ENHANCED
WebAssign

for Fierro's *Mathematics for Elementary School Teachers*

Bringing **Mathematics** to Life

Cengage Learning's **Enhanced WebAssign®** offers an extensive online homework solution to accompany Fierro's *Mathematics for Elementary School Teachers* to encourage the practice that's so critical for concept mastery. The meticulously crafted pedagogy and exercises in this proven text become even more effective in Enhanced WebAssign, supplemented by multimedia tutorial support and immediate feedback as students complete their assignments.

Key Features

- *Read It* interactive eBook pages, *Watch It* videos, and *Chat About It* links
- **Problems** that match end-of-section exercises
- **Cengage YouBook**, an eBook that is interactive and customizable
- *Practice Another Version* feature on many problems allows students to attempt the same question with a new set of values until they feel ready to move on
- *MathPad* makes it easy for students to enter mathematical symbols into their answers
- **Lecture Tutorial Videos** hosted by Dana Mosely help students make better connections with topics and are ideal for individual study and review. These lectures support students in a variety of learning environments

For more information, visit **www.cengage.com/ewa**

Options That SAVE Your Students Money

To Mitchell and Samantha

Contents

My motivation for writing this textbook stems from searching for ways to relate the mathematics in college courses for prospective elementary school teachers to the mathematics in the elementary curriculum.

My goal is to give prospective elementary school teachers a profound understanding of the mathematical content they are expected to know and be able to teach.

My writing has been shaped by reviewing and incorporating the literature and standards from both the National Council of Teachers of Mathematics (NCTM) Standards and Expectations and the Common Core State Standards (CCSS). The standards describe knowledge and skills that students should have, and, in turn, describe what teachers should be able to teach. It was shaped by my experiences teaching prospective elementary school teachers in college classrooms for more than 15 years and by teaching K–6 students during a sabbatical leave, along with hundreds of additional volunteer hours in the elementary classroom during the 6 years of writing this textbook. In addition, the writing was shaped by class testing the material, which gave me the opportunity to incorporate valuable feedback from students and colleagues. These reinforcing factors made it possible to narrow the gap between theory and practice by developing, testing, and refining accessible ways to convey the mathematical content.

As I wrote, researched, and revised the chapters, it was important to answer some key questions.

- What topics are given highest priority by the NCTM Standards and Expectations?
- What recommendations are published in the literature?
- What mathematical strategies promote comprehension?
- What are effective ways to develop the mathematical topics so that prospective elementary school teachers can readily apply them in their own classrooms?
- What examples clarify topics?
- What questions assess understanding and skills?

In this textbook, the quality, quantity, and variety of worked examples and homework questions provide prospective elementary school teachers with opportunities to acquire mathematical knowledge, to develop skills that they can effectively apply in their own classrooms, and to support assessment of the main ideas in the sections, in the spirit of the NCTM standards and CCSS. The worked examples and homework questions reflect my belief that "students learn what they are given opportunities to learn" (Hiebert, 2003).

Enriching the Content through Use of the Standards

The *Principles and Standards for School Mathematics,* published by the NCTM in 2000, represents the most significant and influential collaboration among educators to improve mathematics education at a national level. The relevant NCTM Standards and Expectations appear in the exposition.

The purpose of the NCTM standards is "to ensure quality, to indicate goals, and to promote change" (© NCTM Standards 2011 by National Council of Teachers of Mathematics).

There are two main categories for standards—content standards and process standards—each of which has five subcategories.

Content Standards	Process Standards
Skills, concepts, and understanding that students should acquire for bands of grade levels (Pre-K–2, 3–5, 6–8, and 9–12)	*Ways that students acquire and use knowledge and demonstrate understanding*
Number and operations	Representation
Algebra	Problem solving
Geometry	Reasoning and proof
Measurement	Connections
Data analysis and probability	Communication

The content standards, which include specific goals called expectations, outline the math content that Pre-K–8 students will have to know and understand, which, in turn, indicate the mathematical topics that prospective elementary school teachers will have to understand and teach. The five NCTM process standards highlight ways in which teachers present content; students learn content; and students can demonstrate factual, conceptual, and procedural understanding. "The five process standards are drawn from extensive research on human cognition and mathematics. It is our job as teachers to help students learn how to use these processes appropriately to develop the mathematical knowledge described in the content standards" (Zemelman et al., 2005, p. 112).

I highlight the process standards throughout the textbook in the exposition, worked examples, and homework questions. A colorful icon, which includes the names of the applicable processes, is presented in the margin throughout the book to tie the following process standards to the content.

REPRESENTATION
PROBLEM SOLVING
REASONING
CONNECTION
COMMUNICATION

Representation *is the display of mathematical content using language, tables, algebra, diagrams, and symbols in contextualized situations.* These tools help math instructors teach in ways that make mathematics more accessible, relevant, and enjoyable for prospective teachers. They help prospective teachers "articulate, clarify, justify, and communicate their reasoning to others" (Woleck, 2001) not only in ways they will teach their own students but also in ways they will expect their own students to reason and solve problems. Students with strong representational skills achieve more success in mathematics, because representations make mathematical ideas more comprehensible, spark thought, narrow the gap between abstract and concrete ideas, and help students see connections between mathematical ideas. "Representations should be treated as essential elements in supporting students' understanding of mathematical concepts and relationships; in communicating mathematical approaches, arguments, and understanding of one's self and to others; in recognizing connections among related mathematical concepts; and in applying mathematics to realistic problem situations through modeling" (NCTM, 2000, p. 67).

Problem solving *challenges prospective teachers to apply their knowledge in unfamiliar situations.* It helps build and extend their mathematical knowledge and reasoning abilities.

Reasoning and Proof *form a way of thinking, justifying, and making sense of mathematics and providing an explanation (a proof) in a logical and convincing manner.* Types of reasoning include inductive reasoning, deductive reasoning, algebraic reasoning, additive reasoning, multiplicative reasoning, proportional reasoning, probabilistic reasoning, and geometric reasoning.

Connections *involve recognizing relationships between and among topics and are an indicator of understanding.* Students should be able to explain, for example, how the four arithmetic operations are related; how division and fractions are related; how fractions and decimals are related; how the array model of multiplication and the formula for the area of a rectangle are related; how number systems (counting numbers, whole numbers, integers, rational numbers, irrational numbers, and real numbers) are related; and how to use diagrams to solve classic algebra, ratio, and percent problems. "When students can connect mathematical ideas, their understanding is deeper and more lasting" (NCTM, 2000, p. 64).

Communication *involves expressing written and verbal explanations in a clear and organized manner and supporting the explanations with diagrams and appropriate mathematical notation, symbols, and vocabulary.* The explanations flow in a logical order within the textbook, which builds the habit among students of communicating in an orderly way.

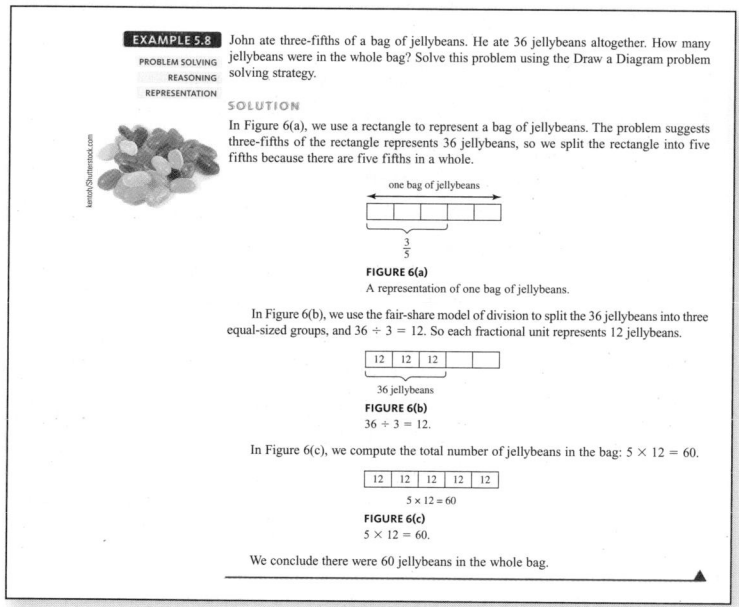

EXAMPLE 5.8
PROBLEM SOLVING
REASONING
REPRESENTATION

John ate three-fifths of a bag of jellybeans. He ate 36 jellybeans altogether. How many jellybeans were in the whole bag? Solve this problem using the Draw a Diagram problem solving strategy.

SOLUTION

In Figure 6(a), we use a rectangle to represent a bag of jellybeans. The problem suggests three-fifths of the rectangle represents 36 jellybeans, so we split the rectangle into five fifths because there are five fifths in a whole.

one bag of jellybeans

$\frac{3}{5}$

FIGURE 6(a)
A representation of one bag of jellybeans.

In Figure 6(b), we use the fair-share model of division to split the 36 jellybeans into three equal-sized groups, and $36 \div 3 = 12$. So each fractional unit represents 12 jellybeans.

| 12 | 12 | 12 |

36 jellybeans
FIGURE 6(b)
$36 \div 3 = 12$.

In Figure 6(c), we compute the total number of jellybeans in the bag: $5 \times 12 = 60$.

| 12 | 12 | 12 | 12 | 12 |

$5 \times 12 = 60$
FIGURE 6(c)
$5 \times 12 = 60$.

We conclude there were 60 jellybeans in the whole bag.

To help students comprehend the five process standards, each worked **Example** illustrates concepts and techniques and an icon indicates which of the five process standards are emphasized in the example.

QUESTIONS FOR SECTION 3.3

REPRESENTATION

Refresher: Representations (language, diagrams, tables, symbols, algebra, manipulatives, and contextualized situations) are important because we use them to organize, record, and communicate mathematical ideas and to make them more comprehensible.

a. List the partial quotients.
b. Find the quotient.   c. Find the remainder.
d. Write an equation involving division.

PROBLEM SOLVING

Refresher: Problem solving (reaching a goal that is not

Many **End-of-Section Questions** are grouped according to the process they emphasize to help students organize their work and to help them understand how processes affect their choice of problems in their own classroom. In each section exercise set, a **Refresher** reminds students of each process standard. The run of exercises that follows gives prospective teachers an opportunity to explore the particular process standard and relate that standard to mathematical content.

b. Find the largest product possible, assuming each digit can be used at most twice.

REASONING AND PROOF

Refresher: Reasoning and proof (thinking and justifying) are important because they help students make sense of mathematics.

7. What two simpler problems does 234×56 require, using the standard multiplication algorithm?

8. A student is multiplying two numbers using the standard multiplication algorithm. The two simpler problems are 345×8 and 345×40. What are the two numbers being multiplied?

9. In the problem $3456 \div b$, a student computed the partial quotients 400, 30, 60, and 3 and the remainder 5.
   a. Find the divisor.
   b. Write an equation involving division.
   c. Check your work.

10. Use properties to multiply 38 and 400.

plication facts. The digits are added along the diagonals, with regrouping as necessary, because each diagonal represents a place value. The digits on the left and bottom edges of the lattice reveal the product: $785 \times 47 = 36{,}895$.

a. Use the given lattice to determine 456×82.

Where Are We Going?

In **Section 10.1**, we introduce geometric language, diagrams, and symbolic notation that students need to describe, compare, and contrast geometric shapes and their properties. We also discuss point and line relationships. In **Section 10.2**, we discuss various angle relationships: vertical angles, complementary angles, supplementary angles, and angles created by a transversal. We also discuss attributes of triangles and parallelograms. In **Section 10.3**, we categorize objects in three dimensions.

How Did Ancient Cultures Use Geometry?

Geometry is the study of shapes and their patterns and properties. Ancient cultures used geometry in different ways according to their needs. The ancient Chinese used geometry to calculate heights and distances of objects in land surveys and to construct buildings and canals. The Mayans applied geometry in the construction of pyramids, temples, terraces, and reservoirs, as well as in their spiritual thinking. Geometry appears in their fabulous symmetric mosaic designs on ceramics and weavings. The ancient Egyptians used geometry to survey land and restore property boundaries after periodic flooding of the Nile and to construct religious temples and public buildings. They also cared about mathematical relationships between geometric figures, such as placing two right triangles together to form a rectangle, but some of their rules were inexact, such as the rule for the area of a circle ($A = 3.11r^2$).

What Is the Greek Influence on Geometry?

Although ancient cultures used geometry for religious, educational, and practical purposes, geometry progressed as an unorganized collection of results. The ancient Greeks, who learned geometry from the Egyptians, changed that by adding structure and logical reasoning, making geometry a subject to study from a mathematical and an abstract point of view. The word *geometry* stems from the Greek word *geometria,* which means "Earth measure." The Greeks' remarkable discoveries, methodical inquiry, and scholarly books led to the understanding and development of geometry in a systematic and organized way.

The step pyramid El Castillo ("the Castle"), built by the Mayans between the 900s and the 1300s.

In addition to the integration of the content and process standards, the text includes many features designed to engage students and prepare them to become elementary school teachers.

The Where Are We Going? **Chapter Opener** motivates the material in the chapter with inviting and brief questions (and their answers). This direct approach will help students navigate the main concepts of the chapter.

Unique **Concept Maps** engage students by showing how concepts relate to one another. The Concept Maps are rich with information and recap ideas in an accessible way.

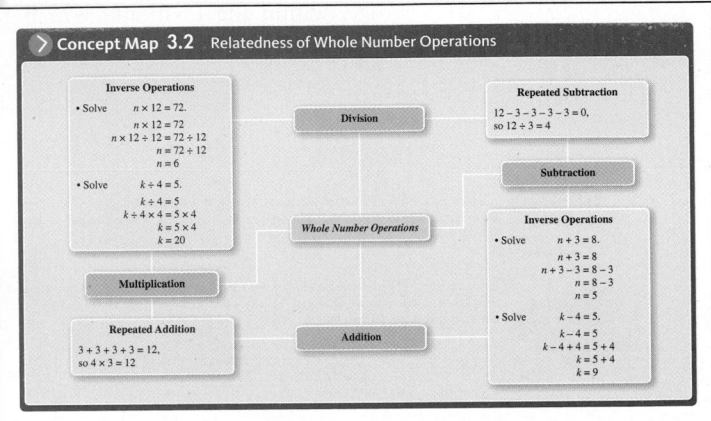

The following Released Items illustrates other situations involving equally likely outcomes.

▶ RELEASED ITEM

- NAEP, 2009

Marty has 6 red pencils, 4 green pencils, and 5 blue pencils. If he picks out one pencil without looking, what is the probability that the pencil will be green?

a. 1 out of 3   **b.** 1 out of 4   **c.** 1 out of 15   **d.** 4 out of 15

38% of fourth graders gave the correct answer.

- NAEP, 2007

(1, 1) (2, 1) (3, 1)
(1, 2) (2, 2) (3, 2)
(1, 3) (2, 3) (3, 3)

A pair of numbers will be chosen at random from the list above. What is the probability that the first number in the pair will be less than the second number in the pair?

33% of eighth graders gave the correct answer. (U.S. Department of Education,

The National Center for Education Statistics administers a nationwide standardized test—the National Assessment of Educational Progress (NAEP), also known as the Nation's Report Card—to a pooled random sample of 4th, 8th, and 12th graders. The NAEP released 25 and 29 questions from 4th- and 8th-grade tests in 1996, respectively; 59 and 67 questions from 4th- and 8th-grade tests in 2003, respectively; 32 and 56 questions from 4th- and 8th-grade tests in 2005, respectively; 54 and 53 questions from 4th- and 8th-grade tests in 2007, respectively; 31 and 34 questions from 4th- and 8th-grade tests in 2009, respectively; and 51 and 47 questions from 4th- and 8th-grade tests in 2011, respectively.

Some NAEP test questions given to 4th- and 8th-grade students appear in this textbook. The NAEP questions are commonly called Released Items because these questions were selectively released to improve student learning. The **Released Items** in the text show prospective teachers types of questions that elementary school students see in standardized assessment tests. The percentage of students who answered the question correctly is given.

In the following Classroom Connection, students use long division or a calculator to classify rational numbers according to their decimal representation.

◆ Classroom Connection

● Harcourt *Math*, Student Edition, Grade 6, p. 247

Rename each fraction as a terminating or repeating decimal. Write terminating or repeating. $\frac{11}{22}$, $\frac{4}{15}$. (© by Harcourt, Inc. Reproduced by permission of the publisher, Houghton Mifflin Harcourt Publishing Company.)

Some homework questions at the end of this section are designed to help you think about "exhibiting rectangles with the same perimeter and different areas or with the same area and different perimeters" (Gr. 3, CCSS). The following student page is an example of an activity that relates the perimeter and area of a rectangle.

(Harcourt *Math*, Student Edition, Grade 6, p. 530)

Pre-K–8 problems from actual elementary mathematics textbooks appear in the exposition as **Classroom Connection** boxes. They give prospective teachers another opportunity to see that the topics they are studying are relevant to the mathematics curriculum. Furthermore, relevant pages from the actual elementary mathematics textbooks are featured. Each Classroom Connection box is placed in context so that prospective teachers can understand how textbooks for elementary school students present the information that they are currently studying in a college classroom.

This textbook includes integrated research results from publications and from Pre-K–8 classroom teachers to develop and clarify mathematical topics. Research results cannot prescribe the "best way" to teach a topic, but they do "show what is possible and what looks promising" (Heibert, 2003). They help determine reasonable approaches for presenting material and increase a prospective teacher's level of confidence in instructional decisions.

Key learning outcomes and ideas of the chapter are summarized in a chapter organizer grid. The **Chapter Organizer** presents the main elements of the chapter in a concise way so that they are accessible to students.

CHAPTER 2 Organizer

Section	What You Should Learn	Review Problems
2.1	**1.** Express ideas about collections of objects using vocabulary and notation.	1–3
	2. Represent sets with a Venn diagram.	4–6
	3. Find the union, intersection, set difference, and Cartesian product of two given sets.	7
	4. Use a Venn diagram to visualize sets and relationships.	8–12
2.2	**1.** Identify basic properties of a numeration system.	13–14
	2. Demonstrate understanding of place value concepts.	15–21
	3. Represent a base ten numeral in various forms.	22–24

Key Terms and Concepts

set 58	period 72	compatible numbers 91
element 58	value 72	decomposition 91
list form 58	standard form 74	identity for addition 92
universal set 58	word form 74	take away model 93
empty set 58	short word form 74	definition of subtraction 94
equal 58	expanded form 74	difference 94
equivalent 59	rounding 75	minuend 94
cardinality 59	Mayan numeration system 77	subtrahend 94
subset 61	Mayan place values 77	missing addend 94
proper subset 61	Babylonian numeration system 78	unknown addend 94
union 62	Babylonian place values 79	addend model 95
intersection 62	base five numeration system 79	comparison model 96
disjoint 62	base twelve numeration system 81	number line model (−) 97

A variety of problems are given in a set of **Review Questions** to increase interest and flexibility in teaching the topics in this textbook.

Review Questions

1. Determine the type of variable.
   a. number of students who ride a bike to school
   b. student identification numbers
   c. letter grade on an assignment
   d. telephone numbers
   e. percentage of students who say their favorite color is blue
   f. age group of survey respondents: 13 to 18, 19 to 25, 26 to 30, 31 to 35, . . .
   g. types of crime (burglary, robbery, and so on)

2. The table shows data for five participants in a survey at an elementary school.

Student	ID	Favorite color	Pets
Janet	415	blue	4
Carlo	213	green	3
Mikey	004	blue	4
Elisa	681	brown	5
Pete	400	purple	0

   a. How many surveyed females were between 46 and 60 years old?
   b. How many males were surveyed?
   c. How many people were surveyed?
   d. What percentage of those surveyed were females?

5. *Consumer Reports* listed the prices of cell phones recommended for its subscribers. The manufacturer, brand of phone, and prices are listed.

Samsung; Impression; $50	Samsung; Solstice; $30
Motorola; Tundra; $180	LG; Rumor Touch; $30
Samsung; Instinct; $100	Samsung; Exclaim; $50
LG; Lotus Elite; $100	Samsung; Alias 2; $50
LG; enV Touch; $80	Casio; G'zOne Rock; $150
LG; enV3; $30	Samsung; Jitterbug J; $150
Samsung; Convoy; $70	Casio; G'zOne Brigade; $250

   Display the data in a frequency table. Create categories that depend on the

The **Chapter Test** provides students an opportunity to reinforce their learning—even as the display of learning outcomes in the chapter tests offers students an opportunity to consider how knowledge acquisition works. The chapter tests are also designed to support the national trend of integrating instruction, assessment, and content and process standards.

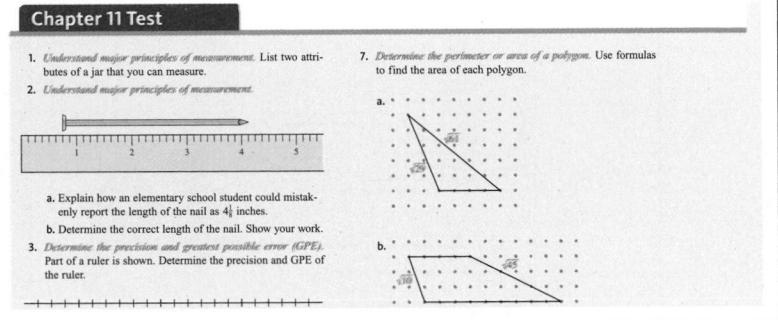

Other Key Features

Historical Notes provide social, cultural, and historical context for select mathematical ideas. They remind students that mathematics is a human activity and an evolving process.

Important **Definitions and Key Theorems and Properties** are set in two types of boxes designed to distinguish them. Definitions briefly describe key terms to learn.

Key terms appear in boldface type to make them easier to locate.

Historical Note

William Playfair (1759–1823), a draftsman and engineer, invented line plots, bar graphs, pie charts, and histograms, publishing them in the books *The Commercial and Political Atlas* and *Statistical Breviary*. In the preface of his atlas, Playfair makes the case that he was the first to represent data with picture graphs (also called pictographs).

Regarding tables, Playfair said, "A man who has carefully investigated a printed table, finds, when done, that he has only a very faint and partial idea of what he has read, and that like a figure imprinted on sand, is soon totally erased and defaced" (*Atlas*, 1801, p. xiv). Regarding graphs, he said, "as much information may be obtained in five minutes as would require whole days to imprint on the memory, in a lasting manner, by a table of figures" (*Atlas*, p. xii) and "Of all the senses, the eye gives the liveliest and most sensible idea of whatever is susceptible of being represented to it" (*Statistical Breviary*, 1801, 14).

Initially, scientists viewed picture representations with suspicion, preferring numbers and formal reasoning instead. Graphs were difficult to publish at that time because of the difficulty of engraving illustrations on copper plates. With improved printing technology and increased acceptance of inductive reasoning, the graphs gradually became acceptable tools for representing data and making reasonable inferences. Graphs today still model Playfair's use of descriptive titles, frames, shading, grid lines, and labels for axes.

Theorem 15

Let a and b represent any whole numbers. Then $a \cdot b = \text{LCM}(a, b) \cdot \text{GCF}(a, b)$.

Noncomputational Definition of $a \times b$

Let the counting number a represent the number of groups and b represent the number of objects in each group. Then the total number of objects in all groups is $a \times b$, which is read as "a times b."

- a is called the **multiplier**, and b is called the **multiplicand**.
- a and b are also called **factors**.
- The number $a \times b$ is also read as "the **product of a and b.**"
- We define $0 \times b$ as equal to zero ($0 \times b = 0$).

A Brief Overview

This textbook:

- focuses on the goal of giving prospective teachers a lasting understanding of the factual, conceptual, and procedural knowledge that they are expected to know and be able to teach.

- includes problems from actual elementary mathematics textbooks, Released Items from the NAEP, and selected NCTM Standards and Expectations and CCSS that link the mathematics prospective teachers study to the mathematics they will teach, as appropriate. This combination helps students answer the questions "What do we need to know?" and "Why do we need to know it?" This combination makes mathematics more relevant for prospective teachers, which will increase their persistence, improve their attitude, and reduce their anxiety. This allows the mathematics instructor to focus on the mathematical content while teaching the course.

- promotes the five processes of mathematics (representation, problem solving, reasoning and proof, connections, and communication). The processes provide a bridge to teaching and learning mathematical content. The processes that a student uses reveal much about the student's level of understanding—which is important for planning, instruction, and assessment.

- contains a variety of homework problems at the end of each section and chapter to increase a student's interest and flexibility in teaching the topics from the textbook. The problems reflect the content and processes that prospective teachers must know and teach. They also reflect the national trend of integrating instruction, assessment, and content and process standards. Although the five processes underlie all questions in the homework, some questions are organized in groups to give prospective teachers a chance to explore a particular process in more depth and to improve their abilities in selecting problems that assess the process. This unique differentiation allows the mathematics instructor to assess a particular aspect of student understanding of a mathematical topic.

- views procedural understanding (*how*) as the culmination of conceptual understanding (*why*), which improves motivation and attitude. The chapter tests found at the end of the chapters reinforce and reconsider these hows and whys by linking problems to specific learning outcomes.

- reflects the belief that prospective teachers should know the content at a deeper level than they teach because they will lead classroom discussions, ask their students questions, and answer questions from their students. The Math Panel Report (2008) supports this assertion: "teachers must know in detail and from a more advanced perspective the mathematical content they are responsible for teaching and the connection of that content to other important mathematics, both prior to and beyond the level they are assigned to teach" (p. 38).

Supplements for the Instructor

Print Supplements

Instructor Edition
(ISBN: 978-1-111-98946-0)
The *Instructor Edition* features an appendix containing the answers to all problems in the book, as well as an appendix denoting which problems can be found in Enhanced WebAssign®.

Instructor's Resource Manual
(ISBN: 978-1-133-36372-9)
Authors: Ricardo D. Fierro and Scott Fallstrom
The *Instructor's Resource Manual* provides detailed solutions to all problems in the text.

Electronic Supplements

PowerLecture with ExamView®
(ISBN: 978-1-133-36373-6)

This CD-ROM (or DVD) provides you with dynamic media tools for teaching. Create, deliver, and customize tests (both print and online) in minutes with ExamView Computerized Testing Featuring Algorithmic Equations. Easily build solution sets for homework or exams using Solution Builder's online solutions manual. Microsoft® PowerPoint® lecture slides and figures from the book are included on this CD-ROM (or DVD).

Solution Builder

This online instructor database offers complete worked solutions to all exercises in the text, allowing you to create customized, secure solutions printouts (in PDF format) matched exactly to the problems you assign in class. For more information, visit www.cengage.com/solutionbuilder.

Enhanced WebAssign
(ISBN: 978-0-538-73810-1)

Exclusively from Cengage Learning®, Enhanced WebAssign combines the exceptional mathematics content that you know and love with the most powerful online homework solution, WebAssign. Enhanced WebAssign engages students with immediate feedback, rich tutorial content, and interactive e-books that help students to develop a deeper conceptual understanding of their subject matter. Online assignments can be built by selecting from thousands of text-specific problems or supplemented with problems from any Cengage Learning textbook.

Enhanced WebAssign: Start Smart Guide for Students
(ISBN: 978-0-495-38479-3)
Author: Brooks/Cole

The Enhanced WebAssign: Start Smart Guide for Students helps students get up and running quickly with Enhanced WebAssign so that they can study smarter and improve their performance in class.

Supplements for the Student

Print Supplements

Student Solutions Manual
(ISBN: 978-1-133-36374-3)
Authors: Ricardo D. Fierro and Scott Fallstrom

Go beyond the answers—see what it takes to get there and improve your grade! This manual provides step-by-step solutions to selected problems in the text, giving you the information you need to truly understand how these problems are solved.

Activities Manual
(ISBN: 978-1-133-36371-2)
Authors: Ricardo D. Fierro and Randa Kress

The Activities Manual is geared toward helping you grasp the main ideas of each section that is covered in the text, with open-ended activities that allow you to practice and apply the knowledge that you have learned.

Math Manipulatives Kit
(ISBN: 978-0-618-19093-5)
Author: ETA Cuisenaire

Get hands-on experience when you use the Manipulatives Kit. By using this tool, you will see benefits that help elementary school students understand mathematical concepts. The kit includes pattern blocks, pentominoes, base ten flats, base ten rods, base ten units, tangrams, and a geoboard.

Mathematics for Elementary School Teachers

RICARDO D. FIERRO
CALIFORNIA STATE UNIVERSITY SAN MARCOS

BROOKS/COLE
CENGAGE Learning·

Australia · Brazil · Japan · Korea · Mexico · Singapore · Spain · United Kingdom · United States

Mathematics for Elementary School Teachers
Ricardo D. Fierro

Publisher: Charlie Van Wagner

Acquisitions Editor: Marc Bove

Developmental Editors: Don Gecewicz;
   Stefanie Beeck

Assistant Editor: Shaun Williams

Editorial Assistant: Zack Crockett

Media Editors: Heleny Wong; Bryon Spencer

Marketing Manager: Gordon Lee

Marketing Communications Manager:
   Mary Anne Payumo

Content Project Manager: Cheryll Linthicum

Art Director: Vernon Boes

Manufacturing Planner: Becky Cross

Rights Acquisitions Specialist: Roberta Broyer

Production and Composition: Graphic World Inc.

Photo Researcher: Bill Smith Group

Text Researcher: Pablo D'Stair

Copy Editor: Graphic World Inc.

Art Editor: Leslie Lahr

Illustrator: Graphic World Inc.

Text Designer: Diane Beasley

Cover Designer: Marsha Cohen

Cover Image: Thomas Dannenberg/Masterfile

For product information and technology assistance, contact us at
Cengage Learning Customer & Sales Support, 1-800-354-9706

For permission to use material from this text or product,
submit all requests online at **www.cengage.com/permissions**
Further permissions questions can be emailed to
permissionrequest@cengage.com

Library of Congress Control Number: 2011944297

Student Edition:

ISBN-13: 978-0-538-49363-5

ISBN-10: 0-538-49363-1

Brooks/Cole
20 Davis Drive
Belmont, CA 94002-3098
USA

Cengage Learning is a leading provider of customized learning solutions with office locations around the globe, including Singapore, the United Kingdom, Australia, Mexico, Brazil, and Japan. Locate your local office at:
www.cengage.com/global.

Cengage Learning products are represented in Canada by Nelson Education, Ltd.

For your course and learning solutions, visit **academic.cengage.com**

Purchase any of our products at your local college store or at our preferred online store **www.CengageBrain.com**

Printed in the United States of America
1 2 3 4 5 6 7 16 15 14 13 12

Electronic Supplements

Enhanced WebAssign: Start Smart Guide for Students
(ISBN: 978-0-495-38479-3)
Author: Brooks/Cole
If your instructor has chosen to package Enhanced WebAssign with your text, this manual will help you get up and running quickly with the Enhanced WebAssign system so that you can study smarter and improve your performance in class.

Enhanced WebAssign
(ISBN: 978-0-538-73810-1)
Enhanced WebAssign (assigned by the instructor) provides you with instant feedback on homework assignments. This online homework system is easy to use and includes helpful links to textbook sections, video examples, and problem-specific tutorials.

Acknowledgments

I would like to thank the many people who reviewed the manuscript throughout various stages. Their thoughtful feedback helped shape this textbook in many ways.

Advisory Reviewers

John Armon, *Illinois Central*
Beth Chance, *Cal Poly at San Luis Obispo*
Eduardo Chappa, *Texas A&M University*
Robert delMas, *University of Minnesota*

Flor de Maria Garcia-Wukovits, *University of the Incarnate Word*
Theresa Johnson, *Los Angeles Pierce College*
Mary Richardson, *Grand Valley State University*

Reviewers

Paul S. Ache, *Kutztown University of Pennsylvania*
Jim Brandt, *Southern Utah University*
Linda Cooke, *University of South Carolina Upstate*
Mark L. Daniels, *University of Texas at Austin*
Julie DePree, *University of New Mexico Valencia Campus*
Monette Elizalde, *Palo Alto College*
Scott Fallstrom, *MiraCosta College*
Thomas W. Fisher, *Front Range Community College*
Linda Fitzpatrick, *Western Kentucky University*

Grant A. Fraser, *California State University at Los Angeles*
Melinda Gann, *Mississippi College*
Cheryl Herrmann, *Front Range Community College*
Randa Kress, *Idaho State University*
Maria Mitchell, *Central Connecticut State University*
Stuart Moskowitz, *Humboldt State University*
Nancy Ressler, *Oakton College*
Vince Schielack, *Texas A&M University*
Rebecca Wong, *West Valley College*

Special thanks to Cheryl Herrmann, Randa Kress, and Vince Schielack for reviewing the manuscript in its entirety. They contributed a great amount of time and feedback.

Mrs. Dietor, Mrs. Dugger, Mrs. Emme, Mrs. Grady, Ms. Klien, Mrs. Kulminski, Ms. Litt, Mrs. Rocha, Mrs. Roncaglia, Mrs. Smith, Mrs. Swan, and Mrs. Verga deserve special thanks for the many hours of discussions and weekly opportunities to teach to and learn from their students in the first, second, third, fourth, fifth, and sixth grades through the years. It's a pleasure to interact with them and their energetic students. Mrs. Smith deserves additional recognition for allowing me to spend a sabbatical leave in her classroom, teaching mathematics to her sixth-grade students.

Former students in mathematics for elementary school teacher courses through the past 15 years also deserve appreciation. Marcia Michel, a former student and current teacher, deserves special thanks for providing comments on drafts of chapters. Tim Eddo, a former undergraduate and graduate student, was helpful in photocopying resources that were unavailable online. Leila Safaralian, Gina Sanders, and Kerry Ferreirae tested drafts in their classrooms and provided useful suggestions.

Thanks to Ray Landis for sharing his experiences of writing a textbook. Gary Sloane, Jim Ho, Richard Hoff, Bill Belko, Jo Anne Moran, Bob Alidaee, Jennifer Smith, Linda Olafson, and Barry Raskin provided welcome diversion by occasionally joining me for food and conversation on the progress of this project. On numerous occasions, Gary Sloane applied his amazing troubleshooting skills and technical expertise to maintain my home computer and network.

This textbook is the result of the coordinated efforts and dedication of many talented people. Thanks to Publisher Charlie Van Wagner for his overall support and giving the green light to this project. Thanks to Acquisitions Editor Marc Bove for coordinating the reviews, replying to e-mails and returning phone calls quickly and enthusiastically, asking prodding questions, providing feedback to raw ideas, and communicating a steady voice of reason and reassurance during the process. Thanks to Development Editor Don Gecewicz for his many efforts, such as filtering and interpreting the reviews to improve the manuscript, infusing ideas, and analyzing pedagogical features. I appreciated his insight and many suggestions. Thanks to Art Editor Leslie Lahr, who ensured the quality of all artwork. I appreciated her stories, sense of humor, and valuable suggestions. Thanks to Art Stylist Lisa Torri, who helped write the specifications for art design, and Art Director Vernon Boes, who managed everything having to do with art and design. Thanks to Marketing Manager Gordon Lee for leading the marketing efforts for this textbook. Thanks to Production Editor Dan Fitzgerald at Graphic World for managing the production schedule and working with the copy editor, proofreader, and composition team to produce the final product. Thanks to Marcia Frobish for checking the accuracy of solutions. Thanks to Zack Crockett, Bryon Spencer, and Michael Ledesma for their contributions. Thanks to Shaun Williams for her efforts in coordinating the tasks involved in producing the *Activities Manual* and *Instructor's Resource Manual*. Thanks to Stefanie Beeck for coordinating many tasks and assisting in reviewing the chapters. In addition, I would like to thank Content Project Manager Cheryll Linthicum, who had the incredible responsibility of overseeing and monitoring the entire project. Cheryll and Stefanie also served as the eagle eyes ensuring that every "i" was dotted and "t" crossed and kept me in line by filtering all my concerns, questions, and ideas.

My dearest children, Mitchell and Samantha, provided continual inspiration and allowed me to visit and teach many of their classes. My memories of those times are priceless. Samantha helped me organize an after-school program called Math Academy, where we experimented and enjoyed success with using diagrams to represent and solve problems and using the tile model to solve equations. Last, but certainly not least, my wife, Nancy, was supportive and understanding during the writing and editing of this textbook. She stood by my side from the conception to the completion of the entire project. I thank her for being an incredible and loving partner on this journey.

1

Problem Solving and Reasoning

Where Are We Going?

In **Section 1.1,** we discuss patterns and inductive reasoning. They are tools to help students learn mathematical principles and solve problems. In **Section 1.2,** we describe teacher George Pólya's four-phase process for problem solving and demonstrate several problem-solving strategies. In **Section 1.3,** we introduce some basic language of algebra, along with additive, multiplicative, and algebraic reasoning. We also use diagrams and algebra to represent and solve problems. In **Section 1.4,** we explore the language of logic and discuss another form of reasoning called deductive reasoning.

What Is Problem Solving?

Problem solving, a major avenue of learning, is a common theme in mathematics, from elementary school to college. The National Council of Teachers of Mathematics' (NCTM's) *Principles and Standards for School Mathematics* states:

> Problem solving is a hallmark of mathematical activity. It is finding a way to reach a goal that is not immediately attainable. (© NCTM Standards 2011 by National Council of Teachers of Mathematics)

It requires curiosity, flexibility, and imagination. In this chapter, we focus on typical problem-solving strategies and demonstrate how to use them to grapple with problems. Many of these strategies form the basis for representation (using diagrams, tables, symbols, algebra, manipulatives, and contextualized situations) and communication (supporting written and verbal explanations with appropriate diagrams and notation) to make mathematical ideas more comprehensible.

What Are the Benefits of Problem-Solving Skills?

As you gain problem-solving skills, many once-formidable problems will become routine, giving you the ability and confidence to tackle more challenging ones and "see" more math. Seeing more math helps you become an effective problem solver and teacher. It improves your attitude toward mathematics and gives you the ability to provide greater learning opportunities for your students.

Patterns and Inductive Reasoning

Patterns and Mathematical Principles

A **pattern** is similarity or regularity in observations that allows you to predict the behavior in the observations or what comes next. A **conjecture** (or **claim**) is a general statement that seems to be true. **Inductive reasoning,** one of the most basic forms of reasoning that humans use, is the process of using patterns to make a conjecture. The word *inductive* stems from the Latin word *inductivis,* which means "leading on."

Inductive reasoning is an accessible and informal form of justification for students. It makes mathematics more engaging and fascinating, and it gives students the power to learn new mathematical ideas and solve problems.

EXAMPLE 1.1

COMMUNICATION

REASONING

Use inductive reasoning to make a conjecture about the sum of two consecutive whole numbers.

SOLUTION

Let's pick some pairs of consecutive numbers and find the sums: $3 + 4 = 7$, $17 + 18 = 35$, $76 + 77 = 153$, and $524 + 525 = 1049$. The sums 7, 35, 153, and 1049 are all odd numbers. These observations support (but do not prove) the claim "the sum of two consecutive whole numbers is an odd number."

▲

The NCTM's reasoning and proof standard for grades pre-K–12 says students should "make and investigate mathematical conjectures." This helps them discover mathematical principles, as illustrated by the problem shown in the following Classroom Connection.

Classroom Connection

● *Math*, Grade 4, p. 147

What happens when you multiply an even number by 5? An odd number? What patterns do you notice? (© 2000 Macmillan/McGraw Hill. Reprinted by permission.)

CONNECTION

In later chapters, we use patterns to draw conclusions or make predictions (statistics and probability); realize the inverse relationship between the size of the measurement unit and the number of units, such as 1 yd = 3 ft and 1 yd = 36 in. (measurement); sort and classify geometric shapes (geometry); and express a function given in table form as a function in equation form (algebra and functions).

Here are some vocabulary words we use in the study of patterns.

Definition

- A **sequence** is an ordered arrangement of objects, such as numbers, letters, equations, or shapes.
- Each object in the sequence is called a **term.**

Because a sequence is ordered, there is an initial term, second term, third term, and so on. We often use inductive reasoning to predict the next likely term in a sequence. The next example illustrates that inductive reasoning can lead to multiple (correct) answers.

EXAMPLE 1.2   Predict the next few terms in the sequence 10110 . . . .

REASONING

SOLUTION

There are several possibilities.

Option 1: The next few terms could be 0111000 (as in the sequence 10 1100 111000 . . .).

Option 2: The next few terms could be 11101111 (as in the sequence 10 110 1110 11110 . . .).

Option 3: The next few terms could be 10110 (as in the sequence 10110 10110 10110 . . .).

▲

Repeating Sequence

A **repeating sequence** is a pattern of recurring digits, letters, symbols, and pictures. For example, 1, 7, 8, 5, 1, 7, 8, 5, 1, 7, 8, 5, 1, . . . is a repeating sequence because it repeats the terms 1, 7, 8, and 5 (it repeats in groups of four). We typically see repeating patterns in decimal numbers, such as 7.5461461461. . . . We also see repeating patterns in textiles (such as rugs), art (such as stained glass), and wallpaper.

The following Released Item indicates that students should be able to recognize a pattern to predict missing terms.

> **RELEASED ITEM**
>
> • NAEP, 2003
> Peter wrote down a pattern of A's and B's that repeats in groups of 3. Here is the beginning of his pattern with some of the letters erased. Fill in the missing letters.
> A B ___ A ___ B ___ ___ ___
> 52% of fourth graders and 65% of eighth graders gave the correct response.
> (U.S. Department of Education, Institute of Education Sciences, National Center for Education Statistics, NAEP)

Using a Pattern to Solve a Problem

Patterns and inductive reasoning are stepping stones that students can use for improving their understanding of mathematical principles, problem solving, and algebraic thinking. Yogi Berra once said, "You can observe a lot just by watching." In that spirit, you can learn a lot just by *observing*. Searching for patterns is an overlooked problem-solving strategy. The following examples demonstrate that we can solve problems by observing patterns.

EXAMPLE 1.3   Determine the 158th term in the repeating sequence 5, 11, 6, 5, 11, 6, 5, 11, 6, ...

CONNECTION
COMMUNICATION
PROBLEM SOLVING
REASONING

SOLUTION

We notice the three terms 5, 11, and 6 repeat, and every third term is a 6 (third term, sixth term, ninth term, and so on). The table shows a pattern in the remainders when we divide the position (1, 2, 3, 4, . . .) by the number of repeating terms (3).

(continued)

position	1	2	3	4	5	6	7	8	9	. . .	158
term	5	11	6	5	11	6	5	11	6	. . .	?
position ÷ 3	0 R1	0 R2	1 R0	1 R1	1 R2	2 R0	2 R1	2 R2	3 R0	. . .	52 R2

For example, $158 \div 3 = 52$ with a remainder of 2 (52 R2). We see that every position divided by 3 that has a remainder of 2 (such as positions 2, 5, and 8) corresponds to the term 11. The pattern suggests that the 158th term of the repeating sequence 5, 11, 6, 5, 11, 6, 5, 11, 6, . . . is 11.

▲

Arithmetic Sequences

Students should be able to "describe, extend, and make generalizations about geometric and numeric patterns" (NCTM, algebra expectations for grades 3–5), which often involves using tables to organize sequences, see patterns, and generalize the sequence using algebra. These experiences prepare students for more advanced algebraic reasoning, as illustrated in the following Classroom Connection.

◆◆ **Classroom Connection**

● Houghton Mifflin *Math Steps*, California Edition, Grade 4, p. 294

Describe the rule using words. Complete the table. Then write the rule as an algebraic equation using the variables given. (© by Houghton Mifflin Company, Inc. Reproduced by permission of the publisher, Houghton Mifflin Harcourt Publishing Company.)

plants (p)	1	2	3	4
flowers (f)	6	12	18	

The most common types of numerical sequences seen in the elementary mathematics curriculum are arithmetic sequences, such as 6, 12, 18, 24, . . . and 5, 12, 19, 26, ... You obtain the next term by adding a constant to the previous term. Now we illustrate how to describe, extend, and generalize an arithmetic sequence.

EXAMPLE 1.4

CONNECTION
REASONING
REPRESENTATION

The sequence 5, 12, 19, 26, . . . is an arithmetic sequence.

a. Describe the sequence using words.

b. Extend the sequence.

c. Generalize the sequence.

SOLUTION

a. We *describe* this sequence using words by saying, "We begin with 5 and obtain the next term by adding 7 to the previous term."

b. We *extend* this sequence by observing a pattern. The next two terms after 26 are 33 and 40.

c. We *generalize* the sequence with a formula for the nth term, which is an equation that relates the position n to the value y of the nth term in the sequence ($n = 1$ corresponds to the initial term, $n = 2$ corresponds to the second term, and so on). Table 1.1 shows the developing pattern and the equations. The table makes the pattern more apparent.

TABLE 1.1 Using a Table to Generalize the Sequence 5, 12, 19, 26, . . .

Position (n)	Value of nth term (y)	Developing pattern	Equation
1	5	5	$5 = 5 + 0 \cdot 7$
2	12	$12 = 5 + 7$	$12 = 5 + 1 \cdot 7$
3	19	$19 = 12 + 7 = 5 + 7 + 7$	$19 = 5 + 2 \cdot 7$
4	26	$26 = 19 + 7 = 5 + 7 + 7 + 7$	$26 = 5 + 3 \cdot 7$

The equation is $y = 5 + 7(n - 1)$, where y is the term and n is the position. In simplified form, the equation is $y = 7n - 2$.

▲

CONNECTION

Arithmetic sequences such as 2, 4, 6, . . . (even numbers); 5, 10, 15, 20, . . . (multiples of 5); and 10, 20, 30, . . . (multiples of 10) are called *skip-counting sequences.* We apply skip counting, for example, to prepare for multiplication and division with whole numbers; to find the least common multiple; to motivate divisibility rules for 2, 5, and 10; and to generate entries in a ratio table.

We can use algebraic notation to define an arithmetic sequence.

Definition

An **arithmetic sequence** is a sequence that begins with the number a; the next term is obtained by adding the constant d to the previous term.

- a is called the **initial term,** and d is called the **common difference.**
- The ***n*th term** y is given by the rule $y = a + d(n - 1)$, for $n = 1, 2, 3, \ldots$.

In the arithmetic sequence 5, 12, 19, 26, . . . , the initial term is 5 and the common difference is 7 (because $12 - 5 = 7$, $19 - 12 = 7$, $26 - 19 = 7$, and so on).

EXAMPLE 1.5

CONNECTION

REPRESENTATION

The sequence 1, 5, 9, 13, 17, . . . is an arithmetic sequence.

a. What are the initial term and the common difference in this sequence?

b. What is the 24th term?

c. In this sequence, 297 is the kth term. Find k.

SOLUTION

a. The initial term is 1, and the common difference is 4 ($5 - 1 = 4$, $9 - 5 = 4$, $13 - 9 = 4, \ldots$).

b. A generalization of the sequence is $y = 1 + 4(n - 1)$, where y is the term and n is the position. Replacing n with 24, we get $y = 1 + 4(24 - 1) = 1 + 4 \cdot 23 = 93$. The 24th term is 93.

c. We need to find k so that $297 = 1 + 4(k - 1)$. Then $296 = 4(k - 1)$. Then $74 = k - 1$. Then $75 = k$. So 297 is the 75th term in the arithmetic sequence.

▲

EXAMPLE 1.6

CONNECTION

REPRESENTATION

How many numbers are in the list 4, 10, 16, 22, . . . , 214?

SOLUTION

We assume 4, 10, 16, 22, . . . , 214 describes an arithmetic sequence with initial term 4 and common difference 6. Then we need to find k such that $214 = 4 + 6(k - 1)$. Then $210 = 6(k - 1)$. Then $35 = k - 1$. Then $36 = k$. This means 214 is the 36th term in the sequence. So there are 36 numbers in the list 4, 10, 16, 22, . . . , 214.

▲

Multiple Representations of a Sequence

The NCTM representation standards affirm that students should "create and use representations to organize, record, and communicate mathematical ideas" and "select, apply, and translate among mathematical representations to solve problems." Multiple representations deepen student understanding of concepts and relationships, and each representation highlights different aspects of the problem.

EXAMPLE 1.7

REPRESENTATION

Represent the arithmetic sequence $-5, -2, 1, 4, \ldots$ using

a. words.

b. a table.

c. algebra.

d. a graph.

SOLUTION

a. We begin with -5 and obtain the next term by adding 3 to the previous term.

b. We make a table with a few terms.

position (n)	1	2	3	4	5
term (y)	-5	-2	1	4	7

c. $y = -5 + 3(n - 1) = -5 + 3n - 3 = -8 + 3n$. So $y = -8 + 3n$.

d. In the graph, we put the "independent" variable n along the horizontal axis and the "dependent" variable y along the vertical axis. The graph shows the first few terms of the arithmetic sequence.

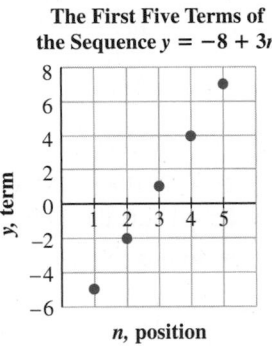

The First Five Terms of the Sequence $y = -8 + 3n$

Classic Savings Problem

The classic savings problem is a model problem for arithmetic sequences.

EXAMPLE 1.8

PROBLEM SOLVING

Mark had $2. Then he saved a fixed amount at the end of each week throughout the year. The table shows the total amount of money he accumulated at the end of each week. When did he have $38 saved?

week (n)	1	2	3	4
total amount saved (y)	$2	$6	$10	$14

SOLUTION

After n weeks, he saved $y = 2 + 4(n - 1)$ dollars, or $y = 4n - 2$ dollars. We need to solve the equation $38 = 4n - 2$. Then $40 = 4n$. Then $10 = n$. At the end of 10 weeks, he had saved $38.

Connections between Whole Numbers and Geometric Patterns

CONNECTION

REPRESENTATION

The sequence 2, 5, 8, 11, 13, . . . is an example of an arithmetic sequence. The sum $2 + 5 + 8 + 11 + 13$ is an example of an arithmetic series. An **arithmetic series** is a sum in which the addends are consecutive terms in an arithmetic sequence. Can you explain why $2 + 5 + 8 + 15$ is not an arithmetic series? Certain whole numbers (triangular numbers, square numbers, and oblong numbers) have close ties to arithmetic series and geometric patterns.

A *triangular number* is an arithmetic series of the form $1 + 2 + 3 + 4 + . . . + n$. The first four triangular numbers are 1, 3, 6, and 10. Each can be represented by an arithmetic series and a triangle.

triangular number	1	3	6	10
arithmetic series representation	1	$1 + 2$	$1 + 2 + 3$	$1 + 2 + 3 + 4$
geometric representation				

What are the next three triangular numbers?

A *square number* is a whole number that has a geometric representation in the shape of a square.

square number	1	4	9	16
arithmetic series representation	1	$1 + 3$	$1 + 3 + 5$	$1 + 3 + 5 + 7$
geometric representation				

What are the next three square numbers? Each square number is an arithmetic series. For example, $1 = 1$, $4 = 1 + 3$, and $9 = 1 + 3 + 5$. Can you express 16 as an arithmetic series?

An *oblong number* is a whole number that has a geometric representation in the shape of the rectangle, where the length and width differ by exactly one unit.

oblong number	·2	6	12	20
product	1×2	2×3	3×4	4×5
geometric representation				

What are the next three oblong numbers? Each oblong number is an arithmetic series. For example, $2 = 2$, $6 = 2 + 4$, and $12 = 2 + 4 + 6$. Can you express 20 as an arithmetic series?

Gauss's Method

CONNECTION

REPRESENTATION

Carl Friedrich Gauss (1777–1855) calculated the sum $1 + 2 + 3 + 4 + . . . + 99 + 100$ in elementary school. To keep the students busy, his teacher asked the class to find the sum. Within minutes, Gauss solved the problem using the following clever method: Let S represent the sum: $S = 1 + 2 + 3 + \ldots + 99 + 100$. Gauss rewrote the sum by reversing the order of the addends:

$$S = 1 + 2 + 3 + \ldots + 98 + 99 + 100$$
$$S = 100 + 99 + 98 + \ldots + 3 + 2 + 1$$

Then by adding the two equalities, he realized the following:

$$2S = 101 + 101 + 101 + \ldots + 101 + 101 + 101$$
$$= 100 \cdot 101 \text{ (because } 1 + 2 + 3 + \ldots + 100 \text{ has 100 addends)}$$

Then he solved for S to get $S = (100 \cdot 101) \div 2 = 5050$. The equation $S = (100 \cdot 101) \div 2$ has the form $S = (\text{number of terms} \cdot \text{sum of the first and last terms}) \div 2$.

The next example suggests that this technique works for other arithmetic series.

EXAMPLE 1.9

CONNECTION
COMMUNICATION
PROBLEM SOLVING
REASONING
REPRESENTATION

Grocery stores often stack merchandise in the shape of a trapezoid to draw attention to the merchandise. A stack has 85 boxes in the first row, 79 boxes in the second row, 73 boxes in the third row, and so on. There are 43 boxes in the last row. How many boxes are in this display?

SOLUTION

The number of boxes in the stack is $85 + 79 + 73 + 67 + 61 + 55 + 49 + 43$. The sum $85 + 79 + 73 + 67 + 61 + 55 + 49 + 43$ is an arithmetic series, because 85, 79, 73, . . . , 43 is an arithmetic sequence with initial term 85 and common difference -6. Using Gauss's method, we let S represent the sum and then rewrite it backward:

$$S = 85 + 79 + 73 + 67 + 61 + 55 + 49 + 43$$
$$S = 43 + 49 + 55 + 61 + 67 + 73 + 79 + 85$$

Then we add

$$2S = 128 + 128 + 128 + 128 + 128 + 128 + 128 + 128.$$

So $2S = (\text{number of times 128 is repeated}) \cdot 128$.

The number of times 128 is repeated equals the position of 43. Note that 43 is a term in the arithmetic sequence 85, 79, 73, . . . , 43 with rule $y = 85 + (-6)(n - 1)$. We need to find n such that $43 = 85 + (-6)(n - 1)$. Solving for n, we get $n = 8$. Then $2S = 8 \cdot 128$, so $S = (8 \cdot 128) \div 2$, which equals 512. There are 512 boxes in the display.

As in Gauss's equation, $S = (8 \cdot 128) \div 2$ has the form $S = (\text{number of terms} \cdot \text{sum of the first and last terms}) \div 2$.

▲

Geometric Sequences

The sequence 2, 6, 18, 54, 162, . . . has initial term 2, and the next term is obtained by multiplying the previous term by 3 ($6 = 2 \cdot 3$, $18 = 6 \cdot 3$, $54 = 18 \cdot 3$, . . .). The terms in this sequence can also be expressed using exponents, as shown in Table 1.2.

REASONING
REPRESENTATION

TABLE 1.2 Expressing Terms in a Geometric Sequence Using Exponential Notation

Position (n)	Term (y)	Developing pattern	Equation
1	2	2	$2 = 2 \cdot 3^0$
2	6	$6 = 2 \cdot 3$	$6 = 2 \cdot 3^1$
3	18	$18 = 3 \cdot 6 = 2 \cdot 3 \cdot 3$	$18 = 2 \cdot 3^2$
4	54	$54 = 3 \cdot 18 = 2 \cdot 3 \cdot 3 \cdot 3$	$54 = 2 \cdot 3^3$

The table is a powerful organizing tool, making it easier to see how the exponent depends on the position. The general formula for the sequence is $y = 2 \cdot 3^{n-1}$, where y is the nth term. The ratio of consecutive terms is constant: $6 \div 2 = 3$, $18 \div 6 = 3$, $54 \div 18 = 3$, and so on. The sequence 2, 6, 18, 54, 162, . . . is called a geometric sequence. We can use algebraic notation to define a geometric sequence.

Definition

A **geometric sequence** is a sequence that begins with the nonzero number a; the next term is obtained by multiplying the previous term by the nonzero number r.
- a is the initial term, and r is called the **common ratio.**
- The nth term y is given by the rule $y = a \cdot r^{n-1}$, for $n = 1, 2, 3, \ldots$.

The phrase *common ratio* means "common quotient." The ratio of a geometric sequence is the quotient of two consecutive terms. For example, we can find the common ratio of the geometric sequence 3, 15, 75, 375, . . . by division: $15 \div 3 = 5$, $75 \div 15 = 5$, and $375 \div 75 = 5$. The common ratio of the geometric sequence 3, 15, 75, 375, . . . is 5, and the nth term y is given by $y = 3 \cdot 5^{n-1}$, for $n = 1, 2, 3, \ldots$.

EXAMPLE 1.10

CONNECTION

Find the initial term and common ratio in each geometric sequence.
a. 10, 100, 1000, 10,000, . . .

b. 125, 25, 5, 1, . . .

c. 4, 4, 4, 4, 4, . . .

SOLUTION

a. $100 \div 10 = 10$, $1000 \div 100 = 10$, and $10{,}000 \div 1000 = 10$. The initial term is 10. The common ratio is 10.

b. $25 \div 125 = \frac{1}{5}$, $5 \div 25 = \frac{1}{5}$, and $1 \div 5 = \frac{1}{5}$. The initial term is 125. The common ratio is $\frac{1}{5}$.

c. $4 \div 4 = 1$, $4 \div 4 = 1$, and $4 \div 4 = 1$. The initial term is 4. The common ratio is 1. ▲

Limitation of Inductive Reasoning

COMMUNICATION

REASONING

Elementary school students enjoy being detectives, searching for patterns in sequences of numbers, letters, shapes, and equations. For example, when students see the equations $3 + 5 = 8$, $1 + 3 = 4$, and $7 + 3 = 10$, they recognize a pattern and then claim that the sum of two odd numbers is an even number. Their claim summarizes their observations. Often, the students are correct. As a result, they believe inductive reasoning is a perfect method. But it is a flawed form of reasoning, because sometimes the observations lead to an incorrect claim. The following Released Item assesses student understanding of the limitation of inductive reasoning.

▶ **RELEASED ITEM**

- NAEP, 2009
  Sam did the following problems. $2 + 1 = 3$, $6 + 1 = 7$. Sam concluded that when he adds 1 to <u>any</u> whole number, his answer will always be odd. Is Sam correct? _____ Explain your answer.
  42% of fourth-grade students answered the question correctly.

TABLE 1.3   Pattern Showing Limitation of Inductive Reasoning

$6 \div 8 = 0.75$
$6 \div 9 = 0.66666\ldots$
$6 \div 10 = 0.6$
$6 \div 11 = 0.545454\ldots$
$6 \div 12 = ?$
$6 \div 13 = ?$
$6 \div 14 = ?$

The following problem illustrates this limitation of inductive reasoning. A whole number divided by a nonzero whole number either has a finite decimal expansion (such as 0.2 and 0.35) or a repeating decimal expansion (such as 0.3333... or 9.128457457457...). Look for a pattern in the computations shown in Table 1.3.

- Predict whether the decimal expansion of $6 \div 12$ is finite or repeating. Check your answer with a calculator. Were you correct?
- Predict whether the decimal expansion of $6 \div 13$ is finite or repeating. Check your answer with a calculator. Were you correct?
- Predict whether the decimal expansion of $6 \div 14$ is finite or repeating. Check your answer with a calculator. Were you correct?

What did you learn about inductive reasoning? Please answer this question before you continue reading.

Inductive reasoning is an imperfect form of reasoning because observations (such as the results in Table 1.3) do not always lead to a true conclusion (such as your prediction). For this reason, scientists, mathematicians, and teachers do not accept examples as proof of a conjecture. However, this flaw of inductive reasoning does not make it a poor method. Students, scientists, mathematicians, and teachers use it all the time to discover patterns that help them recognize relationships, group objects, acquire understanding, and experience some exciting "aha" moments while learning. The NCTM's *Principles and Standards for School Mathematics* say for students in grades 3 to 5, "formulating conjectures and assessing them on the basis of evidence should become the norm."

Mathematicians often use inductive reasoning to make a conjecture, but they always use deductive reasoning to prove the conjecture. Deductive reasoning is the process of making a conclusion based on formal laws of logic (see Section 1.4). In time, teachers help their students shift from inductive reasoning to deductive reasoning. Both inductive and deductive reasoning are vital parts of mathematical reasoning.

QUESTIONS FOR SECTION 1.1

REPRESENTATION

Refresher: Representations (language, diagrams, tables, symbols, algebra, manipulatives, and contextualized situations) are important because we use them to organize, record, and communicate mathematical ideas and to make them more comprehensible.

1. Represent the arithmetic sequence with initial term 1 and common difference 3 in the following ways.
   a. words   b. table   c. algebra   d. graph

2. Identify whether the sequence is an arithmetic sequence, geometric sequence, both, or neither.
   a. 2, 4, 6, 8, 10, . . .   b. 2, 4, 8, 16, 32, . . .
   c. 20, 12, 6, 2, . . .   d. 18, 14, 10, 6, 2, . . .
   e. 4, 4, 4, 4, 4, . . .

3. The equation $y = 7n - 12$ represents an arithmetic sequence.
   a. What is the initial term?
   b. What is the common difference?
   c. Represent the sequence with a table.

4. The following graph shows an arithmetic sequence.

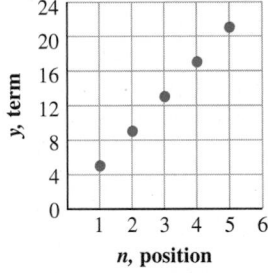

   a. Represent the graph with a table.
   b. What feature of the graph reveals that the sequence is an arithmetic sequence?

5. For the arithmetic sequence 4, 7, 10, 13, . . . ,
   a. find the initial term.   b. find the common difference.
   c. represent the sequence with an equation.
   d. graph the sequence using graph paper.
   e. draw a line through the points on the graph.
   f. find the slope of the line.
   g. discuss the connection between the sequence and the slope of the line.

PROBLEM SOLVING

Refresher: Problem solving (reaching a goal that is not immediately attainable) is important because it helps students think more deeply about what they know and deal with unfamiliar situations.

6. What is the ones digit of 9^{58}? (Hint: Look for a pattern in the ones digit of $9^1, 9^2, 9^3, \ldots$.)

7. A rectangle represents a table, and a dot represents a student sitting at the table. Join the tables according to the diagrams shown.

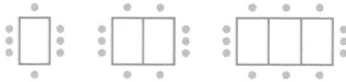

a. How many students can be seated at the tables when 37 tables are joined together?

b. What is the minimum number of tables needed to seat 185 students?

8. Rico saved money in his piggy bank. In the first month he put $11 in the piggy bank. Every month thereafter he deposited a fixed amount in the piggy bank. When he checked his piggy bank, he had $195. What are some possible fixed amounts of money he could have deposited?

9. The shaded cell in the diagram moves clockwise in the order A, B, C, D, A, ...

At time $t = 0$ sec, the shaded square in the diagram is in the upper left corner (A). At time $t = 4$ sec, the shaded square moves to cell B. Every 4 seconds, the shaded square moves to the next cell. Where will the shaded square be after 3 minutes and 10 seconds?

10. If we know the sum $2 + 3 + 4 + 5$, how can we quickly find the sum $6 + 9 + 12 + 15$?

11. There are 23 players in a ping-pong tournament. Each player plays every other player exactly once. How many games will be played? (Hint: Suppose there are simply 2 players, 3 players, 4 players, and so on, and look for a pattern.)

12. The eighth term of an arithmetic sequence is 78. The 26th term is 240. Find the 62nd term.

REASONING AND PROOF

Refresher: Reasoning and proof (thinking and justifying) are important because they help students make sense of mathematics.

13. Use a calculator to determine 37^2, 337^2, 3337^2, and $33{,}337^2$. Use a pattern to predict $3{,}333{,}337^2$.

14. Pick pairs of consecutive whole numbers. Multiply the two numbers in the pair.

a. What pattern did you notice?

b. Make a conjecture about the result.

c. What type of reasoning did you use?

15. 1, 3, 5, and 7 are odd numbers, and $1 = 0 + 1$, $3 = 1 + 2$, $5 = 2 + 3$, and $7 = 3 + 4$.

a. Find the next three equations that continue the pattern.

b. Make a conjecture about a property of odd numbers.

c. What type of reasoning did you use?

16. What is the 247th term in the repeating sequence 8, 20, 41, 25, 8, 20, 41, 25, . . . ?

17. a. How would you use the first and last term in each list to determine the number of terms in the sequence 34, 35, 36? In the sequence 34, 35, 36, 37?

b. Look for a pattern to determine how many terms are in the arithmetic sequence 34, 35, 36, . . . , 621.

CONNECTIONS

Refresher: Connections (linking and applying mathematical ideas) are important because they deepen student understanding and make mathematics more meaningful, flexible, and useful.

18. Do the following.

a. What are the initial term, common difference, and equation for the arithmetic sequence 8, 16, 24, 32, 40, . . . ?

b. What are the initial term, common difference, and equation for the arithmetic sequence 10, 20, 30, 40, 50, . . . ?

c. Arithmetic sequences such as 8, 16, 24, 32, 40, . . . and 10, 20, 30, 40, 50, . . . are called skip-counting sequences. Write a definition for this term.

19. Consider the following sequence of equations: $4^3 = 64$, $4^2 = 16$, $4^1 = 4$, ... Use patterns to help your students evaluate 4^0.

20. Consider the sequence $3 \times 4 = 12$, $2 \times 4 = 8$, $1 \times 4 = 4$, $0 \times 4 = 0$, ... Use patterns to help your students evaluate -1×4 and -2×4.

21. The following equations form a "fact family" for the equation $5 + 3 = 8$: $5 + 3 = 8$, $3 + 5 = 8$, $8 - 3 = 5$, and $8 - 5 = 3$. Look for the pattern in the equations to write the fact family for the equation $n - 7 = 16$. Then circle the equation or equations that help you solve the equation $n - 7 = 16$.

22. Consider the sequence of staircases shown. To obtain the next staircase from the previous staircase, place one new column of squares along the tallest column of the shape, extending one square longer. Each square has a side length of one unit.

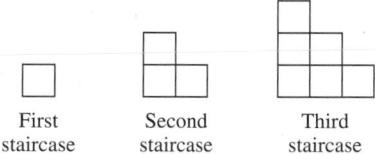

First staircase   Second staircase   Third staircase

a. Draw the next staircase.

b. Find the perimeter of each of the first four staircases and organize the results in a table.

c. Write an equation for the perimeter of nth staircase.

d. The third staircase has 3 steps. What would be the perimeter of a staircase that has 14 steps?

23. A teacher shows her students the division problem $52 \div 15$. Then she demonstrates the following strategy based on skip counting: She writes on the board the sequence 15, 30, 45 and the equation $52 - 45 = 7$. Then she writes $52 \div 15 = 3$ R7. Study the teacher's approach. Use the same approach to solve each division problem.

    a. $85 \div 20$ b. $52 \div 15$ c. $64 \div 12$

24. In the equation $a \div b = q$ Rr, the number a is the dividend, b is the divisor, q is the quotient, and r is the remainder, with $0 \le r < b$. We read $a \div b = q$ Rr as "a divided by b equals q remainder r." The following list shows a few equations.

$$0 \div 3 = 0 \text{ R}0$$
$$1 \div 3 = 0 \text{ R}1$$
$$2 \div 3 = 0 \text{ R}2$$

    a. Complete the next six rows of the list.

    b. Describe the pattern in the remainders for division by 3.

25. Find the next two equations that continue the pattern.

$$1 = 1^2$$
$$1 + 3 = 2^2$$
$$1 + 3 + 5 = 3^2$$
$$1 + 3 + 5 + 7 = 4^2$$

26. Find the next two equations that continue the pattern.

$$2 = 1 \times 2$$
$$2 + 4 = 2 \times 3$$
$$2 + 4 + 6 = 3 \times 4$$
$$2 + 4 + 6 + 8 = 4 \times 5$$

COMMUNICATION

Refresher: Communication (written and verbal explanations using representations and proper mathematical vocabulary) is important because it helps students refine and strengthen their understanding.

27. Answer the following.

    a. What is a pattern?   b. What is a conjecture?

    c. What is inductive reasoning?

    d. What is a limitation of inductive reasoning?

28. $1, 2, 3, 4, \ldots$ is a sequence.

    a. Could it be an arithmetic sequence? Why?

    b. Could it be a geometric sequence? Why?

29. $7, 7, 7, 7, \ldots$ is a sequence.

    a. Could it be a repeating sequence? Why?

    b. Could it be an arithmetic sequence? Why?

    c. Could it be a geometric sequence? Why?

More practice with the ideas of the section

30. Fill in the blank. Choose one of the following words or phrases: *arithmetic, deductive reasoning, exercises, generalize, geometric, inductive reasoning, pattern, problem solving, representations, sequence, skip counting, stretch,* or *wishful thinking.*

    a. _____ help(s) you to reinforce your skill in performing calculations and applying procedures.

    b. _____ is finding a way to reach a goal that is not immediately attainable.

    c. Similarity or regularity in observations that allows you to predict the behavior in the observations or what comes next is called _____.

    d. The process of using several observations to make a conclusion is called _____.

    e. _____ are aids such as tables, graphs, diagrams, and algebra that we use to communicate and learn mathematical ideas.

    f. In a(n) _____ sequence, we add a constant to the previous term to obtain the next term.

    g. $5, 10, 15, 20, 25, \ldots$ is an example of a(n) _____ sequence.

    h. Students are expected to describe, extend, and _____ patterns.

31. Find the next three likely terms in each sequence.

    a. $5, 8, 11, 14, 17,$ ___, ___, ___

    b. $1, 8, 27, 64, 125,$ ___, ___, ___

    c. $5, 10, 20, 40, 80, 160,$ ___, ___, ___

    d. $1, 1, 2, 3, 5, 8, 13, 21,$ ___, ___, ___

    e. $4, 11, 6, 13, 8, 15, 10,$ ___, ___, ___

32. What are the next three likely terms in the sequence $1, 2, 6, 24, \ldots$?

33. Pick a few whole numbers.

    a. Multiply each number by 5.

    b. What pattern do you notice?

    c. Make a conjecture about the result.

    d. What type of reasoning did you use?

34. The sequence $-3, 1, 5, 9, \ldots$ is an arithmetic sequence.

    a. Describe the sequence in words.

    b. Represent the sequence with a table.

    c. Represent the sequence with a graph.

    d. Represent the sequence with an equation.

    e. How many terms are less than 513?

35. Compare $46 \cdot 47$ and $465 \cdot 465$. Compare $134 \cdot 135$ and $1345 \cdot 1345$. Then compare $728 \cdot 729$ and $7285 \cdot 7285$.

    a. Given $36 \cdot 37 = 1332$, predict $365 \cdot 365$.

    b. Given $4725 \cdot 4725 = 22,325,625$, what product can you easily predict?

36. A teacher writes the sequence $5 + 2a, 10 + 3a, 30 + 4a, \ldots$ on the board. He asks the class, "What is the next likely term?" A few minutes later, Marissa shouts, "The next likely term is $120 + 5a$!" Explain how Marissa could be correct.

37. What is the tens digit of the number 21^{84}?

38. Do the following.

    a. Calculate 64^2, 664^2, 6664^2, and $66,664^2$.

    b. Use a pattern to predict $6,666,664^2$.

39. Find the sum of each arithmetic series using Gauss's method.

    a. $204 + 206 + 208 + \ldots + 410$

    b. $88 + 96 + 104 + \ldots + 496$

40. Represent each arithmetic sequence with an equation.

   a. 1, 6, 11, 16, . . . and 5, 10, 15, 20, . . .

   b. 5, 8, 11, 14, . . . and 3, 6, 9, 12, . . .

41. Represent the arithmetic sequence 5, 9, 13, 17, . . . in the following ways.

   a. table   **b.** algebra

42. The sequence 768, 192, 48, . . . is a geometric sequence.

   a. What is the initial term?   **b.** What is the common ratio?

   c. Represent the sequence with an equation.

43. Find a geometric sequence such that the fifth term is 62,500.

44. Use inductive reasoning to find the ones digit of 4^{75}.

45. Use patterns to complete the following equations.

   a. $3 \times 9 =$ ___   **b.** $3 \times 90 =$ ___

   c. $3 \times 900 =$ ___   **d.** $3 \times 9000 =$ ___

46. Find the next three equations that continue the pattern.

$$0 + 1 = 1^2$$
$$1 + 3 = 2^2$$
$$3 + 6 = 3^2$$
$$6 + 10 = 4^2$$
$$10 + 15 = 5^2$$

47. The standard rule of thumb for depreciation of a used car is that it is worth only 85% of its value every year. The manufacturer's suggested retail price of a car is $25,000.

   a. Make a table to show how much the car will be worth in the next 3 years.

   b. When does the vehicle experience the largest decrease in value?

   c. What is the ratio of two consecutive values in the table?

48. Jane arranges cotton swabs to make a chain of triangles. The chain continues by adding one new triangle on the far right of the shape.

   a. Draw the next two shapes.

   b. How many cotton swabs does Jane need to make the seventh shape?

   c. Jane has 68 cotton swabs. Can she use all of them to make a chain of triangles? Explain.

   d. How many cotton swabs does Jane need to make the nth shape?

49. Jim arranges toothpicks as shown. The first arrangement requires 4 toothpicks, and the second one requires 10 toothpicks. How many toothpicks does Jim need to make the sixth shape?

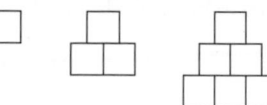

50. The following numbers arranged in the shape of a triangle help form Pascal's triangle:

			1			row 0
		1		1		row 1
	1		2		1	row 2
1		3		3		1 row 3

   a. Each row begins and ends with 1, and we obtain an entry in the row by adding two adjacent numbers. Find row 4 of Pascal's triangle.

   b. Apparently, each row corresponds to some power of 11: $11^0 = 1$, $11^1 = 11$, $11^2 = 121$, and $11^3 = 1331$. Use Pascal's triangle to predict the value of 11^4.

   c. Use a calculator to calculate 11^4. Compare the result to your prediction.

   d. Do entries in row 5 of Pascal's triangle accurately predict 11^5? Explain.

51. The terms in a sequence are shapes consisting of dots.

   a. Sketch the next two shapes in the sequence.

   b. Write an equation that tells you the number of dots in the nth shape. Check your answer.

52. The graph shows two sequences, A and B.

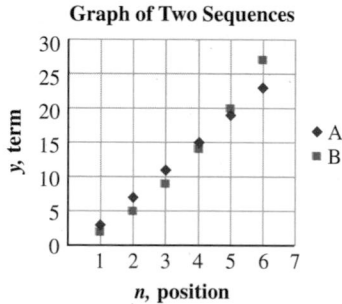

Graph of Two Sequences

   a. Which sequence is an arithmetic sequence?

   b. How can you tell?

Problem-Solving Strategies

Why Problem-Solving Strategies Are Important

We engage in problem solving every day. For example, you hop in your car to go to class. But the car doesn't start. Now a problem needs to be solved. You play the radio to test the battery. You check the gauge to see whether the car has fuel. You open the hood to inspect the engine, hoping for clues. You consider past car problems and think about how you resolved similar problems. Eventually, you solve the problem, even if it means having the car towed to a repair shop. Mathematical problems are similar to car problems in that we try different strategies and usually one of them works. The NCTM problem-solving standards expect K–8 students to "apply and adapt a variety of appropriate strategies to solve problems."

Problem-solving strategies are important for two main reasons. First, they help you solidify and extend your knowledge. Second, several strategies are also representation tools (such as Make a Table or Draw a Diagram) that you will use to understand and teach mathematics.

Problem Solving Is a Four-Phase Process

Chuck Painter/Stanford News Service

George Pólya, a prolific researcher and enthusiastic teacher, was interested in discovering and explaining solutions to problems. His classic book *How to Solve It* (1957) is a systematic study of methods for discovery and solving problems. More than 1 million copies have sold in 21 languages. His ideas still affect how elementary grade students, teachers, and mathematicians approach problem solving. He identified four phases of problem solving and listed strategies suitable for the elementary mathematics curriculum.

This proven process relies on simple principles that will increase your likelihood of solving mathematical problems. We list and interpret each of the four phases in Concept Map 1.1. Read the interpretations periodically and follow the four phases. Teachers with good problem-solving skills can give their students more learning opportunities.

> **Concept Map 1.1**   Problem Solving Is a Dynamic, Four-Phase Process

Phase 1 Understand the problem Read the problem carefully. Identify the question you have to answer. Determine the known and unknown information. You may need to reread or restate the problem, draw a picture, or introduce some notation to gain more clarity about the question.

Phase 2 Devise a plan Explore various strategies until you realize a particular strategy looks promising. This is often the most difficult phase in the problem-solving process—finding a strategy that works—so it's important to be familiar with a variety of strategies. You may need to reread the problem.

Phase 4 Look back Recheck your calculations, review your reasoning, and make sure that your answer agrees with the information given. You may need to make some minor adjustments or reread the problem. When you are satisfied with your solution, rewrite the explanation neatly and carefully in a logical order.

Phase 3 Carry out the plan Implement your plan. Check your calculations and reasoning as you proceed. Make sure you use appropriate units for variables and appropriate labels for diagrams, tables, or lists. Sometimes the strategy you choose will not lead to progress, and you may need to devise a new plan.

Your students should be able to follow the four phases too, although slightly different terms may apply, such as *explore, plan, solve,* and *examine.* You may need to shift from phase to phase until you are satisfied with a solution (as shown by the dashed arrows in the concept map). You not only need basic skills and persistence but also need to ask yourself many questions as you attempt to apply what you already know to solve new problems. You should also examine how changes in the conditions change the solution; doing this helps you achieve a deeper understanding of the problem.

Problem Solving Is Opportunity

There is a difference between an exercise and a problem. Exercises involve performing calculations or applying routine procedures. In contrast, problems help students to think about what they already know, forcing them to extend their knowledge, create connections between old and new ideas, and make sense of mathematics. Together, good problems and problem-solving strategies make it possible for students to think more deeply about mathematical ideas. Eventually, we want past problems to become exercises. Successful problem solvers ask themselves many questions to help apply what they know to solve a problem.

Problem-Solving Strategies

In the previous section, we used two of the strategies described by Pólya, the Look for a Pattern and the Make a Table strategies, to solve problems. Table 1.4 lists Pólya's famous **problem-solving strategies.**

TABLE 1.4   **Problem-Solving Strategies**

Look for a Pattern	Work Backward
Make a Table	Use Direct Reasoning
Guess and Check	Solve an Equation
Make an Orderly List	Consider Special Cases
Solve a Simpler Problem	Eliminate Possibilities
Think of a Similar Problem	Solve an Equivalent Problem
Use a Formula	Use a Model
Draw a Diagram	Be Ingenious

Once you become aware of the possible strategies for solving problems, you'll have a better chance of preparing an organized and convincing solution to a mathematical problem. Often, more than one strategy solves a problem. We now describe some problem-solving strategies.

Guess and Check Strategy   The Guess and Check strategy is an iterative process. The idea is to make a reasonable guess and then adjust the guess based on information in the problem. As students improve their guess, they clarify their understanding of basic relationships in the problem, which helps them solve the problem.

EXAMPLE 1.11

PROBLEM SOLVING

REASONING

A traffic engineer was conducting a traffic safety study at a busy intersection. Altogether, 196 cars and trucks passed through the intersection during the study. There were three times as many cars as trucks. How many trucks passed through the intersection?

SOLUTION

Phase 1 Understand the problem. We must find the number of trucks that passed through the intersection. There were three times as many cars as trucks (for example, one truck and three cars or two trucks and six cars).

Phase 2 Devise a plan. We will use the Guess and Check strategy and organize the results in a table.

(continued)

Phase 3 Carry out the plan. Table 1.5, constructed with appropriate headings, organizes the guesses. We begin by guessing there were 43 trucks. This means there were $3 \cdot 43 = 129$ cars and $43 + 129 = 172$ vehicles. The number of vehicles is too low. So we should increase the number of trucks to increase the number of vehicles. So let's try 51 trucks. This means there were $3 \cdot 51 = 153$ cars and $51 + 153 = 204$ vehicles. The number of vehicles is too high, so we need fewer trucks. This process continues. Eventually, we should determine the correct answer.

TABLE 1.5   **Using a Table to Organize Guesses**

Trucks	Cars	Total vehicles	Total vehicles versus 196
43	129	172	low
51	153	204	high
49	147	196	exact

Phase 4 Look back. The problem states the traffic engineer counted 196 vehicles. Let's double-check our calculations: The number of cars is three times the number of trucks. We guessed 49 trucks. The number of cars is $3 \cdot 49 = 147$. The total number of vehicles is 196, and $49 + 147 = 196$. This agrees with the information given in the question.

▲

An elementary grade textbook used the following problem to illustrate the Guess and Check strategy.

> ◆ **Classroom Connection**
>
> • *Mathematics*, Grade 5, p. 210
>
> A family plans to build a rectangular dog run for their dog Shamrock. The run will be 4 feet longer than it is wide. If 60 feet of fencing is used, what will be the length and width? (From Randall I. Charles. © 2004 by Pearson Education, Inc. or its affiliates. Used by permission. All rights reserved.)

Make an Orderly List Strategy   The Make an Orderly List strategy is useful for determining the number of possible ways to perform a task. It helps guard against missing or repeating possibilities.

Tables and lists look alike because both help organize results. However, we typically use tables to help analyze patterns, while we use lists to count the number of possible ways to perform a task. The next problem illustrates the Make an Orderly List strategy.

 EXAMPLE 1.12   How many ways can you make 16¢ using only dimes, nickels, and pennies?

PROBLEM SOLVING   SOLUTION

Phase 1 Understand the problem. We must find the number of possible ways dimes, nickels, and pennies make 16¢.

Phase 2 Devise a plan. We will use the Make an Orderly List strategy to organize and count the possibilities.

Phase 3 Carry out the plan. We constructed a list with columns for the number of dimes (D), nickels (N), and pennies (P). There are six ways to make 16¢.

D	N	P	total
0	0	16	16¢
0	1	11	16¢
0	2	6	16¢
0	3	1	16¢
1	0	6	16¢
1	1	1	16¢

Phase 4 Look back. We used as many pennies as possible (16 pennies), converted them into nickels, and then converted some nickels into dimes. The organized list suggests there are only six possible ways to make 16¢ with dimes, pennies, and nickels.

▲

The following Classroom Connection asks students to make a list to solve a problem.

 Classroom Connection

● *Mathematics*, Grade 4, p. 328

Make an organized list to solve the problem. Write the answer in a complete sentence.

Andrea and Calvin are decorating for a party. They want to use two colors of crepe paper. Their choices are red, blue, green, orange, and yellow. How many ways can they choose two colors? (From Randall I. Charles. © 2004 by Pearson Education, Inc. or its affiliates. Used by permission. All rights reserved.)

Solve a Simpler Problem Strategy The main idea behind the Solve a Simpler Problem strategy is to solve related, simpler problems in hope of gaining enough insight to solve the original problem. For example, to find 333336^2, we could solve the simpler problems $36^2 = 1296$, $336^2 = 112,896$, and $3336^2 = 11,128,896$; look for a pattern; and then solve the original problem. What is your solution to this problem?

CONNECTION **Think of a Similar Problem Strategy** The Think of a Similar Problem strategy builds on past problem-solving experience to solve a related problem. In Section 1.1, we learned how to "determine the 158th term in the repeating sequence 5, 11, 6, 5, 11, 6, 5, 11, 6, ..." We could use a similar approach to solve the problem "Determine the 200th term in the repeating sequence K, W, 8, 15, H, K, W, 8, 15, H, ..." As another example, we learned how to find the sum $1 + 2 + 3 + \ldots + 100$ using the method of Gauss and then applied the same approach to find the sum $85 + 79 + 73 + 67 + 61 + 55 + 49 + 43$. As you solve problems, you create a bank of problems that you can draw upon to help you solve similar problems. The more math you learn, the more math you see.

Use a Formula Strategy The Use a Formula strategy requires applying known mathematical formulas, such as for perimeter and area.

EXAMPLE 1.13

PROBLEM SOLVING

A farmer has 32 pieces of 4-foot-long by 1-foot-wide planks. He wants to use all of the planks to build a 4-foot-high rectangular fence that encloses the largest area possible for his chickens, without cutting any planks. What are the dimensions of the rectangular fence?

SOLUTION

Phase 1 Understand the problem. We must use 32 planks, each 4 feet long and 1 foot wide, to build a rectangular fence that encloses the largest area possible without cutting any planks. The perimeter is 32 feet. The length and width must be whole numbers.

Phase 2 Devise a plan. We will apply the Use a Formula strategy. We need formulas for the perimeter and area of a rectangle with length l and width w. The formula for the perimeter is $P = 2 \cdot l + 2 \cdot w$, and the formula for the area is given by $A = l \cdot w$. The perimeter is 32 feet, and the length and width must be whole numbers that satisfy the equation $32 = 2 \cdot l + 2 \cdot w$. We need to choose l and w such that this equation is satisfied and the area A is as large as possible.

Phase 3 Carry out the plan. The length and width must satisfy the equation $32 = 2 \cdot l + 2 \cdot w$, or $16 = l + w$. This means l varies from 1 to 15 feet. Table 1.6 organizes the possible dimensions for l and w (in feet) and gives the resulting area $l \cdot w$ (in square feet).

(continued)

TABLE 1.6 Possible Dimensions for *l* and *w*

l	1	2	3	4	5	6	7	8	9	10	11	12	13	14	15
w	15	14	13	12	11	10	9	8	7	6	5	4	3	2	1
l × *w*	15	28	39	48	55	60	63	64	63	60	55	48	39	28	15

Table 1.6 reveals the largest area is 64 square feet. So the rectangular fence that encloses the largest area is actually square; it has a length of 8 feet and width of 8 feet.

Phase 4 Look back. The perimeter of the fence is $(2 \cdot 8) + (2 \cdot 8) = 16 + 16 = 32$ ft, which uses all of the planks as required. The largest product in the table is 64. So the fence that encloses the largest area has a length and a width of 8 feet.

▲

As we mentioned earlier, you will achieve a deeper understanding of a problem when you reflect upon how changes in the problem affect the solution. For example, what if the farmer had 31 planks and each plank was 4 feet long and 2 feet wide? Would he be able to use all of the planks?

Draw a Diagram Strategy The Draw a Diagram strategy is useful for visualizing relationships and understanding problems. Diagrams help represent a situation, make a problem less abstract, evoke thought, and keep track of your progress. Drawing a diagram is a common strategy in the elementary mathematics curriculum. In the next problem, we draw a diagram to help represent and solve the classic fence post problem.

EXAMPLE 1.14

PROBLEM SOLVING
REPRESENTATION

A farmer built a rectangular fence. Each corner of the rectangle had a post. The shorter sides of the fence each had four equally spaced posts, while the longer sides each had six equally spaced posts. How many posts did she use?

SOLUTION

Phase 1 Understand the problem. We must place fence posts on each corner of the fence and then on the sides. We need to determine the total number of fence posts.

Phase 2 Devise a plan. We will use the Draw a Diagram strategy to avoid counting the corners twice.

Phase 3 Carry out the plan. We draw a rectangular fence with fence posts at the corners; see Figure 1(a). The shorter sides each have four fence posts, so we need to add two more to each side; see Figure 1(b). The longer sides have six fence posts, so we need to add four more to each side; see Figure 1(c).

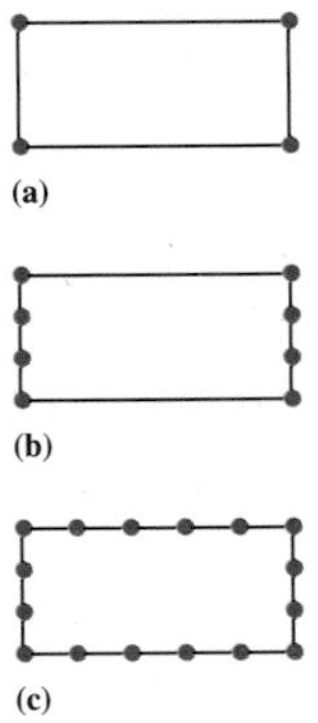

(a)

(b)

(c)

FIGURE 1

Fence posts are placed along the sides of the fence.

Figure 1 shows the pictures that represent the fence. In Figure 1(a), we put posts in the corners, corresponding to the information in the first sentence of the problem statement. In Figure 1(b), we added 2 equally spaced posts on the shorter sides, and in Figure 1(c) we added 4 equally spaced posts on the longer side. We count the posts in Figure 1(c) and conclude the farmer used 16 posts in all.

Phase 4 Look back. Each corner has a post. The shorter sides each have 4 equally spaced fence posts, and the longer sides each have 6 equally spaced fence posts. The farmer used 16 fence posts in all.

▲

Suppose the farmer builds a rectangular fence with posts in the corners, *n* equally spaced posts on each shorter side, and *m* equally spaced posts on the longer sides. How many posts will she use?

Work Backward Strategy The Work Backward strategy may be appropriate when the final result is known or the problem involves a sequence of reversible steps. The familiar

"I'm thinking of a number" problem illustrates how you can work backward to solve a problem. These types of problems challenge students to identify inverse relationships (such as addition and subtraction, multiplication and division, and squares and square roots) and to use proper sequences of events. Ancient Egyptians posed and solved these types of problems thousands of years ago.

EXAMPLE 1.15

CONNECTION
PROBLEM SOLVING
REPRESENTATION

Eight is subtracted from a number. Then the result is divided by 9. Then 3 is added to the result. Then the result is squared. The final result is 49. What was the original number?

SOLUTION

Phase 1 Understand the problem. We need to find the original number.

Phase 2 Devise a plan. We will use the Work Backward strategy and draw a diagram to record the operations and then work backward using inverse operations.

Phase 3 Carry out the plan. First, we draw a diagram to record the sequence of operations.

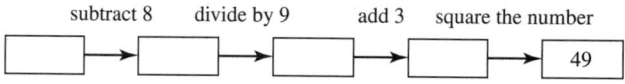

Then, using inverse operations, we work backward to fill in the missing numbers.

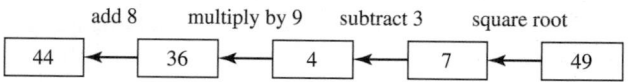

The original number was 44.

Phase 4 Look back. Work forward beginning with 44:

$$44 - 8 = 36 \qquad 36 \div 9 = 4 \qquad 4 + 3 = 7 \qquad 7^2 = 49$$

This calculation agrees with the final result.

Use Direct Reasoning Strategy We illustrate the Use Direct Reasoning strategy with an interesting problem. Suppose a cereal company puts a prize in each box. There are four possible prizes, and you want to get two identical prizes. How many boxes would you need to purchase to guarantee you get two identical prizes?

Say the prizes are A, B, C, and D. You could purchase two boxes and end up with prizes AA or AB, for example, so purchasing two boxes does not guarantee you would get two identical prizes. You could purchase four boxes, and get one A, B, C, and D prize from each box, so purchasing four boxes does not guarantee you would get two identical prizes. However, the fifth box must contain a prize that results in two identical prizes because you already have one of each.

PROBLEM SOLVING

Be Ingenious Strategy The Be Ingenious strategy requires creativity and thinking outside the box. In May 2010, a bus company in China received complaints that its bus drivers sometimes brake too quickly or turn too sharply causing an uncomfortable ride for the passengers. The company hung a large bowl of water in the bus and expected the bus driver to finish the day with the same amount of water. It also installed cameras to discourage bus drivers from adding water to the bowl. The company devised an ingenious way to encourage the bus drivers to drive more carefully.

Combining Strategies We often combine strategies to solve problems.

EXAMPLE 1.16 A farmer built a ladder using 18 rungs. The rungs on the ladder were 14.5 cm apart and 2.4 cm thick. What is the distance from the bottom of the lowest rung to the top of the highest rung?

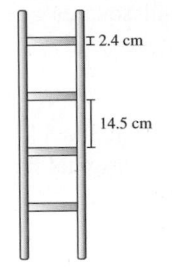

FIGURE 2

The rungs are 2.4 cm wide and 14.5 cm apart.

SOLUTION

Phase 1 Understand the problem. We must find the distance from the bottom of the lowest rung to the top of the highest rung on the ladder.

Phase 2 Devise a plan. We will apply the Solve a Simpler Problem and Draw a Diagram strategies and draw a ladder with four rungs to gain insight into the problem.

Phase 3 Carry out the plan. Figure 2 represents a ladder with four rungs; there are three spaces between the rungs.

REPRESENTATION

The diagram makes it easier to visualize and calculate the distance: $4 \cdot 2.4 + 3 \cdot 14.5 = 53.1$, so the distance is 53.1 cm. This suggests the distance from the bottom of the lowest rung to the top of the highest rung on the ladder with 18 rungs is $18 \cdot 2.4 + 17 \cdot 14.5 = 289.7$ cm.

Phase 4 Look back. The diagram in Figure 2 suggests we multiply the number of rungs by 2.4, multiply one fewer than the number of rungs by 14.5, and then add the products. This is precisely what we did. ▲

REASONING
REPRESENTATION

Multiple Approaches Many problems can be solved with more than one approach. For example, you can solve the following Released Item using the Make a Table or Draw a Diagram strategies.

▶ **RELEASED ITEM**

● NAEP, 2003

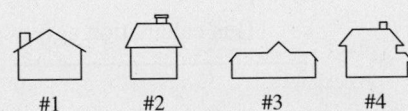

#1   #2   #3   #4

Allen, Bridgitte, Chaz, and Diann each live in a different house on the same side of a street. The houses and their numbers are shown above. Only one of the other three people lives next to Bridgitte. Chaz lives next to Bridgitte and next to Diann. Which person could live in house number 2?

a. Allen only   **b.** Chaz only   **c.** Diann only   **d.** Chaz or Diann   **e.** Any of these four people could live in house number 2.

43% of eighth-grade students chose the correct answer.

The four-phase process and strategies enable you to solve problems in a methodical way, think deeply about the mathematics you know, appreciate the subtleties of mathematics, acquire new knowledge, and change the way you think. Scientists, engineers, and programmers, to name a few, use this same process. They may use markedly different terms, such as *analysis, design, implementation,* and *validation,* but they all deal with understanding a complex problem and developing an appropriate solution in a methodical way. Problems do not have to be exceedingly difficult. They just need to perplex you and make you think of new ways to apply and connect the information you already know.

> ■ **Historical Note**
>
> George Pólya, one of six children, was born on December 13, 1887, in Budapest, Hungary. He received a PhD in mathematics in 1912, then accepted a 2-year post-doctoral position at the University of Göttingen, Germany, a major mathematical center at the time. In 1914, he eagerly accepted an offer for a permanent position with the Swiss Federal Institute of Technology (ETH) in Zurich, Switzerland. Pólya was a prolific researcher who published papers in many areas of math, such as number theory, combinatorics, analysis, and probability. After spending 26 years at ETH, he obtained a position at Stanford University, where he wrote *How to Solve It* in 1945. This book influences the way problem solving is taught in the pre-K–12 mathematics curriculum, as well as mathematics for elementary teaching. Pólya was married for 67 years. This well-respected and well-liked mathematician died on September 7, 1985, in Palo Alto, California. (Alexanderson, 2000)

QUESTIONS FOR SECTION 1.2

REPRESENTATION

Refresher: Representations (language, diagrams, tables, symbols, algebra, manipulatives, and contextualized situations) are important because we use them to organize, record, and communicate mathematical ideas and to make them more comprehensible.

1. Consider the following "I'm thinking of a number" problem: Think of a number. Add 5 to the number. Square the result. Add 15 to the result. Divide the result by 4. The result is 46.

   a. Draw a diagram to organize the operations. Solve the problem.

   b. What was the original number?

2. If you cut a stick into 3094 pieces, how many cuts do you need to make?

3. A fireman used a ladder with 56 rungs. The rungs on the ladder were 14 in. apart and 1.5 in. thick. What is the distance from the bottom of the lowest rung to the top of the highest rung?

4. A rectangular table can seat 12 people: four people can sit at the longer side, and two people can sit at the shorter side. A party planner decides to place 29 of these tables side by side in one long row so that adjacent shorter sides are touching. What is the maximum number of people that can be seated?

5. How many different ways can you make 21¢ with coins?

PROBLEM SOLVING

Refresher: Problem solving (reaching a goal that is not immediately attainable) is important because it helps students think more deeply about what they know and deal with unfamiliar situations.

6. A chapter in a book begins on page 143 and ends on page 851. How many pages are in the chapter?

7. What is the tens digit in the number $3 \times 4 \times 5 \times \ldots \times 343 \times 344$?

8. Tonya, Rosa, and Naomi like different types of ice cream: vanilla, chocolate chip, and pistachio. They each like one type, and no two girls like the same type. Rosa and the girl who likes chocolate chip are sisters. Naomi is the best friend of the girl who likes vanilla. Tonya does not like crunchy things in her ice cream. Which girl likes which flavor?

9. A phone company charges a $4 monthly service fee and $0.25 for every minute of long-distance call time. If your telephone budget is $9.41, what is the maximum number of minutes of long-distance calls you can make?

10. When a teacher divided her students into groups of four, she had three students remaining. When she divided them into groups of five, she had four students remaining. There were fewer than 40 students in the class. How many students could be in the class?

11. A carpenter has a piece of wood that is 51 cm long. He cuts the piece of wood to build every edge of one cube. When he is done, 3 cm of the wood are leftover. What is the length of each edge of the cube?

REASONING AND PROOF

Refresher: Reasoning and proof (thinking and justifying) are important because they help students make sense of mathematics.

12. Pick pairs of consecutive whole numbers. Multiply the two numbers.

    a. What pattern did you notice?

    b. Make a conjecture about the result.

    c. What type of reasoning did you use?

13. A cereal company put a prize in every cereal box. There are six different possible prizes. A mother has triplets and wants to give each child the same prize. How many boxes does she need to purchase to guarantee she obtains three identical prizes?

14. You have eight marbles. Seven of the marbles have the same weight, and one marble is heavier. Explain how you can determine the heavier marble by using a balance scale exactly

   a. three times.   b. two times.

15. You have nine marbles. Eight of the marbles have the same weight, and the other marble is heavier. What is the minimum number of weighings needed to identify the heaviest marble using a balance scale?

16. Mr. and Mrs. Turner have four daughters. Each daughter has two brothers. How many children do Mr. and Mrs. Turner have altogether? Explain.

17. A student opened his book and realized the product of the numbers on the pages facing each other was 215,760. What were the page numbers of the pages facing each other?

18. You have a barrel of water, an 8-quart pail, a 5-quart pail, and an empty barrel. You need to measure 9 quarts of water. Describe how to measure exactly 9 quarts of water using these two pails. Assume you have a large container that will hold as much water as you need.

CONNECTIONS

Refresher: Connections (linking and applying mathematical ideas) are important because they deepen student understanding and make mathematics more meaningful, flexible, and useful.

19. A landscaper pays $18 for each increment of 12 square feet of sod. She needs enough sod for a large yard that is 62 feet long and 52 feet wide. How much will it cost her to put sod across the whole yard?

20. Do the following.

   a. Explain why the hour hand on a cuckoo clock turns at a rate of 0.5 degrees per minute.

   b. How quickly does the minute hand of the clock turn?

21. The video store charges $3 to rent a DVD. Every fifth DVD that a customer rents is free. Gary rented a total of 46 DVDs during the past year. How much did that cost him?

22. Consider the following equation: $4 \div 9 = 0$ R4, where 4 is the smallest whole number that has a remainder of 4 when divided by 9.

   a. What is the second smallest whole number that has a remainder of 4 when it is divided by 9?

   b. What is the third smallest whole number that has a remainder of 4 when it is divided by 9?

   c. What is the 187th smallest whole number that has a remainder of 4 when it is divided by 9?

23. A homeowner uses white and dark tiles to make a patio. She uses the white tiles to form a border around the dark tiles, as shown here.

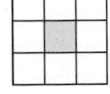 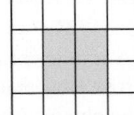 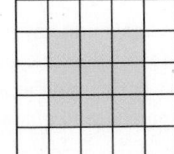

   a. Draw the next shape in the sequence.

   b. How many white tiles are required for the nth shape? Write a general formula.

   c. How many dark tiles are needed in the smallest patio such that the number of dark tiles is at least three times the number of white tiles?

24. A deli is offering a special for its sandwiches. A customer will receive three free sandwiches for every five sandwiches purchased. Jane ordered 634 sandwiches for an office party at a large company. How many sandwiches did Jane have to pay for?

25. Find the area of the shaded region. The line is tangent to both circles. Each circle has a radius of 5 cm. (Hint: The area A of a circle with a radius of r cm is $A = \pi r^2$ cm². Also, the shaded region extends to all three points of tangencies.)

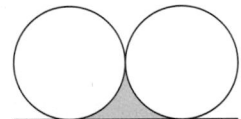

COMMUNICATION

Refresher: Communication (written and verbal explanations using representations and proper mathematical vocabulary) is important because it helps students refine and strengthen their understanding.

26. Why should students be aware of problem-solving strategies?

27. Can a multiple of 6 ever have a ones digit equal to 3? Explain.

28. Polly solved the following problem: "A chapter in a book begins on page 143 and ends on page 851. How many pages are in the chapter?"

   a. Polly's answer was 708 pages. How did she get this answer?

   b. This answer is incorrect. What advice would you give her?

29. A bank offers two checking account options. Option A has a monthly service fee of $3.50, with an additional fee of $0.15 for each check cashed. Option B has a monthly service fee of $5, with an additional fee of $0.09 for each check cashed. Which option should a customer who writes 25 or fewer checks per month choose?

30. A teacher uses the equation $(42 \cdot 4) + (15 \cdot 2) = 198$ to pose a classic barnyard problem: "A farmer wants to know how many horses and ducks are on the farm. He counts 198 legs and 57 animals. How many of each animal are on the farm?"

   a. How does the teacher extract the solution from the equation?

   b. Write your own equation to help you pose and solve a similar barnyard problem.

More practice with the ideas of the section

31. Fill in the blank. Choose one of the following words or phrases: *answers, call a friend, Guess and Check, guess and stop,* How to Solve It, How to Succeed in Math Without Trying, *leave it blank, Think of a Similar Problem, Solve a Simpler Problem, solve an unrelated problem, questions,* or *wishful.*

   a. The main idea in the _____ strategy is to solve related, simpler problems in the hope of gaining enough insight to solve the original problem.

b. The main idea in the _____ strategy is to make a reasonable guess and then adjust the guess based on information in the problem.

c. The main idea in the _____ strategy is to build on past problem-solving experience to solve a related problem.

d. George Pólya, a well-liked and well-respected mathematician, wrote the influential and successful book _____.

e. Successful problem solvers ask themselves many _____ to help apply what they know to the task of solving a problem.

32. It takes a lumberjack 4 minutes to cut a 3-foot log from a piece of timber that is 62 feet long.

a. How many 3-foot pieces can he cut?

b. How long would it take him to make all the cuts?

33. Carli spent two-thirds of her money and then spent $4 more. Then she spent half of her remaining money. It cost her $1 for the bus ride home. She then had $5 left. How much money did she start with?

34. A chef cuts a slab of turkey into 56 slices of meat for sandwiches. How many cuts did he make? Explain.

35. A class sold two types of raffle tickets to raise money for its field trip to the zoo. It sold a total of 43 raffle tickets. Raffle tickets to win a 1-day pass to Disneyland cost $2 per ticket, and raffle tickets to win a set of golf clubs cost $5 per ticket. The class raised $161 altogether. How many raffle tickets to Disneyland did they sell?

36. A video store charges $3.50 to rent a DVD. Every fourth DVD that a customer rents is free. Brooke paid a total of $255.50 last year for renting DVDs. How many free DVDs did she receive?

37. How much is each X and O worth when XOOO is worth 49¢ and XXXOO is worth 91¢?

38. Diane has $1.02 in change consisting of quarters, dimes, nickels, and pennies. She has twice as many dimes as quarters. She has fewer nickels than pennies. What is the least number of coins possible?

39. Determine the ones digit in the number 7^{658}.

40. There are cars and motorcycles in a campus parking lot. The parking attendant noticed there are a total of 294 tires and a total of 85 cars and motorcycles. How many cars and how many motorcycles are in the lot?

41. A carpenter needs to cut a 24-foot piece of wood into two pieces. One piece must be 6 feet longer than the other piece. Find the lengths of the two pieces.

42. What is the minimum number of cards you need to select from a shuffled deck of 52 ordinary playing cards to guarantee you selected

a. two cards with the same suit?

b. three cards with the same suit?

(Hint: Remember, there are four suits: hearts, diamonds, spades, and clubs.)

43. Five horses (Happy-Go-Lucky, Last Chance, You-Too-Slow, You Betcha, and Boomer) raced to the finish line. Boomer placed third. You Betcha finished between Happy-Go-Lucky and Last Chance. Happy-Go-Lucky finished after Last Chance but before You-Too-Slow. In what order did they finish?

44. What is the hundreds digit in the number $1 \times 2 \times 3 \times 4 \times \ldots \times 567$?

45. A farmer has 34 pieces of 1-foot-wide planks. He wants to use the planks to fence a rectangular garden. The length of the rectangle must be at least 5 feet longer than the width. What are the dimensions of the rectangular fence that encloses the largest area without cutting any planks?

46. Mrs. Emme has some candy. She wants to split it evenly among the students in her class who correctly solve a math problem. If four students solve the problem correctly, then there will be two extra pieces of candy. If seven students solve the problem correctly, then there will be three extra pieces of candy. What is the minimum number of pieces of candy Mrs. Emme can have?

47. Zed and Iggy are two snails who like to race. Zed crawls at a rate of 6 cm per hour, while Iggy crawls at a rate of 8 cm per hour. Zed is slower and got a 25-cm head start. If the race were 110 cm, who would win the exciting snail race?

48. Think of a number. Multiply the number by 7. Add 6 to the result. Divide the result by 3. Square the result. The result is 1369. What is the number?

SECTION 1.3 Algebra and Problem Solving

Is It Magic or Algebra?

A magician said to a volunteer from the audience:

Pick a number, but don't tell me what it is.
Add 15 to it.
Multiply your answer by 3.
Subtract 9.
Divide by 3.
Subtract 8.
Now tell me your answer.

"Thirty-two," replied the volunteer. The magician immediately guessed the number that the volunteer had originally chosen: 28. The volunteer nodded in agreement.

How did the magician know so quickly? Think about this problem before reading on. The easiest way to think about this problem is to represent the unknown number with a variable. If we let n stand for the volunteer's number, then we can write an equation.

Pick a number, but don't tell me what it is.	n
Add 15 to it.	$n + 15$
Multiply your answer by 3.	$3(n + 15) = 3n + 45$
Subtract 9.	$3n + 45 - 9 = 3n + 36$
Divide by 3.	$(3n + 36) \div 3 = n + 12$
Subtract 8.	$(n + 12) - 8 = n + 4$
Now tell me your answer.	

Whatever answer the magician hears, he simply subtracts 4 from it and the result is the number the volunteer picked. To the audience, it's magic, but to the magician, it's algebra! The full problem could be written as $[3(n + 15) - 9] \div 3 - 8 = n + 4$.

What Is Algebra?

A **variable** is a letter or other symbol, such as n, x, or $\square$, that represents a quantity. Variables often represent unknown quantities and the relationships between them. For example, suppose Louis has five more coins than Marcos. If we let m represent the number of coins Marcos has, then $m + 5$ represents the number of coins Louis has. **Algebra** is the branch of mathematics that uses variables and rules for operations with variables. **Algebraic reasoning** is the ability to recognize and solve problems involving unknown quantities. Algebra makes many problems easier to solve. In this section, we use algebra to solve classic word problems. The foundation in algebra that elementary school teachers provide is critical to their students' success in later mathematic courses.

> ### ■ Historical Note
>
> The word *algebra* stems from the first word in the title of the ninth-century book *Al-jabr wa'lmuqābalah*, written by a Persian scholar named al-Khowarizmi. The title means "restoring and comparing," referring to the process of solving an algebraic equation. *Al-jabr* (restoring) refers to using addition to remove a subtracted quantity. For example, $x + 4 = 12 - 2x$ becomes $3x + 4 = 12$. *Wa'lmuqābalah* (comparing) refers to subtracting a positive amount from both sides of an equation. For example, $3x + 4 = 12$ becomes $3x = 8$. al-Khowarizmi used words to describe the process of solving an algebraic equation. Symbols in algebraic equations did not appear until the 1500s.

Language of Algebra

A **numerical expression** contains only numbers and operations, such as $3 \times 4 - 5$ and $1 + 18 \div 6$. We evaluate numerical expressions by carrying out the indicated operations. For example, if we evaluate $3 \times 4 - 5$, then we get 7, because $3 \times 4 - 5 = 12 - 5 = 7$. An **algebraic expression** contains at least one variable and possibly numbers and operations, such as $1 + 12 \div n$ and $a - 3b$. Expressions such as $4n$ and $5(n + 2)$ are abbreviated forms of $4 \cdot n$ and $5 \cdot (n + 2)$. We evaluate algebraic expressions by replacing the variable with a specified number and then carrying out the indicated operations.

For example, if we evaluate $4n + 3$ at $n = 5$, then we get 23, because $(4 \cdot 5) + 3 = 20 + 3 = 23$.

Common Core State Standards (CCSS) describe the following characteristics of proficient sixth graders who grasp the use of variables:

> Students understand the use of variables in mathematical expressions. They write expressions and equations that correspond to given situations, evaluate expressions, and use expressions and formulas to solve problems. (© 2010. National Governors Association Center for Best Practices and Council of Chief State School Officers. All rights reserved.)

■ Historical Note

The Greeks were the first to use letters to represent numbers. Francois Vièta (1540–1603) is credited with being the first person to use letters in algebraic equations in his 1591 publication *In Artem Analyticem Isogoge* (translated *Introduction to the Analytic Art*). His work provided the foundation for symbolic algebra. Renè Descartes (1596–1650) is often credited with using *x, y,* and *z* to represent variables in the 1637 publication *La géométrie* (translated *Geometry*).

Five Uses of Variables

Variables do not look like numbers, but we treat them as though they are numbers. The NCTM standards for algebra for grades 6–8 state that students should "develop an initial conceptual understanding of different uses of variables." Concept Map 1.2 shows the five uses of variables.

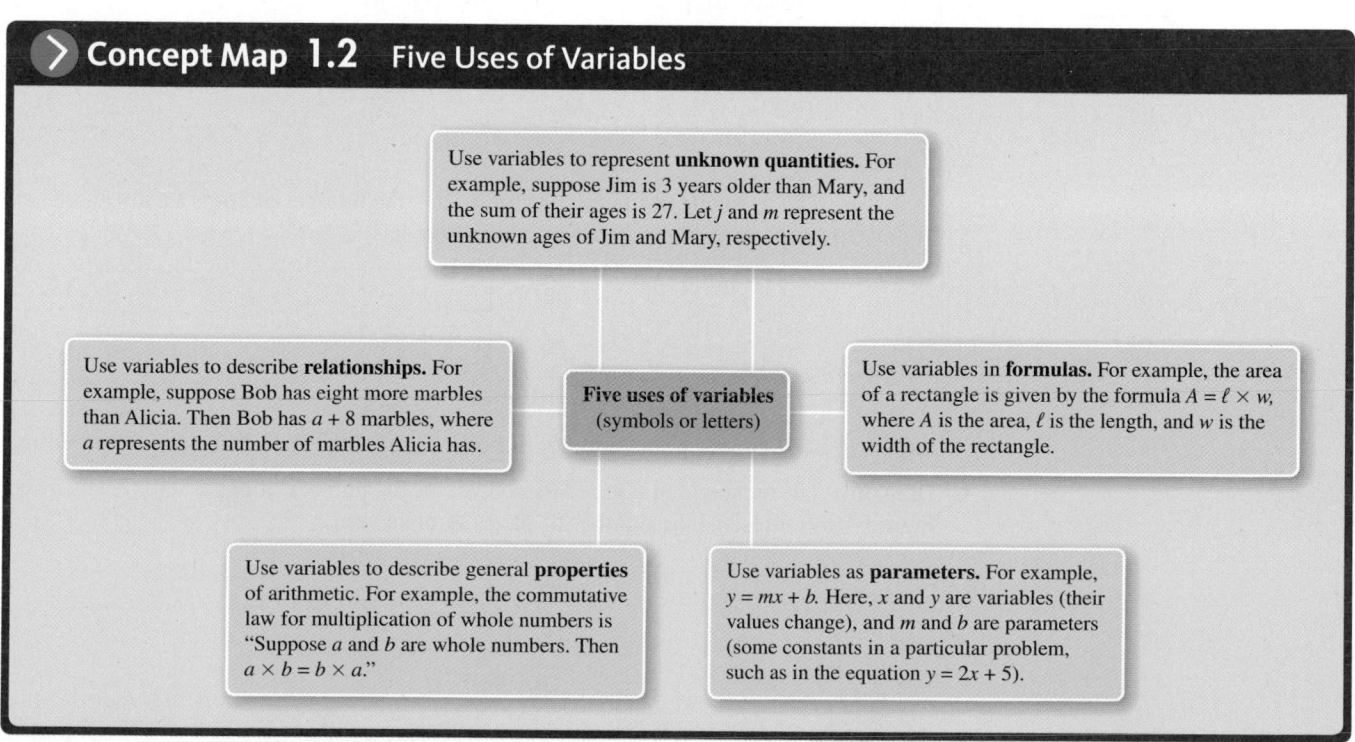

> **Concept Map 1.2**   Five Uses of Variables

Use variables to represent **unknown quantities.** For example, suppose Jim is 3 years older than Mary, and the sum of their ages is 27. Let j and m represent the unknown ages of Jim and Mary, respectively.

Use variables to describe **relationships.** For example, suppose Bob has eight more marbles than Alicia. Then Bob has $a + 8$ marbles, where a represents the number of marbles Alicia has.

Five uses of variables (symbols or letters)

Use variables in **formulas.** For example, the area of a rectangle is given by the formula $A = \ell \times w$, where A is the area, ℓ is the length, and w is the width of the rectangle.

Use variables to describe general **properties** of arithmetic. For example, the commutative law for multiplication of whole numbers is "Suppose a and b are whole numbers. Then $a \times b = b \times a$."

Use variables as **parameters.** For example, $y = mx + b$. Here, x and y are variables (their values change), and m and b are parameters (some constants in a particular problem, such as in the equation $y = 2x + 5$).

The following Released Item defines a variable to represent an unknown quantity, and students must determine the appropriate expression.

> **RELEASED ITEM**
>
> ● NAEP, 2005
>
> N stands for the number of hours of sleep Ken gets each night. Which of the following represents the number of hours of sleep Ken gets in 1 week?
>
> **a.** $N + 7$ **b.** $N - 7$ **c.** $N \times 7$ **d.** $N \div 7$
>
> 61% of fourth-grade students gave the correct answer.

Using a Diagram and Algebra to Represent Relationships

Associating word phrases such as *more than, fewer than,* or *times as many* with an arithmetic operation and algebraic expression is a central aspect of problem solving in the elementary mathematics curriculum. It gives students an algebraic foundation for their future studies in mathematics. Identifying operations and variables in a word problem is challenging for elementary school students and deserves careful attention. Students need to be able to recognize and symbolize variables in context and translate between verbal and algebraic representations.

The following example illustrates a strong visual connection between diagrams and algebraic representations of common word phrases seen in the elementary mathematics curriculum. The rectangle represents the variable and is typically chosen to represent the quantity for which we have the least information. Then the relationships dictate how we use a diagram to represent the other unknown quantities or relationships.

EXAMPLE 1.17

CONNECTION

REPRESENTATION

Represent each relationship using a diagram and algebra.

a. Mike has three more coins than Lenny.

b. Brooke read two fewer pages than Pablo.

c. Raul drove five times as far as Eddie.

SOLUTION

a. Diagram The rectangle in Figure 3(a) represents the number of coins Lenny has. Then Figure 3(b) represents the number of coins Mike has.

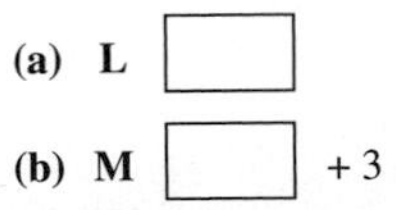

(a) L [ ]

(b) M [ ] + 3

FIGURE 3

Algebra Let L represent the number of coins Lenny has. Then Mike has $L + 3$ coins.

b. Diagram The rectangle in Figure 4(a) represents the number of pages Pablo read. Then Figure 4(b) represents the number of pages Brooke read.

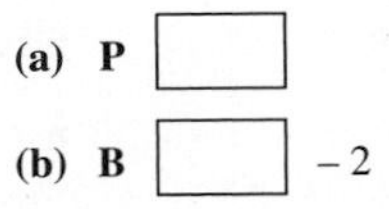

(a) P [ ]

(b) B [ ] − 2

FIGURE 4

Algebra Let P represent the number of pages Pablo read. Then Brooke read $P - 2$ pages.

c. **Diagram**   The rectangle in Figure 5(a) represents the distance Eddie drove. Then Figure 5(b) represents the distance Raul drove.

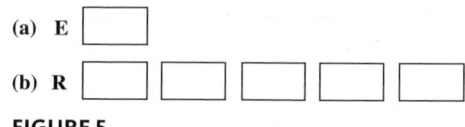

FIGURE 5

Algebra   Let E represent the number of miles Eddie drove. Then Raul drove $E \times 5$ miles.

▲

Many students represent the phrase "3 more than n" with the expression $3 + n$, because the 3 appears first in the phrase. However, the preferable expression is $n + 3$, because "3 more than" implies 3 more than something that is there first. "3 fewer than n" corresponds to the expression $n - 3$, because "3 fewer than" implies 3 fewer than something that is there first.

Solving Word Problems Using a Diagram

The next two examples illustrate word problems that grade 4–6 students should be able to solve. They typically apply the Guess and Check strategy, because they are still learning to use variables. We illustrate how to use the Draw a Diagram strategy to solve these word problems through algebraic reasoning—without using the Guess and Check strategy or algebra explicitly.

EXAMPLE 1.18

PROBLEM SOLVING
REASONING
REPRESENTATION

Mark has 82 coins, which is 3 fewer than five times as many coins as Lisa. How many coins does Lisa have?

SOLUTION

Figure 6 represents the relationships. One rectangle represents the number of coins Lisa has; see Figure 6(a). The arrow and the number 82 indicate that Mark has 82 coins, which is 3 fewer than five times as many coins as Lisa; see Figure 6(b).

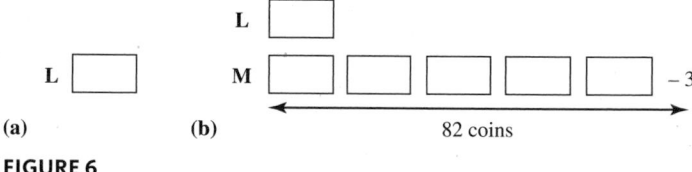

FIGURE 6

The lower five rectangles in the diagram must represent 85 coins, since $85 - 3 = 82$. This leads to Figure 6(c).

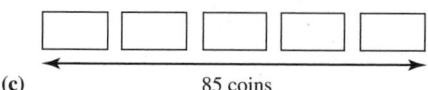

Now we need to split 85 coins into five equal-sized groups: $85 \div 5 = 17$. Each rectangle represents 17 coins, so this means Lisa has 17 coins.

Let's look back: Mark has 82 coins, which is 3 fewer than five times as many coins as Lisa. $5 \cdot 17 - 3 = 85 - 3 = 82$, which is what we expected. So Lisa has 17 coins.

▲

EXAMPLE 1.19

PROBLEM SOLVING

REASONING

REPRESENTATION

George planted two more than three times as many trees as Martha. Together they planted 138 trees. How many trees did each plant?

SOLUTION

Figure 7 represents the relationships. One rectangle in Figure 7(a) represents the number of trees that Martha planted. The arrow and the number 138 in Figure 7(b) indicate that they planted 138 trees altogether.

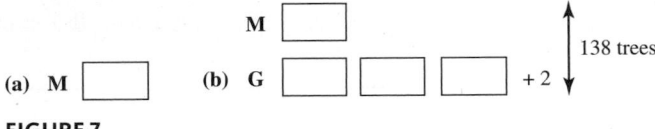

FIGURE 7

The four rectangles in the diagram must represent 136 trees, since $136 + 2 = 138$. This leads to Figure 7(c).

Now we need to split 136 trees into four equal-sized groups: $136 \div 4 = 34$. Each rectangle is worth 34 trees. This means Martha planted 34 trees. The number of trees George planted is $3 \cdot 34 + 2 = 104$. So George planted 104 trees.

Let's look back: $104 \div 24 = 3$ R2, which means George planted two more than three times as many trees as Martha. Also, $34 + 104 = 138$, which is the number of trees they planted altogether.

▲

Translating between Algebraic Representations and Word Phrases

In the previous examples, we solved word problems using diagrams. To solve these problems using algebraic representations, we need to know how to translate between verbal and algebraic expressions. Throughout this textbook, you will develop and apply these skills to solve word problems.

EXAMPLE 1.20

REPRESENTATION

Write an algebraic expression to answer each question.

a. Myesha has six more than three times as many CDs as Cindy. Let c represent the number of CDs Cindy has. How many CDs does Myesha have?

b. Deshawn has seven fewer than four times as many beads as Mia. Let m represent the number of beads Mia has. How many beads does Deshawn have?

SOLUTION

a. $3c + 6$

b. $4m - 7$

▲

Writing a word problem for a given algebraic expression offers students an opportunity to demonstrate understanding of the concept of variables.

EXAMPLE 1.21

COMMUNICATION

REASONING

Write a word problem for the algebraic expression.

a. $n - 5$

b. $4n - 2$

SOLUTION

Answers vary. Here are some possible answers.

a. Marcia has five fewer coins than Natalie. Let n represent the number of coins that Natalie has. Write an algebraic expression that tells how many coins Marcia has.

b. Mia has two fewer than four times as many books as Natalie. Let n represent the number of books Natalie has. Write an algebraic expression that tells how many books Marcia has.

Solving Word Problems Using an Equation

We could use an equation to represent and solve a problem. An **equation** is a mathematical sentence that says two expressions are equal. Some examples are $7 = 5 + 2$, $3 + n = 5$, and $a = b \times q + r$. Numbers and variables are the building blocks of equations. To **solve an equation** means to find values for the variables that make the equation true. For example, to solve $3n - 5 = 13$ means to find a value for n such that 3 times n with 5 then taken away is equal to 13. So $n = 4$ is not a solution to $3n - 5 = 13$ because $(3 \cdot 4) - 5 \neq 13$, but $n = 6$ is a solution to $3n - 5 = 13$ because $(3 \cdot 6) - 5 = 13$.

The following Classroom Connection illustrates a type of problem suitable for the Solve an Equation strategy.

 Classroom Connection

● *Math*, Grade 6, p. 367

Write an equation. Solve for the value given.
Cambridge School has 150 fewer students than twice the number of students at Argyle School. If Cambridge School has 500 students, how many students attend Argyle School? (© 2000 Macmillan/McGraw Hill. Reprinted by permission.)

The following example illustrates the Solve an Equation strategy using one variable. It involves transforming word phrases into expressions, writing an equation, and then solving the equation. Students should be able to "solve multistep word problems posed with whole numbers and having whole-number answers using the four operations and represent these problems using equations with a letter standing for the unknown quantity."

EXAMPLE 1.22

PROBLEM SOLVING

REASONING

REPRESENTATION

Rodney has three more than four times as many coins as William. Together, they have 78 coins. How many coins do they each have?

SOLUTION

Let W represent the number of coins William has. Rodney has three more than four times as many coins as William, so Rodney has $4W + 3$ coins. Altogether, they have 78 coins, so

$$W + 4W + 3 = 78$$
$$5W + 3 = 78$$
$$5W = 75$$
$$W = 75 \div 5$$
$$W = 15$$

So William has 15 coins, and Rodney has $4W + 3 = 4 \cdot 15 + 3 = 60 + 3 = 63$ coins.

Properties of Equality

The substitution principle is a reasonable and useful property.

Substitution Principle

Suppose $a = b$. If an expression contains a, then an equivalent expression is obtained by replacing each a with b.

The substitution principle is a broad property. For example, suppose we know that $n + 3 = 7$. Then $(n + 3)^2 - 2k = 7^2 - 2k$. Also, suppose we know that $a = b \div 3$. Then $9a + 1 = 9(b \div 3) + 1$. The substitution property is also useful for solving equations. For example, suppose we want to solve the equation $-n = 5$. The expression $(-1)(-n)$ equals the expression $(-1)(5)$ because we replaced $-n$ in the expression $(-1)(-n)$ with 5. Then

$$
\begin{array}{ll}
-n = 5 & \text{Original equation} \\
(-1)(-n) = (-1)(5) & \text{Substitution principle} \\
n = -5. & \text{Simplification}
\end{array}
$$

This simple example illustrates how the substitution principle allows us to multiply both sides of an equation by the same number. The following properties of operations, which we apply throughout this textbook, are specific applications of the substitution principle and deserve their own name.

Properties of Equality

Addition Property of Equality

Suppose a and b are any expressions and $a = b$. Let c be any number. Then $a + c = b + c$.

Subtraction Property of Equality

Suppose a and b are any expressions and $a = b$. Let c be any number. Then $a - c = b - c$.

Multiplication Property of Equality

Suppose a and b are any expressions and $a = b$. Let c be any number. Then $a \times c = b \times c$.

Division Property of Equality

Suppose a and b are any expressions and $a = b$. Let c be any nonzero number. Then $a \div c = b \div c$.

We often apply these properties of equality while solving equations. Let's solve the equation $n + 15 = 23$.

$$
\begin{array}{ll}
n + 15 = 23 & \text{Original equation} \\
n + 15 - 15 = 23 - 15 & \text{Subtraction property of equality} \\
n = 23 - 15 & \text{Addition and subtraction are inverse operations} \\
& \text{(see Section 2.3)} \\
n = 8 & \text{Simplification}
\end{array}
$$

Then $n = 8$ solves the equation $n + 15 = 23$.

Let's solve the equation $n \div 5 = 20$.

$n \div 5 = 20$	**Original equation**
$n \div 5 \times 5 = 20 \times 5$	**Multiplication property of equality**
$n = 20 \times 5$	**Multiplication and division are inverse operations (see Section 3.2)**
$n = 100$	**Simplification**

Then $n = 100$ solves the equation $n \div 5 = 20$.

Mistaking a Variable for a Label

Some letters are variables (for example, w is width) while others are labels (for example, L is an abbreviation for liters). Sometimes, students misinterpret a variable as a label, leading to incorrect mathematical expressions. The classic student–professor problem illustrates this phenomenon.

> A university has six times as many students as professors. S is the number of students at the university, and P is the number of professors at the university. Write an equation expressing a relationship between S and P.

The most common incorrect response to this problem is $6 \times S = P$, because many students mistakenly believe S represents "students" and P represents "professors." They treat S and P as *labels* rather than *variables*. The correct response is $S = 6 \times P$, where S represents the *number* of students and P represents the *number* of professors. You can verify incorrect and correct responses by evaluating the algebraic expressions in each of those equations using $S = 6$ and $P = 1$. Which equation holds?

Additive and Multiplicative Reasoning

Additive reasoning is the ability to recognize and solve problems involving addition or subtraction. Typical word problems are

- Mark has 11 pencils. Maria has three fewer pencils than Mark. How many pencils does Maria have?
- Pat has 518 baseball cards. Larry has 32 more baseball cards than Pat. How many baseball cards does Larry have?
- Jenny had $3. Then she earned some money for delivering newspapers. She had $7 altogether. How much did she earn for delivering newspapers?
- Cory had some marbles. He gave five marbles to his sister. Then he had eight left. How many marbles did he have originally?

Multiplicative reasoning is the ability to recognize and solve problems involving multiplication and division. Typical word problems are

- Jerry made four stacks of coins. Each stack has 11 coins. How many coins does he have in all?
- Janet wanted to order a soda. There were three possible cup sizes and 12 possible flavors. How many different cups of soda can she order?
- Larry had 32 baseball cards and gave them to his four friends. He gave each one the same number of baseball cards. How many baseball cards did each friend receive?
- The farmer had 568 avocados. He put eight avocados in each bag. How many bags of avocados did the farmer make?
- The teacher budgeted $200 for expenses. She spent three-fourths of the budget on school supplies. How much money did she spend on school supplies?

- The teacher ordered five slices of pizza for every three students in her class. There were 24 students in her class. How many slices of pizza did the teacher order?
- Mark has 12 pencils. Maria has two more than three times as many pencils as Mark. How many pencils does Maria have?

We apply additive and multiplicative reasoning throughout this book. The language of operations and the structure of the problems provide clues for representing unknown quantities and setting up equations in word problems requiring these types of reasoning.

EXAMPLE 1.23

REASONING

Jenny saved $15. Susan saved $3. Compare the amount of money they saved using

a. additive reasoning.

b. multiplicative reasoning.

SOLUTION

Answers vary. Note that $15 - 3 = 12$ and $15 \div 3 = 5$.

a. Jenny saved $12 more than Susan. Susan saved $12 fewer than Jenny.

b. Jenny saved five times as much as Susan. Susan saved one-fifth the amount Jenny saved. ▲

QUESTIONS FOR SECTION 1.3

REPRESENTATION

Refresher: Representations (language, diagrams, tables, symbols, algebra, manipulatives, and contextualized situations) are important because we use them to organize, record, and communicate mathematical ideas and to make them more comprehensible.

1. Complete the following table.

	Choose one: numerical expression, algebraic expression, equation	Variable, if applicable
$n \div 3$		
$(4 + x) \times 5$		
$(3 + 9) \div 2 = 6$		
$a \times 8 = 25$		
$(7 + 2) \times 3$		
$(b - 3) \div m = 8$		

2. A problem states, "John has five more than four times as many books as Mary." A student writes the expression $4n + 5$. What does n represent?

3. A problem states, "Tanya has three fewer than five times as many coins as Carlos." A student writes the expression $5n - 3$. What does $5n - 3$ represent?

4. Veronica has five more than three times as many pencils as Cory.

   a. Draw a diagram to represent the relationship.

   b. Write a variable expression to represent the relationship. Tell what the variable means.

5. A truck driver noticed that every 5 gallons of gasoline cost $12. Let g represent the number of gallons of gasoline and let c represent the cost (in dollars).

   a. Make a table for values of g and c.

   b. Write an equation that relates the variables g and c.

6. Write a word problem such that the answer is the given algebraic expression.

   a. $n + 3$ b. $n - 5$ c. $3n + 4$ d. $4n - 3$

PROBLEM SOLVING

Refresher: Problem solving (reaching a goal that is not immediately attainable) is important because it helps students think more deeply about what they know and deal with unfamiliar situations.

7. Use a diagram to solve these problems.

   a. Fred has three times as many stamps as Mark. Fred has 45 stamps. How many stamps does Mark have?

   b. Marcos has 41 marbles. He has two more than three times as many marbles as Tony. How many marbles does Tony have?

   c. Pam has 111 beads. She has four fewer than five times as many beads as Amy. How many beads does Amy have?

8. Use a diagram to solve: Matthew and Courtney have 77 coins altogether. Courtney has five more than three times as many coins as Matthew. How many coins do they each have?

9. Marty and Carol played a round of miniature golf. Their combined score was 104. Marty scored 31 less than twice as much as Carol. What were their scores? Let c represent Carol's score. Solve this problem using algebra with one variable.

10. Use a variable to solve: Matthew and Courtney have 116 coins altogether. Courtney has four fewer than twice as many coins as Matthew. How many coins do they each have?

REASONING AND PROOF

Refresher: Reasoning and proof (thinking and justifying) are important because they help students make sense of mathematics.

11. Do the following.
    a. Pick two odd numbers, and then find the sum. Repeat this for several other pairs of odd numbers. Make a conjecture based on your observations.
    b. Prove your conjecture using algebraic reasoning.

12. Mary has three more marbles than Judy.
    a. Make a table that shows how many marbles Mary and Judy could have.
    b. If Judy has j marbles, how many marbles does Mary have?
    c. Let m represent the number of marbles that Mary has. Write an equation expressing a relationship between j and m.

13. Mike has eight fewer books than Cheryl.
    a. Make a table that shows how many books Mike and Cheryl could have.
    b. If Cheryl has c books, how many books does Mike have?
    c. Let m represent the number of books that Mike has. Write an equation expressing a relationship between c and m.

14. Mark has three times as many coins as Fred.
    a. Make a table that shows how many coins Mark and Fred could have.
    b. If Fred has f coins, how many coins does Mark have?
    c. Let m represent the number of coins Mark has. Write an equation expressing a relationship between f and m.

15. Martin has two more pencils than three times the number of pencils Sara has.
    a. Make a table that shows how many pencils Martin and Sara could have.
    b. If Sara has s pencils, how many pencils does Martin have?
    c. Let m represent the number of pencils that Martin has. Write an equation expressing a relationship between s and m.

CONNECTIONS

Refresher: Connections (linking and applying mathematical ideas) are important because they deepen student understanding and make mathematics more meaningful, flexible, and useful.

16. A circle has a radius of r cm. Suppose you double the radius. What happens to the area of the circle? (Hint: The area A of a circle is given by the formula $A = \pi r^2$.)

17. For the arithmetic sequence 2, 6, 10, 14, 18, . . . ,
    a. find the initial term. b. find the common difference.
    c. represent the sequence with an equation.
    d. graph the sequence using graph paper.

    e. draw a line through the points on the graph.
    f. find the slope of the line.
    g. discuss the connection between the sequence and the slope of the line.

COMMUNICATION

Refresher: Communication (written and verbal explanations using representations and proper mathematical vocabulary) is important because it helps students refine and strengthen their understanding.

18. Explain why we represent the phrase "2 more than n" with $n + 2$ rather than $2 + n$.

19. Explain why we represent the phrase "4 fewer than n" with $n - 4$ rather than $4 - n$.

20. Sandra has n pencils. The given expression represents the number of pencils Brian has. Translate each algebraic expression in context.
    a. $7n$ b. $n - 3$ c. $n + 5$ d. $3n + 2$ e. $5n - 3$

21. Use additive reasoning to compare these quantities.
    a. Steve has \$5. Melanie has \$48.
    b. Aaron sold nine books. Marty sold four books.

22. Use multiplicative reasoning to compare the quantities.
    a. Ellen collected seven butterflies. Kate collected 23 butterflies.
    b. Carrie has four marbles, and Bob has 13 marbles.

23. A teacher writes on the board: "Elijah has three times as many coins as Tom, and Mark has twice as many coins as Elijah." Then she asks, "Mark has how many times as many coins as Tom?" A minute later, Cindy shouts, "Five times as many!" Then Andy exclaims, "Six times as many!"
    a. Explain how each student arrived at his/her answer.
    b. Which is the correct answer?
    c. Use a diagram to justify your answer.
    d. Use algebra to justify your answer.

24. You are a magician. Ask an audience member to pick a number, but make sure she doesn't tell you what the number is. Give her these directions: "Subtract 3 from it. Multiply the result by 6. Add 10. Divide by 2." Ask her to tell you the result. How would you determine her original number?

25. Suppose an audience member chooses n.
    a. Write a set of directions that a magician could give that corresponds to the expression $[9(n + 5) + 3 - n] \div 4$.
    b. How would the magician determine n from the audience member's final result?

More practice with the ideas of the section

26. Fill in the blank. Choose one of the following words or phrases: *additive, algebra, algebraic, arithmetic, constant, equal sign, equation, evaluate, inequality, multiplicative, numerical, place value, solution, solve,* or *variable*.
    a. A(n) _____ expression contains only numbers and operations.

b. A(n) _____ expression contains a variable, such as $a - 3 \times b$.

c. _____ is a notational system that involves the use of variables to formalize, generalize, and manipulate mathematical concepts and structure.

d. A(n) _____ is a letter or symbol that is used to represent a quantity.

e. We _____ an algebraic expression by replacing the variable with a specified number.

f. A(n) _____ is an equality between two expressions, such as $7 = 5 + 2$, $3 + n = 5$, or $a = b \times q + r$.

g. _____ reasoning is the ability to recognize situations that involve addition and subtraction.

h. _____ reasoning is the ability to recognize situations that involve multiplication, division, fractions, or proportions.

27. A problem states, "Max has four fewer than three times as many socks as Sam." A student writes $3n - 4$.

    a. What does n tell you?   b. What does $3n - 4$ tell you?

28. A problem states, "Caitlyn has three more than five times as many coins as Jon." A student writes $5n + 3$.

    a. What does n tell you?   b. What does $5n + 3$ tell you?

29. Mark has three times as many stamps as Fred.

    a. Draw a diagram to represent the relationship.

    b. Write a variable expression. Tell what the variable and the variable expression represent.

30. Pam has four fewer than five times as many beads as Amy.

    a. Draw a diagram to represent the relationship.

    b. Write a variable expression. Tell what the variable and the variable expression represent.

31. Tom was saving $3000 for a trip. He initially deposited $200 in a savings account and then deposited a fixed amount every month in the account for the next 5 months. Then he received a check in the mail. The check was three times as much as the total amount he had saved so far. When he deposited the check in his savings account, he had $400 more than he needed. What was the fixed amount he deposited in the savings account during the 5 months?

32. Write a word problem for the following diagram.

33. Write an equation. Tell what each variable stands for.

    a. Amanda is 3 years older than her brother Jerry.

    b. Krista can run three times as fast as Carlo.

    c. Sam has four more than three times as many coins as Cory.

    d. If Ralph had six more stamps, he would have four times as many stamps as Dorothy.

34. Manuel has some nickels and dimes in his piggy bank. He has 26 coins altogether. The number of nickels is 2 fewer than three times the number of dimes. How much money does he have in his piggy bank? Let d represent the number of dimes. Solve this problem using only this variable.

35. Write an algebraic expression for

    a. 2 more than the product of p and 8.

    b. three times the number of marbles in the bag, less five.

    c. eight more than five times the number of flowers.

    d. Brenda is 18 years older than her sister.

36. The sum of 28 consecutive whole numbers is 686. Find the smallest addend in the sum.

37. John deposited $410 in his bank account. The new balance in his bank account was $3215.

    a. How much did he have in his account before the deposit?

    b. Write an equation.   c. Define the variable.

38. A class sold two types of raffle tickets to raise money for their field trip to the zoo. Raffle tickets to win a 1-day pass to Disneyland cost $2 per ticket, and raffle tickets to win a set of golf clubs cost $3. The class raised $139 altogether. If they had sold five more tickets for the golf clubs, the number of tickets for the golf clubs would have been three times the number of tickets for the Disneyland pass. How many of each type of ticket did they sell? Let d represent the number of raffle tickets sold for Disneyland. Solve this problem using only this variable.

39. A movie theater sold a total of 390 adult and child tickets on a certain day. The theater sold 2.25 times as many adult tickets as child tickets. Each adult ticket cost $8, and each child ticket cost $3. How much revenue did the theater generate in ticket sales that day?

40. Pick two consecutive whole numbers. Square each of the numbers. Subtract the smaller result from the larger result to get a positive difference.

    a. Repeat these steps for three pairs of consecutive numbers.

    b. Make a conjecture about the result.

    c. Prove your conjecture using algebraic reasoning.

    d. Suppose the result is 853. What are the two consecutive numbers?

41. A recycling station pays $0.15 for each large glass bottle, $0.03 for each aluminum can, and $30 for each ton of newspaper. Neal brought some bottles, some aluminum cans, and 250 pounds of newspaper to the recycling center. Write an expression that tells how much money he earned.

42. Pick three consecutive numbers. Square the second number. Subtract the product of the first and third numbers. Subtract your result from the square of the second number.

    a. Use inductive reasoning to illustrate the result is always 1.

    b. Express the three numbers using algebraic notation.

    c. Use algebraic reasoning to prove the result is always 1.

43. Write a word problem such that the answer is the given algebraic expression.

    a. $37 - n$ b. $n + 2$ c. $3n - 6$

44. Consider each of the following arithmetic sequences:

$$5, 10, 15, 20, \ldots$$
$$7, 12, 17, 22, \ldots$$
$$73, 78, 83, 88, \ldots$$

    a. Generalize each of the sequences with an equation.

    b. How are the sequences alike?

45. Consider the following sequence:

$$2 \cdot 1 - 1 = 1$$
$$2 \cdot 2 - 2 = 2$$
$$2 \cdot 3 - 3 = 3$$
$$2 \cdot 4 - 4 = 4$$

    a. Use patterns to find the next three terms of the sequence.

    b. Use algebraic notation to explain why the pattern occurs.

    c. Does algebraic notation help make the pattern obvious?

46. A farmer wants to know how many horses and chickens are on the farm. She counted 90 feet and 28 animals. How many of each is there?

47. Andrew has eight fewer coins than Casey. Bob has three more than twice as many coins as Andrew. Altogether, they have 459 coins. How many coins does Bob have?

48. How can you convince students that the letter in the equation $a + 5 = 12$ is a variable?

49. An early draft of Napoleon Bonaparte's will sold for $149,505, while his memoir of early military campaigns to conquer Europe sold for $336,400. Compare these two numbers using

    a. additive reasoning.   **b.** multiplicative reasoning.

50. Do the following.

    a. Pick two consecutive whole numbers, and then find their sum. Repeat this for other pairs of consecutive numbers.

    b. Make a conjecture about the sum of two consecutive whole numbers.

    c. What type of reasoning did you use?

51. Use algebraic reasoning to prove that the sum of two consecutive whole numbers is an odd number.

52. Do the following.

    a. Make a conjecture about the product of two odd numbers.

    b. Prove your conjecture using algebraic reasoning.

53. Mrs. Grady decides to have a party for her class. She orders two large pizzas for every seven students in her class. Let n represent the number of students in her class, and let p represent the number of pizzas she orders.

    a. Complete the table.

		Is the equation $2p = 7n$ true?		Is the equation $2n = 7p$ true?	
p	n	Yes	No	Yes	No
2	7				
4	14				
6	21				

    b. Write an equation that relates variables n and p.

54. A university has 12 times as many students as professors. Let S represent the number of students at the university and P represent the number of professors at the university.

    a. Are there more professors or students?

    b. If there are 24 students, then how many professors are at the university?

    c. Construct a table for possible values of P and S.

    d. Write an equation expressing a relationship between P and S.

55. The sum of three consecutive numbers is 159. Find the three numbers using each strategy.

    a. Guess and Check   **b.** Solve an Equation

SECTION 1.4   Logic and Deductive Reasoning

What Are Logic and Deductive Reasoning?

Inductive reasoning is dependable but also imperfect because sometimes true statements (3, 11, 37, and 41 are prime numbers) may lead to a false conclusion (all prime numbers are odd numbers). (Note: 2 is an even prime number.)

    Logic is the study of using statements to reach conclusions. The word *logic* stems from the Greek word *logos,* which means "word or thought." **Deductive reasoning** is the process of using general statements and logical reasoning to reach a conclusion. The word *deductive* comes from the Latin word *deducere,* which means "to lead down, bring away."

Deductive Reasoning in the Elementary Mathematics Curriculum

CONNECTION
COMMUNICATION
PROBLEM SOLVING
REASONING
REPRESENTATION

Elementary school students should be able to use diagrams, charts, words, algebra, theorems, facts, and models to explain or justify their solutions to problems. The justification should be convincing without major jumps or gaps in their explanations. Teachers apply deductive reasoning to critique their students' explanations. In time, teachers help their students organize their reasoning using complete sentences, proper notation and vocabulary, appropriate representations, and various methods of proof.

Statements and Open Sentences

In logic, a **statement** is a sentence that is either true or false (but not both, such as "I am a liar."). An **open sentence** is an equation that has a variable, so it may be true for some values of the variable and false for others.

EXAMPLE 1.24 Determine whether each of the following is a statement, open sentence, or neither.
a. The United States consists of 50 states.

b. $a + 3 = 5$

c. $4 + 7 = 10$

d. Is anybody home?

e. George Washington received 10 presents on his third birthday.

SOLUTION

a. Statement because the sentence is true.

b. Open sentence because $a + 3 = 5$ is an equation with a variable.

c. Statement because the sentence is false.

d. Neither because the sentence is a question.

e. Statement because the sentence is either true or false, although we cannot determine which one.

▲

Compound Statements

A **compound statement** is a combination of two or more statements. **"P or Q"** and **"P and Q"** are two common compound statements. The words *or* and *and* are logical connectives because they connect statements to form a new statement. Tables 1.7 and 1.8 show how the truth values of the individual statements affect the truth value of the compound statement. "P or Q" is true when at least one statement is true, and "P and Q" is true when both statements are true.

TABLE 1.7   **Truth Values of "P or Q"**

Row 0	Possibilities	P or Q
row 1	P is true, Q is true	true
row 2	P is true, Q is false	true
row 3	P is false, Q is true	true
row 4	P is false, Q is false	false

TABLE 1.8   **Truth Values of "P and Q"**

Row 0	Possibilities	P and Q
row 1	P is true, Q is true	true
row 2	P is true, Q is false	false
row 3	P is false, Q is true	false
row 4	P is false, Q is false	false

EXAMPLE 1.25 Determine whether the compound statement is true or false.

COMMUNICATION
a. $5 + 3 = 10$ or 33 is an odd number.

b. $5 + 3 = 8$ and 9 is an even number.

c. $3 \leq 7$

SOLUTION

a. True. At least one statement (33 is an odd number) is true (see Table 1.7, row 2).

b. False. One of the statements is false (see Table 1.8, row 4).

c. True. The statement "$3 \leq 7$" is the same as "$3 < 7$ or $3 = 7$." The statement "$3 < 7$" is true, so one of the statements of "$3 < 7$ or $3 = 7$" is true (see Table 1.7, row 2). This makes $3 \leq 7$ true.

▲

Quantifiers

COMMUNICATION   The English language has words and phrases such as *much, many, some, any, none, a few, at least one,* and *a little.* These types of words and phrases are quantifiers because they say something about quantity. In mathematics, we use quantifiers that refer to all, none, or at least one of the objects in a set. Quantifiers tell us how many objects under consideration have a certain property.

Universal quantifiers are phrases such as *no, none, all, any,* and *every* because they convey information about every object under consideration. Some examples are "no elephants flew in space," "none of the dogs barked," "all cars are blue," "any whole number is greater than 5," and "every student answered the question."

Existential quantifiers are phrases such as *some, there exists,* and *at least one* because they refer to at least one element of the set and possibly all of them. Some examples are "some cows eat grass," "there exists an even prime number," and "at least one odd number is greater than 10."

A quantifier combined with an open sentence forms a statement. For example, the following are statements:

- There is at least one whole number n such that $n + 5 = 5$. (true, $n = 0$)
- There are no integers x such that $x^2 + 1 = 10$. (false, choose $x = 3$)
- For every whole number n, $n + 3 > 7$. (false, choose $n = 1$)

Negation

The **negation** of a statement has the opposite truth value of the original statement. The negation of $5 > 3$ is $5 \not> 3$, which is the same as $5 \le 3$. The negation of "The Moon is not made of cheese" is "The Moon is made of cheese." The statements "3 feet equal 1 yard" and "$4 + 2 = 10$" have opposite truth values, but we do not consider one statement a negation of the other because they do not have opposite meanings.

We can negate statements that involve quantifiers. Table 1.9 gives some examples, along with the general quantified statements and their corresponding negation. The word *are* can be any form of a verb.

TABLE 1.9 **Negation of Statements with Quantifiers**

Statement	Negation
All cats chase mice.	Some cats do not chase mice.
All A are B.	**Some A are not B.**
No books have pictures.	Some books have pictures.
No A are B.	**Some A are B.**
Some bicycles are trains.	No bicycles are trains.
Some A are B.	**No A are B.**
Some squirrels do not wear hats.	All squirrels wear hats.
Some A are not B.	**All A are B.**

Euler Diagrams

An **Euler diagram** is a representational tool for visualizing relationships in logic statements (in the next chapter, we use similar diagrams, called Venn diagrams, to represent sets of objects). Figure 8 shows Euler diagrams for the statements "All A are B," "No A are B," "Some A are B," and "Some A are not B." The Euler diagram for "Some A are B" includes a dot (•) common to both regions, and "Some A are not B" includes a dot (•) that is in the region for A but not for B. A dot indicates there is at least one object that has a certain characteristic.

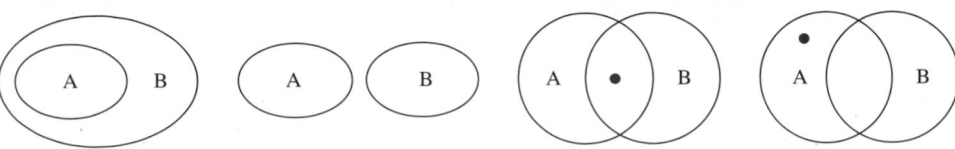

FIGURE 8
Euler diagrams.

EXAMPLE 1.26

CONNECTION
REASONING
REPRESENTATION

Draw the Euler diagram for each statement.
a. All grandmothers bake cookies.
b. Some ants ruin picnics.
c. Some ants do not ruin picnics.

SOLUTION

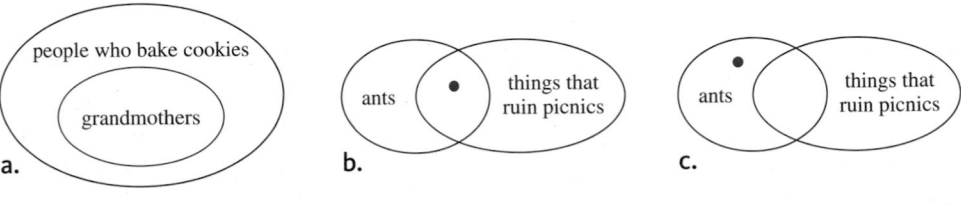

Valid and Invalid Arguments

REASONING

In logic, we use statements called *premises* to reach another statement called the *conclusion*. An **argument** is the collection of premises and the conclusion. In a **valid argument,** the premises guarantee the stated conclusion. This is the main idea behind deductive reasoning: reach a conclusion that logically follows from the given information. In an **invalid argument,** the premises do not guarantee the stated conclusion.

> Mathematically proficient students understand and use stated assumptions, definitions, and previously established results in constructing arguments. They make conjectures and build a logical progression of statements to explore the truth of their conjectures (CCSS, p. 6).
>
> Mathematically proficient students are also able to compare the effectiveness of two plausible arguments, distinguish correct logic or reasoning from that which is flawed, and—if there is a flaw in an argument—explain what it is (CCSS, p. 7).

How to Use an Euler Diagram to Analyze a Simple Argument

A **simple argument** (also called a *syllogism*) consists of two premises and a conclusion. The following steps describe how to use Euler diagrams to analyze simple arguments.

How to Analyze an Argument Using an Euler Diagram

Step 1. Draw circles, and objects in the circles as needed, to represent the premises. There should be one circle for each premise and one circle for the conclusion. Draw all possible diagrams.

Step 2. Analyze the diagram or diagrams. If the conclusion necessarily follows, then the argument is *valid*. If the conclusion does not necessarily follow, then the argument is *invalid*.

In the following example, we see how an Euler diagram reveals an argument is valid.

EXAMPLE 1.27   Analyze the argument using an Euler diagram.

COMMUNICATION

REASONING

REPRESENTATION

Premise: All football players are athletes.

Premise: John plays football.

Conclusion: John is an athlete.

SOLUTION

Due to the first premise, the region representing all football players is completely contained within the region representing all athletes. Due to the second premise, the dot that represents John must be located somewhere in the region representing all football players.

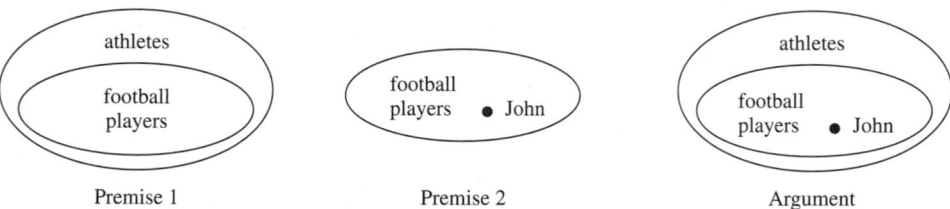

Premise 1   Premise 2   Argument

The dot must be within the region representing all athletes. As a result, the conclusion, "John is an athlete," inescapably follows. Therefore, the argument is valid. ▲

The following example has the same structure as the previous example but contains two false premises and a false conclusion. Yet the argument is still valid. This example reinforces the point that *validity* is a characteristic of the structure of the argument rather than the context of the statements. Enjoy the silly example.

EXAMPLE 1.28   Analyze the argument using an Euler diagram.

COMMUNICATION

REASONING

REPRESENTATION

Premise: All cats are birds.

Premise: Mr. K is a cat.

Conclusion: Mr. K is a bird.

SOLUTION

Due to the first premise, the region representing all cats is completely contained within the region representing all birds. Due to the second premise, the dot that represents Mr. K must be located somewhere in the region representing cats.

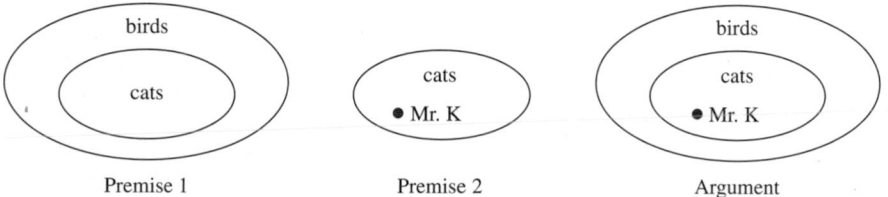

Premise 1   Premise 2   Argument

The only way to combine these diagrams is shown. The dot must be within the region representing all birds. As a result, the conclusion, "Mr. K is a bird" inescapably follows. Therefore, the argument is valid. ▲

The validity of an argument and the truth value of the conclusion are independent. Again, the structure of the argument is important, not the context. If you can draw one Euler diagram to illustrate the argument such that the conclusion does not inescapably follow from the premises, then you have shown the argument is invalid. In the next example, we see how an Euler diagram reveals an argument is invalid.

EXAMPLE 1.29

COMMUNICATION

REASONING

REPRESENTATION

Dean says, "All baseball players are athletes. Mark is an athlete." His friend Mitchell then exclaims, "Mark plays baseball!" Is Mitchell's reasoning correct?

SOLUTION

The Euler diagram in Figure 9(a) represents the first premise. The region representing all baseball players is completely contained within the region representing all athletes. The dot for Mark must be located somewhere in the region representing all athletes. Figures 9(b) and (c) show the two possibilities.

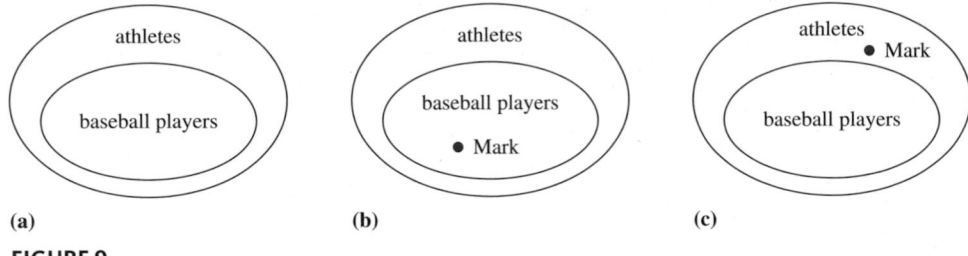

FIGURE 9

Figure 9(b) supports the conclusion that "Mark is an athlete." However, we must consider Figure 9(c) too because that Euler diagram is also possible. Figure 9(c) shows an instance in which the conclusion, "Mark is a baseball player," does not logically follow from the premises. Therefore, the argument is invalid. ▲

In the following example, the conclusion is true but the argument is invalid.

EXAMPLE 1.30

COMMUNICATION

REASONING

REPRESENTATION

Samantha says, "Some animals have fur. All bears have fur." Her friend Megan thinks about these statements and then replies, "Some animals are bears." Is Megan's reasoning correct?

SOLUTION

The argument has the form

Premise: Some A are B.

Premise: All C are B.

Conclusion: Some A are C.

Figures 10(a) and (b) represent the premises.

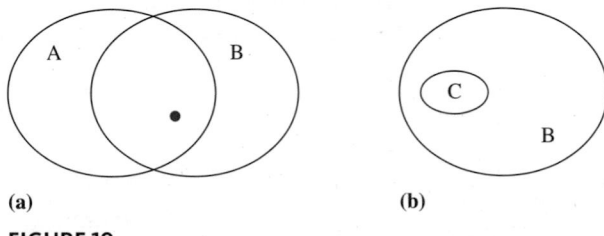

FIGURE 10

Figures 11(a) and (b) show two possible ways to represent the argument.

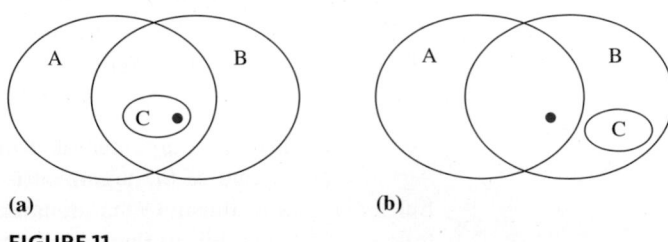

FIGURE 11

Figure 11(a) supports the conclusion "Some A are C." However, we must also consider Figure 11(b), which does not support the conclusion "Some A are C." This is an instance in which the conclusion does not logically follow from the premises. Therefore, the argument is invalid. This means Megan's reasoning is flawed.

▲

EXAMPLE 1.31

COMMUNICATION
REASONING
REPRESENTATION

Analyze the argument.

Premise: Some cats are pets.

Premise: No pets are birds.

Conclusion: No birds are cats.

SOLUTION

A possible Euler diagram is shown.

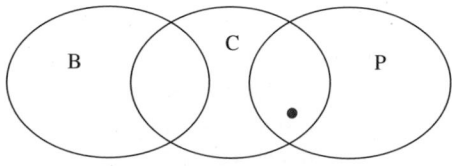

The conclusion does not necessarily follow from the premises because we lack evidence that the common region for B and C is empty. Therefore, the argument is invalid.

▲

> ■ **Historical Note**
>
> Leonhard Euler (1707–1783), born in Basel, Switzerland, is considered one of the greatest mathematicians of all time. Euler diagrams are named in his honor. He graduated from the University of Basel at the age of 15. He was broadly educated, having studied mathematics, theology, medicine, astronomy, physics, and foreign languages. In 1726, he accepted a position at the St. Petersburg Academy of Sciences in Russia. He eventually married, had 13 children, and published more than 800 books and papers. His volume of publication is unsurpassed. Euler established some important mathematical notation in his work that we continue to use today and was largely responsible for the standardization of the symbols e, π, and i. He wrote several influential mathematical textbooks. Euler spoke German but wrote mostly in Latin. In 1741, he accepted a position at the Berlin Academy in Germany. He evolved into the premier mathematician of Europe during his 25-year stay there. He lost his eyesight in 1771 and published nearly half of his work while blind. In 1776, he returned to the Academy of Sciences in Russia, where he remained until he died 7 years later.

© Portrait Essentials/Alamy

Representing the Conditional Statement "if P, then Q" with a Diagram

Many mathematical relationships involve "if/then" statements. We explore these types of statements using everyday situations to make it easier to understand if/then statements.

Statements such as "If you eat your green beans, then you will be healthy" and "If it walks like a duck, then it is a duck" are examples of conditional statements, which are also called *implications*. A **conditional statement** is a statement of the form "if P, then Q" and

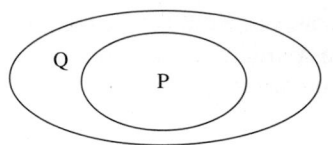

FIGURE 12

How to represent the conditional statement P → Q with an Euler diagram.

is written mathematically as **P → Q**. P is called the *hypothesis* (or *antecedent*), and Q is called the *conclusion* (or *consequent*). We often read P → Q as "P implies Q." Figure 12 shows the Euler diagram for P → Q. Any dot that belongs to the inner ellipse must belong to the outer ellipse.

Many statements can be recast in the form "if P, then Q." For example,

Statement	If P, then Q
All dogs chase cats.	If the animal is a dog, then it chases cats.
You can graduate if you pass this class.	If you pass this class, then you can graduate.
Quadrilaterals are polygons.	If the figure is a quadrilateral, then it is a polygon.
You cannot ride the bike without a helmet.	If you do not have a helmet, then you cannot ride the bike.

Let's examine a famous parental promise: "If you eat your dinner, then you will get dessert." When is this promise true, and when is it false? The hypothesis is P: You eat your dinner. The conclusion is Q: You will get dessert. Let's agree in advance that P → Q is true whenever your parents kept their promise and P → Q is false whenever your parents did not keep their promise.

- Suppose you ate your dinner (P is true), and your parents gave you dessert (Q is true). Then your parents kept their promise (P → Q is true).

- Suppose you ate your dinner (P is true), but your parents did not give you dessert (Q is false). Then you would be disappointed because your parents did not keep their promise (P → Q is false).

- Suppose you did not eat your dinner (P is false), but your parents gave you dessert anyway (Q is true). While you might be surprised to receive dessert, your parents did not lie and therefore they kept their promise (P → Q is true).

- Suppose you did not eat your dinner (P is false), and your parents did not give you dessert (Q is false). Your parents did not lie and therefore they kept their promise (P → Q is true).

Table 1.10 generalizes these results.

TABLE 1.10   Truth Values for "P → Q"

Row 0	Possibilities	P → Q
row 1	P is true, Q is true	T
row 2	P is true, Q is false	F
row 3	P is false, Q is true	T
row 4	P is false, Q is false	T

The conditional statement P → Q is automatically true for any hypothetical statement P that is false. In these cases, we say P → Q is *trivially* true. P → Q is automatically true for any consequential statement Q that is true. The following example provides more practice with the conditional statement.

EXAMPLE 1.32

CONNECTION

REASONING

Determine the truth value of each statement.

a. If $3 + 2 = 5$, then $11 \times 2 = 22$.

b. If 5 is even, then 6 is even.

c. If either 2 or 5 is odd, then the product of 2 and 5 is odd.

d. If George Washington ate cake on his third birthday, then $10 = 8 + 2$.

SOLUTION

a. The hypothesis P is true and the conclusion Q is true. So the conditional statement P → Q is true.

b. The hypothesis P is false, so automatically the conditional statement P → Q is true.

c. The hypothesis P is true and the conclusion Q is false. The conditional statement P → Q is false.

d. The hypothesis P is true or false, but we cannot ascertain the truth value. However, the conclusion Q is true, so the conditional statement P → Q is true.

▲

Related Conditional Statements: Converse, Inverse, and Contrapositive

The symbol ~B represents the negation of B. For example, if B is the statement "Chad went to the store," then ~B is the statement "Chad did not go to the store." If B is the statement "You did not drop the egg," then ~B is the statement "You dropped the egg."

Three conditional statements relate to "if P, then Q":

- The **converse** of P → Q is **Q → P.**
- The **inverse** of P → Q is **~P → ~Q.**
- The **contrapositive** of P → Q is **~Q → ~P.**

EXAMPLE 1.33

CONNECTION

Find the converse, inverse, and contrapositive of "If your course grade is an A, then you pass this class."

SOLUTION

- The converse is "If you pass this class, then your course grade is an A."
- The inverse is "If your course grade is not an A, then you do not pass this class."
- The contrapositive is "If you do not pass this class, then your course grade is not an A."

▲

Figure 13 shows the Euler diagram for "If your course grade is an A, then you pass this class."

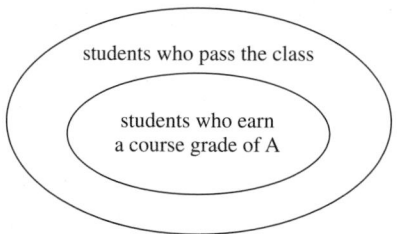

FIGURE 13

The Euler diagram for "If your course grade is an A, then you pass this class."

REASONING
REPRESENTATION

Let's think about the true statement "If your course grade is an A, then you pass this class."

- The contrapositive is true. A dot that represents a student who did not pass the class would be outside the outer ring and would not be in the inner ring of students who earn a course grade of A. In general, *the conditional statement "if P, then Q" and its contrapositive "if not Q, then not P" are logically equivalent,* which means "if P, then Q" and "if not Q, then not P" always have identical truth values.

- The inverse may be true or false. A dot that represents a student who did not get an A must belong outside the inner ring. Suppose the dot belongs outside the outer ring (for example, a student earns a course grade of F). Then the inverse is true. Suppose the dot belongs between the rings (for example, a student earns a course grade of B). Then the inverse is false. In general, *the conditional statement "if P, then Q" and its inverse "if not P, then not Q" are not logically equivalent.*

• The converse may be true or false. A dot that represents a student who passes the class must belong within the outer ring. Suppose the dot belongs to the inner ring. Then the converse is true. Suppose the dot belongs between the rings. Then the converse is false. In general, *the conditional statement "if P, then Q" and its converse "if Q, then P" are not logically equivalent.*

Biconditional Statements

A **biconditional statement** is a compound statement of the form "if P, then Q, and if Q, then P." We represent this relationship as "P if and only if Q." If P and Q have opposite truth values, then the statement "P if and only if Q" is false. If P and Q have identical truth values, then the statement "P if and only if Q" is true. To prove "P if and only if Q" is true, you would need to prove that "if P, then Q" and "if Q, then P" are true.

Three Standard Rules of Deductive Reasoning

An undervalued aspect of deductive reasoning is that it represents an opportunity to understand mathematics. The NCTM's reasoning and proof standard for grades pre-K–12 states that instruction should enable students to "recognize reasoning and proof as fundamental aspects of mathematics" and "develop and evaluate mathematical arguments and proofs." Three standard rules (arguments) of deductive reasoning, which the ancient Greeks analyzed in the third century BCE, are the law of detachment, the law of contraposition, and the chain rule. These rules are valuable because true premises *ensure* the conclusion is true. We analyze these rules with diagrams so that you can help your students analyze arguments involving if/then statements.

Law of Detachment

EXAMPLE 1.34 Analyze the argument.

CONNECTION
REASONING
REPRESENTATION

> Premise: If you play soccer, then you are an athlete.
> Premise: Henry plays soccer.
> ──
> Conclusion: Henry is an athlete.

SOLUTION

The Euler diagram represents the argument.

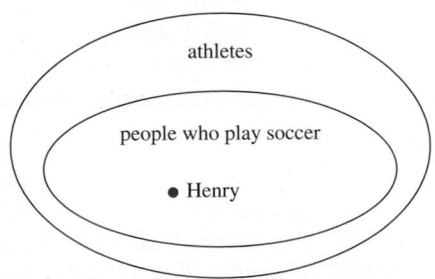

We see that Henry belongs within the ring that represents athletes. The conclusion Henry is an athlete inescapably follows. The argument is valid.

This example illustrates the valid argument called the **law of detachment** (or *modus ponens* from the Latin phrase that means "mode that affirms"). This rule uses two true premises, P → Q and P, to reach the true conclusion Q:

$$P \rightarrow Q$$
$$\underline{P}$$
$$\text{Therefore, Q}$$

The following example illustrates how to apply the law of detachment.

EXAMPLE 1.35

CONNECTION
REASONING

Suppose the following premises are true: If you drive to work, then you listen to the radio. You drive to work. What true conclusion follows from these premises?

SOLUTION

The premises have the form P → Q and P. The conclusion has the form Q. We conclude "you listen to the radio." ▲

Law of Contraposition

EXAMPLE 1.36

CONNECTION
REASONING
REPRESENTATION

Analyze the argument.

Premise: If you play soccer, then you are an athlete.
Premise: Henry is not an athlete.
_____
Conclusion: Henry does not play soccer.

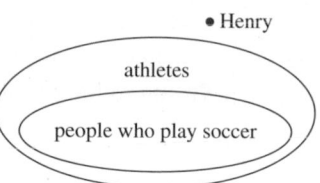

• Henry
athletes
people who play soccer

SOLUTION

The Euler diagram represents the argument.

We see that Henry belongs outside the ring that represents athletes. Then Henry must belong outside the ring of people who play soccer. The conclusion Henry is not an athlete inescapably follows. The argument is valid. ▲

This example illustrates the valid argument called the **law of contraposition** (or *modus tollens* from the Latin phrase that means "mode that denies"). This rule uses two true premises, P → Q and ~Q,—to reach the true conclusion ~P:

$$P \rightarrow Q$$
$$\underline{\sim Q}$$
$$\text{Therefore, } \sim P$$

The following example illustrates how to apply the law of contraposition.

EXAMPLE 1.37

REASONING

Suppose the following premises are true: If you go to the store, then you buy milk. You did not buy milk. What true conclusion follows from the premises?

SOLUTION

The premises have the form P → Q and ~Q. The conclusion has the form ~P. We conclude "you did not go to the store." ▲

Chain Rule

EXAMPLE 1.38

CONNECTION
REASONING
REPRESENTATION

Analyze the argument.

Premise: If it rains, then the grass will get wet.
Premise: If the grass gets wet, then you cannot mow the lawn.
_____
Conclusion: If it rains, then you cannot mow the lawn.

SOLUTION

The following Euler diagram represents the argument.

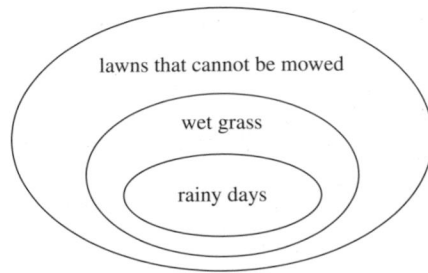

We see that the ring for rainy days must be contained within the ring for lawns that cannot be mowed. The conclusion "if it rains, then you cannot mow the lawn" inescapably follows. The argument is valid. ▲

This example illustrates the valid argument called the **chain rule,** which uses two conditional statements to produce a third conditional statement.

$$P \rightarrow Q$$
$$Q \rightarrow R$$
$$\overline{\text{Therefore, } P \rightarrow R}$$

The following example illustrates how to apply the chain rule.

EXAMPLE 1.39

CONNECTION

REASONING

Suppose the following premises are true: If your car doesn't start, you will have to take the bus. If you take the bus, then you will be late to work. What true conclusion follows from the premises?

SOLUTION

The premises have the form $P \rightarrow Q$ and $Q \rightarrow R$. The conclusion has the form $P \rightarrow R$. We conclude "If your car doesn't start, then you will be late to work." ▲

The following two examples serve two purposes. First, they highlight the difference between inductive and deductive reasoning. Second, they demonstrate a strategy for proving a statement of the form "if P, then Q": we assume P is true and then derive the statement Q.

EXAMPLE 1.40

REASONING

Justify the claim "If n is an even number, then n^2 is an even number" using
a. inductive reasoning.
b. deductive reasoning.

SOLUTION

a. We can use a few examples. We know 2, 8, and 10 are even numbers. Then $2^2 = 4$, $8^2 = 64$, and $10^2 = 100$. So 2^2, 8^2, and 10^2 are even numbers. These observations support the claim "If n is an even number, then n^2 is an even number."
b. Let n be any even number. Then $n = 2k$ for some whole number k that depends on n. Then $n^2 = (2k)^2 = 2k \cdot 2k = 2(2k^2)$. We know $2k^2$ is a whole number, so n^2 equals 2 times a whole number. So n^2 is an even number. ▲

EXAMPLE 1.41

REASONING

Justify the claim "Every odd number is the sum of two consecutive whole numbers" using
a. inductive reasoning.
b. deductive reasoning.

SOLUTION

a. We can use a few examples. Some odd numbers are 3, 51, 91, and 3451. Note that $3 = 1 + 2$; $51 = 25 + 26$; $91 = 45 + 46$; and $3451 = 1725 + 1726$. These observations support the claim that every odd number is the sum of two consecutive numbers.

b. Two examples are as follows: 7 is an odd number and $7 = 3 + 4$, and 21 is an odd number and $21 = 10 + 11$. We need to show this property holds for all odd numbers. The original statement is equivalent to "For all whole numbers x, if x is an odd number, then x is the sum of two consecutive whole numbers." This quantified statement has the logical structure $P \rightarrow Q$. Because deductive reasoning begins with true premises, we may assume P ("x is any odd number") is true. We need to prove Q ("x is the sum of two consecutive numbers") is true. This would prove $P \rightarrow Q$ is true.

We can use variables. Let x represent any odd number. We must show x can be expressed in the form $x = n + (n + 1)$ for some whole number n. x is an odd number, so x can be expressed in the form $x = 2n + 1$ for some whole number n that depends on x. Then

$$x = 2n + 1$$
$$= (n + n) + 1$$
$$= n + (n + 1)$$

Because n is a whole number, it follows that n and $n + 1$ are consecutive whole numbers. Then x is the sum of two consecutive numbers. This proves "Every odd number is the sum of two consecutive whole numbers."

▲

Counterexamples

Students often need to evaluate a simple statement P that involves universal quantifiers, ones that say something about all objects in the given universe. To prove that a statement P is false, we just need to find one example that makes the statement P false. An example that makes P false is called a **counterexample.**

EXAMPLE 1.42

REASONING

Let n be any whole number. Prove the statement "$n^2 + n + 5$ is a prime number" is false by finding a counterexample.

SOLUTION

We know that 2, 3, 5, 7, 11, 13, and 17 are a few prime numbers. The example's statement is true for several values of n: for $n = 0$, we get 5 ($0^2 + 0 + 5 = 5$); for $n = 1$, we get 7 ($1^2 + 1 + 5 = 7$); for $n = 2$, we get 11 ($2^2 + 2 + 5 = 11$); for $n = 3$, we get 17 ($3^2 + 3 + 5 = 17$). But for $n = 4$, we get 25 ($4^2 + 4 + 5 = 25$), which is not a prime number. This proves the statement "$n^2 + n + 5$ is a prime number" is not true for all whole numbers n. The statement "$n^2 + n + 5$ is a prime number" is false by counterexample.

▲

To prove $P \rightarrow Q$ is false by counterexample, we must demonstrate an instance such that P is true and Q is false. In other words, a counterexample is an example that makes the premise (P) true and the conclusion (Q) false.

EXAMPLE 1.43

REASONING

Let a be any whole number. If $a + 7 < 20$, then a is even. Prove that the conditional sentence is false by finding a counterexample.

SOLUTION

The variable a can be any whole number. For the conditional statement "If $a + 7 < 20$, then a is even" to be false, we need to find an example of a whole number a such that "$a + 7 < 20$" is true and "a is even" is false. Consider $a = 5$. This value of a makes $a + 7 < 20$ true because $12 < 20$ is true. However, $a = 5$ is an odd number, so "a is even" is false for this value of a. Then the statement "If $a + 7 < 20$, then a is even" is false by counterexample.

▲

QUESTIONS FOR SECTION 1.4

REPRESENTATION

Refresher: Representations (language, diagrams, tables, symbols, algebra, manipulatives, and contextualized situations) are important because we use them to organize, record, and communicate mathematical ideas and to make them more comprehensible.

1. Match the statement with an Euler diagram.
   a. All dogs chase cats.
   b. Some motorists do not drive fast.
   c. No politicians tell the truth.
   d. If you play baseball, then you are an athlete.

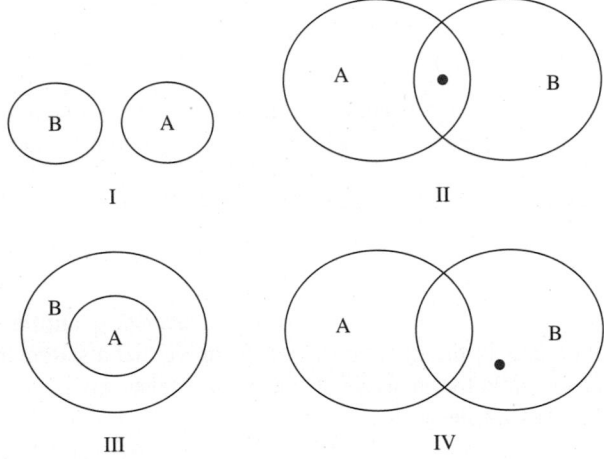

2. Construct an Euler diagram for each statement.
   a. Some dogs chase cats.
   b. Some students do not drink coffee.
   c. There is at least one politician who tells the truth.
   d. If you are a vegetarian, then you like spinach.
3. Do the following.
   a. Draw the Euler diagram for "if P, then Q."
   b. Draw the Euler diagram for "if Q, then P."
   c. What do these two diagrams show?
4. Use an Euler diagram to determine whether the argument is valid or invalid: Ken says, "All mathematicians know how to multiply." Carlo says, "Mike knows how to multiply." Then Lisa concludes, "Mike is a mathematician." Is Lisa's reasoning correct? Justify your answer.
5. Use an Euler diagram to determine whether the argument is valid or invalid.

   Premise: If you read the newspaper, then you are a bird. Premise: Fred is not a bird. Conclusion: Fred does not read the newspaper.

PROBLEM SOLVING

Refresher: Problem solving (reaching a goal that is not immediately attainable) is important because it helps students think more deeply about what they know and deal with unfamiliar situations.

Example 1.40 in this section illustrates one strategy to prove a statement of the form $P \rightarrow Q$. Begin by assuming the statement P is true. Then use definitions and relationships to prove Q is true. Use this approach for questions 6–10 to prove each conditional sentence, where m and n are any whole numbers.

6. If n is an even number, then $n + 2$ is an even number.
7. If n is an odd number, then $n + 4$ is an odd number.
8. If n is an odd number, then n^2 is an odd number. (Hint: An odd number must have the form $2k + 1$ for some whole number k.)
9. If 5 divides the number n, then 10 divides the number $6n$. (Hint: The phrase "5 divides n" means $n = 5k$ for some whole number k.)
10. If n is a multiple of 5, then n^2 is a multiple of 25. (Hint: A multiple of 5 must have the form $5k$ for some whole number k.)

Use diagrams or rules of inference to determine whether the argument is valid or invalid for questions 11 and 12.

11. Premise: If you eat oatmeal for breakfast, then you will win the race. Premise: You did not eat oatmeal for breakfast. Conclusion: You did not win the race.
12. Premise: If it walks like a duck, then it is a duck. Premise: If it is a duck, then it quacks. Conclusion: If it walks like a duck, then it quacks.

REASONING AND PROOF

Refresher: Reasoning and proof (thinking and justifying) are important because they help students make sense of mathematics.

13. The following argument, called the *fallacy of the inverse*, is invalid:

$$\begin{array}{l} \text{Premise: } P \rightarrow Q \\ \underline{\text{Premise: } \sim P} \\ \text{Conclusion: } \sim Q \end{array}$$

The following argument, called the *fallacy of the converse*, is invalid:

$$\begin{array}{l} \text{Premise: } P \rightarrow Q \\ \underline{\text{Premise: } Q} \\ \text{Conclusion: } P \end{array}$$

Draw an Euler diagram for each fallacy that shows that the argument is invalid.

14. Identify which fallacy is used.
   a. Premise: If you eat oatmeal for breakfast, then you drink milk. Premise: You did not eat oatmeal for breakfast. Conclusion: You did not drink milk.

b. Premise: If you studied, then you passed the test. Premise: You passed the test. Conclusion: You studied.

c. Premise: You ate dessert. Premise: If you eat your dinner, then you get dessert. Conclusion: You ate your dinner.

d. Premise: You did not sweep the sidewalk. Premise: If you sweep the sidewalk, then you can use the car. Conclusion: You cannot use the car.

15. Premise: If Jenna is rich, then she will buy a house. Premise: If Jenna subscribes to the *Wall Street Journal,* then she is rich. Premise: Jenna did not buy a house. What conclusions may follow from these statements?

16. Which pairs of statements are equivalent? Supply the form for each statement.

   a. If the price of gasoline increases, then I will take the train.

   b. If I take the train, then the price of gasoline increased.

   c. If the price of gasoline decreases, then I will not take the train.

   d. If I do not take the train, then the price of gasoline decreased.

17. Do the following.

   a. Let P be the statement "$4 + 3 = 7$." Construct a statement Q such that $P \rightarrow Q$ is true.

   b. Let P be the statement "$20 \div 4 = 5$." Construct a statement Q such that $P \rightarrow Q$ is false.

18. Dan is reading a newspaper article about local doctors. The article states that "Some doctors are surgeons" and "Dr. Ruiz is a doctor." Dan concludes, "Dr. Ruiz is a surgeon." Is his reasoning correct? Explain.

19. A class was discussing birds. Julie said, "Some birds eat worms." Mary said, "Some birds bathe in water fountains." Taylor thought about these remarks and then claimed, "Some birds eat worms and bathe in water fountains." Is Taylor's reasoning correct? Explain.

CONNECTIONS

Refresher: Connections (linking and applying mathematical ideas) are important because they deepen student understanding and make mathematics more meaningful, flexible, and useful.

20. Convert each statement into a conditional statement.

   a. No late homework will be accepted.

   b. All mathematicians use calculators.

21. Find a counterexample to prove that each statement is false.

   a. All rectangles are squares.

   b. All whole numbers are greater than 10.

   c. There are no whole numbers a, b, and c such that $a^2 + b^2 = c^2$.

   d. There are no solutions to the equation $x^2 - 5x + 6 = 0$.

   e. All factors of 24 are even numbers.

22. Find a counterexample to prove that each conditional statement is false.

   a. If n is a whole number, then $5n$ is an odd number.

   b. If a and b are any two whole numbers, then $(a - b)^2 = a^2 - b^2$.

c. x is a whole number. If x is an even number, then $2x + 6$ is less than 1000.

d. a and b are any two whole numbers. If $a > b$, then $ab < 500$.

e. Let x be any whole number. If x is greater than 5, then x is an odd number.

COMMUNICATION

Refresher: Communication (written and verbal explanations using representations and proper mathematical vocabulary) is important because it helps students refine and strengthen their understanding.

23. Construct an argument with premises of the form "All A are B" and "x is an A." Provide your own conclusion. Is your argument valid or invalid? Explain.

24. Determine the truth value of each statement. State your reason.

   a. If $3 + 5 = 8$, then Mickey Mouse is a cartoon character.

   b. If the moon is made of cheese, then pigs will fly.

   c. If a triangle has three sides, then a circle is a rectangle.

   d. If 5 is an even number, then 8 is an even number.

25. One of the following conditional statements is true, and the other is false:

"If 4 is an even number, then 6 is an odd number."

"If 6 is an odd number, then 4 is an even number."

Which conditional statement is true? Explain.

26. Construct an argument with premises of the form "Some A are B" and "x is not B." Provide your own conclusion. Is your argument valid or invalid? Explain.

27. Construct an invalid argument. Explain why the argument is invalid.

Use the following information to solve questions 28 and 29. The negation of the statement "A or B" is "not A and not B." For example, the negation of "He read the book or she remembered the name" is "He did not read the book and she did not remember the name." The negation of the statement "A and B" is "not A or not B." For example, the negation of "She walked the dog and he did not ride the bike" is "She did not walk the dog or he rode the bike."

28. Write the negation of each compound statement.

   a. The passengers boarded the train or they could not find a taxi.

   b. He sent an e-mail and purchased stamps at the post office.

   c. Mark does not have a job and walks to school.

   d. Mary called her mother or Jim did not ride the bike.

29. Write the converse, inverse, and contrapositive of each conditional statement.

   a. $P \rightarrow Q$ **b.** $(P \text{ and } Q) \rightarrow R$

   c. $(P \text{ or } Q) \rightarrow R$ **d.** $P \rightarrow (Q \text{ or } R)$

More practice with the ideas of the section

30. Fill in the blank. Choose one the following words or phrases: *argument, cartoons, conditional, contrapositive, converse, existential, invalid, inverse, logical connectives, negation, P, $P \to Q$, $P \to R$, Q, $\sim Q \to \sim P$, $Q \to P$, $\sim P \to \sim Q$, $\sim Q$, statement, truth serum, unconditional, universal, valid, Euler,* or *Vinny.*

a. _____ quantifiers are words or phrases such as *no, none, all, any,* and *every* because they refer to every object under consideration.

b. A(n) _____ is the collection of the premises and the conclusion.

c. _____ quantifiers are words or phrases such as *some, there exists,* or *at least one* because they refer to at least one element of the set and possibly all of them.

d. In a(n) _____ argument, the premises guarantee the stated conclusion.

e. A(n) _____ is a sentence that is either true or false but not both.

f. In a(n) _____ argument, the premises do not guarantee the stated conclusion.

g. _____ diagrams are used to visualize relationships and reason.

h. The _____ of "if P, then Q" is the conditional statement "if Q, then P."

i. The _____ of "if P, then Q" is the conditional statement "if not P, then not Q."

j. The _____ of "if P, then Q" is the conditional statement "if not Q, then not P."

k. A(n) _____ statement is a statement of the form "if P, then Q" and is represented as $P \to Q$.

l. The law of detachment uses two true premises—$P \to Q$ and P—to establish the true conclusion _____.

m. The law of contraposition uses two true premises—$P \to Q$ and $\sim Q$—to establish the true conclusion _____.

n. The chain rule uses two premises—$P \to Q$ and $Q \to R$—to establish the true conclusion _____.

31. Is each of the following a statement? Explain.

a. Stay in school!

b. President Lincoln sneezed as he delivered his famous Gettysburg Address in 1863.

c. $n + 5 = 11$

d. There is a whole number n such that $n - 8 = 30$.

e. There are no whole numbers n such that $n^3 - 3n + 2 = 0$.

32. Write the negation of each statement.

a. There are no computers in the library.

b. Sometimes the lights in the office flicker.

c. All dogs chase cats.   d. No rats play football.

e. There are no fleas on the cat.

f. Some whole numbers are negative integers.

g. There are no cars that do not require fuel.

33. Do the following.

a. Give an example such that $P \to Q$ is true and the converse is true.

b. Give an example such that $P \to Q$ is true and the converse is false.

34. Do the following.

a. Give an example such that $P \to Q$ is true and the inverse is true.

b. Give an example such that $P \to Q$ is true and the inverse is false.

35. Draw a diagram to determine whether the argument is valid or invalid.

Premise: Some wingos are lingos. Premise: Some lingos are bingos. Conclusion: Some wingos are bingos.

36. Do the following.

a. Let P be the statement "$15 - 7 = 8$." Construct a statement Q such that $P \to Q$ is true.

b. Let P be the statement "5 is an odd number." Construct a statement Q such that $P \to Q$ is false.

37. Write each statement in the form "if P, then Q."

a. All whole numbers are greater than -12.

b. $a + 5 < a + 8$ for all whole numbers a.

c. All squares are rectangles.

38. Prove that if m is an odd number and n is an even number, then $m + n$ is an odd number. (Hint: An even number must have the form $2k$ for some whole number k, and an odd number must have the form $2q + 1$ for some whole number q.)

Determine whether the argument is valid or invalid in questions 39–44. State your reason. Assume the premises are true.

39. Premise: Huong will not be charged a late fee if he returns the rented tuxedo on time. Premise: Huong did not return the tuxedo on time. Conclusion: Huong was charged a late fee.

40. Premise: If you are an athlete, then you exercise regularly. Premise: If you exercise regularly, then you are healthy. Conclusion: If you are an athlete, then you are healthy.

41. Premise: If Derek plays basketball, then his parents take him to Disneyland. Premise: Derek plays basketball. Conclusion: His parents take him to Disneyland.

42. Premise: If Latifa eats ice cream, then she cannot eat any cookies. Premise: Latifa ate cookies. Conclusion: Latifa cannot eat ice cream.

43. Premise: If Kobe wins the spelling bee, then he will be accepted to college. Premise: Kobe did not win the spelling bee. Conclusion: Kobe was not accepted to college.

44. Premise: All mathematicians use calculators. Premise: Some teachers are not mathematicians. Conclusion: Some teachers do not use calculators.

CHAPTER 1 REVIEW

CHAPTER 1 Organizer

Section	What You Should Learn	Review Problems
1.1	**1.** Use patterns (inductive reasoning) to make a conjecture (claim).	1–2
	2. Use patterns make predictions.	3
	3. Use patterns to solve problems.	4–7
	4. Use patterns to learn relationships.	8–10
	5. Represent patterns using words, a table, algebra, or a graph.	11–15
	6. Describe and extend a pattern in a sequence.	16
	7. Translate among mathematical representations.	17–18
	8. Explain the limitation of inductive reasoning.	19
1.2	**1.** Apply problem solving strategies.	20–28
1.3	**1.** Know the five uses of variables.	29
	2. Use a diagram to represent relationships and solve problems.	30–32
	3. Explain what a variable in an expression means.	33–35
	4. Compare two quantities using additive or multiplicative reasoning.	36
	5. Use algebra to represent relationships and solve problems.	37–40
1.4	**1.** Determine if the compound statement "P or Q" and "P and Q" is true or false.	41
	2. Write the negation of a statement.	42
	3. Draw the Euler diagram for each statement: "All A are B," "No A are B," "Some A are B," and "Some A are not B."	43
	4. Analyze an argument consisting of two premises and one conclusion using an Euler diagram.	44–48
	5. Draw the Euler diagram for the conditional statement "If P, then Q."	49
	6. Determine if the conditional statement $P \rightarrow Q$ is true or false.	50–51
	7. Write the converse, inverse, and contrapositive of a conditional statement.	52
	8. Analyze arguments involving conditional statements.	53–56

Key Terms and Concepts

pattern 2	arithmetic series 7	solve an equation 29
conjecture (or claim) 2	geometric sequence 8	properties of equality 30
inductive reasoning 2	common ratio 9	additive reasoning 31
sequence 2	problem-solving strategies 15	multiplicative reasoning 31
term 2	variable 24	logic 35
repeating sequence 3	algebra 24	deductive reasoning 35
arithmetic sequence 4	algebraic reasoning 24	statement 36
initial term 5	numerical expression 24	open sentence 36
common difference 5	algebraic expression 24	compound statement 36
nth term 5	equation 29	P or Q, P and Q 36

Key Terms and Concepts

universal quantifiers 37	invalid argument 38	biconditional statement 44
existential quantifiers 37	simple argument 38	law of detachment 44
negation 37	conditional statement 41	law of contraposition 45
Euler diagram 37	converse 43	chain rule 45
argument 38	inverse 43	counterexample 47
valid argument 38	contrapositive 43	

Review Questions

1. Write an even number. Then write the square of that even number. Repeat this several times with other even numbers. Make a conjecture about the square of an even number.

2. Think of an even number and an odd number. Then multiply them. Repeat this several times with other pairs of numbers. Make a conjecture about the product of an even number and an odd number.

3. Do the following.

   a. Evaluate the products:

   $$1551 \times 13 = \underline{}$$
   $$15{,}551 \times 13 = \underline{}$$
   $$155{,}551 \times 13 = \underline{}$$

   b. Use a pattern to predict the next two equations.

4. Do the following.

   a. Find the 345th term in the repeating sequence W, X, Y, Z, W, X, Y, Z, W, X, ...

   b. Find the 240th term in the repeating sequence L, M, N, L, M, N, L, M, ...

5. Find the ones digit of 8×3^{95}.

6. A classic problem in the study of patterns is the "border problem." A landscaper wants to construct a square patio with light and dark bricks. The figure shows a 3-by-3, a 4-by-4, and a 5-by-5 patio.

   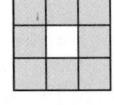 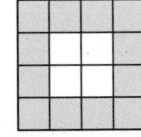 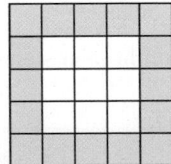

   a. How many dark bricks does a 6-by-6 patio require?

   b. How many dark bricks does a 13-by-13 patio require?

   c. Find a formula for the number of dark bricks needed for an *n*-by-*n* patio.

   d. When does a patio have more light bricks than dark bricks?

7. A homeowner makes a patio using light and dark square tiles that are 1 ft by 1 ft. In the design, the width of the patio is 4 ft, but the length can vary, as shown. Suppose a patio requires 332 tiles altogether. How many dark bricks are needed?

   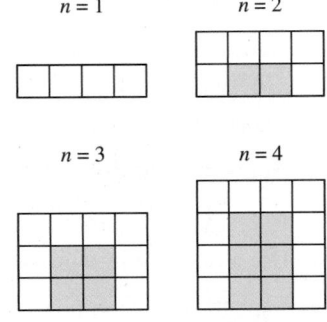

8. A teacher shows his students the division problem $63 \div 12$. Then he demonstrates the following strategy based on skip counting: He writes the sequence 12, 24, 36, 48, 60 and the equation $63 - 60 = 3$ on the board. Then he writes $63 \div 12 = 5$ R3. Study the teacher's approach. Use the same approach to solve each division problem.

   a. $74 \div 15$ b. $145 \div 32$ c. $94 \div 12$

9. Consider the sequence $5^3 = 125$, $5^2 = 25$, $5^1 = 5$, ... Use patterns to help your students evaluate 5^0.

10. Consider the sequence $3 \times 5 = 15$, $2 \times 5 = 10$, $1 \times 5 = 5$, $0 \times 5 = 0$, ... Use patterns to help your students evaluate -1×5 and -2×5.

11. You are given the arithmetic sequence 11, 15, 19, 23, 27, ...

    a. What is the initial term?

    b. What is the common difference?

    c. Represent the sequence with a table.

    d. Generalize the sequence using algebra.

    e. Which term is 3647?

12. A sequence of shapes is shown. Each square has a side whose length is one unit.

    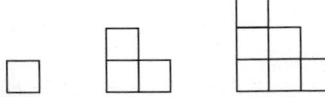

    a. Draw the next shape in the sequence.

    b. Find the number of corners on the perimeter of each of the first four shapes.

    c. Find a formula for the number of corners on the perimeter of the *n*th shape.

13. You are given the geometric sequence 3, 12, 48, 192, ...
    a. What is the initial term?   b. What is the common ratio?
    c. Represent the sequence with a table.
    d. Represent the nth term using algebra.
    e. Which term is 12,288?

14. What is the common difference of an arithmetic sequence such that 3307 is the 15th term and 3 is the initial term?

15. Edmond Halley (1656–1742) was an astronomer who predicted that a particular comet seen in 1682 would return about every 76 years. How many times did the comet appear in the 1900s?

16. Predict the next three likely terms of the sequence: 5, 15, 60, 300, 1800, ... Then describe the pattern that you used.

17. The equation $y = -3n + 8$ represents an arithmetic sequence.
    a. What is the initial term?
    b. What is the common difference?
    c. Represent the sequence with a table.

18. A graph of some terms of an arithmetic sequence is shown.

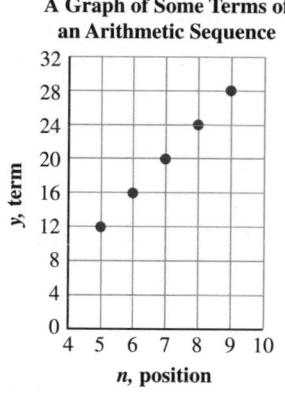

A Graph of Some Terms of an Arithmetic Sequence

n, position / *y*, term

    a. What is the common difference?
    b. What is the initial term?

19. Define the terms *pattern* and *inductive reasoning*. Then explain a limitation of inductive reasoning.

20. Mr. Brown, Mrs. Smith, and Mrs. Grady competed in a school sack race. Mr. Brown finished before Mrs. Grady. Mrs. Smith did not finish last. Mr. Brown greeted Mrs. Smith when she crossed the finished line. In what order did they finish the race?

21. A student opened his book and calculated that the product of the numbers on the pages facing each other was 46,010. What were the numbers of the facing pages?

22. A carpenter takes 15 minutes to saw a log into 3 pieces. At this rate, how long would it take her to saw a log into 28 pieces?

23. A fast-food restaurant gave a customer 2 free hamburgers for every 5 hamburgers they purchased ("buy 5, get 2 free"). How many hamburgers
    a. were free if the customer received 31 hamburgers?
    b. did the customer purchase if he received 766 hamburgers?

24. What is the minimum number of cards you need to select from a shuffled deck of 52 ordinary playing cards to guarantee you selected three face cards? Do not replace any selected cards. (Hint: The "face" cards are the jacks, queens, and kings.)

25. Harry and Larry were decorating cookies at the bakery. Harry can decorate 5 cookies per minute, while Larry can decorate 3 cookies per minute. Together, they decorated 191 cookies. Harry worked 5 fewer minutes than Larry. How many cookies did Harry decorate?

26. Draw a diagram to represent the following "I'm thinking of a number" problem: Think of a number. Add 15 to the number. Square the result. Add 6 to the result. Divide the result by 3. The result is 14. What was the original number?

27. A cereal company put a prize in every cereal box. There are five different possible prizes. A mother has triplets and wants to give each child the same prize. How many boxes does she need to purchase to guarantee she obtains three identical prizes?

28. The video store charges $4 to rent a DVD. Every seventh DVD that a customer rents is free. Chris rented a total of 121 DVDs. How much did that cost him?

29. We use variables to: represent unknown quantities, represent relationships, use in formulas, act as parameters in equations, and describe properties of operations numbers. Identify the use of the variable.
    a. The perimeter P of a rectangle with a length of l units and a width of w units is $P = 2l + 2w$ units.
    b. If a and b are any real numbers, then $ab = ba$.
    c. Bob has three fewer coins than Carrie. A student writes the expression $n - 3$.

30. Use a diagram to solve: Fred has four times as many stamps as Mark. Altogether, they have 340 stamps. How many stamps does Fred have?

31. Use a diagram to solve: Randy has 123 marbles. He has 5 fewer than twice as many marbles as Tony. How many marbles does Tony have?

32. Use a diagram to solve: Pam has 4 fewer than five times as many beads as Sandra. She has 340 more beads than Sandra. How many beads does Pam have?

33. A student is given the problem "Paul has four fewer than five times as many coins as Mike." She writes $5n - 4$.
    a. What does n tell her?   b. What does $5n - 4$ tell her?

34. A student reads the following sentence in a word problem: "Andy has four more than three times as many coins as Cindy." He defines the variable as n = Cindy. Is the definition of the variable acceptable, or can it be improved? Explain.

35. David has three fewer than four times as many marbles as Ann.
    a. Write a variable expression to represent the relationship.
    b. Tell what the variable means.

36. Mitchell has 48 coins. Joey has 14 coins. Compare the quantities using
    a. additive reasoning.   b. multiplicative reasoning.

37. A phone company charges a $5 monthly service fee and $0.30 for every minute of long-distance call time. If your telephone budget is $35, what is the maximum number of minutes of long-distance calls you can make?

38. Nick and Mathew work as couriers for a busy law firm in a busy city. During one week they delivered 390 packages. Nick delivered the packages at a rate of 4 packages per hour, while Mathew delivered the packages at a rate of 6 packages per hour. Nick worked 5 more hours than Mathew. Let m be the number of hours Mathew worked.

   a. What does $m + 5$ represent?

   b. What does $4(m + 5)$ represent?

   c. What does $6m$ represent?

   d. Write an equation that expresses the total number of packages both couriers delivered.

   e. How many hours did each courier work delivering packages that week?

   f. How many packages did each courier deliver?

39. A movie theater sold 221 adult and child tickets one Saturday morning. If it had sold just 4 more adult tickets, then the number of adult tickets sold would have been four times the number of child tickets sold. Each adult ticket cost $6, and each child ticket cost $3. How much revenue did the theater generate in ticket sales that Saturday morning?

40. Mack has 44 coins. The number of dimes is five more than the number of nickels. The number of pennies is one-third the number of dimes. How much money does he have in his piggy bank?

41. Determine whether the compound statement is true or false.

   a. $4 \cdot 5 = 20$ or 8 is an odd number.

   b. $630 \div 42 = 15$ and 8 is an even number.

   c. $24 \cdot 72 = 1728$ or George Washington had five children.

   d. $5 + 3 = 8$ and 33 is an even number.

42. Write the negation of each statement.

   a. Every bird eats worms.

   b. Some skiers do not drink hot chocolate.

   c. None of the cats meowed when the cow appeared.

   d. At least one elephant is not pink.

43. Identify the statement associated with the given Euler diagram. The choices are "All A are B," "No A are B," "Some A are B," and "Some A are not B."

   a.

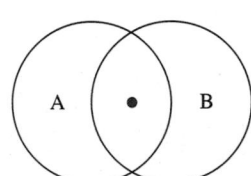

   b.

   c.

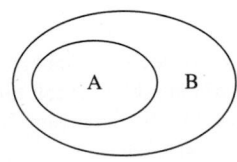

d.

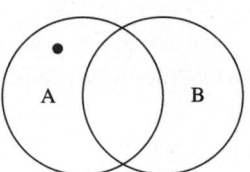

Use an Euler diagram to determine the validity of the argument for questions 59–63.

44. Premise: All employees pay taxes. Premise: Mike does not pay taxes. Conclusion: Mike is not an employee.

45. Premise: Some students play soccer. Premise: Jerry is a student. Conclusion: Jerry plays soccer.

46. Premise: Some mammals are horses. Premise: Black Beauty is a horse. Conclusion: Black Beauty is a mammal.

47. Premise: All students like math. Premise: John is a student. Conclusion: John likes math.

48. Premise: Some students drink coffee. Premise: Mark is not a student. Conclusion: Mark does not drink coffee.

49. Identify the correct Euler diagram for the conditional statement "If A, then B."

   a.

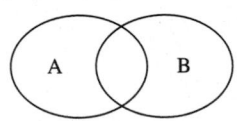

   b.

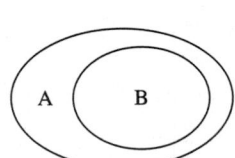

   c.

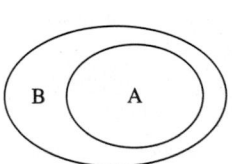

50. Determine the truth value of the conditional statement.

   a. If $6 \cdot 4 = 24$, then 5 is an even number.

   b. If 5 is an even number, then $24 \div 4 = 6$.

   c. If 8 is an odd number, then $24 \div 4 = 7$.

   d. If George Washington ate oatmeal on his 30th birthday, then $5 + 3 = 8$.

51. Do the following.

   a. Let Q be the statement "4 is an odd number." Construct a statement P such that $P \rightarrow Q$ is false.

   b. Let P be the statement "$12 + 3 = 15$." Construct a statement Q such that $P \rightarrow Q$ is true.

52. For the conditional statement "If you read the newspaper, then you will be smart," find the

   a. converse.   **b.** inverse.   **c.** contrapositive.

53. Determine and justify whether the following argument is valid or invalid: Premise: Some yups are eggs. Premise: Some eggs are leaves. Conclusion: Some yups are leaves.

54. Determine and justify whether the following argument is valid or invalid: Premise: If you read the newspaper, then you are smart. Premise: If you are smart, then you will pass the class. Conclusion: If you read the newspaper, then you will pass the class.

55. Determine and justify whether the following argument is valid or invalid: Premise: If Anthony fixes the patio, then Randy will have a birthday party. Premise: Anthony fixed the patio. Conclusion: Randy will have a birthday party.

56. Determine and justify whether the following argument is valid or invalid: Premise: If LeBron passes the class, then he will take a vacation. Premise: LeBron does not pass the class. Conclusion: LeBron will not take a vacation.

Chapter 1 Test

1. *Define key vocabulary words or explain key concepts.*

   a. pattern   **b.** conjecture   **c.** inductive reasoning

2. *Use inductive reasoning to make a conjecture.* Think of three consecutive whole numbers. Then add them. Then divide the sum by 3. Repeat this several times with other choices of three consecutive whole numbers. Make a conjecture about the sum of three consecutive whole numbers.

3. *Represent patterns using words or a table.* For the arithmetic sequence 3, 7, 11, 15, 19, . . . ,

   a. find the initial term.

   b. find the common difference.

   c. describe the sequence with words.

   d. represent the sequence with a table.

4. *Represent patterns using algebra or a graph.* For the arithmetic sequence 1, 4, 7, 10, 13, . . . ,

   a. represent the sequence with an equation.

   b. determine whether 567 is a term in this sequence.

   c. graph the sequence using graph paper.

   d. draw a line through the points on the graph.

   e. find the slope of the line.

   f. discuss the connection between the sequence and the slope of the line.

5. *Use patterns to solve problems or make predictions.* Do the following.

   a. Use a calculator to calculate 56^2, 566^2, 5666^2, and $56,666^2$.

   b. Use a pattern to predict $566,666^2$.

6. *Use patterns to solve problems or make predictions.* Do the following.

   a. Evaluate the products:

   $$2445 \times 13 = \underline{}$$
   $$24,445 \times 13 = \underline{}$$
   $$244,445 \times 13 = \underline{}$$

   b. Use a pattern to predict the next two equations.

7. What is problem solving?

8. *Apply problem-solving strategies.* Determine the 105th term in the repeating sequence H, Q, Y, W, H, Q, Y, W, ...

9. *Apply problem-solving strategies.* A classic problem in the study of patterns is the "border problem." A landscaper wants to construct a patio with light and dark bricks. The figure shows the 2-by-3, 3-by-4, and 4-by-5 patio.

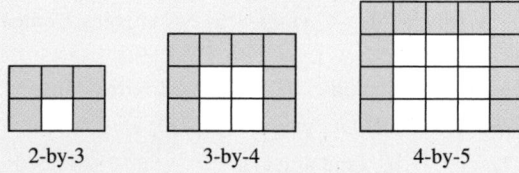

2-by-3   3-by-4   4-by-5

   a. Find a formula for the number of dark bricks needed for an n-by-$(n + 1)$ patio.

   b. Can you make a patio with this pattern that has 456 dark bricks?

10. *Apply problem-solving strategies.* The sum of three consecutive even numbers is 342. Find the largest of the three numbers.

11. *Apply problem-solving strategies.* A rectangle represents a table, and a dot represents a student sitting at the table. The tables are joined by placing two sides together as shown. What is the minimum number of tables required to seat 73 people?

12. *Apply problem-solving strategies.* Marc and Don were painting a room. Marc can paint 4 square feet of wall per minute, and Don can paint 6 square feet of wall per minute. Marc painted 20 more minutes than Don. Together, they painted 720 square feet. How much time did Don spend painting the room?

13. *Use a diagram to solve problems.* Pam has eight more than four times as many beads as Sandra. Sandra has 353 fewer beads than Pam. How many beads does Sandra have? Solve this problem using a diagram.

14. *Define key vocabulary words or explain key concepts.*

   a. algebra   **b.** variable   **c.** equation

15. *Represent a relationship using a variable.*

   a. "Gary has three more than four times as many coins as Dan." A student writes $4n + 3$. What does n tell you? What does $4n + 3$ tell you?

   b. Mario has two fewer than three times as many marbles as Jennifer. Write a variable expression to represent the relationship. Tell what the variable and the variable expression mean.

16. *Use algebra to solve problems.* A movie theater sold adult and child tickets for the midnight showing of *The Calculator Returns!* If it had sold five fewer adult tickets, then the number of adult tickets sold would have been three times the number of child tickets sold.

    a. Let n represent the number of child tickets sold. Write an expression that tells how many adult tickets were sold.

    b. Suppose 253 adult and child tickets were sold altogether. How many child tickets were sold? Solve this problem using algebra.

    c. Suppose each adult ticket cost $11 and each child ticket cost $6. How much revenue did the theater generate in ticket sales?

17. *Compare two quantities using additive or multiplicative reasoning.* Mitchell has 41 coins. Joey has 12 coins. Compare the quantities using

    a. additive reasoning.　　b. multiplicative reasoning.

18. *Define key vocabulary words or explain key concepts.*

    a. premise　　b. valid argument

    c. invalid argument　　d. simple argument

Determine whether the simple argument is valid or invalid, and explain your answer.

19. *Analyze simple arguments using diagrams.* Premise: All cats chase mice. Premise: Felix is a cat. Conclusion: Felix chases mice.

20. *Analyze simple arguments using diagrams.* Joey says, "All mammals breathe air." His friend Mitchell says, "Samantha breathes air." Joey thinks about these premises for a few minutes, and concludes: "Samantha is a mammal!"

21. *Analyze simple arguments using diagrams.* Premise: If the joke is funny, then you will laugh. Premise: You laughed. Conclusion: The joke was funny.

22. *Analyze simple arguments using diagrams.* Premise: If you are an athlete, then you eat granola each day. Premise: You do not eat granola each day. Conclusion: You are not an athlete.

23. *Analyze simple arguments using diagrams.* Premise: Some teachers use calculators. Premise: Some mathematicians are teachers. Conclusion: Some mathematicians use calculators.

2

Sets, Numeration, and Addition and Subtraction with Whole Numbers

Where Are We Going?

In **Section 2.1,** we discuss sets and their operations. They form the conceptual roots of number operations, functions, sample space and events in probability, and shapes in geometry. In **Section 2.2,** we discuss place value concepts and numeration systems—the basis for number sense, estimation, rounding, ordering, and pencil-and-paper methods of addition, subtraction, multiplication, and division. In **Section 2.3,** we discuss models and properties of addition and subtraction. The models describe situations involving joining sets of objects, taking away objects, and comparing objects, while the properties promote number sense. In **Section 2.4,** we examine a variety of addition, subtraction, and estimation methods so that as a teacher you are prepared to query and guide your students to look at numbers and their operations in meaningful and flexible ways.

What Is the Importance of Set Concepts?

Additive reasoning is the ability to recognize and solve word problems that involve addition and subtraction. The NCTM's *Principles and Standards for School Mathematics* states that "Students entering grade 3 should have a grasp of, and much experience with, additive reasoning" (© NCTM Standards 2011 by National Council of Teachers of Mathematics). This means students should have experience with problems that involve combining, separating, and comparing quantities. Set concepts are underlying aspects of these experiences.

What Is the Importance of Place Value Concepts?

The NCTM's *Principles and Standards for School Mathematics* further states, "As students move from third to fifth grade, they should consolidate and practice a small number of computational algorithms for addition, subtraction, multiplication, and division that they understand well and can use routinely. Many students enter third grade with methods for adding and subtracting numbers. In grades 3–5 they should extend these methods to adding and subtracting larger numbers and learn to record their work systematically and clearly. Having access to more than one method for each operation allows students to choose an approach that best fits the numbers in a particular problem" (2000, p. 155). Place value concepts form the foundation of these experiences.

SECTION 2.1 Sets and Operations

Vocabulary and Notation

Nouns are often used to represent a collection of objects. For example, we often use the nouns *pack, kindle, litter, herd,* and *cache* in phrases such as a pack of wolves, a kindle of kittens, a litter of puppies, a herd of cows, and a cache of jewels.

Set theory is the branch of mathematics that deals with collections of objects. The word *set* describes a collection of objects. The terms *set* and *element* are building blocks of set theory.

> **Definition**
>
> - A **set** is an unordered, well-defined collection of objects.
> - An **element** is a member of a set.
>   For example, 3 is an element of the set $\{1, 2, 3, 4\}$.

REPRESENTATION

We typically use capital letters to represent sets. $A = \{1, 4, 5\}$ is read "the set A has elements 1, 4, and 5." $A = \{4, 2, 7, 1\}$ and $B = \{3, 7, 11, 15, \ldots\}$ are representations of sets using the **list form** (or roster form). This is useful when there are just a few objects in the set or the objects in the set follow a pattern that can be continued with an ellipsis ($\ldots$).

The counting numbers $N = \{1, 2, 3, \ldots\}$ and the whole numbers $W = \{0, 1, 2, 3, \ldots\}$ are two common sets. The symbol $\in$ means "is an element of," and $x \in A$ is read **"x is an element of A."** The symbol $\notin$ means "is not an element of," and $x \notin A$ is read **"x is not an element of A."** For example, let $A = \{4, 2, 7, 1\}$. Then $4 \in A$ (4 is an element of A) and $5 \notin A$ (5 is not an element of A).

CONNECTION

The **universal set,** denoted U, is the set of all elements under consideration. For example, the answer to the division problem $9 \div 4$ depends on the universal set under consideration. When students initially study the operation of division, they first consider the set of whole numbers and write $9 \div 4 = 2$ R1. Then they consider the set of fractions and write $9 \div 4 = \frac{9}{4}$. Later they consider the set of decimal numbers and write $9 \div 4 = 2.25$. As they grow in mathematical maturity, their universe expands.

The symbol $\varnothing$ represents the **empty set,** which is the set that does not contain any elements. The list form of $\varnothing$ is $\varnothing = \{\ \}$.

Two sets are equal if and only if they have exactly the same elements. The expression $A = B$ is read "A equals B." The expression $A \neq B$ is read "A is not equal to B." For example, let's define the sets $A = \{1, 2, 3\}$, $B = \{2, 1, 3\}$, and $C = \{2, 3\ 4\}$. Then $A = B$ and $B \neq C$. The following example illustrates some set theory concepts.

EXAMPLE 2.1

REASONING
REPRESENTATION

Indicate true or false.
a. $2 \in \{1, 2, 3\}$
b. $\{2\} \notin \{1, 2, 3\}$
c. $\{2, 1, 3\} = \{3, 1, 2\}$
d. $\{1, 2, 3\} = \{1, 1, 2, 3\}$

SOLUTION

a. True; 2 is an element of $\{1, 2, 3\}$, so $2 \in \{1, 2, 3\}$.

b. True; the elements of $\{1, 2, 3\}$ are 1, 2, and 3. $\{2\}$ does not equal any of the elements of $\{1, 2, 3\}$.

c. True; the order of the elements in a set does not matter.

d. True; the elements of a set may be repeated, but we ignore the copies of elements. So $\{1, 1, 2, 3\} = \{1, 2, 3\}$, which is a more economical representation.

Figure 1 shows different one-to-one correspondences between $A = \{x, y, z\}$ and $B = \{1, 0, 7\}$. Objects in A are paired with objects in B, and each object in A and B belongs to exactly one pair (for example, possible pairings are $x \leftrightarrow 1$, $y \leftrightarrow 0$, and $z \leftrightarrow 7$). We use the representation $A \sim B$, read "A is equivalent to B," to signify a one-to-one correspondence between A and B.

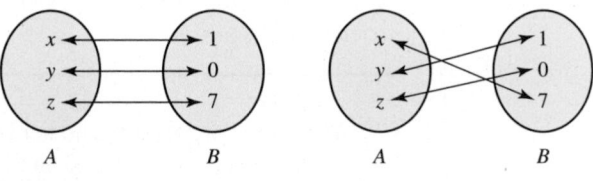

FIGURE 1

Two different diagrams that show $A \sim B$.

This leads to the following definition.

Definition

A is **equivalent** to B, written $A \sim B$, if and only if there is a pairing of the elements in A and B such that the elements of A and B belong to exactly one pair. For example, $\{2, 6, 1\} \sim \{3, a, +\}$.

EXAMPLE 2.2 Determine whether the sets are equal ($=$), equivalent ($\sim$), or both ($=$ and $\sim$). Express your answer using mathematical notation.

a. $A = \{1, 2, 3\}$ and $B = \{u, v, w\}$

b. $C = \{1, 2, 3\}$ and $D = \{u, v, w, x\}$

c. $E = \{1, 2, 3\}$ and $F = \{3, 1, 2\}$

SOLUTION

a. $A \neq B$ and $A \sim B$

b. $C \neq D$ and $C \nsim D$

c. $E = F$ and $E \sim F$

The sets $\{a, b\}$, $\{5, 8\}$, and $\{x, *\}$ are different nonempty sets, but each can be placed in a one-to-one correspondence with the set $\{1, 2\}$. This observation suggests the following definition of the number of elements in a set.

Definition

Let k be a counting number. If the nonempty set A can be placed in a one-to-one correspondence with the set $\{1, 2, 3, \ldots, k\}$, then the **cardinality** of set A, denoted $n(A)$, is k. The cardinality of the empty set $\varnothing$ is defined as 0.

EXAMPLE 2.3 **a.** Explain why the cardinality of $\{\{1, 2\}\}$ is 1.

b. Explain why the cardinality of $\{\{1, 2\}, \{3, 4, 5\}\}$ is 2.

SOLUTION

An element may be a set.

a. We must show $\{\{1, 2\}\} \sim \{1\}$. We create the pairing $\{1, 2\} \leftrightarrow 1$. So $\{\{1, 2\}\} \sim \{1\}$. This means $\{\{1, 2\}\}$ has one element.

b. We must show $\{\{1, 2\}, \{3, 4, 5\}\} \sim \{1, 2\}$. We create the pairings $\{1, 2\} \leftrightarrow 1$ and $\{3, 4, 5\} \leftrightarrow 2$. So $\{\{1, 2\}, \{3, 4, 5\}\} \sim \{1, 2\}$. This means $\{\{1, 2\}, \{3, 4, 5\}\}$ has two elements.

▲

The nonempty set A is said to be *finite* if and only if $n(A) = k$. The empty set is defined to be a finite set. The set A is said to be *infinite* if and only if A is not finite. The set of counting numbers $N = \{1, 2, 3, \ldots\}$ is infinite.

EXAMPLE 2.4

CONNECTION

Determine whether the set is finite or infinite. If the set is finite, determine the cardinality.

a. $A = \{3, 5, 1\}$

b. $B = \{\{0, 1\}, \{2, 3\}, \{4, 5, 6, \ldots\}\}$

c. $C = \{1, 3, 5, 7, \ldots\}$

SOLUTION

a. The one-to-one correspondences $3 \leftrightarrow 1$, $5 \leftrightarrow 2$, and $1 \leftrightarrow 3$ show $A \sim \{1, 2, 3\}$. So A is finite and $n(A) = 3$.

b. The one-to-one correspondences $\{0, 1\} \leftrightarrow 1$, $\{2, 3\} \leftrightarrow 2$, and $\{4, 5, 6, \ldots\} \leftrightarrow 3$ show $B \sim \{1, 2, 3\}$. So B is finite and $n(B) = 3$.

c. C is infinite.

▲

CONNECTION

In Section 2.2, we distinguish the number of objects in a set and the representation of the number of objects in the set (for example, we can represent the number of objects in the set $\{a, b, c, d, e\}$ using |||||, V, or 5). In Section 2.3, we show how teachers use one-to-one correspondence to teach and demonstrate the addition of whole numbers involving combining sets, the subtraction of whole numbers involving taking away objects, and the comparison of two numbers using a one-to-one correspondence.

Historical Note

© INTERFOTO/Alamy

The development of many mathematical topics, such as algebra and geometry, was influenced by many mathematicians and evolved slowly over several centuries. In contrast, the foundational ideas of set theory were mainly established by one person—Georg Cantor (1845–1918). Cantor's original definitions of a set and an element—"By a set we are to understand any collection into a whole M of definite and distinguishable objects of our intuition or our thought. These objects are called the elements of M."—were novel and seemed imprecise at the time, but today we readily accept them, because all attempts to improve the definitions have failed. Cantor also defined the concepts of *equivalent sets* and *cardinality*. In 1900, he finally earned recognition for his remarkable and influential mathematical achievement in set theory (Boyer, 1991).

There are three types of numbers: A *cardinal number,* such as 0, 1, 2, 3, . . . , tells you how many. An *ordinal number,* such as 11th, 12th, 13th, 14th, . . . , tells you what position. Elementary school students should "develop understanding of the relative position and magnitude of whole numbers and of ordinal and cardinal numbers and their connections"

(NCTM, Gr. K–2). A *nominal number* serves as a name or code, such as a number on an athlete's uniform, a telephone number, a ZIP code, or a student identification number (*nominal* means "in name only").

Subsets and Proper Subsets

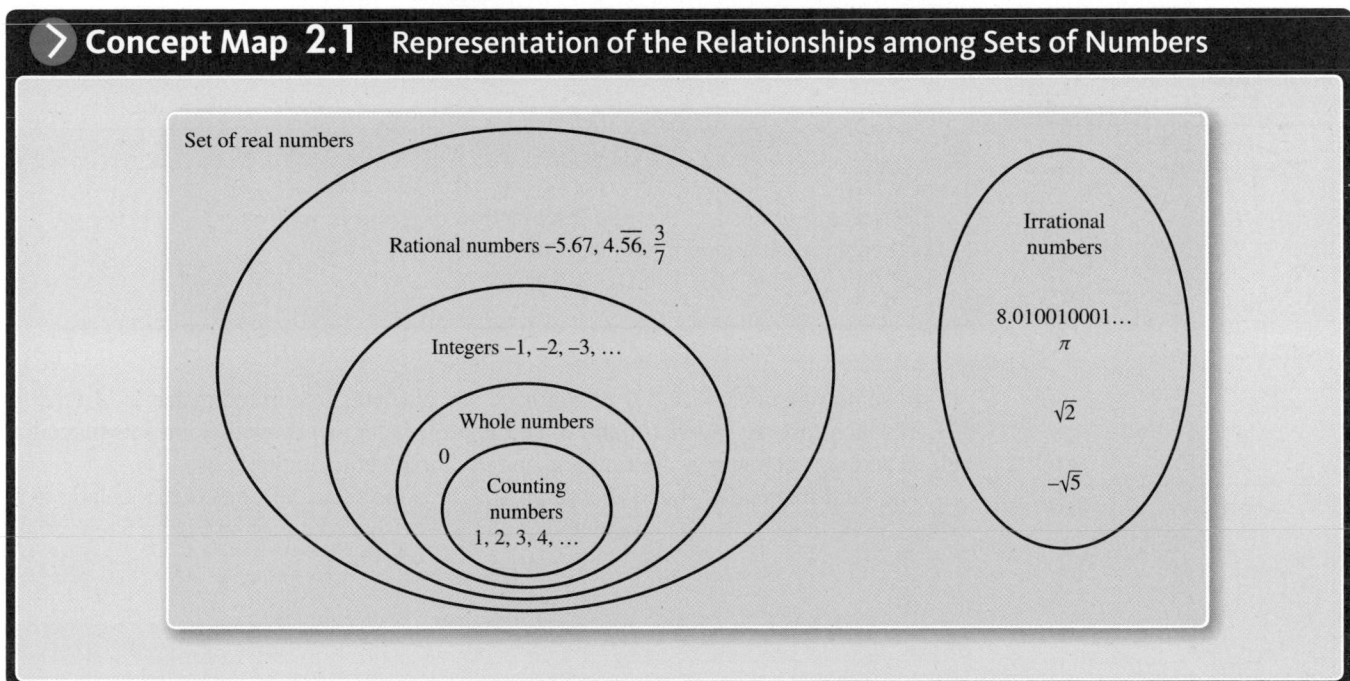

FIGURE 2
$A \subseteq B$.

The sets $\{1, 2, 3\}$ and $\{1, 2, 3, 4\}$ are neither equal nor equivalent. However, every element of $\{1, 2, 3\}$ is an element of $\{1, 2, 3, 4\}$. For some sets A and B, every element of A is also an element of B. The terms *subset* and *proper subset* describe possible relationships between two sets. Figure 2 illustrates a Venn diagram for the concept of subset. The diagram includes the possibility that $A = B$.

> ### Definition
>
> Let A and B represent sets.
> - A is a **subset** of B, written $A \subseteq B$, if and only if every element of A is also an element of B.
> - A is a **proper subset** of B, written $A \subset B$, if and only if $A \subseteq B$ and $A \neq B$.
>
> For example, $\{1, 2, 3\}$ is a subset and proper subset of $\{1, 2, 3, 4, 5\}$.

CONNECTION   A remarkable goal that teachers share is helping their students "understand numbers, ways of representing numbers, relationships among numbers, and number systems" (NCTM, 2000). Concept Map 2.1 uses a Venn diagram to portray the relationships among subsets of numbers in the real number system. For example, it helps you see that every whole number is an integer. What is the universal set in the diagram? What relationships do you see?

> ### ❯ Concept Map 2.1   Representation of the Relationships among Sets of Numbers
>
> Set of real numbers
>
> Rational numbers -5.67, $4.\overline{56}$, $\frac{3}{7}$
>
> Integers $-1, -2, -3, \ldots$
>
> Whole numbers
>
> 0
>
> Counting numbers $1, 2, 3, 4, \ldots$
>
> Irrational numbers
>
> $8.010010001\ldots$
> π
>
> $\sqrt{2}$
>
> $-\sqrt{5}$

Set Operations

Basic set operations (union $\cup$, intersection $\cap$, complement $\sim$, set difference $-$) produce other sets from given sets. By middle school, students become fluent with set concepts.
REPRESENTATION   Before we describe these operations in detail, study Concept Map 2.2 and then describe

$A \cup B$ (read "A union B"), $A \cap B$ (read "A intersect B"), $A - B$ (read "set difference between A and B"), and $\sim A$ (read "complement of A") in words.

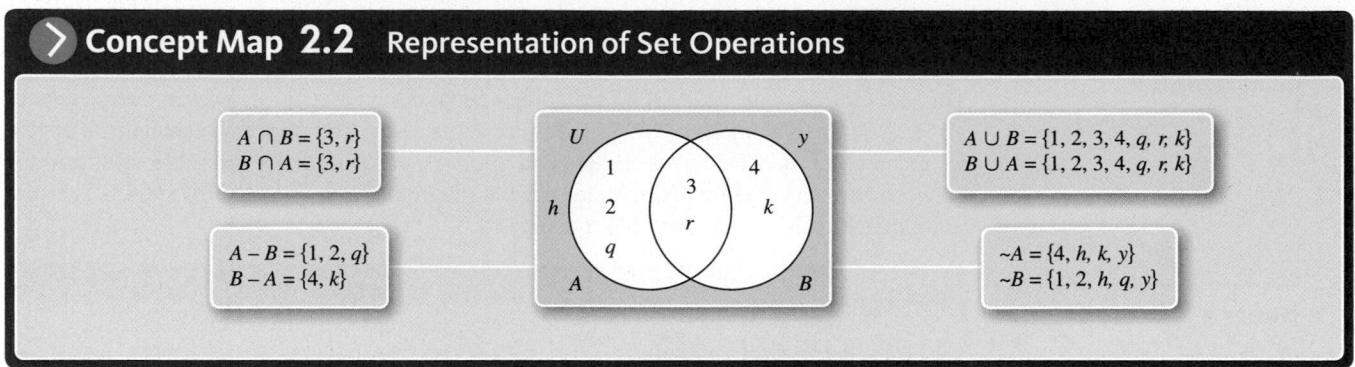

⟩ Concept Map 2.2 Representation of Set Operations

$A \cap B = \{3, r\}$
$B \cap A = \{3, r\}$

$A - B = \{1, 2, q\}$
$B - A = \{4, k\}$

$A \cup B = \{1, 2, 3, 4, q, r, k\}$
$B \cup A = \{1, 2, 3, 4, q, r, k\}$

$\sim A = \{4, h, k, y\}$
$\sim B = \{1, 2, h, q, y\}$

The union of sets A and B, written $A \cup B$, is the set of all elements that belong to A, B, or both. The shaded region in Figure 3 represents $A \cup B$.

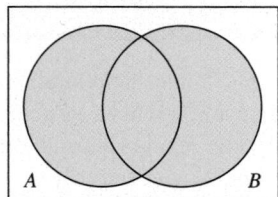

FIGURE 3
$A \cup B$.

Definition

Let A and B represent sets. The **union** of A and B, written $A \cup B$, is the set that contains all elements of A, B, or both. For example, let $A = \{2, 4, 6\}$ and $B = \{1, 4, 6, 7\}$. Then $A \cup B = \{1, 2, 4, 6, 7\}$.

The intersection of sets A and B, written $A \cap B$, is the set of all elements that are common to both A and B. The shaded region in Figure 4 represents $A \cap B$.

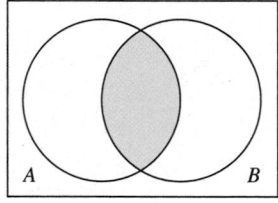

FIGURE 4
$A \cap B$.

Definition

Let A and B represent sets. The **intersection** of A and B, written $A \cap B$, is the set that contains all common elements of A and B. For example, let $A = \{1, 5, 3\}$ and $B = \{0, 3, 5, 10\}$. Then $A \cap B = \{5, 3\}$.

In some situations, A and B do not have any elements in common (that is, $A \cap B = \varnothing$), in which case we say that A and B are **disjoint.** Later, we show disjoint sets playing a role in adding, subtracting, multiplying, and dividing whole numbers.

The set difference of A and B, written $A - B$, is the set of all objects that belong to A except for the objects that belong to both A and B. The shaded region in Figure 5 represents $A - B$.

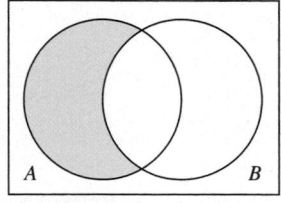

FIGURE 5
$A - B$.

Definition

Let A and B represent sets. The **set difference** of A and B, written $A - B$, is the set that contains the elements of A that do not belong to B. For example, let $A = \{1, 2, 4, 6, 7\}$ and $B = \{4, 6, 9, 11\}$. Then $A - B = \{1, 2, 7\}$.

Later, we use the set difference to conceptualize subtraction using the take-away model.

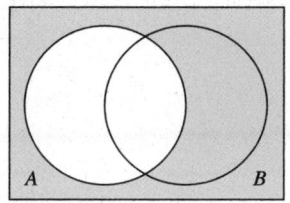

FIGURE 6
~A.

The complement of the set A, written $\sim A$, is the set of elements that belong to the universal set U but not to A. The shaded region in Figure 6 represents $\sim A$.

> **Definition**
>
> Let U represent the universal set and A represent any set. The **complement** of A, written $\sim A$, is the set of elements of U that do not belong to A. For example, let $U = \{1, 2, 3, 4, 5\}$ and $A = \{1, 2\}$. Then $\sim A = \{3, 4, 5\}$.

The following examples provide more practice with set operations.

EXAMPLE 2.5 Let $A = \{3, 4, 5, 6\}$ and $B = \{2, 4, 6, 8\}$. Let $U = \{1, 2, 3, 4, 5, 6, 7, 8, 9, 10\}$. Find

a. $A \cup B$

b. $A \cap B$

c. $A - B$

d. $\sim B$

SOLUTION

a. $A \cup B = \{3, 4, 5, 6\} \cup \{2, 4, 6, 8\} = \{2, 3, 4, 5, 6, 8\}$

b. $A \cap B = \{3, 4, 5, 6\} \cap \{2, 4, 6, 8\} = \{4, 6\}$

c. $A - B = \{3, 4, 5, 6\} - \{2, 4, 6, 8\} = \{3, 5\}$

d. $\sim B = U - B = \{1, 2, 3, 4, 5, 6, 7, 8, 9, 10\} - \{2, 4, 6, 8\} = \{1, 3, 5, 7, 9, 10\}$

▲

EXAMPLE 2.6 Let $A = \{a, e, c, d\}$ and $B = \{a, e, i, o, u\}$.

CONNECTION

COMMUNICATION

REASONING

REPRESENTATION

a. Find $n(A \cap B)$.

b. Compare $n(A \cup B)$ and $n(A) + n(B) - n(A \cap B)$.

SOLUTION

a. $A \cap B = \{a, e\}$, so $n(A \cap B) = 2$.

b. $A \cup B = \{a, e, c, d\} \cup \{a, e, i, o, u\} = \{a, e, c, d, i, o, u\}$, so $n(A \cup B) = 7$.
$n(A) + n(B) - n(A \cap B) = 4 + 5 - 2 = 9 - 2 = 7$. So $n(A \cup B) = n(A) + n(B) - n(A \cap B)$.

▲

The following theorem generalizes the result in the previous example.

> **Theorem 1**
>
> Let A and B represent sets. Then $n(A \cup B) = n(A) + n(B) - n(A \cap B)$.

Let $A = \{1, y\}$ and $B = \{2, 5, 7\}$. The **Cartesian product** of A and B, denoted $A \times B$, is the set of all possible ordered pairs (a, b) such that $a \in A$ and $b \in B$. Table 2.1 illustrates how we can use a table to find all ordered pairs of $A \times B$ for the finite sets A and B.

REPRESENTATION

TABLE 2.1

$A \times B$	2	5	7
1	(1, 2)	(1, 5)	(1, 7)
y	$(y, 2)$	$(y, 5)$	$(y, 7)$

Then $A \times B = \{(1, 2), (1, 5), (1, 7), (y, 2), (y, 5), (y, 7)\}$.

> **Definition**
>
> Let A and B represent sets. The **Cartesian product** of A and B, written $A \times B$, is the set of all possible ordered pairs (a, b) such that $a \in A$ and $b \in B$.

We can extend this definition; for example, the Cartesian product of A, B, and C, denoted $A \times B \times C$, is the set of all possible ordered triplets (a, b, c) such that $a \in A$, $b \in B$, and $c \in C$. Later, we show how the Cartesian product leads to an important counting concept called the fundamental counting principle.

Solving Counting Problems Using Venn Diagrams

The following Classroom Connection shows a problem an elementary mathematics textbook used to introduce Venn diagrams as a way to organize information and solve logical reasoning problems involving counting.

> ### Classroom Connection
>
> ● *Math*, Grade 5, p. 650
>
> Of the students in a fifth-grade class, 15 play on the basketball team. Eighteen students play on the soccer team, and 3 students play on both teams. How many students play on the basketball team, but not the soccer team? on the soccer team but not the basketball team? (© 2000 Macmillan/McGraw Hill. Reprinted by permission.)

CONNECTION
COMMUNICATION
REASONING
REPRESENTATION

The Venn diagram below suggests 12 students play on the basketball team, but not the soccer team.

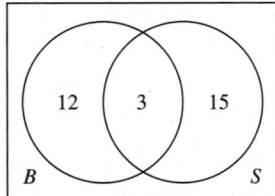

EXAMPLE 2.7 Let S be the set of students who play soccer, D be the set of students who play dodgeball, and B be the set of students who play basketball. Interpret the shaded regions.

a.
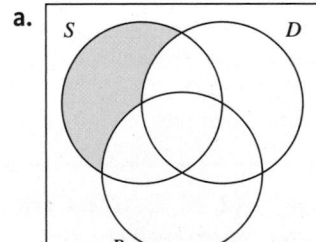

b.
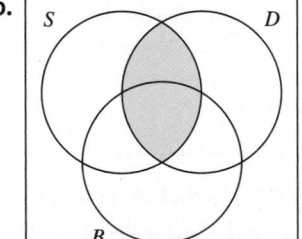

c.
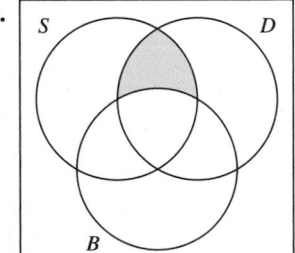

d.
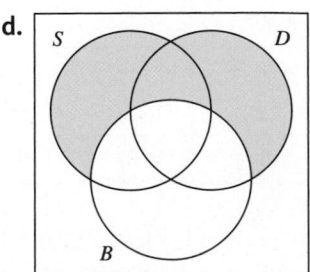

e.
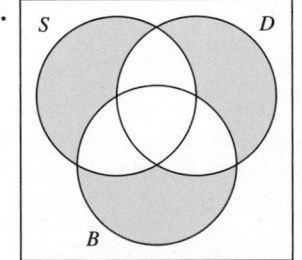

f.
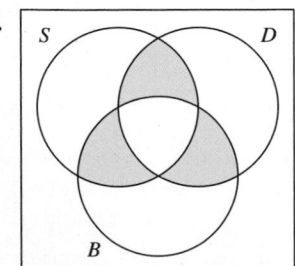

SOLUTION

The shaded region represents the set of students who play

a. soccer only.

b. soccer and dodgeball.

c. only soccer and dodgeball.

d. only soccer or dodgeball.

e. exactly one sport.

f. exactly two sports.

▲

The next example illustrates how we can solve logical reasoning problems involving counting.

EXAMPLE 2.8

CONNECTION

COMMUNICATION

PROBLEM SOLVING

REASONING

REPRESENTATION

In a survey of students who played soccer, dodgeball, or basketball,

- 7 students said they played soccer, dodgeball, and basketball.
- 12 students said they played dodgeball and basketball.
- 11 students said they played soccer and basketball.
- 13 students said they only played soccer.
- 32 students said they played soccer.

How many students played exactly two sports?

SOLUTION

S represents the set of students who played soccer, *D* represents the set of students who played dodgeball, and *B* represents the set of students who played basketball. Figure 7(a) takes into account 7 students who played all three sports and 13 students who played only soccer. Figure 7(b) takes into account 12 students who played dodgeball and basketball and 11 students who played soccer and basketball. Figure 7(c) takes into account 32 students who played soccer.

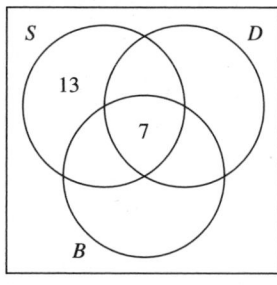
(a)

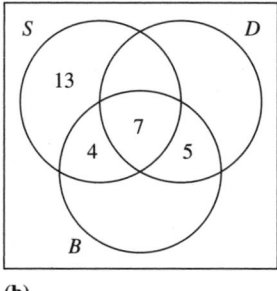
(b)

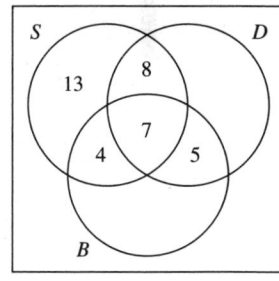
(c)

FIGURE 7
Developing the Venn diagram for the survey.

Then 17 students played exactly two sports $(8 + 4 + 5 = 17)$.

▲

QUESTIONS FOR SECTION 2.1

REPRESENTATION

Refresher: Representations (language, diagrams, tables, symbols, algebra, manipulatives, and contextualized situations) are important because we use them to organize, record, and communicate mathematical ideas and to make them more comprehensible.

1. Draw the Venn diagram for the sets $U = \{0, 1, 2, 3, 4, 5, 6, 7, 8, 9, 10\}$, $A = \{1, 2, 3, 4\}$, $B = \{2, 4, 5, 6, 7\}$, and $C = \{0, 2, 6, 8, 9\}$.

2. Use mathematical symbols to represent each relationship.
   a. x belongs to A.   b. The complement of B is $\{3, 4, 5\}$.
   c. A and B have no common elements.   d. C is nonempty.
   e. The number of objects in $A \cup B$ is 3.
   f. G is not a subset of H.

3. Mrs. Grady surveyed 30 students, 12 of which said they liked basketball, 17 of which said they liked hockey, and 3 of which said they liked both sports.
   a. How many students did not like either sport?
   b. How many students liked exactly one of the sports?

4. In a survey, 15 people said they played basketball, hockey, and volleyball. In addition, 20 people said they played basketball and hockey. Draw a Venn diagram to determine how many people in the survey said they played only basketball and hockey.

5. Let the universal set U be all students at King Elementary School. Let C be the students who like chemistry, H be the students who like history, and M be the students who like math. Interpret the shaded regions.

a.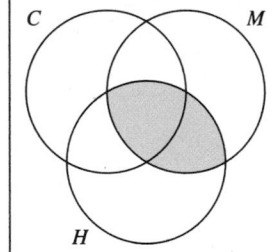

b.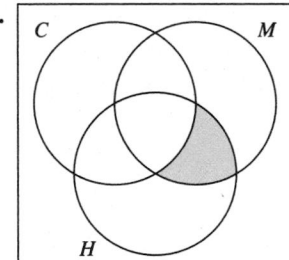

c.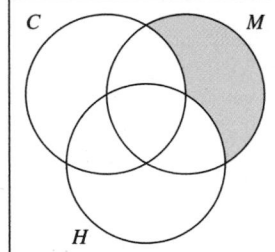

d.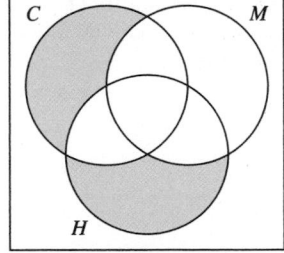

PROBLEM SOLVING

Refresher: Problem solving (reaching a goal that is not immediately attainable) is important because it helps students think more deeply about what they know and deal with unfamiliar situations.

6. A survey of 45 math students revealed
   • 4 students said they like fractions, word problems, and decimals.
   • 7 students said they like fractions and word problems.
   • 5 students said they only like fractions.
   • 16 students said they like word problems and decimals.
   • 2 students said they only like decimals.
   • 26 students said they like fractions or decimals.
   a. How many students like fractions and decimals?
   b. How many students like exactly two topics?
   c. How many students like exactly one topic?

7. An advertiser surveyed 32 customers, 16 of which said they use cell phones regularly, 25 of which said they use e-mail regularly, and 5 of which said they use cell phones and e-mail regularly. Did the customers respond to the survey accurately? Explain.

8. A survey was conducted of 42 students who take math, English, or history. In the survey,
   • 15 students said they take math and history.
   • 2 students said they only take history.
   • 17 students said they take math and English.
   • 12 students said they take math, English, and history.
   • 18 students said they take English and history.

   How many students take only English or only math?

REASONING AND PROOF

Refresher: Reasoning and proof (thinking and justifying) are important because they help students make sense of mathematics.

9. Find $A \cup B$ and $B \cup A$.
   a. $A = \{a, e\}$ and $B = \{e, d, 1\}$
   b. $A = \{1, 2, 3\}$ and $B = \{2, 3, 4\}$
   c. $A = \{4, a, y, 5\}$ and $B = \varnothing$
   d. Use inductive reasoning to make a conjecture based on your observations.

10. Find $A \cap B$ and $B \cap A$.
    a. $A = \{a, f, c, d, e\}$ and $B = \{e, d, 1\}$
    b. $A = \{1, 2, 3, 4, 5, 6\}$ and $B = \{2, 5, 6, 7\}$
    c. $A = \{4, a, y, 1, 7, 8\}$ and $B = \varnothing$
    d. Use inductive reasoning to make a conjecture based on your observations.

11. Find $A - B$ and $B - A$.

    a. $A = \{a, f, c, d, e\}$ and $B = \{e, d, 1\}$

    b. $A = \{1, 2, 3, 4, 5, 6\}$ and $B = \{2, 5, 6, 7\}$

    c. $A = \{4, a, y, 1, 7, 8\}$ and $B = \varnothing$

12. Give an example of sets named A and B such that $A \cup B = \{3, 4, 5, 6, 7\}$ and $A \cap B = \{4, 5\}$.

13. Mr. Smith teaches history and math classes. He has 25 students in both classes combined. He has 17 students in the math class and 15 students in the history class. Is it possible that 12 students are enrolled in both his history and his math classes?

14. Mrs. Smith has 24 students. In a class survey, 16 students said they saw the movie *Happy Feet* and 19 students said they saw the movie *Shrek*. Could there be some students in the class who did not see either movie? Justify your answer.

15. In a survey of 27 people who owned a bird, cat, or dog,
    - 4 people said they owned all three types of pets.
    - 9 people said they owned a cat and a dog.
    - 3 people said they owned only a dog.
    - 10 people said they owned a cat and bird.
    - 8 people said they owned exactly one pet.

    How many people owned both a bird and a dog?

CONNECTIONS

Refresher: Connections (linking and applying mathematical ideas) are important because they deepen student understanding and make mathematics more meaningful, flexible, and useful.

16. Draw a Venn diagram for the following sets: the prime numbers $P = \{2, 3, 5, 7, 11, 13\}$, the even numbers $E = \{0, 2, 4, 6, 8, 10, 12, 14\}$, and the universal set $U = \{0, 1, 2, 3, \ldots, 14, 15\}$.

17. Draw a Venn diagram for the following sets: the odd numbers $O = \{1, 3, 5, 7, 9, 11, 13, 15\}$, the composite numbers $C = \{4, 6, 8, 9, 10, 12, 14, 15\}$, and $U = \{0, 1, 2, 3, \ldots, 14, 15\}$.

18. Draw a Venn diagram for the following sets of geometric objects: quadrilaterals, squares, rectangles, and triangles. Let the universal set be the set of polygons.

COMMUNICATION

Refresher: Communication (written and verbal explanations using representations and proper mathematical vocabulary) is important because it helps students refine and strengthen their understanding.

19. Are there sets A and B such that $n(A \times B) = 5$? Explain.

20. Is there a one-to-one correspondence between the set of counting numbers $N = \{1, 2, 3, 4, \ldots\}$ and the set $S = \{6, 7, 8, 9, \ldots\}$? If so, describe one way to pair the elements of N with the elements of S.

21. Do the following.

    a. Suppose you know $n(A \cup B) = 0$. What can you say about sets A and B?

    b. Suppose you know $n(A \cap B) = 0$. What can you say about sets A and B?

    c. Suppose you know $n(A - B) = 0$. What can you say about sets A and B?

    d. Suppose you know $n(\sim A) = 0$. What can you say about set A?

22. Some students confuse the symbol for union with the symbol for intersection. What advice would you give these students?

23. The Pigeon Inn is a hotel for birds with an infinite number of pigeon holes. The pigeon holes are numbered 1, 2, 3, 4, ... At the moment, every pigeon hole is occupied by one pigeon. If another pigeon were to arrive, describe a process whereby the new pigeon is accommodated with its own pigeon hole—without kicking out any of the currently housed pigeons.

More practice with the ideas of the section

24. Fill in the blank. Choose one of the following words, phrases, or symbols: $A \cup B$, $A \cap B$, $A - B$, $B - A$, $\sim A$, $\sim B$, $A \subseteq B$, $B \subseteq A$, *cardinal*, *equal*, *equivalent*, *finite*, *infinite*, *nominal*, *nominee*, *ordinal*, *ordinary*, *sat*, *set*, *subset*, or *universal*.

    a. A(n) _____ number tells you how many objects are in a finite set.

    b. A(n) _____ is an unordered, well-defined collection of objects.

    c. The _____ set is the collection of all elements under consideration.

    d. $A \not\sim B$ means A is not _____ to B.

    e. _____ is the set of all of objects that belong to A, B, or both.

    f. _____ is the set that contains all common elements of A and B.

    g. _____ is the set of elements that belong to the universal set U but not to B.

    h. _____ is the set of all objects that belong to B except for objects that belong to both A and B.

25. The universal set is $U = \{1, 2, 3, 4, 5, 6, 7, 8\}$. Determine $A \cup B$, $A \cap B$, $A - B$, and $\sim A$ for

    a. $A = \{3, 6, 4\}$ and $B = \{4, 2, 1, 3, 7\}$.

    b. $A = \{2, 4, 6\}$ and $B = \{1, 3, 5\}$.

26. The universal set is $U = \{1, 2, 3, 4, 5, 6, 7\}$. Determine $A \cup B$, $A \cap B$, $A - B$, and $\sim A$.

    a. $A = \{1, 3, 5\}$ and $B = \{1, 2, 3\}$

    b. $A = \{1, 4, 5\}$ and $B = \{1, 2, 3, 4, 5\}$

    c. $A = \{ \}$ and $B = \{1, 2, 3, 4\}$

27. True or false.

    a. $7 \in \{6, 7, 8, 9\}$ b. $\{a, b\} \subset \{a, b, c\}$

    c. $5 \notin \{2, 3, 4\}$ d. $\{1, 2, 5\} \subseteq \{1, 2, 5\}$

    e. $\{a, b, c\} \subset \{a, b, c\}$ f. $\{3\} \not\subseteq \{\{1\}, \{2\}, \{3\}\}$

28. Suppose $A = \{\{2\}, \{4, 6\}, 8\}$.

    a. List two elements of A.   b. List two subsets of A.

29. Determine the cardinality of each set.

    a. $\{1, 6, 0, \{7, 8, 9, \ldots\}\}$ b. $\{\varnothing\}$ c. $\{\{\{4, 5\}\}\}$

30. Suppose $n(X) = 22$ and $n(Y) = 15$.

  a. What is the maximum number of elements $X \cup Y$ can have?

  b. What is the minimum number of elements $X \cup Y$ can have?

31. Do the following.

  a. Suppose you know $n(A \cup B) \neq 0$. What can you say about sets A and B?

  b. Suppose you know $n(A \cap B) \neq 0$. What can you say about sets A and B?

  c. Suppose you know $n(A - B) \neq 0$. What can you say about sets A and B?

  d. Suppose you know $n(\sim A) \neq 0$. What can you say about set A?

32. Do the following.

  a. List all subsets of the set { }.

  b. List all subsets of the set $\{1\}$.

  c. List all subsets of the set $\{1, 2\}$.

  d. List all subsets of the set $\{1, 2, 3\}$.

  e. Make a conjecture about the number of subsets of $\{1, 2, 3, \ldots, k\}$.

33. Mr. Huspek has 17 students. In a class survey, 11 students said they have a dog, 5 students said they have a cat, and 3 students said they have both a cat and a dog. How many students

  a. do not have a dog or cat?

  b. have only a dog or only a cat?

34. A survey of 40 movie patrons revealed 18 said they saw the movie *Scary Fractions* and 32 said they saw the movie *Dr. Venn and Mr. Diagram*. Some people surveyed said they saw both movies. If all movie patrons saw one or both of the movies, how many saw both movies?

35. Mrs. Emme has 23 students. In a class survey, 15 students said they read the book *Charlotte's Web* and 20 students said they read the book *Trumpet of the Swan*. What is the minimum number of students who read both books? Explain.

36. Mr. Kline has 25 students. In a class survey, 16 students said they play a musical instrument and 18 students said they belong to a sports team. What is the maximum number of students who neither play a musical instrument nor belong to a sports team?

37. Let $U = \{a, b, c, d, e\}$. Compare A and $\sim(\sim A)$.

  a. $A = \{a, d\}$ **b.** $A = \{a, b, c\}$ **c.** $A = \varnothing$

  d. Use inductive reasoning to make a conjecture based on your observations.

38. The shaded region in the following diagrams represents the left side of the equation. Fill in the blank with a set that makes the equation true.

  a. $A - B = \sim B \cap$ ___

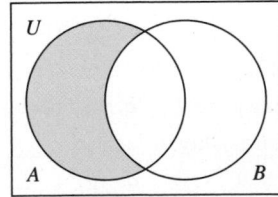

b. $A \cap B = A -$ ___

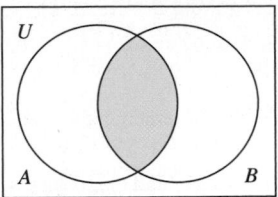

39. Let $U = \{1, 2, 3, \ldots, 10\}$, $A = \{2, 4, 6\}$, and $B = \{4, 5, 6, 7, 8\}$. Write the set that represents the shaded region or regions in each of the following Venn diagrams.

a.
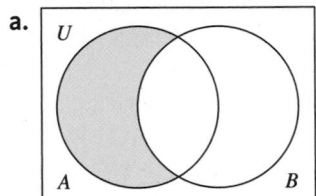

b.
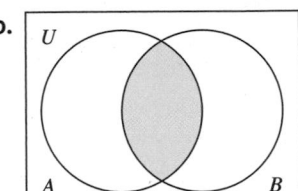

c.
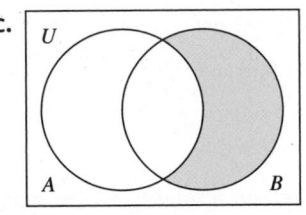

d.
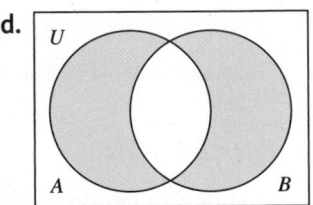

40. Let $A = \{2, 4, 6, 8, 10, \ldots\}$ and $B = \{5, 10, 15, 20, 25, \ldots\}$. Is there a one-to-one correspondence between A and B? Explain.

41. Let B be any set.

  a. How are $B \cup \varnothing$ and B related?

  b. How are $B - \varnothing$ and B related?

  c. What whole number concepts do the preceding parts remind you of?

42. Let B be any set.

  a. How are $B \cap \varnothing$ and $\varnothing$ related?

  b. What whole number concept does this remind you of?

43. Find $A \times B$, $n(A \times B)$, and $n(A) \times n(B)$.

  a. $A = \{x\}$ and $B = \{a, b\}$ **b.** $A = \{x, y\}$ and $B = \{a, b\}$

  c. $A = \{x, y, z\}$ and $B = \{a, b\}$

  d. Use inductive reasoning to make a conjecture about the number of elements $A \times B$ has.

44. Give an example of sets A and B such that $n(A) > 1$, $n(B) > 1$, and $n(A \times B) = 15$.

45. A group of vacationing gamblers were asked which casino games they had played to date.

- 5 gamblers said they played blackjack, roulette, and poker.

- 8 gamblers said they played roulette and poker.

- 11 gamblers said they played blackjack and roulette.

- 12 gamblers said they only played poker.

- 24 gamblers said they played poker.

How many gamblers played exactly two games?

46. Students who had seen either *Jeopardy* or *Wheel of Fortune* were surveyed. The survey found 14 students watched *Jeopardy* and 22 students watched *Wheel of Fortune.*

   a. What is the minimum number of students surveyed?

   b. What is the maximum number of students surveyed?

47. A local computer store performed upgrades for 32 customers to their CPU, hard disk drive, or memory. The customers were asked to participate in a survey. Every person in the survey upgraded at least one piece of hardware. The data showed

- 4 people upgraded their CPU, hard disk drive, and memory.

- 7 customers upgraded their computer's CPU and hard disk drive.

- 8 people upgraded only their memory.

- 9 customers upgraded their computer's hard disk drive and memory.

- 27 people upgraded their memory.

   a. How many customers upgraded exactly one of these items?

   b. Exactly two items?

<h2>SECTION 2.2   Numbers and Numeration</h2>

Numeration Systems

We examine a few numeration (or number) systems that humans have developed through the centuries in the quest to answer the ubiquitous question: "How many?" We focus on the base ten (Hindu–Arabic) numeration system (number system) and use models to clarify its place value structure. The NCTM's *Principles and Standards for School Mathematics* states:

> It is absolutely essential that students develop a solid understanding of the base ten numeration system and place value concepts by the end of grade 2. Students need many instructional experiences to develop their understanding of the system, including how numbers are written. (2000, p. 81)

The base ten models of counting are early concrete and pictorial representations for students. We also discuss the tally, Egyptian, Mayan, and Babylonian numeration systems to make connections to history and culture. Base five and base twelve numeration systems are also discussed. The alternative numeration systems should give you a refreshing appreciation for and understanding of place value numeration systems. This section relies heavily on representation.

Concept of Number

A **numeration system** is a collection of symbols to represent quantities, or **numbers,** using a prescribed set of rules. As civilizations emerged, so did the need to count. Figure 8 shows two sets of objects.

    Although a triangle and crescent are different objects, there is a *one-to-one correspondence* between the two sets. The two sets display the same quantity, or number, of objects. Some cultures represented the same quantity differently—depending on the objects counted. For example, Sumerians used one set of symbols to count produce and a different set of symbols to count animals. Imagine that! Gradually, people began to realize that symbols should not depend on the objects they counted. Historians believe numeration systems probably evolved from finger gestures to words and then to symbols. A numeration system has two basic requirements:

1. The numeration system has a set of symbols.

2. The numeration system has a framework that determines how a sequence of those symbols, called a **numeral,** represents the number of objects counted.

Number (quantity) and numeral (representation) are distinct concepts.

FIGURE 8

Two sets of objects with the same quantity, or number, of objects.

Tally System

© Mary Evans/National Archives/
The Image Works

Early humans did not have numerals or words to describe numbers. They probably used pebbles to represent a one-to-one correspondence needed for the concept of a number. The word *calculate* is based on the Latin word *calculus,* which means "pebble." At some point, primitive man advanced to notches in wood or bones to record numbers. In the tally system, the symbol is a linear notch (|), called a tally mark. We represent numerals by repetition of the tally mark. Numerals in the tally system are |, ||, |||, ||||, |||||, and so on. The word *tally* is based on the French word *tailler,* which means "to cut." The word *write* is based on the Anglo-Saxon word *writan,* which means "to scratch."

■ Historical Note

A tally stick is a stick of wood with tally marks. The British used tally sticks to keep track of financial transactions until the mid-1800s. Suppose you borrowed money from the Bank of England. The banker would mark notches in a stick of wood. Notches of varying widths were used to indicate the amount of money you borrowed. The notches were placed in order of descending values. The tally stick was split down the middle such that each tally mark was split in two pieces. The banker would keep one tally stick and you would keep the other. They could be matched by placing them together. As you repaid your loan, the banker would cut your stick but would keep the cut piece (the one indicating payment) for the bank's records. Before you could withdraw money from your bank account, the banker would have to "check" the tally sticks to make sure the notches lined up (Burton, 1995, pp. 4–5).

Egyptian Numeration System

The ancient Egyptians developed one of the first numeration systems around 3000 BCE. They used symbols that we call *hieroglyphs* (pictures), shown in the first row of Table 2.2, to represent powers of 10 (1, 10, 100, 1000, . . .).

TABLE 2.2   **Egyptian Symbols and the Numbers They Represent**

Egyptian symbols	𒀖	⌐	Ↄ	ℓ	?	∩	I
description	astonished man	tadpole	pointing finger	lotus flower	coiled rope	heel bone	vertical staff
number	1,000,000	100,000	10,000	1000	100	10	1

Strings of these symbols form numerals. We arrange the symbols from largest to smallest. Some examples of numerals are ⌐? ? ? ∩∩ (100,320) and 𒀖 ℓ ℓ ? ? ? ? ∩||| (1,002,413). This system duplicates the symbols as many times as necessary. Regrouping happens whenever 10 copies of a symbol appear:

- |||||||||| is regrouped as the heel bone ∩
- ∩∩∩∩∩∩∩∩∩∩ is regrouped as the coiled rope ?, and so on.

This system needs additional symbols to represent numbers greater than or equal to 10 million, but the ancient Egyptians had no need to represent such large numbers. This numeration system is *additive* in the sense that the position of a symbol does not change the quantity that it represents. For example, the tadpole ⌐ represents 100,000 in each numeral ⌐∩ and ∩⌐. The next example demonstrates addition and subtraction in this system.

EXAMPLE 2.9

REASONING

REPRESENTATION

a. Add: 𝟿𝟿∩∩∩∩∩∩∩∩∩||| + 𓁨𝟿∩∩∩∩∩|||||||||

b. Subtract: 𝟿𝟿𝟿∩∩||| − 𝟿∩∩∩∩∩|||||||||

SOLUTION

a. The vertical staffs | and heel bones ∩ require regrouping. We get

𝟿𝟿∩∩∩∩∩∩∩∩∩||| + 𓁨𝟿∩∩∩∩∩||||||||| = 𓁨𝟿𝟿𝟿∩∩∩∩∩∩∩∩∩∩∩∩∩∩∩∩||||||||||||||

= 𓁨𝟿𝟿𝟿𝟿∩∩|||||||||||||| = 𓁨𝟿𝟿𝟿𝟿∩∩∩||.

b. A heel bone ∩ must be renamed in terms of |, and a coiled rope 𝟿 must be renamed in terms of ∩ before subtraction can occur:

𝟿𝟿𝟿∩∩||| = 𝟿𝟿𝟿∩||||||||||||

= 𝟿𝟿∩∩∩∩∩∩∩∩∩∩∩∩||||||||||||.

Then

𝟿𝟿𝟿∩∩||| − 𝟿∩∩∩∩∩||||||||| =

𝟿𝟿∩∩∩∩∩∩∩∩∩∩∩∩|||||||||||| − 𝟿∩∩∩∩∩||||||||| = 𝟿∩∩∩∩∩∩∩||||

▲

Hindu–Arabic Numeration System

CONNECTION

COMMUNICATION

PROBLEM SOLVING

REASONING

REPRESENTATION

The base ten numeration system we use today is also called the Hindu–Arabic numeration system as a result of its origin. Our historical knowledge of the evolution of this system (such as the origin of zero and the shape of the digits) is imprecise, partly because the system evolved slowly over several centuries and partly because of the lack of ancient science and mathematical records. Historians are uncertain of when this system was fully developed but generally agree the Hindu–Arabic numeration system originated in India around the 200s. By the 800s, it was adopted by the Arabs in Iraq, which was a major center of intellectual activity at the time. It was subsequently transmitted to Western Europe via Middle Eastern trade routes through Spain in the 1100s. The book *Liber Abaci (Book of Counting),* written by the Italian mathematician and merchant Leonardo Fibonacci in the 1200s, is credited with spreading the Hindu–Arabic numeration system throughout Europe. The Hindu–Arabic numeration system replaced the Roman numeration system in Europe by the 1500s with the advent of the printing press.

The Hindu–Arabic numeration system is based on the set of symbols {0, 1, 2, 3, 4, 5, 6, 7, 8, 9}. The symbols are called **digits** because of early counting with fingers. The word *digit* is based on the Latin word *digitus,* which refers to a finger or toe. The digits represent quantities, as illustrated by the dots in Table 2.3.

TABLE 2.3   Digits and the Quantities They Represent

digit	0	1	2	3	4	5	6	7	8	9
number		·	··	···	::	:·:	:::	:·:·	::::	:·:·:

Every numeral is a string of digits, such as 938. Each digit has a **place value** that depends on its position in the numeral. In Table 2.4, we see the place value of the digit 3 in 938 is tens and the place value of the digit 9 is hundreds. We use the grouping of place values into periods to read numerals (the next periods are trillions, quadrillions, and quintillions, which are useful for describing the U.S. national debt, odds in DNA evidence, or astronomical distances).

TABLE 2.4 Place Values for Digits in the Hindu–Arabic Numeration System

Place value	*Billions* period			*Millions* period			*Thousands* period			(no name)		
	Hundred billions	Ten billions	Billions	Hundred millions	Ten millions	Millions	Hundred thousands	Ten thousands	Thousands	Hundreds	Tens	Ones
Numeral												
938										9	3	8
367,850,291				3	6	7	8	5	0	2	9	1

In Figure 9, we model and visualize a few place values using **base ten blocks.** The place value ten represents 10 ones. The place value hundred represents 10 tens or 100 ones. The place value thousand represents 10 hundreds, 100 tens, or 1000 ones.

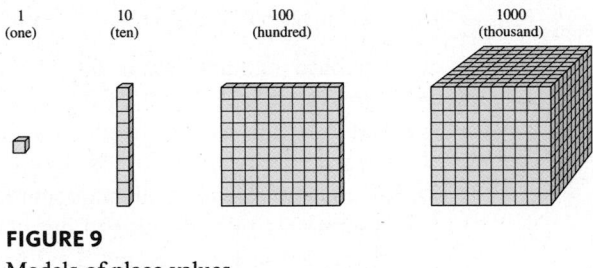

FIGURE 9
Models of place values.

REPRESENTATION

Figure 10 shows how to use base ten blocks to model 2345 and build place value concepts.

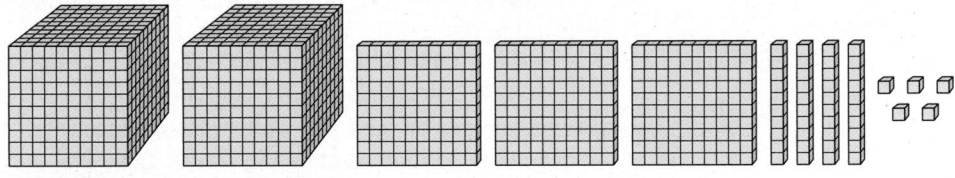

FIGURE 10
Using base ten blocks to model 2345.

CONNECTION
REPRESENTATION

In keeping with NCTM standards, Figure 10 helps students "understand the place-value structure of the base-ten number system" (NCTM, Gr. 3–5) and illustrates two critical place value concepts:

- The place value of a digit indicates the particular base ten block that is repeated.
- The digit in a numeral indicates how often the base ten block is repeated.

Together, the digit and its place value within the numeral indicate the **value** of the digit in the numeral. Let's consider the numeral 2345. The place value of the 2 is *thousands,* and the value of the 2 is two thousand or 2000; the place value of the 3 is *hundreds,* and its value is three hundred or 300; the place value of the 4 is *tens,* and its value is forty or 40; the place value of the 5 is *ones,* and its value is five or 5.

The following example assesses students' understanding of place value concepts.

EXAMPLE 2.10

COMMUNICATION

REASONING

REPRESENTATION

Use place value concepts to answer the following questions.
a. How are the underlined digits in 45<u>4</u>1 alike?
b. How are the underlined digits <u>4</u>5<u>4</u>1 different?

SOLUTION

a. The underlined digits each represent four groups of something (4 thousands and 4 tens).

b. The underlined digits have different values. The value of the 4 in the thousands place is 4000, while the value of the 4 in the tens place is 40.

▲

The Released Item shows that students must associate base ten blocks with numerals and identify the value of a digit.

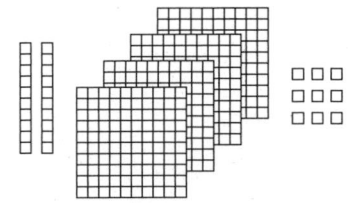

> **RELEASED ITEM**

• NAEP, 2003

Each small square (☐) in this image is equal to 1 (see margin). There are 10 small squares in each strip. There are 100 small squares in each large square. What number is shown?

a. 4029   **b.** 492   **c.** 429   **d.** 249

83% of fourth-grade students gave the correct response. (U.S. Department of Education, Institute of Education Sciences, National Center for Education Statistics, NAEP)

CONNECTION

REPRESENTATION

The base ten blocks illustrate that each place value is a power of 10. Students should know how to represent a numeral in multiple ways. For example, 234 can be written as "2 hundreds, 3 tens, 4 ones" or "1 hundred, 13 tens, 4 ones." This multiple representation relies on the observation base ten blocks can be *regrouped* according to 1 ten = 10 ones, 1 hundred = 10 tens = 100 ones, 1 thousand = 10 hundreds = 100 tens = 1000 ones, and so on. We illustrate multiple representations of 234 as follows:

234 = 2 hundreds, 3 tens, 4 ones   =   1 hundred, 13 tens, 4 ones   =   1 hundred, 11 tens, 24 ones

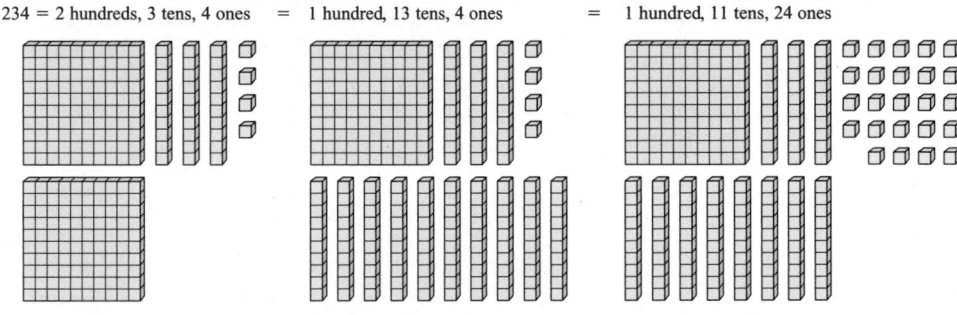

A flexible understanding of the base ten number system reinforces number sense and applies to addition, subtraction, multiplication, and division algorithms.

EXAMPLE 2.11

CONNECTION

REASONING

REPRESENTATION

a. Write three representations of 2046.

b. What is the minimum number of pieces of base ten blocks needed to model 2046?

SOLUTION

a. There are many possible answers. For example, 2046 = 2 thousands, 0 hundreds, 4 tens, 6 ones; 2046 = 1 thousand, 10 hundreds, 4 tens, 6 ones; and 2046 = 1 thousand, 0 hundreds, 102 tens, 26 ones.

b. 12 pieces, because 2046 = 2 thousands, 0 hundreds, 4 tens, 6 ones and 2 + 0 + 4 + 6 = 12

▲

■ Historical Note

Figure 11 shows that the digits we use today have evolved through the centuries (Smith and Karpinski, 1911). The modern shapes of the digits 0, 1, 2, 3, 4, 5, 6, 7, 8, and 9 have remained essentially unchanged since the 1600s.

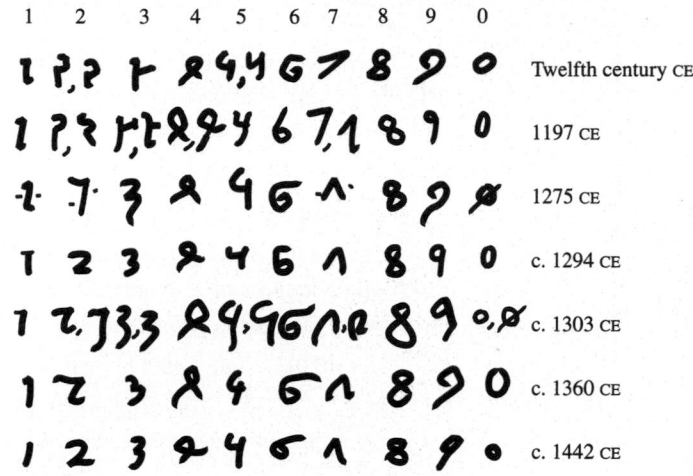

FIGURE 11
Handwritten digits have changed through time.

Reading and Writing Numerals

We represent numerals in several ways. Numerals such as 25 and 672 expressed as a string of digits are said to be in **standard form.** Table 2.5 demonstrates how to write the word form of a few two- or three-digit numerals in standard form. The **word form** is a representation of a numeral using only words. Word forms for two- or three-digit numerals are building blocks of word forms of larger numerals.

TABLE 2.5 Standard Forms and Word Forms of Some Numerals

Standard form	Word form
34	thirty-four
78	seventy-eight
352	three hundred, fifty-two

CONNECTION
REPRESENTATION

Table 2.6 shows the short word form, word form, and various expanded forms of 73,025. The NCTM standards expect students to represent numbers in various ways ($36 = 30 + 6$, $36 = 6 \cdot 6$, $36 = 4 \cdot 8 + 4$, and so on). The **short word form** combines numerals and periods. The **expanded form** represents a numeral as a sum of the values of the digits. An expanded form representation may include products and exponents. As early as second grade, students should be able to "read and write numbers to 1000 using base-ten numerals, number names, and expanded form" (CCSS, Gr. 2).

TABLE 2.6   Different Forms of Representation

Standard form	Representation	Type
73,025	73 thousand, 25	short word form
	seventy-three thousand, twenty-five	word form
	$70{,}000 + 3000 + 0 + 20 + 5$	expanded form
	$7 \cdot 10{,}000 + 3 \cdot 1000 + 0 \cdot 100 + 2 \cdot 10 + 5 \cdot 1$	expanded form with multiplication
	$7 \cdot 10^4 + 3 \cdot 10^3 + 0 \cdot 10^2 + 2 \cdot 10^1 + 5 \cdot 10^0$	expanded form with exponents

We separate the periods with commas to make the standard form, short word form, and word form easier to read. The following Released Item shows students represent numbers in various ways.

> **RELEASED ITEM**
>
> ● NAEP, 2009
> Write a three-digit number using the digits 2, 4, and 6 so that the digit 4 means four tens and the digit 6 means six hundreds.
> 69% of fourth graders answered the question correctly.

The following Classroom Connection indicates that students are expected to know various ways for representing a numeral using place value concepts.

> **Classroom Connection**
>
> ● Houghton Mifflin *Mathematics*, Student Edition, Grade 5, p. 25
>
> Write each number in word form, short word form, and expanded form: 25,064, 693,412, and 231,940. Write each number in expanded form using exponents: 78,056,432,941 and 245,087,705. (© by Houghton Mifflin Company, Inc. Reproduced by permission of the publisher, Houghton Mifflin Harcourt Publishing Company.)

EXAMPLE 2.12

COMMUNICATION

REASONING

REPRESENTATION

Explain how you can use the short word form to lessen the difficulties of translating from the standard form to the word form of a numeral.

SOLUTION

First, write the short word form of the numeral. Second, replace each numeral with its corresponding word form. For example, let's write 435,078,352 in word form. It has the short word form 435 million, 78 thousand, 352. Writing each numeral (435, 78, and 352) in standard form, we get four hundred thirty-five million, seventy-eight thousand, three hundred fifty-two.

Rounding

The distance from Earth to Sun is 149,597,900 km, which is about 150 million km. Which distance do you think students are more likely to remember? A "round number" such as 150 million conveys the same information more effectively because there are fewer non-zero digits to remember. **Rounding** is a systematic process of replacing a number with an approximation using place value concepts.

Rounding a number to a nearest power of 10 (1, 10, 100, 1000, . . .) requires a flexible understanding of place value concepts. For example, let's round 56,834 to the nearest thousand. One name for 56,834 is 56 thousand, 834. Then 56,834 is between 56 thousand and 57 thousand. The number line model in Figure 12 shows 56 thousand and 57 thousand and the midpoint.

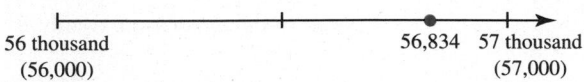

FIGURE 12
Using a number line to round 56,834 to the nearest thousand.

REPRESENTATION

We see 56,834 is closer to 57 thousand. So 56,834 rounded to the nearest thousand is 57 thousand, or 57,000. The next example rounds a number to the nearest ten thousands place.

EXAMPLE 2.13

CONNECTION

REASONING

REPRESENTATION

Round 4,362,815 to the nearest ten thousand. Use a number line to show your thinking.

SOLUTION

The underlined digit in 4,3<u>6</u>2,815 indicates the ten thousands place. One representation of 4,362,815 is 436 ten thousand, 2815. Then 4,362,815 is between 436 ten thousand and 437 ten thousand. The number line model in Figure 13 shows 436 ten thousand and 437 ten thousand and the midpoint.

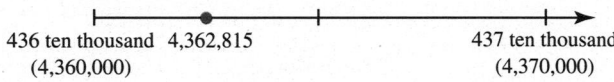

FIGURE 13
Using a number line to round 4,362,815 to the nearest ten thousand.

We see 4,362,815 is closer to 436 ten thousand. So 4,362,815 rounded to the nearest ten thousand is 436 ten thousand, or 4,360,000.

▲

Technically, if a number falls at the midpoint, then the number may be rounded up or down. By convention, elementary students round up to the larger approximation. For example, 25 rounded to the nearest ten is 30. The following Released Item shows that students should understand rounding.

> ▶ **RELEASED ITEM**
>
> • NAEP, 1996
>
>   Which of the following numbers, when rounded to the nearest thousand, becomes 27,000?
>
>   **a.** 26,099   **b.** 26,490   **c.** 27,381   **d.** 27,550   **e.** 27,640
>
>   68% of eighth graders gave the correct answer.

CONNECTION

REASONING

The rounding examples illustrate that the digits to the right of the indicated place value are always zeros. With enough experience, you can use your understanding to develop and apply rounding rules. By grade 4, students should be able to "use place value understanding to round multi-digit whole numbers to any place" (© 2010. National Governors Association Center for Best Practices and Council of Chief State School Officers. All rights reserved.). Some teachers refer to rounding as "skip counting by place value" and do not use a number line. Rounding is useful for reporting large numbers (such as population, national debt, and astronomical distances) and in estimation strategies to check the reasonableness of computations.

Mayan Numeration System

CONNECTION
REASONING
REPRESENTATION

The ancient Maya civilization flourished in the first millennium (about 300–900 CE) in Central America and southern Mexico. The **Mayan numeration system** is a place value system that uses three symbols to form digits. The symbols are 👁, ·, and ——. The seashell symbol 👁 represents 0, the dot · represents 1, and the bar —— represents 5. The Mayan digits and their base ten equivalents appear in Table 2.7.

TABLE 2.7 Mayan Digits

👁	= 0	••••	= 4	•••	= 8	••	= 12	•	= 16
•	= 1	——	= 5	••••	= 9	•••	= 13	••	= 17
••	= 2	•	= 6	——	= 10	••••	= 14	•••	= 18
•••	= 3	••	= 7	•	= 11	——	= 15	••••	= 19

Steyno&Stitch/Shutterstock.com

The **Mayan place values** are 1, 20, 360, 7200, 144,000, . . . and involve powers of 20 ($1 = 20^0$, $20 = 20^1$, $360 = 18 \cdot 20^1$, $7200 = 18 \cdot 20^2$, $144{,}000 = 18 \cdot 20^3$, . . .). The place values are stacked vertically, with the highest place value on top. The lowest level tells you the number of 1s. The next higher level tells you the number of 20s. The next higher level tells you the number of 360s. We might expect this level to represent the number of 400s, because $400 = 20^2$, but it is believed the Mayans chose 360 because their calendar had 360 "ordinary" days and 5 "special" days. The next higher level tells you the number of 7200s, and so on. Place values after 360 increase by a factor of 20. Table 2.8 provides examples of place values and values of digits in Mayan numerals.

TABLE 2.8 Examples of Place Values and Values of Digits in Mayan Numerals

Mayan numeral	Place value of digit	Value of digit	Mayan numeral	Place value of digit	Value of digit	Mayan numeral	Place value of digit	Value of digit
						——	7200	10 · 7200
			••	360	2 · 360	•••	360	8 · 360
•••	20	3 · 20	👁	20	0 · 20	••••	20	19 · 20
•	1	16 · 1	••	1	12 · 1	••	1	7 · 1

EXAMPLE 2.14

CONNECTION
REASONING
REPRESENTATION

Represent the Mayan numeral as a base ten numeral.

a. ••
   ••

b. ••
   👁
   ••
   •••

SOLUTION

a. $17 \cdot 1 + 5 \cdot 20 + 2 \cdot 360 = 837$
b. $8 \cdot 1 + 17 \cdot 20 + 0 \cdot 360 + 2 \cdot 7200 = 14{,}748$

▲

EXAMPLE 2.15

CONNECTION
REASONING
REPRESENTATION

Represent the base ten numeral as a Mayan numeral.
a. 2735
b. 6500

SOLUTION

The Mayan place values in ascending order are 1, 20, 360, 7200, 144,000, ...

a. Because 2735 is between 360 and 7200, we need to represent 2735 in the form $2735 = a \cdot 360 + b \cdot 20 + c \cdot 1$:

Step 1. $2735 \div 360 = 7$ R215

Step 2. $215 \div 20 = 10$ R15.

Step 3. Then $2735 = 7 \cdot 360 + 10 \cdot 20 + 15 \cdot 1$.

The Mayan numeral is

b. Because 16,500 is between 7200 and 144,000, we need to represent 16,500 in the form $16{,}500 = a \cdot 7200 + b \cdot 360 + c \cdot 20 + d \cdot 1$:

Step 1. $16{,}500 \div 7200 = 2$ R2100

Step 2. $2100 \div 360 = 5$ R300

Step 3. $300 \div 20 = 15$ R0.

Step 4. Then $16{,}500 = 2 \cdot 7200 + 5 \cdot 360 + 15 \cdot 20 + 0 \cdot 1$.

The Mayan numeral is

▲

Babylonian Numeration System

CONNECTION
REASONING
REPRESENTATION

The ancient Babylonian civilization flourished in modern-day Iraq. Between approximately 2000–3000 BCE, Babylonians developed a numeration system that used two symbols, ▼ and ◄, to write numerals. They etched numerals in soft clay tablets with a stylus. The triangular wedge symbol ▼ represented 1, and the arrow wedge symbol ◄ represented 10. The examples that follow illustrate the main idea of how to use the two symbols to form Babylonian digits as tightly grouped symbols.

$1 =$ ▼ $5 =$ ▼▼▼ ▼▼ $10 =$ ◄ $17 =$ ◄▼▼▼ ▼▼▼ ▼ $26 =$ ◄◄▼▼▼ ▼▼▼

$33 =$ ◄◄◄▼▼▼ $34 =$ ◄◄◄▼▼▼ ▼ $49 =$ ◄◄◄▼▼▼ ◄ ▼▼▼ ▼▼▼ $58 =$ ◄◄◄▼▼▼ ◄◄ ▼▼▼ ▼▼

The **Babylonian numeration system** is *sexagesimal,* which means **Babylonian place values** are powers of 60 (1, 60, 3600, 216,000, . . .). The place values are ordered from left to right, with the highest place value to the left. For example,

$$\blacktriangledown\blacktriangledown\blacktriangledown\text{...} = 42 \cdot 60^3 + 7 \cdot 60^2 + 31 \cdot 60^1 + 12 \cdot 60^0$$
$$= 9{,}099{,}072.$$

Babylonians used an empty space to skip a place value, two empty spaces to skip two place values, and so on, although this leaves room for ambiguity or confusion. For example, ◄▼ ▼▼▼ could be interpreted as $11 \cdot 60^2 + 0 \cdot 60^1 + 3 \cdot 60^0 = 39{,}603$ or $11 \cdot 60^1 + 3 \cdot 60^0 = 663$, depending on the reader's perception of the spacing. By 300 BCE, the Babylonian numeration system included a symbol for zero, two slash marks //, to occupy empty spaces between digits (but not trailing zeros: they did not use trailing zeros such as ▼▼ // because they did not identify zero as a digit). Thus, ▼▼ // ▼▼▼ represents $2 \cdot 60^2 + 0 \cdot 60^1 + 3 \cdot 60^0$, which equals 7203. Here are a few examples of Babylonian numerals and their base ten equivalents, using the three symbols ◄, ▼, and //. Study these examples:

$$\blacktriangledown\blacktriangledown\blacktriangledown \; \blacktriangledown = 4 \cdot 60^1 + 12 \cdot 60^0 = 252$$

$$\blacktriangledown\blacktriangledown \; // \; \blacktriangledown\blacktriangledown\blacktriangledown = 12 \cdot 60^2 + 0 \cdot 60^1 + 23 \cdot 60^0 = 43{,}223$$

$$\blacktriangledown\blacktriangledown\blacktriangledown \; // \; \blacktriangledown \; \blacktriangledown = 3 \cdot 60^3 + 0 \cdot 60^2 + 1 \cdot 60^1 + 21 \cdot 60^0 = 648{,}081$$

$$\blacktriangledown\blacktriangledown\blacktriangledown \; \blacktriangledown = 9 \cdot 60^1 + 41 \cdot 60^0 = 581$$

EXAMPLE 2.16

CONNECTION
REASONING
REPRESENTATION

a. Convert ▼ // ◄◄◄ to a base ten numeral.

b. Convert 7548 to a Babylonian numeral.

SOLUTION

a. ▼ // ◄◄◄ $= 1 \cdot 60^2 + 0 \cdot 60^1 + 30 \cdot 60^0 = 3630$

b. We know $60^2 = 3600$ and $60^3 = 216{,}000$. Because 7548 is between 3600 and 216,000, we need to represent 7548 in the form $7548 = a \cdot 60^2 + b \cdot 60^1 + c \cdot 60^0$:

Step 1. $7548 \div 3600 = 2$ R348

Step 2. $348 \div 60 = 5$ R48.

Step 3.   So $7548 = 2 \cdot 60^2 + 5 \cdot 60^1 + 48 \cdot 60^0$. Then

$$7548 = \blacktriangledown\blacktriangledown \quad \blacktriangledown\blacktriangledown\blacktriangledown \quad \blacktriangledown\blacktriangledown\blacktriangledown .$$

Base Five Numeration System

The **base five numeration system** is a place value numeration system based on the digits $\{0_{\text{five}}, 1_{\text{five}}, 2_{\text{five}}, 3_{\text{five}}, 4_{\text{five}}\}$, where the subscript *five* indicates they are base five digits (it is OK to use 5, for example, 3_5 and 4_5). The numerals 4_{five}, 342_{five}, and 102_{five} illustrate the convention for writing base five numerals. The numeral 342_{five} is read "three four two base five." The numeral 3102_{five} is read "three one zero two base five." Commas are unnecessary because base five numerals are easy to read without commas. The base five blocks in

Figure 14 help visualize the place values 1_{five}, 10_{five}, 100_{five}, and 1000_{five}. The next place value is 10000_{five}, and so on.

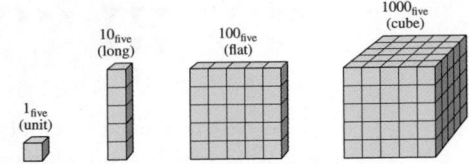

FIGURE 14
Model of base five place values (from lowest to highest).

The *unit* represents 1_{five} units. The *long* represents 10_{five} units. The *flat* represents 100_{five} units or 10_{five} longs. The *cube* represents 10_{five} flats, 100_{five} longs, or 1000_{five} units. We reserve the names *ones, tens, hundreds,* and *thousands* for base ten blocks. Figure 15 shows how to model 3242_{five} with base five blocks.

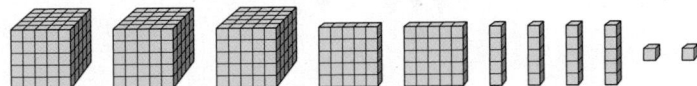

FIGURE 15
Model of 3242_{five} with base five blocks.

EXAMPLE 2.17

CONNECTION

REASONING

REPRESENTATION

a. What is the place value of the underlined digit in $1\underline{4}01_{five}$?

b. What is the value of the underlined digit in $2\underline{3}1_{five}$?

c. Write the expanded form of 3242_{five}.

SOLUTION

a. 100_{five}

b. 30_{five}

c. $3242_{five} = 3000_{five} + 200_{five} + 40_{five} + 2_{five}$ or
$3242_{five} = 3_{five} \cdot 1000_{five} + 2_{five} \cdot 100_{five} + 4_{five} \cdot 10_{five} + 2_{five} \cdot 1_{five}$

▲

Figure 16 shows the base five models of 1_{five}, 2_{five}, 3_{five}, and 4_{five} and that $1_{five} = 1$, $2_{five} = 2$, $3_{five} = 3$, and $4_{five} = 4$, where 1, 2, 3, and 4 refer to base ten digits. Of course, $0_{five} = 0$.

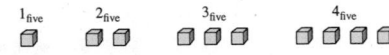

FIGURE 16
Base five models of 1_{five}, 2_{five}, 3_{five}, and 4_{five}.

The next numeral, which is 1 unit more than 4_{five}, is a string of these digits. Figure 17 suggests the next numeral is 10_{five}, which equals 1 long and 0 units.

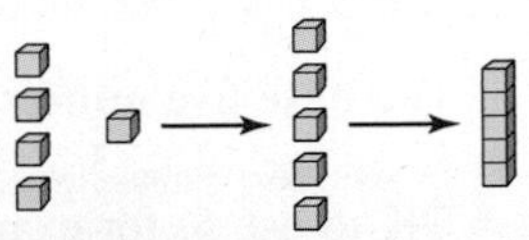

FIGURE 17
One unit more than 4_{five} is 10_{five}.

The next numeral after 10_{five} is 11_{five}. The following array lists more base five whole numbers:

0_{five}	1_{five}	2_{five}	3_{five}	4_{five}
10_{five}	11_{five}	12_{five}	13_{five}	14_{five}
20_{five}	21_{five}	22_{five}	23_{five}	24_{five}
30_{five}	31_{five}	32_{five}	33_{five}	34_{five}
40_{five}	41_{five}	42_{five}	43_{five}	44_{five}
100_{five}	101_{five}	102_{five}	103_{five}	104_{five}

The place values (from lowest to highest) 1_{five}, 10_{five}, 100_{five}, 1000_{five}, and 10000_{five} have respective base ten equivalents: 5^0, 5^1, 5^2, 5^3, and 5^4. The following example shows how to use the expanded form followed by substitutions to represent a base five numeral as a base ten numeral.

EXAMPLE 2.18

CONNECTION
REASONING
REPRESENTATION

Represent 2412_{five} as a base ten numeral.

SOLUTION

$$2412_{\text{five}} = 2_{\text{five}} \cdot 1000_{\text{five}} + 4_{\text{five}} \cdot 100_{\text{five}} + 1_{\text{five}} \cdot 10_{\text{five}} + 2_{\text{five}} \cdot 1_{\text{five}}$$
$$= 2 \cdot 5^3 + 4 \cdot 5^2 + 1 \cdot 5^1 + 2 \cdot 5^0$$
$$= 2 \cdot 125 + 4 \cdot 25 + 1 \cdot 5 + 2 \cdot 1$$
$$= 250 + 100 + 5 + 2$$
$$= 357$$

▲

To represent a base ten numeral as a base five numeral, we reverse the process and divide by powers of 5 ($5^4 = 625$, $5^3 = 125$, $5^2 = 25$, $5^1 = 5$, $5^0 = 1$), beginning with the highest power of 5 that divides the base ten numeral. The following example illustrates the process.

EXAMPLE 2.19

CONNECTION
REASONING
REPRESENTATION

Represent 2234 as a base five numeral.

SOLUTION

Here, we have $5^4 = 5 \cdot 5 \cdot 5 \cdot 5 = 625$ and $5^5 = 5 \cdot 5 \cdot 5 \cdot 5 \cdot 5 = 3125$. We know 2234 is more than 625 but less than 3215, so we begin by dividing by 625 (that is, 5^4):

$2234 \div 5^4 = 3 \text{ R}359$	**Think: $2234 = 3 \cdot 5^4 + 359$**
$359 \div 5^3 = 2 \text{ R}109$	**Think: $2234 = 3 \cdot 5^4 + 2 \cdot 5^3 + 109$**
$109 \div 5^2 = 4 \text{ R}9$	**Think: $2234 = 3 \cdot 5^4 + 2 \cdot 5^3 + 4 \cdot 5^2 + 9$**
$9 \div 5^1 = 1 \text{ R}4$	**Think: $2234 = 3 \cdot 5^4 + 2 \cdot 5^3 + 4 \cdot 5^2 + 1 \cdot 5^1 + 4$**

Then

$$2234 = 3 \cdot 5^4 + 2 \cdot 5^3 + 4 \cdot 5^2 + 1 \cdot 5^1 + 4 \cdot 5^0$$
$$= 3_{\text{five}} \cdot 10000_{\text{five}} + 2_{\text{five}} \cdot 1000_{\text{five}} + 4_{\text{five}} \cdot 100_{\text{five}} + 1_{\text{five}} \cdot 10_{\text{five}} + 4_{\text{five}} \cdot 1_{\text{five}}$$
$$= 32414_{\text{five}}$$

▲

Base Twelve Numeration System

The **base twelve numeration system** requires 12 symbols. We use the digits $\{0_{\text{twelve}}, 1_{\text{twelve}}, 2_{\text{twelve}}, \ldots, 9_{\text{twelve}}, A, B\}$. The base twelve digit A equals the base ten numeral 10, while the base twelve digit B equals the base ten numeral 11 (other textbooks may use

T in place of A and E in place of B). Some place values for base twelve are 10000_{twelve}, 1000_{twelve}, 100_{twelve}, 10_{twelve}, and 1_{twelve}, which have the respective base ten equivalents of 12^4, 12^3, 12^2, 12^1, and 12^0. Like base five numerals, we read base twelve numerals by pronouncing their digits; for example, $25A4B_{twelve}$ is read "two five A four B base twelve."

EXAMPLE 2.20 Represent $2B8A_{twelve}$ as a base ten numeral.

CONNECTION
REASONING
REPRESENTATION

SOLUTION

We expand the numeral and convert the digits (such as $2_{twelve} = 2$, $A = 10$, and $B = 11$) and the place values (such as $10_{twelve} = 12^1$ and $1000_{twelve} = 12^3$):

$$
\begin{aligned}
2B8A_{twelve} &= 2_{twelve} \cdot 1000_{twelve} + B \cdot 100_{twelve} + 8_{twelve} \cdot 10_{twelve} + A \cdot 1_{twelve} \\
&= 2 \cdot 12^3 + 11 \cdot 12^2 + 8 \cdot 12^1 + 10 \cdot 12^0 \\
&= 2 \cdot 1728 + 11 \cdot 144 + 8 \cdot 12 + 10 \cdot 1 \\
&= 3456 + 1584 + 96 + 10 \\
&= 5146
\end{aligned}
$$

▲

To represent a base ten numeral as a base twelve numeral, we reverse the process and divide by powers of 12 ($12^4 = 20{,}736$, $12^3 = 1728$, $12^2 = 144$, $12^1 = 12$, $12^0 = 1$), beginning with the highest power of 12 that divides the base ten numeral. The following example illustrates the process.

EXAMPLE 2.21 Represent 4967 as a base twelve numeral.

CONNECTION
REASONING
REPRESENTATION

SOLUTION

Here, we have $12^3 = 12 \cdot 12 \cdot 12 = 1728$ and $12^4 = 12 \cdot 12 \cdot 12 \cdot 12 = 20{,}736$. Because 4967 is more than 1728 but less than 20,736, we begin by dividing by 1728 (that is, 12^3):

$$
\begin{aligned}
4967 \div 12^3 &= 2 \; R1511 \qquad &&\textbf{Think: } 4967 = 2 \cdot 12^3 + 1511 \\
1511 \div 12^2 &= 10 \; R71 \qquad &&\textbf{Think: } 4967 = 2 \cdot 12^3 + 10 \cdot 12^2 + 71 \\
71 \div 12^1 &= 5 \; R11 \qquad &&\textbf{Think: } 4967 = 2 \cdot 12^3 + 10 \cdot 12^2 + 5 \cdot 12^1 + 11
\end{aligned}
$$

Then

$$
\begin{aligned}
4967 &= 2 \cdot 12^3 + 10 \cdot 12^2 + 5 \cdot 12^1 + 11 \cdot 12^0 \\
&= 2_{twelve} \cdot 1000_{twelve} + A \cdot 100_{twelve} + 5_{twelve} \cdot 10_{twelve} + B \cdot 1_{twelve} \\
&= 2A5B_{twelve}
\end{aligned}
$$

▲

Requirements of a Place Value Numeration System

In a **place value numeration system,** such as the base ten, Mayan, or Babylonian numeration system, the position of a digit is important. There are five requirements of an effective place value numeration system.

> ## Requirements of a Place Value Numeration System
>
> **1.** The numeration system has a set of symbols called *digits*.
> **2.** Each *numeral* is a sequence of digits.
> **3.** Each digit has a *place value* within a numeral that determines the size of a grouping.
> **4.** Each digit in a numeral conveys a *value* that depends on the digit itself and the place value of the digit.
> **5.** One digit, called *zero*, signifies the absence of the grouping associated with its place value.

CONNECTION
REPRESENTATION

Table 2.9 shows a few numbers and corresponding numerals. We see that the numeral depends on the numeration system.

TABLE 2.9 **Representations of Numbers with Numerals from Different Numeration Systems**

Number	Hindu–Arabic	Egyptian	Roman	Greek	Babylonian	Mayan
zero	0				//	⬭
one	1	I	I	α	▼	•
two	2	II	II	β	▼▼	••
three	3	III	III	γ	▼▼▼	•••
four	4	IIII	IV	δ	▼▼▼ ▼	••••
five	5	IIIII	V	ϵ	▼▼▼ ▼▼	—
six	6	IIIIII	VI	ς	▼▼▼ ▼▼▼	⎯•⎯
seven	7	IIIIIII	VII	ζ	▼▼▼ ▼▼▼ ▼	••
eight	8	IIIIIIII	VIII	η	▼▼▼ ▼▼▼ ▼▼	•••
nine	9	IIIIIIIII	IX	θ	▼▼▼ ▼▼▼ ▼▼▼	••••
ten	10	∩	X	τ	◄	═══
fifty	50	∩∩∩∩∩	L	υ	◄◄◄ ◄◄	•• ═══
hundred	100	৭	C	ρ	▼◄◄◄ ◄	⬭
five hundred	500	৭৭৭৭	D	ϕ	▼▼▼ ◄◄ ▼▼▼ ▼▼	•• •• ⬭

QUESTIONS FOR SECTION 2.2

REPRESENTATION

Refresher: Representations (language, diagrams, tables, symbols, algebra, manipulatives, and contextualized situations) are important because we use them to organize, record, and communicate mathematical ideas and to make them more comprehensible.

1. Select the correct expanded form of 423.

   a. $420 + 3$ b. $4 \cdot 100 + 2 \cdot 10 + 3$

   c. $4 \cdot 100 + 2 \cdot 10 + 3 \cdot 1$

2. Clyde Tombaugh discovered Pluto in 1930. Pluto orbits the Sun every 248 years (Earth years). The length of the path it travels as it orbits the Sun is 20,390,000,000 miles. Represent the length of its orbital path in

   a. short word form.   b. word form.

3. Use a number line model to round

   a. 42 to the nearest ten. What is the rounded number?

   b. 286 to the nearest hundred. What is the rounded number?

   c. 436 to the nearest thousand. What is the rounded number?

4. Write each number in standard form.

   a. $20,000 + 3000 + 80 + 7$

   b. 145 million, 241 thousand, 83

   c. three hundred seventy-three billion, fifty-eight million, two hundred sixteen

5. Model 359 using

   a. base ten blocks.   b. Egyptian numerals.

6. Represent the sum as a Mayan numeral.

   a. $4 \cdot 360 + 17 \cdot 20 + 3 \cdot 1$

   b. $11 \cdot 7200 + 6 \cdot 360 + 0 \cdot 20 + 4 \cdot 1$

   c. $15 \cdot 144,000 + 2 \cdot 7200 + 5 \cdot 360 + 12 \cdot 1$

7. Represent the sum as a Babylonian numeral.

   a. $5 \cdot 3600 + 21 \cdot 60 + 8 \cdot 1$

   b. $50 \cdot 216,000 + 12 \cdot 3600 + 0 \cdot 60 + 3 \cdot 1$

   c. $42 \cdot 216,000 + 8 \cdot 3600 + 12 \cdot 60 + 2 \cdot 1$

8. Write the base five numeral.

   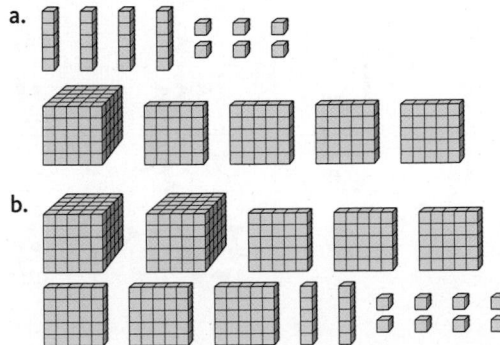

9. Write the base three numeral.

   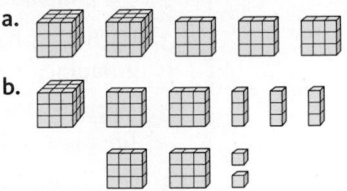

10. Represent each numeral with base three blocks.

    a. 201_{three} b. 101_{three} c. 212_{three}

11. Sketch a cube, flat, long, and unit for base four.

PROBLEM SOLVING

Refresher: Problem solving (reaching a goal that is not immediately attainable) is important because it helps students think more deeply about what they know and deal with unfamiliar situations.

12. In the equation $abc + cb = aaa$, each letter represents a different base ten digit.

    a. Tell what you know about b and c.

    b. Find an example of a, b, and c that makes the equation true.

13. I'm thinking of a two-digit number. The tens digit is 4 more than the ones digit. Both digits are odd. List all possible two-digit numbers.

14. I'm thinking of a three-digit number. The sum of the digits is 15. Two of the digits are even numbers. The hundreds digit is less than the tens digit. The tens digit is less than the ones digit.

    a. Find an example of such a number without the digit 7.

    b. Find an example of such a number with the digit 7.

15. How many digits are in the standard form of 7108×10^{23}? Explain the strategy you used to answer this question.

16. Because $24^2 = 576$, the digit sum of 24^2 is $5 + 7 + 6 = 18$. What is the digit sum of 333332^2? Explain the strategy you used to answer this question.

REASONING AND PROOF

Refresher: Reasoning and proof (thinking and justifying) are important because they help students make sense of mathematics.

17. When we round the number n, we get 48,000. What place values could we have used? Support your answer with examples.

18. The whole number n is rounded to the nearest hundred, and the result is 300.

    a. What is the smallest possible value for n?

    b. What is the largest possible value for n?

    c. How many possible values are there for n?

19. Do the following.

   a. Find a whole number n such that when 4258 and n are each rounded to the nearest thousand, the sum of the rounded numbers is 12,000.

   b. What is the smallest possible value for n?

   c. What is the largest possible value for n?

   d. How many possible values are there for n?

CONNECTIONS

Refresher: Connections (linking and applying mathematical ideas) are important because they deepen student understanding and make mathematics more meaningful, flexible, and useful.

20. Represent the following as a base ten numeral.

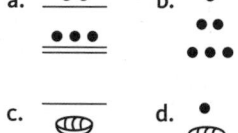

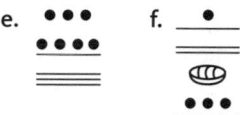

21. Represent the following as a Mayan numeral.

   a. 54   **b.** 348   **c.** 942   **d.** 627   **e.** 17,345

22. Represent the following as a base ten numeral.

   a. ◄▼ // ▼

   b. ◄◄◄ ▼ ◄▼▼

   c. ▼▼▼ ◄▼▼ ▼▼

   d. ◄◄◄ // ▼▼▼ ▼▼▼ ▼▼

   e. ▼ // ◄ // ◄◄▼▼▼ ▼▼

23. Represent the following as a Babylonian numeral.

   a. 54   **b.** 348   **c.** 942   **d.** 627   **e.** 17,345

24. The Babylonian representations did not use the zero (//) as trailing digits. Thus, ▼// was not a valid representation. This means ▼ could actually represent 1, 60, 3600, and so on. Babylonians used the context to interpret the value of ▼. Interpret each numeral for the given situation.

   a. ▼ candles were on the teacher's cake. Does the numeral represent 1, 60, or 3600?

   b. ◄▼▼ people went to a high school football game. Does the numeral represent 12, 720, or 43,200?

25. How are the Hindu–Arabic and Babylonian numeration systems alike? different?

26. How many different digits are needed for

   a. base three?   **b.** base four?   **c.** base fifteen?

27. Represent each numeral in expanded form.

   a. 134_{five} **b.** 725_{eight} **c.** $\text{A47B}_{\text{twelve}}$

28. Represent each numeral as a base ten numeral.

   a. 100_{five} **b.** 100_{six} **c.** 100_{seven}

29. Represent each numeral as a base ten numeral.

   a. 412_{five} **b.** $\text{450B}_{\text{twelve}}$ **c.** 3501_{six}

30. Represent the base ten numeral as a numeral in the indicated base.

   a. $422 = \underline{\hspace{1cm}}_{\text{five}}$ **b.** $6789 = \underline{\hspace{1cm}}_{\text{twelve}}$ **c.** $1865 = \underline{\hspace{1cm}}_{\text{six}}$

31. Fill in the blanks.

   a. $42_{\text{five}}, 43_{\text{five}}, 44_{\text{five}}, \underline{\hspace{0.5cm}}, \underline{\hspace{0.5cm}}$

   b. $\underline{\hspace{0.5cm}}, \underline{\hspace{0.5cm}}, 100_{\text{seven}}, 101_{\text{seven}}, 102_{\text{seven}}$

   c. $8_{\text{twelve}}, 9_{\text{twelve}}, \text{A}, \text{B}, \underline{\hspace{0.5cm}}, \underline{\hspace{0.5cm}}$

COMMUNICATION

Refresher: Communication (written and verbal explanations using representations and proper mathematical vocabulary) is important because it helps students refine and strengthen their understanding.

32. What is a numeration system?

33. What are the two basic requirements of a numeration system?

34. What is a place value numeration system?

35. A teacher writes "3_2_,456,_2_49" on the board and asks the class how the digits are different. One student replies, "The underlined digits have different place values." Another student replies, "The underlined digits have different values." Which reply seems to suggest deeper understanding of place value concepts?

36. How are place values in the Hindu–Arabic numeration system related?

37. How are the Mayan and base ten numeration systems alike? different?

38. Construct your own place value numeration system. Create digits using symbols. Tell what quantity each digit represents. Discuss how regrouping occurs. Relate base ten numerals to numerals in your numeration system. Make an addition table for your numeration system.

More practice with the ideas of the section

39. Fill in the blank. Choose one of the following words or phrases: *place value, value, expanded form, digits, numeral, number, word form, short word form, standard form,* or *rounding.*

   a. The $\underline{\hspace{1.5cm}}$ of a digit depends on the position of the digit.

   b. The $\underline{\hspace{1.5cm}}$ of a digit depends on the digit itself and the position of the digit.

   c. Each numeral in a place value numeration system is a sequence of $\underline{\hspace{1.5cm}}$.

   d. A(n) $\underline{\hspace{1.5cm}}$ is a representation that depends on the numeration system.

   e. A(n) $\underline{\hspace{1.5cm}}$ does not depend on the numeration system.

   f. The $\underline{\hspace{1.5cm}}$ for 53,308 is 53 thousand, 308.

g. The _____ for 1234 is 1000 + 200 + 30 + 4.

h. The _____ for 30 + 6 is 36.

40. Represent each numeral in standard form.

   a. three hundred twenty-eight billion, fifty-two million, two hundred eleven

   b. seventy-eight trillion, thirteen billion, seven thousand, seven hundred eighty-nine

   c. six hundred thirty-nine thousand, three

41. What is the place value of the underlined digit?

   a. 623,705   b. 380,245,701   c. 25,029

42. What is the place value of the underlined digit?

   a. 32,804   b. 125,493   c. 36,790,782,245

43. What is the value of the underlined digit?

   a. 28,710   b. 20,782,499,021   c. 35,428,114

44. What is the value of the underlined digit?

   a. 38,042   b. 4,689,283   c. 50,241

45. Consider the number 382,856,249.

   a. How are the underlined digits alike?

   b. How are they different?

   c. What is the purpose of the commas?

46. Mars is a cold and rocky planet with polar ice caps and magnificent dust storms. On average, Mars is 227,936,640 km from the Sun. Represent the distance in

   a. short word form.   b. word form.

47. Represent each number in standard form.

   a. 72 thousand, 84   b. 53 million, 128 thousand, 421

   c. 21 billion, 12 thousand, 89

48. Represent 45,036 in the following forms.

   a. short word   b. word   c. expanded

   d. expanded with multiplication

   e. expanded with exponents

49. Find the digit in the indicated place value.

   a. 258,645,399 (ten millions)   b. 25,196,001 (hundreds)

   c. 339,245,174,355 (ten billions)

50. Find the place value of the indicated digit.

   a. 798,321,500 (digit 8)   b. 5,364,582,101,000 (digit 6)

   c. 85,403,899 (digit 0)

51. Each letter a, b, and c represents a base ten digit. Give the order from least to greatest, assuming the numerals are written in standard form.

   a. abc, b, ac   b. ab, cba, c

52. We can write 324 = 3 hundreds, 1 ten, 14 ones or 324 = 32 tens, 4 ones. For each problem, find two ways to fill in the blanks.

   a. 456 = ___ hundreds, ___ tens, ___ ones

   b. 623,501 = ___ thousands, ___ tens, ___ ones

   c. 6785 = ___ tens, ___ ones

   d. 7412 = ___ thousands, ___ hundreds, ___ ones

53. Fill in the blanks. Use the most efficient representation possible (that is, the minimum number of base ten pieces possible so that equality holds).

   a. 478 = ___ tens, ___ ones

   b. 1304 = ___ hundreds, ___ tens, ___ ones

   c. 2562 = ___ thousands, ___ ones

   d. 8905 = ___ hundreds, ___ tens, ___ ones

54. Determine the fewest number of base ten pieces needed to represent the base ten numeral.

   a. 5   b. 148   c. 3592   d. 63

55. Use a number line model. Use a dot to indicate the number to be rounded.

   a. Round 870 to the nearest thousand.

   b. Round 425 to the nearest hundred.

   c. Round 3,672,332 to the nearest million.

   d. Round 10,456,788,000 to the nearest billion.

56. Do the following.

   a. Round 12,456,306 to the nearest million.

   b. Round 8,450,251 to the nearest hundred thousand.

   c. Round 985,382,951 to the nearest hundred.

57. Use your calculator to do the following.

   a. Round 842 to the nearest multiple of 15.

   b. Round 5924 to the nearest multiple of 23.

   c. Round 72,950 to the nearest multiple of 41.

58. Represent each number using Egyptian symbols.

   a. 32   b. 2372   c. 34,023   d. 201,485

59. Represent as a base ten numeral.

   a. ◄ // ◄ ▼

   b. ◄◄◄ // ◄▼▼

   c. ◄▼▼▼ // ▼

   d. ◄ // // ◄◄▼ // ▼▼▼

   e. ◄▼▼ // ◄▼▼▼
      ▼

60. Write the expanded form of the numeral.

   a. 678_{nine} b. 1203_{five} c. $A2B8_{twelve}$

61. Represent the base ten numeral as a numeral in the indicated base.

   a. 678 = ___$_{five}$ b. 17,846 = ___$_{twelve}$

   c. 1756 = ___$_{seven}$

62. Represent the numeral as a base ten numeral.

   a. 1234_{five} b. 31021_{five} c. $ABBA_{twelve}$ d. 54321_{seven}

63. Find the missing base.

   a. $18 = 16_?$ b. $24 = 30_?$ c. $16 = 24_?$

64. Use the pattern to fill in the blank.

   a. ___, 100, 101, 102, 103

   b. ___, 100_{five}, 101_{five}, 102_{five}, 103_{five}

   c. ___, 100_{seven}, 101_{seven}, 102_{seven}, 103_{seven}

   d. ___, 100_{twelve}, 101_{twelve}, 102_{twelve}, 103_{twelve}

Models and Properties of Addition and Subtraction

Models for Addition and Subtraction

We begin this section with models (or representations) of situations that require addition and subtraction of whole numbers. The two models for addition are the set model and the number line model. The four models of subtraction are the take-away model, number line model, missing-addend model, and comparison model. We represent these situations that involve addition and subtraction using pictures or symbols, in the spirit of various standards: "use addition and subtraction within 20 to solve word problems involving situations of adding to, taking from, putting together, taking apart, and comparing, with unknowns in all positions, e.g., by using objects, drawings, and equations with a symbol for the unknown number to represent the problem" (CCSS, Gr. 1) and "model situations that involve addition and subtraction of whole numbers, using objects, pictures, and symbols" (NCTM, Gr. PreK–2). Then we discuss various strategies for adding and subtracting that make use of properties.

Two Models That Involve Addition with Whole Numbers

Set Model for Addition The **set model** for addition involves combining two disjoint sets of discrete objects (such as coins, pencils, or marbles) and then determining how many objects there are altogether. For example, "Bob has three coins. Mary has four coins. How many coins do they have altogether?" We can use sets to model the coins they each have, as shown in Figure 18(a), and thus demonstrate that addition is "putting together" or "combining sets" to find the total number of objects. They have seven coins altogether, as shown in Figure 18(b).

Bob has three coins.

(a)

Mary has four coins.

Bob and Mary have seven coins altogether.

(b)

FIGURE 18
Set model of addition.

REPRESENTATION   The coin example illustrates how to define addition in terms of sets.

Definition of Whole Number Addition

Let a and b be two whole numbers. Let A and B represent two disjoint sets (that is, $A \cap B = \varnothing$) such that $a = n(A)$ and $b = n(B)$. Then $a + b$, which is read "a plus b," is the whole number defined by $a + b = n(A \cup B)$.

- a and b are called **addends,** and $a + b$ is called the **sum.**
- $a + b$ is also read "b more than a."

Elementary school students often interpret $a + b$ as something to do such as "add b to a" rather than as a number composed of two other numbers. That explains why many elementary school students faced with the problem $3 + 5 = \_\_ + 2$ fill in the blank with the number 8 rather than 6. Keep in mind that there are three numbers in the expression $a + b$: $a, b,$ and the sum $a + b$.

EXAMPLE 2.22 Use the set model to add 4 + 2.

REPRESENTATION

SOLUTION

We create two disjoint sets, one with four objects and the other with two objects. Then we join the sets and count how many objects there are in all: ○○○○ ○○. We count six objects, so 4 + 2 = 6. ▲

Elementary school students eventually realize they are recounting the four objects in the first set and simply need to continue counting the objects in the second set. They develop the *counting-on strategy* as follows: "Say 'four' out loud. As you continue counting, extend your fingers to record the number of objects in the second set. The last number you say is the sum: 'five, six.' (say 'four' and then count on: 'five, six'). So four plus two equals six."

Number Line Model for Addition The **number line model** is appropriate for finding the sum of continuous quantities, such as weight and distance. The number line in Figure 19 is a geometric representation of the set of whole numbers. It helps students visualize the relative position of numbers. A directed arrow, from left to right, represents a whole number. The whole number is determined by the distance from the initial point to the terminal point of the arrow. Figure 19 illustrates several representations of the number 3 using directed arrows.

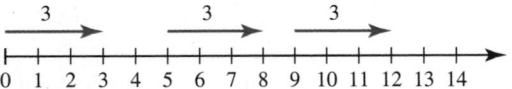

FIGURE 19
Directed arrows, from left to right, representing whole numbers.

REPRESENTATION

Movements on a number line help find a sum, such as 3 + 2. Figure 20 shows how to use a number line to solve the following problem: "John ran 3 miles on Monday. Then he ran 2 miles on Tuesday. How many miles did he run altogether?" Each directed arrow represents an addend. An arrow beginning at 0 and extending from left to right represents the addend 3, while an arrow beginning at 3 and extending from left to right two units represents the addend 2. The location of the terminal point of the second arrow indicates the sum: 3 + 2 = 5. John ran 5 miles altogether.

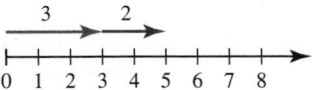

FIGURE 20
Number line model of 3 + 2.

■ **Historical Note**

Mathematicians used various symbols, such as p̃, P, +, and *et,* to represent addition. Johannes Widman (ca. 1462–1498), a German mathematician, is credited with the earliest printed use of the symbol + to represent addition; it appeared in an algebra book he published in 1489. Mathematicians, including Widman, used the symbol + for multiple purposes, such as representing the word *and,* but restricted its use to addition by the early 1600s.

Reunitizing

In some cases addends have different units. For example, "Suppose that 1 gallon of orange juice is mixed with 37 ounces of grape juice. How many ounces of juice are in the mixture?"

$$1 \text{ gal} + 37 \text{ oz} = 128 \text{ oz} + 37 \text{ oz}$$
$$= 165 \text{ oz}$$

This simple example illustrates a basic principle of addition: joining two quantities may require changing the units of one or both of the addends, called *reunitizing* (or *norming*). It is an essential idea of addition that also applies to adding fractions (such as in the problem 2-fifths + 37-eighths).

Mental Arithmetic and Properties of Addition

Mental arithmetic is an early use of properties. For example, $5 + 7 = (2 + 3) + 7 = 2 + (3 + 7) = 2 + 10 = 12$. Properties of addition with simple whole number examples channel elementary school students in making conjectures about operations and help them think about mathematics more deeply. Students should be able to "identify such properties as commutativity, associativity, and distributivity and use them to compute with whole numbers" (NCTM, Gr. 3–5). Fluency with basic number combinations such as $5 + 7$ forms the foundation for success with general examples (such as $325 + 757$), learning basic subtraction facts by relating subtraction and addition (for example, relating $9 - 3 =$ ___ to $3 +$ ___ $= 9$), and solving equations (for example, relating $n - 3 = 7$ and $n = 3 + 7$).

Closure Property of Addition for Whole Numbers Let's choose addends from the set $A = \{0, 4, 5\}$. We can see 0 and 4 belong to A and the sum $0 + 4$ belongs to A. We can also see 4 and 5 belong to A but the sum $4 + 5$ does not belong to A. This means A is not closed under addition. When we say a set is "not closed" under addition, we mean there are at least two elements of the set whose sum does not belong to the set. When we say a set is "closed" under addition, we mean the sum of any two elements of the set also belongs to the set.

EXAMPLE 2.23   Determine whether the following sets are closed under addition.
 a. $\{0, 1\}$
 b. $\{2, 4, 6, 8, \ldots\}$

SOLUTION

 a. We know $1 + 1 = 2$ and 2 does not belong to $\{0, 1\}$; therefore, $1 + 1$ does not belong to $\{0, 1\}$. This means $\{0, 1\}$ is not closed under addition.
 b. We know $24 + 16 = 40$, $2 + 8 = 10$, and $42 + 118 = 160$. Each sum is an even number and belongs to $\{2, 4, 6, 8, \ldots\}$. By inductive reasoning, $\{2, 4, 6, 8, \ldots\}$ is closed under addition.

▲

The closure property is formally stated here.

> **Closure Property of Whole Number Addition**
>
> If a and b are whole numbers, then $a + b$ is a whole number.

Commutative Property of Addition for Whole Numbers Pairs of examples such as $5 + 7 = 12$ and $7 + 5 = 12$, $3 + 5 = 8$ and $5 + 3 = 8$, and $4 + 6 = 10$ and $6 + 4 = 10$ suggest the order of the addends does not change the sum. These arithmetic examples suggest the following algebraic result.

Commutative Property of Whole Number Addition

If a and b are whole numbers, then $a + b = b + a$.

EXAMPLE 2.24

COMMUNICATION

Explain how you could use the commutative property to add $3 + 11$.

SOLUTION

We know $3 + 11 = 11 + 3$. Using the counting-on strategy to find $11 + 3$, we say "eleven" and then count on: "twelve, thirteen, fourteen." So $11 + 3 = 14$. Beginning with the larger addend makes the counting-on strategy more efficient because of the commutative property of addition.

▲

Associative Property of Addition for Whole Numbers Addition is a *binary operation,* which means two whole numbers (a and b) are used to produce another whole number ($a + b$). Let's find the sums $(2 + 3) + 4$ and $2 + (3 + 4)$. Each sum has two addends. The parentheses tell us which numbers to combine first. Figure 21 uses colored cubes to illustrate the result is the same for both sums.

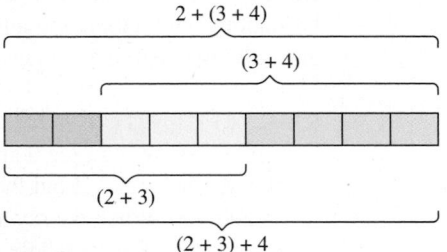

FIGURE 21
Associative property illustrated with colored cubes.

Now we use addition to illustrate the result is the same for both sums.

$$\begin{array}{cc} (2 + 3) + 4 & 2 + (3 + 4) \\ 5 + 4 & 2 + 7 \\ 9 & 9 \end{array}$$

We do not need any parentheses in the expression $(4 + 3) + 2$ or the expression $4 + (3 + 2)$. If $4 + 3 + 2$ is interpreted as $(4 + 3) + 2$, we get 9. If $4 + 3 + 2$ is interpreted as $4 + (3 + 2)$, we still get 9. This example suggests the following algebraic result.

Associative Property of Whole Number Addition

If a, b, and c are whole numbers, then $(a + b) + c = a + (b + c)$.

This implies we can represent $(4 + 3) + 2$ and $4 + (3 + 2)$ as $4 + 3 + 2$ to save ink and reduce clutter in the expression. This property also allows us to interpret $5 + 6 + 7$ as $(5 + 6) + 7$ or $5 + (6 + 7)$.

Number Sense

Number sense is the ability to use numbers and properties flexibly and fluently. It gives teachers a glimpse into student understanding of whole number concepts and operations. Students should "develop a sense of whole numbers and represent and use them in flexible ways, including relating, composing, and decomposing numbers" (NCTM, Gr. PreK–2) and "recognize equivalent representations for the same number and generate them by decomposing and composing numbers" (NCTM, Gr. 3–5). Properties, composition, and decomposition are critical components of number sense. CCSS agree that students should be able to "use strategies such as counting on; making ten (e.g., $8 + 6 = 8 + 2 + 4 = 10 + 4 = 14$); decomposing a number leading to a ten (e.g., $13 - 4 = 13 - 3 - 1 = 10 - 1 = 9$); using the relationship between addition and subtraction (e.g., knowing that $8 + 4 = 12$, one knows $12 - 8 = 4$); and creating equivalent but easier or known sums (e.g., adding $6 + 7$ by creating the known equivalent $6 + 6 + 1 = 12 + 1 = 13$)" (CCSS, Gr. 1).

Composing We can find a sum by using **composition** (or putting together) addends that make an easy combination. For example, $2 + 5 + 8 = 10 + 5 = 15$. We say 2 and 8 are **compatible numbers** because $2 + 8 = 10$ is a common fact. Here's why it works:

$$2 + 5 + 8 = \underbrace{2 + (5 + 8) = 2 + \overbrace{(8 + 5) = (2 + 8)}^{\text{associative property}} + 5}_{\text{commutative property}} = 10 + 5 = 15$$

make 10

Decomposing We can also find a sum by using **decomposition** (or breaking apart or compensating) an addend to make an easy combination. For example, $27 + 8 = 30 + 5 = 35$. Here's why it works:

decompose 8 ↓   make 30 ↓

$$27 + 8 = \underbrace{27 + (3 + 5) = (27 + 3) + 5}_{\text{associative property}} = 30 + 5 = 35$$

CONNECTION

REASONING

Applications of Composing and Decomposing: Making Ten and Making Doubles Composition and decomposition, which involve seeing a number within a number, are a basis for computational fluency in the elementary mathematics curriculum. They arise in early addition strategies as students learn single-digit addition in flexible ways.

EXAMPLE 2.25   **a.** Use the making-tens strategy to add $7 + 5$.

b. Use the making-doubles strategy to add $6 + 8$.

SOLUTION

a. $7 + 5 = 7 + (3 + 2) = (7 + 3) + 2 = 10 + 2 = 12$

b. $6 + 8 = 6 + (6 + 2) = (6 + 6) + 2 = 12 + 2 = 14$

▲

The following Classroom Connection demonstrates that elementary school students apply composing and decomposing throughout their formative years.

> ◆ **Classroom Connection**
>
> ● *Mathematics*, Grade 5
>
> * Find $260 + 190 + 40$ by using compatible numbers. Show why it works. (p. 25)
> * Rosita found $58 + 37$ by thinking $55 + 40$. How did she use compensation? (p. 23) (From Randall I. Charles. © 2004 by Pearson Education, Inc. or its affiliates. Used by permission. All rights reserved.)

Young students learning addition generally progress from combining sets and counting the objects one by one, to applying the counting-on strategy, to composing and decomposing, and finally to showing mastery (for example, "knowing" $7 + 5 = 12$).

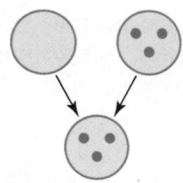

FIGURE 22
Representing the Identity Property of Whole Number Addition.

■ Historical Note

Thomas Harriot (1560–1621) is credited with using the symbols $<$ and $>$ to represent "less than" and "greater than" in his book *Artis Analyticae Praxis ad Aequationes Algebraicas Resolvendas* (translated *Application of Analytical Art to Solving Algebraic Equations*). However, it was published 10 years after his death, and the symbols were introduced by the editors of the publication.

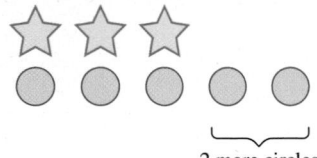

2 more circles

FIGURE 23
Comparing two sets of objects

Identity Property of Whole Number Addition

Figure 22 suggests another property of whole number addition.

> **Identity Property of Whole Number Addition**
>
> Let a represent a whole number. Then $a + 0 = a$ and $0 + a = a$.

Comparing Two Whole Numbers

Two whole numbers must often be compared to determine which number is smaller or larger. The symbols $<$, $>$, $\leq$, and $\geq$ are called *inequalities,* which we use to represent the relationship between two numbers being compared.

- The symbol $<$ means "less than." $a < b$ is read "a is less than b." For example, $3 < 5$ (read "three is less than five").
- The symbol $>$ means "greater than." $a > b$ is read "a is greater than b." For example, $4 > 1$ (read "four is greater than one").
- The symbol $\leq$ means "less than or equal to." $a \leq b$ is read "a is less than or equal to b" and sometimes read "a is at most b." The symbol $\leq$ means there are two mutually exclusive possibilities: a is less than b or a is equal to b. For example, $3 \leq 10$ and $4 \leq 4$ (because 3 is less than 10 and 4 is equal to 4).
- The symbol $\geq$ means "greater than or equal to." $a \geq b$ is read "a is greater than or equal to b" and sometimes read "a is at least b." The symbol $\geq$ means there are two mutually exclusive possibilities: a is greater than b or a is equal to b. For example, $4 \geq 2$ and $7 \geq 7$ (because 4 is greater than 2 and 7 is equal to 7).

   To compare the whole numbers 3 and 5, we could create two sets of objects, the first set with three objects and the second set with five objects, and then match or pair objects between the two sets, as shown in Figure 23. The set with unpaired objects has more elements. There are unpaired circles, so $3 < 5$ (or $5 > 3$).
   Addition can be used to define $<$ and $\leq$.

> **Definition of *less than* in terms of addition**
>
> Let a and b represent any two whole numbers. We say **"a is less than b,"** written $a < b$, if and only if there exists a counting number x such that $a + x = b$.

> **Definition of *less than or equal to* in terms of addition**
>
> Let a and b represent any two whole numbers. We say **"a is less or equal to b,"** written $a \leq b$, if and only if there exists a whole number x such that $a + x = b$.

Algebraic definitions for $>$ and $\geq$ are similar.

EXAMPLE 2.26   **a.** Use the definition of *less than* to show that $3 < 5$.

CONNECTION   **b.** Use the definition of *less than or equal* to write an inequality associated with $4 + 7 = 11$.

REASONING   **c.** True or false: $5 \leq 8$?

SOLUTION

a. We know $3 + 2 = 5$ and 2 is a counting number. The definition of *less than* implies $3 < 5$.

b. There are two possible answers, but the first one is preferable:

We know $4 + 7 = 11$ and 7 is a counting number. The definition of *less than* implies $4 < 11$.

We know $4 + 7 = 11$ and 7 is a whole number. The definition of *less than or equal* implies $4 \leq 11$.

c. True; $5 \leq 8$ if and only if there is a whole number n such that $5 + n = 8$. We know $5 + 3 = 8$, so there is a whole number n such that $5 + n = 8$. So $5 \leq 8$. ▲

Figure 24 shows how to use the number line to compare two numbers (later, we use place value concepts to make such a comparison).

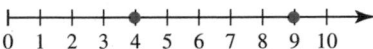

FIGURE 24

On a number line, the number on the left is less than the number on the right.

REPRESENTATION

The number line model gives students a way to "see" the *transitive property* of less than: If a, b, and c are whole numbers such that $a < b$ and $b < c$, then $a < c$. Constructing arguments is a valuable way to understand concepts. The next example uses algebra to prove the transitive property of "less than."

EXAMPLE 2.27 Let a, b, and c be whole numbers such that $a < b$ and $b < c$. Prove $a < c$.

REASONING

SOLUTION

Suppose $a < b$ and $b < c$. To prove $a < c$, we must show a plus some counting number equals c. By the definition of *less than*, $a < b$ means $a + d = b$ for some counting number d. Similarly, $b < c$ means $b + e = c$ for some counting number e.

Then

$$
\begin{array}{ll}
a + d = b & \text{because } a < b \\
(a + d) + e = b + e & \text{by the addition property of equality} \\
a + (d + e) = b + e & \text{by the associative property of addition} \\
a + (d + e) = c. & \text{because } b + e = c
\end{array}
$$

The letters d and e represent counting numbers, so $d + e$ is a counting number by the closure property of addition. This means a plus some counting number equals c. Then $a < c$. ▲

Four Models That Involve Subtraction with Whole Numbers

Elementary school students see four models (or situations) that involve subtraction: the take-away model, missing addend model, comparison model, and number line model. Eventually, they apply basic subtraction facts (for example, they "know" $10 - 7 = 3$) or use place value methods to subtract (for example, they use the standard subtraction algorithm to find the difference $637 - 385$).

Take-Away Model for Subtraction The *take-away model* for subtraction is based on a familiar situation that begins with a discrete collection of objects and is followed by the removal of a *subset* of the objects, as shown in the following example. The quantity of remaining objects answers the question, "How many objects are left?"

EXAMPLE 2.28   Use the take-away model to subtract $7 - 3$.

REPRESENTATION

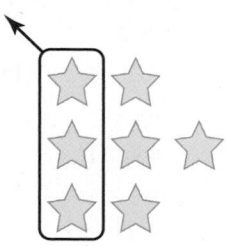

SOLUTION

We draw a set of seven objects, such as seven stars. Then we take away three of the stars. There are four stars remaining, so $7 - 3 = 4$.   ▲

The example links the take-away experience and the symbol $(-)$ for subtraction. The take-away model is the basis for the standard subtraction algorithm in Section 2.4.

Note that $7 - 3 = 4$ (from the diagram) and $3 + 4 = 7$ (from the diagram). This hints that subtraction and addition are related. We could write $7 - 3 = n$, where n is the solution to the equation $7 = 3 + n$. The number n is called a missing or unknown addend because the value of the addend is unknown. This means n is a difference (because $7 - 3 = n$) and an addend (because $7 = n + 3$). Now we are ready to define subtraction.

Definition of Whole Number Subtraction

Let a and b represent whole numbers such that $a \geq b$. The **difference** between a and b, denoted $a - b$ and read "a minus b," is the whole number n (that is, $a - b = n$) if and only if $a = b + n$.

- Also, $a - b = n$ if and only if $a = n + b$ by the commutative property of addition.

- $a - b$ can be read "the difference between a and b," "b fewer than a," and "b less than a."

- a is the **minuend,** b is the **subtrahend,** and n is called the **missing addend** or **unknown addend.**

Equations with one operation, such as $n + 5 = 12$, $15 - k = 8$, $3w = 12$, and $n \div 6 = 24$, are called *one-step equations*. Any one-step equation involving subtraction can be re-expressed in terms of addition and vice versa. For example, $n - 4 = 12$ can be written "$n = 4 + 12$" and $5 + q = 8$ can be written "$q = 8 - 5$."

Students should "understand various meanings of addition and subtraction of whole numbers and the relationship between the two operations" (NCTM, Gr. PreK–2) and "understand subtraction as an unknown-addend problem. For example, subtract $10 - 8$ by finding the number that makes 10 when added to 8" (CCSS, Gr. 1).

A practical application of the missing addend model is learning basic subtraction facts, such as $9 - 3 = $ ___, and solving an equation.

EXAMPLE 2.29   **a.** Use the definition of subtraction to find $9 - 3$.   **Relate subtraction and addition.**

CONNECTION   **b.** Use the definition of subtraction to solve the equation $5 + n = 12$.   **Find a missing addend.**

c. Use the definition of subtraction to solve the equation $x - 6 = 14$.   **Find a missing subtrahend.**

SOLUTION

a. We have $9 - 3 = \underline{\hspace{1em}}$, where $9 = 3 + \underline{\hspace{1em}}$. We know the math fact $9 = 3 + 6$, so $9 - 3 = 6$.

b. We need to solve for the missing addend n in the equation $n + 5 = 12$. According to the definition of subtraction, the equation is equivalent to $n = 12 - 5$. So $n = 7$.

c. We need to solve for the missing subtrahend x in the equation $x - 6 = 14$. According to the definition of subtraction, the equation is equivalent to $x = 6 + 14$. So $x = 20$.

▲

The following Released Item indicates students should be able to relate addition and subtraction to solve equations.

> ▶ **RELEASED ITEM**
>
> ● NAEP, 2009
> $\square - 8 = 21$
> What number should be put in the box to make the number sentence above true?
> Answer: _____
> 69% of fourth-grade students answered the question correctly.

Missing Addend Model for Subtraction   The *missing addend model* applies to situations in which we know the sum and one addend and need to find the other addend. We can use subtraction to answer the question, "How many more are needed?" Maria has four beads. She needs a total of six beads to make a bracelet. How many more beads does she need to make a bracelet?

REPRESENTATION

Say she needs n more beads. The diagram suggests $4 + n = 6$. The number of beads needed, n, is called a missing addend because we do not know its value. We can solve this: $n = 6 - 4 = 2$, so Maria needs two more beads.

EXAMPLE 2.30   **a.** Marty is saving his money for a book that costs $21. He has saved $15 so far. How much more money does he need to save?

CONNECTION

REPRESENTATION   **b.** How are the equations $7 + m = 9$ and $143 + n = 571$ alike? different?

SOLUTION

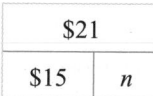

a. The diagram shows how much Marty needs and how much he has saved so far. We see $21 = 15 + n$. We use the definition of subtraction to find the missing addend n to get $n = 21 - 15$, so $n = 6$. Thus, Marty needs to save $6.

b. The equations are alike because each missing addend can be found using subtraction: $m = 9 - 7$ and $n = 571 - 143$. They are different because an elementary school student could use a math fact to solve $7 + m = 9$ but would use a subtraction algorithm to calculate $571 - 143$ to find n.

▲

The following Released Item is a missing addend problem.

> **RELEASED ITEM**
>
> • NAEP, 1996
>
> Kitty is taking a trip on which she plans to drive 300 miles each day. Her trip is 1723 miles long. She has already driven 849 miles. How much farther must she drive?
>
> **a.** 574 miles   **b.** 874 miles   **c.** 1423 miles   **d.** 2872 miles
>
> 64% of fourth graders gave the correct answer.

Comparison Model for Subtraction The *comparison model* uses subtraction to determine how many more or fewer when two known quantities are compared. For example, suppose a mechanic is assembling a machine and has seven bolts and four washers. How many more bolts are there than washers?

We could match the two sets of objects in a one-to-one correspondence, as shown in Figure 25. We "see" there are three more bolts than washers (or three fewer washers than bolts). Because the mechanic already knows there are seven hexagonal bolts and four flat washers, the expression $7 - 4$ tells us how many more bolts there are than washers *without pairing the objects*. Because $7 - 4 = 3$, there are three more bolts.

REPRESENTATION

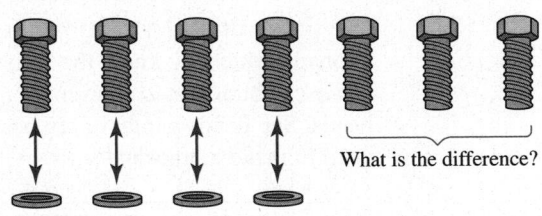

What is the difference?

FIGURE 25
Comparison model.

EXAMPLE 2.31

CONNECTION

a. Alyssa has 11 marbles and Vanessa has 4 marbles. How many more marbles does Alyssa have?

b. Carlo wrote nine poems. Nick wrote three poems. How many fewer poems did Nick write?

SOLUTION

We are comparing two known quantities, so we can use subtraction to tell how many more or fewer.

a. Because $11 - 4 = 7$, Alyssa has seven more marbles than Vanessa.

b. Because $9 - 3 = 6$, Nick wrote six fewer poems than Carlo.

Students usually grasp comparison problems by the third grade. In some situations, one of the quantities is known, along with how many fewer or how many more. Does the phrase "more than" ("fewer than") in these word problems always indicate you should add (subtract) the two numbers? Think about this before reading the following example.

EXAMPLE 2.32

CONNECTION
COMMUNICATION
PROBLEM SOLVING
REASONING
REPRESENTATION

a. Jeremy has seven books. Jeremy has two fewer books than Bianca. How many books does Bianca have?

b. Nick has eight coins. He has five more coins than Rachel. How many coins does Rachel have?

SOLUTION

a. Because $7 + 2 = 9$, Bianca has nine books. **Note: Some students write $7 - 2 = 5$.**

b. Because $8 - 5 = 3$, Rachel has three coins. **Note: Some students write $8 + 5 = 13$.**

▲

EXAMPLE 2.33

PROBLEM SOLVING

REASONING

REPRESENTATION

Brian and Carla have 120 coins altogether. Carla has 36 more coins than Brian. How many coins does Carla have? Solve this problem using

a. a diagram.

b. variables.

SOLUTION

a.

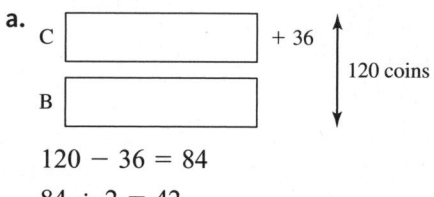

$120 - 36 = 84$

$84 \div 2 = 42$

Brian has 42 coins. Carla has $42 + 36 = 78$ coins.

b. Let b represent the number of coins Brian has. Then Carla has $b + 36$ coins. They have 120 coins altogether, so

$b + (b + 36) = 120$

$(b + b) + 36 = 120$

$2b + 36 = 120$

$2b + 36 - 36 = 120 - 36$

$2b = 84$

$2b \div 2 = 84 \div 2$

$b = 42.$

Then $b + 36 = 42 + 36 = 78$. Brian has 42 coins, and Carla has 78 coins.

▲

Number Line Model for Subtraction The *number line model* for subtraction is like the number line model for addition—it is appropriate for quantities that are of a continuous nature (like distance) rather than a discrete nature (like coins).

Let's consider the problem $8 - 3$. Starting at 0 and facing the whole numbers, we walk eight steps forward. We are at 8. The whole number 3 means walk three steps forward. However, we are at 8 and facing the whole numbers, so three steps forward would put us at 11, which is the wrong answer because $8 - 3 = 5$. To arrive at the correct answer, we must interpret the minus sign as "turn around." As shown in Figure 26, we are at 8, turn around, and then walk three steps forward, which puts us at the correct answer, 5. The minus sign indicates you need to turn around as you walk on the number line.

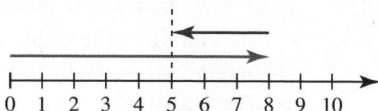

FIGURE 26

Terminal point of the arrow for the subtrahend, indicating the difference.

REPRESENTATION

Same Subtraction Problem in Different Situations

In the next example, the numerical solution to each problem is the same ($13 - 5 = 8$). However, the structures of the word problems are very different. Students need to see addition and subtraction in a variety of situations to strengthen additive reasoning skills.

EXAMPLE 2.34

CONNECTION

REASONING

Determine which subtraction model (take away, missing addend, comparison, or number line) is more appropriate in each situation.

a. A pest control company calculates it needs 5 pounds of chemical to eliminate termites from a house. It has 13 pounds of chemical available in a container on a scale. What should the container weigh to indicate that the house received the prescribed amount of chemical?

b. Samantha had 13 pieces of gum. She gave 5 pieces to her brother. How many did she have left?

c. Ben has 13 pencils, and Holly has 5 pencils. How many more pencils does Ben have?

d. Nicole has $5. She needs $13 to buy her favorite music CD. How much more money does she need?

SOLUTION

a. number line model

b. take-away model

c. comparison model

d. missing addend model

The following Released Item indicates that situations that require both addition and subtraction challenge elementary school students.

> **RELEASED ITEM**
>
> ● NAEP, 2005
>
> A club needs to sell 625 tickets. If it has already sold 184 tickets to adults and 80 tickets to children, how many more does it need to sell?
>
> 44% of fourth-grade students gave the correct answer.

Addition and Subtraction Are Inverse Operations

The recognition that addition and subtraction are **inverse operations** supports other inverse relationships, such as multiplication and division and squaring and square root. Students should "identify and use relationships between operations" (NCTM, Gr. 3–5) and "understand and use the inverse relationships of addition and subtraction to simplify computations and solve problems" (NCTM, Gr. 6–8). The following example makes it clear that subtraction undoes addition and addition undoes subtraction.

EXAMPLE 2.35

CONNECTION

REASONING

Let a and b represent whole numbers.

a. Prove $a + b - b = a$. **Subtraction undoes addition.**

b. Prove $a + b - a = b$. **Subtraction undoes addition.**

c. Suppose with $a \geq b$. Prove $a - b + b = a$. **Addition undoes subtraction.**

SOLUTION

a. The equation $a + b = a + b$ is true. We can view the left-hand side of the equation, $a + b$, as a whole number called the sum because of the closure property of addition. We can view the right-hand side of the equation, $a + b$, as the sum of two whole numbers a and b. By the definition of subtraction, $a + b - b = a$.

b. The equation $a + b = b + a$ is true by the commutative property of addition. We can view the left-hand side of the equation, $a + b$, as a whole number called the sum because of the closure property of addition. We can view the right-hand side of the equation, $b + a$, as the sum of two whole numbers b and a. By the definition of subtraction, $a + b - a = b$.

c. The assumption $a \geq b$ ensures $a - b$ is a whole number. The equation $a - b = a - b$ is true. We can view the left-hand side of the equation, $a - b$, as a single whole number called the difference. We can view the right-hand side of the equation, $a - b$, as the difference between two whole numbers a and b. By the definition of subtraction, $a - b + b = a$.

EXAMPLE 2.36   We know addition and subtraction are inverse operations. Use this to solve the equation.

CONNECTION

REASONING

a. $n + 5 = 12$

b. $12 + n = 30$

c. $k - 8 = 20$

SOLUTION

a.

$n + 5 = 12$	original equation
$n + 5 - 5 = 12 - 5$	**by the subtraction property of equality**
$n = 12 - 5$	**because addition and subtraction are inverse operations**
$n = 7$	**by simplification**

b.

$12 + n = 30$	original equation
$12 + n - 12 = 30 - 12$	**by the subtraction property of equality**
$n = 30 - 12$	**because addition and subtraction are inverse operations**
$n = 18$	**by simplification**

c.

$k - 8 = 20$	original equation
$k - 8 + 8 = 20 + 8$	**by the addition property of equality**
$k = 20 + 8$	**because addition and subtraction are inverse operations**
$k = 28$	**by simplification**

▲

The following portion of a student page shows students how to solve the equation $15 = a + 2$ using properties of equality and inverse operations.

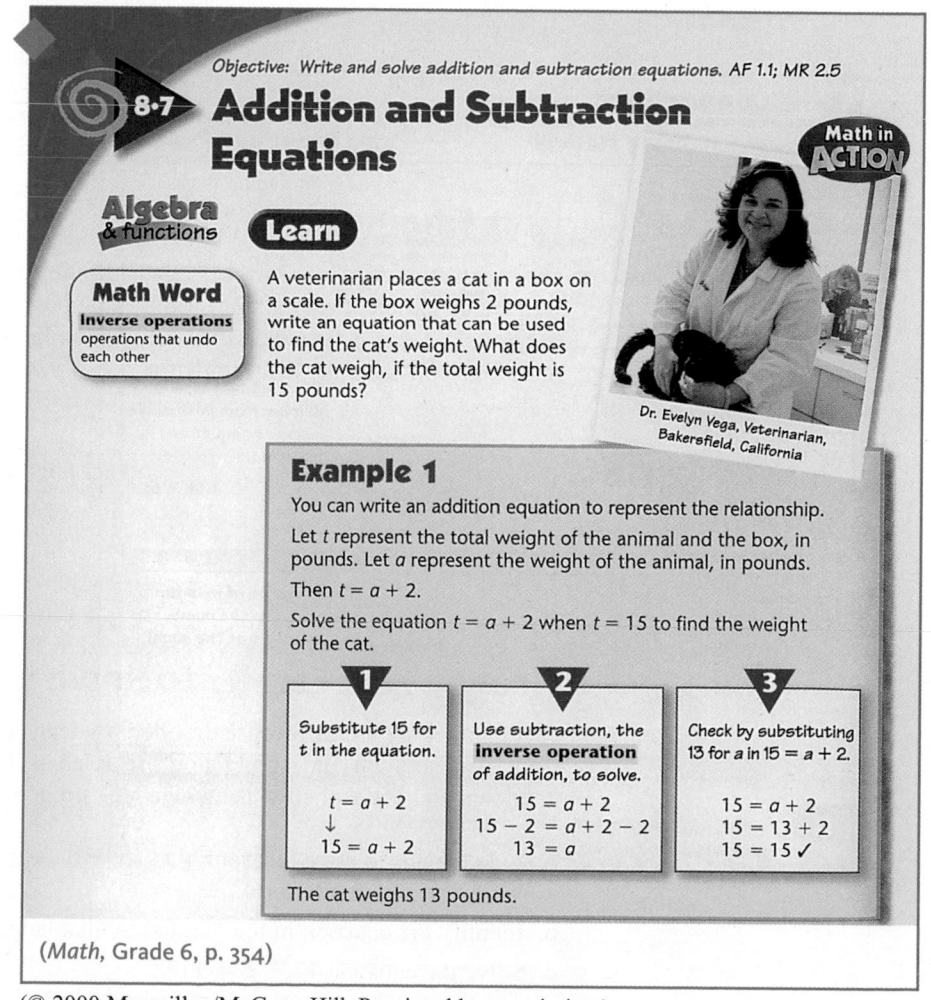

(*Math*, Grade 6, p. 354)

(© 2000 Macmillan/McGraw Hill. Reprinted by permission.)

Connections between Addition and Subtraction

Concept Map 2.3 shows some connections between addition and subtraction.

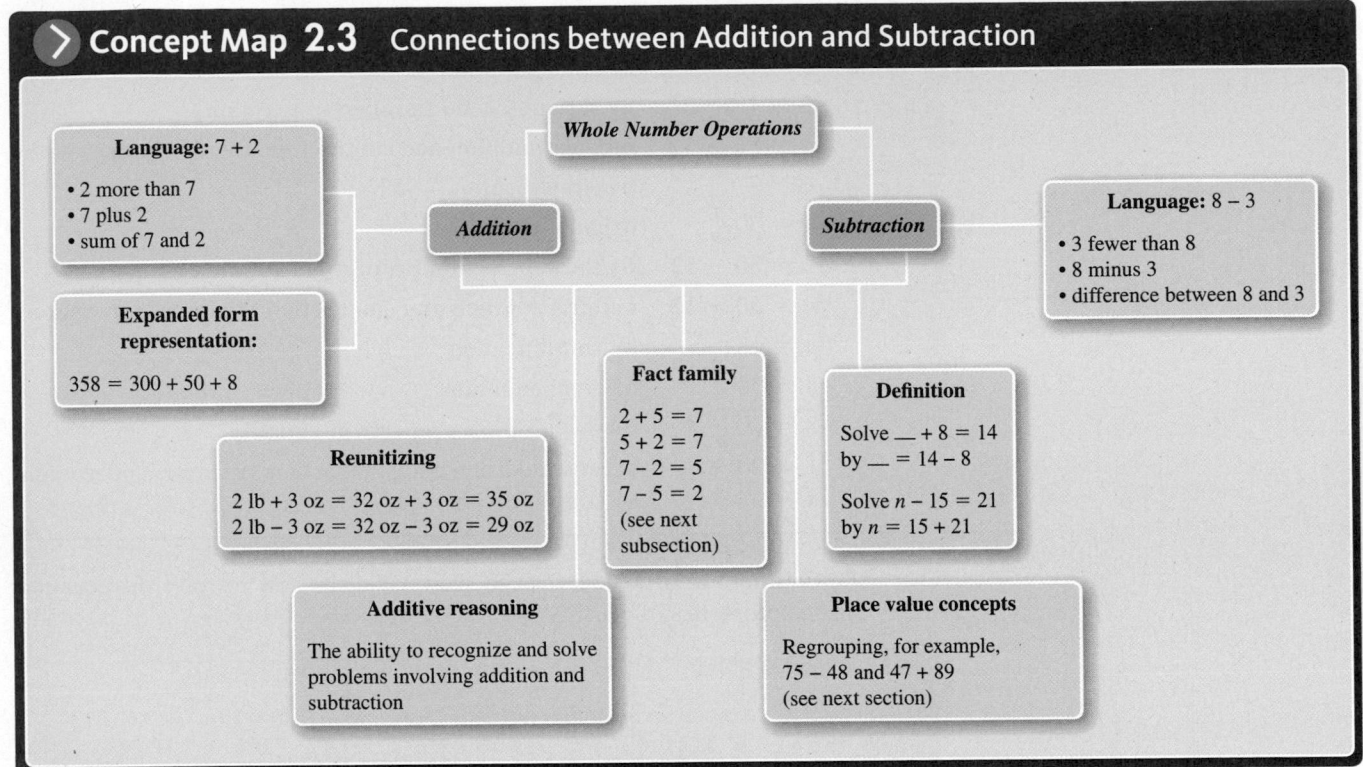

> **Concept Map 2.3** Connections between Addition and Subtraction

Whole Number Operations

Addition

Subtraction

Language: 7 + 2
- 2 more than 7
- 7 plus 2
- sum of 7 and 2

Language: 8 − 3
- 3 fewer than 8
- 8 minus 3
- difference between 8 and 3

Expanded form representation:

$358 = 300 + 50 + 8$

Fact family

$2 + 5 = 7$
$5 + 2 = 7$
$7 − 2 = 5$
$7 − 5 = 2$
(see next subsection)

Definition

Solve __ + 8 = 14
by __ = 14 − 8

Solve $n − 15 = 21$
by $n = 15 + 21$

Reunitizing

2 lb + 3 oz = 32 oz + 3 oz = 35 oz
2 lb − 3 oz = 32 oz − 3 oz = 29 oz

Additive reasoning

The ability to recognize and solve problems involving addition and subtraction

Place value concepts

Regrouping, for example,
75 − 48 and 47 + 89
(see next section)

CONNECTION

Fact Families

The subtraction fact $7 − 3 = 4$ is related to the addition facts $7 = 3 + 4$ and $7 = 4 + 3$ (see the definition of subtraction). Both equations involving addition relate to the subtraction fact $7 − 4 = 3$. Together, the two addition facts and the two subtraction facts form a **fact family.** What is the fact family for $2 + 2 = 4$?

Fact family	
3 + 4 = 7	7 − 4 = 3
4 + 3 = 7	7 − 3 = 4

Using a Fact Family to Solve a One-Step Equation

Fact families are useful because they help students learn basic subtraction facts and remind them that addition and subtraction are related. They also help students solve for an unknown without explicitly using algebraic properties.

EXAMPLE 2.37 A student plans to use a fact family to solve the equation $42 + d = 117$.

CONNECTION
  a. Write the fact family for $42 + d = 117$.
  b. Identify the equation in the fact family that helps you solve this one-step equation.
  c. Solve the equation $42 + d = 117$.

SOLUTION

a. The fact family for $42 + d = 117$ is

$$42 + d = 117$$
$$d + 42 = 117$$
$$117 - d = 42$$
$$d = 117 - 42.$$

b. The equation $d = 117 - 42$ helps solve $42 + d = 117$.

c. From part (b), $d = 117 - 42$. Then $d = 75$. The solution to $42 + d = 117$ is $d = 75$.

QUESTIONS FOR SECTION 2.3

REPRESENTATION

Refresher: Representations (language, diagrams, tables, symbols, algebra, manipulatives, and contextualized situations) are important because we use them to organize, record, and communicate mathematical ideas and to make them more comprehensible.

1. Use the set model to add.
   a. $5 + 2$ **b.** $3 + 6$

2. Use the take-away model to subtract.
   a. $6 - 2$ **b.** $8 - 5$

3. Use the number line model to add.
   a. $2 + 6$ **b.** $4 + 3$

4. The diagram illustrates how to use the empty number line model to add $27 + 32$. You begin by showing a location for the first addend. Then you decompose (break apart) the second addend and add its parts.

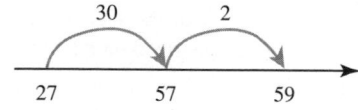

The diagram shows one way to use the empty number line model to add $27 + 32$. The empty number line is a tool, so you do not have to worry about drawing directed arrows to scale. The empty number line does not have confining tick marks. Use the empty number line model to add.

   a. $21 + 74$ **b.** $67 + 15$ **c.** $47 + 29$

PROBLEM SOLVING

Refresher: Problem solving (reaching a goal that is not immediately attainable) is important because it helps students think more deeply about what they know and deal with unfamiliar situations.

5. Maria has 8 fewer coins than Vanessa, who has 70 coins. How many coins does Maria have? Solve using
   a. a diagram.   **b.** algebra.

6. The whole number 2 can be expressed as a sum of two whole numbers in three ways: $0 + 2 = 2$, $1 + 1 = 2$, and $2 + 0 = 2$. How many ways can you express the whole number n as a sum of two whole numbers?

7. Write three word problems that require the calculation $24 - 6$. Make sure the problems' structure differs to reflect the different models of subtraction.

8. The number 24,542 is a palindrome because you obtain the same number when you reverse the order of the digits.
   a. What is the smallest three-digit counting number n such that $24{,}542 + n$ is a palindrome?
   b. What is the smallest four-digit counting number n such that $24{,}542 - n$ is a palindrome?

REASONING AND PROOF

Refresher: Reasoning and proof (thinking and justifying) are important because they help students make sense of mathematics.

9. Do the following. Apply the operations from left to right.
   a. $9 + 4 - 4 = \_\_\_$ **b.** $15 + 5 - 5 = \_\_\_$
   c. $12 + 7 - 7 = \_\_\_$ **d.** $16 + 2 - 2 = \_\_\_$
   e. Use algebra to generalize the results.

10. Do the following. Apply the operations from left to right.
    a. $9 - 4 + 4 = \_\_\_$ **b.** $15 - 5 + 5 = \_\_\_$
    c. $12 - 7 + 7 = \_\_\_$ **d.** $16 - 2 + 2 = \_\_\_$
    e. Use algebra to generalize the results.

11. Solve the one-step equation, knowing that addition and subtraction are inverse operations.
    a. $k - 15 = 22$ **b.** $n + 6 = 14$

12. Many elementary school students see only two whole numbers in the expression $a + b$, namely, a and b. Do you see a third number? Explain.

13. Select the appropriate equation (do not solve).
    a. Paul has 12 coins. He has 3 more coins than Maria. Which equation models the situation: $12 + 3 = n$ or $12 = n + 3$?
    b. Paul has 12 coins. He has 3 fewer coins than Maria. Which equation models the situation: $12 - 3 = n$ or $12 = n - 3$?

14. What property of addition helps you add $4567 + 3000$ quickly?

15. Suppose a, b, and c are whole numbers with $a \leq b$ and $b \leq c$. Prove $a \leq c$. (This is the transitive property of "less than or equal to" for whole numbers. Hint: See Example 2.27).

CONNECTIONS

Refresher: Connections (linking and applying mathematical ideas) are important because they deepen student understanding and make mathematics more meaningful, flexible, and useful.

16. Solve the one-step equation $n - 18 = 25$ using
   a. the definition of subtraction.
   b. addition and subtraction as inverse operations.
   c. a fact family.

17. Solve the one-step equation $n + 14 = 52$ using
   a. the definition of subtraction.
   b. addition and subtraction as inverse operations.
   c. a fact family.

18. a, b, and c are whole numbers. The property "if $a + c = b + c$, then $a = b$" is called the cancellation property of addition. Prove this property, knowing that addition and subtraction are inverse operations (see Example 2.35).

19. You are given the equation $n - 4 = 13$. What two related equations involving addition follow from the definition of subtraction?

20. Which property of addition plays a key role in the pattern in the following sequence of equations: $3 + 5 = 8, 30 + 50 = 80, 300 + 500 = 800, 3000 + 5000 = 8000, \ldots$?

21. The area of a rectangle with length l units and width w units is $l \times w$ square units. Use decomposition to find the area of the given polygonal area.

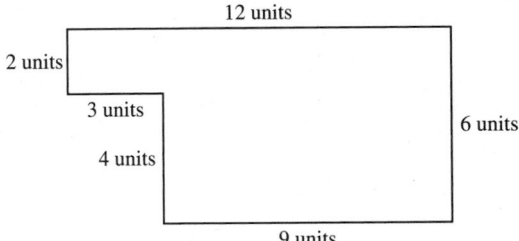

COMMUNICATION

Refresher: Communication (written and verbal explanations using representations and proper mathematical vocabulary) is important because it helps students refine and strengthen their understanding.

22. John has 5 trading cards, and Bob has 11 trading cards. Use additive reasoning to write two sentences that compare the number of trading cards John and Bob have.

23. Start with six coins. Add three more coins. Then take away three coins.
   a. How many coins do you now have?
   b. Repeat this action for other combinations of coins.

   c. Write an equation that generalizes this result, and explain what this equation illustrates.

24. Start with five coins. Take away two coins. Then add two coins.
   a. How many coins do you now have?
   b. Repeat this action for other possible combinations of coins.
   c. Write an equation that generalizes this result, and explain what this equation illustrates.

25. Discuss two possible ways you can teach your elementary school students to solve a one-step equation such as $n - 25 = 41$ or $n + 15 = 61$.

26. Why do we have one term *(addend)* to describe the numbers in a sum but need two terms *(minuend* and *subtrahend)* to describe the numbers in a difference?

27. Describe the pattern in fact families such as $3 + 5 = 8, 5 + 3 = 8, 8 - 3 = 5$, and $8 - 5 = 3$.

28. Write a word problem for each equation.
   a. $14 - n = 5$ b. $n - 7 = 10$

More practice with the ideas of the section

29. Fill in the blank. Choose one of the following words or phrases: *addend, addition, comparing, comparison model, composing, decomposing, difference, joining, minuend, missing addend, number sense, separating, set model, subtraction, subtrahend, sum,* or *take-away model.*
   a. In the expression $7 - 2$, the number 2 is called the _____.
   b. In the expression $8 - 3$, the number 8 is called the _____.
   c. In the equation $5 + n = 12$, the number n is called the _____.
   d. The number $6 - 2$ is called the _____.
   e. The number $5 + 4$ is called the _____.
   f. The equation $5 + 7 = 5 + (5 + 2)$ is an example of _____.
   g. Addition involves _____ sets of objects.
   h. The underlying concept of the take-away model, missing addend model, and comparison model is the _____.
   i. _____ is the ability to use numbers and properties flexibly and fluently.

30. Use the set model to add.
   a. $3 + 5$ b. $2 + 7$

31. Use the number line model to add.
   a. $4 + 7$ b. $2 + 5$

32. Write the appropriate equation.
   a.
   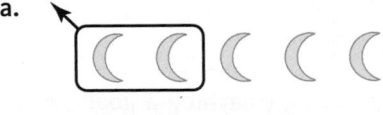

   b.

33. Use the comparison model to show
   a. $4 < 6$. **b.** $3 < 7$.

34. Use the definition of *less than* to show $5 < 9$.

35. Use a number line to compare whole numbers.
   a. 2 and 6 **b.** 5 and 8 **c.** 4 and 7

36. Use the take-away model to subtract.
   a. $5 - 2$ **b.** $9 - 3$

37. Use the number line to illustrate each equation.
   a. $3 + 4 = 4 + 3$ **b.** $2 + (3 + 4) = (2 + 3) + 4$
   c. $5 + 0$

38. Identify an appropriate subtraction model.
   a. Mark has 12 pencils and Mary has 8 pencils. How many more pencils does Mark have?
   b. Lisa needs 43 square yards of cloth to make costumes for the school play. She has 20 square yards of cloth. How much more cloth does she need?
   c. Nicole has 18 books. She sold 3 of them at the garage sale. How many books does she have now?

39. Do the following.
   a. Nick has 20 coins. Carlo has 5 fewer coins than Nick. How many coins does Carlo have?
   b. Carlo has 20 coins. He has 5 fewer coins than Nick. How many coins does Nick have?

40. Select the appropriate equation (do not solve).
   a. Paul has 3 coins. Maria gave him some coins. Then he had 21 coins. Which equation models the situation: $n + 3 = 21$ or $3 + n = 21$?
   b. Paul has some coins. Maria gave him 3 more coins. Then he had 21 coins. Which equation models the situation: $n + 3 = 21$ or $3 + n = 21$?

41. Select the appropriate equation (do not solve).
   a. Paul has 15 coins. He gave Maria some coins. He has 3 coins left. Which equation models the situation: $n + 3 = 15$ or $15 - n = 3$?
   b. Paul has some coins. He gave Maria 3 coins. Now he has 15 coins left. Which equation models the situation: $n + 3 = 15$ or $n - 3 = 15$?

42. Use the number line model to answer the following.
   a. Sam drove 8 miles to work. On the way home, he stopped at the store to buy some groceries. The store is 5 miles from work. How many miles must he drive to get home?
   b. A small aquarium is filled with 6 gallons of water. We drained 2 gallons of water from the tank. How many more gallons of water remain?

43. Write a story problem for each equation.
   a. $8 + 7 = \_\_\_$ **b.** $n - 4 = 12$ **c.** $7 + n = 13$

44. a. Elizabeth has three more marbles than Alley. A student writes $n + 3$. What does n represent?
   b. Ken has four fewer marbles than Lenny. A student writes $n - 4$. What does $n - 4$ represent?

45. Find two subtraction facts related to the given addition fact. The variables are whole numbers.
   a. $5 + 2 = 7$ **b.** $Y + L = E$

46. Find a subtraction fact related to the given subtraction fact.
   a. $345 - w = 5$ **b.** $X - 4 = Y$

47. For each of the following, find a fact family.
   a. $Y + 2 = 9$ **b.** $13 - K = 3$ **c.** 4, 6, 10

48. How are equations $2 + n = 7$ and $943 + n = 15{,}831$
   a. alike? **b.** different?

49. Use composing to add.
   a. $4 + 7 + 6$ **b.** $14 + 7 + 13$ **c.** $12 + 38 + 15$

50. Write the fact family for the equation $k + 5 = 11$. Circle the equation that helps you determine k.

51. Write the fact family for the equation $57 - m = 29$. Circle the equation that helps you determine m.

52. List the addition properties illustrated in the equation.
   a. $(2 + 3) + 6 = 2 + (3 + 6)$ **b.** $1 + 4 = 4 + 1$
   c. $5 + 0 = 5$ **d.** $2 + (3 + 8) = 2 + (8 + 3)$

53. Decompose an addend to make easy combinations for adding (making ten, twenty, thirty, and so on).
   a. $5 + 9$ **b.** $24 + 8$ **c.** $18 + 5$ **d.** $15 + 13$

54. A student uses the counting-on strategy to add two numbers. She says, "Fifteen," and then she says, "sixteen, seventeen, eighteen, nineteen." What two numbers did the student add?

55. Do the following.
   a. Kyle has four more marbles than Amanda. Amanda has eight more marbles than Samantha. How many more marbles does Kyle have than Samantha?
   b. Gabby has three fewer coins than Nick. Nick has seven fewer coins than Taylor. How many fewer coins does Gabby have compared to Taylor?

56. Fill in the blank with a whole number that makes the equation true.
   a. $13 - 9 = 13 - 10 + \_\_\_$ **b.** $24 - 9 = 24 - 10 + \_\_\_$
   c. $56 - 9 = 56 - 10 + \_\_\_$ **d.** $41 - 9 = 41 - 10 + \_\_\_$
   e. Develop a thinking strategy for subtracting 9 from a whole number.

57. Decompose an addend to make easy combinations for adding (making ten, twenty, thirty, and so on). What property are you using?
   a. $14 + 8$ **b.** $27 + 5$ **c.** $17 + 6$ **d.** $18 + 15$

58. Suppose a student knows "doubles" such as $3 + 3 = 6$ and $7 + 7 = 14$. Show how the associative property and doubles can be used to help the student add the following.
   a. $4 + 7$ **b.** $6 + 5$ **c.** $9 + 7$

59. You can decompose to subtract. For example, $14 - 6 = (8 + 6) - 6 = 8$. Use this strategy to subtract the following.
   a. $18 - 5$ **b.** $27 - 5$ **c.** $17 - 6$

60. According to a newspaper article, the incumbent mayor of a large city won by 2108 votes in a recent election. Interestingly, 5547 of the write-in votes cast by voters in favor of the challenger were legally excluded in the election because of technicalities. If the write-in votes happened to be valid, would the challenger have won the race? If so, what would be the margin of victory?

61. Complete the addition table. Shade the squares for doubles (such as 4 + 4), for making tens (such as 7 + 3), for adding one more or two more (such as 5 + 1 or 7 + 2), for the additive identity (such as 3 + 0), and for the commutative property (7 + 2 is shaded, so 2 + 7 should be shaded). What percentage of the squares is shaded?

+	0	1	2	3	4	5	6	7	8	9
0										
1										
2										
3										
4										
5										
6										
7										
8										
9										

62. Is the set closed under addition? If not, explain why.
   a. {5}   b. {0, 1}   c. {7, 14, 21, 28, ...}
   d. {1, 3, 5, 7, ...}   e. {2, 4, 6, 8, ...}

63. The set of whole numbers is closed under addition. Is the set of whole numbers closed under subtraction? Explain your answer, and give some examples to support your conclusion.

SECTION 2.4 Algorithms for Whole Number Addition and Subtraction

Cornerstone of the Various Algorithms

Previously we explored place value concepts and how they help us think about numbers in a flexible way (for example, 534 = 5 hundreds, 3 tens, 4 ones and 534 = 5 hundreds, 2 tens, 14 ones). Then we explored the concepts of addition and subtraction and how properties can be used to find simple sums and differences, such as 18 + 6 = 18 + (2 + 4) = (18 + 2) + 4 = 20 + 4 = 24. In this section we apply these foundational ideas—place value concepts and properties—to develop place value methods for finding sums and differences of any pair of multidigit whole numbers. The concept of **regrouping** is the cornerstone of all of the algorithms (or methods), such as 8 tens + 5 tens = 13 tens = 1 hundred, 3 tens and 24 hundreds = 2 hundreds, 4 tens = 1 hundred, 14 tens. We avoid the terms *carry* and *borrow* because they inaccurately describe the underlying process. Students should be able to

add and subtract within 1000, using concrete models or drawings and strategies based on place value, properties of operations, and/or the relationship between addition and subtraction; relate the strategy to a written method. Understand that in adding or subtracting three digit numbers, one adds or subtracts hundreds and hundreds, tens and tens, ones and ones and sometimes it is necessary to compose or decompose tens or hundreds (CCSS, Gr. 2); Explain why addition and subtraction strategies work, using place value and the properties of operations (CCSS, Gr. 2); Fluently add and subtract within 1000 using strategies and algorithms based on place value, properties of operations, and/or the relationship between addition and subtraction (CCSS, Gr. 3). Fluently add and subtract multidigit whole numbers using the standard algorithm (CCSS, Gr. 4).

Benefit of Knowing Multiple Methods

Knowing more than one way to add and subtract means you are prepared for students who already use alternative strategies or think differently about mathematics. You also deepen your understanding of numbers, properties, and place value concept and are in a position to help your students "develop fluency in adding, subtracting, multiplying, and dividing whole numbers" (NCTM, Gr. 3–5) and "compute fluently and make reasonable estimates" (NCTM, Gr. 3–8). Fluency with operations with whole numbers helps students "develop and analyze algorithms for computing with fractions, decimals, and integers and develop fluency in their use" (NCTM, Gr. 6–8).

Partial Sums Method

Base ten blocks are important for developing and understanding addition methods. Figure 27 models the right-to-left **partial sums method** using base ten blocks to find the sum 265 + 158. This method emphasizes the concept of place value.

Step 1. Model 265 and 158.

FIGURE 27
Right-to-left partial sums method with base ten blocks.

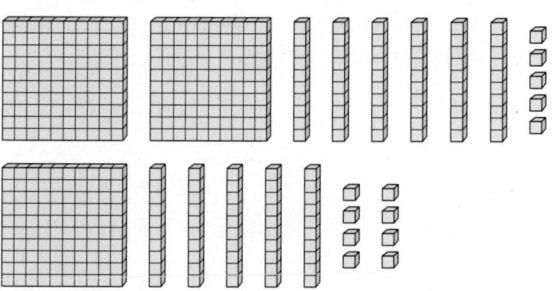

Pencil & Paper

$$
\begin{array}{ccc}
 & 2 & 6 & 5 \\
+ & 1 & 5 & 8 \\
\end{array}
$$

REPRESENTATION **Step 2.** Combine the ones with the ones, the tens with the tens, and the hundreds with the hundreds, with regrouping as necessary: 5 ones + 8 ones = 13 ones = 1 ten, 3 ones = 13. Then join the tens: 6 tens + 5 tens = 11 tens = 1 hundred, 1 ten = 110. Then join the hundreds: 2 hundreds + 1 hundred = 3 hundreds = 300. Then we obtain three partial sums: 13, 110, and 300.

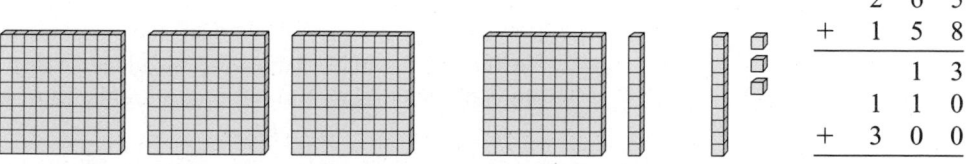

$$
\begin{array}{cccc}
 & & 2 & 6 & 5 \\
+ & & 1 & 5 & 8 \\
\hline
 & & & 1 & 3 \\
 & & 1 & 1 & 0 \\
+ & & 3 & 0 & 0 \\
\end{array}
$$

Step 3. Combine the partial sums, from right to left, with regrouping as necessary.

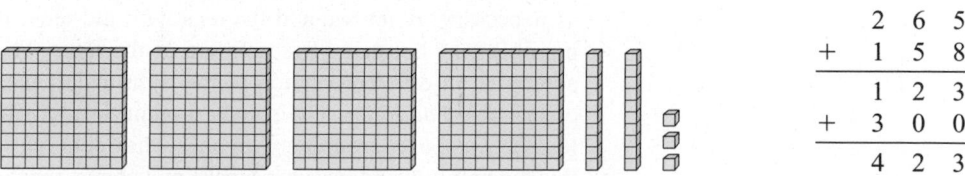

$$
\begin{array}{cccc}
 & & 2 & 6 & 5 \\
+ & & 1 & 5 & 8 \\
\hline
 & & 1 & 2 & 3 \\
+ & & 3 & 0 & 0 \\
\hline
 & & 4 & 2 & 3 \\
\end{array}
$$

Step 4. There are 4 hundreds, 2 tens, and 3 ones, so 265 + 158 = 423.

The partial sums of 265 + 158 are 13, 110, and 300. Regrouping may be required to calculate a partial sum, but it mimics whole number addition with simpler numbers. Then we combine adjacent partial sums and subsequent rows, two rows at a time. Eventually, we obtain the sum: 265 + 158 = 423.

The expanded form of the addends and the commutative and associative properties of addition justify the partial sums method. To see this,

$$
\begin{aligned}
265 + 158 &= 200 + 60 + 5 + 100 + 50 + 8 \\
&= 200 + 100 + 60 + 50 + 5 + 8 \\
&= 300 + 110 + 13 \qquad \leftarrow \text{the partial sums} \\
&= 300 + 123 \\
&= 423
\end{aligned}
$$

EXAMPLE 2.38 Find the sum 789 + 475 using the left-to-right partial sums method. List the partial sums.

CONNECTION

SOLUTION

The following illustrates the left-to-right partial sums method. As the name indicates, we add the digits from left to right:

$$
\begin{array}{r}
7\ 8\ 9 \\
+\ 4\ 7\ 5 \\
\hline
1\ 1\ 0\ 0 \\
1\ 5\ 0 \\
+\ \ \ \ 1\ 4 \\
\hline
1\ 2\ 5\ 0 \\
+\ \ \ \ 1\ 4 \\
\hline
1\ 2\ 6\ 4
\end{array}
$$

The partial sums are 1100, 150, and 14. The sum is 1264. ▲

Although the place values can be added in any order in a partial sums method, the left-to-right and the right-to-left orders are the most common.

Standard Addition Algorithm

In the right-to-left partial sums method, we add the ones with the ones, with regrouping as necessary. When we add the tens with the tens, we do not yet take into account any possible tens because of regrouping of the ones. The **standard addition algorithm** for adding is an efficient version of the right-to-left partial sums method and is sometimes called *short addition*. The standard addition algorithm takes into account any possible tens because of regrouping with ones while it is regrouping the tens. Figure 28 illustrates this algorithm using base ten blocks and shows the corresponding pencil-and-paper algorithm. Each 1 above a digit in the top addend in the pencil-and-paper algorithm indicates a *regrouping*.

Step 1. Represent each addend in the expression 356 + 278 with base ten blocks.

FIGURE 28
Place value concepts and re-groupings used in the standard addition algorithm.

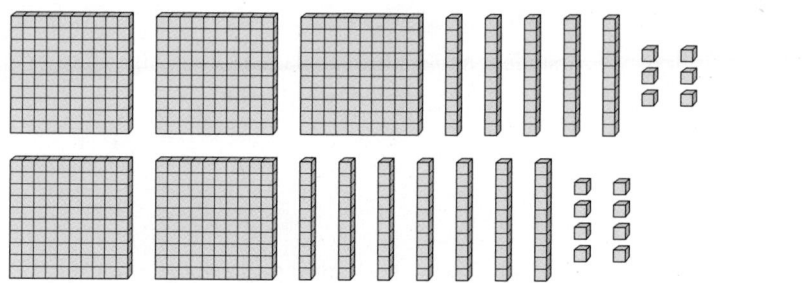

Pencil &
Paper

$$\begin{array}{r} 3\ \ 5\ \ 6 \\ +\ 2\ \ 7\ \ 8 \\ \hline \end{array}$$

CONNECTION
REASONING
REPRESENTATION

Step 2. Add the ones and regroup as necessary:
6 ones + 8 ones = 14 ones = 1 ten, 4 ones

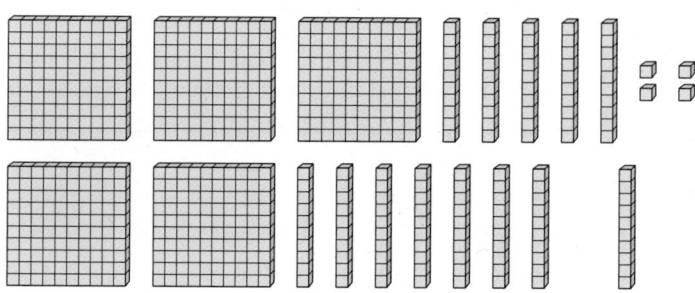

$$\begin{array}{r} \ \ \ \ \ 1 \\ 3\ \ 5\ \ 6 \\ +\ 2\ \ 7\ \ 8 \\ \hline \mathbf{4} \end{array}$$

Step 3. Add all tens and regroup as necessary:
1 ten + 5 tens + 7 tens = 13 tens = 1 hundred, 3 tens

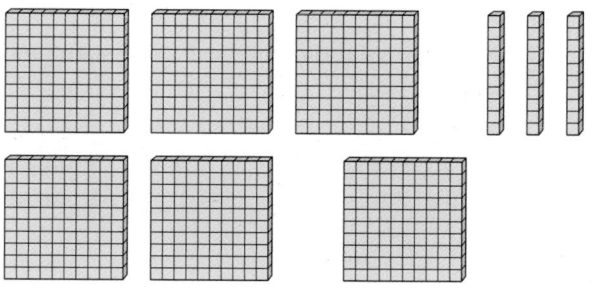

$$\begin{array}{r} 1\ \ \ 1 \\ 3\ \ 5\ \ 6 \\ +\ 2\ \ 7\ \ 8 \\ \hline \mathbf{3}\ \ \mathbf{4} \end{array}$$

Step 4. Add all hundreds and regroup as necessary:
1 hundred + 3 hundreds + 2 hundreds = 6 hundreds

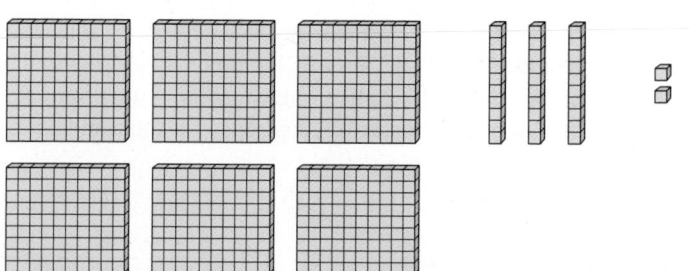

$$\begin{array}{r} 1\ \ \ 1 \\ 3\ \ 5\ \ 6 \\ +\ 2\ \ 7\ \ 8 \\ \hline \mathbf{6}\ \ \mathbf{3}\ \ \mathbf{4} \end{array}$$

So 356 + 278 = 634.

The next example assesses whether students can link conceptual and procedural knowledge.

EXAMPLE 2.39   A student applies the standard addition algorithm to add:

CONNECTION
REASONING
REPRESENTATION

$$\begin{array}{r} {}^{1}\ \ {}^{1}\ \ \\ 4\ \ 8\ \ 5 \\ +\ \ 3\ \ 6\ \ 7 \\ \hline 8\ \ 5\ \ 2 \end{array}$$

a. Explain why the 1 appears above the 8.

b. Explain why the 1 appears above the 4.

SOLUTION

a. Here, 5 ones + 7 ones = 12 ones = 1 ten, 2 ones. The 1 above the 8 represents the 1 ten from regrouping 12 ones as 1 ten, 2 ones.

b. Here, 1 ten + 8 tens + 6 tens = 15 tens = 1 hundred, 5 tens. The 1 above the 4 represents the 1 hundred from regrouping 15 tens as 1 hundred, 5 tens. ▲

Connection between the Left-to-Right Partial Sums and the Standard Addition Algorithm

The following problems illustrate the connection between the right-to-left partial sums method and the pencil-and-paper standard addition algorithm for the sum 28 + 39. Only one row—the sum—appears in the standard addition algorithm. The commutative and associative properties justify both methods.

Right-to-left partial sums method	Standard addition algorithm
$\begin{array}{r} 2\ \ 8 \\ +\ \ 3\ \ 9 \\ \hline 1\ \ 7 \\ +\ \ 5\ \ 0 \\ \hline 6\ \ 7 \end{array}$	$\begin{array}{r} {}^{1}\ \ \ \ \\ 2\ \ 8 \\ +\ \ 3\ \ 9 \\ \hline 6\ \ 7 \end{array}$ 8 ones + 9 ones = 17 ones = 1 ten, 7 ones 1 ten + 2 tens + 3 tens = 6 tens

Lattice Algorithm

The **lattice algorithm,** an ancient strategy, uses a structure of crossed strips, called a *lattice.* The following illustrates this method to find the sum 542 + 89: 2 ones + 9 ones = 11 ones; 4 tens + 8 tens = 12 tens; 5 hundreds + 0 hundreds = 05 hundreds (although 05 is an unconventional way to represent 5). The column entries record the intermediate results: 11 ones, 12 tens, 05 hundreds. Each diagonal in the lattice represents a place value, so this method is a place value method—no gimmick here: 11 ones = 1 ten, 1 one; 12 tens = 1 hundred, 2 tens; 05 hundreds = 0 thousands, 5 hundreds.

REPRESENTATION

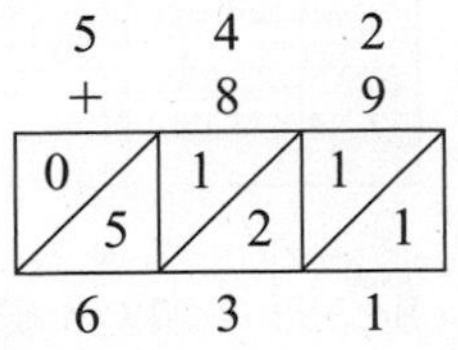

$$\begin{array}{c} 5\quad\ \ 4\quad\ \ 2 \\ +\quad 8\quad\ \ 9 \end{array}$$

EXAMPLE 2.40 Use the lattice algorithm to find 586 + 942 + 97.

SOLUTION

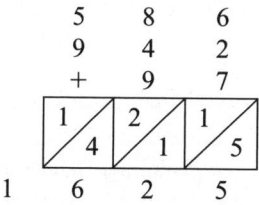

The lattice shows 586 + 942 + 97 = 1625.

Column Addition Method

The following illustrates the **column addition method** to find the sum 486 + 297. The first step involves separating the digits into columns using vertical lines and adding the digits with common place values. Sometimes this leads to a two-digit number in a column. The second step involves combining adjacent columns, two at a time, with regrouping, until each column has a single digit. The row with single digits in each column reveals the sum.

	4	6	5	
+	2	9	7	
	6	15	12	← 6 hundreds, 15 tens, 12 ones
	7	5	12	← 7 hundreds, 5 tens, 12 ones
	7	6	2	← sum

EXAMPLE 2.41 Use the column addition method to find the sum 363 + 257 + 185.

SOLUTION

Refer to the following. We see 363 + 257 + 185 = 805.

	3	6	3
	2	5	7
+	1	8	5
	6	19	15
	7	9	15
	7	10	5
	8	0	5

A common error with the column addition method is finishing early and mistakenly leaving two digits in one place value for a sum.

Scratch Addition Method

Sums such as $34 + 48 + 63 + 54 + 328 + 225$ may be challenging for students because of the memory load. The **scratch addition method** reduces the memory load by using "scratches" to archive the regroupings. The following illustrates the scratch addition method. We add the digits from right to left, one column at a time. A scratch, indicated by the symbol \, is used whenever a regrouping is required, and the current ones digit is recorded next to the scratch. When the digits in the ones column have been added, the number of scratches indicates the number of tens that have been formed because of the regroupings. There are three scratches in the first column, so a 3 is placed above the tens column, and then the tens digits are added. This process is repeated. Then $34 + 48 + 63 + 54 + 328 + 225 = 752$.

$$
\begin{array}{r}
{}^{2}\ {}^{3}\quad\\
3\ 4\\
4\!\!\backslash_0 8\!\!\backslash_2\\
6\ 3\\
5\!\!\backslash_1 4\\
3\ 2\ 8\!\!\backslash_7\\
+2\ 2\ 5\!\!\backslash_2\\
\hline
7\ 5\ 2
\end{array}
$$

Standard Subtraction Algorithm

Figure 29 demonstrates how to use base ten blocks to find the difference $362 - 128$ using the standard subtraction algorithm. The model for the **standard subtraction algorithm** builds the minuend and then applies the take-away model of subtraction, subtracting from lower place values to higher place values. Regrouping occurs as needed.

In Step 1 in Figure 29, we see there are not enough ones to take away 8 ones. In Step 2, we regroup one of the tens as 10 ones, leaving 5 tens. Then 10 ones + 2 ones = 12 ones. Now there are enough ones to take away 8 ones. The take-away model of subtraction that we discussed in Section 2.3 helps students understand the pencil-and-paper version of subtraction in the right-hand column.

Step 1. Represent the minuend 362 with base ten blocks.

FIGURE 29
Standard subtraction algorithm for $362 - 128$.

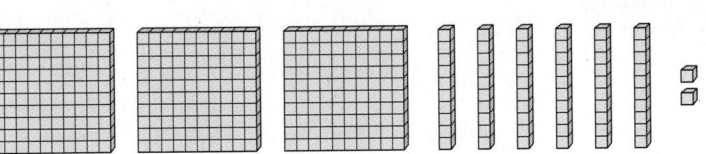
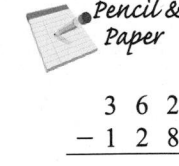

$$
\begin{array}{r}
3\ 6\ 2\\
-\ 1\ 2\ 8\\
\end{array}
$$

Step 2. There are 2 ones, but we need to take away 8 ones. We regroup 1 ten as 10 ones, leaving 5 tens. Then 10 ones + 2 ones = 12 ones.

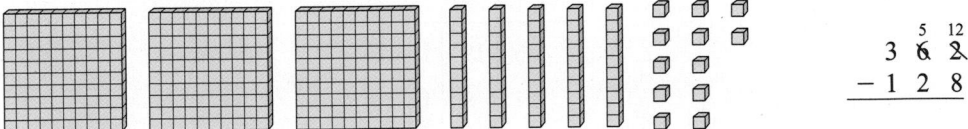

$$
\begin{array}{r}
{}^{5}\ {}^{12}\\
3\ \cancel{6}\ \cancel{2}\\
-\ 1\ 2\ 8\\
\end{array}
$$

Step 3. Now there are enough ones to take away 8 ones. This leaves 4 ones.

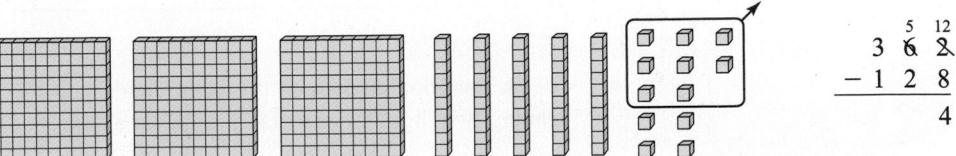

$$
\begin{array}{r}
{}^{5}\ {}^{12}\\
3\ \cancel{6}\ \cancel{2}\\
-\ 1\ 2\ 8\\
\hline
4
\end{array}
$$

Step 4. There are enough tens to take away 2 tens. This leaves 3 tens.

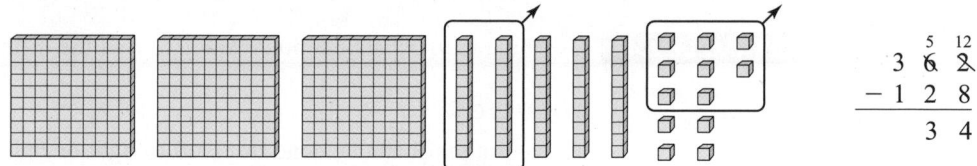

Step 5. There are enough hundreds to take away 1 hundred. This leaves 2 hundreds.

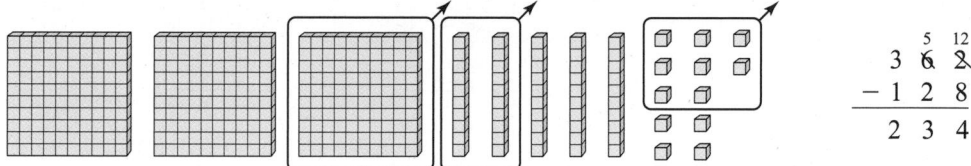

So $362 - 128 = 234$.

The next example assesses whether students can link conceptual and procedural knowledge.

EXAMPLE 2.42

CONNECTION

REASONING

REPRESENTATION

A student applies the standard subtraction algorithm to subtract:

$$\begin{array}{r} \overset{3}{\cancel{4}}\ \overset{12}{\cancel{2}}\ 5 \\ -\ 1\ 7\ 3 \\ \hline 2\ 5\ 2 \end{array}$$

a. Explain why the 3 appears above the 4.

b. Explain why the 12 appears above the 2.

SOLUTION

a. There are 2 tens, and we need to take away 7 tens. There are not enough tens, so we regroup one of the hundreds as 10 tens. This leaves 3 hundreds. The 3 above the 4 represents the 3 hundreds.

b. We regrouped one of the hundreds as 10 tens. Then 10 tens + 2 tens = 12 tens. The 12 above the 2 represents the 12 tens.

▲

The following Released Item shows a subtraction problem that required regrouping.

> **RELEASED ITEM**
>
> ● NAEP, 2009
> Subtract $301 - 75$.
>
> **a.** 226 **b.** 235 **c.** 236 **d.** 374
>
> 67% of fourth graders answered the question correctly.

Trade-First Method

The **trade-first method** is a two-step subtraction method. In the first step, the digits in the minuend (top) are possibly adjusted by means of trading (or regrouping) to make sure they are not less than the corresponding digits in the subtrahend (bottom). We complete all possible trades *before* subtraction. In the second step, subtraction occurs. The following example illustrates this method.

EXAMPLE 2.43 Use the trade-first subtraction method to find the difference 746 − 287.

CONNECTION
REPRESENTATION

SOLUTION

The regroupings can be done from left to right or right to left.

Trade from left to right		Trade from right to left	
Step 1: Trade first	**Step 2: Subtract**	**Step 1: Trade first**	**Step 2: Subtract**
$\begin{array}{r}{}^{13}\\ 6\ \overset{14}{\cancel{4}}\ 16\\ \cancel{7}\ \cancel{4}\ \cancel{6}\\ -\ 2\ 8\ 7\\ \hline \end{array}$	$\begin{array}{r}{}^{13}\\ 6\ \overset{14}{\cancel{4}}\ 16\\ \cancel{7}\ \cancel{4}\ \cancel{6}\\ -\ 2\ 8\ 7\\ \hline 4\ 5\ 9\end{array}$	$\begin{array}{r}{}^{13}\\ 6\ \overset{3}{\cancel{4}}\ 16\\ \cancel{7}\ \cancel{4}\ \cancel{6}\\ -\ 2\ 8\ 7\\ \hline \end{array}$	$\begin{array}{r}{}^{13}\\ 6\ \overset{3}{\cancel{4}}\ 16\\ \cancel{7}\ \cancel{4}\ \cancel{6}\\ -\ 2\ 8\ 7\\ \hline 4\ 5\ 9\end{array}$

Then 746 − 287 = 459. ▲

Same-Change Method

The **same-change method** adds or subtracts the same number to or from the minuend and the subtrahend, resulting in an equivalent but simpler problem. This method requires number sense, because it depends on the numbers involved. It often exploits the ease of subtracting numbers with zeros in the rightmost place values.

EXAMPLE 2.44 Use the same-change method to find the difference.

REASONING
a. 54 − 28
b. 62 − 23

SOLUTION

a. 54 − 28 = 56 − 30   **Add 2 to both the minuend and the subtrahend.**
          = 26

b. 60 − 23 = 57 − 20   **Subtract 3 from both the minuend and the subtrahend.**
          = 37

▲

This same-change subtraction method is based on the equation $a - b = (a + n) - (b + n)$. Why does this method work? The explanation is simple in terms of integers, which we cover in Chapter 4.

Partial Differences Method

The **partial differences method** uses place value concepts to subtract and proceeds from right to left. The following illustrates this method to find the difference 547 − 263. The first subtraction is 7 − 3 = 4. The next subtraction is 40 − 60, −20, which indicates that 2 more tens still need to be subtracted. The next subtraction is 500 − 200 = 300.

$$\begin{array}{r}
547\\
-\ 263\\
\hline
4\\
-\ 20\\
300\\
\hline
4\\
280\\
\hline
284
\end{array}$$

← 2 tens still need to be subtracted

← 300 − 20 = 280
← 280 + 4 = 284

The partial differences are 300, -20, and 4. Students interpret a negative sign ($-$) in a partial difference as a "deficit," meaning that a subtraction still needs to occur. Partial differences make sense because

$$
\begin{aligned}
547 - 263 &= (500 + 40 + 7) - (200 + 60 + 3) \\
&= 500 + 40 + 7 - 200 - 60 - 3 \\
&= (500 - 200) + (40 - 60) + (7 - 3) \\
&= 300 + (40 - 60) + 4 \\
&= 300 + (40 - 40 - 20) + 4 \\
&= 300 - 20 + 4 \\
&= 280 + 4 \\
&= 284.
\end{aligned}
$$

EXAMPLE 2.45 Use the partial differences method to find the difference $726 - 258$.

SOLUTION

Refer to the problem that follows. We see $726 - 258 = 468$.

$$
\begin{array}{r}
7\ \ 2\ \ 6 \\
-\,2\ \ 5\ \ 8 \\
\hline
-\,2 \\
-\,3\ \ 0 \\
5\ \ 0\ \ 0 \\
\hline
-\,2 \\
4\ \ 7\ \ 0 \\
\hline
4\ \ 6\ \ 8
\end{array}
$$

▲

Estimating Sums and Differences

A painter may be quite satisfied with an estimate of the square footage of walls he wants to paint, while a cashier may use an estimate to check the reasonableness of a calculation. Some students often feel uncomfortable with the estimation process because they seem too compelled to learn rules or are conditioned to calculate exact answers.

It's important to remember that **estimation** is a flexible process that depends on the numbers involved, the arithmetic operation, and the estimation strategy, as well as the ability of the student to perform mental arithmetic. Estimation is more of an art than a science and requires number sense and place value understanding. Students should be able to "develop and use strategies to estimate the results of whole-number computations and to judge the reasonableness of such results" (NCTM, Gr. 3–5).

To estimate a sum or difference, simply apply the estimation method to each number before performing the arithmetic operation. The results depend on the numbers involved and the estimation method used. The following examples illustrate how to use rounding to estimate sums and differences.

Round to the nearest ten	
$52 + 68 \approx 50 + 70 = 120$	$73 - 58 \approx 70 - 60 = 10$
$223 + 46 \approx 220 + 50 = 270$	$386 - 37 \approx 390 - 40 = 350$

Round to the nearest hundred	
$475 + 231 \approx 500 + 200 = 700$	$673 - 235 \approx 700 - 200 = 500$
$1378 + 625 \approx 1400 + 600 = 2000$	$826 - 212 \approx 800 - 200 = 600$

Round to the nearest thousand	
$15{,}027 + 8689 \approx 15{,}000 + 9000 = 24{,}000$	$12{,}345 - 4346 \approx 12{,}000 - 4000 = 8000$
$3135 + 4700 \approx 3000 + 5000 = 8000$	$8345 - 2646 \approx 8000 - 3000 = 5000$

Front-end rounding replaces a number with the value of its leftmost digit (highest place value). For example, the front-end estimate of 56,834 is 50,000, the front-end estimate of 486 is 400, and the front-end estimate of 74 is 70.

Front-end estimation	
$52 + 68 \approx 50 + 60 = 110$	$73 - 58 \approx 70 - 50 = 20$
$213 + 46 \approx 200 + 40 = 240$	$386 - 47 \approx 300 - 40 = 260$
$12{,}027 + 8689 \approx 10{,}000 + 8000 = 18{,}000$	$12{,}345 - 4346 \approx 10{,}000 - 4000 = 6000$

The following Released Item illustrates that students should be able to use rounding to estimate.

> ▶ **RELEASED ITEM**
>
> ● NAEP, 2009
> A loaded trailer truck weighs 26,643 kilograms. When the trailer truck is empty, it weighs 10,547 kilograms. About how much does the load weigh?
>
> **a.** 14,000 kilograms **b.** 16,000 kilograms **c.** 18,000 kilograms
> **d.** 36,000 kilograms
>
> 53% of fourth-grade students and 84% of eighth-grade students chose the correct answer.

The NCTM's *Principles and Standards for School Mathematics* states, "Estimation serves as an important companion to computation. It provides a tool for judging the reasonableness of calculator, mental, and pencil-and-paper computations" (2000, p. 155). Estimation helps us judge the reasonableness of a calculation or obtain a ballpark figure, in which case there is no need to check the accuracy of your estimate.

The contemporary teacher who knows alternative methods for adding and subtracting is prepared to help students develop, reinforce, and extend place value concepts; to ask questions to explore students' thinking; and to include students' thinking in their instructional practices.

Base Five Addition and Subtraction

Properties are helpful in establishing addition and subtraction facts in base five (and other bases). For example,

- $4_{\text{five}} + 2_{\text{five}} = 4_{\text{five}} + (1_{\text{five}} + 1_{\text{five}}) = (4_{\text{five}} + 1_{\text{five}}) + 1_{\text{five}} = 10_{\text{five}} + 1_{\text{five}} = 11_{\text{five}}.$
- $4_{\text{five}} + 2_{\text{five}} = 11_{\text{five}},$ so $11_{\text{five}} - 2_{\text{five}} = 4_{\text{five}}$ and $11_{\text{five}} - 4_{\text{five}} = 2_{\text{five}}.$
- $4_{\text{five}} + 3_{\text{five}} = 4_{\text{five}} + (1_{\text{five}} + 2_{\text{five}}) = (4_{\text{five}} + 1_{\text{five}}) + 2_{\text{five}} = 10_{\text{five}} + 2_{\text{five}} = 12_{\text{five}}.$
- $4_{\text{five}} + 3_{\text{five}} = 12_{\text{five}},$ so $12_{\text{five}} - 3_{\text{five}} = 4_{\text{five}}$ and $12_{\text{five}} - 4_{\text{five}} = 3_{\text{five}}.$

Table 2.10 shows the base five addition table. You can also use this table to subtract by applying the definition of subtraction.

TABLE 2.10   Base Five Addition

+	0_{five}	1_{five}	2_{five}	3_{five}	4_{five}
0_{five}	0_{five}	1_{five}	2_{five}	3_{five}	4_{five}
1_{five}	1_{five}	2_{five}	3_{five}	4_{five}	10_{five}
2_{five}	2_{five}	3_{five}	4_{five}	10_{five}	11_{five}
3_{five}	3_{five}	4_{five}	10_{five}	11_{five}	12_{five}
4_{five}	4_{five}	10_{five}	11_{five}	12_{five}	13_{five}

Fluency with Table 2.10 is handy for the pencil-and-paper versions of addition and subtraction algorithms.

Adding base five numerals mimics the algorithms used for the base ten number system. The algorithms depend on adding the digits with common places and regrouping as necessary (such as 10_{five} units = 1_{five} long, 10_{five} longs = 1_{five} flat, 10_{five} flats = 1_{five} cube). Figure 30 models the addition of 223_{five} and 134_{five} in base five. We combine the base five blocks in the order of units, longs, and flats.

Step 1. Model each number.

FIGURE 30

Modeling addition
$223_{five} + 134_{five}$.

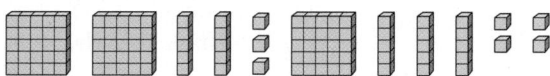

Step 2. Merge both groups.

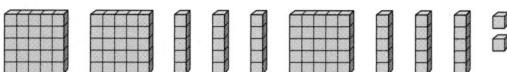

Step 3. Regroup the units (12_{five} = 1_{five} long, 2_{five} units). Then we get 3_{five} flats, 11_{five} longs, and 2_{five} units.

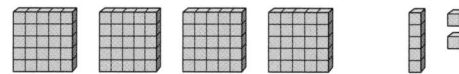

Step 4. Regroup the longs (11_{five} longs = 1_{five} flat, 1_{five} long). Then we get 4_{five} flats, 1_{five} long, and 2_{five} units.

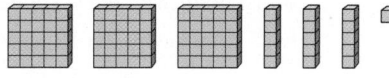

No further regrouping is necessary, so $223_{five} + 134_{five} = 412_{five}$.

Figure 31 models the subtraction of 331_{five} and 134_{five} in base five.

Step 1. Model the minuend 331_{five}.

FIGURE 31

Modeling subtraction
$331_{five} - 134_{five}$.

Step 2. There are not enough units in this representation to take away 4_{five} units, so we need to regroup 1_{five} long as 10_{five} units. Now there are 11_{five} units. We take away 4_{five} units, which leaves 3_{five} flats, 2_{five} longs, and 2_{five} units.

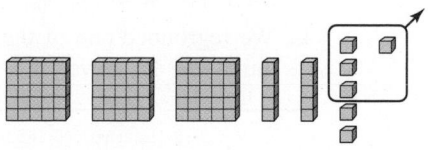

Step 3. Take away 3_{five} longs. There are not enough longs in this representation to take away 3_{five} longs, so we need to regroup 1_{five} flat as 10_{five} longs. Now there are 12_{five} longs. We take away 3_{five} longs, which leaves 2_{five} flats, 4_{five} longs, and 2_{five} units.

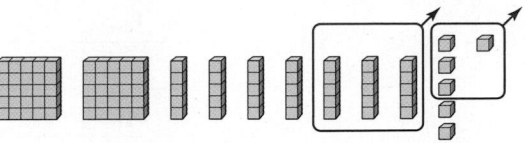

Step 4. Take away 1_{five} flat. This leaves 1_{five} flat, 4_{five} longs, and 2_{five} units.

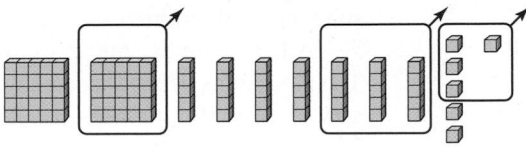

No more base five blocks need to be taken away, so $331_{\text{five}} - 134_{\text{five}} = 142_{\text{five}}$.

The following demonstrates the standard addition algorithm for $324_{\text{five}} + 433_{\text{five}}$. Fluency with base five addition facts and the ability to regroup are keys to the standard addition algorithm.

$$
\begin{array}{r}
{\scriptstyle 1\,1\,1} \\
324_{\text{five}} \\
+\ 433_{\text{five}} \\
\hline
1312_{\text{five}}
\end{array}
$$

Think: 4_{five} units $+ 3_{\text{five}}$ units $= 12_{\text{five}}$ units $= 1_{\text{five}}$ long, 2_{five} units.
Think: 1_{five} long $+ 2_{\text{five}}$ longs $+ 3_{\text{five}}$ longs $= 11_{\text{five}}$ longs $= 1_{\text{five}}$ flat, **1 long.**
Think: 1_{five} flat $+ 3_{\text{five}}$ flats $+ 4_{\text{five}}$ flats $= 13_{\text{five}}$ flats $= 1_{\text{five}}$ cube, 3_{five} **flats.**

The following demonstrates the standard subtraction algorithm for $422_{\text{five}} - 124_{\text{five}} = 243_{\text{five}}$.

$$
\begin{array}{r}
{\scriptstyle 11} \\
{\scriptstyle 3\ \ \cancel{4}\ \ 12} \\
\cancel{4}\ \cancel{2}\ \cancel{2}_{\text{five}} \\
-\ 1\ \ 2\ \ 4_{\text{five}} \\
\hline
2\ \ 4\ \ 3_{\text{five}}
\end{array}
$$

Think: Regroup 2_{five} **longs,** 2_{five} **units as** 1_{five} **long,** 12_{five} **units so** 12_{five} **units** $- 4_{\text{five}}$ **units** $= 3_{\text{five}}$ **units.**
Think: Regroup 4_{five} **flats,** 1_{five} **long as** 3_{five} **flats,** 11_{five} **longs so** 11_{five} **longs** $- 2_{\text{five}}$ **longs** $= 4_{\text{five}}$ **longs.**
Think: 3_{five} **flats** $- 1_{\text{five}}$ **flats** $= 2_{\text{five}}$ **flats.**

EXAMPLE 2.46 Refer to the following problem:

$$
\begin{array}{r}
{\scriptstyle 10} \\
{\scriptstyle 3\ \ \cancel{0}\ \ 12} \\
\cancel{4}\ \cancel{1}\ \cancel{2}_{\text{five}} \\
-\ \ \ \ 3\ \ 4_{\text{five}} \\
\hline
3\ \ 2\ \ 3_{\text{five}}
\end{array}
$$

a. Explain why the 0 appears above the 1.
b. Explain why the 12 appears above the 2.

SOLUTION

a. There are 2_{five} units, and we need to take away 4_{five} units. There are not enough units to take away, so we regrouped one long as 10_{five} units. This leaves 0_{five} longs. The 0 above the 1 represents the 0_{five} longs.

b. We regrouped one of the longs as 10_{five} units. Then 10_{five} units $+ 2_{\text{five}}$ units $= 12_{\text{five}}$ units. The 12 above the 2 represents the 12_{five} units.

You are extremely unlikely to teach your elementary school students how to add and subtract in alternatives bases, but it gives you insight into the issues that your students are likely to face when they make sense of the base ten number system.

QUESTIONS FOR SECTION 2.4

REPRESENTATION

Refresher: Representations (language, diagrams, tables, symbols, algebra, manipulatives, and contextualized situations) are important because we use them to organize, record, and communicate mathematical ideas and to make them more comprehensible.

1. Draw base ten blocks to illustrate the standard algorithms to add or subtract.

   a. $34 - 8$ **b.** $225 - 47$ **c.** $36 + 25$ **d.** $245 + 78$

2. Explain why the 1 appears over the 3.

$$
\begin{array}{ccc}
 & 1 & \\
4 & 3 & 7 \\
+\ 3 & 2 & 8 \\
\hline
7 & 6 & 5
\end{array}
$$

3. Explain why the 5 appears over the 6.

$$
\begin{array}{ccc}
5 & 13 & \\
7 & \cancel{6} & \cancel{3} \\
-\ 6 & 2 & 9 \\
\hline
1 & 3 & 4
\end{array}
$$

4. Explain why the 14 appears over the 4.

$$
\begin{array}{ccc}
 & 6 & 14 \\
8 & \cancel{7} & \cancel{4} \\
-\ 3 & 5 & 8 \\
\hline
5 & 1 & 6
\end{array}
$$

PROBLEM SOLVING

Refresher: Problem solving (reaching a goal that is not immediately attainable) is important because it helps students think more deeply about what they know and deal with unfamiliar situations.

5. Find a pair of possible addends to add using the lattice algorithm.

6. Find a pair of possible addends to add using the partial sums method.

7. Find a pair of possible addends to add using the column addition method.

8. Find a pair of possible addends to add using the column addition method.

REASONING AND PROOF

Refresher: Reasoning and proof (thinking and justifying) are important because they help students make sense of mathematics.

9. A student adds the two numbers $467 + abc$ using the standard addition algorithm, where a, b, and c are digits. What is the largest possible number abc such that

   a. no regroupings are required?

   b. exactly one regrouping is required?

   c. exactly two regroupings are required?

10. How many possible partial sums are there when you add a

    a. 2-digit number and a 3-digit number?

    b. 3-digit number and a 5-digit number?

    c. 100-digit number and a 160-digit number?

11. Do the following.

    a. A student adds the two numbers $3a$ and $b7$. Her work is shown here. What are the values of a and b?

$$
\begin{array}{c}
1 \\
3a \\
+\ b7 \\
\hline
95
\end{array}
$$

    b. What is the largest possible value for k?

$$
\begin{array}{c}
k \\
uv \\
+\ wx \\
\hline
yz
\end{array}
$$

CONNECTIONS

Refresher: Connections (linking and applying mathematical ideas) are important because they deepen student understanding and make mathematics more meaningful, flexible, and useful.

12. What property of addition helps you add $2345 + 5000$ quickly?

13. Find the missing digits: $34,\_\_91 = 34,216 + 3\_\_\ \_\_$.

14. Add $64 + 58$ using the
    a. partial sums method.   b. lattice method.
    c. standard algorithm.   d. column addition method

15. Add 345 and 938 using the
    a. partial sums method.   b. lattice method.

16. Find each sum.

    a.   3 hours 54 minutes 16 seconds
       $+$ 4 hours 12 minutes 45 seconds

    b.   17 hours 35 minutes 50 seconds
       $+$ 20 hours 12 minutes 30 seconds

17. Find each difference.

    a.   12 hours 24 minutes 25 seconds
       $-$ 4 hours 56 minutes 14 seconds

    b.   18 hours 35 minutes 23 seconds
       $-$ 11 hours 47 minutes 30 seconds

18. Each addend in the sum $17,856 + n$ is rounded to the nearest thousand, and the result is 42,000.

    a. What is the smallest possible value for n?
    b. What is the largest possible value for n?
    c. How many possible values are there for n?

COMMUNICATION

Refresher: Communication (written and verbal explanations using representations and proper mathematical vocabulary) is important because it helps students refine and strengthen their understanding.

19. Give an example of a subtraction problem in which it is useful to know $34 = 2$ tens, 14 ones.

20. Give an example of an addition problem in which it is useful to know 15 tens $= 1$ hundred, 5 tens.

21. Discuss how place value understanding is reflected in the lattice algorithm.

22. Discuss how place value understanding is reflected in the partial sums method.

23. Discuss how place value understanding is reflected in the column addition method.

More practice with the ideas of the section

24. Add or subtract. Use base ten blocks to model the process you used.
    a. $34 + 8$ b. $74 + 52$ c. $48 - 35$ d. $236 - 57$

25. Write in standard form.

    a.   3 hundreds $+$ 4 tens $+$ 5 ones
       $+$ 4 hundreds $+$ 8 tens $+$ 9 ones

    b.   7 hundreds $+$ 2 tens $+$ 8 ones
       $+$ 3 hundreds $+$ 5 tens $+$ 7 ones

26. Use the column addition method for $578 + 837$.
    a. Regroup from left to right.
    b. Regroup from right to left.

27. A student adds $382 + abc$ using the standard addition algorithm, where a, b, and c are all nonzero digits. What is the largest possible number abc such that
    a. no regroupings are required?
    b. exactly one regrouping is required?
    c. exactly two regroupings are required?

28. A student subtracts $738 - abc$ using the standard subtraction algorithm, where a, b, and c are nonzero digits. What is the largest possible number abc such that
    a. no regroupings are required?
    b. exactly one regrouping is required?
    c. exactly two regroupings are required?

29. The standard algorithm is used to add. Explain why the 1 appears over the 2.

    $$\begin{array}{r} 1 \\ 2\ 7\ 3 \\ +\ 6\ 5\ 4 \\ \hline 9\ 2\ 7 \end{array}$$

30. The standard algorithm is used to add. Explain why
    a. the 1 appears over the 8.
    b. the 1 appears over the 4.

    $$\begin{array}{r} 1\ \ 1 \\ 4\ 8\ 5 \\ +\ 3\ 6\ 7 \\ \hline 8\ 5\ 2 \end{array}$$

31. Use the partial sums method to add.
    a. $57 + 72$ b. $321 + 36$

32. Use the lattice algorithm to add.
    a. $34 + 55$ b. $76 + 321$ c. $2367 + 487$

33. Use the column addition method to add.
    a. $34 + 55$ b. $76 + 321$ c. $2367 + 487$

34. A student adds the two numbers $27a$ and $5b8$. What are the values of a, b, and c?

    $$\begin{array}{r} 27a \\ +\ 5b8 \\ \hline c54 \end{array}$$

35. Use the scratch algorithm to add.

    a.   25   b.   85
            67   233
            39   546
        $+$ 42 $+$ 79

36. Subtract using the same-change strategy.
    a. $34 - 8$ b. $567 - 24$ c. $5003 - 635$

37. Use compatible numbers to estimate each sum.

    a. $43 + 879$ **b.** $124 + 68$ **c.** $87 + 325$

38. Sketch how you can use base ten blocks to subtract $345 - 97$.

39. Use front-end estimation.

    a. $527 + 62$ **b.** $745 - 97$ **c.** $731 + 398$

40. Use the partial differences method to subtract.

    a. $79 - 15$ **b.** $757 - 83$

41. Use the trade-first method to subtract.

    a. $456 - 273$ **b.** $834 - 46$ **c.** $803 - 51$

42. Calculate mentally. (Show your work; for example, $43 - 28 = 43 - 20 - 8 = 23 - 8 = 15$.)

    a. $57 - 43$ **b.** $65 - 28$ **c.** $131 - 63$

43. Calculate mentally. (Show your work; for example, $43 + 28 = 40 + 20 + 3 + 8 = 60 + 11 = 71$.)

    a. $57 + 43$ **b.** $65 + 28$ **c.** $72 + 25$

44. Use partial sums to add $367 + 487$.

45. Find a pair of possible addends.

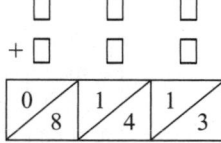

46. Estimate the sum $345 + 687$ by rounding each addend to the nearest

    a. hundreds place.   **b.** tens place.

47. Estimate the difference $868 - 532$ by rounding the minuend and subtrahend to the nearest

    a. hundreds place.   **b.** tens place.

48. Front estimation was used to estimate the sum. What are the smallest and largest possible values for the missing addend?

    a. $245 + n \approx 800$ **b.** $731 + n \approx 1600$

49. Each addend in the sum $4258 + n$ is rounded to the nearest hundred, and the result is 9000.

    a. What is the smallest possible value for n?

    b. What is the largest possible value for n?

    c. How many possible values are there for n? Explain.

50. Add using the standard addition algorithm.

    a. $343_{five} + 324_{five}$ **b.** $214_{five} + 403_{five}$

    c. $A57_{twelve} + 4B7_{twelve}$ **d.** $476_{twelve} + 325_{twelve}$

51. Subtract using the standard subtraction algorithm.

    a. $343_{five} - 124_{five}$ **b.** $240_{five} - 124_{five}$

    c. $45A_{twelve} - B7_{twelve}$ **d.** $92B_{twelve} - 376_{twelve}$

CHAPTER 2 REVIEW

CHAPTER 2 Organizer

Section	What You Should Learn	Review Problems
2.1	**1.** Express ideas about collections of objects using vocabulary and notation.	1–3
	2. Represent sets with a Venn diagram.	4–6
	3. Find the union, intersection, set difference, and Cartesian product of two given sets.	7
	4. Use a Venn diagram to visualize sets and relationships.	8–12
2.2	**1.** Identify basic properties of a numeration system.	13–14
	2. Demonstrate understanding of place value concepts.	15–21
	3. Represent a base ten numeral in various forms.	22–24
	4. Use a diagram to round, demonstrate understanding of rounding.	25–28
	5. Convert numerals to and from a base ten numeral.	29–36
2.3	**1.** Use number sense (decomposing, composing, making ten, using doubles) to add.	37–40
	2. Use the take-away model to subtract.	41–42
	3. Solve an equation using the definition of subtraction, fact family, or the fact that addition and subtraction are inverse operations.	43–44

Section	What You Should Learn	Review Problems
	4. Determine the subtraction model that is more appropriate in a situation.	45
	5. Write a story problem for a given equation.	46
	6. Use additive reasoning to compare two numbers.	47
	7. Add, subtract, or translate phrases.	48–49
2.4	1. Use various place-value methods to add or subtract.	50–58
	2. Estimate sums and differences.	59–60
	3. Add and subtract in other bases.	61–62

Key Terms and Concepts

set 58
element 58
list form 58
universal set 58
empty set 58
equal 58
equivalent 59
cardinality 59
subset 61
proper subset 61
union 62
intersection 62
disjoint 62
set difference 62
complement 63
Cartesian product 63
Venn diagram 64
numeration system 69
number 69
numeral 69
tally system 70
Egyptian numeration system 70
Hindu-Arabic numeration system 71
digits 71
place value 71
base ten blocks 72

period 72
value 72
standard form 74
word form 74
short word form 74
expanded form 74
rounding 75
Mayan numeration system 77
Mayan place values 77
Babylonian numeration system 78
Babylonian place values 79
base five numeration system 79
base twelve numeration system 81
place value numeration system 82
set model 87
definition of addition 87
addend 87
sum 87
counting-on strategy 88
number line model (+) 88
mental arithmetic 89
closure property of addition 89
commutative property of addition 89
associative property of addition 90
number sense 90
composition 91

compatible numbers 91
decomposition 91
identity for addition 92
take away model 93
definition of subtraction 94
difference 94
minuend 94
subtrahend 94
missing addend 94
unknown addend 94
addend model 95
comparison model 96
number line model (−) 97
inverse operations 98
fact family 100
regrouping 104
partial sums method 105
standard addition algorithm 106
lattice algorithm 108
column addition method 109
scratch addition method 110
standard subtraction algorithm 110
trade-first method 111
same-change method 112
partial differences method 112
estimation 113
front-end rounding 114

Review Questions

1. Give an example of each set or relationship.
   a. $x \in A$ b. $A \subseteq B$ c. $\sim A$ d. $A \cap B$ e. $X \cup Y$

2. True or false?
   a. $\{7\} \in \{6, \{7\}, 8, \{9\}\}$ b. $\{7, 8\} \subseteq \{6, \{7\}, 8, \{9\}\}$
   c. $\varnothing \in \{2, 3\}$ d. $\varnothing \subseteq \{2, 3\}$
   e. $\{1, 2, 3\} = \{1, 2, 2, 3\}$ f. $\varnothing = \{ \}$

3. Determine the cardinality of each set.
   a. $A = \{6, 7, 12, 13\}$ b. $A = \{5, 10, 15, 20, \ldots, 185\}$
   c. $\{e, g, 2, 8, 1\} \cap \{1, 2, 3, a, b, c, d, e\}$
   d. $\{3, \{4, 5, 6, 7, \ldots\}, 1\}$ e. $\{\{\varnothing\}\}$

4. Represent the sets with a Venn diagram: A is the set of factors of 12, B is the set of factors of 8, and the universal set is $U = \{1, 2, 3, 4, 5, 6, 7, 8, 9, 10, 11, 12\}$.

5. Write each set in the list form.

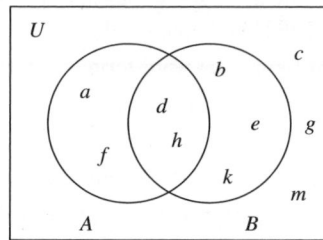

a. A **b.** B **c.** $A \cup B$ **d.** $A \cap B$ **e.** $A - B$

f. $B - A$ **g.** $\sim A$ **h.** $\sim B$ **i.** U

6. Use the diagram to determine each number.

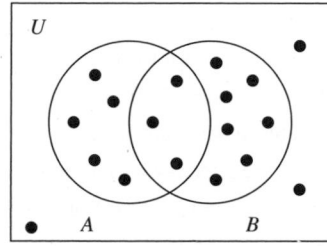

a. $n(A)$ **b.** $n(B)$ **c.** $n(A \cup B)$ **d.** $n(A \cap B)$

e. $n(A - B)$ **f.** $n(B - A)$ **g.** $n(\sim A)$

h. $n(\sim B)$ **i.** $n(U)$

7. $A = \{1, 2, 3\}$, $B = \{5, 6, 7, 11\}$, and $C = \{3, 2, 0\}$. Find

a. $A - C$.   **b.** $B \cup C$.   **b.** $A \cap B$.

8. Use the diagram to verify the equation $n(A \cup B) = n(A) + n(B) - n(A \cap B)$.

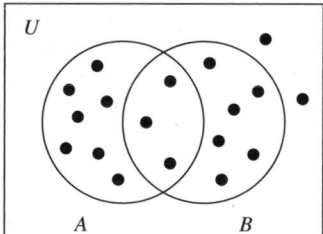

9. Suppose $n(X) = 6$ and $n(Y) = 13$.

a. What is the maximum number of elements $X \cup Y$ can have?

b. What is the minimum number of elements $X \cup Y$ can have?

10. Suppose $n(X) = 5$ and $n(Y) = 9$.

a. What is the maximum number of elements $X \cap Y$ can have?

b. What is the minimum number of elements $X \cap Y$ can have?

11. In a survey, 45 people were asked which of the following three game shows they watched: *Deal or No Deal*, *Minute to Win It*, and *Jeopardy*. The results are displayed in the diagram.

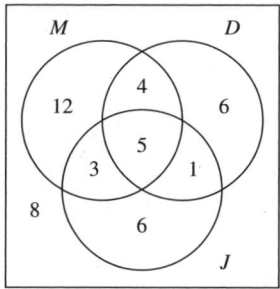

How many people in the survey said they

a. watched *Minute to Win It*?

b. watched only *Minute to Win It* and *Deal or No Deal*.

c. watched only *Jeopardy*?

d. watched exactly one game show?

e. watched exactly two game shows?

f. watched none of the game shows?

12. A teacher surveyed 40 students about two sports: football and baseball. During the survey, 15 students said they liked to play football, 20 students said they liked to play baseball, and 3 students said they liked to play both sports. How many students in his class

a. liked football but not baseball?

b. liked either football or baseball?

c. did not like either sport?

d. liked baseball but not football?

e. liked exactly one sport?

13. Fill in each blank with one of the following choices: *numeral, number, place value, symbols, value:* A numeration system has a set of _____ with a prescribed set of rules that tells how a sequence of those symbols, called a _____, represents the number of objects counted.

14. Select the best answer.

a. A _____ is a quantity. *numeral, number, symbol*

b. A _____ is a representation of a number that consists of a string of symbols. *numeral, number*

c. In the base ten number system, the symbols 0, 1, 2, 3, 4, 5, 6, 7, 8, and 9 are called _____. *numbers, digits*

d. A _____ in a base ten numeral tells you how often a base ten block (ones, tens, hundreds, . . .) is repeated. *place value, digit, value*

e. The _____ of a digit indicates the particular grouping that is represented. *place value, digit, value*

f. In a place value number system, the value of a particular digit depends on its _____. *position, digit*

g. The digit 2 in the base ten numeral 56,201 represents _____. *2, 20, 200*

h. The place value of 2 in the base ten numeral 56,201 is _____. *2, 200, 100*

15. Write the base ten numeral for the base ten block representation shown.

a.
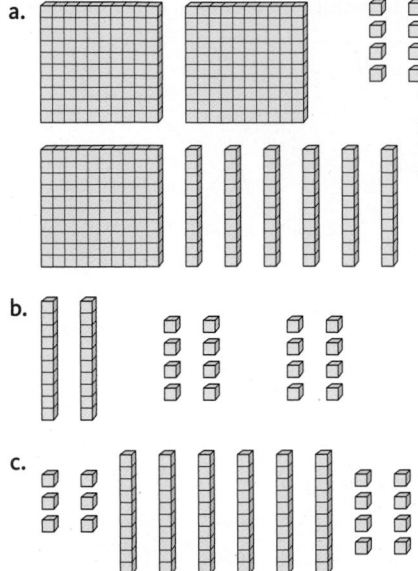

b.

c.

16. Sketch a representation of the numeral using base ten blocks.

a. 512   b. 263

17. Write the numeral using an appropriate base. Regroup as necessary.

a.
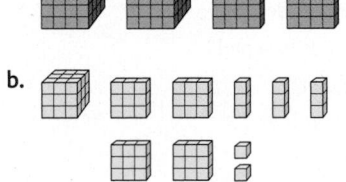

b.

18. Suppose we know that 425 = ___ tens, ___ ones. Then we could write 425 = 42 tens, 5 ones or 425 = 41 tens, 15 ones. But the most efficient representation of 425 in the form 425 = ___ tens, ___ ones is 425 = 42 tens, 5 ones. Fill in the blanks with the most efficient base ten block representation for the given form.

a. 316 = ___ tens, ___ ones

b. 7205 = ___ hundreds, ___ tens, ___ ones

c. 4811 = ___ thousands, ___ ones

d. 562 = ___ hundreds, ___ tens, ___ ones

19. Fill in the blanks:

a. The minimum number of pieces in the most efficient base ten block representation of 354 is _____ pieces.

b. The maximum number of pieces in a base ten block representation of 354 is _____ pieces.

20. Do the following.

a. What is the place value of the underlined digit? 465,3<u>2</u>1

b. What is the value of the underlined digit? 1<u>4</u>,387

c. Find the digit in the hundred thousands place in 1,384,785.

21. The five lowest Mayan place values are 1, 20, 360, 7200, and 144,000. What is the next highest place value?

22. Jupiter is the largest planet in our solar system. Its atmosphere consists of mainly hydrogen and helium. The equatorial radius of Jupiter is 71,492 km. Represent the radius in different forms.

a. short word form   b. word form   c. expanded form

d. expanded form using multiplication

e. expanded form using exponents

23. Find the standard form of each word form.

a. four hundred eighty-two million, one hundred fifty-two thousand, two hundred nineteen

b. seventy-nine million, five hundred six thousand, three hundred four

c. three hundred two billion, fifty-seven thousand, eighty-two

24. Do the following.

a. Represent 46^2 in standard form.

b. Represent 466^2 in standard form.

c. Represent 4666^2 in standard form.

d. Use patterns to represent $466,666^2$ in standard form.

25. A whole number n is rounded to the nearest hundred, and the result is 1200.

a. What is the smallest possible value for n?

b. What is the largest possible value for n?

26. Use a number line to round 3870 to the nearest thousand.

27. Use a number line to round 1435 to the nearest hundred.

28. When we round the number n, we get 1800. What place values could we have used? Support your answer with a possible value of n for each place value that could have been used.

29. Mayan numerals are written vertically in a stack, with the highest place value on top, and in descending order, so the lowest place value is on the bottom of the stack. Convert each Mayan numeral to a base ten numeral.

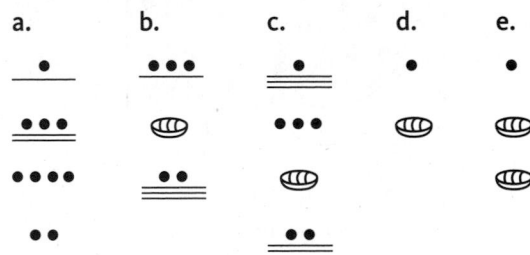

a.   b.   c.   d.   e.

30. Represent the base ten numeral as a Mayan numeral.

a. $3 \cdot 360 + 17 \cdot 20 + 7 \cdot 1$

b. $4 \cdot 7200 + 12 \cdot 360 + 0 \cdot 20 + 8 \cdot 1$

c. $16 \cdot 144,000 + 5 \cdot 7200 + 2 \cdot 360 + 0 \cdot 20 + 15 \cdot 1$

31. Represent the base ten numeral as a Mayan numeral.

a. 5678   b. 10,921

32. The Babylonian place values are 1, 60, 60^2, 60^3, and so on. Use the three symbols (◄, ▼, and //, where ◄ represents 10, ▼ represents 1, and // represents 0), to convert the base ten representations to Babylonian numerals.

a. $7 \cdot 60^1 + 42 \cdot 60^0$

b. $12 \cdot 60^3 + 0 \cdot 60^2 + 4 \cdot 60^1 + 31 \cdot 60^0$

c. $21 \cdot 60^3 + 8 \cdot 60^2 + 0 \cdot 60^1 + 53 \cdot 60^0$

33. Represent each Babylonian numeral as a base ten numeral.

    a. ▼▼▼ ◄◄◄ ▼▼▼
       ▼▼▼   ▼
         ▼▼

    b. ◄◄◄ ▼▼ // ◄◄◄ ▼▼▼
                      ▼▼

    c. ▼▼▼ // ▼◄◄▼

34. Represent the base ten numeral as a Babylonian numeral.

    a. 5678   b. 10,921

35. Represent the base ten numeral as a numeral in the indicated base.

    a. $738 =$ ____$_{five}$ b. $7492 =$ ____$_{five}$

    c. $1231 =$ ____$_{seven}$ d. $8881 =$ ____$_{twelve}$

36. Represent the numeral as a base ten numeral.

    a. 3012_{five} b. 4251_{six} c. $A1B2_{twelve}$

    d. $5B7A_{twelve}$ e. 463_{seven}

37. Which property is illustrated in the equation (commutative, associative, zero identity, and so on).

    a. $(2 + 5) + 9 = 2 + (5 + 9)$ b. $3 + 1 = 1 + 3$

    c. $0 + 6 = 6$ d. $1 + (3 + 8) = 1 + (8 + 3)$

38. Suppose a student knows "doubles," such as $2 + 2 = 4$ and $8 + 8 = 16$. Use doubles to add.

    a. $8 + 6$ b. $9 + 5$

39. How could a student use decomposition to add $8 + 7$?

40. A student used the making-ten strategy to add $n + (2 + 8) = 26 + 10 = 36$. What were the original numbers the student added?

41. Write an appropriate subtraction sentence.

42. Use the take-away model to subtract.

    a. $12 - 4$ b. $7 - 5$

43. Suppose y is a whole number and $y + 3 = 22$.

    a. Solve this equation using the definition of subtraction.

    b. Solve this equation, knowing that addition and subtraction are inverse operations.

    c. Solve this equation using a fact family.

44. Suppose n is a whole number and $n - 15 = 18$.

    a. Solve this equation using the definition of subtraction.

    b. Solve this equation, knowing that addition and subtraction are inverse operations.

    c. Solve this equation using a fact family.

45. Identify the model of subtraction that is most appropriate for each problem. Do not solve the problems.

    a. The Chrysler Building is 1046 feet tall, while the Empire State Building is 1454 feet tall. How much taller is the Empire State Building than the Chrysler Building?

    b. There are 3862 windows in the Chrysler Building. If a window cleaner cleaned 1467 of the windows, how many more windows need to be cleaned?

    c. It takes less than 1 minute to take an elevator from the lobby to the observation deck on the 86th floor of the Empire State Building. There were 58 people waiting for the elevators. When the elevator arrived, only 39 people could fit into it. How many people had to wait for the next elevator?

46. Write a word problem that requires the equation

    a. $n - 8 = 15$.   b. $n + 4 = 9$.   c. $12 - n = 5$.

47. John has 8 trading cards and Bob has 13 trading cards. Use additive reasoning to write two sentences that compare the number of trading cards John and Bob have.

48. Add or subtract.

    a. $4 \text{ oz} + 3 \text{ lb}$ b. $2 \text{ ft} + 16 \text{ in}$ c. $7 \text{ yd} - 5 \text{ ft}$

49. Translate the following phrases using mathematical symbols.

    a. 14 minus h is less than or equal to 8

    b. a plus 5 equals 3 plus 7, which is equal to 10

    c. k take away 5   d. x is at most 14   e. y is at least 12

50. The standard algorithm is used to add:

    $$\begin{array}{r} {}^{1}{}^{1} \\ 4\ 6\ 3 \\ +\ 9\ 2\ 7 \\ \hline 1\ 3\ 9\ 0 \end{array}$$

    Explain why

    a. the 1 appears over the 6.

    b. the 1 appears over the + sign.

51. Use the partial sums method to add.

    a. $857 + 67$ b. $678 + 365$

52. Add $364 + 75$ using the

    a. lattice algorithm.   b. column addition method.

53. The lattice algorithm is used to add. Find a pair of possible addends.

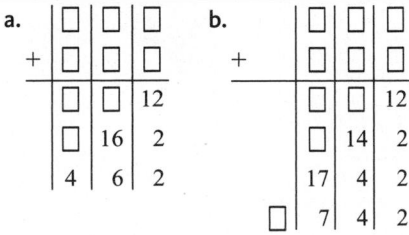

54. The column addition method was used to find the sum. Fill in the blanks with appropriate numbers.

    a.
	☐	☐	☐
+	☐	☐	☐
	☐	☐	12
	☐	16	2
	4	6	2

    b.
	☐	☐	☐
+	☐	☐	☐
	☐	☐	12
	☐	14	2
	17	4	2
☐	7	4	2

55. Find each difference using a base ten model.

    a. $345 - 23$ **b.** $43 - 18$

56. Find a minuend and a subtrahend that yield the partial differences.

    a. $300, -40, -7$ **b.** $400, 60, 2$

57. Use the trade-first method to subtract.

    a. $573 - 48$ **b.** $3456 - 782$

58. Use the partial differences method to subtract.

    a. $456 - 364$ **b.** $734 - 579$

59. Estimate using compatible numbers.

    a. $573 - 85$ **b.** $76{,}421 + 3872$

60. Estimate using rounding.

    a. $16{,}378 - 4632$ **b.** $63{,}234 + 14{,}732$

61. Add using the standard addition algorithm.

    a. $304_{\text{five}} + 123_{\text{five}}$ **b.** $243_{\text{five}} + 13_{\text{five}}$

    c. $7\text{B}6_{\text{twelve}} + 2\text{A}8_{\text{twelve}}$ **d.** $674_{\text{twelve}} + 327_{\text{twelve}}$

62. Subtract using the standard subtraction algorithm.

    a. $304_{\text{five}} - 123_{\text{five}}$ **b.** $243_{\text{five}} - 13_{\text{five}}$

    c. $7\text{B}6_{\text{twelve}} - 2\text{A}8_{\text{twelve}}$ **d.** $674_{\text{twelve}} - 327_{\text{twelve}}$

Chapter 2 Test

1. *Know vocabulary, notation, and diagrams associated with sets.* Indicate true or false.

    a. $3 \in \{1, 0, 3\}$ **b.** $3 \in \{1, 0, \{3\}\}$ **c.** $\{3\} \notin \{1, 0, 3\}$

    d. $\{3, 0, 0, 2\} = \{2, 0, 3\}$ **e.** $\{1, 2, 0\} = \{1, 0, 2\}$

    f. $0 \in \varnothing$ **g.** $\{1, 2, 3\}$ is a proper subset of $\{1, 2, 3\}$

2. *Know vocabulary, notation, and diagrams associated with sets.*

    a. Explain why the cardinality of $\{4, \{0, 1\}\}$ is 2.

    b. Explain why the cardinality of $\{\{5, 2\}, \{1\}, \varnothing\}$ is 3.

    c. Determine whether the set is finite or infinite. If the set is finite, determine the cardinality. $\{\{4, 2\}, \{2, 1\}, \{2, 4, 6, 8, \ldots\}\}$

3. *Know vocabulary, notation, and diagrams associated with sets.* Let $U = \{1, 2, 3, \ldots, 10\}$, $A = \{3, 5, 6, 7, 8\}$, and $B = \{1, 2, 3\}$. Write the set that represents the shaded region in each of the Venn diagrams.

a.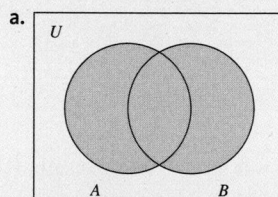

b.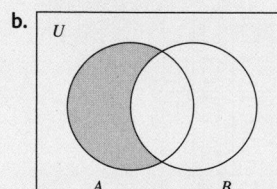

c.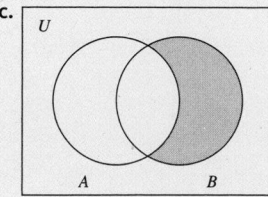

d.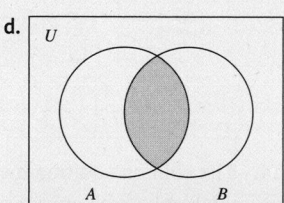

e.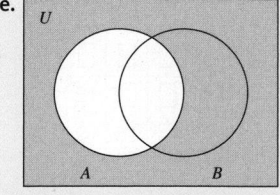

f.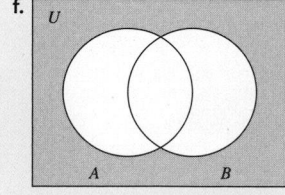

4. *Perform set operations.* $A = \{2, 3, 4, 5\}$ and $B = \{2, 4, 1, 3, 6\}$. The universal set is $U = \{0, 1, 2, 3, 4, 5, 6, 7, 8\}$. Write each set in list form.

    a. $A \cup B$ **b.** $A \cap B$ **c.** $A - B$ **d.** $B - A$ **e.** $\sim A$

5. *Use a Venn diagram to visualize sets and relationships.* Mrs. Dugger surveyed her students to learn how many liked probability, geometry, and measurement. The results of the survey are summarized in the Venn diagram.

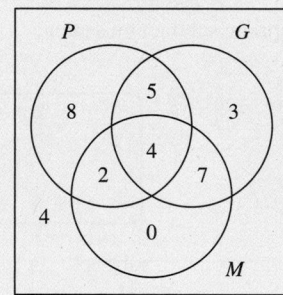

    a. How many students were surveyed?

    b. How many students liked all three subjects?

    c. How many students liked exactly one subject?

    d. How many students liked only geometry?

    e. How many students liked geometry and measurement?

    f. How many students liked only probability and measurement?

6. *Use a Venn diagram to visualize sets and relationships.* Mr. Smith surveyed his class of 23 students to learn how many students liked gum, taffy, or licorice. Every student liked at least one of the types of candy, with 5 students saying they liked only licorice, 9 students saying they liked licorice and gum, 6 students saying they liked all three, 4 students saying they liked only gum, and 12 students saying they liked exactly one of the types of candy.

a. How many students liked only taffy?

b. How many students liked exactly one type of candy?

c. How many students liked licorice and taffy?

7. *Know the basics of a numeration system.* Fill in the blanks. A numeration system has two basic requirements: The numeration system has a set of _____. The numeration system has a framework that determines how a sequence of those symbols, called a _____, represents the number of objects counted. A _____ does not depend on the numeration system.

8. *Know the basics of a numeration system.* For the numeral 4,052,348,

a. what is the place value of the 3?

b. what is the value of the 2?

c. what is the short word form?

d. what is the word form?

9. *Know the basics of a numeration system.* Because $96^2 = 9216$, the standard form of 96^2 is 9216. What is the standard form of $999,996^2$? Explain.

10. *Represent a base ten numeral in various expanded forms.* Represent 345,678 in the following forms.

a. expanded form   b. expanded form with multiplication

c. expanded form with exponents

11. *Use a diagram to round.* Use a number line model to round

a. 57 to the nearest ten.   b. 372 to the nearest hundred.

c. 4278 to the nearest thousand.

12. *Demonstrate understanding of rounding.* A number n is rounded, and the result is 42,000. What place values could have been used? Support your answer with examples.

13. *Demonstrate understanding of rounding.*

a. Find a whole number n such that when 3456 and n are each rounded to the nearest thousand, the sum of the rounded numbers is 14,000.

b. What is the smallest possible value for n?

c. What is the largest possible value for n?

14. *Convert numerals to and from a base ten numeral.* Represent the sum as a Mayan numeral. Then represent the sum as a base ten numeral.

a. $8 \cdot 360 + 12 \cdot 20 + 4 \cdot 1$

b. $14 \cdot 7200 + 0 \cdot 360 + 5 \cdot 20 + 2 \cdot 1$

c. $12 \cdot 144,000 + 0 \cdot 7200 + 4 \cdot 360 + 0 \cdot 20 + 17 \cdot 1$

15. *Convert numerals to and from a base ten numeral.*

a. Represent 2345 as a Mayan numeral.

b. Represent 754,321 as a Babylonian numeral.

c. Represent ◄◄◄ ▼▼ // ◄◄ ▼ as a Hindu–Arabic numeral.

d. Represent 793 as a base five numeral.

e. Represent 4955 as a base twelve numeral.

16. *Use number sense to add.*

a. Use the making-ten strategy to add $8 + 6$.

b. Use the making-doubles strategy to add $7 + 9$.

c. Use decomposing to add $27 + 5$.

d. Use composing to add $12 + 37 + 8$.

17. *Determine the subtraction model that is most appropriate in a situation.* Do not solve the problem.

a. Bob has 56 marbles, and Kamran has 30 marbles. How many fewer marbles does Kamran have?

b. A box of chocolate has 16 chocolate truffles in the flavors raspberry, passion fruit, and orange. Kelly ate 3 of them. How many were left?

18. *Solve an equation using the definition of subtraction, a fact family, or addition and subtraction as inverse operations.* A student solves an equation, knowing that addition and subtraction are inverse operations. Supply the missing reasons.

$n + 35 = 82$	original equation
$n + 35 - 35 = 82 - 35$	a.
$n = 82 - 35$	b.
$n = 47$	simplification
$n - 28 = 64$	original equation
$n - 28 + 28 = 64 + 28$	c.
$n = 64 + 28$	d.
$n = 92$	simplification

19. *Solve an equation using the definition of subtraction, a fact family, or addition and subtraction as inverse operations.*

a. Solve $n + 3 = 8$ using a fact family.

b. Solve $k - 26 = 84$ using the definition of subtraction.

c. Solve $b + 18 = 45$ using the definition of subtraction.

20. *Solve an equation using the definition of subtraction, a fact family, or addition and subtraction as inverse operations.* Solve the equation using the fact that addition and subtraction are inverse operations.

a. $m + 45 = 131$ b. $h - 23 = 68$

21. *Solve an equation using the definition of subtraction, fact family, or addition and subtraction as inverse operations.* A student works the subtraction problem $65 - 38$ and obtains the answer 33. How can the student check his answer?

22. *Use various place value methods to add or subtract.* Add $456 + 328$ using the

a. lattice algorithm.   b. column-addition method.

23. *Use various place value methods to add or subtract.* The standard addition algorithm is used to add:

```
  1 1 1
    4 5 6
  +   7 9 8
  ─────────
  1 2 5 4
```

Explain why

a. the 1 appears over the 5.   b. the 1 appears over the + sign.

24. *Use various place value methods to add or subtract.* The standard subtraction algorithm is used to subtract:

$$
\begin{array}{r}
\overset{7}{\cancel{8}}\ \overset{16}{\cancel{6}} \\
4\ \ \ \ \ \\
-\ 1\ 2\ 7 \\
\hline
3\ 5\ 9
\end{array}
$$

Explain why

a. the 7 appears over the 8.

b. the 16 appears over the 6.

25. *Estimate.* Briefly discuss your strategy.

   a. $567 + 215$ **b.** $52{,}820 + 7285$

   c. $73 - 37$ **d.** $12{,}350 - 4788$

26. *Add and subtract in other bases.*

   a. $402_{\text{five}} + 233_{\text{five}}$ **b.** $402_{\text{five}} - 233_{\text{five}}$

   c. $453_{\text{twelve}} + 248_{\text{twelve}}$ **d.** $4A3_{\text{twelve}} - 148_{\text{twelve}}$

3

Multiplication and Division with Whole Numbers

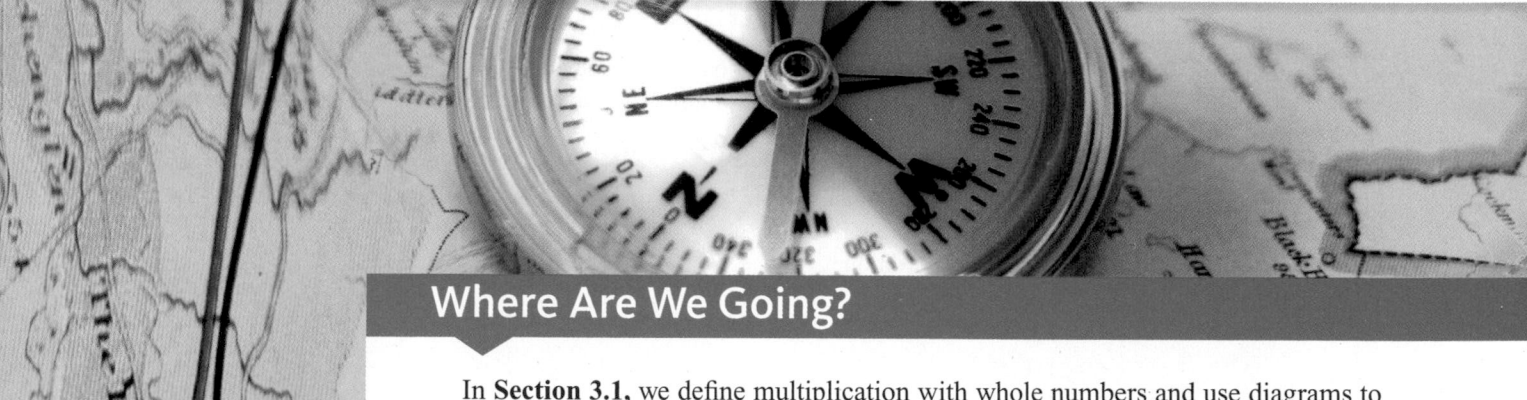

Where Are We Going?

In **Section 3.1,** we define multiplication with whole numbers and use diagrams to illustrate situations (repeated addition, arrays, and Cartesian product) involving multiplication with whole numbers. We use skip counting as an informal method to multiply two whole numbers. Then we discuss properties, number sense, and exponential notation. In **Section 3.2,** we present two models of division with whole numbers. We explain why they provide the same numerical answer and discuss division by zero. We introduce the quotient–remainder theorem and its uses. In **Section 3.3,** we use models, place value concepts, and properties to develop various methods of multiplication and division.

What Situations Involve Multiplication and Division?

Imagine a jar of coins. How could you count them? One way involves organizing them into equal-sized stacks. Now imagine a restaurant has a promotional offer with three types of sandwiches and two types of drinks. How many ways can you order a sandwich and drink? As another example, cars in a parking lot are arranged in a rectangular array. How can we determine the number of cars without counting each car? These seemingly different problems involve multiplication.

Now imagine a teacher needs to teach her students division. How could she explain to her class what division is, show them how to use a diagram to evaluate $12 \div 4$, or help them recognize problems that require division?

What Is Multiplicative Reasoning?

The NCTM's *Principles and Standards for School Mathematics* states:

> In grades 3–5, multiplicative reasoning should become a focus. Multiplicative reasoning is more than just doing multiplication or division. It is about understanding situations in which multiplication or division is an appropriate operation. It involves a way of viewing situations and thinking about them. (© NCTM Standards 2011 by National Council of Teachers of Mathematics)

Models and Properties of Multiplication

Addition answers the question "How many in all?" when disjoint sets are combined. Multiplication answers the same question for situations in which the disjoint sets each have the same number of objects.

Set Model of Multiplication

In the **set model** of multiplication, we join several groups of discrete objects, with each group having the same number of objects. The following problem introduces a connection between two new concepts.

EXAMPLE 3.1

CONNECTION

REPRESENTATION

A customer buys three regular cartons of eggs. How many eggs are there in all? Express the total using the following.

a. Repeated addition

b. Multiplication

SOLUTION

There are 3 cartons, with 12 eggs per carton.

a. In **repeated addition,** all addends are identical. The total number of eggs is $12 + 12 + 12$.

b. We can represent the sum $12 + 12 + 12$ more compactly as 3×12, with the understanding that the 3 indicates the number of groups, the $\times$ sign indicates a new arithmetic operation called **multiplication,** and the 12 indicates the number of objects in each group. ▲

Initially, students calculate 3×12 as $3 \times 12 = 12 + 12 + 12 = 36$. This helps develop their readiness for multiplication. However, thinking of multiplication solely in terms of repeated addition is ineffective for supporting multiplicative thinking in other situations with multiplicative structure, such as arrays, Cartesian products, comparisons, fractions, and measurements. The following noncomputational definition of multiplication supports multiplicative thinking in these various situations.

$3 \times 4 = 12$

|||| |||| ||||

FIGURE 1

A second-grade student interprets 3×4 as three groups of four.

> ### Noncomputational Definition of $a \times b$
>
> Let the counting number a represent the number of groups and b represent the number of objects in each group. Then the total number of objects in all groups is $a \times b$, which is read as "a times b."
>
> - a is called the **multiplier,** and b is called the **multiplicand.**
> - a and b are also called **factors.**
> - The number $a \times b$ is also read as "the **product of a and b.**"
> - We define $0 \times b$ as equal to zero ($0 \times b = 0$).

CONNECTION

Students should be able to "interpret products of whole numbers, e.g., interpret 5×7 as the total number of objects in 5 groups of 7 objects each" (CCSS, Gr. 3). The phrases "three times four" and "three groups of four" mean there are three groups, where each group has four objects, as shown in Figure 1. In this case, there are 3×4, or 12, objects in all, because $3 \times 4 = 4 + 4 + 4 = 12$.

Unlike addition and subtraction, the factors in multiplication may have different units:

- 4 packages $\times$ 3 bottles per package = 4×3 bottles
- $\$15 \times 4$ tickets per dollar = 15×4 tickets
- a groups $\times$ b objects per group = $a \times b$ objects

EXAMPLE 3.2

CONNECTION

A dragonfly has four wings. How many wings do 12 dragonflies have? Give the answer as an expression involving the multiplication sign.

SOLUTION

The dragonflies have 12×4 wings.

▲

 Historical Note

William Oughtred (1574–1660) is credited with using the $\times$ sign to symbolize multiplication in his 1631 publication *Clavis Mathematicae* (translated *Key to Mathematics*). He lived in England and was a mathematician and a minister. He also invented the slide rule.

Connection between Skip Counting and Whole Number Multiplication

CONNECTION **Skip counting** gives students an opportunity to create and recognize patterns and relationships between numbers and operations, and it helps students calculate $a \times b$. The following example illustrates the use of skip counting to evaluate a product.

EXAMPLE 3.3

CONNECTION

Use skip counting to evaluate each product.
a. 4×3
b. 3×5

SOLUTION

a. Skip counting by threes: 3, 6, 9, 12. So $4 \times 3 = 12$.
b. Skip counting by fives: 5, 10, 15. So $3 \times 5 = 15$.

▲

Measurement Model of Multiplication

The **measurement model** is based on the number line and extends the conceptual definition of multiplication to situations in which the quantity that is copied is continuous in nature (such as distance or weight), rather than discrete (such as batteries or eggs). Suppose a painter used 2 gallons of paint per day on a project. He spent 3 days on the project. How much paint did he use? Figure 2 illustrates how to use the number line in the measurement model.

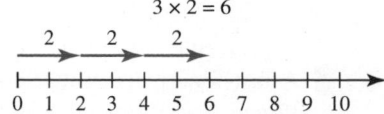

FIGURE 2
The measurement model of multiplication uses the number line.

REPRESENTATION   Each arrow represents the quantity measured. We see the painter used 6 gallons of paint, because $3 \times 2 = 6$. In the number line model for the product $a \times b$, the first factor a indicates the number of times you repeat the arrow and the second factor b tells you the length of the arrow.

Array Model of Multiplication

An **array** is a rectangular arrangement of objects in which each row or column has the same number of objects. We often see cans on grocery shelves, cars in parking lots, and desks in classrooms arranged in an array. The **array model** of multiplication gives the total number of objects in an array *without* counting every object. Figure 3 illustrates the connection between an array of objects and multiplication.

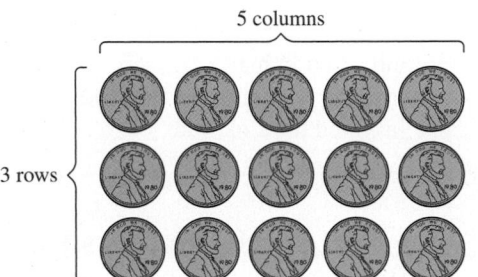

5 columns

3 rows

There are 3 groups of 5 pennies.
There are 3×5 pennies in all.

There are 5 groups of 3 pennies.
There are 5×3 pennies in all.

FIGURE 3
An array of pennies.

REPRESENTATION   The key to seeing that an array has multiplicative structure is seeing that each row (or column) represents a group and that the squares in each column (or row) are the objects in each group. An array of objects with a rows (or columns) and b columns (or rows) has $a \times b$ objects. It is not necessary to count every object in the array to answer the question, "How many in all?" It is more efficient to count the number of rows and the number of columns and then multiply the two numbers.

CONNECTION   We also use arrays to model prime and composite numbers, the associative property of multiplication, and the area formula for a rectangle.

Cartesian Product Model of Multiplication

A collection of objects that has characteristics from two sets has multiplicative structure. For example, there are three shirts and four pairs of pants. An outfit consists of one shirt and one pair of pants. How many different outfits are possible? The **Cartesian product model** of multiplication determines the number of possibilities when choosing one object from each set. The diagram in the following example illustrates the connection between the Cartesian product model and multiplication.

EXAMPLE 3.4   A fast-food restaurant offers a combination meal with a sandwich and potatoes. There are
CONNECTION   three types of sandwiches: ham, turkey, or chicken. There are two types of potatoes: baked
PROBLEM SOLVING   potato or french fries. Draw a tree diagram to organize the list of possibilities. How many
REASONING   possible combinations of sandwiches and potatoes can you order?
REPRESENTATION

SOLUTION

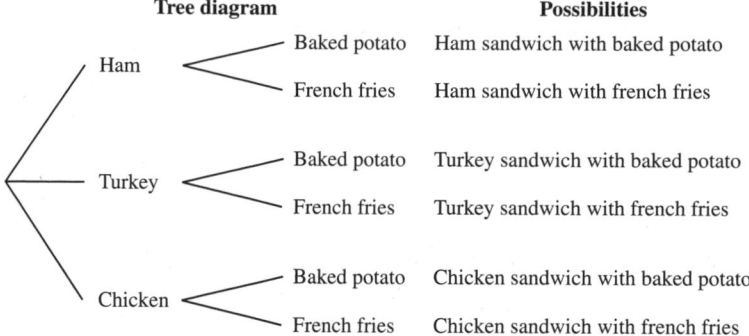

The tree diagram generates a complete list of possibilities that can be partitioned into three groups with two meals per group, so 3×2 meals can be ordered.

TABLE 3.1   All Possible Combinations of Meals

Sandwich types	Potato types	
	b	**f**
h	hb	hf
t	tb	tf
c	cb	cf

CONNECTION

REPRESENTATION

We can use a table to solve this problem too. Let $A = \{h, t, c\}$ and $B = \{b, f\}$, where the elements of A represent the types of sandwiches (ham, turkey, chicken) and the elements of B represent the potato types (baked potato, french fries). Table 3.1 shows the possible combinations. The Cartesian product set $A \times B$ contains all possible ordered pairs: $A \times B = \{(h, b), (h, f), (t, b), (t, f), (c, b), (c, f)\}$. The number of different orders of sandwiches has an array structure, so $n(A \times B) = 6$. Because $n(A \times B) = 6 = 3 \times 2 = n(A) \times n(B)$, the number of possible meals is $n(A \times B) = n(A) \times n(B)$. The following principle generalizes this result.

Fundamental Counting Principle

Let $n(A)$ and $n(B)$ represent the number of objects in sets A and B, respectively. The number of ways you can select one object first from A and then another object from B is $n(A) \times n(B)$.

EXAMPLE 3.5

CONNECTION

PROBLEM SOLVING

REPRESENTATION

Suppose you would like to order a cheese pizza. The sizes are personal, small, medium, large, and extra large. The crust types are thin and deep pan. How many different cheese pizzas can you order?

SOLUTION

There are five sizes of pizzas and two crust types. Because $5 \times 2 = 10$, you can order 10 types of cheese pizzas.

CONNECTION

The Cartesian product model of multiplication also appears in probability when students determine the number of equally likely outcomes in an experiment or draw a tree diagram to list all possible outcomes.

Comparison Model of Multiplication

In the **comparison model** of multiplication, we compare two quantities using the phrase "times as many." Students should be able to "interpret a multiplication equation as a comparison, e.g., interpret $35 = 5 \times 7$ as a statement that 35 is 5 times as many as 7 and 7 times as many as 5" (CCSS, Gr. 4). They should also be able to "represent verbal statements of multiplicative comparisons as multiplication equations" (CCSS, Gr. 4). In addition, they should be able to "multiply or divide to solve word problems involving multiplicative comparison, e.g., by using drawings and equations with a symbol for the unknown number to represent the problem" (CCSS, Gr. 4).

CONNECTION
REPRESENTATION

For example, suppose Tanya has four times as many coins as Alicia and Alicia has three coins. We can represent the number of coins Tanya has with the following diagram.

The phrase "Tanya has four times as many coins" tells us the number of groups, and the phrase "Alicia has three coins" tells us the number of objects in each group. So Tanya has $4 \times 3 = 12$ coins.

EXAMPLE 3.6

CONNECTION

Judith has five coins. Paul has seven times as many coins as Judith. How many coins does Paul have?

SOLUTION

Paul has seven times as many coins as Judith, who has 5 coins. Because $7 \times 5 = 35$, Paul has 35 coins.   ▲

The following Released Item suggests that comparison problems involving multiplication are challenging.

▶ **RELEASED ITEM**

● NAEP, 2003

In Jean's class, there are twice as many boys as girls. If there are 10 girls in the class, how many boys and girls are there in the class?
a. 15 **b.** 20 **c.** 25 **d.** 30

34% of fourth-grade students chose the correct answer. (U.S. Department of Education, Institute of Education Sciences, National Center for Education Statistics, NAEP)

Same Multiplication Problem in Different Situations

The solution to each of the problems in the next example is the same ($7 \times 8 = 56$), but the structure of the problems in the contextualized situations differs.

EXAMPLE 3.7

CONNECTION

Determine which of the following multiplication models is more appropriate in each situation: *set model, measurement model, array model, comparison model,* or *Cartesian product model.*

a. A sixth-grade class must choose a boy and a girl to represent the class in a spelling contest. There are seven boys and eight girls in the class. How many different ways can the class choose their representatives?

b. Mark has eight marbles. Mary has seven times as many marbles as Mark. How many marbles does Mary have?

c. Mike runs 8 miles every day. How many miles does he run in 7 days?

d. Mrs. Grady bought seven bags of candy for her class. Each bag contained eight candy bars. How many candy bars did Mrs. Grady have altogether?

e. A store employee taking inventory counted eight rows of cans of tomato soup. Each row had seven cans of tomato soup. How many cans of tomato soup were there altogether?

SOLUTION

a. Cartesian product model

b. Comparison model

c. Measurement model

d. Set model

e. Array model

▲

In the previous example, what words or phrases helped you identify the model?

Multiplying by Powers of 10

REASONING Multiplying by powers of 10 is an important number sense skill. Students readily see the patterns in Table 3.2 and can use inductive reasoning to make a conjecture about multiplying by powers of 10 before applying formal methods. What patterns do you see?

TABLE 3.2   **Using Patterns to Help Students Multiply by Powers of 10**

$3 \times 10 = 30$	$25 \times 10 = 250$	$163 \times 10 = 1630$
$3 \times 100 = 300$	$25 \times 100 = 2500$	$163 \times 100 = 16,300$
$3 \times 1000 = 3000$	$25 \times 1000 = 25,000$	$163 \times 1000 = 163,000$

Students should be able to "explain patterns in the number of zeros of the product when multiplying a number by powers of 10" (CCSS, Gr. 4) (© 2010. National Governors Association Center for Best Practices and Council of Chief State School Officers. All rights reserved.). One of the three top indicators of estimation ability is the ability to multiply by powers of 10 (the other two indicators are choosing the larger or smaller of two numbers and choosing the larger number in two word problems).

Early Application of Properties of Multiplication

The properties of multiplication give students a way to determine products, such as 12×6 or 7×19, before they learn the standard multiplication algorithm. Properties of whole numbers also provide the foundation for number sense, estimation skills, and algebra. The NCTM standards for algebra expects students to "identify such properties as commutativity, associativity, and distributivity and use them to compute with whole numbers" (NCTM, Gr. 3–5), and the CCSS expects students to "apply properties of operations as strategies to multiply and multiply one-digit whole numbers by multiples of 10 in the range 10–90 (e.g., 9×80, 5×60) using strategies based on place value and properties of operations" (CCSS, Gr. 3).

Closure Property of Multiplication of Whole Numbers

Let's choose factors from the set $A = \{0, 4, 5\}$. Both 0 and 4 belong to A, and the product 0×4 belongs to A. Both 4 and 5 belong to A, but the product 4×5 does not belong to A. When we say, "A set is not closed under multiplication," we mean there are at least two elements of the set whose product does not belong to the set. When we say, "A set is closed under multiplication," we mean the product of any two elements of the set also belongs to the set.

EXAMPLE 3.8 Determine whether the following sets are closed under multiplication.

REASONING a. $\{0, 1\}$

b. $\{5, 6, 7\}$

SOLUTION

a. There are four possible products: $0 \times 0 = 0$, $0 \times 1 = 0$, $1 \times 1 = 1$, and $1 \times 0 = 0$. All of the products belong to $\{0, 1\}$, so the set is closed under multiplication.

b. Although 5 and 6 belong to $\{5, 6, 7\}$, 5×6 does not belong to $\{5, 6, 7\}$, because $5 \times 6 = 30$. This shows there are at least two elements of $\{5, 6, 7\}$ whose product does not belong to the set, so $\{5, 6, 7\}$ is not closed under multiplication.

▲

We know 5×7, 10×3, and 2×0 are whole numbers (because $5 \times 7 = 35$, $10 \times 3 = 30$, and $2 \times 0 = 0$). These examples suggest an important property of multiplication of whole numbers, which is stated algebraically here.

> ### Closure Property of Whole Number Multiplication
>
> Let a and b be whole numbers. Then $a \times b$ is a whole number.

This means $2343 \times 57{,}002$ and $45 \times 67 + 7531$ are whole numbers. Some students disagree because they do not know their actual values. Can you explain why they are whole numbers?

Commutative Property of Multiplication of Whole Numbers

Many students, and even street vendors who make calculations every day in financial transactions, do not easily recognize that 5×7 and 7×5 represent the same number. Why should they? It's not obvious that five groups of seven should equal seven groups of five.

CONNECTION
REASONING
REPRESENTATION

In grocery stores, boxes typically form an array to make counting easier during inventory. Suppose a store clerk notices there are five rows of three cans of soup on a shelf. Are there 5×3 or 3×5 cans in all? Intuitively, both answers are correct, because the number of cans of soup is independent of whether the cans are grouped by rows or columns. Figure 4 suggests a property of multiplication of whole numbers: the *order of the factors* can change without changing the product.

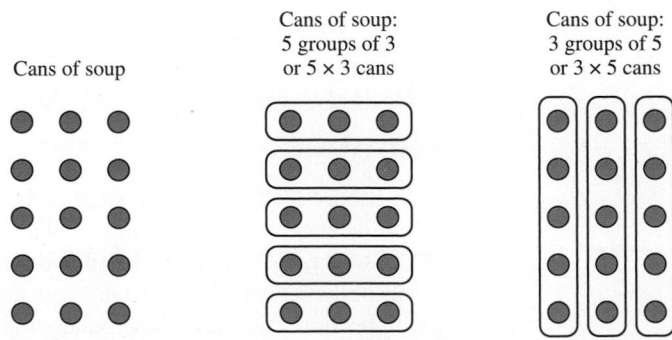

FIGURE 4
An array of objects can be grouped by rows or columns without changing the total. The number of objects is the same, so $5 \times 3 = 3 \times 5$.

This property can be stated algebraically.

> ## Commutative Property of Whole Number Multiplication
>
> Let a and b be whole numbers. Then $a \times b = b \times a$.

The **commutative property of multiplication** is especially helpful when multiplying by 2 or 5, because students are familiar with doubling and counting by fives. For example, $6 \times 2 = 2 \times 6 = 12$ (6, 12), and $5 \times 3 = 3 \times 5 = 15$ (5, 10, 15).

Associative Property of Multiplication of Whole Numbers

Figure 5 represents an array of bags of marbles. Each bag contains exactly three marbles. How many marbles are there altogether?

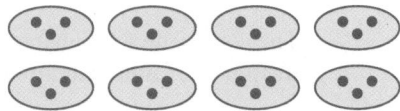

FIGURE 5

An array of bags of marbles to illustrate the associative property.

CONNECTION

REASONING

REPRESENTATION

There are 2×4 bags, and each bag has three marbles, so there are $(2 \times 4) \times 3$ marbles. There are two rows, and each row has 4×3 marbles, so there are $2 \times (4 \times 3)$ marbles. Intuitively, the total number of marbles is independent of the grouping, so $(2 \times 4) \times 3 = 2 \times (4 \times 3)$. Let's check: $(2 \times 4) \times 3 = 8 \times 3 = 24$, and $2 \times (4 \times 3) = 2 \times 12 = 24$. Our intuition is correct. This suggests we can represent either product as $2 \times 4 \times 3$ to save ink and reduce the clutter in the expression, because no matter where we place the parentheses, we get the same result. Figure 5 suggests another property of multiplication of whole numbers: the *order of the groupings* can change without changing the product. This property is stated algebraically here.

> ## Associative Property of Whole Number Multiplication
>
> Let a, b, and c be whole numbers. Then $(a \times b) \times c = a \times (b \times c)$.

EXAMPLE 3.9

REASONING

Use the associative property to simplify the calculation.

a. 32×25

b. 8×400

SOLUTION

a. $32 \times 25 = (8 \times 4) \times 25$

$\qquad = 8 \times (4 \times 25)$

$\qquad = 8 \times 100$

$\qquad = 800$

b. $8 \times 400 = 8 \times (4 \times 100)$

$\qquad = (8 \times 4) \times 100$

$\qquad = 32 \times 100$

$\qquad = 3200$

In the following Released Item, the associative property makes it possible to represent the correct answer 5 × 4 × 3 without parentheses.

> ▶ **RELEASED ITEM**
>
> • NAEP, 1996
>
> The picture in the margin shows the flowerpots in which Kevin will plant flower seeds. He needs 3 seeds for each pot. Which of the following number sentences shows how many seeds Kevin will need for all of the pots?
> **a.** $5 \times 4 \times 3$ **b.** $(5 \times 4) + 3$ **c.** $5 + (4 \times 3)$ **d.** $5 + 4 + 3$
>
> 50% of fourth-grade students chose the correct answer.

Distributive Property of Multiplication of Whole Numbers

The array model illustrates another property of multiplication called the **distributive property of multiplication over addition.** Figure 6 shows a 5-by-6 array.

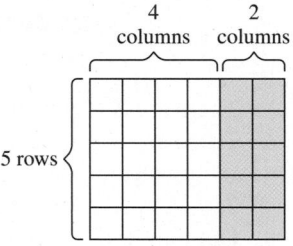

FIGURE 6
How to use the array model to illustrate the distributive property of multiplication over addition.

CONNECTION
REASONING
REPRESENTATION

Then:

Number of squares = 5×6 **Array model**

$= 5 \times (4 + 2)$ **Because 6 = 4 + 2**

Number of squares = Number of unshaded squares + Number of shaded squares

$= 5 \times 4 + 5 \times 2$

Then $5 \times (4 + 2) = 5 \times 4 + 5 \times 2$. The 5 is "distributed" to each addend. This property holds for all whole numbers.

> **Distributive Property of Multiplication over Addition**
>
> Let a, b, and c be any whole numbers. Then $a \times (b + c) = a \times b + a \times c$.

The next example illustrates how to use the distributive property of multiplication over addition to find an unknown product using known facts, and it forms the foundation of methods for multiplication.

EXAMPLE 3.10   Use the distributive property of multiplication over addition to compute the product.

CONNECTION   **a.** 6×12

REASONING   **b.** 4×35

c. 11×14

SOLUTION

a. $6 \times 12 = 6 \times (10 + 2)$
$= 6 \times 10 + 6 \times 2$
$= 60 + 12$
$= 72$

b. $4 \times 35 = 4 \times (30 + 5)$
$= 4 \times 30 + 4 \times 5$
$= 120 + 20$
$= 140$

c. $11 \times 14 = 11 \times (10 + 4)$
$= 11 \times 10 + 11 \times 4$
$= 110 + 44$
$= 154$

▲

EXAMPLE 3.11 Simplify the expression $4(3 + 5a)$. Show all steps.

CONNECTION

SOLUTION

$4(3 + 5a) = 4 \times 3 + 4 \times (5a)$ **Distributive property of multiplication over addition**

$= 4 \times 3 + (4 \times 5)a$ **Associative property of multiplication**

$= 12 + 20a$ **Simplification**

▲

The following example requires students to use definitions and properties to prove other interesting and useful properties of multiplication of whole numbers. The proofs rely on the ability to apply definitions and properties. Proofs represent opportunities to reason, and students should be able to "recognize reasoning and proof as fundamental aspects of mathematics" (NCTM, Pre-K–8).

EXAMPLE 3.12 Let a, b, and c represent whole numbers. Use properties to prove the following.

REASONING

a. $(a + b) \times c = a \times c + b \times c$.

b. If $b - c$ is a whole number, then $a \times (b - c) = a \times b - a \times c$.

SOLUTION

a. $(a + b) \times c = c \times (a + b)$ **Commutative property of multiplication**

$= c \times a + c \times b$ **Distributive property of multiplication over addition**

$= a \times c + c \times b$ **Commutative property of multiplication**

$= a \times c + b \times c$ **Commutative property of multiplication**

Therefore, $(a + b) \times c = a \times c + b \times c$.

b. Suppose $b - c$ is a whole number; that is, $b - c = n$ for some whole number n. Then $b = n + c$ by the definition of subtraction. Then the following is true:

$a \times b = a \times (n + c)$ **Because $b = n + c$**

$= a \times n + a \times c$ **Distributive property of multiplication over addition**

(continued)

Then $a \times b = a \times n + a \times c$. So we can calculate the following:

$$a \times b - a \times c = a \times n \qquad \text{Definition of subtraction}$$
$$= a \times (b - c) \qquad \text{Because } n = b - c$$

Therefore, $a \times (b - c) = a \times b - a \times c$.

▲

This leads to the next important property of whole number multiplication: the **distributive property of multiplication over subtraction.**

Distributive Property of Multiplication over Subtraction

Let a, b, and c be any whole numbers such that $b - c$ is a whole number. Then $a \times (b - c) = a \times b - a \times c$.

We use this property to compute products in the next example.

EXAMPLE 3.13

CONNECTION

REASONING

Use the distributive property of multiplication over subtraction to multiply.
a. 13×9
b. 45×17

SOLUTION

a. $13 \times 9 = 13 \times (10 - 1)$
$\qquad = 13 \times 10 - 13 \times 1$
$\qquad = 130 - 13$
$\qquad = 117$

b. $45 \times 17 = 45 \times (20 - 3)$
$\qquad = 45 \times 20 - 45 \times 3$
$\qquad = 900 - 135$
$\qquad = 765$

▲

Multiplying Whole Numbers by 0 or 1

By definition, $0 \times a = 0$. The expression $a \times 0$ represents the total number of objects when a empty sets are combined, so $a \times 0 = 0$. When joining groups of single objects, the total number of objects is the same as the number of groups, so $3 \times 1 = 3$, $4 \times 1 = 4$, and $5 \times 1 = 5$. Because multiplication is commutative, $1 \times 3 = 3$, $1 \times 4 = 4$, and $1 \times 5 = 5$. These properties can be stated algebraically.

Zero Property of Multiplication of Whole Numbers

Let a be a whole number. Then $a \times 0 = 0 \times a = 0$.

Identity Property of Multiplication of Whole Numbers

Let a be a whole number. Then $a \times 1 = 1 \times a = a$.

Properties and Number Sense

Number sense is a way of thinking about numbers and operations, and it allows students to rely more on properties, patterns, and structure of numbers and less on memorization, as illustrated in the following examples.

- Find $2 \times 3 \times 5$. We could proceed as follows: $2 \times 3 \times 5 = 2 \times (3 \times 5) = 2 \times (5 \times 3) = (2 \times 5) \times 3 = 10 \times 3 = 30$. Here, we recognized that products involving 10 are easy to compute.

- Find 25×28. We could proceed as follows: $25 \times 28 = 25 \times (4 \times 7) = (25 \times 4) \times 7 = 100 \times 7 = 700$. Here, we used the associative law of multiplication and multiplying by powers of 10.

When students use number sense, they are not expected to justify each step.

EXAMPLE 3.14

CONNECTION

REASONING

Use number sense to multiply.

a. 42×3

b. 24×45

c. 15×98

d. 42×103

e. $26 \times 25 \times 24$

SOLUTION

a. $42 \times 3 = (40 + 2) \times 3 = 40 \times 3 + 2 \times 3 = 120 + 6 = 126$

b. $24 \times 45 = 12 \times 2 \times 5 \times 9 = 12 \times 10 \times 9 = 108 \times 10 = 1080$

c. $15 \times 98 = 15 \times (100 - 2) = 1500 - 30 = 1470$

d. $46 \times 103 = 46 \times (100 + 3) = 4600 + 138 = 4738$

e. $26 \times 25 \times 24 = 26 \times 25 \times 4 \times 6 = 26 \times 100 \times 6 = 100 \times 6 \times (20 + 6) = 100 \times (120 + 36) = 100 \times 156 = 15,600$

▲

Repeated Multiplication and Exponential Notation

CONNECTION Some examples of *repeated multiplication* are 5×5, $3 \times 3 \times 3 \times 3$, and $7 \times 7 \times 7 \times 7 \times 7$. Repeated multiplication occurs when all factors are identical. We write products involving identical factors more compactly using **exponential notation.** The examples in Table 3.3 illustrate the connection between repeated multiplication and exponential notation and introduce related terms such as *base* and *exponent*.

TABLE 3.3 Examples of Exponential Notation

Repeated multiplication	Exponential notation	Base	Exponent	Definition
5×5	5^2	5	2	$5^2 = 5 \times 5$
$3 \times 3 \times 3 \times 3$	3^4	3	4	$3^4 = 3 \times 3 \times 3 \times 3$
$10 \times 10 \times 10$	10^3	10	3	$10^3 = 10 \times 10 \times 10$

Table 3.4 shows how to read exponential notation.

TABLE 3.4 Reading Exponential Notation

Exponential notation	How to read exponential notation
17^1	Seventeen
17^2	Seventeen to the second power, or seventeen squared
17^3	Seventeen to the third power, or seventeen cubed
17^4	Seventeen to the fourth power

Now we are ready to define exponents algebraically.

Definition of Exponential Notation for Whole Numbers

Let a and n be whole numbers, with $n \neq 0$. Then a^n, which is read as **a to the nth power,** is defined as

$$\underbrace{a^n = a \times a \times \ldots \times a}_{n \text{ factors}}$$

- a is called the **base,** and n is called the **exponent.**
- We define $a^1 = a$. For $a \neq 0$, we define $a^0 = 1$. The expression 0^0 is undefined.

Many students erroneously think the exponent tells them how many times they multiply rather than how many factors are in the expression. The following example applies the definition of exponential notation.

EXAMPLE 3.15

REPRESENTATION

Rewrite each expression using exponential notation.
a. $4 \cdot 4 \cdot 4 \cdot 4 \cdot 4$
b. $8^4 \cdot 8^3$
c. $(5^4)^3$
d. $(5a)^3$

SOLUTION

a. $4 \cdot 4 \cdot 4 \cdot 4 \cdot 4 = 4^5$
b. $8^4 \times 8^3 = (8 \cdot 8 \cdot 8 \cdot 8)(8 \cdot 8 \cdot 8) = 8 \cdot 8 \cdot 8 \cdot 8 \cdot 8 \cdot 8 \cdot 8 = 8^7$
c. $(5^4)^3 = 5^4 \cdot 5^4 \cdot 5^4$
   $= (5 \cdot 5 \cdot 5 \cdot 5)(5 \cdot 5 \cdot 5 \cdot 5)(5 \cdot 5 \cdot 5 \cdot 5)$
   $= 5 \cdot 5 \cdot 5 \cdot 5 \cdot 5 \cdot 5 \cdot 5 \cdot 5 \cdot 5 \cdot 5 \cdot 5 \cdot 5$
   $= 5^{12}$
d. $(5a)^3 = (5a)(5a)(5a) = (5 \cdot 5 \cdot 5)(a \cdot a \cdot a) = 5^3 a^3$

▲

■ **Historical Note**

Mathematicians experimented with diverse representations for exponential notation. They used $5aaaa$, $5a4$, $5a(4)$, $5(4)\vdots a\vdots$, and $5a^{iv}$, among others, to represent what we write today as $5a^4$. The current exponential notation, promoted by René Descartes in the mid-1600s, became widely accepted by the late 1800s.

We removed the parentheses in the previous example because of the associative property of multiplication.

The following results come from the definition of exponential notation and properties of multiplication.

Multiplication Rules for Exponential Notation

Let a, m, and n be whole numbers, with $m \neq 0$ and $n \neq 0$. Then

- $a^m \times a^n = a^{m+n}$.
- $(a^m)^n = a^{m \times n}$.
- $(a \times b)^m = a^m \times b^m$.

CONNECTION   Exponential notation and its properties are useful in expressing numbers in expanded form, representing numbers in scientific notation, expressing the prime factorization of a number, simplifying formulas and algebraic expressions, and finding the least common multiple and greatest common factor of two or more numbers. Later we discuss division with exponents and fractions with exponents.

Connections between Addition and Multiplication

CONNECTION   Concept Map 3.1 shows various connections between addition and multiplication.

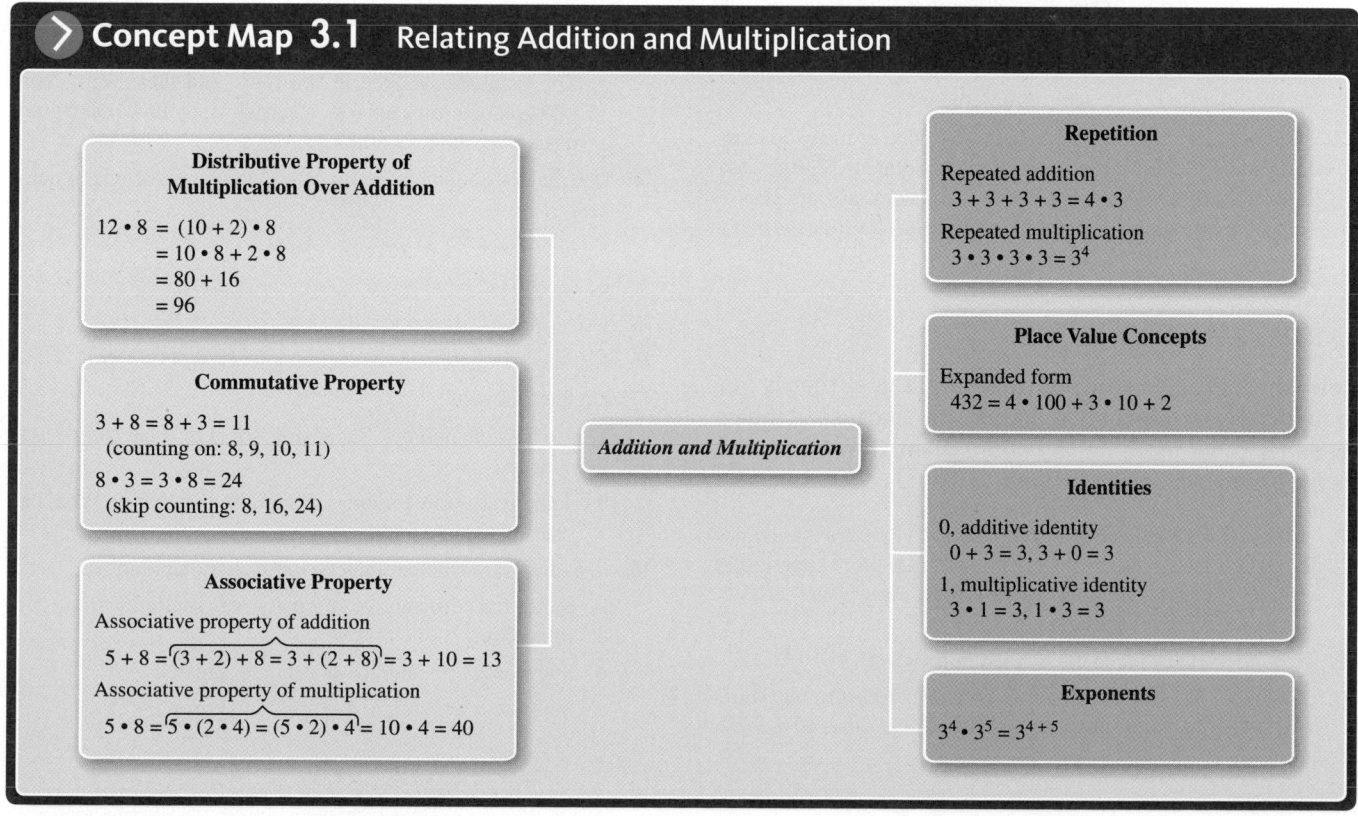

> ### Concept Map **3.1**   Relating Addition and Multiplication

Distributive Property of Multiplication Over Addition

$$12 \cdot 8 = (10 + 2) \cdot 8$$
$$= 10 \cdot 8 + 2 \cdot 8$$
$$= 80 + 16$$
$$= 96$$

Commutative Property

$3 + 8 = 8 + 3 = 11$
   (counting on: 8, 9, 10, 11)
$8 \cdot 3 = 3 \cdot 8 = 24$
   (skip counting: 8, 16, 24)

Associative Property

Associative property of addition
$5 + 8 = (3 + 2) + 8 = 3 + (2 + 8) = 3 + 10 = 13$
Associative property of multiplication
$5 \cdot 8 = 5 \cdot (2 \cdot 4) = (5 \cdot 2) \cdot 4 = 10 \cdot 4 = 40$

Addition and Multiplication

Repetition

Repeated addition
$3 + 3 + 3 + 3 = 4 \cdot 3$
Repeated multiplication
$3 \cdot 3 \cdot 3 \cdot 3 = 3^4$

Place Value Concepts

Expanded form
$432 = 4 \cdot 100 + 3 \cdot 10 + 2$

Identities

0, additive identity
   $0 + 3 = 3, 3 + 0 = 3$
1, multiplicative identity
   $3 \cdot 1 = 3, 1 \cdot 3 = 3$

Exponents

$3^4 \cdot 3^5 = 3^{4+5}$

QUESTIONS FOR SECTION 3.1

REPRESENTATION

Refresher: Representations (language, diagrams, tables, symbols, algebra, manipulatives, and contextualized situations) are important because we use them to organize, record, and communicate mathematical ideas and to make them more comprehensible.

1. Write an expression involving multiplication for the diagram.

   ●●●● ●●●●

2. Use the set model to represent each product.
   a. 5×3 b. 3×5

3. Use the number line model to represent each product.
   a. 5×3 b. 3×5

4. Maria says the following array could represent 5×3. Lenny says the array could represent 3×5.

   ●●●●●
   ●●●●●
   ●●●●●

   a. Explain how Maria could be correct.
   b. Explain how Lenny could be correct.

5. Determine the number of groups and the number of objects in each group in the expression 4×15.

6. A student wants to order a lunch consisting of a sandwich and a drink. There are three types of sandwiches (turkey, pastrami, and ham) and four types of drinks (soda, lemonade, orange juice, and grape juice). Determine the number of different lunches the student can order using a
   a. tree diagram.   b. table of ordered pairs.

7. Lisa and Carol noticed that Martin has twice as many coins as Luis and Kyle has three times as many coins as Martin. Lisa said, "I think Kyle has five times as many coins as Luis." Carol said, "I drew a diagram and it shows Kyle has six times as many coins as Luis." Draw a diagram that shows Carol is correct.

PROBLEM SOLVING

Refresher: Problem solving (reaching a goal that is not immediately attainable) is important because it helps students think more deeply about what they know and deal with unfamiliar situations.

8. A large tire company has 245 employees. There are three times as many mechanics as supervisors and five more supervisors than accountants. How many mechanics, supervisors, and accountants work for the company?

9. How many digits are in the standard form of 456×10^{78}?

10. A shopper has $140 to spend. The shopper wants to buy shirts and hats. Each shirt costs $21, and each hat costs $16. What combination of shirts and hats maximizes the amount of money the shopper can spend?

11. Use the fundamental counting principle to determine how many three-digit numbers consist entirely of odd digits.

12. Because $45^2 = 2025$, the digit sum of 45^2 is $2 + 0 + 2 + 5 = 9$.
    a. Determine the digit sum of 37^2.
    b. Determine the digit sum of 337^2.
    c. Determine the digit sum of 3337^2.
    d. Use patterns to determine the digit sum of 3333337^2.

REASONING AND PROOF

Refresher: Reasoning and proof (thinking and justifying) are important because they help students make sense of mathematics.

13. Specify the appropriate multiplication model, and then write the number sentence for the problem.
    a. A typical driver drives 12,000 miles each year. How many miles does the typical driver drive in 4 years?
    b. A box of cookies has eight packages of cookies. How many packages of cookies are in four boxes of cookies?
    c. A candy vending machine has seven buttons with the letters A through G. It has four buttons with the numbers 1 through 4. To select an item, you need to choose a letter followed by a number. How many different items are there altogether?
    d. Henry ate five times as many strawberries as Tony. Tony ate seven strawberries. How many strawberries did Henry eat?
    e. The graduates walked in two rows, and there were about 200 graduates in each row. Approximately how many graduates were at the ceremony?

14. Use the distributive property of multiplication of whole numbers to prove
    a. $a(b + c + d) = ab + ac + ad$.
    b. $(a + b)(c + d) = ac + ad + bc + bd$.

15. Use $4 \times 6 = 24$ to calculate 12×6.

16. List the two factors in the expression $5(3 + 4)$.

17. Do the following.
    a. b is a whole number. Suppose $4 \times b = 0$. What can you say about b?
    b. a and b are whole numbers. Suppose $a \times b = 0$. What can you say about a and b?

18. a, b, and c are whole numbers, n is a counting number.
    a. State the distributive property of multiplication over subtraction.
    b. Suppose $a \geq b$ and $5 \times a = 5 \times b$. Prove $a = b$.
    c. Suppose $a \geq b$ and $n \times a = n \times b$. Prove $a = b$.

CONNECTIONS

Refresher: Connections (linking and applying mathematical ideas) are important because they deepen student understanding and make mathematics more meaningful, flexible, and useful.

19. When we add a and b, we may call both a and b addends. When we multiply a and b, we may call both a and b factors. When we subtract a from b, we do not define a word that describes both a and b. Explain why.

20. Consider the sequence $2^3 = 8$, $2^2 = 4$, $2^1 = 2$, ... Use patterns to define 2^0.

21. Use skip counting to multiply.

 a. 5×3 **b.** 6×5 **c.** 3×12

22. Show how you can use patterns to define 5^0.

23. 25,000 is a multiple of a power of 10, because $25{,}000 = 25 \times 1000$ and 1000 is a power of 10.

 a. Write 700 as a multiple of a power of 10.

 b. Write 80 as a multiple of a power of 10.

 c. How can you use 7×8 to compute 700×80?

24. In the United States, a Social Security Number (SSN) is a nine-digit number. SSNs are not recycled: when a person with an SSN is deceased, the number is discarded and cannot be reissued. How many nine-digit numbers are there?

25. A lock requires a sequence of five letters of the alphabet. How many possible codes can be created?

COMMUNICATION

Refresher: Communication (written and verbal explanations using representations and proper mathematical vocabulary) is important because it helps students refine and strengthen their understanding.

26. A person asked if $3 + 3 + 3 + 3$ can be represented as 3×4, and one person replied that it would be OK because multiplication is commutative. Do you agree or disagree with that response? Explain.

27. Write a word problem that requires the expression 5×8.

28. $21 \times 481 = 10{,}101$. This product is amazing, because the digits are alternating ones and zeros. Find another amazing product, and then describe the pattern that makes the product amazing in your view.

More practice with the ideas of the section

29. Fill in the blank. Choose one of the following words, phrases, or numbers: *4, 5, addends, additive reasoning, array, associative, closed, common sense, commutative, distributive, estimation, factors, jump rope, multiplicative reasoning, not closed, number sense, open, repeated addition, repeated multiplication,* or *skip counting.*

 a. _____ is the ability to recognize and solve word problems that involve multiplication and division.

 b. $7 + 7 + 7$ is an example of _____.

 c. $7 \times 7 \times 7$ is an example of _____.

 d. In one interpretation of the expression 4×5, we may think of _____ as the number of groups.

 e. In the expression 4×5, both 4 and 5 are called _____.

 f. The example "3, 6, 9, 12, so $4 \times 3 = 12$" illustrates how to use _____ to calculate a product.

 g. A(n) _____ is a rectangular arrangement of objects in which each row or column has the same number of objects.

 h. _____ is a way of thinking about numbers and operations and allows students to rely more on properties, patterns, and structure of numbers and less on memorization.

 i. The equation $5 \times (2 + 4) = 5 \times 2 + 5 \times 4$ illustrates the _____ property.

 j. The compound equation $5 \times 8 = 5 \times (2 \times 4) = (5 \times 2) \times 4 = 10 \times 4 = 40$ applies the _____ property.

 k. The equation $3 \times (4 \times 7) = 3 \times (7 \times 4)$ applies the _____ property.

30. Let $A = \{w, f\}$ and $B = \{0, 1, 2\}$.

 a. Use a tree diagram to determine the number of ways in which you can select an object first from A and then from B. Then write an equation involving multiplication.

 b. Use a table of ordered pairs to determine the number of ways to select an object first from A and then from B. Then write an equation involving multiplication.

31. Although the solution to each of the following problems is the same $(6 \times 12 = 72)$, the situations are different. Determine which of the following multiplication models is more appropriate in each situation: *set model, measurement model, array model, Cartesian model,* or *comparison model.*

 a. A can typically contains 12 ounces of soda. How many ounces are in six cans?

 b. A certain package contains 12 sticks of gum. How many sticks of gum are in six packages?

 c. In a parking lot, there are six rows of cars with 12 cars in each row. How many cars are there in all?

 d. Ernest can lift 12 pounds. Ted can lift six times as much as Ernest. How many pounds can Ted lift?

 e. A small restaurant makes six types of salads and 12 types of soup. Each lunch consists of a soup and a salad. How many different types of lunches can be ordered?

32. Write a word problem for 7×9 that fits the given model.

 a. set model **b.** measurement model **c.** array model

 d. Cartesian product model **e.** comparison model

33. Multiply and express with appropriate units.

 a. 2 days $\times$ 6 miles per day = ___ _____

 b. 10 cars $\times$ 11 pounds per month per car = ___ _____

34. Use properties to simplify the expression. Show all steps.

 a. $7(4 + 8a)$ **b.** $2n \times 7n$

35. Name the property of multiplication that justifies the equation:

 a. $10 \times 11 = 11 \times 10$ **b.** $7 \times 0 = 0$

 c. $8 \times 41 \times 12 = 8 \times 12 \times 41$

   d. $4 \times (10 \times 3) = 4 \times (3 \times 10)$

   e. $5 \times (3 \times 0) = 5 \times 0$ **f.** $15 \times 1 = 15$

   g. $4 \times (11 + 9) = 4 \times 11 + 4 \times 9$

36. Justify the equation $10 \times (11 \times 9) = 11 \times (9 \times 10)$.

37. Fill in the blanks:

   a. $4 \times 17 = 4 \times (10 + \underline{})$

   b. $(7 \times 5) \times 8 = 7 \times (8 \times \underline{})$

   c. $3 \times 9 = 9 \times (2 + \underline{})$

   d. $5 \times 12 = 5 \times \underline{} + 5 \times 3$

   e. $(5 - \underline{}) \times 12 = 2 \times 12$

38. A group of students was organized into six teams with 10 students on each team to play football. Then they played basketball, and there were 5 students on each team. How many basketball teams were there? Use the associative property of multiplication to solve.

39. A national clothing chain must sell 3000 pairs of $35 khakis to cover the cost of replacing a salesperson who quits, including recruiting, training, and lost productivity.

   a. How much revenue is required to cover the cost of a salesperson who quits?

   b. Show how multiplication by a power of 10 and properties of multiplication can help solve the problem.

40. Use properties of multiplication with whole numbers to write each expression as a product. Do not simplify (for example, do not replace 3×5 with 15).

   a. $4 \times 3 + 5 \times 3$ **b.** $3 + w \times 3$

   c. $3 \times a - 3 \times b$ **d.** $(x + y) + (x + y) + (x + y)$

41. Use the distributive property to multiply.

   a. 5×13 **b.** 23×12 **c.** 67×9

42. Use the associative property to multiply.

   a. 4×125 **b.** 15×20 **c.** 30×90 **d.** 5×140

43. In how many different ways can you replace the letters with a digit to make the inequality true?

   a. $2A7B < 2484$ **b.** $6C7D \le 6348$

44. Insert parentheses, $+$, and $\times$ to make the equation true.

   a. $6 \quad 5 \quad 4 \quad 3 \ = 57$ **b.** $6 \quad 1 \quad 5 \quad 3 \ = 38$

45. Write a word problem that requires the equation.

   a. $4 \times n = 32$ **b.** $n \times 4 = 32$

46. Identify the base and the exponent. Then express the number in terms of repeated multiplication.

   a. 5^3 **b.** 23^4 **c.** 2^3 **d.** 3^2

47. Do the following.

   a. Calculate $5^4 \times 5^2$. Compare the result to 5^6.

   b. Calculate $3^3 \times 3^2$. Compare the result to 3^5.

   c. Make a conjecture that generalizes the results of the preceding examples.

48. Anita has five times as many beads as Polly. Polly has three times as many beads as Gretchen. How many beads does Anita have compared to Gretchen?

49. Use inductive reasoning to support the conjecture $(a^m)^n = a^{m \times n}$.

50. A calling card company sells a calling card for $45 for a month of unlimited usage for calls to Germany. Another calling card company charges $4 per month for a service charge and $2 per minute for calls to Germany. Which plan is the better deal?

51. A vendor is selling hot dogs for $3 and sodas for $2. Write an algebraic expression for the total price of h hot dogs and s sodas.

52. Use properties of exponents to verify.

   a. $8^{12} = 2^{36}$ **b.** $(20)^8 = 2^{16} \cdot 5^8$

53. Write a product that encourages students to use the indicated property. Then use the property to calculate the product.

   a. associative property of multiplication

   b. commutative property of multiplication

   c. distribution property of multiplication over addition

54. Justify each equation.

   a. $3h + 5h = 8h$ **b.** $7d - 3d = 4d$

55. Use number sense to multiply 18 and 35.

56. How can you use 4×6 to compute 600×40?

57. How can you use 3×7 to compute 3000×70?

58. Use the fundamental counting principle to determine how many three-digit numbers consist entirely of even digits.

59. Suppose a and b are counting numbers and $a < b$. Prove

   a. $5a < 8a$.   **b.** $5a < 5b$.

60. Discuss the pattern you observe when you multiply 1001 and

   a. a two-digit number of the form aa.

   b. a three-digit number with consecutive digits.

   c. a three-digit number of the form $a0a$.

61. Explain why each set is not closed under multiplication.

   a. $\{5, 6, 7\}$ **b.** $\{0, 2\}$

62. Use inductive reasoning to informally justify that each set is closed under multiplication.

   a. Set of even numbers: $\{0, 2, 4, 6, 8, \ldots\}$

   b. Set of odd numbers: $\{1, 3, 5, 7, 9, \ldots\}$

   c. Set of multiples of 3: $\{0, 3, 6, 9, 12, 15, \ldots\}$

63. $45 \times 67 + 7531$ is a whole number. Some students disagree because the number is not written in standard form. Explain why $45 \times 67 + 7531$ is a whole number. (Hint: The set of whole numbers is closed under multiplication and under addition.)

What Is Division?

Division is the process of separating a collection of objects into equal-sized groups. Division answers two questions: "How many objects per group?" and "How many groups?" In this section, we discuss the two conceptual models of division: the fair share model (or *partitive model*) that answers the question "How many objects per group?" and the repeated subtraction model (or *measurement model*) that answers the question "How many groups?"

"Math Standards & Expectations: Number and Operations" in the NCTM's *Principles and Standards for School Mathematics* supports these goals, stating that students should be able to "understand situations that entail multiplication and division, such as equal groupings of objects and sharing equally" (NCTM, Gr. Pre-K–2) and "understand various meanings of multiplication and division" (NCTM, Gr. 3–5). The CCSS agrees, saying students should be able to "interpret whole-number quotients of whole numbers, e.g., interpret $56 \div 8$ as the number of objects in each share when 56 objects are partitioned equally into 8 shares, or as a number of shares when 56 objects are partitioned into equal shares of 8 objects each" (CCSS, Gr. 3). Division with whole numbers provides students a foundation for other mathematical topics, such as fractions, decimals, and measurement.

Fair Share Model for Division

The **fair share model** for division is appropriate when the total number of objects is known, the number of groups is known, and each group must receive the same number of objects. The fair share model answers the question, "How many objects in each group?"

EXAMPLE 3.16

PROBLEM SOLVING
REPRESENTATION

A teacher wishes to distribute eight cookies among four students so that each student receives a fair share (same number of cookies). How many cookies should each student receive? Write a division sentence.

SOLUTION

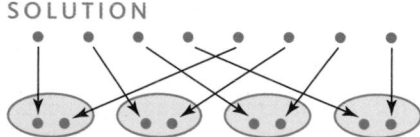

FIGURE 7
Fair share model for $8 \div 4$.

We must separate eight objects into four equal-sized groups. First we draw eight objects and four groups. Then we allocate one object to each group and repeat this step, as modeled in Figure 7. We distribute the objects so that each group receives the same amount. The model shows that each student should receive two cookies. This means eight cookies divided among four students equals two cookies per student. The division sentence is $8 \div 4 = 2$.

▲

Repeated Subtraction Model for Division

The **repeated subtraction model** for division is appropriate when the total number of objects is known, the number of objects in each group is known to be the same, and we want to determine the number of groups that can be formed. The repeated subtraction model answers the question, "How many groups?"

EXAMPLE 3.17

PROBLEM SOLVING
REPRESENTATION

A teacher wants to separate 18 students into teams of 3 students. How many teams can be formed? Write a division sentence.

SOLUTION

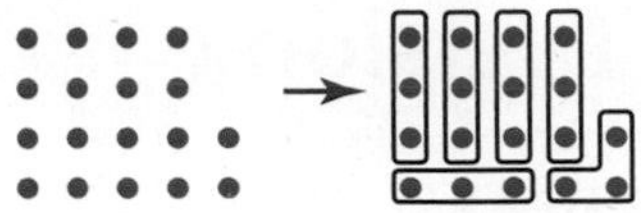

FIGURE 8
Repeated subtraction model for 18 ÷ 3.

The 18 objects must be separated into groups of 3 objects. First we draw 18 objects. Then we circle 3 objects at a time and count the number of groupings, as modeled in Figure 8. The model shows that the teacher can form six groups. This means 18 students divided into groups of 3 students equals six groups. The division sentence is 18 ÷ 3 = 6.   ▲

The repeated subtraction model derives its name from the implicit repeated subtraction involved in the model. For example, 12 ÷ 4 = 3, because three groups of four can be subtracted from 12: 12 − 4 = 8, 8 − 4 = 4, and 4 − 4 = 0.

The following Released Item suggests students should be able to recognize a repeated subtraction division problem.

▶ **RELEASED ITEM**

● NAEP, 1996

Martha planted 32 seeds. She put 8 seeds in each row. How many rows did she plant?

a. 32 + 8   **b.** 32 − 8   **c.** 32 × 8   **d.** 32 ÷ 8

48% of fourth-grade students chose the correct answer.

The following Classroom Connection illustrates that students should be able to solve both types of division problems.

◀◆ **Classroom Connection**

● *Math*, Grade 4, California Edition, p. 282

Florists donate 576 flowers. A youth group puts 3 flowers in each vase. How many vases can they fill? (© 2000 Macmillan/McGraw Hill. Reprinted by permission.)

● *Math*, Grade 4, California Edition, p. 292

A large mosaic kit has 5100 tiles separated equally into 4 bags. How many tiles are in each bag?

Fact Family

CONNECTION   We can write four equations for the array of dots shown in Figure 9: 12 = 4 × 3 and 12 ÷ 4 = 3 (fair share model) for the dotted groupings and 12 = 3 × 4 and 12 ÷ 3 = 4 (fair share model) for the solid groupings. Together, the two multiplication facts and the two division facts form a collection of equations called a fact family, as explained in Chapter 2.

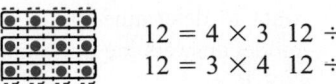

$$12 = 4 \times 3 \quad 12 \div 4 = 3$$
$$12 = 3 \times 4 \quad 12 \div 3 = 4$$

FIGURE 9
The array model motivates the fact family for multiplication and division.

Fact families appear in the elementary mathematics curriculum because they help students relate multiplication and division and help them learn elementary division facts by building on their knowledge of multiplication. For example, to solve $12 \div 3$, a student may either draw a diagram or consider the equation $12 = 3 \times$ ___. The basic multiplication and division facts form the building blocks of multiplication and division algorithms for problems such as 34×58 and $364 \div 26$.

CONNECTION   The next example shows how a fact family can be used to solve an equation.

EXAMPLE 3.18 Solve $58{,}752 \div n = 3456$.

SOLUTION

The fact family for $58{,}752 \div n = 3456$ is shown here.

$58{,}752 \div n = 3456 \quad n \times 3456 = 58{,}752$

$58{,}752 \div 3456 = n \quad 3456 \times n = 58{,}752$

Then $58{,}752 \div 3456 = n$, and with the aid of a calculator, perhaps, we get $n = 17$. ▲

Division by Zero

CONNECTION   Most students (and their parents) have difficulties explaining division by zero. Fact fami-
REASONING   lies can help explain why division by zero is not allowed. Let's consider the prototype division problems $7 \div 0$ and $0 \div 0$.

First, let's consider the fact family for $7 \div 0 = n$. The variable n must be a whole number that makes each equation in the fact family true. The fact family for $7 \div 0 = n$ is $7 = 0 \times n$, $7 \div 0 = n$, $7 = n \times 0$, and $7 \div n = 0$.

The left-hand side of the equation $7 = 0 \times n$ is 7, and the right-hand side is 0 (by the zero property of multiplication). So there is no solution to the equation $7 = 0 \times n$. As a result, we say $7 \div 0$ is **undefined.**

Second, let's momentarily pretend $0 \div 0$ equals n for some whole number n. The fact family for $0 \div 0 = n$ is $0 = 0 \times n$, $0 \div 0 = n$, $0 = n \times 0$, and $0 \div n = 0$. The equation $0 = 0 \times n$ has infinitely many solutions, for example, $0 = 0 \times 5$ and $0 = 0 \times 2$. Then $0 \div 0 = 2$ and $0 \div 0 = 5$; therefore, $5 = 2$, which is a silly conclusion. As a result, we say $0 \div 0$ is **indeterminate.**

Definition of Division with Whole Numbers

The equation $12 \div 3 = 4$ is read as "12 divided by 3 equals 4." The equation $12 \div 3 = 4$ can be interpreted as "12 objects divided into three groups equals 4 objects per group" by the fair share model of division, which implies $12 = 3 \times 4$. The equation can also be interpreted as "12 objects divided into groups of 3 objects equals four groups" by the repeated subtraction model, which implies $12 = 4 \times 3$. This suggests the following definition of division.

> ### Definition of Division with Whole Numbers
>
> Let a and b represent any whole numbers such that $b \neq 0$. Then $a \div b = c$ if and only if $a = b \times c$ for some unique whole number c.
>
> - $a \div b$ is read as "a divided by b."
> - The number a is called the **dividend,** and the number b is called the **divisor.**
> - The number c is called the **quotient, missing factor,** or **unknown factor.**
> - $a \div b = c$ if and only if $a = c \times b$ by the commutative property of multiplication.

The statements "a is divisible by b" and "b divides a evenly" are ways of saying, "There is a whole number c such that $a \div b = c$." The definition of division helps students "understand division as an unknown-factor problem" (CCSS, Gr. 3). For example, $45 \div 9$ is the number n such that $45 = 9 \times n$. Then a student familiar with multiplication facts concludes $n = 5$. Also, $n \div 4 = 12$ can be written as $n = 4 \times 12$, and $3q = 45$ can be written as $q = 45 \div 3$. The following example illustrates how to use the definition to learn basic division facts or solve equations.

EXAMPLE 3.19

CONNECTION

Apply the definition of division with whole numbers to do the following.
a. Divide: $24 \div 3$.
b. Solve for n in the equation $13 \times n = 195$.

SOLUTION

a. $24 \div 3 = c$ if and only if $24 = 3 \times c$. We know $24 = 3 \times 8$ (math fact), so $c = 8$. Therefore, $24 \div 3 = 8$.

b. $13 \times n = 195$ if and only if $n = 195 \div 13$. Using a calculator, we get $n = 15$.

▲

The definition also provides a way to solve a problem that requires determining a missing factor.

EXAMPLE 3.20

CONNECTION

Anna made some bracelets. She used 12 beads for each bracelet. She used 72 beads in all. How many bracelets did she make?

SOLUTION

This problem requires the solution to $n \times 12 = 72$. By the definition of division, $n = 72 \div 12$. So $n = 6$. Anna made six bracelets.

▲

 Historical Note

Johann Rahn (1622–1676) used the $\div$ sign to symbolize division in the 1659 publication *Teutsche Algebra* (translated *Teutonic Algebra*). Before the symbol was standardized, mathematicians often used their own symbols, such as the minus sign ($-$), the colon (:), or the fraction bar (—) to symbolize division. Eventually, mathematicians widely adopted the $\div$ sign to symbolize division.

Multiplication and Division Are Inverse Operations

Students should be able to "understand and use the inverse relationships of multiplication and division to simplify computations and solve problems" (NCTM, Gr. 6–8). The following example proves that multiplication and division with whole numbers are inverse operations.

EXAMPLE 3.21

CONNECTION

REASONING

REPRESENTATION

Let a and b represent whole numbers, with $b \neq 0$.
a. Prove $a \times b \div b = a$.   **Think: Division undoes multiplication.**
b. Prove $a \times b \div a = b$.   **Think: Division undoes multiplication**
c. Suppose $a \div b$ is the whole number c.
   Prove $a \div b \times b = a$.   **Think: Multiplication undoes division.**

SOLUTION

a. The equation $a \times b = a \times b$ is true. We can view the left-hand side of the equation ($a \times b$) as a single whole number by the closure property of multiplication and the right-hand side of the equation ($a \times b$) as the product of two whole numbers a and b. By the definition of division, $a \times b \div b = a$.

b. The equation $a \times b = a \times b$ is true. Then $a \times b = b \times a$ by the commutative property of multiplication. We can view the left-hand side of the equation $(a \times b)$ as a single whole number by the closure property of multiplication and the right-hand side of the equation $(b \times a)$ as the product of two whole numbers a and b. By the definition of division, $a \times b \div a = b$.

c. The equation $a \div b = a \div b$ is true. We know $a \div b$ is the whole number c, so $c = a \div b$. By the definition of division, $a = c \times b$. Now we replace c with $a \div b$ to get $a = a \div b \times b$. Then $a \div b \times b = a$.

▲

Although this example may seem abstract, it proves what we commonly believe: Multiplication and division with whole numbers are inverse operations. The next example shows how you can apply these results.

EXAMPLE 3.22

CONNECTION

REASONING

REPRESENTATION

Multiplication and division are inverse operations. Use this fact to solve each equation.
a. $n \times 8 = 32$
b. $k \div 6 = 42$

SOLUTION

a.

$n \times 8 = 32$	**Original equation**
$n \times 8 \div 8 = 32 \div 8$	**Division property of equality**
$n = 32 \div 8$	**Because multiplication and division are inverse operations**
$n = 4$	**Simplification**

b.

$k \div 6 = 42$	**Original equation**
$k \div 6 \times 6 = 42 \times 6$	**Multiplication property of equality**
$k = 42 \times 6$	**Because multiplication and division are inverse operations**
$k = 252$	**Simplification**

▲

The following portion of a student page shows students how to solve the equation $y \div 5 = 35$ using properties of equality and inverse operations.

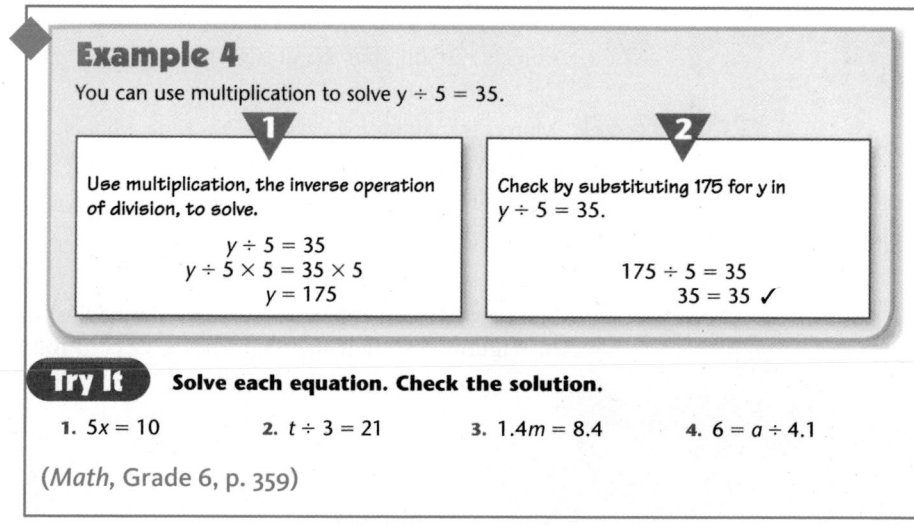

Example 4

You can use multiplication to solve $y \div 5 = 35$.

1

Use multiplication, the inverse operation of division, to solve.

$$y \div 5 = 35$$
$$y \div 5 \times 5 = 35 \times 5$$
$$y = 175$$

2

Check by substituting 175 for y in $y \div 5 = 35$.

$$175 \div 5 = 35$$
$$35 = 35 \checkmark$$

Try It **Solve each equation. Check the solution.**

1. $5x = 10$ **2.** $t \div 3 = 21$ **3.** $1.4m = 8.4$ **4.** $6 = a \div 4.1$

(*Math*, Grade 6, p. 359)

(© 2000 Macmillan/McGraw Hill. Reprinted by permission.)

Connections among the Four Operations

A hallmark of understanding of addition, subtraction, multiplication, and division is being able to explain how these operations are related. The connections among operations give students an early chance to see that mathematics is a collection of related ideas, rather than isolated facts. Concept Map 3.2 shows the connectedness of the operations.

> **Concept Map 3.2**   Relatedness of Whole Number Operations

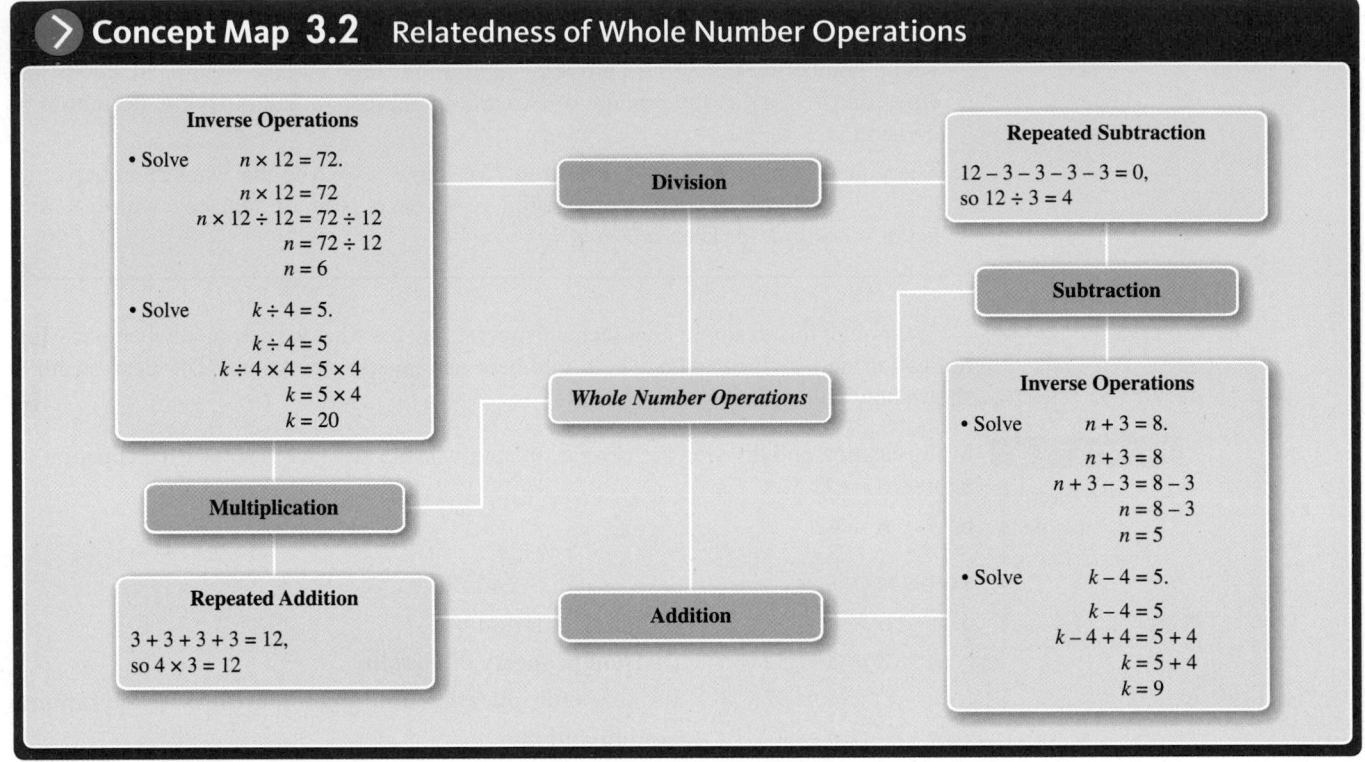

Inverse Operations

- Solve $n \times 12 = 72$.

$$n \times 12 = 72$$
$$n \times 12 \div 12 = 72 \div 12$$
$$n = 72 \div 12$$
$$n = 6$$

- Solve $k \div 4 = 5$.

$$k \div 4 = 5$$
$$k \div 4 \times 4 = 5 \times 4$$
$$k = 5 \times 4$$
$$k = 20$$

Multiplication

Repeated Addition

$$3 + 3 + 3 + 3 = 12,$$
so $4 \times 3 = 12$

Division

Whole Number Operations

Addition

Repeated Subtraction

$$12 - 3 - 3 - 3 - 3 = 0,$$
so $12 \div 3 = 4$

Subtraction

Inverse Operations

- Solve $n + 3 = 8$.

$$n + 3 = 8$$
$$n + 3 - 3 = 8 - 3$$
$$n = 8 - 3$$
$$n = 5$$

- Solve $k - 4 = 5$.

$$k - 4 = 5$$
$$k - 4 + 4 = 5 + 4$$
$$k = 5 + 4$$
$$k = 9$$

Quotient–Remainder Theorem

In the division problems we've considered so far, there were no objects remaining after the groupings. However, the set of whole numbers is not closed under division. For example, $7 \div 3$ is not a whole number. The following problem illustrates division still applies when objects remain after the groupings.

EXAMPLE 3.23

COMMUNICATION

PROBLEM SOLVING

REPRESENTATION

Marco is making toy cars. He has nine wheels. Each toy car requires four wheels.

a. How many toy cars can he make?

b. How many wheels are left over?

SOLUTION

This involves the repeated subtraction model of division.

a. Figure 10 models the nine wheels. Sets of four wheels are grouped.

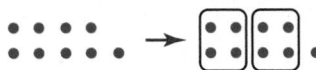

FIGURE 10

Each dot represents a wheel. Each group of four wheels represents a car.

Each group represents one toy car. Marco can make two toy cars.

b. One wheel is left over.

The example shows 9 divided by 4 equals 2 with a remainder of 1; that is, $9 \div 4 = 2 \, R1$.

Now we state the quotient–remainder theorem about the relationship among the dividend, divisor, quotient, and remainder for whole numbers.

Quotient–Remainder Theorem

Let a and b represent any whole numbers such that $b \neq 0$. There exist unique whole numbers q and r such that $a = b \times q + r$, where $0 \leq r < b$.

- a is the dividend, and b is the divisor.
- q is the quotient, and r is called the **remainder.**
- $a \div b = q \, Rr$, which is read as "a divided by b equals q with a remainder of r," is another way to express $a = b \times q + r$.
- If $r = 0$, then we typically write $a \div b = q$ (rather than $a \div b = q \, R0$).

REASONING
COMMUNICATION

Students should be able to "solve multistep word problems posed with whole numbers and having whole-number answers using the four operations, including problems in which remainders must be interpreted" (CCSS, Gr. 4). For example, consider the following classic problem: "Suppose 32 students are going on a field trip in minivans that can hold 5 students each. How many minivans are needed?" Because $32 \div 5 = 6 \, R2$, some students mistakenly believe the number of minivans is "6 R2." What is the correct interpretation of the remainder?

▶ RELEASED ITEM

● NAEP, GRADE 4, 2007

Five classes are going on a bus trip and each class has 21 students. If each bus holds only 40 students, how many buses are needed for the trip?

Answer: _____

36% of 4th graders answered the question correctly.

Three Applications of the Quotient–Remainder Theorem

This theorem serves three main purposes:

1. We can express whole number division problems with zero or nonzero remainders, such as $20 \div 5 = 4$ and $17 \div 3 = 5 \, R2$.

2. We can "check our work." For example, let's verify the equation $27 \div 4 = 6 \, R3$ using the quotient–remainder theorem: $4 \times 6 + 3 = 24 + 3 = 27$, so $27 \div 4 = 6 \, R3$.

3. We can use the theorem to compare two quantities. For example, Mary has 14 apples and John has 3 apples. We know $14 \div 3 = 4 \, R2$. Then we can say, "Mary has two more than four times as many apples as John."

The following example illustrates how we can check our work using the quotient–remainder theorem.

EXAMPLE 3.24   Find the quotient and the remainder: $28 \div 8$. Check your work.

CONNECTION

SOLUTION

A division model yields $28 \div 8 = 3 \, R4$. Let's check our work: $8 \times 3 + 4 = 24 + 4 = 28$. So the quotient is 3 and the remainder is 4.

▲

The following example demonstrates how we can use a calculator to find the quotient and the remainder.

EXAMPLE 3.25   Use a calculator to find the quotient and the remainder of $29 \div 6$. Check your work.

CONNECTION

SOLUTION

Three steps can be followed:

Step 1. $29 \div 6 = 4.83$ (rounded), which means the quotient is $q = 4$.

Step 2. The remainder is $r = a - b \times q = 29 - 6 \times 4 = 29 - 24 = 5$.

Step 3. $29 \div 6 = 4$ R5.

Check your work: $6 \times 4 + 5 = 24 + 5 = 29$. So the quotient is $q = 4$ and the remainder is $r = 5$.

▲

The following problem illustrates how you can use division to compare two quantities.

EXAMPLE 3.26   The library at Park Elementary School has 45 books about lizards and 231 books about kittens. Compare the number of books on kittens and lizards using multiplicative reasoning.

CONNECTION

REASONING

SOLUTION

$231 \div 45 = 5$ R6, so $231 = 5 \times 45 + 6$. There are six more than five times as many books about kittens than there are about lizards.

▲

EXAMPLE 3.27 $133 \div 6 = 22$ R1. Use this to solve $142 \div 6$.

CONNECTION

COMMUNICATION

PROBLEM SOLVING

REASONING

SOLUTION

$133 \div 6 = 22$ R1 means there are 22 groups of 6 objects, and one object is ungrouped. We added 9 more objects to the mix ($142 - 133 = 9$). Then we have 10 ungrouped objects. We can make one more group of 6 with 4 ungrouped objects. This creates 23 groups of 6 with 4 ungrouped objects. So $142 \div 6 = 23$ R4.

▲

■ **Historical Note**

The oldest known remainder problem appeared in Chinese literature in the first century. The problem is as follows: There are certain things whose number is unknown. When divided by 3, the remainder is 2; when divided by 5, the remainder is 3; when divided by 7, the remainder is 2. What will be the number of things? (Burton, 1995, p. 234)

CONNECTION

Concept Map 3.3 relates division and addition with whole numbers.

> **Concept Map 3.3**   Relating Division and Addition

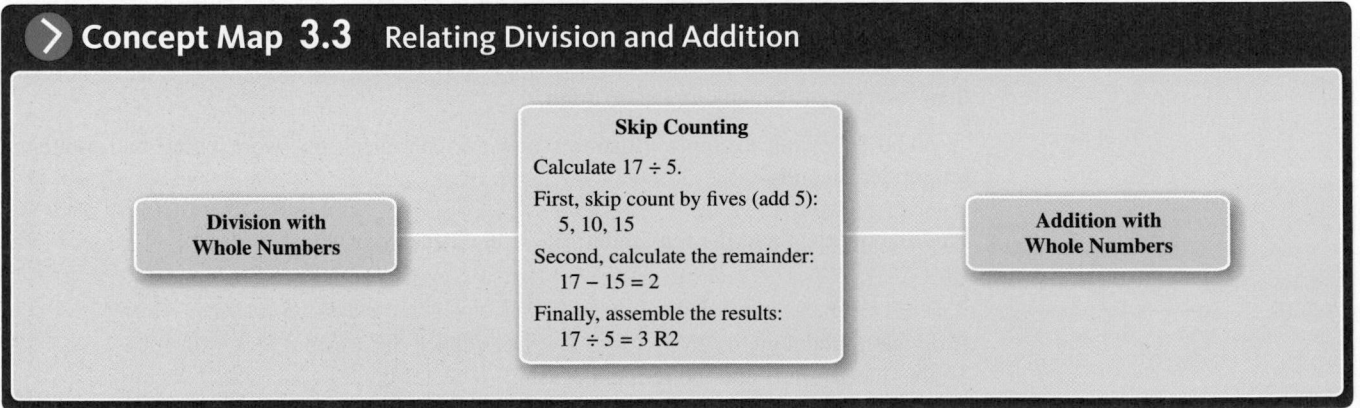

Skip Counting

Calculate $17 \div 5$.

First, skip count by fives (add 5):
5, 10, 15

Second, calculate the remainder:
$17 - 15 = 2$

Finally, assemble the results:
$17 \div 5 = 3$ R2

Division with Whole Numbers

Addition with Whole Numbers

Reducing the Need for Parentheses: Order of Operations

Mathematical expressions contain numbers, arithmetic operators, and possibly letters or variables that represent numbers, such as $3 + 5$, $(3 \times 2) + 1$, $7 + 4y$, and $2^3 + 4 - a$. The expression $6 + 8 \div 2$ is ambiguous because it contains more than one operator; therefore, it could potentially be interpreted as $6 + 8 \div 2 = 6 + (8 \div 2) = 6 + 4 = 10$ or $6 + 8 \div 2 = (6 + 8) \div 2 = 14 \div 2 = 7$. When an expression contains more than one operator, we may use parentheses to indicate the order of operations so that the expression results in only one possible number, as long as it is understood that operators in parentheses must be performed first. For example, $(3 \times 4) + 5 = 12 + 5 = 17$ and $3 \times (4 + 5) = 3 \times 9 = 27$.

To reduce the use of parentheses and make expressions easier to read, we follow a prescribed agreement on the order of operations. Because $3^2 + 4 = 3 \times 3 + 4 = 3 + 3 + 3 + 4$, it makes sense to apply exponential notation before multiplication and multiplication before addition. The following are agreements or rules for the order of operations.

1. Perform the operations in the grouping symbols, such as parentheses ( ) or brackets [ ]. If there are several sets of grouping symbols, then perform the operation in the innermost grouping symbol first. For example,

   - $[(5 + 2) + 2] \times 3 = [7 + 2] \times 3 = 9 \times 3 = 27$.
   - $[(13 + 2) - (4 + 1)] + 2 = [15 - 5] + 2 = 10 + 2 = 12$.

2. Evaluate the numbers with exponents. For example,

   - $2^3 + 4 = 8 + 4 = 12$.
   - $1 + (24 \div 2^3)^2 = 1 + (24 \div 8)^2 = 1 + 3^2 = 1 + 9 = 10$.

3. Multiply or divide, whichever operation comes first from left to right. For example,

   - $30 \div 2 \div 5 = 15 \div 5 = 3$.
   - $(8 + 2) \times 3 \div 15 = 10 \times 3 \div 15 = 30 \div 15 = 2$.

4. Add or subtract, whichever operation comes first from left to right. For example,

   - $3 \times 5 - 3^2 + 10 - 5 = 15 - 9 + 10 - 5 = 6 + 10 - 5 = 16 - 5 = 11$.
   - $5^2 + 4 - (6 \div 3) = 25 + 4 - 2 = 29 - 2 = 27$.

EXAMPLE 3.28   Find the value of each expression:
a. $4 \times 2^3 - (27 \div 3)$
b. $5 \times (10 - 4) \div 3 + 1$
c. $(3 - 1) + 13] \times 2 \div 10$

SOLUTION

a. $\begin{aligned} 4 \times 2^3 - (27 \div 3) &= 4 \times 2^3 - 9 \\ &= 4 \times 8 - 9 \\ &= 32 - 9 \\ &= 23 \end{aligned}$

b. $\begin{aligned} 5 \times (10 - 4) \div 3 + 1 &= 5 \times 6 \div 3 + 1 \\ &= 20 \div 3 + 1 \\ &= 10 + 1 \\ &= 11 \end{aligned}$

c. $\begin{aligned} [(3 - 1) + 13] \times 2 \div 10 &= [2 + 13] \times 2 \div 10 \\ &= 15 \times 2 \div 10 \\ &= 30 \div 10 \\ &= 3 \end{aligned}$

Students should be able to "perform arithmetic operations, including those involving whole number exponents, in the conventional order when there are no parentheses to specify a particular order (Order of Operations)" (CCSS, Gr. 6). We caution that even with the preceding prescribed agreements, students often forget the order of operations. For example, in one published study, eighth graders in a prealgebra class were asked to calculate $14 + 6(3)$. Approximately half of the students correctly answered 32, while the other half incorrectly answered 60. These results are similar to the following Released Item.

▶ RELEASED ITEM

● NAEP, 2004

Complete the equation: $3 + 15 \div 3 - 4 \times 2 =$ ___.

a. -9 **b.** -2 **c.** 0 **d.** 4 **e.** 5

52% of the eighth-grade students answered the question correctly.

■ Historical Note

The Electronic Numerical Integrator Analyzer and Computer (ENIAC), built in 1946, was the first large-scale reprogrammable digital computer. It weighed 30 tons and required 1500 square feet of floor space. In 1 second, the ENIAC could perform 5000 additions, 357 multiplications, or 38 divisions. Today, desktop computers can perform millions of operations per second, while supercomputers can perform trillions of operations per second.

Division and Exponential Notation

Theorem 1 shows how to solve division problems such as $2^7 \div 2^3$ or $a^8 \div a^3$.

Theorem 1

Let a, m, and n represent any whole numbers such that $m \geq n$ and $a \neq 0$. Then $a^m \div a^n = a^{m-n}$.

Let a, m, and n represent any whole numbers such that $m \geq n$ and $a \neq 0$:

$$a^m = a^{n + (m - n)}$$ **Because $m = n + (m - n)$**
$$= a^n \times a^{m-n}$$ **Because $a^{b+c} = a^b \times a^c$**

Then

$$a^m \div a^n = a^{m-n}$$ **Because of the definition of division: $a = b \times c$ if and only if $a \div b = c$.**

When we discuss fractions in Chapter 5, we apply the rule $a^m \div a^n = a^{m-n}$ without requiring $m \geq n$.

EXAMPLE 3.29

CONNECTION

Divide.

a. $7^6 \div 7^4$

b. $x^7 \div x^4$

SOLUTION

a. $7^6 \div 7^4 = 7^{6-4}$
$= 7^2$
$= 49$

b. $x^7 \div x^4 = x^{7-4}$
$= x^3$

▲

Students should be able to "use whole-number exponents to denote powers of 10" (CCSS, Gr. 5) and "write and evaluate numerical expressions involving whole-number exponents" (CCSS, Gr. 6).

Solve Classic Problems Using a Diagram

The following two examples illustrate the Draw a Diagram strategy to solve problems involving multiplicative reasoning without using algebra explicitly.

EXAMPLE 3.30

CONNECTION
COMMUNICATION
PROBLEM SOLVING
REASONING
REPRESENTATION

Marco has 146 coins. He has five more than three times as many coins as Tina. How many coins does Tina have?

SOLUTION

We will draw a diagram to represent the relationships. We need to determine the number of coins Tina has. The rectangle in Figure 11(a) represents the number of coins Tina has.

FIGURE 11(a)

In Figure 11(b) we represent the number of coins Marco has: 146 coins, which is five more than three times as many coins as Tina.

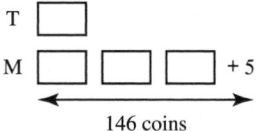

FIGURE 11(b)

The three rectangles corresponding to Marco must represent 141 coins, since 141 + 5 = 146. Then we obtain the results in Figure 11(c).

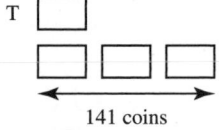

FIGURE 11(c)

Now we divide 141 coins into three equal-sized groups: 141 ÷ 3 = 47. Each rectangle represents 47 coins. Therefore, Tina has 47 coins.

Let's look back: Marco has 141 coins, which is five more than three times as many coins as Tina.

$3 \times 47 + 5 = 141 + 5 = 146$, which is what we expected.

▲

EXAMPLE 3.31

CONNECTION
COMMUNICATION
PROBLEM SOLVING
REASONING
REPRESENTATION

Pam surveyed 489 people who like either Brand A or Brand B. Three fewer than five times as many people preferred Brand A compared to Brand B. How many people in the survey preferred Brand A?

SOLUTION

We will draw a diagram to represent the relationships. The rectangle in Figure 12(a) represents the number of people who preferred Brand B.

B ☐

FIGURE 12(a)

In Figure 12(b) we represent the number of people who preferred Brand A: three fewer than five times as many people who preferred Brand B. We also represent the 489 people in the survey.

FIGURE 12(b)

The six rectangles represent 492 people, since 492 − 3 = 489. Then we obtain the results in Figure 12(c).

FIGURE 12(c)

Now we divide 492 people into six equal-sized groups: 492 ÷ 6 = 82. Each rectangle represents 82 people, so 82 people preferred Brand B. Therefore, the number of people who preferred Brand A is 5 × 82 − 3 = 407.

Let's look back: Pam surveyed 489 people, and 82 + 407 = 489, which is what we expected.

QUESTIONS FOR SECTION 3.2

REPRESENTATION

Refresher: Representations (language, diagrams, tables, symbols, algebra, manipulatives, and contextualized situations) are important because we use them to organize, record, and communicate mathematical ideas and to make them more comprehensible.

1. Use the diagram shown to write a division sentence (equation) that answers the question, "How many groups?"

   a.

   b.

2. Use the diagram shown to write a division sentence (equation) that answers the question, "How many objects in each group?"

   a.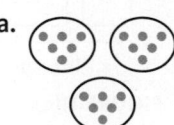

   b.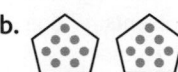

   c.

3. Draw a diagram for the equation $14 \div 4 = 3$ R2 that corresponds to the
   a. fair share model.   b. repeated subtraction model.

PROBLEM SOLVING

Refresher: Problem solving (reaching a goal that is not immediately attainable) is important because it helps students think more deeply about what they know and deal with unfamiliar situations.

4. Matthew and Courtney have 60 coins altogether. Courtney has three times as many coins as Matthew. How many coins do they each have? Use a diagram to solve this question.

5. Matthew and Courtney have 77 coins altogether. Courtney has 5 more than three times as many coins as Matthew. How many coins do they each have? Use a diagram to solve this question.

6. Matthew and Courtney have 116 coins altogether. Courtney has 4 fewer than twice as many coins as Matthew. How many more coins does Courtney have than Matthew? Use a diagram to solve this question.

7. Tyson has 20 coins. He has four times as many coins as Marco. How many coins does Marco have? Solve this problem using
   a. a diagram.   b. algebra.

8. When n is divided by 3 and 4, the remainder is 2.
   a. What is the smallest possible value of n?
   b. What is the second-smallest possible value of n?
   c. What is the 58th-smallest possible value of n?

REASONING AND PROOF

Refresher: Reasoning and proof (thinking and justifying) are important because they help students make sense of mathematics.

9. The average blue whale weighs about 122 tons. A fully loaded Hummer Wagon weighs about 8 tons. Compare the two weights. Show your work.
   a. Use additive reasoning.   b. Use multiplicative reasoning.

10. Solve each problem, and explain your reasoning.
    a. Use the equation $50 = 6 \times 8 + 2$ to find $50 \div 6$.
    b. Use the equation $b = 12 \times y + 5$ to find $b \div 4$.

11. Multiplication and division are inverse operations. Use this to solve each equation.
    a. $k \div 8 = 72$ b. $15 \times n = 105$

12. Use the equation $y = 3q + 2$ to find
    a. $(y + 1) \div 3$.   b. $(y + 2) \div 3$.   c. $(2y - 3) \div 3$.

CONNECTIONS

Refresher: Connections (linking and applying mathematical ideas) are important because they deepen student understanding and make mathematics more meaningful, flexible, and useful.

13. For the diagram shown, write an equation based on the

    a. set model for multiplication.
    b. repeated subtraction model.   c. fair share model.

14. Look for a pattern in the following sequence of letters: A B C D E F A B C D E F A B C D E F . . . . What is the 578th letter in this sequence?

15. A student writes the equation $23 \div 3 = 7$ R2. Check the answer.

16. Write the fact family for each equation. Circle the equation that helps you solve for the variable.
    a. $7 \times b = 21$ b. $72 \div n = 4$

17. Write a word problem that requires the calculation $16 \div 3 = 5$ R1. Pose the question in the problem in such a way that the answer to the problem is
    a. 1.   b. 2.   c. 5.

COMMUNICATION

Refresher: Communication (written and verbal explanations using representations and proper mathematical vocabulary) is important because it helps students refine and strengthen their understanding.

18. What is the relationship between the divisor and the remainder?

19. A fifth-grade student did not know how to solve $n \div 12 = 5$. What advice would you give?

20. $3 \times n = 12$, and $d \times 543 = 225{,}345$.
    a. Which equation can be solved using a multiplication fact?
    b. How would the student solve the other equation?

21. List three uses of the quotient–remainder theorem, and give an example of each.

22. What is the obvious error in the equation?
    a. $23 \div 5 = 3$ R8   b. $36 \div 8 = 72$ R3

23. A presidential candidate in a controversial election was poisoned with dioxin. Tests revealed the level of dioxin in the presidential candidate was 100,000 units per gram of blood fat. The normal range is 15 to 45 units per gram of blood fat. Compare the level of dioxin in the candidate to the normal range. Would it be more appropriate to make an additive or multiplicative comparison? Summarize your comparison in a phrase that might appear in a headline.

More practice with the ideas of the section

24. Fill in the blank. Choose one of the following words or phrases: *additive reasoning, additive raisins, dandy, dividend, division, divisor, fair share, inverse operations, missing factor, missing variable, multiplicative reasoning, quotient, remainder, reindeer, reminder, repeated addition,* or *repeated subtraction.*

    a. _____ is the ability to recognize and solve word problems that involve multiplication and division.

    b. The _____ model answers the question, "How many groups?"

    c. The _____ model answers the question, "How many objects per group?"

    d. The letter n in the equations $4 \times n = 20$ and $n \times 3 = 12$ is called the _____.

    e. In the equation $q \div a = r$ Rw, the number r is called the _____.

    f. _____ involves separating a collection of objects into equal-sized groups.

25. Identify the dividend, divisor, quotient, and remainder in each equation.

    a. $214 \div 12 = 17$ R10 b. $322 \div 14 = 23$

26. Draw a diagram using the fair share model for each division problem. Then write an equation.

    a. $9 \div 4$ b. $14 \div 3$ c. $3 \div 5$

27. Draw a diagram using the repeated subtraction model for each division problem. Then write an equation.

    a. $9 \div 4$ b. $14 \div 3$ c. $3 \div 5$

28. Use repeated subtraction to divide (for example, to find $12 \div 3$, $12 - 3 = 9$, $9 - 3 = 6$, $6 - 3 = 3$, and $3 - 3 = 0$, so $12 \div 3 = 4$).

    a. $24 \div 8$ b. $15 \div 3$ c. $20 \div 4$

29. Use the definition of division with whole numbers to solve the division problem.

    a. $n \div 3 = 5$ b. $n \times 5 = 30$ c. $24 \div n = 8$

30. Write a word problem that requires the calculation $38 \div 5 = 7$ R3. Pose the question in the problem in such a way that the answer to the problem is

    a. 7.   b. 8.   c. 3.   d. 2.

31. Identify all possible values for the remainder r.

    a. $n \div 7 = 3$ Rr b. $a \div 9 = q$ Rr c. $18 \div b = 3$ Rr

32. Use the diagram shown to write a division sentence (equation) for the given model of division.

    a. fair share   b. repeated subtraction

33. Use algebra to solve.

    a. Marcos has 41 marbles. He has 2 more than three times as many marbles as Tony. How many marbles does Tony have?

    b. Jenny has 81 beads. She has 4 fewer than five times as many beads as Amy. How many beads does Amy have?

34. Use a diagram to solve.

    a. Ryan has 453 trading cards, which is 6 more than three times as many cards as Peter. How many trading cards does Peter have?

    b. Amanda read 263 pages this week, which is 5 fewer than four times as many pages as she read last week. How many pages did she read last week?

35. Use a diagram to solve.

    a. Elijah and Michael have 160 coins altogether. Elijah has four times as many coins as Michael. How many coins does each boy have?

    b. Elijah and Michael have 340 coins altogether. Elijah has 4 more than seven times as many coins as Michael. How many coins does each boy have?

    c. Elijah and Michael have 110 coins altogether. Elijah has 5 fewer than four times as many coins as Michael. How many coins does each boy have?

36. Write an equation in the form $a \div b = q$ Rr for each diagram.

    a.

    b.

37. Apply the order of operations to evaluate each expression.

    a. $40 \div 4 \times 2$ b. $40 - 4 \times 2$
    c. $8^2 + (12 - 4) \times 3$ d. $100 - (48 \div 2^3)$

38. Verify the division facts.

    a. $17 \div 2 = 8$ R1 b. $12 \div 7 = 1$ R5 c. $15 \div 3 = 5$

39. Write a fact family.

    a. $28 \div 7 = 4$ b. 4, 5, and 20   c. $a \times 6 = 150$

40. Solve each equation, writing the answer in exponential form.

    a. $23^8 \div 23^3 = a$ b. $425^{19} \div b = 425^4$
    c. $c \div 72^{43} = 72^{25}$

41. Write a word problem that requires the computation $48 \div 6$.

42. Evaluate each expression.

    a. $3 \times (10 - 6) \div 6$ b. $3 \times 10 - 6 \div 2$ c. $24 \div 6 \div 2$
    d. $4 + 3 \times 4 - 15$ e. $[(5 - 1) + 16] \times 2 \div 10 + 3$

43. Is there a whole number a such that $10{,}101 \times a = 1{,}010{,}101$?

44. Look for a pattern in the following sequence of letters: A B C D E A B C D E A B C D E .... What is the 218th letter in this sequence?

45. A bicycle repairman wants to make some tricycles. He has 23 wheels and needs to use 3 wheels for each tricycle. He wants to make as many tricycles as possible. How many wheels are left over?

46. A rocket blasted into space carrying a single experiment to measure the effect of gravity on time and space. The total cost was $700 million, which was five times the original cost estimate. The project took 40 years to complete because it took so much time for emerging technologies to build the necessary scientific instruments. What was the original estimate of the total cost?

47. Fill in the missing numbers.

    a. ___ $\times 12 + 6 = 102$ b. $12 \times$ ___ $+ 5 = 185$
    c. $43 \times 56 +$ ___ $= 2415$

48. Mrs. Emme has some candy. She wants to split it evenly among the students in her class who correctly solve a math problem. If five students solve the problem correctly, then there will be three extra pieces of candy. If seven students solve the problem correctly, then there will be four extra pieces of candy. What is the minimum number of pieces of candy Mrs. Emme can have?

49. According to data from the National Aeronautics and Space Administration, Earth is approximately 149,597,890 km from the Sun, while Saturn is approximately 1,426,725,400 km from the Sun.

    a. Compare these distances using additive reasoning.

    b. Compare these distances using multiplicative reasoning.

    c. Which type of reasoning is more appropriate?

50. According to a fitness calculator, an 85-pound student burns 48 calories per hour watching television but burns 288 calories per hour moving boxes. Compare the number of calories burned by these two activities. Show your work.

    a. Use additive reasoning.   b. Use multiplicative reasoning.

51. Use the definition of division to determine whether 7 is a multiple of 3.

52. If 150 is divided by x, then the remainder is 3. What is the remainder when 296 is divided by x?

53. If 100 is divided by b, then the remainder is 2. What is the remainder when 393 is divided by b?

54. Grocery stores have a large variety of foods on the shelves. The typical American grocer today has 35,000 products, up from 800 products in the 1930s.

    a. Do you think these numbers are exact or the result of rounding?

    b. Write a sentence that compares the number of products in grocery stores in these two periods of time using additive reasoning.

    c. Write a sentence that compares the number of products in grocery stores in these two periods of time using multiplicative reasoning.

55. Do the following.

    a. Find all whole numbers a such that $a \div 14 = 1$.

    b. Find all whole numbers b such that $35 \div b = 1$.

    c. Suppose a and b are whole numbers such that $a \div b = 1$. What can you conclude?

56. Do the following.

    a. A talk show host spent $7,838,400 when she surprised each audience member with a new car worth $28,400. How many audience members were there? Which model is appropriate for this problem? Explain.

    b. The Federal Communications Commission fined 20 CBS-owned television stations for indecent programming during a Super Bowl half-time show. The total fine was $550,000. Each station received the same fine. How much was each station fined? Which model is appropriate for this problem? Explain.

57. Do the following.

    a. Use the equation $108 \div k = d$ to find $108 \div d$.

    b. Use the equation $y \div 17 = h$ to find $y \div h$, where y $\neq$ 0.

58. Is division commutative? That is, if a and b are whole numbers with $a \neq 0$ and $b \neq 0$, is $a \div b = b \div a$? Explain your answer, using an example to support your conclusion.

59. Is this an associative law for division: if a, b, and c are whole numbers with $c \neq 0$, is $(a \div b) \div c = a \div (b \div c)$? Give an example to support your conclusion.

60. Use the equation $y = 5q + 3$ to find

    a. $(y + 4) \div 5$.   b. $(y - 1) \div 5$.   c. $(y + 12) \div 5$.

61. Use the equation $y = 4k + 5$ to find

    a. $(y - 2) \div 4$.   b. $(2y + 1) \div 4$.   c. $(3y - 2) \div 4$.

62. $1002 \times 35 = 35,070$, $1002 \times 60 = 60,120$, and $1002 \times 75 = 75,150$.

    a. Use these examples to predict 1002×84.

    b. Write $1002 \times a$ as a sum, where a is a counting number.

63. Solve the equation $18 \times n = 90$,

    a. knowing multiplication and division are inverse operations.

    b. using the definition of division.

SECTION 3.3 # Algorithms for Whole Number Multiplication and Division

Simpler Calculations Form the Foundation

We used set models, skip counting, and repeated addition and subtraction to demonstrate the concepts of multiplication and division. We also used them as elementary strategies to calculate 4×5 and $24 \div 6$ and used patterns to calculate 23×10 and 23×100. We can also use the distributive property to multiply; for example, $7 \times 12 = 7(10 + 2) = 7 \times 10 + 7 \times 2 = 70 + 14 = 84$. These simpler calculations form the foundation for more complicated calculations such as 347×876 or $245 \div 34$, which in turn form the basis for computing with integers, fractions, and decimals. In this section, we discuss several efficient place value methods for whole number multiplication and division with whole numbers.

Building Blocks of the Standard Multiplication Algorithm

The distributive property is the underpinning of the standard multiplication algorithm. For example, $145 \times 67 = 145 \times (60 + 7) = 145 \times 60 + 145 \times 7$, which are simpler multiplication problems (145×7 is a product involving a single-digit factor, and 145×60 is a product involving a multiple of a power of 10).

Modeling a Product Involving a Single-Digit Factor

Products such as 67×5 and 67×3 involve a factor with one digit and set the stage for more complex problems such as 67×53. The following example illustrates a place value method using base ten blocks to multiply a multidigit number and a single-digit number.

EXAMPLE 3.32

CONNECTION

REPRESENTATION

Use base ten blocks to determine 3×58.

SOLUTION

Four steps can be followed:

Step 1. We need to create three groups of 58. Use base ten blocks to represent the multidigit factor 58.

Step 2. Create three equal-sized groups.

Step 3. Regroup the ones: 3×8 ones $= 24$ ones $= 2$ tens, 4 ones.

Step 4. Regroup the tens: 15 tens $+ 2$ tens $= 17$ tens $= 1$ hundred, 7 tens.

Then $3 \times 58 = 174$. ▲

The following example illustrates the pencil-and-paper algorithm with place value concepts to multiply a multidigit number and a single-digit number.

EXAMPLE 3.33

CONNECTION

COMMUNICATION

Multiply: 3×58.

SOLUTION

We begin by multiplying the ones:

$$\begin{array}{r} \overset{2}{58} \\ \times\ 3 \\ \hline 4 \end{array}$$ **Multiply the ones: 3×8 ones $= 24$ ones $= 2$ tens, 4 ones.**

The 2 above the 5 represents the 2 tens from regrouping 24 ones as 2 tens, 4 ones. Then we multiply the tens:

$$\begin{array}{r} \overset{1\ 2}{58} \\ \times\ 3 \\ \hline 174 \end{array}$$ **Multiply the tens: 3×5 tens $= 15$ tens. Add the tens: 15 tens $+ 2$ tens $= 17$ tens. Regroup the tens: 17 tens $= 1$ hundred, 7 tens.**

The 1 in the hundreds place represents the 1 hundred from adding and regrouping the tens: 3×5 tens $+ 2$ tens $= 15$ tens $+ 2$ tens $= 17$ tens $= 1$ hundred, 7 tens. Then $3 \times 58 = 174$.

▲

EXAMPLE 3.34

CONNECTION
COMMUNICATION
REPRESENTATION

A student writes the following calculation:

$$\begin{array}{r} {}^{5\,4} \\ 87 \\ \times\,6 \\ \hline 522 \end{array}$$

a. Explain why the 4 appears over the 8.

b. Explain why the 5 appears in the hundreds place.

SOLUTION

a. The student multiplied the ones: 6×7 ones $= 42$ ones. The 4 over the 8 represents the 4 tens from regrouping 42 ones as 4 tens, 2 ones.

b. The student multiplied and added the tens: 6×8 tens $+ 4$ tens $= 48$ tens $+ 4$ tens $= 52$ tens. The 5 in the hundreds place represents the 5 hundreds from regrouping 52 tens as 5 hundreds, 2 tens.

▲

The risk of pencil-and-paper multiplication is the possible loss of place value concepts. For example, in the preceding example, a student may think "6 times 7 equals 42, carry the 4; 6 times 8 equals 48, plus 4 equals 52, carry the 5" rather than "6 times 7 ones equals 42 ones, which equals 4 tens, 7 ones; 6 times 8 tens is 48 tens, plus 4 tens equals 52 tens, which equals 5 hundreds, 2 tens."

Multiplying by a Power of 10

In Section 3.1, we used skip counting and patterns to calculate products such as 4×10 (10, 20, 30, 40, so $4 \times 10 = 40$) and 234×100 (append the factor 234 with two zeros, so $234 \times 100 = 23,400$). In Chapter 6, we upgrade our thinking and learn that multiplying by powers of 10 changes the place values of digits and therefore shifts the decimal point.

Multiplying by a Multiple of a Power of 10

CONNECTION
COMMUNICATION
REASONING

Numbers such as 50, 60, and 70 are multiples of 10 ($50 = 5 \times 10$, $60 = 6 \times 10$, and $70 = 7 \times 10$). Numbers such as 500, 600, and 700 are multiples of 100 ($500 = 5 \times 100$, $600 = 6 \times 100$, and $700 = 7 \times 100$). The following example illustrates the thinking process we use when multiplying by a multiple of a power of 10 (such as multiplying by 400).

EXAMPLE 3.35   Use properties to multiply: 38×400.

SOLUTION

$38 \times 400 = 38 \times (4 \times 100) = (38 \times 4) \times 100 = 152 \times 100 = 15,200$

▲

Multiplying by certain multiples of a power of 10 builds on a previous skill: multiplying a multidigit number by a single-digit number. The following Classroom Connection illustrates that students should know how to multiply using the associative property of multiplication.

> ◆◆ **Classroom Connection**
>
> ● Houghton Mifflin *Mathematics*, Student Edition, Grade 4, p. 179
>
> Multiply. Use the associative property. 15×40, 68×20 (© by Houghton Mifflin Company, Inc. Reproduced by permission of the publisher, Houghton Mifflin Harcourt Publishing Company.)

Standard Multiplication Algorithm

We have all the building blocks in place to discuss the standard multiplication algorithm to calculate 487×36. Applying the distributive property, we obtain $487 \times 36 = 487 \times (30 + 6) = 487 \times 30 + 487 \times 6$. Here, we see that the standard multiplication algorithm for 487×36 involves solving two simpler problems, 487×30 and 487×6, in a vertical stack:

$$
\begin{array}{r}
\overset{5\,4}{487} \\
\times\ 36 \\
\hline
2922
\end{array}
\qquad \leftarrow \mathbf{487 \times 6 = 2922}
$$

$$
\begin{array}{r}
\overset{2\,2}{\overset{5\,4}{487}} \\
\times\ 36 \\
\hline
2922 \\
14610
\end{array}
\qquad \leftarrow \mathbf{487 \times 30 = 14{,}610}
$$

$$
\begin{array}{r}
\overset{2\,2}{\overset{5\,4}{487}} \\
\times\ 36 \\
\hline
2922 \\
14610 \\
\hline
17532
\end{array}
\qquad \leftarrow \mathbf{487 \times 36 = 17{,}532}
$$

CONNECTION

COMMUNICATION

REPRESENTATION

So $487 \times 36 = 17{,}532$. In the same way, the product 345×67 requires two simpler problems: 345×7 and 345×60. What two simpler problems does the product 832×49 require?

Concept Map 3.4 highlights some important concepts associated with the standard algorithm for multiplication.

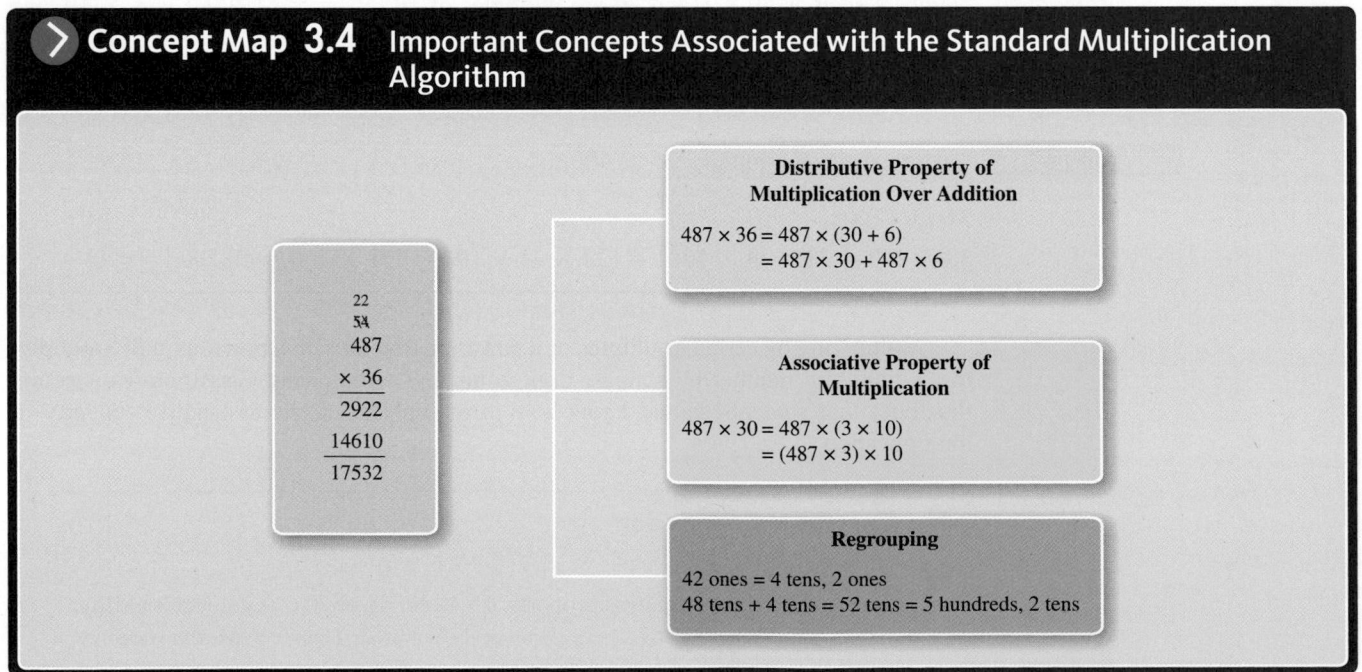

> **Concept Map 3.4** Important Concepts Associated with the Standard Multiplication Algorithm

$$
\begin{array}{r}
\overset{2\,2}{} \\
\overset{5\,4}{} \\
487 \\
\times\ 36 \\
\hline
2922 \\
14610 \\
\hline
17532
\end{array}
$$

Distributive Property of Multiplication Over Addition

$487 \times 36 = 487 \times (30 + 6)$
$= 487 \times 30 + 487 \times 6$

Associative Property of Multiplication

$487 \times 30 = 487 \times (3 \times 10)$
$= (487 \times 3) \times 10$

Regrouping

42 ones = 4 tens, 2 ones
48 tens + 4 tens = 52 tens = 5 hundreds, 2 tens

EXAMPLE 3.36

CONNECTION

REASONING

Write three simpler problems that 234×567 requires using the standard multiplication algorithm.

SOLUTION

There are two possible solutions. First, $234 \times 567 = 234 \times (500 + 60 + 7) = 234 \times 500 + 234 \times 60 + 234 \times 7$. The three simpler problems are 234×500, 234×60, and 234×7.

Alternatively, $567 \times 234 = 567 \times (200 + 30 + 4) = 567 \times 200 + 567 \times 30 + 567 \times 4$. The three simpler problems are 567×200, 567×30, and 567×4. ▲

EXAMPLE 3.37

COMMUNICATION

CONNECTION

REASONING

Jared is using the standard multiplication algorithm to calculate 274×638. Why did he write 0 in the ones and tens places in the last row shown?

$$
\begin{array}{r}
\overset{2\ 1}{\underset{5\ 3}{}} \\
274 \\
\times\ 638 \\
\hline
2192 \\
8220 \\
00
\end{array}
$$

SOLUTION

Jared is calculating the simpler product 274×600, which equals $(274 \times 6) \times 100$. The two zeros anticipate multiplying the product 274×6 by 100. ▲

Partial Products Method

Finding the product 13×24 using the standard multiplication algorithm requires solving two simpler problems: 13×20 and 13×4 (or 24×10 and 24×3). But we can find the product 13×24 using another method called the **partial products method.** In Figure 13, we represent the product 13×24 with an array model. There are 13 rows and 24 columns. We represent 13 and 24 by their expanded forms: $13 = 10 + 3$ and $24 = 20 + 4$. This creates four simpler arrays. Each array creates an intermediate product called a *partial product.* The partial products are 200, 60, 40, and 12 ($10 \times 20 = 200$, $3 \times 20 = 60$, $10 \times 4 = 40$, and $3 \times 4 = 12$). The product 13×24 equals the *sum* of the partial products: $13 \times 24 = 200 + 60 + 40 + 12 = 312$.

CONNECTION

COMMUNICATION

REASONING

REPRESENTATION

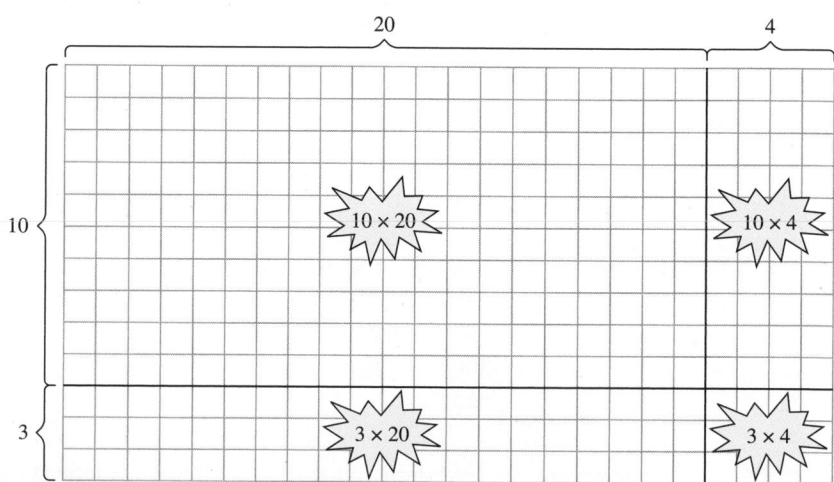

FIGURE 13

The array model makes it easy to see that finding 13×24 using the partial products method requires solving four simpler problems: 10×20, 3×20, 10×4, and 3×4. The partial products for 13×24 are 200, 60, 40, and 12.

CONNECTION

REASONING

In other words, calculating 13×24 involves solving four simpler problems: 10×20, 3×20, 10×4, and 3×4. The distributive property justifies the existence of these partial products (200, 60, 40, and 12):

$$
\begin{aligned}
13 \times 24 &= 13 \times (20 + 4) \\
&= 13 \times 20 + 13 \times 4 \\
&= (10 + 3) \times 20 + (10 + 3) \times 4 \\
&= 10 \times 20 + 3 \times 20 + 10 \times 4 + 3 \times 4 \\
&= 200 + 60 + 40 + 12
\end{aligned}
$$

The partial products method makes it easy to identify student mistakes in place value concepts and relies on basic multiplication facts (for example, $3 \times 2 = 6$ and $3 \times 20 = 60$).

EXAMPLE 3.38 List the partial products.
a. 37×6
b. 532×86

SOLUTION

a. The simpler problems are 7×6 and 30×6. The partial products are 42 and 180, respectively.
b. The simpler problems are 2×6, 30×6, 500×6, 2×80, 30×80, and 500×80. The partial products are 12, 180, 3000, 160, 2400, and 40,000, respectively.

▲

The partial products method arranges the partial products in a vertical format, as shown in the equations below. There are several ways to organize the partial products, each reflecting the place value structure of the number system. We show two possible arrangements here, working from left to right and then right to left.

Work left to right

$$
\begin{array}{r}
13 \\
\times\ 35 \\
\hline
300 \quad \leftarrow 10 \times 30 = 300 \\
50 \quad \leftarrow 10 \times 5 = 50 \\
90 \quad \leftarrow 3 \times 30 = 90 \\
15 \quad \leftarrow 3 \times 5 = 15 \\
\hline
455
\end{array}
$$

Work right to left

$$
\begin{array}{r}
13 \\
\times\ 35 \\
\hline
15 \quad \leftarrow 5 \times 3 = 15 \\
50 \quad \leftarrow 5 \times 10 = 50 \\
90 \quad \leftarrow 30 \times 3 = 90 \\
300 \quad \leftarrow 30 \times 10 = 300 \\
\hline
455
\end{array}
$$

CONNECTION

Working left to right produces the largest partial product first and helps students align the subsequent partial products needed for addition in the final phase.

The following portion of a page from an elementary school textbook shows that using arrays to find partial products may be part of the elementary mathematics curriculum.

◆ **Activity**

How do you record what you showed with the array?

Here is one way to record what you do with grid paper and an array to find the product for 24 × 27.

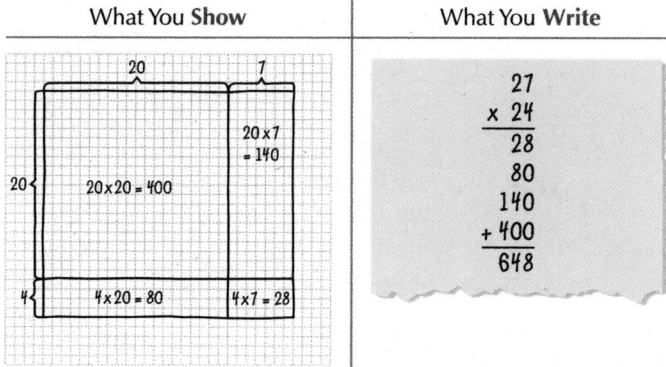

What You **Show**	What You **Write**

a. Use grid paper to draw each rectangle. Follow the method above to find each product.

17 × 25   19 × 32   21 × 29   12 × 38

b. Explain how breaking apart the rectangle for 24 × 27 into smaller rectangles is like solving four simpler problems. What are the simpler problems?

(*Mathematics*, Grade 4, p. 321)

Mental Arithmetic

Students should be able to "compute fluently and make reasonable estimates" (NCTM, Gr. 3–8). **Mental strategies** use the structure of numbers and properties of multiplication to calculate, rather than estimate, the product. Mental arithmetic is a dynamic and flexible process, because it depends on the numbers involved, the operation, and the student's reasoning ability.

Table 3.5 illustrates a mental strategy using *adjustments,* which involves adjusting one or both factors and using properties of multiplication.

TABLE 3.5 Making Adjustments

$99 \times 36 = (100 - 1) \times 36 = 3600 - 36 = 3600 - 30 - 6 = 3570 - 6 = 3564$
$101 \times 45 = (100 + 1) \times 45 = 4500 + 45 = 4545$
$5 \times 462 = 10 \times 231 = 2310$

REASONING

Adjustments often lead to simpler problems. Powers of 10 make computations easier. Mental arithmetic also involves *compatible numbers* to multiply by using properties of multiplication to rearrange factors and form products that are easier to compute, as illustrated in Table 3.6.

TABLE 3.6 Using Compatible Numbers

$4 \times 16 \times 25 = 16 \times 100 = 1600$
$5 \times 347 \times 2 = 10 \times 347 = 3470$
$28 \times 25 = 7 \times 4 \times 25 = 7 \times 100 = 700$

EXAMPLE 3.39

REASONING

Use mental arithmetic to multiply.
a. 5×24
b. 50×142

SOLUTION

a. $5 \times 24 = 5 \times (25 - 1) = 125 - 5 = 120$
b. $50 \times 142 = 50 \times 2 \times 71 = 100 \times 71 = 7100$

▲

Mental arithmetic and number sense involve using operations on numbers in a flexible way that considers the numbers involved in the computation. They involve using the structure and properties of the number system, such as place value, commutative property, associative property, distributive property, factoring, composing, and decomposing, and therefore kindle and reinforce conceptual understanding.

Estimating the Product

Estimation, more of an art than a science, reflects knowledge of basic facts, place value concepts, and number sense. The most common strategies for estimation are rounding to a multiple of 10, front-end estimation, and compatible numbers (including a combination of these strategies).

To measure the number of 1-by-1-foot square tiles needed to tile a 9.4-by-12.7-foot room, a simple overestimate would suffice: 10 feet $\times$ 13 feet = 130 square feet, or 130 square tiles. In this example, we rounded the measurements up to the nearest whole number. You can also round factors to the nearest hundred, thousand, and so on, before you multiply. For example, to estimate 356×21, we can round each factor to the nearest ten to get $356 \times 21 \approx 360 \times 20 = 36 \times 2 \times 100 = 72 \times 100 = 7200$.

EXAMPLE 3.40

REASONING

Estimate using rounding.
a. 856×5675
b. 77×138

SOLUTION

Answers using estimation may vary.
a. Rounding to the nearest thousand: $831 \times 5675 \approx 1000 \times 6000 = 6,000,000$
b. Rounding to the nearest ten: $77 \times 138 \approx 80 \times 140 = 11,200$

▲

A *range estimate* of a product consists of two estimates (a lower bound and an upper bound) by rounding the leftmost digit of each factor. We use two examples to demonstrate this method for range estimates of 347×77 and 432×8891.

- The range estimate of 347×77 is $300 \times 70 \leq 347 \times 77 \leq 400 \times 80$, or $21,000 \leq 347 \times 77 \leq 32,000$.

- The range estimate of 432×8891 is $400 \times 8000 \leq 432 \times 8891 \leq 500 \times 9000$, or $3,200,000 \leq 432 \times 8891 \leq 4,500,000$.

Another estimation strategy consists of replacing the factors with compatible numbers to create products that are easier to evaluate. The next example illustrates that multiples of 10 are good choices.

EXAMPLE 3.41

REASONING

Use compatible numbers to estimate 11×245.

SOLUTION

$11 \times 245 \approx 10 \times 250 = 2500$

▲

Estimation strategies provide good opportunities to demonstrate understanding of place value concepts, arithmetic properties, and mental arithmetic.

Division with Whole Numbers

CONNECTION   The partial quotients method and traditional long division algorithm exploit the place value structure in the division models, leading to efficient methods. Later, we use division to simplify fractions, convert fractions to decimals, scale down ratios, solve missing value problems in proportions, represent counting numbers using a prime factorization, calculate probabilities, and convert measurements.

Partial Quotients Method

The first long division method we discuss is the **partial quotients method,** which builds on repeated subtraction ("How many groups?"), multiplication, subtraction, and number sense. Let's solve $3302 \div 121$. An estimate of the quotient using compatible numbers is $3302 \div 121 \approx 3600 \div 120 = 30$.

The following calculation demonstrates the partial quotients method for $3302 \div 121$. We interpret the dividend as the total and the divisor as the number of objects in each group. Then the quotient tells us how many groups of 121 are in 3302. The dividend diminishes in each step by multiples of the divisor. Each multiplier, called a *partial quotient,* represents the number of groups of 121.

$$
\begin{array}{r}
121\overline{)3302} \\
-1210 \\
\hline
2092 \\
-1210 \\
\hline
882 \\
-484 \\
\hline
398 \\
-363 \\
\hline
35
\end{array}
$$

$121\overline{)3302}$
-1210 $10 \times 121 = 1210$
2092 ↑ **partial quotient**
-1210 $10 \times 121 = 1210$
882 ↑ **partial quotient**
-484 $4 \times 121 = 242$
398 ↑ **partial quotient**
-363 $3 \times 121 = 363$
35 ↑ **partial quotient**
↑ **remainder**

In this case, the partial quotients are 10, 10, 4, and 3. The quotient is the *sum* of the partial quotients, so the quotient is $10 + 10 + 4 + 3 = 27$, which is close to the estimate using compatible numbers. Each partial quotient is a "chunk" of the quotient. The quotient is 27 and the remainder is 35, so $3302 \div 121 = 27$ R35.

The next calculation shows another possibility using the partial quotients method. In this case, the partial quotients are 5, 7, 2, 6, and 7. The quotient is $5 + 7 + 2 + 6 + 7 = 27$, and the remainder is 35, so $3302 \div 121 = 27$ R35.

CONNECTION
REASONING
REPRESENTATION

$121\overline{)3302}$
-605 $5 \times 121 = 605$
2697 ↑ **partial quotient**
-847 $7 \times 121 = 847$
1850 ↑ **partial quotient**
-242 $2 \times 121 = 242$
1608 ↑ **partial quotient**
-726 $6 \times 121 = 726$
882 ↑ **partial quotient**
-847 $7 \times 121 = 847$
35 ↑ **partial quotient**
↑ **remainder**

The two preceding calculations show that the partial quotients method, based on repeated subtraction, is a flexible cycle of estimation, multiplication, and subtraction. This strategy allows students to use number sense, providing them with more options.

Standard Long Division Algorithm

It is easier to illustrate the standard long division algorithm using the fair share model ("How many in each group?") than the repeated subtraction method. To keep ideas simple, we use a single-digit divisor. The single-digit divisor represents the number of groups, and the quotient represents the number of objects in each group. There may be a remainder.

Figure 14 applies place value concepts and the fair share model to calculate 715 ÷ 3.

CONNECTION
REASONING
REPRESENTATION

Step 1. Begin with a place value model of 715 as 7 hundreds, 1 ten, and 5 ones, along with three groups. We know $3 \times 200 = 600$ and $3 \times 250 = 750$, so we expect a quotient between 200 and 250.

FIGURE 14

Applying place value concepts to find 715 ÷ 3.

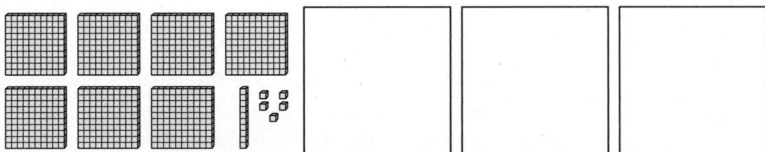

Step 2. Give 2 hundreds to each group, with 1 hundred left over.

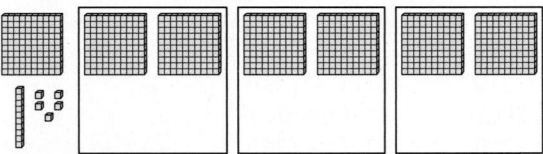

Step 3. Regroup 1 hundred, 1 ten as 11 tens.

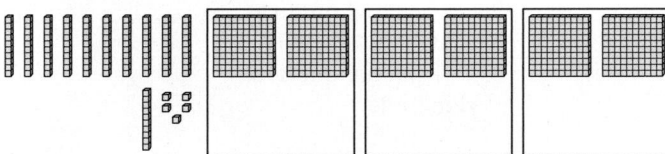

Step 4. Give 3 tens to each group, with 2 tens left over.

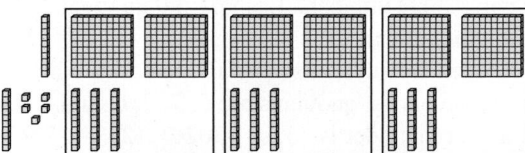

Step 5. Regroup 2 tens, 5 ones as 25 ones.

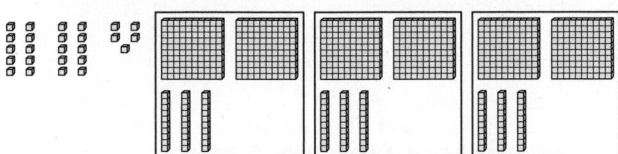

Step 6. Give 8 ones to each group, with a remainder of 1 one.

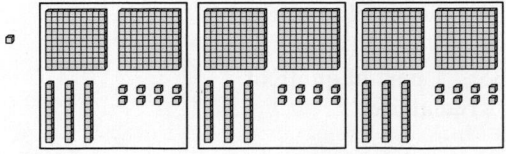

In all, we allocate 2 hundreds, 3 tens, and 8 ones to each group, with a remainder of 1 one. Thus, the quotient is 238 and the remainder is 1. Let's check: $3 \times 238 + 1 = 714 + 1 = 715$. So $715 \div 3 = 238$ R1.

The following Classroom Connection shows that students should know how to use base ten blocks to model division.

> ### ◆ Classroom Connection
>
> ● *Math*, Grade 5, West Virginia Edition, p. 115
>
> Use place-value models to find how many are in each group. $152 \div 8$ (© 2000 Macmillan/McGraw Hill. Reprinted by permission.)

The following is a step-by-step mathematical summary of the model in Figure 14. The "Think" comments relate to place value concepts, while the "Do" comments relate to the procedure for division. We place digits in the quotient according to place value. The conceptual basis for "bringing down a digit" is regrouping.

Step 1.

$3\overline{)715}$ **Do: Set up the problem.**

Step 2.

$$\begin{array}{r} 2 \\ 3\overline{)715} \\ -6\downarrow \\ \hline 1 \end{array}$$

Think: Split 7 hundreds among three groups. Each group gets 2 hundreds: $3 \times 2 = 6$.
Do: Put the 2 above the dividend in the hundreds place.
Subtract: 7 hundreds − 6 hundreds = 1 hundred.
Think: The 1 represents 1 hundred.

Step 3.

$$\begin{array}{r} 2 \\ 3\overline{)715} \\ -6\downarrow \\ \hline 11 \end{array}$$

Do: Bring down the 1.
Think: Regroup 1 hundred, 1 ten as 11 tens.

Step 4.

$$\begin{array}{r} 23 \\ 3\overline{)715} \\ -6\downarrow \\ \hline 11 \\ -9 \\ \hline 2 \end{array}$$

Think: Split 11 tens among three groups. Each group gets 3 tens: $3 \times 3 = 9$.
Do: Put the 3 above the dividend in the tens place.
Subtract: 11 tens − 9 tens = 2 tens.
Think: The 2 represents 2 tens.

Step 5.

$$\begin{array}{r} 23 \\ 3\overline{)715} \\ -6\downarrow \\ \hline 11 \\ -9\downarrow \\ \hline 25 \end{array}$$

Do: Bring down the 5.
Think: Regroup 2 tens, 5 ones as 25 ones.

Step 6.

$$
\begin{array}{r}
238 \\
3\overline{)715} \\
-6\downarrow \\
\hline
11 \\
-9\downarrow \\
\hline
25 \\
-24 \\
\hline
1
\end{array}
$$

Think: Split 25 ones among three groups. Each group gets $3 \times 8 = 24$.
Do: Put the 8 above the dividend in the ones place.
Subtract: 25 ones − 24 ones = 1 one.
Think: The 1 represents 1 one, and 1 is the remainder.

The quotient is 238 and the remainder is 1. So $715 \div 3 = 238$ R1.

In Step 2 of Figure 14, we split 7 hundreds into three groups, and each group received 2 hundreds. We could have asked, "How many 3s in 7?" The answer would be *two*. In Step 4, we split 11 tens into three groups, and each group received 3 tens. We could have asked, "How many 3s in 11?" The answer would be *three*. The "how many" questions tend to marginalize place value concepts.

The following calculation illustrates the long division algorithm for $9126 \div 42$. It includes the typical questions that students ask themselves, such as "How many 42s in 91?" and "How many 3s in 11?"

$$
\begin{array}{r}
217 \\
42\overline{)9126} \\
-84\downarrow \\
\hline
72 \\
-42\downarrow \\
\hline
306 \\
-294 \\
\hline
12
\end{array}
$$

How many 42s in 91? *Two.* $2 \times 42 = 84$.
"Bring down the 2."
How many 42s in 72? *One.* $1 \times 42 = 42$.
"Bring down the 6."
How many 42s in 306? *Seven.* $7 \times 42 = 294$
How many 42s in 12? *None.*
↑ remainder

Thus, the quotient is 217 and the remainder is 12. Check $42 \times 217 + 12 = 9114 + 12 = 9126$. Therefore, $9126 \div 42 = 217$ R12.

EXAMPLE 3.42

CONNECTION
COMMUNICATION
REASONING
REPRESENTATION

Refer to the previous calculation for $42\overline{)9126}$.

a. Explain why the 2 in the quotient appears above the 1 in the dividend.

b. What is going on when we "bring down" the 2?

c. What is going on when we "bring down" the 6?

SOLUTION

a. When we ask, "How many 42s in 9?" the answer is 0. Then we ask, "How many 42s in 91?" The 91 is the result of regrouping 9 thousands, 1 hundred as 91 hundreds. The answer to the question "How many 42s in 91?" is *two,* so we put the 2 above the dividend in the *hundreds* place.

b. We are regrouping 7 hundreds, 2 tens as 72 tens.

c. We are regrouping 30 tens, 6 ones as 306 ones.

▲

> **RELEASED ITEM**
>
> • NAEP, GRADE 4, 2009
>
> Divide: $5\overline{)476}$
>
> **a.** 85 R1 **b.** 95 R1 **c.** 96 **d.** 135 R1
>
> 59% of fourth graders answered the question correctly.

The partial quotients method may seem less efficient than the standard long division algorithm, but it is usually less frustrating to students. In a humorous *Broom Hilda* cartoon, the teacher sends a disruptive student to the board, expecting the student to apply his dedication to disrupting the class to solving the division problem 4,679,951,328 ÷ 641,552. The student senses "a tiny dollop of revenge." Which division method do you prefer for that division problem?

Estimating the Quotient

REASONING   We already know the remainder is less than the divisor, so we usually estimate the quotient. Replacing the dividend, divisor, or both with compatible numbers makes estimating the quotient easier:

$$571 \div 6 \approx 600 \div 6 = 100 \qquad 2147 \div 8 \approx 2100 \div 10 = 21$$
$$460 \div 8 \approx 480 \div 8 = 60 \qquad 8105 \div 41 \approx 8000 \div 40 = 200$$
$$839 \div 37 \approx 800 \div 40 = 20 \qquad 5674 \div 76 \approx 5600 \div 70 = 80$$

Connection among the Four Standard Algorithms

CONNECTION   Concept Map 3.5 illustrates that *regrouping* is a connection among the four standard algorithms for addition, subtraction, multiplication, and division.

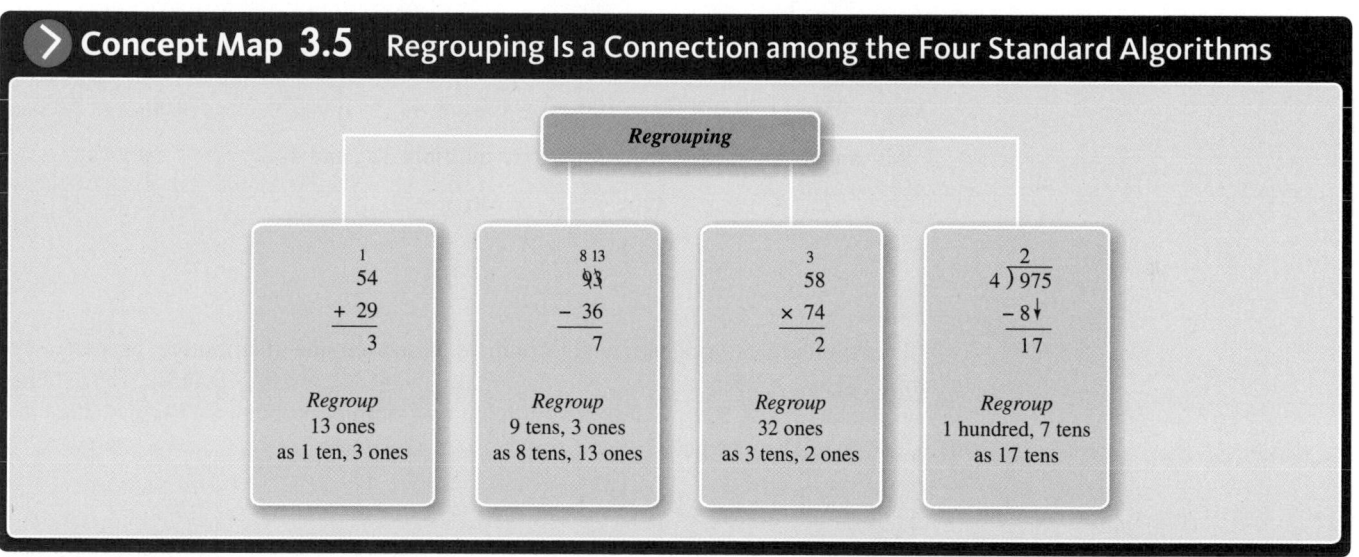

> **Concept Map 3.5**   Regrouping Is a Connection among the Four Standard Algorithms

Base Five Multiplication

Thinking of multiplication as repeated addition helps establish multiplication facts in base five (and other bases). For example,

- $2_{five} \times 4_{five} = 4_{five} + 4_{five} = 4_{five} + 1_{five} + 3_{five} = 10_{five} + 3_{five} = 13_{five}.$
- $3_{five} \times 2_{five} = 2_{five} + 2_{five} + 2_{five} = 4_{five} + 2_{five} = 4_{five} + 1_{five} + 1_{five} = 10_{five} + 1_{five} = 11_{five}.$

Table 3.7 shows the base five multiplication table. Fluency with Table 3.7 is handy for pencil-and-paper versions of multiplication algorithms.

TABLE 3.7 **Base Five Multiplication Table**

$\times$	0_{five}	1_{five}	2_{five}	3_{five}	4_{five}
0_{five}	0_{five}	0_{five}	0_{five}	0_{five}	0_{five}
1_{five}	0_{five}	1_{five}	2_{five}	3_{five}	4_{five}
2_{five}	0_{five}	2_{five}	4_{five}	11_{five}	13_{five}
3_{five}	0_{five}	3_{five}	11_{five}	14_{five}	22_{five}
4_{five}	0_{five}	4_{five}	13_{five}	22_{five}	31_{five}

The expanded form is one way to learn how to multiply by 10_{five}. For example,

$$
\begin{aligned}
423_{\text{five}} \times 10_{\text{five}} &= (4_{\text{five}} \cdot 10^2_{\text{five}} + 2_{\text{five}} \cdot 10^1_{\text{five}} + 3_{\text{five}} \cdot 10^0_{\text{five}}) \times 10_{\text{five}} \\
&= 4_{\text{five}} \cdot 10^2_{\text{five}} \times 10_{\text{five}} + 2_{\text{five}} \cdot 10^1_{\text{five}} \times 10_{\text{five}} + 3_{\text{five}} \cdot 10^0_{\text{five}} \times 10_{\text{five}} \\
&= 4_{\text{five}} \cdot 10^3_{\text{five}} + 2_{\text{five}} \cdot 10^2_{\text{five}} + 3_{\text{five}} \cdot 10^1_{\text{five}} \\
&= 4230_{\text{five}}.
\end{aligned}
$$

Using the same reasoning, we can multiply by higher powers of 10_{five}:

- $10_{\text{five}} \times 10_{\text{five}} = 100_{\text{five}}$
- $12_{\text{five}} \times 100_{\text{five}} = 1200_{\text{five}}$
- $423_{\text{five}} \times 1000_{\text{five}} = 423000_{\text{five}}.$

The moral of the story is that multiplying a number by a power of 10 (for example, 10_{five}, 10^2_{five}, and 10^3_{five}) amounts to appending the number with the appropriate number of zeros.

Multiplying a number by a multiple of a power of 10 (for example, 40_{five}, 120_{five}, and 21300_{five}) is facilitated by the associative property of multiplication. For example,

- $2_{\text{five}} \times 30_{\text{five}} = 2_{\text{five}} \times (3_{\text{five}} \cdot 10_{\text{five}}) = (2_{\text{five}} \times 3_{\text{five}}) \cdot 10_{\text{five}} = 11_{\text{five}} \cdot 10_{\text{five}} = 110_{\text{five}}.$
- $3_{\text{five}} \times 400_{\text{five}} = 3_{\text{five}} \times (4_{\text{five}} \cdot 100_{\text{five}}) = (3_{\text{five}} \times 4_{\text{five}}) \cdot 100_{\text{five}} = 22_{\text{five}} \cdot 100_{\text{five}} = 2200_{\text{five}}.$

We can use the distributive property to multiply 3_{five} and 42_{five}:

$$
\begin{aligned}
3_{\text{five}} \times 42_{\text{five}} &= 3_{\text{five}} \times (40_{\text{five}} + 2_{\text{five}}) \\
&= 3_{\text{five}} \times 40_{\text{five}} + 3_{\text{five}} \times 2_{\text{five}} \\
&= 220_{\text{five}} + 11_{\text{five}} \\
&= 231_{\text{five}}.
\end{aligned}
$$

The standard multiplication algorithm is based on the distributive property. For example, $413_{\text{five}} \times 23_{\text{five}} = 413_{\text{five}} \times (20_{\text{five}} + 3_{\text{five}}) = 413_{\text{five}} \times 20_{\text{five}} + 413_{\text{five}} \times 3_{\text{five}}$. Then the product $413_{\text{five}} \times 23_{\text{five}}$ is found by solving two simpler problems, $413_{\text{five}} \times 20_{\text{five}}$ and $413_{\text{five}} \times 3_{\text{five}}$. Then we get

$$
\begin{array}{r}
\overset{1}{\underset{\text{five}}{\cancel{1}}} \\
413_{\text{five}} \\
\times\ 23_{\text{five}} \\
\hline
2244_{\text{five}} \\
13310_{\text{five}} \\
\hline
21104_{\text{five}}
\end{array}
$$

$\leftarrow 413_{\text{five}} \times 3_{\text{five}} = 2244_{\text{five}}$

$\leftarrow 413_{\text{five}} \times 20_{\text{five}} = 13310_{\text{five}}$

An estimate of $413_{\text{five}} \times 23_{\text{five}}$ is $400_{\text{five}} \times 30_{\text{five}} = 22000_{\text{five}}$, so 21104_{five} is reasonable.

EXAMPLE 3.43 What two simpler problems does $314_{\text{five}} \times 42_{\text{five}}$ require using the standard multiplication algorithm?

SOLUTION

$314_{\text{five}} \times 42_{\text{five}} = 314_{\text{five}} \times (40_{\text{five}} + 2_{\text{five}}) = 314_{\text{five}} \times 40_{\text{five}} + 314_{\text{five}} \times 2_{\text{five}}$. The two simpler problems are $314_{\text{five}} \times 40_{\text{five}}$ and $314_{\text{five}} \times 2_{\text{five}}$.

EXAMPLE 3.44   Amy is multiplying two base five numbers, as shown.
a. Why is there a 1 above the 4?

b. Why did she write 0?

$$\begin{array}{r} \overset{1\,1}{343}_{\text{five}} \\ \times\ 32_{\text{five}} \\ \hline 1241_{\text{five}} \\ 0_{\text{five}} \end{array}$$

SOLUTION

a. Amy multiplied the units: $3_{\text{five}} \times 2_{\text{five}} = 11_{\text{five}}$. The 1 above the 4 represents the 1_{five} long from regrouping 11_{five} units as 1_{five} long and 1_{five} unit.

b. Amy is calculating the simpler product $343_{\text{five}} \times 30_{\text{five}}$, which equals $(343_{\text{five}} \times 3) \times 10_{\text{five}}$. She is anticipating multiplication by 10_{five} because she knows the rightmost digit of $(343_{\text{five}} \times 3) \times 10_{\text{five}}$ must be 0.

▲

EXAMPLE 3.45   Do the following for the product $14_{\text{five}} \times 23_{\text{five}}$.
a. Draw the array model using the expanded form.

b. List the partial products.

c. Find the product using the partial products method.

d. Find the product using the standard multiplication algorithm.

SOLUTION

a. The product $14_{\text{five}} \times 23_{\text{five}}$ is the number of squares in an array with 14_{five} rows and 23_{five} columns. We partition the array using the expanded forms of the factors: $14_{\text{five}} = 10_{\text{five}} + 4_{\text{five}}$ and $23_{\text{five}} = 20_{\text{five}} + 3_{\text{five}}$.

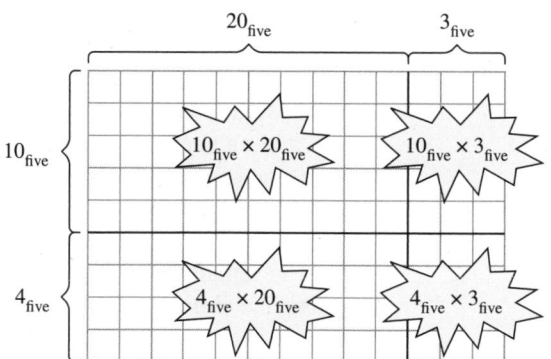

b. The partial products are 200_{five} $(10_{\text{five}} \times 20_{\text{five}})$, 130_{five} $(4_{\text{five}} \times 20_{\text{five}})$, 30_{five} $(10_{\text{five}} \times 3_{\text{five}})$, and 22_{five} $(4_{\text{five}} \times 3_{\text{five}})$.

c. The partial sums method (from right to left) arranges the partial products in a vertical stack and then adds them:

$$\begin{array}{r} 14_{\text{five}} \\ \times\ 23_{\text{five}} \\ \hline 22_{\text{five}} \quad \leftarrow 4_{\text{five}} \times 3_{\text{five}} \\ 30_{\text{five}} \quad \leftarrow 10_{\text{five}} \times 3_{\text{five}} \\ 130_{\text{five}} \quad \leftarrow 4_{\text{five}} \times 20_{\text{five}} \\ 200_{\text{five}} \quad \leftarrow 10_{\text{five}} \times 20_{\text{five}} \\ \hline 432_{\text{five}} \end{array}$$

d. We see the standard algorithm is efficient for representing the partial products.

$$
\begin{array}{r}
\overset{\overset{1}{2}}{14}_{\text{five}} \\
\times\ 23_{\text{five}} \\
\hline
102_{\text{five}} \\
330_{\text{five}} \\
\hline
432_{\text{five}}
\end{array}
$$

$102_{\text{five}}\quad\leftarrow$ **Sum of the partial products 22_{five} and 30_{five}**

$330_{\text{five}}\quad\leftarrow$ **Sum of the partial products 130_{five} and 200_{five}**

▲

Base Five Division

In a whole number division problem, such as $1430_{\text{five}} \div 24_{\text{five}}$, we can view the dividend 1430_{five} as the total number of objects, the divisor 24_{five} as the number of objects in each group, and the quotient as the number of groups of 24_{five} in 1430_{five}. We can divide using the partial quotients method, which builds on repeated subtraction ("How many groups?"), multiplication, subtraction, and number sense. The following calculation demonstrates the partial quotients method for $1430_{\text{five}} \div 24_{\text{five}}$. Each multiplier, called a partial quotient, represents the number of groups of 24_{five}.

$$
\begin{array}{ll}
24_{\text{five}}\overline{)1430_{\text{five}}} & \\
\quad-1030_{\text{five}} & \mathbf{20_{\text{five}} \times 24_{\text{five}} = 1030_{\text{five}}} \\
\quad\ \ 400_{\text{five}} & \uparrow \textbf{partial quotient} \\
\quad-240_{\text{five}} & \mathbf{10_{\text{five}} \times 24_{\text{five}} = 240_{\text{five}}} \\
\quad\ \ 110_{\text{five}} & \uparrow \textbf{partial quotient} \\
\quad\ \ -24_{\text{five}} & \mathbf{1_{\text{five}} \times 24_{\text{five}} = 24_{\text{five}}} \\
\quad\ \ \ \ 31_{\text{five}} & \uparrow \textbf{partial quotient} \\
\quad\ \ -24_{\text{five}} & \mathbf{1_{\text{five}} \times 24_{\text{five}} = 24_{\text{five}}} \\
\quad\ \ \ \ \ 2_{\text{five}} & \uparrow \textbf{partial quotient} \\
\quad\ \ \ \uparrow \textbf{remainder} &
\end{array}
$$

The partial quotients in this calculation are 20_{five}, 10_{five}, 1_{five}, and 1_{five}. The quotient is the *sum* of the partial quotients, so the quotient is $20_{\text{five}} + 10_{\text{five}} + 1_{\text{five}} + 1_{\text{five}} = 32_{\text{five}}$. Each partial quotient is a "chunk" of the quotient. The remainder is 2_{five}. We can check our work as follows: $32_{\text{five}} \times 24_{\text{five}} + 2_{\text{five}} = 1423_{\text{five}} + 2_{\text{five}} = 1430_{\text{five}}$, which equals the dividend. Then $1430_{\text{five}} \div 24_{\text{five}} = 32_{\text{five}}$ R2_{five}.

Other choices of partial quotients are possible, because the partial quotients depend on the size of the groupings chosen. For example, it would be possible to use the partial quotients method for $1430_{\text{five}} \div 24_{\text{five}}$ and obtain the partial quotients 10_{five}, 10_{five}, 10_{five}, and 2_{five}. However, the quotient and the remainder must be the same as before: quotient $= 32_{\text{five}}$ and remainder $= 2_{\text{five}}$. The partial quotients method is a flexible method that gives students the ability to tap into their number sense skills.

EXAMPLE 3.46 The partial quotients method is used to divide:

$$
\begin{array}{ll}
42_{\text{five}}\overline{)24232_{\text{five}}} & \\
\quad-4200_{\text{five}} & \mathbf{100_{\text{five}} \times 42_{\text{five}}} \\
\quad\ 20032_{\text{five}} & \\
\quad-4200_{\text{five}} & \mathbf{100_{\text{five}} \times 42_{\text{five}}} \\
\quad\ 10332_{\text{five}} & \\
\quad-4200_{\text{five}} & \mathbf{100_{\text{five}} \times 42_{\text{five}}} \\
\quad\ \ 1132_{\text{five}} & \\
\quad\ \ -420_{\text{five}} & \mathbf{10_{\text{five}} \times 42_{\text{five}}} \\
\quad\ \ \ 212_{\text{five}} & \\
\quad\ \ \ -42_{\text{five}} & \mathbf{1_{\text{five}} \times 42_{\text{five}}} \\
\quad\ \ \ 120_{\text{five}} & \\
\quad\ \ \ -42_{\text{five}} & \mathbf{1_{\text{five}} \times 42_{\text{five}}} \\
\quad\ \ \ \ \ 23_{\text{five}} &
\end{array}
$$

a. Determine the partial quotients.

b. Determine the quotient.

c. Determine the remainder.

d. Write an equation.

e. Check your work.

SOLUTION

a. The partial quotients are 100_{five}, 100_{five}, 100_{five}, 10_{five}, 1_{five}, and 1_{five}.

b. The quotient is $100_{five} + 100_{five} + 100_{five} + 10_{five} + 1_{five} + 1_{five} = 312_{five}$.

c. The remainder is 23_{five}.

d. $24232_{five} \div 42_{five} = 312_{five} \text{ R}23_{five}$.

e. $312_{five} \times 42_{five} + 23_{five} = 24204_{five} + 23_{five} = 24232_{five}$, which equals the dividend. ▲

The standard long division algorithm is easier to describe using the fair share model of division ("How many objects per group"). For example, let's consider $3443_{five} \div 12_{five}$. If 3443_{five} objects are split into 12_{five} equal-sized groups, how many objects are placed in each group? The quotient is the number of objects in each group.

$$12_{five}\overline{)3443_{five}}^{\,?}$$

Now we describe the steps for this division problem.

Step 1. 3443_{five} represents 3_{five} cubes, 4_{five} flats, 4_{five} longs, and 3_{five} units. There are not enough cubes to give to each of the 12_{five} groups, so we regroup 3_{five} cubes and 4_{five} flats as 34_{five} flats. We can give 2_{five} flats to each of the 12_{five} groups. This leaves 10_{five} flats.

$$12_{five}\overline{)3443_{five}}^{\,2}$$
$$\underline{-24}$$
$$10$$

Think: Regroup 3_{five} cubes and 4_{five} flats as 34_{five} flats.
Think: Split 34_{five} flats among 12_{five} groups. Each group gets 2_{five} flats, and $12_{five} \times 2_{five} = 24_{five}$.
Do: Put the 2 above the dividend in the flats place, and subtract: $34_{five} - 24_{five} = 10_{five}$.
Think: The 10 represents 10_{five} flats.

Step 2. We regroup 10_{five} flats and 4_{five} longs as 104_{five} longs. Procedurally, this means "bring down the 4."

$$12_{five}\overline{)3443_{five}}^{\,2}$$
$$\underline{-24\downarrow}$$
$$104$$

Think: Regroup 10_{five} flats and 4_{five} longs as 104_{five} longs.
Do: Bring down the 4.

Step 3. Now we can give 4_{five} longs to each of the 12_{five} groups. This leaves 1_{five} long.

$$12_{five}\overline{)3443_{five}}^{\,24}$$
$$\underline{-24\downarrow}$$
$$104$$
$$\underline{-103}$$
$$1$$

Think: Split 104_{five} longs among 12_{five} groups. Each group gets 4_{five} longs, and $12_{five} \times 4_{five} = 103_{five}$.
Do: Put the 4 above the dividend in the longs place, and subtract: $104_{five} - 103_{five} = 1_{five}$.
Think: The 1 represents 1_{five} long.

Step 4. We regroup 1_{five} long and 3_{five} units as 13_{five} units. Procedurally, this means "bring down the 3."

$$
\begin{array}{r}
24 \\
12_{five} \overline{)3443_{five}} \\
-24 \\
\hline
104 \\
-103\!\downarrow \\
\hline
13
\end{array}
$$

Think: Regroup 1_{five} long and 3_{five} units as 13_{five} units.
Do: Bring down the 3.

Step 5. We can give 1_{five} unit to each of the 12_{five} groups. This leaves 1_{five} unit.

$$
\begin{array}{r}
241 \\
12_{five} \overline{)3443_{five}} \\
-24 \\
\hline
104 \\
-103\!\downarrow \\
\hline
13 \\
-12 \\
\hline
1
\end{array}
$$

Think: Split 13_{five} units among 12_{five} groups. Each group gets 1_{five} unit, and $12_{five} \times 1_{five} = 12_{five}$.
Do: Put the 1 above the dividend in the units place, and subtract: $13_{five} - 12_{five} = 1_{five}$.
Think: The 1 represents 1_{five} unit.

Step 6. The number of units remaining is less than the divisor, so the procedure terminates. Each of the 12_{five} groups receives 2_{five} flats, 4_{five} longs, and 1_{five} unit. The quotient is 241_{five}, and the remainder is 1_{five}. Let's check our work: $12_{five} \times 241_{five} + 1_{five} = 3442_{five} + 1_{five} = 3443_{five}$, which equals the dividend. Then $3443_{five} \div 12_{five} = 241_{five} \, R1_{five}$.

QUESTIONS FOR SECTION 3.3

REPRESENTATION

Refresher: Representations (language, diagrams, tables, symbols, algebra, manipulatives, and contextualized situations) are important because we use them to organize, record, and communicate mathematical ideas and to make them more comprehensible.

1. Illustrate how to use base ten blocks to multiply: 4×37.

2. For the division problem $863 \div 4$,

   a. estimate the quotient.

   b. illustrate how to use base ten blocks to divide using the fair share model.

3. The partial quotients method is used to solve $3302 \div 121$ as shown.

$$
\begin{array}{rl}
121\overline{)3302} & \\
-363 & \quad 3 \\
\hline
2939 & \\
-1210 & \quad 10 \\
\hline
1729 & \\
-121 & \quad 1 \\
\hline
1608 & \\
-1573 & \quad 13 \\
\hline
35 & \\
\end{array}
$$

   a. List the partial quotients.

   b. Find the quotient.   c. Find the remainder.

   d. Write an equation involving division.

PROBLEM SOLVING

Refresher: Problem solving (reaching a goal that is not immediately attainable) is important because it helps students think more deeply about what they know and deal with unfamiliar situations.

4. Arlene is planning a party. She bought 212 sodas and made 72 cupcakes. If each person drinks 3 sodas and eats 2 cupcakes, how many people can she invite to the party?

5. Find two possible numbers with the given partial products.

   a. 42 and 210   b. 3, 60, 120, and 2400

6. Consider the problem of finding a product using only the digits 2, 3, 4, and 6.

$$
\begin{array}{r}
\square \ \square \ \square \\
\times \ \square \\
\hline
\end{array}
$$

   a. Find the largest product possible, assuming each digit can only be used once.

b. Find the largest product possible, assuming each digit can be used at most twice.

REASONING AND PROOF

Refresher: Reasoning and proof (thinking and justifying) are important because they help students make sense of mathematics.

7. What two simpler problems does 234×56 require, using the standard multiplication algorithm?

8. A student is multiplying two numbers using the standard multiplication algorithm. The two simpler problems are 345×8 and 345×40. What are the two numbers being multiplied?

9. In the problem $3456 \div b$, a student computed the partial quotients 400, 30, 60, and 3 and the remainder 5.
   a. Find the divisor.
   b. Write an equation involving division.
   c. Check your work.

10. Use properties to multiply 38 and 400.

11. Maria computed the partial quotients 1200, 300, 50, and 3 and the remainder 25 for $a \div b$.
   a. Find a possible value for a and for b.
   b. Is your choice of dividend a and divisor b unique? Explain.

12. List all whole numbers y such that a front-end estimate of the product leads to the approximation $y \times 242 \approx 120{,}000$.

13. What is the conceptual reason for
   a. "bringing down the 3"?

$$
\begin{array}{r}
1 \\
5\overline{)731} \\
-5\!\downarrow \\
\hline
23
\end{array}
$$

   b. "bringing down the 7"?

$$
\begin{array}{r}
42 \\
2\overline{)857} \\
-8\!\downarrow \\
\hline
05 \\
-4\!\downarrow \\
\hline
17
\end{array}
$$

14. What is the maximum number of partial products when you multiply an m-digit number by an n-digit number?

CONNECTIONS

Refresher: Connections (linking and applying mathematical ideas) are important because they deepen student understanding and make mathematics more meaningful, flexible, and useful.

15. The given diagram illustrates the lattice algorithm used to calculate 785×47. Mathematicians in India used this method by the twelfth century and eventually transferred it to Europe in the fourteenth century. In a multiplication lattice, the factors are arranged along the top and right edges of the lattice. The diagonals contain the products of digits, which simply require basic multiplication facts. The digits are added along the diagonals, with regrouping as necessary, because each diagonal represents a place value. The digits on the left and bottom edges of the lattice reveal the product: $785 \times 47 = 36{,}895$.

	7	8	5	×
3	2/8	3/2	2/0	4
6	4/9	5/6	3/5	7
	8	9	5	

a. Use the given lattice to determine 456×82.

	4	5	6	×
3	3/2	4/0	4/8	8
7	0/8	1/0	1/2	2
	3	9	2	

b. Use the lattice method to multiply 49 and 36. Verify the product with a calculator.

c. Use the lattice method to multiply 724 and 23. Verify the product with a calculator.

d. Calculate 46×37 using the partial products method and the lattice method.

e. What is the connection between the partial products and the diagonal entries in the lattice method?

f. Explain how the lattice method uses place value concepts.

16. Study the following lattice method for finding a product of polynomials, such as $(3x^2 + 4x + 7)(5x + 2)$.

	$3x^2$	$4x$	7	
	15x³	20x²	35x	5x
$15x^3$	6x²	8x	14	2
	$26x^2$	$43x$	14	

Then $(3x^2 + 4x + 7)(5x + 2) = 15x^3 + 26x^2 + 43x + 14$. Use the lattice method to find each product.

a. $(4x^2 + 8x + 3)(6x + 5)$
b. $(2x^2 + 7x + 4)(8x - 3)$
c. $(3x^2 + 4x - 7)(5x - 2)$

COMMUNICATION

Refresher: Communication (written and verbal explanations using representations and proper mathematical vocabulary) is important because it helps students refine and strengthen their understanding.

17. What is the relationship between the product and the partial products?

18. What is the relationship between the quotient and the partial quotients?

19. A student multiplies 43 and 8 and writes the following calculation:

$$\begin{array}{r} \overset{3\,2}{43} \\ \times\ 8 \\ \hline 344 \end{array}$$

   a. Explain why the 2 appears over the 4.

   b. Explain why the 3 appears in the hundreds place above the multiplication symbol.

20. Monique is using the standard multiplication algorithm to calculate 47×38. Why did she write 0 in the ones place?

$$\begin{array}{r} \overset{5}{47} \\ \times\ 38 \\ \hline 376 \\ 0 \end{array}$$

21. The actual work of a fourth grader is shown. The student did not give the correct answer. Explain how the student possibly made a mistake.

$$\begin{array}{r} 214\ \text{R}5 \\ 6\overline{)749} \\ -6 \\ \hline 14 \\ -12 \\ \hline 29 \\ -24 \\ \hline 5 \end{array}$$

More practice with the ideas of the section

22. Fill in the blank. Choose one of the following words or phrases: *estimation, long division, mental arithmetic, number sense, partial products, partial quotients, rounding,* or *partial quotients.*

   a. It is possible to express a product as a sum of _____.

   b. The _____ method is a flexible method that builds on repeated subtraction, multiplication, subtraction, and number sense.

   c. In the traditional _____ algorithm, the conceptual basis for bringing down a number is regrouping.

23. $a \times b$ has the partial products 21, 120, 140, and 800. What is the product?

24. Compute the following products using partial products.

   a. 45×127 b. 602×27

25. Find two factors that have 1800 as one of the partial products. The digit 0 cannot appear in any factor.

26. Theus is using the standard multiplication algorithm to calculate 342×537. Why did he write 0 in the ones and tens places?

$$\begin{array}{r} \overset{1}{\underset{}{\overset{2\,1}{342}}} \\ \times 537 \\ \hline 2394 \\ 10260 \\ 00 \end{array}$$

27. $a \div b$ has the partial quotients 14, 16, 20, and 2. What is the quotient?

28. In the problem $3421 \div b$, a student computed the partial quotients 10, 10, 10, 5, and 2 and the remainder 17.

   a. Find the divisor.

   b. Write an equation involving division.

   c. Check your work.

29. In the problem $2329 \div b$, a student computed the partial quotients 15, 10, 3, and 1 and the remainder 67.

   a. Find the divisor.

   b. Write an equation involving division.

   c. Check your work.

30. In the problem $a \div 25$, a student computed the partial quotients 100, 30, 8, and 8 and the remainder 12.

   a. Find the dividend.

   b. Write an equation involving division.

   c. Check your work.

31. In the problem $a \div 43$, a student computed the partial quotients 21, 5, 120, and 32 and the remainder 35.

   a. Find the dividend.

   b. Write an equation involving division.

   c. Check your work.

32. Estimate the quotient, and then use the partial quotients method to divide.

   a. $1841 \div 23$ b. $2194 \div 150$

33. Estimate the quotient, and then use the partial quotients method to find the quotient and the remainder.

   a. $2501 \div 30$ b. $5182 \div 125$

34. Estimate the quotient, and then use the standard long division algorithm to find the quotient and the remainder.

   a. $4304 \div 30$ b. $2314 \div 22$

35. Estimate the quotient.

   a. $358 \div 4$ b. $7718 \div 52$ c. $3105 \div 43$

36. The first infamous *Bumfights* video reportedly sold 300,000 copies at $20 per video. Calculate the total amount of money the producers grossed.

37. Bottled water is packed 24 bottles to a carton. To make sure that each of the 421 students has two bottles of water for the day, how many cartons of water must be ordered?

38. U.S. consumers dispose of approximately 133,000 personal computers each day. How many computers do they dispose of in 1 year? (Hint: 1 year = 365 days.)

39. Find the missing digits.

$$\begin{array}{r} 1\ \square\ \square \\ \times\ 2\ \square \\ \hline 3\ \square \\ 1\ 5\ 0 \\ 5\ 0\ 0 \\ \square\ 4\ 0 \\ 6\ 0\ 0 \\ \square\ 0\ 0\ 0 \\ \hline 3\ 4\ 2\ 5 \end{array}$$

40. Fill in the blanks.

   a. ___ × ___ = 2000   **b.** ___ × ___ = 28,000

   c. ___ × ___ × ___ = 60,000,000

41. List all whole numbers y such that the front-end estimate of $34 \times y$ is 2400.

42. Lenny estimates a product of two whole numbers using the front-end strategy. The result is 7200. Find a possible pair of factors.

43. Find a range-based estimate of each product.

   a. 24×365 **b.** 97×547 **c.** 262×67

44. Do the following using mental arithmetic.

   a. How many groups of 15 are in 1470?

   b. How many groups of 18 are in 378?

   c. How many groups of 45 are in 405?

   d. If you have 11 rows of 25 chairs, how many chairs are there in all?

45. You have 9 quarters and 37 nickels. Use mental arithmetic to determine how much money you have.

46. Nick has approximately $212 in his pocket. He wants to buy some $16 T-shirts for himself and his friends. Excluding tax, use mental arithmetic to find how many T-shirts he could buy.

47. Use compatible numbers to multiply.

   a. $2 \times 4 \times 6 \times 5$ **b.** $45 \times 8 \times 5 \times 2$

   c. $5 \times 4 \times 8 \times 6 \times 5$ **d.** $13 \times 4 \times 2 \times 25$

48. Use mental arithmetic to multiply.

   a. 8×12 **b.** 9×35 **c.** 32×41 **d.** 234×50

49. Use mental arithmetic to solve. Rabbits inhabit the town of Hops-A-Lot. Each bunny eats three carrots, two radishes, and four lettuce leaves each day. In 1 week, how many of each vegetable do 52 rabbits consume?

50. Consider the problem of finding a product using only the digits 1, 2, 3, 4, and 5.

   □ □
   × □ □

   a. Find the smallest product possible, assuming each digit can only be used once.

   b. Find the smallest product possible, assuming each digit can be used at most twice.

51. Three students estimate 47×159. Which do you believe to be the closest approximation: 40×100, 50×200, or 50×160? Why?

52. Orange juice comes in six-packs and is packed four six-packs to a carton. Each of 421 students will have orange juice on a trip to the park. How many cartons of orange juice are needed?

53. Gary is building a block wall 6 feet high and 120 feet long. Each block is 16 inches long and 8 inches tall. Approximately how many blocks does he need to buy?

54. If two people each use rounding to estimate a product, are they guaranteed to get the same answer?

55. Amber makes a trip to Harry's Hardware. She is building a rectangular patio with 6-by-6-inch concrete pavers. The dimensions of the patio are 21 by 12 feet. How many pavers should Amber purchase at the store?

56. There were 42 baskets of items in the store. The manager added 32 more items. On the average, each basket then had 20 items. How many items were there altogether in the baskets originally?

57. Farmer Arlene has eight rectangular corn fields and six rectangular wheat fields. Each corn field is l feet long and w feet wide, and each wheat field is s feet long and t feet wide.

   a. What is the total area of the fields?

   b. If the total area of the corn fields was 224 square feet, then what are some possibilities for l and w?

   c. If the total area of the wheat fields was 192 square feet, then what are some possibilities for s and t?

58. Spencer the computer whiz needs to buy printer paper and writable CDs. Each ream of paper costs $4.95 and each spool of CDs cost $8.70. He needs eight reams of paper and six spools of CDs. Use mental math to find the approximate amount of money that he needs to make the purchase (excluding tax).

59. Put a \ symbol in the box if the number can be a partial product. Put a / symbol in the box if the number can be a partial quotient. Put an X in the box if the number can be both.

Number	300	320	11	40	43
\, /, or X					

60. What two simpler problems does $234_{\text{five}} \times 42_{\text{five}}$ require, using the standard multiplication algorithm?

61. A student is multiplying two numbers using the standard multiplication algorithm. The two simpler problems are $241_{\text{six}} \times 4_{\text{six}}$ and $241_{\text{six}} \times 20_{\text{six}}$. What are the two numbers being multiplied?

62. A student is multiplying 43_{five} and 4_{five}. The student makes the following calculation:

$$\begin{array}{r} ^2 \\ 43_{\text{five}} \\ \times 4_{\text{five}} \\ \hline 2_{\text{five}} \end{array}$$

   a. Explain why the 2 appears over the 4.

   b. Complete the calculation.

63. A student determines the partial products for $a \times b$ are 11_{five}, 220_{five}, 40_{five}, and 1300_{five}. What is $a \times b$?

64. Multiply using the partial products method.

   a. $132_{\text{five}} \times 24_{\text{five}}$ **b.** $42_{\text{five}} \times 31_{\text{five}}$

65. Multiply using the standard multiplication algorithm.

   a. $322_{\text{five}} \times 23_{\text{five}}$ **b.** $134_{\text{five}} \times 43_{\text{five}}$

66. The following is an unfinished division problem.

$$\begin{array}{r} 1 \\ 23_{\text{five}} \overline{)3423_{\text{five}}} \\ -23\downarrow \\ \hline 112 \end{array}$$

   a. What is the conceptual reason for "bringing down the 2"?

   b. What does the 112 represent?

67. The following is an unfinished division problem.

$$21_{\text{five}} \overline{\smash{)}3012_{\text{five}}}$$
$$\underline{-21\downarrow}$$
$$4$$

with 1 above the problem.

a. What does the 1 represent above the 0 in the dividend?

b. What does the 4 represent?

68. In the problem $a \div 23_{\text{five}}$, a student computed the partial quotients 10_{five}, 3_{five}, and 1_{five}. The remainder was 2_{five}.

a. Find the dividend.

b. Write an equation involving division.

69. You are given that $3324_{\text{five}} \div 12_{\text{five}} = 231_{\text{five}}$ R2_{five}. Use this result to find

a. $3320_{\text{five}} \div 12_{\text{five}}$.   **b.** $3323_{\text{five}} \div 12_{\text{five}}$.

c. $3330_{\text{five}} \div 12_{\text{five}}$.   **d.** $3332_{\text{five}} \div 12_{\text{five}}$.

70. Draw the array model for the product $22_{\text{five}} \times 32_{\text{five}}$.

71. Use the partial quotients method to divide 4304_{five} by 30_{five}.

72. In the problem $23020_{\text{five}} \div b$, a student computed the partial quotients 100_{five}, 120_{five}, 10_{five}, 2_{five}, and 1_{five} and the remainder 3_{five}.

a. Find the quotient.

b. Explain how you would find the divisor b.

CHAPTER 3 REVIEW

CHAPTER 3 Organizer

Section	What You Should Learn	Review Problems
3.1	**1.** Identify situations requiring multiplication with whole numbers.	1–5
	2. Solve word problems using algebra or a diagram.	6–8
	3. Use properties, mental arithmetic, patterns, or skip-counting to multiply.	9–16
	4. Understand and apply rules of exponents in multiplication.	17–19
3.2	**1.** Distinguish the two models of division.	20–23
	2. Solve problems involving division.	24–25
	3. Apply the relationship between multiplication and division.	26–28
	4. Justify why division by zero is prohibited.	29–30
	5. Apply the Quotient-Remainder Theorem.	31–35
	6. Write a word problem for equations such as $15 \div n = 3$ or $14 \div 3 = 4$ R2.	36
	7. Apply the order of operations.	37–38
3.3	**1.** Use base ten blocks to multiply, for example, 48×3.	39
	2. Decomposes a product of two numbers into simpler multiplication problems using the distributive property.	40-48
	3. Multiply two numbers using various strategies.	49–51
	4. Estimate products.	52
	5. Illustrate division, for example, $745 \div 3$, using base ten blocks.	53
	6. Divide using various strategies.	54–56
	7. Provide a mathematical explanation of bringing down a digit in the standard division algorithm.	57

Key Terms and Concepts

multiplicative reasoning 127

set model 128

repeated addition 128

multiplication 128

multiplier 128

multiplicand 128

factor 128

product 128

skip counting 129

measurement model 129

array 130

array model 130

Cartesian product model 130

fundamental counting
principle 131

comparison model 131

multiplying by powers of 10 133

closure property of
multiplication 134

commutative property of
multiplication 134

associative property of
multiplication 135

distributive property of
multiplication over addition 136

distributive property of multiplication
over subtraction 138

zero property of multiplication 138

identity property of
multiplication 138

number sense 139

repeated multiplication 139

exponential notation 139

base 140

exponent 140

division 145

fair share model 145

repeated subtraction model 145

fact family 146

division by zero 147

definition of division 147

undefined 147

indeterminate 147

dividend 147

divisor 147

quotient 147

missing factor 147

unknown factor 147

inverse operations 148

quotient-remainder theorem 150

remainder 151

order of operations 153

standard multiplication
algorithm 162

partial products method 163

mental arithmetic 165

mental strategies 165

estimation 166

range estimate 166

partial quotients method 167

standard long division
algorithm 168

base five multiplication 171

base five division 174

Review Questions

1. Use the set model to represent each product.

   a. 4×2 **b.** 2×4

2. State which model of multiplication best applies to the word problem: *set model, array model, Cartesian product model, comparison model, measurement model.*

   a. There are five tables in a room. Four children are seated at each table. How many children are there altogether?

   b. Krista is carrying 12 books. Kelly has three times as many books as Krista. How many books does Kelly have?

   c. Jamie drinks two glasses of milk every morning before school. How many glasses of milk did he drink in 7 days?

   d. You can buy barbecue-flavored chips or sour cream and chives–flavored chips in small, medium, or large packages. How many different selections can you make?

   e. Five women agreed to make 100 cookies each for the Carlsbad Street Fair. How many cookies did they make?

   f. Students in the band were marching in a parade. There were five students in a row. As the students marched by, John counted 20 rows. How many students were in the band?

   g. To make a tablecloth, Kelly purchased 3 m of material at $5/m. How much did she spend for the cloth?

3. The Internet Assigned Numbers Authority maintains a registry of Internet protocol (IP) addresses that companies and universities use to connect their networks to the Internet. IP addresses have the "dotted decimal" form, such as 165.25.0.177. Each IP has four blocks of digits, and each block is a number ranging from 0 to 255. With this notation, the IP addresses range from 0.0.0.0 to 255.255.255.255.

   a. Give an example of a valid IP address.

   b. Give an example of an invalid IP address.

   c. Determine the total number of valid IP addresses.

4. Ross goes to the Fancy Pants Clothing Store to buy an outfit. The store offers suits in four different colors, shirts in two different colors, and ties with seven different patterns. Assuming that they all match in any combination, how many outfits does Ross have to choose from?

5. Write a word problem that requires the given equation.

   a. $5 \times 4 = m$ **b.** $3 \times n = 24$ **c.** $k \times 15 = 45$

6. Mary has 12 coins. She has three times as many coins as Verne.

   a. How many coins does Verne have?

   b. Solve this word problem using a diagram.

   c. Solve this problem using algebra.

   d. Some students think the answer is 36 coins. Why do you think they make this mistake?

7. How many digits are in the standard form of 2678×10^{42}?

8. Do the following.

   a. Kenna has twice as many coins as Sammy. Together, they have 702 coins. How many coins does Sammy have?

   b. Kenna has 7 more than five times as many coins as Sammy. Together, they have 439 coins. How many coins does Kenna have?

   c. Kenna has 12 fewer than three times as many coins as Sammy. Together, they have 520 coins. How many coins does Sammy have?

9. Show how you can use skip counting to multiply.

   a. 4×5 b. 3×4

10. Use the distributive property to multiply.

    a. 15×11 b. 7×12

11. Use the associative property to evaluate.

    a. 4×125 b. 25×20 c. 5×120

12. 21×481 is an amazing product, because $21 \times 481 = 10,101$. Use properties of multiplication to find another amazing product equal to 10,101.

13. Do the following.

    a. Use a calculator to evaluate 68^2.

    b. Use a calculator to evaluate 668^2.

    c. Use a calculator to evaluate 6668^2.

    d. Describe any pattern that you noticed.

    e. Predict the standard form of $6,666,668^2$.

14. Show you can use

    a. 4×6 to compute 40×6.

    b. 3×5 to compute 300×50.

15. Simplify the expressions. Show all steps.

    a. $3(5a)$ b. $6n \times 8n$

16. Use mental arithmetic.

    a. How many groups of 18 are in 396?

    b. How many groups of 12 are in 156?

    c. How many groups of 15 are in 1470?

17. Identify the base and the exponent. Then express the number in terms of repeated multiplication.

    a. 7^4 b. 16^5 c. 4^3

18. Consider the sequence $3^3 = 27$, $3^2 = 9$, $3^1 = 3$, ... Use patterns to define 3^0.

19. Use properties of exponents to verify.

    a. $8^4 = 2^{12}$ b. $(24)^5 = 2^{15} \times 3^5$

20. Draw a diagram using the fair share model for division to find each of the following.

    a. $24 \div 8$ b. $14 \div 5$

21. Draw a diagram using the repeated subtraction model for division to find each of the following.

    a. $24 \div 8$ b. $14 \div 5$

22. Tom has 47 pennies and wants to stack them into groups of 8 pennies.

    a. Which division model is appropriate?

    b. How many pennies are left over?

23. Mr. McCormick is organizing a party for the second-grade classes at his school. He estimates 523 paper plates will be needed. There are 25 plates per package.

    a. How many packages does he need to buy?

    b. Which division model is appropriate?

24. Solve each problem using a diagram.

    a. Kyle and Henry have 157 coins altogether. Henry has 5 more than three times as many coins as Kyle. How many more coins does Henry have than Kyle?

    b. Leticia read 4 fewer than three times as many pages as Diane. Leticia read 218 pages. How many pages did Diane read?

25. Look for a pattern in the following repeating sequence of letters: A B C A B C A B C .... What letter will be in the 243th position?

26. A fifth-grade student did not know how to solve $n \div 7 = 84$. What advice would you give?

27. A fifth-grade student did not know how to solve $510 \div n = 15$. What advice would you give?

28. Write the fact family for the equation $n \div 8 = 72$. Circle an equation that helps you solve this equation.

29. A student says $6 \div 0$ is 0, because he is dividing by nothing, he gets nothing. How would you respond to this student to improve his understanding of division by zero?

30. A student says that zero is nothing. So $0 \div 0 = 0$, because nothing divided by nothing is nothing. How would you respond to this student to improve her understanding of division by zero?

31. A student claims that $291 \div 15 = 19$ R6. Check the student's work.

32. Find the variable.

    a. $a \div 6 = 22$ R1   b. $38 \div 3 = 12$ Rr

    c. $77 \div 4 = q$ R1

33. Use a calculator to find the quotient and the remainder of $46 \div 8$. Then check your work.

34. Mrs. Dugger has 460 marbles. She plans to store the marbles in bags. Each bag can hold at most 24 marbles. What is the minimum number of bags needed?

35. Percy has 130 coins. Kenneth has 45 coins. Write a sentence that compares these quantities using

    a. additive reasoning.   b. multiplicative reasoning.

36. Write a word problem that requires each calculation.

    a. $3 \times 5 = 15$ b. $14 \div 3 = 4$ R2

37. Evaluate each expression.

    a. $5 \times 20 - (10 \div 2)^2$ b. $4 \times (10 - 8)^3 \div 8 + 1$

    c. $4 - 3 + 10 \times 3 \div 3$

38. Add parentheses to make the equation true.

    a. $2 + 4 \div 2 \times 3 = 9$ b. $6 + 18 \div 3 \times 2 + 3 = 7$

    c. $9 \div 3 \times 3 + 20 \div 4 + 1 = 13$

    d. $14 \div 6 \div 3 \times 3 + 2 \times 4 = 29$

39. Sketch how you can use base ten blocks to multiply: 27×3.

40. A student uses the standard multiplication algorithm to multiply:

    456
    ×32

    What two simpler multiplication problems does the student need to know?

41. A student uses the standard multiplication algorithm to calculate 456×32 as shown. Why did the student put 0 below the 2 in the ones place?

    $\overset{1\,1}{456}$
    ×32
    ——
    912
      0

42. Which property allows you to decompose 789×62 into the two simpler problems 789×60 and 789×2?

43. Outline or describe the procedure a student should follow to calculate 5274×300.

44. $abc \times f = 2348$ and $abc \times e = 3522$, where each letter is a digit. Determine each product.

    a. $abc \times ef$ **b.** $abc \times fe$

45. Find the missing digits:

    ```
            5 □
        ×   4 □
        ————————
            2 □
        1   5 0
        2 □   0
      □ 0   0 0
      ————————————
      2 4   5 1
    ```

46. What two simpler problems does $412_{\text{five}} \times 23_{\text{five}}$ require, using the standard multiplication algorithm?

47. A student is multiplying two numbers using the standard multiplication algorithm. The two simpler problems are $523_{\text{six}} \times 2_{\text{six}}$ and $523_{\text{six}} \times 30_{\text{six}}$. What are the two numbers being multiplied?

48. Multiply using the standard multiplication algorithm.

    a. $213_{\text{five}} \times 23_{\text{five}}$ **b.** $312_{\text{five}} \times 42_{\text{five}}$

49. Multiply using the partial products method.

    a. 428×73 **b.** 789×48

50. Multiply using the lattice method.

    a. 428×73 **b.** 789×48

51. Multiply using the partial products method.

    a. $213_{\text{five}} \times 23_{\text{five}}$ **b.** $312_{\text{five}} \times 42_{\text{five}}$

52. Estimate each product.

    a. 36×198 **b.** 42×305 **c.** $486,367 \times 72$

53. Sketch how to use base ten blocks to divide 412 by 3.

54. Use the partial quotients method to divide. List your partial quotients.

    a. $4567 \div 123$ **b.** $2010_{\text{five}} \div 14_{\text{five}}$

55. In the division problem $a \div 450$, a student computed the partial quotients 4000, 200, 10, and 8. The remainder was 231.

    a. Find the dividend.

    b. Write an equation involving division.

56. Use the standard division algorithm to divide.

    a. $3460 \div 12$ **b.** $3401_{\text{five}} \div 21_{\text{five}}$

57. What is going on when we "bring down the 3"?

    ```
        2
    4)935
    −8↓   ("bring down the 3")
    ——
     13
    ```

Chapter 3 Test

1. *Identify situations requiring multiplication with whole numbers.* Determine which of the following multiplication models is more appropriate in each situation: *set model, measurement model, array model, comparison model, Cartesian product model.*

    a. Alexis has 15 comic books. Chad has three times as many comic books as Alexis. How many comic books does Chad have?

    b. Mr. Hines loaded 55 cedar planks in his van for building a fence. Each plank weighed 2 pounds. How much did the cedar planks weigh altogether?

    c. Maria organized her coins in stacks. There were 24 stacks, and each stack had 10 coins. How many coins did she have altogether?

    d. The code to a combination lock is a sequence of two letters (A through Z) followed by one digit (from 0 to 9). How many different codes are possible?

    e. The students were in a graduation ceremony. They formed three lines, and each line had 35 students. How many students were there altogether?

2. *Use properties or mental arithmetic.* Use properties to multiply.

    a. 38×400 **b.** 42×103 **c.** 35×98

    d. 44×25 **e.** 11×18

3. *Solve word problems using algebra or a diagram.* A printing company prints shirts for organizations. It charges $60 to set up the equipment to print the logo on the shirts, plus $7 for each shirt ordered.

    a. Write an equation for the cost C for an order of n shirts.

    b. How much will the printing company charge for an order of 124 shirts?

    c. An organization has a budget of $1563. How many shirts can it order?

4. *Solve word problems using algebra or a diagram.* Daniel has 15 coins. He has five times as many coins as Tony. How many coins does Tony have?

    a. Solve this word problem using a diagram.

    b. Solve this problem using algebra.

5. *Solve word problems using algebra or a diagram.* Rachel has three times as many coins as Pam. Together, they have 372 coins. How many coins does each have?

   a. Solve this word problem using a diagram.

   b. Solve this problem using algebra.

6. *Solve word problems using algebra or a diagram.* Kira has 5 fewer than three times as many coins as Leo. Together, they have 307 coins. How many coins does each have?

   a. Solve this word problem using a diagram.

   b. Solve this problem using algebra.

7. *Understand and apply rules of exponents in multiplication.* Rewrite each expression using exponential notation.

   a. $3 \cdot 3 \cdot 3 \cdot 3$ **b.** $7^{43} \cdot 7^{82}$

8. *Understand and apply rules of exponents in multiplication.* Use properties of exponents to verify.

   a. $10^{12} = 2^{12} \cdot 5^{12}$ **b.** $20^{25} \cdot 10^{31} = 2^{81} \cdot 5^{56}$

9. *Distinguish the two models of division.* Identify the model of division (fair share or repeated subtraction), and then write an equation involving division.

   a. A teacher wants to separate 28 students into teams of 7 students. How many teams can be formed?

   b. A teacher wishes to distribute 20 cookies among five students so that each student receives the same number of cookies. How many cookies should each student receive?

10. *Distinguish the two models of division.* For the diagram shown, write an equation based on the

    a. repeated subtraction model.   **b.** fair share model.

    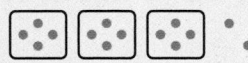

11. *Apply the relationship between multiplication and division.* A student solves an equation, knowing that multiplication and division are inverse operations. Supply the missing reasons.

$n \times 35 = 840$	original equation
$n \times 35 \div 35 = 840 \div 35$	a.
$n = 840 \div 35$	b.
$n = 24$	simplification
$n \div 28 = 64$	original equation
$n \div 28 \times 28 = 64 \times 28$	c.
$n = 64 \times 28$	d.
$n = 1792$	simplification

12. *Apply the relationship between multiplication and division.* Solve the equation $n \div 24 = 120$,

    a. using the definition of division.

    b. knowing that multiplication and division are inverse operations.

13. *Apply the relationship between multiplication and division.* Solve the equation $n \times 24 = 120$,

    a. using the definition of division.

    b. knowing that multiplication and division are inverse operations.

14. *Use properties, mental arithmetic, patterns, or skip counting to multiply.*

    a. Show how you can use skip counting to multiply: 3×8.

    b. Use the distributive property to multiply: 12×8.

15. *Solve problems involving division.* Victor made a stack of cubes that was 1512 mm tall. Each cube had sides 14 mm long. How many cubes were in the stack?

16. *Apply the quotient–remainder theorem.* A student writes the following equation: $44 \div 6 = 7$ R3. How can she check her work?

17. *Apply the quotient–remainder theorem.* Ellen sold 20 rolls of wrapping paper for a fundraiser, while Lenny sold 6 rolls of wrapping paper. Compare the number of rolls of wrapping paper they sold using multiplicative reasoning.

18. *Apply the quotient–remainder theorem.* What is the obvious error in the equation $50 \div 7 = 6$ R8?

19. *Apply the quotient–remainder theorem.* Look for a pattern in the following sequence of letters: P Q R P Q R P Q R . . . . What is the 238th letter in this sequence?

20. *Write a word problem for equations such as $15 \div n = 3$ or $14 \div 3 = 4$ R2.* Write a word problem that requires the student to write the equation given.

    a. $32 \div n = 8$ **b.** $22 \div 4 = 5$ R2

21. *Apply the order of operations.* Evaluate each expression.

    a. $3 + 5 \times 2$ **b.** $48 \div 2 \times 4$ **c.** $49 - 5 + 20$

    d. $180 \div 5 - 3(2)$ **e.** $(3 + 2) \times 4^2 + 18$

22. *Decompose a product of two numbers into simpler multiplication problems using the distributive property.*

    a. Which property allows you to decompose 234×56 into the two simpler problems 234×50 and 234×6?

    b. A student is multiplying two numbers using the standard multiplication algorithm. The two simpler problems are 482×7 and 482×50. What are the two numbers being multiplied?

    c. What two simpler problems does 942×38 require, using the standard multiplication algorithm?

23. *Use various strategies to multiply.*

    a. Use the partial product method to multiply 256×63. List the partial products.

    b. $abc \times f = 2568$ and $abc \times e = 1284$, where each letter is a digit. Determine $abc \times ef$ and $abc \times fe$.

    c. Lisa is using the standard multiplication algorithm to calculate 234×567. Why did she write 0 in the ones and tens places?

$$
\begin{array}{r}
{\scriptstyle 1\ 1} \\
{\scriptstyle \cancel{2}\ \cancel{2}} \\
234 \\
\times 537 \\
\hline
1638 \\
7020 \\
00
\end{array}
$$

24. *Provide a mathematical explanation of bringing down a digit in the standard division algorithm.* Answer the following for the given partially completed calculation.

$$
\begin{array}{r}
6 \\
3\overline{)2051} \\
-18\!\downarrow \\
\hline
25
\end{array}
\quad \text{(``Bring down the 5'')}
$$

a. Why do we place the 6 above the 0?

b. Why do we subtract 18?

c. What is going on when we "bring down the 5"?

25. *Use the partial quotients method or standard division algorithm to divide.*

a. Apply the partial quotients method to divide $47{,}937 \div 412$. List the partial quotients. Write an equation.

b. In the division problem $a \div 234$, a student computed the partial quotients 3000, 100, 20, and 5. The remainder was 145. What is the dividend?

c. In the problem $46{,}263 \div b$, a student computed the partial quotients 1000, 100, 10, 10, 5, and 3. The remainder was 15. What is the divisor?

4

Elementary Number Theory and Integers

Where Are We Going?

In **Section 4.1,** we discuss divisibility vocabulary and concepts and develop divisibility rules. In **Section 4.2,** we discuss prime numbers, composite numbers, a prime factorization theorem, the greatest common factor, and the least common multiple. In **Section 4.3,** we discuss integers, models, and operations with integers.

What Is Elementary Number Theory?

In Chapter 2, we explained how counting numbers are put together by addition. For example, $234 = 200 + 30 + 4$. It turns out that 234 can be put together by multiplication also: $234 = 2 \cdot 3^2 \cdot 13$. Knowing properties of counting numbers and the various ways they are put together is vital to number sense. **Elementary number theory** is the study of properties of counting numbers, their relationships, and ways to represent them. For example, 3888 has several representations: $3888 = 2^4 \cdot 3^5$, $3888 = 3 \cdot 1296$, and $3888 = 15 \cdot 259 + 3$. As we show in this chapter, the equation $3888 = 2^4 \cdot 3^5$ reveals 3888 has two prime factors and 30 factors, $3888 = 3 \cdot 1296$ reveals 3888 is divisible by 3 and 1296, and $3888 = 15 \cdot 259 + 3$ reveals 15 and 259 are not factors of 3888. The numerical representations emphasize some properties of 3888 and de-emphasize other properties. Students should "recognize equivalent representations for the same number and generate them by decomposing and composing numbers" (NCTM, Gr. 3–5) (© NCTM Standards 2011 by National Council of Teachers of Mathematics) and "understand numbers, ways of representing numbers, relationships among numbers, and number systems" (NCTM, Pre-K–8). They should also "use factors, multiples, prime factorization, and relatively prime numbers to solve problems" (NCTM, Gr. 6–8).

What Are Elementary Number Theory Concepts?

Elementary number theory concepts in the elementary mathematics curriculum involve factors, multiples, divisors, divisibility tests, prime factorization, least common multiples, and greatest common factors. Together, these ideas form a foundation for understanding how counting numbers are related through multiplication and division. Many of these number theory concepts form the basis for the secure transmission of sensitive electronic information in the banking, health, computer, telecommunications, and defense industries.

SECTION 4.1   Divisibility of Counting Numbers

Basic Vocabulary

In Section 3.2, we discussed the Quotient–Remainder Theorem: Given any two whole numbers a and b, with $b \neq 0$, there exist whole numbers q and r such that $a = b \cdot q + r$, with $0 \leq r < b$. Another way to express this equation is $a \div b = q$ Rr. For example, given the numbers 13 and 5, we can write

$$13 = 5 \cdot 2 + 3$$

and

$$13 \div 5 = 2 \text{ R}3.$$

The nonrectangular array in Figure 1 represents the equation $13 \div 5 = 2$ R3. In this section, we focus on number relationships in which the remainder is 0. Geometrically, this means we are interested in number relationships described by rectangular arrays. For example, the rectangular array in Figure 2 reflects the number relationships $12 = 4 \cdot 3$, $12 = 3 \cdot 4$, $12 \div 3 = 4$, and $12 \div 4 = 3$. The diagram illustrates 3 is a factor of 12, 12 is a multiple of 3, 3 is a divisor of 12, 3 divides 12, and 12 is divisible by 3.

CONNECTION

REPRESENTATION

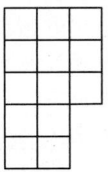

FIGURE 1
Representation of $13 = 5 \cdot 2 + 3$
and $13 \div 5 = 2$ R3.

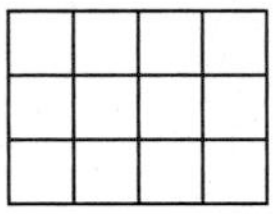

FIGURE 2
Representation of $12 = 4 \cdot 3$, $12 = 3 \cdot 4$,
$12 \div 3 = 4$, and $12 \div 4 = 3$.

We use vocabulary words such as *divisibility, factors,* and *multiples* to describe multiplicative relationships between two numbers.

> **Definition**
>
> Let a and b represent whole numbers with $b \neq 0$. Suppose there is a whole number q such that $a = b \cdot q$. Then we say, **"b is a factor of a"** and **"a is a multiple of b."** We also say, **"b is a divisor of a,"** **"b divides a,"** and **"a is divisible by b."** For example, 4 is a factor of 12, 12 is a multiple of 4, 4 divides 12, and 12 is divisible by 4.

EXAMPLE 4.1   What does the equation $42 = 6 \cdot 7$ reveal?

CONNECTION

COMMUNICATION

REASONING

REPRESENTATION

SOLUTION

Answers vary, such as 6 is a factor of 42, 6 is a divisor of 42, 7 divides 42, or 42 is a multiple of 7.

▲

Positive multiples of 5 are numbers such as 5, 10, 15, 20, . . . , and positive multiples of 8 are numbers such as 8, 16, 24, 32, ... Positive multiples form skip-counting sequences. The following Released Item indirectly asked students to identify a multiple of 6.

> ▶ **RELEASED ITEM**
>
> ● NAEP, 2003
>
> Six students bought exactly enough pens to share equally among themselves.
> Which of the following could be the number of pens they bought?
> **a.** 46 **b.** 48 **c.** 50 **d.** 52
>
> 51% of fourth graders and 83% of eighth graders gave the correct response.
> (U.S. Department of Education, Institute of Education Sciences, National Center for
> Education Statistics, NAEP)

The following example applies the various meanings of divisibility.

EXAMPLE 4.2

CONNECTION
COMMUNICATION
REASONING
REPRESENTATION

a. Prove that 4 is a factor of 68.

b. Let n be any counting number. Suppose b divides 12. Prove b divides $12n$.

SOLUTION

a. $68 = 4 \cdot 17$, so 4 is a factor of 68. Alternatively, $68 \div 4 = 17$, so 4 is a factor of 68.

b. Suppose b divides 12. Then $12 = b \cdot q$ for some counting number q. Let n be any counting number. Then $12n = (b \cdot q)n = b \cdot (qn)$. So $12n = b \cdot (qn)$. The number qn is a counting number. Thus, b divides $12n$.

▲

Theorem 1 generalizes the result in the second part of the example.

> **Theorem 1**
>
> Let a, b, and n be any counting numbers. If b divides a, then b divides $a \cdot n$.

The proof of Theorem 1 is a homework question at the end of this section.

We say, "b does not divide a" if and only if $a \neq b \cdot c$ for any counting number c. In other words, $a \div b = q$ Rr for some whole number q and nonzero remainder r. For example, $14 \div 5 = 2$ R4, so 5 does not divide 14 (or 5 is not a factor of 14).

EXAMPLE 4.3

CONNECTION
REASONING

a. Prove that 8 does not divide 35.

b. What does the equation $46 = 8 \cdot 5 + 6$ reveal?

SOLUTION

a. $35 \div 8 = 4$ R3. The remainder is nonzero; therefore, 8 does not divide 35.

b. $46 = 8 \cdot 5 + 6$ is the same as $46 \div 8 = 5$ R6. This means 8 is not a factor of 46, 8 is not a divisor of 46, 8 does not divide 46, and 46 is not divisible by 8.

▲

EXAMPLE 4.4

CONNECTION
COMMUNICATION
PROBLEM SOLVING
REASONING

How many multiples of 8 are between 107 and 241?

SOLUTION

$107 \div 8 = 13$ R3 and $241 \div 8 = 30$ R1. Multiples of 8 between 107 and 241 are $8 \cdot 14$, $8 \cdot 15$, $8 \cdot 16, \ldots, 8 \cdot 30$. The number of multiples of 8 in this list is the same as the number of terms in the sequence $14, 15, 16, \ldots, 30$. There are 17 numbers in the list, so there are 17 multiples of 8 between 107 and 241.

▲

Divisibility of Sums and Differences

7 divides 63 and 21. Does 7 divide the sum of 63 and 21? Let's check: $63 + 21 = 84$, and $84 \div 7 = 12$. This means 7 divides the sum $63 + 21$. Does 7 divide the difference between 63 and 21? Let's check: $63 - 21 = 42$, and $42 \div 7 = 6$. This means 7 divides the difference. Theorem 2 generalizes these results.

Theorem 2

Let a, b, and n represent counting numbers.
a. If n divides a and n divides b, then n divides $a + b$.
b. If n divides a and n divides b, then n divides $a - b$.

REASONING

Proof of Theorem 2(a): Suppose n divides both a and b. Then $a = nq$ and $b = nc$ for some whole numbers q and c. Then $a + b = nq + nc = n(q + c)$. The sum $q + c$ is a whole number, so n divides the sum $a + b$. The proof of Theorem 2(b) is similar.

Although 7 divides 35, 7 does not divide 18. Does 7 divide the sum of 35 and 18? Let's check: $35 + 18 = 43$, and $43 \div 7 = 6$ R1. This means 7 does not divide the sum $35 + 18$. Does 7 divide the difference between 35 and 18? Let's check: $35 - 18 = 17$, and $17 \div 7 = 2$ R3, so 7 does not divide the difference. Theorem 3 generalizes these results.

Theorem 3

Let a, b, and n represent counting numbers.
a. If n divides a but n does not divide b, then n does not divide $a + b$.
b. If n divides a but n does not divide b, then n does not divide $a - b$.

REASONING

Proof of Theorem 3(a): Suppose n divides a but not b. Then $a \div n = c$ and $b \div n = d$ Rr for some whole numbers c, d, and r with $0 < r < n$. Then $a = nc$ and $b = nd + r$. Then $a + b = nc + (nd + r) = (nc + nd) + r = n(c + d) + r$. Then $(a + b) \div n = (c + d)$ Rr, where $0 < r < n$. Then $(a + b) \div n$ has a nonzero remainder, so n does not divide the sum $a + b$. The proof of Theorem 3(b) is similar.

EXAMPLE 4.5

REASONING

Answer the question without finding the sum or difference.
a. Does 3 divide $6 + 12$?

b. Does 5 divide c in the equation $35 = 20 + c$?

c. Does 2 divide $8 - 3$?

d. Does 2 divide d in the equation $20 = d + 15$?

SOLUTION

a. 3 divides 6, and 3 divides 12. By Theorem 2, 3 divides $6 + 12$.

b. $c = 35 - 20$. 5 divides 35, and 5 divides 20. By Theorem 2, 5 divides $35 - 20$. But $c = 35 - 20$, so 5 divides c.

c. 2 divides 8, but 2 does not divide 3. By Theorem 3, 2 does not divide $8 - 3$.

d. $d = 20 - 15$. 2 divides 20, but 2 does not divide 15. By Theorem 3, 2 does not divide $20 - 15$. But $d = 20 - 15$, so 2 does not divide d.

▲

Divisibility Rules

We can always check whether 3 is a factor of 346 by using division. A **divisibility rule** is a simple procedure to check whether one number divides another number, without performing the actual division. Divisibility rules are one piece of the puzzle in understanding relationships between numbers. Students usually apply rules for divisors 2, 3, 4, 5, 6, 8, 9, and 10. The following Classroom Connection illustrates a typical homework question for divisibility rules.

 Classroom Connection

- *Math,* Grade 5, p. 201

  Use a divisibility rule to tell if each number is divisible by 2, 3, 4, 9, and 10: 126; 5004; 3,172; 6,123. (© 2000 Macmillan/McGraw Hill. Reprinted by permission.)

Theorems 2 and 3 form the basis for elementary divisibility rules. We show how to develop each rule for the four-digit number *ABCD* so that you can see *why* the rules work. The rules are truly logical rather than procedures to memorize. Divisibility rules exploit the expanded form of numbers and involve solving simpler problems. We begin with the simplest rules first. Soon, you will be able to make your own rules.

Divisibility Rules for 2, 5, and 10

Let's devise a rule for divisibility for 2. We begin with the expanded form of the four-digit number *ABCD:*

$$
\begin{aligned}
ABCD &= A \cdot 1000 + B \cdot 100 + C \cdot 10 + D \\
&= A \cdot 500 \cdot 2 + B \cdot 50 \cdot 2 + C \cdot 5 \cdot 2 + D \\
&= \underbrace{(A \cdot 500 + B \cdot 50 + C \cdot 5) \cdot 2}_{\text{divisible by 2}} + \underbrace{D}_{\text{Is } D \text{ divisible by 2?}}
\end{aligned}
$$

By Theorem 2(a), if 2 divides $(A \cdot 500 + B \cdot 50 + C \cdot 5) \cdot 2$ and 2 divides *D,* then 2 divides *ABCD.* We know 2 divides the expression $(A \cdot 500 + B \cdot 50 + C \cdot 5) \cdot 2$ because it is a multiple of 2. If 2 divides *D,* then 2 divides *ABCD* (see Theorem 2). If 2 does not divide *D,* then 2 does not divide *ABCD* (see Theorem 3). Thus, we just need to check divisibility of the ones digit *D* of *ABCD.* This example suggests the following divisibility rule.

Theorem 4

2 divides the whole number *n* if and only if the ones digit of *n* is 0, 2, 4, 6, or 8.

The positive multiples of 2 shaded in Table 4.1 on page 192 form the skip-counting sequence 2, 4, 6, 8, ... These are known as the "even" numbers. Each shaded number *a* can be written in the form $a = 2b$ for some whole number *b* that depends on *a.* The pattern in Table 4.1 suggests the ones digit of multiples of 2 must be 0, 2, 4, 6, or 8.

The same reasoning applies to the divisor 5:

$$
\begin{aligned}
ABCD &= A \cdot 1000 + B \cdot 100 + C \cdot 10 + D \\
&= A \cdot 200 \cdot 5 + B \cdot 20 \cdot 5 + C \cdot 2 \cdot 5 + D \\
&= \underbrace{(A \cdot 200 + B \cdot 20 + C \cdot 2) \cdot 5}_{\text{divisible by 5}} + \underbrace{D}_{\text{Is } D \text{ divisible by 5?}}
\end{aligned}
$$

TABLE 4.1 **Multiples of 2 Are Shaded**

1	2	3	4	5	6	7	8	9	10
11	12	13	14	15	16	17	18	19	20
21	22	23	24	25	26	27	28	29	30
31	32	33	34	35	36	37	38	39	40
41	42	43	44	45	46	47	48	49	50
51	52	53	54	55	56	57	58	59	60
61	62	63	64	65	66	67	68	69	70
71	72	73	74	75	76	77	78	79	80
81	82	83	84	85	86	87	88	89	90
91	92	93	94	95	96	97	98	99	100

Could you adapt this reasoning to motivate the divisibility rule for 10? Try it! These examples suggest the following divisibility rules.

Theorem 5

a. 5 divides the whole number n if and only if the ones digit of n is 0 or 5.
b. 10 divides the whole number n if and only if the ones digit of n is 0.

The following Released Item requires familiarity with the divisibility rule for 5.

▶ RELEASED ITEM

● NAEP, 2000
A whole number is multiplied by 5. Which of these could be the result?
a. 652 **b.** 562 **c.** 526 **d.** 265

54% of fourth-grade students answered the questions correctly.

Divisibility Rules for 3 and 9

Let's devise a rule for divisibility by 3. Again, let's consider the four-digit number $ABCD$:

$$ABCD = A \cdot 1000 + B \cdot 100 + C \cdot 10 + D$$
$$= A \cdot (999 + 1) + B \cdot (99 + 1) + C \cdot (9 + 1) + D$$
$$= (A \cdot 999 + B \cdot 99 + C \cdot 9) + (A + B + C + D)$$
$$= \underbrace{(A \cdot 333 + B \cdot 33 + C \cdot 3) \cdot 3}_{\text{divisible by 3}} + \underbrace{(A + B + C + D)}_{\text{Is the sum divisible by 3?}}$$

By Theorem 2(a), if 3 divides $(A \cdot 333 + B \cdot 33 + C \cdot 3) \cdot 3$ and 3 divides $A + B + C + D$, then 3 divides $ABCD$. We know 3 divides the expression $(A \cdot 333 + B \cdot 33 + C \cdot 3) \cdot 3$ because it is a multiple of 3. If 3 divides the sum $A + B + C + D$, then 3 divides the number $ABCD$. If 3 does not divide $A + B + C + D$, then 3 does not divide the number $ABCD$. This example suggests the divisibility rule for 3 depends on the sum of the digits.

Theorem 6

3 divides the whole number n if and only if 3 divides the sum of the digits of n.

EXAMPLE 4.6   **a.** Test 3456 for divisibility by 3.

CONNECTION   **b.** Test 56,789 for divisibility by 3.

REASONING

SOLUTION

a. The sum of the digits of 3456 is $3 + 4 + 5 + 6 = 18$. Because 18 is divisible by 3, 3456 is divisible by 3.

b. The sum of the digits of 56,789 is $5 + 6 + 7 + 8 + 9 = 35$. But 35 is not divisible by 3, so 56,789 is not divisible by 3.

▲

Let's devise a rule for divisibility by 9. Again, let's consider the four-digit number *ABCD:*

$$ABCD = A \cdot 1000 + B \cdot 100 + C \cdot 10 + D$$
$$= A \cdot (999 + 1) + B \cdot (99 + 1) + C \cdot (9 + 1) + D$$
$$= (A \cdot 999 + B \cdot 99 + C \cdot 9) + (A + B + C + D)$$
$$= \underbrace{(A \cdot 111 + B \cdot 11 + C \cdot 1) \cdot 9}_{\text{divisible by 9}} + \underbrace{(A + B + C + D)}_{\text{Is the sum divisible by 9?}}$$

If 9 divides $(A \cdot 111 + B \cdot 11 + C \cdot 1) \cdot 9$ and 9 divides $A + B + C + D$, then 9 divides *ABCD.* We know 9 divides the expression $(A \cdot 111 + B \cdot 11 + C \cdot 1) \cdot 9$ because it is a multiple of 9. If 9 divides $A + B + C + D$, then 9 divides the number *ABCD.* If 9 does not divide $A + B + C + D$, then 9 does not divide the number *ABCD.* This example suggests the divisibility rule for 9 depends on the sum of the digits.

> ### Theorem 7
>
> 9 divides the whole number *n* if and only if 9 divides the sum of the digits of *n*.

Another way to examine divisibility by 9 is with base ten blocks. Let's see whether 245 is divisible by 9. The diagram in Figure 3 is a base ten block representation of 245. Each group of letters, a's, b's, . . . , k's, represents a group of 9 that has been taken away (repeated subtraction model for division) from 245.

FIGURE 3

Base ten block representation of 245.

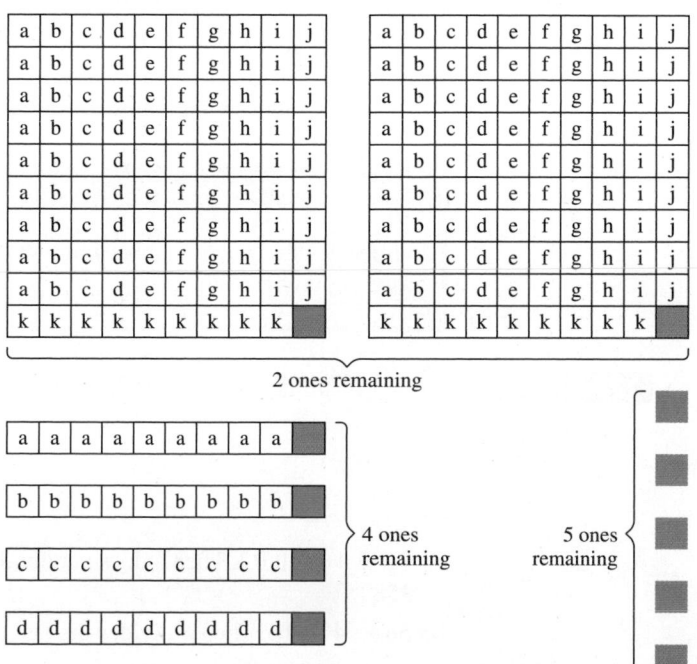

REPRESENTATION The shaded squares represent the remaining ones available to form more groups of 9. There are $2 + 4 + 5 = 11$ remaining ones. From this, we can form one more group of 9, with 2 ones remaining, which cannot form another group of 9. This means 9 does not divide 245. The main point is that the diagram visually illustrates why the sum of the digits $(2 + 4 + 5)$ in the divisibility rule for 9 is reasonable.

EXAMPLE 4.7

CONNECTION
REASONING

Use a divisibility rule to determine whether the whole number is divisible by 9.
a. 3582
b. 1256

SOLUTION

a. The sum of the digits of 3582 is $3 + 5 + 8 + 2$, which equals 18. We know 9 divides 18, so 9 divides 3582.

b. The sum of the digits of 1256 is $1 + 2 + 5 + 6$, which equals 14. We know 9 does not divide 14, so 9 does not divide 1256.

▲

EXAMPLE 4.8

CONNECTION
REASONING

Replace n with a digit so that 9 divides 47,6n2.

SOLUTION

The sum of digits of 47,6n2 is $4 + 7 + 6 + n + 2$, or $19 + n$. We know $19 + n$ must be divisible by 9. Then $19 + n$ must be equal to 27, so $n = 8$.

▲

Divisibility Rule for 4

Let's check whether 4 divides the number $ABCD$. Let's begin with the expanded form of $ABCD$:

$$ABCD = A \cdot 1000 + B \cdot 100 + C \cdot 10 + D$$
$$= A \cdot 250 \cdot 4 + B \cdot 25 \cdot 4 + C \cdot 10 + D$$
$$= (A \cdot 250 + B \cdot 25) \cdot 4 + (C \cdot 10 + D)$$
$$= \underbrace{(A \cdot 250 + B \cdot 25) \cdot 4}_{\text{divisible by 4}} + \underbrace{CD}_{\text{Is } CD \text{ divisible by 4?}}$$

By Theorem 2, if 4 divides the number CD formed by the two rightmost digits of $ABCD$, then 4 divides $ABCD$. By Theorem 3, if 4 does not divide CD, then 4 does not divide $ABCD$. This suggests the following divisibility rule for 4.

Theorem 8

4 divides the whole number n if and only if 4 divides the number formed by the two rightmost digits of n.

EXAMPLE 4.9

CONNECTION
REASONING

Use a divisibility rule to determine whether the whole number is divisible by 4.
a. 3582
b. 1256

SOLUTION

a. $82 \div 4 = 20$ R2. Then 4 does not divide the last two digits of 3582, so 4 does not divide 3582.

b. $56 \div 4 = 14$. Then 4 divides the last two digits of 1256, so 4 divides 1256.

▲

Divisibility Rule for 8

The divisibility rule for 8 is somewhat similar to the divisibility rule for 4.

$$ABCD = A \cdot 1000 + B \cdot 100 + C \cdot 10 + D$$
$$= A \cdot 125 \cdot 8 + (B \cdot 100 + C \cdot 10 + D)$$
$$= \underbrace{(A \cdot 125) \cdot 8}_{\text{divisible by 8}} + \underbrace{BCD}_{\text{Is } BCD \text{ divisible by 8?}}$$

If 8 divides the number BCD formed by the three rightmost digits of $ABCD$, then 8 divides $ABCD$. If 8 does not divide BCD, then 8 does not divide $ABCD$. This suggests the following divisibility rule for 8.

> **Theorem 9**
>
> 8 divides the whole number n if and only if 8 divides the number formed by the three rightmost digits of n.

Divisibility Rule for 6

The multiples of 6 are $6 = 1 \cdot 6$, $12 = 2 \cdot 6$, $18 = 3 \cdot 6$, $24 = 4 \cdot 6$, ... The number 48 is a multiple of 6, and

$$48 = 6 \cdot 8$$
$$= 2 \cdot (3 \cdot 8)$$
$$= 3 \cdot (2 \cdot 8).$$

This means 2 divides 48 and 3 divides 48. Here, 1 is the only common factor of 2 and 3. The number a is divisible by 6 if and only if 2 divides a and 3 divides a.

> **Theorem 10**
>
> 6 divides n if and only if 2 divides n and 3 divides n.

Inventing Divisibility Rules

We can build a new divisibility rule from known divisibility rules.

> **Theorem 11 (Combining Divisibility Rules)**
>
> Suppose 1 is the only common factor of the whole numbers a and b. Then $a \cdot b$ divides n if and only if a divides n and b divides n.

EXAMPLE 4.10   Invent a divisibility rule for 12.

CONNECTION

REASONING   SOLUTION

Here, $12 = 4 \cdot 3$ and 1 is the only common factor of 4 and 3. So by Theorem 11, a divisibility rule for 12 is "12 divides n if and only if 3 divides n and 4 divides n."

It's important that the only common factor of a and b in Theorem 11 is 1. For example, $12 = 2 \cdot 6$. If 2 and 6 each divide n, does that mean 12 divides n? No; the numbers 2 and 6 both divide 18, but 12 does not divide 18.

Connection among Divisibility Rules

Now we discuss another divisibility rule for 12. Let's consider the number $ABCD$. The expanded form is

$$ABCD = A \cdot 1000 + B \cdot 100 + C \cdot 10 + D \cdot 1.$$

Observe:

- $1000 \div 12 = 83$ R4, so $1000 = 83 \cdot 12 + 4$
- $100 \div 12 = 8$ R4, so $100 = 8 \cdot 12 + 4$

Substituting this into the expanded form, we get

$$
\begin{aligned}
ABCD &= A \cdot 1000 + B \cdot 100 + C \cdot 10 + D \cdot 1 \\
&= A \cdot (83 \cdot 12 + 4) + B \cdot (8 \cdot 12 + 4) + C \cdot 10 + D \cdot 1 \\
&= (A \cdot 83 \cdot 12 + B \cdot 8 \cdot 12) + (A \cdot 4 + B \cdot 4 + C \cdot 10 + D \cdot 1) \\
&= \underbrace{(A \cdot 83 + B \cdot 8) \cdot 12}_{\text{divisible by 12}} + \underbrace{(A \cdot 4 + B \cdot 4 + C \cdot 10 + D \cdot 1)}_{\text{Is } A \cdot 4 + B \cdot 4 + C \cdot 10 + D \cdot 1 \text{ divisible by 12?}}
\end{aligned}
$$

The sum of the digits in the number $ABCD$ is $A + B + C + D$. Each digit in the last line of the compound equation is multiplied by a *weight*: $A \cdot 4 + B \cdot 4 + C \cdot 10 + D \cdot 1$. The weights are 4, 4, 10, and 1. This example suggests the following divisibility rule for 12: multiply the digits in the number n according to the following pattern of weights in Table 4.2, and then add the products to obtain a weighted sum of digits. If a weight repeats, then the pattern repeats.

TABLE 4.2 **Weights for the Digits in the Divisibility Rule for 12**

Place value	10,000	1000	100	10	1
Weight of digit	4	4	4	10	1

The divisibility rule for 12 is as follows: 12 divides n if and only if 12 divides the weighted sum of digits using weights given in the table.

EXAMPLE 4.11

CONNECTION

REASONING

a. Use a divisibility rule to test 1236 for divisibility by 12.

b. Use a divisibility rule to test 621,357 for divisibility by 12.

SOLUTION

a. The weighted sum of the digits is $1 \cdot 4 + 2 \cdot 4 + 3 \cdot 10 + 6 \cdot 1 = 48$, and $48 \div 12 = 4$. The weighted sum of digits is divisible by 12, so 1236 is divisible by 12.

b. The weighted sum of the digits is $6 \cdot 4 + 2 \cdot 4 + 1 \cdot 4 + 3 \cdot 4 + 5 \cdot 10 + 7 \cdot 1 = 105$, and $105 \div 12 = 8$ R9. The weighted sum of digits is not divisible by 12, so 621,357 is not divisible by 12.

▲

CONNECTION

You can use this same line of reasoning to conclude *all divisibility rules have a common thread:* they may be expressed in terms of a weighted sum of digits. If a weight repeats, then the pattern of the weights repeats. Tables 4.3–4.8 characterize divisibility rules in terms of weights for the digits.

TABLE 4.3 Weights for the Digits in the Divisibility Rule for 2, 5, and 10

Place value	10,000	1000	100	10	1
Weight of digit	0	0	0	0	1

Is 4567 divisible by 5? The weighted sum of digits is $4 \cdot 0 + 5 \cdot 0 + 6 \cdot 0 + 7 \cdot 1 = 7$. We know $7 \div 5 = 1$ R2. So 5 is not a divisor of 4567.

TABLE 4.4 Weights for the Digits in the Divisibility Rule for 3 and 9

Place value	10,000	1000	100	10	1
Weight of digit	1	1	1	1	1

Is 648 divisible by 9? The weighted sum of digits is $6 \cdot 1 + 4 \cdot 1 + 8 \cdot 1 = 18$. We know $18 \div 9 = 2$. So 9 is a divisor of 648.

TABLE 4.5 Weights for the Digits in the Divisibility Rule for 4

Place value	10,000	1000	100	10	1
Weight of digit	0	0	0	10	1

Is 368 divisible by 4? The weighted sum of digits is $3 \cdot 0 + 6 \cdot 10 + 8 \cdot 1 = 68$. We know $68 \div 4 = 17$. So 4 is a divisor of 368.

TABLE 4.6 Weights for the Digits in the Divisibility Rule for 8

Place value	10,000	1000	100	10	1
Weight of digit	0	0	100	10	1

Is 45,276 divisible by 8? The weighted sum of digits is $4 \cdot 0 + 5 \cdot 0 + 2 \cdot 100 + 7 \cdot 10 + 6 \cdot 1 = 276$. We know $276 \div 8 = 34$ R4. So 8 is a not a divisor of 45,276.

Divisibility Rule for 7

The weights for the divisibility test for 7, from the ten millions place to the ones place, are shown in Table 4.7.

TABLE 4.7 Weights for the Digits in the Divisibility Rule for 7

Place value	1,000,000	100,000	10,000	1000	100	10	1
Weight of digit	1	5	4	6	2	3	1

The weights repeat, so the pattern repeats (for example, . . . , 1, 5, 4, 6, 2, 3, 1). For example, the pattern predicts the weight for the ten millions place is 3, while the weight for the hundred millions place is 2. It is easier to divide a number by 7 than it is to remember the weights in the divisibility rule for 7. For this reason, students do not learn a divisibility rule for 7. They would simply divide the number by 7 to test for divisibility by 7.

Divisibility Rule for 11

Now we discuss a divisibility rule for 11. Let's consider the number $ABCD$. The expanded form is

$$ABCD = A \cdot 1000 + B \cdot 100 + C \cdot 10 + D \cdot 1.$$

It turns out that

- $1001 = 91 \cdot 11$, so $1000 = 1001 - 1 = 91 \cdot 11 - 1$
- $100 = 99 + 1 = 9 \cdot 11 + 1$
- $10 = 11 - 1 = 1 \cdot 11 - 1$

Substituting this into the expanded form, we get

$$
\begin{aligned}
ABCD &= A \cdot 1000 + B \cdot 100 + C \cdot 10 + D \cdot 1 \\
&= A \cdot (1001 - 1) + B \cdot (99 + 1) + C \cdot (11 - 1) + D \cdot 1 \\
&= (A \cdot 1001 + B \cdot 99 + C \cdot 11) + A \cdot (-1) + B \cdot 1 + C \cdot (-1) + D \cdot 1 \\
&= \underbrace{(A \cdot 91 + B \cdot 9 + C \cdot 1) \cdot 11}_{\text{divisible by 11}} + \underbrace{A \cdot (-1) + B \cdot 1 + C \cdot (-1) + D \cdot 1}_{\substack{\text{Is } A \cdot (-1) + B \cdot 1 + C \cdot (-1) + \\ D \cdot 1 \text{ divisible by 11?}}}
\end{aligned}
$$

The weights for the divisibility test for 11 form a repeating pattern with alternating weights 1 and -1, as shown in Table 4.8.

TABLE 4.8   **Weights for the Digits in the Divisibility Rule for 11**

Place value	1000	100	10	1
Weight of digit	-1	1	-1	1

Is 2345 divisible by 11? Let's check: $5 \cdot (1) + 4 \cdot (-1) + 3 \cdot (1) + 2 \cdot (-1) = 5 - 4 + 3 - 2 = 2$. We know 2 is not divisible by 11, so 2345 is not divisible by 11.

QUESTIONS FOR SECTION 4.1

REPRESENTATION

Refresher: Representations (language, diagrams, tables, symbols, algebra, manipulatives, and contextualized situations) are important because we use them to organize, record, and communicate mathematical ideas and to make them more comprehensible.

1. Divide each term in the sequence 4, 7, 10, 13, 16, 19 by the given divisor. Record the result in the form q Rr in a table.

a.

a	4	7	10	13	16	19
$a \div 3$	1 R1					

b.

a	4	7	10	13	16	19
$a \div 5$	0 R4					

2. The diagram represents the equation $18 \div 7 = 2$ Rr. Shade the squares that represent r:

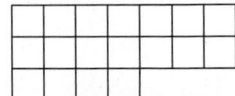

3. Do the following.
   a. Draw a diagram to represent the equation $15 = 5 \cdot 3$.
   b. Explain how the diagram reveals that 5 is a divisor of 15.

4. Do the following.
   a. Draw a diagram to represent the equation $26 \div 3 = 8$ R2.
   b. Shade the parts of the diagram that represent the remainder.
   c. Explain how the diagram reveals that 3 is not a divisor of 26.

PROBLEM SOLVING

Refresher: Problem solving (reaching a goal that is not immediately attainable) is important because it helps students think more deeply about what they know and deal with unfamiliar situations.

5. Leila has 35 yellow marbles and 20 green marbles. She wants to put all of them in boxes to sell. Each box must contain the same number of marbles, and each box can only contain marbles of the same color. How many boxes of marbles can she sell?

6. $4 \div 5 = 0$ R4, and 4 is the smallest counting number that has a remainder of 4 when divided by 5.
   a. What is the second smallest counting number that has a remainder of 4 when divided by 5?
   b. What is the third smallest counting number that has a remainder of 4 when divided by 5?
   c. What is the 57th smallest counting number that has a remainder of 4 when divided by 5?

7. When Mr. Smith arranged his students into groups of 5, he had 2 students left over. When he arranged them into groups of 7, he had 4 students left over. He has fewer than 40 students in his class. How many students does he have in his class?

REASONING AND PROOF

Refresher: Reasoning and proof (thinking and justifying) are important because they help students make sense of mathematics.

8. For the following numbers, is it possible to decide whether the number is divisible by 6 without performing calculations?

   a. $349,437 \cdot 12 + 32$ b. $4,509,231$

   c. $2^5 \cdot 5^3 \cdot 11 \cdot 13^2$ d. $42 \cdot 100,001 + 24 \cdot 333 + 12$

9. Suppose 3 is a factor of k. Prove the following.

   a. 3 is not a factor of $k + 1$

   b. 3 is not a factor of $k + 2$

10. A student claims the sum of three consecutive whole numbers is divisible by 3.

    a. Use inductive reasoning to support this conjecture.

    b. Use deductive reasoning to prove this conjecture.

11. Do the following.

    a. Determine whether 3 divides 1000.

    b. Explain why there are no whole numbers a and b that solve the equation $9a + 36b = 1000$.

12. What is the divisibility rule for

    a. 2^1?   b. 2^2?   c. 2^3?

    d. Make a conjecture about a divisibility rule for 2^4, which equals 16.

    e. Test your conjecture with 92,400 and 197,564,987.

    f. Make a conjecture about a divisibility rule for 2^k $(k = 1, 2, 3, 4, \ldots)$.

13. 30 divides n. Explain why 15 divides n.

CONNECTIONS

Refresher: Connections (linking and applying mathematical ideas) are important because they deepen student understanding and make mathematics more meaningful, flexible, and useful.

14. Suppose $a = 2 \cdot 3 \cdot 5 + 1$.

    a. What is the remainder of $a \div 2$?

    b. What is the remainder of $a \div 3$?

    c. What is the remainder of $a \div 5$?

    d. Is a divisible by 2, 3, or 5? Explain.

15. Multiply the digits of the counting number 35: $3 \cdot 5 = 15$. Multiplying again gives $1 \cdot 5 = 5$. Thus, the "step number" of 35 is 2, because it took two steps of multiplying the digits to arrive at a product with a single digit. As another example, the step number of 347 is 3, because $3 \cdot 4 \cdot 7 = 84$, $8 \cdot 4 = 32$, and $3 \cdot 2 = 6$.

    a. Determine the step number of 42.

    b. Determine the step number of 678.

    c. Determine the step number of 345.

    d. Use number sense to explain why 387 and 647 have the same step number.

    e. Use number sense to determine a four-digit number that has the same step number as 7463.

16. Which counting numbers divide 0?

ISBN is an acronym for International Standard Book Number. Questions 17–23 relate to ISBN numbers. The ISBN number for a book has 13 digits. The ISBN number for the NCTM publication *Principles and Standards for School Mathematics* is 978-0-87353-480-2. The first block of digits on the left reflects the industry (for example, 978 = book publishing). The second block of digits on the left identifies the language of the publication (for example, 0 = English). The third block of digits identifies the publisher. The fourth block of digits is assigned by the publishing company and identifies the title. The fifth block is a digit from 0 to 9 called the *checksum digit,* which is used to detect errors in entering or scanning the digits. The main idea is that an ISBN number is *valid* as long as the *weighted sum of the digits is divisible by 10.* The weights are always 1, 3, 1, 3, 1, ... Let's compute the weighted sum of the given ISBN number 978-0-87353-480-2.

ISBN	9	7	8	0	8	7	3	5	3	4	8	0	2
Weight	1	3	1	3	1	3	1	3	1	3	1	3	1
Weighted sum	\multicolumn{13}{l}{$9 \cdot 1 + 7 \cdot 3 + 8 \cdot 1 + 0 \cdot 3 + 8 \cdot 1$ $+ 7 \cdot 3 + 3 \cdot 1 + 5 \cdot 3 + 3 \cdot 1 + 4 \cdot 3$ $+ 8 \cdot 1 + 0 \cdot 3 + 2 \cdot 1 = 110$}

The weighted sum of the ISBN number is 110. To verify that the ISBN number is a valid ISBN number, we simply need to verify that 110 is divisible by 10. The ones digit of the weighted sum 110 is 0, so 110 is divisible by 10, and we conclude the ISBN number 978-0-87353-480-2 is a valid ISBN number.

17. Answer the following.

    a. Suppose the weighted sum of the 12 leftmost digits of an ISBN number is 134. What is the checksum digit?

    b. Suppose the weighted sum of the 12 leftmost digits of an ISBN number is 142. What is the checksum digit?

    c. Suppose the weighted sum of the 12 leftmost digits of an ISBN number is 90. What is the checksum digit?

    d. When an ISBN number is created, the checksum digit is the last digit to be determined. Why?

18. The ISBN number for the book *The Development of Multiplicative Reasoning in the Learning of Mathematics* is 978-0-7914-1764-5. Verify that the ISBN number is a valid number.

19. The ISBN number for the book *Handbook of Research on Mathematics Teaching and Learning* is 978-1-59-311598-n. Find the checksum digit n.

20. The 12 leftmost digits of an ISBN number are: 978-0-87353-494. Determine the checksum digit n such that 978-0-87353-494-n is a valid ISBN number.

21. The 12 leftmost digits of an ISBN number are: 978-1-80585-876. Determine the checksum digit n such that 978-1-80585-876-n is a valid ISBN number.

22. A customer called the bookstore to order a book. The employee writes the ISBN number on a piece of paper. Later, the store manager decides to order the book and sees the ISBN number 978-1-40201-n58-2, where n represents an unreadable digit. Determine n. Assume the other digits are correct.

23. The ISBN number for a book has 13 digits. An ISBN number is valid as long as the weighted sum of the digits is a multiple of 10. Would the method be more or less prone to errors if the weighted sum had to be a multiple of 3 instead of a multiple of 10?

COMMUNICATION

Refresher: Communication (written and verbal explanations using representations and proper mathematical vocabulary) is important because it helps students refine and strengthen their understanding.

24. Explain and give an example of the following concepts: multiple, factor, divisible, and divides.

25. Is 4 a divisor of $32 + 7$? Justify your answer without calculating the sum.

26. Is 3 a divisor of $42 - 12$? Justify your answer without calculating the difference.

27. Suppose you know 5 is a factor of n. Explain why 5 is not a factor of $n + 1$.

28. What does each equation reveal?

    a. $41 \cdot 28 = 1148$ b. $5481 \div 27 = 203$

    c. $45 \div 6 = 7 \, R3$

29. Explain why there are no whole numbers a and b that solve the equation $4a + 20b = 901$.

More practice with the ideas of the section

30. Fill in the blank. Choose one of the following words, phrases, or symbols: *5, 8, divides, divisibility rules, divisor, does, does not, factor, multiples,* or *number theory.*

    a. _____ is the study of properties of counting numbers, such as factorization and divisibility properties.

    b. The equation $n = 2 \cdot 7 + 4$ reveals 7 _____ divide n.

    c. _____ allow(s) us to determine whether one number divides another number by solving a simpler, but equivalent, problem.

    d. 4, 8, 12, 16, 20, . . . are _____ of 4.

    e. 42 is a(n) _____ of 1050.

31. What does each equation reveal?

    a. $5897 = 53 \cdot 110 + 67$ b. $\sqrt{580} = 24.083$ (rounded)

    c. $5^2 = 25$

32. Answer each question without finding the sum or difference. Justify your answer.

    a. Is 3 a divisor of $6 + 24$?   b. Is 5 a divisor of $15 + 7$?

    c. Is 10 a divisor of $140 + 50$?

    d. Is 3 a divisor of $130 + 8220$?

    e. Is 4 a divisor of $836 - 724$?

    f. Is 4 a divisor of $520 - 311$?

33. 5 is not a divisor of a and 5 is not a divisor of b. Give an example of numbers a and b such that

    a. 5 divides $a + b$.   b. 5 does not divide $a + b$.

34. 3 is not a divisor of a and 3 is not a divisor of b. Give an example of numbers a and b such that

    a. 3 is a divisor of $a - b$.   b. 3 is not a divisor of $a - b$.

35. Suppose a is a divisor of b and b is a divisor of c. Use the definitions of divisibility to prove that a is a divisor of c.

36. Suppose a is a divisor of b and c is a counting number. Prove ac is a divisor of bc.

37. Explain why there are no whole numbers a and b that solve the equation $27a + 9b = 1111$.

38. For $n \geq 1$, let a_n represent a string of n 1s. For example, $a_3 = 111$ and $a_4 = 1111$. For what values of n is a_n divisible by

    a. 3?   b. 5?   c. 6?

39. a and n are counting numbers. A *perfect square* is a counting number that can be expressed in the form n^2. Verify that

    a. 25 is a perfect square.   b. 16 is a perfect square.

    c. a^6 is a perfect square.

40. A *perfect cube* is a counting number that can be expressed in the form n^3. Verify that

    a. 27 is a perfect cube.   b. 125 is a perfect cube.

    c. a^6 is a perfect cube.

41. Do the following.

    a. Test 2,296,492 for divisibility by 4.

    b. Test 20,858 for divisibility by 4.

    c. Construct an even number that is not divisible by 4, and tell how you know the number is not divisible by 4.

42. Do the following.

    a. Test 23,528,656 for divisibility by 8.

    b. Test 365,348 for divisibility by 8.

    c. Determine how many ways you can choose the digit e such that $91,4e8$ is divisible by 8.

43. Do the following.

    a. Test 7410 for divisibility by 6.

    b. Test 3256 for divisibility by 6.

    c. Explain why 6 does not divide an odd number.

44. Do the following.

    a. Test 54,230 for divisibility by 5.

    b. Test 225,099,695 for divisibility by 5.

    c. Test 843,021,024 for divisibility by 5.

45. Do the following.

    a. Construct a rule for divisibility by 24 using two simpler divisibility tests.

    b. Using your rule, determine whether 125,016 is divisible by 24.

    c. Using your rule, determine whether 74,608 is a multiple of 24.

46. Do the following.

    a. Invent a divisibility rule for 15 using two simpler divisibility tests.

    b. Demonstrate your divisibility rule with examples.

    c. Demonstrate your divisibility rule with counterexamples.

47. Do the following.

    a. Construct a rule for divisibility by 25.

    b. Using your rule, determine whether 1,266,389 is divisible by 25.

    c. Using your rule, determine whether 48,375 is a multiple of 25.

48. Answer the following.

    a. How many different ways can you choose the digit d such that $91,43d$ is divisible by 10?

    b. How many different ways can you choose the digit e such that $91,4e8$ is divisible by 10?

    c. How many different ways can you choose the digit e such that $91,4e0$ is divisible by 10?

49. Find a number b such that when each term in the given sequence is divided by b, the remainder is the same.

    a. 2, 6, 10, 14, 18, 22, . . .   b. 3, 8, 13, 18, 23, 28, . . .

50. Suppose 4 divides n and 8 divides n. Does 32 divide n? Explain.

51. Prove Theorem 1: Let a, b, and n be any counting numbers. If b divides a, then b divides $a \cdot n$.

52. Do the following.

    a. Invent a divisibility rule for 20 using two simpler divisibility tests.

    b. Demonstrate your divisibility rule with examples.

    c. Demonstrate your divisibility rule with counterexamples.

53. Fill in the blank with a digit such that the resulting number is divisible by 11.

    a. 362,371,_31   b. 92,818,_21   c. 57,12_,472

54. Divide each term in the sequence 2, 6, 10, 14, 18, 22, . . . by the given divisor. Record the result in the form q Rr in a table. What did you notice about the remainders?

    a. 2   b. 3   c. 4

55. Divide each term in the sequence 3, 8, 13, 18, 23, 28, . . . by the given divisor. Record the result in the form q Rr in a table. What did you notice about the remainders?

    a. 2   b. 3   c. 4

56. Determine whether the following statements are true or false. If a statement is false, then give an example that shows why.

    a. If m is a factor of n, then m is a divisor of $n \cdot p$.

    b. If 14 is not a divisor of x, then 7 is not a factor of x.

    c. If $m + n$ is divisible by 5, then 5 is a factor of m and 5 is a factor of n.

    d. If $x + y$ is divisible by 3, then 9 is a divisor of $x + y$.

    e. If 9 is a divisor of x and 9 is a divisor of y, then 3 is a divisor of $x + y$.

57. Use number sense to answer the following.

    a. Is $10^4 \cdot 3^5 \cdot 17^8$ a factor of $T = 10^2 \cdot 3^4 \cdot 17^6$?

    b. Is 20 a factor of $U = 5^{12} \cdot 2^4 \cdot 11^{600}$?

    c. Is 9 a factor of $V = 6^3 \cdot 5^2 \cdot 17^{345}$?

58. If the sentence is true, then prove the sentence using algebraic reasoning. If the sentence is false, then give an example that shows the sentence is false.

    a. If n is divisible by 6, then n is divisible by 3.

    b. If n is divisible by 5, then n is divisible by 10.

    c. If n is divisible by 4, then n is divisible by 8.

    d. If n is divisible by 100, then n is divisible by 20.

    e. If n is divisible by 20, then n is divisible by 100.

SECTION 4.2   Prime and Composite Numbers, Least Common Multiple, and Greatest Common Factor

Prime and Composite Numbers

We classify numbers to focus on particular aspects of numbers. For example, we can classify whole numbers as *odd* or *even*. We can also classify whole numbers as *prime, composite,* or *neither,* which is based on the nature of their factors. Students should be able to "describe classes of numbers according to characteristics such as the nature of their factors" (NCTM, Gr. 3–5). Figure 4 gives a few geometric representations of prime and composite numbers.

REPRESENTATION

3, prime number
The factors of 3 are 1 and 3.

FIGURE 4(a)

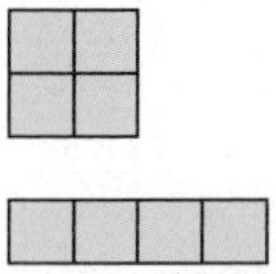

4, composite number
The factors of 4 are 1, 2, and 4.

FIGURE 4(b)

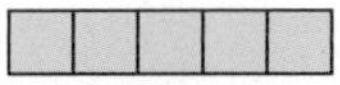

5, prime number
The factors of 5 are 1 and 5.

FIGURE 4(c)

(continued)

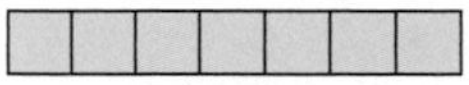

7, prime number
The factors of 7 are 1 and 7.
FIGURE 4(d)

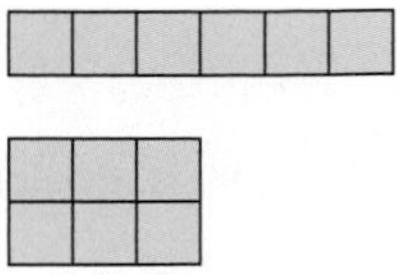

6, composite number
The factors of 6 are 1, 2, 3, and 6.
FIGURE 4(e)

Geometrically, a prime number is a counting number that has exactly one rectangular array representation, and a composite number is a counting number that has more than one rectangular array representation.

> **Definition**
>
> - A **prime number** is a counting number that has exactly two different factors.
> - A **composite number** is a counting number that has more than two different factors.

EXAMPLE 4.12

REASONING

Determine whether the given number is prime, composite, or neither.
a. 11
b. 1
c. 24
d. 0

SOLUTION

a. The number 11 has exactly two factors: 11 and 1. So 11 is a prime number.

b. The number 1 has exactly one factor: 1. Therefore, 1 is neither prime nor composite.

c. Some factors of 24 are 1, 4, and 6. This means 24 has more than two factors. Therefore, 24 is a composite number.

d. Because 0 is not a counting number, 0 is neither prime nor composite. ▲

Through the centuries, mathematicians have developed and studied various classifications of whole numbers (such as odd, even, prime, composite, perfect, deficient, abundant, triangular, square, and cubic). Some homework questions at the end of this section ask you to investigate some of these classifications.

Sieve of Eratosthenes

The sieve of Eratosthenes is a method for determining prime numbers in the list 2, 3, . . . , n. Let's use the sieve to find all prime numbers in the list 2, 3, 4, . . . , 60. First, we list the integers from 2 to 60, as shown in Table 4.9. The number 2 is the first prime number, and we shade prime numbers as we identify them. Then we cross out all subsequent multiples of 2 (every second number), because they are composite numbers.

TABLE 4.9   Sieve of Eratosthenes: Crossing Out Multiples of 2

2	3	4	5	6	7	8	9	10
11	12	13	14	15	16	17	18	19	20
21	22	23	24	25	26	27	28	29	30
31	32	33	34	35	36	37	38	39	40
41	42	43	44	45	46	47	48	49	50
51	52	53	54	55	56	57	58	59	60

The next available number, 3, is a prime number, because it is not a multiple of 2. We shade 3 and cross out all subsequent multiples of 3 (every third number), as shown in Table 4.10, because they are composite numbers.

TABLE 4.10   Sieve of Eratosthenes: Crossing Out Multiples of 3

	2	3	4	5	6	7	8	9	10
11	12	13	14	15	16	17	18	19	20
21	22	23	24	25	26	27	28	29	30
31	32	33	34	35	36	37	38	39	40
41	42	43	44	45	46	47	48	49	50
51	52	53	54	55	56	57	58	59	60

The next available number, 5, is a prime number, because it is not a multiple of any number less than 5, which means it has no factors other than 1 and 5. We shade 5 and then cross out all subsequent multiples of 5 (every fifth number). Then we repeat these steps until all numbers from 2 to 60 are either shaded or crossed out. The shaded numbers are prime numbers. Table 4.11 reveals that the prime numbers from 2 to 60 are 2, 3, 5, 7, 11, 13, 17, 19, 23, 29, 31, 37, 41, 43, 47, 53, and 59.

Historical Note

Eratosthenes (275–195 BCE), born in Cyrene (which is now Libya in North Africa), invented the sieve. He is also known for calculating an accurate measurement of the diameter of Earth.

TABLE 4.11   Shaded Numbers Are Prime Numbers from 2 to 60

	2	3	4	5	6	7	8	9	10
11	12	13	14	15	16	17	18	19	20
21	22	23	24	25	26	27	28	29	30
31	32	33	34	35	36	37	38	39	40
41	42	43	44	45	46	47	48	49	50
51	52	53	54	55	56	57	58	59	60

Factorization and Prime Factorization

In Chapter 2, we used place value concepts to represent a number in expanded form, such as $294 = 200 + 90 + 4$. We can represent 294 with a different expanded form—as a product, rather than a sum, of numbers: $294 = 2 \cdot 3 \cdot 7 \cdot 7$. A **factorization** is an equation of the form "counting number = product of counting numbers." Two more examples of factorizations are $36 = 9 \cdot 4$ and $52 = 2 \cdot 2 \cdot 13$. A **prime factorization** is a factorization where each factor in the product is a prime number. Thus, $90 = 2 \cdot 3 \cdot 3 \cdot 5$ and $245 = 5 \cdot 7 \cdot 7$ are two examples of prime factorizations. However, $12 = 4 \cdot 3$ is not a prime factorization of 12, because 4 is not a prime number.

Using a Tree Diagram to Find a Prime Factorization

Figure 5 shows how to use a tree diagram to find the prime factorization of 120. The idea is to factor every composite number until the ends of the tree consist of prime numbers. Divisibility rules are often helpful.

REPRESENTATION

Figure 5 indicates the prime factorization of 120 is $120 = 2 \cdot 3 \cdot 2 \cdot 2 \cdot 5$. Figure 6 gives an alternative tree diagram and indicates the prime factorization of 120 is $120 = 2 \cdot 5 \cdot 3 \cdot 2 \cdot 2$.

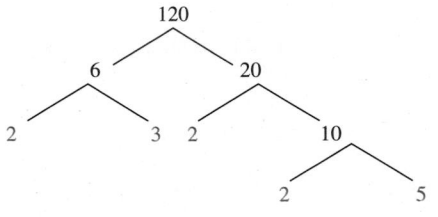

FIGURE 5
A prime factor tree for 120.

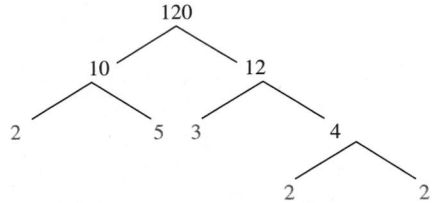

FIGURE 6
An alternative prime factor tree for 120.

The factorizations are equivalent because of properties of multiplication. By convention, we organize the factors in their natural order: $120 = 2 \cdot 2 \cdot 2 \cdot 3 \cdot 5$.

Fundamental Theorem of Arithmetic

In 1801, Carl Friedrich Gauss proved a composite number has exactly one prime factorization (as long as we ignore the order of the prime factors). A prime factorization expresses a composite number as a product of prime numbers, using exponential notation as needed (for example, $6 = 2 \cdot 3$, $8 = 2^3$, and $12 = 2^2 \cdot 3$).

> ### Fundamental Theorem of Arithmetic
>
> - Every composite number n has as a prime factorization $n = p_1^{n_1} \cdot p_2^{n_2} \cdot \ldots \cdot p_k^{n_k}$, where $p_1, p_2, \ldots, p_k$ are different prime numbers and $n_1, n_2, \ldots, n_k$ are counting numbers.
> - The prime factorization of a composite number is unique, as long as we ignore the order of the prime factors.

Carl Gauss at an observatory.

© INTERFOTO/Alamy

EXAMPLE 4.13

COMMUNICATION
PROBLEM SOLVING
REASONING

Let $a = 3 \cdot 5^4 \cdot 11^2 \cdot 13$ and $b = 3 \cdot 10^4 \cdot 11^2 \cdot 13$.

a. How many prime factors does a have?

b. How many prime factors does b have?

SOLUTION

a. The prime factorization of a is $a = 3 \cdot 5^4 \cdot 11^2 \cdot 13$. The prime factorization is unique, so 7, for example, cannot be a prime factor of a. We see a has exactly four prime factors: 3, 5, 11, and 13.

b. The equation $b = 3 \cdot 10^4 \cdot 11^2 \cdot 13$ is a factorization of b, but it is not a prime factorization of b because 10 is not a prime number. The prime factorization of 10 is $10 = 2 \cdot 5$. Then

$$b = 3 \cdot 10^4 \cdot 11^2 \cdot 13$$
$$= 3 \cdot (2 \cdot 5)^4 \cdot 11^2 \cdot 13$$
$$= 3 \cdot 2^4 \cdot 5^4 \cdot 11^2 \cdot 13$$
$$= 2^4 \cdot 3 \cdot 5^4 \cdot 11^2 \cdot 13$$

So $b = 2^4 \cdot 3 \cdot 5^4 \cdot 11^2 \cdot 13$ is a prime factorization of b. The prime factorization is unique, so b has five prime factors: 2, 3, 5, 11, and 13.

EXAMPLE 4.14

REASONING

REPRESENTATION

a. Is 18 a factor of $2 \cdot 3^4 \cdot 5^2 \cdot 11$?

b. Does 24 divide $2 \cdot 3^4 \cdot 5^2 \cdot 11$?

SOLUTION

a. The number 18 is a factor of $2 \cdot 3^4 \cdot 5^2 \cdot 11$ if and only if $2 \cdot 3^4 \cdot 5^2 \cdot 11 = 18q$ for some integer q. The prime factorization of 18 is $18 = 2 \cdot 3^2$. Then

$$2 \cdot 3^4 \cdot 5^2 \cdot 11 = (2 \cdot 3^2) \cdot 3^2 \cdot 5^2 \cdot 11$$
$$= 18 \cdot 3^2 \cdot 5^2 \cdot 11$$

So 18 is a factor of $2 \cdot 3^4 \cdot 5^2 \cdot 11$.

b. The number 24 divides $2 \cdot 3^4 \cdot 5^2 \cdot 11$ if and only if $2 \cdot 3^4 \cdot 5^2 \cdot 11 = 24q$ for some integer q. The prime factorization of 24 is $24 = 2^3 \cdot 3$. Then

$$2 \cdot 3^4 \cdot 5^2 \cdot 11 \overset{?}{=} 24q$$
$$2 \cdot 3^4 \cdot 5^2 \cdot 11 \overset{?}{=} 2^3 \cdot 3q$$

The prime factorization of a composite number is unique. This means the prime factors of the left-hand side of the equation must agree with the prime factors of the right-hand side of the equation, and their exponents must also agree. The prime number 2 appears on both sides of the equation, but the exponent of 2 on the left-hand side of the equation is 1, while the exponent of 2 on the right-hand side of the equation is 3 or higher (because of q). Because of this mismatch, 24 does not divide n.

▲

Using Repeated Division to Find a Prime Factorization

Another way to factor a number is **repeated division**—repeatedly divide by the smallest prime number possible, skipping prime numbers (through trial and error) that create remainders. For example, let's find the prime factorization of 120 using repeated division:

$$
\begin{array}{r}
5 \\
3\overline{)15} \\
2\overline{)30} \\
2\overline{)60} \\
2\overline{)120}
\end{array}
\qquad
\begin{aligned}
120 &= 2 \cdot 2 \cdot 2 \cdot 3 \cdot 5 \\
&= 2^3 \cdot 3 \cdot 5
\end{aligned}
$$

The prime factorization of 120 is $120 = 2 \cdot 2 \cdot 2 \cdot 3 \cdot 5$. We may use exponential notation to represent factors that appear more than once: $120 = 2^3 \cdot 3 \cdot 5$.

How Many Factors Does a Composite Number Have?

The composite number 24 has eight factors: 1, 2, 4, 8, 3, 6, 12, and 24. These factors can be expressed as: $1 = 2^0 \cdot 3^0$, $2 = 2^1 \cdot 3^0$, $4 = 2^2 \cdot 3^0$, $8 = 2^3 \cdot 3^0$, $3 = 2^0 \cdot 3^1$, $6 = 2^1 \cdot 3^1$, $12 = 2^2 \cdot 3^1$, and $24 = 2^3 \cdot 3^1$. From these "clever" factorizations, we see there are four ways to choose powers of 2 (2^0, 2^1, 2^2, and 2^3) and two ways to choose powers of 3 (3^0 and 3^1) to create the factors of 24. The following example illustrates how we can solve simpler problems to determine the number of composite factors based on the prime factorization of 24.

EXAMPLE 4.15

CONNECTION

COMMUNICATION

PROBLEM SOLVING

REASONING

REPRESENTATION

You are given $24 = 2^3 \cdot 3^1$.

a. How many factors does 2^3 have?

b. How many factors does 3^1 have?

c. How many factors does 24 have?

SOLUTION

a. $2^3 = 8$, and the divisors of 8 are 1, 2, 4, and 8. So 2^3 has four factors.

b. $3^1 = 3$, and the divisors of 3 are 1 and 3. So 3^1 has two factors.

c. A prime factorization is unique, so all factors of 24 must have the form $2^x \cdot 3^y$. By part (a) there are four ways to choose x ($x = 0, 1, 2,$ or 3) and by part (b) there are two ways to choose y ($y = 0$ or 1). By the fundamental counting principle (see Section 3.1), there are $4 \cdot 2$ ways to choose the factors of 24. So 24 has eight factors.

▲

We can generalize this result to any composite number.

Theorem 12

If the composite number a has the prime factorization $a = p_1^{n_1} \cdot p_2^{n_2} \cdot \ldots \cdot p_k^{n_k}$, then a has $(n_1 + 1)(n_2 + 1) \ldots (n_k + 1)$ factors.

EXAMPLE 4.16 Answer the following questions for $2^3 \cdot 5^{11} \cdot 13^6$.

CONNECTION   a. How many factors does it have?

REASONING   b. How many prime factors does it have?

REPRESENTATION   c. How many composite factors does it have?

SOLUTION

a. $(3 + 1)(11 + 1)(6 + 1) = 4 \cdot 12 \cdot 7 = 336$, so $2^3 \cdot 5^{11} \cdot 13^6$ has 336 factors.

b. $2^3 \cdot 5^{11} \cdot 13^6$ has three prime factors: 2, 5, and 13.

c. $2^3 \cdot 5^{11} \cdot 13^6$ has 336 factors. The number of composite factors of $2^3 \cdot 5^{11} \cdot 13^6$ is 336 $- 3 - 1 = 332$ (subtract 3 for the number of prime factors, and subtract 1 because the factor 1 is neither prime nor composite).

▲

There Are Infinitely Many Prime Numbers

How many prime numbers are there? It turns out there are infinitely many prime numbers. The mathematician Euclid proved this long ago, about 300 BCE.

Theorem 13

There are infinitely many prime numbers.

COMMUNICATION   We use a small example to outline the spirit of the proof. Suppose there are exactly

REASONING   three prime numbers, say, 2, 3, and 5. We can construct another prime number, which

REPRESENTATION   shows that there cannot be exactly three prime numbers. Let n be the number $n = 2 \cdot 3 \cdot 5$ $+ 1$. n is greater than 1, so n is either a composite number or a prime number. n is not equal to 2, 3, or 5, which supposedly are the only prime numbers, so n must be a composite number. Therefore, n must be divisible by at least one of the prime numbers 2, 3, or 5 because of the fundamental theorem of arithmetic.

- $n = 2(3 \cdot 5) + 1$, so $n \div 2 = 3 \cdot 5$ R1. So 2 does not divide n.
- $n = 3(2 \cdot 5) + 1$, so $n \div 3 = 2 \cdot 5$ R1. So 3 does not divide n.
- $n = 5(2 \cdot 3) + 1$, so $n \div 5 = 2 \cdot 3$ R1. So 5 does not divide n.

Thus, we have a contradiction: "n is divisible by 2, 3, or 5" and "n is not divisible by 2, 3, or 5." We conclude that there cannot be exactly three prime numbers. Like Euclid, we can construct a similar argument assuming there are only k prime numbers $p_1, p_2, \ldots, p_k$, where k is any counting number, and construct another number of the form $n = p_1 \cdot p_2 \cdots p_k + 1$, which can be shown to be prime. Then we reach the same conclusion: there cannot be exactly k prime numbers. This means there are infinitely many prime numbers.

CONNECTION

Theorem 13 means there is no largest prime number. Currently, the largest known prime number is $2^{43112609} - 1$, which has nearly 13 million digits. Go to the Primes Pages (primes.utm.edu/largest.html) for the latest update of the largest known prime number.

Large prime numbers are useful in encryption techniques for the secure transmission of information in electronic payments, ATM machines, cell phones, electronic voting, and confidential information. A popular encryption technique (turning a message into a code) requires the product of two prime numbers. Its related decryption technique (turning the code back into the message) requires knowledge of the prime factorization of the product—that is, the two prime numbers. Effective encryption codes use a product of two prime numbers with several hundred digits each, because factoring a large number having at least 300 digits may take computers millions of years. This makes it extremely difficult for thieves to crack the code and steal information.

ATM encryption PIN pad.

Using Repeated Division to Find All Factors of a Composite Number

Use the following repeated division strategy to list all factors of the composite number a. 1 and a are factors, so put 1 and a in the list. Then divide a by 2. If 2 divides a, then add 2 and $a \div 2$ to the list. Then divide a by 3. If 3 divides a, then add 3 and $a \div 3$ to the list. Repeat this process for divisors 4, 5, 6, . . . , a. Once a factor in the list reappears, then the current list contains all factors of a and the procedure terminates. Students can use this strategy to "find all factor pairs for a whole number in the range 1–100" (CCSS, Gr. 4) (© 2010. National Governors Association Center for Best Practices and Council of Chief State School Officers. All rights reserved.). Try this strategy for 24.

EXAMPLE 4.17 List all factors of 24 using repeated division.

SOLUTION

1 and 24 are factors of 24. $24 \div 2 = 12$, so 2 and 12 are factors of 24. $24 \div 3 = 8$, so 3 and 8 are factors of 24. $24 \div 4 = 6$, so 4 and 6 are factors of 24. $24 \div 5 = 4$ R4, so 5 is not a factor of 24. Next, we try 6, but it is already a factor of 24 on our list. So all factors of 24 have been found. In the order of discovery, the factors of 24 are 1, 24, 2, 12, 3, 8, 4, and 6.

▲

How to Use Division to Determine Whether a Number Is a Prime Number

The sieve of Eratosthenes is useful for determining *all* prime numbers from 2 to n. Sometimes we simply want to determine whether a given number is prime or composite. We could use a Guess and Check Strategy. For example, to determine whether 48 is a prime or composite number, we could simply divide 48 by every prime number less than 48. If one of those prime numbers divides 48, then we know 48 is a composite number. Otherwise, 48 is a prime number. We can ignore composite numbers in the Guess and Check Strategy because the fundamental theorem of arithmetic states every composite number is a product of prime factors.

REASONING

To check whether n is a composite number, do we have to check whether every prime number less than n divides n? It turns out we only need to check the prime numbers less than or equal to $\sqrt{n}$, which reduces the amount of work. To see this, suppose all prime factors of the composite number n are greater than $\sqrt{n}$. Then n has at least two prime factors greater than $\sqrt{n}$, say p and q with $p > \sqrt{n}$ and $q > \sqrt{n}$. Then

$$
\begin{aligned}
n &= p \cdot q \cdot c && \textbf{For some counting number } c \\
&\geq p \cdot q && \textbf{Because } c \geq 1 \\
&> \sqrt{n} \cdot q && \textbf{Because } p > \sqrt{n} \\
&> \sqrt{n} \cdot \sqrt{n} && \textbf{Because } q > \sqrt{n} \\
&= n
\end{aligned}
$$

Then $n > n$, which is false. So all prime factors of the composite number n cannot be larger than $\sqrt{n}$. This means there is at least one prime factor f of the composite number n such that $f \leq \sqrt{n}$. By squaring both sides, this also means $f^2 \leq n$. This reasoning suggests the following generalization.

Theorem 14 (Square Root Test)

Let n be a counting number greater than 1, and let f represent the largest whole number such that $f^2 \leq n$.

- If any prime number less than or equal to f divides n, then n is a composite number.

- If no prime numbers less than or equal to f divide n, then n is a prime number.

EXAMPLE 4.18   Is 359 a prime number or composite number?

CONNECTION

REASONING

REPRESENTATION

SOLUTION

$18^2 = 324$ and $19^2 = 361$, so 18 is the largest whole number such that $18^2 \leq 359$. We just need to check whether any prime numbers less than or equal to 18 (2, 3, 5, 7, 11, 13, and 17) divide 359. We quickly rule out 2, 3, and 5 by the divisibility rules. Now, $359 \div 7 = 51$ R2, $359 \div 11 = 32$ R7, $359 \div 13 = 27$ R8, and $359 \div 17 = 21$ R2. This means the prime numbers 2, 3, 5, 7, 11, 13, and 17 do not divide 359. We conclude 359 is not a composite number. It is greater than 1, so 359 must be a prime number. ▲

Students can use this strategy or divisibility tests to "determine whether a given whole number in the range 1–100 is prime or composite" (CCSS, Gr. 4).

Least Common Multiple

CONNECTION

PROBLEM SOLVING

REASONING

Positive multiples of 3 are 3, 6, 9, 12, 15, . . . , and positive multiple of 4 are 4, 8, 12, 16, 20, ... The numbers 3 and 4 have infinitely many common multiples: 12, 24, 36, ... Common multiples have many uses. Consider these example problems:

- In 1988, Jupiter and Saturn were aligned with the Sun. It takes Jupiter 12 Earth years and Saturn 30 Earth years to revolve around the Sun. When will these planets be aligned with the Sun again?

- Alex and Desiree are playing a song for their grandparents. Alex strikes the drum every 4 seconds. Desiree shakes the tambourine every 3 seconds. How often will their grandparents hear both instruments simultaneously in 5 minutes?

Definition

The **least common multiple (LCM)** of the whole numbers a and b, denoted LCM(a, b), is the smallest positive common multiple of a and b.

Visualizing the LCM

REPRESENTATION   You can visualize the LCM using rods. Let's find the LCM of 4 and 6. We consider rods of the length 4 units and rods of the length 6 units. Place rods of the same type together, without gaps or overlap, to create two chains of rods, as shown in Figure 7. The LCM of 4 and 6 is the shortest identical length of both chains. In Figure 7, we see LCM(4, 6) = 12.

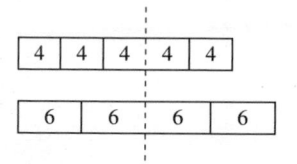

FIGURE 7

Visualizing the LCM of 4 and 6 using rods.

Find the LCM Using the List Method

When we find the LCM using the **list method,** first we list multiples of each number (that is, create skip-counting sequences), then we identify the common multiples in the lists, and finally we choose the least number in the list of common multiples. The list method is suitable for "friendly" numbers and introducing the basic ideas.

EXAMPLE 4.19   Use the list method to find LCM(4, 6).

CONNECTION

REASONING   SOLUTION

REPRESENTATION   The multiples of 4 are 4, 8, 12, 16, 20, 24, 28, 32, ... The multiples of 6 are 6, 12, 18, 24, 30, ... The common multiples of 4 and 6 are 12, 24, 36, ... Then LCM(4, 6) = 12.

▲

Find the LCM Using the Prime Factorization Method

The list method can be used to show that LCM(120, 36) = 360. Let's compare the prime factorizations of 120, 36, and 360.

$$120 = 2^3 \cdot 3^1 \cdot 5$$
$$36 = 2^2 \cdot 3^2$$
$$360 = 2^3 \cdot 3^2 \cdot 5 \quad \textbf{LCM(120, 36)}$$

All prime factors of 120 and 36 (2, 3, and 5) are prime factors of the LCM, and the exponent of each prime factor of the LCM corresponds to the *maximum* exponent.

This suggests the prime factorization method for finding the LCM of two numbers, which we describe and demonstrate to find the LCM of 132 and 600:

1. Write the prime factorizations of the numbers $132 = 2^2 \cdot 3 \cdot 11$ and $600 = 2^3 \cdot 3 \cdot 5^2$.
2. For the prime factors 2, 3, 5, and 11 in these factorizations, choose each of these prime numbers with their maximum exponents, breaking ties arbitrarily: 2^3, 3, 5^2, and 11.
3. Multiply the prime factors and exponents chosen: $LCM(132, 600) = 2^3 \cdot 3 \cdot 5^2 \cdot 11$. The following equation summarizes this process:

REPRESENTATION

$$132 = 2^2 \cdot ③ \cdot ⑪$$
$$600 = ②^3 \cdot 3 \cdot ⑤^2$$
$$LCM(132, 600) = 2^3 \cdot 3 \cdot 5^2 \cdot 11$$

The following example extends this procedure to finding the LCM of several numbers or algebraic expressions. We treat variables the same way—as if they were prime numbers.

EXAMPLE 4.20   Use the prime factorization method to find

REASONING   **a.** LCM(42, 294, 44).

REPRESENTATION   **b.** LCM($15x^3y$, $12x^2y^2$).

SOLUTION

We factor each number or algebraic expression and choose the maximum exponent of each factor.

a. $42 = 2 \cdot 3 \cdot 7$
$294 = 2 \cdot 3 \cdot 7^2$
$44 = 2^2 \cdot 11$
$\text{LCM}(42, 294, 44) = 2^2 \cdot 3 \cdot 7^2 \cdot 11 = 6468$

b. $15x^3y = 3 \cdot 5 \cdot x^3 \cdot y$
$12x^2y^2 = 2^2 \cdot 3 \cdot x^2 \cdot y^2$
$\text{LCM}(15x^3y, 12x^2y^2) = 2^2 \cdot 3 \cdot 5 \cdot x^3 \cdot y^2 = 60x^3y^2$

▲

Greatest Common Factor

A factor divides a whole number. The factors of 12 are 1, 2, 3, 4, 6, and 12. The factors of 18 are 1, 2, 3, 6, 9, and 18. The *common factors* of 12 and 18 are 1, 2, 3, and 6. The *greatest common factor* of 12 and 18 is 6.

> **Definition**
>
> The **greatest common factor (GCF)** of the whole numbers a and b, denoted $\text{GCF}(a, b)$, is the largest common factor of a and b.

Visualizing the GCF

You can use rods to visualize the GCF of two numbers. For example, let's find the GCF of 6 and 8. We create rods of the length 1, 2, 3, 4, 5, 6, 7, and 8 units. Then we place them end to end, without gaps or overlaps, as shown in Figure 8. Can you "see" factors of 6? of 8? common factors of 6 and 8? The GCF of 6 and 8 is 2.

CONNECTION

REPRESENTATION

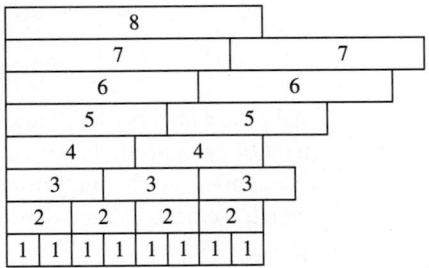

FIGURE 8
Visualizing factors and common factors of 6 and 8.

Find the GCF Using the List Method

When we find the GCF using the list method, first we list factors of each number, then we identify the common factors in the lists, and then we choose the greatest number in the list of common factors.

EXAMPLE 4.21 Use the list method to find the GCF of 15 and 20.

REASONING

REPRESENTATION SOLUTION

The factors of 15 are 1, 3, 5, and 15. The factors of 20 are 1, 2, 4, 5, 10, and 20. The common factors of 15 and 20 are 1 and 5. Therefore, the GCF of 15 and 20 is 5; that is, $\text{GCF}(15, 20) = 5$.

▲

Find the GCF Using the Prime Factorization Method

The factors of 36 are 1, 2, 3, 4, 6, 9, 12, 18, and 36. Of these factors, the greatest factor that also divides 120 is 12. Then GCF$(120, 36) = 12$. Let's compare the prime factorizations of 120, 36, and 12.

$$120 = 2^3 \cdot 3^1 \cdot 5$$
$$36 = 2^2 \cdot 3^2$$
$$12 = 2^2 \cdot 3^1 \quad \textbf{GCF}(120, 36)$$

The prime factorization of the GCF of 120 and 36 contains only *common* prime factors of 120 and 36 (namely, 2 and 3), along with their *minimum* exponents.

This suggests the prime factorization method for finding the GCF of two numbers, which we describe and demonstrate to find the GCF of 132 and 600:

1. Write their prime factorizations: $132 = 2^2 \cdot 3 \cdot 11$ and $600 = 2^3 \cdot 3 \cdot 5^2$.
2. For the common prime factors 2 and 3 in these factorizations, choose each of these prime numbers with their minimum exponents, breaking ties arbitrarily: 2^2 and 3.
3. Multiply the common prime factors and exponents chosen: GCF$(132, 600) = 2^2 \cdot 3$. The following equation summarizes this process:

REPRESENTATION

$$132 = \boxed{2^2} \cdot 3 \cdot 11$$
$$600 = 2^3 \cdot \boxed{3} \cdot 5^2$$
$$\text{GCF}(132, 600) = 2^2 \cdot 3$$

The following example extends this procedure to finding the GCF of several numbers or algebraic expressions. We treat variables the same way—as if they were prime numbers.

EXAMPLE 4.22 Use factorizations to find

REASONING **a.** GCF$(336, 3000, 1800)$.

REPRESENTATION **b.** GCF$(24x^3y^2, 180x^4y)$.

c. GCF$(7, 10)$.

SOLUTION

a. $336 = 2^4 \cdot 3 \cdot 7$
$3000 = 2^3 \cdot 3 \cdot 5^3$
$1800 = 2^3 \cdot 3^2 \cdot 5^2$
The common prime factors are 2 and 3, and we select their minimum exponents: GCF$(336, 1500, 1800) = 2^3 \cdot 3 = 24$.

b. $24x^3y^2 = 2^3 \cdot 3 \cdot x^3 \cdot y^2$
$180x^4y = 2^2 \cdot 3^2 \cdot 5 \cdot x^4 \cdot y$
The common factors are 2, 3, x, and y, and we select their minimum exponents: GCF$(24x^3y^2, 180x^4y) = 2^2 \cdot 3 \cdot x^3 \cdot y = 12x^3y$.

c. $7 = 7$
$10 = 2 \cdot 5$
There are no common prime factors, so GCF$(7, 10) = 1$.

▲

If there are no common prime factors of a and b, then GCF$(a, b) = 1$. We say a and b are **relatively prime** if and only if GCF$(a, b) = 1$. For example, GCF$(5, 42) = 1$, so 5 and 42 are relatively prime. GCF$(24, 32) \neq 1$, so 24 and 32 are not relatively prime.

The following Classroom Connection shows that students should know how to find the LCM and the GCF using multiple methods.

Classroom Connection

- Houghton Mifflin *Mathematics*, Student Edition, Grade 6, p. 71

Use a list or prime factorization method to find the LCM of each pair or group of numbers. (© by Houghton Mifflin Company, Inc. Reproduced by permission of the publisher, Houghton Mifflin Harcourt Publishing Company.)

12, 20   12, 16, 24

- Houghton Mifflin *Mathematics*, Student Edition, Grade 6, p. 67

Find the GCF of each group of numbers. Use either a list of factors or prime factorization.

84, 120   24, 36, 45

Euclidean Algorithm for Finding the GCF

The Greek mathematician Euclid described in his famous book *The Elements* a systematic method, called the **Euclidean algorithm,** for finding the GCF of two numbers using division. This method is based on the simple but powerful idea that if a and b are whole numbers with $b \le a$ and $a = q \cdot b + r$ (that is, $a \div b = q$ Rr), then any number that divides both a and b must divide the remainder r too. For example, $80 = 3 \cdot 24 + 8$. So any number that divides 80 and 24 must also divide 8. To find the GCF of 80 and 24, we just need to focus on the simpler problem of finding the GCF of 8 and 24.

The Euclidean algorithm is especially suited for finding the GCF of two large numbers. We illustrate the method with friendly numbers for learning purposes. The Euclidean algorithm replaces the larger number with the remainder to obtain a simpler problem.

EXAMPLE 4.23 Use the Euclidean algorithm to find GCF(48, 18).

CONNECTION

REASONING

REPRESENTATION SOLUTION

$$\begin{array}{r} 2 \\ 18\overline{)48} \\ -36 \\ \hline 12 \end{array}$$ **Think: 48 = 2 · 18 + 12, and the GCF of 48 and 18 must divide 12. Then GCF(48, 18) = GCF(12, 18).**

$$\begin{array}{r} 1 \\ 12\overline{)18} \\ -12 \\ \hline 6 \end{array}$$ **Think: 18 = 1 · 12 + 6, and the GCF of 18 and 12 must divide 6. Then GCF(12, 18) = GCF(12, 6).**

$$\begin{array}{r} 2 \\ 6\overline{)12} \\ -12 \\ \hline 0 \end{array}$$ **Think: 12 = 2 · 6 + 0, and the GCF of 12 and 6 must divide 0. Then GCF(12, 6) = GCF(0, 6).**

Because 6 divides both 0 and 6, GCF(0, 6) = 6. Therefore, GCF(48, 18) = 6.

The Euclidean algorithm terminates when the remainder is 0 or 1, because the GCF is simple to find: $GCF(0, n) = n$ and $GCF(1, n) = 1$. You can always terminate the algorithm prematurely when the GCF becomes obvious.

Connections between the LCM and the GCF

The LCM and the GCF have several properties, such as $GCF(a, b) = GCF(b, a)$, $LCM(a, b) = LCM(b, a)$, and $GCF(a, b) \leq LCM(a, b)$. But one remarkable relationship is worth exploring further, as shown in Table 4.12. What relationship do you see between $a \cdot b$ and $GCF(a, b) \cdot LCM(a, b)$?

TABLE 4.12 **Discovering the Relationship between $a \cdot b$ and $GCF(a, b) \cdot LCM(a, b)$**

a	b	$a \cdot b$	$GCF(a, b)$	$LCM(a, b)$	$GCF(a, b) \cdot LCM(a, b)$
4	6	24	2	12	24
3	5	15	1	15	15
9	12	108	3	36	108

We formalize this relationship in a theorem.

Theorem 15

Let a and b represent any whole numbers. Then $a \cdot b = LCM(a, b) \cdot GCF(a, b)$.

EXAMPLE 4.24 Maria discovered that $GCF(48, 18) = 6$. Use this information to find $LCM(48, 18)$.

CONNECTION

SOLUTION

$$LCM(48, 18) \cdot GCF(48, 18) = 48 \cdot 18$$
$$LCM(48, 18) = (48 \cdot 18) \div GCF(48, 18)$$
$$= (48 \cdot 18) \div 6$$
$$= 144$$

▲

Although the procedure for finding the LCM and the GCF using prime factorizations works for two or more numbers, the relationship in Theorem 15 only holds for two numbers.

Concept Map for the LCM and the GCF

Students should be able to "find the greatest common factor of two whole numbers less than or equal to 100 and the least common multiple of two whole numbers less than or equal to 12" (CCSS, Gr. 6). Concept Map 4.1 on the next page summarizes the main ideas for the LCM and the GCF. Ratios and adding, subtracting, and simplifying fractions will be covered in Chapter 5.

❯ Concept Map 4.1 LCM and GCF Connections

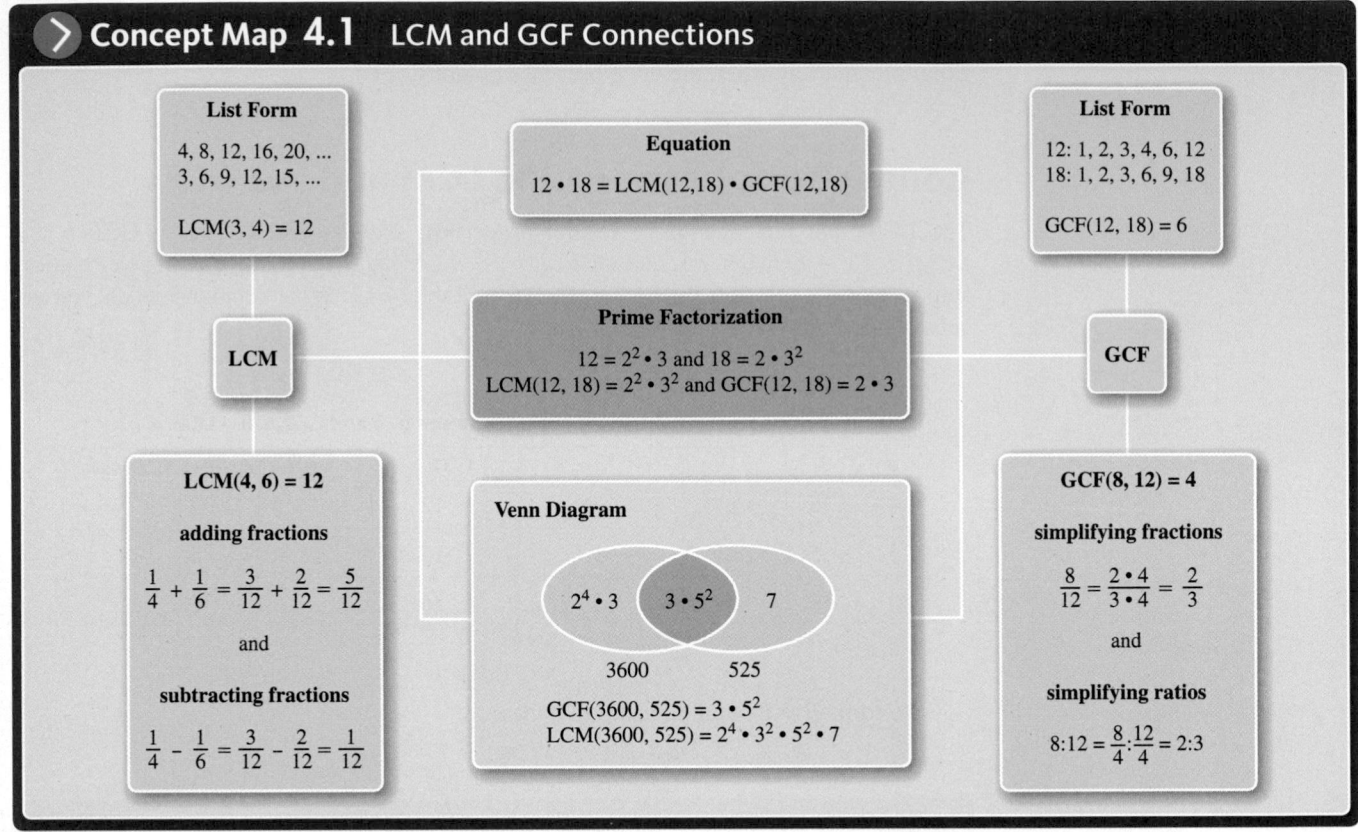

List Form

4, 8, 12, 16, 20, ...
3, 6, 9, 12, 15, ...

LCM(3, 4) = 12

Equation

$12 \cdot 18 = \text{LCM}(12,18) \cdot \text{GCF}(12,18)$

List Form

12: 1, 2, 3, 4, 6, 12
18: 1, 2, 3, 6, 9, 18

GCF(12, 18) = 6

LCM

Prime Factorization

$12 = 2^2 \cdot 3$ and $18 = 2 \cdot 3^2$
$\text{LCM}(12, 18) = 2^2 \cdot 3^2$ and $\text{GCF}(12, 18) = 2 \cdot 3$

GCF

LCM(4, 6) = 12

adding fractions

$\frac{1}{4} + \frac{1}{6} = \frac{3}{12} + \frac{2}{12} = \frac{5}{12}$

and

subtracting fractions

$\frac{1}{4} - \frac{1}{6} = \frac{3}{12} - \frac{2}{12} = \frac{1}{12}$

Venn Diagram

$2^4 \cdot 3$ $3 \cdot 5^2$ 7

3600   525

$\text{GCF}(3600, 525) = 3 \cdot 5^2$
$\text{LCM}(3600, 525) = 2^4 \cdot 3^2 \cdot 5^2 \cdot 7$

GCF(8, 12) = 4

simplifying fractions

$\frac{8}{12} = \frac{2 \cdot 4}{3 \cdot 4} = \frac{2}{3}$

and

simplifying ratios

$8{:}12 = \frac{8}{4}{:}\frac{12}{4} = 2{:}3$

QUESTIONS FOR SECTION 4.2

REPRESENTATION

Refresher: Representations (language, diagrams, tables, symbols, algebra, manipulatives, and contextualized situations) are important because we use them to organize, record, and communicate mathematical ideas and to make them more comprehensible.

1. Draw a diagram to show that and explain why 10 is a composite number.

2. Use the sieve of Eratosthenes to find all prime numbers from 2, 3, 4, . . . , 125.

3. Does $3^2 \cdot 8^5$ represent a prime factorization of a number? Why or why not?

4. The Venn diagram displays the prime factorizations of 90 and 144. Use the Venn diagram to find

   a. GCF(90, 144).   **b.** LCM(90, 144).

   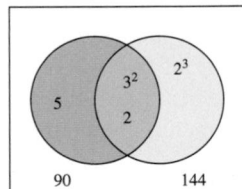

5. Do the following.

   a. Represent the prime factorizations of 72 and 132 with a Venn diagram.

   b. Use the Venn diagram to find GCF(72, 132) and LCM(72, 132).

   c. Some students confuse the GCF and the LCM. Discuss how a Venn diagram could help your students distinguish the GCF and the LCM.

6. The Venn diagram displays partial information about the prime factorizations of a and b. Suppose we know GCF$(a, b) = 75$. Determine a and b.

   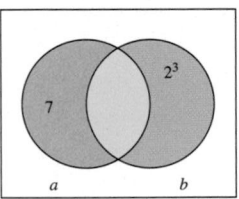

7. Use the prime factorizations $a = 2^4 \cdot 3^4 \cdot 5^3 \cdot 7^2$ and $b = 2^3 \cdot 3 \cdot 5^4 \cdot 11$ to find the prime factorization of

   a. LCM(a, b).   **b.** GCF(a, b).

8. Use a tree diagram to find the prime factorization of 48.

9. The diagram shows the prime factorization of *a*.

    a. Find *a*, *b*, *c*, and *d*.

    b. Write the prime factorization of *a*.

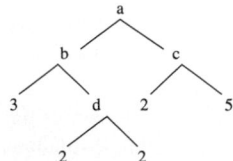

PROBLEM SOLVING

Refresher: Problem solving (reaching a goal that is not immediately attainable) is important because it helps students think more deeply about what they know and deal with unfamiliar situations.

10. Anita had 48 tulips and 32 daffodils. She sold all of them in small containers. Each container contained the same number of flowers. Each container had the same type of flower. What is the maximum number of flowers Anita could have put in each container?

11. David has some candy. He wants to give it all to his friends. What is the least number of pieces of candy he should have if he wants to divide it equally with up to five friends?

12. A bike store sold the same model of mountain bikes on Monday and Tuesday. On Monday, it generated $6720 in revenue. On Tuesday, it generated $7680 in revenue. Determine the maximum price the store could have charged for each bike. Assume the price is a whole number.

13. Alex and Desiree are practicing a song for their grandparents. Alex strikes the drum every 4 seconds. Desiree shakes the tambourine every 3 seconds. How often will their grandparents hear both instruments simultaneously in 1 minute?

14. In 1988, Earth, Jupiter, Saturn, and Uranus were aligned with the Sun. The number of (Earth) years it takes for each planet to revolve around the Sun are: Earth, 1 year; Jupiter, 12 years; Saturn, 30 years; and Uranus, 84 years.

    a. In how many years will Jupiter and Saturn be aligned with the Sun again?

    b. In how many years will Jupiter, Saturn, and Uranus be aligned with the Sun again?

    c. In how many years will Earth, Jupiter, Saturn, and Uranus be aligned with the Sun again?

REASONING AND PROOF

Refresher: Reasoning and proof (thinking and justifying) are important because they help students make sense of mathematics.

15. Use mental math to explain why the LCM of 35 and 428 cannot be 1432.

16. Use mental math to explain why the LCM of 3 and 17 cannot be 102.

17. $\text{GCF}(260, b) = 4$. $\text{LCM}(260, b) = 35{,}620$. Find *b*.

18. Suppose you know $n = 15b + 3$, where *b* is a counting number. Are there any values for *b* that make *n* a prime number? Justify your answer.

19. Find a composite number *n* with exactly 12 divisors, three of which are prime divisors.

20. Explain why there is no whole number *n* that satisfies the equation $5n = 24$ by comparing the prime factorization of each side of the equation.

21. Is there a composite number *n* with exactly 5 divisors, two of which are prime? Explain.

22. The GCF of *a* and *b* is 54.

    a. Find the prime factorization of 54.

    b. How many divisors does 54 have?

    c. *a* and *b* have eight common factors. Why?

CONNECTIONS

Refresher: Connections (linking and applying mathematical ideas) are important because they deepen student understanding and make mathematics more meaningful, flexible, and useful.

23. A Mersenne prime is a prime number of the form $2^n - 1$. The prime number $2^{1,257,787} - 1$, discovered in 1996, has 378,632 digits. When printed in newspaper-sized type, it fills about 12 newspaper pages. Another Mersenne prime is $2^{24,036,583} - 1$. Discovered in 2004, it has 7,235,733 digits (Prime Pages, http://primes.utm.edu/largest.html).

    a. Estimate the number of newspaper pages needed to print the standard form of $2^{24,036,583} - 1$.

    b. Is it possible to write the word form of $2^{24,036,583} - 1$?

24. Use the list method to find each number.

    a. $\text{LCM}(6, 8)$ b. $\text{GCF}(28, 98)$

    c. $\text{LCM}(42, 24)$ d. $\text{GCF}(42, 78)$

25. Use $\text{GCF}(336, 1500) = 12$ to find $\text{LCM}(336, 1500)$.

26. List all factors of 32 using repeated division.

27. Use the GCF to factor the sum (this means express the sum in the form $a(b + c)$, where *a* is the GCF and *b* and *c* have no common factors other than 1).

    a. $24 + 32$ b. $45x + 30xy$ c. $124x^4y^2 + 42x^3y^5$

COMMUNICATION

Refresher: Communication (written and verbal explanations using representations and proper mathematical vocabulary) is important because it helps students refine and strengthen their understanding.

28. Which strategy would you use to find the prime numbers in a collection of numbers 2, 3, . . . , *n*?

29. Which strategy would you use to determine whether a given number is a prime number?

30. Explain why 2 and 3 are the only consecutive prime numbers.

31. Explain why 3 does not have a prime factorization.

32. Suppose p is a prime number greater than 2. Is $p + 1$ a prime number or a composite number? Explain.

33. How can you tell from the prime factorizations of a and b that the LCM of a and b is $a \cdot b$?

34. How can you tell from the prime factorizations of a and b that the LCM of a and b is less than $a \cdot b$?

35. Mrs. Smith showed her students the sieve of Eratosthenes and asked them to look at the ones digit of all prime numbers and make a conjecture about the ones digit of all prime numbers greater than 5. After a few minutes, Sara exclaimed, "The ones digit of prime numbers greater than 5 must be 1, 3, 7, or 9!" Explain why the ones digit cannot be 0, 2, 4, 6, 8, or 5.

More practice with the ideas of the section

36. Fill in the blank. Choose one of the following words, phrases, or symbols: *3, 4, 12, 16, 48, 3 · 4, 12 · 16, 105, composite, GCF, factorization, finite, infinite, list, LCM, number theory, prime, prime factorization,* or *sieve of Eratosthenes.*

    a. _____ is the study of properties of counting numbers, such as factorization and divisibility properties.

    b. The number $2^4 \cdot 3^6 \cdot 7^2$ has _____ factor(s).

    c. The number $2^4 \cdot 3^6 \cdot 7^2$ has _____ prime factor(s).

    d. $2^4 \cdot 3^6 \cdot 7^2$ is an example of a(n) _____.

    e. $2^4 \cdot 10^6 \cdot 7^2$ is an example of a(n) _____.

    f. Elementary school teachers often introduce their students to the _____ method for finding the LCM and the GCF of two numbers because this method is accessible.

    g. 51 is a(n) _____ number.

    h. The _____ is useful for finding relatively small prime numbers, but today we use computers to find large prime numbers.

    i. The _____ of 24 and 18 is 6.

    j. LCM(12, 16) · GCF(12, 16) = _____.

37. List all factors of 42 using repeated division.

38. Write the prime factorizations of the following composite numbers using a factor tree.

    a. 240   b. 3375

39. Determine the number of factors of each number.

    a. $3^5 \cdot 2^7$ b. $5^4 \cdot 11^8 \cdot 17^2$

    c. $2^4 \cdot 7^6 \cdot 5$ d. $10^2 \cdot 2^4 \cdot 17^5$

40. How many of the divisors of $3^5 \cdot 7^4 \cdot 11^2$ are

    a. prime?   b. composite?

41. How many of the divisors of $20^5 \cdot 3^4 \cdot 13^2$ are

    a. prime?   b. composite?

42. How many divisors of 360 are

    a. prime?   b. composite?

43. Find a composite number with exactly six divisors, two of which are prime divisors.

44. Three people buy raffle tickets in the hope of winning a trip. Each raffle ticket cost the same. Person A spent $32. Person B spent $84. Person C spent $48. What is the maximum price for each raffle ticket?

45. The GCF of a and b is 24. a and b have eight common factors. Why?

46. The right-turn signal on a truck blinks every 6 seconds. The right-turn signal on a car blinks every 8 seconds.

    a. Suppose you noticed that both turn signals blinked at the same time. When will the turn signals blink at the same time again?

    b. What is the maximum number of times the right-turn signals of these vehicles blink simultaneously in a 5-minute period?

47. A divisor b of a is called a "proper divisor" if and only if b is a divisor of a and $b \neq a$. Define a prime number in terms of proper divisors.

48. 1, 4, 9, 16, 25, and 36 are examples of *perfect squares* ($1 = 1^2$, $4 = 2^2$, $9 = 3^2$, $16 = 4^2$, $25 = 5^2$, and $36 = 6^2$). 1 has 1 factor, 4 has 3 factors, 9 has 3 factors, 16 has 5 factors, 25 has 3 factors, and 36 has 9 factors.

    a. What does the number of factors in these examples have in common?

    b. Make a conjecture about the number of factors of a perfect square.

    c. The perfect square $p = 1$ has just one factor, so it has an odd number of factors. A perfect square $p > 1$ has the form $p = a^2$ for some counting number $a > 1$. We can express a in the form $a = p_1^{k_1} \cdot p_2^{k_2} \cdot \ldots \cdot p_n^{k_n}$, where $p_1, p_2, \ldots, p_n$ are prime numbers and $k_1, k_2, \ldots, k_n$ are counting numbers (for example, if $a = 5$, then $p_1 = 5$ and $k_1 = 1$). Then $p = (p_1^{k_1} \cdot p_2^{k_2} \cdot \ldots \cdot p_n^{k_n})^2$. Then p has the prime factorization $p = p_1^{2k_1} \cdot p_2^{2k_2} \cdot \ldots \cdot p_n^{2k_n}$. Explain why the perfect square $p > 1$ must have an odd number of factors.

49. A positive integer n is called a *perfect number* if n equals the sum of its proper divisors. For example, the factors of $n = 6$ are 1, 2, 3, and 6. The proper divisors are 1, 2, and 3. The sum of the proper divisors of 6 is $1 + 2 + 3 = 6$. Therefore, 6 is a perfect number. Determine whether the given number is a perfect number.

    a. 28   b. 12   c. 39

50. A positive integer n is called a *deficient number* if n is less than the sum of its proper divisors. For example, the factors of 8 are 1, 2, 4, and 8. The proper divisors of 8 are 1, 2, and 4. The sum of the proper divisors is $1 + 2 + 4 = 7$. Because $7 < 8$, 8 is a deficient number. Determine whether the given number is a deficient number.

    a. 10   b. 6   c. 12   d. any prime number

51. If n and $n + 2$ are prime numbers, then n and $n + 2$ are called *twin primes*. Give an example of twin primes.

52. A positive integer n is called an *abundant number* if n is more than the sum of its proper divisors. For example, the factors of 12 are 1, 2, 3, 4, 6, and 12. The proper divisors are 1, 2, 3, 4, and 6. The sum of the proper divisors of 12 is $1 + 2 + 3 + 4 + 6 = 16$. Because $16 > 12$, 12 is an abundant number. Determine whether the given number is an abundant number.

    a. 18   b. 12   c. 14   d. any prime number

53. For each problem, construct a composite number a with the indicated property.

    a. a has 12 factors, 2 of which are prime.

    b. a has seven factors and is less than 1500.

    c. a has 10 factors, is even, and is divisible by 7.

54. Using your calculator, enter any three-digit number and then repeat the number. For example, choose 453 and enter 453,453. Now divide the number by 7. Divide the result by 11. Divide the result by 13. What happens and why?

55. Use the Venn diagram to determine

    a. a. b. b. c. LCM(a, b). d. GCF(a, b).

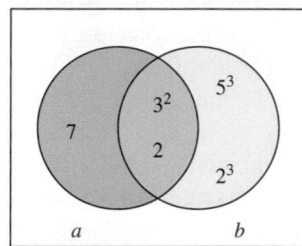

56. Suppose you know $n = 12b + 4$, where b is a counting number. Are there any values for b that make n a prime number? Justify your answer.

57. Use the given factorizations to find LCM(a, b). Write your answer in terms of a factorization.

    a. $a = 2^4 \cdot 3 \cdot 5^3 \cdot 7^2$ and $b = 2^3 \cdot 3^4 \cdot 5^4 \cdot 11$

    b. $a = 3^4 \cdot 5^2 \cdot 11^5 \cdot 13^2$ and $b = 2^3 \cdot 5^4 \cdot 7^4 \cdot 13$

    c. $a = 24x^3y^2$ and $b = 15x^4y^3$

58. Is the given number a prime number or a composite number? Justify your answer using the square root test.

    a. 173 b. 921 c. 719 d. 221

59. Use the given factorizations to find GCF(a, b). Write your answer in terms of a factorization.

    a. $a = 2^4 \cdot 3 \cdot 5^3 \cdot 7^2$ and $b = 2^3 \cdot 3^4 \cdot 5^4 \cdot 11$

    b. $a = 3^4 \cdot 5^2 \cdot 11^5 \cdot 13^2$ and $b = 2^3 \cdot 5^4 \cdot 7^4 \cdot 13$

    c. $a = 24x^3y^2$ and $b = 15x^4y^3$

60. Find two numbers a and b such that

    a. GCF$(a, b) = 2^3 \cdot 5^2 \cdot 7^4 \cdot 11$.

    b. LCM$(a, b) = 2^3 \cdot 5^2 \cdot 7^4 \cdot 11$.

61. Do the following.

    a. Suppose LCM$(a, b) = 1$. What is GCF(a, b)?

    b. Suppose GCF$(a, b) = 1$. What is LCM(a, b)?

62. The GCF of a and b is 20. List all common factors of a and b.

63. Use repeated division to find the prime factorization of

    a. 48. b. 300.

64. Do the following.

    a. GCF$(240, 372) = 12$. Use this information to find LCM$(240, 372)$.

    b. GCF$(336, 192) = 48$. Use this information to find LCM$(336, 192)$.

65. For the given a and b, use the Euclidean algorithm to find GCF (a, b). Then use the GCF(a, b) to find LCM(a, b).

    a. $a = 234, b = 420$ b. $a = 580, b = 18,300$

SECTION 4.3 Integers

r69photo/Shutterstock.com

Does the Equation $n + 4 = 0$ Have a Solution?

Ancient mathematicians knew that if you owed the tax collector five coins and you only gave him three coins, then you still owed the tax collector two coins. However, they were unable to calculate $3 - 5$. They also knew how to solve equations such as $5n - 20 = 0$ ($n = 4$) and $n^2 - 5n + 6 = 0$ ($n = 3$ or $n = 2$). However, they believed $n + 4 = 0$ lacked a solution and $n^2 - n - 6 = 0$ had only one solution ($n = 3$). Ancient mathematicians were correct in a sense, because they had not yet developed integers. However, by the first century, Hindu and Chinese mathematicians had learned how to solve these types of problems; they extended the set of whole numbers $\{0, 1, 2, 3, \ldots\}$ to a new set of numbers $\{\ldots, -3, -2, -1, 0, 1, 2, 3, \ldots\}$, called **integers.** But European mathematicians did not readily accept negative integers until the seventeenth century.

Notation and Models for Integers

The lowest and highest air temperatures ever recorded in the United States are 80 degrees Fahrenheit below zero in Prospect Creek Camp, Alaska, on January 23, 1971, and 134 degrees Fahrenheit above zero in Death Valley, California, on July 10, 1913, respectively. We can represent these extreme air temperatures as $-80°F$ and $134°F$. The numbers -80 and 134 are examples of integers.

> **Definition**
>
> The set of integers, denoted by I, is the set $I = \{\ldots, -3, -2, -1, 0, 1, 2, 3, \ldots\}$.
>
> - The set of **negative integers** is the subset $I^- = \{-1, -2, -3, \ldots\}$.
> - -1 is read as "negative one," -2 is read as "negative 2," and so on.
> - The set of **positive integers** is the subset $I^+ = \{1, 2, 3, \ldots\}$.
> - 0 is an integer that is neither negative nor positive.

The negative sign appears with just one number, such as -4, while the minus sign appears with two numbers, such as $5 - 2$. Later, we formally state a key property of negative integers as *additive inverses* (for example, $-3 + 3 = 0$ and $3 + -3 = 0$, so -3 is the solution to the equations $3 + n = 0$ and $n + 3 = 0$, and -3 is called the additive inverse of 3).

Figure 9 introduces the **chip model** to represent integers. A black chip represents -1, and a white chip represents 1. Then three black chips represent -3, and three white chips represent 3. A pair of black and white chips is called a *zero pair*, because it represents the integer 0. Figure 9 also shows how zero pairs lead to multiple representations of -3 and 3.

●	○	●●●	○○○	●○	●●●●○	○○○○○●●
-1	1	-3	3	0	-3	3
				(zero pair)		

FIGURE 9
The chip model for -1, 1, -3, 3, 0 and multiple ways to represent -3 and 3.

REPRESENTATION   Elementary mathematics textbooks use the chip model with a variety of pairs of colors (such as black and white or yellow and red), but they always use two distinct colors consistently. Some elementary mathematics textbooks refer to the chips as *counters*. Chips that you can hold are concrete representations of integers; chips that you draw are pictorial representations of integers; and expressions such as 3 and -3 are symbolic representations of integers.

Integers were originally associated with debts and assets, but we use them to represent elevation and temperature as well. The following example describes integers in practical situations and helps students "develop meaning for integers" (NCTM, Gr. 6–8).

EXAMPLE 4.25

REPRESENTATION

Represent each situation with an integer.
a. The store sold each shirt for \$3 above cost.
b. The canyon is 150 m below sea level.
c. The temperature is 20 degrees below zero.

SOLUTION
a. 3
b. -150
c. -20

▲

The number line in Figure 10 is a geometric metaphor of the set of integers.

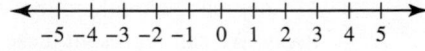

$$-5\ -4\ -3\ -2\ -1\ \ 0\ \ 1\ \ 2\ \ 3\ \ 4\ \ 5$$

FIGURE 10
The number line model for the set of integers.

REPRESENTATION

You can use the number line to compare integers, as with whole numbers. Simply graph both integers. The integer on the left is less than the integer on the right. For example, $-5 < 1$ and $-7 < -3$. Students should be able to "interpret statements of inequality as statements about the relative position of two numbers on a number line diagram. For example, interpret $-3 > -7$ as a statement that -3 is located to the right of -7 on a number line oriented from left to right" (CCSS, Gr. 6).

■ **Historical Note**

Brahmagupta (598–670 CE) was a Hindu mathematician and astronomer who lived in the first century. His book *Brahmasphutasiddhanta* (translated *The Opening of the Universe*), written in 628 CE, is credited with the first appearance of rules for operations with negative and positive integers. He used negative integers to represent debts and positive integers to represent assets. For example, 2 could represent that a person has two coins, and -3 could represent that a person owes three coins. The Chinese also demonstrated knowledge of negative integers in their oldest existing book on arithmetic, *Jiuzhang suanshu* (translated *Nine Chapters on the Mathematical Art*), written over a period of years, approximately 200 BCE to 50 CE. This book, which contains 246 practical problems in nine chapters on trade, taxation, distribution, and engineering, represents a summary of mathematics that the Chinese had learned over several centuries. Chapter 8 in *Jiuzhang suanshu* discusses the concept of negative and positive integers, as well as addition and subtraction of negative and positive integers. The Chinese used black bamboo rods on a counting board to represent negative integers and red bamboo rods to represent positive integers. For example, ⦀≣T represents -456 and ⦀≣T represents 456.

Absolute Value

The **absolute value** of an integer n, denoted $|n|$, is the distance between n and 0. In Figure 11, we see $|5| = 5$ and $|-3| = 3$. The absolute value plays a key role in developing rules for adding two integers.

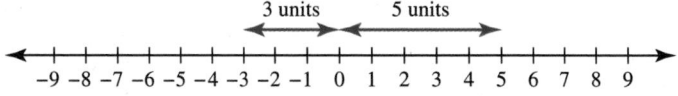

FIGURE 11
Absolute value $|-3| = 3$ and $|5| = 5$.

Integer Addition

The chip model, number line model, pattern model, and charged field model are informal strategies for teaching addition and subtraction with integers. (A homework question at the end of this section introduces the charged field model for adding integers.)

Figure 12 demonstrates how to apply the chip model to calculate $3 + -3$ and $5 + -3$. In the chip model, we model each addend using chips, combine the chips, and then identify and ignore the zero pairs. The remaining chips represent the sum.

REPRESENTATION

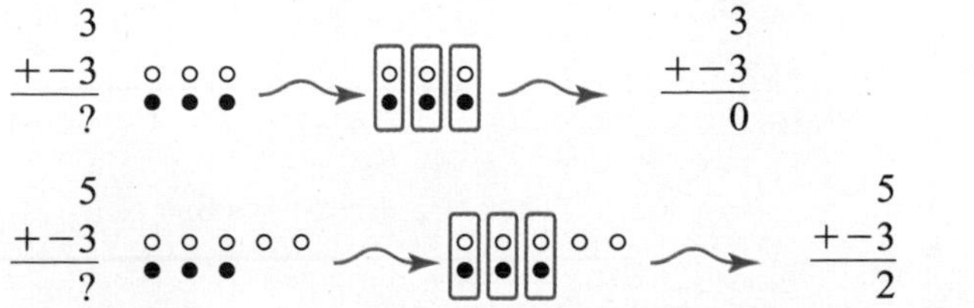

$$\begin{array}{r} 3 \\ +-3 \\ \hline ? \end{array} \quad \circ\circ\circ \atop \bullet\bullet\bullet \quad \rightsquigarrow \quad \rightarrow \quad \begin{array}{r} 3 \\ +-3 \\ \hline 0 \end{array}$$

$$\begin{array}{r} 5 \\ +-3 \\ \hline ? \end{array} \quad \circ\circ\circ\circ\circ \atop \bullet\bullet\bullet \quad \rightsquigarrow \quad \rightarrow \quad \begin{array}{r} 5 \\ +-3 \\ \hline 2 \end{array}$$

FIGURE 12
Using the chip model to add the following: $3 + -3$ and $5 + -3$.

EXAMPLE 4.26 Use the chip model to add: $-4 + 2$.

SOLUTION

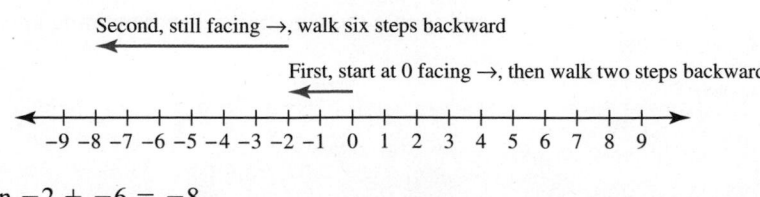

The following Classroom Connection shows students should be able to model integers and write word problems with integers.

> ◆ **Classroom Connection**
>
> ● *Math*, Grade 5, p. 399
>
> Add. You may use counters. $-4 + -7$, $12 + -8$. (© 2000 Macmillan/McGraw Hill. Reprinted by permission.)

We can use movements on a number line to model adding two integers. You begin at 0 and face toward the positive integers. A positive integer always means you take steps forward in the direction you are facing, while a negative integer always means you take steps backward. Figure 13 illustrates how to use the number line model to find the sums $2 + 6$, $2 + -6$, and $-2 + 6$. The small arrow → indicates the direction you are facing while you walk. The tip of the second arrow indicates the sum.

REPRESENTATION

FIGURE 13(a)
The number line model for adding integers is like walking. Positive integers mean step forward, while negative integers mean step backward.

$2 + 6 = 8$

Second, still facing →, walk six steps forward

First, start at 0 facing →, then walk two steps forward

−9 −8 −7 −6 −5 −4 −3 −2 −1 0 1 2 3 4 5 6 7 8 9

FIGURE 13(b)

$2 + -6 = -4$

Second, still facing →, walk six steps backward

First, start at 0 facing →, then walk two steps forward

−9 −8 −7 −6 −5 −4 −3 −2 −1 0 1 2 3 4 5 6 7 8 9

FIGURE 13(c)

$-2 + 6 = 4$

Second, still facing →, walk six steps forward

First, start at 0 facing →, then walk two steps backward

−9 −8 −7 −6 −5 −4 −3 −2 −1 0 1 2 3 4 5 6 7 8 9

EXAMPLE 4.27 Use the number line model to add: $-2 + -6$.

REPRESENTATION

SOLUTION

Second, still facing →, walk six steps backward

First, start at 0 facing →, then walk two steps backward

−9 −8 −7 −6 −5 −4 −3 −2 −1 0 1 2 3 4 5 6 7 8 9

Then $-2 + -6 = -8$.

The pattern model is another way to promote addition with integers. In the **pattern model,** we *build on known facts* (such as whole number addition), and use patterns to reveal new facts (such as sums involving negative integers). The following sequences of equations show how patterns are used to calculate $-2 + 6$. There are two changing patterns: 3, 2, 1, 0, . . . and 9, 8, 7, 6, ... The pattern in the first sequence suggests $-2 + 6 = 4$, as shown in the second sequence.

known facts	patterns reveal new facts
$3 + 6 = 9$	$3 + 6 = 9$
$2 + 6 = 8$	$2 + 6 = 8$
$1 + 6 = 7$	$1 + 6 = 7$
$0 + 6 = 6$	$0 + 6 = 6$
?	$-1 + 6 = 5$
?	$-2 + 6 = 4$
?	$-3 + 6 = 3$

Rules for adding integers appeared in the earliest known books on arithmetic dating from the first century. Here are rules for adding two integers:

- **Rule for adding an integer and its additive inverse.** You can use any of the models to verify that $4 + -4 = 0$, $-2 + 2 = 0$, $5 + -5 = 0$, and $-3 + 3 = 0$. The integer -4, which is read as "negative four," is also called the **additive inverse** (or **opposite**) of 4, because $4 + -4 = 0$. Similarly, the integer 3 is called the additive inverse (or opposite) of -3, because $-3 + 3 = 0$. The additive inverse of 0 is 0. These examples suggest that the sum of an integer and its additive inverse is 0. For example, let's apply this rule to determine $-7 + 7$. The integer -7 is the additive inverse of 7, so $-7 + 7 = 0$.

- **Rule for adding two integers with the same signs.** You can use any of the models to verify that $4 + 2 = 6$, $-4 + -2 = -6$, $5 + 3 = 8$, and $-5 + -3 = -8$. These examples suggest that if we add two integers with the same signs, then the sum has the same sign as both addends. Here is a rule for *adding two integers with the same sign:* First, add the absolute values of the integers; then the sign of the result has the same sign as the integers. For example, let's apply this rule to determine $-5 + -3$. First, we add their absolute values: $|-5| + |-3| = 5 + 3 = 8$. Because -5 and -3 are negative integers, $-5 + -3$ is negative: $-5 + -3 = -8$.

- **Rule for adding two integers with different signs.** You can use any of the models to verify that $5 + -2 = 3$, $7 + -1 = 6$, $-8 + 5 = -3$, and $-3 + 2 = -1$. These examples suggest that if we add two integers with different signs, then the sum has the sign of the addend with the larger absolute value. Here is a rule for *adding two integers with opposite signs:* First, subtract the absolute values of the integers so that the difference is positive; then the sign of the result has the same sign as the addend with the larger absolute value. For example, let's apply this rule to determine $-5 + 3$. First, we subtract their absolute values to obtain a non-negative integer: $|-5| - |-3| = 5 - 3 = 2$. Because -5 has a larger absolute value than -3, $-5 + 3$ is negative: $-5 + 3 = -2$. We would not apply this rule to determine sums such as $-5 + 5$, because we already know the sum is 0.

EXAMPLE 4.28 Apply the rules for adding two integers.
   a. $85 + -85$
   b. $-14 + 29$
   c. $-35 + -21$

SOLUTION

a. 85 and -85 are opposites, so $85 + -85 = 0$.

b. -14 and 29 have different signs. $|29| - |-14| = 29 - 14 = 15$, so $-14 + 29 = 15$.

c. -35 and -21 are negative integers. $|-35| + |-21| = 35 + 21 = 56$, so $-35 + -21 = -56$.

Properties of Integer Addition

Many properties of addition with integers resemble properties for addition with whole numbers. This is to be expected, because every whole number is an integer.

> ### Properties of Addition with Integers
>
> Let a, b, and c represent any integers.
>
> **Commutative Property**
> If a and b are any integers, then $a + b = b + a$.
>
> **Associative Property**
> If a, b, and c are any integers, then $(a + b) + c = a + (b + c)$.
>
> **Additive Inverse Property**
> If a is any integer, then $a + -a = 0$ and $-a + a = 0$.
>
> **Additive Identity Property**
> If a is any integer, then $a + 0 = a$ and $0 + a = a$.

Homework questions at the end of this section ask you to prove that (1) the additive inverse is unique (this means, for example, the only additive inverse of 3 is -3) and (2) 0 is the only additive identity. We can use these basic properties to solve equations.

EXAMPLE 4.29   Use the properties of integers to solve the equation $-4 + a = 8$.

SOLUTION

$-4 + a = 8$	**Original equation**
$4 + (-4 + a) = 4 + 8$	**Addition property of equality**
$(4 + -4) + a = 4 + 8$	**Associative property of addition**
$0 + a = 4 + 8$	**Additive inverse property**
$a = 4 + 8$	**Additive identity property**
$a = 12$	**Simplification**

So the solution to $-4 + a = 8$ is $a = 12$.

▲

REASONING   The basic properties also help us simplify expressions such as $-(-n)$, read as "the opposite of negative n." These types of expressions arise in a method for subtraction when we add the opposite.

EXAMPLE 4.30   Let a be any integer. Prove that if a is any integer, then $-(-a) = a$.

REASONING

SOLUTION

$0 = a + -a$	**Additive inverse property**
$0 + -(-a) = (a + -a) + -(-a)$	**Addition property of equality**
$-(-a) = (a + -a) + -(-a)$	**Additive identity property**
$-(-a) = a + [-a + -(-a)]$	**Associative property of addition**
$-(-a) = a + 0$	**Additive inverse property**
$-(-a) = a$	**Additive identity property**

▲

EXAMPLE 4.31

REASONING

Let a and b represent positive integers.

a. Use inductive reasoning to support the conjecture $-a + -b = -(a + b)$.

b. Use deductive reasoning to prove the conjecture $-a + -b = -(a + b)$.

SOLUTION

a. We know $-4 + -3 = -7 = -(4 + 3)$, because $7 = 4 + 3$. So $-4 + -3 = -(4 + 3)$. Similarly, $-2 + -4 = -(2 + 4)$ and $-8 + -4 = -(8 + 4)$. The examples support the conjecture $-a + -b = -(a + b)$.

b. The equation $-a + -b = -(a + b)$ means $-a + -b$ equals the opposite of $a + b$. We must prove $-a + -b + (a + b) = 0$.

$$
\begin{aligned}
(-a + -b) + (a + b) &= (-a + -b) + (b + a) && \textbf{Commutative property} \\
&&& \textbf{of addition} \\
&= (-a + -b) + b] + a && \textbf{Associative property} \\
&&& \textbf{of addition} \\
&= [-a + (-b + b)] + a && \textbf{Associative property} \\
&&& \textbf{of addition} \\
&= (-a + 0) + a && \textbf{Additive inverse property} \\
&= -a + a && \textbf{Additive identity property} \\
&= 0 && \textbf{Additive inverse property}
\end{aligned}
$$

So $(-a + -b) + (a + b) = 0$, which means $-a + -b$ is the additive inverse of $a + b$. Therefore, $-a + -b = -(a + b)$.

Integer Subtraction

There are several approaches for subtracting integers. The chip model, number line model, pattern model, and charged field model are informal strategies (a homework question introduces the charged field model for subtracting integers), while the missing addend model and add-the-opposite model are formal strategies.

Figure 14 illustrates how to use the chip model to calculate $-3 - 5$. We model the minuend (-3) with three black chips and need to take away five white chips. To do this, we need to insert enough zero pairs to prepare for subtraction using the take-away model. The chips that remain model the difference.

REPRESENTATION

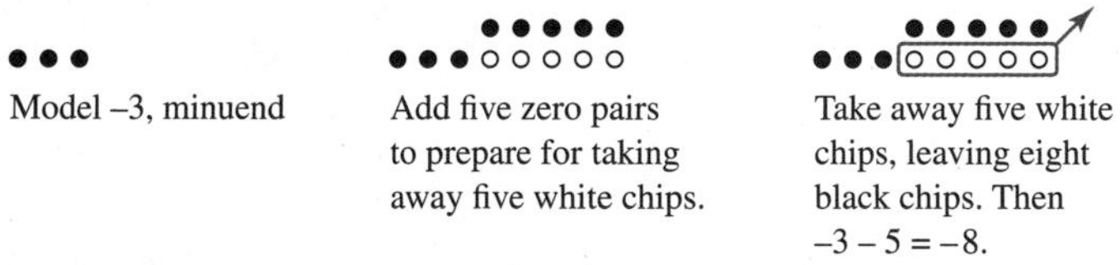

Model –3, minuend

Add five zero pairs to prepare for taking away five white chips.

Take away five white chips, leaving eight black chips. Then $-3 - 5 = -8$.

FIGURE 14

Calculating $-3 - 5$ using the chip model.

EXAMPLE 4.32

CONNECTION

REASONING

REPRESENTATION

Use the chip model to subtract the following: $4 - 6$.

SOLUTION

We build the minuend 4 with four white chips. We need to take away six white chips. This calls for inserting two zero pairs to prepare for subtraction.

4, minuend

Add two zero pairs.

Take away six white chips, leaving two black chips.

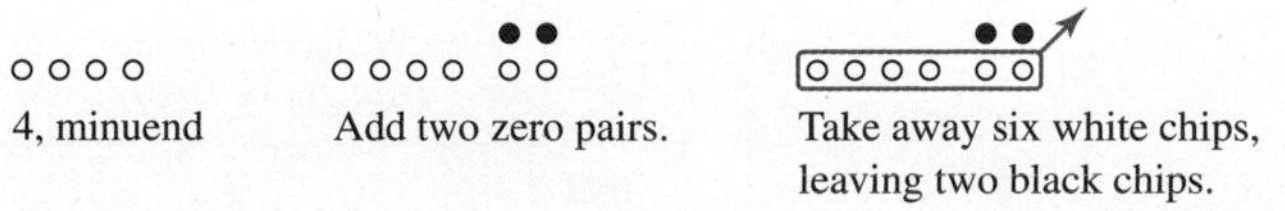

We see $4 - 6 = -2$.

The chip model for the problems such as $4 - -3$ and $-2 - -5$ are similar.

EXAMPLE 4.33 Write the subtraction problem for the chips shown.

CONNECTION

REASONING

REPRESENTATION

a.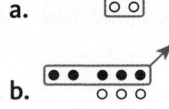

b.

SOLUTION

a. $-3 - 2 = -5$

b. $-2 - -5 = 3$

A page from an elementary mathematics textbook for fifth graders shows that any two-color set of chips can be used to model integer subtraction. The chips give students a physical way to visualize integer subtraction and connect to procedures for addition and subtraction with integers.

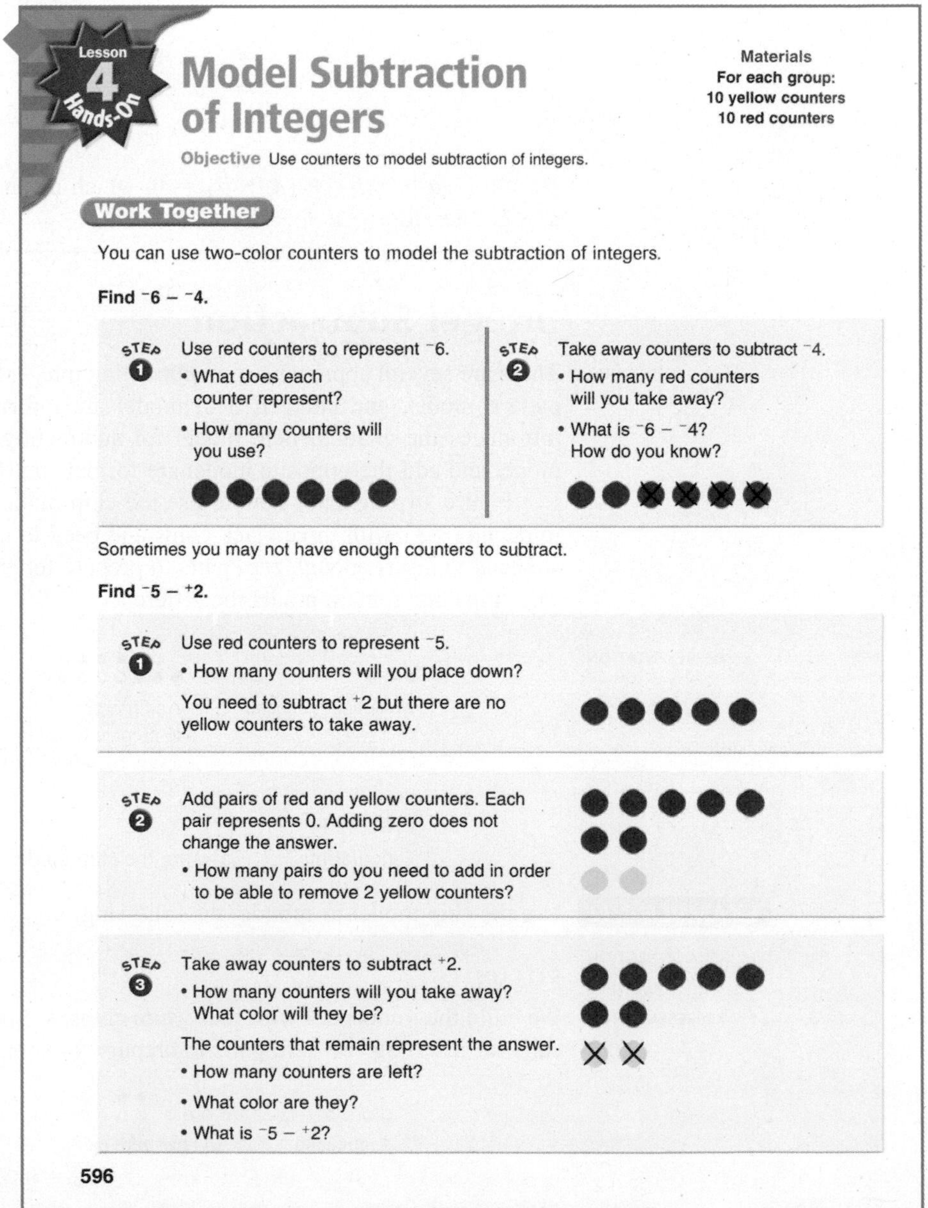

Lesson 4 Hands-On

Model Subtraction of Integers

Materials
For each group:
10 yellow counters
10 red counters

Objective Use counters to model subtraction of integers.

Work Together

You can use two-color counters to model the subtraction of integers.

Find ⁻6 − ⁻4.

STEP **1** Use red counters to represent ⁻6.
- What does each counter represent?
- How many counters will you use?

STEP **2** Take away counters to subtract ⁻4.
- How many red counters will you take away?
- What is ⁻6 − ⁻4? How do you know?

Sometimes you may not have enough counters to subtract.

Find ⁻5 − ⁺2.

STEP **1** Use red counters to represent ⁻5.
- How many counters will you place down?

You need to subtract ⁺2 but there are no yellow counters to take away.

STEP **2** Add pairs of red and yellow counters. Each pair represents 0. Adding zero does not change the answer.
- How many pairs do you need to add in order to be able to remove 2 yellow counters?

STEP **3** Take away counters to subtract ⁺2.
- How many counters will you take away? What color will they be?

The counters that remain represent the answer.
- How many counters are left?
- What color are they?
- What is ⁻5 − ⁺2?

596

(Harcourt *Math*, California, Student Edition, Grade 5, p. 596)

(© by Harcourt, Inc. Reproduced by permission of the publisher, Houghton Mifflin Harcourt Publishing Company.)

The number line model for subtraction uses the same interpretation of positive and negative integers as before. As with whole numbers, the minus sign is the sole indication that you need to turn around as you walk on the number line. Figure 15 shows how to use the number line model to calculate $-3 - -7$. The difference is 4.

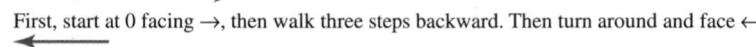

Second, facing ←, −7 means walk seven steps backward

First, start at 0 facing →, then walk three steps backward. Then turn around and face ←

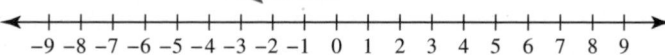

$$-9\ -8\ -7\ -6\ -5\ -4\ -3\ -2\ -1\ \ 0\ \ 1\ \ 2\ \ 3\ \ 4\ \ 5\ \ 6\ \ 7\ \ 8\ \ 9$$

FIGURE 15

Calculating $-3 - -7$ using the number line model.

CONNECTION
REPRESENTATION

The activity of walking provides a meaningful way to make sense of addition and subtraction with integers. Unfortunately, the number line model for addition and subtraction with integers does not naturally extend to multiplication with integers.

We can also use patterns to model subtraction. The following sequences of equations use patterns to subtract the following: $-3 - 4$. We always begin with "known facts," such as $-3 - -2 = -1$ (three black chips take away two black chips equals one black chip) as shown in the first sequence of equations, and then extend the pattern, as shown in the second sequence, to reveal "unknown" facts.

CONNECTION
REASONING
REPRESENTATION

known facts	patterns reveal new facts
$-3 - -2 = -1$	$-3 - -2 = -1$
$-3 - -1 = -2$	$-3 - -1 = -2$
$-3 - -0 = -3$	$-3 - -0 = -3$
?	$-3 - \ \ 1 = -4$
?	$-3 - \ \ 2 = -5$
?	$-3 - \ \ 3 = -6$
?	$-3 - \ \ 4 = -7$

The pattern model naturally extends to multiplication with integers.

We already know that a subtraction problem with whole numbers can be turned into an addition problem by finding a missing addend. This also applies to subtraction problems involving integers.

Definition of Subtraction of Integers

Let a and b be any integers. Then $a - b = c$ if and only if $a = b + c$.

- c is called the **difference**; c is also called the *missing addend*.
- Also, $a - b = c$ if and only if $a = c + b$.

The difference c is still a missing addend. The definition relates subtraction and addition and helps students learn basic subtraction facts.

EXAMPLE 4.34   Subtract by finding the missing addend for $5 - -2$.

CONNECTION

SOLUTION

$5 - -2 = c$ if and only if $5 = -2 + c$. We know $5 = -2 + 7$, so $5 - -2 = 7$.

Table 4.13 shows several pairs of equations, which can be verified using the chip model or number line model. A difference is paired with a sum. The pairs suggest that subtraction can be turned into addition by "adding the opposite" of the subtrahend.

TABLE 4.13 **Arithmetic Examples Suggest Subtraction Can Be Accomplished by Adding the Opposite**

Difference	$-2 - 4 = -6$	$-4 - -6 = 2$	$3 - 5 = -2$	$1 - -8 = 9$
Sum	$-2 + -4 = -6$	$-4 + 6 = 2$	$3 + -5 = -2$	$1 + 8 = 9$

The arithmetic examples in Table 4.13 lead to the following algebraic definition of subtraction.

Subtracting Integers by Adding the Opposite

Let a and b be any integers. Then $a - b = a + (-b)$.

The following example demonstrates how to implement the formula for adding the opposite.

EXAMPLE 4.35

CONNECTION

Subtract by adding the opposite. Simplify the final result.
a. $5 - -2$
b. $-7 - 3$

SOLUTION
a. $5 - -2 = 5 + -(-2) = 5 + 2 = 7$
b. $-7 - 3 = -7 + -3 = -10$

▲

The following Classroom Connection indicates students use the add-the-opposite method to subtract integers.

Classroom Connection

● *Mathematics*, Grade 5, p. 719

Rewrite each subtraction using addition. Then find the answer. Use a number line to check. $-2 - -6$ (From Randall I. Charles. © 2004 by Pearson Education, Inc. or its affiliates. Used by permission. All rights reserved.)

Subtraction can be used to calculate the distance between the integers m and n. In Figure 11 (see p. 219) we see the distance between 5 and -3 is 8 units. Here, $|5 - -3| = |5 + -(-3)| = |5 + 3| = |8| = 8$ and $|-3 - 5| = |-3 + -5| = |-8| = 8$. The absolute value of both differences gives the correct answer. This suggests the following definition for the distance between two integers.

Definition of Distance between Any Two Integers

Let m and n be any integers. The distance between m and n is $|m - n|$.

EXAMPLE 4.36 This morning, the temperature was $-12°F$. Now the temperature is $4°F$. How much has the temperature risen?

CONNECTION

SOLUTION

We need to calculate the distance between -12 and 4.

$$|-12 - 4| = |-12 + -4|$$
$$= |-16|$$
$$= 16$$

The temperature increased by $16°F$.

▲

Integer Multiplication

We can use the pattern model for multiplication with integers. We *build on known facts,* such as whole number multiplication, and use patterns to reveal products involving negative integers. Consider the following sequences of equations. The first sequence begins with known facts, and the sequence equation extends the patterns. The third sequence also begins with known facts, and the fourth sequence again extends the patterns.

known facts	patterns reveal new facts
$3 \times 4 = 12$	$3 \times 4 = 12$
$2 \times 4 = 8$	$2 \times 4 = 8$
$1 \times 4 = 4$	$1 \times 4 = 4$
$0 \times 4 = 0$	$0 \times 4 = 0$
?	$-1 \times 4 = -4$
?	$-2 \times 4 = -8$
?	$-3 \times 4 = -12$

known facts	patterns reveal new facts
$5 \times 3 = 15$	$5 \times 3 = 15$
$5 \times 2 = 10$	$5 \times 2 = 10$
$5 \times 1 = 5$	$5 \times 1 = 5$
$5 \times 0 = 0$	$5 \times 0 = 0$
?	$5 \times -1 = -5$
?	$5 \times -2 = -10$
?	$5 \times -3 = -15$

The next sequence begins with results established in the second sequence of the preceding equations for a negative integer times a positive integer, and the final sequence extends the patterns.

known facts	patterns reveal new facts
$-5 \times 3 = -15$	$-5 \times 3 = -15$
$-5 \times 2 = -10$	$-5 \times 2 = -10$
$-5 \times 1 = -5$	$-5 \times 1 = -5$
$-5 \times 0 = 0$	$-5 \times 0 = 0$
?	$-5 \times -1 = 5$
?	$-5 \times -2 = 10$
?	$-5 \times -3 = 15$

Now we can generalize the patterns with the sign rules for multiplication.

Sign Rules for Multiplying Integers

Let a and b represent positive integers so that $-a$ and $-b$ are negative integers. Then

- $a \cdot b$ is the usual product of two whole numbers.
- $(-a) \cdot (-b) = a \cdot b.$
- $(-a) \cdot b = -(a \cdot b).$
- $a \cdot (-b) = -(a \cdot b).$

Applying the sign rules to multiply two integers means following a two-step process:

1. Ignore any signs and solve the related whole number multiplication problem.

2. Adjust the signs, as necessary: if the two factors have the same sign, then the product is positive; if the two factors have different signs, then the product is negative.

EXAMPLE 4.37 Use the sign rules to multiply.

CONNECTION

a. $5 \cdot -2$

b. $-7 \cdot -6$

SOLUTION

a. The factors have different signs, so the product is negative. $5 \cdot 2 = 10$, so $5 \cdot -2 = -10$.

b. The factors have the same signs, so the product is positive. $7 \cdot 6 = 42$, so $-7 \cdot -6 = 42$. ▲

Properties of Integer Multiplication

Suppose a and b are any integers. The algebraic definition for multiplying integers cannot help simplify the expression $(-a) \cdot (-b)$, because we cannot be sure that $-a$ and $-b$ are negative integers (for example, a could be 7 or -7). To simplify the expression $(-a) \cdot (-b)$, we need to use general properties of multiplication of integers, which mimic and extend the general properties of multiplication for whole numbers.

Properties of Multiplication of Integers

Commutative Property of Multiplication of Integers
Let a and b be any integers. Then $a \cdot b = b \cdot a$.

Associative Property of Multiplication of Integers
Let a, b, and c be any integers. Then $(a \cdot b) \cdot c = a \cdot (b \cdot c)$.

Zero Multiplication Property of Multiplication of Integers
Let a and b be any integers. If $a \cdot b = 0$, then $a = 0$, $b = 0$, or both.

Identity Property of Multiplication of Integers
Let a be any integer. Then $a \cdot 1 = 1 \cdot a = a$.

Distributive Property of Multiplication of Integers
Let a, b, and c be any integers. Then $a \cdot (b + c) = a \cdot b + a \cdot c$.

Now we can use the properties and algebra to simplify the expression $(-a) \cdot (-b)$. The key is to express $-a$ as $(-1) \cdot a$ (the opposite of a equals negative 1 times a), as shown in the following example.

EXAMPLE 4.38

CONNECTION
COMMUNICATION
PROBLEM SOLVING
REASONING
REPRESENTATION

a. Let a be any integer. Prove $-a = (-1) \cdot a$.

b. Let a and b be any integers. Prove $(-a) \cdot (-b) = a \cdot b$.

c. Simplify $-(4k - 3)$.

SOLUTION

a. We must show that the opposite of a equals $(-1) \cdot a$.

$0 = a \cdot 0$ **Zero multiplication property**

   $= a \cdot (1 + -1)$ **$0 = 1 + -1$**

     $= a \cdot 1 + a \cdot (-1)$ **Distributive property of multiplication over addition**

     $= a + a \cdot (-1)$ **Identity property of multiplication**

     $= a + (-1) \cdot a$ **Commutative property of multiplication**

Then $0 = a + (-1) \cdot a$, so the opposite of a is $(-1) \cdot a$; that is, $-a = (-1) \cdot a$.

b. We know $-a = (-1) \cdot a$ and $-b = (-1) \cdot b$. Then

$(-a) \cdot (-b) = ((-1) \cdot a) \cdot ((-1) \cdot b)$ **By substitution; for example, replace $-a$ with $(-1) \cdot a$**

   $= ([(-1) \cdot a] \cdot (-1)) \cdot b$ **Associative property of multiplication**

   $= ((-1) \cdot [a \cdot (-1)]) \cdot b$ **Associative property of multiplication**

   $= ((-1) \cdot [(-1) \cdot a]) \cdot b$ **Commutative property of multiplication**

   $= ([(-1) \cdot (-1)] \cdot a) \cdot b$ **Associative property of multiplication**

   $= ((1 \cdot 1) \cdot a) \cdot b$ **Multiplying two negative integers**

   $= (1 \cdot a) \cdot b$ **Identity property of multiplication**

   $= a \cdot b$ **Identity property of multiplication**

c. $-(4k - 3) = (-1) \cdot (4k - 3) = (-1) \cdot (4k + -3) = (-1) \cdot (4k) + (-1) \cdot (-3) = -4k + 3$

▲

Caution: Some students erroneously believe the negative sign $(-)$ equals -1. This example proves the relationship $-a = (-1) \cdot a$, it does not prove the negative sign equals -1.

Integer Division

As expected, the definition of division for whole numbers extends to integers.

> ### Definition of Division with Integers
>
> Let a and b represent any integers such that $b \neq 0$. Then $a \div b = c$ if and only if $a = b \cdot c$ for some unique integer c.

CONNECTION

The quotient c is a "missing factor." The definition relates division to multiplication and helps us *predict* the sign of the quotient:

- Solve $15 \div 3 = c$. Think $15 = 3 \cdot c$. Then c is positive.
  We know $15 = 3 \cdot 5$, so $15 \div 3 = 5$.
- Solve $-21 \div -7 = c$. Think $-21 = -7 \cdot c$. Then c is positive.
  We know $-21 = -7 \cdot 3$, so $-21 \div -7 = 3$.
- Solve $-16 \div 8 = c$. Think $-16 = 8 \cdot c$. Then c is negative.
  We know $-16 = 8 \cdot -2$, so $-16 \div 8 = -2$.
- Solve $32 \div -4 = c$. Think $32 = -4 \cdot c$. Then c is negative.
  We know $32 = -4 \cdot -8$, so $32 \div -4 = -8$.

Now we can generalize the results with the sign rules for division.

Sign Rules for Dividing Integers

Let a and b represent positive integers so that $-a$ and $-b$ are negative integers. Then

- $a \div b$ is the usual product of two whole numbers.
- $(-a) \div (-b) = a \div b.$
- $(-a) \div b = -(a \div b).$
- $a \div (-b) = -(a \div b).$

Applying the sign rules to divide two integers means following a two-step process:

1. Ignore any signs and solve the related whole number division problem.

2. Adjust the signs, as necessary: if the two integers have the same sign, then the quotient is positive; if the two integers have different signs, then the quotient is negative.

EXAMPLE 4.39   Use the sign rules to divide.

CONNECTION
a. $42 \div -6$

b. $-24 \div -8$

SOLUTION

a. The two integers have different signs, so the quotient is negative. $42 \div 6 = 7$, so $42 \div -6 = -7$.

b. The two integers have the same signs, so the quotient is positive. $24 \div 8 = 3$, so $-24 \div -8 = 3$.

▲

The following Classroom Connection shows that students should be able to relate the sign rules for multiplication and division.

Classroom Connection

- Harcourt *Math*, California, Student Edition, Grade 5, p. 261

Tell how the sign rules for multiplying two integers compare with the sign rules for dividing two integers. (© by Harcourt, Inc. Reproduced by permission of the publisher, Houghton Mifflin Harcourt Publishing Company.)

In the following Historical Note, we see that ancient mathematicians knew the sign rules and how the sign rules for multiplication and division were connected.

■ Historical Note

Brahmagupta, the Hindu mathematician and astronomer, developed rules for adding, subtracting, multiplying, and dividing integers. Historians view the rules as a considerable mathematical accomplishment for that period. The sign rules for nonzero multiplication and division are as follows (debts are negative integers, and assets are positive integers):

- The product or quotient of two fortunes is one fortune.
- The product or quotient of two debts is one fortune.
- The product or quotient of a debt and a fortune is a debt.
- The product or quotient of a fortune and a debt is a debt.

QUESTIONS FOR SECTION 4.3

REPRESENTATION

Refresher: Representations (language, diagrams, tables, symbols, algebra, manipulatives, and contextualized situations) are important because we use them to organize, record, and communicate mathematical ideas and to make them more comprehensible.

1. Write the integer represented by the chip model, where

   ● ○
   −1   1

   a. ●○●○   **b.** ●●○○●●●   **c.** ○●○○○○

   d. ○○○   **e.** ○○○●●○○●●●

2. Use the chip model to add.

   a. $-3 + -2$ **b.** $-2 + 4$ **c.** $-1 + -3$

3. Use the chip model to subtract.

   a. $-3 - 4$ **b.** $1 - -4$ **c.** $-2 - 5$

4. Write an equation involving the *sum* of two integers for the diagram.

   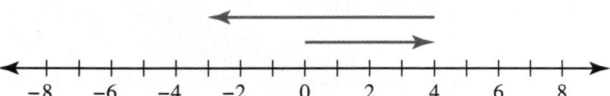

5. Use the number line model to add.

   a. $-3 + -2$ **b.** $-2 + 5$ **c.** $2 + -5$

6. Write an equation involving the *difference* of two integers for the diagram.

   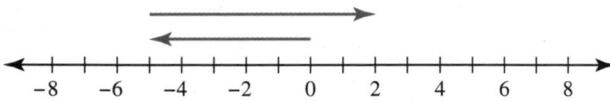

7. Use the number line model to subtract.

   a. $-3 - 4$ **b.** $3 - -4$ **c.** $-2 - -6$

8. Write a subtraction sentence.

   a.
   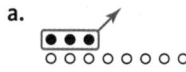

   b.
   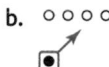

   c.

9. The *charged field model* is another way to represent integers. Let + represent 1, let − represent −1, and let − + represent a zero pair. What integer does each diagram represent?

   a. + + − −   **b.** + + +   **c.** − − − −

   d. + + − − −   **e.** + − + − + + − − − −

   f. + + + − + +

10. We can use the charged field model to add or subtract. For example, to solve $4 + -7$, we represent each addend with charges and form any zero pairs; the remaining charges represent the sum:

    Represent each addend:

    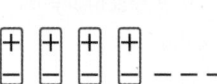

    Ignore zero pairs:

    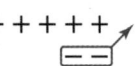

    Remaining charges represent
    the sum: $4 + -7 = -3$

    For example, to solve $3 - -2$, we first represent the minuend 3, then add zero pairs as necessary to prepare to take away -2, and finally take away charges represented by the subtrahend -2. The remaining charges represent the difference:

    Represent the minuend: + + +

    Add zero pairs to prepare to take away: + + + + +
                                                − −

    Take away -2:   + + + + +
                                    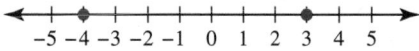

    Remaining charges represent the difference: $3 - -2 = 5$

    Use the charged field model to add and subtract.

    a. $7 + -4$ **b.** $5 - -3$ **c.** $-5 + 3$

    d. $-4 - -3$ **e.** $-5 - 2$

11. What inequality does the diagram represent?

    −5 −4 −3 −2 −1 0 1 2 3 4 5

PROBLEM SOLVING

Refresher: Problem solving (reaching a goal that is not immediately attainable) is important because it helps students think more deeply about what they know and deal with unfamiliar situations.

12. Joe purchased stock. By the end of the first month, the stock slid by $7 per share. The next month, it increased by $3 per share. The next month, it increased by $2 per share. Then Joe sold the stock for $68 per share. How much did he originally pay for each share?

13. A mechanical assembler can assemble 15 units in an hour. She currently has 68 units assembled. How many units did she have assembled 3 hours ago?

14. A busboy is docked $2 out of his pay for every dish he breaks during his shift. The busboy works a 7-hour shift and makes $6 per hour. If the busboy is paid $34 at the end of his shift, how many dishes did he break?

REASONING AND PROOF

Refresher: Reasoning and proof (thinking and justifying) are important because they help students make sense of mathematics.

15. Answer the following.

   a. How are the integers 5, 76, 21, and 0 alike?

   b. How are the integers -6, 0, -145, and -72 alike?

16. Justify each step for solving the equation $4 - n = 7$.

Equation	Reason
$4 - n = 7$	Original equation
$4 = n + 7$	Definition of subtraction
$4 + -7 = (n + 7) + -7$	a.
$4 + -7 = n + (7 + -7)$	b.
$4 + -7 = n + 0$	c.
$4 + -7 = n$	d.
$-3 = n$	Simplification

17. Justify each step for solving the equation $4 - n = 7$.

Equation	Reason
$4 - n = 7$	Given
$4 = 7 + n$	a.
$4 - 7 = n$	b.
$-3 = n$	c.

18. Suppose n is a nonzero integer.

   a. What is the sign of $n \cdot n$?

   b. What is the sign of $n \cdot n \cdot n$?

19. Use patterns to calculate 4×-3.

20. The additive identity element of integers is 0. For any integer a, we know $a + 0 = a$. Suppose x is an integer such that $a + x = a$. The following equations prove that x equals 0 (that is, prove the additive identity element of the set of integers is unique). Supply the missing reasons.

Equation	Reason
$a + x = a$	Original equation
$-a + (a + x) = -a + a$	a.
$-a + (a + x) = 0$	b.
$(-a + a) + x = 0$	c.
$0 + x = 0$	d.
$x = a$	e.

21. Let a be any integer. The integer $-a$ represents the additive inverse of a. We know $a + -a = 0$. Suppose x is an integer such that $a + x = 0$. The following equations prove that x equals $-a$ (that is, prove the additive inverse of a is unique). Supply the missing reasons.

Equation	Reason
$a + x = 0$	Given
$-a + (a + x) = -a + 0$	a.
$-a + (a + x) = -a$	b.
$(-a + a) + x = -a$	c.
$0 + x = -a$	d.
$x = -a$	e.

22. Answer and explain the following.

   a. Is the set of whole numbers closed under subtraction?

   b. Is the set of integers closed under subtraction?

CONNECTIONS

Refresher: Connections (linking and applying mathematical ideas) are important because they deepen student understanding and make mathematics more meaningful, flexible, and useful.

23. The highest and lowest air temperatures ever recorded in Asia are 122°F and -67°F, respectively. Find the difference between these air temperatures.

24. The Dead Sea, the saltiest body of water on Earth, is 400 m below sea level, making it the lowest point on the surface of Earth. The summit of Mount Everest is 8850 m above sea level, making it the highest point on the surface of Earth. What is the change in elevation from the Dead Sea to the summit of Mount Everest?

25. Simplify each expression. Then determine whether the integer is negative or positive.

   a. -5 b. $-(-5)$

   c. $-(-(-5))$ d. $-(-(-(-5)))$

   e. Describe the pattern. How can you use the pattern to determine whether the integer is negative or positive?

26. Study the equations. Use patterns to write the next equation in each sequence.

   a. $3 \cdot 4 = 12$ b. $3 \cdot 3 = 9$ c. $4^3 = 64$
   $\ 2 \cdot 4 = 8$ $\ 3 \cdot 2 = 6$ $\ 4^2 = 16$
   $\ 1 \cdot 4 = 4$ $\ 3 \cdot 1 = 3$ $\ 4^1 = 4$
   $\ 0 \cdot 4 = 0$ $\ 3 \cdot 0 = 0$

27. I is the set of integers. $I^- = \{\ldots, -3, -2, -1\}$ is the set of negative integers. $I^+ = \{1, 2, 3, \ldots\}$ is the set of positive integers (which is the set of counting numbers). $W = \{0, 1, 2, 3, \ldots\}$ is the set of whole numbers. Find each set.

   a. $I^- \cap I^+$ b. $I^- \cup I^+$ c. $I^- \cap W$

   d. $W - I^+$ e. $I - I^-$ f. $I^+ \cup \{0\}$

COMMUNICATION

Refresher: Communication (written and verbal explanations using representations and proper mathematical vocabulary) is important because it helps students refine and strengthen their understanding.

28. Write a word problem that requires the equation $-7 + 3 = -4$.

29. Write a word problem that requires the equation $-3 - 7 = -10$.

30. Do the following.

   a. Evaluate $-3 - 5$ and $5 - -3$.

   b. Evaluate $-6 - -1$ and $-1 - -6$.

   c. Make a conjecture about what these examples suggest.

31. Explain how a student should evaluate $32 \div -8$.

More practice with the ideas of the section

32. Fill in the blank. Choose one of the following words, phrases, or symbols: *−0, 0, −3, 3, add the opposite, addition, additive inverse, additive identity, bank accounts, concrete, debts and assets, integer, multiplicative identity, negative, pictorial, positive, sign rules,* or *symbolic.*

   a. The chip model is a(n) _____ representation of the set of integers.

   b. The number line model is a(n) _____ representation of the set of integers.

   c. The number −2 is a(n) _____ representation of an integer.

   d. The number 5 is a(n) _____ integer.

   e. The number −7 is a(n) _____ integer.

   f. The number 1 is the _____ element of the set of integers.

   g. The number 0 is the _____ element of the set of integers.

   h. The additive inverse of 3 is _____.

   i. The additive inverse of −3 is_____.

   j. _____ is/are neither positive nor negative.

   k. _____ allow(s) you to predict the sign of a product or quotient.

   l. Integers were originally devised to keep track of _____.

33. Find the additive inverse of each expression. All variables represent integers.

   a. 3   **b.** −5   **c.** b **d.** $-(-8)$ **e.** 0   **f.** $p + q$

34. Insert < or >.

   a. 4 ___ 10   **b.** −10 ___ 2   **c.** −5 ___ −100

35. Explain why every negative integer is less than any positive integer.

36. Simplify the expression $-(4 - 5n)$. Show your work, and state what properties you used.

37. Solve $-4 - 3$ using the following models.

   a. chip model   **b.** number line model

38. Solve each equation. Show your work.

   a. $n - -3 = 8$ **b.** $4n + 3 = -21$

39. Subtract by adding the opposite.

   a. $3 - -5$ **b.** $-2 - 8$ **c.** $-5 - -11$ **d.** $10 - 14$

40. Gary purchased electronic equipment for $1000 on his new credit card. Later, he made a $650 payment to the credit card company. Write an integer that expresses the debt.

41. Use patterns to find the next three terms in each sequence.

   a. $3 + 2 = 5$ **b.** $-4 + 6 = 2$
   $3 + 1 = 4$ $-4 + 5 = 1$
   $3 + 0 = 3$ $-4 + 4 = 0$
   $3 + -1 = 2$ $-4 + 3 = -1$

42. Use patterns to compute

   a. $-3 + 4.$ **b.** $3 - -2.$

43. Use patterns to compute

   a. $-3 \cdot 4.$ **b.** $3 \cdot -2.$

44. Use patterns to compute $-3 \cdot -2.$

45. Use the sign rules to multiply.

   a. 3×-9 **b.** -4×7 **c.** 12×5 **d.** -4×-9

46. Use the sign rules to divide.

   a. $36 \div -9$ **b.** $-42 \div 7$ **c.** $20 \div 5$ **d.** $-24 \div -4$

47. Use properties of multiplication to prove

   a. $-2n - 6n = -8n.$ **b.** $4n - 7n = -3n.$

48. Use the standard order of operations to simplify each of the following.

   a. $5 - 3 - 8$ **b.** $h - 4 - (3 + -h)$

   c. $2 + 7 - 12$ **d.** $-a + (3 - (-a - 3))$

49. Evaluate each expression.

   a. $-3 - 5 + -7$ **b.** $3 + - (-4 + 5)$

   c. $-4 - -5 - -6$

50. Evaluate each expression.

   a. $|-3 + 4|$ **b.** $-|-7 - -2|$ **c.** $0 - -|4|$

51. The stock price of a telecommunications company traded at $82 per share. A year later, the price dropped to $51 per share. Express the change in price per share as an integer.

52. Water drains out of a hole in a bucket at a rate of 1 L per minute. Beth pours water into the bucket at a rate of 3 L per minute. If the initial amount of water in the bucket was 3 L, how much water is in the bucket 2 minutes later?

53. Answer and explain the following.

   a. a, b, and c are any whole numbers. Is subtraction associative; that is, is $(a - b) - c = a - (b - c)$?

   b. a, b, and c are any integers. Is subtraction associative; that is, is $(a - b) - c = a - (b - c)$?

54. Factor each expression.

   a. $-12x + 8y$ **b.** $18x^2y^5 - 12x^7y^2$

55. Find the distance between the integers.

   a. −3 and 5   **b.** 4 and −9   **c.** −12 and −5   **d.** 8 and 5

56. $-6, -13, -20, -27, \ldots$ is an arithmetic sequence.

   a. Determine the initial value.

   b. Determine the common difference.

   c. Give an expression for the nth term.

   d. What is the 53rd term in the sequence?

   e. Is −72 a term in the sequence?

57. Find each arithmetic sum.

   a. $-5 + -6 + -7 + -8 + \ldots + -56$

   b. $-46 + -45 + -44 + \ldots + 79 + 80 + 81$

58. Find an arithmetic sequence such that the 14th term is −22 and the 167th term is −634.

59. How many integers are there

   a. from −9 to −2?   **b.** from −12 to 31?

   c. from a to 30, with $a < 30$?

60. Do the following.

   a. Write $|n - 7| = 10$ without absolute value notation. Write two different equations.

   b. Represent the distance between 7 and −3 using absolute value notation.

61. Find all integers n such that

  a. $|n - 2| = 8$.   **b.** $|n + 6| = 37$.   **c.** $|n - 35| = 24$.

62. Written rules for multiplying and dividing integers were known more than 2000 years ago. Let a and b be any positive integers. Represent the written rule using algebra.

  a. The product of a positive integer and a negative integer is a negative integer.

  b. The product of a negative integer and a negative integer is a positive integer.

  c. The quotient of a negative integer and a negative integer is a positive integer.

  d. The quotient of a negative integer and a positive integer is a negative integer.

63. a and b are any integers. Determine whether the equation is true or false.

  a. $a < |a|$ **b.** $|a + b| = |a| + |b|$

  c. $|a + b| < |a| + |b|$ **d.** $|a + b| \leq |a| + |b|$

  e. $|a + b| > |a| + |b|$ **f.** $|a| - |b| \leq |a + b|$

64. Step 1. Choose integers a and b such that $a < b$.

  Step 2. Choose a positive integer n, and calculate $a \cdot n$ and $b \cdot n$.

  Step 3. Compare $a \cdot n$ and $b \cdot n$ using an inequality.

  Step 4. Repeat steps 1 through 3. Make a conjecture.

65. Step 1. Choose integers a and b such that $a < b$.

  Step 2. Choose a negative integer n, and calculate $a \cdot n$ and $b \cdot n$.

  Step 3. Compare $a \cdot n$ and $b \cdot n$ using an inequality.

  Step 4. Repeat steps 1 through 3. Make a conjecture.

CHAPTER 4 REVIEW

CHAPTER 4 Organizer

Section	What You Should Learn	Review Problems
4.1	**1.** Apply the meaning of the phrases "b is a factor of a," "a is a multiple of b," "b is a divisor of a," and "a is divisible by b."	1–4
	2. Apply basic divisibility theorems about sums, differences, and products.	5–13
	3. State, justify, or apply the divisibility rules for 2, 3, 4, 5, 6, 8, 9, and 10.	14–17
	4. Construct divisibility rules.	18–19
4.2	**1.** Model prime and composite numbers with arrays.	20–21
	2. Determine whether a number is a prime or composite number.	22–26
	3. Distinguish the phrases factorization and prime factorization.	27
	4. Use a tree diagram to write a prime factorization.	28
	5. Use repeated division to determine the factors of a composite number.	29–30
	6. Determine the number of factors, prime factors, or composite factors a number has.	31–34
	7. Use the square root test to determine if a given number is a prime or composite number.	35
	8. Use various methods to find the greatest common factor and least common multiple of two numbers.	36–42

4.3	1. Model positive and negative integers.	43–44
	2. Model addition and subtraction of integers.	45–48
	3. Apply "add the opposite" strategy for subtracting integers.	49
	4. Use patterns to add integers.	50
	5. Use patterns to multiply integers.	51
	6. Use the sign rules to multiply or divide integers.	52–54
	7. Use properties of integers.	55–56
	8. Solve problems involving integers.	57–58

Key Terms and Concepts

elementary number theory   187

factor of   188

multiple of   188

divisor of   188

divides   188

divisible by   188

does not divide   190

divisibility rule   191

prime number   202

composite number   202

Sieve of Eratosthenes   202

factorization   203

prime factorization   203

tree diagram   203

Fundamental Theorem of
   Arithmetic   204

repeated division   205

square root test   208

least common multiple (LCM)   208

list method for LCM   209

prime factorization method for
   LCM   209

greatest common factor (GCF)   210

list method for GCF   210

prime factorization method for
   GCF   211

relatively prime   211

Euclidean algorithm   212

integers   217

negative integers   218

positive integers   218

chip model   218

zero pair   218

absolute value   219

integer addition   219

pattern model   220

rules for integer addition   221

additive inverse (opposite)   221

properties of integer addition   222

integer subtraction   223

difference   225

subtracting integers by adding the
   opposite   226

integer multiplication   227

sign rules for multiplying
   integers   228

properties of integer
   multiplication   228

integer division   229

sign rules for dividing integers   230

Review Questions

1. The diagram represents the equation $17 \div 3 = 5 \text{ R} r$. Shade the squares that represent r.

2. Draw a diagram to represent the equation $12 = 4 \times 3$. Explain how the diagram reveals that 4 is a divisor of 12.

3. Do the following.

   a. Draw a diagram to represent the equation $23 \div 4 = 5 \text{ R} 3$.

   b. Shade the parts of the diagram that represent the remainder.

   c. Explain how the diagram reveals that 4 is not a divisor of 23.

4. Answer the following.

   a. Is 4 a factor of 12?   b. Is 12 a divisor of 3?

   c. Is 5 a multiple of 15?   d. Is 24 a multiple of 6?

   e. Is 28 divisible by 7?   f. Is 42 a divisor of 6?

5. 8 is not a divisor of a, and 8 is not a divisor of b. Give an example of numbers a and b such that

   a. 8 divides $a + b$.   b. 8 does not divide $a + b$.

6. Answer each question without finding the sum.

   a. Does 2 divide $712 + 930$?

   b. Does 2 divide $811 + 538$?

   c. Does 10 divide $120 + 30$?

   d. Does 10 divide $81 + 720$?

7. 4 is not a divisor of a, and 4 is not a divisor of b. Give an example of numbers a and b such that

  a. 4 divides the difference $a - b$.

  b. 4 does not divide the difference $a - b$.

8. Answer each question without finding the difference.

  a. Does 5 divide $1532 - 120$?

  b. Does 5 divide $7320 - 810$?

  c. Does 10 divide $1620 - 730$?

  d. Does 10 divide $7263 - 620$?

9. What does each equation reveal?

  a. $78 \cdot 382 = 29{,}796$ **b.** $285 \cdot 36 + 40 = 10{,}300$

  c. $\sqrt{456} = 21.354$ (rounded)   **d.** $2296 \div 56 = 41$

  e. $n = 2^3 \cdot 3^2 \cdot 5 \cdot 7$ **f.** $5^3 = 125$

10. For the following equations, is it possible to decide whether the number is divisible by 13 without performing calculations?

  a. $349{,}437 \times 26 + 39$ **b.** $5{,}021{,}313$ **c.** $24 \cdot 13 + 5$

  d. $4{,}509{,}232$ **e.** $2^5 \cdot 5^3 \cdot 11 \cdot 13^2$ **f.** $13^4 \cdot 15 + 26$

11. Suppose 12 is a factor of n. Of all factors of n that are greater than 1, explain why 12 is not the least factor.

12. Suppose you know 4 is a factor of n. Explain why 4 is not a factor of $n + 3$.

13. Answer the following, and justify your answer.

  a. Let $M = 3^{250} \cdot 7^{50} \cdot 11^{14}$. Is M divisible by 49?

  b. Let $Q = 2^{140} \cdot 7^{168} \cdot 5^3$. Is Q a multiple of 10?

  c. Let $R = 5^4 \cdot 6^7 \cdot 11^2$. Is $5^2 \cdot 6^3$ a factor of R?

14. Explain why 6 does not divide the given number.

  a. 2356   **b.** 6987

15. Fill in the blank with the largest digit such that the resulting number is divisible by 4.

  a. 43,_08   **b.** 6_,624,472   **c.** 80,456,5_2   **d.** 678,35_

16. Fill in the blank with the largest digit such that the resulting number is divisible by 6.

  a. 14,_70   **b.** 5,12_,752   **c.** 4,76_,078

17. Suppose 3 divides the three-digit number abc. Using only the letters a, b, and c, determine another number that is divisible by 3.

18. Do the following.

  a. Construct a test to determine whether a number is divisible by 14.

  b. Using your test, determine whether 43,848 is divisible by 14.

  c. Using your test, determine whether 10,140 is divisible by 14.

19. Do the following.

  a. Construct a test to determine whether a number is divisible by 22.

  b. Use your test to determine whether 2706 is divisible by 22.

  c. Use your test to determine whether 928 is divisible by 22.

20. Do the following.

  a. Define a prime number.

  b. Use a model or diagram to show that 3 is a prime number.

21. Do the following.

  a. Define a composite number.

  b. Use a model or diagram to show that 6 is a composite number.

22. Each list shows all factors of a number. Determine whether the number is a prime number or composite number.

  a. 1, 2, 4, 8   **b.** 1, 6829   **c.** 1, 2, 5, 10   **d.** 1, 5743

23. Indicate which of the following are composite or prime numbers, and justify your answer.

  a. 381   **b.** 193   **c.** 203   **d.** 401   **e.** 1375

24. Suppose you know $B = 24 \cdot A + 8$. Are there any whole numbers A that make B a prime number? Explain.

25. Suppose you know $B = 5 \cdot A + 4$. Are there any whole numbers A that make B a prime number? Explain.

26. Are there any perfect squares (such as 9 or 25) that are prime numbers? Explain.

27. Give an example of a factorization that

  a. is not a prime factorization.

  b. is a prime factorization.

28. Find the prime factorizations of the following composite numbers using a prime factor tree.

  a. 1485   **b.** 600   **c.** 225×12

29. Use repeated division to list all factors of the given composite number.

  a. 60   **b.** 42

30. Use repeated division to find the prime factorization of the given composite number.

  a. 76   **b.** 354

31. How many factors, prime factors, and composite factors does the number have?

  a. $2^3 \cdot 5^6 \cdot 11^2$ **b.** $7^3 \cdot 11^6 \cdot 17$ **c.** $5^3 \cdot 6^5 \cdot 11^2$

  d. 110   **e.** 342

32. Answer the following.

  a. How many divisors of 420 are prime?

  b. How many divisors of 244 are composite?

33. I am the smallest number greater than 350 with three prime factors, and I am also divisible by 63. What number am I?

34. Suppose p has m factors and q has n factors. Suppose the only common factor of p and q is 1. How many factors does $p \cdot q$ have? (Hint: Use examples, and look for a pattern.)

35. The first 12 prime numbers are 2, 3, 5, 7, 11, 13, 17, 19, 23, 29, 31, and 37. Use the square root test to determine whether the given number is a prime number or a composite number.

  a. 451   **b.** 311   **c.** 563   **d.** 341

36. The Venn diagram displays the prime factorizations of 6300 and 12,500. Use the Venn diagram to find GCF(6300, 12,500) and LCM(6300, 12,500).

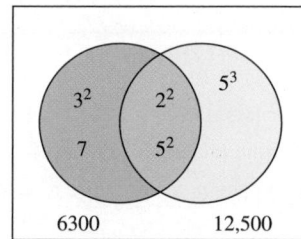

37. Use the list method to find the GCF and the LCM of the two given numbers.

    a. 12 and 15   **b.** 18 and 24   **c.** 5 and 8

38. Use the given prime factorization to find LCM(a, b). Write your answer in terms of a prime factorization.

    a. $a = 2^3 \cdot 3^4 \cdot 5^2 \cdot 7, b = 2^3 \cdot 5^2 \cdot 13$

    b. $a = 5^3 \cdot 11^4 \cdot 13^2, b = 2^3 \cdot 7^2 \cdot 11$

    c. $a = 3^6 \cdot 7^2 \cdot 11 \cdot 13 \cdot 17^3, b = 2^3 \cdot 11 \cdot 13^3 \cdot 17$

39. Use the given prime factorization to find GCF(a, b). Write your answer in terms of a prime factorization.

    a. $a = 2^3 \cdot 3^4 \cdot 5^2 \cdot 7, b = 2^3 \cdot 5^2 \cdot 13$

    b. $a = 5^3 \cdot 11^4 \cdot 13^2, b = 2^3 \cdot 7^2 \cdot 11$

    c. $a = 3^6 \cdot 7^2 \cdot 11 \cdot 13 \cdot 17^3, b = 2^3 \cdot 11 \cdot 13^3 \cdot 17$

40. Use the Euclidean algorithm to find GCF(a, b).

    a. $a = 346, b = 68$ **b.** $a = 1232, b = 64$

    c. $a = 1044, b = 300$

41. Use the Euclidean algorithm to find LCM(a, b).

    a. $a = 15, b = 36$ **b.** $a = 330, b = 260$

    c. $a = 312, b = 124$

42. Three friends are running around a track. It takes Felisha 70 seconds to finish one lap, Janet 90 seconds, and Carla 110 seconds. If they start at the same time, when will they all be in the start position again?

43. Model zero using the chip model. Show two different representations.

44. Model the integer −3 using the chip model. Show two different representations.

45. Add −5 + 3 using the following models.

    a. chip model   **b.** number line model

46. Add −5 + −3 using the following models.

    a. chip model   **b.** number line model

47. Subtract −5 − −3 using the following models.

    a. chip model   **b.** number line model

48. Subtract −4 − 3 using the following models.

    a. chip model   **b.** number line model

49. Subtract by adding the opposite.

    a. 4 − −7   **b.** −5 − 12   **c.** −3 − −21

50. Use patterns to find the next two terms in the sequence.

    a. 2 + 2 = 4   **b.** −3 + 5 = 2
        2 + 1 = 3   −3 + 4 = 1
        2 + 0 = 2   −3 + 3 = 0
       2 + −1 = 1   −3 + 2 = −1

51. Show how to use patterns to compute each product. Assume students know how to multiply two whole numbers.

    a. $(-2) \cdot 5$ **b.** $4 \cdot (-3)$

52. Use the sign rules to multiply.

    a. $2 \cdot (-8)$ **b.** $(-5) \cdot 9$ **c.** $15 \cdot 3$ **d.** $(-8) \cdot (-5)$

53. Use the sign rules to divide.

    a. $18 \div -6$ **b.** $-24 \div 6$ **c.** $-42 \div -7$

54. Suppose you are multiplying five negative numbers and three positive numbers. Is the result positive or negative?

55. A student solved the integer equation $8 - n = 15$ as follows. Write the reasons.

Statement	Reason
$8 - n = 15$	Original equation
$8 - n + n = 15 + n$	a.
$8 = 15 + n$	Addition and subtraction are inverse operations
$-15 + 8 = -15 + (15 + n)$	b.
$-15 + 8 = (-15 + 15) + n$	c.
$-15 + 8 = 0 + n$	d.
$-15 + 8 = n$	e.
$-7 = n$	Simplification

56. Solve the integer equation $a - 5 = -12$. Show each step, listing the properties you used.

57. At 5 p.m., the temperature was 73°F in San Diego, California. At 11 p.m., the temperature fell to 64°F. How many degrees did the temperature fall from 5 p.m. to 11 p.m.?

58. James is playing a gambling game in which each round that he wins, he wins $4, and each round that he loses, he loses $3. If James played the game for 11 rounds and won 4 rounds, how much money does he have after playing, assuming he started with $50 in his pocket?

Chapter 4 Test

1. *Apply the meaning of the phrases "b is a factor of a," "a is a multiple of b," "b is a divisor of a," and "a is divisible by b."*

   a. Is 6 a factor of 18?   **b.** Is 15 a divisor of 5?

   c. Is 7 divisible by 28?   **d.** Is 42 a multiple of 14?

2. *Apply the meaning of the phrases "b is a factor of a," "a is a multiple of b," "b is a divisor of a," and "a is divisible by b."* What does each equation reveal?

   a. $45 \cdot 123 = 5535$ **b.** $3 \cdot 17 + 6 = 57$

   c. $1856 \div 32 = 58$ **d.** $n = 3^3 \cdot 5^2 \cdot 7 \cdot 11$

3. *Apply the meaning of the phrases "b is a factor of a," "a is a multiple of b," "b is a divisor of a," and "a is divisible by b."* What is the largest multiple of 14 less than 567?

4. *Apply basic divisibility theorems about sums, differences, and products.*

   a. Suppose 15 divides n. Of all factors of n greater than 1, explain why 15 is not the least factor of n.

   b. Each letter is a digit. a and d are nonzero digits. The sum $abc + de$ is divisible by 9. Find another sum that is divisible by 9.

5. *Apply basic divisibility theorems about sums, differences, and products.* Justify your answer.

   a. Let $B = 5^{214} \cdot 7^{43} \cdot 11^{10}$. Is B divisible by 175?

   b. Let $K = 2^{175} \cdot 5^{38} \cdot 7^{368}$. Is K divisible by 112?

6. *State, justify, or apply the divisibility rules for 2, 3, 4, 5, 6, 8, 9, and 10.* Fill in the blank with the largest digit such that the resulting number

   a. is divisible by 4: 821,197,_08.

   b. is divisible by 6: 31,_04.

   c. is divisible by 8: 21,992,_16.

7. *Construct divisibility rules.* Do the following.

   a. Invent a divisibility rule for 18 using two simpler divisibility tests.

   b. Using your rule, determine whether 9972 is divisible by 18.

   c. Using your rule, determine whether 12,082 is a multiple of 18.

8. *Use a tree diagram to write a prime factorization.* Construct a tree diagram to find the prime factorization of 2520.

9. *Determine whether a number is a prime or a composite number.*

   a. What is a prime number?

   b. What is a composite number?

   c. Is 51 a prime or a composite number? Tell how you know.

10. *Determine whether a number is a prime or a composite number.* Suppose you know $B = 6n + 15$. Are there any whole numbers n that make B a prime number? Explain.

11. *Determine the number of factors, prime factors, or composite factors a number has.* List all factors of 140 using repeated division.

12. *Determine the number of factors, prime factors, or composite factors a number has.* Answer the following questions for $5^3 \cdot 7^8 \cdot 11^{14}$.

    a. How many factors does it have?

    b. How many prime factors does it have?

    c. How many composite factors does it have?

13. *Determine the number of factors, prime factors, or composite factors a number has.* How many factors does $12^3 \cdot 5^4 \cdot 11^{15}$ have?

14. *Use the square root test to determine whether a given number is a prime or a composite number.* Indicate which of the following are composite or prime numbers. Justify your answer.

    a. 217   **b.** 257

15. *Use various methods to find the GCF and the LCM of two numbers.* The Venn diagram displays the prime factorizations of 43,904 and 54,432. Use the Venn diagram to find GCF(43,904, 54,432) and LCM(43,904, 54,432).

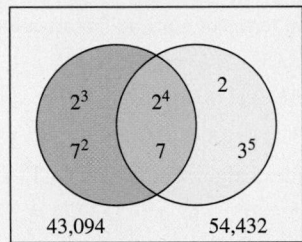

16. *Use various methods to find the GCF and the LCM of two numbers.* Use the list method to find the

    a. GCF of 18 and 15.   **b.** LCM of 18 and 15.

17. *Use various methods to find the GCF and the LCM of two numbers.* Use the given factorization to find LCM(a, b). Write your answer in terms of a prime factorization.

    a. $a = 2^4 \cdot 3^4 \cdot 7^2$, $b = 2^2 \cdot 3^7 \cdot 13$

    b. $a = 2^3 \cdot 5^4 \cdot 11$, $b = 5^3 \cdot 11^2 \cdot 13$

    c. $a = 10^6 \cdot 7^2 \cdot 11 \cdot 13$, $b = 5^3 \cdot 11 \cdot 13^3 \cdot 17$

18. *Use various methods to find the GCF and the LCM of two numbers.* Use the given factorization to find GCF(a, b). Write your answer in terms of a prime factorization.

    a. $a = 2^4 \cdot 3^4 \cdot 7^2$, $b = 2^2 \cdot 3^7 \cdot 13$

    b. $a = 2^3 \cdot 5^4 \cdot 11^2$, $b = 5^3 \cdot 11^2 \cdot 13$

    c. $a = 10^6 \cdot 7^2 \cdot 11 \cdot 13$, $b = 5^3 \cdot 11 \cdot 13^3 \cdot 17$

19. *Use various methods to find the GCF and the LCM of two numbers.* Use the Euclidean algorithm to find GCF(a, b).

    a. $a = 7520$, $b = 1728$ **b.** $a = 1068$, $b = 72$

20. *Use various methods to find the GCF and the LCM of two numbers.* The LCM of 12 and 42 is 84. Use this information to find the GCF of 12 and 42.

21. *Use patterns or rules to add or subtract integers.* Explain how a student would apply sign rules to solve $24 + -40$.

22. *Apply the add-the-opposite strategy for subtracting integers.* Subtract by adding the opposite.

a. $-5 - 3$ b. $145 - -24$ c. $24 - 42$

23. *Use patterns to multiply integers.* Show how to use patterns to compute $(-2) \times 6$. Assume students know how to multiply two whole numbers.

24. *Use the sign rules to multiply or divide integers.* Use the sign rules to multiply or divide.

a. $2 \times (-8)$ b. $(-3) \times (-7)$

c. $24 \div -4$ d. $-48 \div -8$

25. *Use properties of integers.* A student solves the integer equation $-5 + a = 14$ as shown here. List the properties used.

Statement	Reason
$-5 + a = 14$	Original equation
$5 + (-5 + a) = 5 + 14$	a.
$5 + (-5 + a) = 19$	Simplification
$(5 + -5) + a = 19$	b.
$0 + a = 19$	c.
$a = 19$	d.

26. *Solve problems involving integers.* Write a word problem for each equation.

a. $5 \times -7 = -35$ b. $-42 \div 6 = -7$

5 Rational Numbers and Fractions

Where Are We Going?

In **Section 5.1,** we discuss how to represent fractions with words, diagrams, and symbols. We use diagrams and multiplicative reasoning to solve word problems with fractions. We illustrate that a fraction is a quotient and discuss the vital concept of equivalent fractions. We use common fractions, rounding, estimation, benchmarks, and cross-products to compare fractions and discuss the density property of fractions. In **Section 5.2,** we explain the conceptual basis for the procedures for adding and subtracting fractions and discuss related properties. We show how to solve relevant equations using multiple approaches. In **Section 5.3,** we explain the conceptual basis for the procedures for multiplying and dividing fractions and discuss related properties. We show how to solve relevant equations using multiple approaches and discuss comparison problems. In **Section 5.4,** we discuss ratios and proportions, as well as their connections to fraction concepts. Worked examples illustrate five strategies—tables, diagrams, algebra, unit rates, and proportions—to solve ratio problems.

What Is a Fraction?

A **fraction** is any number that can be expressed in the form $\frac{a}{b}$, where a and b are numbers and $b \neq 0$. We can also write the fraction $\frac{a}{b}$ in the form a/b. A **rational number** is any number that can be expressed in the form $\frac{a}{b}$, where a and b are integers and $b \neq 0$. Some examples of rational numbers are $\frac{4}{5}$, $\frac{12}{7}$, $\frac{-2}{3}$, and $\frac{4}{-7}$. This means a rational number is a special type of fraction.

Elementary school students initially work with fractions composed of two positive numbers, such as $\frac{4}{5}$ or $\frac{12}{7}$, because that allows them to think of a fraction as a collection of equal-sized parts, represent fractions with diagrams, build on their understanding of whole number and integer operations, apply fractions to contextualized situations, and develop procedures for operating with fractions. So we focus on fractions composed of two positive numbers, such as 4 and 5 in $\frac{4}{5}$, to develop procedures and properties for operations with rational numbers.

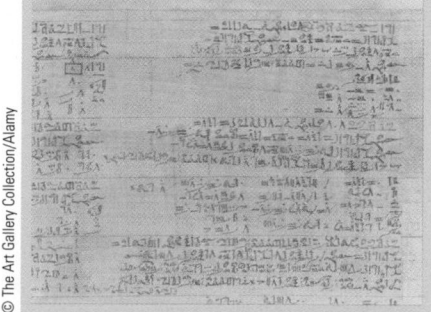

The Egyptian Rhind papyrus from the second century BCE contained many problems involving fractions.

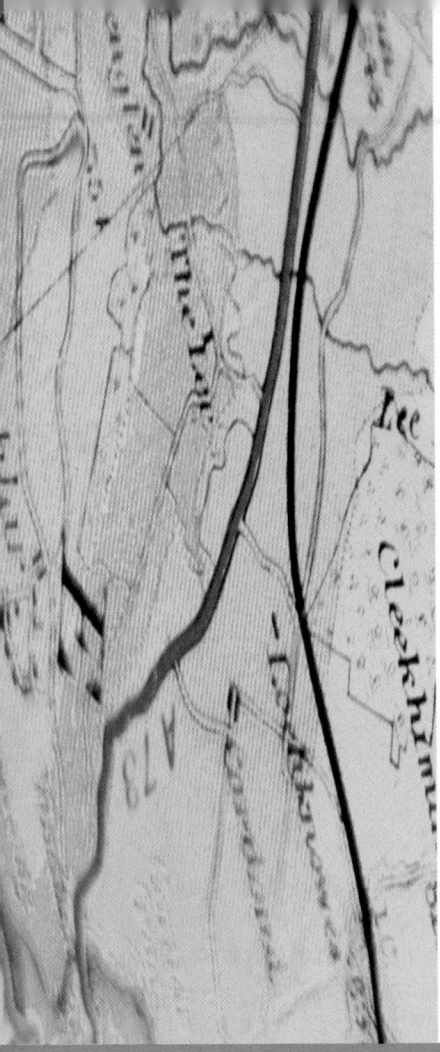

What Are Some Early Uses of Fractions?

Most mathematical problems in ancient written records, such as the Egyptian Rhind papyrus scroll in the second century BCE and the Chinese *Nine Chapters on the Mathematical Art* in the first century BCE, involved fractions, often dividing a commodity (such as bread, grain, or money) equally among several people (for example, "Divide 7 loaves among 10 men"). Later, fractions played a role in expressing measurements and calculating exchanges of currency. Symbolic representations of fractions varied across cultures and time, but the present symbolic representation became widespread in the 1500s.

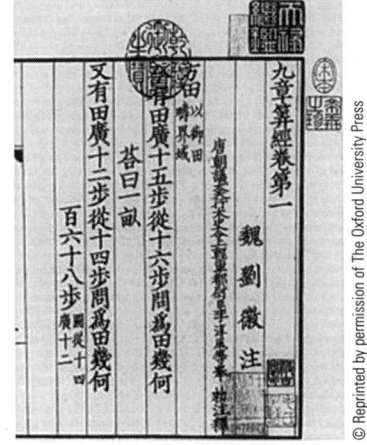

Nine Chapters on the Mathematical Art.

SECTION 5.1 | Concept of Fractions and Representations

The NCTM *Principles and Standards for School Mathematics* (2000) asserts that students should know multiple representations of fractions, benchmark and equivalent fractions, strategies to compare and order fractions, the density property of fractions, and the diverse uses of fractions in their quest to acquire fraction literacy:

- In grades 3–5, "students should build their understanding of fractions as parts of a whole and as division. They will need to see and explore a variety of models of fractions, focusing primarily on familiar fractions such as halves, thirds, fourths, fifths, sixths, eighths, and tenths. By using an area model in which part of a region is shaded, students see parts of a whole, and find equivalent fractions. They should develop strategies for ordering and comparing fractions, often using benchmarks such as 1/2 and 1. . . . They should also begin to understand that between any two fractions, there is always another fraction" (© NCTM Standards 2011 by National Council of Teachers of Mathematics).

- In grades 6–8, "students should expand their repertoire of meanings, representations, and uses for nonnegative rational numbers. They should recognize and use fractions not only in the ways they have in lower grades—as measures, quantities, parts of a whole, locations on a number line, and indicated divisions—but also in new ways. For example, they should encounter problems involving ratios (e.g., 3 adult chaperones for every 8 students), rates (e.g., scoring a soccer goal on 3 of every 8 penalty kicks), and operators (e.g., multiplying by 3/8 means generating a number that is 3/8 of the original number)" (p. 216).

Three models for representing fractions are the area model, set model, and number line model. These models give you a chance to "see" fractions. They set the stage for conceptual understanding of fractions, representing fractions using symbolic notation, solving contextualized problems involving fractions, and later making sense of operations with fractions. In the study of fractions, students in grades 3–5 focus more on learning fraction concepts, and students in grades 6–8 focus more on fraction computations.

Representing a Fraction Using the Area Model

The word *fraction* stems from the Latin word *fractere,* which means "act of breaking." The **area model,** a versatile representation tool, involves breaking a region, called the **whole,** into equal-sized parts. The equal-sized parts may represent equal-sized portions of length, area, volume, weight, time, objects, or other characteristics. A **unit fraction** consists of exactly one equal-sized part of the whole. The shaded regions in Figure 1 represent the unit fractions one-half, one-third, and one-fourth.

the whole   one-half

one-third   one-fourth

FIGURE 1
Diagrams of unit fractions using the
area model (with bars).

REPRESENTATION

We can represent unit fractions with other shapes, such as circles, as shown in Figure 2.

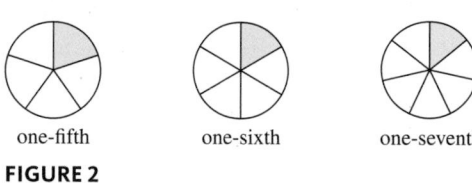

one-fifth   one-sixth   one-seventh

FIGURE 2
Diagrams of unit fractions using the area model
(with circles).

 **EXAMPLE 5.1**

COMMUNICATION

REASONING

a. Eight college students ordered food from a restaurant. They agreed to split the total cost evenly. How much of the total cost should each student pay?

b. How many equal-sized parts in the whole does the unit fraction $\frac{1}{10}$ indicate?

SOLUTION

a. Each student should pay one-eighth of the total cost.

b. The unit fraction indicates 10 equal-sized parts in the whole.

▲

CONNECTION

A homework question at the end of this section describes a procedure by the U.S. Food and Drug Administration (FDA) to help manufacturers determine the serving size of food products served in slices, such as pizzas or cakes, in terms of a unit fraction.

The shaded regions in Figure 3 represent the nonunit fractions two-thirds, three-fourths, seven-fifths, and nine-sixths.

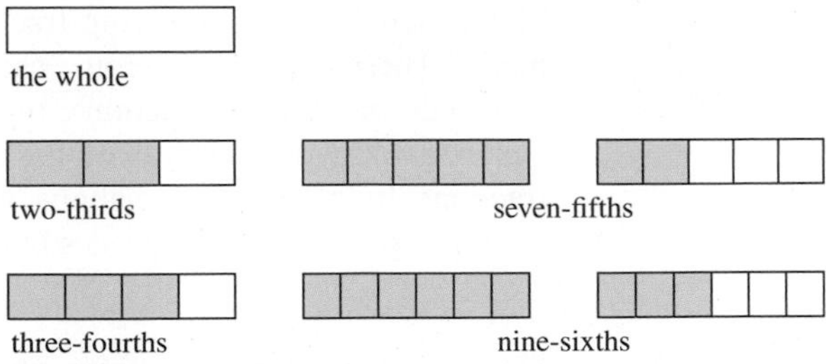

FIGURE 3
Diagrams of nonunit fractions.

REPRESENTATION

Table 5.1 shows how to juxtapose integers to symbolize fractions.

TABLE 5.1 How to Represent Fractions with Symbols

Fraction	eight halves	one-eighth	three-fourths	seven-thirds	12-ninths
Notation	$\dfrac{8}{2}$	$\dfrac{1}{8}$	$\dfrac{3}{4}$	$\dfrac{7}{3}$	$\dfrac{12}{9}$

Think of a Fraction as a Collection of Equal-Sized Parts

The area model helps us think of a fraction as a collection of equal-sized parts.

> **Definition of a Fraction and Its Parts**
>
> Let a and b represent whole numbers with $b \neq 0$. Then $\frac{a}{b}$ is a fraction.
>
> - The number a is called the **numerator.**
> - The number b is called the **denominator.**
> - The line segment in the fraction notation is the fraction bar.
>
> Each fraction is a collection of equal-sized parts. For example, in the fraction $\frac{3}{4}$, the 3 indicates that $\frac{3}{4}$ is a collection of three equal-sized parts, and the 4 indicates that each equal-sized part in the collection is called one-fourth.

Historical Note

In the 600s, the Hindus represented a fraction by placing the numerator over the denominator, but without a fraction bar. The origin of the horizontal fraction bar is uncertain, but historical documents indicate the Arabs used it in the 1100s.

Elementary school students should be able to "read and write fractions and relate the notation to the meaning of these numbers" (NCTM, Gr. 3–5) "and understand a fraction $1/b$ as the quantity formed by 1 part when a whole is partitioned into b equal parts; understand a fraction a/b as the quantity formed by a parts of size $1/b$" (CCSS, Gr. 3) (© 2010. National Governors Association Center for Best Practices and Council of Chief State School Officers. All rights reserved.).

EXAMPLE 5.2

COMMUNICATION

REASONING

REPRESENTATION

$\frac{7}{5}$ is a fraction.

a. Identify the numerator and denominator.

b. What does the 7 indicate?

c. What does the 5 indicate?

SOLUTION

a. The numerator is 7, and the denominator is 5.

b. The collection consists of seven equal-sized parts.

c. Each equal-sized part is called one-fifth.

Elementary school students often view four-sixths as four parts out of six equal-sized parts. This "part to whole" interpretation is the most accessible and common interpretation of fractions in the elementary mathematics curriculum. However, students who view fractions solely in terms of the part-to-whole interpretation struggle to conceptualize a fraction such as six-fifths because they wonder how you can have six parts out of five parts.

Representing a Fraction Using the Set Model

The set model is useful to illustrate fraction concepts when the whole is a small collection of discrete objects. It provides a tactile learning opportunity for students using coins, marbles, and beans, for example. Table 5.2 illustrates the set model for some fractions, where the whole is a bag of marbles.

TABLE 5.2 **The Whole Is a Bag of Four Marbles (● ● ● ●)**

Marbles	●	● ●	● ● ●	● ● ● ●	● ● ● ● ●	● ● ● ● ● ●
Fraction	$\frac{1}{4}$ bag	$\frac{2}{4}$ bag	$\frac{3}{4}$ bag	$\frac{4}{4}$ bag	$\frac{5}{4}$ bags	$\frac{6}{4}$ bags

EXAMPLE 5.3

REASONING

REPRESENTATION

Name the fraction associated with the figure. The whole is ● ● ● ● ● ●.

a. ● ●

b. ● ● ● ● ●

c. ● ● ● ● ● ● ● ● ● ● ●

SOLUTION

a. $\frac{2}{6}$

b. $\frac{5}{6}$

c. $\frac{11}{6}$

▲

The following example illustrates that three objects could represent three-fifths or three halves, depending on how the whole is defined.

EXAMPLE 5.4

REASONING

REPRESENTATION

Determine the fraction that ●●● represents.

a. The whole is ●●●●●.

b. The whole is ● ●.

SOLUTION

a. $\frac{3}{5}$

b. $\frac{3}{2}$

▲

Representing a Fraction Using the Number Line Model

REPRESENTATION   We can represent fractions as numbers on a number line, which is especially useful in measurement with rulers. Students should "understand a fraction as a number on the

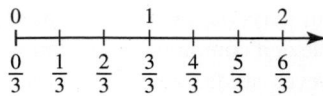

number line" and "represent fractions on a number line diagram" (CCSS, Gr. 3). The whole numbers on the following number line provide a frame of reference.

EXAMPLE 5.5 Write the fraction indicated on the ruler.

CONNECTION
REPRESENTATION

a.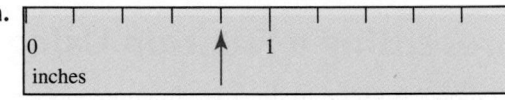

b.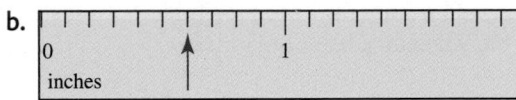

SOLUTION

a. $\dfrac{4}{5}$

b. $\dfrac{6}{10}$

Reversal Task: Given a Fraction, Determine the Whole

A fraction indicates a relationship between the collection of parts and the whole. A **reversal task** challenges student understanding of fractions: given a model of a fraction, determine the whole.

EXAMPLE 5.6 The rectangle is an area model of $\frac{5}{3}$. What does a model of the whole look like?

CONNECTION
REASONING
REPRESENTATION

SOLUTION

We know that $\frac{5}{3}$ represents five fractional units and that each fractional unit is $\frac{1}{3}$. Figure 4(a) is a representation of $\frac{5}{3}$. Each equal-sized part represents $\frac{1}{3}$.

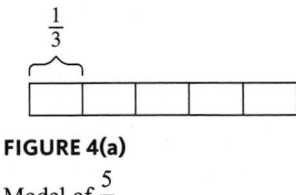

FIGURE 4(a)

Model of $\dfrac{5}{3}$.

Then three equal-sized parts represent the whole. Figure 4(b) represents the whole.

whole unit

FIGURE 4(b)

Model of the whole unit.

Using a Diagram to Solve Problems Involving Fractions

The following Classroom Connection illustrates that students should be able to use diagrams to solve problems involving fraction concepts. For elementary school students, representing, reasoning, and solving problems with diagrams are more accessible than formulas and algebra.

 Classroom Connection

• Houghton Mifflin *Mathematics*, Student Edition, Grade 6, p. 279

Draw a diagram to solve each problem. A pod of dolphins swam 182 meters above the ocean floor. This was 7/10 of the distance to the surface. How far from the surface were the dolphins? (© by Houghton Mifflin Company, Inc. Reproduced by permission of the publisher, Houghton Mifflin Harcourt Publishing Company.)

Students should be able to solve problems using diagrams. Key ideas are (1) think of a fraction as a collection of parts; (2) know that one whole has two halves, three thirds, four fourths, and so on; and (3) use division to split a quantity into equal-sized groups. The next two examples apply this medley of ideas.

EXAMPLE 5.7

PROBLEM SOLVING

REASONING

REPRESENTATION

A rancher stored 420 pounds of hay in the barn. He fed three-fifths of the hay to his horses. How many pounds of hay did the rancher use? Solve this problem using the Draw a Diagram problem solving strategy.

SOLUTION

In Figure 5(a), we represent 420 pounds of hay with an area model.

FIGURE 5(a)
Representation of the hay.

In Figure 5(b), we partition the region into five equal-sized parts.

FIGURE 5(b)
Partition 420 pounds of hay into equal-sized parts called fifths.

In Figure 5(c), we split 420 pounds into five equal-sized groups, and $420 \div 5 = 84$. Each fractional unit represents 84 pounds of hay.

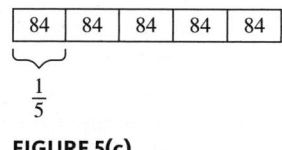

| 84 | 84 | 84 | 84 | 84 |

$\dfrac{1}{5}$

FIGURE 5(c)
$420 \div 5 = 84$.

In Figure 5(d), we select three equal-sized parts, and $3 \times 84 = 252$.

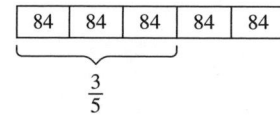

| 84 | 84 | 84 | 84 | 84 |

$\dfrac{3}{5}$

FIGURE 5(d)
$3 \times 84 = 252$.

Therefore, the rancher fed his horses 252 pounds of hay.

EXAMPLE 5.8

PROBLEM SOLVING

REASONING

REPRESENTATION

John ate three-fifths of a bag of jellybeans. He ate 36 jellybeans altogether. How many jellybeans were in the whole bag? Solve this problem using the Draw a Diagram problem solving strategy.

SOLUTION

In Figure 6(a), we use a rectangle to represent a bag of jellybeans. The problem suggests three-fifths of the rectangle represents 36 jellybeans, so we split the rectangle into five fifths because there are five fifths in a whole.

one bag of jellybeans

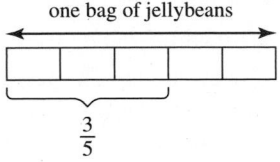

$$\frac{3}{5}$$

FIGURE 6(a)
A representation of one bag of jellybeans.

In Figure 6(b), we use the fair-share model of division to split the 36 jellybeans into three equal-sized groups, and $36 \div 3 = 12$. So each fractional unit represents 12 jellybeans.

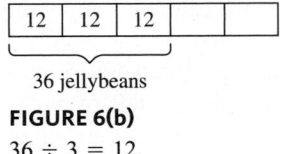

36 jellybeans

FIGURE 6(b)
$36 \div 3 = 12$.

In Figure 6(c), we compute the total number of jellybeans in the bag: $5 \times 12 = 60$.

12	12	12	12	12

$5 \times 12 = 60$

FIGURE 6(c)
$5 \times 12 = 60$.

We conclude there were 60 jellybeans in the whole bag.

Fraction as a Quotient

CONNECTION

Diagrams make it easier to see that a fraction is also a quotient. This represents another opportunity for elementary school students to see the relationship between fractions and multiplicative thinking. For example, a teacher splits four cookies among three people. How much cookie does each person get?

The problem implies that four cookies must be split into three equal-sized groups, so we need to evaluate the arithmetic expression $4 \div 3$. We can represent the people with the letters A, B, and C and model a cookie with an area model. We can split one cookie fairly among three people by giving each person $\frac{1}{3}$ cookie. We repeat this process for the remaining cookies, as shown in Figure 7.

REPRESENTATION

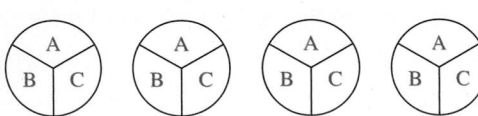

FIGURE 7
Splitting four cookies (circles) among three people (A, B, C).

Each letter (A, B, and C) appears four times. When four cookies are split fairly among three people, each person receives $\frac{4}{3}$ cookies. Then $4 \div 3 = \frac{4}{3}$, where 4 is the dividend, 3 is the divisor, and $\frac{4}{3}$ is the quotient.

This can be generalized as follows:

> **Fraction As a Quotient**
>
> Let a and b represent whole numbers with $b \neq 0$. Then $a \div b = \frac{a}{b}$.

This also means $\frac{a}{b} = a \div b$. Students should be able to "develop meaning for fractions as parts of a unit whole, as part of a collection, as numbers, and as a division of numbers" (NCTM, Gr. 3–5), as well as be able to "interpret a fraction as division of the numerator by the denominator $(a/b = a \div b)$" (CCSS, Gr. 5). Later, we apply the relationship $\frac{a}{b} = a \div b$ to represent a fraction as a decimal number (for example, $\frac{3}{8} = 3 \div 8 = 0.375$).

The following example provides two ways to view a whole number as a fraction.

EXAMPLE 5.9

CONNECTION

REASONING

a. Use inductive reasoning to support the conjecture that every whole number is a fraction.

b. Use deductive reasoning to prove every whole number is a fraction.

SOLUTION

a. We use a few examples. $5 = 5 \div 1 = \frac{5}{1}$, so $5 = \frac{5}{1}$. $12 = 12 \div 1 = \frac{12}{1}$, so $12 = \frac{12}{1}$. $9 = 9 \div 1 = \frac{9}{1}$, so $9 = \frac{9}{1}$. The examples support the conjecture that every whole number is a fraction.

b. Let n be any whole number. Then $n = n \div 1 = \frac{n}{1}$. Therefore, every whole number is a fraction.

▲

Students should be able to "express whole numbers as fractions, and recognize fractions that are equivalent to whole numbers. Examples: express 3 in the form $3 = 3/1$; recognize that $6/1 = 6$" (CCSS, Gr. 3).

Equivalent Fractions Represent the Same Number

The expressions $3 \cdot 8$ and $4 \cdot 6$ are different, but they represent the same number: 24. Similarly, $\frac{1}{3}$ and $\frac{2}{6}$ are different fractions, but they represent the same number, as shown in Figure 8. We say $\frac{1}{3}$ and $\frac{2}{6}$ are **equivalent fractions** (or equal fractions), written $\frac{1}{3} = \frac{2}{6}$.

REPRESENTATION

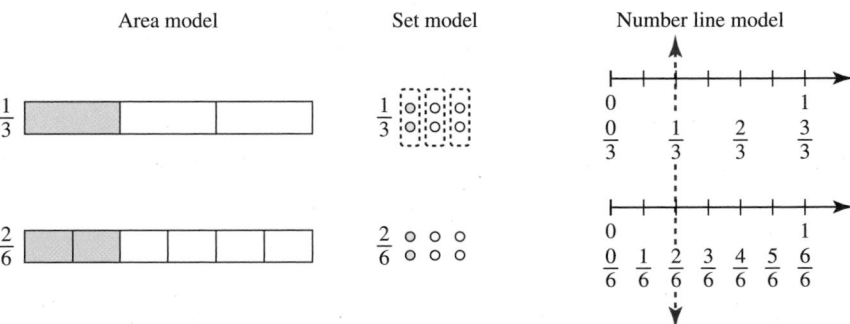

FIGURE 8

Representations of equivalent fractions.

Students should be able to "explain why the fractions are equivalent, e.g., by using a visual fraction model" (CCSS, Gr. 3); "explain why a fraction a/b is equivalent to a fraction $(n \times a)/(n \times b)$ by using visual fraction models, with attention to how the number and size of the parts differ even though the two fractions themselves are the same size and use this principle to recognize and generate equivalent fractions" (CCSS, Gr. 4). The concept of equivalent fractions is a key element of fractions concepts, because we use the idea to simplify and compare fractions, add and subtract fractions, and solve ratio problems.

Use Multiplication to Generate Equivalent Fractions

You can use a model to verify $\frac{2}{3}$ is equivalent to $\frac{4}{6}$ and $\frac{8}{12}$, that is, $\frac{2}{3} = \frac{4}{6}$ and $\frac{2}{3} = \frac{8}{12}$. Then

- $\frac{4}{6} = \frac{2 \cdot 2}{3 \cdot 2}$ using substitution (that is, replace 4 with $2 \cdot 2$ and 6 with $3 \cdot 2$).
- $\frac{8}{12} = \frac{2 \cdot 4}{3 \cdot 4}$ using substitution (that is, replace 8 with $2 \cdot 4$ and 12 with $3 \cdot 4$).

Therefore, $\frac{2}{3} = \frac{4}{6} = \frac{2 \cdot 2}{3 \cdot 2}$ and $\frac{2}{3} = \frac{8}{12} = \frac{2 \cdot 4}{3 \cdot 4}$. This means $\frac{2}{3} = \frac{2 \cdot 2}{3 \cdot 2}$ and $\frac{2}{3} = \frac{2 \cdot 4}{3 \cdot 4}$.

The fundamental law of fractions generalizes how to use multiplication to generate equivalent fractions.

> ### Fundamental Law of Fractions
>
> Let $\frac{m}{n}$ be any rational number and p be any nonzero integer. Then $\frac{m}{n}$ and $\frac{mp}{np}$ are **equivalent fractions** (or equal fractions), that is, $\frac{m}{n} = \frac{mp}{np}$.

This law implies $\frac{3}{7} = \frac{3 \cdot 2}{7 \cdot 2} = \frac{6}{14}$, $\frac{3}{7} = \frac{3 \cdot 5}{7 \cdot 5} = \frac{15}{35}$, and $\frac{3}{7} = \frac{3 \cdot 8}{7 \cdot 8} = \frac{24}{56}$. Every fraction has an infinite number of possible symbolic representations.

Here, $\frac{4}{-7} = \frac{-4}{7}$, because $\frac{4}{-7} = \frac{-1 \cdot 4}{-1 \cdot -7} = \frac{-4}{7}$. Also, $\frac{-4}{-7} = \frac{4}{7}$, because $\frac{-4}{-7} = \frac{-1 \cdot -4}{-1 \cdot -7} = \frac{4}{7}$.

Use Division to Generate Equivalent Fractions

The following example illustrates that we can also use division to generate equivalent fractions.

EXAMPLE 5.10 Verify $\frac{24}{32}$ and $\frac{24 \div 4}{32 \div 4}$ are equivalent fractions.

CONNECTION

SOLUTION

$$\frac{24}{32} = \frac{6 \cdot 4}{8 \cdot 4} \qquad \text{By substitution: } 24 = 6 \cdot 4 \text{ and } 32 = 8 \cdot 4$$

$$= \frac{6}{8} \qquad \text{Fundamental law of fractions}$$

$$= \frac{24 \div 4}{32 \div 4} \qquad \text{By substitution: } 6 = 24 \div 4 \text{ and } 8 = 32 \div 4$$

So $\frac{24}{32} = \frac{24 \div 4}{32 \div 4}$.

You should verify the equations $\frac{64}{48} = \frac{64 \div 8}{48 \div 8}$ and $\frac{42}{74} = \frac{42 \div 2}{74 \div 2}$ using the same line of reasoning.

If p is a nonzero number, then we can generate equivalent fractions by multiplying (or dividing) both the numerator and the denominator by p. The NCTM standards suggest students should "work flexibly with equivalent fractions" (NCTM, Gr. 6–8). Multiplication and division give students that flexibility. The following page from an elementary mathematics textbook shows that students should know how to use both multiplication and division to generate equivalent fractions.

> ### ◆ **Multiply or Divide**
>
> You can multiply the numerator and the denominator by any number except zero to find equivalent fractions. Sometimes you can divide to find equivalent fractions.
>
> **Find equivalent fractions for $\frac{4}{6}$.**
>
> | **One Way** | **Another Way** |
> |---|---|
> | Multiply the numerator and denominator by the same number. Try 3. | Divide the numerator and denominator by the same number. Try 2. |
> | $$\frac{4}{6} = \frac{4 \times 3}{6 \times 3} = \frac{12}{18}$$ | $$\frac{4}{6} = \frac{4 \div 2}{6 \div 2} = \frac{2}{3}$$ |
> | So, $\frac{4}{6}$ is equivalent to $\frac{12}{18}$. | So, $\frac{4}{6}$ is equivalent to $\frac{2}{3}$. |
>
> If you continue to divide until 1 is the only number that can be divided into the numerator and the denominator evenly, you find the fraction in **simplest form**. So, $\frac{4}{6}$ in simplest form is $\frac{2}{3}$.
>
> (Harcourt *Math*, Student Edition, Grade 4, p. 321)

(© by Harcourt, Inc. Reproduced by permission of the publisher, Houghton Mifflin Harcourt Publishing Company.)

Algebra of Equivalent Fractions

The **cross-products** associated with the pair $\frac{4}{10}$ and $\frac{6}{15}$ are $4 \cdot 15$ and $10 \cdot 6$. Cross-products appear when we write the fractions $\frac{4}{10}$ and $\frac{6}{15}$ as equivalent fractions with the common denominator $10 \cdot 15$:

REASONING

$$\frac{4}{10} = \frac{4 \cdot 15}{10 \cdot 15} = \frac{4 \cdot 15}{150} \quad \text{and} \quad \frac{6}{15} = \frac{10 \cdot 6}{10 \cdot 15} = \frac{10 \cdot 6}{150}$$

Then $\frac{4}{10} = \frac{6}{15}$ if and only if $4 \cdot 15 = 10 \cdot 6$.

This example suggests the following definition.

> ### Definition
>
> Let $\frac{a}{b}$ and $\frac{c}{d}$ represent any two rational numbers. $\frac{a}{b}$ and $\frac{c}{d}$ are **equivalent fractions** (or equal fractions), denoted $\frac{a}{b} = \frac{c}{d}$, if and only if $a \cdot d = b \cdot c$.

EXAMPLE 5.11 Use cross-products to verify the fractions $\frac{18}{24}$ and $\frac{12}{16}$ are equivalent.

CONNECTION

SOLUTION

The cross-products of $\frac{18}{24}$ and $\frac{12}{16}$ are $18 \cdot 16 = 288$ and $24 \cdot 12 = 288$. The cross-products are equal, so $\frac{18}{24} = \frac{12}{16}$. ▲

Comparing Two Fractions

Students should be able to "compare and order rational numbers efficiently and accurately" (NCTM, Gr. 6–8), "compare two fractions with the same numerator or the same denominator by reasoning about their size" (CCSS, Gr. 3), and "compare two fractions with different numerators and different denominators, e.g., by creating common denominators or numerators, or by comparing to a benchmark fraction such as 1/2" (CCSS, Gr. 4).

One way to compare two unit fractions is to think about the shaded regions they represent in a circle. For example, the shaded parts in Figure 9 illustrate $\frac{1}{5}$ and $\frac{1}{8}$ using two equal-sized circles. Which fraction is larger? What inequality does the diagram suggest?

COMMUNICATION

REASONING

REPRESENTATION

We can compare $\frac{3}{7}$ and $\frac{5}{9}$ by rewriting each of the fractions as equivalent fractions with any common denominator, which turns the problem into a simpler problem of comparing whole numbers:

$$\frac{3}{7} = \frac{3 \cdot 9}{7 \cdot 9} = \frac{27}{63} \text{ and } \frac{5}{9} = \frac{7 \cdot 5}{7 \cdot 9} = \frac{35}{63}$$

Because $27 < 35$, we conclude $\frac{27}{63} < \frac{35}{63}$. Therefore, $\frac{3}{7} < \frac{5}{9}$. This strategy involves rewriting each fraction as an equivalent fraction with a common denominator, and leads to the following result.

$\frac{1}{5}$ $\frac{1}{8}$

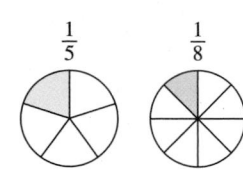

FIGURE 9
Comparing two unit fractions.

Theorem 1

Let $\frac{a}{b}$ and $\frac{c}{d}$ represent rational numbers with $b > 0$ and $d > 0$. $\frac{a}{b} < \frac{c}{d}$ if and only if $ad < bc$.

Proof:

There are two parts to the proof of the "if and only if" statement.

REASONING

PART 1. Suppose $\frac{a}{b} < \frac{c}{d}$. Writing each fraction as an equivalent fraction with the common denominator bd, we get $\frac{ad}{bd} < \frac{bc}{bd}$. Both fractions have a common positive denominator, so $ad < bc$.

PART 2. Suppose $ad < bc$, where $b > 0$ and $d > 0$. Then $\frac{ad}{bd} < \frac{bc}{bd}$. Then $\frac{a}{b} < \frac{c}{d}$ by the fundamental law of fractions.

EXAMPLE 5.12   Use cross-products to compare the fractions $\frac{6}{4}$ and $\frac{7}{3}$.

CONNECTION

SOLUTION

The cross-products of $\frac{6}{4}$ and $\frac{7}{3}$ are $6 \cdot 3 = 18$ and $4 \cdot 7 = 28$. We know $18 < 28$, so $\frac{6}{4} < \frac{7}{3}$. ▲

It is also possible to compare two fractions using a common numerator. We could represent $\frac{3}{7}$ and $\frac{5}{9}$ as the equivalent fractions $\frac{15}{35}$ and $\frac{15}{27}$. In this case, how would we identify the larger fraction?

Approximating Fractions with Benchmark Fractions

Benchmark fractions (or everyday fractions) such as $\frac{1}{2}, \frac{1}{3}, \frac{1}{4}, \frac{1}{5}, \frac{2}{3}, \frac{3}{4}, \frac{2}{5}, \frac{3}{5}$, and $\frac{4}{5}$ are easy to visualize and critical for fraction sense. They typically have the denominator 2, 3, 4, 5, 8, or 10. We can use equivalent fractions and benchmark fractions to comprehend and approximate the magnitude of $\frac{66}{80}$:

$$\frac{66}{80} = \frac{33}{40} \approx \frac{30}{40} = \frac{3}{4}$$

Classifying Fractions: Proper Fractions, Improper Fractions, Mixed Numbers, and Complex Fractions

Some examples of proper fractions are $\frac{1}{3}, \frac{2}{5}$, and $\frac{24}{32}$. If m and n are positive integers and $m < n$, then $\frac{m}{n}$ is called a **proper fraction.** Proper fractions have a part-to-whole interpretation: the proper fraction $\frac{m}{n}$ can be viewed as "m out of n parts." A proper fraction is in its simplest form when the GCF of the numerator and the denominator is 1. The simplest form is the easiest form to relate to. The simplest form of $\frac{6}{10}$ is $\frac{3}{5}$.

Two examples of mixed numbers are $1\frac{2}{3}$ and $2\frac{1}{4}$. A **mixed number** is the sum of a counting number and a positive fraction. The mixed number $1\frac{2}{3}$ is read as "one and two-thirds." The mixed number $2\frac{1}{4}$ is read as "two and one-fourth." $\frac{5}{4}$, $\frac{2}{1}$, and $\frac{3}{3}$ are examples of improper fractions. If m and n are positive integers and $m \geq n$, then $\frac{m}{n}$ is an **improper fraction.**

Figure 10(a) represents a whole, while Figures 10(b) and (c) represent improper fractions and mixed numbers, respectively.

REPRESENTATION

FIGURE 10(a)

Representation of a whole.

FIGURE 10(b)

Shaded region representing $\frac{5}{3}$ or $1\frac{2}{3}$.

FIGURE 10(c)

Shaded region representing $\frac{9}{4}$ or $2\frac{1}{4}$.

The model of $1\frac{2}{3}$ in Figure 10(b) illustrates $1\frac{2}{3}$ means $1 + \frac{2}{3}$, not $1 \times \frac{2}{3}$.

An improper fraction is in its simplest form when it is written as a mixed number such that the fraction part is a proper fraction in simplest form. For example, to write $\frac{17}{5}$ in its simplest form, we would write $3\frac{2}{5}$. The simplest form of $5\frac{4}{6}$ is $5\frac{2}{3}$. A **complex fraction,** such as the fraction in Figure 11, is a fraction in which the numerator, denominator, or both are fractions. Later, we use complex fractions to motivate the invert-and-multiply procedure to find the quotient of two fractions.

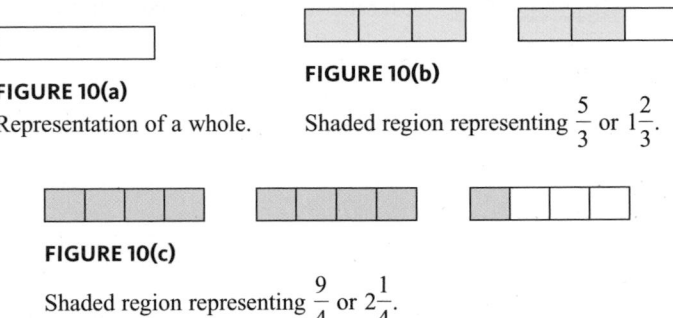

$$\frac{\frac{4}{5}}{\frac{2}{3}}$$

FIGURE 11

Complex fraction.

Connection between Improper Fractions and Mixed Numbers

The following example illustrates strategies to represent an improper fraction and a mixed number, and vice versa.

EXAMPLE 5.13

CONNECTION

REPRESENTATION

a. Represent $\frac{13}{5}$ as a mixed number.

b. Represent the mixed number $3\frac{4}{5}$ as an improper fraction.

SOLUTION

a. Here are two possible approaches.

METHOD 1. Use the meaning of $\frac{13}{5}$: 13 fifths = 10 fifths + 3 fifths = $2 + \frac{3}{5} = 2\frac{3}{5}$.

METHOD 2. Represent $\frac{13}{5}$ with a diagram, as shown.

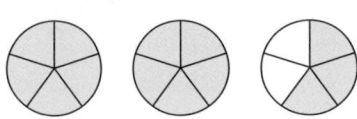

We see $\frac{13}{5}$ equals 2 and 3 fifths. Then $\frac{13}{5} = 2\frac{3}{5}$.

b. $3\frac{4}{5} = 3 + \frac{4}{5} = 15$ fifths + 4 fifths = 19 fifths = $\frac{19}{5}$. (A shortcut for the numerator is $3 \cdot 5 + 4 = 19$).

▲

CONNECTION

Writing an improper fraction as a mixed number makes it easier to approximate the fraction with a whole number, gauge its position on a number line, and estimate computations that involve improper fractions. Students should be able to convert a mixed number to an improper fraction and convert an improper fraction to a mixed number. This skill becomes important when they add, subtract, multiply, and divide fractions and mixed numbers.

The FDA's Center for Food Safety and Applied Nutrition (vm.cfsan.fda.gov) lists the allowable fractions that can be used in specifying serving size for foods that are usually measured in cups, such as dry oatmeal. Some allowable serving sizes are $\frac{1}{4}$, $\frac{1}{3}$, $\frac{1}{2}$, $\frac{2}{3}$, $\frac{3}{4}$, 1, $1\frac{1}{4}$, $2\frac{2}{3}$, and $3\frac{3}{4}$ cups. All proper fractions and mixed numbers in serving sizes must be expressed in simplified form.

EXAMPLE 5.14   Order the fractions $\frac{5}{3}$, $\frac{3}{8}$, and $\frac{6}{4}$ from least to greatest.

REASONING

SOLUTION

METHOD 1.   Use benchmarks: $\frac{3}{8} < 1$, $1 < \frac{5}{3} = 1\frac{2}{3}$, and $1 < \frac{6}{4} = 1\frac{1}{2} < 1\frac{2}{3}$. So $\frac{3}{8} < \frac{6}{4} < \frac{5}{3}$.

METHOD 2.   Use common denominators: $\frac{5}{3} = \frac{40}{24}$, $\frac{3}{8} = \frac{9}{24}$, and $\frac{6}{4} = \frac{36}{24}$. We know $\frac{9}{24} < \frac{36}{24} < \frac{40}{24}$, so $\frac{3}{8} < \frac{6}{4} < \frac{5}{3}$.

Density Property of Fractions

There are no whole numbers between 0 and 1. But you can always find a fraction between two given fractions. For example, let's find fractions between $\frac{1}{3}$ and $\frac{2}{3}$, as shown in Figure 12. When we represent $\frac{1}{3}$ and $\frac{2}{3}$ as the equivalent fractions $\frac{2}{6}$ and $\frac{4}{6}$, we easily see $\frac{3}{6}$ is between $\frac{1}{3}$ and $\frac{2}{3}$. When we represent $\frac{1}{3}$ and $\frac{2}{3}$ as the equivalent fractions $\frac{3}{9}$ and $\frac{6}{9}$, we easily see more fractions between $\frac{1}{3}$ and $\frac{2}{3}$. We could continue doing this with equivalent fractions with ever larger denominators. Figure 12 is a representation of the **density property** of fractions: there are infinitely many fractions between any two distinct fractions.

REPRESENTATION

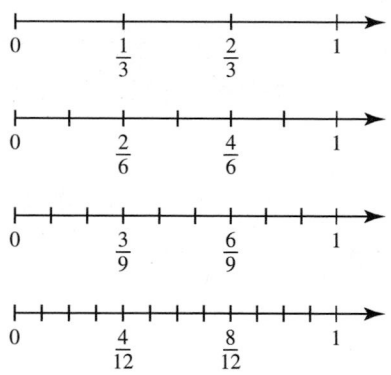

FIGURE 12
Representation of the density property of fractions.

Density Property of Fractions

Suppose $\frac{a}{b} \neq \frac{c}{d}$. There are infinitely many fractions between $\frac{a}{b}$ and $\frac{c}{d}$.

Multifaceted Nature of Fractions

CONNECTION
REPRESENTATION

Concept Map 5.1 conveys the multifaceted nature of fractions. Once you understand the intricate nature of fractions, you will be in a better position to help your students recognize the various situations that may involve fractions, such as measurement (for example, $\frac{3}{4}$ inch), a number on a number line, and ratios (for example, three out of every four). Fraction literacy includes understanding, connecting, and applying the multiple representations and uses of fractions.

> **Concept Map 5.1** Multifaceted Nature of Fractions

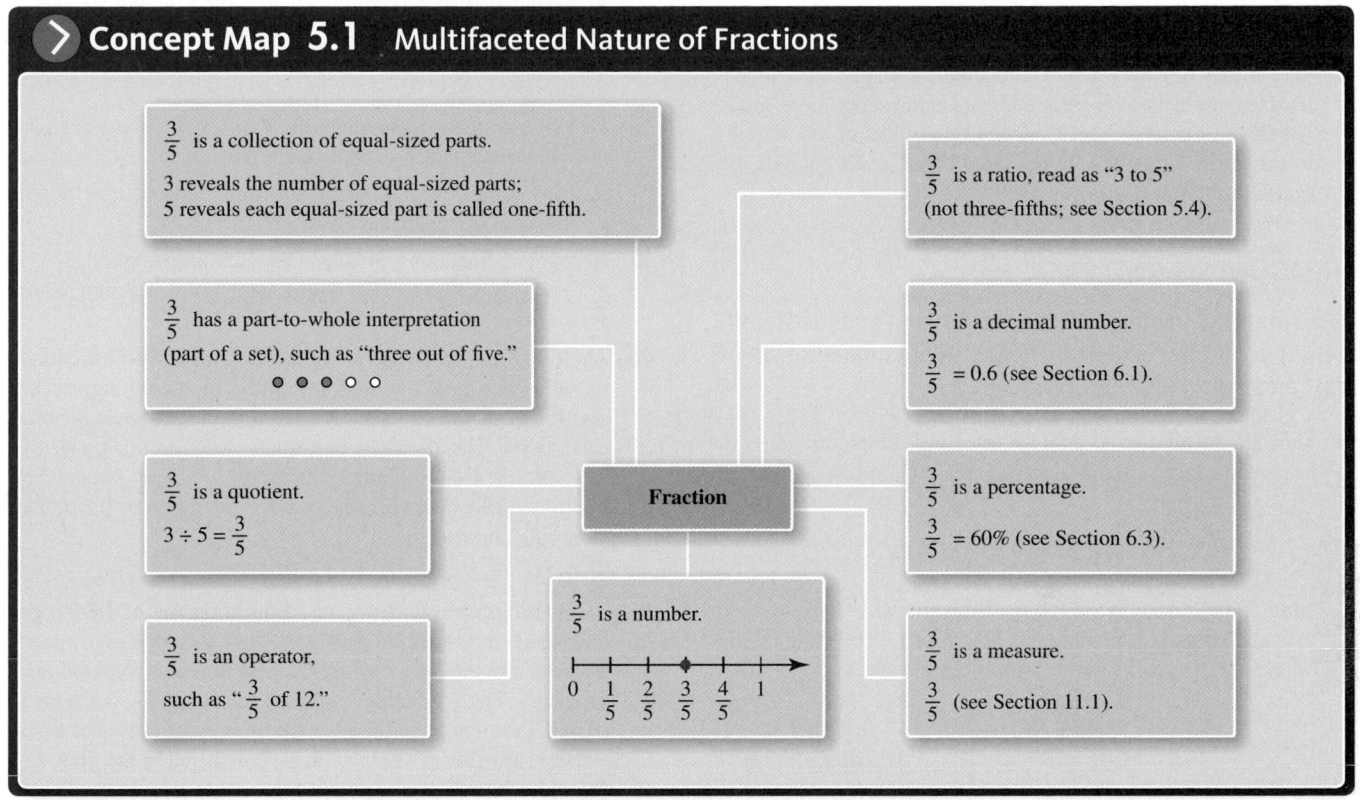

$\frac{3}{5}$ is a collection of equal-sized parts.

3 reveals the number of equal-sized parts;
5 reveals each equal-sized part is called one-fifth.

$\frac{3}{5}$ has a part-to-whole interpretation
(part of a set), such as "three out of five."

$\frac{3}{5}$ is a quotient.
$3 \div 5 = \frac{3}{5}$

$\frac{3}{5}$ is an operator,
such as "$\frac{3}{5}$ of 12."

Fraction

$\frac{3}{5}$ is a number.

$\frac{3}{5}$ is a ratio, read as "3 to 5"
(not three-fifths; see Section 5.4).

$\frac{3}{5}$ is a decimal number.
$\frac{3}{5} = 0.6$ (see Section 6.1).

$\frac{3}{5}$ is a percentage.
$\frac{3}{5} = 60\%$ (see Section 6.3).

$\frac{3}{5}$ is a measure.
$\frac{3}{5}$ (see Section 11.1).

QUESTIONS FOR SECTION 5.1

REPRESENTATION

Refresher: Representations (language, diagrams, tables, symbols, algebra, manipulatives, and contextualized situations) are important because we use them to organize, record, and communicate mathematical ideas and to make them more comprehensible.

1. $\frac{3}{5}$ is a collection of equal-sized parts.
   a. What does the 3 indicate?
   b. What does the 5 indicate?
   c. Show a representation of the fraction $\frac{3}{5}$.

2. $\frac{9}{7}$ is a collection of equal-sized parts.
   a. What does the 9 indicate?
   b. What does the 7 indicate?
   c. Show a representation of the fraction $\frac{9}{7}$.

3. Model the fraction five-thirds using the
   a. area model.   b. set model.   c. number line model.

4. Represent $8 \div 3$ as a fraction.

5. Show that $\frac{3}{5}$ and $\frac{6}{10}$ are equivalent fractions using each model.
   a. area model   b. set model   c. number line model

6. Represent the indicated fraction on the ruler with a
   a. fraction.   b. mixed number.

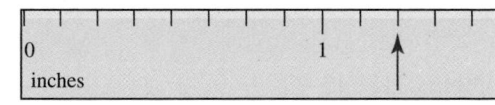

7. The circle is the whole unit. Represent the shaded region with a
   a. fraction.   b. mixed number.

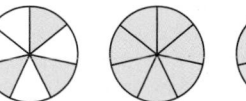 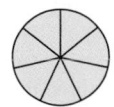  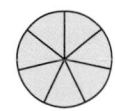

PROBLEM SOLVING

Refresher: Problem solving (reaching a goal that is not immediately attainable) is important because it helps students think more deeply about what they know and deal with unfamiliar situations.

8. Use a diagram to solve: 1120 people voted for the mayor, or five-sevenths of the voters. How many people voted in the election?

9. Use a diagram to solve: 240 birds were sitting in a tree. Three-fifths of the birds flew away. How many birds remained?

10. Use a diagram to solve: Five-eighths of the students in the class are boys. There are 12 more boys than girls. How many students are there altogether?

11. Use algebra to solve: There are 6 green marbles in a small bucket that has 48 marbles altogether. Latifah pours all the marbles into a large bucket and then adds some more green marbles to the large bucket so that three-fifths of the marbles in the large bucket are green. How many green marbles did Latifah add to the large bucket?

REASONING AND PROOF

Refresher: Reasoning and proof (thinking and justifying) are important because they help students make sense of mathematics.

12. How are the phrases "3 pencils" and "four-fifths" alike?

13. The diagram represents $\frac{2}{5}$ of a box. Draw $\frac{3}{4}$ of the box. Explain your drawing.

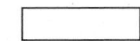

14. Molly says you can write the shaded region as $\frac{1}{4}$. Ben says you can write it as $\frac{3}{4}$. Both students are correct, depending on the whole unit. Draw the whole unit for each student.

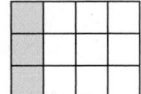

15. Use cross-products to find the missing number.
$$\frac{18}{42} = \frac{n}{112}$$

16. Kimberly spilled $\frac{3}{5}$ of the beads from the jar. There were 300 beads remaining in the jar. How many beads were in the jar before Kimberly spilled the beads? Draw a diagram and show your work.

CONNECTIONS

Refresher: Connections (linking and applying mathematical ideas) are important because they deepen student understanding and make mathematics more meaningful, flexible, and useful.

17. Each diagram represents three-fifths. Draw one-fifth.
    a. ○ ○ ○ ○ ○ ○

    b. ▭

    c. |———————|——————→
       0          $\frac{3}{5}$

18. Approximately 300,000 Americans require total knee replacements each year. Patients who undergo the traditional knee

replacement surgery can expect a three-day hospital stay followed by an extensive recovery period. However, a more promising outpatient knee replacement procedure is being developed as a possible alternative for qualified patients (such as those younger than 80 years and with no previous knee replacements). The doctor who developed the new procedure estimates that two-fifths of all knee replacement surgeries will use the new procedure.

   a. Use a diagram to estimate the number of Americans who will use the new procedure each year.

   b. How many days of hospital stay due to knee surgeries will this new procedure save overall?

19. Benchmark fractions typically have a denominator of 2, 3, 4, 5, 8, or 10. Approximate $\frac{440}{760}$ with a benchmark fraction. Show your work.

20. The FDA's Center for Food Safety and Applied Nutrition lists the allowable unit fractions permitted in specifying serving size for foods that are usually served in pieces, such as pizza, cake, or pie. The allowable unit fractions are 1/2, 1/3, 1/4, 1/5, 1/6, 1/8, 1/9, 1/10, 1/12, and smaller unit fractions obtained by multiplying the denominator by 2 or 3. Is the given fraction an allowable unit fraction?

   a. 1/24   b. 1/27   c. 1/14   d. 1/22

21. The Nutrition and Labeling and Education Act of 1990 regulates terms used on food packages. This act requires manufacturers to provide formatted food labels for most prepared food products. The "reference amount customarily consumed" (RACC) for a prepared food is the amount of food that a person typically eats in one meal. It is determined by the FDA. For example, the reference amount for a heavy weight cake, such as cheesecake, is 125 g, while the reference amount for a light weight cake, such as angel food cake, is 55 g. The serving size of a food product is a fraction of the total amount of food in the package, calculated by the manufacturer.

For food items that are typically served in pieces, such as pizza, cake, or melon, manufacturers must state the serving size as an "allowable fraction" of the food product, using 1/2, 1/3, 1/4, 1/5, 1/6, 1/8, 1/9, 1/10, 1/12, and any other unit fraction obtained by dividing the listed fractions by 2 or 3, according to federal regulations. The serving size is the allowable fraction of the product that most closely approximates the reference amount. Again, heavy cake has a reference amount of 125 g. The following table shows how the serving size would be determined for a heavy cake product weighing 538 g.

Size of one slice of cake as a unit fraction	$\frac{1}{2}$	$\frac{1}{3}$	$\frac{1}{4}$
Weight of one slice of cake that weighs 538 g	538 ÷ 2 ≈ 179 g	538 ÷ 3 ≈ 135 g	538 ÷ 4 ≈ 108 g

135 g is closest to the reference amount of 125 g, so the serving size is stated as $\frac{1}{3}$ (135 g).

   a. The reference amount for angel food cake is 55 g. Calculate the serving size for angel food cake that weighs 290 g.

   b. The reference amount for cheesecake is 125 g. Find the serving size for cheesecake that weighs 1234 g.

COMMUNICATION

Refresher: Communication (written and verbal explanations using representations and proper mathematical vocabulary) is important because it helps students refine and strengthen their understanding.

22. Explain why $\frac{3}{7}$ is more than $\frac{3}{8}$, without comparing cross-products.

23. Explain why $\frac{3}{7}$ is less than $\frac{5}{8}$, without comparing cross-products.

24. Answer the following.

    a. We must share 11 cookies fairly among four students. How much cookie does each student receive?

    b. We must share 11 marbles fairly among four students. How many marbles does each student get?

    c. How are these word problems alike?

    d. How are these word problems different?

25. Each story problem requires the calculation of $8 \div 5$. For each part, fill in the blank in the right-hand side of the equation $8 \div 5 =$ ___.

    a. Eight pizzas are split among five people. How much pizza does each person get?

    b. Eight pencils are split among five people. How many pencils does each person get?

26. Write a story problem that requires the calculation.

    a. $7 \div 3 = 2\,R1$ b. $7 \div 3 = \frac{7}{3}$

27. The fraction $\frac{10}{15}$ can be written as the equivalent fraction $\frac{2}{3}$ by "canceling" factors:

    $$\frac{10}{15} = \frac{\overset{2}{\cancel{10}}}{\underset{3}{\cancel{15}}} = \frac{2}{3}$$

    Explain why this method works.

28. Without making any calculations, explain why $\frac{4}{5}$ and $\frac{2}{7}$ cannot be equivalent fractions.

More practice with the ideas of the section

29. Fill in the blank. Choose one of the following words or phrases: *denominator, dividend, division, fraction, friction, improper, partitioning, practitioner, proper, numerator,* or *quotient.*

    a. The equation $7 \div 3 = 7/3$ illustrates a fraction is a(n) _____.

    b. _____ is the process of dividing a whole into equal-sized parts.

    c. _____ means "to count" and tells you how many equal-sized parts are in the collection.

    d. _____ means "to name" and tells you the size of the equal-sized part in the collection and the number of equal-sized parts in the whole.

    e. Seven-thirds is a(n) _____ fraction.

    f. Three-eighths is a(n) _____ fraction.

30. Consider the fraction seven-thirds.

    a. What does "seven" indicate?

    b. What does "thirds" indicate?

    c. Draw an area model of seven-thirds.

31. Use a diagram to solve each problem. Show your work.

    a. Mark had $35. He spent two-fifths of the money on a gift card. How much did the gift card cost?

    b. A chef had 72 g of sugar. She spilled five-eighths of the sugar. How many grams of sugar does she have left?

    c. Ed has 240 nickels, which is three-eighths of the number of coins Fred has. How many coins does Fred have?

    d. Luis ran 252 m. Jeremy ran $1\frac{2}{7}$ times as far as Luis. How far did Jeremy run?

32. Use a diagram to solve each problem. Show your work.

    a. Yvonne earns $2040 each month. She spends three-eighths of her monthly salary on housing. How much does she spend on housing each month?

    b. James has 420 dimes in a piggy bank, which is four-sevenths of the number of coins in the piggy bank. How many coins are in the piggy bank?

33. Use multiplication to find two equivalent fractions.

    a. $\dfrac{3}{4}$ b. $\dfrac{7}{3}$ c. $\dfrac{12}{5}$

34. Use division to find two equivalent fractions.

    a. $\dfrac{24}{32}$ b. $\dfrac{42}{14}$ c. $\dfrac{120}{200}$

35. Find the cross-products associated with the pairs of fractions. Which pairs represent equivalent fractions?

    a. $\dfrac{4}{7}$ and $\dfrac{6}{11}$ b. $\dfrac{324}{4}$ and $\dfrac{4617}{57}$ c. $\dfrac{3}{7}$ and $\dfrac{4}{9}$

36. Show that $\frac{6}{4}$ and $\frac{12}{8}$ are equivalent fractions using three computational strategies.

37. Express in simplest form.

    a. $\dfrac{48}{36}$ b. $5\dfrac{12}{9}$ c. $\dfrac{36}{42}$ d. $\dfrac{12}{15}$ e. $8\dfrac{4}{6}$

38. OOOO represents two-thirds. Draw a model of one-half.

39. Represent $a \div b$ in the form $a \div b = q\,Rr$.

    a. $1543 \div 35 = 44\dfrac{3}{35}$ b. $990 \div 42 = 23\dfrac{24}{42}$

40. Represent $a \div b$ as a mixed number.

    a. $41 \div 12 = 3\,R5$ b. $398 \div 15 = 26\,R8$

41. Locate the following on the number line.

    a. $1\dfrac{1}{2}$

    b. $\dfrac{3}{4}$

42. Draw a model for each fraction. Identify the whole unit.

    a. two-fifths   b. seven-thirds   c. six-fourths

43. Do the following.

    a. Mark the number line between 0 and 1 with fourths.

    b. Mark the number line between 0 and 1 with eighths.

    c. Mark the number line between 0 and 1 with sixteenths.

    d. Determine the property of fractions this illustrates. Explain your answer.

    ```
    ├─────────────────────────────┤
    0                             1
    ```

44. The diagram represents $1\frac{1}{4}$. Draw a representation of $\frac{2}{3}$. Explain your drawing.

    ```
    ┌──────────┐
    │          │
    └──────────┘
    ```

45. Use number sense to compare $\frac{4}{7}$ and $\frac{8}{17}$.

46. What does  represent, assuming

    a. ▢▢▢ represents one batch.

    b. ▢▢▢▢▢▢▢ represents one bag.

    c. ▢▢▢▢ represents one box.

47. Estimate the fraction with a benchmark fraction.

    a. $\dfrac{298}{408}$ b. $\dfrac{435}{821}$ c. $\dfrac{425}{1340}$

48. Find whole number values for the variables so that the fractions are equivalent.

    a. $\dfrac{x}{8}$ and $\dfrac{84}{6}$ b. $\dfrac{4}{7}$ and $\dfrac{12}{10+y}$ c. $\dfrac{2}{n-5}$ and $\dfrac{4}{n}$

49. Do the following.

    a. Order the fractions $\frac{1}{2}$, $\frac{1}{8}$, and $\frac{1}{6}$ from least to greatest.

    b. Order the fractions $\frac{1}{12}$, $\frac{1}{15}$, and $\frac{1}{10}$ from least to greatest.

    c. Devise a strategy for ordering unit fractions.

50. Do the following.

    a. Order the fractions $\frac{12}{25}$, $\frac{9}{25}$, and $\frac{18}{25}$ from least to greatest.

    b. Order the fractions $\frac{108}{32}$, $\frac{27}{32}$, and $\frac{12}{32}$ from least to greatest.

    c. Devise a strategy for ordering fractions with common denominators.

51. Order the fractions $\frac{m-2}{m}$ and $\frac{n-2}{n}$ from least to greatest, where $m < n$.

52. Use estimation to approximate the following fractions with one of these unit fractions: $\frac{1}{5}$, $\frac{1}{4}$, $\frac{1}{3}$, or $\frac{1}{2}$.

    a. $\dfrac{27}{80}$ b. $\dfrac{23}{99}$ c. $\dfrac{64}{131}$ d. $\dfrac{88}{260}$

53. Which number is larger? Explain.

    a. $\dfrac{8}{5}$ and $\dfrac{9}{5}$ b. $\dfrac{12}{7}$ and $\dfrac{12}{8}$ c. $\dfrac{4}{5}$ and $\dfrac{7}{6}$

54. Find two fractions between the given pair of fractions.

    a. $\dfrac{1}{4}$ and $\dfrac{2}{4}$ b. $\dfrac{7}{11}$ and $\dfrac{8}{11}$ c. $\dfrac{15}{7}$ and $\dfrac{15}{8}$

55. Use prime factorizations to simplify $\frac{48}{72}$.

56. Last year, Acme Inc. earned $20 million and Widget Co. earned $6 million. This year, Acme's revenue was $25 million and Widget's revenue was $10 million. Which company had a better year? Make a case for each company.

57. What is the largest natural number n such that

    a. $\dfrac{634}{787} < \dfrac{360}{n}$?   b. $\dfrac{45}{26} < \dfrac{84}{n+2}$?   c. $\dfrac{n-3}{8} > \dfrac{24}{5}$?

58. Are the fractions equivalent?

    a. $\dfrac{4}{7}$ and $\dfrac{32}{28}$ b. $\dfrac{6}{5}$ and $\dfrac{162}{135}$

    c. $\dfrac{3}{8}$ and $\dfrac{144}{385}$ d. $\dfrac{11}{5}$ and $\dfrac{616}{840}$

59. Simplify when possible.

    a. $\dfrac{5n+15}{10}$ b. $\dfrac{10m+1}{10}$ c. $\dfrac{0}{3}+3$ d. $\dfrac{6^{100}-6^{98}}{6^{100}+6^{98}}$

60. Use a diagram to solve: Sara ran two-fifths of the race. She needs to run 120 m more to finish the race. What is the length of the race?

61. Use a diagram to solve each problem. Explain your answer.

    a. Mike and Angela have 480 stamps altogether. Angela has $1\frac{2}{3}$ times as many stamps as Mike. How many stamps does Angela have?

    b. Fred is saving money for a gift. He saved $84, which is four-sevenths of the amount he needs to buy the gift. How much does the gift cost?

    c. Mark read $\frac{2}{5}$ of the book so far. He needs to read 30 more pages to finish the book. How many pages are in the book altogether?

    d. Natalie has $1\frac{1}{2}$ times as many beads as her sister Cindy. Altogether, they have 420 beads. How many beads does Natalie have?

62. Instruments on an airplane use airflow to determine airspeed. However, at high altitudes, the actual airspeed is higher than the airspeed measurements because of the thinner atmosphere at high altitude. At 10,000 feet, a pilot is traveling one-fifth faster than the indicated airspeed. Determine the actual speed of the airplane if the airspeed instrument reads

    a. 450 mph.   b. 810 mph.   c. 360 mph.

63. Do the following.

    a. Find the next two likely terms in the sequence. Then find an expression for the nth term in the sequence: $\frac{5}{2} = \frac{10}{4}$, $\frac{5}{2} = \frac{15}{6}$, $\frac{5}{2} = \frac{20}{8}$, . . .

    b. Find the next two likely terms in the sequence. Then find an expression for the nth term in the sequence: $\frac{3}{4} = \frac{9}{12}$, $\frac{3}{4} = \frac{15}{20}$, $\frac{3}{4} = \frac{21}{28}$, . . .

    c. Explain the concept these sequences illustrate.

64. Consider the arithmetic sequence $\frac{3}{5}$, $1\frac{2}{5}$, $2\frac{1}{5}$, 3, . . .

    a. List the next three terms.

    b. Determine the 23rd term in the sequence.

Addition and Subtraction with Rational Numbers

We use whole number ideas to add and subtract fractions with like denominators. Building on these ideas, we use fraction strips and equivalent fractions to develop and justify general procedures to add and subtract fractions with unlike denominators. Students should be able to "add and subtract fractions with unlike denominators (including mixed numbers) by replacing given fractions with equivalent fractions in such a way as to produce an equivalent sum or difference of fractions with like denominators. For example, 2/3 + 5/4 = 8/12 + 15/12 = 23/12 (in general, $a/b + c/d = (ad + bc)/bd$)" (CCSS, Gr. 5). This section is another opportunity to "recognize and use connections among mathematical ideas and understand how mathematical ideas interconnect and build on one another to produce a coherent whole" (NCTM, Gr. Pre-K–8).

Addition with Like Denominators

Adding two whole numbers with common units involves counting the total number of units:

- 2 dozen eggs + 5 dozen eggs = 7 dozen eggs
- 4 yd + 2 yd = 6 yd

A fraction is a collection of parts. The *numerator* of a fraction indicates the number of fractional parts, while the *denominator* indicates the fractional part counted. Adding fractions with common fractional parts is a connection to adding whole numbers.

- two-thirds + five-thirds = seven-thirds
- four-tenths + two-tenths = six-tenths

CONNECTION

REASONING
Students who reason $\frac{4}{10} + \frac{2}{10}$ is $\frac{6}{10}$ because they are counting tenths connect the meaning of fractions and the definition of addition with whole numbers. $\frac{4}{10} + \frac{2}{10} = \frac{4 + 2}{10} = \frac{6}{10}$. We use algebra to represent the general case.

> ### Definition of Sum of Rational Numbers with Like Denominators
>
> Let $\frac{a}{n}$ and $\frac{b}{n}$ represent any two rational numbers with a common denominator. Then $\frac{a}{n} + \frac{b}{n} = \frac{a + b}{n}$.

EXAMPLE 5.15   Add: $\dfrac{2}{6} + \dfrac{5}{6}$.

CONNECTION

SOLUTION

According to the definition of adding fractions with like denominators, $\frac{2}{6} + \frac{5}{6} = \frac{2 + 5}{6} = \frac{7}{6}$.

Addition with Unlike Denominators

CONNECTION

REASONING
Adding two whole numbers with different units requires renaming one or both quantities in terms of a common unit (also called *norming* or *unitizing*):

- 2 dozen eggs + 3 eggs = 24 eggs + 3 eggs = 27 eggs
- 4 yd + 18 ft = 4 yd + 6 yd = 10 yd

Renaming applies to adding two fractions with unlike denominators. We use equivalent fractions to rename one or both fractions. The following example combines two problem solving strategies—solve a simpler problem and draw a diagram—to add two fractions with unlike denominators.

EXAMPLE 5.16

CONNECTION
COMMUNICATION
PROBLEM SOLVING
REASONING
REPRESENTATION

Marie ate $\frac{1}{2}$ candy bar and Alex ate $\frac{2}{3}$ candy bar. How much candy bar did they eat altogether? Write an equation.

SOLUTION

The sum $\frac{1}{2} + \frac{2}{3}$ involves two collections of fractional parts: a collection of halves and a collection of thirds. We rename each fraction to turn this problem into an equivalent but simpler problem that involves counting the same fractional parts. In Figure 13(a), we represent both addends with fraction strips.

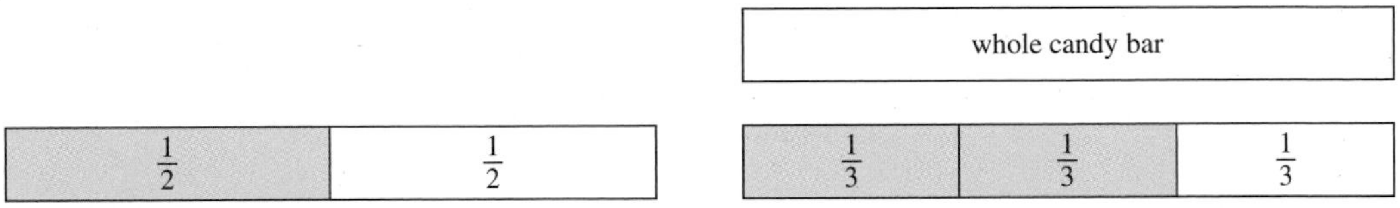

FIGURE 13(a)
Represent both addends with fraction strips.

In Figure 13(b), we rename each fraction as equivalent fractions with common denominators.

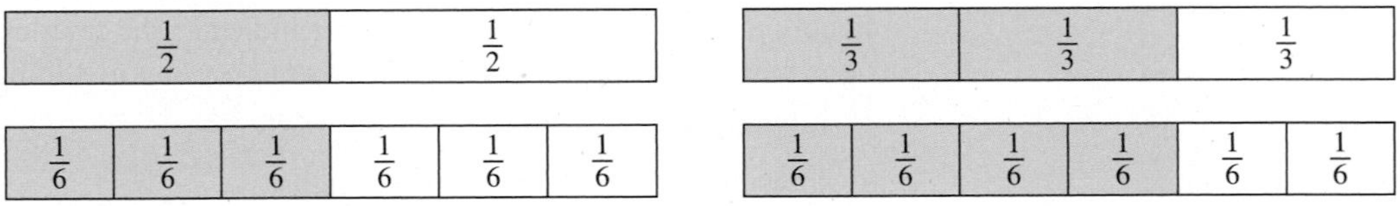

FIGURE 13(b)
Rename each fraction.

The problem $\frac{1}{2} + \frac{2}{3}$ is transformed into the equivalent but simpler problem $\frac{3}{6} + \frac{4}{6}$ that involves counting the same objects—sixths. So $\frac{1}{2} + \frac{2}{3} = \frac{3}{6} + \frac{4}{6} = \frac{7}{6}$. This means Marie and Alex ate $\frac{7}{6}$ candy bars altogether.

▲

The example suggests an approach using equivalent fractions. $\frac{1}{2}$ is equivalent to $\frac{3}{6}$, because $\frac{1}{2} = \frac{1 \cdot 3}{2 \cdot 3} = \frac{3}{6}$, and $\frac{2}{3}$ is equivalent to $\frac{4}{6}$, because $\frac{2}{3} = \frac{2 \cdot 2}{3 \cdot 2} = \frac{4}{6}$. So $\frac{1}{2} + \frac{2}{3}$ is equivalent to $\frac{3}{6} + \frac{4}{6}$, which is $\frac{7}{6}$. So $\frac{1}{2} + \frac{2}{3} = \frac{7}{6}$. The following example illustrates two pencil-and-paper versions for adding fractions.

EXAMPLE 5.17

CONNECTION

Add $\dfrac{8}{6} + \dfrac{7}{4}$.

SOLUTION

METHOD 1. Use the LCM to rename fractions. The LCM of 6 and 4 is 12. Then

$$\frac{8}{6} + \frac{7}{4} = \frac{8 \cdot 2}{6 \cdot 2} + \frac{3 \cdot 7}{3 \cdot 4} = \frac{16}{12} + \frac{21}{12} = \frac{16 + 21}{12} = \frac{37}{12} = 3\frac{1}{12}.$$

METHOD 2. Use the product of the denominators to rename fractions. The product is $6 \cdot 4 = 24$.

$$\frac{8}{6} + \frac{7}{4} = \frac{8 \cdot 4}{6 \cdot 4} + \frac{6 \cdot 7}{6 \cdot 4} = \frac{32}{24} + \frac{42}{24} = \frac{32 + 42}{24} = \frac{74}{24} = 3\frac{2}{24} = 3\frac{1}{12}.$$

▲

The product of the denominators easily produces a common denominator. We generalize this result using algebra.

Theorem 2

Let $\frac{a}{b}$ and $\frac{c}{d}$ represent any two rational numbers. Then $\frac{a}{b} + \frac{c}{d} = \frac{ad + bc}{bd}$.

The following Classroom Connection illustrates that students may initially use fraction strips to learn to add fractions with unlike denominators.

Classroom Connection

- *Math,* Grade 6, p. 259

Add. You may use fraction strips. $\frac{2}{5} + \frac{1}{2}$.
(© 2000 Macmillan/McGraw Hill. Reprinted by permission.)

Additive Inverse

As we discussed in Section 4.3, there is a pair of integers such that the sum of the two integers is zero, for example, $4 + -4 = 0$ and $-3 + 3 = 0$. We say 4 is the additive inverse of -4 and -4 is the additive inverse of 4. As shown in Table 5.3, there is a pair of fractions such that the sum of the two fractions is zero.

TABLE 5.3   **Additive Inverse**

$\frac{3}{4} + \frac{-3}{4} = \frac{3 + -3}{4} = \frac{0}{4} = 0$	$\frac{5}{9} + \frac{-10}{18} = \frac{10}{18} + \frac{-10}{18} = \frac{10 + -10}{18} = \frac{0}{18} = 0$

The additive inverse of $\frac{3}{4}$ is $\frac{-3}{4}$ because $\frac{3}{4} + \frac{-3}{4} = 0$, and the additive inverse of $\frac{-3}{4}$ is $\frac{3}{4}$ because $\frac{-3}{4} + \frac{3}{4} = 0$. In general, the **additive inverse** of $\frac{m}{n}$ is the fraction $\frac{-m}{n}$. This means every fraction has an additive inverse. For example, $\frac{-2}{3}$ has the additive inverse $\frac{-(-2)}{3}$, which is the same as $\frac{2}{3}$, and $\frac{10}{4}$ has the additive inverse $\frac{-10}{4}$.

The symbol $-\frac{m}{n}$ is often used to represent the additive inverse of $\frac{m}{n}$, so the fraction $-\frac{3}{4}$ equals $\frac{-3}{4}$, and the fraction $\frac{-m}{n}$ equals $-\frac{m}{n}$. But we already know $\frac{-m}{n}$ and $\frac{m}{-n}$ are equivalent fractions. This means the negative sign can be in three places: $-\frac{3}{4} = \frac{-3}{4} = \frac{3}{-4}$. Also, the additive inverse of the additive inverse of $-\frac{m}{n}$ is $\frac{m}{n}$; that is, $-\left(-\frac{m}{n}\right) = \frac{m}{n}$.

EXAMPLE 5.18

REASONING

Convert $-5\frac{4}{7}$ to a fraction.

SOLUTION

$5\frac{4}{7}$ is equivalent to $\frac{39}{7}$, so $-5\frac{4}{7}$ is equivalent to $-\frac{39}{7}$, which represents $\frac{-39}{7}$. ▲

Subtraction with Like Denominators

We build on whole number concepts and use the take-away model for subtraction involving two fractions with common denominators (that is, the same equal-sized parts).

EXAMPLE 5.19

CONNECTION
COMMUNICATION
PROBLEM SOLVING
REASONING
REPRESENTATION

Anastasiya Smirnova/Shutterstock.com

Madison had $\frac{5}{6}$ m of ribbon. She used $\frac{2}{6}$ m of ribbon to make a bow. How much ribbon did she have left? Write an equation.

SOLUTION

The shaded region in Figure 14 models $\frac{5}{6}$ m of ribbon. As with the take-away model for whole numbers, we take away parts to represent subtraction. We take away $\frac{2}{6}$ m.

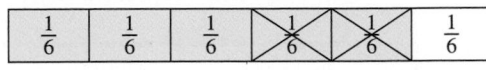

FIGURE 14
five-sixths − two-sixths = ___.

We see $\frac{3}{6}$ m of ribbon remain. The equation is $\frac{5}{6} - \frac{2}{6} = \frac{3}{6}$.

This leads to the following definition.

Definition of Difference of Rational Numbers with Like Denominators

Let $\frac{a}{n}$ and $\frac{b}{n}$ represent any two rational numbers with a common denominator. Then $\frac{a}{n} - \frac{b}{n} = \frac{a-b}{n}$.

Subtraction with Unlike Denominators

Now we know how to solve subtraction problems with fractions that have common denominators using the take-away model of subtraction. To solve a new subtraction problem with fractions that have unlike denominators, we turn this into a problem we already know how to solve by finding a common denominator. The following contextualized situation illustrates the subtraction of fractions with unlike denominators using fraction strips.

EXAMPLE 5.20

CONNECTION
COMMUNICATION
PROBLEM SOLVING
REASONING
REPRESENTATION

thumb/Shutterstock.com

Alex poured $\frac{2}{3}$ cup of sugar in a bowl. Marie realized it was too much and removed $\frac{1}{2}$ cup of sugar from the bowl. How much sugar remained in the bowl? Write an equation.

SOLUTION

We need to find the difference: $\frac{2}{3} - \frac{1}{2}$. We rename each fraction with a common denominator to turn this problem into an equivalent but simpler problem that we already know how to solve. In Figure 15(a), we represent both fractions with fraction strips.

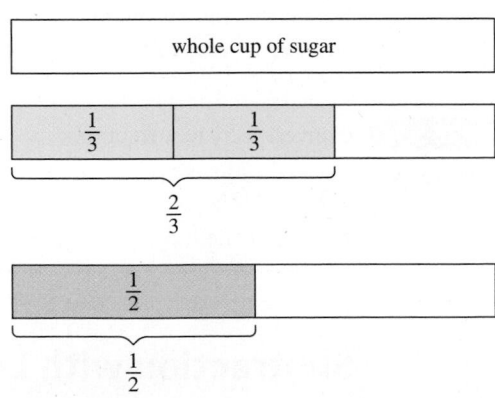

FIGURE 15(a)
Represent both fractions with fraction strips.

In Figure 15(b), we rename each fraction as equivalent fractions with common denominators. A common multiple of 2 and 3 is 6. $\frac{2}{3}$ is equivalent to $\frac{4}{6}$, and $\frac{1}{2}$ is equivalent to $\frac{3}{6}$.

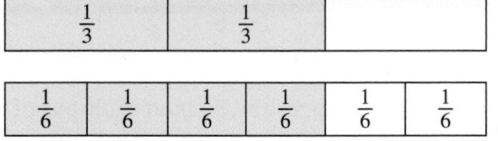   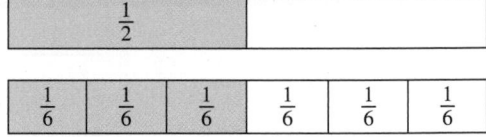

FIGURE 15(b)
Rename the fractions.

In Figure 15(c), we begin with $\frac{2}{3}$ (or $\frac{4}{6}$) and take away $\frac{1}{2}$ (or $\frac{3}{6}$).

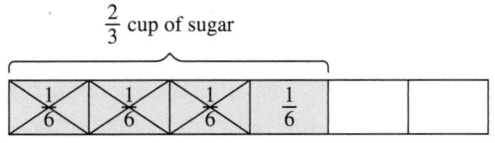

FIGURE 15(c)

$$\frac{2}{3} - \frac{1}{2} = \frac{4}{6} - \frac{3}{6} = \frac{1}{6}$$

The difference is $\frac{1}{6}$. This means $\frac{1}{6}$ cup of sugar remained in the bowl. We see $\frac{2}{3} - \frac{1}{2} = \frac{4}{6} - \frac{3}{6} = \frac{1}{6}$.

The following Classroom Connection illustrates students may initially use fraction strips to learn to add fractions with unlike denominators.

◆◆ Classroom Connection

● *Math*, Grade 6, p. 261

Subtract. You may use fraction strips. $\frac{5}{6} - \frac{1}{4}$.
(© 2000 Macmillan/McGraw Hill. Reprinted by permission.)

EXAMPLE 5.21

CONNECTION

Subtract by finding a common denominator.

a. $\dfrac{3}{4} - \dfrac{-11}{8}$

b. $\dfrac{3}{4} - \dfrac{5}{6}$

SOLUTION

a. $\dfrac{3}{4} - \dfrac{-11}{8} = \dfrac{2 \cdot 3}{2 \cdot 4} - \dfrac{-11}{8} = \dfrac{6}{8} - \dfrac{-11}{8} = \dfrac{6 - -11}{8} = \dfrac{6 + 11}{8} = \dfrac{17}{8} = 2\dfrac{1}{8}$

b. Here are two possible approaches:

METHOD 1.   Use equivalent fractions based on the product of the denominators. This approach is initially easier because the common denominator is easier to determine, but it could lead to more steps.

$$\frac{3}{4} - \frac{5}{6} = \frac{6 \cdot 3}{6 \cdot 4} - \frac{4 \cdot 5}{4 \cdot 6} = \frac{18}{24} - \frac{20}{24} = \frac{18 - 20}{24} = \frac{-2}{24} = \frac{-1}{12}$$

(continued)

METHOD 2. Use equivalent fractions based on the LCM of the denominators. This approach may initially require some work to find the LCM, but it could lead to fewer steps.

$$\frac{3}{4} - \frac{5}{6} = \frac{3 \cdot 3}{3 \cdot 4} - \frac{2 \cdot 5}{2 \cdot 6} = \frac{9}{12} - \frac{10}{12} = \frac{9 - 10}{12} = \frac{-1}{12}$$

▲

The previous examples suggest a common multiple of the denominators forms the basis for a pencil-and-paper strategy for subtracting fractions with unlike denominators. We represent the general case (product of the denominators) with algebra.

> **Theorem 3**
>
> Let $\frac{a}{b}$ and $\frac{c}{d}$ represent any two rational numbers. Then $\frac{a}{b} - \frac{c}{d} = \frac{ad - bc}{bd}$.

The difference between two whole numbers or integers is a missing addend. The same is true with rational numbers.

> **Definition of Subtraction with Rational Numbers**
>
> Let $\frac{a}{b}$, $\frac{c}{d}$, and $\frac{e}{f}$ represent rational numbers. Then $\frac{a}{b} - \frac{c}{d} = \frac{e}{f}$ if and only if $\frac{a}{b} = \frac{e}{f} + \frac{c}{d}$.

EXAMPLE 5.22 Use the definition of subtraction to solve $n - \frac{4}{5} = \frac{1}{3}$.

CONNECTION
REASONING

SOLUTION

$n - \frac{4}{5} = \frac{1}{3}$	**Original problem**
$n = \frac{4}{5} + \frac{1}{3}$	**Definition of subtraction**
$n = \frac{4 \cdot 3 + 5 \cdot 1}{5 \cdot 3}$	**Rule for adding rational numbers**
$n = \frac{17}{15}$	**Simplification**
$n = 1\frac{2}{15}$	**Simplification**

▲

In Section 4.3 on integers, we discussed how to convert subtraction to addition by adding the opposite. The next example proves that we can extend this procedure to rational numbers.

EXAMPLE 5.23 Let $\frac{a}{b}$ and $\frac{c}{d}$ represent any two rational numbers. Prove $\frac{a}{b} - \frac{c}{d} = \frac{a}{b} + \frac{-c}{d}$.

CONNECTION
REASONING

SOLUTION

$\dfrac{a}{b} - \dfrac{c}{d} = \dfrac{ad}{bd} - \dfrac{bc}{bd}$	**Equivalent fractions $\frac{a}{b} = \frac{ad}{bd}$ and $\frac{c}{d} = \frac{bc}{bd}$**
$= \dfrac{ad - bc}{bd}$	**Rule for subtracting rational numbers with like denominators**
$= \dfrac{ad + -(bc)}{bd}$	**Adding the opposite rule for integers: $x - y = x + -y$**
$= \dfrac{ad + b(-c)}{bd}$	**Rule for multiplying integers: $x(-y) = -(xy)$**
$= \dfrac{ad}{bd} + \dfrac{b(-c)}{bd}$	**Rule for adding rational numbers with like denominators**
$= \dfrac{a}{b} + \dfrac{-c}{d}$	**Equivalent fractions $\frac{ad}{bd} = \frac{a}{b}$ and $\frac{b(-c)}{bd} = \frac{-c}{d}$**

▲

This leads to the following result of subtraction of rational numbers by adding the opposite.

> **Theorem 4**
>
> Let $\frac{a}{b}$ and $\frac{c}{d}$ represent any two rational numbers. Then $\frac{a}{b} - \frac{c}{d} = \frac{a}{b} + \frac{-c}{d}$.

EXAMPLE 5.24 Subtract by adding the opposite: $\frac{3}{4} - \frac{6}{5}$.

CONNECTION

SOLUTION

$$\frac{3}{4} - \frac{6}{5} = \frac{3}{4} + \frac{-6}{5} = \frac{3 \cdot 5 + 4(-6)}{4 \cdot 5} = \frac{-9}{20}$$

▲

Algebraic Properties of Rational Numbers

Rational numbers have algebraic properties that resemble integer properties.

> **Basic Properties of Addition and Subtraction with Rational Numbers**
>
> Let $\frac{a}{b}$, $\frac{c}{d}$, and $\frac{e}{f}$ represent rational numbers. Then we have the following properties.
>
> **Closure Property of Addition**
> $\frac{a}{b} + \frac{c}{d}$ is a rational number.
>
> **Commutative Property of Addition**
> $\frac{a}{b} + \frac{c}{d} = \frac{c}{d} + \frac{a}{b}$
>
> **Associative Property of Addition**
> $\left(\frac{a}{b} + \frac{c}{d} \right) + \frac{e}{f} = \frac{a}{b} + \left(\frac{c}{d} + \frac{e}{f} \right)$
>
> **Additive Identity Property**
> $\frac{a}{b} + 0 = \frac{a}{b}$ and $0 + \frac{a}{b} = \frac{a}{b}$
>
> **Additive Inverse Property**
> $\frac{a}{b} + \frac{-a}{b} = 0$ and $\frac{-a}{b} + \frac{a}{b} = 0$
>
> **Adding the Opposite Property**
> $\frac{a}{b} - \frac{c}{d} = \frac{a}{b} + \frac{-c}{d}$

The following example shows how we can use properties to solve an equation.

EXAMPLE 5.25 Solve $\frac{3}{4} + y = \frac{7}{8}$. Use the basic properties of rational numbers.

CONNECTION
REASONING

SOLUTION

$\frac{3}{4} + y = \frac{7}{8}$	**Original problem**
$\frac{-3}{4} + \left(\frac{3}{4} + y \right) = \frac{-3}{4} + \frac{7}{8}$	**Addition property of equality**
$\left(\frac{-3}{4} + \frac{3}{4} \right) + y = \frac{-3}{4} + \frac{7}{8}$	**Associative property of addition**
$0 + y = \frac{-3}{4} + \frac{7}{8}$	**Additive inverse property**
$y = \frac{-3}{4} + \frac{7}{8}$	**Additive identity property**
$y = \frac{-3 \cdot 8 + 4 \cdot 7}{4 \cdot 8}$	**Rule for adding rational numbers**
$y = \frac{4}{32}$	**Simplification**
$y = \frac{1}{8}$	**Simplification**

Let's check the answer: $\frac{3}{4} + \frac{1}{8} = \frac{6}{8} + \frac{1}{8} = \frac{7}{8}$. So $y = \frac{1}{8}$ solves the equation $\frac{3}{4} + y = \frac{7}{8}$.

EXAMPLE 5.26   Solve $n - \frac{3}{4} = \frac{2}{5}$.

CONNECTION   a. Use the definition of subtraction.

REASONING   b. Use the fact that addition and subtraction are inverse operations.

c. Use the basic properties of rational numbers.

SOLUTION

a.

$n - \dfrac{3}{4} = \dfrac{2}{5}$	**Original problem**
$n = \dfrac{3}{4} + \dfrac{2}{5}$	**Definition of subtraction**
$n = \dfrac{3 \cdot 5 + 4 \cdot 2}{4 \cdot 5}$	**Rule for adding rational numbers**
$n = \dfrac{23}{20}$	**Simplification**
$n = 1\dfrac{3}{20}$	**Simplification**

b.

$n - \dfrac{3}{4} = \dfrac{2}{5}$	**Original problem**
$n - \dfrac{3}{4} + \dfrac{3}{4} = \dfrac{2}{5} + \dfrac{3}{4}$	**Addition property of equality**
$n = \dfrac{2}{5} + \dfrac{3}{4}$	**Addition and subtraction are inverse operations.**
$n = \dfrac{2 \cdot 4 + 5 \cdot 3}{5 \cdot 4}$	**Rule for adding rational numbers**
$n = \dfrac{23}{20}$	**Simplification**
$n = 1\dfrac{3}{20}$	**Simplification**

c.

$n - \dfrac{3}{4} = \dfrac{2}{5}$	**Original problem**
$n + \dfrac{-3}{4} = \dfrac{2}{5}$	**Subtraction by adding the opposite**
$\left(n + \dfrac{-3}{4}\right) + \dfrac{3}{4} = \dfrac{2}{5} + \dfrac{3}{4}$	**Addition property of equality**
$n + \left(\dfrac{3}{4} + \dfrac{-3}{4}\right) = \dfrac{2}{5} + \dfrac{3}{4}$	**Associative property of addition**
$n + 0 = \dfrac{2}{5} + \dfrac{3}{4}$	**Additive inverse property**
$n = \dfrac{2}{5} + \dfrac{3}{4}$	**Additive identity property**
$n = \dfrac{2 \cdot 4 + 5 \cdot 3}{5 \cdot 4}$	**Rule for adding rational numbers**
$n = \dfrac{23}{20}$	**Simplification**
$n = 1\dfrac{3}{20}$	**Simplification**

Adding and Subtracting Mixed Numbers

Adding and subtracting two mixed numbers builds on operations with whole numbers and proper and improper fractions. With mixed numbers, we add or subtract the whole number and fraction parts separately, much as we can add whole numbers in any order because of multiple applications of the commutative and associative properties of addition. At times, we need the flexibility to rename a mixed number to find the sum or difference.

EXAMPLE 5.27   Rename the mixed number.

CONNECTION

REASONING

a. $7\dfrac{13}{10} = 8\dfrac{3}{10}$

b. $7\dfrac{8}{12} = 6\dfrac{20}{12}$

SOLUTION

a.
$$7\frac{13}{10} = 7 + \frac{13}{10} \qquad \textbf{Definition of a mixed number}$$

$$= 7 + 1\frac{3}{10} \qquad \textbf{Simplification of an improper fraction}$$

$$= 7 + \left(1 + \frac{3}{10}\right) \qquad \textbf{Definition of a mixed number}$$

$$= (7 + 1) + \frac{3}{10} \qquad \textbf{Associative property of addition}$$

$$= 8 + \frac{3}{10} \qquad \textbf{Simplification}$$

$$= 8\frac{3}{10} \qquad \textbf{Definition of a mixed number}$$

b.
$$7\frac{8}{12} = 7 + \frac{8}{12} \qquad \textbf{Definition of a mixed number}$$

$$= (6 + 1) + \frac{8}{12} \qquad \textbf{Decomposition: 7 = 6 + 1}$$

$$= 6 + \left(1 + \frac{8}{12}\right) \qquad \textbf{Associative property of addition}$$

$$= 6 + 1\frac{8}{12} \qquad \textbf{Definition of a mixed number}$$

$$= 6 + \frac{20}{12} \qquad \textbf{Converting a mixed number to a fraction}$$

$$= 6\frac{20}{12} \qquad \textbf{Definition of a mixed number}$$

▲

The following example illustrates a use of representation that we often apply in an elementary-school classroom.

EXAMPLE 5.28   Calculate the sum or difference.

CONNECTION

REPRESENTATION

a.
$$\begin{array}{r} 7\frac{2}{3} \\ -2\frac{3}{4} \\ \hline \end{array}$$

b.
$$\begin{array}{r} 4\frac{3}{5} \\ +2\frac{9}{10} \\ \hline \end{array}$$

SOLUTION

a. The sum is approximately $8 - 3 = 5$.

$$7\frac{2}{3} = 7\frac{8}{12} = 6\frac{20}{12}$$
$$-2\frac{3}{4} = -2\frac{9}{12} = -2\frac{9}{12}$$
$$\overline{\hphantom{-2\frac{3}{4} = -2\frac{9}{12} = }4\frac{11}{12}}$$

So $7\frac{2}{3} - 2\frac{3}{4} = 4\frac{11}{12}$.

b. The sum is approximately $5 + 3 = 8$.

$$4\frac{3}{5} = 4\frac{6}{10}$$
$$+2\frac{9}{10} = 2\frac{9}{10}$$
$$\overline{\hphantom{+2\frac{9}{10} = }6\frac{15}{10}} = 7\frac{5}{10} = 7\frac{1}{2}$$

So $4\frac{3}{5} + 2\frac{9}{10} = 7\frac{1}{2}$.

The vertical format reveals the reasoning process and makes it easier to identify any errors. Adding the whole numbers to the whole number and the fraction parts to the fraction parts, with renaming as necessary, is much like adding the ones to the ones, tens to the tens, and so on.

Estimation and Mental Math

Estimating sums of fractions or mixed numbers usually involves rounding down to the next whole number, rounding up to the next whole number, rounding to the nearest whole number, or rounding to the nearest half. Many students struggle to estimate sums, even when they are able to compute the precise sum. For example, one study showed 33% of the students who could calculate $\frac{12}{13} + \frac{7}{8}$ exactly were unable to provide a reasonable estimate of the sum. What is your reasonable estimate of the sum?

Tables 5.4 and 5.5 illustrate various estimation approaches for mixed numbers.

TABLE 5.4   Estimating Sums

Round addends to the nearest $\frac{1}{2}$	$4\frac{2}{3} + 13\frac{1}{5} \approx 4\frac{1}{2} + 13 = 17\frac{1}{2}$
Round addends to the nearest whole number	$4\frac{2}{3} + 13\frac{1}{5} \approx 5 + 13 = 18$
Round addends down to the nearest whole number	$4\frac{2}{3} + 13\frac{1}{5} \approx 4 + 13 = 17$
Round addends up to the nearest whole number	$4\frac{2}{3} + 13\frac{1}{5} \approx 5 + 14 = 19$

TABLE 5.5 Estimating Differences

Round the minuend and the subtrahend to the nearest $\dfrac{1}{2}$	$12\dfrac{3}{5} - 4\dfrac{2}{3} \approx 12\dfrac{1}{2} - 4\dfrac{1}{2} = 8$
Round the minuend and the subtrahend to the nearest whole number	$12\dfrac{3}{5} - 4\dfrac{2}{3} \approx 13 - 5 = 8$
Round the minuend up and the subtrahend down to the nearest whole number	$12\dfrac{3}{5} - 4\dfrac{2}{3} \approx 13 - 4 = 9$
Round the minuend down and the subtrahend up to the nearest whole number	$12\dfrac{3}{5} - 4\dfrac{2}{3} \approx 12 - 5 = 7$

QUESTIONS FOR SECTION 5.2

REPRESENTATION

Refresher: Representations (language, diagrams, tables, symbols, algebra, manipulatives, and contextualized situations) are important because we use them to organize, record, and communicate mathematical ideas and to make them more comprehensible.

1. Use a diagram to add: $\dfrac{2}{4} + \dfrac{3}{4}$.

2. Use a diagram to add: $\dfrac{1}{4} + \dfrac{3}{8}$.

3. Use a diagram to subtract: $\dfrac{7}{5} - \dfrac{3}{5}$.

4. Use a diagram to subtract: $\dfrac{6}{4} - \dfrac{5}{8}$.

5. Estimate the sum. Then calculate the sum.

   a. $5\dfrac{3}{4}$ b. $8\dfrac{3}{6}$ c. $2\dfrac{3}{10}$

   $+3\dfrac{2}{3}$ $+5\dfrac{5}{8}$ $+7\dfrac{13}{100}$

6. Estimate the difference. Then calculate the difference.

   a. $8\dfrac{5}{6}$ b. $9\dfrac{3}{8}$ c. $6\dfrac{7}{10}$

   $-3\dfrac{3}{4}$ $-4\dfrac{5}{8}$ $-2\dfrac{23}{100}$

PROBLEM SOLVING

Refresher: Problem solving (reaching a goal that is not immediately attainable) is important because it helps students think more deeply about what they know and deal with unfamiliar situations.

7. Kayla added $4\dfrac{2}{3}$ cups of water to a bucket with water. Then the bucket contained $9\dfrac{3}{4}$ cups of water altogether. How many cups of water were in the bucket before Kayla added water?

8. John went to the local hardware store to buy $17\dfrac{3}{4}$ yards of wire. The store only sells wire in 20-yard spools. How much wire will he have left over?

9. A tire company has three types of employees: mechanics, supervisors, and secretaries. Of the employees, $\dfrac{3}{4}$ are mechanics and $\dfrac{3}{32}$ are supervisors. What fraction of employees are secretaries?

10. Express the following as a fraction.

    a. $\dfrac{1}{2} + \dfrac{1}{4}$ b. $\dfrac{1}{2} + \dfrac{1}{4} + \dfrac{1}{8}$

    c. $\frac{1}{2} + \frac{1}{4} + \frac{1}{8} + \ldots + \frac{1}{1024}$ (Hint: Use patterns.)

REASONING AND PROOF

Refresher: Reasoning and proof (thinking and justifying) are important because they help students make sense of mathematics.

11. Suppose $\dfrac{x}{y}$ and $\dfrac{u}{v}$ are additive inverses of $\dfrac{a}{b}$. Prove that $\dfrac{x}{y} = \dfrac{u}{v}$.

12. Do the following.

    a. Use inductive reasoning to support the closure property of addition of rational numbers.

    b. Use deductive reasoning to prove the closure property of addition of rational numbers.

13. Suppose $\dfrac{a}{b} = \dfrac{e}{f} + \dfrac{c}{d}$. Use properties to prove $\dfrac{a}{b} - \dfrac{c}{d} = \dfrac{e}{f}$.

14. Insert a $<$, $>$, or $=$ in the box using number sense and estimation.

    a. $6\dfrac{7}{10}\ \square\ 4\dfrac{11}{75} + 3\dfrac{3}{34}$ b. $-2\dfrac{3}{4} + 5\ \square\ \dfrac{2}{5}$

    c. $20\dfrac{3}{5} - 13\dfrac{8}{9}\ \square\ 7$ d. $3 + \left(\dfrac{2}{3}\right)^{100}\ \square\ 3\dfrac{2}{3}$

15. Mark and Fred shared a pizza. Is the given situation possible? Explain your answer.

    a. Mark ate $\dfrac{3}{5}$ of the pizza, and Fred ate $\dfrac{4}{7}$ of the pizza.

    b. Mark ate $\dfrac{5}{8}$ of the pizza, and Fred ate $\dfrac{2}{7}$ of the pizza.

16. Solve $n - \frac{3}{8} = \frac{5}{6}$.

  a. Use the definition of subtraction.

  b. Use the fact that addition and subtraction are inverse operations.

  c. Use the basic properties.

17. The number line shows equally spaced tick marks. What is the value of point A?

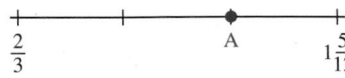

$$\frac{2}{3} \qquad A \qquad 1\frac{5}{12}$$

CONNECTIONS

Refresher: Connections (linking and applying mathematical ideas) are important because they deepen student understanding and make mathematics more meaningful, flexible, and useful.

18. Fill in the blank.

  a. 4 pencils + 8 pencils = ___ pencils

  b. 4 thirds + 8 thirds = ___ thirds

  c. 3 birds + 9 birds = ___ birds

  d. 3 sevenths + 9 sevenths = ___ sevenths

19. According to a newspaper report, the height of the infield and outfield grass in a new baseball park was $\frac{7}{8}$ inch. The tall grass slowed the baseball, which gave the fielders time to grab the baseball and prevent some multibase hits. This discouraged the home team and robbed the fans of excitement. The grass was shortened to $\frac{5}{8}$ inch. How much was the grass shortened?

20. Ancient Egyptians wrote quotients to division problems as the sum of distinct unit fractions. For example, suppose seven loaves of bread are to be divided among 12 students. Six loaves split among 12 students yields one-half loaf per student. The remaining loaf split among the 12 students yields 1/12 of a loaf per student. The result is $7 \div 12 = \frac{1}{2} + \frac{1}{12}$. Think like an Egyptian and write each quotient as the sum of distinct unit fractions.

  a. $3 \div 8$ **b.** $5 \div 8$ **c.** $5 \div 6$

21. What is the length of the nail?

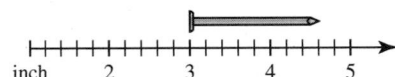

inch   2   3   4   5

COMMUNICATION

Refresher: Communication (written and verbal explanations using representations and proper mathematical vocabulary) is important because it helps students refine and strengthen their understanding.

22. When adding fractions, why do we rewrite the fractions in terms of a common denominator instead of a common numerator?

23. Describe a situation that involves adding two fractions.

24. Describe a situation that involves subtracting two fractions.

25. Discuss a strategy to find two fractions with unlike denominators that have the

  a. sum $\frac{5}{7}$.   **b.** difference $\frac{3}{5}$.

More practice with the ideas of the section

26. Fill in the blank. Choose one of the following words or phrases: *adding the opposite, additive inverse, denominator, fraction strips, like, unlike, rename, remove,* or *numerator.*

  a. $\frac{-7}{3}$ is the _____ of $\frac{7}{3}$.

  b. To find the sum $4\frac{5}{6} + 2\frac{3}{4}$, we would first _____ the fractional parts of the mixed numbers.

  c. The fractions $\frac{5}{6}$ and $\frac{3}{4}$ have _____ denominators.

  d. To find the sum $\frac{5}{6} + \frac{3}{4}$, we would rename each fraction with a like _____.

  e. You could use _____ to represent addition and subtraction with a diagram.

  f. Rewriting $\frac{5}{6} - \frac{2}{6}$ as $\frac{5}{6} + \frac{-2}{6}$ is an example of _____.

27. Fill in the blank.

  a. 9 books − 5 books = ___ books

  b. 9 thirds − 5 thirds = ___ thirds

  c. \$14 − \$8 = \$___

  d. 14 sevenths − 8 sevenths = ___ sevenths

28. Fill in each blank with a mixed number.

  a. 18 ft + 42 in. = ___ ft   **b.** 5 lb + 3 oz = ___ lb

29. Fill in the blank.

  a. 8 lb + ___ lb = 14 lb

  b. 8 sevenths + ___ sevenths = 14 sevenths

  c. ___ cakes + 3 cakes = 10 cakes

  d. ___ fifths + 3 fifths = 10 fifths

  e. 6 ft − ___ ft = 2 ft

  f. 6 eighths − ___ eighths = 2 eighths

  g. ___ hours − 3 hours = 12 hours

  h. ___ fifths − 3 fifths = 12 fifths

30. Find and simplify the sum $\frac{5}{6} + \frac{7}{8}$.

  a. Use the LCM of the denominators to add.

  b. Use the rule for adding fractions.

31. Find and simplify the difference $\frac{7}{8} - \frac{5}{6}$.

  a. Use the LCM of the denominators to subtract.

  b. Use the rule for subtracting fractions.

  c. Subtract by adding the opposite.

32. Solve the equation $\frac{4}{3} + n = \frac{9}{5}$.

  a. Use the definition of subtraction.

  b. Use the fact that addition and subtraction are inverse operations.

  c. Use the basic properties.

33. Solve the equation $\frac{3}{4} - y = \frac{5}{6}$.

  a. Use the definition of subtraction.

  b. Use the fact that addition and subtraction are inverse operations.

34. The number line shows equally spaced tick marks. What is the value of point A?

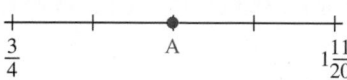

35. Select the appropriate equation (do not solve).

a. Paul put $1\frac{2}{3}$ cups of flour in a bowl. Then Maria put some more flour in the bowl. Then there were $5\frac{3}{4}$ cups of flour in the bowl altogether. Which equation models the situation: $n + 1\frac{2}{3} = 5\frac{3}{4}$ or $1\frac{2}{3} + n = 5\frac{3}{4}$?

b. Paul poured some flour in a bowl. Then Maria poured $2\frac{1}{3}$ cups of flour in the bowl. Then there were $4\frac{1}{5}$ cups of flour in the bowl altogether. Which equation models the situation: $n + 2\frac{1}{3} = 4\frac{1}{5}$ or $2\frac{1}{3} + n = 4\frac{1}{5}$?

36. Select the appropriate equation (do not solve).

a. Maria ran $3\frac{4}{5}$ miles. She ran $1\frac{2}{3}$ miles farther than Paul. Which equation models how far Paul ran: $3\frac{4}{5} = n + 1\frac{2}{3}$ or $n = 3\frac{4}{5} + 1\frac{2}{3}$?

b. Maria ran $3\frac{4}{5}$ miles. She ran $1\frac{2}{3}$ fewer miles than Paul ran. Which equation models how far Paul ran: $n = 3\frac{4}{5} - 1\frac{2}{3}$ or $3\frac{4}{5} = n - 1\frac{2}{3}$?

37. Select the appropriate equation (do not solve).

a. Paul has $4\frac{2}{3}$ feet of ribbon. He gave Maria $1\frac{1}{4}$ feet of ribbon. Which equation models how much ribbon Paul has left: $n + 1\frac{1}{4} = 4\frac{2}{3}$ or $4\frac{2}{3} - 1\frac{1}{4} = n$?

b. Paul has $4\frac{2}{3}$ feet of ribbon. He gave Maria some ribbon. He has $1\frac{1}{4}$ feet of ribbon left. Which equation models the situation: $n + 1\frac{1}{4} = 4\frac{2}{3}$ or $4\frac{2}{3} - n = 1\frac{1}{4}$?

c. Paul has some ribbon. He gave Maria $1\frac{1}{4}$ feet of ribbon. He has $4\frac{2}{3}$ feet of ribbon left. Which equation models how much ribbon Paul had originally: $n - 1\frac{1}{4} = 4\frac{2}{3}$ or $4\frac{2}{3} - n = 1\frac{1}{4}$.

38. How much longer is nail A than nail B?

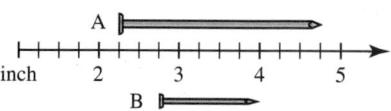

39. Find the additive inverse (opposite).

a. $\frac{5}{7}$ b. $\frac{11}{3}$ c. $\frac{-5}{4}$

40. Verify that each fraction solves the equation $\frac{4}{3} + n = 0$.

a. $\frac{-4}{3}$ b. $\frac{-8}{6}$ c. $\frac{-12}{9}$

41. Convert the mixed numbers to fractions.

a. $5\frac{4}{7}$ b. $-12\frac{5}{6}$

42. Convert the fractions to mixed numbers.

a. $\frac{43}{20}$ b. $\frac{42}{11}$ c. $\frac{-55}{16}$ d. $\frac{-17}{3}$

43. Find each difference using Theorem 3 for subtracting fractions. Then find each difference by adding the opposite. Then compare your results.

a. $\frac{2}{3} - \frac{8}{3}$ b. $\frac{4}{7} - \frac{-3}{4}$

44. Find all values of n such that

a. $\frac{5n}{4} + 2 = 19\frac{1}{2}$.

b. $5 + n < -7n + 120$.

45. Use mental math to determine whether $70\frac{5}{11} - 20\frac{9}{16}$ is less than, greater than, or equal to 50. Explain your answer.

46. Fill each box with a fraction.

a. $10\frac{8}{5} = 11\square$ b. $4\frac{2}{5} = 3\square$

47. Estimate each sum or difference.

a. $12\frac{1}{5} + 7\frac{5}{6}$ b. $24\frac{3}{17} - 2\frac{4}{5}$

c. $65\frac{1}{2} + 30\frac{15}{31}$ d. $54 - 6\frac{1}{8}$

e. $42\frac{3}{8} + 31\frac{5}{7}$ f. $100\frac{5}{11} - 20\frac{7}{13}$

48. The number line shows equally spaced tick marks. What is the value of point A?

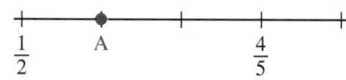

49. Solve for n.

a. $\frac{n}{3} + \frac{5}{3} = 7$ b. $\frac{3}{n} + \frac{4}{5} = 1\frac{8}{35}$

50. A local middle school consists of sixth, seventh, and eighth graders. Three-sevenths of the students are sixth graders and one-fourth are seventh graders. What fraction of the students are eighth graders?

51. A magic square is a 3-by-3 table filled with numbers so that the sum of each row, column, and diagonal is the same. Determine whether each table is a magic square.

a.

$\frac{4}{5}$	$\frac{1}{10}$	$\frac{3}{5}$
$\frac{3}{10}$	$\frac{1}{2}$	$\frac{7}{10}$
$\frac{2}{5}$	$\frac{9}{10}$	$\frac{1}{5}$

b.

$1\frac{1}{5}$	$1\frac{2}{5}$	$\frac{2}{5}$
$\frac{1}{5}$	1	$1\frac{4}{5}$
$1\frac{3}{5}$	$\frac{3}{5}$	$\frac{4}{5}$

52. A recipe for a cake calls for $5\frac{1}{4}$ cups of flour. The chef adds $2\frac{3}{4}$ cups of flour to the mixture. How much more flour does the chef need to add to the mixture?

53. A recipe for a cake calls for $5\frac{3}{4}$ cups of flour. The chef mistakenly adds $7\frac{2}{3}$ cups of flour to the mixture. How much flour does the chef need to remove from the mixture?

54. Explain why the fraction or mixed number is not in its simplest form.

a. $\frac{48}{20}$ b. $12\frac{4}{3}$ c. $6\frac{8}{8}$ d. $3\frac{4}{10}$

55. Find the three next likely terms in each sequence.

a. $\frac{2}{5}, \frac{6}{5}, \frac{10}{5}, \frac{14}{5}, \dots$ b. $\frac{1}{2}, \frac{3}{4}, \frac{5}{6}, \frac{7}{8}, \dots$

SECTION 5.3 Multiplication and Division with Rational Numbers

In this section we use models to understand and develop the traditional algorithms for multiplying and dividing rational numbers. We also use diagrams and algebra to solve word problems involving rational numbers and use the commutative, associative, and distributive properties to solve equations involving rational numbers.

Multiplication and Diagrams

Chapter 3 showed that combining a groups of b objects has multiplicative structure: a groups of b objects per group equals $(a \times b)$ objects, where a and b are whole numbers. We *extend* this conceptual model of multiplication in a meaningful way to fractions using contextualized situations. Students should "understand a multiple of a/b as a multiple of $1/b$, and use this understanding to multiply a fraction by a whole number. For example, use a visual fraction model to express $3 \times (2/5)$ as $6 \times (1/5)$, recognizing this product as $6/5$. (In general, $n \times (a/b) = (n \times a)/b$.)" (CCSS, Gr. 4). Students should also be able to "interpret the product $(a/b) \times q$ as a parts of a partition of q into b equal parts; equivalently, as the result of a sequence of operations $a \times q \div b$. For example, use a visual fraction model to show $(2/3) \times 4 = 8/3$, and create a story context for this equation. Do the same with $(2/3) \times (4/5) = 8/15$. (In general, $(a/b) \times (c/d) = ac/bd$.)" (CCSS, Gr. 5).

EXAMPLE 5.29

CONNECTION
COMMUNICATION
PROBLEM SOLVING
REASONING
REPRESENTATION

Grandma wants to make four batches of cookie dough. Each batch requires $\frac{2}{3}$ cup of sugar. How much sugar does Grandma need?

SOLUTION

This problem has multiplicative structure: 4 batches $\times \frac{2}{3}$ cup of sugar per batch $= 4 \times \frac{2}{3}$ cups of sugar. The shaded region in the diagram in Figure 16 represents the product $4 \times \frac{2}{3}$.

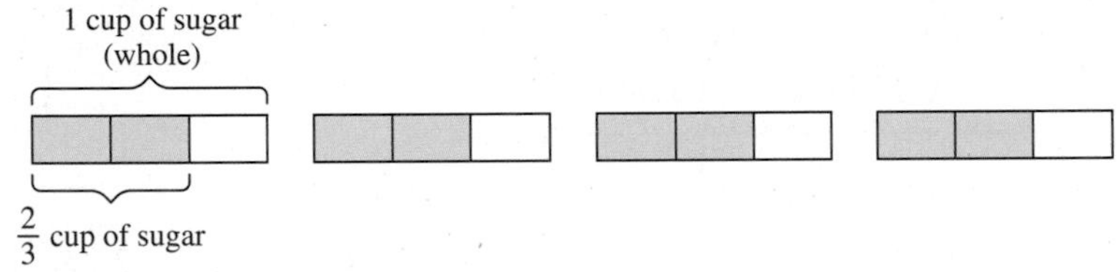

1 cup of sugar (whole)

$\frac{2}{3}$ cup of sugar

FIGURE 16
Model of $4 \times \frac{2}{3}$.

Each shaded region represents one-third, so eight shaded regions represent eight-thirds. So $4 \times \frac{2}{3} = \frac{8}{3}$. Grandma needs $\frac{8}{3}$ cups of sugar.

EXAMPLE 5.30

CONNECTION
COMMUNICATION
PROBLEM SOLVING
REASONING
REPRESENTATION

Grandma wants to make three-quarters of a batch of cookie dough. Her recipe calls for 2 cups of dry oatmeal per batch. How much dry oatmeal does Grandma need?

SOLUTION

We need to find how many cups of oatmeal are in a three-quarter batch of 2 cups of dry oatmeal per batch. $\frac{3}{4}$ batch $\times 2$ cups of dry oatmeal per batch $= \frac{3}{4} \times 2$ cups of dry oatmeal. Figure 17(a) shows the whole is 2 cups of dry oatmeal.

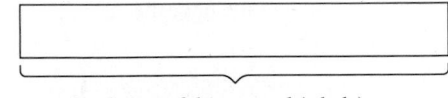

2 cups of dry oatmeal (whole)

FIGURE 17(a)
The whole is 2 cups of dry oatmeal.

Figure 17(b) shows $\frac{1}{4}$ of 2 cups of dry oatmeal, where each fractional part is $2 \div 4 = \frac{2}{4}$ cup of oatmeal.

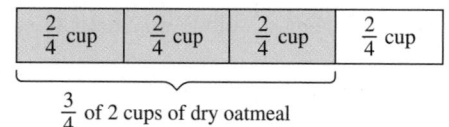

$\frac{2}{4}$ cup	$\frac{2}{4}$ cup	$\frac{2}{4}$ cup	$\frac{2}{4}$ cup

$\underbrace{}$
$\frac{1}{4}$ of 2 cups of dry oatmeal

FIGURE 17(b)

$2 \div 4 = \frac{2}{4}$, so each equal-sized part represents $\frac{2}{4}$ cup of sugar.

Figure 17(c) applies the meaning of $\frac{3}{4}$ as three equal-sized fractional parts, where each fractional part is $\frac{1}{4}$ of the whole (2 cups of dry oatmeal).

$\frac{2}{4}$ cup	$\frac{2}{4}$ cup	$\frac{2}{4}$ cup	$\frac{2}{4}$ cup

$\underbrace{}$
$\frac{3}{4}$ of 2 cups of dry oatmeal

FIGURE 17(c)

$\frac{3}{4}$ is three equal-sized parts.

$\frac{2}{4}$ cup $+ \frac{2}{4}$ cup $+ \frac{2}{4}$ cup $= \frac{6}{4}$ cups, so $\frac{3}{4} \times 2 = \frac{6}{4}$. Grandma needs $\frac{6}{4}$ cups of oatmeal. ▲

Examples 5.29 and 5.30 show $4 \times \frac{2}{3} = \frac{4 \times 2}{3}$ and $\frac{3}{4} \times 2 = \frac{3 \times 2}{4}$, respectively. We generalize these results using algebra.

Definition of Multiplying a Rational Number and a Whole Number

Let $\frac{a}{b}$ represent any rational number and c represent any whole number. Then $\frac{a}{b} \times c = \frac{a \times c}{b}$ and $c \times \frac{a}{b} = \frac{c \times a}{b}$.

EXAMPLE 5.31

CONNECTION

Multiply: $3\frac{7}{10} \times 15$.

SOLUTION

An estimate is $3\frac{7}{10} \times 15 \approx 4 \times 15 = 60$. We represent the mixed number as a fraction and then use the formula to multiply. $3\frac{7}{10} \times 15 = \frac{37}{10} \times 15 = \frac{37 \times 15}{10} = \frac{555}{10} = 55\frac{1}{2}$. ▲

Now we use a five-step process to show our thought process for modeling the product of two proper fractions. A clear conceptualization of the whole is a crucial aspect of multiplication with fractions.

EXAMPLE 5.32

CONNECTION
COMMUNICATION
PROBLEM SOLVING
REASONING
REPRESENTATION

Grandma wants to make four-fifths of a batch of cookies. Her recipe calls for $\frac{2}{3}$ cup of sugar for a batch. How much sugar does Grandma need?

SOLUTION

This problem has the form "a groups of b," which fits the framework of a multiplication problem: $\frac{4}{5}$ batches of $\frac{2}{3}$ cup of sugar per batch $= \frac{4}{5} \times \frac{2}{3}$ cup of sugar. We evaluate $\frac{4}{5} \times \frac{2}{3}$ using the five-step procedure in Figure 18. In step 1, we draw a rectangle to represent the whole, which is 1 cup of sugar. In step 2, we shade two-thirds of the region, which represents $\frac{2}{3}$ cup of sugar. In step 3, we partition the $\frac{2}{3}$ cup of sugar into five equal-sized pieces. In step 4, we shade four-fifths of two-thirds. The cross-hatched region represents $\frac{4}{5} \times \frac{2}{3}$. In step 5, we extend the partition, and we see each equal-sized part equals $\frac{1}{15}$ cup of sugar.

(continued)

step 1   step 2   step 3   step 4   step 5

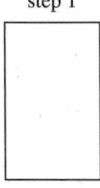 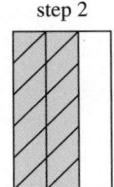 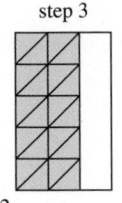 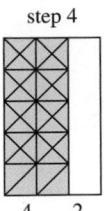

1 (whole cup $\frac{2}{3}$ cup of sugar $\frac{2}{3}$ cup of sugar $\frac{4}{5}$ of $\frac{2}{3}$ $\frac{4}{5} \times \frac{2}{3} = \frac{8}{15}$
of sugar)

FIGURE 18

Using a diagram to calculate $\frac{4}{5} \times \frac{2}{3}$.

Thus, $\frac{4}{5} \times \frac{2}{3} = \frac{8}{15}$. So Grandma needs $\frac{8}{15}$ cup of sugar.

EXAMPLE 5.33 Draw a model to calculate each product.

REASONING
REPRESENTATION   **a.** $\dfrac{2}{5} \times \dfrac{3}{4}$

b. $\dfrac{3}{4} \times \dfrac{2}{5}$

SOLUTION

a. 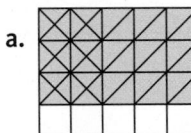 $\dfrac{2}{5} \times \dfrac{3}{4} = \dfrac{6}{20}$

b. 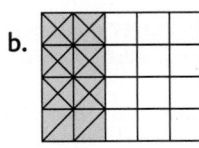 $\dfrac{3}{4} \times \dfrac{2}{5} = \dfrac{6}{20}$

The following Classroom Connection illustrates that students should be able to use models to find the product of two fractions.

> **Classroom Connection**
>
> • Houghton Mifflin *Mathematics*, Student Edition, Grade 5, p. 313
>
> Use models to find each product. Write each product in simplest form. $\frac{3}{4} \times \frac{4}{5}$
> (© by Houghton Mifflin Company, Inc. Reproduced by permission of the publisher, Houghton Mifflin Harcourt Publishing Company.)

Examples 5.32 and 5.33 illustrate $\frac{4}{5} \times \frac{2}{3} = \frac{4 \times 2}{5 \times 3}$ and $\frac{2}{5} \times \frac{3}{4} = \frac{2 \times 3}{5 \times 4}$, respectively. We generalize these results using algebra.

> **Definition of Multiplying Two Rational Numbers**
>
> Let $\frac{a}{b}$ and $\frac{c}{d}$ represent any two rational numbers. Then $\frac{a}{b} \times \frac{c}{d} = \frac{a \times c}{b \times d}$.

EXAMPLE 5.34 Multiply: $3\dfrac{3}{4} \times 2\dfrac{5}{6}$.

CONNECTION   SOLUTION

An estimate of the product is $3\frac{3}{4} \times 2\frac{5}{6} \approx 4 \times 3 = 12$. We represent each mixed number as an improper fraction and then use the formula to multiply: $3\frac{3}{4} \times 2\frac{5}{6} = \frac{15}{4} \times \frac{17}{6} = \frac{15 \times 17}{4 \times 6} = 3\frac{255}{24} = 10\frac{15}{24} = 10\frac{5}{8}$.

Multiplicative Inverse (Reciprocal)

You can verify that $\frac{4}{3} \times \frac{3}{4} = 1$ and $\frac{4}{3} \times \frac{6}{8} = 1$. $\frac{3}{4}$ and $\frac{6}{8}$ are equivalent fractions. It turns out that every fraction $\frac{c}{d}$ that satisfies the equation $\frac{4}{3} \times \frac{c}{d} = 1$ is equivalent to $\frac{3}{4}$. We give a special name to the fraction obtained by switching the positions of the numerator and denominator: the **multiplicative inverse (reciprocal)** of $\frac{m}{n}$ is $\frac{n}{m}$, provided $m \neq 0$. For example, the reciprocal of $\frac{6}{2}$ is $\frac{2}{6}$. The reciprocal of $\frac{-5}{2}$, namely, $\frac{2}{-5}$, is equivalent to $\frac{-2}{5}$. The fraction $\frac{0}{3}$ does not have a reciprocal. In general, a nonzero fraction and its reciprocal have a special relationship: $\frac{m}{n} \times \frac{n}{m} = 1$, as long as $m \neq 0$. Every fraction $\frac{x}{y}$ that satisfies the equation $\frac{m}{n} \times \frac{x}{y} = 1$ is equivalent to $\frac{n}{m}$, that is, $\frac{x}{y} = \frac{n}{m}$.

Algebraic Properties of Multiplication with Rational Numbers

Now we list some algebraic properties of fraction multiplication.

> ### Algebraic Properties of Multiplication with Rational Numbers
>
> Let $\frac{a}{b}$, $\frac{c}{d}$, and $\frac{e}{f}$ represent rational numbers. Then we have the following properties.
>
> **Closure Property**
>
> $\frac{a}{b} \times \frac{c}{d}$ is a fraction.
>
> **Commutative Property of Multiplication**
>
> $\frac{a}{b} \times \frac{c}{d} = \frac{c}{d} \times \frac{a}{b}$
>
> **Associative Property of Multiplication**
>
> $\left(\frac{a}{b} \times \frac{c}{d}\right) \times \frac{e}{f} = \frac{a}{b} \times \left(\frac{c}{d} \times \frac{e}{f}\right)$
>
> **Distributive Property of Multiplication over Addition**
>
> $\frac{a}{b} \times \left(\frac{c}{d} + \frac{e}{f}\right) = \frac{a}{b} \times \frac{c}{d} + \frac{a}{b} \times \frac{e}{f}$
>
> **Distributive Property of Multiplication over Subtraction**
>
> $\frac{a}{b} \times \left(\frac{c}{d} - \frac{e}{f}\right) = \frac{a}{b} \times \frac{c}{d} - \frac{a}{b} \times \frac{e}{f}$
>
> **Multiplicative Inverse Property**
>
> If $\frac{a}{b} \neq 0$, then $\frac{a}{b} \times \frac{b}{a} = 1$.
>
> **Identity Property of Multiplication**
>
> $\frac{a}{b} \times 1 = \frac{a}{b}$ and $1 \times \frac{a}{b} = \frac{a}{b}$
>
> **Zero Property of Multiplication**
>
> $\frac{a}{b} \times 0 = 0$ and $0 \times \frac{a}{b} = 0$

EXAMPLE 5.35 Prove the distributive property of multiplication over subtraction for rational numbers.

CONNECTION

REASONING

SOLUTION

Let $\frac{a}{b}$, $\frac{c}{d}$, and $\frac{e}{f}$ represent rational numbers. Then $\frac{a}{b} \times \left(\frac{c}{d} - \frac{e}{f}\right) = \frac{a}{b} \times \left(\frac{cf}{df} - \frac{de}{df}\right) = \frac{a}{b} \times \left(\frac{cf - de}{df}\right) = \frac{a(cf - de)}{bdf} = \frac{acf - ade}{bdf} = \frac{acf}{bdf} - \frac{ade}{bdf} = \frac{ac}{bd} - \frac{ae}{bf} = \frac{a}{b} \times \frac{c}{d} - \frac{a}{b} \times \frac{e}{f}$. ▲

Can you justify each step in the proof for the example we just worked?

The following Classroom Connection illustrates that students should be able to write and solve equations in word problems involving fractions.

> ### ◆ Classroom Connection
>
> ● *Math*, Grade 6, p. 367
>
> Write an equation. Solve for the given value. Greenwich School has 125 more than $\frac{1}{10}$ the number of students at Clifton School. If Greenwich School has 525 students, how many students attend Clifton School? (© 2000 Macmillan/McGraw Hill. Reprinted by permission.)

The following example explains in detail how to apply properties to solve an equation.

EXAMPLE 5.36 Use algebraic properties of multiplication to solve $\frac{3}{8} \times y = 15$.

CONNECTION

REASONING

SOLUTION

$$\frac{3}{8} \times y = 15 \qquad \text{Original problem}$$

$$\frac{8}{3} \times \left(\frac{3}{8} \times y\right) = \frac{8}{3} \times 15 \qquad \text{Multiplication property of equality}$$

$$\left(\frac{8}{3} \times \frac{3}{8}\right) \times y = \frac{8}{3} \times 15 \qquad \text{Associative property of multiplication}$$

$$1 \times y = \frac{8}{3} \times 15 \qquad \text{Multiplicative inverse property}$$

$$y = \frac{8}{3} \times 15 \qquad \text{Identity property of multiplication}$$

$$y = \frac{8 \times 15}{3} \qquad \text{Rule for multiplying a fraction and whole number}$$

$$y = \frac{120}{3} \qquad \text{Simplification}$$

$$y = 40 \qquad \text{Simplification}$$

Let's check the answer: $\frac{3}{8} \times 40 = \frac{3 \times 40}{8} = \frac{3 \times 5 \times 8}{8} = 3 \times 5 = 15$. So $y = 40$ solves $\frac{3}{8} \times y = 15$. ▲

Multiple Strategies to Solve Word Problems Involving Fractions

The following problem illustrates two strategies used to solve some word problems.

EXAMPLE 5.37 Allie has 5 more than three-fourths times as many coins as William. They have 229 coins altogether. How many coins does each have?

CONNECTION

COMMUNICATION

PROBLEM SOLVING

REASONING

REPRESENTATION

SOLUTION

METHOD 1. Use the Draw a Diagram strategy. The rectangle in Figure 19(a) represents the number of coins William has and is split into four equal-sized parts.

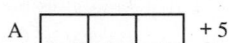

FIGURE 19(a)

A representation of the number of coins William has.

The rectangle in Figure 19(b) represents the number of coins Allie has, which is 5 more than three-fourths the number of coins William has.

A ⬜⬜⬜ +5

FIGURE 19(b)

A representation of the number of coins Allie has.

Figure 19(c) represents that Allie and William have 229 coins altogether.

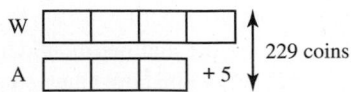

FIGURE 19(c)

William and Allie have 229 coins altogether.

Figure 19(c) means the seven equal-sized parts plus 5 coins equals 229 coins, so the seven equal-sized parts must equal 224 coins ($229 - 5 = 224$). Then the 224 coins must be split into seven equal-sized groups, so each equal-sized group represents 32 coins ($224 \div 7 = 32$). Figure 19(d) reflects this line of reasoning.

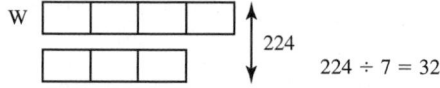

$$224$$
$$224 \div 7 = 32$$

FIGURE 19(d)
Each equal-sized part represents 32 coins.

William has $4 \cdot 32 = 128$ coins. Allie has $3 \cdot 32 + 5 = 101$ coins.

METHOD 2. Use the Solve an Equation strategy. Let W represent the number of coins William has. Then Allie has $\frac{3}{4}W + 5$ coins. They have 229 coins altogether, so

$$W + \left(\tfrac{3}{4}W + 5\right) = 229$$
$$\left(W + \tfrac{3}{4}W\right) + 5 = 229$$
$$\left(1 + \tfrac{3}{4}\right)W + 5 = 229$$
$$\tfrac{7}{4}W + 5 = 229$$
$$\tfrac{7}{4}W = 224$$
$$W = 224 \times \tfrac{4}{7}$$
$$W = 128$$

So William has 128 coins. Allie has $128 + 5 = 96 + 5 = 101$ coins.

Division with Rational Numbers

The repeated subtraction and fair share models of division also apply to division involving rational numbers.

EXAMPLE 5.38

CONNECTION
REASONING

Each problem requires $8\frac{2}{3} \div 2\frac{3}{4}$. Identify the division model for each situation.
a. A chef has $8\frac{2}{3}$ cups of flour in a sack. He realizes there is enough flour to make $2\frac{3}{4}$ pizzas. How much flour does the chef need to make each pizza?
b. Kelly has $8\frac{2}{3}$ feet of ribbon. Each bow she makes uses $2\frac{3}{4}$ feet of ribbon. How many bows (or parts of a bow) can she make?

SOLUTION

a. fair share model of division
b. repeated subtraction model of division

In the homework questions at the end of this section, you are asked to write a word problem that is appropriate for division problems such as $3\frac{2}{3} \div \frac{1}{6}$. This type of problem challenges students to associate operations and contextualized situations. The following Released Item suggests that students struggle with these types of division problems in word problems.

> **RELEASED ITEM**
>
> ● GRADES 4 AND 8, NAEP, 2003
> Jim has 3/4 of a yard of string which he wishes to divide into pieces, each 1/8 of a yard long. How many pieces will he have?
> **a.** 3 **b.** 4 **c.** 6 **d.** 8
>
> 27% of fourth graders and 55% of eighth graders gave the correct response.
> (U.S. Department of Education, Institute of Education Sciences, National Center for Education Statistics, NAEP)

The repeated subtraction model for division is an effective model for division with fractions with common denominators. We show you how this gives us one path to "interpret and compute quotients of fractions, and solve word problems involving division of fractions by fractions, e.g., by using visual fraction models and equations to represent the problem" (CCSS, Gr. 6), and leads to a general procedure to evaluate expressions such as $\frac{14}{5} \div \frac{3}{4}$ and $8\frac{2}{3} \div 2\frac{3}{4}$.

EXAMPLE 5.39

CONNECTION

COMMUNICATION

PROBLEM SOLVING

REASONING

REPRESENTATION

Grandma has $\frac{13}{5}$ cups of sugar. She needs $\frac{3}{5}$ cup of sugar to make each batch of cookies. How many batches of cookies can she make?

SOLUTION

This is the division problem $\frac{13}{5} \div \frac{3}{5}$, because $\frac{13}{5}$ cups of sugar must be divided into equal-sized groups of $\frac{3}{5}$ cup of sugar. We evaluate the expression $\frac{13}{5} \div \frac{3}{5}$ using the repeated subtraction model of division and a diagram. The diagram in Figure 20(a) represents $\frac{13}{5}$ cups of sugar. The whole is 1 cup of sugar, and an equal-sized part represents $\frac{1}{5}$ cup of sugar.

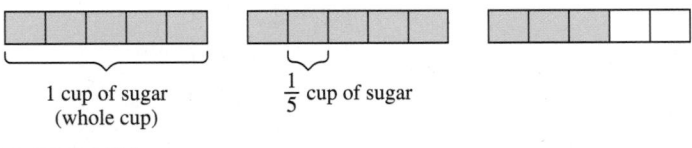

FIGURE 20(a)

Representation of $\dfrac{13}{5}$ cups of sugar.

The diagram in Figure 20(b) represents a batch of cookies and a fraction of a batch of cookies. Three equal-sized parts represent a batch of cookies, because each batch needs just $\frac{3}{5}$ cup of sugar. So the whole is a batch of cookies, and an equal-sized part represents one-third batch of cookies.

FIGURE 20(b)

Representation of a batch of cookies.

In Figure 20(c), the shaded region represents $\frac{13}{5}$ cups of sugar, and each ring represents both $\frac{3}{5}$ cup of sugar and one batch of cookies. An equal-sized part has two possible interpretations: $\frac{1}{5}$ cup of sugar or one-third batch of cookies. We are determining the number of batches, so the correct interpretation of the remainder is one-third batch of cookies.

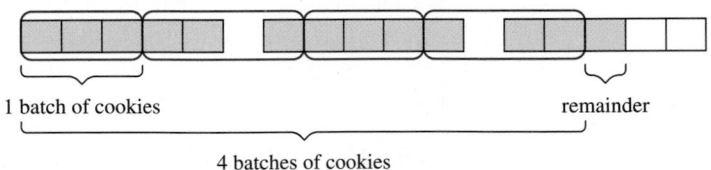

FIGURE 20(c)

Repeated subtraction model for division: $\dfrac{13}{5} \div \dfrac{3}{5}$.

So $\frac{13}{5} \div \frac{3}{5} = 4 + \dfrac{1}{3} = 4\frac{1}{3}$. Grandma can make $4\frac{1}{3}$ batches of cookies. ▲

There are two ways to express the total: $\frac{13}{5} \div \frac{3}{5} = 4\frac{1}{3} = \frac{13}{3}$. Table 5.6 contains a few more examples of division problems involving fractions with common denominators. You should verify these results using the area model.

TABLE 5.6   Division Involving Fractions with Common Denominators

$\frac{13}{7} \div \frac{5}{7} = \frac{13}{5}$	$\frac{13}{8} \div \frac{5}{8} = \frac{13}{5}$	$\frac{4}{9} \div \frac{21}{9} = \frac{4}{21}$	$\frac{4}{16} \div \frac{21}{16} = \frac{4}{21}$	$\frac{17}{3} \div \frac{9}{3} = \frac{17}{9}$	$\frac{17}{2} \div \frac{9}{2} = \frac{17}{9}$

The models and patterns in the examples motivate the procedure for division involving fractions with common denominators.

> ### Rule for Division Involving Rational Numbers with Common Denominators
>
> If $\frac{a}{b}$ and $\frac{c}{b}$ are fractions such that $c \neq 0$, then $\frac{a}{b} \div \frac{c}{b} = \frac{a}{c}$.

EXAMPLE 5.40   Use the Solve a Simpler Problem strategy to express $\frac{12}{5} \div \frac{3}{4}$ as a product of fractions.

CONNECTION

SOLUTION

$$\frac{12}{5} \div \frac{3}{4} = \frac{12 \times 4}{5 \times 4} \div \frac{5 \times 3}{5 \times 4} \quad \textbf{Equivalent fractions}$$

$$= \frac{12 \times 4}{5 \times 3} \quad \textbf{Rule for division involving rational numbers with common denominators}$$

$$= \frac{12}{5} \times \frac{4}{3} \quad \textbf{Definition of multiplying rational numbers}$$

▲

This example shows $\frac{12}{5} \div \frac{3}{4} = \frac{12}{5} \times \frac{4}{3}$. It suggests the **invert and multiply rule** to handle division problems involving rational numbers with unlike denominators.

> ### Invert and Multiply Rule for Dividing Fractions
>
> If $\frac{a}{b}$ and $\frac{c}{d}$ are rational numbers such that $c \neq 0$, then $\frac{a}{b} \div \frac{c}{d} = \frac{a}{b} \times \frac{d}{c}$.

REASONING   Suppose $\frac{a}{b}$ and $\frac{c}{d}$ are fractions such that $c \neq 0$. Then $\frac{a}{b} \div \frac{c}{d} = \frac{ad}{bd} \div \frac{bc}{bd} = \frac{ad}{bc} = \frac{a}{b} \times \frac{d}{c}$. This means that to divide $\frac{a}{b} \div \frac{c}{d}$, we simply need to solve $\frac{a}{b} \times \frac{d}{c}$, which we know how to do.

EXAMPLE 5.41   Use the invert and multiply rule to divide: $6\frac{3}{8} \div \frac{12}{5}$.

CONNECTION

SOLUTION

We can apply the rule after each mixed number is turned into fraction form:

$$6\frac{3}{8} \div \frac{12}{5} = \frac{51}{8} \div \frac{12}{5} = \frac{51}{8} \times \frac{5}{12} = \frac{\overset{17}{\cancel{51}} \times 5}{8 \times \underset{4}{\cancel{12}}} = \frac{85}{32} = 2\frac{21}{32}$$

▲

The invert and multiply rule is one connection between multiplication and division with rational numbers. A comparison of the rows in Table 5.7 suggests that the definition of division of whole numbers extends to rational numbers in a natural way, and this provides another connection.

TABLE 5.7 Relating Multiplication and Division

Division	$12 \div 4 = 3$	$\dfrac{2}{7} \div \dfrac{3}{9} = \dfrac{6}{7}$	$\dfrac{12}{5} \div \dfrac{6}{8} = \dfrac{16}{5}$	$\dfrac{8}{5} \div \dfrac{7}{3} = \dfrac{24}{35}$
Multiplication	$12 = 4 \times 3$	$\dfrac{2}{7} = \dfrac{3}{9} \times \dfrac{6}{7}$	$\dfrac{12}{5} = \dfrac{6}{8} \times \dfrac{16}{5}$	$\dfrac{8}{5} = \dfrac{7}{3} \times \dfrac{24}{35}$

CONNECTION   We use algebra to extend the relationship between multiplication and division for fractions more generally. Sometimes this is called the *missing factor* definition of division, because the quotient $\frac{e}{f}$ is also a factor.

> ### Definition of Division with Rational Numbers
>
> Let $\frac{a}{b}$ and $\frac{c}{d}$ be rational numbers with $c \neq 0$. Then $\frac{a}{b} \div \frac{c}{d} = \frac{e}{f}$ if and only if $\frac{a}{b} = \frac{c}{d} \times \frac{e}{f}$. Also, $\frac{a}{b} \div \frac{c}{d} = \frac{e}{f}$ if and only if $\frac{a}{b} = \frac{e}{f} \times \frac{c}{d}$.

You can use the definition to check your work, as shown in the next example.

EXAMPLE 5.42 A student writes the equation $\frac{5}{8} \div \frac{3}{4} = \frac{20}{24}$. Check the student's work.

CONNECTION

SOLUTION

$$\frac{3}{4} \times \frac{20}{24} = \frac{3 \times 20}{4 \times 24} = \frac{3 \times 5 \times 4}{4 \times 3 \times 2 \times 4} = \frac{5}{8}. \text{ So } \frac{5}{8} \div \frac{3}{4} = \frac{20}{24}.$$

◀

The following example demonstrates three approaches to solve a missing dividend problem.

EXAMPLE 5.43 Solve $n \div \dfrac{3}{4} = \dfrac{7}{5}$.

a. Use the definition of division.

b. Use the fact that multiplication and division are inverse operations.

c. Use the invert and multiply rule.

SOLUTION

a. $n \div \dfrac{3}{4} = \dfrac{7}{5}$ **Original equation**

$n = \dfrac{3}{4} \times \dfrac{7}{5}$ **Definition of division**

$n = \dfrac{3 \times 7}{4 \times 5}$ **Rule for multiplying fractions**

$n = \dfrac{21}{20}$ **Simplification**

$n = 1\dfrac{1}{20}$ **Simplification**

b. $n \div \dfrac{3}{4} = \dfrac{7}{5}$ **Original equation**

$n \div \dfrac{3}{4} \times \dfrac{3}{4} = \dfrac{7}{5} \times \dfrac{3}{4}$ **Multiplication property of equality**

$n = \dfrac{7}{5} \times \dfrac{3}{4}$ **Multiplication and division are inverse operations**

$n = \dfrac{7 \times 3}{5 \times 4}$ **Rule for multiplying fractions**

$$n = \frac{21}{20} \qquad \text{Simplification}$$

$$n = 1\frac{1}{20} \qquad \text{Simplification}$$

c.
$$n \div \frac{3}{4} = \frac{7}{5} \qquad \text{Original equation}$$

$$n \times \frac{4}{3} = \frac{7}{5} \qquad \text{Invert and multiply rule}$$

$$\left(n \times \frac{4}{3}\right) \times \frac{3}{4} = \frac{7}{5} \times \frac{3}{4} \qquad \text{Multiplication property of equality}$$

$$n \times \left(\frac{3}{4} \times \frac{4}{3}\right) = \frac{7}{5} \times \frac{3}{4} \qquad \text{Associative property of multiplication}$$

$$n \times 1 = \frac{7}{5} \times \frac{3}{4} \qquad \text{Multiplicative inverse property}$$

$$n = \frac{7}{5} \times \frac{3}{4} \qquad \text{Multiplicative identity property}$$

$$n = \frac{7 \times 3}{5 \times 4} \qquad \text{Rule for multiplying fractions}$$

$$n = \frac{21}{20} \qquad \text{Simplification}$$

$$n = 1\frac{1}{20} \qquad \text{Simplification}$$

▲

The following example demonstrates how to use the definition of division to solve a missing divisor problem.

EXAMPLE 5.44   Use the definition of division to help solve the equation $\frac{2}{3} \div n = \frac{5}{4}$.

CONNECTION

SOLUTION

The definition of division relates division and multiplication $\frac{2}{3} \div n = \frac{5}{4}$, so $\frac{2}{3} = n \times \frac{5}{4}$. Then $\frac{2}{3} \div \frac{5}{4} = n$. $\frac{2}{3} \times \frac{4}{5} = n$. So $n = \frac{8}{15}$.

▲

Exponents and Rational Numbers

For counting numbers a, b, m, and n, we already know $a^0 = 1$ (definition); $a^n = a \cdot a \cdot \ldots \cdot a$, where the factor a appears n times (definition); $a^m \cdot a^n = a^{m+n}$ (product rule); $(a^m)^n = a^{mn}$ (power rule); and $(a \cdot b)^n = a^n \cdot b^n$ (power of a product rule). Our goal is to extend these rules to rational number bases and integer exponents and to create other rules as appropriate. As we look at particular examples, it may be interesting to predict the equation that generalizes the result.

CONNECTION   To extend the product rule $a^m \cdot a^n = a^{m+n}$ to any nonzero rational number a (the base) and any integer n (the exponent), we need to define a^{-2} so that it satisfies the equation $a^2 \cdot a^{-2} = 1$ (an application of the product rule: $a^2 \cdot a^{-2} = a^{2 + -2} = a^0 = 1$). This means we should view a^{-2} as the multiplicative inverse of a^2. This equation shines a light on how to define a^{-2} as a fraction:

$$a^2 \cdot a^{-2} = 1 \qquad \text{Definition of multiplicative inverse}$$

$$a^{-2} = 1 \div a^2 \qquad \text{Definition of division}$$

$$= 1 \times \frac{1}{a^2} \qquad \text{Invert and multiply rule}$$

$$= \frac{1}{a^2} \qquad \text{Rule for multiplying a whole number and a fraction}$$

The same reasoning can be used to show $a^2 = \frac{1}{a^{-2}}$. The following is a generalization of the result.

> ### Definition of a^{-n}, the Multiplicative Inverse of a^n
>
> Let a represent any nonzero rational number and n be any integer. Then $a^{-n} = \frac{1}{a^n}$.

The definition allows us to write $3^{-5} = \frac{1}{3^5}$, $4^7 = \frac{1}{4^{-7}}$, and $a^n = \frac{1}{a^{-n}}$.

Now we explore expressions that involve exponential expressions with the same base to motivate rules for $a^m \cdot a^n$ and $\frac{a^m}{a^n}$, where a is any nonzero rational number and m and n are any integers.

- $a^5 \cdot a^{-2} = a^5 \cdot \dfrac{1}{a^2} = \dfrac{a^5}{a^2} = a^3 = a^{5+-2}$, so $a^5 \cdot a^{-2} = a^{5+-2}$ and $\dfrac{a^5}{a^2} = a^{5+-2}$

- $a^{-5} \cdot a^2 = \dfrac{1}{a^5} \cdot a^2 = \dfrac{a^2}{a^5} = \dfrac{1}{a^3} = a^{-3} = a^{-5+2} = a^{2-5}$, so $a^{-5} \cdot a^2 = a^{-5+2}$ and $\dfrac{a^2}{a^5} = a^{2-5}$

- $a^{-5} \cdot a^{-2} = \dfrac{1}{a^5} \cdot \dfrac{1}{a^2} = \dfrac{1}{a^7} = a^{-7} = a^{-5+-2}$, so $a^{-5} \cdot a^{-2} = a^{-5+-2}$

The following is a generalization of the results.

> ### Theorem 5
>
> Let a represent any nonzero rational number and m and n be any integers. Then we have the following rules.
>
> **Product Rule** **Quotient Rule**
>
> $a^m \cdot a^n = a^{m+n}$ $\dfrac{a^m}{a^n} = a^{m-n}$

Let's explore the integer power of a quotient. $\left(\frac{a}{b}\right)^2 = \frac{a}{b} \cdot \frac{a}{b} = \frac{a^2}{b^2}$. Also,

$$\left(\frac{a}{b}\right)^{-2} = \frac{1}{\left(\dfrac{a}{b}\right)^2} = \frac{1}{\dfrac{a^2}{b^2}} = 1 \div \frac{a^2}{b^2} = 1 \times \frac{b^2}{a^2} = \frac{b^2}{a^2} = b^2 \times \frac{1}{a^2} = \frac{1}{b^{-2}} \times a^{-2} = \frac{a^{-2}}{b^{-2}}$$

This also shows $\left(\frac{a}{b}\right)^{-2} = \frac{b^2}{a^2} = \left(\frac{b}{a}\right)^2$. The following is a generalization of the results.

> ### Theorem 6 (Power of a Quotient Rule)
>
> Let $\frac{a}{b}$ represent any nonzero rational number and n be any integer. Then $\left(\frac{a}{b}\right)^n = \frac{a^n}{b^n}$ and $\left(\frac{a}{b}\right)^{-n} = \left(\frac{b}{a}\right)^n$.

Now we explore expressions that involve exponential expressions with the same base to motivate rules for $(a^m)^n$ and $(ab)^n$, where a and b are any rational numbers and m and n are any integers.

- $\left(\left(\dfrac{x}{y}\right)^2\right)^3 = \left(\dfrac{x^2}{y^2}\right)^3 = \dfrac{(x^2)^3}{(y^2)^3} = \dfrac{x^6}{y^6} = \left(\dfrac{x}{y}\right)^6 = \left(\dfrac{x}{y}\right)^{2 \cdot 3}$

- $\left(\dfrac{3}{4} \cdot \dfrac{x}{y}\right)^2 = \dfrac{3}{4} \cdot \dfrac{x}{y} \cdot \dfrac{3}{4} \cdot \dfrac{x}{y} = \dfrac{3}{4} \cdot \dfrac{3}{4} \cdot \dfrac{x}{y} \cdot \dfrac{x}{y} = \left(\dfrac{3}{4}\right)^2\left(\dfrac{x}{y}\right)^2$

The following is a generalization of the results.

> ### Theorem 7
>
> Let a and b represent any nonzero rational numbers and m and n be any integers. Then we have the following rules.
>
> | **Power Rule** | **Power of a Product Rule** |
> |---|---|
> | $(a^m)^n = a^{mn}$ | $(ab)^n = a^n b^n$ |

The following example illustrates how to simplify expressions using these rules.

EXAMPLE 5.45 Write each expression in its simplest form, using positive exponents in the answer.

a. $(2x)^{-3}$

b. $\dfrac{x^4 y^{-5}}{(x^{-2} y^4)^3}$

c. $\left(\dfrac{x^3}{2y^{-2}}\right)^{-4}$

SOLUTION

a. $(2x)^{-3} = \dfrac{1}{(2x)^3} = \dfrac{1}{2^3 x^3} = \dfrac{1}{8x^3}$

b. $\dfrac{x^4 y^{-5}}{(x^{-2} y^4)^3} = \dfrac{x^4 y^{-5}}{(x^{-2})^3 (y^4)^3} = \dfrac{x^4 y^{-5}}{x^{-6} y^{12}} = \dfrac{x^4}{x^{-6}} \cdot \dfrac{y^{-5}}{y^{12}} = x^{4--6} y^{-5-12} = x^{10} y^{-17} = \dfrac{x^{10}}{y^{17}}$

c. $\left(\dfrac{x^3}{2y^{-2}}\right)^{-4} = \left(\dfrac{2y^{-2}}{x^3}\right)^4 = \dfrac{(2y^{-2})^4}{(x^3)^4} = \dfrac{2^4 (y^{-2})^4}{x^{12}} = \dfrac{16 y^{-8}}{x^{12}} = \dfrac{16}{x^{12} y^8}$

Multiplicative Comparison with Fractions

In Chapter 2, we used additive reasoning to compare two quantities, using phrases such as "five more coins" or "eight fewer coins." In Chapter 3, we used multiplicative reasoning to compare two quantities, using phrases such as "three times as many." Comparisons such as "two-thirds more coins" or "20% fewer calories" also involve multiplicative reasoning. The key to comparisons is to pay attention to what you are referring to. For example, are you short or tall? It depends on whom we compare your height with. If we compare your height with the height of a picnic ant, then we would say you are tall. However, if we compare your height with the height of the tallest NBA player, then we would say you are short.

Figure 21(a) shows a representation of the number of coins Latifah and Ken have.

There are several ways to write a comparison using multiplicative reasoning.

In Figure 21(b), we can make a comparison that refers to the number of coins Latifah has, so the group of rectangles for Latifah represent the whole unit:

- Ken has two-fifths fewer coins than Latifah.
- Ken has three-fifths of the number of coins Latifah has.

FIGURE 21(a)

Writing a comparison of the number of coins that Latifah and Ken have depends on how the whole unit is defined.

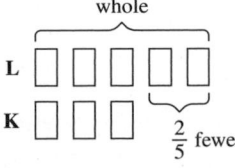

FIGURE 21(b)

Comparing to the number of coins Latifah has.

In Figure 21(c), we can make a comparison that refers to the number of coins Ken has, so the group of rectangles for Ken represent the whole unit:

*   Latifah has two-thirds more coins than Ken.
*   Latifah has $1\frac{2}{3}$ times as many coins as Ken.

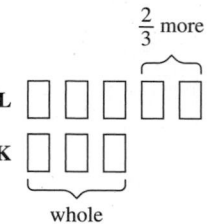

FIGURE 21(c)
Comparing to the number of coins Ken has.

EXAMPLE 5.46

REASONING

REPRESENTATION

The diagram represents the number coins Linn and Dave each have. Fill in each blank with a fraction or mixed number.

L ☐☐☐☐☐☐☐
D ☐☐☐☐

a. Linn has ___ more coins than Dave.
b. Linn has ___ times as many coins as Dave.
c. Dave has ___ fewer coins than Linn.
d. Dave has ___ times as many coins as Linn.

SOLUTION

The comparisons in parts (a) and (b) refer to the number of coins Dave has. Each equal-sized part represents one-quarter the number of coins Dave has.

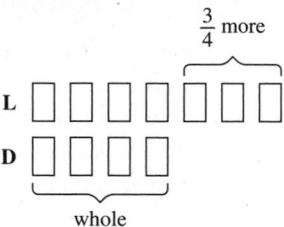

a. Linn has $\frac{3}{4}$ more coins than Dave.
b. Linn has $1\frac{3}{4}$ times as many coins as Dave.

The comparisons in parts (c) and (d) refer to the number of coins Linn has. Each equal-sized part represents one-seventh the number of coins Linn has.

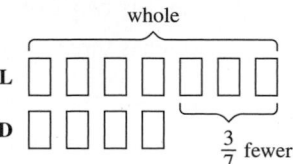

c. Dave has $\frac{3}{7}$ fewer coins than Linn.
d. Dave has $\frac{4}{7}$ times as many coins as Linn.

EXAMPLE 5.47

COMMUNICATION
REASONING
REPRESENTATION

Fill in the blank with a fraction or mixed number: Carlo has three-sevenths fewer coins than Marie. Carlo has ___ of the number of coins Marie has.

SOLUTION

We solve this problem using the Draw a Diagram strategy. The comparison refers to the number of coins Marie has. There are 7 sevenths in a whole unit, so we draw seven rectangles to represent the number of coins Marie has. Then we have the following diagram.

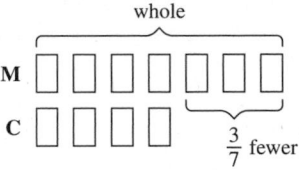

So Carlo has $\frac{4}{7}$ of the number of coins Marie has.

The following example makes comparisons from actual quantities.

EXAMPLE 5.48

COMMUNICATION
REASONING
REPRESENTATION

The Michelangelo Art School purchased 56 brushes and 32 pencils. Use fractions to compare.

a. Use the word *more*.

b. Use the word *fewer*.

c. Use the phrase *times as many*.

SOLUTION

We use the Draw a Diagram strategy.

Brushes	32	24

Pencils	32

a. There are 24 *more* brushes than pencils. This comparison refers to the 32 pencils, which serves as the whole. The fraction $\frac{24}{32}$ is equivalent to $\frac{3}{4}$. There are $\frac{3}{4}$ more brushes than pencils.

b. There are 24 *fewer* pencils than brushes. This comparison refers to 56 brushes, which serves as the whole. The fraction $\frac{24}{56}$ is equivalent to $\frac{3}{7}$. There are $\frac{3}{7}$ fewer pencils than brushes.

c. $\frac{56}{32} = 1\frac{24}{32} = 1\frac{3}{4}$. There are $1\frac{3}{4}$ *times as many* brushes as pencils.

QUESTIONS FOR SECTION 5.3

REPRESENTATION

Refresher: Representations (language, diagrams, tables, symbols, algebra, manipulatives, and contextualized situations) are important because we use them to organize, record, and communicate mathematical ideas and to make them more comprehensible.

1. Express each diagram as a product of fractions in an equation of the form $\frac{a}{b} \times \frac{c}{d} = \frac{e}{f}$.

a.
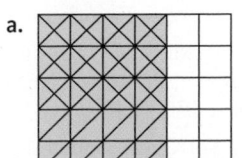

b.
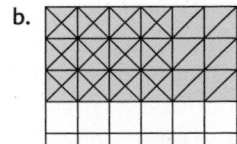

2. Use a diagram to compute each product.

   a. $\frac{3}{4} \times \frac{2}{5}$ b. $\frac{2}{5} \times \frac{3}{4}$

3. Represent each quotient as a product of fractions.

   a. $\frac{13}{4} \div \frac{5}{7}$ b. $\frac{10}{3} \div \frac{4}{9}$

4. Ellie has 4 more than three-fifths the number of coins Kate has. Altogether, they have 500 coins. How many coins does Ellie have? Solve this problem using the diagram shown (do not use algebra).

5. Neal has 3 fewer than two-sevenths the number of coins Mike has. Altogether, they have 105 coins. How many coins does Neal have? Solve this problem using the diagram shown (do not use algebra).

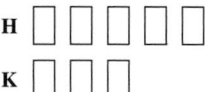

6. Use the diagram to fill in the blank with a fraction.

   H ☐☐☐☐☐
   K ☐☐☐

   a. Kyle has ___ fewer stamps than Hannah.
   b. Hannah has ___ more stamps than Kyle.
   c. Kyle has ___ as many stamps as Hannah.
   d. Hannah has ___ times as many stamps as Kyle.

PROBLEM SOLVING

Refresher: Problem solving (reaching a goal that is not immediately attainable) is important because it helps students think more deeply about what they know and deal with unfamiliar situations.

7. Maria solved all of the math problems in the chapter review to prepare for her exam. She solved four-sevenths of the problems in the morning. She completed the remaining 27 problems in the afternoon. How many math problems did she solve in the morning? Solve this problem using the

   a. Draw a Diagram strategy.   b. Solve an Equation strategy.

8. Erin and David have 536 beads altogether. David has three-fifths of the number of beads Erin has. How many beads does David have? Solve this problem using the

   a. Draw a Diagram strategy.   b. Solve an Equation strategy.

9. Erin and David have 671 beads altogether. David has 6 more than two-fifths the number of beads Erin has. How many beads does David have? Solve this problem using the

   a. Draw a Diagram strategy.   b. Solve an Equation strategy.

10. Erin and David have 401 beads altogether. David has 5 fewer than three-fourths the number of beads Erin has. How many beads does Erin have? Solve this problem using the

    a. Draw a Diagram strategy.   b. Solve an Equation strategy.

REASONING AND PROOF

Refresher: Reasoning and proof (thinking and justifying) are important because they help students make sense of mathematics.

11. Prove the commutative property of multiplication with rational numbers.

12. Prove the associative property of multiplication with rational numbers.

13. According to a report called "Mathematics Equals Opportunity" in the late 1990s, two-thirds of all U.S. high school students take introductory algebra and geometry courses and four-fifths of those students go to college. What is the fraction of students who take introductory algebra and geometry courses and go to college? Write your answer in the form of a product of fractions.

14. When Barry planted a sunflower plant, it was 2 cm tall. When Linda planted a tomato plant, it was $4\frac{1}{2}$ cm tall. Later, they measured the plants. The sunflower plant was 5 cm tall, and the tomato plant was $8\frac{1}{4}$ cm tall. Barry said his plant grew more. Linda said her plant grew more. Explain how each person could be correct.

15. Complex fractions may be used to justify the invert and multiply rule. Fill in the blank for the reason for each step.

$$\frac{a}{b} \div \frac{c}{d} = \frac{\frac{a}{b}}{\frac{c}{d}}$$ a. Because a fraction is a _____

$$= \frac{\frac{a}{b} \times \frac{d}{c}}{\frac{c}{d} \times \frac{d}{c}}$$ b. _____ law of fractions

$$= \frac{\frac{a}{b} \times \frac{d}{c}}{1}$$ c. _____ property of multiplication

$$= \frac{a}{b} \times \frac{d}{c}$$ d. Because _____

CONNECTIONS

Refresher: Connections (linking and applying mathematical ideas) are important because they deepen student understanding and make mathematics more meaningful, flexible, and useful.

16. Solve the equation $y \times \frac{5}{6} = 24$ using

    a. algebraic properties of multiplication.
    b. the definition of division.
    c. the fact that multiplication and division are inverse operations.

17. Solve the equation $y \div \frac{7}{3} = 65$ using the

    a. fact that multiplication and division are inverse operations.

    b. definition of division.

    c. invert and multiply rule.

18. For an initiative to appear on a ballot, a certain number of signatures must be collected. A group collected 126,000 signatures, or three-quarters of the required number of signatures. Determine the number of signatures needed for the initiative to appear on the ballot. Solve this problem using

    a. the Draw a Diagram strategy.

    b. the Solve an Equation strategy.

According to the U.S. Environmental Protection Agency (EPA), gasoline-powered vehicles tend to be more efficient during highway driving than city driving. The average fuel cost depends on the average number of miles driven per year and the fraction of time spent in city driving and highway driving. Questions 19 and 20 ask you to estimate annual fuel costs. Round your final answers to the nearest hundred dollars.

19. Suppose your car gets 24 mpg in city driving and 42 mpg in highway driving. One-sixth of your mileage is city driving and five-sixths is highway mileage. Suppose gas costs $3.50 per gallon. Estimate the annual fuel cost for your vehicle based on an average of

    a. 12,000 miles driven per year. Show your work.

    b. 30,000 miles driven per year. Show your work.

20. Suppose your car gets 16 mpg in city driving and 28 mpg in highway driving. You spend two-thirds of your mileage in city driving and one-third of your mileage in highway driving. Suppose gas costs $3 per gallon. Estimate the annual fuel cost for your vehicle based on an average of

    a. 24,000 miles driven per year. Show your work.

    b. 42,000 miles driven per year. Show your work.

21. According to the FDA's Center for Food Safety and Applied Nutrition, the food label on brand X can state that the product has fewer calories than brand Y when brand X has three-fourths of the number of calories of brand Y or fewer. Determine whether the label on brand X can state that the product has fewer calories than those of brand Y.

    a. brand X: 85 Cal   brand Y: 105 Cal

    b. brand X: 520 Cal   brand Y: 700 Cal

    c. brand X: 360 Cal   brand Y: 500 Cal

    d. brand X: 27 Cal   brand Y: 32 Cal

COMMUNICATION

Refresher: Communication (written and verbal explanations using representations and proper mathematical vocabulary) is important because it helps students refine and strengthen their understanding.

22. Explain why $\frac{0}{3}$ does not have a reciprocal.

23. Describe a situation that involves multiplying two fractions.

24. Describe a situation that involves dividing two fractions.

25. Some students perform the following operation: $8\frac{3}{5} \times 6\frac{2}{7} = 48\frac{6}{35}$.

    a. How do they arrive at that answer?

    b. Is their reasoning correct?

26. Discuss a strategy to find

    a. two nonunit fractions that have the product $\frac{5}{7}$.

    b. two fractions with unlike denominators that have the quotient $\frac{3}{5}$.

27. Write a word problem for $6\frac{2}{3} \div \frac{3}{4}$.

More practice with the ideas of the section

28. Solve each problem using the Draw a Diagram strategy.

    a. Jerry had 150 lollipops to sell for a school fundraiser. He sold two-fifths of the lollipops. How many lollipops did he sell?

    b. Mitchell read 57 pages in a book, which was three-fourths of the number of pages in the book. How many pages were in the book altogether?

    c. Erica has to earn $350 to buy a bike. She earned four-sevenths of the money selling art crafts. How much more money does she need to earn?

29. Use the invert and multiply rule to divide. Write the quotient in its simplified form.

    a. $\frac{2}{3} \div \frac{3}{4}$ **b.** $\frac{14}{20} \div \frac{7}{45}$ **c.** $8\frac{3}{4} \div 3\frac{2}{5}$

30. Solve the equation $\frac{4}{7} \times y = 12$ using

    a. the fact that multiplication and division are inverse operations.

    b. the definition of division.

    c. algebraic properties of multiplication.

31. Solve the equation $y \div \frac{2}{5} = \frac{3}{4}$ using the

    a. fact that multiplication and division are inverse operations.

    b. definition of division.

32. Use a diagram to compute $\frac{2}{3} \times \frac{3}{4}$.

33. Write the cross-hatched region as a product of fractions.

    a.

    b.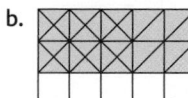

34. What fraction of the class consists of girls? Represent each relationship with a diagram.

    a. There are three times as many girls as boys.

    b. There are two-thirds as many girls as boys.

35. What fraction of the class consists of boys? Represent each relationship with a diagram.

    a. There are four times as many boys as girls.

    b. There are three-fourths as many boys as girls.

36. Use a diagram to solve: Joshua earned money to buy a remote control car. He earned $18 by recycling aluminum cans. Then he earned the rest of the money, which was five-eighths of the price of the car, by mowing lawns. How much did the remote control car cost?

37. Use a diagram to solve: Kendra and Oliver spilled milk. Kendra spilled three-fifths of the milk. Oliver spilled two-thirds of the remaining milk. There were 6 ounces of milk left in the container. How much milk was originally in the container?

38. George and Martha planted 135 apple trees altogether. George planted $1\frac{1}{4}$ times the number of apple trees Martha planted. How many apple trees did Martha plant? Solve this problem using the

    a. Draw a Diagram strategy.   b. Solve an Equation strategy.

39. George and Martha planted 432 apple trees altogether. George planted 5 more than $1\frac{1}{3}$ times the number of apple trees Martha planted. How many apple trees did George plant? Solve this problem using the

    a. Draw a Diagram strategy.   b. Solve an Equation strategy.

40. George and Martha planted 172 apple trees altogether. George planted 8 fewer than $1\frac{1}{2}$ times the number of apple trees Martha planted. How many apple trees did George plant? Solve this problem using the

    a. Draw a Diagram strategy   b. Solve an Equation strategy

41. Write a word problem for $\frac{4}{7} \times \frac{2}{3}$.

42. Solve the equation $4\frac{2}{3}y + 5 = 17$.

43. Two common temperature scales are the Fahrenheit (F) and Celsius (C). The temperatures are related by the equation $F = \frac{9}{5}C + 32$. Find F when C equals

    a. 60°C.   b. −10°C.   c. 85°C.   d. −20°C.

44. The Fahrenheit and Celsius temperatures are related by the equation $F = \frac{9}{5}C + 32$.

    a. Write the Celsius degrees as a function of Fahrenheit degrees.

    b. Find C when F equals 50°F.

    c. Find C when F equals −13°F.

45. Give reasons for each equal sign:

$$\frac{4}{y} \times \left(\frac{a}{6} - \frac{5}{6}\right) = \frac{4}{y} \times \left(\frac{a-5}{6}\right)$$ a. _____

$$= \frac{4 \times (a-5)}{y \times 6}$$ b. _____

$$= \frac{4 \times a - 4 \times 5}{y \times 6}$$ c. _____

$$= \frac{4 \times a}{y \times 6} - \frac{4 \times 5}{y \times 6}$$ d. _____

$$= \frac{4}{y} \times \frac{a}{6} - \frac{4}{y} \times \frac{5}{6}$$ e. _____

46. The Mid-Atlantic Ridge, an underwater mountain ridge between Africa and South America, expands at the rate of about 1/5 cm per month. How many centimeters would the seafloor expand over a period of 2000 years?

47. According to an annual school bus driver survey with 456 usable responses, three-fourths of school bus drivers surveyed were satisfied with their job. How many bus drivers in the survey were satisfied with their job?

    a. Does this problem require evaluating $456 \times \frac{3}{4}$ or $\frac{3}{4} \times 456$? Explain.

    b. Determine the number of bus drivers in the survey satisfied with their job.

48. Use a diagram to divide.

    a. $\frac{9}{4} \div \frac{5}{4}$ b. $\frac{3}{2} \div \frac{5}{2}$

49. Do the following.

    a. $\frac{5}{6} \times \frac{c}{d} = 1$. What can you say about $\frac{c}{d}$?

    b. $\frac{5}{6} \div \frac{c}{d} = 1$. What can you say about $\frac{c}{d}$?

50. A student writes the equation shown. Check the student's work using multiplication.

    a. $\frac{35}{18} \div \frac{7}{6} = \frac{5}{3}$ b. $\frac{8}{5} \div \frac{2}{3} = 2\frac{3}{5}$

51. Bela has three-fifths more beads than Tyra. Fill in the blank with a fraction or a mixed number.

    a. Tyra has ____ fewer beads than Bela.

    b. Bela has ____ times as many beads as Tyra.

    c. Tyra has ____ times as many beads as Bela.

52. Sara has two-sevenths fewer books than Julie. Fill in the blank with a fraction or a mixed number.

    a. Julie has ____ times as many books as Sara.

    b. Sara has ____ times as many books as Julie.

    c. Julie has ____ more books than Sara.

53. Amelia has 28 books. Nancy has 36 books. Fill in the blank with a fraction.

    a. Amelia has ____ fewer books than Nancy.

    b. Amelia has ____ times as many books as Nancy.

    c. Nancy has ____ more books than Amelia.

    d. Nancy has ____ times as many books as Amelia.

54. Cory has 18 trophies. Erica has 30 trophies. Fill in the blank with a fraction.

    a. Cory has ____ fewer trophies than Erica.

    b. Cory has ____ times as many trophies as Erica.

    c. Erica has ____ more trophies than Cory.

    d. Erica has ____ times as many trophies as Cory.

55. Find numbers that makes the open number sentence true.

    a. $\frac{43}{\square} \div \frac{5}{8} = \frac{43}{5}$ b. $\frac{17}{8} \div \frac{\square}{3} = \frac{\square}{40}$

56. State the reasons for the steps.

$$y \div \frac{3}{4} = \frac{5}{8} \quad \text{Original equation}$$

$$y \div \frac{3}{4} \times \frac{3}{4} = \frac{5}{8} \times \frac{3}{4} \qquad \text{a. _____}$$

$$y = \frac{5}{8} \times \frac{3}{4} \qquad \text{b. _____}$$

$$y = \frac{5 \times 3}{8 \times 4} \qquad \text{c. _____}$$

$$y = \frac{15}{32} \qquad \text{d. _____}$$

57. We can use division to make multiplicative comparisons. For example, let's compare $\frac{3}{4}$ and $2\frac{2}{5}$. The equation $2\frac{2}{5} \div \frac{3}{4} = 3\frac{1}{5}$ means $2\frac{2}{5}$ is $3\frac{1}{5}$ times as large as $\frac{3}{4}$. Use this example as a guide to make a multiplicative comparison for each problem.

a. Jenny walked $4\frac{1}{2}$ miles, and Hillary walked $\frac{2}{3}$ mile.

b. Ken spent $7\frac{1}{4}$ hours on his project. Larry spent $2\frac{3}{8}$ on his project.

c. A compact car gets 34 mpg, whereas a heavily armored combat tank gets $\frac{3}{5}$ mpg.

58. A pitcher of water is three-fourths full. Five cups of water are served from the pitcher. Then the pitcher is two-thirds full. How many cups of water can the pitcher hold?

59. Ellen paid \$84 for a new textbook in the fall semester. At the end of the fall semester, she sold it to the bookstore for three-sevenths of the original price. Then the bookstore sold the textbook to Tyler at a \$24 profit for the spring semester. How much did Tyler pay for the textbook?

60. Identify the base and the exponent.

a. 8^5 **b.** $(-3)^4$ **c.** $\left(\frac{2}{3}\right)^{-4}$ **d.** $(-5a)^7$

61. Match the expression with the rule that would be used to simplify the expression: *power rule, product rule, quotient rule, power of a product rule, power of a quotient rule.*

a. $5x^4a^2x^7$ **b.** $(4xy^5)^3$ **c.** $\left(\frac{a}{b}\right)^3$ **d.** $\frac{4h^5}{3h^{-2}}$

62. Write each expression in its simplest form, using positive exponents in the answer.

a. $(2x^4)^3$ **b.** $(3x)^{-2}$ **c.** $\frac{x^{-5}y^{-2}}{(x^{-3}y)^4}$ **d.** $\left(\frac{-x^4}{y^{-5}}\right)^{-3}$

63. Write each expression in its simplest form, using positive exponents in the answer.

a. $(5x^3)^2x^4x$ **b.** $36a\left(\frac{3}{4}\right)^{-2}$ **c.** $\frac{a^4b^{-2}c}{a^{-2}b^5}$

SECTION 5.4   Ratios and Proportional Reasoning

Ratios Are Used to Compare Two Quantities

A wild animal park has five elephants and three pandas. When we say, "There are two more elephants than pandas" or "There are two fewer pandas than elephants," we are making an additive comparison of the number of elephants and pandas. When we say, "The number of pandas is three-fifths of the number of elephants" or "There are one and two-thirds times as many elephants as pandas," we are making a multiplicative comparison. Additive comparisons involve adding and subtracting. In contrast, multiplicative comparisons involve multiplying and dividing.

The comparison "the ratio of elephants to pandas is 5 to 3" is an alternative multiplicative comparison, which is the same as saying, "There are five elephants for every three pandas." In this section, we focus on how to use ratios to compare two quantities and how to use ratios in proportions to study two quantities that vary. The *Principles and Standards for School Mathematics* (2000) states:

> Facility with proportion involves much more than setting two ratios equal and solving for the missing term. It involves recognizing quantities that are related proportionally and using numbers, tables, graphs, and equations to think about the quantities and their relationship. (p. 217)

We use tables, diagrams, and equations to make sense of ratios and proportions so that you can teach your students the same topics with meaning and enthusiasm. You will learn how to solve ratio problems using multiple strategies—an important characteristic of good problem solvers (along with independence, flexibility, and determination).

Multiple Representations of a Ratio

Let's formally define a ratio.

> **Definition**
>
> A **ratio** is an ordered pair of numbers in the form $a{:}b$ and is read as "*a* to *b*." The number a is called the **first term,** and b is called the **second term.**

Sometimes, we represent a ratio with a fraction symbol. The statement "the ratio of elephants to pandas is $\frac{5}{3}$" is read as "the ratio of elephants to pandas is 5 to 3." If the fraction symbol $\frac{5}{3}$ represents a ratio, then we read it as "five to three," not "five-thirds."

EXAMPLE 5.49

REPRESENTATION

Represent a ratio symbolically in three ways.

SOLUTION

3:4, 3 to 4, or $\dfrac{3}{4}$

In the following example, we express a ratio using the household phrase "for every."

EXAMPLE 5.50

COMMUNICATION

Pavers are bricks made of water and cement for sidewalks, patios, and driveways. The water-to-cement ratio of typical pavers is 27 to 33 pounds. Reword the ratio using the phrase "for every."

SOLUTION

Pavers consist of 27 pounds of water for every 33 pounds of cement.

Students should "understand the concept of a ratio and use ratio language to describe a ratio relationship between two quantities" (CCSS, Gr. 6). The next example illustrates how to represent ratio relationships using diagrams.

EXAMPLE 5.51

REPRESENTATION

Draw a diagram to represent the relationship.

a. Ken has 3 coins for every 5 coins Latifah has. Altogether, they have 32 coins.

b. Fred has 18 more marbles than Mark. Mark has 2 marbles for every 5 marbles Fred has.

SOLUTION

a.
K ☐☐☐
L ☐☐☐☐☐ } 32

b.
18
F ☐☐☐☐☐
M ☐☐

Concept Map 5.2 illustrates various ways we use ratios in contextualized situations.

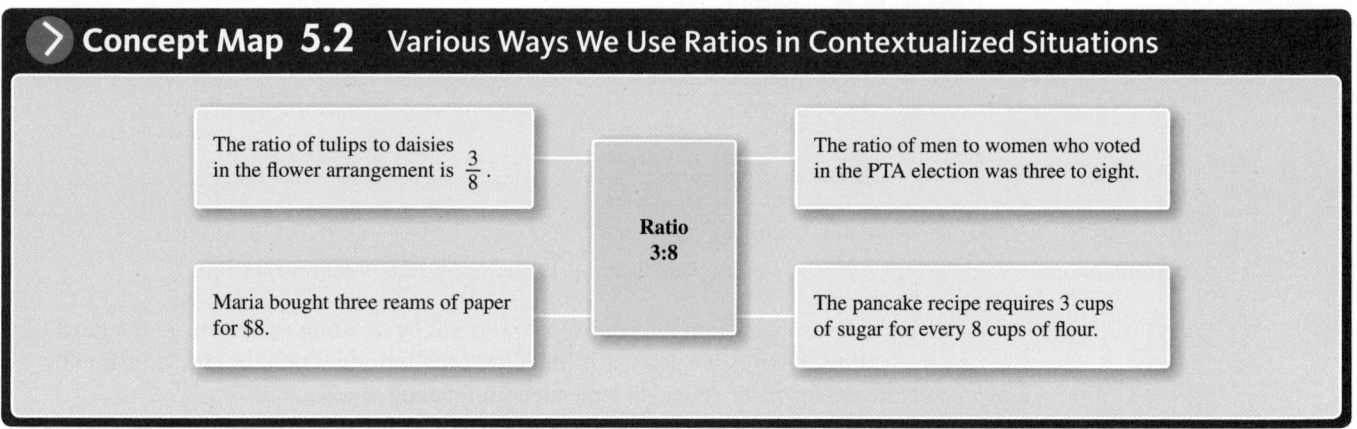

> **Concept Map 5.2** Various Ways We Use Ratios in Contextualized Situations

The ratio of tulips to daisies in the flower arrangement is $\frac{3}{8}$.

The ratio of men to women who voted in the PTA election was three to eight.

Ratio 3:8

Maria bought three reams of paper for $8.

The pancake recipe requires 3 cups of sugar for every 8 cups of flour.

Part-to-Part, Part-to-Whole, and Whole-to-Part Comparisons

Suppose there are three pennies and five nickels. The statement "there are three pennies for every five nickels" is a part-to-part comparison. The statement "three out of every eight coins are pennies" is a part-to-whole comparison. Can you make a whole-to-part comparison?

Equivalent Ratios

Equivalent ratios are two ratios that describe the same multiplicative relationship. Figure 22(a) illustrates the ratio of 3 stars to 5 circles.

☆ ☆ ☆   ○ ○ ○ ○ ○

FIGURE 22(a)
A representation of the ratio 3:5.

Figure 22(b) illustrates two groups of three stars and five circles. We maintain the same 3:5 ratio but also create another ratio, 6:10, that preserves the relationship.

☆ ☆ ☆   ○ ○ ○ ○ ○
☆ ☆ ☆   ○ ○ ○ ○ ○

FIGURE 22(b)
The diagram illustrates that the ratio 3:5 is equivalent to 6:10.

We can turn 3:5 into the equivalent ratio 6:10 by *multiplying* each term in the ratio 3:5 by 2. **Scaling up** is the process of multiplying each term in a ratio by the same number. Figure 23(a) illustrates the ratio of 12 stars to 8 circles.

☆ ☆ ☆   ○ ○
☆ ☆ ☆   ○ ○
☆ ☆ ☆   ○ ○
☆ ☆ ☆   ○ ○

FIGURE 23(a)
A representation of the ratio 12:8.

In Figure 23(b), we split the stars and circles into four equal-sized groups of three stars and two circles. We maintain the same 12:8 ratio but create another ratio, 3:2, that preserves the relationship.

FIGURE 23(b)
The diagram illustrates that the ratio 12:8 is equivalent to 3:2.

We can turn 12:8 into the equivalent ratio 3:2 by *dividing* each term in the ratio 12:8 by 4. **Scaling down** is the process of dividing each term in a ratio by the same number. Now we formally define an equivalent ratio using algebra.

> **Definition**
>
> If c is any nonzero number, then $a{:}b$ and $ac{:}bc$ are equivalent ratios and $a{:}b$ and $\frac{a}{c}{:}\frac{b}{c}$ are equivalent ratios.

Alina Bakker/Shutterstock.com

EXAMPLE 5.52 Use scaling to find an equivalent ratio.
a. \$3 to 10 books is equivalent to \$15 to ___ books.

b. 3 apples to 32 cents is equivalent to ___ apples to 4 cents.

SOLUTION

a. \$15 to 50 books (scale up: $3 \times 5 = 15$, so $10 \times 5 = 50$)

b. $\frac{3}{8}$ apple to 4 cents (scale down: $3{:}32 = \frac{3}{8}{:}\frac{32}{8} = \frac{3}{8}{:}4$)

▲

Problems involving ratios entail multiplicative thinking (rather than additive thinking) because we use multiplication and division (rather than addition and subtraction) to create equivalent fractions.

The following Released Item shows that students should be able to identify an equivalent ratio.

> **▶ RELEASED ITEM**
>
> ● NAEP, 2003
> Which of the following ratios is equivalent to the ratio of 6 to 4?
> **a.** 12 to 18   **b.** 12 to 8   **c.** 8 to 6   **d.** 4 to 6   **e.** 2 to 3
>
> 60% of eighth-grade students answered the question correctly.

We can also represent a ratio with a table. Table 5.8 represents the ratio "There are three cats for every five birds," and each column in the table is a ratio that is equivalent to 3:5.

TABLE 5.8 Using a Table to Represent the Ratio "There Are Three Cats for Every Five Birds"

Number of cats	3	6	9	12	15
Number of birds	5	10	15	20	25

Students should be able to "make tables of equivalent ratios relating quantities with whole number measurements" (CCSS, Gr. 6).

Rates and Unit Rates

Rates are ratios that involve comparing two different measurement units, such as dollars and books or miles and hours. Two examples of rates are "$65 for every four books" and "40 miles in 3 hours." A **unit rate** is a rate of the form $a:1$ (or $1:a$). Unit rates answer the question, "How many for one?" The rate 9 pounds for $5 is equivalent to the unit rate $1\frac{4}{5}$ pounds per dollar (*per* means "for every"). Unit rates make it easier to compare rates. One of the goals for students is to "understand the concept of a unit rate a/b associated with a ratio $a:b$ with $b \neq 0$, and use rate language in the context of a ratio relationship. For example, 'This recipe has a ratio of 3 cups of flour to 4 cups of sugar, so there is 3/4 cup of flour for each cup of sugar.' 'We paid $75 for 15 hamburgers, which is a rate of $5 per hamburger.'" (CCSS, Gr. 6).

Numerical comparisons involve comparing two ratios using scaling (multiplication and division). Numerical comparisons answer questions such as who ran faster or which purchase is the better buy.

EXAMPLE 5.53

REASONING

Natalie ran 45 yards in 12 seconds. Susan ran 22 yards in 5 seconds. Who ran faster?

SOLUTION

Unit rates are easier to compare. $45:12 = \frac{45}{12}:\frac{12}{12} = 3\frac{3}{4}:1$ and $\frac{22}{5} = \frac{22}{5}:\frac{5}{5} = 4\frac{2}{5}:1$. Natalie ran $3\frac{3}{4}$ yards per second and Susan ran $4\frac{2}{5}$ yards per second. Susan ran faster. ▲

Missing Value Problems

Shawn Pecor/Shutterstock.com

Missing value problems involve two equivalent ratios in which one ratio is known and only one of the terms of the other ratio is known. We determine the unknown term of the second ratio, called the missing value, by multiplication or division.

In the following missing value problem, we demonstrate how to use a unit rate to find the missing value.

EXAMPLE 5.54

PROBLEM SOLVING

REASONING

A vendor sells sugar at the rate of 4 pounds for $5.

a. At this rate, how much should you pay for 13 pounds of sugar?

b. At this rate, how much sugar can you buy for $7?

SOLUTION

a. $4:5 = \frac{4}{4}:\frac{5}{4} = 1:\frac{5}{4} = 1 \cdot 13:\frac{5}{4} \cdot 13 = 13:16.25$. Then 13 pounds of sugar cost $16.25.

b. $4:5 = \frac{4}{5}:\frac{5}{5} = \frac{4}{5}:1 = \frac{4}{5} \cdot 7:1 \cdot 7 = 5\frac{3}{5}:7$. Then you can purchase $5\frac{3}{5}$ pounds of sugar for $7. ▲

The previous example models how students can "solve unit rate problems including those involving unit pricing and constant speed. For example, if it took 7 hours to mow 4 lawns, then at that rate, how many lawns could be mowed in 35 hours? At what rate were lawns being mowed?" (CCSS, Gr. 6).

Proportional Reasoning

Proportional reasoning is the ability to recognize and solve problems involving ratios. The concept of proportion is important in the study of similarity, scaling, and conversion of measurement units. It is a framework for algebra, probability, and geometry and a form of multiplicative reasoning, because it involves multiplication and division. Students should "understand and use ratios and proportions to represent quantitative relationships" (NCTM, Gr. 6–8).

The method of unit rates is a popular strategy for elementary school students solving proportional reasoning problems. The concept of *proportion* is the centerpiece of an alternative approach based on equivalent fractions. We define a proportion and then see how it relates to equivalent fractions.

Definition

Let $a{:}b$ and $c{:}d$ represent equivalent ratios. The equation $a{:}b = c{:}d$ is called a **proportion** and is read as "a is to b as c is to d."

CONNECTION
REASONING
REPRESENTATION

A proportion is an equation between two equivalent ratios. Assuming, $b \neq 0$ and $d \neq 0$, we can turn $a{:}b$ and $c{:}d$ into equivalent unit ratios by scaling down:

$$a{:}b = \frac{a}{b}{:}1$$

and

$$c{:}d = \frac{c}{d}{:}1$$

To compare the ratios $a{:}b$ and $c{:}d$, we simply compare their corresponding unit ratios $\frac{a}{b}{:}1$ and $\frac{c}{d}{:}1$. Unit ratios are easy to compare, because we simply need to compare the first terms $\frac{a}{b}$ and $\frac{c}{d}$. This suggests the ratios $a{:}b$ and $c{:}d$ are equivalent if and only if the fractions $\frac{a}{b}$ and $\frac{c}{d}$ are equivalent fractions. We already know that $\frac{a}{b}$ and $\frac{c}{d}$ are equivalent fractions if and only if their cross-products are equal. Writing a proportion $a{:}b = c{:}d$ in the form $\frac{a}{b} = \frac{c}{d}$ using fraction notation taps students' prior knowledge of equivalent fractions.

Theorem 8

$\frac{a}{b} = \frac{c}{d}$ is a proportion if and only if $ad = bc$.

The products ad and bc are called **cross-products.**

Proportions lead directly to our previous experience with equivalent fractions, where we can cross multiply to form cross-products.

EXAMPLE 5.55

a. Is the equation $\frac{12}{15} = \frac{16}{20}$ a proportion?

b. Is the equation $\frac{4}{7} = \frac{3}{5}$ a proportion?

c. Find the missing value so that the equation $\frac{42}{50} = \frac{n}{15}$ is a proportion.

SOLUTION

a. The cross-products are $12 \cdot 20 = 240$ and $15 \cdot 16 = 240$. The cross-products are equal, so the equation is a proportion.

b. The cross-products are $4 \cdot 5 = 20$ and $7 \cdot 3 = 21$. The cross-products are not equal, so the equation is not a proportion.

c. The cross-products must be equal: $50n = 42 \cdot 15$. Then $50n = 630$. Then $n = 630 \div 50$. Then $n = 12.6$.

▲

The following snapshot of a student page shows that students should be able to use cross-products to find a missing value in a proportion.

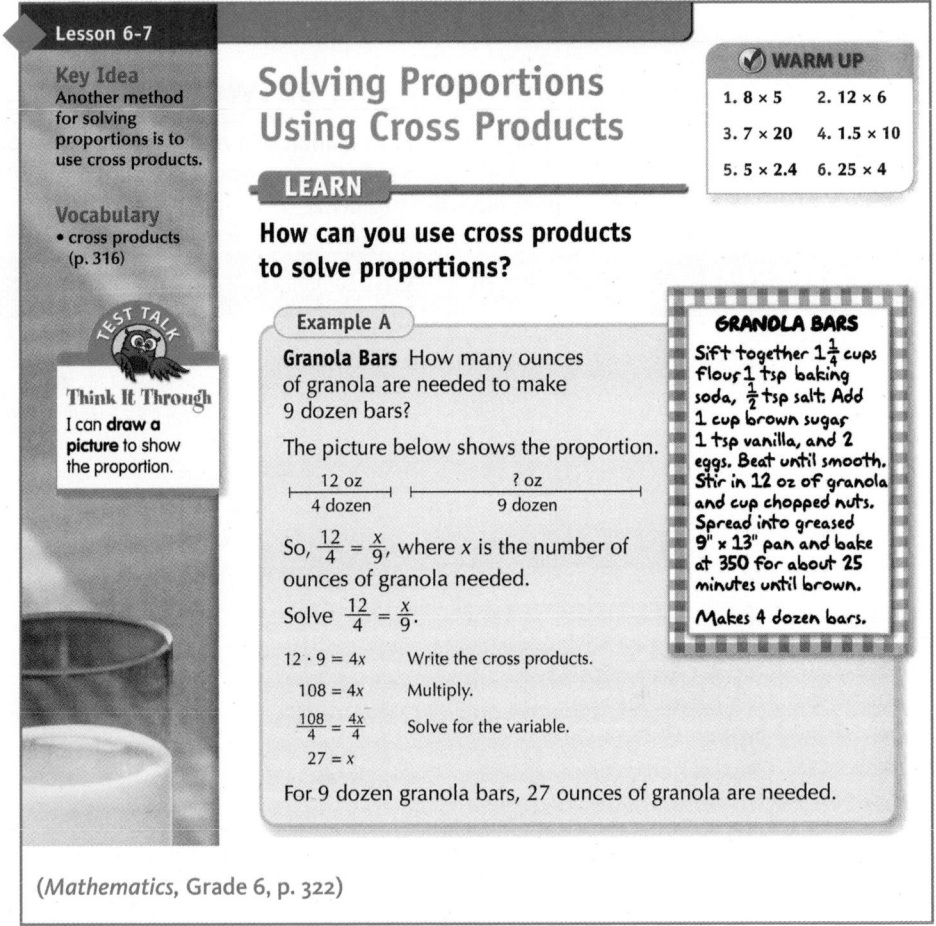

Lesson 6-7

Key Idea
Another method for solving proportions is to use cross products.

Vocabulary
• cross products (p. 316)

TEST TALK

Think It Through
I can **draw a picture** to show the proportion.

✅ **WARM UP**
1. 8×5 2. 12×6
3. 7×20 4. 1.5×10
5. 5×2.4 6. 25×4

Solving Proportions Using Cross Products

▶ **LEARN**

How can you use cross products to solve proportions?

Example A

Granola Bars How many ounces of granola are needed to make 9 dozen bars?

The picture below shows the proportion.

12 oz	? oz
4 dozen	9 dozen

So, $\frac{12}{4} = \frac{x}{9}$, where x is the number of ounces of granola needed.

Solve $\frac{12}{4} = \frac{x}{9}$.

$12 \cdot 9 = 4x$ Write the cross products.

$108 = 4x$ Multiply.

$\frac{108}{4} = \frac{4x}{4}$ Solve for the variable.

$27 = x$

For 9 dozen granola bars, 27 ounces of granola are needed.

GRANOLA BARS
Sift together $1\frac{1}{4}$ cups flour, 1 tsp baking soda, $\frac{1}{2}$ tsp salt. Add 1 cup brown sugar, 1 tsp vanilla, and 2 eggs. Beat until smooth. Stir in 12 oz of granola and 1 cup chopped nuts. Spread into greased 9" x 13" pan and bake at 350 for about 25 minutes until brown.

Makes 4 dozen bars.

(*Mathematics*, Grade 6, p. 322)

(From Randall I. Charles. © 2004 by Pearson Education, Inc. or its affiliates. Used by permission. All rights reserved.)

In the following missing value problem, we use a table to set up the proportion to find the missing value. The table, along with labels and units, helps students avoid mixing up the terms.

EXAMPLE 5.56

CONNECTION
COMMUNICATION
PROBLEM SOLVING
REASONING
REPRESENTATION

A caterer wants to serve 2 pounds of fruit for every 5 guests at a party. He anticipates 325 guests at the party. How many pounds of fruit will he need? Solve this problem using a proportion.

SOLUTION

We solve this problem by setting up a proportion. Let the variable x represent the amount of fruit needed. We make a ratio table to organize the information and represent the ratios.

Pounds of fruit	2	x
Number of guests	5	325

The table leads directly to the proportion $\frac{2}{5} = \frac{x}{325}$. By cross-multiplication, we get $2 \cdot 325 = 5x$. Then $650 = 5x$. Then $x = 650 \div 5 = 130$. The caterer needs 130 pounds of fruit for the party.

Diagrams and tables are representations of ratios that make the comparison or analysis more accessible for elementary school students. These students often favor the unit rate strategy over proportions for solving missing value problems. Both strategies entail proportional reasoning. Students acquire proportional reasoning skills gradually over several years.

CONNECTION
Connections between Ratios and Fractions

A ratio is a representation of a multiplicative relationship. Concept Map 5.3 illustrates the close connection between ratios and fractions in word problems. Can you think of more possible word problems?

> **Concept Map 5.3** Several Possible Word Problems for the Same Diagram

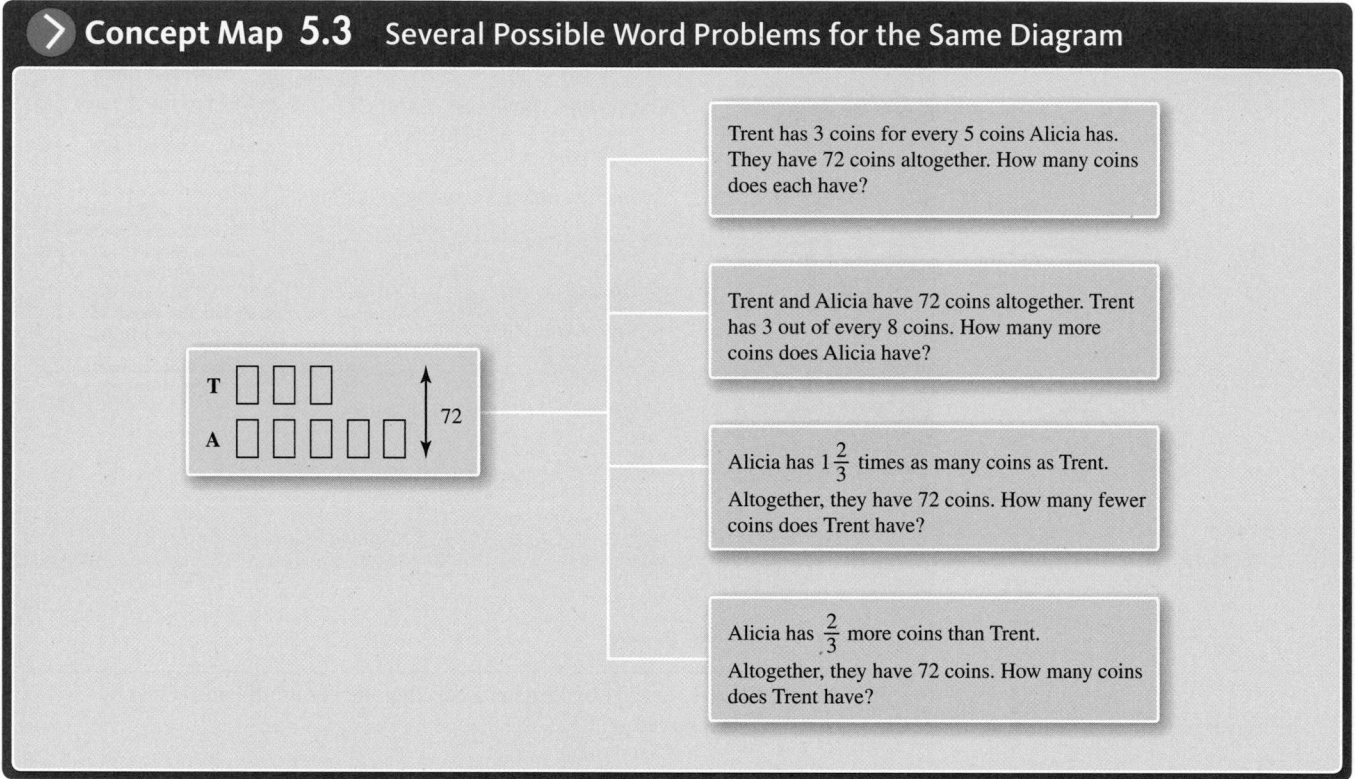

Trent has 3 coins for every 5 coins Alicia has. They have 72 coins altogether. How many coins does each have?

Trent and Alicia have 72 coins altogether. Trent has 3 out of every 8 coins. How many more coins does Alicia have?

Alicia has $1\frac{2}{3}$ times as many coins as Trent. Altogether, they have 72 coins. How many fewer coins does Trent have?

Alicia has $\frac{2}{3}$ more coins than Trent. Altogether, they have 72 coins. How many coins does Trent have?

Multiple Strategies to Solve a Ratio Word Problem

Now we illustrate how to solve a proportional reasoning problem using multiple strategies.

EXAMPLE 5.57

CONNECTION
COMMUNICATION
PROBLEM SOLVING
REASONING
REPRESENTATION

Barack is mixing cranberry juice and apple juice to make punch for a party. He adds 5 cups of cranberry juice for every 3 cups of apple juice. He wants to make 32 cups of punch altogether. How much cranberry juice should Barack use?

SOLUTION

METHOD 1 Make a Table strategy. Use a ratio table to organize information and generate equivalent ratios.

Cranberry juice (cups)	5	10	15	20	25
Apple juice (cups)	3	6	9	12	15
Total	8	16	24	32	40

$20 + 12 = 32$, so Barack needs 20 cups of cranberry juice.

Aaron Amat/Shutterstock.com

METHOD 2 Draw a Diagram strategy   The diagram represents the ratio of 5 cups of cranberry juice to 3 cups of apple juice, and there are 32 cups altogether.

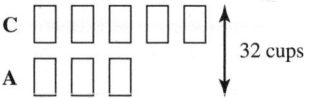

Split 32 into eight equal-sized parts. This requires division: $32 \div 8 = 4$, so each box in the diagram is worth 4 cups. Barack needs $5 \times 4 = 20$ cups of cranberry juice.

METHOD 3 Solve an Equation strategy.   The ratio of cranberry juice to apple juice is 5 cups to 3 cups. Multiplying both terms of the ratio by the positive number n yields the equivalent ratio $5n{:}3n$. We can organize the data in a table.

Cranberry juice (cups)	5	$5n$
Apple juice (cups)	3	$3n$

The expression $5n + 3n$ represents the total number of cups of punch. So solve the equation $5n + 3n = 32$. Then $8n = 32$. Then $n = 32 \div 8 = 4$. Because $5n$ represents the total amount of cranberry juice in the punch and $n = 4$, Barack needs $5 \times 4 = 20$ cups of cranberry juice.

METHOD 4 Unit rate.   Organize the information in a table.

Cranberry juice (cups)	5	n
Apple juice (cups)	3	
Total	8	32

Express the ratio $5{:}8$ as the equivalent ratio $n{:}32$. By scaling down, $5{:}8$ is equivalent to $\frac{5}{8}{:}1$; by scaling up, this is equivalent to $32 \cdot \frac{5}{8}{:}32 \cdot 1$, or $20{:}32$. Barack needs 20 cups of cranberry juice.

METHOD 5 Write a proportion.   Organize the information in a table.

Cranberry juice (cups)	5	n
Apple juice (cups)	3	
Total	8	32

Then $\frac{5}{8} = \frac{n}{32}$. Then $8n = 5 \cdot 32$. Then $8n = 160$. Then $n = 160 \div 8 = 20$. Barack needs 20 cups of cranberry juice. ▲

The ratio table provides a slow but steady solution to the problem and is suitable for "friendly numbers." The diagram builds on multiplicative thinking established for whole number concepts and is a visualization of the algebraic approach. The algebraic approach and proportions can handle a range of values, such as mixing cranberry juice and apple juice in a 3.5:4.1 ratio to make 102.6 cups of punch.

Write an Equation

Teachers often use numerical comparisons (for example, "Which is the better deal?") and missing value problems (for example, "There are three stars for every 5 triangles. How many stars are there if there are 30 triangles?") to assess proportional reasoning. Another way is to ask students to "represent proportional relationships by equations. For example, if total cost t is proportional to the number n of items purchased at a constant price p, the relationship between the total cost and the number of items can be expressed as $t = pn$" (CCSS, Gr. 7). The following example illustrates how to use a table to help determine the correct equation.

EXAMPLE 5.58

REASONING

REPRESENTATION

A party planner ordered five plastic cups for every three people who said they would attend the party. Let c represent the number of cups and p represent the number of people. Write an equation expressing a relationship between c and p.

SOLUTION

We can use the given variables in a ratio table.

Number of cups	5	c
Number of people	3	p

Then $\frac{5}{3} = \frac{c}{p}$. By cross-multiplying, we get $3c = 5p$. By dividing, we get $c = \frac{5}{3}p$. ▲

CONNECTION

REASONING

REPRESENTATION

Geometric Connection between Equivalent Ratios

Students can use graphs to "decide whether two quantities are in a proportional relationship" (CCSS, Gr. 7) and "graph proportional relationships" (CCSS, Gr. 8) in a coordinate plane to learn the geometric connection between two equivalent ratios and the slope of the line through the two equivalent ratios.

The ratios 2:3 and 4:6 are equivalent, but 2:3 and 5:4 are not equivalent ratios. Let's graph these ratios by plotting the first term of the ratio along the horizontal axis and the second term along the vertical axis. Each point on the graph represents a ratio; for example, (2, 3) represents 2:3. Then draw a straight line through each pair of ratios. Figure 24 shows the results.

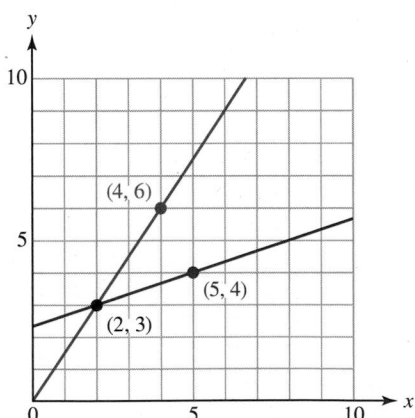

FIGURE 24

Lines through the pair of ratios 2:3 and 4:6 and the pair of ratios 2:3 and 5:4.

Consider the pair of ratios 2:4 and 4:8 and the pair of ratios 2:4 and 5:7. We know 2:4 and 4:8 are equivalent ratios and 2:4 and 5:7 are not equivalent ratios. Carefully graph these ratios onto Figure 24. Then use a straightedge to draw a line through each pair of ratios. What do the lines connecting pairs of equivalent ratios (the pair 2:3 and 4:6 and the pair 2:4 and 4:8) have in common? How would you characterize equivalent ratios using geometric terminology?

Now turn the ratio 2:3 into a unit ratio in the form a:1. Turn the ratio 4:6 into a unit ratio of the form a:1. Then calculate the slope of the line through the points (2, 3) and (4, 6). What is the relationship between the unit rates and the slope of line?

QUESTIONS FOR SECTION 5.4

REPRESENTATION

Refresher: Representations (language, diagrams, tables, symbols, algebra, manipulatives, and contextualized situations) are important because we use them to organize, record, and communicate mathematical ideas and to make them more comprehensible.

1. For every four stars, there are five moons. Represent the ratio of stars to moons in three ways.

2. Draw a diagram to show that the ratio of 3 boys to 4 girls is equivalent to the ratio of 9 boys to 12 girls.

3. Use scaling up (multiplication) to show the ratio of 3 to 4 is equivalent to the ratio of 9 to 12.

4. Use scaling down (division) to show that the ratio of 12 to 15 is equivalent to the ratio of 4 to 5.

5. There are three pens for every seven pencils. Make a ratio table to show how many pens and pencils there could be.

6. Write two different, but equivalent, ratios for the diagram.

● ● ● ● □ □ □ □

PROBLEM SOLVING

Refresher: Problem solving (reaching a goal that is not immediately attainable) is important because it helps students think more deeply about what they know and deal with unfamiliar situations.

7. Julie and Ann have 480 beads altogether. Julie has 3 beads for every 5 beads Ann has. How many beads does Ann have? Solve this problem using each strategy.
   a. Draw a Diagram   b. Write a Proportion
   c. Solve an Equation

8. Two local politicians, Smith and Jones, competed for a seat on the city council. Smith spent $4500 more than Jones in advertising during the campaign. In fact, Smith spent $5 for every $3 Jones spent. How much money did Smith and Jones each spend? Solve this problem using each strategy.
   a. Draw a Diagram   b. Solve an Equation

9. Acme Inc. spent $840 less on postage than on supplies. The ratio of postage costs to supply costs was 2 to 5. How much did Acme spend on postage? Solve this problem using algebra.

10. Mark saved $258 more than Neal. In fact, Mark saved $7 for every $4 Neal saved. How much money did Mark save? Solve this problem using the Solve an Equation strategy.

REASONING AND PROOF

Refresher: Reasoning and proof (thinking and justifying) are important because they help students make sense of mathematics.

11. How are a:b and $\frac{a}{b}$ alike? different?

12. Answer the following.
    a. Suppose x:1 = 3:1. What is x?
    b. Suppose x:1 = y:1. How are x and y related?

13. A painter mixes blue and yellow paint.
    a. Complete the table. Express all improper fractions as mixed numbers in simplified form.

Blue paint (oz)	7	14	
Yellow paint (oz)	5	10	
Additive comparison	$7 - 5 = 2$		
Multiplicative comparison	$7 \div 5 = 1\frac{2}{5}$		

   b. Fill in the blank: The painter added 7 ounces of blue paint for every ___ ounces of yellow paint.
   c. Fill in the blank: The amount of blue paint in the mixture is ___ times as much as the amount of yellow paint.
   d. Are equivalent ratios related by addition and subtraction or by multiplication and division?

14. Suppose k is a nonzero number (for example, $k = 3$, $k = -2$, or $k = 1/5$). Under what conditions is the ratio a to b equivalent to the ratio
    a. $a + k$ to $b + k$?   b. ak to bk?

15. Use mental math to fill in the blank.
    a. 6 calories is to 5 minutes as ___ calories is to 45 minutes.
    b. 5 m is to 3 days as ___ m is to 1 day.
    c. 3 pounds is to ___ books as 12 pounds is to 32 books.

16. There are 30 students in a class. What are some possible ratios of boys to girls for the class?

CONNECTIONS

Refresher: Connections (linking and applying mathematical ideas) are important because they deepen student understanding and make mathematics more meaningful, flexible, and useful.

17. The ratio of cats to mice in a barn is 3:7. If there are 15 cats in the barn, how many mice are there? Solve this problem using each strategy.

    a. Make a Table   b. Draw a Diagram   c. Unit Rate

    d. Write a Proportion   e. Solve an Equation

18. A shade of green paint is made by mixing 3 pints of white paint with 7 pints of blue paint. How much white paint should be mixed with 3 gallons of blue paint to get the same shade of green paint? (Hint: 8 pints = 1 gallon.)

19. The "fundraising ratio" is the ratio of costs incurred to raise funds to the amount of funds raised.

    a. What is the fundraiser ratio if it costs $3000 to raise $45,000?

    b. Express this ratio as a unit ratio, and then interpret your result.

20. The ratio of apples to oranges in a fruit basket is 2 to 3. What fraction of the fruit basket consists of apples?

21. The ratio of birds to nests is 7:3. Let b represent the number of birds and n represent the number of nests. Write an equation expressing a relationship between b and n in the form $b = \_\_\_$.

22. According to the U.S. Department of Energy (www.fueleconomy.gov/feg/driveHabits.shtml), excessive speeds can decrease fuel economy. Each 5 mph you drive over 60 mph is like paying an additional 20 cents per gallon of fuel.

    a. What is the additional cost of driving at 78 mph?

    b. What is the additional cost of driving 93 mph?

23. Use the diagram to fill in the blank with a ratio or a fraction.

    a. The ratio of pennies to nickels is _____.

    b. _____ of the coins are pennies.

    c. The ratio of pennies to coins is _____.

    d. There are _____ fewer nickels than pennies.

COMMUNICATION

Refresher: Communication (written and verbal explanations using representations and proper mathematical vocabulary) is important because it helps students refine and strengthen their understanding.

24. The ratio of boys to girls in a class is 3 to 5. There are 12 boys. A student concludes there are 14 girls in the class.

    a. How did the student arrive at this incorrect answer?

    b. What advice would you give to correct the student's thinking?

    c. How many girls are in the class?

25. List two significant differences between the fraction $\frac{a}{b}$ and the ratio $\frac{a}{b}$.

26. Maria is making unsweetened lemonade. She adds 5 cups of water for every 2 cups of lemon juice. Tom is making unsweetened lemonade too. He adds 8 cups of water for every $3\frac{1}{2}$ cups of lemon juice. Which lemonade is sourer?

27. Consider the seven letters A, A, B, B, B, B, B. Write a sentence that uses ratios to compare the numbers of As and Bs. Make a

    a. part-to-part comparison.   b. part-to-whole comparison.

    c. whole-to-part comparison.

More practice with the ideas of the section

28. Make a ratio table for 2:5.

29. The ratio of pennies to nickels in a jar is 3:7. If there are 28 nickels in the jar, how many pennies are there? Solve this problem using a proportion.

30. A recipe calls for $2\frac{1}{4}$ cups of flour for every 1/2 teaspoon of salt. Suppose you put 6 cups of flour in a mixing bowl. How much salt should you add?

31. Here's one way to approximate the minimum amount of water you should drink each day to stay hydrated (it's good for nutrient transport, cushioning joints, and temperature regulation): First, divide your body weight in half to determine the baseline number of ounces of water you need each day. Second, for every 20 minutes of exercise, add 8 ounces of water. Finally, round the computation to the nearest whole number. Estimate the daily amount of water a person needs who weighs

    a. 180 pounds and exercises 45 minutes per day.

    b. 210 pounds and exercises 30 minutes per day.

    c. 195 pounds and exercises 67 minutes per day.

32. A 110-pound student burns 11 calories while playing Frisbee for 4 minutes. How many calories does he burn while playing Frisbee for 30 minutes? Use the given strategy.

    a. Unit Rate   b. Write a Proportion

33. In a newspaper article, a university representative said the campus planned to increase the number of parking spaces to 8200. This would maintain the ratio of four parking spaces for every 10 people on campus. Use unit rates to calculate the number of people the university expects to have on campus.

34. According to a newspaper article, 6 out of 10 people voted for a proposition to increase the pay of city council members in a certain small town. What was the ratio of people who voted for the proposition to people who did not vote for the proposition?

35. Grocer A is selling 9 pounds of sugar for $2.25, and grocer B is selling 12 pounds of sugar for $2.50. Which grocer is offering the better buy?

36. Gary mixes 2 cups of water, 1 cup of sugar, and 1/2 cup of lemon juice to make lemonade. His sister Sue adds 4 cups of water. How much additional sugar and lemon juice should Gary add so that the lemonade tastes the same?

37. The principal at an elementary school wants to maintain a teacher-to-student ratio of 2:37. During the summer, she learns that 756 students plan to enroll in the school. What is the minimum number of teachers needed so that the principal has enough teachers? Use the unit rate strategy to solve this problem.

38. Marvin has 252 more marbles than Kyle. Marvin has 5 marbles for every 2 marbles Kyle has. How many marbles does Kyle have? Solve this problem using each strategy.

   a. Draw a Diagram   b. Solve an Equation   c. Unit Rate

39. At a school dance, the ratio of boys to girls is 7 to 5. What fraction of students at the dance consists of girls?

40. The ratio of cats to mice is 8:5. Let c represent the number of cats and m represent the number of mice. Write an equation expressing a relationship between c and m in the form $m =$ ___.

41. At Bulk Store, toilet paper comes in packs of 72 rolls and costs $14.75. What would be a good price for another store that sells toilet paper in packs of 6 rolls so that it can compete with Bulk Store?

42. Mrs. Emme's class and Mrs. Smith's class have the same ratio of girls to boys. Mrs. Emme's class has 2 girls for every 3 boys. Explain why Mrs. Smith cannot have 24 students in her class.

43. Jamahl the basketball player shoots 420 free throws. He makes 3 out of every 7 shots. His goal is to make half of his shots. He plans to take 600 more shots. He calculates he now needs to make 11 out of every 20 shots. Justify this calculation.

44. Mitchell and Joey have 1312 pennies altogether. If Joey had 8 more pennies, then Joey would have 3 pennies for every 8 pennies Mitchell has. How many coins does each have?

45. In chemistry, a molecule is two or more atoms bonded together. The sulfuric acid molecule has two hydrogen atoms and four oxygen atoms for every sulfur atom. Suppose a beaker has pure sulfuric acid and has 500 million oxygen atoms. How many hydrogen atoms are there?

46. When mixing cement, the strength of concrete is primarily based on the ratio of the volume of water to the volume of cement. The cement becomes weaker as the volume of water increases. Organize the following ratios of water to cement in order of increasing strength of cement: 23:42, 12:23, and 8:6.

47. According to a news report, many top basic cable channels lost subscribers, with losers outnumbering gainers overall by a 5-to-3 ratio. If there were 200 top basic cable channels, how many of them gained subscribers?

48. Rewrite each sentence in terms of a ratio.

   a. Four-sevenths of the coins were pennies.

   b. The number of boys was three times the number of girls.

49. Pose and solve a word problem involving ratios for the diagram.

50. Pose and solve a word problem involving ratios for the diagram.

CHAPTER 5 REVIEW

CHAPTER 5 Organizer

Section	What You Should Learn	Review Problems
5.1	1. Explain the meaning of m and n in the expression m/n.	1–2
	2. Represent a fraction using the area, set, or number line model.	3–4
	3. Use diagrams to solve word problems involving fractions.	5–7
	4. Solve problems that make use of the fact a fraction is a quotient.	8–9
	5. Use multiplication or division to generate equivalent fractions.	10–12
	6. Compare and approximate fractions using benchmarks, common denominators, common numerators, or cross-products.	13–15

5.2	1. Explain the connection between adding two whole numbers and adding two fractions with common fractional parts.	16
	2. Use a diagram to model or use rules to find the sum and the difference of two fractions.	17–18
	3. Apply various strategies to solve an equation involving addition or subtraction with rational numbers.	19–22
	4. Make a reasonable estimate of a sum or difference of two rational numbers.	23
	5. Calculate the sum or difference of two rational numbers.	24
	6. Convert mixed numbers and fractions.	25
5.3	1. Draw a model for a product of fractions.	26–27
	2. Apply various strategies to solve an equation involving multiplication or division with rational numbers.	28–30
	3. Solve word problems involving fractions.	31–33
	4. Make comparisons using phrases such as "two-thirds more," "three-fourths fewer," or "$2\frac{3}{4}$ times as many."	34–35
	5. Justify and apply the invert and multiply strategy for dividing fractions.	36–37
	6. Write story problems for expressions such as $\frac{3}{4} \times \frac{2}{5}$ or $5\frac{2}{3} \div \frac{3}{4}$.	38
	7. Apply exponent rules for rational numbers.	39–40
5.4	1. Represent a ratio symbolically in three ways.	41
	2. Use diagrams to generate equivalent ratios.	42
	3. Solve a ratio problem in various ways, such as make a table, draw a diagram, use a unit rate, solve an equation, and write a proportion.	43–48
	4. Use ratios to compare two quantities.	49–51

Key Terms and Concepts

Review Questions

1. Fill in the blank with a word or phrase: In the fraction $\frac{5}{3}$, the numerator indicates a collection of _____ equal-sized parts, while the denominator indicates each equal-sized part is called _____.

2. Consider the fraction three-eighths.
   a. What is the equal-sized part?
   b. How many copies of the equal-sized part are there in the fraction?

3. Model the fraction five-eighths using
   a. a number line.   b. an area model.   c. a set model.

4. a. $\frac{3}{2}$ candy bars are shown.

   Draw $\frac{3}{4}$ of a candy bar.

5. Erin and David have 364 coins altogether. David has two-fifths of the number of coins Erin has. How many coins does David have? Solve this problem using each strategy.
   a. Draw a Diagram   b. Solve an Equation

6. David has two-fifths of the number of coins Erin has. Erin has 243 more coins than David does. How many coins does David have? Solve this problem using each strategy.
   a. Draw a Diagram   b. Solve an Equation

7. Erin and David have 302 coins altogether. David has 8 fewer than two-thirds the number of coins Erin has. How many coins does David have? Solve this problem using each strategy.
   a. Draw a Diagram   b. Solve an Equation

8. Write an appropriate equation for each fair-share word problem.
   a. A teacher divides seven pencils among three students. How many pencils does each student get?
   b. A teacher divides seven candy bars among three students. How much candy bar does each student get?

9. Write a word problem that requires the given computation.
   a. $9 \div 4 = 2 \text{ R} 1$ b. $9 \div 4 = \frac{9}{4}$

10. Show $\frac{3}{4}$ and $\frac{9}{12}$ are equivalent fractions using
    a. an area model.   b. a number line.   c. cross-products.

11. Use division to find two equivalent fractions of $\frac{210}{672}$.

12. Use multiplication to find two equivalent fractions of $\frac{7}{9}$.

13. a. What are the cross-products for the fractions $\frac{a}{b}$ and $\frac{c}{d}$?
    b. Suppose you know $\frac{a}{b} < \frac{c}{d}$. How are the cross-products of $\frac{a}{b}$ and $\frac{c}{d}$ related?

14. Compare $\frac{3}{4}$ and $\frac{5}{8}$ by finding a common denominator, and tell how you decided which fraction is larger.

15. Lisa makes trail mix by combining 2 cups of raisins with 5 cups of peanuts. Mark combines 3 cups of raisins with 8 cups of peanuts. Lisa said her mixture has more raisins. Mark said his mixture has more raisins. Explain how each could be correct.

16. Choose the best answer: Students can reason $\frac{4}{10} + \frac{3}{10}$ is $\frac{7}{10}$ because they are "counting": thirds, fourths, sevenths, or tenths.

17. Use a diagram to model the sum or difference of two fractions, then write an equation.
    a. $\frac{2}{3} + \frac{1}{4}$ b. $\frac{2}{3} - \frac{1}{4}$

18. How much longer is nail B than nail A?

    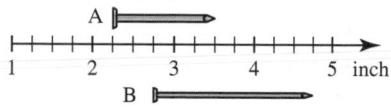

19. Use basic algebraic properties to solve the equation $y + \frac{5}{3} = \frac{9}{4}$.

20. Use the definition of subtraction to solve the equation $y + \frac{5}{3} = \frac{9}{4}$.

21. Use the fact that addition and subtraction are inverse operations to solve the equation $y - \frac{5}{3} = \frac{9}{4}$.

22. Use the definition of subtraction to solve the equation $y - \frac{5}{3} = \frac{9}{4}$.

23. Estimate each sum or difference.
    a. $\frac{4}{5} + \frac{7}{8}$ b. $\frac{4}{7} - 7\frac{1}{3}$ c. $8\frac{3}{5} + 14\frac{6}{7}$

24. Calculate the sum or difference.
    a. $3\frac{2}{5}$ b. $12\frac{1}{3}$
    $+8\frac{9}{10}$ $-5\frac{3}{4}$

25. Convert the mixed numbers to fractions, and convert the fractions to mixed numbers.
    a. $2\frac{5}{8}$ b. $-8\frac{5}{6}$ c. $\frac{45}{7}$ d. $\frac{-17}{3}$

26. Express the cross-hatched region as a product of fractions.
    a.
    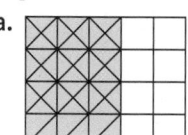

    b.
    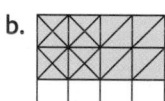

27. Represent each product with a diagram, and then write an appropriate equation.
    a. $\frac{4}{7} \times \frac{2}{3}$ b. $\frac{2}{5} \times \frac{3}{4}$

28. Solve $\frac{4}{5} \times y = 32$ for y using basic algebraic properties of fractions.

29. Solve $\frac{3}{5} \times y = 45$ using the definition of division.

30. Solve $n \div \frac{3}{5} = 28$ using the fact that multiplication and division are inverse operations.

31. Use a diagram to solve each problem.

    a. Jake has 18 coins. Carlos has 2 fewer than two-thirds times as many coins as Jake. How many coins does Carlos have?

    b. 420 people waited to buy tickets for the concert on Saturday. The tickets sold out before 2 more than three-fourths of the people could buy tickets. How many people purchased tickets?

32. In a poll, two-fifths of Americans were concerned that they or a friend might lose a job because an employer would shift the job to a foreign country. The poll surveyed 1005 people. How many people in the poll actually shared this concern?

33. A computer programmer had to find a new job when his employer released him to streamline operations. The computer programmer found a new job, but it only paid two-thirds of his previous salary. His new salary is $48,000. What was his previous salary?

34. The diagram represents how many coins each person has. Fill in each blank with a fraction or mixed number.

    K □□□□□□
    A □□□

    a. Kamran has ___ more coins than Allia.

    b. Kamran has ___ times as many coins as Allia.

    c. Allia has ___ fewer coins than Kamran.

    d. Allia has ___ times as many coins as Kamran.

35. Fill in the blank with the appropriate fraction or mixed number.

    a. Mary has 28 coins. John has 20 coins. Mary has ___ more coins than John. Mary has ___ times as many coins as John.

    b. Mary has 60 coins. John has 36 coins. Mary has ___ more coins than John. Mary has ___ times as many coins as John.

    c. Mary has 30 coins. John has 21 coins. Mary has ___ more coins than John. Mary has ___ times as many coins as John.

36. Use the invert and multiply algorithm to divide.

    a. $\frac{23}{7} \div \frac{21}{4}$ b. $3\frac{5}{7} \div \frac{7}{5}$ c. $12 \div \frac{3}{4}$

37. How could you teach your students the basis for the invert and multiply rule? (Hint: Use complex fractions.)

38. Write a story problem for each expression.

    a. $\frac{3}{4} \times \frac{2}{3}$ b. $4\frac{2}{5} \div \frac{3}{4}$

39. Simplify each expression.

    a. $3^0 \cdot 4^{-2}$ b. $6^{-2} + \left(\frac{2}{3}\right)^2$

40. Simplify each expression. Write the answer in terms of positive exponents.

    a. $\frac{3a^{-3}(bc)^{-2}}{(-4)^2 b^{-5} c^3}$ b. $(3^{-2}a)^{-3}$

    c. $\left(\frac{b^2}{a^4 b^{-3}}\right)^{-3}$ d. $\left(\frac{3a^{-1}}{b}\right)^{-2} \frac{a^{-5}}{b^3}$

41. There are three boys for every seven girls. Represent this ratio in three ways.

42. Use a diagram to show that the ratio 2:3 is equivalent to the ratio 4:6. Explain your drawing.

43. The ratio of cats to dogs is 3 to 5. We can represent the relationship with a diagram, as shown.

    C □□□
    D □□□□□

    a. If there are 72 cats and dogs altogether, then how many dogs are there?

    b. If there are 42 more dogs than cats, then how many dogs are there?

44. Use the Unit Rate strategy to answer the following questions.

    a. It costs $6 for 25 pounds of flour. At this rate, how much does 7 pounds of flour cost?

    b. A hiker walks 8 miles in 3 days. At this rate, how many days does it take to walk 21 miles?

    c. On a map 1 inch represents 4 miles. Two cities are $2\frac{3}{4}$ inches apart. What is the actual distance between the cities?

45. Three local department stores are having sales on T-shirts: store A is selling five shirts for $20, store B is selling four shirts for $15, and store C is selling three shirts for $12. Which store has the best deal?

46. A mixture of light blue paint consists of 3 pints of white paint and 7 pints of blue paint. Another mixture of light blue paint consists of 5 parts of white paint and 9 parts of blue paint. Are the colors in these two mixtures the same shade of light blue paint? Explain.

47. Shehan is mixing cement. The ratio of bags of cement to gallons of water is 2:5. If he has eight bags of cement, then how much water does he need? Solve this problem using each strategy.

    a. Make a Table   b. Draw a Diagram   c. Unit Rate

    d. Solve an Equation   e. Write a Proportion

48. Suppose the ratio of boys to girls in a class is 4 to 7, and there are 12 boys in the class. Suppose a student concludes there are 15 girls in the class. How did the student arrive at this answer? What advice would you give the student to correct his thinking?

49. The ratio of cats to dogs is 3 to 5. We can represent the relationship with a diagram, as shown.

    C □□□
    D □□□□□

    Fill in each blank with the appropriate fraction or mixed number.

    a. There are ___ more dogs than cats.

    b. There are ___ fewer cats than dogs.

    c. There are ___ times as many dogs as cats.

    d. The number of cats is ___ of the number of dogs.

50. The ratio of cats to dogs is 5 to 9. Fill in each blank with the appropriate fraction or mixed number.

    a. There are ____ more dogs than cats.

    b. There are ____ fewer cats than dogs.

    c. There are ____ times as many dogs as cats.

    d. The number of cats is ____ of the number of dogs.

51. According to a news article in *National Geographic,* insects form a traditional part of the diet of many cultures around the world. Insect farming is arguably more efficient than cattle production: 100 pounds of feed yields 10 pounds of beef, while the same amount of feed yields 45 pounds of cricket. Compare the yield of 100 pounds of feed. Use

    a. additive reasoning.   **b.** multiplicative reasoning.

Chapter 5 Test

1. *Explain the meaning of m and n in the expression m/n.* The fraction $\frac{8}{6}$ is a collection of equal-sized parts.

    a. What is the equal-sized part?

    b. How many copies of the equal-sized part are there in the collection?

2. *Explain the meaning of m and n in the expression $\frac{m}{n}$.* ▪▪▪▪ represents one package. Write the fraction that ▪▪▪▪▪▪▪▪▪ represents.

3. *Use diagrams to solve word problems involving fractions.* Benny has 3 fewer than two-fifths the number of marbles that Dallas has. Dallas has 189 more marbles than Benny.

    a. Draw a diagram to represent the situation.

    b. How many marbles does Benny have?

4. *Use diagrams to solve word problems involving fractions.* Bill and Jim have 578 coins altogether. If Bill had 2 more coins, then he would have three-sevenths of the number of coins Jim has.

    a. Draw a diagram to represent the situation.

    b. How many coins does Bill have?

5. *Solve problems that make use of the fact that a fraction is a quotient.* Write an appropriate equation for each fair-share word problem needed to solve the problem.

    a. A teacher divides 11 markers among four students. How many markers does each student get?

    b. A teacher divides 11 pounds of clay among four students. How much clay does each student get?

6. *Solve problems that make use of the fact that a fraction is a quotient.* Write a word problem that requires the computation.

    a. $17 \div 5 = 3 \text{ R2}$ **b.** $17 \div 5 = \frac{17}{5}$

7. *Compare and approximate fractions using benchmarks, common denominators, common numerators, or cross-products.* Are $\frac{59}{32}$ and $\frac{21,476}{11,648}$ equivalent fractions? Tell how you know.

8. *Find the sum and difference of two fractions using rules.* Calculate the sum or difference.

    a.
$$3\frac{4}{5}$$
$$+\,15\frac{3}{7}$$
    b.
$$4\frac{2}{5}$$
$$-\,12\frac{4}{7}$$

9. *Convert mixed numbers and fractions.* Convert the mixed numbers to fractions, and convert the fractions to mixed numbers.

    a. $6\frac{4}{5}$ **b.** $-7\frac{3}{5}$ **b.** $\frac{235}{18}$ **b.** $\frac{-35}{8}$

10. *Draw a model for a product of fractions.* Represent the product $\frac{4}{7} \times \frac{5}{6}$ with a diagram. Write an equation.

11. *Draw a model for a product of fractions.* Write a product of fractions modeled by the diagram.

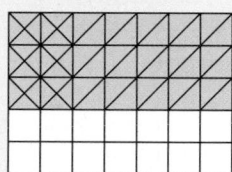

12. *Apply various strategies to solve an equation involving addition or subtraction with rational numbers.* Solve $y - \frac{7}{5} = \frac{2}{3}$ using the definition of subtraction.

13. *Apply various strategies to solve an equation involving addition or subtraction with rational numbers.* Solve $y + \frac{5}{8} = \frac{4}{3}$ using the fact that addition and subtraction are inverse operations.

14. *Apply various strategies to solve an equation involving multiplication or division with rational numbers.* Solve $\frac{7}{5}y = \frac{2}{3}$ using the fact that multiplication and division are inverse operations.

15. *Apply various strategies to solve an equation involving multiplication or division with rational numbers.* Solve $\frac{8}{3} \times y = 60$ using the definition of division.

16. *Apply various strategies to solve an equation involving multiplication or division with rational numbers.* Solve $n \div \frac{3}{5} = 45$ using algebraic the definition of rational numbers.

17. *Apply various strategies to solve an equation involving multiplication or division with rational numbers.* Solve $\frac{3}{4} \times n = 6$ using algebraic properties of rational numbers.

18. *Make comparisons using phrases such as "two-thirds more," "three-fourths fewer," or "$2\frac{3}{4}$ times as many."* The diagram represents how many coins each person has. Fill in the blank with the appropriate fraction or mixed number.

    T □□□□□□□□
    L □□□□□

    a. LeBron has ____ fewer coins than Tanya.

    b. LeBron has ____ times as many coins as Tanya.

c. Tanya has ___ more coins than LeBron.

d. Tanya has ___ times as many coins as LeBron.

19. *Make comparisons using phrases such as "two-thirds more," "three-fourths fewer," or "$2\frac{3}{4}$ times as many."* Vera has 32 coins. Omar has 18 coins. Fill in the blank with the appropriate fraction or mixed number.

   a. Vera has ___ more coins than Omar.

   b. Vera has ___ times as many coins as Omar.

   c. Omar has ___ fewer coins than Vera.

   d. Omar has ___ times as many coins as Vera.

20. *Apply the invert and multiply strategy for dividing fractions.* Use the invert and multiply algorithm to divide.

   a. $\dfrac{42}{15} \div \dfrac{12}{5}$ b. $14\dfrac{5}{7} \div 3\dfrac{3}{4}$

21. *Apply exponent rules for rational numbers.* Simplify each expression. Write the answer in terms of positive exponents.

   a. $\dfrac{(3a^{-1})^2 b^4}{12a^{-4}(bc^{-2})^3}$ b. $(2^{-1}b^2)^{-4}$

   c. $\left(\dfrac{-a^2 b}{a^{-3}b^5}\right)^{-4}$ c. $\left(\dfrac{5b^{-1}}{a^3 c}\right)^{-2} \times \dfrac{b^{-3}}{a^4}$

22. *Solve a ratio problem in various ways, such as make a table, draw a diagram, use a unit rate, solve an equation, and write a proportion.* The ratio of cars to trucks is 4 to 7. We can represent the relationship with a diagram, as shown.

   C ☐☐☐☐

   T ☐☐☐☐☐☐☐

   a. If there are 924 cars and trucks altogether, then how many trucks are there?

   b. If there are 420 fewer cars than trucks, then how many cars are there?

23. *Solve a ratio problem in various ways, such as make a table, draw a diagram, use a unit rate, solve an equation, and write a proportion.* A recipe for punch calls for 3 parts lemon juice, 5 parts pineapple juice, and 1 part orange juice. Kerry wants to make 60 cups of punch in a large bowl for a party. How many cups of pineapple juice should she put in the bowl? Solve this problem using the Write a Proportion strategy.

24. *Solve a ratio problem in various ways, such as make a table, draw a diagram, use a unit rate, solve an equation, and write a proportion.* The aspect ratio describes the shape of a picture. It is a ratio of the width (horizontal direction) to the height (vertical direction). A photographer has a picture with an aspect ratio of 3 to 5. Can the photographer fit the picture exactly on paper that has a width of 12 inches and a height of 20 inches? Solve this problem using the Unit Rate strategy.

25. *Solve a ratio problem in various ways, such as make a table, draw a diagram, use a unit rate, solve an equation, and write a proportion.* Ravi is stocking the shelves with canned goods in a large warehouse. There are 4 cans of corn for every 7 cans of green beans. There are 924 more cans of green beans than of corn. How many cans of green beans are there? Solve this problem using the Solve an Equation strategy.

6

Decimals, Real Numbers, and Percents

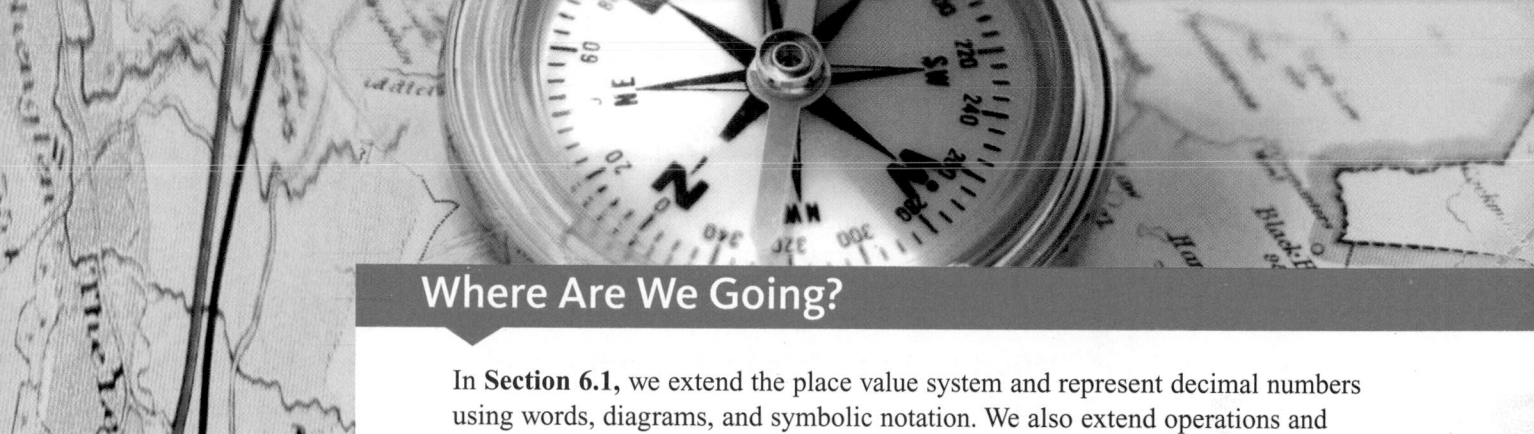

Where Are We Going?

In **Section 6.1,** we extend the place value system and represent decimal numbers using words, diagrams, and symbolic notation. We also extend operations and algorithms to decimal numbers. We focus on terminating decimals and their connections to fractions. Whole numbers, integers, and fractions are representations of decimal numbers but lack the decimal point. In **Section 6.2,** we discuss repeating decimals and irrational numbers, the real number system, square roots and *n*th roots, rational exponents, and scientific notation. In **Section 6.3,** we examine percents defined as ratios and then as fractions. We demonstrate how to use diagrams and algebra to represent and solve classic percent problems. We also explore connections among fractions, decimals, and percents.

What Is a Decimal Number?

The place value system for whole numbers organizes objects into groups, such as *hundreds, tens,* and *ones.* The place value system extends in a natural way to regrouping smaller equal-sized parts: *tenths, hundredths, thousandths,* and so on. The NCTM's *Principles and Standards for School Mathematics* asserts, "The foundation of students' work with decimal numbers must be an understanding of whole numbers and place value. In grades 3–5, students should have learned to think of decimal numbers as a natural extension of the base-ten place value system to represent quantities smaller than 1" (© NCTM Standards 2011 by National Council of Teachers of Mathematics).

A **decimal number** is any number that we can represent using the usual digits 0, 1, 2, 3, 4, 5, 6, 7, 8, or 9 with a dot (.), called the **decimal point,** after the ones place. For example, 3.24 and 0.00251 are decimal numbers. The place values after the decimal point are *tenths, hundredths, thousandths,* and so on. As we show later, $\frac{2}{3}$ and $\frac{3}{4}$ are decimal numbers too.

Every number on the real number line can be written as one of the following three types of decimal numbers:

- A *terminating decimal number* is a decimal number with a finite number of digits to the right of the decimal point, such as 0.028, 56.0, and 1457.6001. As we show later, any terminating decimal can be expressed as a fraction in the form $\frac{a}{b}$, where *a* and *b* are integers.

- A *repeating decimal number* is a decimal number with a repeating pattern of digits, such as 18.67343434 . . . and 47.035210210210 . . . . There are infinitely many digits to the right of the decimal point, with a block of digits that repeats. As we show later, any repeating decimal can be expressed as a fraction in the form $\frac{a}{b}$, where a and b are integers.

- An *irrational number* is a decimal number with infinitely many digits to the right of the decimal point but without a repeating pattern, such as 5.47010010001 . . . . A pattern is present in 5.47010010001 . . . , but it is not a *repeating* pattern. As we show later, numbers such as $\sqrt{2}$ and $\sqrt{3}$ are also irrational numbers.

Every decimal number has two parts: the integer part and the decimal part (fractional part). The **integer part** consists of the digits before the decimal point. The **decimal part (fractional part)** consists of the decimal point and the digits after the decimal point. For example, 12.034 has the integer part 12 and the decimal part .034. For terminating decimals, the "number of decimal places" is the number of digits after the decimal point. For example, 12.034 has three decimal places while 12.03470 has five decimal places.

What Is the Origin of Procedures with Decimal Numbers?

A **decimal fraction** is a fraction that can be written with a denominator of 10, 100, 1000, or any other positive power of 10, such as 324/100 and 95,642/1000. In 1585, Simon Stevin wrote a 36-page book that described a new but cumbersome decimal notation for representing a decimal fraction without a fraction bar and provided the first understandable and systematic methods to add, subtract, multiply, and divide decimal fractions. He detailed how operations with decimal numbers are first performed as operations with integers and then followed by inserting the decimal point in the correct position. His goal was to teach everyone "how to perform, with an ease unheard of, all computations necessary between men by integers without fractions" (Stevin, 1585). Today, elementary school students follow the same procedures that Stevin described to add, subtract, multiply, and divide decimal numbers. The modern decimal notation was developed in the late 1590s and popularized in the early 1620s.

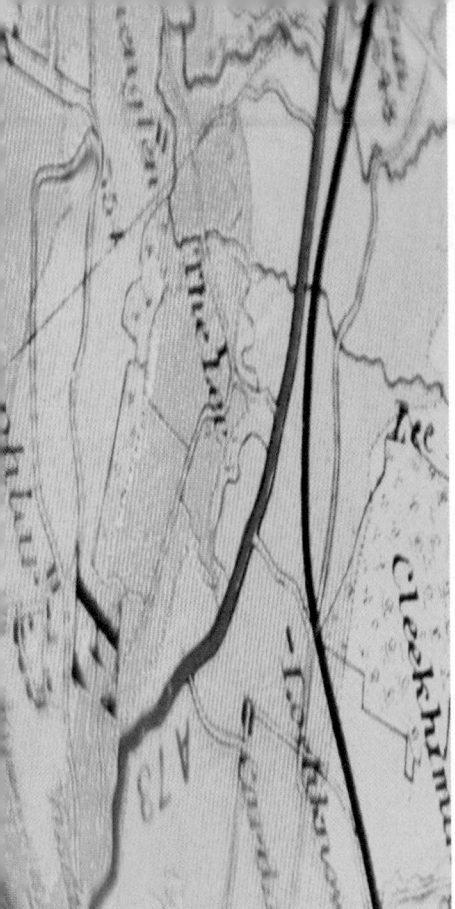

decimal fraction

$$\frac{95{,}642}{1000} \left(\text{or } 95\frac{642}{1000} \right)$$

Stevin notation

⓪ ① ② ③

95   6   4   2

decimal notation

95.642

Decimals and Operations

Models of Place Values: Tenths and Hundredths

The shaded region in the decimal square in Figure 1(a) represents one (1). The shaded region in the decimal square in Figure 1(b) represents **one-tenth,** denoted numerically as $\frac{1}{10}$ or 0.1. The shaded region in the decimal square in Figure 1(c) represents **one-hundredth,** denoted numerically as $\frac{1}{100}$ or 0.01.

Smaller equal-sized pieces are thousandths ($\frac{1}{1000}$ or 0.001), ten-thousandths ($\frac{1}{10{,}000}$ or 0.0001), hundred-thousandths ($\frac{1}{100{,}000}$ or 0.00001), millionths ($\frac{1}{1{,}000{,}000}$ or 0.000001), and so on.

CONNECTION

REPRESENTATION

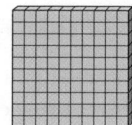

FIGURE 1(a)

Shaded part models one (1).

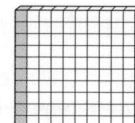

FIGURE 1(b)

Shaded part models one-tenth $\left(\frac{1}{10} \text{ or } 0.1\right)$.

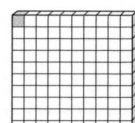

FIGURE 1(c)

Shaded part models one-hundredth $\left(\frac{1}{100} \text{ or } 0.01\right)$.

The decimal squares in Figure 2 model three decimal numbers.

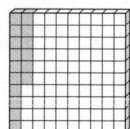

FIGURE 2(a)

Sixteen-hundredths $\left(\frac{16}{100} \text{ or } 0.16\right)$.

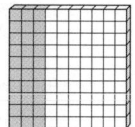

FIGURE 2(b)

Three-tenths $\left(\frac{3}{10} \text{ or } 0.3\right)$.

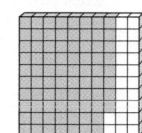

FIGURE 2(c)

Seventy-eight hundredths $\left(\frac{78}{100} \text{ or } 0.78\right)$.

Each Digit Has a Place Value and a Value

Table 6.1 illustrates that each digit in a decimal number has a place value and a value that depend on the digit's location.

TABLE 6.1 Each Digit in a Decimal Number Such As 3827.452 Has a Place Value and a Value

	Place Value of the Digit							
	Thousands	**Hundreds**	**Tens**	**Ones**	**.**	**Tenths**	**Hundredths**	**Thousandths**
3827.452	3	8	2	7		4	5	2
Value of the digit (decimal form)	3000	800	20	7		0.4	0.05	0.002
Value of the digit (fraction form)	3000	800	20	7		$\frac{4}{10}$	$\frac{5}{100}$	$\frac{2}{1000}$

The value of each digit to the right of the decimal point has a decimal form and a fraction form. Table 6.1 suggests that the places are symmetric about the ones place (tens and tenths, hundreds and hundredths, thousand and thousandths, and so on), and asymmetric about the decimal point (ones and tenths, tens and hundredths, hundreds and thousandths, and so on). The ones place is the focal point of the decimal system, not the decimal point.

The next example assesses place value concepts for decimal numbers.

EXAMPLE 6.1

CONNECTION

REASONING

REPRESENTATION

a. How are the underlined digits in 38<u>2</u>7.45<u>2</u> alike?

b. How are the underlined digits in 38<u>2</u>7.45<u>2</u> different?

c. What is the place value of the underlined digit in 3827.4<u>5</u>2?

d. What is the value of the underlined digit in 3827.4<u>5</u>2?

SOLUTION

a. Each represents two groups (two tens and two thousandths).

b. They have different values (20 versus 0.002).

c. hundredths, $\frac{1}{100}$, or 0.01

d. 0.05 or $\frac{5}{100}$

▲

Multiple Representations of Decimals

In Chapter 2, we described various ways to represent a whole number, for example, $642 = 6$ hundreds, 4 tens, 2 ones; $642 = 64$ tens, 2 ones; or $642 = 642$ ones. The multiple representations were important for the regrouping needed for operations with whole numbers.

The decimal square in Figure 3 helps students develop more flexible thinking about decimal numbers needed for naming and renaming decimal numbers, as well as performing operations with decimal numbers:

$$
\begin{aligned}
0.36 &= 3 \text{ tenths, } 6 \text{ hundredths} &&(3 \text{ columns, } 6 \text{ squares}) \\
&= 2 \text{ tenths, } 16 \text{ hundredths} &&(2 \text{ columns, } 16 \text{ squares}) \\
&= 1 \text{ tenth, } 26 \text{ hundredths} &&(1 \text{ column, } 26 \text{ squares}) \\
&= 36 \text{ hundredths} &&(0 \text{ columns, } 36 \text{ squares})
\end{aligned}
$$

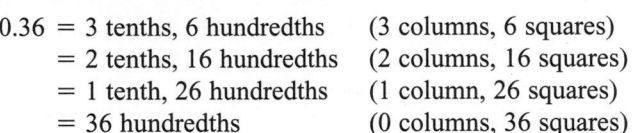

FIGURE 3
A model of 0.36.

Another way to see this using decimal fractions is as follows:

$$
\begin{aligned}
0.36 &= 3 \text{ tenths, } 6 \text{ hundredths} \\
&= \frac{3}{10} + \frac{6}{100} \\
&= \frac{30}{100} + \frac{6}{100} \\
&= \frac{36}{100}
\end{aligned}
$$

CONNECTION
REPRESENTATION

As another example, we can think of 0.0127 in various ways. For example,

1. $0.0127 = 0$ tenths, 1 hundredth, 2 thousandths, 7 ten-thousandths.

2. $0.0127 = 127$ ten-thousandths. (The place value of the 7 is ten-thousandths.)

3. $0.0127 = \dfrac{127}{10{,}000}$.

Knowing multiple representations of a decimal number promotes knowing how to "read and write decimals to thousandths using base-ten numerals, number names, and expanded form, e.g., $347.392 = 3 \times 100 + 4 \times 10 + 7 \times 1 + 3 \times (1/10) + 9 \times (1/100) + 2 \times (1/1000)$" (CCSS, Gr. 5) (© 2010. National Governors Association Center for Best Practices and Council of Chief State School Officers. All rights reserved.) and being able to "fluently add, subtract, multiply, and divide multi-digit decimals using the standard algorithm for each operation" (CCSS, Gr. 6).

Word Forms and Expanded Forms

The following example describes how to write the short word and word forms of a decimal.

EXAMPLE 6.2

CONNECTION
REASONING
REPRESENTATION

Represent 68.01275 in
a. short word form.
b. word form.

SOLUTION

68.01275 has integer part 68 and fractional part .01275, which represents 1275 equal-sized parts. The place value of the rightmost digit in the fractional part is hundred-thousandths, so the equal-sized parts are hundred-thousandths.

a. The short word form is 68 and 1 thousand 275 hundred-thousandths.

b. The word form is sixty-eight and one thousand, two hundred seventy-five hundred-thousandths.

The keys to translating from word form to short word or standard form are to identify the word *and* (which represents the decimal point) and to pay attention to the *ths* place (tenths place, hundredths place, thousandths place, ten-thousandths place, and so on) in the word form.

EXAMPLE 6.3

CONNECTION

REPRESENTATION

Represent 4135.0026 in
a. short word form.
b. word form.

SOLUTION

The place value of the rightmost digit in the fractional part .0026 is ten-thousandths.

a. 4 thousand, 135 and 26 ten-thousandths

b. four thousand, one hundred thirty-five and twenty-six ten-thousandths

▲

EXAMPLE 6.4

CONNECTION

REPRESENTATION

Write two hundred thirty-five and ninety-three ten-thousandths in
a. short word form.
b. standard form.

SOLUTION

a. 235 and 93 ten-thousandths

b. 235.0093 (Make sure the digit 3 in the fractional part is in the ten-thousandths place.)

▲

The expanded forms of decimal numbers—natural extensions of the expanded forms of whole numbers—are useful for understanding procedures for adding, subtracting, multiplying, and dividing decimals.

EXAMPLE 6.5

CONNECTION

REPRESENTATION

Represent 3827.452 in expanded form with
a. decimals.
b. fractions.
c. multiplication.
d. exponents.

SOLUTION

a. $3827.452 = 3000 + 800 + 20 + 7 + 0.4 + 0.05 + 0.002$

b. $3827.452 = 3000 + 800 + 20 + 7 + \dfrac{4}{10} + \dfrac{5}{100} + \dfrac{2}{1000}$

c. $3827.452 = 3 \cdot 1000 + 8 \cdot 100 + 2 \cdot 10 + 7 \cdot 1 + 4 \cdot 0.1 + 5 \cdot 0.01 + 2 \cdot 0.001$

d. $3827.452 = 3 \cdot 10^3 + 8 \cdot 10^2 + 2 \cdot 10^1 + 7 \cdot 10^0 + 4 \cdot 10^{-1} + 5 \cdot 10^{-2} + 2 \cdot 10^{-3}$

▲

EXAMPLE 6.6

CONNECTION

COMMUNICATION

REASONING

REPRESENTATION

a. Represent 0.452 as a fraction.
b. Represent 3821.078 as a mixed number.

SOLUTION

a. $0.452 = 452 \text{ thousandths} = \dfrac{452}{1000}$

b. $3821.078 = 3821 \text{ and } 78 \text{ thousandths} = 3821\frac{78}{1000}$

▲

The Classroom Connection shows that students should be able to read and write decimal numbers.

> **Classroom Connection**
>
> ● *Math,* Grade 5, p. 8
>
> Write the word name and expanded form: 8.20; 47.034
> (© 2000 Macmillan/McGraw Hill. Reprinted by permission.)

Reading a decimal such as 0.45 as "forty-five hundredths" instead of "point forty-five" reminds students that terminating decimals are fractions (even though it's easier to say the latter).

The next example illustrates strategies for converting a fraction or mixed number to a decimal.

EXAMPLE 6.7

REPRESENTATION

Represent each fraction as a decimal number.

a. $\dfrac{43}{1000}$

b. $2\frac{3}{4}$

SOLUTION

a. $\frac{43}{1000}$ = 43 thousandths = 0.043 (The digit 3 is in the thousandths place.)

b. $2\frac{3}{4} = 2 + \frac{3}{4} = 2 + \frac{3 \cdot 25}{4 \cdot 25} = 2 + \frac{75}{100}$ = 2 and 75 hundredths = 2.75 (The digit 5 is in the hundredths place.) ▲

In fourth grade, students should "use decimal notation for fractions with denominators 10 or 100" (CCSS, Gr. 4).

> ■ **Historical Note**
>
> Long ago, mathematicians used various symbols to separate the integer part from the fractional part in a decimal (such as 93,687|045 or 93,687⁰⁴⁵). Many historians credit Christoph Clavius with introducing the decimal point in his publication *Astrolabium* in 1593. A few years later, John Napier used the dot as a separator in his book on logarithms, which paved the way for its current prominence. European nations, however, use a comma to separate the integer and decimal part but then use a thin space to separate groups of three digits in the integer part (for example, 34,567.89 is written as 34 567,89).

Ordering Decimals

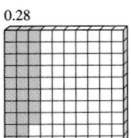 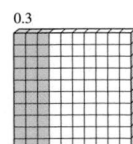

FIGURE 4
Using base ten blocks to compare 0.28 and 0.3.

When elementary school students compare whole numbers, they eventually realize that the whole number with the most digits is automatically larger. As a result, when they compare decimal numbers, they often mistakenly think the decimal number with the most digits is automatically larger. For example, many elementary school students mistakenly believe 0.28 > 0.3 because 28 > 3. In Figure 4, we use a diagram to challenge this flawed thinking and help students "compare two decimals to hundredths by reasoning about their size" (CCSS, Gr. 4).

The diagram suggests $0.28 < 0.3$, so the decimal number with more digits is not automatically larger. In the next example, we suggest two methods to compare decimal numbers. Students should be able to "compare two decimals to thousandths based on meanings of the digits in each place, using $>$, $=$, and $<$ symbols to record the results of comparisons" (CCSS, Gr. 5).

EXAMPLE 6.8

REASONING

REPRESENTATION

Compare 524.67 and 524.632.

SOLUTION

METHOD 1. Build on what we know: $524.67 = 524\frac{67}{100} = 524\frac{670}{1000}$ and $524.63 = 524\frac{632}{1000}$. Each decimal number has the same integer part, so compare their fractional parts: $\frac{670}{1000} > \frac{632}{1000}$. This means $524\frac{67}{100} > 524\frac{632}{1000}$. So $524.67 > 524.632$.

METHOD 2. Make a place value chart for the decimal numbers. Then annex zeros in the fractional part as needed to serve as placeholders (the conceptual basis for annexing zeros to serve as placeholders is regrouping: 67 hundredths = 670 thousandths). Then compare the leftmost place values and digits in each decimal number. In the event of a tie, move to the next place value to the right, much like the strategy for comparing whole numbers.

Hundreds	Tens	Ones	.	Tenths	Hundredths	Thousandths
5	2	4	.	6	7	0
5	2	4	.	6	3	2

↑   ↑   ↑   ↑
tie   tie   tie   tie $3 < 7$

3 is less than 7, so $524.632 < 524.67$.

▲

Adding and Subtracting Decimals

We use base ten blocks to model the algorithm for adding decimals, much like the process for adding whole numbers. The main idea is to combine similarly sized blocks, with regrouping as necessary. Figure 5 illustrates how to use base ten blocks to find the sum $1.34 + 2.81$.

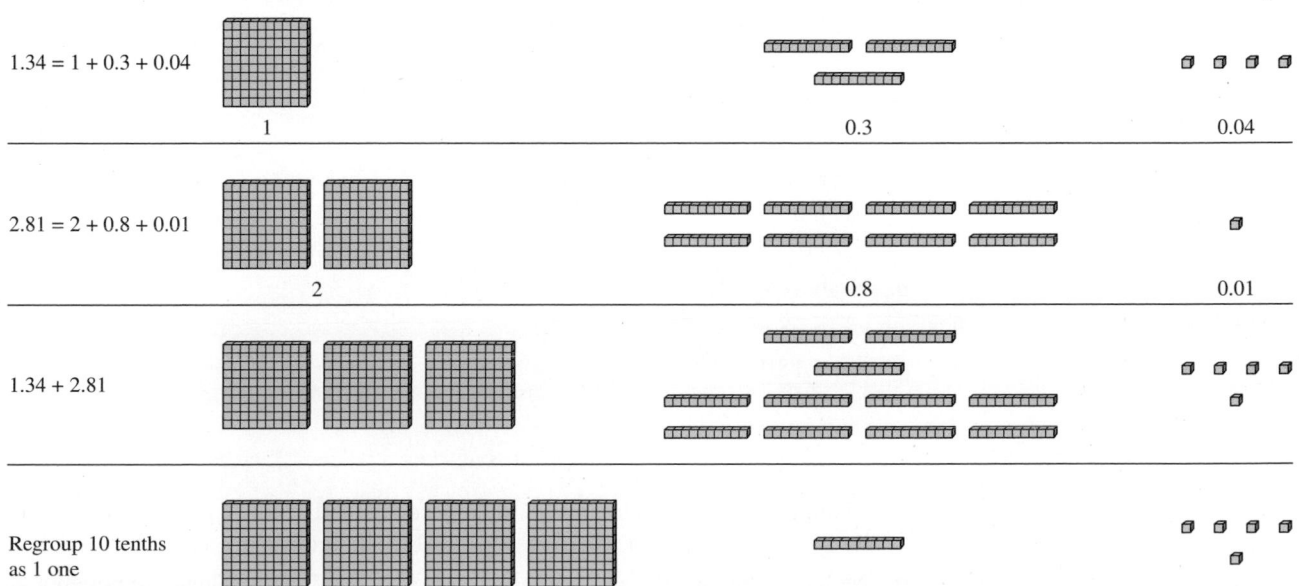

$1.34 = 1 + 0.3 + 0.04$ 1   0.3   0.04

$2.81 = 2 + 0.8 + 0.01$ 2   0.8   0.01

$1.34 + 2.81$

Regroup 10 tenths as 1 one

FIGURE 5

Using base ten blocks to model addition of decimals. $1.34 + 2.81 = 4.15$

CONNECTION
REPRESENTATION

We could also use base ten blocks to model subtraction of decimal numbers, using the take-away approach. Strategies for adding and subtracting decimal numbers rely on lining up the decimal points. The conceptual basis for lining up the decimal points in addition and subtraction is the action of combining or taking away similar groupings (for example, combine hundredths with hundredths, tenths with tenths, ones with ones, tens with tens, and so on, or take away hundredths from hundredths, tenths from tenths, ones from ones, tens from tens, and so on). In one study, less than 33% of elementary school students could explain the conceptual basis for lining up the decimal point for adding or subtracting decimals.

We can illustrate the algorithm for 68.35 + 5.274. The conceptual basis for annexing a zero in 68.35 is representing 35/100 as the equivalent fraction 350/1000 to prepare for adding similar groupings (add tens to tens, ones to ones, tenths to tenths, and so on).

Line up the decimal points. Insert zeros as placeholders, if necessary.	Add the digits. Regroup.	Insert the decimal point in the sum to separate the ones and tenths place values.
$\begin{array}{r} 68.350 \\ +\ 5.274 \\ \hline \end{array}$	$\begin{array}{r} ^{1}\ ^{1} \\ 68.350 \\ +\ 5.274 \\ \hline 73\ 624 \end{array}$	$\begin{array}{r} ^{1}\ ^{1} \\ 68.350 \\ +\ 5.274 \\ \hline 73.624 \end{array}$

This example involved regrouping skills: 0 thousandths + 4 thousandths = 4 thousandths, and 5 hundredths + 7 hundredths = 12 hundredths = 1 tenth, 2 hundredths. So the 1 above the 3 indicates the 1 tenth when we regroup 12 hundredths as 1 tenth and 2 hundredths. The following series illustrates the algorithm for 6.572 − 1.18.

Line up the decimal points. Insert zeros as placeholders, if necessary.	Subtract the digits. Regroup.	Insert the decimal point in the difference to separate the ones and tenths place values.
$\begin{array}{r} 6.572 \\ -\ 1.180 \\ \hline \end{array}$	$\begin{array}{r} ^{4\,17} \\ 6.5\not{7}2 \\ -\ 1.180 \\ \hline 5\ 392 \end{array}$	$\begin{array}{r} ^{4\,17} \\ 6.5\not{7}2 \\ -\ 1.180 \\ \hline 5.392 \end{array}$

This example involves regrouping skills: before we could take away 8 hundredths, we regrouped 5 tenths as 4 tenths and 10 hundredths, resulting in 10 + 7 = 17 hundredths. Then 17 hundredths take away 8 hundredths equals 9 hundredths.

EXAMPLE 6.9

COMMUNICATION
REASONING

What is the conceptual basis for the

a. 1 above the 2?

$$\begin{array}{r} ^{1} \\ 74.24 \\ +\ 5.38 \\ \hline 79.62 \end{array}$$

b. 13 above the 3?

$$\begin{array}{r} ^{4\,13} \\ 9.\not{5}\not{3}7 \\ -\ 5.180 \\ \hline 4.357 \end{array}$$

SOLUTION

a. 4 hundredths + 8 hundredths = 12 hundredths = 1 tenth, 2 hundredths. The 1 above the 2 represents 1 tenth when we regroup 12 hundredths as 1 tenth, 2 hundredths.

b. We have 3 hundredths and need to take away 8 hundredths. There are not enough hundredths. We regroup 1 tenth as 10 hundredths. Then 10 hundredths + 3 hundredths = 13 hundredths.

▲

Estimation

We can extend whole number skills to estimate sums, differences, products, and quotients of decimals. Generally, we look at the numbers and replace each with a number that makes the estimate easier to calculate. Thus, estimation is more of an art than a science.

- $1.34 + 2.81 \approx 1 + 3 = 4$
- $154.6423 + 28.262 \approx 155 + 30 = 185$, or $154.6423 + 28.262 \approx 150 + 30 = 180$
- $174.678 - 32.16 \approx 170 - 30 = 140$, or $174.678 - 32.16 \approx 175 - 30 = 145$
- $85.16 - 32.72 \approx 85 - 33 = 52$
- $3.89 \times 80.003 \approx 4 \times 80 = 320$
- $48.72 \div 5.235 \approx 48 \div 6 = 8$, or $48.72 \div 5.235 \approx 50 \div 5 = 10$
- $8734 \div 9.214 \approx 9000 \div 9 = 1000$

We use estimation to approximate a computation or judge the reasonableness of a computation.

Multiplying and Dividing by Powers of 10

The following example illustrates what happens to the decimal point when multiplying or dividing 4.32 by 10.

EXAMPLE 6.10

CONNECTION

REASONING

Verify the calculations using the expanded form of 4.32.

a. $4.32 \times 10 = 43.2$

b. $4.32 \div 10 = 0.432$

SOLUTION

a. $4.32 \times 10 = (4 \cdot 10^0 + 3 \cdot 10^{-1} + 2 \cdot 10^{-2}) \times 10^1 = 4 \cdot 10^1 + 3 \cdot 10^0 + 2 \cdot 10^{-1}$
$$= 43.2$$

b. $4.32 \div 10 = 4.32 \times \dfrac{1}{10} = 4.32 \times 10^{-1} = (4 \cdot 10^0 + 3 \cdot 10^{-1} + 2 \cdot 10^{-2}) \times 10^{-1}$
$$= 4 \cdot 10^{-1} + 3 \cdot 10^{-2} + 2 \cdot 10^{-3} = 0.432$$

▲

The expanded form and the property of exponents clarify why the decimal point shifts left or right. How many places does the decimal point shift when you multiply by 100? How many places does the decimal point shift when you divide by 1000? The number of zeros in 100 or 1000 is the critical clue. You can also use a calculator to multiply (4.32×10, 4.32×100, 4.32×1000) and divide ($4.32 \div 10$, $4.32 \div 100$, $4.32 \div 1000$) to see what happens to the decimal point. Does the decimal point shift left or right? Students should be able to "explain patterns in the placement of the decimal point when a decimal is multiplied or divided by a power of 10" (CCSS, Gr. 5).

Multiplying Decimals

The product 2.14×7.034 is about 2×7, so a reasonable estimate of 2.14×7.034 is 14. To multiply two decimals, we could first express them as fractions, then multiply the fractions, and finally express the fraction as a decimal.

CONNECTION

$$2.14 \times 7.034 = \frac{214}{100} \times \frac{7034}{1000} \qquad \textbf{Writing each decimal as an equivalent fraction}$$

$$= \frac{214 \times 7034}{100 \times 1000} \qquad \textbf{Applying the rule for multiplying fractions}$$

$$= \frac{1,505,276}{100,000} \qquad \textbf{Simplification}$$

$$= 15.05276 \qquad \textbf{Dividing by } 10^5 \textbf{, which amounts to shifting the decimal point five places to the left}$$

This example suggests the following three-step procedure to calculate a product of decimals such as 2.14×7.034:

1. *Ignore* the decimal points temporarily and compute the product of the resulting whole numbers: $214 \times 7034 = 1{,}505{,}276$.

2. *Add* the number of decimal digits in the fractional part of each factor: $2 + 3 = 5$. This means the product 2.14×7.034 has five decimal digits.

3. *Insert* the decimal point in the product of whole numbers to create a decimal number with the correct number of decimal digits determined in the previous step. Thus, insert the decimal point in 1505276 to create a decimal number with five decimal digits to get 15.05276. Then $2.14 \times 7.034 = 15.05276$.

EXAMPLE 6.11

CONNECTION
REASONING

a. What whole number multiplication problem does 3.40×6.7 involve?

b. Without making any calculations, insert the decimal point in the proper position in the number on the right-hand side of the equation: $81.7 \times 5.025 = 4105425$.

SOLUTION

a. By ignoring the decimal points, 3.40×6.7 involves the whole number product 340×67.

b. We can use two approaches.

METHOD 1. The number of decimal digits in the fractional parts is $1 + 3 = 4$, so $81.7 \times 5.025 = 410.5425$.

METHOD 2. $81.27 \times 5.025 \approx 80 \times 5 = 400$, so $81.7 \times 5.025 = 410.5425$. ▲

The following Classroom Connection shows that students should be familiar with the process of multiplying two decimal numbers.

> ### Classroom Connection
>
> Harcourt *Math*, Student Edition, Grade 5, p. 72
>
> Explain how you would place the decimal point in the product 0.27×0.476.
> Tell the number of decimal places there will be in the product 4.04×5.2.
> Copy the problem. Place the decimal point in the product 0.7×4.1.
> (© by Harcourt, Inc. Reproduced by permission of the publisher, Houghton Mifflin Harcourt Publishing Company.)

Dividing Decimals

In the following example, we use base ten blocks and the repeated subtraction model of division to calculate $1.2 \div 0.3$. This example shows students that it is possible and meaningful to divide by a decimal.

EXAMPLE 6.12

CONNECTION
COMMUNICATION
PROBLEM SOLVING
REASONING
REPRESENTATION

Mary used 1.2 pounds of sugar to make cookies. She used 0.3 pounds of sugar in each batch of cookies. How many batches of cookies did she make?

SOLUTION

The problem involves splitting 1.2 into equal-sized groups of 0.3, so we need to calculate $1.2 \div 0.3$. In Figure 6(a), we represent 1.2 with a diagram. We use the repeated subtraction model of division.

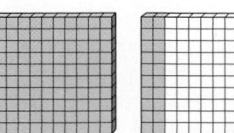

FIGURE 6(a)
Model of 1.2.

In Figure 6(b), we create equal-sized groups of 0.3.

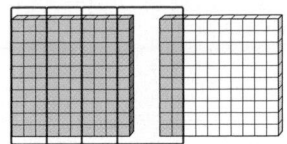

FIGURE 6(b)
Creating equal-sized groups of 0.3.

There are four equal-sized groups, so $1.2 \div 0.3 = 4$. This means Mary made four batches of cookies. ▲

We can use equivalent fractions to motivate a procedure for handling division problems that build on division with whole number divisors:

CONNECTION

- $150.765 \div 26.46 = \frac{150.765}{26.46} = \frac{150.765 \times 100}{26.46 \times 100} = \frac{15,076.5}{2646} = 15,076.5 \div 2646$
- $240.072 \div 5.6 = \frac{240.072}{5.6} = \frac{240.072 \times 10}{5.6 \times 10} = \frac{2400.72}{56} = 2400.72 \div 56$

Each division problem now involves a whole number divisor. These two examples suggest the following strategy when the divisor has a fractional part: shift the decimal point of the divisor to the right to obtain a whole number divisor, and then shift the decimal point of the dividend to the right the same number of places. The conceptual basis for shifting the decimal point to the right is multiplying the dividend and divisor by the same positive power of 10 (10, 100, 1000, . . .).

The following example illustrates the internal dialogue that underlies meaningful division with decimals. It mimics the internal dialogue we should have with division with whole numbers using the fair share model of division. Regrouping skills are paramount for understanding division with decimals.

EXAMPLE 6.13 Divide: $85.128 \div 2.4$.

CONNECTION
COMMUNICATION
REASONING
REPRESENTATION

SOLUTION

First, we shift the decimal point one place value to the right. Then we divide, using the fair share interpretation of division (split 851.28 into 24 groups; how much per group?) The steps show the internal dialogue that helps students make sense of division.

$2.4\overline{)8\,5.1\,2\,8}$ **Shift the decimal point, because $85.128 \div 2.4 = 851.28 \div 24$.**
$\quad \rightarrow \quad \rightarrow$

$\begin{array}{r} 3 \\ 24\overline{)8\,5\,1.2\,8} \\ -7\,2 \\ \hline 1\,3 \end{array}$ **Regroup: 8 hundreds, 5 tens = 85 tens.**
$24 \times 3 = 72$, so each group gets 3 tens.
Take away 72 tens: $85 - 72 = 13$ tens.

$\begin{array}{r} 3 \\ 24\overline{)8\,5\,1.2\,8} \\ -7\,2\downarrow \\ \hline 1\,3\,1 \end{array}$ **"Bring down the 1," which means regroup 13 tens, 1 one as 131 ones.**

$\begin{array}{r} 3\,5. \\ 24\overline{)8\,5\,1.2\,8} \\ -7\,2\downarrow \\ \hline 1\,3\,1 \\ -1\,2\,0 \\ \hline 1\,1 \end{array}$ **$24 \times 5 = 120$, so each group gets 5 ones.**
Take away 120 ones: 131 ones − 120 ones = 11 ones.

(continued)

$$
\begin{array}{r}
3\,5. \\
24\overline{)8\,5\,1.2\,8} \\
-7\,2\downarrow \\
\hline
1\,3\,1
\end{array}
$$

$-1\,2\,0\downarrow$ "Bring down the 2," which means regroup 11 ones, 2 tenths as
$\overline{1\,1\,2}$ **112 tenths.**

$$
\begin{array}{r}
3\,5.4 \\
24\overline{)8\,5\,1.2\,8} \\
-7\,2\downarrow \\
\hline
1\,3\,1 \\
-1\,2\,0\downarrow
\end{array}
$$

 **24 × 4 = 96, so each group gets 4 tenths.**
$\overline{1\,1\,2}$ **Take away 96 tenths: 112 tenths − 96 tenths = 16 tenths.**
$-9\,6$
$\overline{1\,6}$

$$
\begin{array}{r}
3\,5.4 \\
24\overline{)8\,5\,1.2\,8} \\
-7\,2\downarrow \\
\hline
1\,3\,1 \\
-1\,2\,0\downarrow \\
\hline
1\,1\,2
\end{array}
$$

$-9\,6\downarrow$ "Bring down the 8," which means regroup 16 tenths, 8 hundredths as
$\overline{1\,6\,8}$ **168 hundredths.**

$$
\begin{array}{r}
3\,5.4\,7 \\
24\overline{)8\,5\,1.2\,8} \\
-7\,2\downarrow \\
\hline
1\,3\,1 \\
-1\,2\,0\downarrow \\
\hline
1\,1\,2
\end{array}
$$

$-9\,6\downarrow$ **7 × 24 = 168, so take away 168 hundredths:**
$\overline{1\,6\,8}$ **168 hundredths − 168 hundredths = 0 hundredths.**
$-1\,6\,8$ **There are no more hundredths, thousandths, and so on, to give away,**
$\overline{0}$ **so the procedure terminates.**

So $85.128 \div 2.4 = 35.47$.

▲

Terminating Decimals and Fractions

A **terminating decimal number** is a decimal with a finite number of digits to the right of the decimal point, such as 0.028, 56.0, and 1457.6001. A rational number is any number that can be expressed in the form $\frac{a}{b}$, where a and b are integers and $b \neq 0$. The following examples suggest a connection between rational numbers and terminating decimals using inductive reasoning. At the end of this section, these connections are proved using deductive reasoning (we postpone the proofs to maintain the flow of the main ideas).

EXAMPLE 6.14

CONNECTION

REASONING

A student claims that any positive terminating decimal can be represented as a positive rational number with a positive power of 10 as the denominator. Use inductive reasoning to support this claim.

SOLUTION

Let's explore this claim with a few examples: $0.028 = \frac{28}{1000}$, $56.3 = \frac{563}{10}$, $1457.6001 = \frac{14,576,001}{10,000}$, and $3.2 = \frac{32}{10}$. These examples support the claim that any positive terminating decimal can be represented as a positive rational number with a positive power of 10 as the denominator.

▲

EXAMPLE 6.15

CONNECTION

REASONING

A student claims that any positive rational number with a positive power of 10 as the denominator can be represented as a positive terminating decimal. Use inductive reasoning to support this claim.

SOLUTION

Let's explore this claim with a few examples: $345/1000 = 0.345$, $234/10 = 23.4$, and $7180/100 = 71.80$. These examples support the claim that any positive rational number with a positive power of 10 as the denominator can be represented as a positive terminating decimal.

▲

Some rational numbers can be converted to a fraction with a power of 10 in the denominator by multiplying the numerator and denominator by a suitable power of 2 or 5. For example, $\frac{7}{8} = \frac{7}{2^3} = \frac{7 \times 5^3}{2^3 \times 5^3} = \frac{7 \times 5^3}{(2 \times 5)^3} = \frac{7 \times 5^3}{10^3}$, so $\frac{7}{8}$ can be expressed as a terminating decimal. The rational number $\frac{2}{3}$ cannot be written as a terminating decimal, because it's impossible to express the denominator as a power of 10. What about the rational number $\frac{21}{6}$? The common factor of 21 and 6 is 3, so $\frac{21}{6} = \frac{7 \times 3}{2 \times 3} = \frac{7}{2} = \frac{7 \times 5}{2 \times 5} = \frac{35}{10}$, which means $\frac{21}{6}$ can be expressed as a terminating decimal.

The prime numbers 2 and 5 are the only prime factors of the positive powers of 10 (10, 100, 1000, and so on). We now reformulate the main results of the preceding examples as a theorem.

> **Theorem 1**
>
> Suppose the only common factor of the whole numbers a and b is 1 and $b > 1$. The rational number $\frac{a}{b}$ is a terminating decimal if and only if all prime factors of b belong to the set $\{2, 5\}$.

The following example applies this result.

EXAMPLE 6.16

REASONING

Explain why

a. $\frac{7}{40}$ is a terminating decimal.

b. $\frac{18}{48}$ is a terminating decimal.

c. $\frac{7}{2^4 \cdot 11^3 \cdot 5^8}$ is not a terminating decimal.

SOLUTION

a. $\frac{7}{40}$ is in its simplest form. The prime factorization of 40 is $40 = 2^3 \cdot 5$. The only prime factors of 40 are 2 and 5. By Theorem 1, $\frac{7}{40}$ is a terminating decimal.

b. $\frac{18}{48}$ has $\frac{3}{8}$ as its simplest form. The prime factorization of 8 is $8 = 2^3$. The only prime factor of 8 is 2. By Theorem 1, $\frac{3}{8}$ is a terminating decimal. Then $\frac{18}{48}$ is a terminating decimal.

c. $\frac{7}{2^4 \cdot 11^3 \cdot 5^8}$ is in its simplest form. The denominator has the prime factors 2, 5, and 11. By Theorem 1, $\frac{7}{2^4 \cdot 11^3 \cdot 5^8}$ is not a terminating decimal.

▲

Concept Map 6.1 summarizes the main results in the last two examples, which helps students "know that the decimal form of a rational number terminates in 0s or eventually repeats" (CCSS, Gr. 7).

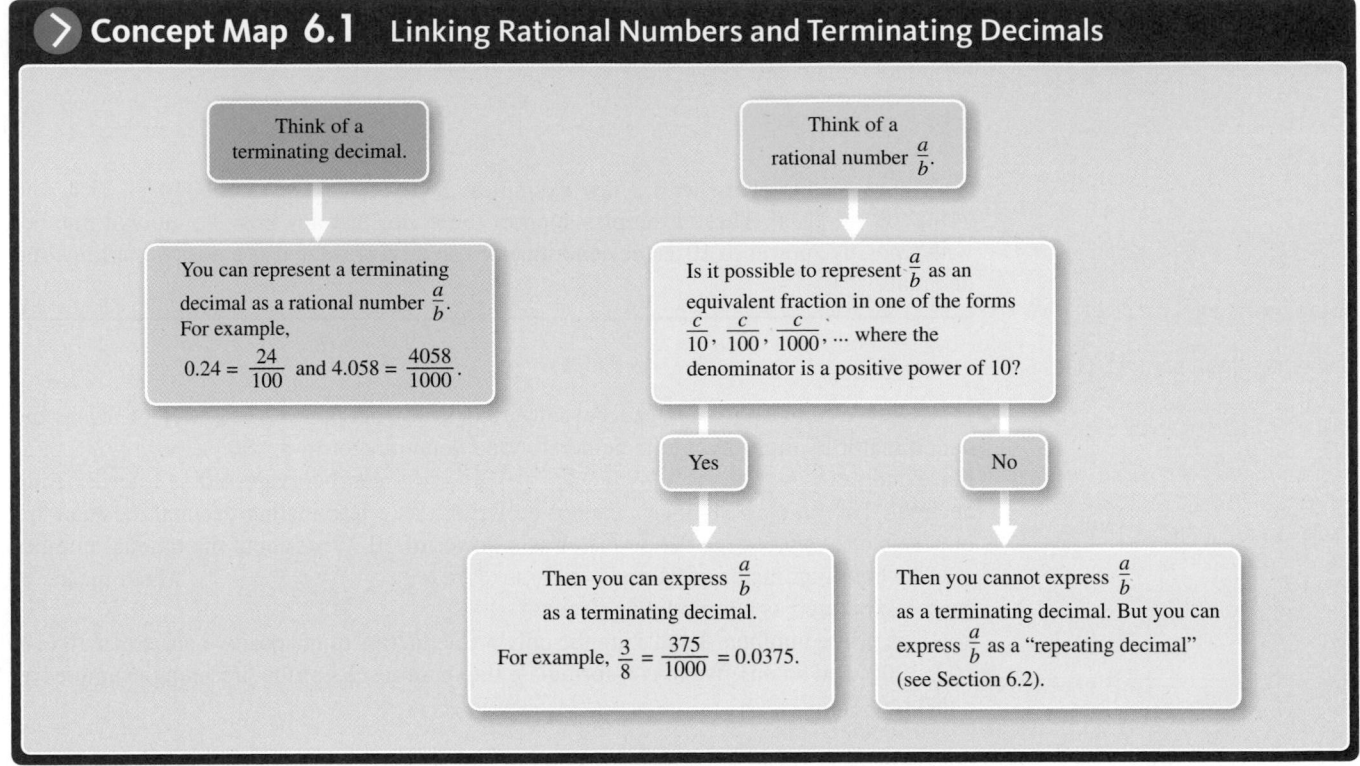

> **Concept Map 6.1**   Linking Rational Numbers and Terminating Decimals

Think of a terminating decimal.

Think of a rational number $\frac{a}{b}$.

You can represent a terminating decimal as a rational number $\frac{a}{b}$. For example,

$$0.24 = \frac{24}{100} \text{ and } 4.058 = \frac{4058}{1000}.$$

Is it possible to represent $\frac{a}{b}$ as an equivalent fraction in one of the forms $\frac{c}{10}, \frac{c}{100}, \frac{c}{1000}, \dots$ where the denominator is a positive power of 10?

Yes

No

Then you can express $\frac{a}{b}$ as a terminating decimal.

For example, $\frac{3}{8} = \frac{375}{1000} = 0.0375$.

Then you cannot express $\frac{a}{b}$ as a terminating decimal. But you can express $\frac{a}{b}$ as a "repeating decimal" (see Section 6.2).

Multiplication Makes Bigger, Division Makes Smaller Myth

"Math Standards & Expectations" in the NCTM's *Principles and Standards for School Mathematics* states that students should "understand the meaning and effects of arithmetic operations with fractions, decimals, and integers" (NCTM, Gr. 6–8). When multiplying and dividing with positive decimals, many students apply their experience with counting numbers and incorrectly make the generalization that "multiplication makes bigger (MMB), division makes smaller (DMS)." You could use diagrams to model 0.5×6 (show one-half of a group of six objects is three objects) to challenge the MMB generalization and $1.2 \div 0.4$ (show there are three groups of 0.4 in 1.2) to challenge the DMS generalization. The next example uses algebraic reasoning to prove that in some cases a product of decimal numbers is less than one of the factors.

EXAMPLE 6.17   Let a and b be nonzero positive decimals with $0 < b < 1$. Prove $a \cdot b < a$.

SOLUTION

Suppose a and b are nonzero positive decimals and $0 < b < 1$. We know b is positive and less than 1, so there is a positive decimal c such that $b + c = 1$ (just choose c equal to $1 - b$). Then $a \cdot (b + c) = a \cdot 1$. Then $a \cdot b + a \cdot c = a \cdot 1$. Then $a \cdot b + a \cdot c = a$. Both a and c are positive, so $a \cdot c$ is positive. The definition of "less than" implies $a \cdot b < a$. Thus, the product $a \cdot b$ is less than the factor a, that is, $a \cdot b < a$.

Rounding

The process of rounding decimals is similar to that of rounding whole numbers.

EXAMPLE 6.18

CONNECTION
REASONING

a. Round 5286.34721 to the nearest hundredth.

b. Round 35.18928 to the nearest thousandth.

SOLUTION

a. The nearby hundredths are 5286.34 and 5286.35, and 5286.34721 is closer to 5286.35.

b. The nearby thousandths are 35.189 and 35.190, and 35.18928 is closer to 35.189.

▲

Additive and Multiplicative Reasoning

The additive and multiplicative reasoning skills we developed with whole numbers and fractions extend to decimal numbers. The next example illustrates additive and multiplicative reasoning to compare decimal numbers.

EXAMPLE 6.19

CONNECTION
COMMUNICATION
REASONING

Jupiter is 890.8 million miles from the Sun, while Earth is 93 million miles from the Sun. Compare the distances using

a. additive reasoning.

b. multiplicative reasoning.

SOLUTION

a. $890.8 - 93 = 797.8$. Jupiter is about 800 million miles farther from the Sun than Earth.

b. $890.8 \div 93 \approx 9.6$. Jupiter is about 9.6 times as far from the Sun as Earth.

▲

Now we provide the proof of Theorem 1.

- *Any positive terminating decimal can be represented as a positive rational number with a positive power of 10 as the denominator.* A positive terminating decimal can be written in the form $a + \frac{b}{10^n}$, for some whole numbers a, b, and n, where a is the whole number part and $\frac{b}{10^n}$ is the fractional part. Then $a + \frac{b}{10^n} = \frac{a \cdot 10^n + b}{10^n}$. By the closure properties of multiplication and addition, $a \cdot 10^n + b$ is a whole number. The numerator and denominator are whole numbers, and the denominator is a positive power of 10. This proves the claim that any positive terminating decimal can be represented as a positive rational number with a positive power of 10 as the denominator.

- *Any positive rational number with a positive power of 10 as the denominator can be represented as a positive terminating decimal.* Let $\frac{w}{10^n}$ represent a positive rational number with a positive power of 10 as the denominator, where w is a whole number with digits $w = a_1 a_2 \ldots a_k$ such that $a_1 \neq 0$. For example, $\frac{w}{10^n}$ could be $\frac{789}{10^5}$, where w is a whole number with the expanded form $w = 7 \cdot 10^2 + 8 \cdot 10^1 + 9 \cdot 10^0$. In general, w has the expanded form $w = a_1 \cdot 10^{k-1} + a_2 \cdot 10^{k-2} + \ldots + a_k \cdot 10^0$. Our goal is to show that $\frac{w}{10^n}$ is a terminating decimal.

$$\frac{w}{10^n} = w \cdot 10^{-n}$$
$$= (a_1 \cdot 10^{k-1} + a_2 \cdot 10^{k-2} + \ldots + a_k \cdot 10^0) \cdot 10^{-n}$$
$$= a_1 \cdot 10^{k-1-n} + a_2 \cdot 10^{k-2-n} + \ldots + a_k \cdot 10^{-n}$$

The expanded form of $\frac{w}{10^n}$ has a finite number of addends, and each addend indicates a place value, so $\frac{w}{10^n}$ is a terminating decimal. This proves the claim that any positive rational number with a positive power of 10 as the denominator can be represented as a positive terminating decimal.

QUESTIONS FOR SECTION 6.1

REPRESENTATION

Refresher: Representations (language, diagrams, tables, symbols, algebra, manipulatives, and contextualized situations) are important because we use them to organize, record, and communicate mathematical ideas and to make them more comprehensible.

1. The large decimal square represents 1 unit. Identify the decimal represented by the shaded region.

   a. 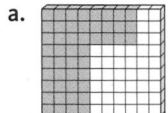   b.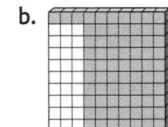

2. The large decimal square represents 1 unit. Shade the decimal square to represent the given decimal with a diagram.

   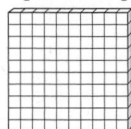

   a. 0.03   b. 0.26   c. 0.74

3. Some elementary school students think 0.35 is greater than 0.8 because they inappropriately compare whole numbers.

   a. What whole numbers are they comparing?

   b. Draw decimal squares to compare the two decimal numbers.

4. Represent 0.6 on a number line.

5. Represent 0.42 on a number line.

6. Represent each decimal in standard form.

   a. three hundred forty-seven and four hundred twenty-three thousandths

   b. twenty-eight thousand, three hundred seventy-four and two hundred thirty-five hundred-thousandths

   c. fifty-eight and thirteen ten-thousandths

7. Represent each decimal in short word form.

   a. 9.05   b. 56,835.708   c. 14.0037

8. Represent each decimal in word form.

   a. 3.84123   b. 62.04021   c. 0.0036

9. In the decimal 5146.7321, specify the digit in the

   a. tenths place.   b. ten-thousandths place.

PROBLEM SOLVING

Refresher: Problem solving (reaching a goal that is not immediately attainable) is important because it helps students think more deeply about what they know and deal with unfamiliar situations.

10. A phone company has a plan called the California Classic. Under this plan, local calls cost $0.0349 per minute and state-to-state calls cost $0.049 per minute. There is no monthly fee.

    a. Your telephone budget is $72. What is the maximum number of minutes of local calls that can be made?

    b. Your telephone budget is $37. What is the maximum number of minutes of state-to-state calls that can be made?

    c. Write an expression that represents the monthly charge for x minutes of local calls and y minutes of state-to-state calls.

    d. Suppose your current monthly bill was $51.04 and you spent about five-eighths of your total minutes on local calls. Approximate the number of minutes you spent on each type of call.

11. Determine the tenths digit in $0.8 - (0.5)^{40}$.

12. A legal assistant charges $35 for 15 minutes of work and $5 for every 3 minutes thereafter. What is the charge for a legal assistant who spends 38 minutes on a task?

13. A brand of clay brick tiles has the dimensions $3\frac{5}{8}$ by $7\frac{5}{8}$ by $\frac{1}{2}$ inch. These thin bricks are commonly used for floors. Estimate the cost to tile the floor of a 12-by-17-foot room. Each clay brick tile sells for $0.72. Round your final answer to the nearest hundred.

14. The Gregorian calendar has 365.2425 days per year. The tropical calendar has 365.24220 days per year. Over a century, by how many days do the two calendars differ?

REASONING AND PROOF

Refresher: Reasoning and proof (thinking and justifying) are important because they help students make sense of mathematics.

15. Use a calculator.

    a. Multiply: $34.12 \cdot 10^1$, $34.12 \cdot 10^2$, $34.12 \cdot 10^3$, and $34.12 \cdot 10^4$.

    b. Make a conjecture about the effect of multiplying by a positive power of 10.

16. Use the expanded form of 2.345 and properties of exponents to verify that $2.345 \times 100 = 234.5$.

17. Use a calculator.

    a. Divide: $456.12 \div 10^1$, $456.12 \div 10^2$, $456.12 \div 10^3$, and $456.12 \div 10^4$.

    b. Make a conjecture about the effect of dividing by a positive power of 10.

18. Use the expanded form of 567.8 and property of exponents to verify that $567.8 \div 100 = 5.678$.

19. What whole number multiplication problem does 34.8×0.0023 require?

20. What division problem does $22.231 \div 4.3$ require such that the divisor in the new division problem is a whole number?

21. Every number n in the interval $2.75 \leq n < 2.85$ equals 2.8 when n is rounded to the nearest tenth. Find the largest possible interval such that all numbers in the interval equal

    a. 5.6, rounded to the nearest tenth.

    b. 7.23, rounded to the nearest hundredth.

    c. 15.000, rounded to the nearest thousandth.

22. Use estimation to insert the decimal point.

    a. $13.845 \div 3.25 = 426$ **b.** $88.5495 \div 4.75 = 18642$

    c. $487.24 \times 9.38 = 45703112$

    d. $75.7341 \times 3.45 = 261282645$

23. Find the next two terms in the sequence.

$$20 \div 10 = 2$$
$$20 \div 5 = 4$$
$$20 \div 2.5 = 8$$

24. The following table is based on 2008 data from the U.S. Census Bureau in the 2006–2008 American Community Survey.

Highest education level	Average (median) salary
High school dropout	$19,989
High school diploma	$27,448
Bachelor's degree	$47,853
Graduate or professional degree	$63,174

    a. Compare the salary earned by a high school dropout to the salary earned by a high school graduate. Use additive reasoning, and then use multiplicative reasoning.

    b. Compare the salary earned by a high school graduate to the salary earned by a college graduate with a bachelor's degree. Use additive reasoning, and then use multiplicative reasoning.

CONNECTIONS

Refresher: Connections (linking and applying mathematical ideas) are important because they deepen student understanding and make mathematics more meaningful, flexible, and useful.

25. What simpler whole number multiplication problem do you need to solve to calculate 4.50×0.32?

26. A teacher asks her students, "What simpler whole number multiplication problem do you need to solve to calculate 8.20×5.216?" Carlos realizes an answer and shouts, "820×5216!" Explain why Carlos is correct.

27. What simpler division problem do you need to solve to calculate $43.5 \div 0.75$?

28. A driver fills up his car's tank with 20 gallons of gas. After he drives 350 miles, he stops for fuel, and 12.5 gallons are needed to fill the tank. How many miles per gallon did he get?

29. The ratio of a picture's width to height is known as its aspect ratio.

    a. TV programming is usually formatted to a screen with a 4:3 aspect ratio. Many TV shows are adopting a 16:9 screen format. Which screen looks more like a square? Justify your answer.

    b. You can express an aspect ratio as an equivalent unit ratio in the form $a{:}1$. An image with an aspect ratio greater than 1 is called a landscape image. An image with an aspect ratio less than 1 is called a portrait image. Determine the type of image for the following aspect ratios: 4:3 and 5:9.

30. Some scientists examine bubbles of air trapped in ice sheets to study changes in Earth's climate. The bubbles of air in the ice sheets capture the mix of gasses in the atmosphere. Some scientists say that high levels of methane point to periods of global warming. In a special vacuum, 2 tons of ice from a glacier must be melted to produce a 200-L sample of air, which nets 0.1 mmol of methane for analysis.

    a. How many tons of ice must be melted to produce 710.25 L of air?

    b. How many liters of air are required to produce 0.15 mmol of methane gas?

31. The price per share in stocks is computed to the nearest ten-thousandth of a dollar.

    a. Suppose you own 450 shares with a total value of $12,000. What is the price per share?

    b. Suppose you own 247 shares with a total value of $389. What is the price per share?

32. Pavers are bricks made of water and cement for sidewalks, patios, and driveways. The water-to-cement ratio of typical pavers is 0.27 to 0.33 pounds, according to the Interlocking Pavement Concrete Institute.

    a. How many pounds of water should you add to 90 pounds of cement?

    b. How many pounds of cement should you add to 60 pounds of water?

    c. How many pounds of water and cement would you use to make 90 pounds of pavers?

COMMUNICATION

Refresher: Communication (written and verbal explanations using representations and proper mathematical vocabulary) is important because it helps students refine and strengthen their understanding.

33. Explain why the ones place is the focal point of the decimal number system.

34. Explain how you know 0.4 and 0.40 represent the same amount.

35. Without computing the quotient, explain why $6 \div 0.2$ is greater or less than 6.

36. A student may think 0.32 is greater than 0.7.

    a. Explain why the student may reach this conclusion.

    b. Use decimal squares to compare the two numbers.

37. Answer the following.

    a. What is really going on when we bring down the 2?

    b. What is the digit in the tenths place of the quotient?

    c. What is the digit in the hundredths place of the quotient?

$$\begin{array}{r} 3. \\ 15\overline{)46.26} \\ -45\downarrow \\ \hline 1\,2 \end{array}$$

More practice with the ideas of the section

38. Fill in the blank. Choose one of the following words, phrases, or symbols: *0.002, .23, 23, 40, 80, 400, 800, decimal, decimal fractions, fraction, fractions, hundredths, nonterminating, rational number, tenths, terminating,* or *thousandths.*

    a. $\frac{45}{100}$ and $\frac{7}{20}$ are examples of _____.

    b. 4.15 is an example of a(n) _____ decimal.

    c. In 5.4821, the place value of the digit 8 is _____.

    d. 5.48<u>2</u>1, the value of the underlined digit is ___.

    e. The fractional part of 6.23 is ___.

39. Represent each decimal in standard form.

    a. two hundred seventy-eight and three hundred five ten-thousandths

    b. thirty-six and two hundred thirteen millionths

40. In the decimal 4375.09286, specify the digit in the

    a. tenths place.   **b.** thousands place.

    c. ten-thousandths place.

41. Represent the decimal in short word form.

    a. fifty-two and twenty-four hundredths

    b. thirty-eight and twenty-four ten-thousandths

    c. fifteen thousand, three hundred forty-nine and three hundred forty-nine millionths

42. Fill in the blank.

    a. 1 tenth = ___ hundredths   **b.** 2 hundredths = ___ tenths

    c. 4 ones = ___ tenths   **d.** 3 tenths = ___ hundredths

43. In the decimal number 1.131567098, specify the place value of the given digit.

    a. 3 **b.** 5 **c.** 0 **d.** 8

44. In the decimal number 56.3082, specify the value of the given digit.

    a. 3 **b.** 5 **c.** 0 **d.** 8

45. Represent each decimal in short word form.

    a. 8.015 **b.** 801.00450 **c.** 0.00082

46. Represent each decimal as a fraction or mixed number.

    a. 3.84123 **b.** 62.04021 **c.** 0.0036

47. Write each decimal as a fraction in its simplified form.

    a. 0.45 **b.** 0.450

48. Write the word form of each fraction.

    a. 0.45 **b.** 0.450

49. Round

    a. 34.5678 to the nearest hundredth.

    b. 567.234 to the nearest hundred.

    c. 7341.0038 to the nearest thousandth.

    d. 8765.0076 to the nearest thousand.

50. All numbers n in the interval $4.55 \le n < 4.65$ equal 4.6 when rounded to the nearest tenth. Use this example to find the largest possible interval such that all numbers in the interval equal

    a. 12.7, rounded to the nearest tenth.

    b. 12.70, rounded to the nearest hundredth.

51. A phone plan for state-to-state calls is $0.50 for 10 minutes or less and $0.05 for each additional minute. Determine the cost of a call that lasts

    a. 5 minutes. **b.** 15 minutes. **c.** 24 minutes.

52. Why does the 1 appear above the

    a. 5? **b.** 2?

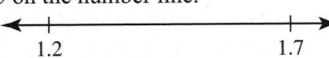

$$\begin{array}{r} \overset{1}{4}2.\overset{1}{6}58 \\ +\ 3.734 \\ \hline 46.392 \end{array}$$

53. Answer the following.

    a. Why does the 2 appear above the 3?

    b. Why does the 16 appear above the 6?

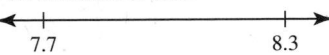

$$\begin{array}{r} \overset{2}{4}\overset{16}{\cancel{3}}.\cancel{6}58 \\ -\ 1.732 \\ \hline 41.926 \end{array}$$

54. Answer the following.

    a. What is really going on when we bring down the 6?

    b. What is the digit in the tenths place of the quotient?

    c. What is the digit in the hundredths place of the quotient?

$$\begin{array}{r} 3. \\ 18\overline{)55.62} \\ -54\downarrow \\ \hline 1\,6 \end{array}$$

55. Locate 1.45 on the number line.

$$\overset{\longleftarrow\quad\quad\quad\quad\quad\quad\longrightarrow}{\underset{\underset{1.2}{|}\qquad\qquad\qquad\underset{1.7}{|}}{}}$$

56. Locate 8.15 on the number line.

$$\overset{\longleftarrow\quad\quad\quad\quad\quad\quad\longrightarrow}{\underset{\underset{7.7}{|}\qquad\qquad\qquad\underset{8.3}{|}}{}}$$

57. Represent each sum as a decimal.

    a. $35 + \dfrac{7}{10}$ **b.** $\dfrac{5}{1000} + \dfrac{3}{10,000}$

    c. $200 + 8 + \dfrac{3}{100} + \dfrac{5}{10,000}$

58. Multiply. Show all steps you would expect your elementary school students to show.

    a. 4.34×2.6 **b.** 12.7×0.06 **c.** 0.034×0.28

59. Divide. Show your work.

    a. $7.8 \div 2.4$ **b.** $3.144 \div 0.6$ **c.** $0.6152 \div 0.04$

60. Which sum is easier to express as a decimal, $3 + \frac{4}{10} + \frac{8}{100}$ or $3 + \frac{4}{7}$? Explain.

61. Use examples to support that a terminating decimal is a rational number.

62. Suppose $a \div b = 1.75$. Find
   a. $(10a) \div b$.   **b.** $a \div (10b)$.

63. Without using a calculator, determine whether the fraction can be written as a terminating decimal. Justify your answer.
   a. $\dfrac{5}{8}$ **b.** $\dfrac{4^{10}}{7^{12} \times 5^{20}}$ **c.** $\dfrac{33}{15}$ **d.** $\dfrac{105}{72}$

64. Use division to convert each fraction into a decimal. Round your answer to the nearest hundredth.
   a. $\dfrac{6}{8}$ **b.** $\dfrac{7}{15}$ **c.** $\dfrac{13}{70}$

65. Three packs of paper and six markers cost $4.38. Eleven markers and seven packs of paper cost $9.26. How much does one marker cost?

66. A magic square is a 3-by-3 table filled with numbers so that the sum of each row, column, or diagonal is the same.
   a. Is the table a magic square?

0.8	0.1	0.6
0.3	0.5	0.7
0.4	0.9	0.2

   b. Create a new magic square filled with decimals such that the smallest entry is 2.08.

67. Cheryl is publishing a book with 150 pages. She needs 153 copies. There are 500 sheets of paper in a ream. How many reams of paper does she need?

68. At the local movie theater, the ticket cost for a senior citizen (age 60 and over) is $6, while the ticket cost for an adult is $6.50 and a child is $5.25. Jean has a coupon for $4.25 per ticket. She treats her 68-year-old friend and her four young daughters, as well as herself, to a movie. How much can Jean save by using the coupon?

69. When you multiply 0.003 and 0.64, you need to multiply 3 and 64 and then insert zeros in the product. Write and multiply two other decimals that require you to insert additional zeros in the product.

70. The U.S. Bank Tower, built in 1989, is the tallest building in Los Angeles. Los Angeles City Hall, built in 1926, is the 26th tallest building is Los Angeles.

Building	Height
US Bank Tower	310 m
Los Angeles City Hall	134 m

   The tower is about 2.3 times taller than city hall. Find similar data at the Emporis website (www.emporis.com/en/), and write a sentence that compares the data using decimals.

Repeating Decimals, Irrational Numbers, and Real Numbers

What Are Nonterminating Decimals?

In this section, we examine **nonterminating decimals**. These decimal numbers have *infinitely* many digits after the decimal point, with a least one of the digits being nonzero, such as 5.07242424 . . . (infinitely many decimal digits with a repeating pattern) and 5.010010001 . . . (infinitely many decimal digits without a repeating pattern).

CONNECTION
REASONING

Some Rational Numbers Are Repeating Decimal Numbers

In the previous section, we learned that to represent $\frac{3}{11}$ as a *terminating* decimal, we would need to be able to express $\frac{3}{11}$ as an equivalent fraction in the form $\frac{a}{10^n}$ for some whole numbers a and n. Then the property of equivalent fractions implies $11a = 3 \cdot 10^n$. Do you think this is possible? Think about this before continuing.

The prime factorization of a number is unique, so the set of prime factors of $11a$ would have to equal the set of prime factors of $3 \cdot 10^n$. The set of prime factors of $11a$ includes 11, while the set of prime factors of $3 \cdot 10^n$ is $\{3, 2, 5\}$. This means $11a$ and $3 \cdot 10^n$ do not have the same set of prime factors, so it's impossible to express $\frac{3}{11}$ as an equivalent fraction in the form $\frac{a}{10^n}$. This means it's impossible to represent $\frac{3}{11}$ as a terminating decimal. Then $\frac{3}{11}$ is a nonterminating decimal, which means it must have an infinite number of decimal digits.

CONNECTION   What does the decimal representation of $\frac{3}{11}$ look like? We know $\frac{3}{11} = 3 \div 11$, so we can divide to convert a rational number to a decimal number. Students should know how to "convert a rational number to a decimal using long division" (CCSS, Gr. 7). Let's use the fair share model to divide and to determine the decimal representation of $\frac{3}{11}$. To begin, we must split 3 ones into 11 equal-sized groups.

In step 1, we see each group gets 0 ones.

Step 1.

$$11\overline{)3}^{0.}$$

In step 2, we rename the 3 ones as 30 tenths.

Step 2.

$$11\overline{)3.0}^{\,0.}\qquad \leftarrow \textbf{Rename 3 ones as 30 tenths.}$$

In step 3, we see that each of the 11 groups gets 2 tenths. The 2 is in the tenths place.

Step 3.

$$
\begin{array}{r}
0.2 \\
11\overline{)3.0} \\
-22 \\
\hline
8
\end{array}
$$
$\leftarrow$ **11 × 2 = 22. Subtract: 30 tenths −22 tenths = 8 tenths.**
$\leftarrow$ **8 tenths remain.**

There are 8 tenths remaining. In step 4, we renamed the 8 tenths as 80 hundredths.

Step 4.

$$
\begin{array}{r}
0.2 \\
11\overline{)3.0} \\
-22 \\
\hline
80
\end{array}
$$
$\leftarrow$ **Rename 8 tenths as 80 hundredths.**

In step 5, we see each of the 11 groups gets 7 hundredths.

Step 5.

$$
\begin{array}{r}
0.27 \\
11\overline{)3.0} \\
-22 \\
\hline
80 \\
-77 \\
\hline
3
\end{array}
$$
$\leftarrow$ **11 × 7 = 77. Subtract: 80 hundredths − 77 hundredths = 3 hundredths.**
$\leftarrow$ **3 hundredths remain.**

There are 3 hundredths remaining. In step 6, we renamed the 3 remaining hundredths as 30 thousandths.

Step 6.

$$
\begin{array}{r}
0.27 \\
11\overline{)3.0} \\
-22 \\
\hline
80 \\
-77 \\
\hline
30
\end{array}
$$
$\leftarrow$ **Rename 3 hundredths as 30 thousandths.**

In step 7, we see each of the 11 groups gets 2 thousandths. There are 8 thousandths remaining.

Step 7.

$$
\begin{array}{r}
0.272 \\
11\overline{)3.0} \\
-22 \\
\hline
80 \\
-77 \\
\hline
30 \\
-22 \\
\hline
8
\end{array}
$$

← $11 \times 2 = 22$. Subtract: 30 thousandths − 22 thousandths = 8 thousandths

← 8 thousandths remain.

We can use an ellipsis to indicate that the pattern continues: $\frac{3}{11} = 0.272727\ldots$. The decimal representation of $\frac{3}{11}$ continues forever with a block of repeating digits. A **repeating decimal number** is a nonterminating decimal number with a block of repeating digits. The **repetend** is the block of repeating digits, and the **period** of the repetend is the number of digits in the repetend. $\frac{3}{11}$ is a repeating decimal with a repetend of 27 and a period of 2. We typically use a bar to represent the repetition $\left(\frac{3}{11} = 0.\overline{27}\right)$, placing the bar above the repeating digits. Use the least number of digits possible to represent a repeating decimal. For example, represent $8.5242424\ldots$ with $8.5\overline{24}$, rather than $8.5\overline{2424}$ or $8.\overline{5242}$.

EXAMPLE 6.20

REPRESENTATION

Think about the decimal number $5.03\overline{6812}$.

a. What is the repetend?

b. What is the period of the repetend?

c. Round the decimal number to the nearest thousandth.

SOLUTION

a. 6812 (the block of repeating digits)

b. 4 (the number of digits in the repetend)

c. The nearby thousandths are 5.036 and 5.037; that is, $5.036 < 5.03\overline{6812} < 5.037$. $5.03\overline{6812}$ rounded to the nearest thousandth is 5.037.

▲

The following student page illustrates that students should be able to represent a repeating fraction by writing a bar over the repeating part.

> **Guided Practice** ·   **Ask Yourself**
>
> Write each fraction as a decimal. If the decimal is a repeating decimal, use a bar to show repeating digits.
>
> **1.** $\frac{5}{12}$ **2.** $\frac{4}{6}$ **3.** $\frac{3}{4}$ **4.** $\frac{1}{11}$
>
> **5.** $\frac{2}{9}$ **6.** $\frac{4}{5}$ **7.** $\frac{10}{90}$ **8.** $\frac{4}{25}$
>
> • Did I stop dividing too soon?
> • Did I place a bar over all the repeating digits?
>
> TEST TIPS
>
> **TEST TIPS** **Explain Your Thinking** ▶ Do $0.23\overline{888}$, $0.23\overline{88}$, and $0.23\overline{8}$ name different repeating decimals? Explain.
>
> (Houghton Mifflin *Mathematics*, Student Edition, Grade 6, p. 165)

(© by Houghton Mifflin Company, Inc. Reproduced by permission of the publisher, Houghton Mifflin Harcourt Publishing Company.)

How To Represent a Repeating Decimal as a Fraction

It turns out you can represent *any* repeating decimal as a rational number. The following example illustrates the reasoning and process. The key idea is to multiply the repeating decimal by appropriate powers of 10 to create two repeating decimals with the same fractional part so that when you subtract them the result is a whole number. You have to identify the repetend (the block of repeating digits in the fractional part of the decimal) to decide which powers of 10 are appropriate. Students should be able to "convert a decimal expansion which repeats eventually into a rational number" (CCSS, Gr. 8).

EXAMPLE 6.21

REASONING

REPRESENTATION

Represent $5.3\overline{47}$ as a rational number.

SOLUTION

Let's define $n = 5.3\overline{47} = 5.3474747\ldots$ We need to multiply n by appropriate powers of 10 to create two decimals numbers with the same fractional part.

Both $10n = 53.474747\ldots$ and $1000n = 5347.474747\ldots$ have the fractional part $.474747\ldots$, so the fractional part of the difference $(5347.474747\ldots - 53.474747\ldots)$ is 0.

$$1000n - 10n = 5347.474747\ldots - 53.474747\ldots$$
$$990n = 5347.474747\ldots - 53.474747\ldots$$
$$990n = 5347 - 53$$
$$990n = 5294$$
$$n = \frac{5294}{990}$$

Therefore, $5.3\overline{47} = \frac{5294}{990}$.

▲

You can follow the same steps to write any repeating decimal number as a rational number. Try it for $45.3\overline{467}$. The answer is $\frac{453,014}{9990}$. Amazingly, you could apply the same reasoning to prove $0.999\ldots = 1$.

Rational Numbers

As mentioned earlier, a rational number is a number that can be expressed in the form $\frac{a}{b}$, where a and b are integers and $b \neq 0$. The following result characterizes all rational numbers in terms of decimal numbers.

> **Theorem 2**
>
> Suppose a and b are integers with $b \neq 0$. The rational number $\frac{a}{b}$ is a terminating decimal or a repeating decimal.

REASONING

In other words, the set of rational numbers can also be viewed as the set of all numbers that can be expressed as terminating decimals or repeating decimals. To see this, think of the positive rational number $\frac{m}{n}$, where m and n are counting numbers. We know $\frac{m}{n} = m \div n$, and when dividing by n the only possible remainders are $0, 1, 2, \ldots,$ or $n - 1$ by the Quotient–Remainder theorem. So when dividing, the remainders must terminate or repeat (as in the steps shown earlier in this section) before or on the nth division (for example, $0.4936 \div 4$ requires four divisions until the remainders terminate, while $\frac{2}{3}$ requires two divisions until the remainders repeat).

EXAMPLE 6.22

REASONING

Refer to Theorems 1 and 2. Classify the rational number as a terminating decimal or a repeating decimal.

a. $\dfrac{7}{40}$

b. $\dfrac{6}{15}$

c. $\dfrac{3}{7}$

SOLUTION

a. The rational number $\frac{7}{40}$ is in its simplified form. The prime factors of 40 are 2 and 5. So $\frac{7}{40}$ is a terminating decimal number.

b. The rational number $\frac{6}{15}$ is equivalent to the simplified fraction $\frac{2}{5}$. The prime factor of the denominator is 5. So $\frac{6}{15}$ is a terminating decimal.

c. The rational number $\frac{3}{7}$ is in its simplified form. The prime factor of the denominator is 7. Then $\frac{3}{7}$ is not a terminating decimal. So $\frac{3}{7}$ is a repeating decimal number. ▲

In the following Classroom Connection, students use long division or a calculator to classify rational numbers according to their decimal representation.

Classroom Connection

● Harcourt *Math*, Student Edition, Grade 6, p. 247

Rename each fraction as a terminating or repeating decimal. Write terminating or repeating. $\frac{11}{25}$, $\frac{4}{15}$. (© by Harcourt, Inc. Reproduced by permission of the publisher, Houghton Mifflin Harcourt Publishing Company.)

Connections between Rational Numbers and Decimal Representations

Now we summarize the connections between rational numbers and decimal numbers.

Connections between Rational and Decimal Representations

Let a and b represent integers, with $b \neq 0$.

• The rational number $\frac{a}{b}$ is a terminating decimal or a repeating decimal.

• A terminating decimal can be expressed as a rational number $\frac{a}{b}$.

• A repeating decimal can be expressed as a rational number $\frac{a}{b}$.

Irrational Numbers

An **irrational number** is a nonterminating, nonrepeating decimal number, which is a decimal number that has an infinite number of digits to the right of the decimal point *and* does not repeat. Two examples are 5.12122122212222 . . . (it has a pattern but not a repeating pattern) and $\pi = 3.141592654\ldots$ (which can be proved to be irrational, but that is beyond the scope of this book). The set of irrational numbers is the set of nonterminating, nonrepeating decimal numbers. Students should "know that numbers that are not rational are called irrational" (CCSS, Gr. 8).

The following example makes an important point: a fraction with integers cannot represent an irrational number.

EXAMPLE 6.23

COMMUNICATION

REASONING

A fraction has a numerator that is an integer and a denominator that is a nonzero integer. Can the fraction be an irrational number?

SOLUTION

No. By definition, it is a rational number. Therefore, it cannot be an irrational number. ▲

EXAMPLE 6.24

COMMUNICATION

REASONING

Label the decimal as rational or irrational. Justify your answer.
a. 58.002341
b. 72.093121212 . . .
c. 49.12112111211112 . . .

SOLUTION

a. Every terminating decimal is a rational number, so 58.002341 is a rational number.

b. Every repeating decimal is a rational number, so 72.093121212 . . . is a rational number.

c. The decimal has an infinite number of nonzero digits to the right of the decimal point and does not have a repeating block of digits, so 49.12112111211112 . . . is an irrational number. ▲

■ **Historical Note**

Followers of the Greek mathematician Pythagoras discovered the first irrational number by accident. They tried to represent the length of the diagonal of a square as a rational number and then discovered it was mathematically impossible. They used the phrase *irrational number* to classify the new type of number, with the idea that *irrational* means the number cannot be written as a quotient of whole numbers. Mathematicians have since proved there are many more irrational numbers than rational numbers.

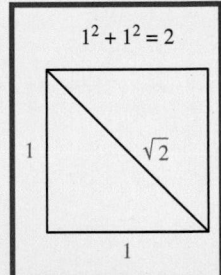

$1^2 + 1^2 = 2$

Set of Real Numbers

CONNECTION

REPRESENTATION

The **set of real numbers** is the union of the set of rational numbers and the set of irrational numbers. Concept Map 6.2 represents the relationships among decimal numbers, rational numbers, and irrational numbers needed for fraction and decimal literacy.

> **Concept Map 6.2** Linking Real Numbers, Rational Numbers, and Irrational Numbers

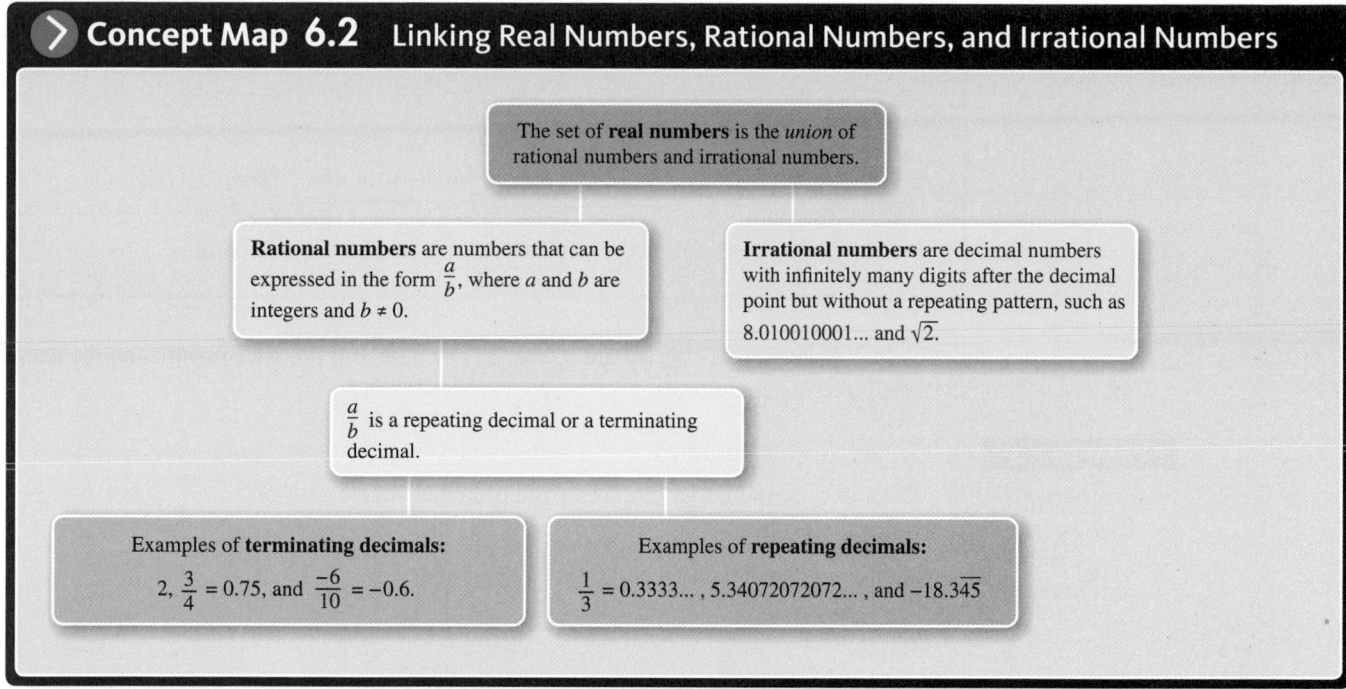

The Venn diagram in Concept Map 6.3 shows the relationships among the different number systems: counting (natural) numbers, whole numbers, integers, rational numbers, and irrational numbers.

> **Concept Map 6.3** Venn Diagram Depicting Relationships among Different Number Systems

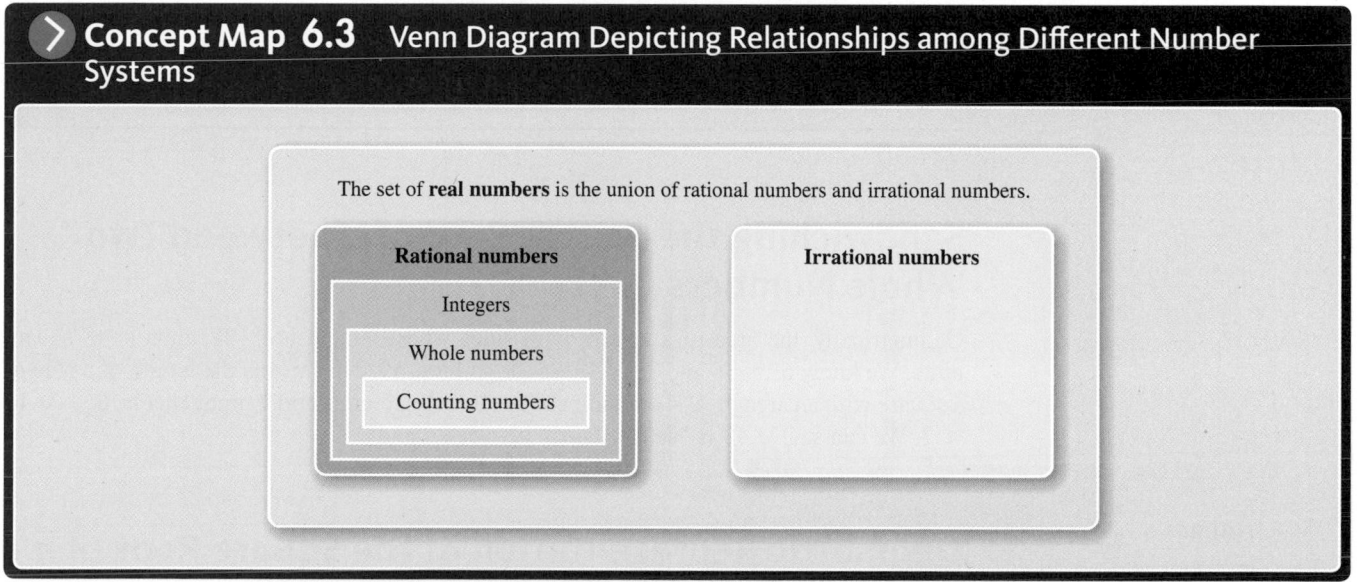

CONNECTION

REPRESENTATION

Square Roots

Any integer x that satisfies the equation $x^2 = 49$ is said to be a *square root* of 49. The integers 7 and -7 are square roots of 49, because $(7)^2 = 7 \cdot 7 = 49$ and $(-7)^2 = (-7) \cdot (-7) = 49$. The symbol $\sqrt{49}$ represents the *nonnegative* solution to $x^2 = 49$, so $\sqrt{49} = 7$. The number $\sqrt{49}$ is read as "the principal square root of 49." It is incorrect to write $\sqrt{49} = -7$, because $\sqrt{49}$ must be nonnegative. The equation $x^2 = 10$ has a positive solution and a negative solution. The symbol $\sqrt{10}$ represents the *nonnegative* solution to $x^2 = 10$, so the two solutions are $\sqrt{10}$ and $-\sqrt{10}$.

> ## Definition of a Square Root
>
> Let a be a nonnegative number.
>
> - A **square root** of a is a real number x such that $x^2 = a$.
> - The symbol $\sqrt{a}$, read as "the principal square root of a," represents the nonnegative solution x to $x^2 = a$.
> - The symbol $\sqrt{}$ is called the **radical**, and a is called the **radicand**.

$\sqrt{a}$ is often read as "the square root of a" when there is no risk of confusing the negative and positive square roots.

EXAMPLE 6.25

CONNECTION
COMMUNICATION
REASONING
REPRESENTATION

a. List the square roots of 25.

b. Write an expression that represents the principal square root of 7.

c. Simplify $\sqrt{64}$.

d. Explain why there is no real number x such that $x^2 = -6$.

e. Find all solutions to $x^2 = 3$.

SOLUTION

a. 5 and -5

b. $\sqrt{7}$

c. $\sqrt{64}$ represents the nonnegative solution to $x^2 = 64$. We know $8 \times 8 = 64$, so $\sqrt{64} = 8$.

d. The left-hand side of the equation $x^2 = -6$ is a nonnegative number, but the right-hand side is a negative number. So there is no real number x that satisfies $x^2 = -6$.

e. $x = \sqrt{3}$ is the nonnegative solution to the equation $x^2 = 3$. The other solution is $x = -\sqrt{3}$. So the two solutions are $x = \sqrt{3}$ and $x = -\sqrt{3}$.

▲

Sandwiching the Square Root of n between Two Whole Numbers

Geometrically, the area of a square with sides whose length is $\sqrt{48}$ units is 48 square units. We know $6^2 = 36$ and $7^2 = 49$, so $36 < 48 < 49$. This means the length of a side of a square with an area of $\sqrt{48}$ square units is between 6 units and 7 units; that is, $6 < \sqrt{48} < 7$. We can say $\sqrt{48}$ is "sandwiched" between 6 and 7.

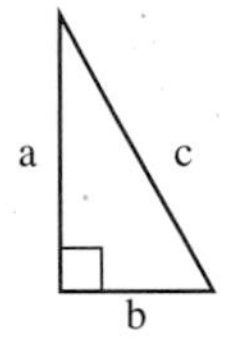

FIGURE 7
$a^2 + b^2 = c^2$.

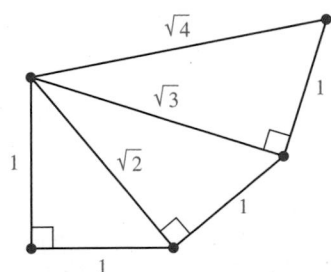

FIGURE 8
The spiral of square roots.

Geometric Representation of the Square Root of n

The Pythagorean theorem relates the lengths of the sides of a right triangle (see Section 11.3). Figure 7 shows a right triangle with legs whose lengths are a units and b units and with a hypotenuse whose length is c units. For right triangles, the Pythagorean theorem guarantees $a^2 + b^2 = c^2$. The spiral of square roots shows line segments with the lengths $\sqrt{2}$ units, $\sqrt{3}$ units, $\sqrt{4}$ units, and so on.

Here is how we sketched the spiral of square roots. Construct a right triangle with legs whose length is 1 unit. Then the length of the hypotenuse is c units, where $c^2 = 1^2 + 1^2$. Then $c^2 = 2$. Then $c = \sqrt{2}$ units. See Figure 8. Now draw a line segment whose length is 1 unit perpendicular to the hypotenuse. Form another triangle. The length of the new hypotenuse is c units, where $c^2 = (\sqrt{2})^2 + 1^2$. Then $c^2 = 2 + 1 = 3$, so $c = \sqrt{3}$. Continuing in this way, we get a spiral of square roots $\sqrt{2}$, $\sqrt{3}$, $\sqrt{4}$, and so on.

Classifying $\sqrt{n}$ as Rational or Irrational

Is $\sqrt{2}$ a rational number or an irrational number? By definition, $\sqrt{2}$ is the positive solution to the equation $x^2 = 2$.

We know $1 \cdot 1 < 2 < 2 \cdot 2$, so $1 < \sqrt{2} < 2$. This means $\sqrt{2}$ is between 1 and 2, so $\sqrt{2}$ is not a counting number. The following result says $\sqrt{2}$ must be an irrational number. Students should "know that $\sqrt{2}$ is irrational" (CCSS, Gr. 8).

Theorem 3

Let n be a counting number. If there is a counting number c such that $c^2 < n < (c + 1)^2$, then $\sqrt{n}$ is an irrational number.

Interpretation:

- c^2 and $(c + 1)^2$ are two consecutive perfect squares.
- Consecutive perfect squares are 1, 4, 9, 16, 25, 36, 49, 64, 81, 100, ...
- If n is between two consecutive perfect squares, then $\sqrt{n}$ is an irrational number.

EXAMPLE 6.26 Prove that $\sqrt{17}$ is an irrational number.

COMMUNICATION
REASONING

SOLUTION

$16 \leq 17 < 25$. This means 17 is between two consecutive perfect squares. By Theorem 3, $\sqrt{17}$ is an irrational number. ▲

How can you create an irrational number? If you choose a counting number n that does not belong to the sequence of perfect squares 1, 4, 9, 16, 25, 36, 49, 64, 81, 100, . . . , then $\sqrt{n}$ is an irrational number. Another way is to create a decimal number with infinitely many decimal digits that do not contain a block of repeating digits, such as 5.010010001 . . . .

COMMUNICATION
REASONING

Now we will prove Theorem 3. Suppose n is a counting number and there is a counting number c such that $c^2 < n < (c + 1)^2$. Then $c < \sqrt{n} < c + 1$. Then $\sqrt{n}$ is between two consecutive counting numbers.

We know $\sqrt{n}$ is either a rational number or an irrational number. For the moment, we assume $\sqrt{n}$ is a rational number. We just showed $\sqrt{n}$ is between two consecutive counting numbers, so it cannot be a counting number. Then $\sqrt{n}$ is a rational number such that $\sqrt{n} = \frac{a}{b}$ for some counting numbers a and b, with $b \neq 1$, and we may assume $\text{GCF}(a, b) = 1$ (because we can always simplify the fraction $\frac{a}{b}$).

Because $\sqrt{n} = \frac{a}{b}$, we know $n = \frac{a^2}{b^2}$. Then $a^2 = nb^2$. The counting numbers a and b are greater than 1, so each has at least one prime factor. Let q be a prime factor of b (our goal is to show that q is a prime factor of a too). Then q is a prime factor of b^2. Then q is a prime factor of nb^2. We know that $a^2 = nb^2$, q is a prime factor of nb^2, and the prime power representation of a number is unique, so q must be a prime factor of a^2.

The set of prime factors of a^2 equals the set of prime factors of a, so q must be a prime factor of a. This means the prime number q, which is greater than 1, is a factor of both a and b, so $\text{GCF}(a, b) > 1$. Then $\text{GCF}(a, b) = 1$ and $\text{GCF}(a, b) > 1$, which is impossible. Then $\sqrt{n}$ cannot be a rational number. Then $\sqrt{n}$ is an irrational number.

EXAMPLE 6.27 Prove that $5\sqrt{2}$ is an irrational number.

CONNECTION
COMMUNICATION
REASONING

SOLUTION

$1 < 2 < 4$. This means 2 is between two consecutive perfect squares. So $\sqrt{2}$ is an irrational number. $5\sqrt{2}$ is a rational number or an irrational number. Suppose for the moment $5\sqrt{2}$ is a rational number. Then $5\sqrt{2} = \frac{a}{b}$ for some counting numbers a and b. Then $\sqrt{2}$

(continued)

$= \frac{a}{5b}$. The numerator and denominator are counting numbers, so $\sqrt{2}$ is a rational number. Then $\sqrt{2}$ is an irrational number and $\sqrt{2}$ is a rational number, which is a contradiction. Therefore, $5\sqrt{2}$ is not a rational number. Therefore, $5\sqrt{2}$ is an irrational number. ▲

More generally, the product of a rational number and an irrational number is an irrational number. Must the product of two irrational numbers be an irrational number?

EXAMPLE 6.28

CONNECTION
COMMUNICATION
REASONING

Label each number as rational or irrational. Explain your answer.

a. 7.34802

b. $\frac{4}{3} \times \sqrt{3}$

SOLUTION

a. rational, because 7.34802 is a terminating decimal

b. irrational, because the product of a rational number and an irrational number is an irrational number ▲

*n*th Roots (*n* Is Odd)

Let a be a real number, and let n be a number such that $n^3 = a$. Then n is called the cube root of a. Here are two examples: $(-4)^3 = -64$, so the cube root of -64 is -4, and $5^3 = 125$, so the cube root of 125 is 5. The symbol $\sqrt[3]{a}$ represents the cube root of a, so $\sqrt[3]{-64} = -4$ and $\sqrt[3]{125} = 5$, respectively.

Let a be a real number, and let n be a number such that $n^5 = a$. Then n is called the fifth root of a. Here are two examples: $(-2)^5 = -32$, so the fifth root of -32 is -2, and $3^5 = 243$, so the fifth root of 243 is 3. The symbol $\sqrt[5]{a}$ represents the fifth root of a, so $\sqrt[5]{-32} = -2$ and $\sqrt[5]{243} = 3$, respectively.

The following defines the *n*th root of a when n is an odd number.

Definition of the *n*th Root of a Number (*n* Is an Odd Number)

Let a be a real number and n be an odd number.

- $\sqrt[n]{a}$ is called the *n*th root of a. (If $n = 3$, then we call it the **cube root of *a*.**)
- $\sqrt[n]{a}$ represents the solution to $x^n = a$, where a can be positive or negative.
- For $\sqrt[n]{a}$, the symbol $\sqrt{}$ is the **radical,** n is the **index,** and a is the **radicand.**
- The number $\sqrt[n]{a}$ is also represented as $a^{\frac{1}{n}}$.

EXAMPLE 6.29

a. Simplify $\sqrt[3]{\dfrac{1}{125}}$.

b. Find all real solutions to the equation $x^9 = -15$.

SOLUTION

a. $\sqrt[3]{\dfrac{1}{125}} = \sqrt[3]{\dfrac{1}{5^3}} = \sqrt[3]{\left(\dfrac{1}{5}\right)^3} = \dfrac{1}{5}$, so $\sqrt[3]{\dfrac{1}{125}} = \dfrac{1}{5}$

b. $x = \sqrt[9]{-15}$ (which is about -1.35 using a calculator) ▲

*n*th Roots (*n* Is Even)

We already studied the case in which a is a positive number and n is a number such that $n^2 = a$. Now let a be a positive number and n be a number such that $n^4 = a$. Then n is called the fourth root of a. Here are two examples: $(-2)^4 = 16$ and $2^4 = 16$, so -2 and 2 are fourth roots of 16, and $(-3)^4 = 81$ and $3^4 = 81$, so -3 and 3 are fourth roots of 81. $\sqrt[4]{a}$, called the principal fourth root of a, represents the *positive* fourth root of a. So $\sqrt[4]{16} = 2$ and $\sqrt[4]{81} = 3$, respectively. The term *principal nth root* is used to distinguish the positive root and the negative root of a.

The following defines the *n*th root and the principal *n*th root of a when a is a positive number and n is an even number and shows how to represent solutions to the equation $x^n = a$.

Definition of the *n*th Root of a Number (*n* Is an Even Number)

Let a be a positive number and n be an even number.

- $\sqrt[n]{a}$ and $-\sqrt[n]{a}$ are called the *n*th roots of a.
- $\sqrt[n]{a}$ is called the **principal *n*th root of *a*.** (If $n = 2$, then we call it the **principal square root of *a*.**)
- For any positive number a, the equation $x^n = a$ has two solutions: $x = \sqrt[n]{a}$ and $x = -\sqrt[n]{a}$.
- $\sqrt[n]{a}$ represents the *positive solution* to $x^n = a$.
- For $\sqrt[n]{a}$, the symbol $\sqrt{}$ is the radical, n is the index, and a is the radicand.
- The number $\sqrt[n]{a}$ is also represented as $a^{\frac{1}{n}}$.

EXAMPLE 6.30

CONNECTION

REASONING

REPRESENTATION

a. List the sixth roots of 20.

b. Write an expression that represents the principal sixth root of 7.

c. Find all solutions to the equation $x^{10} = 15$.

d. Write an equation that has the solution $\sqrt[6]{8}$ such that the equation does not involve a radical sign.

SOLUTION

a. $\sqrt[6]{20}$ and $-\sqrt[6]{20}$

b. $\sqrt[6]{7}$

c. $x = \sqrt[10]{15}$ and $x = -\sqrt[10]{15}$ ($\sqrt[10]{15} \approx 1.31$ using a calculator)

d. $x^6 = 8$ (there are other possibilities, such as $5x^6 = 40$ or $2x^6 + 4 = 20$).

The following example explains why some expressions such as $\sqrt[4]{-8}$ are not real numbers.

EXAMPLE 6.31

CONNECTION

COMMUNICATION

REASONING

Explain why $\sqrt[4]{-8}$ is not a real number.

SOLUTION

$\sqrt[4]{-8}$ represents the solution to the equation $x^4 = -8$. The left-hand side of the equation is a nonnegative number, and the right-hand side is a negative number. So the equation $x^4 = -8$ does not have a solution. This means $\sqrt[4]{-8}$ is not a real number.

In general, if n is even and a is negative, then $\sqrt[n]{a}$ is undefined (for example, $\sqrt[4]{-5}$ is undefined), because there is no real number solution to the equation $x^4 = -5$. If n is odd, then $\sqrt[n]{a}$ and $\sqrt[n]{-a}$ are defined. The most common roots that students experience are the square roots and cube roots of a number, and students should be able to "use square root and cube root symbols to represent solutions to equations of the form $x^2 = p$ and $x^3 = p$, where p is a positive rational number" (CCSS, Gr. 8).

Rational Exponents

We now explore rational exponents for a positive number a (for simplicity). For the integers m and n, we already know $(a^m)^n$ and $(a^n)^m$ represent the same number a^{mn}: $(a^m)^n = a^{mn}$ and $(a^n)^m = a^{mn}$. We extend this property for rational exponents. Let's consider the simple case $(64^2)^{\frac{1}{3}}$:

$$
\begin{aligned}
(64^2)^{\frac{1}{3}} &= (64 \times 64)^{\frac{1}{3}} \\
&= ((4 \times 4 \times 4)(4 \times 4 \times 4))^{\frac{1}{3}} \\
&= ((4 \times 4)(4 \times 4)(4 \times 4))^{\frac{1}{3}} \\
&= 4 \times 4 \\
&= 64^{\frac{1}{3}} \times 64^{\frac{1}{3}} \\
&= (64^{\frac{1}{3}})^2
\end{aligned}
$$

The expressions $(64^2)^{\frac{1}{3}}$ and $(64^{\frac{1}{3}})^2$ represent the same number, and a natural choice for their common representation is $64^{\frac{2}{3}}$, especially because $2 \times \frac{1}{3} = \frac{2}{3}$ and $\frac{1}{3} \times 2 = \frac{2}{3}$. Similar examples suggest the following natural way to define rational exponents algebraically for positive numbers (negative numbers require more care).

Definition

Let a be a positive number. Then $a^{\frac{m}{n}} = (a^m)^{\frac{1}{n}} = \sqrt[n]{a^m}$ and $a^{\frac{m}{n}} = (a^{\frac{1}{n}})^m = (\sqrt[n]{a})^m$.

EXAMPLE 6.32   Evaluate $\sqrt{16^3}$.

SOLUTION

$$\sqrt{16^3} = (16^3)^{\frac{1}{2}} = 16^{\frac{3}{2}} = (16^{\frac{1}{2}})^3 = 4^3 = 64$$

The multiplicative inverse of 5 is $\frac{1}{5}$, because $5 \cdot \frac{1}{5} = 1$. In general, the multiplicative inverse of the nonzero number a is the number $\frac{1}{a}$. What is the multiplicative inverse of a^2? We know $a^2 \cdot \frac{1}{a^2} = \frac{a^2}{a^2} = 1$, so the multiplicative inverse of a^2 is $\frac{1}{a^2}$. In general, for any nonzero number a and any rational number n, the multiplicative inverse of a^n is $\frac{1}{a^n}$, and we can use the symbol a^{-n} to represent $\frac{1}{a^n}$.

Properties of rational exponents are the same as those for integer exponents.

Properties of Rational Exponents

Let a and b be any real numbers and m and n be rational numbers. Then, as long as the expression is defined, the following are true.

Representation of Multiplicative Inverse of a^n	**Power Rule**
$a^{-n} = \dfrac{1}{a^n}$	$(a^m)^n = a^{mn}$
Product Rule	**Power of a Product**
$a^m \cdot a^n = a^{m+n}$	$(a \cdot b)^n = a^n \cdot b^n$
Quotient Rule	**Power of a Quotient**
$\dfrac{a^m}{a^n} = a^{m-n}$	$\left(\dfrac{a}{b}\right)^n = \dfrac{a^n}{b^n}$

EXAMPLE 6.33   Write each expression in a simpler form.

a. $\sqrt{32}$

b. $27^{-\frac{5}{3}}$

c. $\sqrt{2} \cdot \sqrt{3}$

d. $\sqrt[4]{\dfrac{1}{625}}$

SOLUTION

a. $\sqrt{32} = \sqrt{16 \cdot 2} = \sqrt{16} \cdot \sqrt{2} = 4\sqrt{2}$

b. $27^{-\frac{5}{3}} = 27^{\frac{-5}{3}} = (27^{\frac{1}{3}})^{-5} = 3^{-5} = \dfrac{1}{3^5} = \dfrac{1}{243}$

c. $\sqrt{2} \cdot \sqrt{3} = 2^{\frac{1}{2}} \cdot 3^{\frac{1}{2}} = (2 \cdot 3)^{\frac{1}{2}} = 6^{\frac{1}{2}} = \sqrt{6}$

d. $\sqrt[4]{\dfrac{1}{625}} = \sqrt[4]{\dfrac{1}{5^4}} = \sqrt[4]{\left(\dfrac{1}{5}\right)^4} = \dfrac{1}{5}$

▲

EXAMPLE 6.34   Write each expression in a simpler form with positive exponents.

a. $(8a)^{\frac{2}{3}}$

b. $\left(\dfrac{a}{4}\right)^{\frac{3}{2}}$

c. $\dfrac{a^{\frac{3}{4}}b^2}{a^{\frac{1}{3}}b^6}$

SOLUTION

a. $(8a)^{\frac{2}{3}} = 8^{\frac{2}{3}}a^{\frac{2}{3}} = (8^{\frac{1}{3}})^2 a^{\frac{2}{3}} = 2^2 a^{\frac{2}{3}} = 4a^{\frac{2}{3}}$

b. $\left(\dfrac{a}{4}\right)^{\frac{3}{2}} = \dfrac{a^{\frac{3}{2}}}{4^{\frac{3}{2}}} = \dfrac{a^{\frac{3}{2}}}{(4^{\frac{1}{2}})^3} = \dfrac{a^{\frac{3}{2}}}{2^3} = \dfrac{a^{\frac{3}{2}}}{8}$

c. $\dfrac{a^{\frac{3}{4}}b^2}{a^{\frac{1}{3}}b^6} = \dfrac{a^{\frac{3}{4}}}{a^{\frac{1}{3}}} \cdot \dfrac{b^2}{b^6} = a^{\frac{3}{4}-\frac{1}{3}}b^{2-6} = a^{\frac{5}{12}}b^{-4} = \dfrac{a^{\frac{5}{12}}}{b^4}$

▲

Scientific Notation

Scientific notation is a way to represent small or large numbers, such as the weight of an electron (0.00000000000000000000000000091093826 g) or the speed of light (29,979,245,800 cm per second), more conveniently using exponential notation. Students should "develop an understanding of large numbers and recognize and appropriately use exponential, scientific, and calculator notation" (NCTM, Gr. 6–8).

> **Definition**
>
> - A positive number expressed in **scientific notation** has the form $a \times 10^n$, where $1 \leq a < 10$ and n is an integer.
> - The number of **significant digits** of the number $a \times 10^n$ is the number of digits in a.
> - The **order of magnitude** of the number $a \times 10^n$ is the integer n.
>
> For example, according to the world population clock (www.census.gov/main/www/popclock.html), there were an estimated 6,879,011,682 people in the world on November 2, 2010. Using scientific notation, we could express this number as 6.9×10^9 (two significant digits with an order of magnitude of 9) or 6.88×10^9 (three significant digits with an order of magnitude of 9).

EXAMPLE 6.35 Determine the number of significant digits and the order of magnitude of 4.00320×10^8.

SOLUTION

The number of significant digits is six, and the order of magnitude is 8. ▲

The order of magnitude leads to a simple estimate of a number. For example, the order of magnitude of 4.0032×10^8 is 8, so $4.0032 \times 10^8 \approx 10^8$. The order of magnitude of 6.0×10^{-3} is -3, so $6.0 \times 10^{-3} \approx 10^{-3}$.

Table 6.2 illustrates how to express some numbers using scientific notation.

TABLE 6.2 **Scientific Notation, Significant Digits, and Order of Magnitude**

	Scientific Notation				
Number	**One significant digit**	**Two significant digits**	**Three significant digits**	**Four significant digits**	**Order of magnitude**
0.0000925037	9×10^{-5}	9.3×10^{-5}	9.25×10^{-5}	9.250×10^{-5}	-5
347,602,102.052	3×10^8	3.5×10^8	3.48×10^8	3.476×10^8	8
4.65472	4×10^0	4.7×10^0	4.65×10^0	4.655×10^0	0

EXAMPLE 6.36

CONNECTION
REASONING
REPRESENTATION

According to the world population clock, there were an estimated 311,730,873 people in the United States on July 10, 2011. Represent this number using scientific notation. State the number of significant digits and the order of magnitude of the number.

SOLUTION

Answers vary; for example, 3.1×10^8 (two significant digits, order of magnitude is 8) or 3.12×10^8 (three significant digits, order of magnitude is 8) ▲

EXAMPLE 6.37

CONNECTION
COMMUNICATION
REASONING

How are 7.3×10^5 and 7.30×10^5 alike? different?

SOLUTION

7.3×10^5 and 7.30×10^5 are alike because we can represent them with the same point on the number line. They are also alike because they have the same order of magnitude. However, 7.3×10^5 and 7.30×10^5 are different because 7.3×10^5 has two significant digits but 7.30×10^5 has three significant digits. ▲

The following Released Item shows that students should know how to translate between standard form and scientific notation.

> ### RELEASED ITEM
>
> ● NAEP, 2005
> The mean distance from Venus to the Sun is 1.08×10^8 km. Which of the following quantities is equal to this distance?
> **a.** 10,800,000 km   **b.** 108,000,000 km   **c.** 1,080,000,000 km
> **d.** 10,800,000,000 km   **e.** 108,000,000,000 km
>
> 41% of eighth graders gave the correct answer. (U.S. Department of Education, Institute of Education Sciences, National Center for Education Statistics, NAEP)

The following example illustrates how to add, subtract, multiply, and divide two numbers written in scientific notation. Students should be able to "perform operations with numbers expressed in scientific notation, including problems where both decimal and scientific notation are used" (CCSS, Gr. 8).

EXAMPLE 6.38

CONNECTION
COMMUNICATION
REASONING

Write each expression in scientific notation.
a. $2.71 \times 10^5 + 3.5 \times 10^3$
b. $4.6 \times 10^4 - 8.26 \times 10^1$
c. $(3.58 \times 10^5)(7.1 \times 10^3)$
d. $(2.105 \times 10^2) \div (8.42 \times 10^6)$

SOLUTION

a. $2.71 \times 10^5 + 3.5 \times 10^3 = 271 \times 10^3 + 3.5 \times 10^3 = (271 + 3.5) \times 10^3$
$= 274.5 \times 10^3 = 2.745 \times 10^5$

b. $4.6 \times 10^4 - 8.26 \times 10^1 = 4600 \times 10^1 - 8.26 \times 10^1 = (4600 - 8.26) \times 10^1$
$= 4591.74 \times 10^1 = 4.59174 \times 10^4$

c. $(3.58 \times 10^5)(7.1 \times 10^3) = (3.58)(7.1)(10^5)(10^3) = (25.418)(10^8) = 2.5418 \times 10^9$

d. $(2.105 \times 10^2) \div (8.42 \times 10^6) = \dfrac{2.105 \times 10^2}{8.42 \times 10^6} = \dfrac{2.105}{8.42} \times \dfrac{10^2}{10^6} = 0.25 \times 10^{-4}$
$= 2.5 \times 10^{-5}$

▲

We can use scientific notation to estimate products and quotients. For example,

• $0.00031 \times 76.78 \approx 3 \times 10^{-4} \times 75 = 225 \times 10^{-4} \approx 0.02$.

• $360{,}000{,}821 \div 0.0000053 \approx (4 \times 10^8) \div (5 \times 10^{-6}) = \dfrac{4 \times 10^8}{5 \times 10^{-6}} = \dfrac{4}{5} \times \dfrac{10^8}{10^{-6}} \approx 10^{14}$.

The following table is designed to help students "interpret scientific notation that has been generated by technology" (CCSS, Gr. 8).

Calculator display	Meaning
1.234567890 e+3 or 1.234567890 E+3	1.234567890×10^3
1.234567890 e3 or 1.234567890 E3	1.234567890×10^3
1. 234567890 e−3 or 1.234567890 E−3	$1.234567890 \times 10^{-3}$

We studied operations with whole numbers in Chapters 2 and 3. The equations we solved, such as $n + 12 = 18$ and $a \times 7 = 14$, were chosen carefully to ensure whole number solutions. But the equation $n + 5 = 3$ does not have a whole number solution, so we introduced a new set of numbers called integers in Chapter 4. Again, some equations lacked integer solutions, such as $6n = 10$, so we introduced a new set of numbers called rational numbers (fractions) in Chapter 5. The properties of the extended number systems inherit the properties of the previous number systems, and we added a few new properties along the way. Then we extended the base ten number system to decimal numbers in this chapter. A decimal number is either a rational number or an irrational number. The set of real numbers—the union of the sets of rational numbers and irrational numbers—forms the apex of the number systems for K–8 teaching. Now we summarize the properties of operations with real numbers.

Properties of Operations with Real Numbers

Closure Properties
- If a and b are real numbers, then $a + b$ is a real number.
- If a and b are real numbers, then ab is a real number.

Commutative Properties
- If a and b are real numbers, then $a + b = b + a$.
- If a and b are real numbers, then $ab = ba$.

Associative Properties
- If a, b, and c are real numbers, then $a + (b + c) = (a + b) + c$.
- If a, b, and c are real numbers, then $a(bc) = (ab)c$.

Identity Properties
- If a is any real number, then $a + 0 = a$ and $0 + a = a$.
- If a is any real number, then $a \cdot 1 = a$ and $1 \cdot a = a$.

Zero Multiplication Properties
- If a is any real number, then $a \cdot 0 = 0$ and $0 \cdot a = 0$.
- Let a and b represent real numbers. If $ab = 0$, then $a = 0$ or $b = 0$.

Distributive Properties
- If a, b, and c are real numbers, then $a(b + c) = ab + ac$.
- If a, b, and c are real numbers, then $(a + b)c = ac + bc$.

Inverse Properties
- The additive inverse of the real number a, denoted $-a$, satisfies the equations $a + -a = 0$ and $-a + a = 0$. (If a is nonzero, then a and $-a$ have opposite signs.)
- The multiplicative inverse of a, denoted a^{-1}, satisfies the equations $aa^{-1} = 1$ and $a^{-1}a = 1$. (The multiplicative inverse of a is also read as "the reciprocal of a," because a^{-1} is the number $\frac{1}{a}$.)

Density Property

There are infinitely many real numbers between any two distinct real numbers. (Given two real numbers a and b with $a < b$, the number $a + \frac{b-a}{2n}$ is between a and b for any counting number n).

QUESTIONS FOR SECTION 6.2

REPRESENTATION

Refresher: Representations (language, diagrams, tables, symbols, algebra, manipulatives, and contextualized situations) are important because we use them to organize, record, and communicate mathematical ideas and to make them more comprehensible.

1. Represent $\frac{52}{220}$ as a decimal number.

2. Draw a visual representation of $\sqrt{5}$.

3. Use exponents to represent the solution to the equation $x^3 = 42$.

4. $x = \sqrt[3]{25}$ represents the solution to the equation $x^3 = 25$. Write another possible equation.

5. Explain why $\frac{3}{2\cdot2\cdot2\cdot5\cdot5\cdot5\cdot5}$ represents a terminating decimal.

6. Explain why $\frac{3}{2\cdot2\cdot5\cdot5\cdot5\cdot7}$ represents a repeating decimal.

7. Represent each decimal as a fraction.
   a. $0.\overline{35}$ b. $0.2\overline{182}$ c. $6.80\overline{341}$

8. The teacher asked her students to write an irrational number. David wrote $\sqrt{14}$. Explain why $\sqrt{14}$ represents an irrational number.

9. Use scientific notation to represent each number with the stated number of significant digits.

	Two significant digits	Three significant digits	Four significant digits
87,291			
0.0045063			

PROBLEM SOLVING

Refresher: Problem solving (reaching a goal that is not immediately attainable) is important because it helps students think more deeply about what they know and deal with unfamiliar situations.

10. What is the 87th digit of the fractional part of $5.03\overline{4789}$?

11. What is the repetend of $\frac{1}{333,333,333}$?

REASONING AND PROOF

Refresher: Reasoning and proof (thinking and justifying) are important because they help students make sense of mathematics.

12. Give an example of irrational numbers a and b such that
   a. $a - b$ is an irrational number.
   b. $a + b$ is a rational number.
   c. $a \cdot b$ is an irrational number.   d. $a \cdot b$ is a rational number.
   e. $\frac{a}{b}$ is an irrational number.   f. $\frac{a}{b}$ is a rational number.

13. Is 43.1789789789 . . . an irrational number? Justify your answer.

14. Fill in the blank with one of the following words: *all, some, no.* Choose the best possible answer.
   a. _____ whole numbers are integers.
   b. _____ rational numbers are integers.
   c. _____ repeating decimal numbers are rational numbers.
   d. _____ integers are whole numbers.
   e. _____ rational numbers are terminating decimal numbers.
   f. _____ irrational numbers are integers.
   g. _____ integers are rational numbers.
   h. _____ irrational numbers are repeating decimal numbers.
   i. _____ real numbers are irrational numbers.
   j. _____ whole numbers are irrational numbers.
   k. _____ irrational numbers are whole numbers.
   l. _____ terminating decimal numbers are rational numbers.
   m. _____ rational numbers are irrational numbers.
   n. _____ whole numbers are not irrational numbers.
   o. _____ repeating decimal numbers are irrational numbers.
   p. _____ irrational numbers are not integers.

15. Use mental arithmetic to explain why $\frac{1}{13}$ must have a nonterminating decimal representation.

16. Is $\sqrt{12}$ a rational number or an irrational number? Explain your answer.

CONNECTIONS

Refresher: Connections (linking and applying mathematical ideas) are important because they deepen student understanding and make mathematics more meaningful, flexible, and useful.

17. Do the following.
   a. Use a calculator to express each fraction as a decimal: $\frac{154}{99}$, $\frac{155}{99}$, and $\frac{156}{99}$.
   b. Predict the decimal representation of $\frac{157}{99}$. Check your result with a calculator.

18. What is the 57th digit of the fractional part of $2.04\overline{715398}$?

19. Write an equation without a radical that has the solution $x = \sqrt[5]{-38}$.

20. Do the following.
   a. Determine whether $\sqrt{3}$ is a rational number or an irrational number, and explain your answer.
   b. Use a spiral to draw a triangle so that one side has the length $\sqrt{3}$.
   c. Use the result from part (b) to plot $2 + \sqrt{3}$ on the number line.

21. Use a calculator as needed.

    a. Compare $\sqrt{2} \cdot \sqrt{3}$ and $\sqrt{2 \cdot 3}$.

    b. Compare $\sqrt{5} \cdot \sqrt{7}$ and $\sqrt{5 \cdot 7}$.

    c. Make a conjecture about $\sqrt{m} \cdot \sqrt{n}$ and $\sqrt{mn}$.

22. Use a calculator as needed.

    a. Compare $\frac{\sqrt{8}}{\sqrt{5}}$ and $\sqrt{\frac{8}{5}}$. b. Compare $\frac{\sqrt{10}}{\sqrt{4}}$ and $\sqrt{\frac{10}{4}}$.

    c. Make a conjecture about $\frac{\sqrt{m}}{\sqrt{n}}$ and $\sqrt{\frac{m}{n}}$.

23. The ordered pair (a, b) lies on the graph of the function $y = \sqrt{2}x$ if and only if $b = \sqrt{2}a$. Monica and Kendall correctly agreed that $\sqrt{2}$ is an irrational number. Then Monica said, "I think there are integers a and b such that (a, b) lies on the graph of $y = \sqrt{2}x$." Maria thought about this and then exclaimed, "That cannot happen, because that would suggest $\sqrt{2}$ is a rational number!" Explain why Maria is correct.

24. The ordered pair (a, b) lies on the graph of the function $y = 5x$ if and only if $b = 5a$. Explain why it is impossible to find an irrational number a such that the ordered pair $(a, 14)$ lies on the graph of $y = 5x$.

COMMUNICATION

Refresher: Communication (written and verbal explanations using representations and proper mathematical vocabulary) is important because it helps students refine and strengthen their understanding.

25. What do we mean when we say $\sqrt{5}$ is an irrational number?

26. Explain how you know the positive solution to the equation $x^2 = 65$ is an irrational number.

27. Explain why a real number x does not exist such that $x^2 = -54$.

28. How are 2 and 2.0 alike? different?

29. Do the following.

    a. List the solutions to $x^2 = 100$.

    b. Ken said you could write $\sqrt{100} = -10$ because $(-10)^2 = 100$. Explain why Ken is incorrect.

30. Tell how you know 7.04004000400004 . . . is an irrational number.

31. A teacher asks a student to write a real number that is a terminating decimal. The student writes $(2 \cdot 2 \cdot 5 \cdot 5 \cdot 5 \cdot 5 \cdot 5)^{-1}$. Is the student correct? Why?

32. A teacher asks a student to write a real number that is a repeating decimal. The student writes $(2 \cdot 2 \cdot 5 \cdot 5 \cdot 5 \cdot 5 \cdot 17)^{-1}$. Is the student correct? Why?

More practice with the ideas of the section

33. Fill in the blank. Choose one of the following words, phrases, or symbols: *4, 6, 7, $-\sqrt[3]{21}$, $\sqrt[3]{21}$, irrational number, order, period, principal square root, rational number, repeating decimal, repetend,* or *square root.*

    a. 23.070070007 . . . is a(n) _____.

    b. A(n) _____ is any number that can be represented in the form a/b, where a and b integers and $b \neq 0$.

    c. The _____ of $0.047\overline{153}$ . . . is 3.

d. The _____ of $83.017\overline{1456}$ is 1456.

e. 0.005367×10^{12} has ___ significant digits.

f. $\sqrt{5}$ is the _____ of 5.

g. The solution to $x^3 = 21$ is _____.

34. Label the decimal as rational or irrational.

    a. 23.0041212   b. 63.21$\overline{35}$ c. $\sqrt{32}$

    d. 82.16116111611116 . . .   e. $\sqrt{49}$

35. Find a number a greater than 2 such that

    a. $\frac{a}{15}$ is a terminating decimal.

    b. $\frac{a}{15}$ is a nonterminating decimal.

36. Use the digits 4, 5, and 6 to create a decimal number of the given type. You can use each digit more than once.

    a. terminating decimal   b. repeating decimal

    c. nonterminating, nonrepeating decimal

37. Use a calculator to represent each fraction as a decimal.

    a. $\dfrac{147}{99}$ b. $\dfrac{147}{999}$ c. $\dfrac{147}{9999}$

38. State the number of significant digits in each number.

    a. 4.5203×10^6 b. 7.00005×10^8

    c. 3.0×10^{-4} d. 0.001356×10^{-2}

39. Express 0.000506083 in scientific notation. Use

    a. two significant digits.   b. three significant digits.

    c. four significant digits.

40. Do the following.

    a. Use a calculator to express each fraction as a decimal: $\frac{254}{99}$, $\frac{255}{99}$, and $\frac{256}{99}$.

    b. Predict the decimal representation of $\frac{257}{99}$. Check your result with a calculator.

41. Find a real number n with the given property.

    a. 254 is the repetend for n.

    b. n is a terminating decimal that can be represented as a fraction with a denominator of 56.

    c. The period of n is 4.

    d. n is a repeating decimal less than 1.

    e. 0027 is the repetend for n.   f. n is an irrational number.

    g. $n \div \pi$ is a rational number.

42. Do the following.

    a. Explain why $\sqrt{18}$ is an irrational number.

    b. You know a nonzero rational number times an irrational number is an irrational number. Use this fact and part (a) to explain why $\sqrt{1800}$ is an irrational number.

43. Do the following.

    a. Explain why $\sqrt{317}$ is an irrational number.

    b. You know a nonzero rational number times an irrational number is an irrational number. Use this fact and part (a) to explain why $\sqrt{3.17}$ is an irrational number.

44. The average distance between the Sun and Pluto is 3,660,000,000 miles. Express this distance in scientific notation, using the following number of significant digits.

    a. 2   b. 3   c. 4   d. 5

45. Evaluate the following expressions.

a. $\sqrt{25^3}$ b. $\sqrt[3]{81^2}$ c. $\sqrt[5]{32^4}$

46. $\sqrt{20} = (20)^{1/2} = (4 \times 5)^{1/2} = 4^{1/2} \times 5^{1/2} = 2 \times 5^{1/2} = 2\sqrt{5}$. The simplest form of $\sqrt{20}$ is $2\sqrt{5}$. Find the simplest form of each square root.

a. $\sqrt{48}$ b. $\sqrt{700}$ c. $\sqrt{1350}$

47. Find all solutions in simplest form.

a. $8x^3 = 12$ b. $x^2 + 15 = 78$ c. $x^2 - 12 = 168$

48. Write an equation without a radical sign that has the given solution.

a. $x = \sqrt[3]{5}$ b. $x = \sqrt[5]{8} + 1$

49. Use a calculator to express each fraction as a decimal.

a. $\dfrac{1514}{999}$ b. $\dfrac{1515}{999}$ c. $\dfrac{1516}{999}$

50. The ordered pair (a, b) lies on the graph of the function $y = \sqrt{3x}$ if and only if $b = \sqrt{3a}$. Charles and Maria correctly agreed that $\sqrt{3}$ is an irrational number. Then Charles said, "I think there is a point (a, b) in the xy-plane such that a and b are integers and (a, b) lies on the graph of $y = \sqrt{3x}$." Maria thought about this, and then exclaimed, "That cannot happen, because that would suggest $\sqrt{3}$ is a rational number!" Explain why Maria is correct.

51. What is the repetend of $\frac{1}{4444}$?

52. What is the period of $\frac{1}{5555}$?

53. Use the Guess and Check strategy to approximate each real number with the nearest whole number. Show your work.

a. $\sqrt{373}$ b. $\sqrt[5]{721}$

54. Is $\dfrac{\sqrt{48}}{\sqrt{12}}$ a rational number or an irrational number? Explain.

55. The ordered pair (a, b) lies on the graph of the function $y = 3x$ if and only if $b = 3a$. Are there any irrational numbers a and b such that the ordered pair (a, b) lies on the graph of $y = 3x$? Explain.

56. What does $\sqrt[5]{8}$ mean to you?

57. Place Xs in the boxes that correspond to the set of numbers.

	Rational	Irrational
-7.8		
$3/7$		
$43.26787878\ldots$		
-689		
0.00079		
$5.242442444\ldots$		
$\sqrt{27}$		
$-\dfrac{15}{3}$		

58. Classify each of the following numbers as rational or irrational.

a. $\sqrt{167}$ b. $\sqrt{4.7}$ c. $\sqrt{81}$ d. $-\sqrt{100}$

59. Create your own irrational number. Express the irrational number as a decimal.

60. Create your own irrational number. Express the irrational number using a square root sign.

61. Is the given number rational or irrational?

a. $\sqrt{2} + 1$ b. $(\sqrt{2} + 1)^2$
c. $(\sqrt{2} + 1)^2 + (\sqrt{2} - 1)^2$

62. Are there real solutions to the equation?

a. $y^2 + 28 = 8y^2$ b. $\sqrt{y} + 12 = -3\sqrt{y}$
c. $\dfrac{-y}{16} > y$ d. $y^{12} = -150$

63. Do the following.

a. List the fifth root of 28.

b. Write an expression that represents the principal fourth root of 12.

c. Find all solutions to the equation $x^{18} = 35$.

d. Write an equation that has the solution $\sqrt[9]{20}$ such that the equation does not involve a radical sign.

64. Find all solutions to the equation $x^7 = 10$.

65. Find all solutions to the equation $x^{24} = 95$.

66. Use scientific notation to help estimate the number.

a. $70{,}092 \times 4058$ b. $7{,}500{,}821.32 \div 5082$

67. $\sqrt{3}$ is an irrational number. Prove that $8\sqrt{3}$ is an irrational number.

68. $\sqrt{3}$ is an irrational number. Prove that $6 + \sqrt{3}$ is an irrational number.

69. Simplify the expression. Write the answer using positive exponents.

a. $(64w)^{\frac{2}{3}}$ b. $(a^4 b)^{\frac{3}{2}}$ c. $\dfrac{a^{\frac{5}{6}} b^5}{a^2 b^3}$

SECTION 6.3 Percent and Percent Change

thumb/Shutterstock.com

What Is a Percent?

Percent is a multifaceted concept with strong connections to ratios, fractions, proportions, variables, representation, and equations. A percent may be a symbolic representation of a ratio in which the second term is 100 (for example, "32 percent" means "32 parts of this to 100 parts of that"). A percent may also be a symbolic representation of a fraction in which the denominator is 100 (for example, 32 percent = 32/100). Both interpretations build on prior knowledge and help students make informed decisions in a world that uses percents in polls, news reports, commissions, interest, taxes, gratuities, probability, markups, discounts, and grades. Students should be able to "use proportional relationships to solve multistep ratio and percent problems. Examples: simple interest, tax, markups and markdowns, gratuities and commissions, fees, percent increase and decrease, percent error" (CCSS, Gr. 7).

First, we view a percent as a ratio. We use a bar diagram to visualize relationships between quantities and help analyze the underlying structure of problems before computations. With diagrams, students do not need to know how to convert percents to fractions or decimals, an advantage because conversions sometimes create confusion for students. The NCTM representation standard asserts that students should be able to flexibly and appropriately "create and use representations to organize, record, and communicate mathematical ideas" (NCTM, 2001). When elementary school students "gain access to mathematical representations and the ideas they represent, they have a set of tools that significantly expands their capacity to think mathematically" (NCTM, p. 67) and improve their understanding of quantitative situations.

Second, we view a percent as a fraction and use the equation method to compare one quantity to another. With this approach, students convert percents to fractions and decimal numbers. The NCTM's *Principles and Standards for School Mathematics* (2000) states that students in grades 3–5 should be able to "recognize and generate equivalent forms of commonly used fractions, decimals, and percents." This approach reinforces those skills. These students should also be able to write and solve equations involving a variable.

Hallmarks of Understanding Percents

As you study the topic of percents, keep in mind the following five hallmarks of understanding this topic:

1. Representing a percent using a diagram
2. Connecting fractions, decimals, and percents
3. Applying benchmarks to percent problems
4. Using mental calculations to perform some percent computations
5. Judging the reasonableness of a computation or an answer to a percent problem

COMMUNICATION

REASONING

Percent as a Ratio

Each month Terrell earns $20 for chores and Mary earns $32 for chores. Terrell received a $6 pay raise and Mary received an $8 pay raise. Who received the larger pay raise? Terrell says he received the larger pay raise. Mary says she received the larger pay raise. Can you explain how both could be correct? Think about this before you continue reading.

The answer to this problem depends on how you make the comparison. On an absolute scale, Mary received a larger pay raise (8 > 6). Yet Terrell received a pay raise of $30 per $100 (6:20 = 30:100), while Mary received a pay raise of $25 per $100 (8:32 = 1:4 = 25:100). On a relative scale, Terrell received a larger pay raise.

Relative comparisons on the scale of *per hundred* tend to be easier to comprehend and represent. We use the term *percent* and symbol % to represent relative comparisons on the scale of per hundred.

> **Definition**
>
> p% is read as "p percent" and means "p parts per 100 parts." Think of p% as "p parts of this to 100 parts of that."

EXAMPLE 6.39

REPRESENTATION

Model each percent using a 10-by-10 grid.

a. 36%

b. 100%

c. 142%

SOLUTION

A 10-by-10 grid contains 100 equal-sized parts.

a. 36% means 36 parts per 100 parts. The shaded region in Figure 9(a) represents 36%.

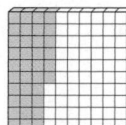

FIGURE 9(a)
Model of 36%.

b. 100% means 100 parts per 100 parts. The shaded region in Figure 9(b) represents 100%.

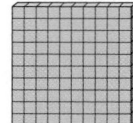

FIGURE 9(b)
Model of 100%.

c. 142% means 142 parts per 100 parts. The shaded region in Figure 9(c) represents 142%.

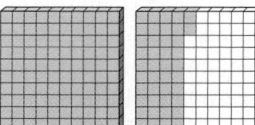

FIGURE 9(c)
Model of 142%.

EXAMPLE 6.40

COMMUNICATION

Explain what 20% means.

SOLUTION

20% means 20 parts of this for every 100 parts of that. For example, suppose 20% of the students at a school play a musical instrument. Then 20 students play musical instruments for every 100 students at the school.

The following two examples apply percents in situations that compare two different quantities. In both examples, we turn one ratio into an equivalent ratio in which the second term is 100.

EXAMPLE 6.41

CONNECTION
COMMUNICATION
PROBLEM SOLVING
REASONING
REPRESENTATION

The ratio of boys to students at the school is 7 to 20. What percent of the students in the school are boys?

SOLUTION

Our goal is to determine the number of boys for every 100 students at the school. The ratio of boys to students is 7:20. We can scale up by multiplying each term in the ratio by 5, obtaining 35:100. This means there are 35 boys of every 100 students. Therefore, 35% of the students at the school are boys.

▲

EXAMPLE 6.42

CONNECTION
REASONING
REPRESENTATION

The ratio of boys to students at the school is 5 to 8. What percent of the students in the school are boys?

SOLUTION

Our goal is to determine the number of boys for every 100 students at the school. The ratio of boys to students is 5:8. We need to express 5:8 as an equivalent ratio in the form b:100.

$$5:8 = \frac{5}{8}:\frac{8}{8} \qquad \textbf{Scale down}$$

$$= \frac{5}{8}:1 \qquad \textbf{Simplify}$$

$$= \left(\frac{5}{8}\right) \cdot 100:1 \cdot 100 \quad \textbf{Scale up}$$

$$= 62.5:100 \qquad \textbf{Simplify}$$

The calculations show 5:8 is equivalent to 62.5:100. Therefore, 62.5% of the students are boys.

▲

How to Use the Bar Diagram to Solve Classic Percent Problems

We can use a bar diagram to solve classic percent problems. The bar diagram eliminates the need to convert percents to fractions and decimals, provides a visual representation of the information, helps students analyze the underlying structure of contextualized problems, promotes reasoning in percent problems, and allows students to grasp the percent problem. The bar diagram relates percents to proportions and is easy to draw. It easily handles fractions, mixed numbers, decimal numbers, and percents such as 0.05% and 17.03%.

Figure 10 is a **bar diagram** that illustrates percents of $12 using benchmark percents such as 25%, 50%, and 75%. We picked a friendly number such as 12 and benchmark percents such as 25% and 50% to keep ideas simple. The benchmark percents allow students to use intuition, patterns, and experience with *partitioning* to create a bar diagram.

The $12 corresponds to 100%, $6 corresponds to 50%, $3 corresponds to 25%, and so on. The numbers in each row always increase in their natural order (like a dual number line). The numbers in the top row display actual amounts, while the numbers in the bottom row display relative amounts.

CONNECTION
REASONING
REPRESENTATION

Actual amount ($)	0	3	6	9	12	15	18	21	24

Relative amount (%)	0	25	50	75	100	125	150	175	200

FIGURE 10
Using a bar diagram to visualize percents of $12.

The numbers in Table 6.3, taken from Figure 10, form a ratio table.

TABLE 6.3

Dollars	3	6	9	12	15	18	21	24
Percent	25	50	75	100	125	150	175	200

This means the bar diagram is a tool used to organize information and translate percent problems into proportional reasoning problems, thus building on what we already know. The next few examples illustrate how to use a bar diagram to solve classic percent problems. Once students recognize the two quantities being compared, they need to decide which one serves as the basis of comparison and then associate the 100 parts with that quantity.

EXAMPLE 6.43

CONNECTION
COMMUNICATION
PROBLEM SOLVING
REASONING
REPRESENTATION

Jerry purchased a new bike for $543. He sold it 3 years later to Tom for 72% of the purchase price. How much did Tom pay?

SOLUTION

We are comparing the price of the used bike to the price of the new bike. The price of the new bike corresponds to 100% (100 parts). Let n represent the price of the used bike. Then n corresponds to 72%. This makes sense because Jerry received $72 for every $100 of the purchase price. Then we obtain the following diagram:

Dollars n 543

Percent   72   100

The diagram leads to the part-to-part proportion $\frac{n}{72} = \frac{543}{100}$. Then $100n = 72 \cdot 543$, and $n = \frac{72 \cdot 543}{100} = 390.96$. Tom paid $390.96. The part-to-whole proportion $\frac{n}{543} = \frac{72}{100}$ would lead to the same answer.

▲

EXAMPLE 6.44

CONNECTION
COMMUNICATION
PROBLEM SOLVING
REASONING
REPRESENTATION

This year, 5678 people attended the fair. That is 136% of the number of people who attended the fair last year. How many people attended the fair last year?

SOLUTION

We are comparing the attendance this year to the attendance last year. Let n represent the number of people who attended the fair last year. Then n corresponds to 100% and 5678 corresponds to 136%. This makes sense because 136 people attended the fair this year for every 100 people who attended the fair last year. Then we obtain the following diagram:

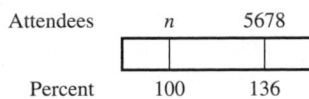

Attendees n 5678

Percent   100   136

The diagram leads to the part-to-part proportion $\frac{n}{100} = \frac{5678}{136}$. Then $136n = 100 \cdot 5678$, and $n = \frac{100 \cdot 5678}{136} = 4175$. So 4175 people attended the fair last year. The whole-to-part proportion $\frac{n}{5678} = \frac{100}{136}$ would lead to the same answer.

▲

EXAMPLE 6.45

CONNECTION

COMMUNICATION

PROBLEM SOLVING

REASONING

REPRESENTATION

A company had 6250 employees. Of those, 420 employees carpooled to work. What percent of the employees carpooled to work?

SOLUTION

We are comparing the number of employees who carpooled, 420, to the total number of employees, 6250. The total of 6250 employees corresponds to 100%. Let k% represent the unknown percent. Then k corresponds to the 420 employees. Then we obtain the following diagram:

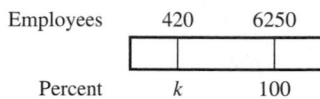

The diagram leads to the part-to-part proportion $\frac{420}{k} = \frac{6250}{100}$. Then $420 \cdot 100 = 6250k$, and $k = \frac{420 \cdot 100}{6250} = 6.72$. This means 6.72% of the employees carpool to work. The part-to-whole proportion $\frac{420}{6250} = \frac{k}{100}$ would lead to the same answer. ▲

> ■ **Historical Note**
>
> Early historical uses of percent-like concepts appeared in commerce for computation of interest, such as 12 coins on every 100 coins, and taxes, such as 12 units of grain for every 100 units of grain produced. These are part-to-whole comparisons. Today, the concept of percent appears in magazines, news reports, and store advertisements, and percents may be larger than 100%. You can read a fantastic comprehensive history of percent in a journal article by Parker and Leinhardt (1995).

Change and Percent Change

Phrases such as "increased by $30," "decreased by 45 cars," "15 more coins," and "24 fewer marbles" indicate absolute change. We measure **change** (increase or decrease) using subtraction. Change is a form of additive reasoning. We may also represent change with percents. Here are a few examples:

• Convention business is down 25% this year compared to last year.

• The company plans to increase its research expenditures by 8% to $3 billion in 2011.

• Internet advertising revenue was 28% more than last year.

• Fifteen percent fewer crimes were committed in the city.

• The company's earnings slid 4% from $5 million last year.

• There are 42% fewer salmon than halibut at the fish market.

Percent change (percent increase or percent decrease) is a representation of absolute change (increase or decrease) as a percent. Percent change is a form of multiplicative reasoning.

"Students use their understanding of ratios and proportionality to solve a wide variety of percent problems, including those involving percent increase or decrease" (CCSS, p. 47). Phrases that represent percent change, such as "24% more" and "32% fewer," may be challenging for students because they have difficulty identifying the quantity the percent refers to and organizing the information.

The following contextualized situations illustrate that we already have the representation tools to solve percent change problems.

EXAMPLE 6.46

CONNECTION
COMMUNICATION
PROBLEM SOLVING
REASONING
REPRESENTATION

Last week, there were 525 cars in the parking lot on campus. This week, there were 651 cars in the parking lot.

a. Find the increase in the number of cars in the parking lot.

b. Find the percent increase in the number of cars in the parking lot.

SOLUTION

a. $651 - 525 = 126$. Interpretation: There were 126 more cars in the parking lot this week than last week.

b. Our goal is to represent the increase as a percent change. We are comparing 651 cars this week to 525 cars last week.

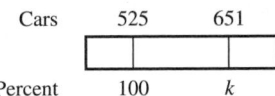

Then $\frac{525}{100} = \frac{651}{k}$. Then $525k = 651 \cdot 100$. Then $k = \frac{651 \cdot 100}{525} = 124$. This leads to the following diagram:

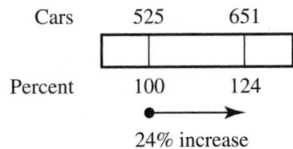

Interpretation: The number of cars in the parking lot increased by 24% this week compared to last week.

▲

Thus, in the preceding example, if there were 100 cars in the parking lot last week, then there are 124 cars in the parking lot this week. If there were 200 cars in the parking lot last week, then there are 248 cars in the parking lot this week.

The following Classroom Connection illustrates that elementary school students should know how to represent change as a percent, that is, find the percent increase or percent decrease.

 Classroom Connection

• *Mathematics*, Grade 6, p. 385

A $20 item is increased to $25. Find the percent increase or decrease. If necessary, round answers to the nearest tenth of a percent. (From Randall I. Charles. © 2004 by Pearson Education, Inc. or its affiliates. Used by permission. All rights reserved.)

EXAMPLE 6.47

CONNECTION
COMMUNICATION
PROBLEM SOLVING
REASONING
REPRESENTATION

This month, 68 students played basketball after school, an increase of 240% compared to last month. How many students played basketball after school last month?

SOLUTION

We are comparing the number of students who played basketball this month to the number of students who played last month. So the number of students who played basketball last month, denoted by n, corresponds to 100%. This leads to the following diagram:

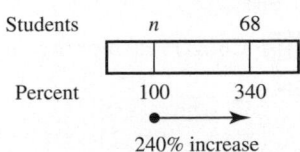

Then $\frac{n}{100} = \frac{68}{340}$. Then $340n = 68 \cdot 100$. Then $n = \frac{68 \cdot 100}{340} = 20$. This means 20 students played basketball after school last month.

▲

EXAMPLE 6.48

CONNECTION
COMMUNICATION
PROBLEM SOLVING
REASONING
REPRESENTATION

A manufacturer claims its new potato chips are crunchier and more flavorful, with only 153 calories per serving. The manufacturer also claims its new potato chips have 32% fewer calories than classic potato chips. How many calories are in one serving of classic potato chips?

SOLUTION

We are comparing the number of calories per serving of new potato chips to classic potato chips. The number of calories per serving of classic potato chips, denoted by *n*, corresponds to 100%. This leads to the following diagram:

Calories	153	*n*

Percent	68	100

32% decrease

Then $\frac{153}{68} = \frac{n}{100}$. Then $68n = 153 \cdot 100$. Then $n = \frac{153 \cdot 100}{68} = 225$. This means the classic potato chips have 225 calories per serving. ▲

From the diagrams, we see another way to view "153 calories is a 32% decrease" is "153 calories is 68% of the calories per serving of the classic potato chips."

Percent as a Fraction

As we mentioned in the beginning of this section, you can also represent a percent as a fraction. This representation allows you to solve percent problems using algebra and requires translating percents to fractions and decimals.

CONNECTION

> **Definition**
>
> $p\%$ is read as "*p* percent," means "*p* parts per 100 parts," and is defined as $p\% = \frac{p}{100}$.

A percent is another way to represent a fraction that has a denominator of 100. Here are some benchmark percents.

$$1\% = \frac{1}{100} = 0.01 \qquad 2\% = \frac{2}{100} = 0.02 \qquad 3\% = \frac{3}{100} = 0.03 \qquad \ldots$$

$$10\% = \frac{10}{100} = \frac{1}{10} = 0.10 \quad 20\% = \frac{20}{100} = \frac{1}{5} = 0.20 \quad 30\% = \frac{30}{100} = \frac{3}{10} = 0.30 \quad \ldots$$

$$25\% = \frac{25}{100} = \frac{1}{4} = 0.25 \qquad 50\% = \frac{50}{100} = \frac{1}{2} = 0.50 \qquad 75\% = \frac{75}{100} = \frac{3}{4} = 0.75$$

$$100\% = \frac{100}{100} = 1 \qquad 200\% = \frac{200}{100} = 2 \qquad 300\% = \frac{300}{100} = 3 \qquad \ldots$$

The following example shows how to convert some fractions and decimal numbers to percents without a calculator.

EXAMPLE 6.49

CONNECTION

Convert each of the numbers to a percent.

a. $\dfrac{57}{100}$

b. $\dfrac{15}{25}$

c. 0.012

d. 335.751

e. $\dfrac{3}{7}$

SOLUTION

First, write each number as a fraction with 100 as the denominator. Second, express the fraction using percent notation.

a. $\dfrac{57}{100} = 57\%$

b. $\dfrac{15}{25} = \dfrac{15 \times 4}{25 \times 4} = \dfrac{60}{100} = 60\%$

c. $0.012 = 0.012 \times \dfrac{100}{100} = \dfrac{0.012 \times 100}{100} = \dfrac{1.2}{100} = 1.2\%$

d. $335.751 = 335.751 \times \dfrac{100}{100} = \dfrac{335.751 \times 100}{100} = \dfrac{33{,}575.1}{100} = 33{,}575.1\%$

e. $\dfrac{3}{7} = \dfrac{3}{7} \times \dfrac{100}{100} = \dfrac{\frac{3}{7} \times 100}{100} = \dfrac{\frac{300}{7}}{100} = \dfrac{300}{7}\% = 42\dfrac{6}{7}\%$

EXAMPLE 6.50

CONNECTION

Convert each percent to a decimal.

a. 427%

b. 12.317%

c. 0.0048%

SOLUTION

a. $427\% = \dfrac{427}{100} = 4.27$

b. $12.317\% = \dfrac{12.317}{100} = 0.12317$

c. $0.0048\% = \dfrac{0.0048}{100} = 0.000048$

Common mistakes in converting between percents and decimals are 124% = 124 (ignoring the % sign) and 158% = 0.158 (putting the decimal point to the left of the numeral). The following example relates ratios, fractions, and percents.

EXAMPLE 6.51

CONNECTION
COMMUNICATION
PROBLEM SOLVING
REASONING
REPRESENTATION

Brenda is making unsweetened lemonade. She adds 3 ounces of lemon juice for every 5 ounces of water. What percent of the mixture is lemon juice?

SOLUTION

The ratio of ounces of lemon juice to ounces of water is 3:5. The ratio of lemon juice to mixture is 3:8. This means three-eighths of the mixture is lemon juice. Then

$$\frac{3}{8} = \frac{\frac{3}{8} \times 100}{100} = \frac{0.375 \times 100}{100} = \frac{37.5}{100} = 37.5\%.$$

37.5% of the mixture is lemon juice.

Write an Equation to Solve Percent and Percent Change Problems

Students should be able to "work flexibly with fractions, decimals, and percents to solve problems" (NCTM, Gr. 6–8). The following example illustrates types of percent problems.

EXAMPLE 6.52

PROBLEM SOLVING

REPRESENTATION

Edyta Pawlowska/Shutterstock.com

Solve each problem using algebra.

a. In a survey, 75% of students said they recycle plastic grocery bags. We know 140 students participated in the survey. How many students in the survey recycle plastic bags?

b. In a survey, 105 out of 140 students said they recycle plastic grocery bags. What percent of the students in the survey recycle plastic bags?

c. In a survey, 75% of the students, or 105 students, said they recycle plastic grocery bags. How many students participated in the survey?

SOLUTION

a. The number of students a in the survey who recycle plastic bags is 75% of 140. Then

$$a = 75\% \cdot 140$$
$$= 0.75 \cdot 140$$
$$= 105$$

So 105 students in the survey said they recycle plastic bags.

b. In a survey, $\frac{105}{140}$ is the fraction of students who said they recycle plastic bags. We need to convert the fraction to a percentage. $\frac{105}{140} = 0.75 = \frac{0.75 \times 100}{100} = \frac{75}{100} = 75\%$. This means 75% of the students in the survey said they recycle plastic bags. Another approach is to think, "105 is what percent of 140?" Then we obtain the equation $105 = p\% \times 140$. This leads to the following steps:

$$105 = p\% \cdot 140$$
$$105 = \frac{p}{100} \cdot 140$$
$$\frac{105}{140} = \frac{p}{100}$$
$$\frac{105}{140} \cdot 100 = p$$
$$75 = p$$

So $105 = 75\% \cdot 140$. This means 75% of the students in the survey said they recycle plastic bags.

c. Let n represent the total number of students in the survey.

$$75\% \cdot n = 105$$
$$0.75 \cdot n = 105$$
$$n = 105 \div 0.75$$
$$n = 140$$

This means 140 students participated in the survey. ▲

The equation $a = p\% \cdot n$ is called the **percent equation.** The variable expressions are a (part or percentage), $p\%$ (percent), and n (base or whole). Table 6.4 summarizes the possibilities and provides examples. We mention the cases to highlight their similarities (variations of the same equation) rather than their differences (variations of the unknown). Students should be able to "solve problems involving finding the whole, given a part and the percent" (CCSS, Gr. 6).

TABLE 6.4 The Three Classic Percent Problems Are Variations of the Percent Equation $a = p\% \cdot n$

Task	Unknown	Examples
Finding a part of a number	Part or percentage (a)	$a = 15\% \cdot 420$ $a = \dfrac{15}{100} \cdot 420$ $a = 0.15 \cdot 420$
Representing one number as a percentage of another number	Percent ($p\%$)	$18 = p\% \cdot 72$ $18 = \dfrac{p}{100} \cdot 72$
Finding the base number when the percentage of that number is known	Base or whole (n)	$24 = 162\% \cdot n$ $24 = \dfrac{162}{100} \cdot n$ $24 = 1.62 \cdot n$

The cases are similar because each equation involves two known quantities and one unknown quantity. Now we turn our attention to expressing percent change (percent increase or percent decrease) in terms of algebra.

Percent Change Equation

Suppose b is compared to a.

- b is a $p\%$ increase of a if and only if $b = a + p\% \cdot a$.
- b is a $p\%$ decrease of a if and only if $b = a - p\% \cdot a$.

EXAMPLE 6.53

PROBLEM SOLVING

REPRESENTATION

a. The regular price of a calculator is $72. It was on sale for $56. Express the change in price as a percent.

b. The number of students who marched in the annual parade rose by 12.5% to 63 students. How many students marched in the parade last year?

SOLUTION

a. The sales price is equal to the regular price minus a percent of the regular price. We are comparing the sale price $56 to the regular price $72. We write an equation to find the percent decrease:

$$56 = 72 - p\% \cdot 72$$

$$56 = 72 - \frac{p}{100} \cdot 72$$

$$\frac{p}{100} \cdot 72 = 72 - 56$$

$$\frac{p}{100} \cdot 72 = 16$$

$$p = (16 \div 72) \cdot 100$$

$$p = 22.2 \text{ (rounded to nearest tenth)}$$

Here, $\frac{p}{100} = \frac{22.2}{100} = 22.2\%$. The change in price is -22.2%.

(continued)

b. The number of students who marched this year is equal to the number of students who marched last year plus a percentage of the number of students who marched last year. Let n represent the number of people who marched in the parade last year. Then

$$63 = n + 12.5\% \cdot n$$
$$63 = n + 0.125 \cdot n$$
$$63 = 1 \cdot n + 0.125 \cdot n$$
$$63 = (1 + 0.125)n$$
$$63 = (1.125)n$$
$$n = \frac{63}{1.125}$$
$$n = 56$$

This means 56 students marched in the parade last year. ▲

The distributive property can be used to simplify calculations. For example, a 25% increase is equivalent to multiplying the original quantity by 1.25 because $a + 25\% \cdot a = 1 + 0.25a = (1 + 0.25)a = 1.25a$. A 25% decrease is equivalent to multiplying the original quantity by 0.75 because $a - 25\% \cdot a = 1 - 0.25a = (1 - 0.25)a = 0.75a$.

Concept Map 6.4 illustrates that we can use fractions, decimals, ratios, and percents to make comparisons of the same quantities.

> **Concept Map 6.4** **Using Fractions, Decimals, Ratios, and Percents to Make Comparisons of the Same Quantities**

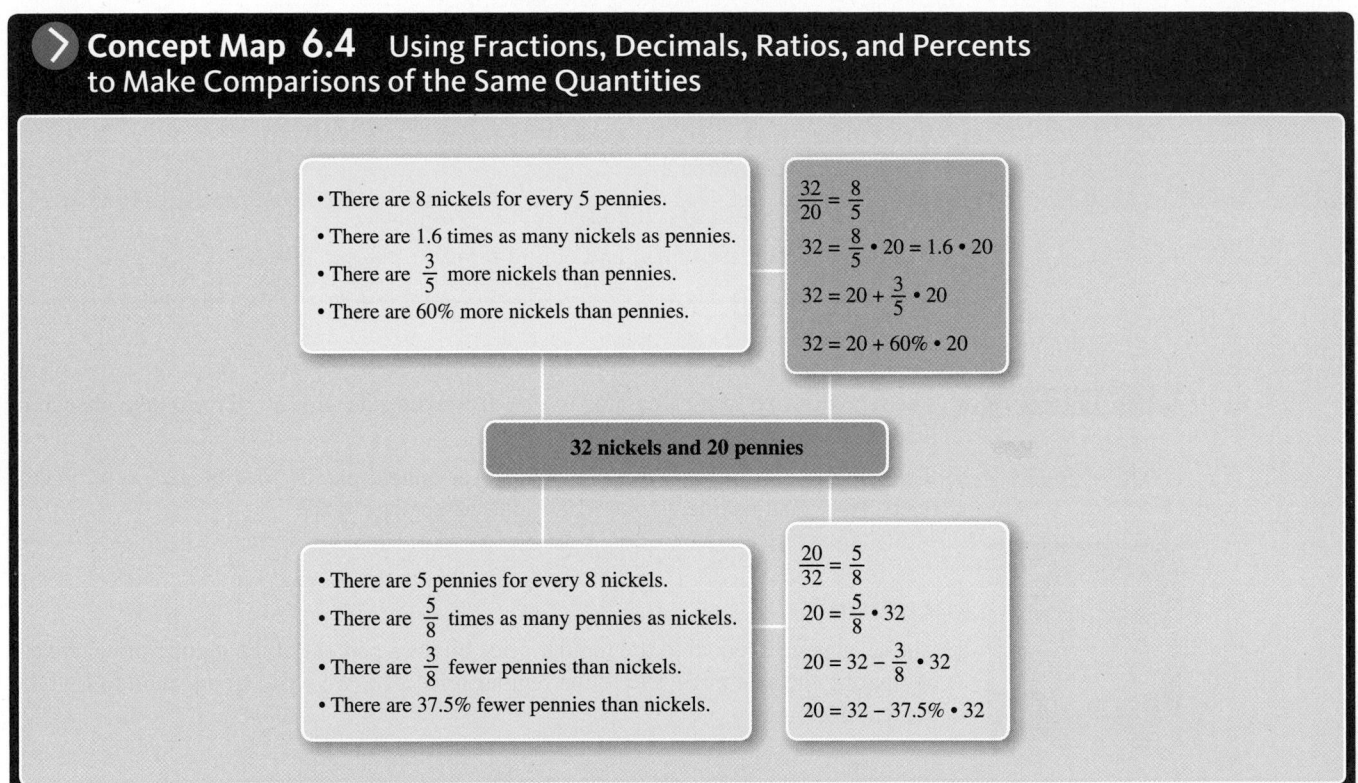

- There are 8 nickels for every 5 pennies.
- There are 1.6 times as many nickels as pennies.
- There are $\frac{3}{5}$ more nickels than pennies.
- There are 60% more nickels than pennies.

$$\frac{32}{20} = \frac{8}{5}$$
$$32 = \frac{8}{5} \cdot 20 = 1.6 \cdot 20$$
$$32 = 20 + \frac{3}{5} \cdot 20$$
$$32 = 20 + 60\% \cdot 20$$

32 nickels and 20 pennies

- There are 5 pennies for every 8 nickels.
- There are $\frac{5}{8}$ times as many pennies as nickels.
- There are $\frac{3}{8}$ fewer pennies than nickels.
- There are 37.5% fewer pennies than nickels.

$$\frac{20}{32} = \frac{5}{8}$$
$$20 = \frac{5}{8} \cdot 32$$
$$20 = 32 - \frac{3}{8} \cdot 32$$
$$20 = 32 - 37.5\% \cdot 32$$

QUESTIONS FOR SECTION 6.3

REPRESENTATION

Refresher: Representations (language, diagrams, tables, symbols, algebra, manipulatives, and contextualized situations) are important because we use them to organize, record, and communicate mathematical ideas and to make them more comprehensible.

1. There are 250 first graders in the school district. Of this group, 48% are boys. How many first graders are boys? Solve this problem using

   a. a bar diagram.   **b.** the percent equation.

2. Sandra has a collection of beads. Of the beads, 45% are silver. She has 126 silver beads. How many beads are in her collection? Solve this problem using

   a. a bar diagram.   **b.** the percent equation.

3. In a survey, 45 of 125 people liked the movie *I Dropped the Calculator Again*. What percent of the people in the survey liked the movie? Solve this problem using

   a. a bar diagram.   **b.** the percent equation.

4. Hillary purchased a ring for $230. Later, she sold it for $333.50. Fill in the blank with a percent, using the diagram: Hillary sold the ring for _____ more than she paid for it.

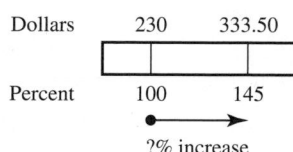

5. Mark purchased a painting for $61. Later, he sold it for $373.93. Fill in the blank with a percent, using the diagram: Mark sold the painting for _____ more than he paid for it.

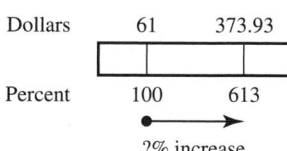

6. There are 372 calories in each serving of Homemade potato chips. There are 465 calories in each serving of Grandma Kettle potato chips. Fill in the blank with a percent, using the diagram: Homemade potato chips have _____ fewer calories than Grandma Kettle potato chips.

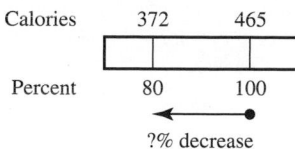

7. Kendall consumed 550 calories at breakfast and 352 calories at lunch. Fill in the blank with a percent, using the diagram: At lunch he consumed ____ fewer calories.

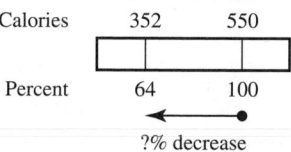

PROBLEM SOLVING

Refresher: Problem solving (reaching a goal that is not immediately attainable) is important because it helps students think more deeply about what they know and deal with unfamiliar situations.

8. The manager of a clothing store paid $35 for a shirt. She wants to set the regular price of the shirt so that she can make a $10 profit after she sells the shirt at a 15% discount. What should the regular price of the shirt be? Show your work.

9. Of the 450,000 ants at an annual picnic, about 15% of the ants preferred bread crumbs. That is a 25% decrease from the number of ants who preferred bread crumbs last year. How many ants preferred bread crumbs at the picnic last year? Show your work.

10. Suppose you purchased some stock and at the end of the first year the stock loses 14% of its value. Ed says, "In the second year, your stock needs to increase by approximately 16.28% to recover your losses." Use algebra to show that Ed is correct. Let A represent the original investment. Let B represent the value of the stock after the first year.

11. A fuel mixture consists of 3 parts oil and 11 parts gasoline. The oil costs $0.75 per liter, and the gasoline costs $1.60 per liter. A mechanic makes 392 liters of the mixture.

    a. How much oil does he use?

    b. How much gasoline does he use?

    c. What is the minimum amount the mechanic should charge for each liter of the fuel mixture to guarantee at least 15% profit?

REASONING AND PROOF

Refresher: Reasoning and proof (thinking and justifying) are important because they help students make sense of mathematics.

12. There are three girls for every five boys. Use a bar diagram to fill in the blank with a percent.

    a. There are _____ fewer girls than boys.

    b. The number of girls is _____ of the number of boys.

13. There are three girls for every five boys. Use a bar diagram to fill in the blank with a percent.

    a. There are _____ more boys than girls.

    b. The number of boys is _____ of the number of girls.

14. There are 10 girls and 14 boys. Use a bar diagram to fill in the blank with a percent.

    a. There are _____ fewer girls than boys.

    b. The number of girls is _____ of the number of boys.

15. There are 10 girls and 14 boys. Use a bar diagram to fill in the blank with a percent.

    a. There are _____ more boys than girls.

    b. The number of boys is _____ of the number of girls.

16. Fill in the blank with a decimal number.

    a. The number of girls is 100% more than the number of boys. The number of girls is ___ times the number of boys.

    b. The number of girls is 200% more than the number of boys. The number of girls is ___ times the number of boys.

    c. The number of girls is 250% more than the number of boys. The number of girls is ___ times the number of boys.

    d. The number of girls is 128% more than the number of boys. The number of girls is ___ times the number of boys.

    e. The number of girls is 15% more than the number of boys. The number of girls is ___ times the number of boys.

17. If 12% of a number is 70, what is 30% of the number? Solve this problem using mental arithmetic.

CONNECTIONS

Refresher: Connections (linking and applying mathematical ideas) are important because they deepen student understanding and make mathematics more meaningful, flexible, and useful.

18. A piggy bank with only pennies and nickels has 28 nickels for every 52 pennies. What percent of the coins are nickels? Solve this problem using

    a. a bar diagram.   b. the percent equation.

19. Temperatures reached 104°F during the sizzling heat wave in Europe in the summer of 2003. The highest temperature recorded in the United States was 29% higher, occurring in July 1913 in Death Valley, California. What was the temperature in Death Valley?

20. The duck population in the United States and Canada fell 11% from 2003 to 2004 to 32.2 million. Determine the duck population in the United States and Canada in 2003. Solve this problem using a

    a. bar diagram.   b. percent change equation.

21. J.D. Power & Associates is a company that conducts customer satisfaction surveys. Every year it releases the results of a survey of new car owners. In May 2003, it reported the 6400-pound Hummer H2 had 225 complaints per 100 vehicles, while the highly rated Lexus had fewer complaints—only 76 complaints per 100 vehicles. Express the difference in the complaints per 100 vehicles as a percent. Solve using a

    a. bar diagram.   b. percent change equation.

22. There are 15 cars and 27 trucks in the parking lot. Fill in the blank, rounding to the nearest tenth.

    a. In the parking lot, ___% of the vehicles are trucks.

    b. There are ___% fewer cars than trucks.

    c. There are ___% more trucks.

    d. The number of cars is ___% of the number of trucks.

COMMUNICATION

Refresher: Communication (written and verbal explanations using representations and proper mathematical vocabulary) is important because it helps students refine and strengthen their understanding.

23. Explain why unions usually negotiate the same percent raise for its union members rather than the same raise.

24. Can you have a percent increase that is more than 100%?

25. Can you have a percent decrease that is more than 100%?

26. Building A has 62,000 square feet. Building B has 88,000 square feet. The janitor claims Building B has approximately 30% more square footage than building A. What mistake did the janitor make?

27. In 2010, the population of San Marcos was 51,000. In 2007, the population was 57,600.

    a. Find the change in the population. Then interpret your answer in a sentence.

    b. Represent the change as a percent. Then interpret your answer in a sentence.

28. Last year, there were 520 registered vehicles in the town of Winkler. This year there are only 442.

    a. Find the change in the number of registered vehicles. Then interpret your answer in a sentence.

    b. Represent the change as a percent. Then interpret your answer in a sentence.

29. Option A: You get a 5% annual raise followed by a 12% annual raise 1 year later. Option B: You get a 12% annual raise followed by a 5% annual raise 1 year later. Which option is better? Justify your answer.

More practice with the ideas of the section

30. Fill in the blank. Choose one of the following words or phrases: *additive, change, finding a number when the percent of that number is known, finding a percent of a number, multiplicative, percent, percent change, percent equation,* or *representing one number as a percent of another number.* Use a word or phrase more than once if necessary.

    a. Phrases such as "35 more" and "35 fewer" indicate _____ reasoning.

    b. Phrases such as "35% more" and "35% fewer" indicate _____ reasoning.

    c. $a = p\% \times b$ is the _____.

    d. The equation $a = 15\% \times 420$ is an example of _____.

    e. The equation $65 = 21\% \times n$ is an example of _____.

    f. The equation $16 = p\% \times 70$ is an example of _____.

g. Change is a form of _____ reasoning.

h. Percent change is a form of _____ reasoning.

31. Kendall ate breakfast, consuming 350 calories. At lunch he consumed 22% fewer calories.

   a. Represent the situation with a bar diagram.

   b. Use the bar diagram to set up a proportion to determine how many calories he consumed at lunch.

32. Kim read 80 pages. Lennie read 35% more pages.

   a. Represent the situation with a bar diagram.

   b. Use the bar diagram to set up a proportion to determine the number of pages Lennie read.

33. Last year, a company spent $1200 on advertising. This year it spent $1650 on advertising.

   a. Find the change in the amount spent on advertising. Then interpret your answer in a sentence.

   b. Represent the change as a percent. Then interpret your answer in a sentence.

34. There are 42 boys in the first grade. There are 20% more boys than girls. How many girls are there? Solve this problem using a

   a. bar diagram.   **b.** percent change equation.

35. The average published tuition and fee charges at public 4-year universities and colleges was $7605 in academic year 2010–2011, according to the College Board Advocacy & Policy Center (trends.collegeboard.org). This represents a 64.4% increase from inflation-adjusted charges in academic year 2000–2001. What were the charges in academic year 2000–2001? Solve using a

   a. bar diagram.   **b.** percent change equation.

36. According to the Alternative Fuels and Advanced Vehicles Data Center (AFDC) of the U.S. Department of Energy, "Hybrid electric vehicles (HEVs) are powered by conventional or alternative fuels as well as electric power stored in a battery. HEVs combine the benefits of high fuel economy and low emissions with the power and range of conventional vehicles." Based on AFDC data, a total of 290,271 HEVs were sold in the United States in 2009. This represents a 7.08% decrease from 2008. Estimate the number of HEVs sold in 2008. Solve using a

   a. bar diagram.   **b.** percent change equation.

37. A hybrid sports utility vehicle (SUV) operates by a hybrid engine, which switches from a gasoline-powered engine to an electric-powered engine during deceleration to save gasoline. A conventional SUV operates by a conventional gasoline-powered V-6 engine. A particular hybrid SUV gets approximately 35 mpg in the city. Its conventional counterpart SUV gets 20 mpg in the city. Represent the difference as a percent of the conventional fuel efficiency using a

   a. bar diagram.   **b.** percent change equation.

38. Mary's annual salary decreased by $3800, which represents a 9% decrease.

   a. Represent the situation with a bar diagram.

   b. Use the bar diagram to set up a proportion to determine her previous salary.

39. Answer the following.

   a. Mary's annual salary is $40,000. She received a 6% pay raise. What is her new salary?

   b. Mary received a 6% pay raise. Her new annual salary is $43,000. What was her previous salary?

40. Use mental arithmetic to solve.

   a. 50% of 452 is ___.   **b.** 40% of 20 is ___.

   c. 30% of 90 is ___.   **d.** 5% of 240 is ___.

41. Do the following.

   a. Compute 16% of 94 and 16 × 94.

   b. Compute 23% of 35 and 23 × 35.

   c. Let a and b be whole numbers. What is the relationship between $a\% \times b$ and $a \times b$?

42. Give an example of two whole numbers a and b such that a is 35% more than b. Show your work.

43. Give an example of two whole numbers a and b such that a is 22% less than b. Show your work.

44. Round

   a. 14.67% to the nearest 1%.

   b. 0.678% to the nearest 0.5%.

   c. 134.53% to the nearest 0.1%.

   d. 142.45% to the nearest 5%.

45. Benchmark percents help students develop number sense. Using the definition of a percent as a fraction, devise a strategy to find

   a. 10% of a number.   **b.** 25% of a number.

   c. 40% of a number.   **d.** 50% of a number.

46. Express each decimal as a percent.

   a. 4.57   **b.** 0.00256   **c.** 158.6

47. Express each fraction or mixed number as a percent.

   a. $\dfrac{17}{20}$ **b.** $12\dfrac{4}{5}$ **c.** $5\dfrac{2}{3}$

48. Solve for y.

   a. $15\% \times 240 = y$ **b.** $320 \times y\% = 400$

   c. $1400 \times 0.05\% = y$

49. Solve using algebra. Round to the nearest whole number or whole percent as appropriate.

   a. What percent of 6.2 feet is 4.5 feet?

   b. What is 254% of $9?

   c. What percent is 67 books of 20 books?

50. Solve using algebra.

   a. What is 40% of 0.035 m?

   b. What percent of 7.2 pounds is 25 pounds?

   c. 38 feet is what percent of 242 feet?

51. Dave the musician makes 4% of the amount for which he sells every CD. If he sold 2,045,000 CDs and each CD sells for $12, then how much money does he make?

52. Use mental arithmetic to solve.

   a. 10% of n is 42. What is 15% of n?

   b. 5 is 10% of 50. What is 40% of 50?

   c. 8 is 10% of h. What is 5% of h?

53. The Bureau of Transportation Statistics, a branch of the U.S. Department of Transportation, handles complaints about airline service. In June 2010 it received 1419 complaints, and in June 2009 it received 748 complaints. Find the change and percent change in the number of complaints about airline service from June 2009 to June 2010. Then interpret each result in sentence form.

54. Pedometers are electronic devices walkers wear to count the number of steps taken on a walk. Japanese industry standards require that they be accurate to within 3%. The following data are based on an informal study by a reporter for the *San Diego Union Tribune* that was published in August 2004.

  a. The Sharper Image talking pedometer was off by 43 steps in a 1000-step test. Did this pedometer meet the Japanese standards in this test?

  b. The Walk4Life pedometer was off by at most 1 step in 1000-step tests. Did this pedometer meet the Japanese standards in this test?

  c. The Go Active Stepometer, given away by McDonald's as a free promotion, was off by 4% in tests. What is the minimum and the maximum possible number of steps recorded in a 1521-step test?

  d. The Digiwalker was off by 2% in tests. What is the minimum and the maximum possible number of steps recorded in a 3209-step test?

55. Last year, 280 people participated in the annual Calculator Parade. This year, only 245 people participated in the parade.

  a. Find the change in the number of people who participated in the parade. Then interpret your answer in a sentence.

  b. Represent the change as a percent. Then interpret your answer in a sentence.

56. Suppose you just purchased some stock. At the end of the first year, the stock loses 24% of its value. At the end of the second year, your stock needs to increase by approximately ___% to recover your losses. Justify your answer.

57. The formula used to calculate the monthly payment amount of a loan is given by

$$m = \frac{A \times \dfrac{r}{12}}{1 - \left(1 + \dfrac{r}{12}\right)^{-n}}$$

where

$$A = \text{original loan amount}$$
$$m = \text{monthly payment}$$
$$r = \text{interest rate expressed as a decimal}$$
$$n = \text{number of months of the loan}$$

  a. Suppose a loan amount of $25,000 must be repaid within 5 years and the interest rate is 6.3% per year. Calculate the monthly payment. Then calculate the total amount of interest paid on the original loan amount.

  b. Suppose a loan amount of $10,000 must be repaid within 4 years and the interest rate is 9.2% per year. Calculate the monthly payment. Then calculate the total amount of interest paid on the original loan amount.

58. Seven percent of a number is 18 more than 3% of the number. Find the number.

59. What is the discount for 42% off a regular price of $380?

60. A mountain bicycle is on sale for 80% of the regular price. The regular price is $1225. What is the sale price?

61. A sporting goods store reduced all prices 22% for a sale. What is the sale price for a $37 sweatshirt?

62. A bag of green peas in the pods sold for $2.00 after a discount of 20%. What was the regular price?

63. A gallon of orange juice sold for $3.20 after a discount of 5%. What was the regular price?

CHAPTER 6 REVIEW

CHAPTER 6 Organizer

Section	What You Should Learn	Review Problems
6.1	**1.** Represent a decimal with a decimal square, and know multiple representations.	1–2
	2. Write the place value and value of a digit in a decimal number.	3
	3. Use place value concepts to represent a decimal using word and expanded forms.	4–6
	4. Use place value concepts to order and round decimals.	7–10
	5. Justify and predict the effect that multiplying and dividing by positive powers of 10 (for example, 10, 100, and 1000) has on the decimal point.	11

	6. Describe the connection between operations with whole numbers and operations with decimal numbers.	12–16
	7. Determine whether the fraction is a terminating decimal.	17
6.2	**1.** Represent a fraction as a terminating or repeating decimal, and vice versa.	18–20
	2. Predict which fractions have terminating and which have repeating decimal representations.	21
	3. Define and distinguish rational and irrational numbers.	22–23
	4. Represent decimal numbers using scientific notation.	24
	5. Demonstrate understanding of nth roots.	25–26
	6. Use exponential notation to simplify or represent expressions.	27–29
6.3	**1.** Explain the concept of the percent in terms of a ratio.	30–31
	2. Use benchmarks to find the percent of a number.	32
	3. Solve percent problems using ratios, diagrams, proportions, and algebra.	33–36
	4. Solve percent increase and percent decrease problems.	37–42
	5. Translate among fractions, decimals, and percents.	43
	6. Make comparisons in terms of percents.	44–45

Key Terms and Concepts

decimal number   307
decimal point   307
integer part   308
decimal part (fractional part)   308
decimal fraction   308
one-tenth   308
one-hundredth   308
word form   310
expanded form   310
short word form   310
ordering decimals   312
adding decimals   313
subtracting decimals   313
multiplying and dividing decimals by powers of 10   315
multiplying decimals   315
dividing decimals   316
terminating decimal number   318

nonterminating decimal   325
repeating decimal number   327
repetend   327
period   327
connections between rational numbers and decimal representations   329
irrational number   329
set of real numbers   330
square root   332
radical   332
radicand   332
classifying $\sqrt{n}$ 333
nth root (n is odd)   334
index   334
nth root (n is even)   335
principal nth root   335
principle square root   335

properties of rational exponents   336
scientific notation   338
significant digits   338
order of magnitude   338
properties of operations with real numbers   340
percent as a ratio   344
how to use the bar diagram to solve classic percent problems   346
bar diagram   346
change   348
percent change   348
percent as a fraction   350
write an equation to solve percent and percent change problems   352
percent equation   352
percent change equations   353

Review Questions

1. The large decimal square represents 1 unit. Shade the decimal square to represent the decimal with a diagram.

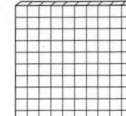

   a. 0.06   **b.** 0.34

2. Fill in the blank for an equivalent representation.

   a. 3 tenths = ___ hundredths

   b. 14 hundredths = ___ tenths

   c. 23 ones = ___ tenths   **d.** 2 tenths = ___ hundredths

3. In 2.232561097, specify the place value of the digit.

   a. 3   **b.** 5   **c.** 6   **d.** 0

4. Represent the standard form of the number.

   a. four hundred thirty-two and forty-five thousandths

   b. two hundred five and ninety-eight millionths

5. Represent 716.034 in expanded form with

   a. decimals.   **b.** fractions.

   c. multiplication.   **d.** exponents.

6. Write the short word form of the number.

   a. 17,432.082   **b.** 17,432.0082   **c.** 17,432.00082

7. Write 54.302 in expanded form using multiplication.

8. Some elementary school students think 0.28 is greater than 0.4 because they inappropriately apply whole number concepts.

   a. What two whole numbers are they comparing?

   b. Draw decimal squares to compare the two decimal numbers.

9. Round

   a. 82.982 to the nearest tenth.

   b. 72.931578 to the nearest hundredth.

   c. 416.3476 to the nearest thousandth.

   d. 872.02 to the nearest tenth.

10. Every number n in the interval $2.75 \leq n < 2.85$ equals 2.8 when n is rounded to the nearest tenth. Find the largest possible interval such that all numbers in the interval equal

    a. 2.97, rounded to the nearest hundredth.

    b. 67.035, rounded to the nearest thousandth.

11. Order the decimals from least to greatest: 0.4, 8.004, 32.84, 46.1, 7.000999, 7.0021, 0.38.

12. Answer the following.

    a. Suppose you multiply 4.72 by 10. What happens to the decimal point? Justify your answer.

    b. Suppose you divide 4.72 by 10. What happens to the decimal point? Justify your answer.

13. Answer the following.

    a. When we add 34.35 and 1.28 using a vertical format, as shown here, why do we line up the decimal points?

    $$\begin{array}{r} \overset{1}{34.35} \\ +1.28 \\ \hline 35.63 \end{array}$$

    b. Why does a 1 appear above the 3?

14. Answer the following.

    a. When we subtract 6.19 from 9.84 using a vertical format, as shown here, why do we line up the decimal points?

    $$\begin{array}{r} \overset{7\ 14}{9.8\cancel{4}} \\ -6.19 \\ \hline 3.65 \end{array}$$

    b. Why does a 14 appear above the 4?

15. Show that that 0.0053×32.7 requires the calculation 53×327.

16. Turn each decimal into a fraction and show that $567.3 \div 4.02$ requires the calculation $56{,}730 \div 402$.

17. Use estimation to insert the decimal point.

    a. $27.15 \times 4.88 = 132492$

    b. $28.815 \div 4.25 = 678$

18. Without using a calculator, determine whether the fraction is a terminating decimal.

    a. $\dfrac{21}{2 \cdot 5 \cdot 7}$ **b.** $\dfrac{17}{2 \cdot 5 \cdot 5 \cdot 5 \cdot 5}$ **c.** $\dfrac{4}{42}$

19. Think about the decimal number $18.0\overline{627}$.

    a. What is the repetend?

    b. What is the period of the repetend?

20. Use a calculator to divide, and then represent the fraction as a repeating decimal. Use proper notation to signify the repetend.

    a. $\dfrac{34}{99}$ **b.** $\dfrac{857}{999}$

21. Represent the repeating decimal as a fraction.

    a. $12.52525252\ldots$ **b.** $15.84123123123\ldots$

22. Without using a calculator, determine whether the fraction is a terminating decimal or a repeating decimal.

    a. $\dfrac{24}{4 \cdot 4 \cdot 5 \cdot 5 \cdot 5 \cdot 3}$ **b.** $\dfrac{42}{2 \cdot 5 \cdot 5 \cdot 5 \cdot 5 \cdot 7}$

    c. $\dfrac{10}{35}$ **d.** $\dfrac{4}{55}$ **e.** $\dfrac{5}{8}$ **f.** $\dfrac{18}{21}$

23. Tell how you know $\sqrt{12}$ is an irrational number.

24. Determine whether the given number is rational or irrational.

    a. $\sqrt{7}$ **b.** $\sqrt{25}$ **c.** $623.1\overline{962}$ **d.** $\dfrac{5}{8}$

    e. $23.45607007000700007\ldots$

25. Use scientific notation to represent each number with the stated number of significant digits.

	Two significant digits	Three significant digits
185.73		
0.0004561		

26. Do the following.
    a. Write an expression for the principal square root of 24.
    b. List the square roots of 24.
    c. Find all solutions to the equation $x^2 = 24$.

27. How many real solutions does the equation have?
    a. $x^5 = 72$ b. $x^9 = -32$ c. $x^6 = 85$ d. $x^{40} = -5$

28. The simplest form of $\sqrt{20}$ is $2\sqrt{5}$. Write each expression in a simpler form.
    a. $\sqrt[3]{4^3 \cdot 5^2 \cdot 8^6}$ b. $\sqrt{7^3 \cdot 5^2 \cdot 3^6}$
    c. $\sqrt[3]{24a^4b^5}$ d. $\dfrac{a^5b^3}{a}$ e. $4^{\frac{-3}{2}}$

29. Simplify each expression, and write the final answer using positive exponents.
    a. $\left(\dfrac{a^2b}{ab}\right)^3$ b. $\dfrac{a^3b^5}{a^{-1}b^2}$ c. $\dfrac{a^{\frac{4}{3}}b^6}{a^5b^{\frac{3}{4}}}$ d. $\dfrac{a^{-4}b^{-2}}{a^3b^{-5}}$

30. Use properties of radicals to simplify each expression.
    a. $\sqrt{3} \cdot \sqrt{5}$ b. $(\sqrt[3]{5})^6$ c. $\sqrt{3} \cdot \sqrt{6}$

31. What does 35% mean to you?

32. There are five cars for every three trucks. What percent of the vehicles are cars? Use ratios to solve this problem.

33. Benchmark percents help students develop number sense. Using the definition of a percent, devise a strategy to find
    a. 10% of a number. b. 15% of a number.
    c. 20% of a number. d. 30% of a number.

34. Solve each problem using a bar diagram.
    a. In a survey, 65% of students said they recycle plastic grocery bags. We know 180 students participated in the survey. How many students in the survey recycle plastic bags?
    b. In a survey, 68 out of 85 students said they recycle plastic grocery bags. What percentage of the students in the survey recycle plastic bags?
    c. In a survey, 28% of the students, or 84 students, said they recycle plastic grocery bags. How many students participated in the survey?

35. There are 200 first graders in the school district. Of them, 55% are boys. How many first graders are boys? Solve this problem using
    a. a bar diagram. b. the percent equation.

36. Cindy has a collection of beads. Of the beads, 45% are silver. She has 360 silver beads. How many beads are in her collection? Solve this problem using
    a. a bar diagram. b. the percent equation.

37. In a survey, 72 of 400 people liked the movie *The Case of the Missing Calculator*. What percent of the people in the survey liked the movie? Solve this problem using
    a. a bar diagram. b. the percent equation.

38. Ken spent $450 on utility bills this month. That was 32% less than last month. What was his bill last month? Solve using
    a. a bar diagram. b. algebra.

39. Diane read 330 pages. She read 65% more pages than Pam. How many pages did Pam read? Solve using a
    a. bar diagram. b. percent change equation.

40. According to data from the Center for Applied Biodiversity Science, the wild chimpanzee population has declined by an estimated 400,000 in the past 30 years, or about 66%. Estimate the number of wild chimpanzees remaining today. Solve using a
    a. bar diagram. b. percent change equation.

41. The top five Internet search engines for July 2010 were, in order, (1) Google Search, (2) Yahoo! Search, (3) Bing Search, (4) Ask.com Search, and (5) AOL Search.

    In July 2009, there were approximately 10.5 billion Internet searches altogether. In July 2010, there were approximately 8.8 billion Internet searches, according to the ACNielsen/Nielsen Media Research.
    a. What is the change in the number of Internet searches? Interpret your answer in a sentence.
    b. Represent the change as a percent. Then interpret your answer in a sentence.

42. Adults with a university degree earn, on the average, approximately 72% more than adults with just a high school diploma.
    a. Suppose the average income of an adult with a university degree is $84,000. What is the average income of an adult with just a high school diploma?
    b. Suppose the average income of an adult with just a high school diploma is $84,000. What is the average income of an adult with a university degree?

43. The manager of a clothing store paid $28 for a shirt. He wants to set the regular price of the shirt so that he can make a 20% profit after he sells the shirt at a 25% discount. What should the regular price of the shirt be?

44. Complete the table of equivalent representations.

Percentage	Fraction	Decimal
20%	$\frac{20}{100}$	0.20
172%		
	$\frac{15}{24}$	
		0.0042

45. There are 25 nickels and 40 dimes. Fill in the blank, rounding decimals and percentages to the nearest tenth.
    a. The number of dimes is _____ times the number of nickels.
    b. The ratio dimes to nickels is _____.

c. Of the coins, ___% are dimes.

d. There are ___% fewer nickels than dimes.

e. There are ___% more dimes.

f. The number of nickels is ___% of the number of dimes.

46. 2800 warblers and 1260 hawks migrated to a wild refuge. Fill in the blank, rounding to the nearest whole number.

a. ___ percent more warblers than hawks migrated to the wildlife refuge.

b. ___ percent fewer hawks than warblers migrated to the wildlife refuge.

Chapter 6 Test

1. *Write the place value and value of a digit in a decimal number.* Specify the digit in 5.320864 that is in the

   a. hundredths place.   b. thousandths place.

   c. millionths place.

2. *Write the place value and value of a digit in a decimal number.* In 67.0921, specify the place of the digit.

   a. 9   b. 1   c. 6

3. *Use place value concepts to represent a decimal using word and expanded forms.* Write the standard form of the number six hundred two and eighty-three hundred-thousandths.

4. *Use place value concepts to represent a decimal using word and expanded forms.* Write the short word form of 305,632.04237.

5. *Use place value concepts to represent a decimal using word and expanded forms.* Represent 73.105 in expanded form with

   a. decimals.   b. fractions.

   c. multiplication.   d. exponents.

6. *Describe the connection between operations with whole numbers and operations with decimal numbers.*

   a. What whole number multiplication problem does 34.708×1.42 require?

   b. What simpler division problem does $347.268 \div 42.05$ require?

7. *Describe the connection between operations with whole numbers and operations with decimal numbers.*

   a. Why does a 15 appear above the 5?

   $$\begin{array}{r} \overset{3\ 15}{7.\cancel{4}\cancel{5}} \\ -4.28 \\ \hline 3.17 \end{array}$$

   b. Why does a 1 appear above the 4?

   $$\begin{array}{r} \overset{1\ \ 1}{38.47} \\ +2.06 \\ \hline 40.53 \end{array}$$

8. *Represent a fraction as a terminating or repeating decimal, and vice versa.*

   a. Represent $62.35\overline{18}$ as a fraction.

   b. Represent $456 \div 990$ as a decimal number.

9. *Predict which fractions have terminating and which have repeating decimal representations.* Without using a calculator, determine whether the fraction is a terminating decimal or repeating decimal.

   a. $\dfrac{3^4 \cdot 5^{10} \cdot 7^{30}}{2^{10} \cdot 5^{40} \cdot 7^8}$ b. $\dfrac{3^9 \cdot 5^{12} \cdot 14^{60}}{2^{10} \cdot 21^4}$

   c. $\dfrac{a}{2^b \cdot 5^c}$, where a, b, and c are counting numbers.

   d. $\dfrac{15 \times 10^{60}}{a \times 36 \times 10^{20}}$, where a is a counting number.

10. *Define and distinguish rational and irrational numbers.*

    a. Tell how you know $\sqrt{15}$ is an irrational number.

    b. Tell how you know $\frac{3}{4} \times \sqrt{15}$ is an irrational number.

    c. Tell how you know $6.315311531115311115\ldots$ is an irrational number.

11. *Represent decimal numbers using scientific notation.*

    a. How many significant digits does 3.057×10^{12} have?

    b. Represent 5,748,216 using scientific notation with three significant digits.

    c. What is the order of magnitude of 14.38×10^{-5}?

12. *Demonstrate understanding of nth roots.*

    a. List the sixth root or roots of 18.

    b. Write an expression that represents the fifth root of 4.

13. *Demonstrate understanding of nth roots.*

    a. Find all solutions to the equation $4x^{12} - 6 = 28$.

    b. Write an equation that has the solution $\sqrt{15}$ such that the equation does not involve a radical sign.

    c. Write an equation that has the solution $2\sqrt{15}$ such that the equation does not involve a radical sign.

14. *Demonstrate understanding of nth roots.* Explain why $\sqrt[6]{-10}$ is not a real number.

15. *Solve percent problems using ratios, diagrams, proportions, and algebra.* In 2009, 28 governors belonged to the Democratic Party and 22 governors belonged to the Republican Party, according to the 2010 Statistical Abstract of the United States. What percent of governors belonged to the Democratic Party? Solve this problem using a diagram, then interpret your answer in a sentence.

16. *Solve percent problems using ratios, diagrams, proportions, and algebra.* Taylor spent $245 on car repairs this year. That was 18% less than last year. How much did he spend on car repairs last year? Solve this problem using an equation, then interpret your answer in a sentence.

17. *Solve percent problems using ratios, diagrams, proportions, and algebra.* Kim has a collection of books. She has 84 nonfiction books, which is 35% of her collection. How many books does she have? Solve this problem using a diagram or an equation.

18. *Solve percent increase and percent decrease problems.* There were 14,507 thousand full-time and part-time students enrolled in college degree–granting institutions in 1998. College enrollment increased by 31.7% from 1998 to 2008, based on data from the 2009 Digest of Education Statistics.

a. Represent the situation with a diagram.

b. Determine the number of college students in 2008. Then interpret your answer in a sentence.

19. *Solve percent increase and percent decrease problems.* There were 162,000 marriages in New York in 2000. The number of marriages decreased by 19.4% in New York from 2000 to 2007, based on data from the 2010 Statistical Abstract of the United States.

a. Represent the situation with a diagram.

b. Determine the number of marriages in 2007. Then interpret your answer in a sentence.

20. *Solve percent increase and percent decrease problems.* In 1997, there were 3,138 thousand elementary and secondary school teachers. In 2007, there were 3,634 thousand, according to the 2010 Statistical Abstract of the United States.

a. What is the change in the number of teachers? Interpret your answer in a sentence.

b. Represent the change as a percentage. Then interpret your answer in a sentence.

21. *Translate among fractions, decimals, and percents.* Convert each of the numbers to a percent. Show your work.

a. 0.0046   **b.** 586.3

22. *Translate among fractions, decimals, and percents.* Convert each of the numbers to a percent. Show your work.

a. $\dfrac{4}{7}$ **b.** $\dfrac{5}{8}$

23. *Translate among fractions, decimals, and percents.* Convert each percent to a decimal. Show your work.

a. 312%   **b.** 18.4%   **c.** 0.0024%

24. *Make comparisons in terms of percents.* There are 24 cars and 38 trucks in the parking lot. Round each answer to the nearest tenth.

a. ___ percent of the vehicles in the parking lot are trucks.

b. There are ___% fewer cars than trucks.

c. There are ___% more trucks than cars.

d. The number of cars is ___% of the number of trucks.

e. The number of trucks is ___% of the number of cars.

7

Algebra and Functions

Where Are We Going?

In **Section 7.1,** we discuss the concept of a function, which we use to relate two variables. We can represent a function using a table, a graph, an equation, or words. The multiple representations highlight different aspects of the relationship. Connections among the representations lead to a deeper understanding of the relationship between the two variables. We also discuss the algebra of functions, or ways to build a new function from existing functions. In **Section 7.2,** we discuss the connection between solving an equation and finding a point on the graph of a function. Then we represent and solve word problems that involve two equations and two unknowns. In **Section 7.3,** we discuss the tile model for representing and solving one- and two-step equations.

How Does Fuel Efficiency Depend on Speed?

A function is a special relationship between two related variables. For example, fuel efficiency (miles per gallon, or mpg) depends on speed (miles per hour, or mph). The following graph shows how speed affects fuel efficiency. We see that fuel efficiency increases as speed increases from 5 to 55 mph. We also see that fuel efficiency drops for speeds past 55 mph, which leads to higher fuel consumption because you need more fuel than usual for your trip, which in turn leads to higher costs. The U.S. Department of Energy (www.fueleconomy.gov/feg/driveHabits.shtml) estimates that every 5 mph over 60 mph is like paying an additional 20 cents per gallon (assuming gasoline costs $3 per gallon).

Why Is the Concept of Function Critical to Understanding Mathematics?

The concept of function is a unifying idea because it integrates many mathematical topics: tables, graphs, variables, algebraic expressions, representations, quantifying relationships with equations, arithmetic operations and their properties, evaluating expressions, and solving equations. Functions afford students powerful opportunities to comprehend advanced mathematics.

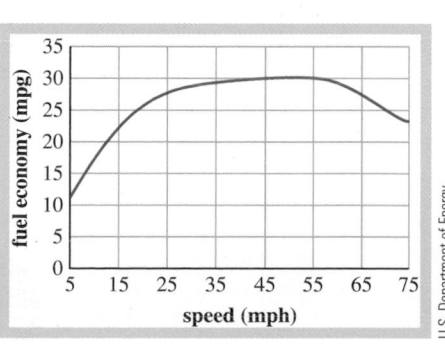

AmanaImagesRF/Getty Images

U.S. Department of Energy.

365

SECTION 7.1 | Representing and Creating Functions

We may represent a function (with numerical inputs and outputs) using a table, a graph, an equation, or words. Given one representation of the function, students should be able to create other representations of the function. For example, given a table, students should be able to draw a graph, describe the function in words, and write an equation. Students should be able to see that a table records and organizes the data to help them explore a pattern, a graph lets them "see" the relationship between two variables, words help describe the story, and an equation allows them to quantify the relationship and obtain ordered pairs that may be infeasible to obtain from a table or graph. Both the table and the graph illustrate the dynamic relationship between the two variables.

The NCTM *Principle and Standards for School Mathematics* advocates multiple representations, stating students should be able to "solve problems in which they use tables, graphs, words, and symbolic expressions to represent and examine functions and patterns of change" (© NCTM Standards 2011 by National Council of Teachers of Mathematics). In addition, the NCTM's standards and expectations states that students should be able to "represent and analyze patterns and functions, using words, tables, and graphs" (Gr. 3–5) and "relate and compare different forms of representation for a relationship" (Gr. 6–8).

Concepts and Representation

Informally, a function is a predictable relationship between two variables. Elementary school students typically relate values in a table, draw the ordered pairs in a rectangular graph, express the function as a rule (for example, Marcia has two fewer than three times as many coins as Tim), and finally generalize the relationship in the form of an equation (for example, $m = 3t - 2$). A thorough understanding of the concept of function requires new terminology and notation.

A game consists of spinning two spinners, spinner A and spinner B, as shown in Figure 1.

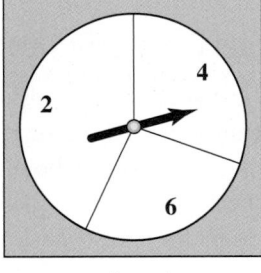 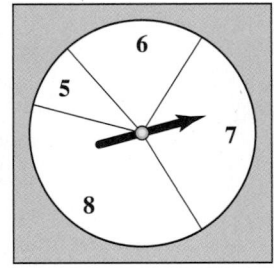

spinner A   spinner B

FIGURE 1

Spinners A and B.

If the number from spinner A divides the number from spinner B, then you win a prize (please see your instructor). This problem requires thinking about two variables at the same time (the number from spinner A and the number from spinner B). The winning possibilities are

- spinner A points to 2 and spinner B points to 6.
- spinner A points to 2 and spinner B points to 8.
- spinner A points to 4 and spinner B points to 8.
- spinner A points to 6 and spinner B points to 6.

REPRESENTATION You can use ordered pairs to represent these relationships more compactly. An **ordered pair** is a pair of elements x and y written in the form (x, y). Both x and y are called **coordinates**. We say x is the **first coordinate** and y is the **second coordinate**. In this example, the first coordinate is the result from spinner A and the second coordinate is the result from spinner B. Thus, the list of winning outcomes is the set $\{(2, 6), (2, 8), (4, 8), (6, 6)\}$.

Let A represent the set $\{2, 4, 6\}$ and B represent the set $\{5, 6, 7, 8\}$. The Cartesian product $A \times B$ is the set of all possible outcomes from spinning both spinners, which is the set of all ordered pairs (x, y) such that x belongs to A and y belongs to B. Then $A \times B = \{(2, 5), (2, 6), (2, 7), (2, 8), (4, 5), (4, 6), (4, 7), (4, 8), (6, 5), (6, 6), (6, 7), (6, 8)\}$.

The set of winning outcomes $\{(2, 6), (2, 8), (4, 8), (6, 6)\}$ is an example of a relation. A **relation from set A to set B** is a *subset* of the Cartesian product $A \times B$. Any relation from A to itself is called a relation on A. A relation does not have to be meaningful—any subset of $A \times B$ is a relation. It is helpful to think of a relation as some type of relationship between two sets or varying quantities. Table 7.1 shows a few illustrative examples.

TABLE 7.1   **Examples of Relations from A to B**

Sets A and B	Set $A \times B$	Relations from A to B
$A = \{0, 1\}$ $B = \{q, r\}$	$A \times B = \{(0, q), (0, r), (1, q), (1, r)\}$	$M = \{(0, q), (1, r)\}$ $N = \{(0, q), (0, r), (1, q)\}$
$A = \{1, 2, 3\}$ $B = \{h, 5\}$	$A \times B = \{(1, h), (1, 5), (2, h), (2, 5),$ $(3, h), (3, 5)\}$	$P = \{(1, 5), (2, h), (2, 5)\}$ $Q = \{(1, h), (2, 5), (3, 5)\}$

We can think of relations in terms of ordered pairs. We can also use rules (words) to describe some relations and then represent the relationship as a set of ordered pairs.

EXAMPLE 7.1

CONNECTION
REASONING
REPRESENTATION

Let $A = \{3, 4, 6\}$ and $B = \{3, 6, 7\}$. Let W be the relation from A to B consisting of ordered pairs (x, y) such that $x + y$ is an even number. Represent W as a set of ordered pairs.

SOLUTION

The possible sums are $3 + 3 = 6$, $3 + 6 = 9$, $3 + 7 = 10$, $4 + 3 = 7$, $4 + 6 = 10$, $4 + 7 = 11$, $6 + 3 = 9$, $6 + 6 = 12$, and $6 + 7 = 13$. The sums 6, 10, and 12 are even numbers, so $W = \{(3, 3), (3, 7), (4, 6), (6, 6)\}$.

▲

COMMUNICATION
REASONING

An ordered pair (x, y) has two coordinates. We often think of the first coordinate x as the **input** (or **independent variable**) and the second coordinate y as the **output** (or **dependent variable**). It is helpful to think of the independent variable as the quantity that we can specify and the dependent variable as the quantity that we measure or calculate. This thinking is useful for relating two variables in a contextualized situation.

EXAMPLE 7.2

Identify the independent and the dependent variables.

a. A cook is making a pot of soup. He adds some salt. Then he tastes the soup and adds some more salt.

b. A student is studying the relationship between the area of a square and the length of a side of the square. She wants to know if doubling the length of the side doubles the area and creates the table shown.

Length of side (s)	1	2	4	8
Area (A)	1	4	16	64

c. A student wants to graph the solutions of the equation $2h + 3q = 48$. He labels the horizontal axis as the "h-axis" and the vertical axis as the "q-axis."

SOLUTION

The independent variable is the variable that can be specified, and the dependent variable is the variable that is measured.

a. The independent variable is the amount of salt added, and the dependent variable is the taste of the soup.

(continued)

b. The independent variable is the length of the side of the square, and the dependent variable is the area.

c. By convention, the horizontal axis corresponds to the independent variable and the vertical axis corresponds to the dependent variable. The student labels the horizontal axis as the "*h*-axis," so *h* is the independent variable. He labels the vertical axis as the "*q*-axis," so *q* is the dependent variable.

▲

A relation is a relationship between a set of inputs and a set of outputs.

EXAMPLE 7.3

COMMUNICATION

REASONING

Let $A = \{1, 2, 3\}$ and $B = \{t, u, v, w\}$. Define the relation Q from A to B by $Q = \{(1, t), (2, t), (2, w)\}$. According to the relation Q,

a. if the input is 1, what is the corresponding output?

b. if the input is 2, what is the corresponding output?

c. if the input is 3, what is the corresponding output?

SOLUTION

a. $(1, t)$ is the only ordered pair with a first coordinate of 1, so the corresponding output is t. This means that if you know the input is 1, then you can predict the corresponding output, because there is exactly one choice t.

b. $(2, t)$ and $(2, w)$ both belong to Q, so the corresponding output is either t or w. This means that if you know the input is 2, then you cannot predict the corresponding output, because there are two possible choices: t or w.

c. There is no ordered pair in Q with a first coordinate of 3. Based on the information in Q, the answer to the question is "I don't know; Q does not specify an output for 3."

▲

EXAMPLE 7.4

COMMUNICATION

REASONING

Let $A = \{1, 2, 3\}$ and $B = \{t, u, v, w\}$. Define the relation R from A to B by $R = \{(1, t), (2, t), (3, w)\}$. According to relation R,

a. if the input is 1, what is the corresponding output?

b. if the input is 2, what is the corresponding output?

c. if the input is 3, what is the corresponding output?

SOLUTION

a. $(1, t)$ is the only ordered pair with a first coordinate of 1, so the corresponding output is t. This means that if you know the input is 1, then you can predict the corresponding output, because there is exactly one choice t.

b. $(2, t)$ is the only ordered pair with a first coordinate of 2, so the corresponding output is t. This means that if you know the input is 2, then you can predict the corresponding output, because there is exactly one choice t.

c. $(3, w)$ is the only ordered pair with a first coordinate of 3, so the corresponding output is w. This means that if you know the input is 3, then you can predict the corresponding output, because there is exactly one choice w.

▲

Function as a Special Relation

The relation Q in Example 7.3 created some ambiguity ("t or w") or puzzlement ("I don't know"). But the relation R in Example 7.4 was "well behaved," because each possible input has exactly one output. A relation like R is called a function, which describes a predictable relationship.

> ## Definition
>
> A **function** is a relation from set A to set B such that each element of A (the inputs) corresponds to exactly one element of B.
>
> - The set of first coordinates (the inputs) of the function is the set A and is called the **domain** of the function.
> - The set of second coordinates (the outputs) of the function is called the **range** of the function.
> - The set B is called the **codomain** of the function. (The range is a subset of set B.)

EXAMPLE 7.5   Use set notation to represent the domain and range of the function shown in the table.

REPRESENTATION

Inputs	1	2	−3	4
Outputs	3	3	2	0

SOLUTION

The domain is the set of inputs: {1, 2, −3, 4}. The range is the set of outputs: {0, 2, 3}.

Students are expected to "understand that a function is a rule that assigns to each input exactly one output" and "understand that functions describe situations where one quantity determines another" (© 2010. National Governors Association Center for Best Practices and Council of Chief State School Officers. All rights reserved.). The following Classroom Connection illustrates that students should be able to distinguish relations and functions in tables.

> **Classroom Connection**
>
> - *Mathematics*, Grade 6, p. 446
>
> Tell whether each relation is a function. (From Randall I. Charles. © 2004 Pearson Education, Inc. or its affiliates. Used by permission. All rights reserved.)
>
> | x | 2 | 1 | 0 | −1 |
> |---|---|---|---|---|
> | y | 6 | 5 | 4 | 3 |
>
> | x | −3 | 0 | 0 | 3 |
> |---|---|---|---|---|
> | y | 0 | 2 | −2 | 0 |

EXAMPLE 7.6   Each table shows ordered pairs. Is y a function of x?

REPRESENTATION

a.

x	1	2	3	4
y	3	3	2	0

b.

x	1	2	2	4
y	8	3	5	0

SOLUTION

a. Each input value produces exactly one output value. For example, 1 always corresponds to 3, 2 always corresponds to 3, and 4 always corresponds to 0. Therefore, the relation is a function.

b. The input 2 corresponds to 3 or 5, so the input 2 corresponds to more than one output. Therefore, the relation is a not function.

The following example explains how to visualize relationships with diagrams, which may be easier than inspecting a table or set of ordered pairs.

EXAMPLE 7.7

REPRESENTATION

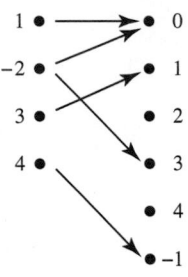

FIGURE 2

Representation of Q using an arrow diagram.

Determine whether the relation $Q = \{(1, 0), (-2, 0), (3, 1), (4, -1), (-2, 3)\}$ is a function from $A = \{1, -2, 3, 4\}$ to $B = \{0, 1, -1, 2, 3, 4\}$.

a. Use an arrow diagram.

b. Use a rectangular coordinate graph.

SOLUTION

a. Figure 2 illustrates an arrow diagram. The left-hand side of the diagram lists the domain, and the right-hand side of the diagram lists the codomain. For each ordered pair (a, b) in the relation, an arrow begins at input a and then extends to output b. We see the input -2 produces two output values: 0 and 3. The input -2 corresponds to more than one output, so the relation Q is not a function.

b. Figure 3 illustrates a rectangular (or Cartesian) coordinate graph. The graph has two perpendicular axes in the horizontal and vertical directions. The location of every point on the graph is specified with an ordered pair (a, b). The coordinate a in (a, b) tells you what direction along the horizontal axis to move and how far, and the coordinate b in (a, b) tells you what direction along the vertical axis to move and how far. We see the input -2 produces two output values: 0 and 3. The input -2 corresponds to more than one output, so the relation Q is not a function.

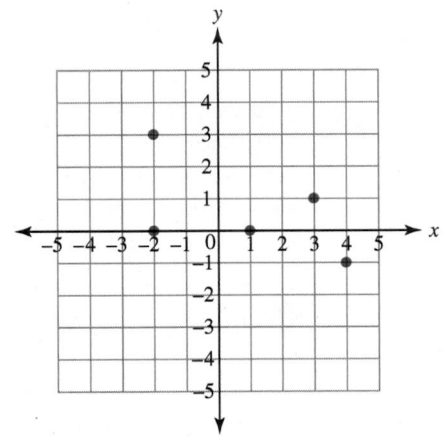

FIGURE 3

Representation of Q using a rectangular coordinate graph.

EXAMPLE 7.8

REASONING

Assume the domain is appropriate in each case.

a. Is the perimeter of a rectangle a function of the area of the rectangle?

b. Is the number of digits in a whole number a function of the whole number?

SOLUTION

Think about any possible input. If the corresponding output is unique, then the relation describes a function. However, if you can think of an input with two distinct outputs, then the relation is not a function.

a. We consider ordered pairs of the form (A, P), where A is the area and P is the perimeter of the rectangle. Figure 4 shows two rectangles. A rectangle with an area of 24 square units ($3 \cdot 8$ or $4 \cdot 6$) could have a perimeter of 22 units ($2 \cdot 3 + 2 \cdot 8$) or of 20 units ($2 \cdot 4 + 2 \cdot 6$). Therefore, the perimeter of a rectangle is not a function of the area of the rectangle.

b. We consider ordered pairs of the form (w, d), where w is the whole number and d is the number of digits in the whole number. The whole number 462, for example, has exactly three digits. Every whole number has a unique number of digits. Therefore, the number of digits in a whole number is a function of the whole number.

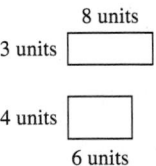

FIGURE 4

Rectangles with the same area but different perimeters.

EXAMPLE 7.9

CONNECTION
REPRESENTATION

Mary has five fewer than three times as many coins as Tim.

a. Make a table that shows how many coins each could have.

b. Explain why the table represents a function.

c. Express the function using variables.

SOLUTION

a. Suppose Tim has one coin. Then $3 \cdot 1 - 5 = -2$, which is impossible (Mary cannot have -2 coins). Suppose Tim has two coins. Then $3 \cdot 2 - 5 = 1$, so Mary has one coin. Suppose Tim has three coins. Then $3 \cdot 3 - 5 = 4$, so Mary has four coins. Suppose Tim has four coins. Then $3 \cdot 4 - 5 = 7$, so Mary has seven coins.

The following table shows how many coins each could have.

Number of coins Tim has (t)	2	3	4	5	6	7
Number of coins Mary has (m)	1	4	7	10	13	16

b. The table represents a function because each input value t corresponds to a unique output m.

c. Let the variable m represent the number of coins Mary has. Let the variable t represent the number of coins Tim has. The variables m and t are related by the equation $m = 3t - 5$, where $t = 2, 3, 4, 5, \ldots$.

▲

Function Notation

The previous problem stated that "Mary has five fewer than three times as many coins as Tim." If you know how many coins Tim has, then you can predict how many coins Mary has. The equation $m = 3t - 5$ is an algebraic representation of the function.

CONNECTION
REASONING
REPRESENTATION

Another way to write the equation $m = 3t - 5$ is $m(t) = 3t - 5$. The function notation $m(t)$, read as "m of t," is a symbol that conveys three significant messages:

1. The variable m depends on the variable t, so each ordered pair has the form (t, m).

2. t is the independent (input) variable, and m is the dependent (output) variable.

3. The equation $m(t) = 3t - 5$ describes a function and tells how the input t is related to exactly one output m.

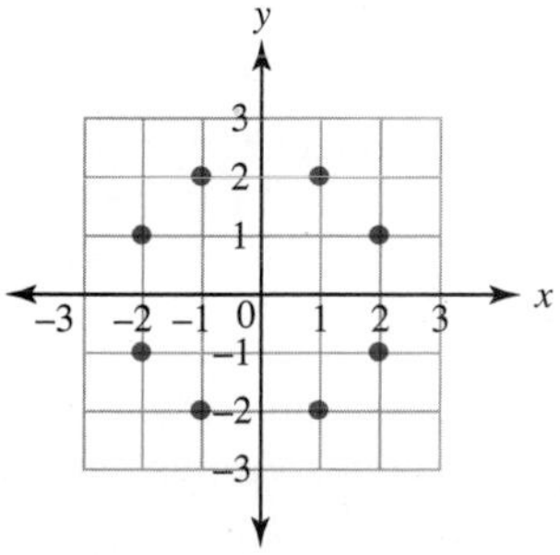

FIGURE 5

Graph of the equation $x^2 + y^2 = 5$, where x and y are integers.

> **Definition of Function Notation**
>
> - $f(x)$ is read as "f of x."
> - $y = f(x)$ is read as "y equals f of x" or "y is a function of x."
> - The notation $y = f(x)$ means that the variable y is a function of the variable x, where x is the independent variable and y is the dependent variable.

Some equations do not describe a function. Let's say the integers x and y are related through the equation $x^2 + y^2 = 5$. Figure 5 is the graph of this relationship. Do you "see" why the equation is not the equation of a function?

You can use any lowercase or uppercase letter to represent an output variable (such as *f, C, A,* or *d*), but we usually use a lowercase letter to represent an input variable (such as *x, n, r,* or *t*).

> ### ■ Historical Note
>
> Leonhard Euler (1707–1783), considered one of the greatest mathematicians of all time, invented the notation $f(x)$ for a function of *x* in 1734. His influential publications on functions paved the way for a flood of remarkable mathematical developments in the eighteenth century.

In contextualized situations, we usually choose letters that suggest what the variables represent to recall the meaning more easily. We often represent the cost *C* to purchase *n* items with $C(n)$, the area *A* of a circle of radius *r* units with $A(r)$, and the distance *d* traveled after *t* units of time with $d(t)$, and so on.

EXAMPLE 7.10

REPRESENTATION

Use function notation to represent each relationship.

a. Gary has three more marbles than Ellen.

b. The length of the rectangle is 4 cm fewer than three times the width of the rectangle.

c. A sales representative receives a monthly salary of $3200 plus a commission of 6%.

SOLUTION

a. Let *g* and *e* represent the number of marbles that Gary and Ellen have, respectively. The variable *g* depends on *e,* and $g = e + 3$. Using function notation, we write $g(e) = e + 3$.

b. Let *l* represent the length and *w* represent the width. The variable *l* depends on *w,* and $l = 3w - 4$. Using function notation, we write $l(w) = 3w - 4$.

c. Let *E* and *s* represent the monthly earnings and sales, respectively. The variable *E* depends on *s,* and $E = 0.06s + 3200$. Using function notation, we write $E(s) = 0.06s + 3200$.

▲

The next example illustrates a function in another contextualized situation.

EXAMPLE 7.11

CONNECTION
PROBLEM SOLVING
REASONING
REPRESENTATION

A male cricket chirps to attract female crickets. The warmer the air temperature, the more frequently the cricket chirps. You can estimate the air temperature, in degrees Fahrenheit (°F), by counting the number of chirps it makes in 15 seconds and adding 40.

a. Express the temperature as a function of the number of chirps in 15 seconds.

b. Estimate the air temperature when the cricket chirps 24 times in 15 seconds.

c. How many times will the cricket chirp in 1 minute when the temperature is 72°F?

d. At what temperature will the cricket stop chirping?

SOLUTION

Let *n* represent the number of times the cricket chirps in 15 seconds, and let $T(n)$ represent the temperature in degrees Fahrenheit when the cricket chirped *n* times in 15 seconds.

a. $T(n) = n + 40$, for $0 \le n$.

b. $T(24) = 24 + 40 = 64$. The air temperature is about 64°F.

c. When the temperature is 72°F, the cricket chirps *n* times in 15 seconds, where $72 = n + 40$. Then $n = 32$, so the cricket will chirp 32 times in 15 seconds. At this rate, the cricket will chirp $4 \times 32 = 128$ times in 1 minute.

d. $n = 0$ means the cricket has stopped chirping. $T(0) = 0 + 40 = 40$. This means the cricket will stop chirping when the temperature is 40°F.

▲

Bill Fehr/Shutterstock.com

Translating Among Representations

CONNECTION
REASONING
REPRESENTATION

The NCTM representation standards state that students should be able to "select, apply, and translate among mathematical representations to solve problems" (Gr. K–8). The following student page illustrates that students should be able to translate among the different representations of a function.

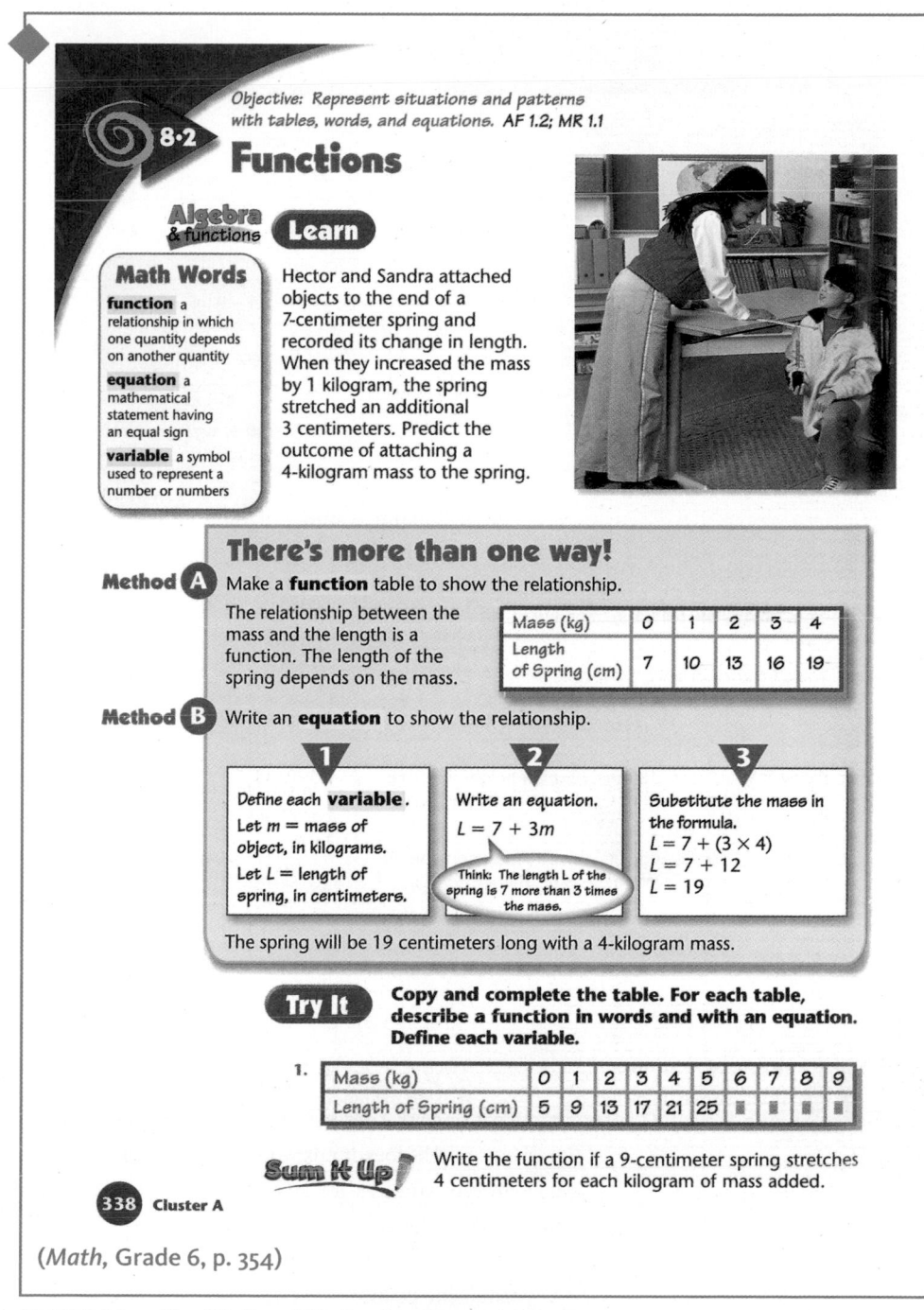

(*Math*, Grade 6, p. 354)

(© 2000 Macmillan/McGraw Hill. Reprinted by permission.)

Concept Map 7.1 summarizes the various representations: rule (words), table, equation, and graph.

> **Concept Map 7.1** Various Representations of a Function

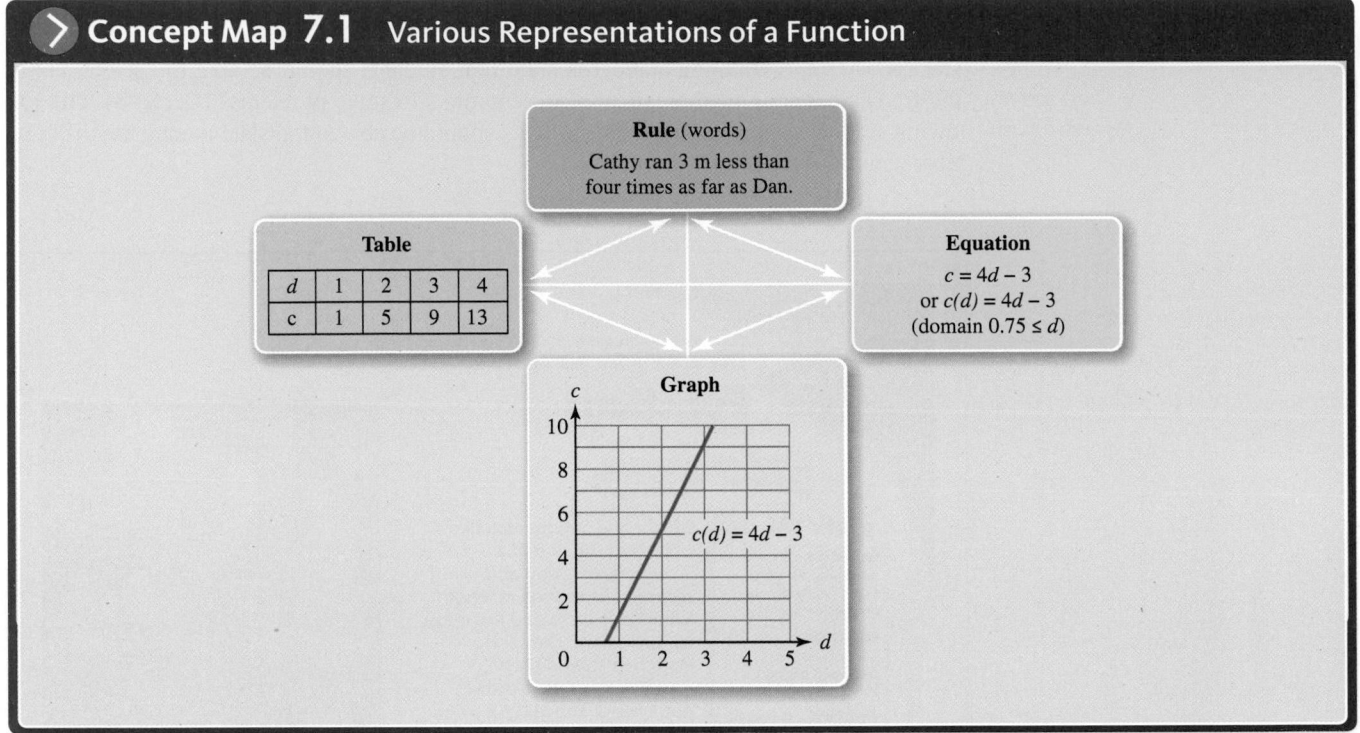

The following example requires students to translate among various representations of functions to solve a problem.

EXAMPLE 7.12

CONNECTION

PROBLEM SOLVING

REASONING

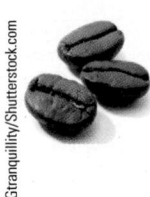

The graph shows the total cost C, in dollars, that a customer pays for n pounds of coffee from an online coffee merchant. The total cost includes a fixed fee for shipping.

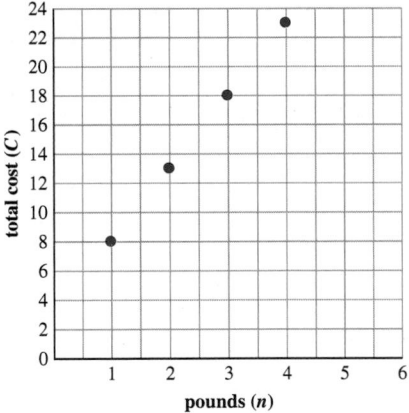

a. What does the ordered pair (2, 13) mean?

b. How much does it cost to order 4 pounds of coffee?

c. Carolyn paid $18 for an order. How many pounds of coffee did she order?

d. Ignoring the shipping cost, how much does each pound of coffee cost?

e. What is the shipping cost for each order?

f. Predict the cost to order 12 pounds of coffee.

SOLUTION

a. The ordered pair (2, 13) means that an order for 2 pounds of coffee costs $13.

b. From the graph, we see that the cost to order 4 pounds of coffee is $23.

c. From the graph, we see that $18 corresponds to 3 pounds of coffee.

d. We see $13 - 8 = 5$, $18 - 13 = 5$, $23 - 18 = 5$, and $28 - 23 = 5$. The cost for an additional pound is $5. So each pound of coffee costs $5.

e. It costs $8 to order 1 pound of coffee. Each pound of coffee costs $5. The shipping cost is the difference: $8 − $5 = $3.

f. We represent the cost (C) as a function of the number pounds (n) of coffee. The graph leads to the following table of ordered pairs:

n	1	2	3	4	5
C	8	13	18	23	28

The costs 8, 13, 18, 23, 28, . . . are generalized by the equation $C(n) = 5n + 3$. The cost to order 12 pounds of coffee is $C(12) = 5 \cdot 12 + 3 = 60 + 3 = \$63$.

▲

The following Classroom Connection shows that elementary school students should be able to translate among the various representations of a function.

◀◀◆ **Classroom Connection**

● Harcourt *Math*, Student Edition, Grade 6, p. 446

Use a rule to complete the table. Write the ordered pairs, and then make a graph. (© by Harcourt, Inc. Reproduced by permission of the publisher, Houghton Mifflin Harcourt Publishing Company.)

x	2	4	6	8	10
y	1	2	3		

The following Released Item shows that students solve similar problems—determine an equation given a table of x and y values.

▶ **RELEASED ITEM**

● NAEP, 2005

Which of the following equations represents the relationship between x and y shown in the table?

x	0	1	2	3	10
y	−1	2	5	8	29

a. $y = x^2 + 1$ **b.** $y = x + 1$ **c.** $y = 3x - 1$ **d.** $y = x^2 - 3$ **e.** $y = 3x^2 - 1$

54% of eighth graders answered the question correctly. (U.S. Department of Education, Institute of Education Sciences, National Center for Education Statistics, NAEP)

Functions also arise in fraction and proportional reasoning problems.

EXAMPLE 7.13

CONNECTION

a. Two-sevenths of the coins in the piggy bank are nickels. Express the number of nickels as a function of the number of coins.

b. There are three boys for every five girls at the elementary school. Express the number of boys as a function of the number of girls.

SOLUTION

a. Let c represent the number of coins in the piggy bank, and let n represent the number of nickels in the piggy bank. Then $n = \frac{2}{7}c$. Using function notation, $n(c) = \frac{2}{7}c$.

b. Let the variable b represent the number of boys and the variable g represent the number of girls. Then $\frac{b}{g} = \frac{3}{5}$. Then $b = \frac{3}{5}g$. Using function notation, $b(g) = \frac{3}{5}g$.

▲

Algebra of Functions: Creating New Functions

Input: x

Output: $f(x)$

A function f can be viewed as a machine that accepts an input x and then produces as an output $f(x)$. The number x enters the machine, and the number $f(x)$ exits the machine.

Scientific calculators have various functions, such as the square root key, that act as machines. If you enter 4 in the calculator and push the square root button, then the calculator displays 2.

The domain and range of many functions are subsets of the set of real numbers. Suppose x belongs to the domain of f and g. We can create new functions using arithmetic operations, much like creating new sets using set operations. Because $f(x)$ and $g(x)$ are real numbers, we can add, subtract, multiply, and divide the two numbers (as long as we avoid dividing by zero). The inputs must have identical units, and the output units must be compatible. The new functions are symbolized by $f + g$ (add the outputs), $f - g$ (subtract the outputs), $f \cdot g$ (multiply the outputs), and f/g (divide the outputs). The following examples illustrate how to evaluate the functions $f + g$, $f - g$, $f \cdot g$, and f/g.

f	Input	0	1	2	3
	Output	4	-1	6	3

g	Input	0	1	2	3
	Output	3	5	2	-1

$f + g$	Input	0	1	2	3
	Output	7	4	8	2

$f - g$	Input	0	1	2	3
	Output	1	-6	4	4

$f \cdot g$	Input	0	1	2	3
	Output	12	-5	12	-3

f/g	Input	0	1	2	3
	Output	$\frac{4}{3}$	$\frac{-1}{5}$	3	-3

Algebraic notation helps define the new functions $f + g$, $f - g$, $f \cdot g$, and f/g.

Definition

Let f and g represent functions of real numbers defined with appropriate domains and codomains. Then $f + g$, $f - g$, $f \cdot g$, and f/g are functions defined by the algebraic rules

- $(f + g)(x) = f(x) + g(x)$.
- $(f - g)(x) = f(x) - g(x)$.
- $(f \cdot g)(x) = f(x) \cdot g(x)$.
- $(f/g)(x) = \dfrac{f(x)}{g(x)}$, as long as $g(x) \neq 0$.

EXAMPLE 7.14

CONNECTION

REASONING

REPRESENTATION

Define the functions $f(x = x^2 + 1$ and $g(x) = 3x + 1$. Find
a. $(f + g)(2)$.
b. $(f - g)(2)$.
c. $(f \cdot g)(-1)$.
d. $(f/g)(4)$.

SOLUTION

a. $(f + g)(2) = f(2) + g(2) = (2^2 + 1) + (3 \cdot 2 + 1) = 5 + 7 = 12$
b. $(f - g)(1) = f(1) - g(1) = (1^2 + 1) + (3 \cdot 1 + 1) = 2 - 4 = -2$

c. $(f \cdot g)(-1) = f(-1) \cdot g(-1) = ((-1)^2 + 1) \cdot (3 \cdot (-1) + 1) = 2 \cdot (-2) = -4$

d. $(f/g)(x)(4) = \dfrac{f(4)}{g(4)} = \dfrac{4^2 + 1}{3 \cdot 4 + 1} = \dfrac{17}{13}$

▲

The next example illustrates that many functions can be viewed as some combination of simpler functions.

EXAMPLE 7.15 Express each rule as a combination of other rules.

CONNECTION

REASONING

REPRESENTATION

a. $f(x) = 4x$

b. $f(x) = 4x^2 + 2x - 5$

c. $f(x) = 4x(5 + x^2)$

d. $f(x) = \dfrac{3x - 7}{x + 1}$

SOLUTION

Answers vary.

a. Define $g(x) = 4$ and $h(x) = x$. Then $f(x) = g(x) \cdot h(x)$.

b. Define $g(x) = 4x^2$ and $h(x) = 2x - 5$. Then $f(x) = g(x) + h(x)$.

c. Define $g(x) = 4x$ and $h(x) = 5 + x^2$. Then $f(x) = g(x) \cdot h(x)$.

d. Define $g(x) = 3x$, $h(x) = 7$, and $n(x) = x + 1$. Then $f(x) = \dfrac{g(x) - h(x)}{n(x)}$.

▲

QUESTIONS FOR SECTION 7.1

REPRESENTATION

Refresher: Representations (language, diagrams, tables, symbols, algebra, manipulatives, and contextualized situations) are important because we use them to organize, record, and communicate mathematical ideas and to make them more comprehensible.

1. Select the correct equation for the function in the table.

x	4	-3	2	7
y	5	-9	1	11

$y(x) = -x^2 - 3$ $y(x) = x + 1$

$y(x) = 2x - 3$ $y(x) = -3x + 1$

2. A teacher states the following rule to her class: the output is two more than three times the input. Express this rule as an equation using function notation.

3. Let $q(x) = 5x - 4$ be a function with the domain $\{-2, -1, 0, 1, 2\}$. Express the function using a

a. rule (words).   **b.** table.   **c.** set of ordered pairs.

d. rectangular coordinate graph.

4. The graph shows the total cost C, in dollars, that a hobby store charges for a mail order of n pounds of modeling clay.

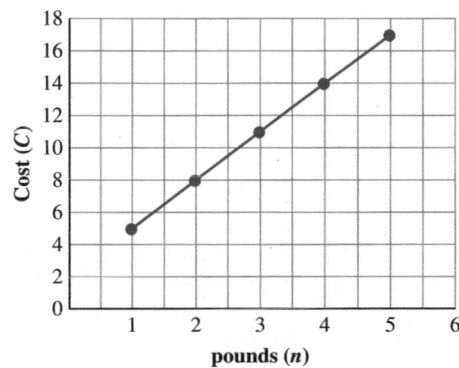

a. What does the ordered pair $(3, 11)$ mean?

b. How much does the store charge to mail 4 pounds of clay?

c. Steve paid \$14 for an order. How many pounds of clay did he order?

d. What is the shipping cost for each order?

e. Predict the cost to order 21 pounds of clay.

5. Write a function that expresses a relationship between the variables.

   a. A car salesman receives a monthly salary of $1985 plus a commission of 4% of his monthly sales.

   b. Fred has three more than five times as many coins as Amber.

   c. One number is 248 less than another number.

   d. There are four cars for every seven trucks in the parking lot.

   e. Four-fifths of the people in the survey supported the proposition.

6. Rewrite each equation using function notation.

   a. $y = 4x - 5$ b. $y = 2x^2 + x - 3$
   c. $10x + 3y = 6$ d. $A = l \times w$

PROBLEM SOLVING

Refresher: Problem solving (reaching a goal that is not immediately attainable) is important because it helps students think more deeply about what they know and deal with unfamiliar situations.

7. A taxi company charges $1.60 for the first fifth of a mile and then $0.30 each successive fifth or part of a mile. Let m represent the number of miles to complete a trip.

   a. What is the cab fare for a 1-mile ride?

   b. What is the cab fare for a 2-mile ride?

   c. Express the cab fare C as a function of m.

   d. Use the function to calculate the cab fare for a 7.4-mile ride.

   e. Suppose the cab fare was $26.80. How many miles was the taxi ride?

8. A homeowner uses black and white tiles to make a patio. The white tiles form a border around the black tiles, as shown.

   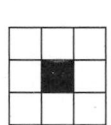 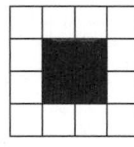 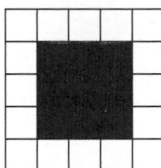

   a. Write an equation that expresses the number of black tiles b in an n-by-n patio as a function of n.

   b. How many black tiles are in an 18-by-18 patio?

   c. A patio has 2401 black tiles. What are the dimensions of the patio?

   d. Is it possible to build a patio with exactly 346 black tiles? Justify your answer.

   e. What does the function $w(n) = n^2 - b(n)$ represent?

9. A company makes widgets and sells each one for $25. It has determined the cost to make w widgets is $C(w) = 0.05w^2 + \$3$. The cost increases because of the need to hire more workers, rent storage space, and pay for additional transportation costs.

   a. Express the revenue $R(w)$ the company generates, in dollars, as a function of selling w widgets.

   b. How much revenue does it generate when it sells 145 widgets?

   c. How many widgets does it need to sell to generate revenue of $900?

   d. Express the amount of profit $P(w)$ the company makes as a function of selling w widgets.

   e. How much profit does it make when it sells 41 widgets?

   f. How many widgets does it need to sell to make a profit of at least $1275?

   g. At what point will the cost to produce w widgets exceed the revenue generated?

REASONING AND PROOF

Refresher: Reasoning and proof (thinking and justifying) are important because they help students make sense of mathematics.

10. Each table defines a relation. Is the relation also a function of x? Justify your answer.

    a.

x	1	3	4	6
y	4	-3	1	1

    b.

x	3	2	1	3
y	1	1	1	-4

11. Does each rule specify a function?

    a. Let A be a finite set. Let $f(A)$ be the number of elements in A.

    b. Let B be a whole number. Let $g(B)$ be a set with B elements.

    c. Let x be the number of boys in a family. Let $f(x)$ be the number of people in a family with x boys.

    d. Let y be the number of children in a family. Let $g(y)$ be the number of children in that family that are boys.

12. Answer the following.

    a. Is an exam score a function of the number of hours of preparation?

    b. Is the number of hours spent preparing for an exam a function of the exam score?

    c. Is the letter grade in a course a function of the overall numerical score in the course?

    d. Is the overall numerical score in a course a function of the letter grade in the course?

13. A farmer uses 600 feet of wire fencing to build a rectangular fence with one side parallel to a wall, as shown in the diagram. The farmer does not use any of the wire fencing along the wall.

    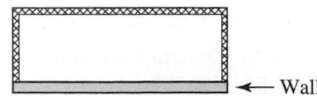
    ← Wall

a. A student writes the area A of the region enclosed by the fence as $A(x) = x(600 - 2x)$ square feet. Explain how this formula could be correct.

b. A student writes the area A of the region enclosed by the fence as $A(x) = x(300 - 0.5x)$ square feet. Explain how this formula could be correct.

CONNECTIONS

Refresher: Connections (linking and applying mathematical ideas) are important because they deepen student understanding and make mathematics more meaningful, flexible, and useful.

14. In some cases, when oil spills in the ocean, the area of the oil that spreads on the surface of the water can be approximated by the area of a circle $A = \pi r^2$, where r is the radius, due to its circular shape.

   a. What is the area of the oil slick when the radius is 11 m? Round your answer to the nearest square meter.

   b. Suppose the area of the oil slick was 152 m². Approximate the radius of the circular oil slick to the nearest meter.

15. A rectangular box with a square base has a volume of 80 cm³.

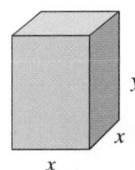

   a. Express the surface area of the box as a function of the length x of an edge of the base. ($V = x^2 y$ and $S = 2x^2 + 4xy$).

   b. Verify that the surface area is 232 cm² when $x = 10$ cm.

16. The length of a rectangle is 4 feet more than 3 times the width. ($A = \ell \times w$ and $P = 2\ell + 2w$)

   a. Express the area A as a function of the width w.

   b. Express the perimeter P as a function of the length ℓ.

17. The atmosphere (atm) unit is the pressure we feel on us because of the weight of the air above us at sea level. A diver that descends in the ocean feels additional pressure because of the volume of water above her. Thus, the diver experiences pressure because of both air and water. The following table shows how much pressure the diver experiences because of the volume of air and water combined.

Depth (d) in feet	0	33	66	99
Pressure (P) in atmospheres	1	2	3	4

   a. What is the pressure on a diver at the surface of the water?

   b. What is the pressure on a diver who is 33 feet below the surface of the water?

   c. What is the pressure on a diver who is 66 feet below the surface of the water?

   d. Write pressure as a function of depth.

   e. What is the pressure on a diver who is 20 feet below the surface of the water?

   f. A diver experiences a pressure of 2.4 atm. What is the depth of the diver?

COMMUNICATION

Refresher: Communication (written and verbal explanations using representations and proper mathematical vocabulary) is important because it helps students refine and strengthen their understanding.

18. What does the notation $h(x)$ mean to you?

19. A math problem involves the equation $k(x) = 7x + 2$.

   a. Identify the independent variable.

   b. Identify the dependent variable.

   c. Explain how you arrived at your decisions.

20. A math problem involves the equation $x(y) = 4y - 3$.

   a. Identify the independent variable.

   b. Identify the dependent variable.

   c. Explain how you arrived at your decisions.

21. Variables x and y are related by the equation $25 = x + y$. What happens to the value of y as the value of x increases?

22. Variables x and y are related by the equation $y = 3x$. What happens to the value of y when the value of x is doubled?

23. A student represented the arithmetic sequence 5, 8, 11, 14, 17, . . . with the function $f(x) = 3x + 2$.

   a. What does x represent?   b. What does $f(x)$ represent?

More practice with the ideas of the section

24. Fill in the blank. Choose one of the following words, phrases, or symbols: *d, dependent variable, equation, function, graph, h, horizontal, independent variable, input, output, relation, table, vertical,* or *y.*

   a. In the expression $h(d)$, the variable _____ is the dependent variable.

   b. In the expression $h(y)$, the variable _____ is the independent variable.

   c. In the graph of a function, the independent variable corresponds to the _____ axis.

   d. In the graph of a function, the dependent variable corresponds to the _____ axis.

   e. Any subset of $A \times B$ describes a(n) _____ from A to B.

   f. A(n) _____ is a relation from A to B such that each element of A appears as the first coordinate of some ordered pair with one corresponding output from set B.

   g. We may describe a function using words, a table, a graph, or a(n) _____.

25. Determine whether each rule specifies a function.

   a. Is an item selected from a menu a function of the cost?

   b. Is cost a function of an item selected from a menu?

   c. Is the income of a buyer of a new car a function of the car selected?

d. Is the car purchased a function of the income of the buyer?

e. Is the income tax rate a function of income?

f. Is income a function of the income tax rate?

26. The table defines a function.

x	1	2	3	4	5	6
y	5	8	11	14	17	20

a. Express the function in words.

b. Express the function using an equation.

27. The table defines a function.

n	4	6	8	13	15	20
T	11	15	19	29	33	43

a. Express the function in words.

b. Express the function using an equation.

28. Let $f(x) = x^2 + 3$ be a function with the domain $\{0, 1, -1, 2\}$. Express f using

a. words. **b.** a table.

c. a set of ordered pairs. **d.** a graph.

29. Graph the function $y(x) = 2x - 3$ for the given domain.

a. $\{0, 1, 2, 3\}$ **b.** $0 \leq x \leq 3$

30. Consider the equation $h(w) = 4w - 5$.

a. Identify the independent variable.

b. Identify the dependent variable.

c. Fill in the blanks with the correct variables: _____ is a function of _____.

31. Do the following.

a. Juan has five more than four times as many stamps than Angel. Let a represent the number of stamps Angel has, and let j represent the number of stamps Juan has. Write a function that expresses the number of stamps Juan has.

b. Suppose Angel has 68 stamps. How many stamps does Juan have? Use your function in part (a) to solve this problem.

c. Can Juan have 135 stamps? Use your function in part (a) to answer this question, and justify your answer.

32. A store advertises that all its prices are reduced by 25%. Let x represent the regular price of a customer's merchandise, and let $f(x)$ represent the sale price (excluding any possible taxes). A student correctly writes the equation $f(x) = x - 0.25x$. What does the expression $0.25x$ represent?

33. A store advertises that all its prices are reduced by 15%. Let x represent the regular price of a customer's merchandise.

a. What does $0.15x$ represent?

b. What does $f(x) = x - 0.15x$ represent?

34. Do the following.

a. Mark has five fewer than three times as many coins than Neal. Let n represent the number of coins Neal has. Write a function T that expresses the number of coins Mark and Neal have altogether in terms of n.

b. Suppose they have 299 coins altogether. How many coins does Neal have? Use your function in part (a) to solve this problem.

c. Is it possible that they have 568 coins altogether? Use your function in part (a) to answer this question, and justify your answer.

35. An arithmetic sequence appears in the table.

n	1	2	3	4	5	6
T	−1.5	−1	−0.5	0	0.5	1

a. Write an equation that expresses the term T in the sequence as a function of the position n.

b. How can you check your equation in part (a)?

c. Using your function, verify that the 33rd term is 14.5.

d. Is 90.5 a term? Use your function to answer this question.

36. A farmer uses 800 feet of wire fencing to build a rectangular fence with one side along a wall that does not need wire fencing. Let x be the length of the side of the fence parallel to the wall. Write an equation for the area A enclosed by the fence as a function of x.

37. A homeowner uses black and white tiles to make an n-by-$(n + 1)$ patio. The white tiles form a border around the black tiles, as shown.

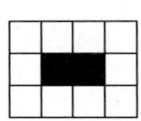 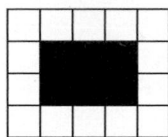 

a. What does the expression $n(n + 1)$ tell you?

b. What does the expression $(n - 2)(n - 1)$ tell you?

c. Write an equation that expresses the number of black tiles b in an n-by-$(n + 1)$ patio as a function of n.

d. How many black tiles are in a 34-by-35 patio?

e. Write an equation that expresses the number of white tiles w in an n-by-$(n + 1)$ patio as a function of n.

f. How many white tiles are in a 34-by-35 patio?

g. A patio has 226 white tiles. What are the dimensions of the patio?

h. Is it possible to build a patio with exactly 419 white tiles? Justify your answer.

38. The width of a rectangular garden is 24 m ($A = l \times w$ and $P = 2l + 2w$).

a. Express the area as a function of the length.

b. Express the area as a function of the perimeter.

39. The length of a rectangle is 3 feet fewer than four times the width ($A = l \times w$ and $P = 2l + 2w$).

a. Express the area as a function of the width.

b. Express the perimeter as a function of the length.

40. A rectangular garden with an area of 36 square meters has length l meters and width w meters. Express the perimeter P of the rectangular garden as a function of the width.

41. Each week a first-grade class sells snow cones to raise money to donate to charity. The first graders charge $0.75 for each snow cone. The weekly cost for the machine rental is $5. The ice, cups, straws, and flavoring are donated by a parent.

  a. Make a table that records the relationship between the weekly profit p and the number of snow cones sold n.

  b. Write an equation that relates the weekly profit p from selling n snow cones.

  c. Use the equation to determine the weekly profit for selling 120 snow cones.

42. Do the following.

  a. An airplane travels 600 miles in 3 hours at a constant speed. Find the speed of the airplane.

  b. An airplane travels at a constant speed of 525 mph for 4 hours. How far did it travel?

  c. An airplane travels 400 miles at a constant speed. Express the speed S of the airplane as a function of the number of hours t it was flying.

43. The volume V of a cylinder with radius r and height h is $V(r, h) = \pi r^2 h$. This is an example of a function that has two inputs and one output.

  a. What is the volume of the cylinder that has a radius of 3 cm and a height of 7 cm?

  b. Using function notation, express the height of the cylinder as a function of the volume and the radius.

44. A publisher gives an author $100,000 to write a sequel to a best-selling western novel. The author also receives a royalty of 6% of the revenue.

  a. Express the author's total income I from writing the sequel as a function of the revenue r.

  b. How much does the author receive if the revenue is $750,000?

  c. Suppose the author received a total of $214,000. What is the revenue for book sales?

45. The cost of using a certain calling card is $0.07 per minute plus a $0.50 surcharge for each call.

  a. Express the cost C of a phone call in terms of the number of minutes n of the phone call.

  b. Suppose you only have $3.25 remaining on the calling card. What is the maximum number of remaining minutes?

46. A rental car company charges $100 to rent a car for 1 week, plus $0.20 per mile after 300 miles. Determine the total cost for renting a car for 1 week and traveling

  a. 500 miles. **b.** 720 miles.

47. A boat travels at a constant speed of 48 mph in still water. Let c denote the speed of the current in a certain river in miles per hour.

  a. Write the speed d of the boat in the river as a function of the current of the river when the boat travels downstream (with the current).

  b. Suppose the current is 4 mph. What is the speed of the boat when it travels downstream? How far has it traveled after 2 hours?

  c. Write the speed of the boat as a function $u(c)$ of the current of the river when it goes upstream (against the current).

  d. Suppose the current is 6 mph. What is the speed of the boat when it travels upstream? How far has it traveled after 2 hours?

  e. Suppose you take a roundtrip ride on your boat on the river. It takes you 3 hours to get there while traveling downstream, and it takes you 5 hours to get back while traveling upstream. What is the speed of the current? (Hint: The distance each way is the same, and speed = distance/time.)

48. A company makes custom shirts for local sports teams. Each shirt has a fixed price, but the company also charges a setup fee. The graph shows the total cost for a customer that orders n shirts.

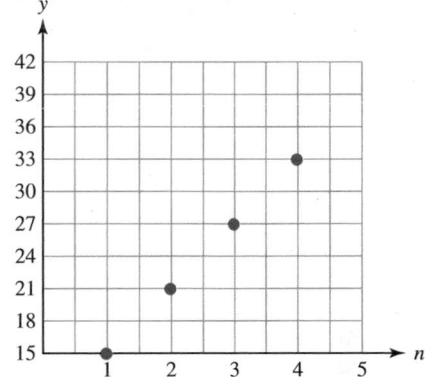

  a. What is the cost of each shirt?

  b. What is the setup fee?

  c. Express the total cost y as a function of the number of shirts n ordered.

  d. How much would an order of 30 shirts cost?

49. Let f and g be the functions defined in the tables shown. Does it make sense to define the function $f + g$? Explain.

f	Input	1	2	3	4	5
	Output	3	−4	2	6	8

g	Input	0	1	2	3	4
	Output	−6	4	2	3	4

50. Let f and g be the functions defined in the tables shown. Complete the tables for the functions $f + g$, $f - g$, $f \cdot g$, and f/g.

f	Input	1	2	3	4	5
	Output	3	−4	2	6	8

g	Input	1	2	3	4	5
	Output	−6	4	2	3	4

$f + g$	Input					
	Output					

$f - g$	Input					
	Output					

$f \cdot g$	Input					
	Output					

f/g	Input					
	Output					

$f \cdot g$	Input	1	2	3	4	5
	Output	4	−1	2	0	3

51. Let $f(x) = 4x - 1$ and $g(x) = 2x + 1$. Find
 a. $(f + g)(-3)$. **b.** $(f/g)(2)$.
 c. $(f - g)(0)$. **d.** $(f \cdot g)(3)$.

52. Let $f(x) = x^2 + 2x - 3$ and $g(x) = 3x + 2$. Find
 a. $(f + g)(2)$. **b.** $(f \cdot g)(-1)$.
 c. $(f - g)(0)$. **d.** $(f/g)(2)$.

53. Make tables for functions f and g that would result in the following table for $f \times g$.

f	Input					
	Output					

g	Input					
	Output					

54. The graph of $y = f(x)$ is shown. Use the information to draw the graph of $y = f(x) - 2$ and $y = f(x) + 1$. Label your graphs.

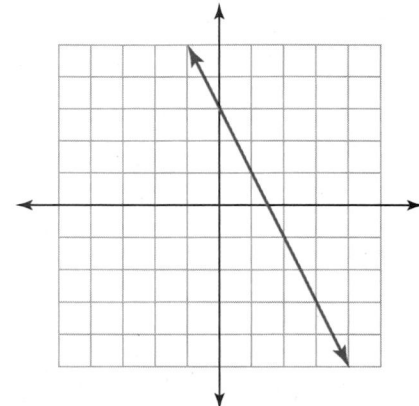

SECTION 7.2 | Solving Equations

Solve $y = f(x)$

COMMUNICATION

Some students are confused by directions to homework problems that ask them to "solve" an equation. In Section 1.3, we learned that to solve an equation such as $4n + 5 = 17$, we needed to find all values for n that makes the equation true. Now we define what it means to solve the equation $y = f(x)$. Remember that the equation $y = f(x)$, which is read as "y equals f of x," is an algebraic representation that means y is a function of x, the variables x and y are related, x is the input variable, and y is the output variable.

> **Definition: The Meaning of "Solve $y = f(x)$"**
>
> To "solve" the equation $y = f(x)$ means to find all values for x and y that make the equation true.
>
> **Algebraic Connection**
>
> $x = a$ and $y = b$ are solutions to the equation $y = f(x)$ if and only if $f(a) = b$.
>
> **Graphical Connection (Cartesian Connection)**
>
> $x = a$ and $y = b$ are solutions to the equation $y = f(x)$ if and only if (a, b) lies on the graph of f.

The definition states the connection between the algebraic and the graphical representations of functions. The next two examples apply these connections.

EXAMPLE 7.16

CONNECTION

Determine whether the given values solve the equation $y = x^2 - 3x + 4$.

a. $x = 1, y = 2$

b. $x = 7, y = 5$

SOLUTION

Replace each variable with a number and evaluate both sides of the equation.

a. Replace x with 1 and y with 2:

$$y = x^2 - 3x + 4$$
$$2 \stackrel{?}{=} (1)^2 - 3(1) + 4$$
$$2 = 2$$

$x = 1, y = 2$ is a solution to $y = x^2 - 3x + 4$.

b. Replace x with 7 and y with 5:

$$y = x^2 - 3x + 4$$
$$5 \stackrel{?}{=} (7)^2 - 3(7) + 4$$
$$5 \neq 32$$

$x = 7, y = 5$ is a not a solution to $y = x^2 - 3x + 4$.

▲

EXAMPLE 7.17 The graph of function f is shown. Use the graph to find a solution to the equation $y = f(x)$.

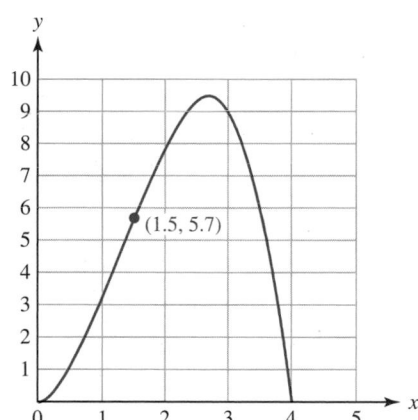

SOLUTION

The ordered pair $(1.5, 5.7)$ lies on the graph; that is, $f(1.5) = 5.7$. Therefore, $x = 1.5$ and $y = 5.7$ is a solution to the equation $y = f(x)$.

▲

The following Classroom Connection challenges student understanding of the Cartesian connection.

> **◆◆ Classroom Connection**
>
> ● *Mathematics,* Grade 6, p. 469
>
> Explain why $(6, -1)$ is not a point on the graph of the equation $y = 4 - x$.
> (From Randall I. Charles. © 2004 Pearson Education, Inc. or its affiliates. Used by permission. All rights reserved.)

The Released Item shows an ordered pair is another way to represent a solution to an equation.

RELEASED ITEM

- NAEP, 1996

Which of the following ordered pairs (x, y) is a solution to the equation $2x - 3y = 6$?

a. $(6, 3)$ **b.** $(3, 0)$ **c.** $(3, 2)$ **d.** $(2, 3)$ **e.** $(0, 3)$

41% of eighth-grade students gave the correct answer.

These types of examples help students see the algebraic and graphical connections to solutions of the equation $y = f(x)$.

Linear and Nonlinear Functions and Intercepts

A **linear function** is a function that has a graph that lies along a nonvertical line. Figure 6 illustrates two linear functions, v and w. A **nonlinear function** is a function whose graph is not a straight line. Nonlinear graphs have bends and curves. Figure 7 illustrates two nonlinear functions, p and q. Students should be able to "identify functions as linear or nonlinear and contrast their properties from tables, graphs, or equations" (Gr. 6–8, NCTM).

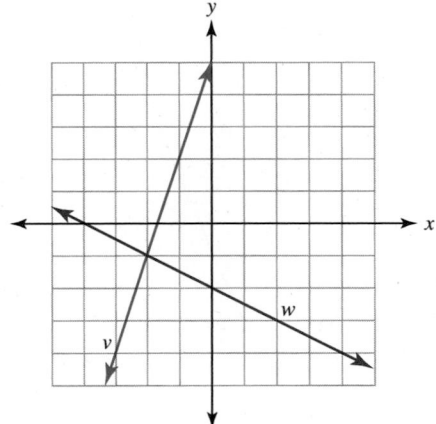

FIGURE 6
Examples of linear functions v and w.

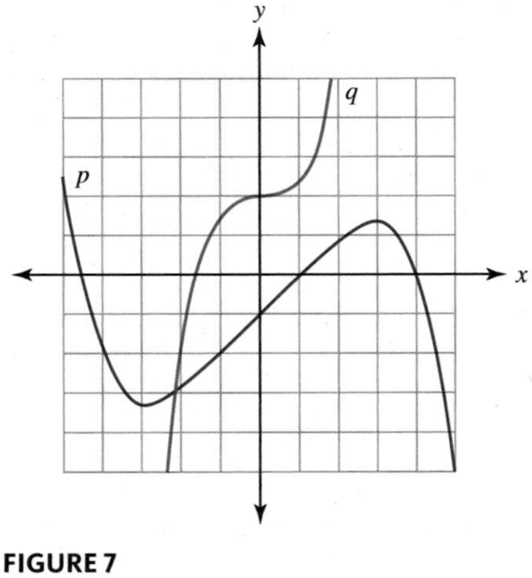

FIGURE 7
Examples of nonlinear functions p and q.

The graphs of some functions intersect (touch or cross) the horizontal axis, the vertical axis, or both. An ***x*-intercept** of a function f is a point where the graph of f touches or crosses the x-axis. In Figure 8, we see that the graph of f crosses the x-axis at $(-1, 0)$ and $(3, 0)$, so we say the x-intercepts of f are $(-1, 0)$, and $(3, 0)$. A ***y*-intercept** of a function f is the point where the graph of f touches or crosses the y-axis. In Figure 8, we also see that the graph crosses the y-axis at $(0, 3/2)$, so the y-intercept of f is $(0, 3/2)$.

You can find the x-intercept or x-intercepts, if any exist, of the function $f(x)$ algebraically by *solving* the equation $f(x) = 0$ for x and find the y-intercept, if it exists, of the function $f(x)$ by *evaluating* the equation $y = f(0)$. A function can have more than one x-intercept but at most one y-intercept.

The following example illustrates the difference between finding an x-intercept and finding a y-intercept.

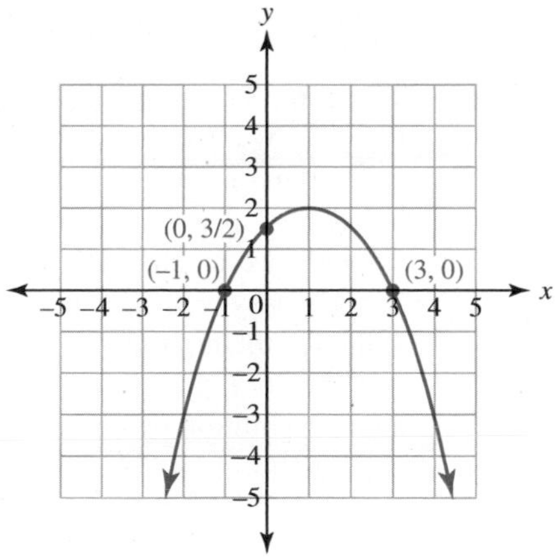

FIGURE 8

The x-intercepts of f are $(-1, 0)$, and $(3, 0)$. The y-intercept of f is $(0, 3/2)$.

EXAMPLE 7.18

CONNECTION

Find the x- and y-intercepts, if they exist, of the graph of the function $f(x) = x^2 + 2x - 8$.

SOLUTION

To find the x-intercepts, we have to solve the equation $f(x) = 0$.

$$x^2 + 2x - 8 = 0$$
$$(x + 4)(x - 2) = 0$$
$$x = -4 \text{ or } x = 2$$

The x-intercepts are $(-4, 0)$ and $(2, 0)$.

The y-intercept is obtained by setting $x = 0$: $f(0) = 0^2 + 2 \cdot 0 - 8 = -8$. The y-intercept is $(0, -8)$.

▲

EXAMPLE 7.19

CONNECTION
COMMUNICATION
REASONING

A company manufactures tables. Each table costs \$150 to manufacture. The company has daily fixed costs of \$718 (such as rent and insurance premiums). The function $C(x) = 150x + 718$ describes the cost, in dollars, as a function of the x number of tables manufactured each day. Explain the significance of the y-intercept.

SOLUTION

To find the y-intercept, we set $x = 0$. Then $y = 150 \cdot 0 + 718 = 718$. The y-intercept is $(0, 718)$. This means that if the company does not manufacture any tables ($x = 0$), its daily cost will be \$718.

▲

EXAMPLE 7.20

CONNECTION
COMMUNICATION
REASONING

You are driving on the freeway to Disneyland and your GPS indicates you are 220 miles from the freeway exit. You plan to drive at a constant speed of 55 mph on the freeway until you get to the freeway exit. After x hours of driving, you are $d(x) = -55x + 220$ miles from the exit. Explain the significance of the x-intercept.

SOLUTION

To find the x-intercepts, we solve the equation $d(x) = 0$.

$$d(x) = 0$$
$$-55x + 220 = 0$$
$$-55x = -220$$
$$x = 4$$

The x-intercept is $(4, 0)$. This means it will take 4 hours to get to the Disneyland freeway exit.

▲

How to Graph a Linear Equation

The graph of any equation written in the form $y = mx + b$ is a straight line. To graph $y = mx + b$, we need to find two sets of ordered pairs that satisfy the equation, plot the two ordered pairs, and then use a straightedge (say, a ruler) to draw a line through the dots. This is because of a geometry axiom (see Chapter 10) that says that there is exactly one line through two given points in the plane.

It's easy to find a solution to a linear equation, such as $y = -2x + 5$. First, choose a value for the input x, say, $x = 3$. Second, replace x with 3 and solve for y. Then $y = -2(3) + 5 = -6 + 5 = -1$. Then $(3, -1)$ is a solution to the equation $y = -2x + 5$. Let's find another solution by choosing $x = 0$. Then $y = -2 \cdot 0 + 5 = 5$. So $(0, 5)$ is a solution to the equation $y = -2x + 5$. Figure 9 shows the graph of $y = -2x + 5$.

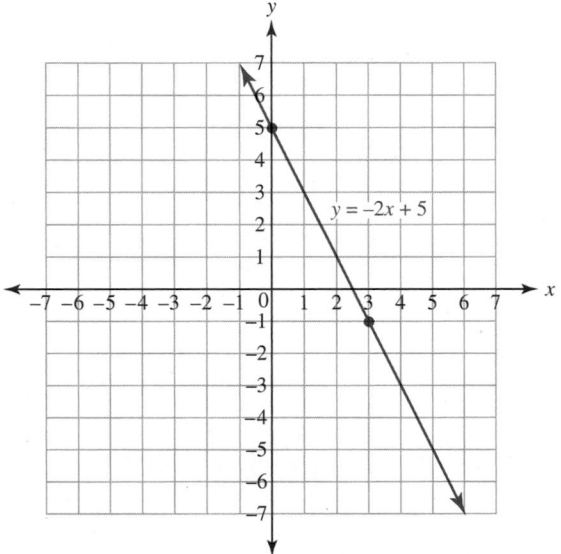

FIGURE 9
Graph of $y = -2x + 5$.

Vertical, horizontal, and oblique lines are explored in Section 13.1.

System of Linear Equations

Middle school students should be able to solve a system of two linear equations. A *system* is just a collection of two or more equations. To "solve" the system means to find all ordered pairs that satisfy the equations simultaneously. For example, a problem could be *Solve the system of linear equations:*

$$y = 3x - 4$$
$$y = -4x + 5$$

This means we need to find all ordered pairs (u, v) that satisfy both equations: $v = 3u - 4$ and $v = -4u + 5$. In this example, the solution is $(9/7, -1/7)$.

Students should be able to "analyze and solve pairs of simultaneous linear equations" (Gr. 8, CCSS). Three common strategies are used to solve two equations with two unknowns. One strategy is the intersection method. The intersection method involves graphing the equations of two lines. Another strategy is the substitution method. Yet another strategy is the elimination method. The substitution and elimination methods require that students be able to "solve systems of two linear equations in two variables algebraically" (Gr. 8, CCSS). You can use any of these strategies to solve the following problems in the Classroom Connection.

> ### Classroom Connection
>
> ● *Pre-Algebra*, California Edition, p. 424
>
> Solve each problem using a system of linear equations.
>
> • There are 11 animals in a barnyard. Some are chickens, and some are cows. There are 38 legs in all. Let *x* be the number of chickens and *y* be the number of cows. How many of each animal are in the barnyard?
>
> • The perimeter of a rectangle is 24 ft. Its length is five times its width. Let *x* be the length and *y* be the width. What is the area of the rectangle? (From David M. Davidson. © 2001 Pearson Education, Inc. or its affiliates. Used by permission. All rights reserved.)

As we explore the methods for solving two linear equations (for example, solve $3x + 5y = 12$ and $4x - 6y = 7$) with two unknowns (usually *x* and *y*), keep in mind that a system of two linear equations may have one solution (the two lines intersect at one point), no solutions (the two lines are parallel and distinct), or infinitely many solutions (the two lines are identical), as shown in Figure 10. Students are expected to "solve systems of two linear equations in two variables and relate the systems to pairs of lines in the plane; these intersect, are parallel, or are the same line" (Gr. 8, CCSS).

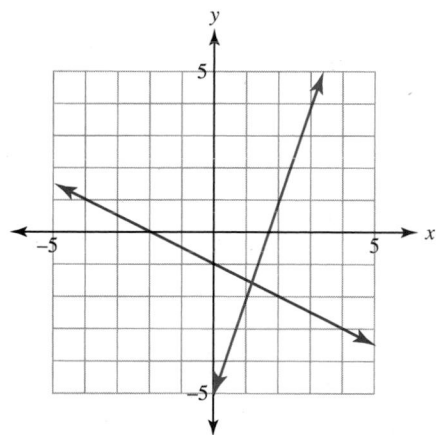

(a) The lines intersect at one point. (There is one solution.)

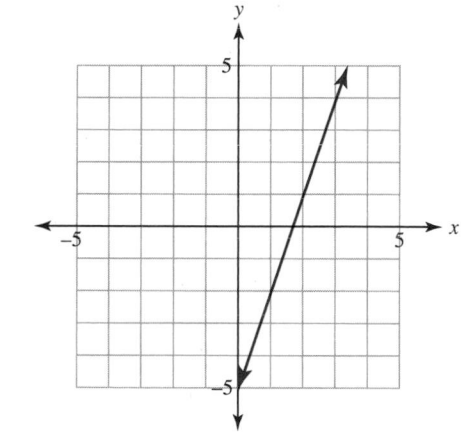

(b) The lines are parallel. (There are no solutions.)

(c) The lines overlap (same line). (There are infinitely many solutions.)

FIGURE 10

Solving Two Linear Equations Using the Intersection Method

In some cases, we can find a solution graphically using the **intersection method:**

1. Graph the lines $y = ax + b$ and $y = cx + d$.

2. Locate the point (u, v) of intersection of the lines.

This is the most common way students learn to solve a system of two linear equations, because it builds on their graphing techniques and they can "see" the solution to the system, which is the intersection of the two lines. The following example illustrates how students can learn and "understand that solutions to a system of two linear equations in two variables correspond to points of intersection of their graphs, because points of intersection satisfy both equations simultaneously" (Gr. 8, CCSS).

EXAMPLE 7.21

CONNECTION
COMMUNICATION
PROBLEM SOLVING
REASONING
REPRESENTATION

The sum of two numbers is 10. The larger number is 4 more than twice the smaller number. Find the two numbers using the intersection method.

SOLUTION

To apply the intersection method, we first need to derive two linear equations. Let x represent the larger number and y represent the smaller number. Then the two numbers satisfy the following equations:

$$x + y = 10$$
$$x = 2y + 4$$

Then we graph each equation as shown.

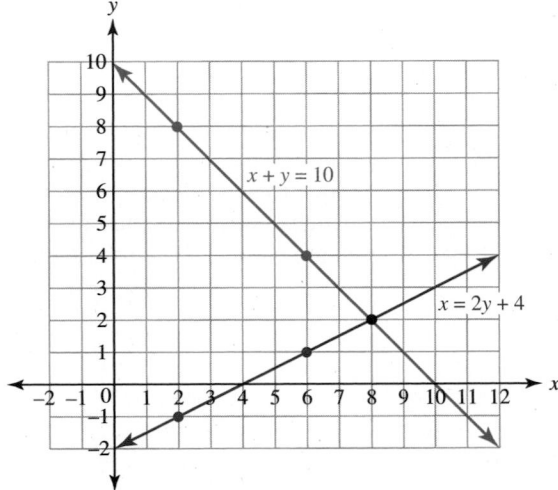

Finally, we see $(8, 2)$ is the intersection of the lines, so $(8, 2)$ solves both equations. The solution is $x = 8$ and $y = 2$. The two numbers are 8 and 2.

▲

The usefulness of the intersection method is limited to situations in which the functions intersect at a point with integer coordinates.

Solving Two Linear Equations Using the Substitution Method

The main idea behind the **substitution method** is to use *substitution* to turn a pair of equations (say, $N + B = 43$ and $B = N + 7$) into a single equation with one variable ($N + N + 7 = 43$), a simpler problem that we already know how to solve. Once the value for the variable has been determined ($N = 18$), we can solve an additional one- or two-step equation ($18 + B = 43$) to obtain the value of the other variable ($B = 25$).

EXAMPLE 7.22

CONNECTION
REASONING
REPRESENTATION

Solve the system of linear equations using the substitution method.

$$3x + 5y = 7$$
$$y = 2x - 9$$

SOLUTION

The second equation is $y = 2x - 9$, so we can replace the y in the first equation with the expression $2x - 9$. This creates a new equation with a single variable, x. Then we can find x.

$$3x + 5y = 7 \qquad \text{First equation in the system}$$
$$3x + 5(2x - 9) = 7 \qquad \text{Replacing } y \text{ with } 2x - 9$$
$$3x + 10x - 45 = 7 \qquad \text{Distributive property}$$
$$13x - 45 = 7 \qquad \text{Simplifying to obtain a two-step equation}$$
$$13x = 52 \qquad \text{Adding 45 to both sides to obtain a one-step equation}$$
$$x = 4 \qquad \text{Dividing both sides by 13}$$

So $x = 4$. To find the value of y, we replace x with 4 in one of the equations. Let's choose the second equation in the system: $y = 2x - 9 = 2 \cdot 4 - 9 = 8 - 9 = -1$. So the solution is $x = 4$ and $y = -1$.

▲

The next example is slightly more challenging but also illuminating.

EXAMPLE 7.23

CONNECTION
REASONING
REPRESENTATION

Solve the system of two linear equations using the substitution method.

$$-2x + 4y = 14$$
$$4x - 6y = -4$$

SOLUTION

The first equation can be re-expressed as $-2x = -4y + 14$, or $x = 2y - 7$. We can replace the x in the second equation with the expression $2y - 7$. This creates a new equation with a single variable, y. Then we can find y.

$$4x - 6y = -4 \qquad \text{Second equation in the system}$$
$$4(2y - 7) - 6y = -4 \qquad \text{Replacing } x \text{ with } 2y - 7$$
$$8y - 28 - 6y = -4 \qquad \text{Distributive property}$$
$$2y - 28 = -4 \qquad \text{Simplifying to obtain a two-step equation}$$
$$2y = 24 \qquad \text{Adding 28 to both sides to obtain a one-step equation}$$
$$y = 12 \qquad \text{Dividing both sides by 2}$$

Now we know $y = 12$. To find x, we can choose either of the equations and replace y with 12 to obtain a two-step equation in terms of x.

$$-2x + 4y = 14 \qquad \text{First equation in the system}$$
$$-2x + 4 \cdot 12 = 14 \qquad \text{Replacing } y \text{ with } 12$$
$$-2x + 48 = 14 \qquad 4 \cdot 12 = 48$$
$$-2x = -34 \qquad \text{Subtracting 48 from both sides}$$
$$x = 17 \qquad \text{Dividing both sides by 2}$$

Then $x = 17$ and $y = 12$. To check the solution, we just need to replace x with 12 and y with 17 in one of the original equations.

$$-2x + 4y = 14 \qquad\qquad\qquad 4x - 6y = -4$$
$$-2(17) + 4(12) \stackrel{?}{=} 14 \qquad \text{or} \qquad 4(17) - 6(12) \stackrel{?}{=} -4$$
$$-34 + 48 \stackrel{?}{=} 14 \qquad\qquad\qquad 68 - 72 \stackrel{?}{=} -4$$
$$14 = 14 \qquad\qquad\qquad -4 = -4$$

So $x = 17$ and $y = 12$ solves the equations $-2x + 4y = 14$ and $4x - 6y = -4$.

▲

Solving Two Linear Equations Using the Elimination Method

A solution for two equations can be determined using the **elimination method.** The main idea is to add or subtract equations to eliminate a variable. The result is a one-step equation, a simpler problem we already know how to solve.

EXAMPLE 7.24

CONNECTION

REASONING

REPRESENTATION

Use the elimination method to solve the following equations:

$$4x + y = 11$$
$$-4x - 6y = -26$$

SOLUTION

Beginning with $4x + y = 11$, we add different but equivalent expressions to each side to eliminate a variable:

$4x + y = 11$	**First equation**
$4x + y + (-4x - 6y) = 11 + (-26)$	**Because $-4x - 6y$ equals -26**
$4x + y - 4x - 6y = -15$	**Simplifying**
$-5y = -15$	**Simplifying**
$y = 3$	**Dividing both sides by -5**

As usual, to find the value for x, just pick one of the original equations and replace y with 3 to create a one- or two-step equation and solve for x.

$4x + y = 11$	**First equation**
$4x + 3 = 11$	**Replacing y with 3**
$4x = 8$	**Subtracting 3 from both sides**
$x = 2$	**Dividing both sides by 4**

Then $x = 2$ and $y = 3$. To check the solution, we just need to replace x with 2 and y with 3 in each of the original equations:

$$
\begin{array}{ccc}
4x + y = 11 & & -4x - 6y = -26 \\
4(2) + 3 \overset{?}{=} 11 & \text{or} & -4(2) - 6(3) \overset{?}{=} -26 \\
8 + 3 \overset{?}{=} 11 & & -8 - 18 \overset{?}{=} -26 \\
11 = 11 & & -26 = -26
\end{array}
$$

So the solution is $x = 2$ and $y = 3$. ▲

We may need to use multiplication, division, or both to produce equations that have at least one variable with opposite coefficients. The following example illustrates how we can solve a contextualized problem using a system of linear equations in two variables.

EXAMPLE 7.25

CONNECTION

COMMUNICATION

PROBLEM SOLVING

REASONING

Lee purchased four packs of erasers and three boxes of pencils for $23.25. Kyle purchased five packs of erasers and two boxes of pencils for $20.75. How much did each pack of erasers and box of pencils cost?

SOLUTION

Let e represent the price of each pack of erasers, and let p represent the price of each box of pencils. Then

$$4e + 3p = 23.25$$
$$5e + 2p = 20.75$$

Let's use the elimination method. Multiply both sides of the first equation by 5, and multiply both sides of the second equation by -4. Then the variable e in the equations has opposite coefficients. Then the new, but equivalent, set of equations is

$$5(4e + 3p) = 5(23.25)$$
$$-4(5e + 2p) = -4(20.75)$$

and becomes

$$20e + 15p = 116.25$$
$$-20e - 8p = -83$$

The variable e has opposite coefficients: 20 and -20. Then we could add the equations to obtain a one-step equation:

$$20e + 15p = 116.25$$
$$20e + 15p + (-20e - 8p) = 116.25 + (-83)$$
$$20e + 15p - 20e - 8p = 33.25$$
$$7p = 33.25$$
$$p = 4.75$$

This means each box of pencils costs $4.75. We can now replace p with 4.75 in either equation and solve for e:

$$5e + 2p = 20.75$$
$$5e + 2(4.75) = 20.75$$
$$5e + 9.50 = 20.75$$
$$5e = 11.25$$
$$e = 2.25$$

This means each pack of erasers costs $2.25. Let's verify the values $e = 2.25$ and $p = 4.75$:

$$4e + 3p = 23.25 \qquad\qquad 5e + 2p = 20.75$$
$$4(2.25) + 3(4.75) \stackrel{?}{=} 23.25 \quad \text{or} \quad 5(2.25) + 2(4.75) \stackrel{?}{=} 20.75$$
$$9 + 14.25 \stackrel{?}{=} 23.25 \qquad\qquad 11.25 + 9.50 \stackrel{?}{=} 20.75$$
$$23.25 = 23.25 \qquad\qquad 20.75 = 20.75$$

The equations check, so $e = 2.25$ and $p = 4.75$ is the solution to the equations $4e + 3p = 23.25$ and $5e + 2p = 20.75$. Each pack of erasers costs $2.25, and each box of pencils costs $4.75. ▲

There is a humorous *Peanuts* cartoon that shows Peppermint Patty reading a word problem (dealing with coins), thinking, and then applying a new problem-solving strategy—screaming for help! The word problem, similar to the one here, leads to two linear equations.

> *Marcia has 24 nickels and quarters. If the nickels were quarters and the quarters were nickels, then she would have 80 cents less than now. How many nickels does she have now? How many quarters does she have now?*

The word *now* refers to the original number of coins (before the switch).

Let's use variables and write equations to solve this problem.

$$n = \text{the number of nickels she has now}$$

$$q = \text{the number of quarters she has now}$$

Then Marcia has $n + q$ coins. She has 24 coins, so $n + q = 24$. She now has $5n + 25q$ cents.

Let's make some sense of the second statement, "If the nickels . . . ," by solving a simpler problem. Suppose she originally had two nickels and three quarters. If the nickels were quarters and the quarters were nickels, then she would have two quarters and three nickels:

| 2 nickels now | 3 quarters now | becomes | 2 quarters | 3 nickels |
| n nickels now | q quarters now | becomes | n quarters | q nickles |

She has n nickels and q quarters now, and she would have q nickels and n quarters then. As a result, Marcia would then have $5q + 25n$ cents. Then

$$\text{money she would have with the switch} = \text{money she has now} - 80$$
$$5q + 25n = (5n + 25q) - 80$$

So the variables n and q must satisfy the following two equations:

$$n + q = 24$$
$$5q + 25n = 5n + 25q - 80$$

We leave it to you to find n and q using one of the strategies we discussed in this section to determine how many dimes Marcia has now and then how many quarters she has now.

QUESTIONS FOR SECTION 7.2

REPRESENTATION

Refresher: Representations (language, diagrams, tables, symbols, algebra, manipulatives, and contextualized situations) are important because we use them to organize, record, and communicate mathematical ideas and to make them more comprehensible.

1. The graph of function f is shown. Use the graph to find a solution to the equation $y = f(x)$.

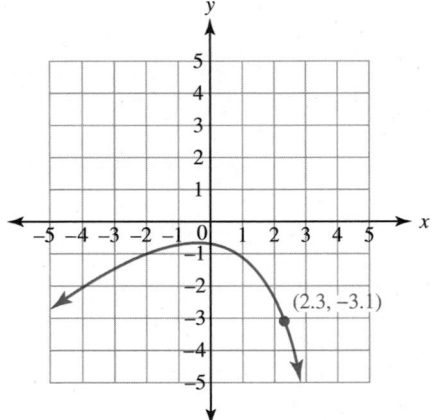

2. The graph of two equations is shown. What ordered pair solves both equations?

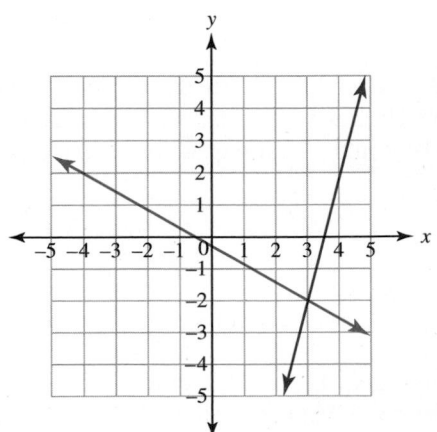

3. The table shows a function y of x.

x	0	2	4	5	-3	1
y	3	0	5	8	0	4

   a. Identify the x-intercepts, if any exist.
   b. Identify the y-intercept, if it exists.
   c. Find a solution to the equation $11 = 2 \cdot y(x) + 3$.

4. Use the graph of f to find a solution to the given equation.

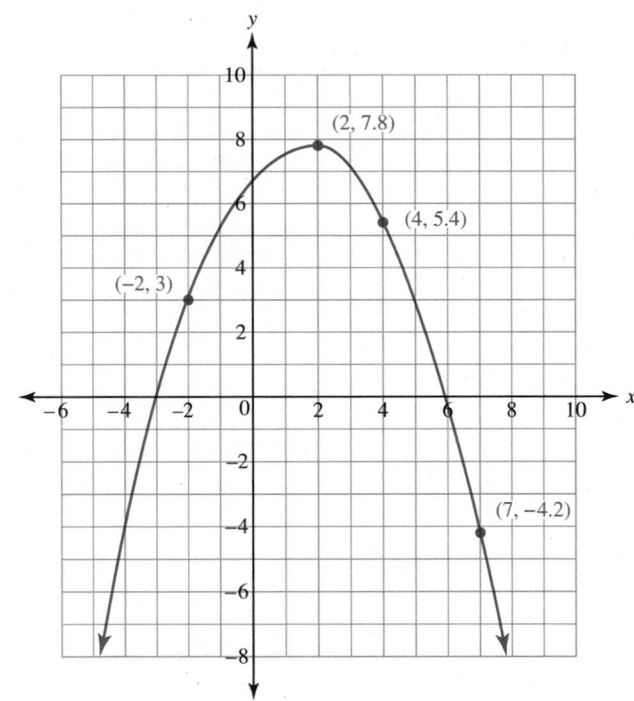

   a. $-4.2 = f(x)$ b. $f(x) = 7.8$ c. $f(x) + 2 = 5$
   d. $1.5 - f(x) = -3.9$ e. $0 = f(x)$

5. Write a system of linear equations that represents the situation.

   a. Alex is 5 years older than her sister Chloe. The sum of their ages is 29. Use variables a and c.

   b. Ken has $20 less than his sister Lennie. Altogether they have $112. Use variables k and l.

   c. Daniel has 8 fewer than three times as many jellybeans as his sister Hannah. Together they have 112 jellybeans. Use variables d and h.

6. Find the solution to the system of linear equations $y = 5x + 2$ and $y = -3x + 10$ using the intersection method. Check your answer.

7. Write a system of linear equations that represents the situation.

   a. Two bottles of milk and five containers of yogurt cost $18.50. Four bottles of milk and two containers of yogurt cost $17.

   b. Dallas has 9 fewer than twice the number of pieces of candy Holly has. They have 375 pieces of candy altogether.

PROBLEM SOLVING

Refresher: Problem solving (reaching a goal that is not immediately attainable) is important because it helps students think more deeply about what they know and deal with unfamiliar situations.

8. A supervisor of a recycling company has determined that her daily cost is $y = 40x + \$130$, where x is the number of tons of recycled material that the company processes.

   a. What is the daily cost to recycle 14 tons?

   b. What is the cost to recycle the 14th ton?

9. A truck driver is $d(t) = 500 - 60t$ miles from his destination after driving t hours. He drives at a constant rate.

   a. Interpret the ordered pair $(5, 200)$.

   b. After driving 3 hours, how far is he from his destination?

   c. How far did he go in his third hour of driving?

10. A class sold two types of raffle tickets to raise money for a field trip to the zoo. Raffle tickets for a fancy dinner cost $2 per ticket, and raffle tickets for a sightseeing tour cost $3. The class raised $183 altogether. The number of dinner raffle tickets sold was four more than twice the number of raffle tickets for the sightseeing tour.

   a. Write a system of linear equations that represents the situation.

   b. How many tickets of each did the class sell?

11. On Saturday, the store sold 17 reams of paper and 12 DVDs for a total of $112.50. On Sunday, the store sold 8 reams of paper and 21 DVDs for a total of $99. Determine the cost of each ream of paper and each DVD.

12. A telephone company offers two calling plans. Plan A costs $12 each month for local calls, plus $0.05 for each minute for long-distance calls. Plan B costs $18 each month, plus $0.03 for each minute for long-distance calls. Which plan do you recommend? Justify your recommendation.

REASONING AND PROOF

Refresher: Reasoning and proof (thinking and justifying) are important because they help students make sense of mathematics.

13. A system of linear equations may lack a solution. Consider the equations $y = x + 4$ and $-3x + 3y = 6$.

   a. Graph the linear equations.

   b. Explain how the graph illustrates there are no solutions to the system of linear equations.

   c. Use the substitution method to solve the equations and see what happens.

   d. Use the elimination method to solve the equations and see what happens.

14. There are no solutions to each system (I, II, and III) of linear equations.

   System I $\quad -2x + y = 5 \quad$ and $y = 2x - 1$
   System II $\quad 12x - 3y = 2 \quad$ and $y = 4x + 7$
   System III $\quad 5x - 7y = 3 \quad$ and $7y - 5x = -8$

   a. Use substitution to solve each system.

   b. Make a conjecture based on the pattern you observe.

15. A system of linear equations may have infinitely many solutions. Consider the equations $y = 3x + 4$ and $-6x + 2y = 8$.

   a. Graph the linear equations.

   b. Explain how the graph illustrates there are infinitely many solutions to the system of linear equations.

   c. Use the substitution method to solve the equations and see what happens.

   d. Use the elimination method to solve the equations and see what happens.

16. There are infinitely many solutions to each system (I, II, and III) of linear equations.

   System I $\quad x - y = 8 \quad$ and $2y = 2x - 16$
   System II $\quad 5y = 3x + 20 \quad$ and $-12x + 20y = 80$
   System III $\quad x - 3y = 6 \quad$ and $15y + 30 = 5x$

   a. Use substitution to solve each system.

   b. Make a conjecture based on the pattern you observe.

CONNECTIONS

Refresher: Connections (linking and applying mathematical ideas) are important because they deepen student understanding and make mathematics more meaningful, flexible, and useful.

17. Is the ordered pair a solution to the system of equations $3y + 2x = 18$ and $2x^2 + 5y = 38$?

   a. $(-3, 8)$ **b.** $(3, 4)$

18. Does the ordered pair lie on the graph of the given function?

   a. $(2, -3), f(x) = 3x^2 - 9$ **b.** $(45, 75), f(x) = 2x - 15$

   c. $(-5, -43), f(x) = -3x^2 + 32$

   d. $(3, 10), f(x) = 5x - 4$

19. There are no solutions to each system (I, II, and III) of linear equations.

   System I $\quad -2x + y = 5$ and $y = 2x - 1$
   System II $\quad 12x - 3y = 2$ and $y = 4x + 7$
   System III $\quad 5x - 7y = 3$ and $7y - 5x = -8$

   a. Write each equation in the form $y = mx + b$.

   b. Make a conjecture based on the pattern you observe.

20. Find the value of A such that there is no solution to the system of linear equations $Ax + 3y = 8$ and $7y - 2x + 10 = 0$.

21. The area of a rectangle is 70 cm². The perimeter of the rectangle is 38 cm. Find the length and width of the rectangle. Show your work.

22. The area of a rectangle is 44 cm². The longer side is 1 cm less than three times the shorter side.

    a. Write a system of equations for this situation. Use the variables l and w to represent the longest side and the shorter side of the rectangle, respectively.

    b. Solve the system of equations. Identify the method you used.

23. A student needs to solve the equation $3x - 2 = 4$. How could the student solve this graphically?

COMMUNICATION

Refresher: Communication (written and verbal explanations using representations and proper mathematical vocabulary) is important because it helps students refine and strengthen their understanding.

24. Explain why a function can have at most one y-intercept.

25. A teacher writes an equation with two variables x and y (such as $x^2 + y = 5$ or $4y - 3 = 2$).

    a. Maria replaces x with 0 and solves for y. Explain what she is calculating.

    b. Nicole replaces y with 0 and solves the equation for x. Explain what she is calculating.

26. Explain why a function with the domain [3, 12] cannot have a y-intercept.

27. Consider the following equations: $18 = 3 \cdot 6$ and $18 + 6 = 24$. From these two equations, we can create the following word problem: "Beth has three times as many beads as Anne. Altogether, they have 24 beads. Let A equal the number of beads Anne has and B equal the number of beads Beth has. How many beads does each have? Solve this problem using a system of linear equations." This word problem leads to the system of linear equations $B = 3 \cdot A$ and $B + A = 24$. The system of linear equations has the solution $A = 6$ and $B = 18$.

    a. Write two equations similar to $18 = 3 \cdot 6$ and $18 + 6 = 24$.

    b. Use your equations from part (a) to create a word problem similar to the one given.

    c. Write two linear equations that follow from your word problem in part (b).

    d. Solve the system of linear equations.

28. Consider the following equations: $20 = 3 \cdot 6 + 2$ and $20 + 6 = 26$. From these two equations, we can create the following word problem: "Beth has 2 more than three times as many beads as Anne. Altogether, they have 26 beads. Let A equal the number of beads Anne has and B equal the number of beads Beth has. How many beads does each have? Solve this problem using a system of linear equations." This word problem leads to the system of linear equations $B = 3 \cdot A + 2$ and $B + A = 26$. The system of linear equations has the solution $A = 6$ and $B = 20$.

    a. Write two equations similar to $20 = 3 \cdot 6 + 2$ and $20 + 6 = 26$.

    b. Use your equations in part (a) to create a word problem similar to the one given.

    c. Write two linear equations that follow from your word problem in part (b).

    d. Solve the system of linear equations.

29. A student wants to solve the system of linear equations $y = 3x - 5$ and $y = -2x + 1$. Explain why the student could begin by solving the equation $3x - 5 = -2x + 1$ for x.

More practice with the ideas of the section

30. Fill in the blank. Choose one of the following words, phrases, equations, or symbols: (a, b), (b, a), $f(b) = a$, $f(a) = b$, *system of linear equations*, *x-intercept*, *y-intercept*, *solve*, or *zero*.

    a. If $f(b) = a$, then the ordered pair _____ lies on the graph of f.

    b. Suppose we wish to find a solution that solves both equation $y = 3x - 4$ and equation $5x + 3y = 12$. The two equations are an example of a(n) _____.

    c. Suppose we are given the function $f(x) = 3x^2 + 5x - 4$. A student who evaluates the expression $f(0)$ could be finding the _____.

    d. If the ordered pair (a, b) lies on the graph of f, then _____.

    e. Suppose we are given the function $f(x) = 3x^2 + 5x - 4$. A student who solves the equation $f(x) = 0$ could be finding the _____.

    f. To _____ the equation $3x + 5 = 18$ means to find all values of x such that the equation is true.

31. Use the graph of f to find an exact solution to the given equation.

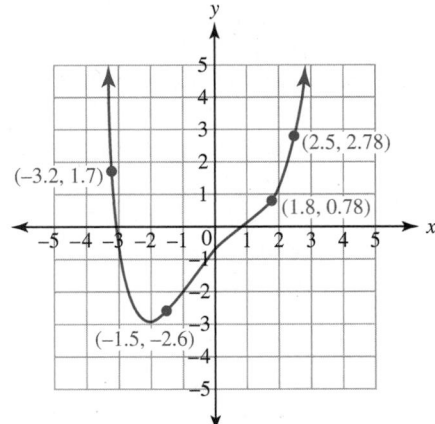

    a. $-2.6 = f(x)$

    b. $f(x) + 3.5 = 5.2$

    c. $f(x) + 2 = 2.78$

32. Write the system of linear equations to represent the following relationships: Fred and Mark have 240 coins altogether. Mark has three times as many coins as Fred.

33. Write the system of linear equations to represent the following relationships: Fred and Mark have 200 coins altogether. Mark has 8 more than three times as many coins as Fred.

34. Is it possible to plot a solution to the equation $Ax + 3y = -6$ without knowing the value of A? Explain how you would do this.

35. Is it possible to plot a solution to the equation $5x - By = 8$ without knowing the value of B? Explain how you would do this.

36. A class sold two types of raffle tickets to raise money for a field trip to the zoo: raffle tickets for a sightseeing tour and raffle tickets for a fancy dinner. The class sold 386 tickets altogether. The number of dinner raffle tickets sold was 8 more than twice the number of raffle tickets for the sightseeing tour.

  a. Write a system of linear equations that represents the situation.

  b. How many tickets of each did the class sell?

37. Sketch the graph of a function f such that the function has

  a. three x-intercepts and one y-intercept.

  b. one x-intercept and no y-intercept.

  c. no x-intercepts and one y-intercept.

38. Find the solution to the system of linear equations using the intersection method. Check your answer.

  a. $y = 5x + 2$ and $y = -3x + 10$

  b. $-3x + 2y = -10$ and $y = -2x + 9$

  c. $x = 4y - 8$ and $y = 3x - 9$

In questions 39–42, solve the system of equations using the substitution method and then check your answer.

39. $-3x + 8y = 38, 4x + 12y = 40$

40. $2x - y = 1, 3x + 4y = 29$

41. $5x + 6y = 14, 7x + 3y = 25$

42. $3x - 2y = 11, x + 5y = 15$

In questions 43–46, solve the system of equations using the elimination method and then check your answer.

43. $5x + 2y = 24, -5x + 6y = -8$

44. $3x + 5y = 17, 2x + 4y = 14$

45. $2x - y = 1, 3x + 4y = 29$

46. $-3x + 4y = -17, -3x - 6y = 3$

47. Solve the following problem (Gr. 6, Harcourt, p. 311): Elliot has nickels and dimes in his pocket. He has twice as many dimes as nickels. If the total value of the coins is $1, how many of each coin does he have?

48. Consider the following problem: "Mary has three-fifths as many marbles as Anne. Together, they have 32 marbles. How many marbles does each have?" To solve this problem, we could let M be the number of marbles Mary has and A be the number of marbles Anne has. Then we get the two linear equations $M = (3/5)A$ and $M + A = 32$.

  a. Write two similar equations.

  b. Write a word problem that uses the two equations.

  c. Solve the problem.

49. Consider the following problem: "Mary has 4 more than three-fifths as many marbles as Anne. Together, they have 36 marbles. How many marbles does each have?" To solve this problem, we could let M be the number of marbles Mary has and A be the number of marbles Anne has. Then we get the two linear equations $M = (3/5)A + 4$ and $M + A = 36$.

  a. Write two similar equations.

  b. Write a word problem that uses the two equations.

  c. Solve the problem.

50. Suppose Marcia collects 15 dimes and 6 quarters. She now has 21 coins, and they are worth $15(\$0.10) + 6(\$0.25) = \$3$. If the dimes were quarters and the quarters were dimes, then she would have 6 dimes and 15 quarters, which would be worth $6(\$0.10) + 15(\$0.25) = \$4.35$. She would have $1.35 more than she does now, because $\$4.35 - \$3 = \$1.35$. Here's the corresponding coin problem: "Marcia has 21 dimes and quarters. If the dimes were quarters and the quarters were dimes, then she would have $1.35 more than she has now. How many dimes does she have now? How many quarters does she have now?"

  a. Write the equations that would be used to solve this problem. Let d be the number of dimes and q be the number quarters.

  b. Solve the system in part (a) to verify the solution is 15 dimes and 6 quarters.

51. Marc has 11 nickels and quarters. If the nickels were quarters and the quarters were nickels, then he would have 60 cents more than he has now.

  a. Write the equations that would be used to solve this problem. Let n be the number of nickels he has now and q be the number of quarters.

  b. How many nickels does he have now?

  c. How many quarters does he have now?

SECTION 7.3 Algebra Tiles

Linear Equations with One Variable

A linear equation with one variable is an equation that involves one variable, such as x, that has the exponent 1. Some examples of linear equations with one variable are $2x = 12, x + 3 = 8, 2x - 4 = 12, -4x + 2 = 8, 3x + 5 = 2(x - 5)$, and $-4x + 3 = 2x - 3(1 - x)$. To "solve" a linear equation means to find all values of x that make the equation true. For example, $x = 8$ solves the linear equation $2x - 4 = 12$ because $2 \cdot 8 - 4 = 16 - 4 = 12$. We usually solve an equation by transforming an equation into a simpler one that we already know how to solve.

Again, a linear equation may have one solution, infinitely many solutions, or no solutions. The equation $x + 3 = 5$ has one solution, because it has the simpler form $x = 2$. The equation $x + 3 = x + 3$ has infinitely many solutions, because it has the simpler form $3 = 3$. The equation $x + 3 = x + 5$ has no solutions, because it has the simpler form $3 = 5$. Students should be able to "give examples of linear equations in one variable with one solution, infinitely many solutions, or no solutions" and "show which of these possibilities is the case by successively transforming the given equation into simpler forms, until an equivalent equation of the form $x = a$, $a = a$, or $a = b$ results (where a and b are different numbers)" (Gr. 8, CCSS).

One- and two-step equations are two of the simplest types of linear equations in one variable. **One-step equations,** such as $2x = 12$ and $x + 3 = 8$, involve one inverse operation to solve for x:

$$2x = 12 \qquad\qquad x + 3 = 8$$
$$2x \div 2 = 12 \div 2 \qquad x + 3 - 3 = 8 - 3$$
$$x = 6 \qquad\qquad x = 5$$

Two-step equations, such as $2x - 4 = 12$ and $-4x + 2 = 8$, involve two inverse operations to solve for x:

$$2x - 4 = 12 \qquad\qquad -4x + 2 = 8$$
$$2x - 4 + 4 = 12 + 4 \qquad -4x + 2 - 2 = 8 - 2$$
$$2x = 16 \qquad\qquad -4x = 6$$
$$2x \div 2 = 16 \div 2 \qquad -4x \div -4 = 6 \div -4$$
$$x = 8 \qquad\qquad x = \frac{6}{-4}$$
$$x = -1\frac{1}{2}$$

We used symbolic algebra for solving one- and two-step equations. After you study this section, you will develop the skills needed to help your students visualize and solve linear equations using manipulatives called **algebra tiles.** Symbolic algebra and algebra tiles give you more options for teaching elementary school students with different learning styles. These students typically learn how to solve one- and two-step equations involving whole numbers. Later, these skills provide the foundation for working with linear equations involving integers, fractions, and decimals.

Modeling Whole Number Expressions with Algebra Tiles

The algebra tiles in Figure 11 are suitable for solving equations that are restricted to whole numbers. Each rectangular tile (called an *n*-tile) represents the variable *n*, and each square tile (called a 1-tile) represents 1 unit.

The next two examples illustrate how we can represent various expressions with algebra tiles.

FIGURE 11

How to represent *n* and 1 using algebra tiles.

REPRESENTATION

EXAMPLE 7.26

CONNECTION
COMMUNICATION
REASONING
REPRESENTATION

Represent each algebra tile model with an algebraic expression.

a. 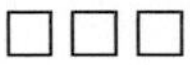 ☐☐☐   **b.** 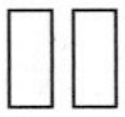 ▯▯   **c.**  ▯▯☐   **d.** 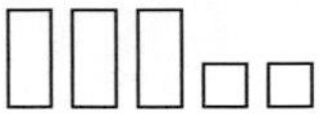 ▯▯▯☐☐

SOLUTION

a. 3   **b.** $2n$ **c.** $2n + 1$ **d.** $3n + 2$

▲

EXAMPLE 7.27   Represent $3(2n + 1)$ with algebra tiles.

SOLUTION

We make three copies of the model for $2n + 1$:

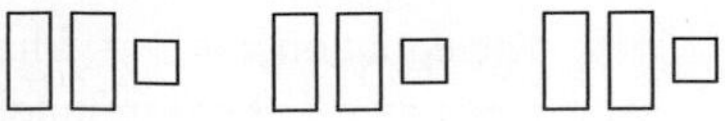

▯▯☐   ▯▯☐   ▯▯☐

▲

Solving Whole Number Equations with Algebra Tiles

The concept of equality is central to algebraic thinking. We split a rectangular mat in two halves. Each half of the mat represents one side of the equation. The tile mat in Figure 12 represents the two-step equation $2n + 1 = 7$. The left side of the mat represents $2n + 1$, and the right side of the mat represents 7.

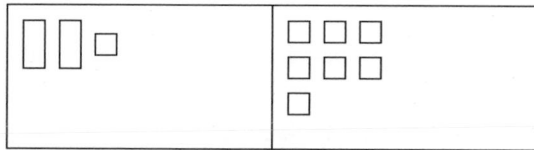

FIGURE 12

Representation of the equation $2n + 1 = 7$ using a tile mat.

EXAMPLE 7.28 Write the equation that represents the given tile mat.

CONNECTION

REASONING

REPRESENTATION

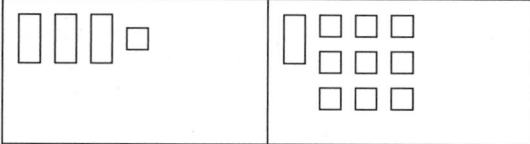

SOLUTION

$3n + 1 = n + 9$

Let's solve the one-step equations $n + 3 = 7$ and $3n = 12$. The goal is to transform the original equation into a form such as $n = 5$, because this type of equation reveals the solution. One-step equations form a foundation for two-step equations. The symbol $\boxtimes$ in the diagrams indicates a tile that has been removed, that is, subtracted.

EXAMPLE 7.29 Solve $n + 3 = 7$ using algebra tiles.

CONNECTION

REASONING   SOLUTION

REPRESENTATION   We sketch the algebra tiles and write the corresponding equations.

Tile representation		Symbolic representation
▯ □ □ □	□ □ □ / □ □ □ / □	$n + 3 = 7$
▯ ⊠ ⊠ ⊠	□ □ □ / ⊠ ⊠ □ / ⊠	$n + 3 - 3 = 7 - 3$
▯	□ □ □ / □	$n = 4$

According to the tile representation, the solution to $n + 3 = 7$ is $n = 4$.

EXAMPLE 7.30

CONNECTION
COMMUNICATION
REASONING
REPRESENTATION

Simplify the expression $3n \div 3$ using algebra tiles.

SOLUTION

The tile model for $3n$ is as follows.

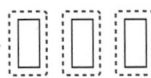

According to the fair share model of division, the tile model for $3n \div 3$ is as follows.

$3n \div 3$ means $3n$ is split into three equal-sized groups. We see there is one n in each group. So $3n \div 3 = n$.

▲

Next, we use algebra tiles to solve the one-step equation $3n = 12$. The fair share model for division, which answers the question "How many per group?" is crucial.

EXAMPLE 7.31

CONNECTION
REASONING
REPRESENTATION

Solve $3n = 12$ using algebra tiles.

SOLUTION

We sketch the algebra tiles and write the corresponding equations.

Tile representation	Symbolic representation
	$3n = 12$
	$3n \div 3 = 12 \div 3$
	$n = 4$

$n = 4$ is the solution to $3n = 12$.

▲

We can apply the one-step procedures to solve the two-step equation $2n + 3 = 11$ with algebra tiles.

EXAMPLE 7.32

CONNECTION
REASONING
REPRESENTATION

Use the tile model to solve $2n + 3 = 11$.

SOLUTION

We sketch the algebra tiles and write the corresponding equations.

Tile representation	Symbolic representation
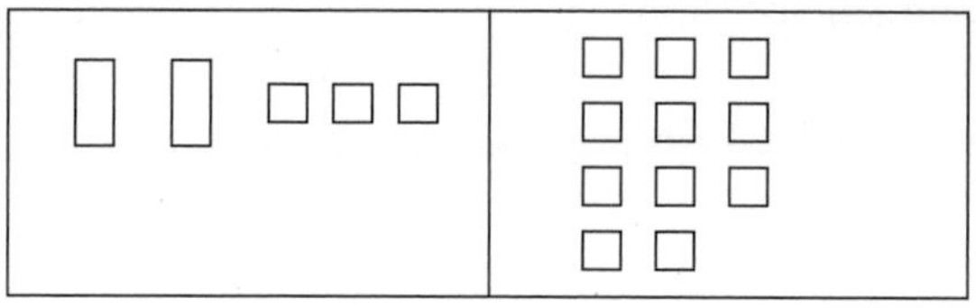	$2n + 3 = 11$
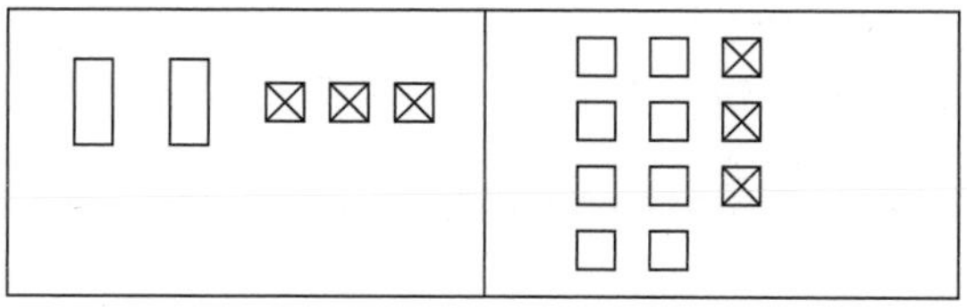	$2n + 3 - 3 = 11 - 3$
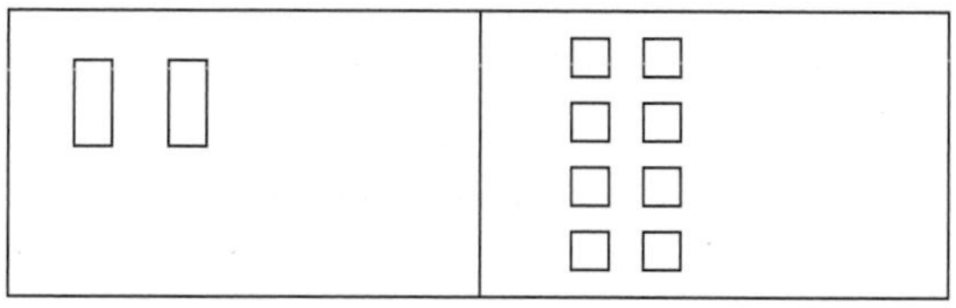	$2n = 8$
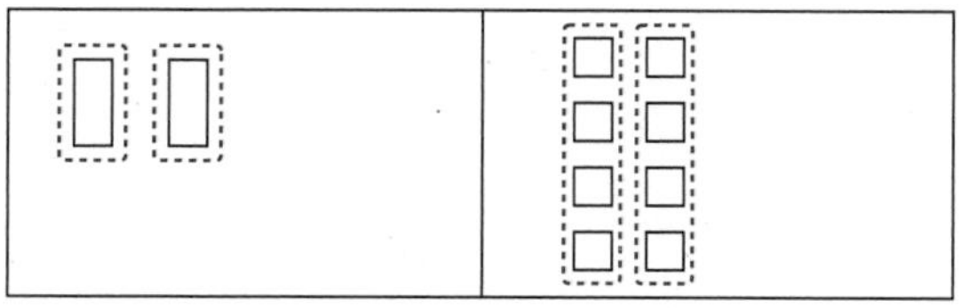	$2n \div 2 = 8 \div 2$
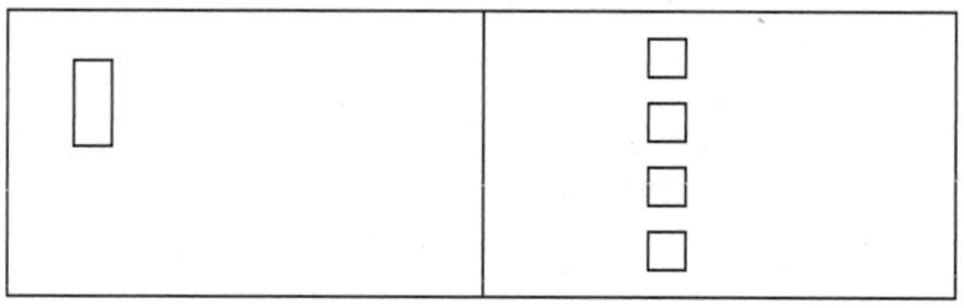	$n = 4$

Let's check our answer: $2 \cdot 4 + 3 = 8 + 3 = 11$. The answer checks, so the solution is $n = 4$. ▲

Modeling Integer Expressions with Algebra Tiles

We can use algebra tiles to solve equations such as $3n + 5 = n - 1$. Like the chip model for integers, we need two colors to distinguish positive and negative integers. Figure 13 shows the representations of n, $-n$, 1, and -1.

Zero pairs are representations of zero. Figure 14 shows two possible zero pairs in the tile model. There are multiple representations of zero in the tile model, much like the chip model or charged field model for integers.

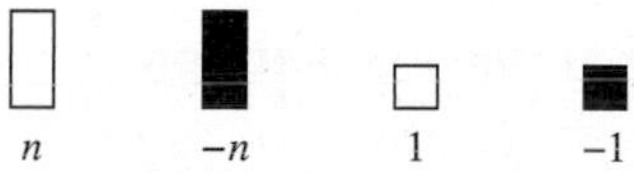

FIGURE 13
Tile models of n, $-n$, 1, and -1.

FIGURE 14
Zero pairs.

EXAMPLE 7.33

CONNECTION

REPRESENTATION

Build the tile model for the given expression.
a. $3n + -1$ **b.** $-2n + 3$

SOLUTION

a. 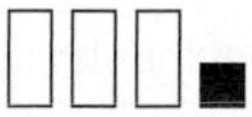 **b.**

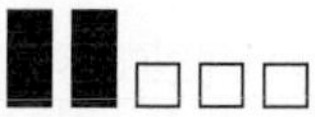

▲

The following example shows how to represent algebraic expressions involving subtraction.

EXAMPLE 7.34

CONNECTION

REPRESENTATION

Sketch the tile model for each algebraic expression.
a. $2n - 3$
b. $-4n - 5$

SOLUTION

a. Express $2n - 3$ as $2n + (-3)$ by adding the opposite.

b. Express $-4n - 5$ as $-4n + (-5)$ by adding the opposite.

Solving Integer Equations with Algebra Tiles

The tile model for solving one- and two-step equations with integers mimics the model for one- and two-step equations with whole numbers. So we use the tile model to solve a multistep equation involving integers.

EXAMPLE 7.35

CONNECTION

REPRESENTATION

Use the tile model to solve $2n - 1 = -n - 7$.

SOLUTION

The model in Figure 15 represents the equation $2n - 1 = -n - 7$. We express $2n - 1$ as $2n + (-1)$ and $-n - 7$ as $-n + (-7)$ by adding the opposite. Then we strategically add tiles to create zero pairs and thus separate the rectangles from the squares and remove zero pairs as needed.

The final step suggests one n-tile is equal to two -1-tiles, or $n = -2$. Let's check our work: $2(-2) - 1 = -4 - 1 = -5$, and $-(-2) - 7 = 2 - 7 = -5$. If $n = -2$, then both sides equal -5. The solution is $n = -2$.

The following Classroom Connection illustrates students should be able to solve two-step equations with algebra tiles.

> **Classroom Connection**
>
> ● *Middle Grades Math Tools for Success*, p. 453
>
> Use algebra tiles to solve each equation.
> **a.** $5x - 2 = -7$
> **b.** $3x - 4 = 2$
> (From Suzanne H. Chapin. © 1999 Pearson Education, Inc. or its affiliates. Used by permission. All rights reserved.)

The following examples relate the symbolic approach to solving an equation and the corresponding actions in the tile model.

	Tile representation	Symbolic representation
Step 1	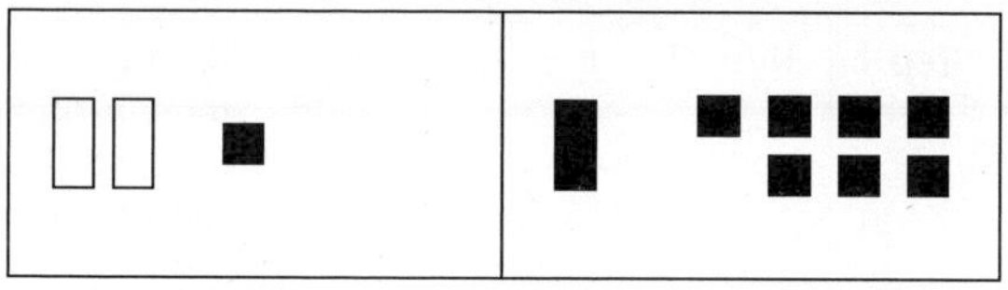	$2n - 1 = -n - 7$
Step 2	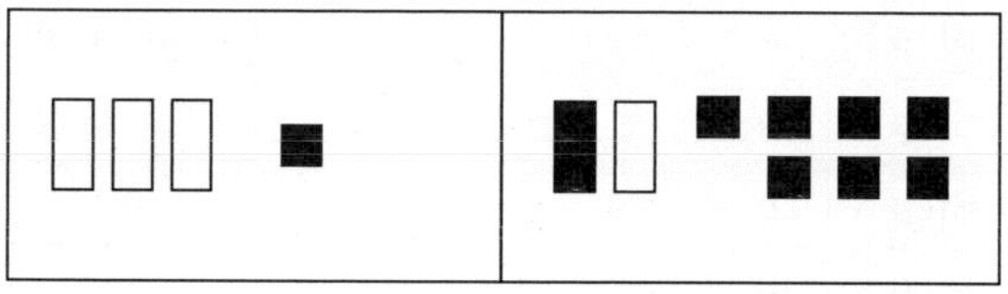	$2n - 1 + n = -n - 7 + n$
Step 3	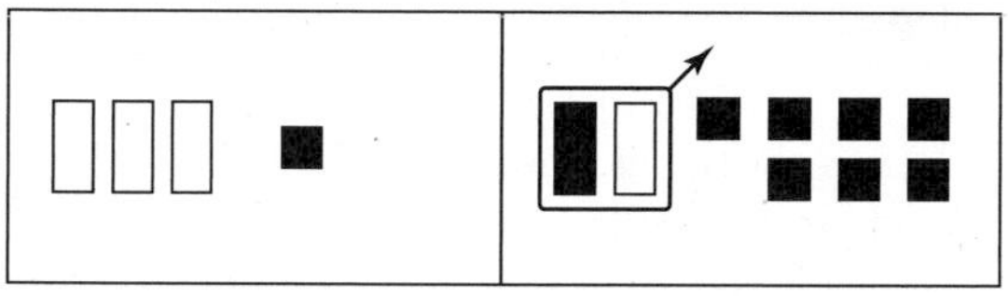	$3n - 1 = -7$
Step 4	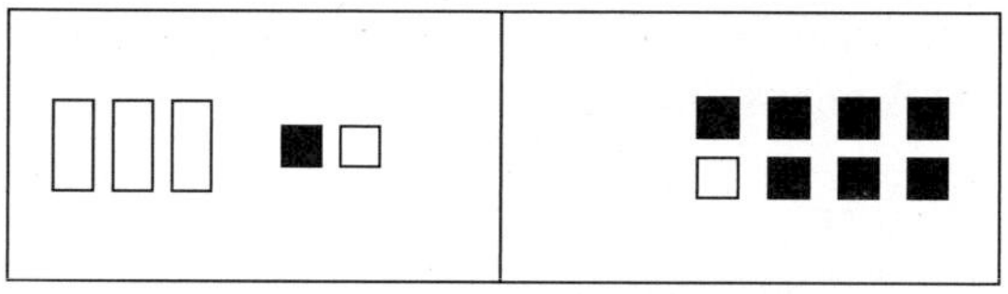	$3n - 1 + 1 = -7 + 1$
Step 5	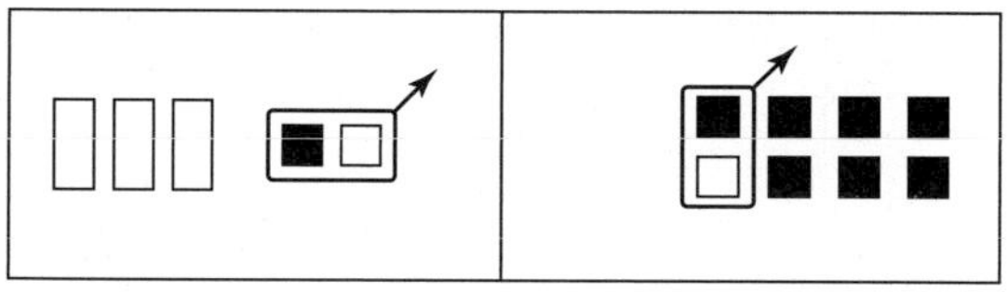	$3n = -6$
Step 6	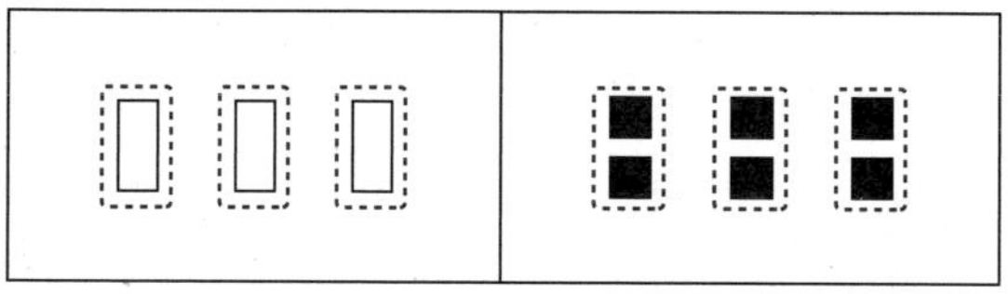	$3n \div 3 = -6 \div 3$
Step 7	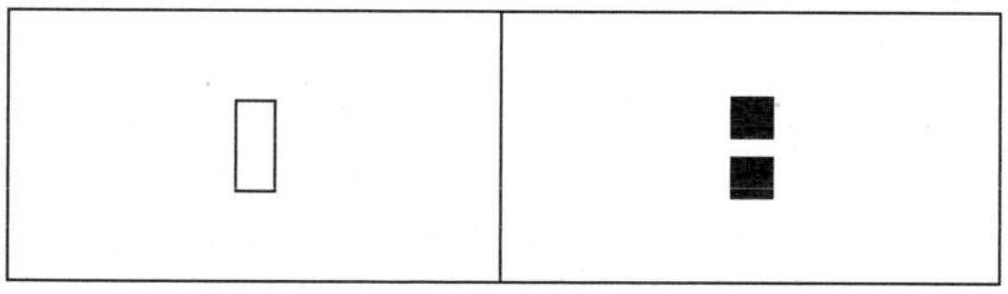	$n = -2$

FIGURE 15
Using algebra tiles to solve integer equations.

EXAMPLE 7.36

CONNECTION
COMMUNICATION
REASONING
REPRESENTATION

Solve $3n + 2 = n - 12$ using algebra. Relate the symbolic action to the tile model. Check your solution.

SOLUTION

	Symbolic representation	Tile representation
Step 1	$3n + 2 = n - 12$	Represent the equation with algebra tiles. Place three n-tiles and two 1-tiles on the left-hand side of the mat. Place 1 n-tile and twelve -1-tiles on the right-hand side of the mat.
Step 2	$3n + 2 - 2 = n - 12 - 2$	Add two -1-tiles to each side.
Step 3	$3n = n - 14$	Remove all zero pairs.
Step 4	$3n - n = n - 14 - n$	Take away one n-tile from each side.
Step 5	$2n = -14$	Simplify.
Step 6	$2n \div 2 = -14 \div 2$	Divide each side into two groups.
Step 7	$n = -7$	One n-tile equals seven -1-tiles.

Let's check our work: $3 \cdot (-7) + 2 = -21 + 2 = -19$, and $-7 - 12 = -19$. So the solution is $n = -7$. ▲

EXAMPLE 7.37

CONNECTION
COMMUNICATION
REASONING
REPRESENTATION

Solve $3(2n - 1) = 2n + 9$ using algebra. Relate the symbolic action to the tile model. Check your solution.

SOLUTION

	Symbolic representation	Tile representation
Step 1	$3(2n - 1) = 2n + 9$	Represent the equation with algebra tiles. Place three groups of two n-tiles and one -1-tile on the left-hand side of the mat. Place two n-tiles and nine 1-tiles on the right-hand side of the mat.
Step 2	$6n - 3 = 2n + 9$	There are six n-tiles and three -1-tiles on the left-hand side of the mat. There are two n-tiles and nine 1-tiles on the right-hand side of the mat.
Step 3	$6n - 3 + 3 = 2n + 9 + 3$	Add three 1-tiles to both sides of the mat.
Step 4	$6n = 2n + 12$	Remove all zero pairs and combine the 1-tiles.
Step 5	$6n - 2n = 2n + 12 - 2n$	Take away two n-tiles from each side.
Step 6	$4n = 12$	Simplify.
Step 7	$4n \div 4 = 12 \div 4$	Divide each side into four groups.
Step 8	$n = 3$	One n-tile equals three 1-tiles.

Let's check our work: $3(2 \cdot 3 - 1) = 3(6 - 1) = 3(5) = 15$, and $2 \cdot 3 + 9 = 6 + 9 = 15$. So the solution is $n = 3$. ▲

Linear equations in one variable arise, for example, in age problems.

EXAMPLE 7.38   Mr. Andrews is 38 years older than Billy. In 9 years, Mr. Andrews will be three times as old as Billy will be. How old is Billy?

SOLUTION

Let x equal the age of Billy. Then Mr. Andrews is $x + 38$ years old. In 9 years, Billy will be $x + 9$ years old, Mr. Andrews will be $(x + 38) + 9$ years old, and $(x + 38) + 9 = 3(x + 9)$, because Mr. Andrews will be three times as old Billy will be. Then

$$(x + 38) + 9 = 3(x + 9)$$
$$x + 47 = 3x + 27$$
$$20 = 2x$$
$$10 = x$$

Billy is 10 years old.

You can also use linear equations in one variable, for example, to help solve the system of linear equations $y = 3x - 10$ and $y = -5x + 6$. Here's how: First, solve the equation $3x - 10 = -5x + 6$ to obtain $x = 2$. Then pick one of the equations and replace x with 2: $y = 3x - 10 = 3(2) - 10 = -4$. Finally, $x = 2$ and $y = -4$ solves the system of linear equations.

QUESTIONS FOR SECTION 7.3

REPRESENTATION

Refresher: Representations (language, diagrams, tables, symbols, algebra, manipulatives, and contextualized situations) are important because we use them to organize, record, and communicate mathematical ideas and to make them more comprehensible.

1. Write the equation represented by the tile model.

   a.

   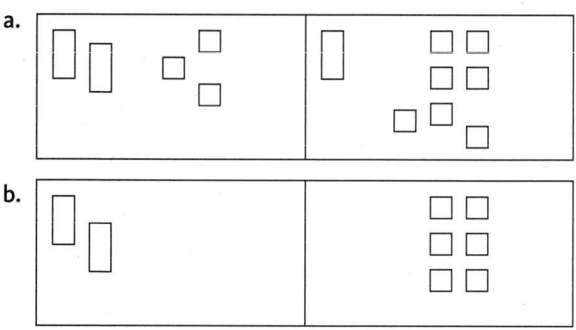

   b.

2. Represent the equation with a tile model.

   a. $3n + 1 = n + 5$ **b.** $2n + 1 = 7$

3. Write the equation represented by the tile model.

   a.

   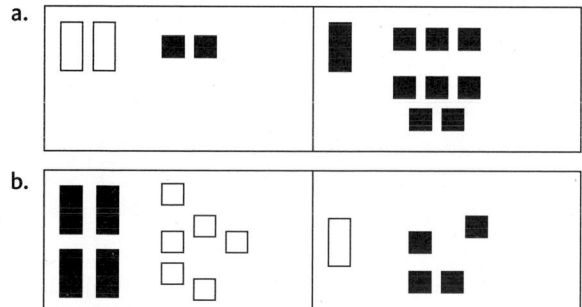

   b.

4. Use algebra tiles to represent each expression.

   a. $3n - 1$ **b.** $-3n - 2$ **c.** $4 - n$

5. Use algebra tiles to represent each equation.

   a. $1 - n = 2n - 5$ **b.** $2(1 - n) = 5n + 7$

PROBLEM SOLVING

Refresher: Problem solving (reaching a goal that is not immediately attainable) is important because it helps students think more deeply about what they know and deal with unfamiliar situations.

6. I'm thinking of a number. If you multiply it by 5 and add 3, then the result is 23. What equation would you use to solve the problem, and what is the number?

7. A jar of coins consists of pennies, nickels, and quarters. The number of pennies is four more than twice the number of quarters, and the number of nickels is eight fewer than five times the number of quarters. The jar has the same number of pennies and nickels. What equation would you use to solve the problem, and how many quarters are in the jar?

REASONING AND PROOF

Refresher: Reasoning and proof (thinking and justifying) are important because they help students make sense of mathematics.

8. In Example 7.30, we used the fair share model to simplify the algebraic expression $3n \div 3$. An alternative method uses inductive reasoning.

   a. Complete the table by filling in the blank using the order of operations and showing your work.

1	$3 \cdot 1 \div 3 = $ ___
2	$3 \cdot 2 \div 3 = $ ___
3	$3 \cdot 3 \div 3 = $ ___
4	$3 \cdot 4 \div 3 = $ ___

   b. Make a conjecture.

9. Each mat represents steps in solving a multistep algebraic equation. Write the corresponding equation for each mat to determine the solution, and then check your answer.

a.
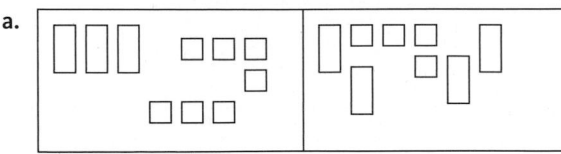

b.
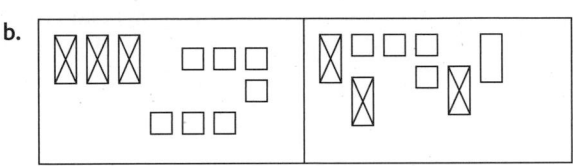

c.
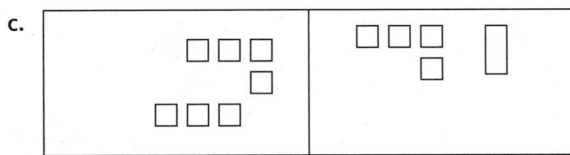

d.
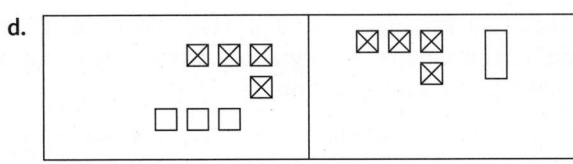

e.
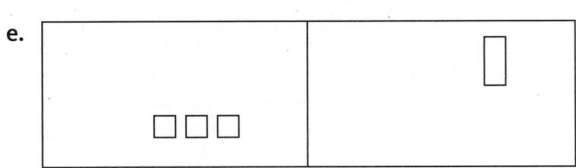

10. Show how to use algebra tiles to solve the equation $-n = 4$.

11. Show how to use algebra tiles to solve the equation $4n = 8$.

CONNECTIONS

Refresher: Connections (linking and applying mathematical ideas) are important because they deepen student understanding and make mathematics more meaningful, flexible, and useful.

12. Do the following.

   a. Draw the first mat of algebra tiles that you would use to solve the equation $3n + 4 = -n + 16$.

   b. Explain how you could use part (a) to solve the system of linear equations $y = 3n + 4$ and $y = -n + 16$.

13. Draw the first mat of algebra tiles that you could use to solve the system of linear equations $y = x + 5$ and $y = 4x - 1$.

14. Draw the first mat of algebra tiles that you would use to solve the system of linear equations $y = x + 1$ and $2y = x + 4$.

COMMUNICATION

Refresher: Communication (written and verbal explanations using representations and proper mathematical vocabulary) is important because it helps students refine and strengthen their understanding.

15. What is a one-step equation?

16. What is a two-step equation?

17. What is a multistep equation?

18. A student writes the following explanation for solving an equation: "Place two groups of three n-tiles and five -1-tiles on the left side of the mat. Place eight 1-tiles on the right side of the mat. Then there are six n-tiles and ten -1-tiles on the left side of the mat, which equals eight 1-tiles on the right side of the mat. Add ten 1-tiles to each side. This leaves six n-tiles on the left side and eighteen 1-tiles on the right side. Divide each side into six equal-sized groups. Then one n-tile equals three 1-tiles." Write the corresponding equations.

19. Write a paragraph that explains how to solve the equation $3(2x - 1) = 9$ using algebra tiles.

More practice with the ideas of the section

20. Fill in the blank. Choose one of the following words or phrases: *algebra tiles, ceramic tiles, equations, multistep, one-step,* or *two-step*.

   a. Equations such as $2x = 12$ and $x + 3 = 8$ are called _____ equations because they involve one inverse operation to solve for x.

   b. Equations such as $2x - 4 = 12$ and $-4x + 2 = 8$ are called _____ equations because they involve two inverse operations to solve for x.

   c. _____ are manipulatives for solving algebraic equations and provide a basis for understanding and justifying the symbolic process of solving algebraic equations.

21. Write the equation represented by the tile model.

a.
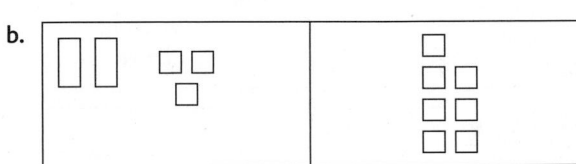

b.

22. Identify the equation as one-step, two-step, or multistep.

   a. $2n + 6 = 14$ **b.** $n + 5 = 23$ **c.** $5n = 10$

   d. $5n + 2 = 3n - 8$ **e.** $n + 10 = 4(22 - n)$

23. Use algebra tiles to solve $3n = 6$.

24. Use algebra tiles to solve $3n + 4 = 10$.

25. Use algebra tiles to solve $2n = 8$.

26. Use algebra tiles to solve $4n + 5 = 13$.

27. Use algebra tiles to solve $3n = -6$.

28. Use algebra tiles to solve $2n + 3 = -9$. Show the corresponding algebraic representation.

29. Use algebra tiles to solve $5n + 2 = 3n + 8$. Show the corresponding algebraic representation.

30. Use algebra tiles to solve $n + 1 = -3$. Show the corresponding algebraic representation.

31. Use algebra tiles to solve $-5n - 6 = 4 - 3n$. Show the corresponding algebraic representation.

32. Use algebra to solve $n + 1 = 7$. Show the corresponding representation using algebra tiles.

33. Use algebra to solve $n - 1 = 7 - n$. Show the corresponding representation using algebra tiles.

34. Write a two-step equation, and then use algebra tiles to represent the equation.

35. Write and solve a multistep equation, showing the correspondence between the algebra and the algebra tiles.

36. Miguel is 28 years older than Bella. In 5 years, Miguel will be three times as old as Bella will be.

   a. Write a single equation that represents the age relationships.

   b. Solve the equation to verify that Bella is 9 years old.

37. Miguel is four times as old as Bella. In 8 years, he will be three times as old as Bella will be.

   a. Write a single equation that represents the age relationships.

   b. Solve the equation to verify that Miguel is 64 years old.

CHAPTER 7 REVIEW

CHAPTER 7 Organizer

Section	What You Should Learn	Review Problems
7.1	**1.** Determine if a relation or graph is a function.	1–2
	2. Communicate about functions using appropriate vocabulary and notation.	3–8
	3. Represent a function using various representations: words, table, graph, or equation.	9–14
	4. Use the concept of functions to solve word problems that involve varying relationships between two variables.	15–19
	5. Describe how a change in one variable affects the value of a related variable.	20–22
	6. Create new functions from two existing functions.	23–24
7.2	**1.** Understand the connection between a solution to an equation and the graph of the equation.	25–31
	2. Determine or estimate the x- and y-intercepts, if any, from the graph of a function or from the equation of a function.	32–34
	3. Solve a system of equations using various methods: intersection method, substitution method, and elimination method.	35–42
7.3	**1.** Use algebra tiles to represent expressions and equations.	43–45
	2. Use algebra tiles to solve one-step and two-step equations.	46–48

Key Terms and Concepts

ordered pair 366	output (dependent variable) 367	function notation 371
coordinates 366	function 369	algebra of functions 376
first coordinate 366	domain 369	solve $y = f(x)$ 382
second coordinate 366	range 369	algebraic connection 382
relation from set A to set B 367	codomain 369	graphical connection (Cartesian connection) 382
input (independent variable) 367	rectangular coordinate graph 370	

Key Terms and Concepts

linear function 384	intersection method 387	algebra tiles 396
nonlinear function 384	substitution method 388	modeling whole numbers with algebra tiles 396
x-intercept 384	elimination method 389	
y-intercept 384	one-step equation 396	modeling integers with algebra tiles 396
system of linear equations 386	two-step equation 396	

Review Questions

1. Each table defines a relation. Is the relation a function? If it is not, justify your answer.

   a.

Input	3	4	8	2	1	0
Output	5	−1	2	−3	5	4

   b.

Input	1	2	3	4	5	2
Output	4	0	−2	−1	6	1

2. Does the graph represent a function?

   a.

   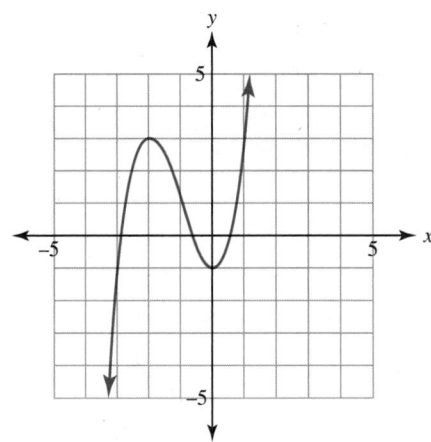

   b.

   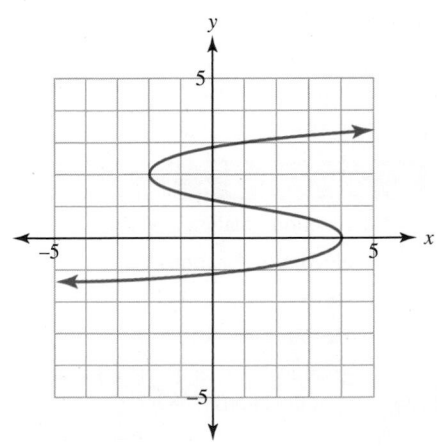

3. Match the representation tool with its benefit.

Tool	Benefit
a. Words	(i) let(s) you "see" the relationship between two variables.
b. Table	(ii) allow(s) you to quantify the relationship and obtain ordered pairs that may be infeasible from other tools.
c. Graph	(iii) record(s) and organize(s) the data to help you explore a pattern.
d. Equation	(iv) help(s) describe the story.

4. Fill in the blank with the appropriate word, phrase, or expression.

   a. In the equation $y = f(x)$, it is helpful to think of x as the independent variable and y as the _____ variable, because the value of y depends on the value of x.

   b. A(n) _____ is a relation from set A to set B such that each element of A appears as the first coordinate of some ordered pair with one corresponding output from B.

   c. Sets, _____, graphs, and equations are representational tools that make the concept of the function understandable.

   d. $(4, -2)$ is an example of a(n) _____.

   e. The 4 in $(4, -2)$ is called the _____.

   f. The -2 in $(4, -2)$ is called the _____.

5. Does the given rule specify a function?

   a. Let w be the weight of a letter that will be mailed from Austin to Boston. Let $P(w)$ be the amount of postage required.

   b. Let w be the postage on a letter mailed from Austin to Boston. Let $P(w)$ be the weight of the letter.

   c. Let n be the number of items you purchased at a store. Let $C(n)$ be the total cost of the n items.

   d. Let n be the total cost of the items you purchased at the store. Let $C(n)$ be the number of items you purchased.

6. Use function notation to represent each relationship. Tell what each variable means.

   a. Kamran has five fewer marbles than Bob.

   b. The width of the rectangle is 3 cm more than four times the length of the rectangle.

   c. There are two cats for every seven birds.

   d. Three-fourths of the coins in the piggy bank are nickels.

7. Complete the table so that it does not represent a function.

Input	A	B	
Output	1	6	1

8. A math problem involves the function $x(y) = 2y - 5$.

   a. Identify the independent variable.

   b. Identify the dependent variable.

   c. Explain how you arrived at your decisions.

9. An online store sells a series of four books for $8 per book. The shipping charge for each order is $6. Represent the cost C to order n books ($n = 1, 2, 3$, or 4) using

   a. a table.   **b.** a set of ordered pairs.

   c. a graph.   **d.** an equation.

10. The stopping distance d for a car is proportional to the square of the velocity v of the car (ignoring the reaction time, slope of the road, coefficient of friction of the tires on the road, and so on). This means a car traveling v mph has stopping distance d where $d = kv^2$ feet for some number k. Suppose a car traveling 50 mph required 60 feet to stop.

   a. Find the value of k.

   b. What is the stopping distance for the same car traveling at 15 mph?

   c. What is the stopping distance for the same car traveling at 30 mph?

   d. If you double the speed of the car, what happens to the stopping distance?

   e. Interpret the ordered pair $(70, 117.6)$.

11. The table represents a function. Write an equation for the function.

x	1	2	3	4	5
y	4	1	-2	-5	-8

12. The width of a rectangle is 3 feet less than four times the length. Write a formula for the area as a function of the length.

13. The boiling point of water is 100°C at sea level. The elevation E (in meters) at which the boiling point of water is t (in degrees Celsius) is determined by the equation $E(t) = 1000(100 - t) + 580(100 - t)^2$. What happens to the elevation as the boiling point of water increases? (Hint: make a table.)

14. A farmer hired a tractor from a company to prepare his field for planting. He paid an initial fee plus an additional charge for each hour the tractor was needed. The graph shows the total cost C, in dollars, for a job that lasts h hours.

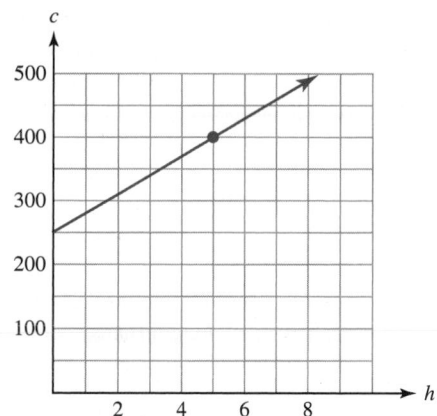

   a. What does the ordered pair $(5, 400)$ mean?

   b. What is the cost for hiring the company for a job that lasts 10 hours?

   c. The farmer paid $475. How many hours did the job take?

   d. What is the initial fee?

   e. Ignoring the initial fee, how much does each additional hour cost?

15. A truck driver is $d(t) = 630 - 40t$ miles from her destination after driving t hours. She drives at a constant rate.

   a. How far from her destination is she after driving 4 hours?

   b. How far did she drive during her fifth hour of driving?

16. A taxi company charges $1.45 for the first fourth of a mile, and then $0.30 each successive fourth or part of a mile. Let m represent the number of miles to complete a trip.

   a. What is the cab fare for a 1-mile ride?

   b. Express the cab fare F as a function of m for any trip that is at least 1 mile.

   c. Determine $F(1)$, the cab fare for a 1-mile ride, and whether it agrees with your answer in part (a).

   d. Use the function to calculate the cab fare for an 8.5-mile ride.

   e. Suppose the cab fare was $19.15. Approximately how many miles was the taxi ride?

17. A plane travels at a constant speed of 420 mph in the absence of winds. Let w denote the speed of the prevailing wind, in miles per hour. A tailwind is wind that travels in the same direction as the airplane. A headwind is wind that the airplane flies directly into.

   a. Suppose the speed of the wind is 40 mph. What is the speed of the airplane when the wind is a tailwind? How far has it traveled after 3 hours?

   b. Write the speed of the plane as a function $T(w)$ of the wind when the wind is a tailwind.

   c. Suppose the speed of the wind is 60 mph. What is the speed of the airplane when the wind is a headwind? How far has it traveled after 3 hours?

   d. Write the speed of the plane as a function $H(w)$ of the wind when the wind is a headwind.

18. A contractor determined that $b(f) = 2 + 15f$ bags of concrete are required to pour f linear feet of sidewalk. How many bags of concrete are needed to pour

   a. 10 linear feet of sidewalk?

   b. 11 linear feet of sidewalk?

   c. the 11th foot of sidewalk?

   d. 27 linear feet of sidewalk?

   e. the 27th foot of sidewalk?

19. A telephone company charges a monthly service fee, plus a fixed rate for each hour of long-distance phone calls. The graph shows the total monthly telephone charges for a customer who chats for h hours.

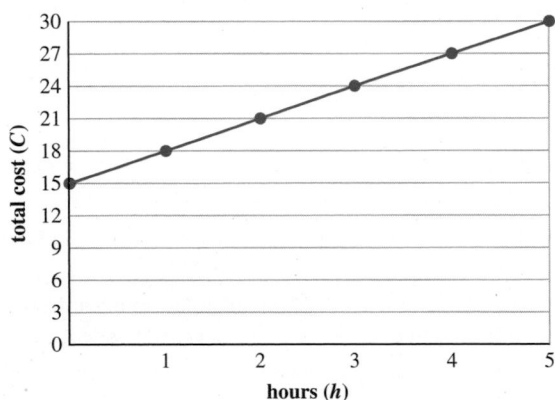

   a. What is the total monthly cost to chat for 3 hours?

   b. What is the monthly service charge?

   c. What is the rate for 1 hour of long-distance calls?

   d. Express the total monthly cost as a function of the number of hours of long-distance calling.

20. Variables x and y are related by the equation $12 = x - y$. What happens to the value of y as the value of x increases?

21. Variables x and y are related by the equation $xy = 15$. What happens to the value of y when the value of x decreases?

22. Variables x and y are related by the equation $12 = 4x + y$. What happens to the value of y as the value of x increases?

23. The function table for $g(x)$ is given.

x	1	2	3	4	5	6
$g(x)$	5	−1	2	0	4	1

Determine the function table for

   a. $g(x) + 2$.   **b.** $3 \times g(x)$.

24. $R(n)$ is the revenue a company earns for selling n items, and $C(n)$ is the cost the company incurs to produce the n items. What function describes the profit the company earns for selling n items?

25. Do the given values solve the equation $y = 2x^2 - 3x - 1$?

   a. $x = 2, y = 3$

   b. $x = 1, y = -2$

26. Explain the connection between the graph of $f(x) = 4x + 1$ and all solutions to the equation $f(x) = 4x + 1$.

27. Find one solution to the equation $210y^2 - 4x = 4$.

28. Find one solution to the equation $Ax + 2y = -8$, where A is a number (but unknown).

29. What is the relationship between the point $(4, -3)$ and the graph of the function $y(x) = 2x - 11$?

30. The graph of the equation $-4x + 9y = -2$ is shown. Is there an obvious solution, based on the graph, to the equation $-4x + 9y = -2$? If yes, give the solution.

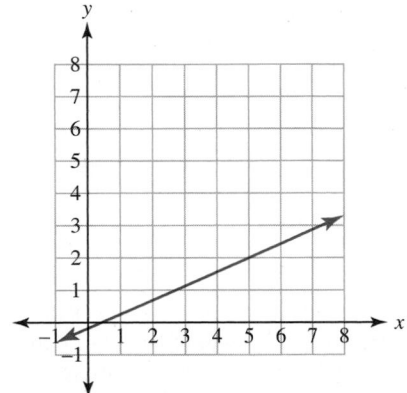

31. The graph of function f is shown. Use the graph to find a solution to the equation $y = f(x)$.

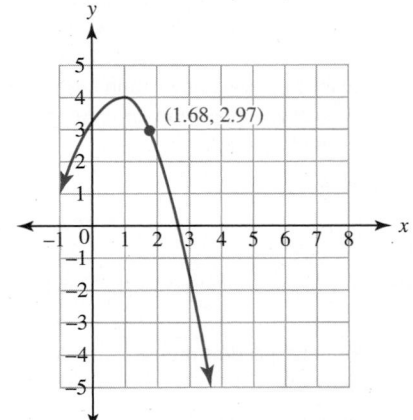

32. Determine the x- and y-intercepts, if they exist.

   a. $y = -x + 10$ **b.** $x = -2.5$ **c.** $y = 6.5$

   d. $3y - 6x = 27$

33. Estimate the x- and y-intercepts of the function with the given graph.

   a.

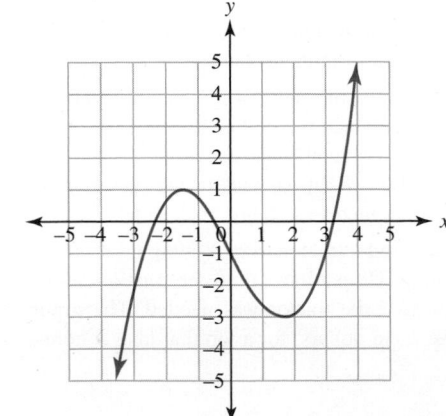

b.

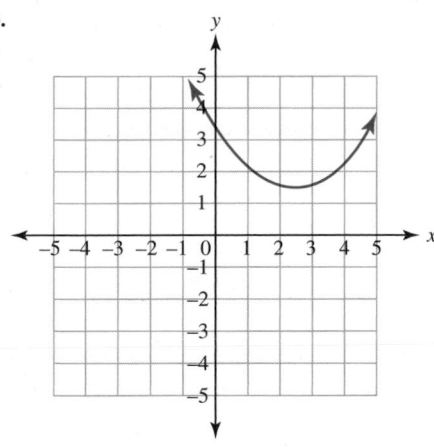

34. The graph shows the number of moviegoers p in a theater t minutes after the movie ends.

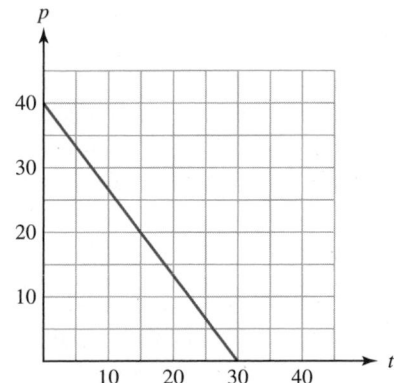

a. How many moviegoers are in the theater 15 minutes after the movie ends?

b. Interpret the p- and t-intercepts.

35. Using the intersection method, find a solution to the system of linear equations $y = 2x - 6$ and $y = -3x + 4$.

36. Using the intersection method, find a solution to the system of linear equations $y = -4x + 5$ and $y = 2x - 7$.

37. Solve the system of linear equations using the method of substitution.

$$12x - 3y = -6$$
$$-5x + 4y = 19$$

38. Solve the system of linear equations using the method of substitution.

$$-3x + 4y = -17$$
$$-3x - 6y = 3$$

39. Solve the system of linear equations using the method of elimination.

$$x - 5y = 27$$
$$-6x + 7y = -47$$

40. Solve the system of linear equations using the method of elimination.

$$2y = -3x + 24$$
$$5y - 2x = 41$$

41. Set up a system of equations for the problem, and then solve the problem: Fred and Mark have 417 coins altogether. Mark has 6 fewer than twice as many coins as Fred. How many coins does each have?

42. A telephone company offers two calling plans. Plan A costs $5 each month for local calls, plus $0.03 for each minute for long-distance calls. Plan B costs $2 each month, plus $0.05 for each minute for long-distance calls. Which plan do you recommend? Show your work, and then explain your answer.

43. Use algebra tiles to model each of the following.

a. $5n$ b. $-4n$ c. $-3n + 4$ d. $-(1 - 3n)$

44. Write the equation represented by the tile model.

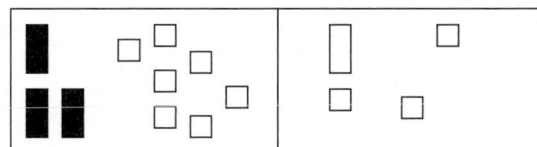

45. Use algebra tiles to model each equation.

a. $6 - 2n = n$ b. $2n - 3 = 1$ c. $2(n - 1) = 4$

46. Use algebra tiles to solve the equation $2n + 4 = 12$.

47. Use algebra tiles to solve the equation $2n = -8$.

48. Use algebra tiles to solve $9 + 2n = 6n - 3$. Show the corresponding algebraic representation.

Chapter 7 Test

1. *Determine whether a relation or graph is a function.* Does each relation specify a function? Justify your answer. Assume the set of inputs is appropriate.

   a. $A = \{(3, 2), (4, 5), (1, 0), (7, 8)\}$

   b. $B = \{(1, 2), (5, 5), (3, 0), (1, 8)\}$

2. *Determine whether a relation or graph is a function.* Does each table specify a function? Justify your answer.

   a.

x	-1	0	5	-2
y	1	2	1	0

   b.

x	-3	0	4	-3
y	1	2	3	4

3. *Determine whether a relation or graph is a function.* Does each rule specify a function?

   a. Let $C(w)$ be the cost to mail a package with weight w.

   b. Let $W(p)$ be the weight of the package that costs p to mail.

   c. Let n be the number of inches of rainfall recorded in Pocatello, Idaho, and let $D(n)$ be the date Pocatello recorded the rainfall.

   d. Let a be a date, and let $n(a)$ be the number of inches of rain recorded in Pocatello, Idaho, on that date.

4. *Communicate about functions using appropriate vocabulary and notation.* A math problem involves the equation $x(y) = 7y + 2$.

   a. Identify the independent variable.

   b. Identify the dependent variable.

5. *Communicate about functions using appropriate vocabulary and notation.* Let $W(n)$ be the number of windows cleaned by a professional window washing company after n hours.

   a. Interpret $W(4) = 180$.

   b. The company cleaned 120 windows in 3.5 hours. Express this using function notation.

6. *Communicate about functions using appropriate vocabulary and notation.* Fill in the blank with the appropriate word, phrase, or expression.

   a. The expression $h(t)$ tells us that h is a(n) _____ of t.

   b. In the equation $y = f(x)$, we think of x as the _____ variable.

   c. In the equation $y = f(x)$, we think of y as the _____ variable.

   d. An equation such as $h(w) = 4w^2 - 3w + 2$ is an example of a relationship between two variables h and w expressed in _____ notation.

7. *Communicate about functions using appropriate vocabulary and notation.* Use function notation to represent each relationship. Tell what each variable means.

   a. The length of the rectangle is 5 cm less than three times the width of the rectangle.

   b. There are five mice for every three cats.

8. *Represent a function using various representations: words, a table, a graph, or an equation.* A hotel rents a conference hall for $400 per day. It charges $150 to cover the cost of setting up the chairs and tables for the conference.

   a. What is the charge to rent to the hall for 5 days?

   b. Express the total cost C to rent the hall for d days.

   c. What is the domain of the function?

9. *Use the concept of functions to solve word problems that involve varying relationships between two variables.* The water company charges a fixed cost of $3.50 per month to deliver water and maintain the infrastructure (reservoirs, pipes, pumps, meter reading, and billing), plus $0.003 for each gallon of water used.

   a. Represent the function with a table. Choose appropriate input values.

   b. Write an equation that expresses the monthly water bill b as a function of the number of gallons g used.

   c. What is the monthly water bill for a household that uses 1546 gallons of water? Round to the nearest penny.

10. *Use the concept of functions to solve word problems that involve varying relationships between two variables.* Taxi companies in Boston charge $2.60 for the first seventh of a mile and then $0.40 each successive seventh or part of a mile. Let m represent the number of miles to complete a trip.

    a. What is the cab fare for a 1-mile ride?

    b. What is the cab fare for a 2-mile ride?

    c. Express the cab fare C as a function of m.

    d. Use the function to calculate the cab fare for an 8-mile ride.

    e. Suppose the cab fare was $128.20. How many miles was the taxi ride?

11. *Use the concept of functions to solve word problems that involve varying relationships between two variables.* The equation $c(t) = 331.3 + 0.606t$ relates the speed of sound c (in meters per second) in air to the temperature t (in degrees Celsius) of the air.

    a. What is the speed of sound when the temperature is 29°C? Round to the nearest whole number.

    b. What happens to the speed of sound as the temperature increases?

    c. Suppose the speed of sound in the air is 360.4 m per second. What is the air temperature, to the nearest degree?

12. *Describe how a change in one variable affects the value of a related variable.* The equation $C = \frac{5}{9}(F - 32)$ relates the temperature C in degrees Celsius to the temperature F in degrees Fahrenheit.

    a. What happens to the Celsius temperature as the Fahrenheit temperature increases?

    b. The average temperature in San Diego, California, in November is 61.8°F. What is the temperature in degrees Celsius? Round your answer to the nearest tenth of a degree.

13. *Describe how a change in one variable affects the value of a related variable.* Most of the ocean exists in darkness. The photic zone of a body of water, such as a lake or ocean, is the depth of the water for which sufficient light is present in the water to support photosynthesis (the process by which plants, algae, and bacteria use light to produce compounds such as sugar and oxygen that sustain life). The level of algae is one factor that affects the photic zone, because algae blocks sunlight. What happens to the photic zone as the concentration of algae in a body of water increases? Assume all other influencing factors, such as turbidity (which stirs mud and silt), remain constant.

14. *Understand the connection between a solution to an equation and the graph of the equation.* The graph of function *f* is shown.

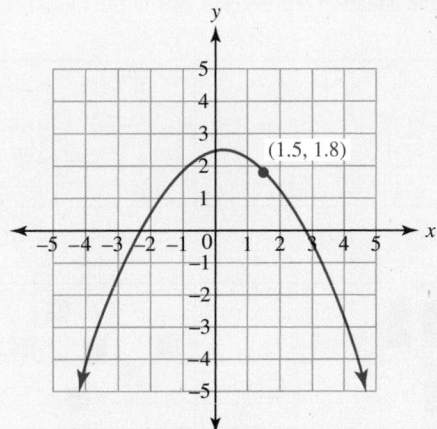

 a. Use the graph to find a solution to the equation $y = f(x)$.

 b. How many solutions are there to the equation $-2 = f(x)$?

 c. How many solutions are there to the equation $4 = f(x)$?

 d. How many solutions are there to the equation $y = f(x)$?

15. *Understand the connection between a solution to an equation and the graph of the equation.* The graph of function *f* is shown. Solve each equation.

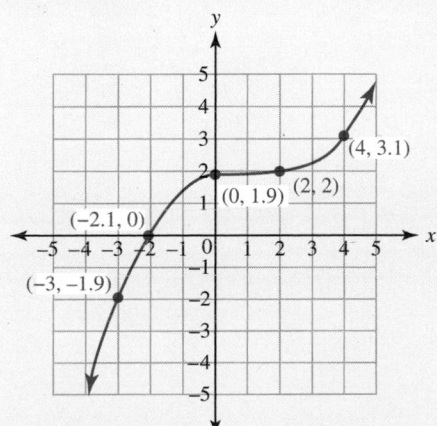

 a. $1.9 = 3.8 + f(x)$

 b. $f(x) - 1.9 = 1.2$

 c. $0 = f(x)$

16. *Understand the connection between a solution to an equation and the graph of the equation.* Does the ordered pair lie on the graph of the equation $4y^2 + 10x = 59$?

 a. $(3, 7)$ b. $(5, 1.5)$

17. *Understand the connection between a solution to an equation and the graph of the equation.* Find an ordered pair that lies on the graph of the equation $3y^2 - 8x = 100$.

18. *Understand the connection between a solution to an equation and the graph of the equation.* The graph of an equation is shown.

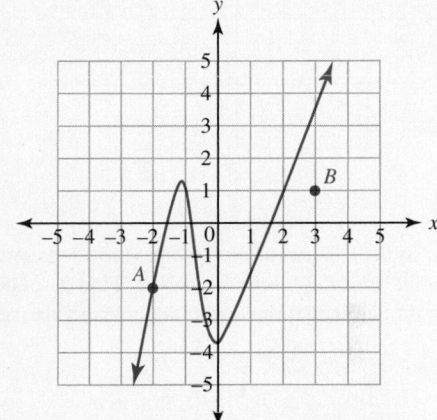

 a. Explain why the coordinates of *A* solve the equation.

 b. Explain why the coordinates of *B* do not solve the equation.

19. *Understand the connection between a solution to an equation and the graph of the equation.*

 a. Is it possible to plot a solution to the equation $Ax - 2y = 6$ without knowing the value of *A*? Explain your answer.

 b. Is it possible to plot a solution to the equation $4x - By = 20$ without knowing the value of *B*? Explain your answer.

20. *Determine or estimate the x- and y-intercepts, if they exist, from the graph of a function or from the equation of a function.* Estimate the *x*- and *y*-intercepts, if they exist, from the graph of the function.

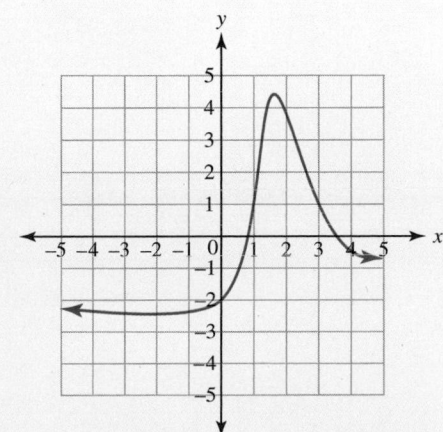

21. *Determine or estimate the x- and y-intercepts from the graph or from the equation of a function.* Find the *x*- and *y*-intercepts, if they exist, of the function $y = 5x^2 + 7$.

22. *Solve a system of equations using various methods: intersection, substitution, and elimination.* The graph of two linear equations is shown. Find a solution to the system of linear equations.

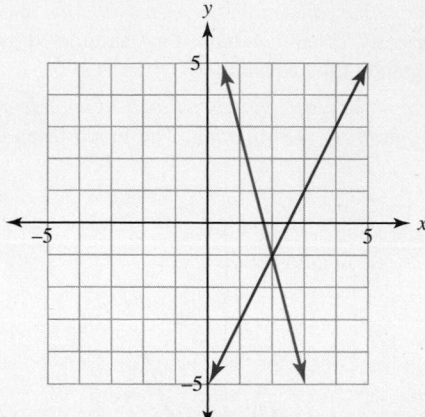

23. *Solve a system of equations using various methods: intersection, substitution, and elimination.* Find a solution to the system of linear equations using the intersection method.

$$y = -3x + 7$$
$$y = -3x - 8$$

24. *Solve a system of equations using various methods: intersection, substitution, and elimination.* Solve the system of linear equations using the method of substitution.

$$4x + 5y = 2$$
$$7y - x = -17$$

25. *Solve a system of equations using various methods: intersection, substitution, and elimination.* Solve the system of linear equations using the method of elimination.

$$-2x + 3y = -14$$
$$-5y = -3x + 22$$

26. *Solve a system of equations using various methods: intersection, substitution, and elimination.*

a. Find the value of A such that there is no solution to the system of equations $Ax - 8y = 12$ and $12y - 10x + 5 = 0$.

b. A student solves a system of two linear equations and arrives at the equation $3 = 3$. What does this tell you about the system of equations?

c. A student solves a system of two linear equations and arrives at the equation $8 = 3$. What does this tell you about the system of equations?

27. *Use algebra tiles to represent expressions and equations.* Use algebra tiles to model each expression.

a. 2 **b.** $4n$ **c.** $2(n - 1)$ **d.** $5 - 3n$

28. *Use algebra tiles to represent expressions and equations.* Write the equation represented by the tile model.

a.

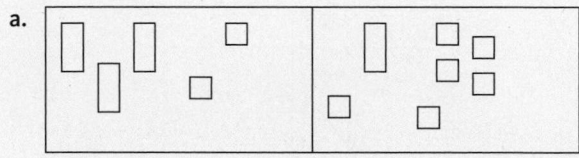

b.

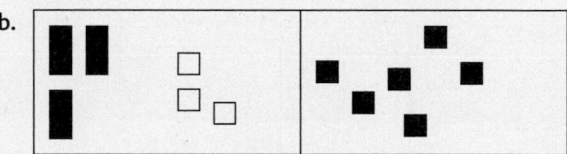

29. *Use algebra tiles to solve one-step and two-step equations.* Use algebra tiles to solve $3n - 2 = -n + 10$. Show the corresponding algebraic representation.

8

Descriptive Statistics

Where Are We Going?

In **Section 8.1,** we discuss the two types of variables: categorical (qualitative) and numerical (quantitative) variables. Variables lead us to data. We discuss the various ways to visualize data: frequency tables, bar and pie charts, line graphs, scatterplots, histograms, and pictographs. Graphing skills give students the opportunity to explore data, look for patterns, and make convincing arguments. In **Section 8.2,** we discuss various ways to summarize numerical data using numbers. We focus on three measures of center: mean, median, and mode. We use stem-and-leaf plots and dot plots to visualize the distribution of numerical data and then select an appropriate measure of center. We discuss three measures of variation: range, mean absolute deviation, and minimum and maximum usual values. In **Section 8.3,** we discuss percentiles and demonstrate how to use them to measure variation, create box plots, and detect outliers.

What Are Data?

Data basically means information. The word *data* stems from the Latin word *datum,* which means "thing given." We can obtain data from surveys, such as asking students their favorite ice cream flavor; from measurements, such as measuring heights of students; from observations, such as counting the number of cars that enter an intersection; or from experiments, such as studying the effectiveness of a particular brand of lawn fertilizer. More than 200 years ago, it was common practice to display data in a table similar to Table 8.1, which contains 2009 foreign trade data for the three leading trading partners with the United States.

Tables make it easier to store and retrieve data, but patterns and trends are difficult to recognize in tables loaded with data. Eighteenth-century draftsman William Playfair invented line graphs, bar graphs, and pie charts to make it easier to see patterns and trends in the blink of an eye. He used charts to visualize economic data, especially trade between England and other countries, such as the line graph shown of imports and exports between England and both Italy and Venice.

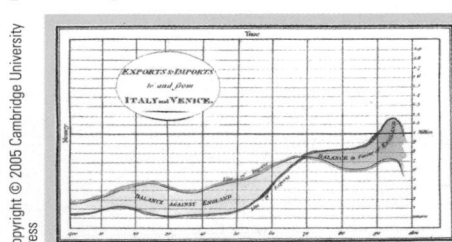

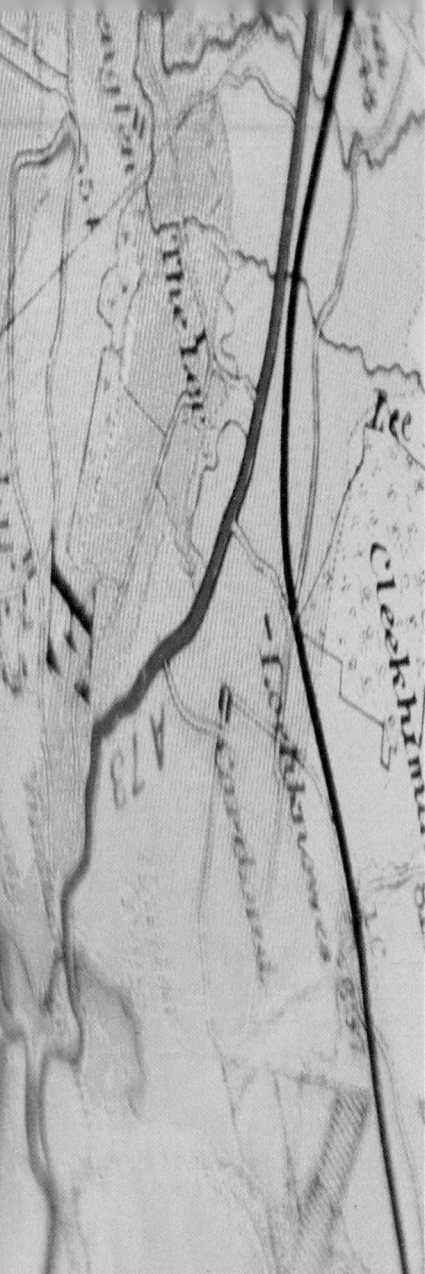

TABLE 8.1 Example of Data

Rank	Country	Exports (in billions)	Imports (in billions)	Total trade (in billions)	Percentage of total trade with U.S.
1	Canada	$204.7	$224.9	$429.6	16.4
2	China	$69.6	$296.4	$366.0	14.0
3	Mexico	$129.0	$176.5	$305.5	11.7

SOURCE: U.S. Census Bureau, Foreign Trade Statistics, www.census.gov/foreign-trade/statistics.

What Is Statistics?

Statistics is the science of collecting, organizing, visualizing, summarizing, and analyzing data. Governments use statistics to make policies and decisions that affect social and economic aspects of our lives, such as health, education, housing, and employment. Manufacturers use statistics to improve quality of products, reduce production costs, and develop marketing strategies. Consumers need to know statistics to read, understand, and evaluate claims in newspapers and journals. Teachers often use statistics to make connections between mathematics and science in their instruction.

There are two branches of statistics: descriptive statistics and inferential statistics. **Descriptive statistics** involves visualizing and summarizing data. We *visualize* data with graphs (for example, a bar graph or pictograph) and *summarize* data with numerical measures (such as the mean or range). Descriptive statistics may include making initial conclusions or predictions from the data, much like making conclusions or predictions based on patterns. Students initially learn and apply descriptive statistics in elementary school, where they should be able to pose questions worth answering; collect data; display the data using tables, graphs, or both; perhaps verify predictions; and sometimes look "beyond" or "behind" the data and draw preliminary conclusions from the data. *Inferential statistics* involves using probability theory and data to test a claim or to generalize. Students initially learn and apply inferential statistics in high school or college. As you might expect, in this chapter we only focus on descriptive statistics.

SECTION 8.1   # Graphical Representations of Data

According to researchers and the NCTM standards for data analysis and probability for grades K–8, there are four phases of data analysis (© NCTM Standards 2011 by National Council of Teachers of Mathematics).

> **Four Phases of Data Analysis**
>
> 1. Ask a question worth answering.
> 2. Collect and organize data.
> 3. Explore and analyze the data with appropriate methods.
> 4. Display the data and communicate conclusions based on the data.

Two Types of Variables: Categorical and Numerical Variables

A **variable** is a characteristic that varies from one object to another. If the objects are people, then the variables could be height, age, or hair color. If the objects are books, then the variables could be number of pages, weight, and binding type. **Data** are observations or measurements from one or more variables. For example, Table 8.2 displays a small collection of data.

TABLE 8.2   **Example of Data**

Person	Height	Age	Hair color
Mrs. A	5′7″	53	brown
Mr. B	6′2″	21	black
Ms. C	5′1″	42	red

NCTM expectations assert students should be able to "recognize the differences in representing categorical and numerical data" (Gr. 3–5). The ability to classify a variable influences the ability to explore and display data appropriately.

A **categorical variable** (also known as a **qualitative variable**) has values that are labels or categories. The value of a categorical variable answers the question, "Which category does the object belong to?" Here are a few examples of categorical variables:

- Hair color, with values such as black, brown, or red
- Type of movie, with values such as comedy, drama, horror, or adventure
- Political affiliation, with values such as Democrat, Republican, or Independent
- Zip code, such as 92009 or 10278

When we collect information about a categorical variable, we should make sure the categories do not overlap. A categorical variable may look like a number, such as zip code 10278, but arithmetic operations such as addition and division with these values do not make sense (for example, the "average" zip code is meaningless).

EXAMPLE 8.1

COMMUNICATION

Describe a categorical variable. List some possible values for the variable.

SOLUTION

Answers vary. "Employment status" is a variable, because it differs among people. It is a categorical variable, and some possible values are unemployed, part time, full time, and retired.

▲

EXAMPLE 8.2

COMMUNICATION

REASONING

Classify movies using a categorical variable.

SOLUTION

Answers vary. Students could classify movies according to how well they liked the movie, using categories such as "not recommended," "recommended," and "highly recommended."

An independent board of parents rates movies using the categories "G" (general audiences), "PG" (parental guidance suggested, some material may not be suitable for children), "PG-13" (parents strongly cautioned, some material may be inappropriate for children under 13), "R" (restricted, children under 17 require accompanying parent or adult guardian), and "NC-17" (no one 17 and under admitted).

▲

A **numerical variable** (also known as a **quantitative variable**) has values that represent counts or measurements. The values answer the question "How many?" or the question "How much?" Here are a few examples of numerical variables:

- The number of pets in homes is a numerical variable, because the value is determined by counting.
- The weight of a person is a numerical variable, because it must be measured with a device.

Values for numerical variables often have measurement units, such $35, 2.3 miles, and 4.75 pounds. A numerical variable may be *discrete* (such as the number of pets and the number of students) or *continuous* (such as weight and time). Continuous variables have scales that can be cut into different increments, whereas discrete values have pre-established increments.

EXAMPLE 8.3

COMMUNICATION

REASONING

Determine the type of variable. Explain your answer.

a. number of students in a survey who like history

b. social security numbers (SSNs)

c. letter grades in a class

d. percent of students in a survey who voted for Proposition A

SOLUTION

a. numerical, because it involves counting

b. categorical, because addition and subtraction of SSNs gives meaningless results

c. categorical, because the letters are categories

d. numerical, because the variable is a percent and percents are numbers

---

Concept Map 8.1 summarizes the two types of variables.

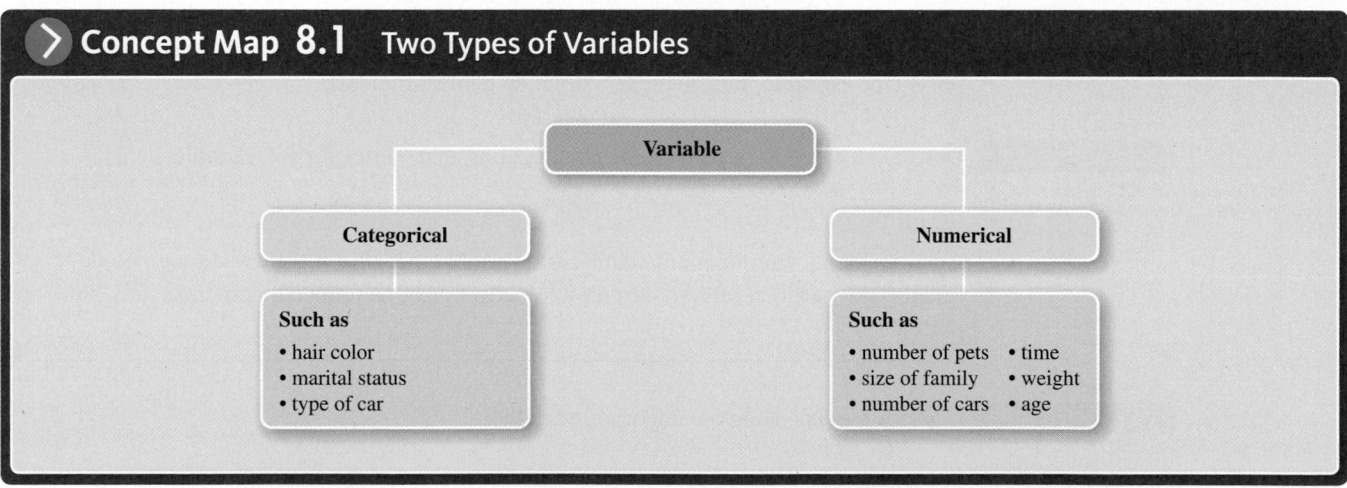

Concept Map 8.1 Two Types of Variables

When we collect data, we often organize it in a table or spreadsheet.

EXAMPLE 8.4

COMMUNICATION

REASONING

REPRESENTATION

The table shows data for four participants in an exercise survey.

a. Explain how the table records the data associated with each participant.

b. Determine the variables of interest and type of each variable.

c. Explain how the table records the data for each variable.

Participants	E-mail address	Height	Age (in years)	Exercise level
Mrs. K	mrsk@gmail.com	5′3″	56	low
Mr. Y	mry@yahoo.com	6′0″	24	medium
Mr. Q	mrq@aol.com	5′6″	45	low
Ms. A	msa@roadrunner.com	5′7″	23	high

SOLUTION

a. The data associated with each participant are reported in the rows. For example, the data in the first row indicate Mrs. K has the e-mail address mrsk@gmail.com, her height is 5 feet 3 inches, she is 56 years old, and her exercise level is low.

b. The variables of interest are height, age, and exercise level. Height is a numerical variable, age is a numerical variable, and exercise level is a categorical variable.

c. Data for each variable appear in the columns. For example, from top to bottom, the data associated with the variable exercise level are low, medium, low, and high. The data associated with the variable age are 56, 24, 45, and 23.

▲

EXAMPLE 8.5

COMMUNICATION
REASONING
REPRESENTATION

Describe the variable of interest and identify the type of variable.

a. The mayor of a town surveys some citizens about the ownership status of their housing unit (such as home, condominium, or mobile home). There were 368 respondents who reported they owned their housing unit.

b. The following table obtained in an observational study gives the number of vehicles that entered the Main Street and First Street intersection during rush hour.

Day	Mon	Tues	Wed	Thurs	Fri
Vehicles	640	537	588	520	485

c. The average highest temperatures in Chicago Heights, Illinois, for the months of January, April, July, and October are given in the following table.

Month	January	April	July	October
Temperature (°F)	29.2	58.1	83.7	63.0

SOLUTION

a. The variable of interest is the ownership status of the respondent. The possible responses to the question in the survey are "owner" or "renter," so the type of variable is a categorical variable.

b. The variable of interest is the number of vehicles, which involves counting. The type of variable is a numerical variable.

c. The variable of interest is the average high temperature each month, which involves measuring. The type of variable is a numerical variable.

▲

Organizing and Representing Data with Tables

REPRESENTATION

Students should know how to "represent data using tables" (NCTM, Gr. 3–5), as well as "organize, represent, and interpret data with up to three categories" (Grade 1, CCSS) and "ask and answer questions about the total number of data points, how many in each category, and how many more or less are in one category than in another" (Gr. 1, CCSS). A **tally table,** as shown in Table 8.3, is a table that shows the categories for one variable and tally marks that indicate the number of observations that belong to each category. A **frequency table,** as shown in Table 8.4, is a table that shows the categories for one variable and the number of observations that belong to each category. A **relative frequency table,** as shown in Table 8.5, is a table that shows the categories for one variable and the percent of all observations that belong to each category.

TABLE 8.3   Tally Table

Type of pet	Tally
dog	||
cat	⊬⊬ |||
bird	||||
other	|||

TABLE 8.4   Frequency Table

Type of pet	Frequency
dog	2
cat	8
bird	4
other	3

TABLE 8.5   Relative Frequency Table

Type of pet	Relative frequency
dog	11.8%
cat	47.1%
bird	23.5%
other	17.6%

Frequency and relative frequency tables also serve as intermediate tools for organizing data in preparation of creating a graph, such as a bar graph, pie chart, or histogram.

EXAMPLE 8.6

REPRESENTATION

A teacher surveys the students in the class. He asks the question, "How do you get to school: bus, car, bike, or walk?" The following table records the results for the mode of transportation variable.

Student		Student		Student	
1	bike	6	walk	11	walk
2	walk	7	walk	12	bike
3	bike	8	walk	13	bike
4	walk	9	car	14	walk
5	car	10	bus		

a. Create a frequency table for the data.

b. Create a relative frequency table for the data.

SOLUTION

a. We make a table with a list of possible values of the variable and then use the tally method to record the counts. Then we count the tallies to record the number of observations (frequency) in a category. Then we obtain the frequency table.

Tally Table	
How students get to school	**Tally**
bike	||||
walk	⊬⊬ ||
car	||
bus	|

Frequency Table	
How students get to school	**Frequency**
bike	4
walk	7
car	2
bus	1

b. We divide each frequency by the total number of students surveyed to obtain a relative frequency table, rounding each percent to the nearest tenth of a percent: $4/14 \approx 28.6\%$, $7/14 = 50\%$, $2/14 \approx 14.3\%$, and $1/14 \approx 7.1\%$.

How students get to school	Relative frequency
bike	28.6%
walk	50%
car	14.3%
bus	7.1%

The following example illustrates that the question asked (which in turn affects the choice of the variable) may reveal different aspects of the data.

EXAMPLE 8.7

COMMUNICATION
REASONING
REPRESENTATION

A sedan is a car that has at least 33 cubic feet of interior space. Consumer Reports listed 15 sedans that cost $25,000 or less that achieved the best gas mileage in their tests. The data are given in the table. Display the data with a relative frequency table to help answer each question.

a. Are the sedans primarily made by domestic or foreign manufacturers?

b. What is the gas mileage of most of the sedans?

Sedan	Gas mileage (mpg)	Manufacturer	Sedan	Gas mileage (mpg)	Manufacturer
Toyota Camry Hybrid	34	foreign	Nissan Altima 2.5 S (4-cyl.)	26	foreign
Ford Fusion Hybrid	34	domestic	Toyota Camry LE (4-cyl.)	26	foreign
Volkswagen Jetta TDI	33	foreign	Subaru Legacy 2.5i (4-cyl.)	25	foreign
Nissan Altima Hybrid	32	foreign	Acura TSX	25	foreign
Lexus HS Hybrid 250h Premium	31	foreign	Suzuki Kizashi SE	25	foreign
BMW 335d	28	foreign	Chevrolet Malibu LT (4-cyl.)	25	domestic
Hyundai Sonata GLS	27	foreign	Kia Optima LX (4-cyl.)	25	foreign
Honda Accord LX-P (4-cyl., manual transmission)	26	foreign			

SOLUTION

a. The categorical variable would be the type of manufacturer, with the categories "domestic" and "foreign." A count shows 2 cars in the list are domestic and 13 cars are foreign. Then 2/15 ≈ 13.3% and 13/15 ≈ 86.7%. We summarize the results with a relative frequency table with percents rounded to the nearest tenth of a percent.

Manufacturer	Percent
domestic	13.3
foreign	86.7

The table shows that foreign manufacturers produced about 87% of the sedans.

b. Although the average gas mileage of a vehicle is a numerical variable, we could create the categorical variable "gas mileage (mpg) range" by grouping the gas mileage into intervals (much like grouping ages using the categories "16–19," "20–23," and so on). Possible categories for this problem are "25–26," "27–28," "29–30," "31–32," and "33–34." We summarize the results with a relative frequency table with percents rounded to the nearest tenth of a percent.

Gas mileage (mpg) range	Percent
25–26	53.3
27–28	13.3
29–30	0
31–32	13.3
33–34	20

The percents do not total 100% because of rounding. The table shows that most sedans achieved an average of 25 to 26 mpg.

Although the intervals must account for all data, there are no firm rules for choosing the intervals, so choosing them may require some experimentation. Try to create intervals with the same size or choose intervals that seem natural for the data. For example, a possible alternative grouping for this problem is 25 to 27, 28 to 30, and 31 to 34. Intervals that are too narrow or too wide may not be useful. Again, you may need to experiment with different interval sizes to extract useful information.

▲

Graphs and Exploratory Data Analysis

Graphs are visual representations for exploring, identifying, interpreting, and communicating important features of data sets. They also make text more interesting. Students should be able to "draw a picture graph and a bar graph (with a single-unit scale) to represent a data set with up to four categories" (CCSS, Gr. 2) (© 2010. National Governors Association Center for Best Practices and Council of Chief State School Officers. All rights reserved.) and answer simple questions about the graphs, for example, "solve one- and two-step 'how many more' and 'how many less' problems using information presented in scaled bar graphs" (Gr. 3, CCSS). Students in grades 3–5 tend to focus on graphs for analyzing one set of data. Students in grades 6–8 tend to focus on how to use graphs to compare two different data sets and explore relationships between variables.

Skills for creating various types of graphs are important for **exploratory data analysis,** where you create multiple graphs for data and then select the graph that reveals important or unexpected features of the data and best supports the conclusion. Students should be able to "compare different representations of the same data and evaluate how well each representation shows important aspects of the data" (Gr. 3–5, NCTM), examine different graphs of the data to make sense of the data and make predications or conclusions, and "begin to compare the effectiveness of various types of displays in organizing the data for further analysis or in presenting the data clearly to an audience" (NCTM, p. 49).

As your students become detectives and use exploratory data analysis to make sense of data, they also solidify their understanding of graphs and engage in genuine data analysis.

Readers focus on graph components such as legends and labels for axes to understand the graph. The title for a chart is an opportunity to insert an interpretative statement about the data, using phrases such as "The fish population declined steadily since 1985," "Voters overwhelmingly approved of Proposition A," "More people have tattoos," and "Gasoline prices are rising steadily." The NCTM standards assert that even students in grades

Pre-K–2 should be encouraged to make interpretative statements about the data, such as "Most students in the class have lost only two teeth" (p. 113). Creative titles suggest the graph maker comprehends the data.

■ **Historical Note**

William Playfair (1759–1823), a draftsman and engineer, invented line plots, bar graphs, pie charts, and histograms, publishing them in the books *The Commercial and Political Atlas* and *Statistical Breviary*. In the preface of his atlas, Playfair makes the case that he was the first to represent data with picture graphs (also called pictographs).

Regarding tables, Playfair said, "A man who has carefully investigated a printed table, finds, when done, that he has only a very faint and partial idea of what he has read, and that like a figure imprinted on sand, is soon totally erased and defaced" (*Atlas,* 1801, p. xiv). Regarding graphs, he said, "as much information may be obtained in five minutes as would require whole days to imprint on the memory, in a lasting manner, by a table of figures" (*Atlas,* p. xii) and "Of all the senses, the eye gives the liveliest and most sensible idea of whatever is susceptible of being represented to it" (*Statistical Breviary,* 1801, 14).

Initially, scientists viewed picture representations with suspicion, preferring numbers and formal reasoning instead. Graphs were difficult to publish at that time because of the difficulty of engraving illustrations on copper plates. With improved printing technology and increased acceptance of inductive reasoning, the graphs gradually became acceptable tools for representing data and making reasonable inferences. Graphs today still model Playfair's use of descriptive titles, frames, shading, grid lines, and labels for axes.

Bar Graphs

Bar graphs are mainly used to display categorical data and are useful for comparing categories. Bar graphs use rectangles separated by equally spaced gaps. Each rectangle represents a category, the rectangles have a common width, and the height of a rectangle is proportional to the frequency or relative frequency of the category.

EXAMPLE 8.8

REASONING

REPRESENTATION

Mrs. Smith surveyed her sixth-grade class to learn what type of juice her students prefer for the end-of-the-year party. The choices were apple, orange, grape, and tomato juice.

Favorite type of juice	Frequency
apple juice	16
orange juice	5
grape juice	7
tomato juice	0

a. Display the data using a bar graph.

b. What juice should Mrs. Smith bring to the class party for her students next year to satisfy the majority of students?

c. What juice should Mrs. Smith avoid bringing to the class party for her students next year?

SOLUTION

a. The frequency determines the height of the bars.

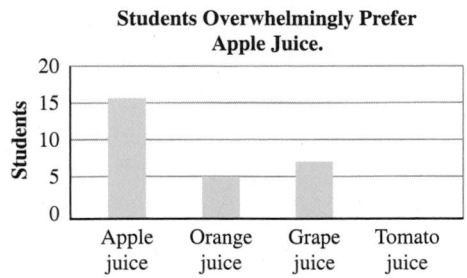

Students Overwhelmingly Prefer Apple Juice.

b. The data suggest apple juice would be a safe choice for the party next year.

c. The data suggest she should avoid tomato juice.

▲

In the next example, we compare data in a frequency table called a **two-way table.** In a two-way table, each object is grouped according to two categorical variables. Sometimes the data are called *bivariate data,* because they depend on two variables. For example, suppose a teacher conducts a survey to investigate any possible association between the average number of hours of sleep per night a student gets and that student's interest in mathematics. Table 8.6 shows a possible two-way table that can be used to summarize the results. Each student (object) is asked about amount of sleep (5–6 hours, 6–8 hours, or 8–10 hours) and level of interest in mathematics (low, moderate, or high). Each student in the survey would belong to one cell in the table. The cells in the table would record the frequencies or relative frequencies.

TABLE 8.6   Two-Way Table

	Level of interest in mathematics		
Average number of hours of sleep per night	**Low**	**Moderate**	**High**
5–6 hours			
6–8 hours			
8–10 hours			

Students should "understand that patterns of association can also be seen in bivariate categorical data by displaying frequencies and relative frequencies in a two-way table and be able to construct and interpret a two-way table summarizing data on two categorical variables collected from the same subjects" (Gr. 8, CCSS).

Bar graphs can help visualize the data in two-way tables. In the next chapter, we use two-way tables to verify some probability concepts and formulas.

EXAMPLE 8.9

CONNECTION
REPRESENTATION

The following table summarizes the percentage of people with some type of health insurance in three chosen states. For example, a 50-year-old person from California would be part of the 79.4% of people with some type of health insurance. Draw a bar graph to visualize the data.

	Percentage of People with Some Type of Health Insurance	
State	**Under 65 years**	**65 years and older**
California	79.4	97.3
Maryland	84.5	98.8
Texas	72.8	96.8

SOURCE: U.S. Census Bureau.

SOLUTION

There are two approaches to displaying the data because of the rows and columns of the table. The bar graphs in Figures 1 and 2 represent the data in the two-way table, but each highlights different aspects of the data.

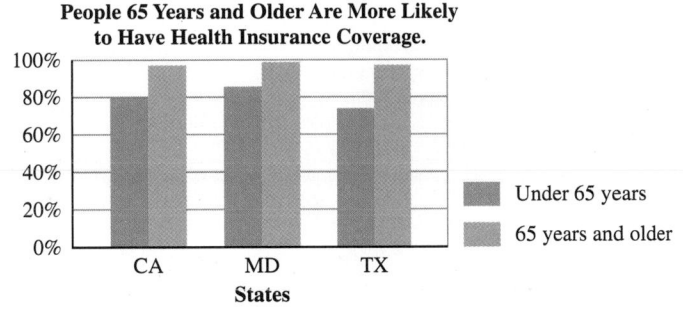

FIGURE 1

This bar graph emphasizes a comparison between age groups (for each state).

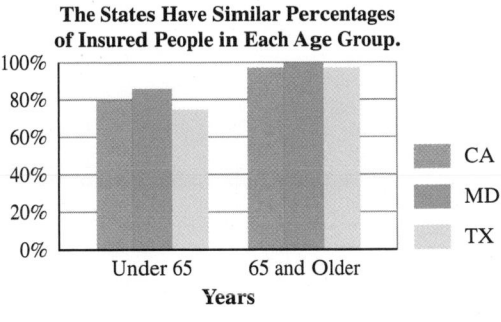

FIGURE 2

This bar graph emphasizes a comparison among states (for each age group).

The following Classroom Connection illustrates that students should know how to represent a two-way table with a bar graph (called a *double-bar graph* in this problem). This problem may involve categories that are not mutually exclusive, because there may be some students who participate in more than one event (for example, the long jump and 100-meter dash).

◆ Classroom Connection

● *Math*, Grade 5, p. 162

Use data from the chart to make a double-bar graph. (© 2000 Macmillan/McGraw Hill. Reprinted by permission.)

Students Participating in the East Vernon Track and Field Olympics		
Event	Sixth-grade students	Fifth-grade students
100-meter dash	12	15
High jump	13	8
Long jump	9	9
Javelin throw	4	7

Pictograph (Picture Graph)

A **pictograph** (or **picture graph**) uses symbols (or icons) to represent quantities. A symbol represents a certain value, and the number of symbols is proportional to the quantity represented. Sometimes this means the pictograph contains part of the symbol rather than the whole symbol. A pictograph is similar to a bar graph.

EXAMPLE 8.10

CONNECTION

REPRESENTATION

The table shows the estimated number of arrests for certain crimes in 2008, based on data from law enforcement agencies. Make a pictograph for the categorical variable "type of crime."

Type of crime	burglary	motor vehicle theft	liquor laws
Crimes	308,479	98,035	625,939

SOURCE: Federal Bureau of Investigation.

SOLUTION

We used the fingerprint symbol to represent 100,000 arrests. A legend shows the amount represented by the symbol. We see the number of arrests for liquor law violations is about six times the number of arrests for motor vehicle thefts and twice the number of arrests for burglaries.

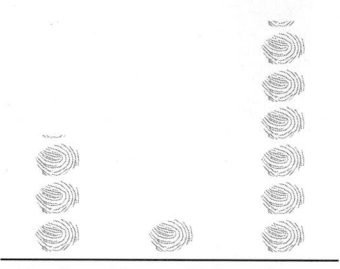

Arrests for Liquor Law Violations Exceed Arrests for Burglary and Motor Vehicle Thefts in 2008.

= 100,000 arrests

Burglary   Motor vehicle   Liquor
                 theft   laws

Pie Chart (Pie Graph)

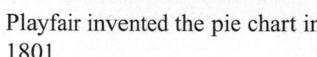

Playfair invented the pie chart in 1801.

We can visualize numerical or categorical data using a **pie chart** (also called a pie graph) to show part-to-whole relationships, much like fractions and percentages. Pie charts require nonoverlapping categories. The main idea is the circular region represents the whole, and each sector (or slice) has a central angle that is proportional to the quantity that the sector represents.

Suppose 5 out of 32 respondents in a survey said they would vote for Proposition A. There are 360 degrees in a circle, and the central angle x of the sector in the pie that represents the 5 people is determined by a proportion:

$$\frac{x}{360} = \frac{5}{32}$$

So $x = \frac{5}{32} \cdot 360 \approx 56.$

The central angle is 56°.

EXAMPLE 8.11

CONNECTION
COMMUNICATION
REASONING
REPRESENTATION

The frequency table shows the number of males under the age of 24 years who were injured in collisions that involved drivers who had been drinking in California in a particular year. The categorical variable is the age group, with categories that are age intervals: "15–17," "18–20," and "21–23." Make a pie chart for the data.

Age group	Injuries
15–17	269
18–20	1486
21–23	2147
total	**3902**

SOLUTION

The central angle for a sector corresponding to an age group is proportional to the number of injuries in the age group. Then

Age group	Proportion	Central angle of sector
15–17	$\dfrac{a}{360} = \dfrac{269}{3902}$	$a = (269/3902) \cdot 360° \approx 6.89\% \cdot 360° \approx 25°$
18–20	$\dfrac{b}{360} = \dfrac{1486}{3902}$	$b = (1486/3902) \cdot 360° \approx 38.08\% \cdot 360° \approx 137°$
21–23	$\dfrac{c}{360} = \dfrac{2147}{3902}$	$c = (2147/3902) \cdot 360° \approx 55.02\% \cdot 360° \approx 198°$

The title in the corresponding pie chart steers the reader toward a conclusion that uses multiplicative reasoning $(2147 \div 269 \approx 8$ or $55\% \div 7\% \approx 8)$.

A 21–23 Year-Old Male Is 8 Times as Likely to be Injured in an Alcohol-Related Vehicle Collision Than a 15–17 Year-Old Male

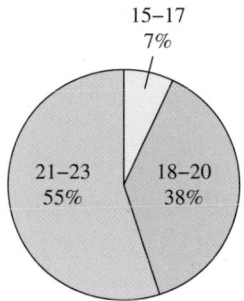

Also, you could use the title as an opportunity to note that the legal drinking age in California is 21 years and the riskiest age group for males under the age of 24 years is 21 to 23 years.

▲

In the following example, we illustrate how to use a bar graph and a pie chart to visualize numerical data. We create "categories" and lose the individual bowling scores. This form of data compression is fine when we do not need to retain the individual numerical values.

EXAMPLE 8.12

CONNECTION

REPRESENTATION

The table shows the bowling scores of a class of students.

65	100	51	82	75	91
86	73	110	88	48	82
81	62	83	86	72	
73	78	123	92	73	

Represent the data using a
a. bar graph.
b. pie chart.

SOLUTION

A frequency table is an aid for organizing information and a transition tool for creating graphs. We create the categories "69 or fewer," "70–79," "80–89," "90–99," and "100 or more" for the scores and record the number of observations that belong to each category (other categories are possible, such as "50–59," "60–69," and so on).

Score	69 or fewer	70–79	80–89	90–99	100 or more
Frequency	4	6	7	2	3

There are 22 students in the class. The angle of the sector corresponding to the category 69 or fewer is $(4/22) \cdot 360° \approx 18°$. The other central angles are $(6/22) \cdot 360° \approx 27°$, $(7/22) \cdot 360° \approx 32°$, $(2/22) \cdot 360° \approx 9°$, and $(3/22) \cdot 360° \approx 14°$. The bar and pie charts are shown here.

a.

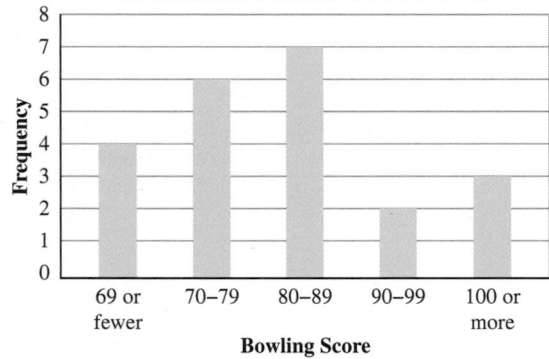

Most Students Scored in the 70s and 80s.

b. Most Students Scored in the 70s and 80s

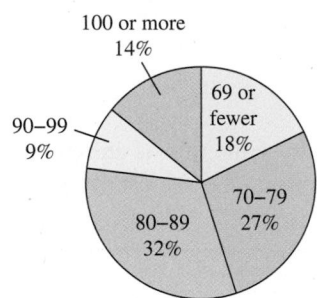

The following Released Item illustrates the use of a pie chart when part-to-whole comparisons are possible.

> **RELEASED ITEM**
>
> ● NAEP, 2003
>
> The pie chart shows the portion of time Pat spent on homework in each subject last week. If Pat spent 2 hours on mathematics, about how many hours did Pat spend on homework altogether?
>
>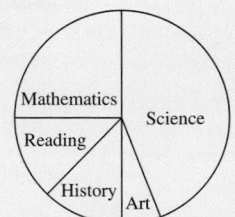
>
> **a.** 4 **b.** 8 **c.** 12 **d.** 16
>
> 51% of fourth graders gave the correct answer. (U.S. Department of Education, Institute of Education Sciences, National Center for Education Statistics, NAEP)

Line Graph

A **line graph** is suitable for visualizing two related numerical variables, x and y. We plot the ordered pairs (x, y) and connect the ordered pairs with line segments to visualize any trends. A time series plot (or time series graph) is another name for a line graph in which the horizontal axis represents a time variable, as in the following example.

EXAMPLE 8.13

CONNECTION

REPRESENTATION

The table shows the number of burglaries per 1000 households in the United States from 1994 to 2002, according to the National Crime Victimization Survey published by the Bureau of Justice Statistics. Make a line graph for the data. What does the graph show?

Year	1994	1995	1996	1997	1998	1999	2000	2001	2002
Burglaries per 1000 households	56.3	49.3	47.2	44.6	38.5	34.1	31.8	28.7	27.7

SOLUTION

We plot the ordered pairs (1994, 56.3), (1995, 49.3), . . . , (2002, 27.7) and connect the ordered pairs with line segments.

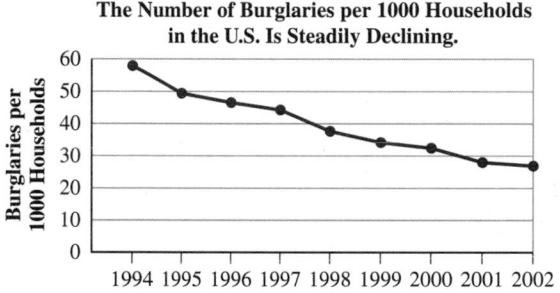

The line graph shows the burglary rate is steadily declining.

A line graph is affected by the scale of the axes and the physical size of the graph. For example, by changing the scale of the y-axis and the size of the graph, as shown in Figure 3, the number of burglaries per 1000 households seems to be *rapidly* declining. Changing the scale may exaggerate minor changes.

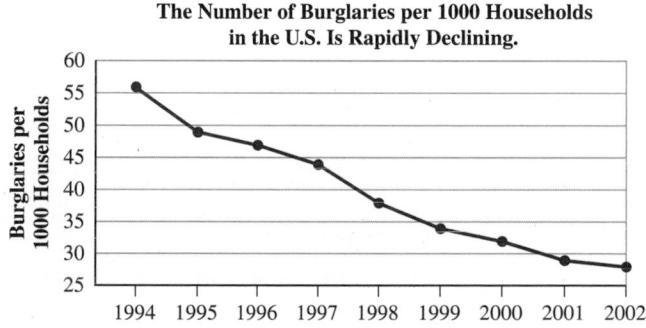

FIGURE 3

Changing the scale and size of the graph may exaggerate minor changes.

If you use software programs to create graphs, then you can experiment with different scales and dimensions of the graph. Some scales may exaggerate minor changes. For example, if you are a salesperson, you may want to avoid exaggerating minor declines in revenue. Or if you are a police chief, you may want to avoid exaggerating minor increases in crime. Regardless, a line graph is not suitable for categorical data.

Scatterplot (Scatter Plot)

A **scatterplot** (or **scatter plot**) is a graph of a collection of ordered pairs (x, y), where x and y are numerical variables. The purpose of a scatterplot is to make it easier to see whether there is a possible *association* between the variable x (along the horizontal axis) and the variable y (along the vertical axis). In a scatterplot, we do not connect the ordered pairs with line segments. Figure 4 shows four illustrative scatterplots of some possible associations between x and y. In scatterplots, we look at the direction and the shape of the dots.

CONNECTION

REASONING

REPRESENTATION

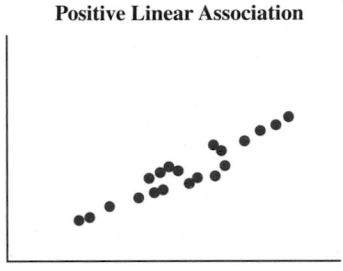

Positive Linear Association

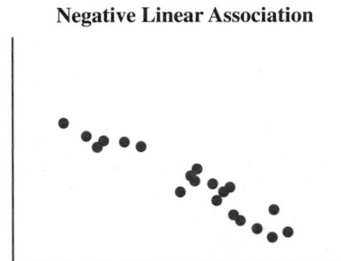

Negative Linear Association

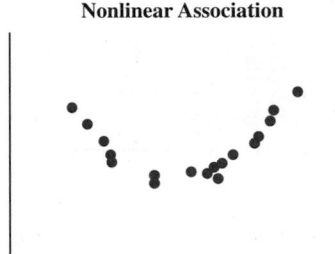

Nonlinear Association

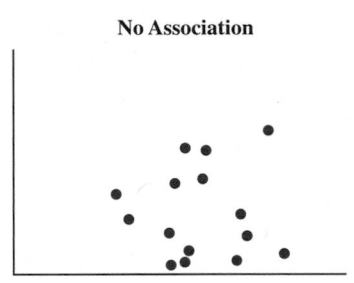

No Association

FIGURE 4
Examples of scatterplots.

EXAMPLE 8.14

CONNECTION

REASONING

REPRESENTATION

A student draws scatterplots for four sets of ordered pairs (x, y), as shown in Figure 4. Let's suppose x represents the number of songs on a CD and y represents the number of CDs sold. Interpret the association between x and y for the following:

a. positive linear association

b. negative linear association

c. nonlinear association

d. no association

SOLUTION

a. As the number of songs on the CD increases, then the number of CDs sold steadily increases.

b. As the number of songs on the CD increases, then the number of CDs sold steadily decreases.

c. The number of songs on the CD and the number of CDs sold seem to be related, because the ordered pairs seem to follow a curve. The number of CDs sold decreases, but then at some point it begins to increase.

d. There is no apparent association between the number of songs on the CD and the number of CDs sold.

The scatterplot provides a quick way to see whether there is an apparent association between two variables, such as the cost of an airline ticket and the number of miles to the destination. Students should be able to "construct and interpret scatter plots for bivariate measurement data to investigate patterns of association between two quantities and describe patterns such as clustering, outliers, positive or negative association, linear association, and nonlinear association" (Gr. 8, CCSS).

The following Released Item illustrates that students should be able to interpret a scatterplot.

<blockquote>

▶ RELEASED ITEM

● NAEP, 2007

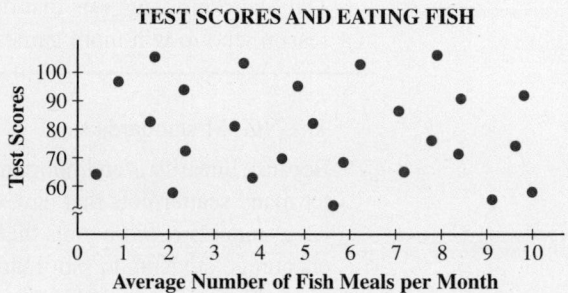

For a science project, Marsha made the scatterplot above that gives the test scores for the students in her math class and the corresponding average number of fish meals per month. According to the scatterplot, what is the relationship between test scores and the average number of fish meals per month?

a. There appears to be no relationship.

b. Students who eat fish more often score higher on tests.

c. Students who eat fish more often score lower on tests.

d. Students who eat fish 4–6 times per month score higher on tests than those who do not eat fish that often.

e. Students who eat fish 7 times per month score lower on tests than those who do not eat fish that often.

62% of eighth graders gave the correct answer.

</blockquote>

EXAMPLE 8.15

COMMUNICATION
CONNECTION
REASONING
REPRESENTATION

The following table shows the total number of points scored and the number of wins by the 32 NFL teams during a regular season. Does there appear to be a correlation between the number x of points scored and the number y of regular season games won? Construct and analyze a scatterplot for the data.

x	589	252	268	267	402	393	380	275	450	411	379	301	412	320	283	226
y	16	7	4	1	10	10	7	5	13	11	8	10	11	7	4	4

x	455	373	336	334	435	365	346	334	334	267	259	404	379	393	263	219
y	13	10	8	9	13	8	7	7	9	7	4	8	7	10	3	5

SOLUTION

We draw and label the axes and then plot the ordered pairs (x, y). The ordered pairs seem to have a positive relationship along a straight line. One ordered pair seems noticeably far away from the others.

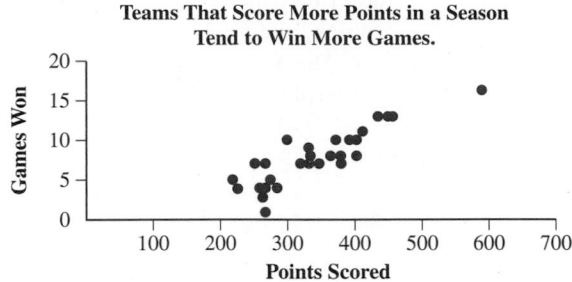

Teams That Score More Points in a Season Tend to Win More Games.

The scatterplot suggests that during the regular season, teams that score more points in a season tend to win more games overall.

▲

The NCTM standards say,

Because linearity is an important idea in the middle grades, students should encounter many scatterplots that have a nearly linear shape. . . . But teachers should also have students explore plots that represent nonlinear relationships. Teachers should encourage students to plot many data sets and look for relationships in the plots; computer graphing software and graphing calculators can be helpful in this work. Students should see a range of examples in which plotting data sets suggests linear relationships, nonlinear relationships, and no apparent relationship at all. When a scatterplot suggests that a relationship exists, teachers should help students determine the nature of the relationship from the shape and direction of the plot. (p. 253)

Histogram

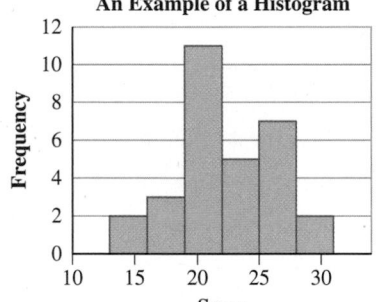

An Example of a Histogram

A **histogram** is a visual representation of a frequency or relative frequency table for a numerical variable and is especially suitable for displaying and visualizing a large collection of numbers. Students should be able to "display numerical data in plots on a number line, including dot plots, histograms, and box plots" (Gr. 6, CCSS).

For example, you may want to run a computer program 1000 times and display the running times using a histogram. Alternatively, you may want to measure the heights of 120 students and display the heights using a histogram. In many situations, the shape of the data is important too. For example, you may want to display a data set with a histogram to see whether it has a bell-shaped pattern or to see the variability in the data.

There are several visual differences between histograms and bar graphs. Generally, the rectangles in a histogram touch, whereas the rectangles in a bar graph are separated by arbitrary, but equally spaced, gaps. Also, the rectangles in a histogram graph must appear in their natural order along a number line, whereas the rectangles in a bar graph can appear in any order.

Constructing histograms requires some experimentation with selecting the number of groups to obtain a shape that reveals a useful or interesting characteristic of the data. The groups are inequalities of the form $a \leq x < b$. Each group should have equal width. Usually, 5 to 20 groups are adequate, and choosing the appropriate number of groups may require experimentation to depict an interesting aspect of the data. Too few groups may give the histogram a "skyscraper" profile (narrow and tall), while too many groups may give the histogram a "pancake" profile (wide and short).

The following example shows a possible way to visualize data from the eruption time of the geyser Old Faithful, which spouts water an average of 130 feet in the air.

EXAMPLE 8.16

CONNECTION

REPRESENTATION

The following data represent 107 measurements of the durations of eruptions, in minutes, of the geyser Old Faithful. Represent the data using a histogram.

3.5	4.28	4.13	4.37	1.68	4.35	4.25	4.05	4	1.83	4.63	1.97	4.07	3.8
3.92	3.72	4.4	3.87	3.92	2.33	3.58	4.25	3.67	4.13	4.5	3.7	2.27	1.85
4.25	3.95	4.1	4	3.68	3.83	3.8	3.33	1.67	1.83	1.82	3.5	4.43	1.85
2.27	4.58	1.9	4.03	3.1	1.88	3.77	2	4.6	4.65	1.97	4	4	
4.5	1.95	4.83	3.5	4.03	4.6	3.75	4.33	1.67	4.2	3.43	4.62	3.43	
4.12	4.57	4.93	4.08	1.77	1.8	2.5	2.93	4	3.93	3.73	2.93	4.18	
1.73	3.2	3.58	2.25	4.08	4.73	4.5	4.58	1.8	4.33	1.73	4.62	3.52	
4.53	1.9	3.7	4.7	1.75	1.77	4.1	1.9	4.42	1.83	3.73	4.63	2.03	

SOURCE: Data and Story Library, lib.stat.cmu.edu/DASL.

SOLUTION

There is great flexibility in constructing a histogram. You get to choose the number of groups. Each group is an interval of the form $a \leq x < b$. Each group should have equal width (where width $= b - a$). Make sure every measurement belongs to some group and the groups do not overlap. Try different choices and see what the graph looks like. Choose the histogram that seems to display an interesting feature. A common way to determine the groups depends on the extreme values and the number of groups you prefer, which in turn determine the width of each interval.

STEP 1 **Calculate the difference between the extreme values.**   The highest and lowest measurements are 4.93 minutes and 1.67 minutes. The difference is 4.93 − 1.67 = 3.26.

STEP 2 **Choose the number of groups.**   Let's create eight groups.

STEP 3 **Determine the width of each group.**   3.26 ÷ 8 = 0.4075. Choose a width slightly larger than 0.4075 so that the largest value 4.93 minutes in the data set belongs to the last group. Let's make the width slightly larger at 0.41, because it seems convenient.

STEP 4 **Create the groups.**   The lowest measurement is 1.67. Then 1.67 + 0.41 = 2.08. The first group is the interval $1.67 \leq x < 2.08$, and it automatically contains the lowest measurement. Now we just add 0.41 to the lower and upper boundaries of the first group to obtain the second group. Then 2.08 + 0.41 = 2.49, and the second group is $2.08 \leq x < 2.49$. As before, we add 0.41 to the lower and upper boundaries of the second group to obtain the third group. Then 2.49 + 0.41 = 2.90, and the third group is $2.49 \leq x < 2.90$. We repeat this process, making sure the last group contains the highest measurement (otherwise, go back to step 2 and choose a width between 4.075 and 0.41).

STEP 5 **Create a frequency table.**   The table records the number of observations that belong to each category. The sum of the counts is 107.

Groups	1.67–2.08	2.08–2.49	2.49–2.90	2.90–3.31	3.31–3.72	3.72–4.13	4.13–4.54	4.54–4.95
Frequency (Relative Frequency)	25 (23.4%)	4 (3.7%)	1 (0.1%)	4 (3.7%)	13 (12.1%)	27 (25.2%)	19 (17.8%)	14 (13.1%)

STEP 6 **Create the graph.**   Be sure to use good habits and include a title and label the axes. There are no arbitrary gaps between the groups (unless a group has a frequency of 0), and the groups must be placed in their natural order. Report the *midpoint* of each category on the number line. For example, (1.67 + 2.08)/2 = 1.875, (2.08 + 2.49)/2 = 2.285, and (2.49 + 2.90)/2 = 2.695. (Some textbooks or instructors may say to report the lower limit, upper limit, or both of each group.)

(Continued)

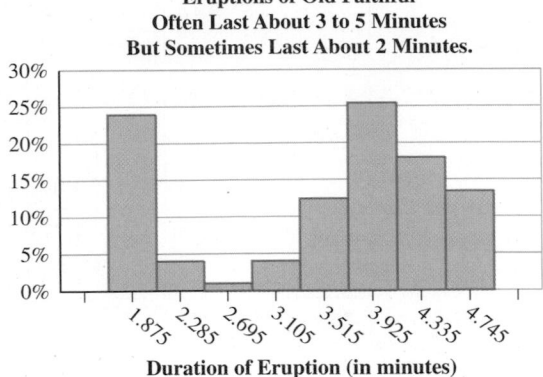

Eruptions of Old Faithful
Often Last About 3 to 5 Minutes
But Sometimes Last About 2 Minutes.

The following student page shows how an elementary mathematics textbook introduces histograms to students.

LESSON

5

HANDS ON

Histograms

▶ **Explore**

A **histogram** is a bar graph that shows the number of times data occur within intervals.

The data show the number of minutes some students spent on homework each night.

MINUTES SPENT ON HOMEWORK						
15	20	25	35	10	10	45
30	20	15	40	25	5	10
20	25	20	30	45	35	

Follow the steps to make a histogram of the data.

STEP 1

- Find the range of the data. Range: 45 − 5 = 40

- Decide on the scale. The scale could be 0 to 50 minutes.

- Select an interval to divide the data equally. Use 5 intervals of 10 minutes.

The intervals are used to show the number of times data occur within them.

STEP 2

- Make a frequency table with the intervals.

- Tally the data for each interval.

- Record the frequencies.

Number of Minutes Frequency	Tally	
0–10 minutes	IIII	4
11–20 minutes	⊬ I	6
21–30 minutes	⊬	5
31–40 minutes	III	3
41–50 minutes	II	2

STEP 3

- Use the frequency table to make the histogram.

- The intervals are along one axis. The scale for the frequencies is along the other axis.

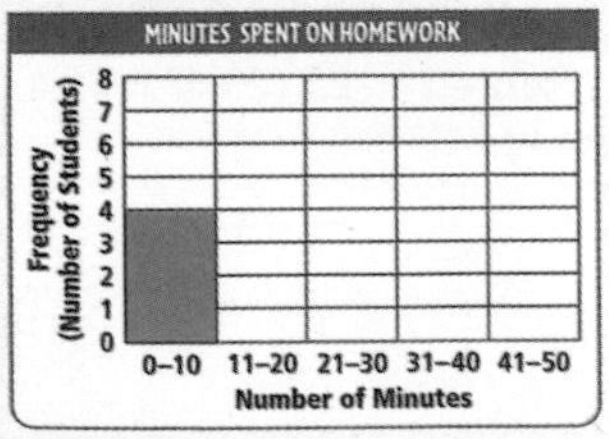

MINUTES SPENT ON HOMEWORK

(Harcourt *Math*, Student Edition, Grade 6, p. 128)

QUESTIONS FOR SECTION 8.1

Remember to include a descriptive title and appropriate labels in your charts. For best results, draw your charts on grid paper.

REPRESENTATION

Refresher: Representations (language, diagrams, tables, symbols, algebra, manipulatives, and contextualized situations) are important because we use them to organize, record, and communicate mathematical ideas and to make them more comprehensible.

1. A student records the results of a brief survey of some classmates' preferences.

Student	Soda or juice
Mary	soda
Tanya	juice
Luke	juice
Mitch	juice
Ken	soda
Lisa	juice
Wanda	juice
Jennifer	juice

Use each type of table listed here to represent the students' preferences for soda or juice.

a. tally table   b. frequency table

c. relative frequency table

2. A student surveys a few classmates. She asks them, "Do you prefer smooth or chunky peanut butter?" The results are as follows.

Boy (B) or Girl (G)	B	G	B	B	G	B	B	G
Smooth (S) or Chunky (C)	S	S	C	C	S	S	S	C

Complete the two-way frequency table to summarize the collection of data.

	Smooth	Chunky
Boy		
Girl		

3. A student represents data with a pictograph using the symbol shown. Draw the symbol needed to represent 24 beads.

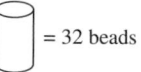 = 32 beads

4. McDonald's Double Quarter Pounder with Cheese is a burger that has 770 calories, while Burger King's Double Whopper with Cheese has 1070 calories (www.fatcalories.com).

a. Make a pictograph to compare the calorie content of both burgers. Let the icon you choose represent 50 calories.

b. Make a pictograph to compare the calorie content of both burgers. Let the icon you choose represent 150 calories.

c. Compare the pictographs. Does your impression depend on the choice of the icon? Explain your answer.

5. A student records the results of a brief survey of some classmates. If you were to represent the data with a pie chart, what is the angle for the sector for

a. apples?   b. oranges?   c. pears?

Student	Favorite fruit
Mary	pears
Tanya	apples
Luke	oranges
Joey	pears
Ken	pears
Lisa	apples
Wanda	apples
Sammy	oranges
Mitchell	apples

PROBLEM SOLVING

Refresher: Problem solving (reaching a goal that is not immediately attainable) is important because it helps students think more deeply about what they know and deal with unfamiliar situations.

6. The following bar graph shows the number of a particular brand of helmets a bike store sold February through July.

a. Which months experienced an increase in sales (compared to the previous month)?

b. Which month experienced the greatest increase in sales (compared to the previous month)?

c. Which months experienced a decrease in sales (compared to the previous month)?

d. Which month experienced the greatest decrease in sales?

e. What is the minimum number of helmets the store should keep in inventory? Explain your answer.

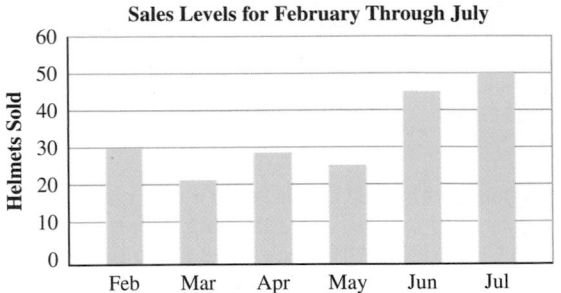

7. The following two-way table represents the results of scores from an exam worth 100 points.

	<50	50–59	60–69	70–79	80–89	90–100
Nonmath majors	3	5	1	12	5	2
Math majors	2	4	4	5	10	5

a. How many nonmath majors took the exam?

b. How many students scored fewer than 50 points?

c. What percent of students taking the exam scored in the 70s?

d. What percent of students taking the test were math majors?

8. The data show how people spend their time using the Internet for the top 7 activities.

Activity	Percent
social networks	22.7
online games	10.2
e-mail	8.3
portals	4.4
instant messaging	4.0
videos/movies	3.9
search	3.5

SOURCE: blog.nielsen/nielsenwire.com

a. How much time altogether is spent on the top 3 activities listed in the table?

b. Do the percents add up to 100%? If not, give the total percentage.

c. Explain why there should be eight sectors (slices of the pie) in a pie chart based on this table for how people spend their time on the Internet.

d. Determine the central angle of each of the seven listed activities in a pie chart for the data. Round to the nearest degree.

e. Represent the data with a pie chart.

f. Represent the data with a bar graph.

9. Mr. Waterworth's bar graph compares the number of fourth- and fifth-grade students who participated in activities.

a. Write a descriptive title for the graph.

b. How many more fifth graders than fourth graders did push-ups?

c. Identify the most challenging activity.

d. Represent the chart with a two-way table.

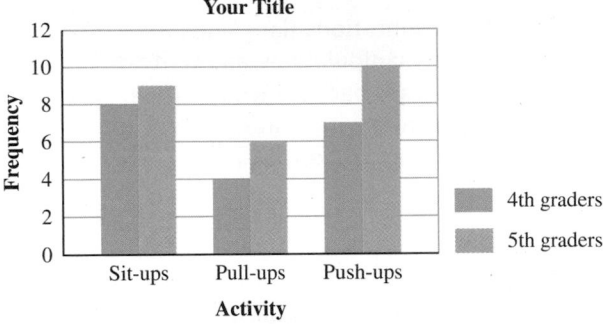

REASONING AND PROOF

Refresher: Reasoning and proof (thinking and justifying) are important because they help students make sense of mathematics.

10. Determine the type of variable.

a. life span of paper money (such as $1 bills)

b. number on jerseys of football players

c. nationality of survey respondents

d. age group of the survey respondent 16 to 19 years, 20 to 24 years, 25 to 32 years, and 33 to 55 years

e. salaries of teachers

f. telephone numbers

g. percent of people in a survey who voted "no" in the California recall election

h. weights of people in a sample of elevator passengers

11. An investor collected data about homes he was interested in buying. Identify the variables of interest and their type.

Address	Monthly homeowner fees	Square footage	ZIP code	Type of residence
2567 Lava Lane	$350	1588	92009	condominium
6534 Pisa Circle	$200	3200	95616	house
123 Main Street	$85	1850	94293	house

12. A teacher gives her students a questionnaire that asks them to rate the effectiveness of her reviews for exams on a 1-to-4 scale, with 1 meaning "ineffective" and 4 meaning "effective." The variable of interest is "teaching effectiveness." Why is this a categorical variable?

13. The table shows the life expectancy for males and females born in the given year.

	Male	**Female**
2002	74.3	79.5
2003	74.5	79.6
2004	74.9	79.9
2005	74.9	79.9
2006	75.1	80.2

SOURCE: U.S. Census Bureau.

a. Make a line graph of life expectancy for males and females by drawing both line graphs on the same graph.

b. What does the graph mainly show?

14. The table shows the median income level for various age groups, based on the most recent U.S. census data available (www.census.gov). Make a bar graph for the data, and include an inference from the chart in the form of a descriptive title for the chart.

Age group (in years)	Median income of males and females
21–24	$20,502
25–34	$30,187
35–44	$35,764
45–54	$38,145
55–64	$36,119

SOURCE: U.S. Census Bureau.

15. The following two-way table lists the median income of males and females by age groups, based on the most recent U.S. census data available.

Age group (in years)	Median income of males	Median income of females
21–24	$21,393	$19,108
25–34	$32,085	$26,788
35–44	$40,741	$27,520
45–54	$44,836	$30,950
55–64	$42,313	$28,360

SOURCE: U.S. Census Bureau.

Here are two bar graphs for the table of median incomes. Based on these graphs,

a. which graph highlights differences in median earnings between males and females?

b. which graph highlights differences among the age groups?

c. write a descriptive title for graph A.

d. write a descriptive title for graph B.

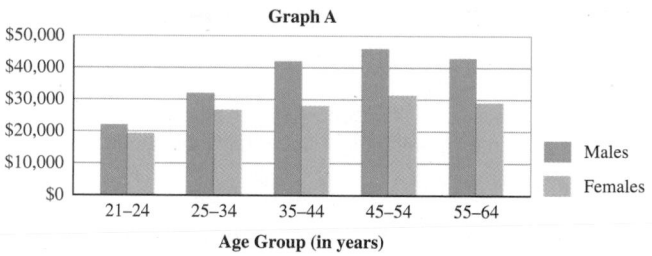

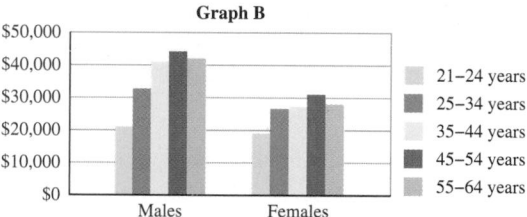

16. The two-way table summarizes casualty data from the *Titanic* ship that sank on its maiden voyage April 15, 1912.

Type of passenger	Passengers	Survivors
men, first class	175	57
men, second class	168	14
men, third class	462	75

a. Did the type of accommodation affect survival? Explain your answer.

b. Make a graph for the data. Include a creative title that supports your conclusion.

17. Grants, loans, and scholarships are three common sources of financial aid for college students. The following line graph shows the share of loans and grants as a percent of all aid sources beginning with the academic year 1980–1981, based on data from the 2003 Status Report on the Federal Education Loan Programs (p. 10).

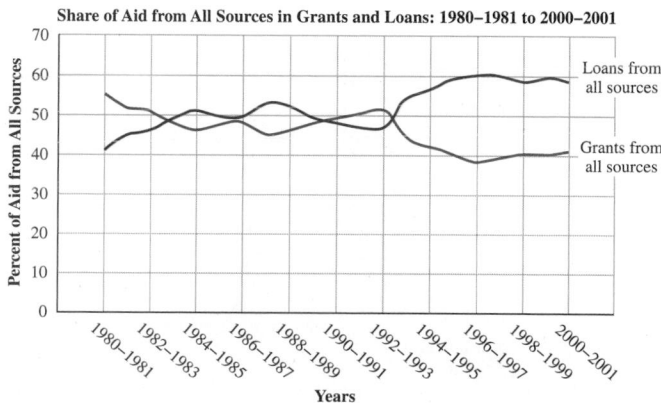

a. Estimate the share of aid from grants in the academic year 2000–2001.

b. Estimate the share of aid from loans in the academic year 1985–1986.

c. Identify the academic years that grants were the predominant form of aid.

d. What academic year experienced the greatest difference between loans and grants as sources of financial aid?

e. Formulate a conclusion from the graph.

CONNECTIONS

Refresher: Connections (linking and applying mathematical ideas) are important because they deepen student understanding and make mathematics more meaningful, flexible, and useful.

18. Find an example of a pie chart from a newspaper, magazine, or nonacademic Internet website.

    a. Is the title accurate and interpretative?

    b. Are the categories clearly labeled?

    c. Are the slices of the pie proportional to the percentages they represent?

19. Find an example of a bar graph from a newspaper, magazine, or nonacademic Internet website.

    a. Is the title creative or suggestive?

    b. Are the axes labeled properly?

    c. Are the data categorical or numerical?

    d. Are the heights of the bars proportional to the numbers they represent?

20. The Gallup Organization conducted a national survey to compare attitudes toward a ban on smoking in all workplaces, bars, and restaurants. Among the women, 63% supported such a ban, and 35% opposed it. Among the men, 52% supported such a ban, and 45% opposed it. Make a bar graph to compare the gender support for the ban on smoking in all workplaces, bars, and restaurants. Be sure to include a descriptive title and appropriate labels.

21. The pie chart shows the breakdown of water consumption in Smallville. Overall, the town used 741,800 acre-feet of water. One acre-foot is the volume of water that supplies two families for 1 year.

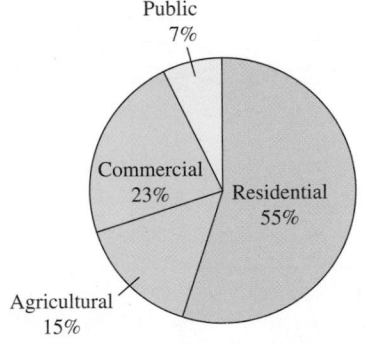

a. Create a title for the pie chart.

b. Calculate the number of acre-feet of water consumed by public use.

c. How many more acre-feet of water were consumed for commercial use compared to agricultural use?

d. Fill in the blank: The amount of water consumed for residential use was _____ times as much as the water consumed for commercial use. (Round to the nearest tenth.)

e. Fill in the blank: The amount of water consumed for commercial use was _____ times as much as the water consumed for agricultural use. (Round to the nearest tenth.)

22. The following bar graph summarizes how students in a class spend their time after school.

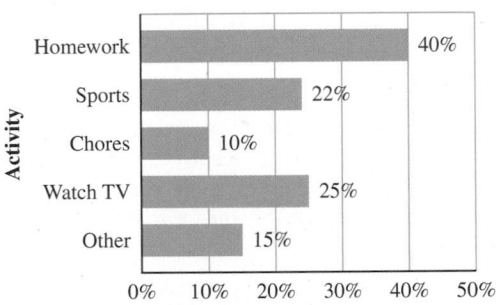

a. Write a title for the graph.

b. Give a logical explanation as to why the percentages do or do not sum to 100%.

COMMUNICATION

Refresher: Communication (written and verbal explanations using representations and proper mathematical vocabulary) is important because it helps students refine and strengthen their understanding.

23. What is statistics?

24. What is a variable?

25. What are data?

26. What are graphs?

27. What are essential components of graphs?

28. Why is it important to include axis labels, legends, grid lines, and tick marks as necessary on a graph?

29. The four steps of data analysis are listed here but in incorrect order. Identify the correct order by enumerating the steps with 1, 2, 3, or 4.

    _____ Present the data in a graph or table and communicate conclusions.

    _____ Analyze the data with appropriate methods.

    _____ Formulate a question worth answering.

    _____ Collect and organize data.

30. How are scatterplots and line graphs alike? different?

More practice with the ideas of the section

31. Fill in the blank. Choose one of the following words or phrases: *apple pie, bar graph, frequency table, histamine, histogram, line graph, pictograph, pie chart,* or *scatterplot.*

    a. A(n) _____ is a graph that shows the categories and the proportion of observations that belong to each category using sectors of a circle.

    b. A(n) _____ is useful for determining whether a relationship exists between two numerical variables.

    c. A(n) _____ is useful for showing a trend or change between two numerical variables by connecting consecutive ordered pairs with line segments and is especially useful for showing the trend when the independent variable is time, such as years.

    d. A(n) _____ is a table that shows the categories and the number of observations that belong to each category.

    e. A(n) _____ shows quantities using a symbol or icon to represent some amount.

    f. A(n) _____ is useful for presenting a large set of numerical data; requires the intermediate step of summarizing the data using a frequency table, typically with equal-sized intervals; often requires experimenting with 5 to 20 intervals; and is more of an art than a science.

    g. A(n) _____ is a graph that shows the categories and the number of observations that belong to each category using rectangles.

32. Indicate whether each sentence is true or false.

    a. Line graphs require horizontal and vertical axes.

    b. A pie chart requires horizontal and vertical axes.

    c. Pie charts are appropriate to compare several variables.

    d. A title is a good opportunity to express your conclusion.

    e. Creative titles and axis labels help students understand what they see and imply comprehension of the data.

    f. More than 2000 years ago, it was common practice to display data with a bar graph.

33. When 21 people were asked how they would vote for Proposition B, 10 said they would vote yes, 4 said they would vote no, and 7 said they were undecided.

    a. Calculate the percent of responses for each category to the nearest tenth of a percent.

    b. Do the percentages add up to 100%? Explain your answer.

    c. If you drew a pie chart for the data, what would be the central angles for the sectors of the pie? Round the angles to the nearest degree.

34. The table that follows shows data for four participants in a survey by an automotive dealer.

    a. Explain how the table records the data associated with each participant.

    b. Determine the variables and their type.

    c. Explain how the table records the data for each variable.

Customer	Color of car	Gas mileage (mpg)	Customer satisfaction (scale 1–4)
Mrs. A	brown	23	4
Mr. B	silver	34	1
Ms. C	white	21	2
Ms. D	white	15	4

35. A teacher recorded the following data.

	Cool day	Hot day
Sit-ups	6	5
Pull-ups	10	6
Push-ups	15	12

    a. Make a bar graph for the frequency table. Use the categories "hot day" and "cool day" to label the horizontal axis. Use frequencies along the vertical axis.

    b. Make a bar graph for the frequency table. Use the categories "sit-ups," "pull-ups," and "push-ups" to label the horizontal axis. Use frequencies along the vertical axis.

    c. Which graph suggests the particular activity had a greater effect on student performance?

    d. Which graph suggests the temperature had a greater effect on student performance?

36. The two-way table summarizes casualty data from the *Titanic*.

Type of passenger	Passengers	Survivors
women, first class	144	140
women, second class	93	80
women, third class	165	76

    a. Did the type of accommodation affect survival?

    b. Make a graph for the data. Include a creative title that supports your conclusion.

37. Make a line graph for the data, from the 2003 Status Report on the Federal Education Loan Programs (p. 11), showing the total amount of money that college students borrowed at 4-year and 2-year institutions. The reported amounts are in millions of constant 2002 dollars to take inflation into account and make comparisons fair.

Year	4-year	2-year
1996	$15,486	$1788
1997	$16,689	$1856
1998	$16,723	$1860
1999	$16,165	$1732
2000	$17,127	$1778

38. The following table shows the fuel efficiency (in miles per gallon, mpg) and the carbon footprint (the number of tons per year of carbon dioxide) for some 2012 convertible vehicles. (Source: Based on data from www.fueleconomy.com.)

    a. Make a scatterplot for the data.

    b. Describe the apparent relationship between the two variables.

mpg (city)	carbon footprint (tons of CO_2 per year)
27	6.5
23	7.2
22	7.5
21	7.5
21	7.8
20	7.5
20	8.1
19	8.1
18	8.5
18	8.9
17	9.3
16	9.8
15	10.4
14	11
13	11.6
13	12.4
12	13.3

39. The following graphs are based on a CNN/*USA Today*/Gallup poll to gain insight on Americans' perception of rising gasoline prices. They were asked the question, "Now, thinking of the cost of gasoline, would you say the country is in—a state of crisis, has major problems, has minor problems, or has no problems at all?"

    a. Write a conclusion highlighted by each graph.

    b. Which graph is easier to follow? Explain your answer.

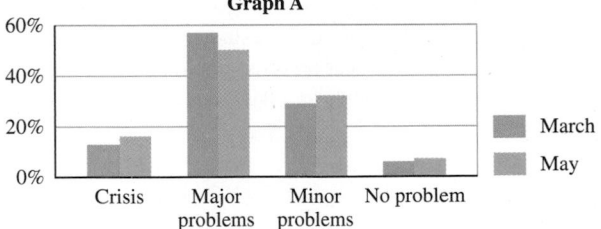

Graph A

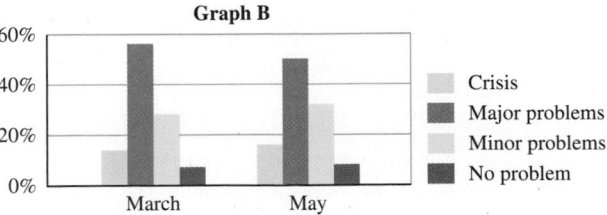

Graph B

40. Find an example of a pictograph from a newspaper, magazine, or nonacademic Internet website.

    a. State your source.

    b. Is the title creative or suggestive?

    c. Are the categories clearly labeled?

    d. Is the value of the icon clearly labeled?

    e. Are the icons proportional to the amount they represent?

41. The following data show the percentage of young (age 25–29) advanced degree holders (higher than a bachelor's degree) by gender. The data are based on a survey of approximately 100,000 addresses nationwide. Display the data using an appropriate graph. Express your conclusion using a descriptive title.

	Total holders (age 25–29)	Men	Women
1960	416,000	78%	22%
1970	783,000	73%	27%
1980	1,474,000	58%	42%
1990	1,384,000	53%	47%
2000	994,000	42%	58%
2009	1,579,000	42%	58%

SOURCE: U.S. Census Bureau.

42. The following data show the percentage of adults 25 and older with an advanced degree (higher than a bachelor's degree) by gender. The data are based on a survey of approximately 100,000 addresses nationwide. Display the data using an appropriate graph. Express your conclusion using a descriptive title.

	Both men and women	Men	Women
1960	3.0%	4.4%	1.7%
1970	4.3%	6.3%	2.4%
1980	7.2%	9.8%	5.0%
1990	8.8%	10.9%	6.9%
2000	8.6%	10.0%	7.3%
2009	10.6%	11.1%	10.1%

SOURCE: U.S. Census Bureau.

43. The table shows the percentage of students scoring 600 or above on the SAT for the verbal and math portions of the exams.

Year	Verbal score	Math score
1990	20.3%	20.4%
1995	21.9%	23.4%
2000	21.1%	24.2%
2005	22.5%	26.5%
2006	21.4%	25.8%
2007	21.2%	24.5%
2008	21.0%	25.0%

SOURCE: U.S. Census Bureau.

a. Draw a scatterplot for the verbal and math scores.

b. Do the percentages seem closely related for students scoring 600 or above on the verbal and on the math portion of the SAT?

44. The table shows the overall miles per gallon and weight for selected four-door vehicles, based on data from Consumer Reports studies.

Gas mileage (mpg)	Weight (lb)	Gas mileage (mpg)	Weight (lb)
27	2895	24	3120
20	3365	26	2715
32	2850	19	3925
17	4190	24	2920
25	2555	16	4340
18	4345		

a. Make a scatterplot for the data. Label the x-axis and the y-axis. Include a descriptive title.

b. Which variable makes the most sense to choose as the independent variable? Explain your decision.

45. The following table shows the distribution of achievement levels in mathematics for fourth-grade students on the 2007 NAEP test.

Level	below basic	basic	proficient	advanced
Percent	18	42	34	6

a. Represent the data with a graph.

b. Explain why you chose the type of graph.

46. The data show, in thousands, the total number of teachers in elementary and secondary schools from 2003 to 2007, according to the *Digest of Education Statistics* (2007, Table 4; this annual publication, freely available online, highlights educational statistics).

Year	Total (in thousands)
2001	3440
2002	3476
2003	3490
2004	3537
2005	3588

a. Display the data in an appropriate graph.

b. Use the graph to predict the number of teachers in 2006.

47. Most students in the United States aged 5 to 17 years attend public or private schools. However, many students are schooled at home. The following data show the number of homeschooled students, in thousands, by household income level for 2007

(based on the latest data available at time of publication from the National Center for Education Statistics).

Household income	Homeschooled (in thousands)
$25,000 or less	239
$25,001 to $50,000	364
$50,001 to $75,000	405
$75,001 or more	501

a. How many students were homeschooled?

b. What percent of students were homeschooled in households that earned $50,000 or less?

c. Make a pie chart for the data, and include a descriptive title.

d. Make a bar graph for these data, and include a descriptive title.

48. A veterinarian conducted a survey of the number of pets people have and their annual household income. The group "3; $25,000" means the respondent has three pets and has an annual household income of $25,000.

3; $25,000	1; $40,000	1; $75,000
0; $41,000	2; $21,000	3; $41,000
1; $46,500	5; $52,000	0; $21,000
2; $32,000	1; $27,000	2; $75,000
1; $53,000	1; $38,500	4; $45,000
5; $38,000	2; $30,000	3; $52,000
0; $38,000	0; $53,000	1; $46,500
2; $75,000	5; $48,500	4; $35,000

a. Draw a scatterplot of these data.

b. Is there an association between income level and number of pets?

49. The following line graph shows the number of federal correction facilities in Canada from 2000 to 2008.

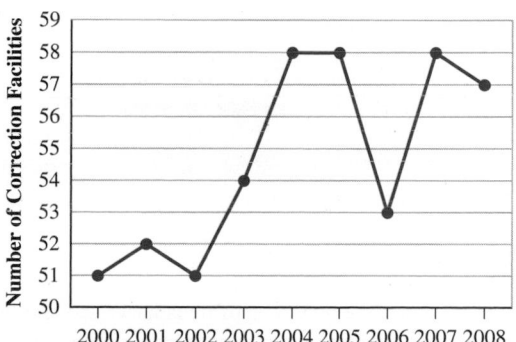

SOURCE: Statistics Canada.

a. Which years experienced an increase in facilities (compared to the previous year)?

b. Which year experienced the greatest increase in facilities (compared to the previous year)?

c. Which years experienced a decrease in facilities (compared to the previous year)?

d. Which year experienced the greatest decrease in facilities?

50. The line graph shows the employment rate of full-time post-secondary students 15 to 24 years old in Canada for the academic years 2004–2005, 2005–2006, 2006–2007, 2007–2008, 2008–2009, and 2009–2010. Write a sentence about the employment pattern in the graph that highlights

a. gender differences.

b. age differences.

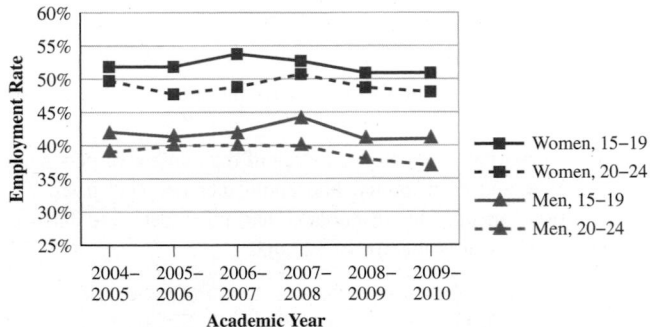

51. Sal the car salesman made two graphs showing the number of cars he sold during the past few months. If Sal wanted to ask his boss for a raise, which graph should Sal show his boss? Explain your answer.

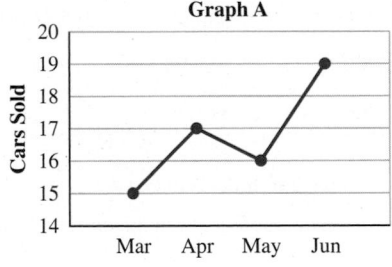

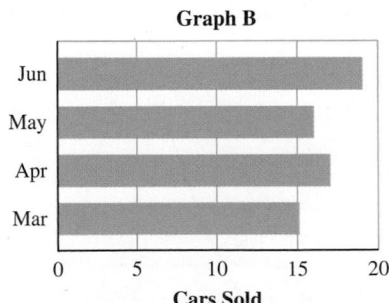

52. The table shows the total area of trees harvested and the total area of trees replenished by planting seedlings for 2001, in square meters, for different locations in Canada. Is there a relationship between the number of square meters harvested and the area replenished by planting seedlings? Explain your answer.

Location	Harvested	Replenished
Newfoundland and Labrador	434	46
Prince Edward Island	49	17
Nova Scotia	533	108
New Brunswick	1115	170
Quebec	3017	751
Ontario	1857	922
Manitoba	156	90
Saskatchewan	232	123
Alberta	674	380
British Columbia	2045	1610

SOURCE: Statistics Canada, Analysing Provincial Forestry Practices Using Bar Graphs and Scatter Graphs, www.statcan.ca/english/Estat/guide/scatter.htm.

53. The histogram shows the average number of points scored per game by basketball players.

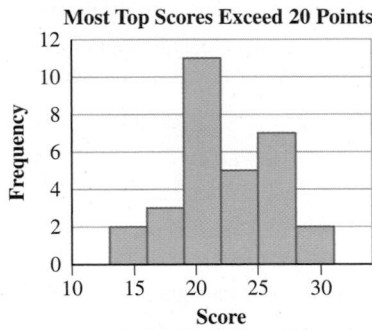

a. Complete the frequency table for the histogram (add more rows as necessary).

Interval	Frequency
$13 \leq x < 16$	2
$16 \leq x < 19$	
. . .	. . .

b. What percentage of the players averaged at least 25 points per game?

54. The table shows the percentage of eighth-grade students who scored at or above basic proficiency on the NAEP test for mathematics in 2007.

State	Percent	State	Percent
AL	55	MT	79
AK	73	NE	74
AZ	66	NV	60
AR	65	NH	78
CA	59	NJ	77
CO	75	NM	57
CT	73	NY	70
DE	74	NC	73
FL	68	ND	86
GA	64	OH	76
HI	59	OK	66
ID	75	OR	73
IL	70	PA	77
IN	76	RI	65
IA	77	SC	71
KS	81	SD	81
KY	69	TN	64
LA	64	TX	78
ME	78	UT	72
MD	74	VT	81
MA	85	VA	77
MI	66	WA	75
MN	81	WV	61
MS	54	WI	76
MO	72	WY	80

SOURCE: U.S. Census Bureau.

a. Complete the frequency table (add more rows as necessary).

Interval	Frequency
below 50	
$50 \le x < 55$	
. . .	. . .
$85 \le x < 90$	
above 90	

b. Construct a histogram for the data. Use grid paper. Be sure to label the axes and include a descriptive title.

55. The table shows the number of new residential housing permits approved by each state in a certain year (in thousands, so 24.1 represents 24,100).

State	Permits (in thousands)	State	Permits (in thousands)
AL	24.1	MT	3.4
AK	1.6	NE	6.6
AZ	55.6	NV	26.7
AR	10.8	NH	4.8
CA	107.7	NJ	17.1
CO	30.4	NM	12.3
CT	7.1	NY	20.0
DE	5.0	NC	82.7
FL	146.2	ND	2.3
GA	86.1	OH	27.5
HI	5.6	OK	14.1
ID	14.8	OR	19.9
IL	37.9	PA	33.1
IN	24.4	RI	1.8
IA	10.3	SC	41.7
KS	11.1	SD	4.0
KY	13.5	TN	39.2
LA	23.8	TX	162.8
ME	6.5	UT	22.6
MD	17.9	VT	2.1
MA	10.9	VA	39.0
MI	24.8	WA	35.6
MN	20.9	WV	5.2
MS	14.1	WI	19.6
MO	19.9	WY	3.1

SOURCE: U.S. Census Bureau.

a. Represent the data with a frequency table.

b. Construct a histogram for the data.

SECTION 8.2 | Measures of Center and Measures of Variation

Three Characteristics of a Collection of Numerical Measurements

We often collect data to answer a question. For a collection of numerical values, we are often interested in a measure of center, a measure of variation, and the distribution. A **measure of center** (such as mean, median, or mode) is a representative value of a collection of numbers. A **measure of variation** (such as range, mean absolute deviation, interquartile range, or minimum and maximum usual values) quantifies the amount of spread in the set of numbers. Students should be able to "find, use, and interpret measures of center and spread, including mean and interquartile range" (Gr. 6–8, NCTM). The **distribution** tells you the possible values of the variable and how often these values occur.

To visualize the distribution of numerical data, we often use a graph of the data. A histogram, for example, provides a visual representation of the distribution. In this section, we introduce two additional ways to visualize a distribution: the stem-and-leaf plot and the dot plot (or line plot). Measures of center and spread provide supporting information about the distribution. Students should "understand that a set of data collected to answer a statistical question has a distribution which can be described by its center, spread, and overall shape" (Gr. 6, CCSS).

Concept Map 8.2 may help you organize important information as you move forward in this chapter.

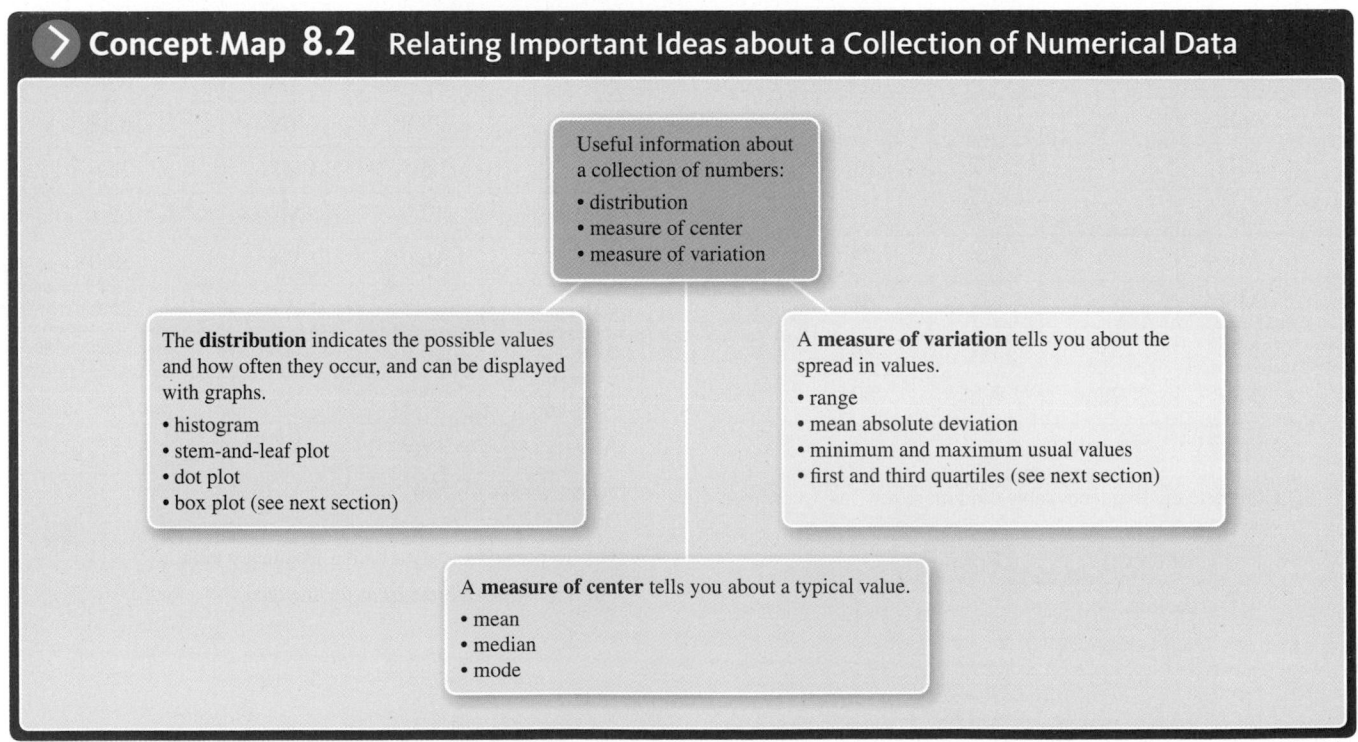

> **Concept Map 8.2** Relating Important Ideas about a Collection of Numerical Data

Useful information about a collection of numbers:
- distribution
- measure of center
- measure of variation

The **distribution** indicates the possible values and how often they occur, and can be displayed with graphs.
- histogram
- stem-and-leaf plot
- dot plot
- box plot (see next section)

A **measure of variation** tells you about the spread in values.
- range
- mean absolute deviation
- minimum and maximum usual values
- first and third quartiles (see next section)

A **measure of center** tells you about a typical value.
- mean
- median
- mode

Measures of Center

Maria is a middle school student elected to serve as president of her class. Part of her job is to represent the views and interests of her classmates. In mathematics, a measure of center is a single number that represents a collection of numbers. It is one of the most important ways to summarize numerical data, especially in the sciences. Students should recognize that "a measure of center for a numerical data set summarizes all of its values with a single number" (Gr. 6, CCSS). Three common choices are mean, median, and mode.

Mean Contextualized situations involving the mean are level values, fair comparisons, fair share, reduction of error in measurements, and estimation of the total.

We illustrate how to use manipulatives to model the mean with *level values* (the same or a constant amount).

EXAMPLE 8.17

COMMUNICATION
CONNECTION
PROBLEM SOLVING
REASONING
REPRESENTATION

In the given figures, move the cubes so that each stack has the same number of cubes.
a. In Figure 5, each stack has about how many cubes?

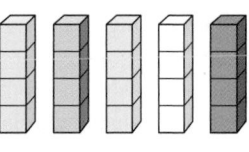

FIGURE 5

b. In Figure 6, each stack has about how many cubes?

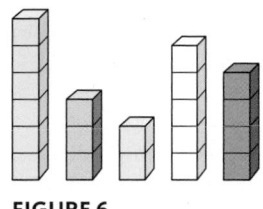

FIGURE 6

SOLUTION

a. Each stack already has the same number of cubes. Each stack has four cubes.
b. The cubes in Figure 6 can be moved as shown in Figure 7.

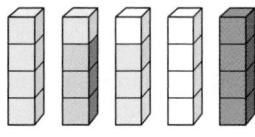

FIGURE 7

Each stack has four cubes.

▲

We can think of the *mean* as the number of cubes in each equal-sized stack. We can use this leveling approach to solve a word problem using algebra rather than cubes.

EXAMPLE 8.18

COMMUNICATION
CONNECTION
PROBLEM SOLVING
REASONING
REPRESENTATION

Carlo purchased a pencil for 19 cents, a pen for 32 cents, and a marker for 30 cents. If each item cost the same amount, what would be the cost of each item?

SOLUTION

If each item cost the same, say n cents, then we would have $n + n + n = 19 + 32 + 30$, which leads to the equation $3n = 81$, and $n = 81/3 = 27$. If each item cost the same amount, then the cost would be 27 cents per item.

▲

The level amount is a representative value determined by finding a sum, $19 + 32 + 30$ in the preceding example, and then dividing the sum by the number of addends—in this case, 3. This numerical value is called the mean.

> **Definition of the Mean**
>
> Let $x_1, x_2, \ldots, x_n$ represent a collection of n numbers. The **mean,** denoted $\bar{x}$ and read as "x bar," is the number defined by $\bar{x} = \dfrac{x_1 + x_2 + \ldots + x_n}{n}$.
>
> - n is the number of values.
> - The total is the sum $x_1 + x_2 + \ldots + x_n$.
> - The number $n \cdot \bar{x}$ equals the total.

We can use the mean to make *fair comparisons* between two data sets. These types of motivating problems challenge students to think and build on their intuitions.

EXAMPLE 8.19

COMMUNICATION
CONNECTION
PROBLEM SOLVING
REASONING
REPRESENTATION

Two classes raised money in a fundraiser. The table shows the results. How can the principal decide which class performed better?

	Amount of money raised	Students
Fifth-grade class	$350	20
Sixth-grade class	$441	28

SOLUTION

The sixth-grade class raised more money, but it also has more students. A fair comparison takes into account the number of students. If each fifth grader raised the same amount of money, then each fifth grader would have raised *total* $\div n$ = \$350/20 = \$17.50. If each sixth grader raised the same amount of money, then each sixth grader would have raised *total* $\div n$ = \$441/28 = \$15.75. Each fifth grader raised an average of \$17.50, while each sixth grader raised an average of \$15.75. The fifth-grade class performed better. ▲

The mean is also suitable in situations involving *fair share.*

EXAMPLE 8.20

COMMUNICATION
CONNECTION
PROBLEM SOLVING
REASONING
REPRESENTATION

Kyle, Maria, and Andy are waiters at the same restaurant. They agree to combine their tips at the end of the day and split the total evenly. Kyle earned $30, Maria earned $80, and Andy earned $40 in tips. How much money does each get in tips?

SOLUTION

Altogether, they collected \$30 + \$80 + \$40. The total must be split among three people: $(30 + 80 + 40) \div 3 = 50$. Each waiter gets \$50, which is the mean of the numbers 30, 80, and 40. ▲

We can also use the mean in situations for the **reduction of error in measurements,** such as repeated blood pressure readings, because repeated measurements are subject to differences that result from variations depending on time, human error, or equipment. The idea is that some errors in the measurements will be positive and some errors will be negative; therefore, when you add the measurements, the absolute value in the error in the mean could be lower because of cancellation. For example, suppose three hikers measure the distance between two landmarks on their trail. They obtain the measurements 204, 197, and 205 feet, but the true distance between the landmarks is actually 200 feet. The errors in the measurements are 4, −3, and 5 feet, with absolute values of 4, 3, and 5 feet. The mean distance is 202 feet. The absolute value of the error in the mean is 2, because $|202 - 200| = 2$. Let's see how the errors could cancel.

$$\text{absolute value of the} = |\text{mean} - \text{true measurement}|$$
error in the mean

$$= |202 - 200|$$

$$= \left| \frac{204 + 197 + 205}{3} - 200 \right|$$

$$= \left| \frac{204 + 197 + 205}{3} - \frac{3 \cdot 200}{3} \right|$$

$$= \left| \frac{(204 - 200) + (197 - 200) + (205 - 200)}{3} \right|$$

$$= \left| \frac{4 + -3 + 5}{3} \right|$$

$$= \left| \frac{1 + 5}{3} \right| \qquad \text{**Some cancellation occurred because of the opposite signs.**}$$

$$= 2$$

In this situation, the measurement with the lowest error absolute value is the mean, as some of the errors canceled. This simple example illustrates that the mean measurement could result in a lower error.

EXAMPLE 8.21

CONNECTION

Shawn measured the air pressure, recorded in pounds per square inch, in his tire four times with an electronic gauge. The measurements were 34.3, 32.8, 35.1, and 34.6 psi. What is the average pressure reading?

SOLUTION

The sum of the four measurements is 34.3 + 32.8 + 35.1 + 34.6 = 136.8. Then 136.8/4 = 34.2. The average pressure reading is 34.2 psi. ▲

In the following example, we use the mean to *estimate a total*.

EXAMPLE 8.22

CONNECTION

REASONING

REPRESENTATION

There are approximately five dots in each square. Estimate the total number of dots without counting each dot.

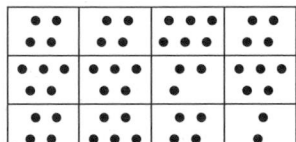

SOLUTION

The squares are arranged in a 3-by-4 array, and 3 · 4 = 12. So there are 12 squares altogether. Then 12 · 5 = 60. So there are about 60 dots altogether. ▲

■ **Historical Note**

According to an ancient Indian story written in the fourth century, Rituparna used estimation to count the number of leaves on a branch by counting the number of leaves on a typical twig on the branch and then multiplying that number by the number of twigs on the branch.

EXAMPLE 8.23

CONNECTION
PROBLEM SOLVING
REASONING
REPRESENTATION

A teacher surveyed her students to determine the average number of books in their backpacks.

Books	Frequency
3	2
4	1
5	3
6	2

a. How many students were surveyed?

b. What is the average number of books in their backpacks?

SOLUTION

a. $2 + 1 + 3 + 2 = 8$, so eight students were surveyed.

b. To find the average number of books per backpack, we need to find the total number of books: $2 \cdot 3 + 1 \cdot 4 + 3 \cdot 5 + 2 \cdot 6 = 37$. Then $37 \div 8 = 4.6$ (rounded to the nearest tenth). On average, there were 4.6 books per backpack.

▲

The following Released Item expects students to apply a clear understanding of the mean, as required in the previous example, rather than simply applying the formula.

> **RELEASED ITEM**
>
> • NAEP, 2003
>
> The table shows the scores of a group of 11 students on a history test. What is the average (mean) score of the group to the nearest whole number?
>
> | Scores | Students |
> |--------|----------|
> | 90 | 1 |
> | 80 | 3 |
> | 70 | 4 |
> | 60 | 0 |
> | 50 | 3 |
>
> 19% of eighth-grade students answered the question correctly.

Making Sense of an Average of 2.5 Children per Family

The mean represents a group of individual values. A result such as "an average of 2.5 children per family" is mathematically possible, although no family actually has 2.5 children. How can we make sense of this statement?

If you randomly select two families, then it would be reasonable to imagine there would be five children altogether. The mean is not a ratio, so if you select two families, there may be fewer or more than five children.

Many elementary-school students have difficulty grasping that a measure of center represents the *group* of values rather than *individual* values. A helpful analogy is that we elect a mayor to represent all citizens of the town rather than any particular citizen in the town.

Median The U.S. Patent and Trademark Office (www.uspto.gov) keeps records of U.S. patents issued to inventors from foreign countries. Table 8.6 gives the total number of patents issued to inventors from certain countries in 2009.

TABLE 8.6 **Number of U.S. Patents Issued**

Country	Denmark	South Africa	Luxembourg	Thailand	New Zealand
Patents	537	139	56	39	198

A possible choice for a representative number of the *sorted* list (39, 56, 139, 198, 537) is the middle number, 139. The **median** is the middle number in a list sorted from lowest to highest, and it takes into account the position of all numbers.

EXAMPLE 8.24

REPRESENTATION

Determine the median in each set of data.
a. 7, 78, 22, 5, 14
b. 8, 11, 33, 1

SOLUTION

We write each list in its natural order, from lowest to highest.
a. The ordered list is 5, 7, 14, 22, 78. The middle number is 14. The median is 14.
b. The ordered list is 1, 8, 11, 33. Both 8 and 11 are in the middle, so any number between 8 and 11 can be a median. However, it is standard to report the average of 8 and 11 as the median: $(8 + 11)/2 = 9.5$. The median is 9.5. ▲

The following Released Item expects students to determine the median of an unsorted list of numbers.

> ▶ **RELEASED ITEM**
>
> ● NAEP, 2003
>   4, 8, 3, 2, 5, 8, 12.
>   What is the median of the numbers above?
>   **a.** 4 **b.** 5 **c.** 6 **d.** 7 **e.** 8
>
> 57% of eighth grade students gave the correct answer.

Choosing between the Mean and the Median The following problem illustrates an important difference between the mean and the median.

EXAMPLE 8.25

REPRESENTATION

Calculate the mean and the median of each collection of numbers.
a. 3, 5, 7, 12, 20
b. 3, 5, 7, 12, 300

SOLUTION

Each list is already written from lowest to highest.
a. The mean is $(3 + 5 + 7 + 12 + 20)/5 = 47/5 = 9.4$. The median is 7.
b. The mean is $(3 + 5 + 7 + 12 + 300)/5 = 327/5 = 65.4$. The median is 7. ▲

COMMUNICATION
REASONING

The example illustrates the mean is *sensitive* to relatively low or high values (think about leveling the cubes: you have significantly fewer or more cubes to move around), because it depends on the sum of all values. The median is *resistant* to extreme values, because it focuses on the positions of the numbers. If some values have a dramatic effect on the mean, then the median would be a better choice than the mean to represent a "typical" value in the distribution. Here are some situations that use the mean and the median:

- mean SAT scores, reported by the College Entrance Examination Board
- mean amount of time children spend on various activities, reported by the National Endowment for the Arts
- median weekly earnings among women in various occupations, reported by the U.S. Department of Labor
- median amount of federal student loans that college graduates borrow, reported by the U.S. Department of Education

Which measure of center would you choose to represent average home values in your town?

The NCTM standards note the following:

In the middle grades, students should learn to use the mean, and continue to use the median and the mode, to describe the center of a set of data. . . . Students need to understand that the mean "evens out" or "balances" a set of data and that the median identifies the "middle" of a data set. They should compare the utility of the mean and the median as measures of center for different data sets. (p. 251)

Mode The **mode** is the most frequently occurring value in the data set. The following example illustrates the main ideas for determining the mode.

EXAMPLE 8.26

REPRESENTATION

Find the mode or modes, if any exist.

a. 3, 4, 8, 1, 2, 3

b. 1, 2, 3

c. 3, 4, 1, 2, 3, 4

SOLUTION

a. 3

b. No value repeats, so there is no mode.

c. 3 and 4

▲

The following Classroom Connection illustrates that students should be able to select an appropriate measure of center (referred to as the "average").

◆◆ **Classroom Connection**

● *Math*, Grade 6, p. 118

Find the mean, median, and mode for each set of data. Round to the nearest tenth, if necessary. Which of these is the most appropriate average? Explain your answer. (© 2000 Macmillan/McGraw Hill. Reprinted by permission.)

a. 17, 18, 19, 20, 21, 40

b. payments to the actors in a movie: Dirk, $500,000; Holly, $4,000,000; Ralph, $200,000; Olga, $30,000; Glen, $30,000; Myra, $30,000

Stem-and-Leaf Plot

A **stem-and-leaf plot** displays a numerical variable using artifacts called stems and leaves. The **stems** determine the groupings, and the **leaves** distinguish the data. Typically, a leaf consists of the rightmost digit and the stem consists of the other digits.

EXAMPLE 8.27

REPRESENTATION

Draw a stem-and-leaf plot for the scores of 23 third graders tested after 8 weeks of the usual reading curriculum.

42	43	55	26	62	37
33	41	19	54	26	85
46	10	17	60	53	42
37	42	55	28	48	

SOURCE: StatLib, lib.stat.cmu.edu.

SOLUTION

The stem-and-leaf plot for this data set is shown here. The leaves are the ones digits, and the stems are the remaining digits. The stems appear vertically in their natural order. It helps to include a legend in the graph, for example, $3|4 = 34$ (instead of, say, 340 or 3.4). In this problem, $2|068$ indicates the scores 20, 26, and 28. The absence of leaves corresponding to the stem 7 indicates there were no scores in the 70s. The leaves are customarily lined up and ordered from lowest to highest.

Stem	Leaf $3|4 = 34$
1	079
2	668
3	377
4	1222368
5	3455
6	02
7	
8	5

Slightly more than half of the scores were in the 40s and 50s. The largest grouping of scores was in the 40s. The scores are distributed over a range of values.

▲

A different class of 21 third graders received the usual reading curriculum, along with directed reading activities, and took the same test after the 8-week period. A back-to-back stem-and-leaf plot, based on data for this scenario taken from StatLib (lib.stat.cmu.edu), can be used to compare both classes, as shown.

Directed Reading Activities		**No Directed Reading Activities**
6|5 = 56 Leaf	**Stem**	**Leaf 3|7 = 37**
	1	079
4	2	668
3	3	377
9964333	4	1222368
98776432	5	3455
721	6	02
1	7	
	8	5

In the back-to-back stem-and-leaf plot, 721\|6 indicates the scores 61, 62, and 67, while 6\|02 indicates the scores 60 and 62. The stem-and-leaf plot makes the differences more apparent. The directed reading activities seem more effective in improving the test scores.

The following Released Item illustrates how to use stem-and-leaf plots for decimal numbers.

▶ **RELEASED ITEM**

● NAEP, 2003

Gloria's diving scores from a recent competition are represented in the stem-and-leaf plot shown. In this plot, 3\|4 would be read as 3.4. What was her lowest score for this competition?

5	2 5
6	1
7	7
8	0 2

a. 0.02 **b.** 1.0 **c.** 2.5 **d.** 5.2 **e.** 8.0

73% of eighth graders gave the correct answer.

Dot Plot (Line Plot)

A **dot plot** (also called a **line plot**) is another graph for numerical variables where the individual values are plotted as dots (or other symbols, such as x).

EXAMPLE 8.28 The data show the prices of various models of inkjet printers. Make a dot plot for the data.

CONNECTION
REPRESENTATION

$150	$225	$150	$130	$100	$300	$100	$250
$150	$60	$150	$70	$200	$250	$100	

SOLUTION

The dot plot shows the prices and their frequencies.

Most Printers Cost Less Than $200.

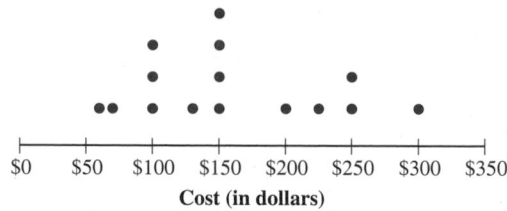

Cost (in dollars)

Students should be able to take repeated measurements and "show the measurements by making a line plot, where the horizontal scale is marked off in whole-number units" (Gr. 2, CCSS), or "make a line plot to display a data set of measurements in fractions of a unit (1/2, 1/4, 1/8)" (Gr. 5, CCSS).

The problems on the following student page illustrate that students should be able to read stem-and-leaf plots, as well as dot plots, and compute numerical summaries from them.

Extra Practice

Set A (Lesson 2, pp. 194–197)

Make a line plot for each set of data. Identify any clusters or gaps. Then find the mean, median, mode, and range.

1. number of CD's owned
   15, 22, 5, 10, 23, 18,
   24, 14, 19, 4, 22

2. class attendance
   28, 24, 23, 26, 14, 29,
   20, 18, 25, 29, 26, 14

3. test scores
   101, 98, 100, 97, 100,
   87, 103, 98, 99, 100

Find the mean, median, and mode of each set of data.

4. 45, 46, 39, 47, 49, 42,
   38, 46, 49, 43

5. 68, 59, 67, 66, 54, 67,
   68, 70, 63, 66, 61

6. 120, 118, 117, 107, 123,
   121, 119, 120, 120, 118

Set B (Lesson 3, pp. 198–199)

Use the stem-and-leaf plot for Problems 1–4.

1. How many amusement parks are represented in the data?

2. How many parks had fewer than 20 rides?

3. What is the greatest number of rides at any amusement park?

4. Find the mean, median, mode, and range of the data.

Kinds of Rides in Amusement Parks	
Stem	**Leaf**
0	9
1	2 4 5 5 6 8 9
2	0 0 0 1 2 4 4 5 5 6 6 7 7 8 8 9
3	0

1 | 2 means 12 rides.

Set C (Lesson 5, pp. 204–209)

Use the data from the line plot for Problems 1–5.

1. How many days had a low temperature below 5°?

2. How long was the winter break?

3. Which low temperatures occurred more than once?

4. Find the mean, median, mode, and range of the data.

5. Use the mean, median, or mode to predict the normal low temperature for Green Bay in February. Explain your answer.

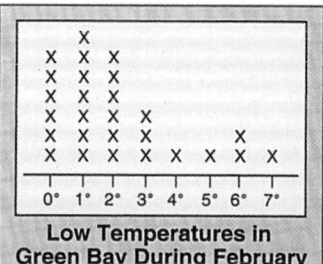

Low Temperatures in Green Bay During February

(Houghton Mifflin *Mathematics*, Student Edition, Grade 5, p. 209)

(© by Houghton Mifflin Company, Inc. Reproduced by permission of the publisher, Houghton Mifflin Harcourt Publishing Company.)

Measures of Variability

Figures 8 and 9 show histograms for two collections of numbers with the same mean. The data in Figure 8 seem to have less variability (because they are more closely spaced) than the data in Figure 9.

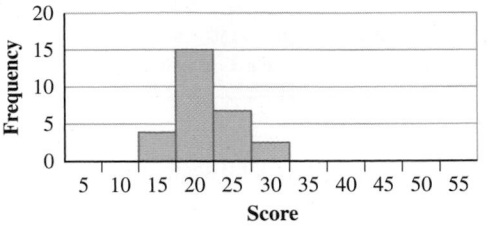

FIGURE 8

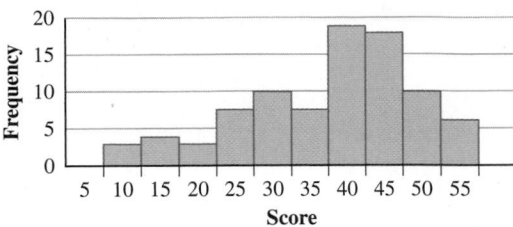

FIGURE 9

We can "visualize" variability with a histogram, stem plot, or dot plot. We can "measure" variability with the range, mean absolute deviation, minimum and maximum usual values, and interquartile range and percentiles (see the next section). Students should be able to summarize data by "giving quantitative measures of center (median and/or mean) and variability (interquartile range and/or mean absolute deviation), as well as describing any overall pattern and any striking deviations from the overall pattern with reference to the context in which the data were gathered" (Gr. 6, CCSS).

Range The **range** is the distance between the highest value and the lowest value. The range always has the same units as the data. The measurements 43, 42, 23, 63, 12, 34, and 58 m have a range of 51 m (range = highest value − lowest value = 63 − 12 = 51 m). Elementary-school students often use the range as a measure of variability because of its simplicity. As shown in the previous section, the range is useful for determining the width of intervals in histograms.

Deviation from the Mean Let $\bar{x}$ denote the mean of the numbers x_1, x_2, and x_3. A natural question to ask is, "How different are the values x_1, x_2, and x_3 from the mean $\bar{x}$?" The *deviation* of x from the mean $\bar{x}$ is the number $x - \bar{x}$. The *absolute deviation* of x from the mean $\bar{x}$ is the number $|x - \bar{x}|$. For example, suppose the data are 1, 5, and 6. Then the mean is 4, the deviation of 1 from the mean is −3, and the absolute deviation of 1 from the mean is 3.

Mean Absolute Deviation (MAD) Let's say the data x_1, x_2, and x_3 have the mean $\bar{x}$. The sum of the deviations $(x_1 - \bar{x}) + (x_2 - \bar{x}) + (x_3 - \bar{x})$ seems like a measure of spread or variation of the data. But it turns out that this sum is 0. Here's why:

$$(x_1 - \bar{x}) + (x_2 - \bar{x}) + (x_3 - \bar{x}) = (x_1 + x_1 + x_1) - 3\bar{x}$$

$$= (x_1 + x_1 + x_1) - 3 \cdot \frac{x_1 + x_2 + x_3}{3}$$

$$= (x_1 + x_1 + x_1) - (x_1 + x_1 + x_1)$$

$$= 0$$

One way to measure the spread of the data x_1, x_2, and x_3 is to sum their *absolute deviations* from $\bar{x}$ and then divide by 3 to obtain the mean of the absolute deviations. This number is called the mean absolute deviation (MAD):

$$\text{MAD} = \frac{|x_1 - \bar{x}| + |x_2 - \bar{x}| + |x_3 - \bar{x}|}{3}$$

The MAD tells us how much each score, on average, deviates from the mean. If x_1, x_2, and x_3 are close to $\bar{x}$, then the MAD will be smaller. If some values of x_1, x_2, and x_3 are far from $\bar{x}$, then the MAD will be larger.

EXAMPLE 8.29   Mr. Lin grew 250 tomato plants. After the first week, he selected four tomato plants and measured their height: 5, 6, 3, and 10 cm. Calculate the MAD of the heights.

SOLUTION

The mean is $\bar{x} = \dfrac{(5 + 6 + 3 + 10)}{4} = \dfrac{24}{4} = 6$ cm. Then

$$
\begin{aligned}
\text{MAD} &= \frac{|5 - 6| + |6 - 6| + |3 - 6| + |10 - 6|}{4} \\
&= \frac{|-1| + |0| + |-3| + |-4|}{4} \\
&= \frac{1 + 0 + 3 + 4}{4} \\
&= \frac{8}{4} \\
&= 2
\end{aligned}
$$

So the MAD is 2 cm (a representation of the spread of the heights).

If you choose the mean as your measure of center, then you could choose the MAD as your measure of variation (in Section 9.3, we discuss another measure of variation that we could use with the mean, called the *standard deviation*). The formula for the MAD extends to n values in a natural way.

Definition of Mean Absolute Deviation

Let $\bar{x}$ represent the mean of $x_1, x_2, \ldots, x_n$. The **mean absolute deviation,** denoted by MAD, is defined by $\text{MAD} = \dfrac{|x_1 - \bar{x}| + |x_2 - \bar{x}| + \ldots + |x_n - \bar{x}|}{n}$.

Using the MAD to Grasp Variation   **Usual values** are values that you would expect to occur. Knowing the minimum usual value and the maximum usual value would be helpful in understanding variation. For example, suppose you know the minimum usual value is 35 and the maximum usual value is 62.

- These values give you a sense of the variation of the data, because you would know "typical values" of the variable vary from 35 to 62.
- These values help you identify whether a score is unusual or usual. For example, 25 would be considered an unusually low value and 55 would be considered a usual value.

We can use the MAD to determine an interval of usual values.

A Rule of Thumb for Making Sense of the MAD

Let $\bar{x}$ and MAD represent the mean and the MAD of a collection of numbers.

- Usual values of the data belong to the interval $[\bar{x} - 2.5 \cdot \text{MAD}, \bar{x} + 2.5 \cdot \text{MAD}]$.
- The **minimum usual value** is $\bar{x} - 2.5 \cdot \text{MAD}$.
- The **maximum usual value** is $\bar{x} + 2.5 \cdot \text{MAD}$.
- If $x < \bar{x} - 2.5 \cdot \text{MAD}$ or $\bar{x} + 2.5 \cdot \text{MAD} < x$, then x is considered an **unusual value.**

This is a "rule of thumb," which means it has some impreciseness but is simple, useful, and reliable for providing a sense of the variation of the values in a data set, especially for data that have a bell-shaped histogram, which is one of the most common shapes for numerical data (we describe later how we arrived at this rule). The mean $\bar{x}$ is the center of the interval $[\bar{x} - 2.5 \cdot \text{MAD}, \bar{x} + 2.5 \cdot \text{MAD}]$.

EXAMPLE 8.30

CONNECTION

REASONING

A teacher gives a test. The average is 80, and the MAD is 5.

a. Find the interval of usual values.

b. Would a score of 70 be usual or unusual?

c. Would a score of 94 be usual or unusual?

SOLUTION

a. $\bar{x} - 2.5 \cdot \text{MAD} = 80 - 2.5 \cdot 5 = 67.5$, and $\bar{x} + 2.5 \cdot \text{MAD} = 80 + 2.5 \cdot 5 = 92.5$. According to the rule of thumb, usual scores are from 67.5 to 92.5.

b. usual

c. unusually high

We use two collections of numbers with bell-shaped histograms, shown in Figures 10 and 11, to motivate this rule of thumb.

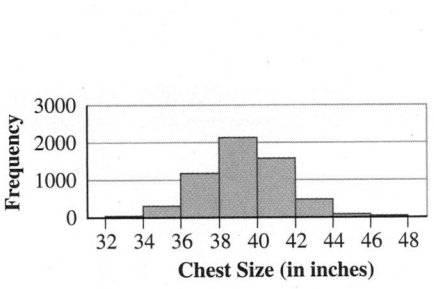

FIGURE 10

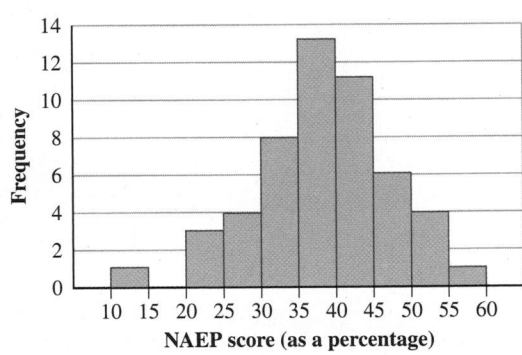

FIGURE 11

COMMUNICATION

CONNECTION

REASONING

REPRESENTATION

- Figure 10 shows the distribution of the chest sizes, measured in inches, of 5738 Scottish militiamen in the early nineteenth century, based on data from an online library of data sets (lib.stat.cmu.edu/DASL). The three lowest chest sizes were each 33 inches. The three highest chest sizes were 47, 47, and 48 inches.

- Figure 11 shows the distribution of the percentage of fourth graders who scored "at or above proficient" on the math portion of the NAEP tests in 2007 for the 50 states and the District of Columbia. The three lowest percentages were 14%, 21%, and 24%. The three highest percentages were 52%, 52%, and 58%.

Tables 8.7 and 8.8 show intervals, each with the midpoint $\bar{x}$, and the percentage of data within the interval.

TABLE 8.7 Chest Size Intervals and Percentages

Chest sizes (in inches) $\bar{x} = 39.83''$, MAD $= 1.63''$		Data within the interval
$[\bar{x} - \text{MAD}, \bar{x} + \text{MAD}]$	[38.20, 41.46]	46%
$[\bar{x} - 1.5 \cdot \text{MAD}, \bar{x} + 1.5 \cdot \text{MAD}]$	[37.38, 42.28]	78%
$[\bar{x} - 2 \cdot \text{MAD}, \bar{x} + 2 \cdot \text{MAD}]$	[36.57, 43.09]	92%
$[\bar{x} - 2.5 \cdot \text{MAD}, \bar{x} + 2.5 \cdot \text{MAD}]$	[35.75, 43.91]	95%
$[\bar{x} - 3 \cdot \text{MAD}, \bar{x} + 3 \cdot \text{MAD}]$	[34.94, 44.72]	99%

TABLE 8.8 **Test Result Intervals and Percentages**

NAEP results for fourth graders (as a percentage) $\bar{x} = 38.67\%$, MAD = 6.58%		Data within the interval
$[\bar{x} - \text{MAD}, \bar{x} + \text{MAD}]$	[32.09, 45.24]	58%
$[\bar{x} - 1.5 \cdot \text{MAD}, \bar{x} + 1.5 \cdot \text{MAD}]$	[28.80, 48.53]	69%
$[\bar{x} - 2 \cdot \text{MAD}, \bar{x} + 2 \cdot \text{MAD}]$	[25.51, 51.82]	86%
$[\bar{x} - 2.5 \cdot \text{MAD}, \bar{x} + 2.5 \cdot \text{MAD}]$	[22.23, 55.11]	94%
$[\bar{x} - 3 \cdot \text{MAD}, \bar{x} + 3 \cdot \text{MAD}]$	[18.94, 58.40]	98%

From the tables, we observe the following:

- The intervals $[\bar{x} - \text{MAD}, \bar{x} + \text{MAD}]$ and $[\bar{x} - 1.5 \cdot \text{MAD}, \bar{x} + 1.5 \cdot \text{MAD}]$ capture a low percentage of the values, so these intervals are too narrow.
- The interval $[\bar{x} - 2 \cdot \text{MAD}, \bar{x} + 2 \cdot \text{MAD}]$ captures an inconsistent percentage of the values, whereas the interval $[\bar{x} - 2.5 \cdot \text{MAD}, \bar{x} + 2.5 \cdot \text{MAD}]$ steadily captures roughly 95% of the values.
- The interval $[\bar{x} - 3 \cdot \text{MAD}, \bar{x} + 3 \cdot \text{MAD}]$ captures too much of the data, so this interval is too wide.

The percentages of observations that fall within the interval $[\bar{x} - 2.5 \cdot \text{MAD}, \bar{x} + 2.5 \cdot \text{MAD}]$ are consistent and contain a reasonable amount of data (about 95%), which enable us to define usual values. We use this observation to justify the rule of thumb for estimating usual values, which in turn provides some sense of the variation of the values. This rule is supported by the statistical literature for large values of n (typically $30 \le n$), but we often use small values of n in worked examples and homework questions to simplify computations and thus get the main ideas across.

EXAMPLE 8.31

COMMUNICATION
CONNECTION
PROBLEM SOLVING
REASONING
REPRESENTATION

Automakers are introducing gasoline–electric hybrid vehicles to improve fuel economy and reduce emissions. According to the label for a hybrid pickup truck, the city fuel mileage is between 20 and 28 mpg. Assume they are the minimum and the maximum usual values, respectively.
a. Estimate the mean fuel efficiency for city driving.
b. Estimate the MAD.

SOLUTION

a. The mean is the midpoint of the interval [20, 28], so $\bar{x} = (20 + 28)/2 = 24$. The mean fuel efficiency for city driving for this car is approximately 24 mpg.
b.
$$28 \approx \bar{x} + 2.5 \cdot \text{MAD}$$
$$28 \approx 24 + 2.5 \cdot \text{MAD}$$
$$4 \approx 2.5 \cdot \text{MAD}$$
$$4/2.5 \approx \text{MAD}$$
$$1.6 \approx \text{MAD}$$

The MAD of the fuel efficiency is approximately 1.6 mpg.

▲

QUESTIONS FOR SECTION 8.2

REPRESENTATION

Refresher: Representations (language, diagrams, tables, symbols, algebra, manipulatives, and contextualized situations) are important because we use them to organize, record, and communicate mathematical ideas and to make them more comprehensible.

1. Identify the measure of center that seems more appropriate for the data displayed.

   a.
   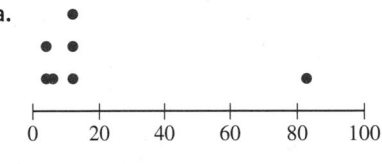

   b.
   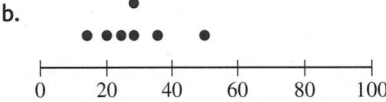

2. The following data give the life span (in hours) before charging of a few types of cell phone batteries (rounded to the nearest hour): 4, 5, 8, 3, 4, 5, 3, 6, 5, 5, and 3.

   a. Represent the data with a dot plot.

   b. Determine an appropriate measure of center for the data, and justify your decision.

3. A teacher asked her students how many pets they have. Here are the results.

Pets	Frequency
0	2
1	5
2	3
3	1

   a. How many students were surveyed?

   b. On average, how many pets does each student have? Round your answer to the nearest tenth.

4. Write the data set represented by the stem-and-leaf plot.

Stem	Leaf 4|2 = 4.2
1	03
2	4566
3	
4	0012

5. Determine the mean, median, and mode of the data represented by the dot plot.

   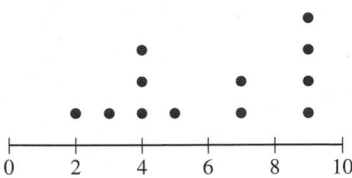

PROBLEM SOLVING

Refresher: Problem solving (reaching a goal that is not immediately attainable) is important because it helps students think more deeply about what they know and deal with unfamiliar situations.

6. A teacher gave the same test to two classes. In the class with 50 students, the mean score was 76. In the class with 30 students, the mean score was 84. What was the mean score for all students?

7. A customer bought $120 worth of coffee at $15 per pound and $72 worth of coffee at $18 per pound. On average, how much did the customer pay for each pound of coffee?

8. An advertisement for a laptop computer said the battery lasts 6.5 hours. To test the claim, a student charged the battery five times and recorded the following durations: 4, 5.4, 7, 4.5, and 5 hours. Does the advertised operating time of 6.5 hours seem credible?

9. There are n numbers $x_1, x_2, \ldots, x_n$ with $x_1 \leq x_2 \leq x_3 \leq \ldots \leq x_n$.

   a. Suppose n is an odd number. Write a formula for the median.

   b. Suppose n is an even number. Write a formula for the median.

REASONING AND PROOF

Refresher: Reasoning and proof (thinking and justifying) are important because they help students make sense of mathematics.

10. A student calculated the median of the data set 5, 7, 2, 1, 8. The student said the answer was 2. What mistake do you think the student made?

11. The mean number of sit-ups for a group of five students was seven. Every student managed at least one sit-up.

    a. What is the maximum number of sit-ups one of these students could have reported? Explain your answer.

    b. One student did 20 sit-ups. What is the maximum number of sit-ups another student could have done? Explain your answer.

12. Calculate the mean, median, and mode for each data set. Then suggest an appropriate measure of center for each data set.

   a. 3, 5, 8, 55

   b. 3, 3, 3, 3, 5, 9

   c. 7, 7, 8, 10, 12, 15

13. For each part, give an example of five numbers such that

   a. the median is less than the mean.

   b. the mean equals the median.

   c. the median is more than the mean.

   Give the median and mean for each example.

14. A teacher recorded the number of students who missed a certain math problem through the years: 5, 3, 6, 4, 5, 7, and 4. When she puts this problem on the next test, how many students do you think would miss this problem? Why?

15. A teacher gives a test for which the average is 72.8 and the MAD 4.7. Assume the histogram for the test scores is approximately bell shaped.

   a. Would a score of 65 be usual or unusual?

   b. Would a score of 87 be usual or unusual?

16. The teacher announces the average on the exam was 72.1 and the MAD was 4.5. Jerry cannot remember what his friend scored, but he knows it was either 57 or 75. What score do you think his friend received? Why?

CONNECTIONS

Refresher: Connections (linking and applying mathematical ideas) are important because they deepen student understanding and make mathematics more meaningful, flexible, and useful.

17. Find the mean and the MAD of the data. Round the final answers to one additional decimal place than the data.

   a. 3, 5, 2, 11, 3

   b. 4.1, 7.1, 12.1, 5.1, 2.1

18. The table shows the median age of males and females at first marriage. Explain why the median may be more appropriate than the mean as a measure of center.

Year	2000	2001	2002	2003	2004	2005
Males	26.8	26.9	26.9	27.1	27	27.5
Females	25.1	25.1	25.3	25.3	25.5	25.9

SOURCE: U.S. Census Bureau.

19. Consider the algebraic expression

$$(x - 2) + (x - 5) + (x - 4) + (x - 10).$$

   a. Find the mean $\bar{x}$ of the data set 2, 5, 4, 10.

   b. Evaluate the algebraic expression using $x = \bar{x}$ from part (a).

   c. Evaluate the algebraic expression using $x = 3$.

   d. Evaluate the algebraic expression using $x = 6$.

   e. Evaluate the algebraic expression using your own choice of x.

   f. If $(a - 2) + (a - 5) + (a - 4) + (a - 10)$ is closest to zero, then we say the number a is "closest" to all numbers $x_1, x_2, \ldots, x_n$. Do your results support the idea that the mean $\bar{x}$ is the number that is closest to all numbers $x_1, x_2, \ldots, x_n$?

20. Krista purchased a bag of chips for $2.25, a soda for $1.65, and a sandwich for $2.55. If each item cost the same, how much would each item cost?

21. A teacher used a frequency table to summarize scores from a 10-question true-or-false quiz.

Score	Frequency
50	2
60	3
70	8
80	9
90	5
100	3

   a. What is the mode of the scores?

   b. What is the median of the scores?

   c. What is the mean of the scores?

22. Leila, Cindy, and Shawn sell hot dogs and hamburgers at an amusement park. They take turns operating the food stand. They decided to combine the tips they earned and share them evenly. Leila earned $41, Cindy earned $25, and Shawn earned $54.

   a. How much money in tips does each get?

   b. Find the mean of the three numbers 41, 25, and 54.

23. A common way to measure the clarity of a lake is to lower a white disc (about 8 to 12 inches in diameter) in the lake and measure the distance at which the disc disappears from view. A rope is tethered to the center of the disc, which is slowly lowered into the water. Typically, several measurements are taken from several locations in the lake. The mean is then taken as the measurement of the clarity; this Secchi depth is named after the person who first experimented with this method in the mid-1800s. Calculate the Secchi depth of a lake with the four measurements 35.4, 32.7, 34.8, and 33.6 feet.

Use the following information to answer questions 24–26.

The quotient $(x - \bar{x})/\text{MAD}$ is a relative measure of the difference between the value x and the mean $\bar{x}$. The quotient can be negative (x is below the mean) or positive (x is above the mean). Two values from different collections of numbers can be compared by comparing their quotients. For example, suppose Marc received 84 points on a quiz in a math class, with $\bar{x} = 78$ points and MAD $= 10$ points, while Don received 80 points on a quiz in a history class, with $\bar{x} = 75$ points and MAD $= 8$ points. A direct comparison suggests Marc performed better, because $84 > 80$. Math and psychology are considerably different subjects, however, and that makes a direct comparison questionable. Instead, we can ask, "Who performed *relatively* better on his quiz?" Then $(84 - 78)/10 = 0.6$, and $(80 - 75)/8 = 0.625$. This suggests Don scored more points above the mean of his history class than Marc scored above the mean of his math class. Use this information to answer Questions 24–26.

24. Maria received her results for two tests, in math and history, and calculated the quotient $(x - \bar{x})/MAD$ for each test. In math, her test score corresponded to the quotient 1.8. In history, her test score corresponded to the quotient 1.2. On which test did she perform relatively better? Explain your answer.

25. Pete the painter collected data for costs of brushes and rollers. The mean cost for a brush was $5.30 with a MAD of $2.11. The mean cost of a package of rollers was $2.87 with a MAD of $0.85. Which is relatively more expensive, a brush for $8 or a package of rollers for $4?

26. A survey of stores in a city reveals the mean price of a gallon of milk is $3.50 with a MAD of $0.65 and the mean price for a 16-ounce bottle of orange juice is $2.50 with a MAD of $0.25. A store charges $3.20 for a gallon of milk and $2.25 for a 16-ounce bottle of orange juice. Which is relatively more expensive, the gallon of milk or the bottle of orange juice? Explain your answer.

COMMUNICATION

Refresher: Communication (written and verbal explanations using representations and proper mathematical vocabulary) is important because it helps students refine and strengthen their understanding.

27. A scientist obtains the measurements 4.25, 4.23, and 4.22 m. Explain why the scientist would be inclined to use the average of the three measurements as the reported measurement.

28. A student is asked to calculate the mean of the numbers 7, 6, 2, and 0. The student gives the answer 5. Explain how the student arrived at the faulty answer.

29. The data sets show the life span, in hours, of two brands of batteries.

Brand A:	4.3, 4.5, 5, 5.5, 5.5, 5.8, 6.5, 7
Brand B:	3, 3.7, 4, 5.5, 5.5, 6.7, 6.9, 8.7

a. Calculate the mean, median, and mode for each data set.

b. Draw a dot plot for each data set.

c. Which battery do you prefer? Explain your answer.

30. A teacher asks his students, "How many pets do you have?" After collecting the data, he determines that, on average, each student has 1.5 pets. Many elementary-school students struggle with this result because it has no physical counterpart in reality; a student cannot have a fraction of a pet. How can you help your students make sense of this measure of center?

31. Explain how the U.S. Census Bureau uses the median to define the "wage gap" between men and women. (Hint: Use an Internet search.)

More practice with the ideas of the section

32. Fill in the blank. Choose one of the following words or phrases: *average, center, estimates, extreme values, insensitive, large, mean, mean absolute deviation, median, medium, mode, quantifies, range, representative, resistant, sensitive, small, stem-and-leaf plot, variation,* or *variety.*

   a. A measure of center (such as mean, median, or mode) is a(n) _____ value of a collection of numbers.

   b. A measure of variation (such as range or MAD) _____ the degree of variability in the collection of numbers.

   c. The mean is _____ to extreme values.

   d. The median is _____ to extreme values.

   e. The _____ would be a good choice to summarize house prices in a large city.

   f. If a plot reveals some _____, then it would be a good idea to choose the median.

   g. A(n) _____ displays a numerical variable using artifacts called stems and leaves.

   h. Histograms, stem plots, and dot plots "illustrate" variability, while the _____ and the MAD "measure" variability.

   i. If x_1, x_2, and x_3 are close together, then the MAD of x_1, x_2, and x_3 will be _____.

   j. If you choose the mean as your measure of center, then you should choose the _____ as your measure of spread.

33. A teacher gives three tests with a maximum score of 100 points on any test. What is the lowest score a student can receive on a test and still maintain an average of 93 or higher?

34. Use the leveling approach to find the mean for the data set: 3, 5, 2, 11, 3.

35. At recess, the boys and girls in a class tossed a beanbag. On average, the boys tossed it 11.2 feet. On average, the girls tossed it 8.8 feet. There were 12 boys and 15 girls. What was the average distance (to the nearest tenth) of the beanbag toss for the class combined? Explain your answer.

36. Suppose 5 gallons of orange juice costing a total of $16 are mixed with 3 gallons of cranberry juice costing a total of $10. Find the average cost for 1 gallon of the mixture.

37. A person counted the number of cars that traveled through an intersection on four consecutive days. The results were 3, 2, 11, and 9 cars.

   a. Find the mean value $\bar{x}$.

   b. Does the mean have to be a whole number to make sense?

   c. Calculate the deviation $x - \bar{x}$ for each number x ($x = 3, 2, 11,$ or 9).

   d. Compute the MAD.

38. Let 4, 6, 2, and 5 pounds represent the weights of four backpacks filled with math books.

   a. Find the mean weight of the backpacks.

   b. Suppose a math book weighing 3 pounds is added to each backpack. What is the mean weight of the backpacks?

   c. Suppose a math book weighing 7 pounds is added to each backpack. What is the mean weight of the backpacks?

d. Suppose a math book weighing k pounds is added to each backpack. What is the mean weight of the backpacks?

39. Let 2, 3, and 7 feet represent the heights of three trees.

a. Find the mean height of the trees.

b. Suppose each tree grows six times its height in 1 year. What is the mean height of the trees after 1 year?

c. Suppose each tree grows 10 times its height in 1 year. What is the mean height of the trees after 1 year?

d. Suppose each tree grows k times its height in 1 year. What is the mean height of the trees after 1 year?

40. A teacher asks her students, "How many pairs of shoes do you have?" After collecting the data, she determines each student has an average of 1.4 pairs of shoes. Some elementary school students struggle with this answer because it has no physical counterpart in reality; a student cannot have a fraction of a pair of shoes. How can you help your students make sense of this measure of center?

41. Two classes raised money for a fundraiser. Which class performed better?

	Students	Amount raised
Second graders	15	$219
Third graders	23	$294.40

42. Trains A and B both offer a route from point A to point B. The data show the number of minutes the two trains were late in arriving at their destination. Which train do you prefer? Explain your answer.

Train A	4	3	2	14	16	15	9	
Train B	9	6	18	9	9	9	7	5

43. The mean of 22 measurements is 47 cm. The collection of data includes the measurement 36 cm. Suppose the measurement 36 cm is replaced with 63 cm. What is the new mean? Explain your answer.

44. The mean of 35 measurements is 25 cm. The collection of data includes the measurement 40 cm. Suppose the measurement 40 cm is deleted. What is the new mean? Explain your answer.

45. Every year the Federal Bureau of Investigation (FBI) publishes the Uniform Crime Report (UCR). The data in the UCR are based on crime statistics reported by local law enforcement agencies throughout the United States. The city of Boston, Massachusetts, reported 27,876 property crimes (burglary, theft, and motor vehicle theft), and the city of Scottsdale, Arizona, reported 9475 property crimes. According to the U.S. census reports, there were approximately 2.7 times as many people in Boston as in Scottsdale. Which city is safer? Explain your answer.

46. Circle all that apply.

a. This measure of center is sensitive to very low or very high values.

    mean   mode   median

b. This measure of center is unique.

    mean   mode   median

c. This measure of center may not be unique.

    mean   mode   median

d. This measure of center can be used for numerical, or quantitative, data.

    mean   mode   median

e. This measure of center can be used for categorical, or qualitative, data.

    mean   mode   median

f. This measure of center is often used to describe the average home price.

    mean   mode   median

g. This measure of center should be used when the collection of data contains extremely low or high values compared to other values.

    mean   median

h. This measure of spread may be used with the mean.

    mean deviation   mean absolute deviation

47. The table shows the cost of types of soup and the number of items a customer purchased. Find the mean, median, and mode of the cost.

Type of soup	Cost	Items
noodle	$1.50	4
rice	$2.00	2
mushroom	$1.65	5

48. The table records the total monthly rainfall at Fly Fast Airport, in both millimeters and inches, for a 3-month period.

Month	Jan	Feb	Mar
mm	139.7	106.68	93.98
in	5.5	4.2	3.7

Do the following, rounding the final results to the nearest hundredth.

a. Calculate the mean rainfall in millimeters.

b. Calculate the mean rainfall in inches.

c. Convert both means to centimeters (1 cm = 10 mm and 1 cm = 2.54 inches).

49. The mean score on an exam for a class of 15 students is 78 points. Five students earn 4 points each in extra credit for the exam to be added to their scores. What is the new mean of the 15 tests? Explain your answer.

50. The following tables, based on data from the Bureau of Labor Statistics (www.stats.bls.gov) for a particular year, list the rates of nonfatal injuries and illnesses (number of cases per 100 full-time workers) in manufacturing of durable and nondurable goods.

Manufacturing durable goods	Recordable cases with days away from work, job transfer, or restriction
lumber and wood products	5.7
furniture and fixtures	6.0
stone, clay, and glass products	5.4
primary metal industries	5.5
fabricated metal products	5.1
industrial machinery and electrical equipment	3.3
electronic equipment	2.4
transportation equipment	5.8
instruments and related products	1.9
misc. manufacturing industries	3.4

Manufacturing nondurable goods	Recordable cases with days away from work, job transfer, or restriction
food and similar products	6.1
tobacco products	2.1
textile mill products	3.0
apparel and other textile products	2.7
paper and allied products	3.1
printing and publishing	2.2
chemicals and allied products	1.9
petroleum and coal products	2.2
rubber and misc. plastic products	5.1
leather and leather products	4.3

a. Construct a back-to-back stem-and-leaf plot to compare the data sets.

b. Briefly discuss the conclusion you might reach based on your plot, and then explain why the conclusion is probably valid.

51. A student receives the following scores on four quizzes (out of 100 points each): 85, 90, 92, and 91. The student is preparing for a fifth quiz. Is it possible for the student to earn a 93 average score over the five quizzes? Explain your answer.

52. There are five situations in which we could use the mean: level values, fair comparisons, fair share, reduction of error in measurements, and estimation of the total. Identify the situation that applies.

a. Cindy, Andy, and Marissa go to a restaurant. Here is the cost of each meal: Cindy, $25, Andy, $40, and Marissa, $26. They decide to split the bill evenly. How much money does each person have to pay?

b. A teacher asked four students to measure the length of a fish. The reported measurements were 35, 38, 34, and 37 mm. What is the average length of the fish?

c. Carlo purchased a ruler for 58 cents, a protractor for 80 cents, and a ruler for 65 cents. If each item cost the same amount, what would be the cost of each item?

d. On average, 20 students visit the tutoring center each hour. The tutoring center is open from 9 a.m. to 4 p.m. Estimate the number of students who visit the tutoring center each day.

e. Two classes read books. The table shows the results. How can the principal decide fairly which class read the most books?

	Books	Students
Fifth-grade class	177	15
Sixth-grade class	215	19

53. A local elementary school held a reading contest. A fourth-grade class read 12,345 pages altogether. A fifth-grade class read 15,000 pages altogether. The number of fourth graders is 80% of the number of fifth graders. Which class should win the reading contest? Explain your answer.

54. Find the mean and median of the data represented by the stem plot.

a.

Stem	Leaf 4|2 = 4.2
1	0
2	466
3	4
4	013

b.

Stem	Leaf 4|2 = 42
1	0
2	466
3	4
4	013

55. The following data show the median annual income, in dollars, by education level.

	Women	Men
Less than high school graduate	$14,682	$23,638
High school graduate (includes equivalency)	$21,711	$33,506
Some college or associate's degree	$27,663	$41,861
Bachelor's degree	$39,571	$59,079
Graduate or professional degree	$52,301	$79,276

SOURCE: U.S. Census Bureau.

a. Why do you think the bureau reports the median income rather than the mean income for each group?

b. Represent the data with an appropriate graph.

c. What trends do you see?

56. The following data show the time (in minutes) it takes for some students to complete a quiz: 26, 31, 24, 40, 20, 26, and 29. Calculate the

a. mean of the data.

b. MAD of the data.

c. minimum and maximum usual values.

57. The teacher announces that most scores on the test were from 40 to 85. Assume they are the minimum and maximum usual values. Find the

a. mean of the scores.

b. MAD of the scores.

58. A telemarketer is taking a survey of customers who purchased brand A or brand B batteries for radios. Brand A has a mean life span of 5.0 hours and a MAD of 0.4 hours. Brand B has a mean life span of 4.4 hours and a MAD of 1.3 hours. A particular customer cannot remember the brand of the battery he purchased, but he knows it lasted 6.6 hours. Which brand do you think the customer purchased, brand A or brand B? Explain your answer.

SECTION 8.3   Percentile, Box Plot, and Outliers

Convert a Given Number to a Percentile

Table 8.9 shows the average scores of eighth graders for each of the 50 states on the NAEP test for data analysis, statistics, and probability for 2009, the most recent year available as of publication.

TABLE 8.9   Scores for Eighth Graders on the 2009 NAEP Test for Data Analysis, Statistics, and Probability

MS	265	AR	278	TX	285	IN	291	MD	295
CA	267	TN	278	IL	286	OH	291	SD	295
NM	268	GA	279	NE	286	VA	291	WA	295
AL	269	MI	279	UT	286	DE	292	NH	296
HI	271	AK	282	WY	286	WI	292	CN	297
WV	273	FL	282	NC	287	CO	293	NJ	297
LA	275	RI	282	IA	288	MN	293	ND	298
NV	275	NY	283	OR	288	MT	294	VT	298
OK	275	KY	284	MO	289	PA	294	MN	300
AZ	278	SC	284	ID	290	KS	295	MA	304

SOURCE: U.S. Department of Education, Institute of Education Sciences, National Center for Education Statistics, NAEP, 2009 Mathematics Assessment.

The scores are sorted from lowest to highest, moving from the upper left and down each column to end at the lower right corner. The three highest scores are 304 (Massachusetts), 300 (Minnesota), and 298 (Vermont and North Dakota). We could rank the scores using ordinal numbers: first, second, third, fourth, and so on. We could also rank the scores using percentiles.

> ### Definition of Percentile
>
> If we say the number y has the rank **pth percentile,** then we mean $p\%$ of the numerical data $x_1, x_2, \ldots, x_n$ are less than y.

The following procedure outlines how to find the percentile of a number.

> ### How to Find the Percentile, Given a Number y
>
> **STEP 1.** Arrange the n numerical values in order from lowest to highest: $x_1, x_2, \ldots, x_n$.
>
> **STEP 2.** Count the number of observations k less than y.
>
> **STEP 3.** Round the decimal number $\frac{k}{n} \cdot 100$ to the nearest whole number to obtain p.
>
> **STEP 4.** The number y has the rank pth percentile.

There is no standard approach for calculating percentiles, so your calculator, software program, and the preceding definition could give you slightly different results. A percentile is not a number; it is an indication of rank (position).

EXAMPLE 8.32

COMMUNICATION
CONNECTION
REASONING

The percentile of the score 283 (New York) in Table 8.9 is 34%.

Interpret the result.

SOLUTION

Thirty-four percent of the states had a score less than 283.

▲

EXAMPLE 8.33

CONNECTION
REASONING

Find the percentile of the score 294 in Table 8.9.

SOLUTION

We follow the approach outlined earlier.

STEP 1. The numbers are already arranged from lowest to highest.

STEP 2. Of 50 observations, 37 are less than 294.

STEP 3. $\frac{37}{50} \cdot 100 = 74$ (which is already a whole number, so no rounding is needed).

STEP 4. The rank for 294 is the 74th percentile (both Pennsylvania and Montana scored 294).

▲

Health care professionals use percentiles, for example, in growth charts from the Centers for Disease Control and Prevention (www.cdc.gov/growthcharts), to monitor aspects of infants, children, and adolescents, such as weight and height. For example, the body mass index (BMI) is based on weight and height measurements. The formula is $\text{BMI} = 703(W/H^2)$, where W is weight in pounds and H is height in inches. The chart in Figure 12 is a gender-specific graph that uses both the age and the BMI of boys to determine the percentile ranking for the weight status of the boy.

CONNECTION
REPRESENTATION

Health care professionals use charts like Figure 12 to determine whether the patient is underweight, normal, at risk for being overweight, or overweight. In particular, they use the guidelines in Table 8.10 to interpret percentiles.

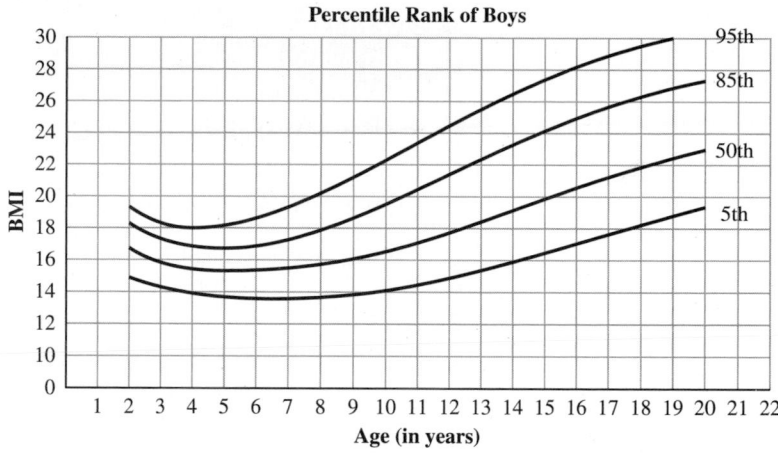

FIGURE 12

BMI for age for boys.

TABLE 8.10   Guidelines for Interpreting Percentiles for Children and Teens

Weight status	Percentile range
underweight	less than 5th percentile
healthy weight	5th percentile to less than 85th percentile
at risk of being overweight	85th percentile to less than 95th percentile
overweight	95th percentile or above

SOURCE: Centers for Disease Control and Prevention.

According to Figure 12, the ordered pair $(12, 20)$ corresponds to a percentile between the 50th and the 85th percentile. According to Table 8.10, this means the boy has a healthy weight. The ordered pair $(10, 24)$ corresponds to a percentile above the 95th percentile, which means the boy is overweight.

EXAMPLE 8.34

CONNECTION

a. Determine the weight status of a 14-year-old boy with a weight of 105 pounds and a height of 63 inches using the BMI calculation and the BMI-for-age graph.

b. Estimate the minimum healthy weight of a 12-year-old boy with a height of 65 inches.

SOLUTION

a. BMI $= 703(W/H^2) = 703(105/63^2) \approx 18.6$. Using Figure 12, the ordered pair $(14, 18.6)$ indicates a percentile slightly below the 50th percentile curve. The percentile is within the "5th percentile to less than 85th percentile" interval, and we conclude the boy has a healthy weight.

b. According to the graph, a 12-year-old boy with BMI ≈ 16 has a healthy weight, because the ordered pair $(12, 16)$ is slightly above the 5th percentile curve. We need to solve $16 = 703(W/65^2)$ for W. Then $W = 16 \cdot 65^2/703 \approx 96$ pounds. The minimum healthy weight is approximately 96 pounds.

▲

A homework question asks you similar percentile questions for girls.

Convert a Given Percentile to a Number

In some situations, you are given a percentile, such as the 40th percentile, and would like to determine the score y that is in that percentile. Here are the steps to find the score y corresponding to a given percentile.

> ### How to Find the Value y That Represents the pth Percentile, Given a Number p
>
> **STEP 1.** Arrange the n numerical values in order from lowest to highest: $x_1, x_2, \ldots, x_n$.
>
> **STEP 2.** Given the pth percentile, let $i = \left(\dfrac{p}{100}\right)n$.
>
> **STEP 3.** If i is a whole number, then let $y = (x_i + x_{i+1})/2$. If i is not a whole number, then round i upward to the nearest whole number k and let $y = x_k$.
>
> **STEP 4.** The pth percentile is the number y.

The following example illustrates the procedure.

EXAMPLE 8.35

CONNECTION

a. Find the 20th percentile of the numbers 4, 8, 2, 15, 20, 10, 16, 22, 17, 15, 19, and 24.

b. Find the 40th percentile of the numbers 5, 2, 6, 12, 15, 15, 16, 20, 28, 24, 22, 14, 10, 11, and 17.

SOLUTION

We follow the approach outlined earlier.

a. There are 12 numbers, so $n = 12$.

STEP 1. The ordered list is 2, 4, 8, 10, 15, 15, 16, 17, 19, 20, 22, 24.

STEP 2. $i = \left(\dfrac{p}{100}\right)n = \left(\dfrac{20}{100}\right) \cdot 12 = 2.4$.

STEP 3. $i = 2.4$ is not a whole number, so we round i up to the nearest whole number to find k and $y = x_k$: $i = 2.4$, $k = 3$, and $y = x_3 = 8$.

STEP 4. The 20th percentile is 8.

b. There are 15 numbers, so $n = 15$.

STEP 1. The ordered list is 2, 5, 6, 10, 11, 12, 14, 15, 15, 16, 17, 20, 22, 24, 28.

STEP 2. $i = \left(\dfrac{p}{100}\right)n = \left(\dfrac{40}{100}\right) \cdot 15 = 6$.

STEP 3. $i = 6$ is a whole number, so we average x_6 and x_7: $y = (x_6 + x_7)/2 = (12 + 14)/2 = 13$.

STEP 4. The 40th percentile is 13.

▲

The following example illustrates one way to summarize data using percentiles.

EXAMPLE 8.36

COMMUNICATION

CONNECTION

PROBLEM SOLVING

REASONING

REPRESENTATION

A teacher recorded the prices of different brands of school supplies. Summarize the data with percentiles in a table.

Marker	\$0.68, \$0.72, \$0.75, \$0.77, \$0.78, \$0.80, \$0.81, \$0.82, \$0.83, \$0.83, \$0.85, \$0.89, \$0.90, \$0.92
Binder	\$2.85, \$2.90, \$2.94, \$2.95, \$3.00, \$3.00, \$3.05, \$3.10, \$3.20, \$3.21
Paper	\$1.60, \$1.72, \$1.75, \$1.85, \$1.90, \$1.94, \$2.00, \$2.20, \$2.32, \$2.35, \$2.40, \$2.51

SOLUTION

Answers vary. We chose to report the 20th and 80th percentiles for each item in a table format, following the procedure outlined earlier for finding the values that represent the 20th and 80th percentiles.

	Percentile		
Item	**20th**	**80th**	**Observations**
marker	$0.75	$0.89	14
binder	$2.92	$3.15	10
paper	$1.75	$2.35	12

The 20th and 80th percentiles give the chart's reader a sense of the variation. Another possibility would be to report the 25th, 50th, and 75th percentiles.

▲

Presenting several percentiles at one time often provides some indication of the variation in the data.

Suppose a researcher compares the lifespan of two brands of batteries and summarizes the data in the following table:

	25th percentile	**75th percentile**
Brand A	6.1 hours	8.4 hours
Brand B	3.5 hours	7.6 hours

For brand A, 50% of the values vary from 6.1 to 8.4 hours, while for brand B, 50% of the values vary from 3.5 to 7.6 hours. Subtracting, we get $8.4 - 6.1 = 2.3$ and $7.6 - 3.5 = 4.1$. From the data, we could conclude that the lifespan of brand B batteries has more variation compared to brand A batteries. The 25th and 75th percentiles are common percentiles for gaining some insight of variation based on percentiles.

In situations that could involve very low and very high numerical values, such as home prices or annual salaries, we tend to avoid percentiles such as the 1st percentile and 99th percentile because a few extreme values may affect these percentiles and therefore distort the picture of the variation in the data. The 5th and 95th percentiles, or the 10th and 90th percentiles, are safer bets for representing lower and upper percentiles.

Table 8.11 is a fantastic use of percentiles to summarize the results of a hospital survey from approximately 620 hospitals. The data are percentages (the proportion of positive responses in the survey). The table presents several percentiles, as well as the minimum and maximum values.

Five-Number Summary

The **five-number summary** of a collection of numbers consists of the lowest number, the 25th percentile, the 50th percentile, the 75th percentile, and the highest number. Suppose the lowest number is 15, the 25th percentile is 22, the 50th percentile is 40, the 75th percentile is 45, and the highest number is 130. We could report the five-number summary in list form or table form.

List form of a five-number summary:

15, 22, 40, 45, 130

Table form of a five-number summary:

Minimum	**25th percentile**	**50th percentile**	**75th percentile**	**Maximum**
15	22	40	45	130

TABLE 8.11 **How Researchers Used Percentiles to Summarize a Hospital Survey**

Patient safety culture composites	Hospitals	Composite Positive Response						
		Minimum value	10th percentile	25th percentile	Median (50th percentile)	75th percentile	90th percentile	Maximum value
teamwork within units	621	52%	72%	76%	80%	83%	87%	97%
supervisor/manager expectations and actions promoting patient safety	622	47%	66%	70%	75%	79%	83%	95%
organizational learning—continuous improvement	621	39%	61%	66%	71%	76%	80%	94%
management support for patient safety	620	37%	57%	64%	71%	78%	84%	97%
overall perceptions of patient safety	621	27%	52%	58%	64%	70%	77%	89%
feedback and communication about error	618	32%	52%	57%	62%	68%	74%	90%
communication openness	619	40%	54%	58%	61%	66%	70%	98%
frequency of events reported	617	33%	50%	55%	60%	66%	71%	84%
teamwork across units	621	14%	44%	49%	56%	65%	72%	91%
staffing	620	25%	42%	48%	54%	62%	69%	87%
handoffs and transitions	622	19%	30%	36%	42%	51%	61%	93%
nonpunitive response to error	621	14%	34%	38%	43%	49%	55%	82%

SOURCE: U.S. Department of Health and Human Services, Agency for Healthcare Research and Quality, Hospital Survey on Patient Safety Culture.

The lowest number (minimum), 25th percentile (lower quartile or first quartile), 50th percentile (median), 75th percentile (upper quartile or third quartile), and highest number (maximum) split a data set into four groups such that each group captures 25% of the data. Figure 13 illustrates the groups.

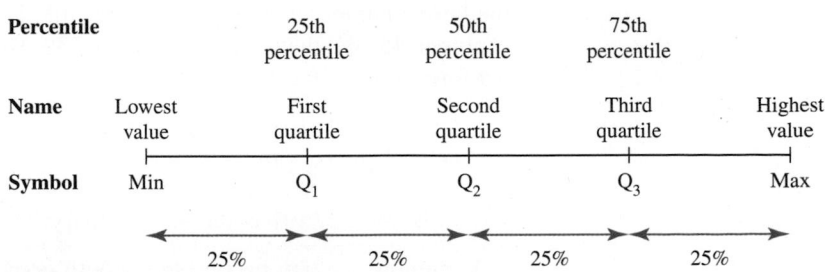

FIGURE 13
The quartiles split the data into four groups.

CONNECTION
REPRESENTATION

The distance between the numbers Min, Q_1, Q_2, Q_3, and Max do not have to be the same; for example, a possibility is Min $= 5$, $Q_1 = 15$, $Q_2 = 17$, $Q_3 = 57$, and Max $= 100$.

The five-number summary contains a great deal of information:

- Approximately 25% of the data belong to each interval [Min, Q_1] and [Q_3, Max].
- Approximately 50% of the data are less than Q_2.
- Approximately 75% of the data are less than Q_3.
- Approximately 50% of the data belong to the interval [Q_1, Q_3].
- The typical value is indicated by the median Q_2.

Also,

- The numbers Q_1 and Q_3 give an indication of the spread (variation) of the data set, because the interval [Q_1, Q_3] contains the middle 50% of the data.
- The **interquartile range (IQR),** defined by IQR $= Q_3 - Q_1$, is the range of the middle 50% of the data.

Five-Number Summary

The five-number summary of any collection of numbers $x_1, x_2, \ldots, x_n$ contains the lowest number (Min), first quartile (Q_1), median (Q_2), third quartile (Q_3), and the highest number (Max).

The following example finds the five-number summary for a data set.

EXAMPLE 8.37   Hank Aaron played baseball for the Atlanta Braves for 23 seasons from 1954 to 1976. The table shows the number of home runs he hit each year, from lowest to highest. Find the five-number summary.

10	12	13	20	24	26	27	29	30	32	34	34
38	39	39	40	40	44	44	44	44	45	47	

SOURCE: www.baseball-reference.com.

SOLUTION

The lowest value is Min $= 10$, the first quartile is $Q_1 = 26$, the median is $Q_2 = 34$, the third quartile is $Q_3 = 44$, and the highest value is Max $= 47$. The five-number summary is 10, 26, 34, 44, 47. We could represent the five-number summary in a table, as follows:

Min	Q_1	Q_2	Q_3	Max
10	26	34	44	47

▲

Box Plot (Box-and-Whisker Plot)

A **box plot** (or **box-and-whisker plot**) is a visual representation of the five-number summary. Figure 14 shows the box plot corresponding to the five-number summary of the annual number of home runs hit by Hank Aaron over his 23-year career.

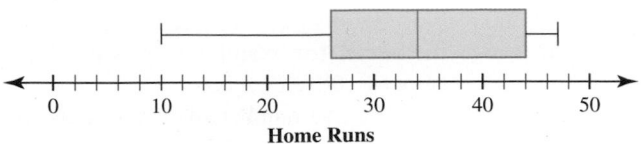

FIGURE 14

A box plot for the five-number summary of the annual home runs hit by Hank Aaron: lowest value = 10, 25th percentile = 26, median = 34, 75th percentile = 44, highest value = 47.

CONNECTION
REPRESENTATION
    The quartiles $Q_1 = 26$ and $Q_3 = 44$ correspond to the edges of the box, the vertical line in the box corresponds to the median $Q_2 = 34$, and the endpoints of the whiskers correspond to the lowest value Min = 10 and the highest value Max = 47 (called *extreme values*). The whiskers extend from a quartile to an extreme value. The line in the box represents the measure of center. Students should be able to "display numerical data in plots on a number line, including dot plots, histograms, and box plots" (Gr. 6, CCSS).

> ◼ **Historical Note**
>
> John Tukey (1915–2000) was a researcher for Bell Labs and a professor at Princeton University. He invented the box plot to display the five-number summary, describing it in his book *Explanatory Data Analysis* (1977) in the chapter titled "Box-and-Whisker Plots."
>
> *Time & Life Pictures/Getty Images*

    Stem-and-leaf plots and dot plots are excellent ways to visualize single small sets of data. Box plots are useful for comparing the centers and spread of multiple sets of data. We compare the centers by comparing the lines in the box (median), and we compare the variability by comparing the length of the boxes (IQR).

    Figure 15 shows the box plot of the number of nonfatal occupational injuries per 100 full-time workers for durable goods manufacturing (for example, lumber products, furniture, metal products, and glass products) and nondurable goods manufacturing (for example, tobacco, textile, paper, and leather products), based on data from the Bureau of Labor Statistics.

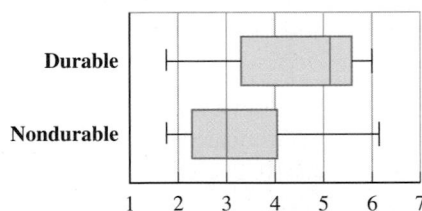

FIGURE 15

Box plot of the incidence of nonfatal occupational injuries per 100 full-time workers for durable and nondurable goods manufacturing.

    Can you think of a title for this graph?

    A possible title of the graph could be "The durable goods workforce tends to experience more days away from work because of injuries or illnesses."

CONNECTION
REPRESENTATION
    The locations of the medians show there are fewer injuries or illnesses, on average, for occupations in nondurable goods manufacturing. The widths of the boxes (IQR) show there is more variation in the number of injuries or illnesses for occupations in durable goods manufacturing.

Detecting Outliers and Creating Outlier Box Plots

An **outlier** is a number that is much smaller or much larger than other numbers in the data set. There are several possible causes of outliers:

AP Photo

- An outlier may represent a rare occurrence because of diversity and chance. For example, Guinness World Records recognizes Robert Pershing Wadlow, pictured in the photo, as the tallest man in the world at 8 feet 11.1 inches.
- An outlier may represent a malfunction in equipment.
- An outlier may represent a value from a different population. For example, a researcher gathering data about rainbow trout may accidentally include measurements from a brown trout.
- An outlier may represent an error in recording. For example, the number 258 could be entered instead of 25.8 in the following table.

	A
1	meters
2	24.2
3	21.6
4	258
5	18.9

Outliers should be identified, because by definition they are extremely unusual and warrant further study. Why did the outlier occur? Also, outliers could distort graphs and descriptive summaries such as the mean or the MAD. There is a way, developed by statisticians, to detect outliers using a formula.

How to Use Quartiles to Identify Outliers

Let the measurement y belong to a collection of numbers $x_1, x_2, \ldots, x_n$ with the quartiles Q_1 and Q_3 and IQR $= Q_3 - Q_1$.

- If $y < Q_1 - 1.5 \cdot \text{IQR}$, then y is an outlier (y is extremely low).
- If $Q_3 + 1.5 \cdot \text{IQR} < y$, then y is an outlier (y is extremely high).

This means that

- if y is much less than the first quartile (25th percentile), then y is an outlier.
- if y is much greater than the third quartile (75th percentile), then y is an outlier.

EXAMPLE 8.38

CONNECTION

REASONING

Identify outliers, if any, in the data set.

$-6, -3, 10, 17, 18, 22, 24, 25, 34, 34, 36, 41, 42, 52, 53, 53, 55, 56, 56, 78, 113, 120$

SOLUTION

The list is sorted from lowest to highest. We need to find Q_1, Q_3, and IQR: $Q_1 = 22$, $Q_3 = 55$, and IQR $= Q_3 - Q_1 = 55 - 22 = 33$.

Now, let's check for outliers that are extremely low: $Q_1 - 1.5 \cdot \text{IQR} = 22 - 1.5 \cdot 33 = -27.5$. All numbers y less than -27.5 are outliers. There are no numbers in the data set less than -27.5.

Let's check for outliers that are extremely high: $Q_3 + 1.5 \cdot \text{IQR} = 55 + 1.5 \cdot 33 = 104.5$. Both 113 and 120 are greater than 104.5, so 113 and 120 are outliers.

▲

The following example illustrates how to draw an **outlier box plot.**

EXAMPLE 8.39

CONNECTION

REASONING

REPRESENTATION

Draw a box plot of the data. Use a mark such as a dot (•) to indicate outliers, if any.

$$3, 5, 7, 12, 14, 22, 25, 28, 29, 30, 33, 35, 35, 38, 72$$

SOLUTION

The list is sorted from lowest to highest. We need to find the quartiles and IQR: $Q_1 = 12$, $Q_2 = 28$, $Q_3 = 35$, and IQR = $35 - 12 = 23$. We must choose endpoints of the whiskers that are not outliers.

Now, let's check for values that are extremely low: $Q_1 - 1.5 \cdot IQR = 12 - 1.5 \cdot 23 = -22.5$. There are no values less than -22.5, so there are no extremely low values. This means 3 is the endpoint of a whisker.

Let's check for outliers that are extremely high: $Q_3 + 1.5 \cdot IQR = 35 + 1.5 \cdot 23 = 69.5$. $69.5 < 72$, so 72 is an outlier. $69.5 \not< 38$, so 38 is not an outlier, which means 38 is the endpoint of a whisker. Then we can draw the outlier box plot.

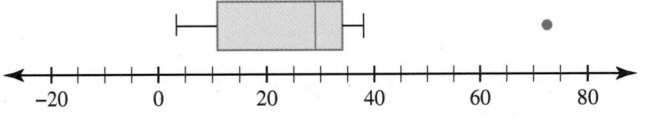

CONNECTION

REPRESENTATION

Fuel economy is important because it reduces toxic emissions, saves oil, and lowers operating costs. In the city, the Chrysler Sebring (a compact car) gets 15 mpg, the Honda Accord (a midsize car) gets 26 mpg, the Toyota Avalon (a large car) gets 21 mpg, and the Jeep Liberty (an SUV) gets 17 mpg. We generally believe smaller vehicles are more efficient than large vehicles, although we can find examples that violate our intuition. So we looked at city fuel efficiency estimates of 194 compact cars, 122 midsize cars, 51 large cars, and 300 SUVs available from the U.S. EPA to get an overall view of the differences in city fuel efficiency for these classes of vehicles. Figure 16 shows the box plot for the mileage of each class of vehicle. The asterisks indicate outliers.

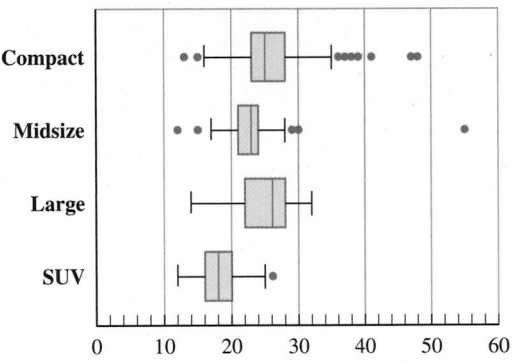

FIGURE 16

Outlier box plot with outliers (•).

We see the large cars have the most variability (a larger IQR), while midsize cars have the least variability (a smaller IQR). One midsize car has strikingly better fuel efficiency compared to all vehicles, and it turns out to be a rare occurrence—a hybrid model—rather than a data entry error. Several compact cars have unusually high fuel efficiency. Large cars, which offer more space and power, are comparable to many compact and midsize cars in terms of fuel efficiency.

As noted in the NCTM standards, "Box plots do not convey as much specific information about the data set, such as where clusters occur, as histograms do. But box plots can provide effective comparisons between two data sets because they make descriptive characteristics such as median and interquartile range readily apparent" (p. 251). Box plots make it easier to compare multiple collections of numbers.

QUESTIONS FOR SECTION 8.3

REPRESENTATION

Refresher: Representations (language, diagrams, tables, symbols, algebra, manipulatives, and contextualized situations) are important because we use them to organize, record, and communicate mathematical ideas and to make them more comprehensible.

1. Find the five-number summary for the data summarized by the following box plot.

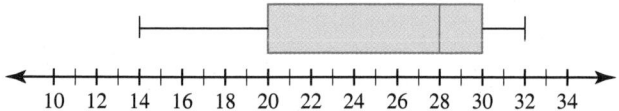

2. The five-number summary for the number of phone calls per hour for a technical support hotline is 4, 12, 15, 20, 22. Draw the corresponding box plot. Be sure to use appropriate tick marks on the axis.

3. A Federal Trade Commission survey on consumer fraud in the United States provided the first systematic analysis of fraud in the past decade. Percentiles were used to estimate the cost per incident of fraud across types of fraud. The table demonstrates a wonderful use of percentiles, because it shows a measure of central tendency (50th percentile) and the lower and upper quartiles (25th percentile and 75th percentile), which provide a measure of variation (for example, 50% of club membership fraud is between $25 and $100).

Type of fraud	Cost per Incident			Observations
	Percentile			
	25th	50th	75th	
billed for Internet service you did not agree to purchase	$40	$60	$100	11
billed for buyers' clubs memberships you did not agree to purchase	$25	$50	$100	22
purchased credit repair	$100	$300	$1000	14

a. On average, which type of fraud is the most costly for consumers? Explain your answer.

b. Which type of fraud shows the most variation? Explain your answer.

4. A teacher recorded the prices of different brands of inkjet printers: $150, $385, $150, $130, $150, $300, $100, $250, $150, $60, $150, $70, $200, $350, $100, and $100. Summarize the data with the 25th percentile, 50th percentile, and 75th percentile by completing the table.

	Percentile		
	25th	50th	75th
Cost for different brands of inkjet printers			

5. The box plot shows the overall ranking of small and large air conditioners based on cost.

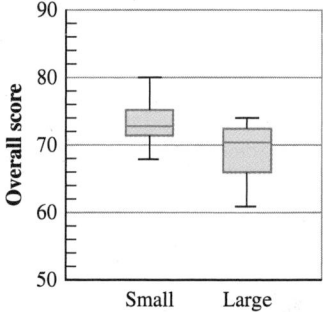

a. Which category of air conditioners typically has a higher ranking? Explain how you know.

b. Which category of air conditioners shows more variation in ranking? Explain how you know.

PROBLEM SOLVING

Refresher: Problem solving (reaching a goal that is not immediately attainable) is important because it helps students think more deeply about what they know and helps them deal with unfamiliar situations.

6. A set of data has the five-number summary 40, 46, 60, 66, 72.

a. What is the lowest possible value in the data set that is not an outlier?

b. What is the highest possible value in the data set that is not an outlier?

7. Shawn has a credit card for purchasing gasoline. The company keeps a record of the distance from the gas station to Shawn's house for each purchase with the credit card. If the company notices any unusual purchases, then the company makes an effort to contact Shawn to verify the card is being properly used to guard against fraudulent use. The data show the non-zero distances, in miles rounded to the nearest 5 miles, of several recent purchases. Determine a distance based on quartiles that must be exceeded for the company to contact Shawn.

   20, 15, 15, 35, 40, 10, 10, 60, 20, 120, 220, 140, 80, 75, 65, 50

8. Tim the tire dealer wants to set the warranty on a particular brand of tires so that 15% of the customers, at most, return tires because of premature wear. Tim obtains the following representative data on the life span of a sample of tires from some

of his customers (mileage rounded to the nearest mile). What mileage should Tim guarantee in his warranty?

15,483	17,759	24,313	27,210
15,595	18,957	24,417	27,964
16,507	21,008	25,775	28,490
17,493	21,812	26,158	29,233
17,531	23,809	26,241	33,578

REASONING AND PROOF

Refresher: Reasoning and proof (thinking and justifying) are important because they help students make sense of mathematics.

9. Find a possible value for the missing number in the data set that results in the graph shown.

   a. Box plot A has the data set 12, 15, 15, a, 22, 23, 26.

   b. Box plot B has the data set b, 15, 18, 19, 20, 23, 25.

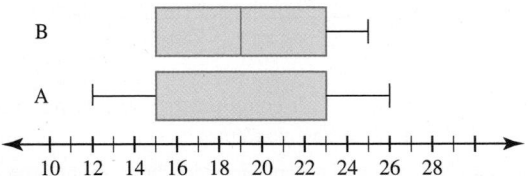

10. A data set has a range of 25 and an IQR of 8. Find a possible five-number summary for the data.

11. What number is the range of the middle 50% of the data? Choose the correct answer: *median, range, IQR.*

CONNECTIONS

Refresher: Connections (linking and applying mathematical ideas) are important because they deepen student understanding and make mathematics more meaningful, flexible, and useful.

12. If a "20 percentile wage" is $23,000, then 20% of workers in that occupation earn less than $23,000 and 80% of workers in that occupation earn $23,000 or more. The table shows the percentile wages for elementary-school teachers (excluding special education teachers).

Percentile	10th	25th	50th	75th	90th
Annual wage	$33,830	$40,850	$50,510	$63,600	$78,720

SOURCE: Bureau of Labor Statistics, 2009.

   a. What is the 25th percentile wage for elementary school teachers?

   b. What percentage of elementary school teachers earn $33,830 or more?

   c. What percentage of elementary school teachers earn less than $63,600?

13. Refer to the BMI-for-age chart in Figure 12 and use the BMI calculation.

   a. Determine the weight status of a 12-year-old boy with a weight of 113 pounds and a height of 58 inches.

   b. Estimate the minimum healthy weight of a 14-year-old boy with a height of 62 inches.

14. The table shows the worst 20 starting salaries for 2010 graduates.

College degree	Starting pay
child and family studies	$29,500
elementary education	$31,600
social work	$31,800
athletic training	$32,800
recreation and leisure	$33,300
art	$33,500
interior design	$34,400
theology	$34,700
religious studies	$34,700
horticulture	$35,000
paralegal studies/law	$35,100
education	$35,100
graphic design	$35,400
interdisciplinary studies	$35,600
culinary arts	$35,900
special education	$36,000
music	$36,700
art history	$39,400
dietetics	$40,400
nutrition	$42,200

SOURCE: 20 Worst-Paying College Degrees in 2010, Lynn O'Shaughnessy, August 12, 2010, finance.yahoo.com.

   a. Which salaries appear to be outliers?

   b. Identify any actual outliers in the starting salaries.

COMMUNICATION

Refresher: Communication (written and verbal explanations using representations and proper mathematical vocabulary) is important because it helps students refine and strengthen their understanding.

15. A student scored an 85 on a test. This score corresponds to the 78th percentile. What does this mean?

16. What does the length of the whiskers in a regular box plot tell you?

17. What does the length of the box in a box plot tell you?

18. List four possible sources of outliers.

19. Kelly's score on a math test ranked in the 96th percentile. What does this mean?

More practice with the ideas of the section

20. Fill in the blank. Choose one the following acronyms, words, or phrases: *25th percentile, 50th percentile, 75th percentile, bar graph, box plot, different, five-number summary, identical, IQR, greater, high, histogram, length, less, line, low, negative, ordinal number, outliers, percentage, percentile, positive,* or *MAD.*

a. A(n) _____ is a graph that makes the median and IQR readily apparent.

b. Spread (or variability) could be measured by the range, quartiles, or _____.

c. _____ are numerical values that are unusual and can affect some summary measures, such as mean and MAD, and even the graphical representation of the data.

d. A standard box plot is based on the _____.

e. A(n) _____ is a rank that tells you the relative number of observations less than a given number.

f. If $y < Q_1 - 1.5 \cdot IQR$, then y is an outlier that is unusually _____.

g. If $Q_3 + 1.5 \cdot IQR < y$, then y is an outlier that is unusually _____.

h. Q_1 represents the _____.

i. A(n) _____ in the box represents the measure of center.

j. The _____ of the box represents the measure of variability.

k. There is no standard approach for calculating percentiles, so your calculator, software program, and the guidelines in this section could give you _____ results.

21. Find the five-number summary for the given data.

18	19	22	24	26	31	33	33	35	38
38	40	42	48	51	53	58	61	75	76
78	80	82							

22. A data set of the number of minutes Gina practiced piano has the following five-number summary: 70, 108, 125, 135, 143. Draw the corresponding box plot. Be sure to use appropriate tick marks on the horizontal axis.

23. Software for cameras is important for organizing and editing digital pictures. A photographer ranked cameras sold with software, using a numerical score from 0 to 100. Draw an appropriate box plot of the data.

75, 33, 48, 62, 75, 50, 15, 32, 36, 43

24. The given data are for cost, in cents, to print one page of text for 20 printers.

	A	B	C	D
1	1.8	3.3	4.8	6.2
2	1.9	3.4	5.2	6.4
3	2.0	3.5	5.3	6.5
4	3.2	3.6	5.8	6.8
5	3.3	4.0	5.8	7.1

a. Find the percentile corresponding to 5.3.

b. Find the percentile corresponding to 4.0.

c. Find the percentile corresponding to 3.3.

d. Find the price that represents the 72nd percentile.

e. Find the price that represents the 58th percentile.

f. Find the price that represents the 30th percentile.

25. Pete the painter recorded the price per gallon, in dollars, for samples of two types of paint: flat and semigloss.

Flat paint			Semigloss paint	
9	17	20	11	26
9	17	21	14	29
11	18	21	15	32
12	18	25	17	32
14	18	26	18	34
15	18	26	18	34
15	18	27	21	35
16	19	29	23	

a. Complete the table.

Type of paint	Price per Gallon			Observations
	Percentile			
	25th	**50th**	**75th**	
flat				
semigloss				

b. On average, which type of paint is more expensive?

c. Which type of paint shows the most variation? Explain your answer.

26. Naomi drove the following number of miles each day, rounded to the nearest mile: 16, 17, 18, 19, 19, 20, 20, 21, 22, 22, 22, 22, 23, 24, 27, 35, 33, 33, and 38. Summarize the data with percentiles in a table.

27. Is a percentile a number? If not, what is it?

28. Find the value of x that represents the pth percentile of a collection of n numbers in increasing order.

   a. $p = 50, n = 64, x_{31} = 125, x_{32} = 150, x_{33} = 156$

   b. $p = 62, n = 50, x_{31} = 124, x_{32} = 150, x_{33} = 181$

   c. $p = 40, n = 120, x_{47} = 62, x_{48} = 70, x_{49} = 74$

   d. $p = 72, n = 258, x_{184} = 88, x_{185} = 94, x_{186} = 103$

29. The top 10 companies in the computer industry with the most patents in 2008 were as follows.

Rank	Company	Patents
1	IBM	4186
2	Samsung	3515
3	Canon	2114
4	Microsoft	2030
5	Intel	1776
6	Matsushita	1745
7	Toshiba	1609
8	Fujitsu	1494
9	Sony	1485
10	Hewlett-Packard	1424

   a. Which values appear to be outliers?

   b. Use the IQR to identify any actual outliers.

30. Give an example of a situation in which you would prefer to have the rank 90th percentile rather than 60th percentile.

31. Give an example of a situation in which you would prefer to have the rank 60th percentile rather than 90th percentile.

32. The graph shows the BMI for age for girls.

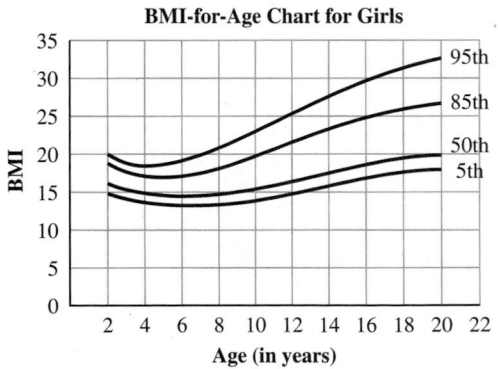

BMI-for-Age Chart for Girls

Refer to this BMI-for-age chart for girls and Table 8.10 and use the formula $\text{BMI} = 703(W/H^2)$ to do the following.

   a. Determine the weight status of a 16-year-old girl with a BMI of 24.

   b. Determine the weight status of a 13-year-old girl with a weight of 105 pounds and a height of 56 inches.

   c. Estimate the minimum healthy weight of a 14-year-old girl with a height of 66 inches.

33. The following table shows recent expenditures per student for fall enrollment in public elementary and secondary schools. Are there any outliers in the data? If yes, indicate which expenditures are outliers.

Type of expenditure	Cost per student
salaries	$5562
employee benefits	$1789
purchased services	$881
supplies	$747
tuition and other	$175
capital outlay	$1168
interest on debt	$292

SOURCE: National Education Center for Statistics.

34. The data show a few average math scores of fourth graders on the NAEP test in 2008 for 11 states: 214, 229, 232, 235, 237, 238, 240, 242, 242, 243, and 252.

   a. Which values, if any, appear to be outliers?

   b. Use quartiles to identify any actual outliers.

35. Draw an outlier box plot for each data set. Use a circle ($\cdot$) for any outliers.

   a. 21, 23, 44, 56, 67, 82, 115, 119, 125, 133, 240, 260

   b. 20, 30, 67, 82, 112, 114, 115, 119, 120, 122, 124, 124, 125, 128, 129, 130, 142

36. The following table of 51 values represents the percentages of fourth graders who scored "at or above proficiency" (solid academic performance) on an NAEP reading test for the 50 states plus the District of Columbia.

14	DC	28	OR	34	DE	36	OH
19	MS	29	AR	34	UT	36	WA
20	LA	29	AK	34	FL	36	WY
23	CA	29	AL	35	NE	37	MN
24	NM	29	NC	35	ID	38	VA
24	AZ	30	TX	35	ND	39	MT
24	NV	31	RI	36	WI	40	PA
26	HI	32	MO	36	ME	41	VT
26	SC	32	IL	36	MD	41	NH
27	OK	32	MI	36	NY	41	CT
27	TN	33	IN	36	IA	43	NJ
28	WV	33	KY	36	KS	49	MA
28	GA	34	SD	36	CO		

   a. Which values, if any, appear to be outliers?

   b. Use quartiles to identify any actual outliers.

37. In a study by the Insurance Institute for Highway Safety, cars traveled at 10 mph and crashed into the rear bumper of a parked SUV. The data reflect the cost to repair the SUVs in seven pairs of vehicles: $1053, $1338, $1428, $1872, $2091, $2208, and $6015. Make a box plot for these data. Indicate outliers, if any, with a circle or an asterisk. A surprise awaits you.

38. The following table records the percentage of citizens of the 50 states plus the District of Columbia who were registered voters in 2008.

HI	59.1	WY	69.3	MA	72.6	NC	75.7
UT	59.7	KS	69.7	KY	73.0	NH	76.0
TN	64.5	OK	70.1	OH	73.0	IA	76.3
AR	64.9	PA	70.1	OR	73.0	WI	76.4
NY	65.8	FL	70.4	CT	73.5	SD	76.9
WV	66.1	IL	70.9	AK	73.7	MS	77.0
NV	66.9	NJ	70.9	DE	73.8	MI	77.1
TX	67.3	GA	71.0	MD	73.9	DC	78.3
IN	68.1	MT	71.3	VA	74.3	LA	78.3
CA	68.2	AL	71.6	MO	74.5	ME	79.7
AZ	68.9	WA	71.7	SC	74.5	MN	79.7
ID	68.9	CO	72.2	NE	74.9	ND	83.7
NM	69.3	VT	72.5	RI	75.5		

SOURCE: U.S. Census Bureau.

a. Which values, if any, appear to be outliers?

b. Use quartiles to identify any actual outliers.

39. The table shows the number of bushels of soybeans (in millions of bushels, where 1 bushel = 60 pounds) grown by leading states.

1	12	55	161
1	15	56	191
3	17	70	226
5	17	78	244
5	18	105	264
9	31	120	428
10	47	124	445
12	50	138	

SOURCE: U.S. Census Bureau.

a. Which values, if any, appear to be outliers?

b. Use quartiles to identify any actual outliers.

40. The table shows the number of bushels of corn per acre (in millions of bushels, where 1 bushel = 60 pounds) grown by leading states.

65	125	137	160
78	125	137	163
104	130	138	164
105	133	140	165
108	133	140	170
115	134	144	171
116	134	144	179
118	135	144	180
121	136	155	195
124	136	157	200
			205

SOURCE: U.S. Census Bureau.

a. Which values, if any, appear to be outliers?

b. Use quartiles to identify any actual outliers.

41. *Consumer Reports* defines the *blind zone distance* of a car as the distance a 28-inch traffic cone had to be before the driver could see the cone in the rearview mirror. It depends on the height of the driver and the design of the vehicle. The dot plot shows the blind zone distance for some of the worst vehicles for a driver with a height of 5 feet 1 inch.

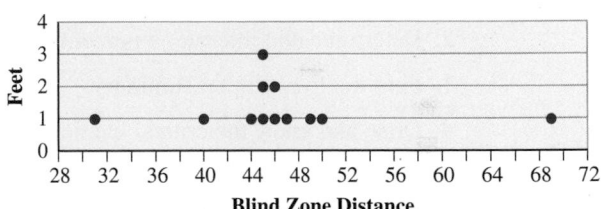

a. Which values, if any, appear to be outliers?

b. Use quartiles to identify any actual outliers.

42. The basic box plot shown is based on data from a study by the Insurance Institute for Highway Safety. In the study, the SUVs traveled at 10 mph and crashed into the rear bumper of a parked car. The box plot summarizes the damage to the vehicles. The study involved seven pairs of vehicles.

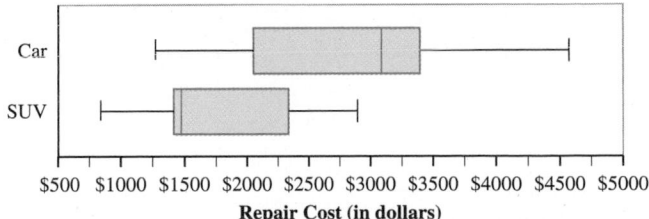

An SUV Crashes into a Parked Car.

a. Which type of vehicle, on average, suffered costlier damage? Explain how you know.

b. Which type of vehicle shows more variation in the costs? Explain how you know.

CHAPTER 8 REVIEW

CHAPTER 8 Organizer

Section	What You Should Learn	Review Problems
8.1	**1.** Recognize and distinguish the two types of variables: categorical variable and numerical variable.	1–2
	2. Use a tally table, frequency table, or relative frequency table to organize data.	3–5
	3. Include appropriate title, key, units, and scale in a graph.	6–7
	4. Create and read a pie graph and bar graph to visualize categorical data.	8–12
	5. Create and read a line graph, scatterplot, histogram, and pictograph to visualize numerical data.	13–16
	6. Use a scatterplot to see if there is a relationship between two variables.	17–18
	7. Construct a histogram.	19
8.2	**1.** Calculate three measures of center: mean, median, mode.	20
	2. Recognize and use the mean in various situations.	21–28
	3. Determine the appropriateness of the mean or median as a measure of center.	29
	4. Calculate the mean absolute deviation and range of a data set.	30–31
	5. Calculate the minimum usual and maximum usual scores.	32–33
	6. Create or use stem-and-leaf plots or dot plots.	34–35
8.3	**1.** Compare two scores.	36
	2. Determine and interpret a percentile.	37–39
	3. Find the five-number summary.	40–42
	4. Draw and know the critical elements of a box-and-whisker plot.	43–44
	5. Compare several numerical variables using box plots.	45–46
	6. Detect outliers using quartiles.	47–48
	7. Draw an outlier box plot.	49–50

Key Terms and Concepts

statistics   414

descriptive statistics   414

four phases of data analysis   414

variable   415

data   415

categorical variable
   (qualitative variable)   415

numerical variable
   (quantitative variable)   416

tally table   418

frequency table   418

relative frequency table   418

graphs   420

exploratory data analysis   420

bar graph   421

two-way table   422

pictograph (picture graph)   423

pie chart   424

line graph   427

scatterplot (scatter plot)   428

histogram   430

measure of center   442

measure of variation   442

distribution   442

mean   444

reduction of error in
   measurements   444

median   447

choosing mean or median   447

mode   448

stem-and-leaf plot   449

stems   449

leaves   449

dot plot (line plot)   450

measures of variability   452

range   452

deviation from the mean   452

mean absolute deviation (MAD)   452

usual values   453

minimum usual value   453

maximum usual value   453

unusual value   453

percentile   462

five-number summary   465

measuring variation with IQR   465

interquartile range (IQR)   467

box plot (box-and-whisker plot)   467

outlier   469

using quartiles to detect outliers   469

outlier box plot   470

Review Questions

1. Determine the type of variable.

   a. number of students who ride a bike to school

   b. student identification numbers

   c. letter grade on an assignment

   d. telephone numbers

   e. percentage of students who say their favorite color is blue

   f. age group of survey respondents: 13 to 18, 19 to 25, 26 to 30, 31 to 35, . . .

   g. types of crime (burglary, robbery, and so on)

2. The table shows data for five participants in a survey at an elementary school.

Student	ID	Favorite color	Pets
Janet	415	blue	4
Carlo	213	green	3
Mikey	004	blue	4
Elisa	681	brown	5
Pete	400	purple	0

   a. Explain how the table records the data associated with each participant.

   b. Determine the variables of interest and type of each variable.

   c. Explain how the table records the data for each variable.

3. A teacher surveys students with pets. She asks the question, "What is your favorite animal?" The choices were dog, cat, bird, or other. The following table records the results.

Student	Type	Student	Type
1	dog	6	other
2	bird	7	cat
3	bird	8	other
4	cat		
5	none		

   Summarize the data in the following formats.

   a. tally table   b. frequency table

   c. relative frequency table

4. The following frequency table shows the number of participants who favor Proposition 123. The table groups the results by gender and age group.

	<30	30–45	46–60	61–75	>75
Male	5	2	7	1	4
Female	4	3	7	8	2

   a. How many surveyed females were between 46 and 60 years old?

   b. How many males were surveyed?

   c. How many people were surveyed?

   d. What percentage of those surveyed were females?

5. *Consumer Reports* listed the prices of cell phones recommended for its subscribers. The manufacturer, brand of phone, and prices are listed.

Samsung; Impression; $50	Samsung; Solstice; $30
Motorola; Tundra; $180	LG; Rumor Touch; $30
Samsung; Instinct; $100	Samsung; Exclaim; $50
LG; Lotus Elite; $100	Samsung; Alias 2; $50
LG; enV Touch; $80	Casio; G'zOne Rock; $150
LG; enV3; $30	Samsung; Jitterbug J; $150
Samsung; Convoy; $70	Casio; G'zOne Brigade; $250

   Display the data in a frequency table. Create categories that depend on the

   a. manufacturer.   b. price range.

6. Write a creative or interpretative title for the graph.

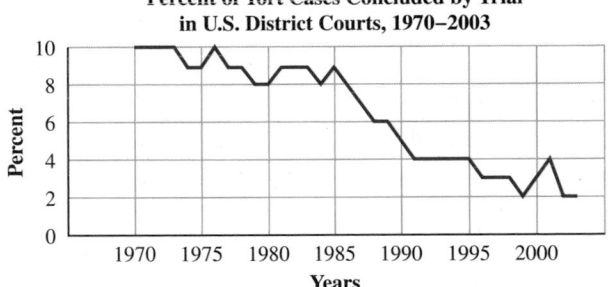

Percent of Tort Cases Concluded by Trial in U.S. District Courts, 1970–2003

SOURCE: Bureau of Justice Statistics.

7. According to the Bureau of Justice Statistics, "Drug abuse violations are defined as state or local offenses relating to the unlawful possession, sale, use, growing, manufacturing, and making of narcotic drugs, including opium or cocaine and their derivatives, marijuana, synthetic narcotics, and dangerous non-narcotic drugs such as barbiturates. Juveniles are defined as persons under age 18 years. Adults are defined as persons age 18 and older" (bjs.ojp.usdoj.gov/content/glance/drug.cfm). Write a creative or interpretative title for the graph.

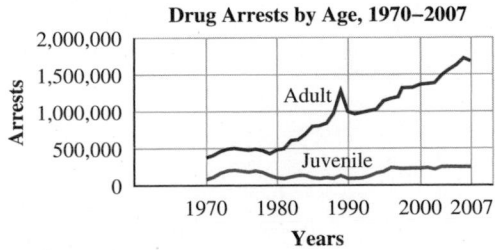

Drug Arrests by Age, 1970–2007

SOURCE: Bureau of Justice Statistics.

8. In a survey, 18 people were asked how they would vote for Proposition 246. Of the respondents, 8 said they would vote yes, 6 said they would vote no, and the others said they were undecided. If you drew a pie chart for the data, what would be the central angles for the sectors of the pie? Round your results to the nearest degree.

9. The two-way table summarizes casualty data from the *Titanic*.

Type of passenger	Passengers	Survivors
men, first class	175	57
men, second class	168	14
men, third class	462	75
women, first class	144	140
women, second class	93	80
women, third class	165	76

  a. Did class affect survival? Make a graph for the data. Write a descriptive title for the graph.

  b. Did gender affect survival? Make a graph for the data. Write a descriptive title for the graph.

10. The following bar graph shows the number of packages of a particular brand of gum sold at Candies-R-Us from July through December.

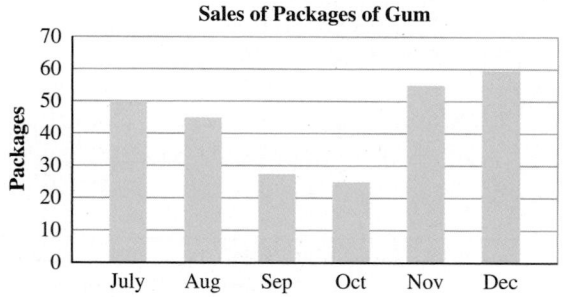

  a. Which months experienced an increase in sales (compared to the previous month)?

  b. Which month experienced the greatest increase in sales?

  c. Which months experienced a decrease in sales (compared to the previous month)?

  d. Which month experienced the greatest decrease in sales?

  e. What is the minimum number of packages of gum the store should keep in inventory?

11. The U.S. Census Bureau lists the number of health care visits, as percentages, to doctor's offices, to emergency departments, and as home visits during 2001 according to age groups.

Age (in years)	None	1–3 visits	4–9 visits	10 or more visits
under 18	11.5%	54.6%	26.1%	7.6%
18–44	23.3%	46.1%	18.9%	11.8%
45–64	16.6%	42.9%	25.7%	15.9%
65 and older	7.1%	32.3%	35.6%	25%

Graphs A and B are two different bar graphs of the data in the table.

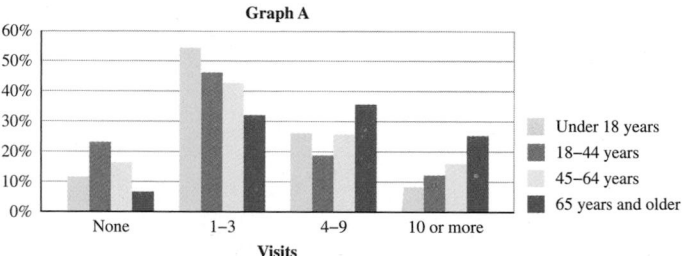

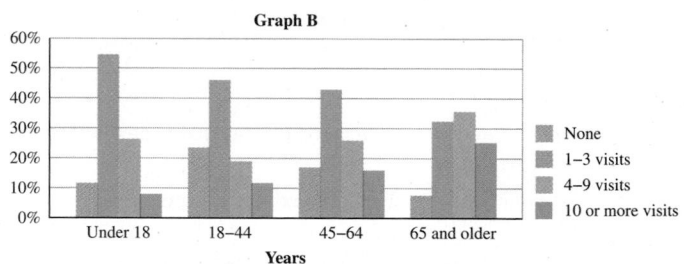

  a. Which graph highlights differences among the age groups?

  b. Which graph highlights differences among the number of health care visits?

12. The following table records per capita consumer expenditures (in dollars) for three types of health care.

Types of expenditures	2004	2005	2006
hospital care	$1920	$2040	$2163
home health care	$145	$162	$176
nursing home care	$392	$407	$417

SOURCE: U.S. Census Bureau, Statistical Abstract of the United States: 2009.

Graphs A and B are two different bar graphs of the data in the table.

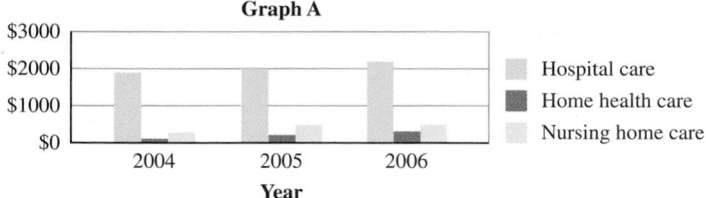

Graph A

a. Which graph highlights differences in the years?

b. Which graph highlights differences among the types of expenditures?

c. Write a descriptive title for graph A.

d. Write a descriptive title for graph B.

13. The following data show the percentage (rounded to the nearest percent) of students who play sports at a certain school. Create a bar graph that highlights differences

a. between girls and boys.

b. among the listed sports.

Sport	Girls	Boys
basketball	21	60
softball	55	15
hockey	8	3
other	16	22

14. The following table lists the four leading exporters of crude oil for 2008, as well as the amount of crude oil produced, rounded to the nearest hundred thousand. Graph the data using a pictograph.

Country	Oil (in millions of barrels per day)
Saudi Arabia	8.0
Russia	7.0
United Arab Emirates	2.5
Iran	2.3

15. Graphs A and B are two preliminary graphs of the following data.

Year	Dollars	Year	Dollars
2005	40	2007	62
2006	45	2008	68

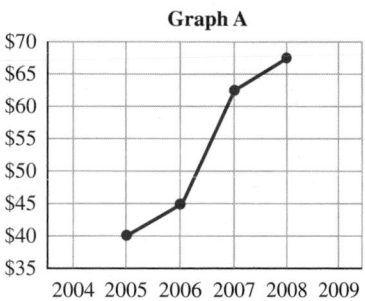

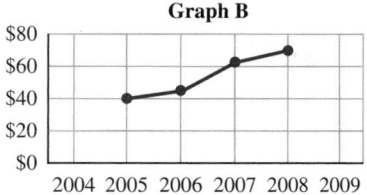

a. Which graph exaggerates small changes?

b. What characteristics of the graph exaggerate minor changes?

16. Construct a line graph for the mean age (in years) of the mother when she first gives birth. Include a descriptive title for your graph.

1980	22.7	1995	24.5
1985	23.7	2000	24.9
1990	24.2	2005	25.2

SOURCE: U.S. Census Bureau, Statistical Abstract of the United States: 2009.

17. Rolling resistance ("the force at the axle in the direction of travel required to make a loaded tire roll") affects fuel efficiency. Tires with lower rolling resistance lead to higher fuel efficiency. Tires with lower slide numbers help the driver maintain safer control of the vehicle due to better traction, which is important in stopping distance. More information is available from the National Highway Transportation & Safety Administration (http://www.nhtsa.gov). The table is based on data from the NHSTA. The first column of the table indicates the tire brand, the second indicates the rolling resistance of the tire, and the third column of sliding numbers indicates the dry traction rating of the tire on asphalt. Is there a correlation between the rolling resistance (horizontal axis) and dry trac-

tion ratings (vertical axis) of the tires? Construct and analyze a scatter plot for the data.

Tire	Rolling resistance	Slide number (dry surface)
B10	12.02	93.83
B11	10.13	94.77
B12	15.22	103.9
B13	15.01	94.87
B14	13.9	101.5
B15	13.99	90.64
D10	13.56	94.6
G10	12.09	98.53
G11	10.02	97.45
G8	9.83	94.41
G9	11.27	98.25

18. The following data from the NHTSA estimate the amount of money spent on media advertisement and enforcement of the Click It or Ticket programs for improving seat belt use.

State	Dollars spent per person	Citations per 10,000 people
Alaska	$0.50	38.2
Arkansas	$0.67	45.4
Connecticut	$1.74	144.1
Idaho	$0.36	208.3
Illinois	$0.32	123.9
Indiana	$0.45	131.2
New York	$0.02	153.3
North Dakota	$0.74	82.7
Ohio	$0.27	99.4
South Dakota	$0.17	25.5

a. Construct a scatterplot for the data.

b. Does there appear to be a correlation between the number of dollars spent per person and the number of citations per 10,000 people? Explain your answer.

19. The following table shows the number of U.S. patents awarded by state in 2009, from the U.S. Patent and Trademark Office in a report from April 2010.

AL	2869	LA	315	OH	3023
AK	55	ME	130	OK	446
AZ	1759	MD	1445	OR	2014
AR	154	MS	4038	PA	3066
CA	23,354	MI	3516	RI	305
CO	1968	MN	2972	SC	579
CT	1661	MS	144	SD	56
DE	342	MO	877	TN	785
FL	2899	MT	91	TX	6436
GA	1666	NE	226	UT	855
HI	96	NV	426	VT	500
ID	985	NH	608	VA	1209
IL	3615	NJ	3259	WA	4856
IN	1246	NM	329	WV	102
IA	730	NY	6127	WI	1887
KS	509	NC	2298	WY	417
KY	457	ND	92		

a. Create a tally table for the data using the groupings $0 \leq x < 500$, $500 \leq x < 1000$, $1000 \leq x < 1500$, $1500 \leq x < 2000, \ldots, 6000 \leq x < 6500$, and 6500 or more.

b. Create a frequency table for the data using the same groupings.

c. Display the data with a histogram.

20. Calculate the mean and median for each data set.

a. 11, 15, 17, 19, 24, 28   b. 15, 17, 19, 24

c. 15, 17, 19, 100

21. Martha purchased a song, a blank CD, and a marker for a total of $2.04. What is the average cost for each item?

22. Two classes raised money for a fundraiser. The table shows the results. How can the principal fairly decide which class performed better?

	Money raised	Students
Third-grade class	$380	25
Fourth-grade class	$450	30

23. Pam, Sandra, and Cindy are teachers who collected cash donations from merchants to buy school supplies for their classes. They agreed to combine their donations and split the total evenly. Pam collected $200, Sandra collected $185, and Cindy collected $242. How much money does each get?

24. Ellen, Connie, and Tanya measured the height of a flower. They obtained the measurements 14.5, 15.1, and 14.5 cm. What is a reasonable measurement to record for the height of the flower? Explain your answer.

25. A teacher surveyed her class to determine the average number of pencils each student has at his or her desk. The results are shown in the frequency table.

Quantity	Frequency
0	2
1	3
2	8
3	12

   a. How many students were surveyed?

   b. What is the average number of pencils each student has?

26. A collection of 20 measurements with a mean of 54 cm includes the measurement 42 cm. Suppose the measurement 42 cm is replaced with 70 cm. What is the new mean? Explain your answer.

27. The teacher measured the heights of his students. On average, the boys were 65 cm tall and the girls were 60 cm tall. There were 14 boys and 12 girls. What was the average height of a student in the class? Explain your answer.

28. A student is asked to calculate the mean of the numbers 0, 3, 8, and 10. The student gives the answer 7. Explain how the student arrived at the faulty answer.

29. Calculate the mean and median for the data set 6, 10, 15, 35, 72, 100, 315. Which average seems more appropriate? Explain your answer.

30. The following data, from the U.S. Census Bureau's 2009 Statistical Abstract of the United States, represent the annual per capita consumption of nonalcoholic beverages (such as milk, tea, juice, bottled water, and coffee) from 2002 to 2006: 149.3, 151.0, 152.8, 152.8, and 154.0 gallons. Use the following statistical ideas to quantify the variation in the per capita consumption over this period. Round the final calculation to the nearest hundredth.

   a. range   b. MAD

   c. minimum and maximum usual values

   d. first and third quartiles

31. The following data show the distance (in feet) a ball is thrown on six throws: 21, 24, 30, 36, 38, and 42. The concept of variation is an important idea in statistics. Use the following statistical ideas to quantify the variation in the distance. Round the final calculation to the nearest tenth.

   a. range   b. MAD

   c. minimum and maximum usual values

   d. first and third quartiles

32. The teacher returned tests to her students. The average on the tests was 82 points, and the MAD was 5.2 points. Suppose Ken scored 66, Erin scored 73, Lisa scored 93, and Phil scored 97. Identify the unusual scores, if any.

33. Ken wants to buy a used car. He plans to choose car A or car B. The annual operating expense for car A is $1280, with a MAD of $275. The annual operating expense for car B is $1450, with a MAD of $105.

   a. What are the minimum and maximum usual operating expenses for car A?

   b. What are the minimum and maximum usual operating expenses for car B?

   c. Ken must take into account his limited budget of $150 for monthly operating expenses. If the cars are similar in all other respects, which car might Ken choose? Why?

34. Calculate the mean, median, and mode for the data displayed in the stem-and-leaf plot.

   a.

Stem	Leaf 1|2 = 12
0	2334
1	23
2	012

   b.

Stem	Leaf 1|2 = 1.2
0	2334
1	23
2	012

35. Determine the mean, median, and mode of the data represented by the dot plot. All data are whole numbers.

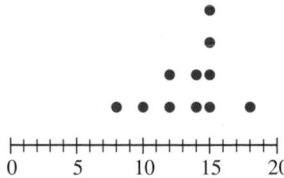

36. The data show the results of tests taken by Mitchell in psychology and Samantha in history. Who scored relatively better on a test? (Refer to the directions for questions 24–26 in Section 8.2.)

Student	Test score	Mean	MAD
Samantha	76	68	4
Mitchell	82	70	7

37. The table shows the times (in seconds) for a sack race with 20 participants.

28.2	39.1	46.0	52.4
28.8	40.2	46.3	61.0
31.5	42.3	47.0	62.0
33.1	43.1	47.7	62.8
37.2	43.1	51.3	67.2

a. Find the 44th percentile.   b. Find the 90th percentile.

c. What is the percentile rank of the time 43.1 seconds?

d. What is the percentile rank of the time 33.1 seconds?

e. Give the five-number summary for the data.

38. The given data are based on the U.S. Census Bureau's 2009 Statistical Abstract of the United States. Do the following.

    a. A 23-year-old male has a height of 6 feet 1 inch, which corresponds to the 85th percentile for males in their 20s. What does the 85th percentile mean in this situation?

    b. A 22-year-old female has a weight of 150 pounds, which corresponds to the 55th percentile for females in their 20s. What does the 55th percentile mean in this situation?

39. Mike sells solar lighting systems and wants to set the warranty on a particular brand of solar lighting so that 20% of the customers, at most, are eligible for free repairs because of malfunctions. Mike obtains the following representative data on the life span of solar lighting from some of his customers (hours rounded to the nearest whole number). How many hours should Mike guarantee in his warranty? Explain your answer.

4005	5162	7399
4025	5224	8079
4083	5470	8236
4210	5553	8837
4231	6388	8851
4686	6527	9879
4894	7316	9990

40. The table shows the number of students who were absent in a class during the first 3 weeks of class.

0	0	8	2	1
3	2	4	5	4
1	2	3	9	0

Represent the data using a

a. five-number summary.   b. dot plot.

41. The box plot summarizes the number of people who attended a play each day during a 4-week period. All the data are whole numbers.

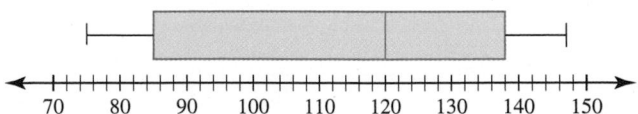

a. What interval captures the middle 50% of the number of people who attended the play?

b. What is the 75th percentile of the data?

c. What is the range of the attendance?

42. The box plot is a representation of the number of books read by a class each day during a contest.

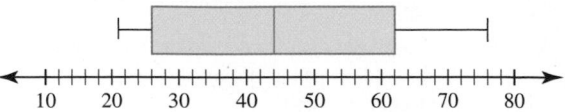

a. Are the upper 50% of the data more spread apart than the lower 50% of the data? Explain how you can tell from the box plot.

b. Find the five-number summary for the data.

43. Draw a box plot for the following measurements of running times (in seconds) in a race at a track meet: 62, 63, 65, 70, 72, 75, 76, 78, 81.

44. The following data represent the total scores for 15 competitors in an archery competition.

1102	1024	938	866
1040	993	934	862
1037	988	892	850
1027	939	884	

a. Determine the five-number summary for these data.

b. What is the IQR for these data?

c. Make a box plot for the data.

d. Are the upper 50% of the data more spread apart than the lower 50% of the data? Explain how you can answer this question using the box plot.

45. The following box plot compares the repair costs for two types of cars at a local automotive shop.

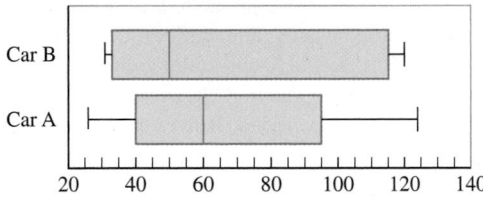

a. Which car has a lower average repair cost? Tell how you know.

b. Which car has a larger variation in repair costs? Tell how you know.

46. The following box plot compares the fuel efficiency (in miles per gallon) for two types of trucks.

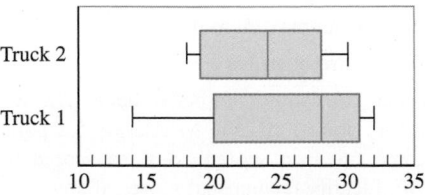

a. Which truck gets more miles per gallon, on average? Tell how you know.

b. Which truck has less variation in fuel efficiency? Tell how you know.

47. The following data show the number of boxes of cookies sold by different youth organizations: 19, 22, 45, 48, 51, 52, 55, 56, 61, 62, 84.

   a. Which number or numbers appear to be outliers?

   b. Identify any outliers in the data.

48. The following data show the number of jumping jacks by 15 students: 2, 7, 10, 17, 18, 18, 19, 19, 20, 21, 21, 23, 26, 31, 33.

   a. Which number or numbers appear to be outliers?

   b. Identify any outliers in the data.

49. The diagram shows an outlier box plot.

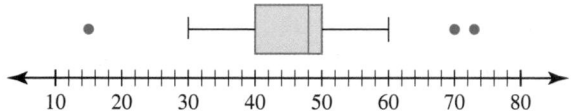

   a. How many outliers are there?

   b. What are their numerical values?

50. A website shows the demographics of its Internet visitors from the top 12 countries.

Origin	Percent
United States	42.1
India	10.1
United Kingdom	8.0
Canada	4.7
Netherlands	2.5
Australia	2.3
Germany	2.0
Sweden	1.7
France	1.7
Spain	1.4
Italy	1.3
Singapore	1.3

   a. Make a standard box plot for the data.

   b. Identify any outliers using the IQR.

   c. Make an outlier box plot.

   d. Which graph do you prefer? Explain your answer.

Chapter 8 Test

1. *Recognize and distinguish the two types of variables: categorical and numerical.* Determine the type of variable.

   a. television rating system in Canada (E, exempt; C, children; C8+, viewers 8 years and older; G, general programming, suitable for all audiences; PG, parental guidance; 14+, viewers 14 years and older; and 18+, adult programming)

   b. number of text messages that a person sends

   c. ratings for songs (0, 1, 2, 3, 4, and 5) on your music play list where 0 means "avoid" and 5 means "favorite"

   d. numerical grades on your homework assignments

   e. your opinion on the affordability of health care (very satisfied, somewhat satisfied, somewhat dissatisfied, very dissatisfied, or no opinion)

   f. month (1 = January, 2 = February, . . . , 12 = December) of the date of birth of people in a survey

   g. air pollution index (for example, 234 parts per million)

   h. service rating (excellent, good, fair, or poor)

   i. salary of workers

   j. number of words you can memorize in a memory study

2. *Use a tally table, frequency table, or relative frequency table to organize data.* Students completed a written survey. One of the questions asked was, "What is your favorite subject?" The choices were math, history, and writing. The following table summarizes the results of 10 students.

Student	Subject	Student	Subject
1	math	6	math
2	history	7	math
3	history	8	writing
4	writing	9	math
5	history	10	math

Summarize the data in the following formats.

   a. tally table

   b. frequency table

   c. relative frequency table

3. *Use a tally table, frequency table, or relative frequency table to organize data.* The following frequency table shows the number of people in a survey who favor Proposition ABC. The table groups the results by gender and age group. Altogether, 85 people were surveyed.

	<20	21–35	36–50	51–65	>65
Male	6	8	3	5	4
Female	3	12	7	7	5

a. How many females in the survey between 36 and 50 years old supported Proposition ABC?

b. What percentage of those surveyed between 51 and 65 years old supported Proposition ABC?

c. What percentage of males surveyed supported Proposition ABC?

4. *Create and read a pie chart and a bar graph to visualize categorical data.* The data in the table show the median income (in 2008 dollars) of people 25 or older based on their educational attainment. The educational levels represent categories. Make a bar chart to compare the categories. Include a descriptive title for the graph.

Educational attainment	Median income
less than high school graduate	$19,989
high school graduate (including equivalency)	$27,448
some college courses or associate's degree	$33,838
bachelor's degree	$47,853
graduate or professional degree	$63,174

SOURCE: U.S. Census Bureau, 2006–2008 America Community Survey.

5. *Create and read a pie chart and a bar graph to visualize categorical data.* The data show the top 5 search engines in the United States for July 2010. Create a pie chart to compare the share of the search engines.

Rank	Brand	Share of search
1	Google Search	64.2%
2	Yahoo! Search	14.3%
3	Bing Search	13.6%
4	Ask.com Search	2.1%
5	AOL Search	1.9%

SOURCE: The Nielsen Company.

6. *Create and read a pie chart and a bar graph to visualize categorical data.* The data show the year-to-year percent change in the share of searches for the top 5 search engines in the United States for July 2010. Create a bar graph to compare the percent change in the categories.

Rank	Brand	Percent change
1	Google Search	−1%
2	Yahoo! Search	−17%
3	Bing Search	51%
4	Ask.com Search	24%
5	AOL Search	−38%

SOURCE: The Nielsen Company.

7. *Create and read a pie chart and a bar graph to visualize categorical data.* The table shows the rental vacancy rate (as a percentage) in the United States from 2007 to 2009 for each quarter.

	Q1	Q2	Q3	Q4
2007	10.1	9.5	9.8	9.6
2008	10.1	10	9.9	10.1
2009	10.1	10.6	11.1	10.7

SOURCE: Adapted from data from the U.S. Census Bureau, 2010.

The following are two bar graphs for the table.

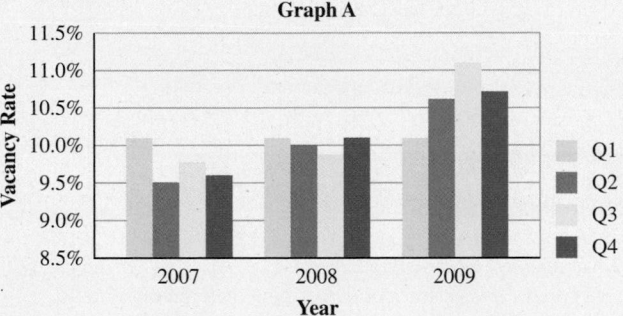

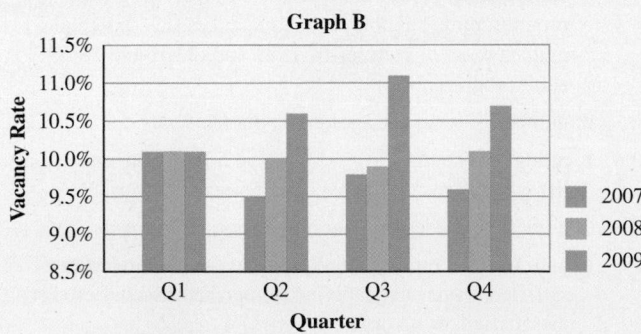

a. Which bar graph highlights differences in the years? Explain your answer.

b. Which bar graph highlights differences among the quarters? Explain your answer.

c. Discuss any interesting features of the graphs.

8. *Create and read a line graph or pictograph to visualize numerical data.* The table shows the number of workplace injuries (in thousands) in the food service and drinking places for various years. Possible injuries include slipping on floors, burns from hot equipment, and muscle strains from heavy lifting.

Year	Workplace injuries (in thousands)
2005	236
2006	240
2007	246
2008	222
2009	202

SOURCE: U.S. Bureau of Labor Statistics, 2010.

Represent the table with the following line graphs. Include a descriptive title for each graph.

a. Use a scale for the vertical axis that exaggerates minor changes.

b. Use a scale for the vertical axis that seems to represent the data fairly.

9. *Create and read a line graph or pictograph to visualize numerical data.* The line graph shows the U.S. unemployment rate for people over the age of 25 by educational attainment.

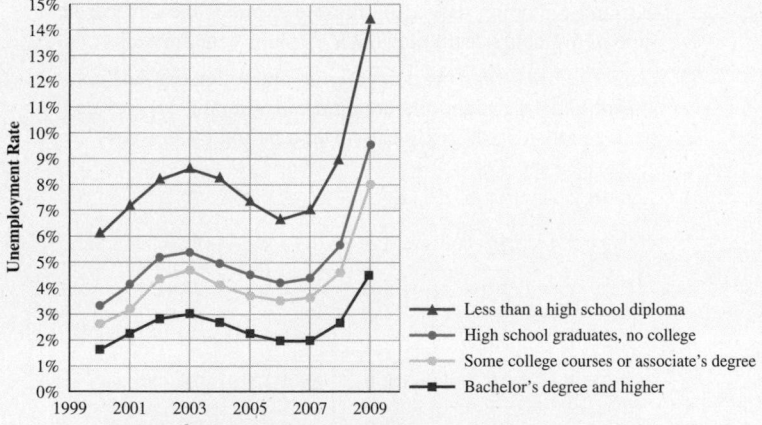

SOURCE: U.S. Bureau of Labor Statistics, 2010.

a. Which group of people seems most vulnerable when the economy experiences a downturn?

b. How does the graph display cycles of economic expansion and contraction?

c. Write a title that interprets the graph for the reader.

10. *Create and read a line graph or pictograph to visualize numerical data.* The table shows the mean SAT total scores for two groups of students, "took PSAT" and "no PSAT," in the classes of 2000 to 2004 in the Montgomery County Public Schools system in Maryland. The "took PSAT" group of students took the PSAT before taking the SAT, whereas the "no PSAT" group of students did not take the PSAT before taking the SAT. Make a graph to compare the performance of both groups of students on the same graph. Include a descriptive title for the graph.

	No PSAT	Took PSAT
2000	903	965
2001	899	962
2002	904	957
2003	855	922
2004	855	922

11. *Create and read a line graph or pictograph to visualize numerical data.* The line graph shows the percentage of workers 65 and older according to their work schedule: "usually full-time" and "usually part-time." What trend does the graph show?

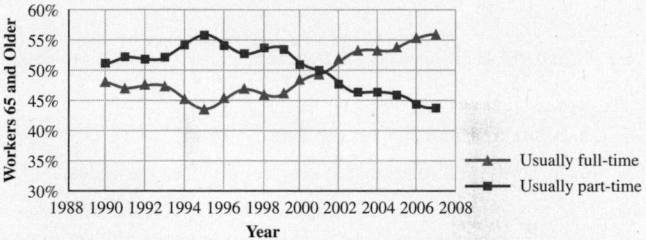

SOURCE: U.S. Bureau of Labor Statistics, 2008.

12. *Use a scatterplot to see whether there is a relationship between two variables.* For each graph, describe the relationship between the two variables as a strong positive linear relationship, weak positive linear relationship, strong negative linear relationship, weak negative linear relationship, or no apparent relationship.

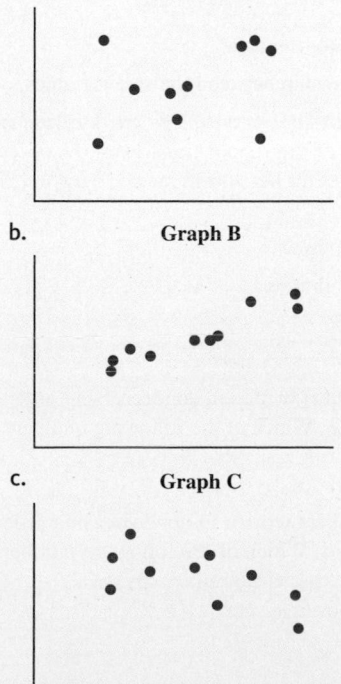

13. *Use a scatterplot to see whether there is a relationship between two variables.* The following table shows the fuel efficiency (in miles per gallon) and the carbon footprint (in tons per year of carbon dioxide) for some hybrid vehicles for 2011.

Fuel efficiency (mpg)	CO₂ footprint (tons/year)
51	3.8
34	5.8
41	4.8
35	5.4
22	8.1
30	6.5
28	6.7
32	6.2

SOURCE: Based on data from the U.S. Department of Energy, www.fueleconomy.com.

  a. Make a scatterplot for the data.

  b. Describe the relationship between the two variables.

14. *Use a scatterplot to see whether there is a relationship between two variables.* The following table shows the estimated fuel efficiency (in miles per gallon) for city and highway driving for some diesel vehicles for 2011.

City	30	23	22	19	19	18	18	17	17
Highway	42	36	33	28	26	25	24	25	21

SOURCE: Based on data from the U.S. Department of Energy, www.fueleconomy.com.

  a. Make a scatterplot for the data.

  b. Describe the relationship between the two variables.

15. *Calculate three measures of center: mean, median, and mode.* Samantha, a member of the school track team, recorded the following running times for her 400-m races: 73.2, 71.1, 75.4, and 72.4 seconds.

  a. Calculate the mean time.

  b. Calculate the median time.

  c. Determine the mode.

16. *Calculate three measures of center: mean, median, and mode.*

  a. There are 401 numbers written in nondecreasing order: $x_1 \le x_2 \le \ldots \le x_{401}$. Which of the following numbers is the median: $x_{199}, x_{200}, x_{201}, (x_{199} + x_{200}) \div 2$, $(x_{200} + x_{201}) \div 2$, or $(x_{201} + x_{202}) \div 2$?

  b. There are 824 numbers written in nondecreasing order: $x_1 \le x_2 \le \ldots \le x_{750}$. Which of the following numbers is the median: $x_{411}, x_{412}, x_{413}, (x_{411} + x_{412}) \div 2$, $(x_{412} + x_{413}) \div 2$, or $(x_{413} + x_{414}) \div 2$?

17. *Determine the appropriateness of the mean or median as a measure of center.* Maria organized a bake sale for the sixth-grade class. The data show the number of yummy chocolate chip cookies sold on Mondays and Fridays for seven weeks. Which measure of center, the median or the mean, would be appropriate to determine the average number of cookies sold on the given weekday? Explain your answer.

  a. Monday: 118, 122, 124, 126, 132, 134, 148

  b. Friday: 112, 122, 125, 125, 128, 130, 180

18. *Calculate the mean absolute deviation and range of a data set.* Several factors affect fuel efficiency, such as quick acceleration and breaking, driving at high speeds, vehicle condition, and where you drive. A driver calculated his fuel efficiency (in miles per gallon) on four separate occasions. The results were 34, 38, 32, and 35 mpg.

  a. Calculate the mean of the data. Round your answer to the nearest tenth.

  b. Calculate the MAD of the data. Round your answer to the nearest tenth.

19. *Calculate the minimum and maximum usual values.* The mean height of students in a sixth-grade class is 62.8 inches, with a MAD of 2.4 inches. Determine the minimum and maximum usual heights for the students.

20. *Calculate the minimum and maximum usual values.* An advertisement for a laptop computer said the battery lasts 5.4 hours. To test the claim, a student charged the battery seven times and recorded the following durations: 4.7, 4.8, 4.9, 5.0, 5.2, 5.3, and 5.7 hours. Based on these data, does the advertised time of 5.4 hours seem plausible? Explain your answer.

21. *Determine and interpret a percentile.* The following data consist of the total weight of aluminum cans (in pounds) recycled per week by a sixth-grade class over a period of 35 weeks.

20.8	31.7	42.1	56.8	72.6
21.1	32.5	44.4	59.3	74.5
22.3	33.9	44.4	61.2	75.0
23.4	37.9	45.2	61.6	78.1
28.7	38.7	48.9	64.1	78.1
31.6	38.9	49.0	66.9	79.7
31.7	39.3	52.7	67.1	79.8

  a. What is the percentile of the weight 44.4 pounds?

  b. What is the percentile of the weight 74.5 pounds?

  c. What weight represents the 70th percentile?

  d. What weight represents the 60th percentile?

22. *Determine and interpret a percentile.* Misha scored in the 85th percentile on her exam. What does this mean?

23. *Find the five-number summary.* The table shows the average number of hours a person 15 years or older spent in a sport or activity. Find the five-number summary for the data.

Sports and exercise activities	Hours per day (average)
cycling	1.2
swimming, surfing, waterskiing	1.7
racquet sports	1.9
basketball	2.0
soccer	2.1
dancing	2.3
baseball, softball	2.4
bowling	2.5
football	2.5
hiking	2.6
golfing	3.3

SOURCE: U.S. Bureau of Labor Statistics, 2008.

24. *Draw and know the critical elements of a box plot.* Write the five-number summary for the box plot. All data are whole numbers.

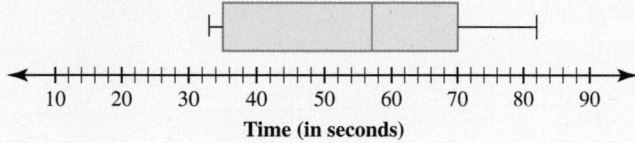

Time (in seconds)

25. *Compare several numerical variables using box plots.* Each member of a team threw a baseball, and the distance was recorded for each player. The box plot summarizes the distances for each team, team A and team B.

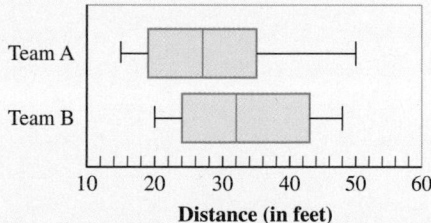

Distance (in feet)

a. Which team threw the baseball farther, on average? Explain how you arrived at your answer.

b. Which team exhibited more variation in the distances? Explain how you arrived at your answer.

26. *Detect outliers using quartiles.* The table shows the number of fatal work injuries per 100,000 workers for each age group.

Age group (in years)	Rate per 100,000
16–17	0.9
18–19	2.6
20–24	3.0
25–34	3.1
35–44	3.4
45–54	4.1
55–64	4.6
65 and over	10.0

SOURCE: U.S. Bureau of Labor Statistics, 2009.

a. Which rates, if any, seem like outliers?

b. Use quartiles to detect any actual outliers. Explain what any such outliers mean.

27. *Draw an outlier box plot.* The table shows the worst 20 mid-career salaries, approximately 15 years into a career.

College degree	Midcareer pay
child and family studies	$38,400
elementary education	$44,400
social work	$44,900
athletic training	$45,700
culinary arts	$50,600
horticulture	$50,800
theology	$51,300
paralegal studies/law	$51,300
recreation and leisure	$53,200
special education	$53,800
dietetics	$54,200
religious studies	$54,400
art	$54,800
education	$54,900
interdisciplinary studies	$55,700
interior design	$56,600
nutrition	$56,700
graphic design	$56,800
music	$57,000
art history	$57,100

SOURCE: 20 Worst-Paying College Degrees in 2010, Lynn O'Shaughnessy, August 12, 2010, finance.yahoo.com.

a. Which salaries, if any, appear to be outliers?

b. Use quartiles to detect any actual outliers.

c. Draw an appropriate box plot for the data.

9

Probability

Where Are We Going?

In **Section 9.1,** we discuss the vocabulary and basic concepts of probability. We discuss the connection between experimental probability and theoretical probability and give a simple probability rule for experiments with equally likely outcomes. In **Section 9.2,** we discuss mutually exclusive events, dependent and independent events, and rules for handling events involving *or* and *and,* and we show how to use a tree diagram to analyze multistage experiments. In **Section 9.3,** we discuss expected value, standard deviation, the normal distribution, simulations, and odds.

What Is the Origin of Probability?

The ancient Egyptians, Chinese, Romans, and Greeks enjoyed dice games. Interest in dice games has a long history. People used dice to determine the will of the gods, to make decisions, or to play a game of chance for entertainment. Thinking of games of chance in terms of mathematics is a relatively recent phenomenon. In the mid-1600s, a gambler named Chevalier de Méré (1607–1684) frequently bet he would roll at least one 6 within 4 rolls of a standard die. He played another game in which he bet he would roll at least one pair of 6s within 24 rolls of two standard dice. He realized he won more money rolling one die than rolling two dice. He asked a friend, the French mathematician Blaise Pascal (1623–1665), for an explanation. Pascal corresponded with his colleague Pierre de Fermat (1601–1655), and together they explained why de Méré won more money with one die. Historians generally regard their correspondence on questions related to dice games and other games of chance as the birth of probability theory.

What Is Probability?

Probability is a measure of the chance that a particular event will occur. It helps us makes informed decisions despite uncertainty. Insurance companies use probability to set rates for insurance policies for drivers and homeowners. Pharmaceutical companies use probability to determine whether improvements in patients result from the drug they are testing. Casinos use probability theory to analyze dice and card games to make sure the rules favor profits for the

Ancient Roman dice made from bone.

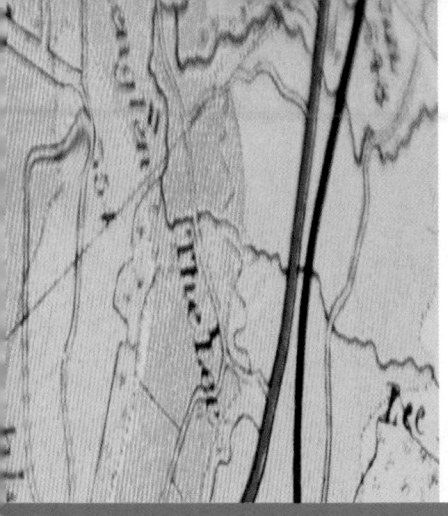

casino. Medical researchers use probability to study the spread of disease and epidemics. Physicists use probability to study the movement of particles in fluid. A judge even used the familiar game of chance called "rock, paper, scissors" to settle a dispute between two attorneys who could not agree upon a neutral site in which to interview a witness for an insurance lawsuit. Nevada law allows candidates to break ties in elections by tossing a coin, drawing straws, or picking a card. Students actively experience probability in all stages of elementary school, for example, tossing a coin, spinning a spinner, and drawing a tree diagram to represent and analyze a probability situation.

SECTION 9.1 | Basics of Probability

Qualitative Phrases in Probability

Words and phrases such as "impossible," "unlikely," "likely," and "certain to occur" are qualitative phrases that we often use to informally characterize the level of uncertainty in a situation. Students should be able to "describe events as likely or unlikely and discuss the degree of likelihood using such words as *certain, equally likely,* and *impossible*" (Gr. 3–5, NCTM).

EXAMPLE 9.1

COMMUNICATION

REASONING

Decide whether the situation is impossible, unlikely, likely, or certain to occur.
a. You will win the lottery.
b. Your pet will learn how to build a spaceship.
c. You will stay awake during the lecture.

SOLUTION

a. unlikely

b. impossible

c. likely

▲

Elementary school students initially engage in explorative activities such as flipping a coin, spinning a spinner, or drawing marbles from a bag and use terms such as *always, maybe, sometimes, never, likely, unlikely, certain,* and *impossible* to describe the chance that a situation will occur.

EXAMPLE 9.2

COMMUNICATION

REASONING

A teacher shows his class a bag containing 3 blue marbles, 15 red marbles, and 72 green marbles. The teacher randomly selects a marble from the bag. Use the word *impossible, unlikely, likely,* or *certain* to describe how likely it is that the teacher will draw a
a. blue marble.

b. red marble.

c. green marble.

SOLUTION

a. There are few blue marbles in the bag compared to the total number of marbles in the bag, so the teacher is unlikely to draw a blue marble.

490

b. Less than half of the marbles in the bag are red marbles, so the teacher is unlikely to draw a red marble.

c. More than half of the marbles in the bag are green marbles, so the teacher is likely to draw a green marble.

▲

In the previous example, the teacher is likely to draw a green marble. However, the teacher may draw a blue marble. Probability tells us what *should* happen in an experiment, it does not tell us what *will* happen in an experiment.

Language of Probability

Here are a few formal vocabulary words related to probability.

Definition

An **experiment** is a procedure in which something happens but the result is not known in advance. An **outcome** is the result of an experiment. The **sample space** is the set of all possible outcomes of an experiment. An **event** is a collection of outcomes. By convention, the letter S represents the sample space, and other capital letters $(A, B, C, \ldots)$ represent events.

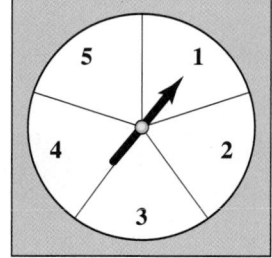

FIGURE 1
1–5 spinner.

An experiment consists of spinning the 1–5 spinner in Figure 1 and recording the number to which the arrow points. The sample space is $S = \{1, 2, 3, 4, 5\}$. $A = \{1\}$ is the event in which the spinner lands on 1, and $B = \{1, 2\}$ is the event in which the spinner lands on 1 or 2. A is an example of a **simple event,** because it consists of exactly one outcome. B is an example of a **compound event,** because it consists of more than one outcome.

EXAMPLE 9.3

COMMUNICATION

REASONING

An experiment consists of rolling a standard die and recording the number that shows on the top side.
a. List the sample space.
b. Describe event $E = \{1, 4\}$ in words.
c. Describe event $E = \{1, 3, 5\}$ in words.

SOLUTION

a. $S = \{1, 2, 3, 4, 5, 6\}$

b. E is the event of rolling a 1 or a 4.

c. E is the event of rolling an odd number, or E is the event of rolling a 1, a 3, or a 5.

▲

EXAMPLE 9.4

COMMUNICATION

REPRESENTATION

Refer to the 1–5 spinner in Figure 1. Consider the events $A = \{2, 4\}$ and $B = \{1, 4\}$.
a. If the spinner points to 3, did event A occur? Explain your answer.
b. If the spinner points to 1, did event B occur? Explain your answer.

SOLUTION

a. A is the event that the spinner points to 2 or 4. The spinner landed on 3, so event A did not occur.

b. B is the event that the spinner points to 1 or 4. The spinner landed on 1, so event B occurred.

▲

Using Numbers from 0 to 1 to Represent Probability

The expression $P(E)$ represents the probability (or likelihood or chance) that event E will occur. You can quantify probability with a fraction, percent, or decimal number.

- If event E is impossible, then we say the chance of E occurring is 0, that is, $P(E) = 0$. In a bag containing blue and yellow marbles, the chance of selecting a green marble is 0.
- If event E is certain to occur, then we say the chance of E is 1, that is, $P(E) = 1$. In the 1–5 spinner in Figure 1, we are certain the arrow will point to a number less than 8.
- If we are uncertain whether event E will or will not occur, then $0 \leq P(E) \leq 1$.
- The closer $P(E)$ is to 0, the less likely E is to occur.
- The closer $P(E)$ is to 1, the more likely it is that E will occur.

REPRESENTATION Students should "understand and use 0 to represent the probability of an impossible event and 1 to represent the probability of a certain event, and they should use common fractions to represent the probability of events that are neither certain nor impossible" (© NCTM Standards 2011 by National Council of Teachers of Mathematics). In addition, they should "know that a probability near 0 indicates an unlikely event, a probability around 1/2 indicates an event that is neither unlikely nor likely, and a probability near 1 indicates a likely event" (CCSS, Gr. 7) (© 2010. National Governors Association Center for Best Practices and Council of Chief State School Officers. All rights reserved.). Concept Map 9.1 relates qualitative phrases with quantities from 0 to 1.

> **Concept Map 9.1** Relating Qualitative Phrases to Quantities from 0 to 1

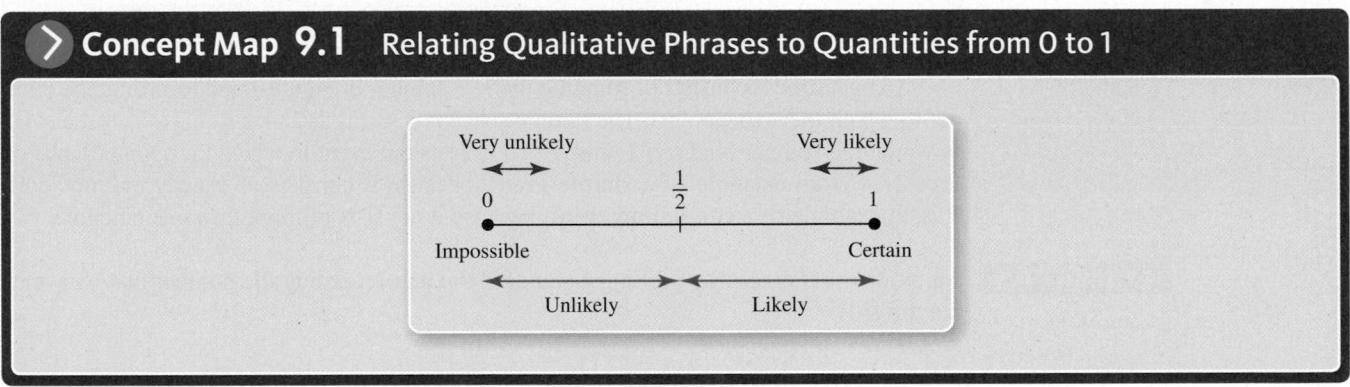

Experimental Probability

Suppose you observed that event E occurred f times when you repeated an experiment n times. The **experimental probability** that event E will occur is the fraction f/n. Experimental probability depends on observations.

EXAMPLE 9.5

CONNECTION
PROBLEM SOLVING
REPRESENTATION

An experiment consists of rolling two standard dice and then multiplying the numbers shown on the top of each die. For example, if one die shows 4 and the other die shows 2, then the outcome is $4 \cdot 2 = 8$.

a. What is the experimental probability of getting a 3 or a multiple of 5?

b. Suppose you repeat this experiment 60 times. Based on the experimental probability in part (a), how often would you expect to get a 3 or a multiple of 5?

SOLUTION

a. The event of getting a 3 or a multiple of 5 is $E = \{3, 5, 10, 15, 20, 25, 30\}$. We rolled the dice 32 times. The actual outcomes were as follows:

15	6	8	8	8	6	6	6	2	18	24	3	12	3	15	24
12	30	4	15	3	5	2	4	36	4	12	15	10	2	6	8

The frequency table is shown.

$E = \{3, 5, 10, 15, 20, 25, 30\}$	Frequency
times E occurred	卌 卌
times E did not occur	卌 卌 卌 卌 𝍦

So, $f = 10$ and $n = 32$. Then the experimental probability of getting a 3 or a multiple of 5 is $10/32 \approx 31\%$.

b. Based on the results in part (a), we expect event E will occur 10 times for every 32 rolls. This leads to the proportion $\frac{10}{32} = \frac{a}{60}$, where a is the number of times we expect event E will occur when we roll the dice 60 times. Then $32a = 10 \cdot 60$, and $a = (10 \cdot 60)/32 = 18.75 \approx 19$. Based on the experimental results, we expect the event to occur 19 times when we roll the dice 60 times. ▲

Another sample of 32 rolls of the dice could yield $f = 15$ and therefore a different experimental probability ($15/32 \approx 47\%$), because the experimental probability depends on the observed frequency f and the number n of repetitions.

Short-Term and Long-Term Behavior of Experiments

It is likely the 1–2 spinner in Figure 2 would land on 2. We *expect* the spinner to land on 2 in 75% of the spins. Let's examine our hunch. Table 9.1 displays some experimental results (generated by a computer), where n is the number of spins, f is the number of times the spinner landed on 2, and f/n is the fraction of times the spinner lands on 2.

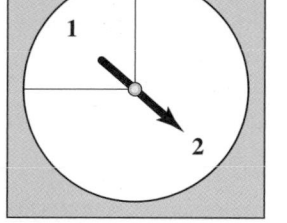

FIGURE 2

1–2 spinner.

TABLE 9.1   **Sample Data for the 1–2 Spinner**

Spins (n)	Frequency (f)	Fraction (f/n, nearest 0.001)
25	17	0.680
65	54	0.831
325	254	0.782
3065	2291	0.747
4945	3719	0.752

Figure 3 shows the graph of the ordered pairs $(n, f/n)$. The fraction f/n is always a number from 0 to 1.

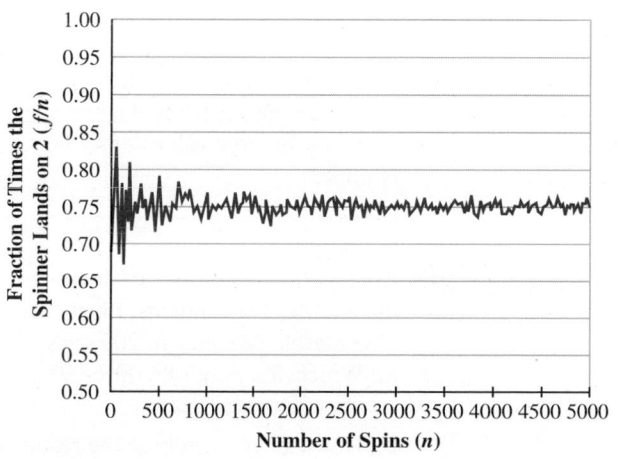

FIGURE 3

Graph of the fraction of times the 1–2 spinner landed on 2.

Small values of n represent **short-term behavior,** and large values of n represent **long-term behavior.** The graph reveals f/n fluctuates widely for small values of n, but the number f/n tends to hover near our expectation 0.75 for large values of n. The data in Table 9.1 and Figure 3 suggest experimental results are unpredictable for a low number of repetitions of an experiment (f/n varies from 0.680 to 0.831) but are more predictable for a large number of repetitions (f/n consistently hovers near 0.75). For larger n, we would see the graph settle more closely to 0.75. Students should be able to "approximate the probability of a chance event by collecting data on the chance process that produces it and observing its long-run relative frequency and predict the approximate relative frequency given the probability" (Gr. 7, CCSS).

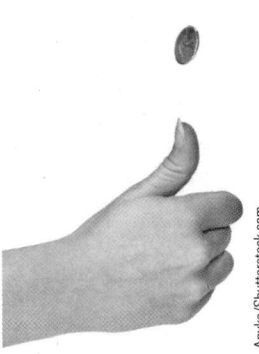

Anyka/Shutterstock.com

Students know the probability that a fair coin lands on tails is 0.50 (or $\frac{1}{2}$ or 50%). They could easily calculate the relative frequency f/n and see that f/n settles near 0.50 as n increases. With this type of problem, students can learn that experimental probabilities approach their expectation as the number of repetitions increases. This gives students the opportunity to relate experimental results (f/n) to their intuition (0.50). It also reinforces that we can *estimate* the probability of an event with the fraction f/n, where f is the number of times the event occurred, and n is the total number times the experiment was repeated.

Law of Large Numbers and Theoretical Probability

CONNECTION   The values of f/n in Figure 3 tend to settle near the number 0.75 for large values of n. This supports our hunch that the number between 0 and 1 that best quantifies the chance the 1–2 spinner lands on 2 is 0.75. **Theoretical probability** is the expected long-term behavior of experimental results. The theoretical probability of the arrow landing on 2 for the spinner in Figure 3 is 0.75.

The **Law of Large Numbers,** proved in the early 1700s, states that the fraction of times an event E occurs when an experiment is repeated n times approaches a fixed number as n increases. That fixed number is the theoretical probability that E occurs.

> ### Law of Large Numbers
>
> Suppose event E occurs f times when an experiment is repeated n times. As n increases, the fraction f/n approaches the theoretical probability that E occurs.

EXAMPLE 9.6

COMMUNICATION
REASONING

Maria observed that event E occurred 5 times when she repeated an experiment 12 times. Ken observed that event E occurred 10 times when he repeated the same experiment 15 times. Their experimental probabilities are $5/12 \approx 0.42$ and $10/15 \approx 0.67$. Explain the noticeable discrepancy between these results.

SOLUTION

An experimental probability f/n depends on both the observed frequency f and the number of times n the experiment is repeated. Noticeable discrepancies may occur for small values of n, but for large values of n, the results will be quite similar because of the Law of Large Numbers.

▲

EXAMPLE 9.7

COMMUNICATION
CONNECTION
REASONING

An experiment consists of drawing one marble from a bag, noting the color, and replacing the marble. Two students, Shawna and Leila, performed this experiment. Shawna picked a blue marble 48 times in 200 tries. Leila picked a blue marble 95 times in 500 tries.

a. Which fraction, 48/200 or 95/500, do you prefer as an estimate of the probability of drawing a blue marble?

b. How can you combine the results to obtain another estimate of the probability of drawing a blue marble?

SOLUTION

a. The experimental probability $95/500 = 0.19$ is preferred because of the greater number of repetitions.

b. By combining the results, we observed that a blue marble is picked $48 + 95 = 143$ times in $200 + 500 = 700$ tries. Then $143/700 \approx 0.20$ is another estimate of the probability of drawing a blue marble. We do not know which estimate ($48/200 = 0.24$, $95/500 = 0.19$, or $143/700 \approx 0.20$) is more accurate, but the Law of Large Numbers suggests the estimate $143/700$ is preferable.

▲

The following Classroom Connection illustrates that students that should be able to apply experimental results, as well as make predictions.

 Classroom Connection

● *Mathematics,* Grade 6, p. 666

Sean dropped his buttered bread 200 times. It landed butter-side-up 62 times. (From Randall I. Charles. © 2004 by Pearson Education, Inc. or its affiliates. Used by permission. All rights reserved.)

a. Estimate the probability, given as a percent, that next time Sean drops the bread, it will land buttered-side-up.

b. How many times might Sean expect the bread to land buttered-side-up the next 350 times he drops it?

Practical Applications of the Law of Large Numbers

CONNECTION How would you find the probability that if you toss a tack, then it lands point down? Or the probability that a newly manufactured lightbulb is not defective? Or the probability that a 40-year-old person dies between 40 and 45 years? We cannot calculate theoretical probabilities for these types of situations. But we can reliably estimate theoretical probabilities with experimental probability.

Interpreting a Probability

The following example illustrates how we can interpret a probability.

EXAMPLE 9.8

CONNECTION
REASONING
REPRESENTATION

An experiment consists of spinning a spinner with the colors blue, green, and yellow. The teacher states that the theoretical probability of the spinner landing on blue is 35%. What does this mean?

SOLUTION

If you spin the spinner many times, then you expect 35% of the spins to land on the color blue. For example, if you spin the spinner 856 times, then you expect the spinner to land on blue approximately 300 times because $35\% \cdot 856 \approx 300$.

▲

Students often have experience with number cubes (dice) or spinners to relate probability and frequency. The NCTM standards assert that "through these experiences, students encounter the idea that although they cannot determine an individual outcome, such as which color the spinner will land on next, they can predict the frequency of various outcomes" (p. 181).

Equally Likely Outcomes

Let $S = \{x_1, x_2, \ldots, x_k\}$ denote the sample space. If the outcomes are **equally likely,** then all outcomes have the same chance of occurring. Mathematically, this means $P(x_1) = P(x_2) = \ldots = P(x_k)$, where $P(x)$ represents the probability of outcome x. Here are three examples:

- Let $S = \{T, H\}$ be the sample space for tossing a fair coin, where T is tails and H is heads. Then $P(T) = P(H) = 1/2$.

- Let $S = \{1, 2, 3, 4, 5, 6\}$ be the sample space for rolling a standard die. Then $P(1) = P(2) = P(3) = P(4) = P(5) = P(6) = 1/6$.

- A bag contains eight green marbles, three blue marbles, and one yellow marble. An experiment consists of randomly drawing one marble from the bag without peeking. Each marble has the same chance of being picked (but the color of the marble is most likely to be green, because most of the marbles are green).

For experiments with equally likely outcomes, we can use theoretical probability rather than experimental probability. The French mathematician Pierre-Simon Laplace (1749–1827) stated the following classical result that plays a large role in probability in the elementary mathematics curriculum.

How to Calculate the Theoretical Probability of Event E When the Sample Space Consists of Equally Likely Outcomes

Suppose all outcomes in an experiment are equally likely. Then the theoretical probability that event E will occur, denoted $P(E)$, is given by

$$P(E) = \frac{\text{number of ways } E \text{ can occur}}{\text{number of equally likely outcomes in the sample space}}.$$

The definition of probability makes it clear that the ability to count the number of outcomes in the event, as well as the sample space, is crucial for problems involving equally likely outcomes. Students should "understand that, just as with simple events, the probability of a compound event is the fraction of outcomes in the sample space for which the compound event occurs" (Gr. 7, CCSS).

EXAMPLE 9.9

COMMUNICATION

CONNECTION

PROBLEM SOLVING

REASONING

REPRESENTATION

An experiment consists of rolling a standard die and recording the number on the top face of the die. Determine the probability of rolling

a. a 1 or a 5.

b. an even number.

SOLUTION

The die is fair, which means all outcomes $S = \{1, 2, 3, 4, 5, 6\}$ are equally likely.
a. Let A represent the event of rolling a 1 or a 5. Then $A = \{1, 5\}$. There are two ways A can occur and six equally likely outcomes in the sample space, so $P(A) = 2/6 = 1/3$.

b. Let B represent the event of rolling an even number. Then $B = \{2, 4, 6\}$. There are three ways B can occur and six equally likely outcomes in the sample space, so $P(B) = 3/6 = 1/2$.

▲

EXAMPLE 9.10

CONNECTION

REASONING

A bag contains eight green marbles, three blue marbles, and one yellow marble. An experiment consists of drawing one marble from the bag without peeking. What is the probability of drawing a green marble?

SOLUTION

Each marble has an equal chance of being drawn because they are presumably the same size and feel the same, so this experiment consists of equally likely outcomes. In the bag, 8 marbles are green and there are 12 marbles altogether, so the probability of drawing a green marble is 8/12 ≈ 67%.

▲

EXAMPLE 9.11

CONNECTION

REASONING

An experiment consists of drawing a card from a standard deck of 52 cards. What is the probability of drawing a club or a queen?

SOLUTION

Each card has an equal chance of being drawn because they are presumably the same size and feel the same, so this experiment consists of equally likely outcomes. There are 13 clubs (A♣, 2♣, 3♣, 4♣, 5♣, 6♣, 7♣, 8♣, 9♣, 10♣, J♣, Q♣, and K♣) and four queens (Q♣, Q♠, Q♥, and Q♦). The event is the union of these sets: $E = \{$A♣, 2♣, 3♣, 4♣, 5♣, 6♣, 7♣, 8♣, 9♣, 10♣, J♣, Q♣, K♣, Q♠, Q♥, Q♦$\}$ (we count Q♣ once). There are 16 ways to draw a club or queen, and there are 52 equally likely outcomes altogether, so the probability of drawing a club or queen is 16/52 ≈ 31%.

▲

The following Released Items illustrates other situations involving equally likely outcomes.

> **RELEASED ITEM**
>
> ● NAEP, 2009
>
> Marty has 6 red pencils, 4 green pencils, and 5 blue pencils. If he picks out one pencil without looking, what is the probability that the pencil will be green?
>
> **a.** 1 out of 3   **b.** 1 out of 4   **c.** 1 out of 15   **d.** 4 out of 15
>
> 38% of fourth graders gave the correct answer.
>
> ● NAEP, 2007
>
> (1, 1)   (2, 1)   (3, 1)
> (1, 2)   (2, 2)   (3, 2)
> (1, 3)   (2, 3)   (3, 3)
>
> A pair of numbers will be chosen at random from the list above. What is the probability that the first number in the pair will be less than the second number in the pair?
>
> 33% of eighth graders gave the correct answer. (U.S. Department of Education, Institute of Education Sciences, National Center for Education Statistics, NAEP)

Another sample space with equally likely outcomes occurs by rolling a pair of standard dice. Suppose an experiment consists of rolling a pair of dice and adding the numbers that appear on top. How many ways can we obtain a sum of 3? Many students claim there is one way, not realizing that there are actually two ways to obtain a 3. Colored dice make it easier to "see" this. Table 9.2 provides a systematic way to list all possible outcomes in a simple experiment that consists of a single toss of two dice, supposing one is green and the other is blue.

TABLE 9.2 **Sample Space for Rolling Two Dice and Observing the Number of Dots Appearing on the Top Face of Each Die**

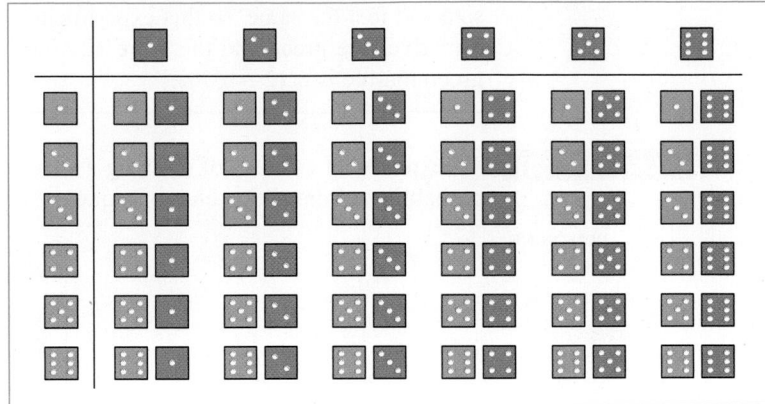

There are 36 possible ordered pairs in this sample space. The ordered pair $(2, 3)$ means the number showing on the green die is 2 and the number showing on the blue die is 3. Similarly, $(4, 5)$ means the number showing on the green die is 4 and the number showing on the blue die is 5. Each ordered pair is equally likely. For example, $(1, 1)$, $(4, 5)$, and $(6, 6)$ are equally likely to occur.

EXAMPLE 9.12

An experiment consists of tossing two standard dice and recording the *sum* of the number of dots showing on the top face of each die. Determine the probability of rolling

a. a 5.

b. a 3 or a 5.

SOLUTION

Table 9.3 shows the possible outcomes.

TABLE 9.3 **Sum of Two Dice**

Sum	•	••	•••	••••	•••••	••••••
•	2	3	4	5	6	7
••	3	4	5	6	7	8
•••	4	5	6	7	8	9
••••	5	6	7	8	9	10
•••••	6	7	8	9	10	11
••••••	7	8	9	10	11	12

a. There are four possible ways to obtain a sum of 5, so the probability of rolling a 5 is 4/36, or $P(5) = 1/9$.

b. There are $2 + 4 = 6$ ways to obtain a 3 or a 5, so the probability of rolling a 3 or a 5 is 6/36, or $P(3 \text{ or } 7) = 6/36 = 1/6$.

We could create different experiments with the two dice by recording the product, the difference, or the maximum rather than the sum.

The probability of an equally likely outcome depends on the model (for example, coins, dice, spinners, cubes, chips, or cards), and students should be able to "develop a uniform [equally likely] probability model by assigning equal probability to all outcomes and use the model to determine probabilities of events" (Gr. 7, CCSS)

Sum of Probabilities

Table 9.4 shows the outcomes and probabilities for a bag of three blue marbles (B), two green marbles (G), and one yellow marble (Y).

TABLE 9.4   Marble Outcomes and Probabilities

Outcome	B	G	Y
Probability	$\dfrac{3}{6}$	$\dfrac{2}{6}$	$\dfrac{1}{6}$

Then $P(\text{B}) + P(\text{G}) + P(\text{Y}) = \dfrac{3}{6} + \dfrac{2}{6} + \dfrac{1}{6} = 1.$

Table 9.5 shows the outcomes and probabilities for the 1–3 spinner in Figure 4.

TABLE 9.5   Probabilities for the 1–3 Spinner

Outcome	1	2	3
Probability	0.20 (72/360)	0.30 (108/360)	0.50 (180/360)

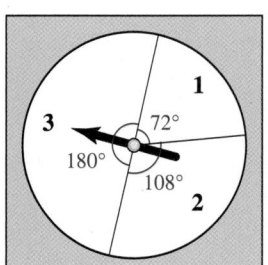

FIGURE 4
1–3 spinner.

Then $P(1) + P(2) + P(3) = 0.20 + 0.30 + 0.50 = 1.$ The marble (see Table 9.4) and spinner (see Table 9.5) examples illustrate the following important property of probability.

Sum of the Probabilities of All Outcomes in the Sample Space

If the sample space of an experiment is $S = \{x_1, x_2, \ldots, x_k\}$, then
$$P(x_1) + P(x_2) + \ldots + P(x_k) = 1.$$

Complementary Event

An experiment consists of rolling a fair die and recording the number of dots on the top face. Let S be the sample space. Let E be the event of rolling a 3, and let $\sim E$ be all outcomes in the S that do not belong to E. The symbol $\sim E$ represents the complement of E. Then $S = \{1, 2, 3, 4, 5, 6\}$, $E = \{3\}$, and $\sim E = \{1, 2, 4, 5, 6\}$.

$$P(E) = \frac{1}{6} \quad \text{and} \quad P(\sim E) = \frac{5}{6}$$
$$= 1 - \frac{1}{6}$$
$$= 1 - P(E)$$

If we know the probability of E, then we can use the following complement rule to find the probability that E does not occur.

> ### Complement Rule
>
> Let S represent the sample space of an experiment and E be any event.
>
> - The **complement of E,** denoted $\sim\!E$, consists of all outcomes in the sample space S that do not belong to E.
> - $P(\sim\!E)$ is the probability that E does not occur.
> - $P(\sim\!E) = 1 - P(E)$.

EXAMPLE 9.13

CONNECTION

Do the following.

a. On a test, 85% of students gave the correct answer to a particular problem. What is the likelihood that a randomly selected student did not give the correct answer?

b. An experiment consists of randomly drawing a card from a standard deck of cards. What is the probability that the card is not a 7?

SOLUTION

a. $1 - 0.85 = 0.15$. There is a 15% chance that a randomly selected student did not give the correct answer.

b. The probability of drawing a 7 is 4/52. Then the probability of not drawing a 7 is $1 - 4/52 = 48/52 \approx 92\%$. The probability that the card is not a 7 is about 92%.

▲

Comparing Probabilities

It is common to compare probabilities using phrases such as "25% more likely," "30% less likely," or "four times as likely." These are multiplicative (not additive) comparisons, because they involve multiplication, percent, or both. We have seen these types of comparisons before, but now we are applying them to probability situations.

- The phrase "A is 60% more likely than B" means $P(A) = P(B) + 60\% \cdot P(B)$. For example, people who suffered a stroke were 60% *more likely* to develop Alzheimer's disease than those who never suffered a stroke, according to the *Seattle Times*. Here's an example: Suppose $P(A) = 0.7$ and $P(B) = 0.5$. Then

$$P(A) = P(B) + k \cdot P(B)$$
$$0.7 = 0.5 + k \cdot 0.5$$
$$0.7 - 0.5 = k \cdot 0.5$$
$$0.2 = k \cdot 0.5$$
$$\frac{0.2}{0.5} = k$$
$$0.40 = k$$
$$40\% = k$$

Then A is 40% more likely to occur than B.

- The phrase "*A* is 15% less likely than *B*" means $P(A) = P(B) - 15\% \cdot P(B)$. For example, a study showed women with cardiovascular disease are 15% *less likely* to receive medication to reduce high LDL cholesterol levels compared to men with cardiovascular disease, according to the Endocrine Society. Here's an example: Suppose $P(A) = 0.61$ and $P(B) = 0.73$. Then

$$P(A) = P(B) - k \cdot P(B)$$
$$0.61 = 0.73 - k \cdot 0.73$$
$$0.61 - 0.73 = -k \cdot 0.73$$
$$-0.12 = -k \cdot 0.73$$
$$\frac{-0.12}{-0.73} = k$$
$$0.16 \approx k$$
$$16\% \approx k$$

Then *A* is 16% less likely to occur than *B*.

- The phrase "*A* is three times as likely to occur as *B*" means $P(A) = 3 \cdot P(B)$. For example, a study showed that agricultural workers exposed to pesticides were three times as likely to experience a steep decline in mental process, such as performing basic calculations or categorizing objects, compared to agricultural workers who were not exposed to pesticides (www.suite101.com). Here's an example: Suppose $P(A) = 0.48$ and $P(B) = 0.17$. Then

$$P(A) = k \cdot P(B)$$
$$0.48 = k \cdot 0.17$$
$$\frac{0.48}{0.17} = k$$
$$2.8 \approx k$$

Then *A* is 2.8 times as likely to occur as *B*.

The media and researchers often report probability comparisons using the casual phrases "times more likely" and "times less likely" rather than the phrase "times as many."

- **Times more likely.** Students who participate in the arts are four *times more likely* to earn recognition for academic achievement (www.artsusa.org). The phrase "*A* is four times more likely to occur than *B*" means $P(A) = 4 \cdot P(B)$. Thus, "four times more likely" really means "four times as likely."

- **Times less likely.** A study showed patients with surgeries scheduled at about 9 a.m. were four *times less likely* to request pain medication than patients with surgeries scheduled at about 4 p.m., according to the journal *Quality & Safety in Health Care*. The phrase "*B* is four times less likely to occur than *A*" means $P(B) = (1/4) \cdot P(A)$. Thus, "four times less likely" really means "one-fourth times as likely."

Concept Map 9.2 illustrates probability comparisons using words, equations, and diagrams.

> **Concept Map 9.2** **Probability Comparisons**

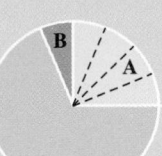

Words:
B is $\frac{1}{4}$ times as likely to occur as A.

Equation:
$P(B) = \frac{1}{4} \cdot P(A)$

Wording from the media and researchers:
B is four times less likely to occur than A.

Words:
A is four times as likely to occur as B.

Equation:
$P(A) = 4 \cdot P(B)$

Wording from the media and researchers:
A is four times more likely to occur than B.

Words:
B is 25% less likely to occur than A.

Equation:
$P(B) = P(A) - 25\% \cdot P(A)$

Words:
B is $\frac{1}{4}$ less likely to occur than A.

Equation:
$P(B) = P(A) - \frac{1}{4} \cdot P(A)$

Words:
A is 33% more likely to occur than B.

Equation:
$P(A) = P(B) + 33\% \cdot P(B)$

Words:
A is $\frac{1}{3}$ more likely to occur than B.

Equation:
$P(A) = P(B) + \frac{1}{3} \cdot P(B)$

EXAMPLE 9.14

CONNECTION

Determine $P(A)$.

a. $P(B) = 0.36$, and event A is 2.4 as likely as event B.

b. $P(B) = 0.20$, and event A is 35% more likely than event B.

c. $P(B) = 0.56$, and event A is 42% less likely than event B.

SOLUTION

a. Event A is 2.4 times as likely as event B, so $P(A) = 2.4 \cdot P(B)$. Then $P(A) = 2.4 \cdot 0.36 \approx 0.86$.

b. Event A is 35% more likely than event B, so $P(A)$ is more than $P(B)$. Then

$$P(A) = P(B) + 35\% \cdot P(B)$$
$$= 0.20 + 0.35 \cdot 0.20$$
$$= 0.27$$

c. Event A is 42% less likely than event B, so $P(A)$ is less than $P(B)$. Then

$$P(A) = P(B) - 42\% \cdot P(B)$$
$$= 0.56 - 0.42 \cdot 0.56$$
$$\approx 0.32$$

▲

EXAMPLE 9.15

CONNECTION

REASONING

An experiment consists of randomly drawing a marble from a jar containing green, blue, yellow, and white marbles. $P(\text{green}) = 5/20$, $P(\text{blue}) = 4/20$, and $P(\text{yellow}) = 3/20$, and $P(\text{white}) = 8/20$. Verify each statement.

a. A green marble is 1.25 times as likely to be drawn as a blue marble.

b. A green marble is 1.6 times less likely to be drawn than a white marble.

c. A yellow marble is 25% less likely to be drawn than a blue marble.

SOLUTION

a. We need to verify the equation $P(\text{green}) = 1.25 \cdot P(\text{blue})$.

$$P(\text{green}) \stackrel{?}{=} 1.25 \cdot P(\text{blue})$$

$$\frac{5}{20} \stackrel{?}{=} 1.25 \cdot \frac{4}{20}$$

$$0.25 = 0.25$$

This verifies that a green marble is 1.25 times as likely to be drawn as a blue marble.

b. We need to verify $P(\text{white}) = 1.6 \cdot P(\text{green})$.

$$P(\text{white}) \stackrel{?}{=} 1.6 \cdot P(\text{green})$$

$$\frac{8}{20} \stackrel{?}{=} 1.6 \cdot \frac{5}{20}$$

$$0.40 = 0.40$$

This verifies that a green marble is 1.6 times less likely to be drawn than a white marble.

c. We need to verify the equation $P(\text{yellow}) = P(\text{blue}) - 25\% \cdot P(\text{blue})$.

$$P(\text{yellow}) \stackrel{?}{=} P(\text{blue}) - 25\% \cdot P(\text{blue})$$

$$\frac{3}{20} \stackrel{?}{=} \frac{4}{20} - 0.25 \cdot \frac{4}{20}$$

$$0.15 \stackrel{?}{=} 0.2 - 0.05$$

$$0.15 = 0.15$$

This verifies that a yellow marble is 25% less likely to be drawn than a blue marble.

QUESTIONS FOR SECTION 9.1

REPRESENTATION

Refresher: Representations (language, diagrams, tables, symbols, algebra, manipulatives, and contextualized situations) are important because we use them to organize, record, and communicate mathematical ideas and to make them more comprehensible.

1. An experiment consists of spinning the 1–3 spinner shown and recording the outcome.

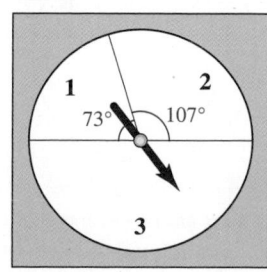

   a. List the sample space.
   b. Determine the probability of each outcome.
   c. Verify $P(1) + P(2) + P(3) = 1$.

2. An experiment consists of spinning a 3–8 spinner and recording the number the arrow points to. What does $E = \{3, 6, 7\}$ represent?

3. A student repeated an experiment of randomly drawing one letter from a bag that contained six letters and recorded the frequency table shown.

Outcome	g	r	a	d	e	s
Frequency	4	5	1	7	3	5

Find the experimental probability of each event.

   a. {r}   b. {e, a}

4. The table shows data for Raj, Gina, and Taylor.

Name	Times *E* occurred	*n*
Raj	68	120
Gina	147	250
Taylor	260	400

a. For each student, determine the experimental probability that *E* occurred.

b. Which experimental probability seems like the best estimate of $P(E)$?

c. How could these results be combined in some way to obtain a potentially better estimate of $P(E)$?

5. A student flips a fair penny several times and records the number of tails in a table. The letter *n* represents the number of times the student tossed the coin. One table shows experimental results (generated by a computer), and the other table shows phony data (generated by the author). Identify the table with the experimental results, and explain how you decided the other table consists of phony data.

Table A

n	10	855	1724	5267
Tails	1	396	840	2588

Table B

n	10	748	1832	4368
Tails	4	300	1329	2764

6. A bag has *b* blue marbles, *y* yellow marbles, and *g* green marbles. There are *n* marbles altogether. An experiment consists of randomly drawing a marble from the bag. What does each fraction represent?

a. y/n b. g/n c. $(b + g)/n$

PROBLEM SOLVING

Refresher: Problem solving (reaching a goal that is not immediately attainable) is important because it helps students think more deeply about what they know and deal with unfamiliar situations.

7. An experiment consists of randomly drawing a card from a standard deck of 52 cards. Find the probability of drawing

a. a 3 or a 5.   b. a diamond or a 7.

c. a face card (the cards with faces on them).

8. Two people play a dice game, rolling two standard dice. The outcome is determined by the difference of the larger number and the smaller number. For example, if the two dice show a 2 and a 5, then the outcome is 3 $(5 - 2 = 3)$. Player A wins if the difference is 1 or 2. Player B wins if the difference is 3, 4, or 5.

a. Find the probability that player A wins.

b. Find the probability that player B wins.

c. Find the probability of a tie.

d. If they play 250 games, how many games would you expect player B to win?

9. A bag contains 450 blue and yellow marbles. The probability of drawing a yellow marble is 36%. How many blue marbles are in the bag?

10. A bag contains four blue marbles, five green marbles, and three yellow marbles. How many blue marbles should you add to the bag so that the probability of drawing a blue marble is 0.80?

REASONING AND PROOF

Refresher: Reasoning and proof (thinking and justifying) are important because they help students make sense of mathematics.

11. In a bag of marbles, 1/4 are blue, 1/6 are green, 1/2 are yellow, and 1/12 are black. If you randomly draw one marble from the bag, which color is most likely?

12. Bag A contains 25 blue marbles and 33 yellow marbles. Bag B contains 32 blue marbles and 45 yellow marbles. If you hoped to draw a blue marble, which bag would you choose to draw from? Why?

13. A die with six faces has letters on each face. Each face is equally likely to occur. Suppose the probability that the die lands on the letter H is 1/3. How many faces on the die have the letter H? Justify your answer.

14. A jar contains pennies and nickels. There are three times as many pennies as nickels.

a. Make a table to show how many pennies and nickels could be in the jar.

b. An experiment consists of randomly picking one coin from the jar. What is the probability of picking a penny?

15. A bag contains marbles. The probability of randomly picking a blue marble is 25%, and the probability of randomly picking a green marble is 60%. Show that the ratio of blue marbles to green marbles is 5:12.

16. Suppose *A* and *B* are two events that cannot occur at the same time and *A* is four times as likely to occur as *B*, that is, $P(A) = 4 \cdot P(B)$. A diagram that represents this situation is shown. Use the inequality $P(A) + P(B) \le 1$ to write $P(A) \le 1 - P(B)$, and plug this into the equation $P(A) = 4 \cdot P(B)$ to get $4 \cdot P(B) \le 1 - P(B)$. This leads to $5 \cdot P(B) \le 1$, which in turn leads to $P(B) \le 1/5$, or $P(B) \le 20\%$.

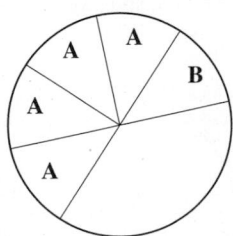

Now suppose *A* and *B* are two events that cannot occur at the same time and *A* is *seven* times as likely to occur as *B*. Verify that the largest possible value for $P(B)$ is 12.5%.

17. A teacher surveyed her class. She asked her students whether they preferred donuts or ice cream. She learned that 63% of the students preferred donuts and 37% preferred ice cream. Verify each statement.

    a. Students are about 1.7 times as likely to prefer donuts as ice cream.

    b. Students are about 41% less likely to prefer ice cream than donuts.

CONNECTIONS

Refresher: Connections (linking and applying mathematical ideas) are important because they deepen student understanding and make mathematics more meaningful, flexible, and useful.

18. When we toss a two-sided coin, we cannot predict the outcome of a single toss. Therefore, we cannot predict the next term in the sequence HHTTHHTTHH . . . , where H represents the coin landing on heads and T represents the coin landing on tails.

    a. What aspect of the sequence is predictable if we toss the coin 5000 times?

    b. What aspect of the sequence is unpredictable, besides the result of the next toss, if we toss the coin 15 times?

19. A bag contains green and blue marbles. For every three green marbles, there are five blue marbles.

    a. Make a table to show how many green and blue marbles there could be in the bag.

    b. An experiment consists of randomly picking one marble from the bag. What is the probability that the marble will be green?

20. In a fourth-grade class, 75% of the students are boys. You randomly select a student from this class. What is the probability that the student is a boy?

21. The table shows the target distribution of questions on the NAEP by grade and content area for grades 4 and 8 for 2007.

Content area	Gr. 4	Gr. 8
number and operations	40%	20%
measurement	20%	15%
geometry	15%	20%
data analysis and probability	10%	15%
algebra	15%	30%

SOURCE: U.S. Department of Education.

An experiment consists of randomly picking a question.

    a. If a question for grade 4 is randomly chosen, which content area is most likely to be picked?

    b. If a question for grade 8 is randomly chosen, which content area is most likely to be picked?

    c. If a question for grade 4 is randomly chosen, what is the likelihood that it is a question for data analysis and probability?

    d. If a question for grade 8 is randomly chosen, what is the likelihood that it is a question for measurement or algebra?

22. A study showed 1.2% of European diabetic patients and 20% of American diabetic patients use or have access to insulin pump therapy. An insulin pump delivers precise insulin doses, taking the place of multiple daily injections and providing better blood sugar control (www.medtronic.com). Because $0.20/0.012 \approx 16.7$, we can say that American diabetic patients are 16.7 times more likely to use insulin pump therapy than European diabetic patients or European diabetic patients are 16.7 times less likely to use insulin pump therapy than American diabetic patients. Use this example to write two probability comparisons based on the given percents using the casual phrases "times more likely" and "times less likely" for each of the following situations.

    a. A poll found 30% of the students prefer cheese pizza but 5% of the students prefer ham pizza.

    b. In the survey, 15% of registered voters said they would vote for Proposition A, and 48% said they would vote against Proposition A.

    c. In the bag, 35% of the marbles are blue, and 20% of the marbles are green.

23. The table records the number of hits, walks, strikeouts, ground-outs, and flyouts for a baseball player.

Result	hits	walks	strike-outs	ground-outs	flyouts
Frequency	40	15	22	20	8

    a. What is the probability that the baseball player gets a walk?

    b. What is the probability that the baseball player makes an out?

    c. How many hits do you expect the batter to get in the next 48 at-bats?

24. A spinner has two outcomes: *A* and *B*. Determine the angle measurement (in degrees) of the sector that determines *A* in each situation.

    a. The probability that the arrows lands on *A* is four times as likely as the probability that the arrow lands on *B*.

    b. The probability that the arrows lands on *A* is 30% more likely than the probability that the arrow lands on *B*. (Hint: Begin with the equation $P(A) = P(B) + 0.30 \cdot P(B)$. Then use $P(B) = 1 - P(A)$ and replace $P(B)$ with $1 - P(A)$ to create an equation in terms of $P(A)$. Then solve the equation for $P(A)$.)

COMMUNICATION

Refresher: Communication (written and verbal explanations using representations and proper mathematical vocabulary) is important because it helps students refine and strengthen their understanding.

25. An experiment consists of randomly picking one marble from a bag. A teacher states the probability of picking a green marble is 32%. What does this mean?

26. What is the difference between an outcome and an event?

27. What is the connection between experimental probability and theoretical probability?

28. Explain how you would determine the probability that a randomly chosen student at your school has two pets.

29. A researcher conducts an experiment by tossing a foam cup and noting whether it lands on its side, top, or bottom. The goal is to determine the probability that the cup lands on its side. Would the researcher rely on experimental probability or theoretical probability? Explain your answer.

More practice with the ideas of the section

30. Fill in the blank. Choose one of the following words or phrases: *certainty, chance, event, experiment, experimental probability, outcome, probability, qualitative, quantitative, sample space, probability,* or *uncertainty.*

  a. _____ is a measure of the chance that an event will occur.

  b. Words and phrases such as "impossible," "unlikely," "likely," and "certain to occur" are _____ phrases that we can use to characterize the level of uncertainty in a situation.

  c. A(n) _____ is a procedure in which something happens but the specific outcome cannot be predicted in advance.

  d. A(n) _____ is the result of an experiment.

  e. The _____ is the set of all possible outcomes.

  f. A(n) _____ is a collection of outcomes.

  g. Suppose event E occurs f times when an experiment is repeated n times. The fraction f/n is called a(n) _____.

31. Decide whether the event is impossible, unlikely, likely, or certain to occur.

  a. randomly picking a green marble from a jar that has 15 blue marbles, 12 green marbles, and 500 red marbles

  b. tossing a single standard die and getting a 5 or lower number

32. An experiment consists of randomly drawing a card from a standard deck of 52 cards. Find the probability of drawing

  a. a 2 or an 8.   **b.** a heart or a 3.

33. A student claims that the probability that the spinner lands on blue is 1.2. What advice would you give to the student?

34. There are seven chips in a bag, numbered 1 through 7. If you draw one chip from the bag, what is the probability that the chip's number will be even?

35. What is the probability that a randomly chosen number from 1 to 100 is not a multiple of 6?

36. A jar has six green marbles, three blue marbles, and five yellow marbles. An experiment consists of randomly picking a marble from the jar.

  a. What is the probability of picking a green marble?

  b. What is the probability of picking a green or yellow marble?

37. A 1–3 spinner has the following properties: $P(1) = 0.3$ and $P(2) = 0.25$. Calculate $P(3)$.

38. Philip flipped a fair coin 500 times. Mark flipped the same coin 20 times. One of these students observed that he obtained tails 65% of the time. Which student do you think it was? Justify your answer.

39. Decide whether the situation would involve experimental probability or theoretical probability.

  a. the likelihood that the temperature exceeds 80°F on November 30 in Kalamazoo, Michigan

  b. the chance of picking a 7 in a deck of standard playing cards

  c. the probability of catching a fish at Lake Mary

40. Find the central angles of a spinner with two outcomes, A and B, such that the likelihood that the spinner lands on A is 3.5 times the likelihood that it lands on B. (Hint: Begin with the equation $P(A) = 3.5 \cdot P(B)$. Then use $P(A) = 1 - P(B)$ to create an equation in terms of $P(B)$. Then solve for $P(B)$. Then calculate the central angles.

41. An experiment has exactly three outcomes a, b, and c. Suppose $P(a) = 0.20$ and $P(b) = 0.35$. Find the probability that

  a. c occurs.

  b. c does not occur.

42. Bill and Ken buy raffle tickets consisting of four digits from 0000 to 9999. Bill chooses 5555 and Ken chooses 3781. Does Bill have a higher chance, a lower chance, or the same chance of winning as Ken? Justify your answer.

43. The table shows the number of minutes customers waited in line at a bank during the lunch hour, and the corresponding frequencies.

Minutes spent waiting	Frequency
1	7
2	10
3	4
4	3
5	2
6 or more	1

Find the probability of each event.

  a. A customer waited 4 minutes.

  b. A customer waited 3 or 4 minutes.

  c. A customer waited less than 4 minutes.

  d. A customer waited 5 or more minutes.

44. The table shows data for Mary, Bob, and Tina.

Name	Times E occurred	n
Mary	3	15
Bob	6	24
Tina	10	32

a. Determine the experimental probability for each person.

b. Which experimental probability seems like the best estimate of $P(E)$?

c. How could the data be combined in some way to obtain a potentially better estimate of $P(E)$?

45. Mary, Bob, and Tina each calculated experimental estimates of $P(E)$. The table shows their results.

Name	$P(E)$	n
Mary	0.58	12
Bob	0.60	70
Tina	0.80	40

a. Which empirical probability seems like the best estimate of $P(E)$? Explain your answer.

b. How could these estimates be used to obtain a potentially better estimate of $P(E)$?

46. The spinner has four outcomes: *W, X, Y,* and *Z.*

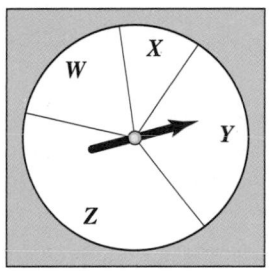

a. Use a protractor to determine the measure of each central angle.

b. Use your results in part (a) to determine the probability of each outcome.

47. An experiment consists of rolling a pair of standard dice, and the outcome is the maximum of the numbers that appear (for example, rolling a 3 and a 5 is recorded as a 5). Find the probability of rolling

a. a 4.   **b.** a 3.   **c.** an even number.

d. a number less than 3.

48. A trading card company puts a coupon for a free shirt in some of its packs. The probability that a pack has a coupon is 0.075. Predict how many packs you should expect to purchase to get three coupons.

49. A dice game consists of rolling one die and moving a stone (•) resting at point A the number of spaces indicated on the top face of the die. The game ends when the stone lands on or past point B. A friend bets you $1 that the game would end on the second roll.

A •								B

a. Play this game several times. Record your results in a tally table.

b. How much money would you expect to win or lose each game, on average?

50. Do the following.

a. A gambler bets you he can roll at least one 6 within four rolls of one die. What do you think his chance of winning is?

b. An experiment consists of rolling one die four times. Repeat this experiment 50 times. Use a tally table to determine the experimental probability of rolling at least one 6 within four rolls of a die.

51. An experiment consists of drawing two marbles from a bag. E is the event that both marbles have the same color. The graph shows experimental results of the probability of E for various values of n. Examine the graph to estimate $P(E)$.

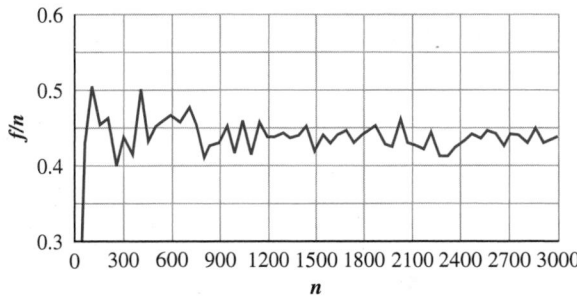

52. Many students believe that if $P(E) = 50\%$, then "E might or might not happen." Give a better interpretation of $P(E) = 50\%$.

53. Event A is 2.7 times as likely to occur as event B. Rewrite this sentence using the casual phrase "times more likely."

54. A is 3.4 times as likely to occur as event B. Rewrite this sentence using the casual phrase "times more likely."

55. A is 2.8 times more likely to occur than event B. Rewrite this sentence using the phrase "times as likely."

56. A is 4.2 times more likely to occur than event B. Rewrite this sentence using the phrase "times as likely."

57. A is 6.2 times less likely to occur than event B. Rewrite this sentence using the phrase "times as likely."

58. A is five times less likely to occur than event B. Rewrite this sentence using the phrase "times as likely."

59. A is eight times as likely to occur as event B. Rewrite this sentence using the casual phrase "times less likely."

60. A is 1.7 times as likely to occur as event B. Rewrite this sentence using the casual phrase "times less likely."

61. Suppose $P(A) = 0.38$ and $P(B) = 0.48$. Verify that

a. A is about 21% less likely than B.

b. B is about 26% more likely than A.

c. B is about 1.26 times as likely as A.

62. Suppose $P(A) = 0.34$ and $P(B) = 0.55$. Verify that

a. A is about 38% less likely than B.

b. B is about 62% more likely than A.

c. B is about 1.6 times as likely as A.

63. According to insurance statistics, 26% of homes are damaged by floods and 9% of homes are damaged by fire over the course of a 30-year mortgage.

    a. Verify that homes are nearly three times as likely to be damaged by floods than by fires.

    b. Verify that homes are 189% more likely to be damaged by floods than by fires.

64. According to the Centers for Disease Control and Prevention (CDC), diabetic patients, ages 18 to 44, have a 27.6% chance of having arthritis—2.5 times the rate of the general population.

    a. What is the likelihood that a randomly chosen person from the general population has arthritis?

    b. If you randomly choose 580 people from the general population, how many of them would you expect to have arthritis?

65. Let p be the probability that a person develops type II diabetes. A study claimed that a person who drinks one glass of juice each day has an 18% higher chance of developing type II diabetes. What is the probability that a person who drinks one glass of juice each day develops type II diabetes? Justify your answer, writing it in terms of p.

66. Let p be the probability that a person at a 4-year college applies for federal financial aid. A study claimed that students at community colleges are 24% less likely to apply for federal financial aid than students at 4-year colleges. What is the probability that a student at a community college applies for federal financial aid? Justify your answer, writing it in terms of p.

67. A teacher surveyed 30 students about the sport they should play on Friday. Eight students preferred basketball, and 20 students preferred soccer. Verify each statement.

    a. A student is 2.5 times as likely to choose soccer as basketball.

    b. A student is 60% less likely to choose basketball than soccer.

SECTION 9.2   Probability Rules

In some situations, we know the probability of event A and the probability of event B. In this section, we explain how to use $P(A)$ and $P(B)$ to determine the probability that "A or B" will occur, as well as the probability that "A and B" will occur.

Determining the Probability of Event "*A* or *B*" for Mutually Exclusive Events

The event "A or B" is one event consisting of the union of the outcomes in events A and B.

EXAMPLE 9.16

CONNECTION

REPRESENTATION

List all outcomes that belong to the event "A or B."

a. $A = \{1, 3\}$ and $B = \{4, 6\}$

b. $A = \{1, 3\}$ and $B = \{3, 6\}$

SOLUTION

a. A is the event of getting a 1 or a 3, and B is the event of getting a 4 or a 6. So the event "A or B" is the event of getting a 1, a 3, a 4, or a 6. So A or $B = \{1, 3, 4, 6\}$.

b. A is the event of getting a 1 or a 3, and B is the event of getting a 3 or a 6. So the event "A or B" is the event of getting a 1, a 3, or a 6. So A or $B = \{1, 3, 6\}$.

    In Example 9.16(a), the events A and B do not share any common outcomes. This means both events cannot occur at the same time. If you know A occurred, then you also know B did not occur. If you know B occurred, then you also know A did not occur. In mathematics, we say, "A and B are mutually exclusive." As another example, turning left and turning right at an intersection are mutually exclusive events, because they cannot occur at the same time. Students should "understand and use appropriate terminology to describe complementary and mutually exclusive events" (Gr. 3–5, NCTM).

> **Definition**
>
> A and B are **mutually exclusive events** when events A and B cannot possibly occur at the same time (they do not have any common outcomes).

EXAMPLE 9.17

REASONING
REPRESENTATION

Determine whether the events A and B are mutually exclusive.

a. An experiment consists of spinning a 1–7 spinner (a spinner with the outcomes 1, 2, 3, 4, 5, 6, and 7). Define $A = \{2, 5, 6\}$ and $B = \{4, 7\}$.

b. An experiment consists of randomly drawing a card from a standard deck of 52 cards. Let A be the event that the card is a spade, and let B be the event that the card is a 7.

SOLUTION

a. Events A and B do not have any outcomes in common, so A and B are mutually exclusive.

b. The 7 card belong to both A and B, so A and B are not mutually exclusive. ▲

The following Classroom Connection illustrates that elementary school students should understand the concept of mutually exclusive.

> ◆ **Classroom Connection**
>
> ● *Mathematics*, Grade 6, p. 699
>
> Suppose you toss a number cube. Give an example of an event that is mutually exclusive to tossing an odd number. Give an example of an event that is *not* mutually exclusive to tossing an odd number. (From Randall I. Charles. © 2004 by Pearson Education, Inc. or its affiliates. Used by permission. All rights reserved.)

If we know in advance that event A and event B are mutually exclusive, then we could find the probability of event "A or B" in terms of $P(A)$ and $P(B)$. For example, an experiment consists of drawing a card from a standard deck of cards. The experiment consists of 52 equally likely outcomes. What is the probability of drawing a 7 or a face card? Figure 5 shows the event "7 or face card."

FIGURE 5
Event of drawing a 7 or a face card.

Figure 5 shows there are 16 ways the event "7 or face card" can occur. So $P($7 or face card$) = \frac{16}{52}$. The probability of drawing a 7 is $P(7) = \frac{4}{52}$. The probability of drawing a face card is $P($face card$) = \frac{12}{52}$. Then

$$P(7 \text{ or face card}) = \frac{16}{52}$$

$$= \frac{4 + 12}{52}$$

$$= \frac{4}{52} + \frac{12}{52}$$

$$= P(7) + P(\text{face card})$$

So, $P($7 or face card$) = P(7) + P($face card$)$. This example motivates the following definition.

> **Definition**
>
> If A and B are mutually exclusive events, then $P(A \text{ or } B) = P(A) + P(B)$.

EXAMPLE 9.18

CONNECTION

REASONING

The following data are based on a report by the CDC from the National Hospital Ambulatory Medical Care Survey for outpatient department visits.

a. What is the likelihood that a patient visited the outpatient department because of an acute problem or for preventive care?

b. Interpret your result from part (a).

Reason	acute problem	chronic problem	follow-up	preventive care	unknown
Percent	0.36	0.36	0.04	0.18	0.06

SOLUTION

a. Let A represent the event that a patient visited the outpatient department because of an acute problem, and let B represent the event that a patient visited the outpatient department for preventive care. These events are mutually exclusive, because visits for acute problems are unexpected emergencies, whereas visits for preventive care are scheduled. Because the sets A and B are mutually exclusive, we can use the formula $P(A \text{ or } B) = P(A) + P(B)$. Then $P(A \text{ or } B) = P(A) + P(B) = 0.36 + 0.18 = 0.54$. The probability that a patient visited the outpatient department for an acute problem or preventive care is 54%.

b. This means we should expect 54 of every 100 patients visiting the outpatient department would be seen either for an acute problem or for preventive care.

▲

EXAMPLE 9.19

CONNECTION

REASONING

The following table is based on a report called "The Worker Health Chartbook, 2004" from the Bureau of Labor Statistics. The table shows the number, in thousands, of employed workers in the United States in 2001 by age group.

Age group	16–19	20–24	25–34	35–44	45–54	55–64	65 and older
Employed workers (in thousands)	6889	13,361	29,697	36,226	30,592	14,133	4174

Determine the probability that a randomly chosen employed worker is

a. in the 20 to 24 age group.

b. in the 20 to 24 or 35 to 44 age group.

c. between 20 and 44 years old.

SOLUTION

The total number of workers, in thousands, is 135,072.

a. There were 13,361 thousand employed workers in the 20 to 24 age group. The probability of choosing an employed worker in the 20 to 24 age group is 13,361/135,072 ≈ 9.9%.

b. There were 13,361 + 36,226 = 49,587 thousand workers in the 20 to 24 or 35 to 44 age groups. The probability that a randomly chosen employed worker is in the 20 to 24 or 35 to 44 age group is 49,587/135,072 ≈ 36.7%.

c. The employed workers from 20 to 44 years old belong to the 20 to 24 or 25 to 34 or 35 to 44 age groups. There were 13,361 + 29,697 + 36,226 = 79,284 thousand employed workers in these age groups. The probability that a randomly chosen employed worker is from 20 to 44 years old is 79,284/135,072 ≈ 58.7%.

▲

Determining the Probability of Event "*A* or *B*" for Any Events

Suppose an experiment consists of rolling a standard die and then recording the number of dots that appear on the top face. Let $A = \{2, 4\}$ and $B = \{2, 3, 5\}$. What is the probability of event "*A* or *B*"? Events A and B are not mutually exclusive, because A and B can occur at the same time by rolling a 2, so we cannot apply the formula $P(A \text{ or } B) = P(A) + P(B)$. We know the following:

- $S = \{1, 2, 3, 4, 5, 6\}$

- $P(A) = \dfrac{2}{6}$ and $P(B) = \dfrac{3}{6}$

- A or $B = \{2, 3, 4, 5\}$ and $P(A \text{ or } B) = \dfrac{4}{6}$

- A and $B = \{2\}$ and $P(A \text{ and } B) = \dfrac{1}{6}$

What is the probability of event "*A* or *B*"?

$$
\begin{aligned}
P(A \text{ or } B) &= \frac{4}{6} \\
&= \frac{5}{6} - \frac{1}{6} \\
&= \frac{2}{6} + \frac{3}{6} - \frac{1}{6} \\
&= P(A) + P(B) - P(A \text{ and } B)
\end{aligned}
$$

This example motivates the following definition to determine $P(A \text{ or } B)$ without listing all outcomes in the event "*A* or *B*."

Definition

If A and B are any events, then $P(A \text{ or } B) = P(A) + P(B) - P(A \text{ and } B)$.

EXAMPLE 9.20

CONNECTION

REASONING

An experiment consists of drawing a card from a standard deck of cards. What is the probability of drawing a spade or an ace?

SOLUTION

There are two events, drawing a spade and drawing an ace. The ace of spades belongs to both events, so the events are not mutually exclusive. There are 13 spades, so $P(\text{spade}) = \frac{13}{52}$. There are four aces, so $P(\text{ace}) = \frac{4}{52}$. One card is both a spade and an ace (A♠), so $P(\text{spades and ace}) = \frac{1}{52}$. Then $P(\text{spades or ace}) = P(\text{spades}) + P(\text{ace}) - P(\text{spades and ace}) = \frac{13}{52} + \frac{4}{52} - \frac{1}{52} = \frac{16}{52} \approx 30.8\%$.

▲

Determining the Probability of Event "A and B" for Independent Events

Suppose an experiment consists of drawing one card from a standard deck of cards and rolling a die. We know that the probability that the die lands on an even number is 3/6. We then draw a king from the deck of cards. The probability that the die lands on an even number is still 3/6, because the event of drawing a king does not affect the probability of rolling an even number. We say the two events "drawing a king" and "rolling an even number" are *independent events.*

Suppose Cindy and Andy are each drawing a card from a standard deck of cards and have agreed that the person with the lower card has to do the dishes (2 is the lowest, and ace is the highest). Cindy draws the first card but keeps it hidden from Andy as she eagerly waits to see which card Andy will draw so that they can compare cards. There are two possibilities:

- If Cindy did not draw an ace, then Andy would have a 4/51 chance of drawing an ace.
- If Cindy did draw an ace, then Andy would have a 3/51 chance of drawing an ace.

The probability that Andy draws an ace depends on the card that Cindy first chooses. We say the two events "Cindy draws an ace" and "Andy draws an ace" are *dependent events.*

Definition

- When we say the two events *A* and *B* are **independent events,** we mean that the occurrence of *A* does not affect the probability that event *B* will occur.
- When we say the two events *A* and *B* are **dependent events,** we mean that the occurrence of *A* does affect the probability that event *B* will occur.

EXAMPLE 9.21

COMMUNICATION

REASONING

a. Determine the probability of drawing an ace from a standard deck of cards.

b. An experiment consists of drawing two cards from a standard deck of cards, **with replacement.** This means we return the first card to the deck before drawing the second card. *A* is the event that the first card is a 5, and *B* is the event that the second card is an ace. Explain why event *A* and event *B* are independent.

c. An experiment consists of drawing two cards from a standard deck of cards, **without replacement.** This means we do not return the first card to the deck before drawing the second card. *A* is the event that the first card is a 5, and *B* is the event that the second card is an ace. Explain why event *A* and event *B* are dependent.

SOLUTION

a. The probability of drawing an ace is 4/52.

b. Assume event *A* occurred (a 5 was drawn and then returned to the deck). There are four aces in the deck of 52 cards. Then the probability of drawing an ace is 4/52. The occurrence of event *A* did not affect the probability of drawing an ace; it is still 4/52. So event *A* and event *B* are independent.

c. Assume event *A* occurred (a 5 was drawn but not returned to the deck). There are four aces in the 51 cards remaining in the deck. The probability of drawing an ace is now 4/51. The occurrence of event *A* affected the probability of drawing an ace; it changed from 4/52 to 4/51. So event *A* and event *B* are dependent.

▲

We return to our problem of drawing a card and rolling a die. There are 52 possible outcomes for the card and 6 possible outcomes for the die. By the fundamental counting principle, there are 52 · 6 possible outcomes for the sequence of drawing a card and rolling a die. Some possible outcomes are (2♣, 1) (draw a 2 of clubs and roll a 1) and (Q♠, 4) (draw a queen of spades and roll a 4). Each outcome is equally likely. There are four ways to draw a king and three ways to roll an even number. By the fundamental counting principle, there are 4 · 3 ways to draw a king and roll an even number. There are 4 · 3 ways the event "draw a king and roll an even number" can occur, and there are 52 · 6 equally likely outcomes in the sample space. Then

$$P\begin{pmatrix}\text{drawing a king and die}\\\text{landing on an even number}\end{pmatrix} = \frac{4 \cdot 3}{52 \cdot 6} \quad \begin{array}{l}\leftarrow \textbf{4 · 3, number of favorable outcomes}\\\leftarrow \textbf{52 · 6, number of possible outcomes}\end{array}$$

$$= \frac{4}{52} \cdot \frac{3}{6}$$

$$= P(\text{drawing a king}) \cdot P(\text{die landing on an even number})$$

This example motivates the following definition.

Definition

If events *A* and *B* are independent events, then the probability that both *A* and *B* will occur is $P(A \text{ and } B) = P(A) \cdot P(B)$.

EXAMPLE 9.22

CONNECTION
PROBLEM SOLVING
REASONING
REPRESENTATION

An experiment consists of drawing two cards from a standard deck of cards, with replacement. What is the probability that the first card is a spade and the second card is an ace?

SOLUTION

Because we are drawing cards with replacement, the probability that any card is an ace is $\frac{4}{52}$. The event that the first card is a spade and the event that the second card is an ace are independent events. So $P(\text{spade and ace}) = P(\text{spade}) \cdot P(\text{ace}) = \frac{13}{52} \cdot \frac{4}{52} = \frac{1}{52} \approx 1.92\%$.

▲

Drawing several cards with replacement, or tossing a coin repeatedly, involves independent events and therefore multiplying probabilities.

EXAMPLE 9.23

COMMUNICATION
REASONING

An experiment consists of tossing a fair coin five times in a row. Which outcome is more likely, HTHHT or TTTTT?

SOLUTION

Tossing a coin repeatedly involves independent events. For example, the outcome of the first coin toss does not affect the probability of getting tails on the second toss. On any toss, $P(H) = 1/2$ and $P(T) = 1/2$. Then

$$P(\text{HTHHT}) = P(H) \cdot P(T) \cdot P(H) \cdot P(H) \cdot P(T)$$

$$= \frac{1}{2} \cdot \frac{1}{2} \cdot \frac{1}{2} \cdot \frac{1}{2} \cdot \frac{1}{2}$$

$$= \frac{1}{32}$$

(continued)

and

$$P(\text{TTTTT}) = P(\text{T}) \cdot P(\text{T}) \cdot P(\text{T}) \cdot P(\text{T}) \cdot P(\text{T})$$
$$= \frac{1}{2} \cdot \frac{1}{2} \cdot \frac{1}{2} \cdot \frac{1}{2} \cdot \frac{1}{2}$$
$$= \frac{1}{32}$$

The outcomes TTTTT and HTHHT are equally likely.

▲

Many students think that HTHHT is more likely than TTTTT, because intuitively they know that getting a mixture of Hs and Ts is more likely than getting all Ts.

> **■ Historical Note**
>
> In 1756, Abraham de Moivre (1667–1754) wrote a book on probability and games of chance called *The Doctrine of Chances: or, A Method of Calculating the Probabilities of Events in Play.* He wrote: "Two Events are independent, when they have no connexion one with the other, and that the happening of one neither forwards nor obstructs the happening of the other. Two Events are dependent, when they are so connected together as that the Probability of either's happening is altered by the happening of the other."

Conditional Probability

In some probability experiments, the outcome of one event affects the probability of another event.

Let's draw two cards from a standard deck of 52 cards, one at a time, *without replacement.* This means the drawn cards are not returned to the deck. Consider two examples:

- What is the probability that the second card is an ace, given that the first card is not an ace? Because the first card is not an ace, there are four aces in the remaining 51 cards, and each of the 51 cards is equally likely to be drawn. The probability that the second card is an ace is 4/51, given that the first card is not an ace.

- What is the probability that the second card is an ace, given that the first card is an ace? Because the first card is an ace, there are three aces in the remaining 51 cards, and each of the 51 cards is equally likely to be drawn. The probability that the second card is an ace is 3/51, given that the first card is an ace.

The probabilities in these examples are called *conditional probabilities* because of the imposed condition "given that." Problems involving conditional probability require that we think carefully about what is possible after the first event occurs.

> **Definition**
>
> Let A and B represent two events. The probability that B will occur, given that A already occurred, is called the **conditional probability** of B and is denoted $P(B \mid A)$, which is read as "the probability of B given A."

EXAMPLE 9.24

COMMUNICATION

PROBLEM SOLVING

REASONING

A bag contains three blue marbles, two green marbles, and one yellow marble. An experiment consists of drawing two marbles from the bag, one at a time, without replacement. This means we do not replace the first marble after it is drawn. Determine the probability that

a. the second marble is green, given that the first marble is blue.

b. the second marble is green, given that the first marble is green.

SOLUTION

a. We know the first marble is blue. Five marbles remain: two blue marbles, two green marbles, and one yellow marble. The probability that the second marble is green is 2/5. So $P(\text{green} \mid \text{blue}) = 2/5$.

b. We know the first marble is green. Five marbles remain: three blue marbles, one green marble, and one yellow marble. The probability that the second marble is green is 1/5. So $P(\text{green} \mid \text{green}) = 1/5$.

▲

The probability that a youth age 11 to 18 uses a tanning bed is 10%, according to American Cancer Society. However, given that the parent used a tanning bed within the past year, the probability jumps to 30%.

Determining the Probability of Event "A and B" for Any Events

Suppose an experiment consists of drawing two marbles from a jar, one at a time, without replacement. This means we do not replace the first marble that we pick. The jar contains three blue marbles, two green marbles, and one yellow marble. What is the probability that the first marble is blue and the second marble is green?

The probability of drawing a blue marble on the first draw is $P(\text{blue}) = 3/6$. The probability of drawing a green marble on the first draw is $P(\text{green}) = 2/6$. However, given that the first marble selected is blue, then the probability of drawing a green marble is $P(\text{green} \mid \text{blue}) = 2/5$. The event that the first marble is blue and the event that the second marble is green are dependent, because knowing the first marble is blue affects the probability that the second marble is green.

COMMUNICATION
CONNECTION
REASONING

Although some of the marbles have the same color, they are different marbles. There are six marbles to choose from on the first draw and five marbles to choose from on the second draw. By the fundamental counting principle, there are $6 \cdot 5$ possible pairs of marbles. There are three ways to choose a blue marble on the first draw and two ways to choose a green marble on the second draw. So there are $3 \cdot 2$ ways to draw a blue marble and a green marble in that order. So $3 \cdot 2$ of the $6 \cdot 5$ possible pairs of marbles have a blue marble and a green marble in that order. All pairs of marbles (without regard for color) are equally likely, because the marbles are the same size and feel the same. Then

$$P(\text{first marble is blue and second marble is green}) = \frac{3 \cdot 2}{6 \cdot 5}$$

$$= \frac{3}{6} \cdot \frac{2}{5}$$

$$= P(\text{blue}) \cdot P(\text{green} \mid \text{blue})$$

This example motivates the following definition.

> **Definition**
>
> Let A and B represent any two events. Then $P(A \text{ and } B) = P(A) \cdot P(B \mid A)$.

This probability formula agrees with the one for independent events, because if A and B are independent events, then A does not affect the probability of B, which means $P(B \mid A) = P(B)$.

EXAMPLE 9.25

COMMUNICATION
CONNECTION
PROBLEM SOLVING
REASONING
REPRESENTATION

Mikey has 24 pens in a container. He knows 5 of the 24 pens are defective, because they do not have any ink.

a. Mikey randomly picks 1 pen. What is the probability that the pen is defective?

b. Mikey randomly picks 2 pens, one at a time, without replacement. What is the probability that both pens are defective?

SOLUTION

Let A represent the event that the first pen is defective, and let B represent the event that the second pen is also defective.

a. $P(A) = 5/24 \approx 20.8\%$

b. $P(A \text{ and } B) = P(A) \cdot P(B \mid A) = \dfrac{5}{24} \cdot \dfrac{4}{23} \approx 3.6\%$

▲

The following student page on page 517 shows some problems an elementary school student may see for both independent and dependent events. Two similar experiments are given: one with replacement (leading to independent events) and one without replacement (leading to dependent events).

A two-way table summarizes the frequencies or percents of two possibly related categorical variables. The rows are categories for one variable, and the columns are categories for the other variable. A two-way table may have just two rows and two columns, but it may have more than two rows or columns.

EXAMPLE 9.26

COMMUNICATION
CONNECTION
PROBLEM SOLVING
REASONING

A teacher surveyed her 30 students about their pizza preference for a class party. She summarized the results in the following table.

	Cheese	Pepperoni	Vegetable
Boys	10	5	1
Girls	8	2	4

Suppose we randomly select a student from this class.

a. What is the probability that the student prefers a cheese pizza, given that the student is a boy?

b. What is the probability that the selected girl prefers a cheese pizza?

c. What is the probability that the student is a girl or prefers pepperoni pizza?

SOLUTION

a. $P(\text{cheese} \mid \text{boy}) = 10/16 = 62.5\%$. The probability that the student prefers a cheese pizza, given that the student is a boy, is 62.5%.

b. We can solve this problem in two ways:

METHOD 1. $P(\text{girl and cheese}) = P(\text{girl}) \cdot P(\text{cheese} \mid \text{girl}) = \dfrac{14}{30} \cdot \dfrac{8}{14} = \dfrac{8}{30} \approx 26.7\%$

METHOD 2. There are eight girls who prefer cheese pizza, and there are 30 students altogether. So $P(\text{girl and cheese}) = 8/30 \approx 26.7\%$.

CHECK ✓

For another example, see Set 11-15 on p. 691.

For 1–5, give each probability as a
fraction and a percent rounded to
the nearest tenth of a percent.

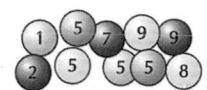

You select one letter without looking,
replace it, and then select another.

1. Find P(A, G).   **2.** Find P(vowel, M).

You select one letter without looking, do
not replace it, and then select another.

3. Find P(A, G).   **4.** Find P(vowel, M).

5. Reasoning Suppose you toss a coin 3 times. Find P(H, H, H).

PRACTICE

For more practice, see Set 11-15 on p. 695.

A Skills and Understanding

For Exercises 6–15, use the balls at the right.
Give each probability as a fraction and a
percent rounded to the nearest tenth of a percent.

You select a ball without looking, replace it, and then select another.

6. Find P(1, 8).   **7.** Find P(5, 9).   **8.** Find P(prime, even).

You select a ball without looking, do not replace it, and then
select another.

9. Find P(1, 8).   **10.** Find P(5, 9).   **11.** Find P(prime, 9).

Suppose you toss a number cube twice.

12. Find P(2, 5).   **13.** Find P(even, 3).   **14.** Find P(even, 2).

15. Reasoning Suppose you toss a coin 4 times. Find P(T, T, T, T).

Think It Through
I need to **decide if
the events are
independent or
dependent** before
I start to compute
the probability.

B Reasoning and Problem Solving

16. There are 6 gray socks and 14 white socks thrown loosely into Ted's
sock drawer. If Ted pulls out a sock without looking, sets it on the bed,
and pulls out another sock, does he have at least a 50% chance of
choosing a pair of white socks?

17. **Writing in Math** Your teacher draws 2 names at random to pick the two
co-captains of a team. Are these independent or dependent events? Explain.

Mixed Review and Test Prep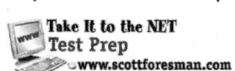

18. Suppose you toss 2 number cubes. Find P(sum of 3 or sum of 10).

19. Find the area of a triangle with base 5 cm and height 12 cm.

   A. 17 cm²   **B.** 30 cm²   **C.** 34 cm²   **D.** 60 cm²

All text pages available online and on CD-ROM.   **Section C Lesson 11-15**   **673**

(*Mathematics*, Grade 6, p. 673)

c. $P(\text{girl or pepperoni}) = P(\text{girl}) + P(\text{pepperoni}) - P(\text{girl and pepperoni})$

$$= \frac{14}{30} + \frac{7}{30} - \frac{2}{30}$$

$$= \frac{19}{30}$$

$$\approx 63\%$$

The probability that the student is a girl or prefers pepperoni pizza is 63%.

Using Tree Diagrams to Represent and Analyze Probability Problems

A key mathematical process in the teaching and learning of mathematics is representation. Many probability problems can be solved using the approaches we already discussed, but it is easier to analyze more complex probability situations using a tree diagram when they involve several stages, such as randomly drawing several cards, randomly picking several marbles, and rolling several die. These types of experiments are *multistage experiments*. The main idea of a tree diagram is to represent the outcomes using branches (line segments) and represent probabilities using numerical labels on the branches. Students should be able to "represent sample spaces for compound events using methods such as organized lists, tables and tree diagrams" (Gr. 7, CCSS).

> **Definition**
>
> A **probability tree diagram** is a representational tool for systematically organizing the outcomes and probabilities of probability problems that involve several stages.

Now we demonstrate how to use a tree diagram to represent, analyze, and solve a few probability problems. Jar 1 has two blue marbles and three yellow marbles. Jar 2 has three blue marbles, one yellow marble, and five green marbles.

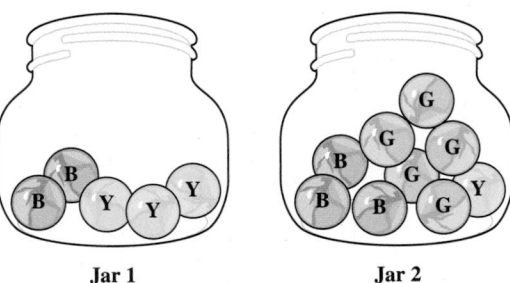

Jar 1   Jar 2

A marble is randomly drawn from jar 1 and then placed in jar 2. Then a marble is randomly drawn from Jar 2. What is the probability that both drawn marbles have the same color? We can analyze this two-stage probability experiment using a tree diagram:

- Figure 6 uses a tree diagram to list all possible outcomes of the first draw and the probability for each outcome in this stage. The labels for the outcomes at each stage appear at the end of the branch.

- Figure 7 creates more branches. Given that a yellow marble is chosen from jar 1 and placed in jar 2, there are now two yellow marbles in jar 2 and 10 marbles in jar 2 altogether. So the probability of drawing a yellow marble from jar 2, given that a yellow marble was drawn from jar 1, is 2/10. Similarly, the probability of drawing a blue marble from jar 2, given that a yellow marble was drawn from jar 1, is 3/10, and so on. The probabilities on the branches in the second stage are conditional probabilities.

CONNECTION
REASONING
REPRESENTATION

To complete the probability tree diagram, we need to list the outcomes and assign a probability for each outcome. The outcome YY represents that the first marble is yellow *and* the second marble is yellow, given that the first marble is yellow.

$P(\text{YY}) = P(\text{first marble is yellow and second marble is yellow})$

$= P(\text{first marble is yellow}) \times P(\text{second marble is yellow, given that the first marble is yellow})$

$= \dfrac{3}{5} \cdot \dfrac{2}{10} = \dfrac{6}{50}$

FIGURE 6
First stage of the jar problem.

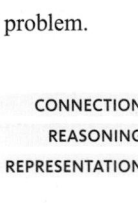

FIGURE 7
First and second stages of the jar problem.

Similarly, the outcome YB represents that the first marble is yellow *and* the second marble is blue.

$$P(\text{YB}) = P(\text{first marble is yellow and second marble is blue})$$
$$= P(\text{first marble is yellow}) \cdot P(\text{second marble is blue,}$$
$$\text{given that the first marble is yellow})$$
$$= \frac{3}{5} \cdot \frac{3}{10} = \frac{9}{50}$$

We obtain the probabilities by simply multiplying the probabilities along the branches. Figure 8 shows the completed probability tree diagram.

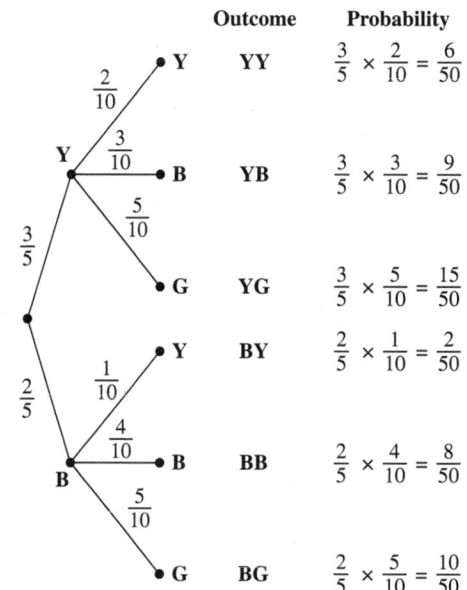

	Outcome	Probability
Y	YY	$\frac{3}{5} \times \frac{2}{10} = \frac{6}{50}$
B	YB	$\frac{3}{5} \times \frac{3}{10} = \frac{9}{50}$
G	YG	$\frac{3}{5} \times \frac{5}{10} = \frac{15}{50}$
Y	BY	$\frac{2}{5} \times \frac{1}{10} = \frac{2}{50}$
B	BB	$\frac{2}{5} \times \frac{4}{10} = \frac{8}{50}$
G	BG	$\frac{2}{5} \times \frac{5}{10} = \frac{10}{50}$

FIGURE 8
Completed probability tree diagram for the jar problem.

The event E that both marbles have the same color is $E = \{\text{YY, BB}\}$, so $P(E) = P(\{\text{YY, BB}\}) = P(\text{YY}) + P(\text{BB}) = \frac{6}{50} + \frac{8}{50} = \frac{14}{50} = 28\%$.

The tree diagram gives us the probability distribution; that is, it tells us what the possibilities are (YG, BB, . . .) and how often they should occur (15/50, 8/50, . . .).

EXAMPLE 9.27

COMMUNICATION
CONNECTION
PROBLEM SOLVING
REASONING
REPRESENTATION

Two marbles are drawn, as follows. A marble is randomly drawn from box 1. If the marble from box 1 is white, then it is placed in box 2 and a marble is randomly drawn from box 2. If the marble from box 1 is black, then it is placed in box 3 and a marble is randomly drawn from box 3. What is the probability that the second marble drawn is black?

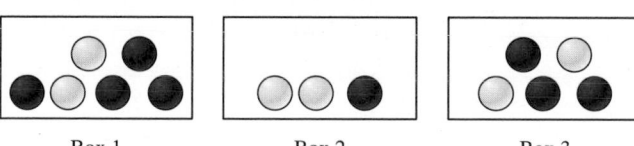

Box 1   Box 2   Box 3

SOLUTION

The second marble must be black, so the event is $E = \{\text{WB, BB}\}$, where WB represents that the first marble is white *and* the second marble is black, and BB represents that the first marble is black *and* the second marble is black. Figure 9 is the probability tree diagram.

(continued)

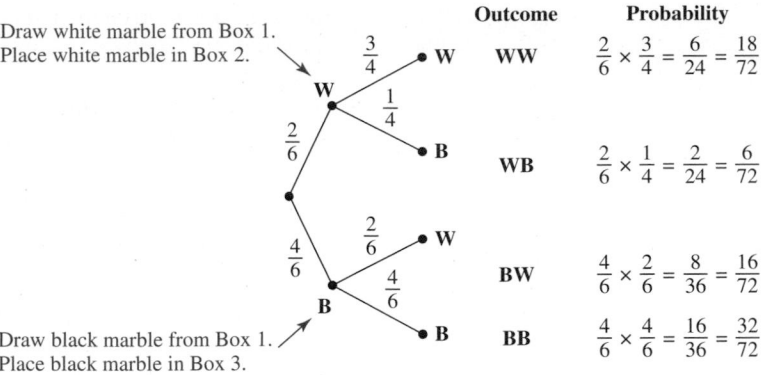

Draw white marble from Box 1.
Place white marble in Box 2.

Draw black marble from Box 1.
Place black marble in Box 3.

FIGURE 9
Representing and analyzing the experiment with a tree diagram.

Given that a white marble is drawn, the tree diagram shows the possible outcomes for the second draw: a white marble or a black marble. The white marble is placed into box 2, so now box 2 contains three white marbles and one black marble. Given that a black marble is chosen, the tree diagram shows the possible outcomes for the second draw: a white marble or a black marble. The black marble is placed into box 3, so now box 3 contains two white marbles and four black marbles. The sample space is {WW, WB, BW, BB}, and the probabilities for the outcomes are found by multiplying the probabilities along the branches. The probability that the second marble is black is

$$P(E) = P(\{WB, BB\}) = P(WB) + P(BB) = \frac{6}{72} + \frac{32}{72} = \frac{38}{72} \approx 53\%.$$

That is, the probability that the second marble is black is about 53%.

The next example illustrates that sometimes you do not have to draw the complete probability tree diagram.

EXAMPLE 9.28

COMMUNICATION
CONNECTION
PROBLEM SOLVING
REASONING
REPRESENTATION

A jar contains four blue marbles and two yellow marbles. Marbles are drawn randomly, one at a time without replacement, until a yellow marble is chosen. Determine the probability of the following events.

a. Exactly one draw is needed.
b. Exactly two draws are needed.
c. Exactly three draws are needed.

SOLUTION

a. One draw is needed, provided that a yellow marble is drawn first. The probability of a yellow marble is 2/6. This means we expect to pick a yellow marble on the first try 33% of the time.

b. The first marble must be blue, and the second must be yellow. The partial tree diagram is shown.

$$\frac{4}{6} \qquad \frac{2}{5}$$

B — Y   Outcome   Probability

first second   BY $\frac{4}{6} \times \frac{2}{5} = \frac{8}{30} \approx 27\%$
draw   draw

Then $P(BY) \approx 27\%$, so we expect to pick a yellow marble on the second try about 27% of the time.

c. Three draws are needed, provided that the first two marbles are blue and a yellow marble is drawn third. The partial tree diagram is shown.

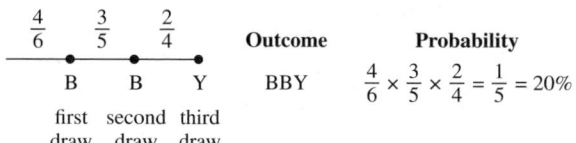

Then $P(\text{BBY}) = 20\%$. This means we expect to pick a yellow marble on the third try 20% of the time.

▲

The following Classroom Connection illustrates that elementary school students should know how to use a tree diagram to represent and analyze a probability situation.

> ◆ **Classroom Connection**
>
> ● *Math*, Grade 6, p. 684
>
> Make a tree diagram for each experiment. List the probability for each outcome. Experiment: Select two marbles at random from a bag of 5 red marbles and 2 green marbles. Do not replace the first marble before selecting the second marble. (© 2000 Macmillan/McGraw Hill. Reprinted by permission.)

QUESTIONS FOR SECTION 9.2

REPRESENTATION

Refresher: Representations (language, diagrams, tables, symbols, algebra, manipulatives, and contextualized situations) are important because we use them to organize, record, and communicate mathematical ideas and to make them more comprehensible.

1. Consider the events $A = \{1, 2, 6\}$ and $B = \{3, 5\}$ and the sample space $S = \{1, 2, 3, 4, 5, 6\}$.

  a. Make a Venn diagram for these sets.

  b. Explain how a Venn diagram for events A and B would reveal A and B are mutually exclusive.

2. Consider the events $A = \{1, 2, 6\}$ and $B = \{2, 3, 6\}$ and the sample space $S = \{1, 2, 3, 4, 5, 6\}$.

  a. Make a Venn diagram for these sets.

  b. Explain how a Venn diagram for events A and B would reveal A and B are not mutually exclusive.

3. What does the expression $P(A \mid B)$ mean?

4. The Venn diagram represents events A and B for a sample space S with equally likely outcomes.

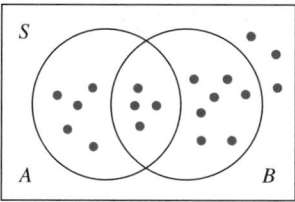

  a. Explain why $P(A) = 9/19$.

  b. Explain why the probability of B occurring, given that A has occurred, is 4/9.

5. The Venn diagram represents events A and B for a sample space S with equally likely outcomes.

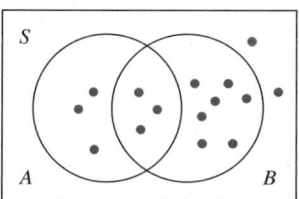

  a. What is the probability that event A will occur?

  b. What is the probability that event B will occur?

c. What is the probability that event "*A* and *B*" will occur?

d. What is the probability that event "*A* or *B*" will occur?

e. What is the probability that event *A* will occur, given that event *B* has occurred?

f. What is the probability that event *B* will occur, given that event *A* has occurred?

g. What is the probability that event *B* will occur, given that event *A* did not occur?

6. A tree diagram for an experiment involving drawing colored marbles is shown. List the outcomes and corresponding probabilities.

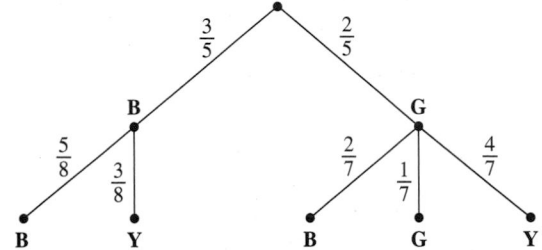

7. A probability experiment consists of drawing two marbles, one at a time, without replacement. There are two blue marbles (B), one green marble (G), and three yellow marbles (Y). The probability tree diagram is shown.

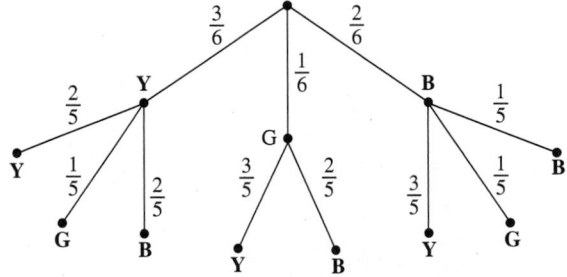

a. Determine the probability that the second marble is yellow, given that the first marble is green.

b. Determine the probability that the second marble is yellow, given that the first marble is yellow.

c. Determine the probability that the first marble is blue and the second marble is green.

d. Determine the probability that the first marble is yellow and the second marble is blue.

e. Determine the probability that the second marble is yellow.

8. An experiment begins with drawing a marble from box 1. If a white marble from box 1 is selected, then the marble is placed in box 3 and a marble is then selected from box 3. If a black marble from box 1 is selected, then the marble is placed in box 2 and a marble is selected from box 2.

a. Determine the likelihood that the second marble is black, given that the first marble is black.

b. Determine the likelihood that the second marble is white, given that the first marble is white.

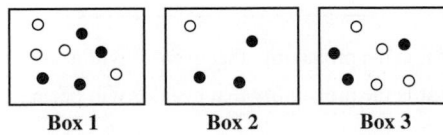

PROBLEM SOLVING

Refresher: Problem solving (reaching a goal that is not immediately attainable) is important because it helps students think more deeply about what they know and deal with unfamiliar situations.

9. Suppose you have a jar with 17 red marbles and 23 black marbles. You randomly select a marble from the jar without replacement. If the marble is red, then you add 7 yellow marbles to the jar and randomly select another marble from the jar. If the first marble is black, then you add 13 blue marbles to the jar and randomly select another marble from the jar. Determine the probability that

a. the second marble is a black marble, given that the first marble was a red marble.

b. the second marble is a red marble, given that the first marble was a black marble.

c. the second marble is a yellow marble.

d. the second marble is a blue marble.

10. The thyroid gland regulates metabolism and is important for proper brain development. Statistics from the *New England Journal of Medicine* indicate 1 in 50 pregnant women have hypothyroidism. A study showed 19% of children born to mothers with hypothyroidism have intelligence quotient (IQ) scores lower than 86, while 5% of children born to mothers without hypothyroidism have IQ scores lower than 86. The average IQ score of a high school graduate is 104.

a. What is the probability that a pregnant woman will have hypothyroidism?

b. What is the likelihood that a child will have an IQ score lower than 86, given that the child is born to a mother with hypothyroidism?

c. What is the probability that a pregnant woman will have hypothyroidism and the child will have an IQ score lower than 86?

d. What is the probability that a pregnant woman will not have hypothyroidism?

e. What is the likelihood that a child will have an IQ score lower than 86, given that the child was born to a mother without hypothyroidism?

f. What is the probability that a pregnant woman will not have hypothyroidism and the child will have an IQ score lower than 86?

g. What is the probability that a pregnant woman will not have hypothyroidism and the child will not have an IQ score lower than 86?

11. Two cards are randomly chosen from an ordinary deck of 52 cards, without replacement. Determine the probability of each event.

a. The first card is a face card.

b. The second card is a face card, given that the first card is an ace.

REASONING AND PROOF

Refresher: Reasoning and proof (thinking and justifying) are important because they help students make sense of mathematics.

12. Given that $P(A) = 0.3$, $P(B) = 0.5$, and A and B are independent events, compute each probability.

    a. $P(A \text{ and } B)$ **b.** $P(A \text{ or } B)$

13. Given that $P(A) = 0.42$, $P(B) = 0.75$, and A and B are independent events, compute each probability.

    a. $P(A \text{ and } B)$ **b.** $P(A \text{ or } B)$

14. Suppose $P(A) = 0.42$ and $P(B) = 0.75$. Can events A and B be mutually exclusive events? Explain your answer.

15. Suppose $P(A) = 0.24$, $P(B) = 0.55$, and $P(B \mid A) = 0.3$. Compute $P(A \text{ and } B)$.

16. Suppose $P(A) = 0.35$, $P(B) = 0.22$, and $P(B \mid A) = 0.15$. Compute $P(A \text{ or } B)$.

17. A bag contains 300 blue marbles, 100 green marbles, and 200 yellow marbles. Two marbles are drawn one at a time.

    a. Determine the probability of drawing 2 blue marbles. Assume you draw with replacement.

    b. Determine the probability of drawing 2 blue marbles. Assume you draw without replacement.

    c. In this problem, the number n of selections was much smaller than the number N of objects to choose from ($n = 2$ and $N = 600$). Does the choice of replacement ("with replacement" or "without replacement") have a large impact on the probability in these situations?

18. A bag contains three blue marbles, two green marbles, and one yellow marble. Two marbles are drawn one at a time.

    a. Determine the probability of drawing 2 blue marbles. Assume you draw with replacement.

    b. Determine the probability of drawing 2 blue marbles. Assume you draw without replacement.

    c. In this problem, the number n of selections was not much smaller than the number N of objects to choose from ($n = 2$ and $N = 7$). Does the choice of replacement ("with replacement" or "without replacement") have a large impact on the probability in these situations?

CONNECTIONS

Refresher: Connections (linking and applying mathematical ideas) are important because they deepen student understanding and make mathematics more meaningful, flexible, and useful.

19. Do the following.

    a. An experiment consists of rolling a die. What is the probability that a 6 does not appear?

    b. A game consists of rolling a die four times. What is the probability that a 6 does not appear on any of the four rolls?

    c. The gambler de Méré frequently bet he would roll at least one 6 within four rolls of a standard die. What is the probability that he would win his bet?

20. Do the following.

    a. An experiment consists of rolling two dice. What is the probability that a pair of 6s does not appear?

    b. A game consists of rolling two dice 24 times. What is the probability that a pair of 6s does not appear on any of the 24 rolls?

    c. The gambler de Méré played a game in which he bet he would roll at least one pair of 6s within 24 rolls of two standard dice. What is the probability that he would win his bet?

21. The Bureau of Justice classifies crimes as personal (for example, assault, purse snatching, violence, and robbery) and property (for example, burglary and theft). According to Bureau of Justice data from 2005, 77% of all crimes are property crimes. Of these property crimes, 5.4% are motor vehicle thefts. Determine the probability that a crime is classified as

    a. a property crime.

    b. a motor vehicle theft, given that it is known the crime is a property crime.

    c. a property crime and a motor vehicle theft.

22. Statistics published in the *San Diego Union Tribune* show that 60,000 police officers, or 10% of America's cops, are hurt in the line of duty every year. Of the injured officers, 25% will become permanently disabled. Determine the chance that a randomly selected police officer

    a. is hurt in the line of duty.

    b. becomes permanently disabled, given that the officer is hurt in the line of duty.

    c. is hurt in the line of duty and becomes permanently disabled.

23. A jewelry store owner decided to record the buying habits of his customers. He noticed 340 people walked past his store. Of these people, 75 walked into the store, and 40 of those people made a purchase. Use these data to estimate each probability.

    a. A person who walks by the store enters the store.

    b. A person who walks into the store makes a purchase.

    c. A person enters the store and buys something.

COMMUNICATION

Refresher: Communication (written and verbal explanations using representations and proper mathematical vocabulary) is important because it helps students refine and strengthen their understanding.

24. Suppose $P(A) = 0.6$ and $P(B) = 0.7$. Explain why events A and B cannot be mutually exclusive events.

25. A jar contains seven pennies, three dimes, and five quarters. An experiment consists of selecting a coin from the jar. The coin is replaced after it is selected, before the next selection.

    a. B is the event that the coin is a penny. Determine the probability that B will occur.

    b. A is the event that the coin is a dime. Determine the probability that B will occur, given that A has already occurred.

    c. Explain why event A and event B are independent events.

26. A jar contains seven pennies, three dimes, and five quarters. An experiment consists of selecting a coin from the jar. The coin is not replaced after it is selected.

    a. *B* is the event that the coin is a penny. Determine the probability that *B* will occur.

    b. *A* is the event that the coin is a dime. Determine the probability that *B* will occur, given that *A* has already occurred.

    c. Explain why event *A* and event *B* are dependent events.

27. In June 2010, a man from St. Louis won a lottery worth $1 million with a "scratchers" ticket. In September, the same man won another lottery, worth $2 million, with another "scratchers" ticket. A Missouri lottery official said the probability of winning either game is about 1 in 2.3 million. When asked about the chance of winning both games, the Missouri lottery official said that because the two games are independent, it was impossible to calculate the probability of winning both games. Do you agree or disagree with the lottery official? Explain your answer.

More practice with the ideas of the section

28. Fill in the blank. Choose one of the following words or phrases: *independent, mutually exclusive,* or *probability tree diagram.*

    a. The phrase "*A* and *B* are _____" means events *A* and *B* cannot occur at the same time (they do not have any common outcomes).

    b. A(n) _____ is a representational tool for systematically organizing the outcomes and probabilities of probability problems that involve several stages.

    c. When we say, "The two events *A* and *B* are _____," we mean that the occurrence of *A* does not affect the probability that event *B* will occur.

29. Suppose $P(A) = 0.4$ and $P(B) = 0.3$.

    a. Is it possible for $P(A \text{ or } B) = 0.5$? Explain your answer.

    b. Is it possible for $P(A \text{ or } B) = 0.8$? Explain your answer.

30. An experiment consists of rolling a standard die and recording the number that appears on the top face. *A* is the event that the die is a 4, and *B* is the event that the die is a 1. Are events *A* and *B* mutually exclusive? Explain your answer.

31. A teacher randomly picks a card from a standard deck of cards. If the card is not a face card, then the teacher flips a coin. If the card is a face card, then the teacher draws a marble from a bag containing three blue marbles and two green marbles. Draw a probability tree diagram for this experiment.

32. Player A and player B are playing a dice game. Two dice are rolled. Player A wins if the sum is 3 or 9. Player B wins if the sum is 7. The dice are rolled until one of the players win.

    a. The probability that the game ends on the first roll is 12/36. Verify this calculation.

    b. The probability that the game ends on the fourth roll is about 10%. Verify this calculation.

33. Player A and player B are playing a dice game. Two dice are rolled. Player A wins if the dice differ by 1 (for example, a 2 and a 3, a 3 and a 2, or a 4 and a 5). Player B wins if the dice match (for example, a 3 and a 3). The dice are rolled until one of the players win.

    a. The probability that the game ends on the first roll is 16/36. Verify this calculation.

    b. The probability that the game ends on the third roll is about 14%. Verify this calculation.

34. An experiment consists of drawing two cards from a standard deck of cards, with replacement. Determine the probability that

    a. the first card is a 7 and the second card is a face card.

    b. the first card is a queen and the second card is a 2.

35. An experiment consists of drawing two marbles, without replacement, from a bag containing six blue marbles, three red marbles, and five green marbles. Determine the probability that

    a. the first marble is blue and the second marble is green.

    b. both marbles have the same color.

36. Melvin and Kelly purchased raffle tickets with five digits. Melvin got 88888 and Kelly got 72481. Select the best answer.

    a. Melvin has a higher chance of winning.

    b. Kelly has a higher chance of winning.

    c. They have the same chance of winning.

37. A box contains 15 blue marbles, 3 red marbles, and 7 green marbles. A marble is drawn from the box, with replacement, until a green marble is picked. Determine the probability of each event, and explain how you arrived at your answer.

    a. Two draws are needed.   b. Three draws are needed.

38. A box contains 15 blue marbles, 3 red marbles, and 7 green marbles. A marble is drawn from the box, without replacement, until a green marble is picked. Determine the probability of each event, and explain how you arrived at your answer.

    a. Two draws are needed.   b. Three draws are needed.

39. A gumball machine has 25 yellow gumballs, 15 blue gumballs, and 10 green gumballs. Samantha wants a green gumball. What is the probability that she will get the green gumball on her third try?

40. Two candidates in an election in Nevada received the same number of votes. The candidates agreed to determine the winner by drawing cards. The candidate with the highest card would be declared the winner. Aces are higher than kings, kings are higher than queens, queens are higher than jacks, and so on. If both candidates draw the same type of card (for example, both draw 7s), then the suit on the card would determine the winner in the following order from highest to lowest: spades, clubs, hearts, and diamonds. The first candidate selected a queen of clubs. What is the probability that the second candidate will win the election?

41. The Spikers and Blockers volleyball teams in the National Volleyball League (NVL) have advanced to the NVL championship final. The first team to win three games is the champion. During the NVL regular season, the Spikers volleyball team won 60% of the games it played against the Blockers volleyball team. Based on these data, determine each probability.

    a. The Blockers will win in three games.

    b. A team will win in three games.

42. An experiment begins by drawing a marble from box 1. If a white marble from box 1 is selected, then the marble is placed in box 3 and a marble is then chosen from box 3. If a black

marble from box 1 is selected, then the marble is placed in box 2 and a marble is selected from box 2.

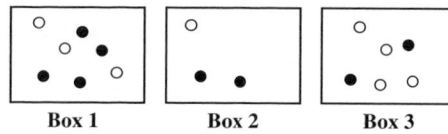

Box 1   **Box 2**   **Box 3**

a. Draw a probability tree diagram for this experiment.

b. Determine the likelihood that the second marble is black, given that the first marble is black.

c. Determine the probability that both marbles have the same color.

43. Amy flipped a coin 10 times in a row. Select the best answer.

a. TTTTTHHHHH is more likely to occur.

b. THHHTHTHHT is more likely to occur.

c. TTTTTHHHHH and THHHTHTHHT have the same chance of occurring.

44. Spinner A is spun. If the outcome of spinner A is an odd number, then spinner B is spun. If the outcome of spinner A is an even number, then spinner C is spun. The results of both spins are added together. What is the probability that the sum is an odd number?

Spinner	A		B			C	
outcome	1	2	4	7	2	6	3
probability	0.2	0.8	0.2	0.3	0.5	0.6	0.4

45. An experiment consists of spinning two spinners and adding the outcomes of the spinners.

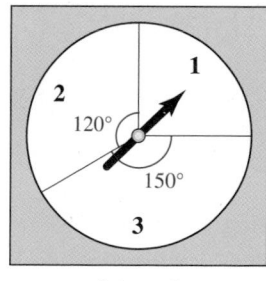   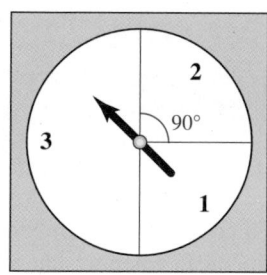

Spinner 1   Spinner 2

a. Draw the probability tree diagram.

b. What is the probability that the outcome is an even number?

46. A lottery consists of picking five digits. Melvin bets that all digits in the winning number will be identical, such as 00000 or 22222. Kelly bets that all digits will not be identical. Select the best answer.

a. Melvin has a higher chance of winning.

b. Kelly has a higher chance of winning.

c. They have the same chance of winning.

47. When we toss a fair coin, we cannot predict the outcome of a single toss. Therefore, we cannot predict the next term in the sequence HTHHT . . . , where H represents that the coin landed

on heads and T represents that the coin landed on tails. However, what aspect of the sequence is predictable if we toss the coin a large number of times, say, 5000 times?

The following two-way table shown is based on a June 2004 report by the CDC on data from the National Hospital Ambulatory Medical Care Survey for outpatient department visits in 2002. The table gives the number of patient visits by major reason for visit, according to gender, in thousands. Use this table to answer Questions 48 and 49.

	Male	**Female**	**Total**
Acute problem	12,489	17,414	29,903
Chronic problem	12,165	18,142	30,307
Follow-up	1573	1803	3376
Preventive care	4280	10,745	15,025
Unknown	1818	2910	4728
Total	32,325	51,014	83,339

48. An outpatient is randomly selected.

a. What is the probability that the outpatient was a male, given that the outpatient had an acute problem?

b. What is the probability that the outpatient had an acute problem, given that the outpatient was a female?

49. An outpatient is randomly selected.

a. What is the probability that the outpatient was a male and visited the outpatient clinic for a follow-up visit or for a chronic problem?

b. What is the probability that the outpatient visited the outpatient clinic for an acute or chronic problem?

c. Let *A* be the event that a randomly chosen outpatient visited the outpatient department for an acute problem. Let *B* be the event that a randomly chosen outpatient was a male. Are *A* and *B* independent events? Explain your answer.

Three players are playing "Odd Man Out." In this game, players A, B, and C each flip a coin. If two players have coins that land on heads and the other player has a coin that lands on tails, then the player with tails wins. If two players have coins that land on tails and the other player has a coin that lands on heads, then the player with heads wins. The players repeat the coin toss whenever all three coins have the same outcome. Questions 50 and 51 pertain to this game.

50. Do the following.

a. Suppose the coin for player A has a 0.5 probability of landing on heads, the coin for player B has a 0.5 probability of landing on heads, and the coin for player C has a 0.5 probability of landing on heads. Which player is favored to win the game?

b. Suppose the coin for player A has a 0.5 probability of landing on heads, the coin for player B has a 0.6 probability of landing on heads, and the coin for player C has a 0.7 probability of landing on heads. Which player is favored to win the game?

51. Do the following.

    a. Suppose the coin for player A has a 0.3 probability of landing on heads, the coin for player B has a 0.8 probability of landing on heads, and the coin for player C has a 0.6 probability of landing on heads. Which player is favored to win the game?

    b. Suppose the coin for player A has a 0.25 probability of landing on heads, the coin for player B has a 0.35 probability of landing on heads, and the coin for player C has a 0.6 probability of landing on heads. Which player is favored to win the game?

Church groups and college sports teams often use 15-passenger vans for transportation. The following two-way table of known injury severity of occupants in a 15-passenger van involved in single-vehicle crashes for 1990–2002 is based on a federal report released in 2004 by the National Center for Statistics and Analysis.

Restraint use	Fatally injured	Survived	Total
unrestrained	517	1816	2333
restrained	95	1055	1150
total	612	2871	3483

Use the data in the table to answer Questions 52 and 53.

52. Suppose an occupant in a single-vehicle crash of a 15-passenger van is randomly selected.

    a. What is the probability that the occupant was fatally injured, given that the occupant was restrained?

    b. What is the probability that the occupant was fatally injured, given that the occupant was unrestrained?

53. Suppose an occupant in a single-vehicle crash of a 15-passenger van is randomly selected.

    a. Determine the probability that the occupant survived.

    b. Determine the probability that the occupant survived, given that the occupant was restrained.

    c. Let A be the event that a randomly chosen occupant was restrained. Let B be the event that a randomly chosen occupant survived. Are A and B independent or dependent events? Explain your answer.

SECTION 9.3 Expected Value, Normal Distribution, Simulations, and Odds

Expected Value

Earlier, we calculated the mean of a collection of numbers using the expression $(x_1 + x_2 + \ldots + x_n)/n$. Now we calculate the mean when we know the probability associated with each numerical outcome in a sample space. In this situation, the mean is called the *expected value*.

Let's suppose you are playing a board game and your piece advances the number of spaces equal to the number where the arrow stops on the spinner shown.

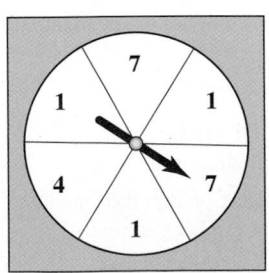

The outcomes and probabilities are:

Outcome	1	4	7
Probability	$\dfrac{3}{6}$	$\dfrac{1}{6}$	$\dfrac{2}{6}$

If the spinner stops at 4, then your piece would advance four spaces. On average, how many spaces would your piece advance on each spin? If we spin the spinner 6 times, then *ideally* we expect a 1 to occur 3 times, a 4 to occur 1 time, and a 7 to occur 2 times. For these ideal outcomes, we get

$$\text{mean} = \frac{1 + 1 + 1 + 4 + 7 + 7}{6} \qquad \leftarrow \textbf{Definition of the mean}$$

$$= \frac{3 \cdot 1 + 1 \cdot 4 + 2 \cdot 7}{6} \qquad \leftarrow \textbf{Expressing repeated addition as multiplication}$$

$$= \frac{3 \cdot 1}{6} + \frac{1 \cdot 4}{6} + \frac{2 \cdot 7}{6} \qquad \leftarrow \textbf{Breaking apart the fraction}$$

$$= 1 \cdot \frac{3}{6} + 4 \cdot \frac{1}{6} + 7 \cdot \frac{2}{6} \qquad \leftarrow \textbf{Expressing each fraction as a product}$$

$$= 1 \cdot P(1) + 4 \cdot P(4) + 7 \cdot P(7) \qquad \leftarrow \textbf{Expressing in terms of probability}$$

The sum $1 \cdot P(1) + 4 \cdot P(4) + 7 \cdot P(7)$, obtained by multiplying outcomes and their probabilities, is 3.5 for this spinner. Then we should expect the piece to advance 3.5 spaces per spin, on average. We replace the word *mean* with the phrase "expected value" when we compute *a mean* by multiplying outcomes and probabilities.

Definition

Suppose an experiment has k numerical outcomes $x_1, x_2, \ldots, x_k$ with the corresponding probabilities $P(x_1), P(x_2), \ldots, P(x_k)$. Then the **expected value** e of the experiment is

$$e = x_1 \cdot P(x_1) + x_2 \cdot P(x_2) + \ldots + x_k \cdot P(x_k).$$

EXAMPLE 9.29

COMMUNICATION
CONNECTION
PROBLEM SOLVING
REASONING
REPRESENTATION

An organization holds a lottery as a fund-raiser. It sells 1000 tickets. There are 10 winning tickets, where 1 winning ticket pays $750, 3 winning tickets pay $200 each, and 6 winning tickets pay $50 each. What is the expected value of a lottery ticket?

SOLUTION

The table shows the outcomes and probabilities for the lottery.

Outcome	$0	$50	$200	$750
Probability	$\dfrac{990}{1000}$	$\dfrac{6}{1000}$	$\dfrac{3}{1000}$	$\dfrac{1}{1000}$

The expected value (or average payout per lottery ticket) is

$$e = 0 \cdot \frac{990}{1000} + 50 \cdot \frac{6}{1000} + 200 \cdot \frac{3}{1000} + 750 \cdot \frac{1}{1000} = \$1.65.$$

▲

The expected value does not mean that the payout for each ticket is $1.65 because each ticket pays $0, $50, $200, or $750. The expected value means that if you play this game many times, then the average payout will be $1.65 per ticket. That makes sense, because the organization will pay a total of $1650 in prize money for the 1000 tickets, which amounts to paying out an average of $1.65 per ticket. To make a profit, the organization should charge more than $1.65 per ticket.

EXAMPLE 9.30

COMMUNICATION
CONNECTION
PROBLEM SOLVING
REASONING
REPRESENTATION

In a board game, a player rolls two dice. If the difference between the higher and lower numbers on the dice is 3, 4, or 5, then the player advances six spaces on the board. Otherwise, the player advances the number of spaces indicated by the difference. For example, a player who rolls a 3 and a 1 advances 2 spaces because $3 - 1 = 2$. On average, how many spaces can a player expect to advance per roll?

SOLUTION

The table of differences is shown.

	•	⠃	⠒	⠲	⠢	⠿
•	0	1	2	3	4	5
⠃	1	0	1	2	3	4
⠒	2	1	0	1	2	3
⠲	3	2	1	0	1	2
⠢	4	3	2	1	0	1
⠿	5	4	3	2	1	0

The following table shows the possible outcomes and corresponding probabilities.

Number of spaces	0	1	2	6
Probability	$\dfrac{6}{36}$	$\dfrac{10}{36}$	$\dfrac{8}{36}$	$\dfrac{12}{36}$

The expected value is $e = 0 \cdot \frac{6}{36} + 1 \cdot \frac{10}{36} + 2 \cdot \frac{8}{36} + 6 \cdot \frac{12}{36} = \frac{98}{36} \approx 2.72$. On average, a player can expect to advance 2.72 spaces per roll.

▲

Standard Deviation

Let $\bar{x}$ denote the mean of the numbers x_1, x_2, x_3, and x_4. A natural question to ask is "How different are the values x_1, x_2, x_3, and x_4 from the mean $\bar{x}$?" In the previous chapter, we averaged the absolute values of the deviations to obtain the MAD as a measure of spread. Another measure of spread of the numbers x_1, x_2, x_3, and x_4 is the **standard deviation,** denoted s, which uses the square (rather than the absolute value) of the deviations:

$$s = \sqrt{\frac{(x_1 - \bar{x})^2 + (x_2 - \bar{x})^2 + (x_3 - \bar{x})^2 + (x_4 - \bar{x})^2}{4}}.$$

EXAMPLE 9.31 Wally grew four sunflower plants. Their heights were 171.6, 174.6, 174.4, and 175.4 cm. Calculate the standard deviation of the heights of the sunflower plants.

SOLUTION

The mean is $\bar{x} = \frac{171.6 + 174.6 + 174.4 + 175.4}{4} = 174$ cm. We can use a table to help organize the computations required to calculate the standard deviation

$$s = \sqrt{\frac{(171.6 - 174)^2 + (174.6 - 174)^2 + (174.4 - 174)^2 + (175.4 - 174)^2}{4}}.$$

1. List the data.	2. Compute the deviation from the mean.	3. Square the deviations.	4. Sum the squares of the deviations.	5. Compute the standard deviation.
171.6	$171.6 - 174 = -2.4$	$(-2.4)^2 = 5.76$	5.76	$s = \sqrt{\dfrac{8.24}{4}}$
174.6	$174.6 - 174 = 0.6$	$(0.6)^2 = 0.36$	$+ 0.36$	$= \sqrt{2.06}$
174.4	$174.4 - 174 = 0.4$	$(0.4)^2 = 0.16$	$+ 0.16$	≈ 1.44 cm
175.4	$175.4 - 174 = 1.4$	$(1.4)^2 = 1.96$	$+ 1.96$	
			8.24	

The standard deviation is 1.44 cm (a representation of the spread of heights).

▲

The standard deviation always has the same units as the data and the mean. The formula for the standard deviation extends to n numbers $x_1, x_2, \ldots, x_n$ in a natural way:

$$\text{standard deviation: } s = \sqrt{\frac{(x_1 - \bar{x})^2 + (x_2 - \bar{x})^2 + \cdots + (x_n - \bar{x})^2}{n}}.$$

As we demonstrate, the standard deviation helps us "compare apples and oranges" and identify an interval of usual values.

Measure of Position Using a z-Score

Sometimes we want to compare two scores from different collections of numbers. For example, suppose Ken received 84 points on a quiz in a math class, which had a mean of 78 points and standard deviation of 10 points. Lennie received 80 points on a quiz in a history class, which had a mean of 75 points and standard deviation of 8 points. A direct comparison suggests Ken performed better, because 84 is greater than 80. Math and history are considerably different subjects, and that makes a direct comparison questionable. Instead, we can ask, "Who performed relatively better on his quiz?" The z-score can be used to measure relative standings so that we can compare apples and oranges.

Definition of z-Score

Let x be a number from a collection of numbers. The **z-score** for x is the number

$$z = \frac{x - \text{mean}}{\text{standard deviation}}.$$

- If z is negative, x is to the left of the mean.
- If z is positive, x is to the right of the mean.
- z represents the number of standard deviations x is from the mean.
- We can think of x as a "raw" score and z as a "standardized" score.

If the number 18 has z-score 1.7, then 18 is 1.7 standard deviations *above* the mean. If the number 5 has z-score -2.4, then 5 is 2.4 standard deviations *below* the mean.

EXAMPLE 9.32 The average monthly rainfall in London is 6.3 cm per month with a standard deviation of 1.14 cm per month, and the average monthly rainfall in Seattle is 8.08 cm per month with a standard deviation of 4.57 cm per month (www.worldclimate.com). Suppose during a particular month it rained 7.67 cm in London and 12.88 cm in Seattle. Which city received relatively more rain than usual?

SOLUTION

We are comparing the rainfall amounts 7.67 and 12.88 cm for two cities that have different means and standard deviations. So, we compare their z-scores to make a relative comparison:

- The z-score for the rainfall of 7.67 cm in London is $z = (7.67 - 6.3)/1.14 \approx 1.20$.
- The z-score for the rainfall of 12.88 cm in Seattle is $z = (12.88 - 8.08)/4.57 \approx 1.05$.

The rainfall in London is 1.20 standard deviations above the mean, while the rainfall for Seattle is 1.05 standard deviations from the mean. Therefore, London received relatively more rain than Seattle compared to the city's usual amount.

▲

Normal Probability Distributions

In Section 8.2, we mentioned three important aspects of a quantitative variable: measure of center, measure of variation, and distribution. The **distribution** tells the shape and pattern of the possible values. We can use a graph to display the shape and pattern of the values. The distribution also gives you a sense of the possible values of the variable and how often these values occur.

For a discrete variable (such as the outcomes when we roll a die or spin a spinner), we could use a table to display the distribution. For example, let's consider a spinner with eight equal-sized sectors that have the numbers 1, 4, 4, 5, 6, 7, 7, and 14. Then the mean is 6 and the standard deviation is 3.5 (rounded). We can display the distribution of the discrete values using probabilities.

x	1	4	5	6	7	14
$P(x)$	0.125	0.25	0.125	0.125	0.25	0.125

For many variables (such as height or blood pressure), we can use a histogram to display a "big picture" of the shape and the relative frequency with which values occur in intervals. In many situations, the histogram is symmetric with the shape of a bell, such as the one in Figure 10.

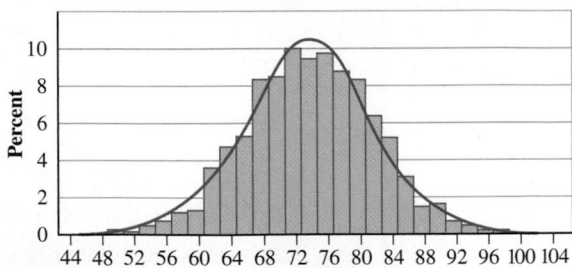

FIGURE 10
Histogram that is symmetric with the shape of a bell.

This is a common shape for many quantitative variables, such as scores on tests, heights of students, results of memory tests, response times of police, red blood cell count per milliliter of whole blood, incubation period of chickens, life span of electronic parts, and errors in repeated measurements. If quantitative data have a symmetric bell-shaped histogram, then the variable is said to have a **normal distribution** (also called a bell-shaped curve). The peak of the bell is above the mean. If the histogram displays the relative frequencies (percents), then the total area of the rectangles is 1. A famous example comes from a study published in 1846, which reported the chest size, in inches, of 5738 Scottish militiamen. Figure 11 shows the histogram for that data, and we see that the histogram is symmetric and has the shape of a bell, which suggests the chest size of militiamen was normally distributed.

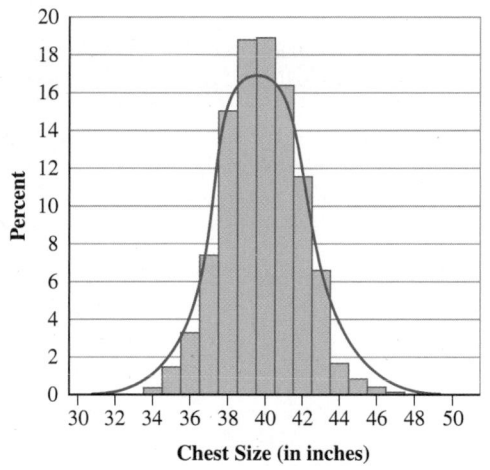

FIGURE 11

Histogram of the chest size of 5738 Scottish militiamen.

Suppose we say that the height of students is "normally distributed." What does this mean? It means that if you take a random sample of many students, measure their heights, and then create a histogram for the data, you would expect to see a histogram that is symmetric with the shape of a bell. The actual histogram depends on your sample, but you can still have expectations of what you might see. So it tells us a pattern.

EXAMPLE 9.33   Suppose the scores on the SAT are "normally distributed." What does this mean?

SOLUTION

It means that if you take a random sample of many SAT scores and then create a histogram for the data, then you should expect to see a histogram that is symmetric with the shape of a bell.

▲

68-95-99.7 Rule for Normal Distributions

An amazing aspect of a variable (such as for heights or test scores) that is normally distributed is that we can say something about the percent (and therefore probability) of observations that should belong to intervals. All we need to know is that the shape of the histogram meets our description (symmetric in the shape of a bell), along with the mean and the standard deviation of the data.

68-95-99.7 Rule for Normal Distributions

Suppose data have a histogram that is symmetric and shaped like a bell.

- Approximately 68% of the data values fall within 1 standard deviation of the mean: $[\bar{x} - s, \bar{x} + s]$.
- Approximately 95% of the data values fall within 2 standard deviations of the mean: $[\bar{x} - 2s, \bar{x} + 2s]$.
- Approximately 99.7% of the data values fall within 3 standard deviations of the mean: $[\bar{x} - 3s, \bar{x} + 3s]$.

Concept Map 9.3 is one way to visualize the 68-95-99.7 rule.

❯ Concept Map **9.3**   Visualizing the 68-95-99.7 Rule

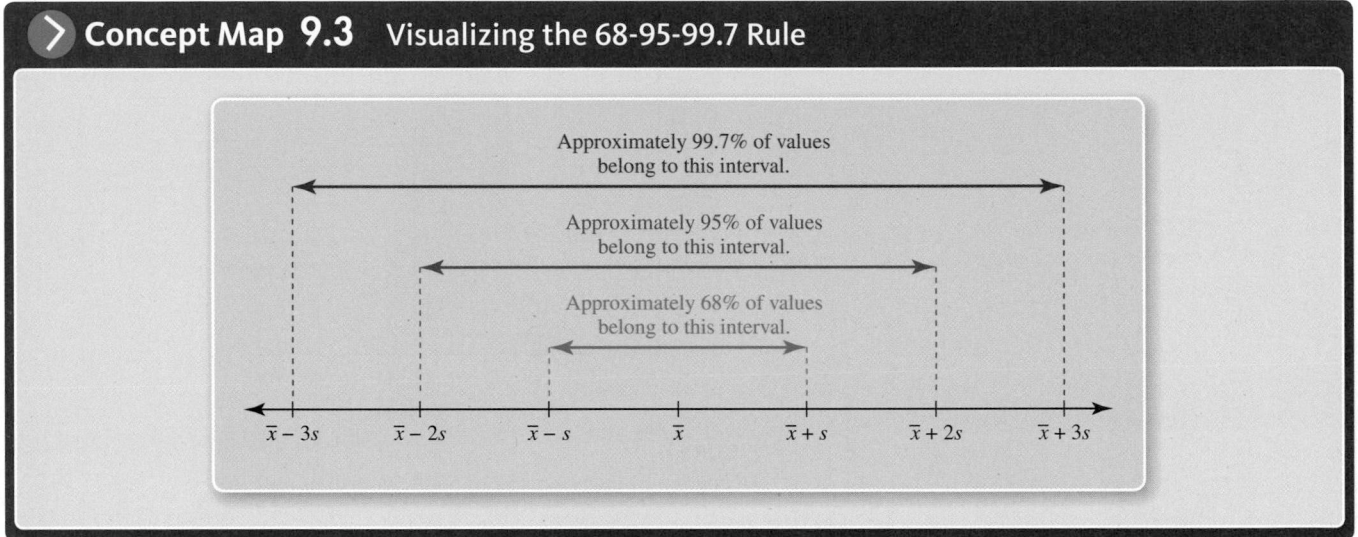

The following examples apply the 68-95-99.7 rule.

EXAMPLE 9.34

CONNECTION

REASONING

Suppose the numbers in your data set are normally distributed with a mean of 25 and standard deviation of 6. What are the maximum and minimum values that you might expect?

SOLUTION

Because of the 68-95-99.7 rule, we can expect 99.7% of the values to be within 3 standard deviations of the mean. Then $25 - 3 \cdot 6 = 7$ and $25 + 3 \cdot 6 = 43$. So we "expect" a minimum value of 7 and maximum value of 43.

▲

The following table shows 300 numbers from a normal distribution with a mean of 25 and standard deviation of 6, randomly generated with software. We see the minimum value is close to 7 and the maximum value is close to 43.

1	8.58609
2	10.57025
3	10.96053
⋮	⋮
298	39.92263
299	40.23564
300	41.15834

EXAMPLE 9.35

COMMUNICATION
CONNECTION
PROBLEM SOLVING
REASONING
REPRESENTATION

The mean SAT score for high school students on the mathematics portion of the test in 2010 was 516, with a standard deviation of 116. Assume the scores are normally distributed. Estimate the percent of students with the following scores.

a. between 400 and 632

b. between 400 and 748

c. less than 400

d. more than 284

SOLUTION

We draw a number line with the mean of 516 in the center. Then we number the equally spaced tick marks that are 1, 2, and 3 standard deviations from the mean. For example, $516 - 116 = 400$ (one tick mark to the left of the mean) and $516 - 2 \cdot 116 = 284$ (two tick marks to the left of the mean).

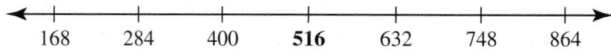

Then we use the symmetry and the 68-95-99.7 rule to calculate the percents for each interval. For example, 68% of the scores are between 400 and 632 (1 standard deviation of the mean), so 34% of the scores belong in each half of the interval. In addition, 95% of the scores are between 284 and 748, and $(95 - 68)/2 = 13.5$. So 13.5% of scores fall between 284 and 400, as well as between 632 and 748. That leaves 5% of the scores below 284 and above 784. Because of symmetry, that means 2.5% of the scores are below 284 and 2.5% of the scores are above 748.

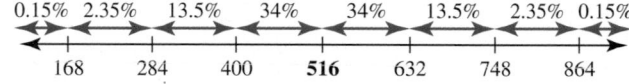

Now we are ready to answer the questions.

a. 68%

b. 81.5%

c. 16%

d. 97.5%

▲

EXAMPLE 9.36

COMMUNICATION
CONNECTION
PROBLEM SOLVING
REASONING
REPRESENTATION

Suppose the scores of a test are normally distributed with a mean of 80 and standard deviation of 5. What is the probability that a randomly chosen student scored between 70 and 85?

SOLUTION

The probability equals the percent of scores between 70 and 85. We apply the 68-95-99.7 rule and draw the number line as shown.

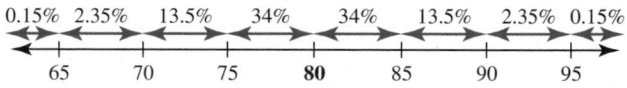

The probability is 81.5%, because $0.135 + 0.34 + 0.34 = 0.815 = 81.5\%$.

▲

Let's consider data (generated by software) that have the symmetric and bell-shaped histogram shown in Figure 12.

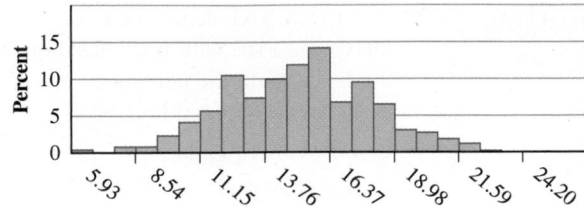

FIGURE 12
Histogram of 500 numbers that is approximately symmetric in the shape of a bell.

There were 500 numbers in the data set, which had a mean of $\bar{x} = 15.16$ and standard deviation of $s = 3.02$. For these data, the software determined the following:

- 67% of the data were within 1 standard deviation of the mean, in the interval [12.14, 18.18].
- 96.6% of the data were within 2 standard deviations of the mean, in the interval [9.12, 21.20].
- 99.8% of the data were within 3 standard deviations of the mean, in the interval [6.10, 24.22].

The data in the histogram in Figure 12 have percents that support the 68-95-99.7 rule.

Usual Values

We can define a "usual value" to be one that seems reasonable or expected.

> ### Rule of Thumb for Using the Standard Deviation to Identify Usual and Unusual Values
>
> Let $\bar{x}$ and s represent the mean and standard deviation of a collection of numbers that can be displayed with a histogram that is symmetric and shaped like a bell.
>
> - If x has a z-score from -2 to 2, then x is considered a usual value.
> - If x has a z-score less than -2, then x is considered an unusual value.
> - If x has a z-score more than 2, then x is considered an unusual value.
> - The minimum usual value is $\bar{x} - 2s$ (which has a z-score equal to -2).
> - The maximum usual value is $\bar{x} + 2s$ (which has a z-score equal to 2).

EXAMPLE 9.37

CONNECTION

The heights of 19-year-old males are approximately normally distributed with a mean of 69.9 inches and a standard deviation of 3.5 inches (based on information from National Health Statistics Reports). Is the given height of a 19-year-old male a usual or unusual measurement?

a. 73 inches

b. 79 inches

SOLUTION

The z-score for the height x inches is $z = (x - \bar{x})/s$. All heights that are considered usual have a z-score from -2 to 2.

a. The z-score for 73 is $(73 - 69.9)/3.5 \approx 0.89$. Then 73 inches is a usual height.

b. The z-score for 79 is $(79 - 69.9)/3.5 = 2.6$. Then 79 inches is an unusual height.

"Usual values" are especially important in medicine. For example, some researchers aimed to define usual values of hemoglobin (a protein in red blood cells that carries oxygen from the lungs to tissues and carbon dioxide from tissues to the lungs) at high altitudes so that unusual values could be used to help diagnose chronic mountain sickness. This condition leads to shortness of breath, fatigue, headache, dizziness, and muscle pain and can even be fatal. The researchers defined "normal" (usual) as values within 2 standard deviations of the mean. They determined that, in part, hemoglobin levels above 21 g per deciliter for males and 19 g per deciliter for females were outside the normal range. However, the field of medicine often defines "normal" values in other ways by using different cutoff values. For example, bone mineral density (BMD) tests are used to evaluate bone strength and diagnose osteoporosis (a debilitating disease that causes brittle bones, leading to fractures of the spine, neck, hip, and so on). The World Health Organization states the following:

- A BMD value within 1 standard deviation of the mean is a normal measurement.

- A BMD value from 1 standard deviation to 2.5 standard deviations below the mean indicates low bone mass, which in turn indicates a higher fracture risk compared to that for young, healthy adults.

- A BMD value more than 2.5 standard deviations below the mean indicates osteoporosis.

Guidelines for Numerical Summaries of Data

Students should be knowledgeable in "relating the choice of measures of center and variability to the shape of the data distribution and the context in which the data were gathered" (Gr. 6, CCSS). Here are helpful guidelines relating measures of center and variability:

- If the histogram of the data is approximately symmetric and has the shape of a bell without outliers, then the data could be summarized with the mean and standard deviation (about 95% of the data are within 2 standard deviations of the mean) or the mean and MAD (about 95% of the data are within 2.5 MADs of the mean).

- If a histogram of the data does not have the shape of a bell and the data do not have any outliers, then the data could be summarized with the five-number summary.

- If the data contain outliers, then the data could be summarized with the 25th, 50th, and 75th percentiles. The 50th percentile (median) is a measure of center, and the 25th and 75th percentiles provide a measure of the variation of the middle 50% of the data. (Researchers sometimes report the 10th, 25th, 50th, 75th, and 90th percentiles, or the 5th, 25th, 50th, 75th, and 95th percentiles.)

Simulations

A **simulation** is a representation or imitation of a process. The experimental results from a simulation provide estimates of theoretical probabilities. Simulations help students develop correct intuitions about probability and predict outcomes. For example, what is the probability that a tack tossed in the air will land with the point down? Simply toss the tack n times and record the frequency f of the number of times it landed point down. Then f/n is an estimate of the probability that a tack tossed in the air will land with the point down. Students should be able to "use proportionality and a basic understanding of probability to make and test conjectures about the results of experiments and simulations" (Gr. 6–8, NCTM). They should be able to "design and use a simulation to generate frequencies for compound events. For example, use random digits as a simulation tool to approximate the answer to the question: If 40% of donors have type A blood, what is the probability that it will take at least 4 donors to find one with type A blood?" (Gr. 7, CCSS).

In some cases, we can use a coin or a table of random digits to determine an experimental probability f/n as an estimate of a theoretical probability.

EXAMPLE 9.38

COMMUNICATION
CONNECTION
PROBLEM SOLVING
REASONING
REPRESENTATION

A couple plans to have five children. Use a simulation to estimate the probability that they will have three boys.

SOLUTION

We assume the probability of a boy is 1/2 and the probability of a girl is 1/2. Using a fair coin, let heads (H) represent a boy and tails (T) represent a girl. The coin properly represents the simple probabilities of 1/2 and 1/2. The couple plans to have five children, so an experiment consists of tossing the coin five times and recording the results of each toss. The event occurs when a sequence has exactly three Hs. We repeat the experiment 25 times ($n = 25$) and count the number of times the event occurs ($f = ?$). The sequences in blue indicate three boys in the family with five children.

HHTTT	THHTH	HHHHH	HHHTH	HHTHH
HTTTH	THTTT	HHTHT	HHHHH	THTHH
HTHHT	TTTHH	TTHHT	TTHTT	TTTHH
THHTT	TTTTT	THHHT	TTTHT	HHHHH
HTTHT	HTHTH	HTTTT	TTTTH	TTTHH

The 25 experimental results show six families that have three boys, so $f = 6$, $n = 25$, and $f/n = 6/25 = 0.24$. The experimental probability that a family with five children will have three boys is 0.24.

▲

We could obtain a different experimental probability using a different n, such as $n = 30$ or $n = 47$. Our estimate will be more accurate if we repeat the experiment a very large number of times. Table 9.6 is a table of random digits, which is applied in the following examples.

EXAMPLE 9.39

COMMUNICATION
CONNECTION
PROBLEM SOLVING
REASONING
REPRESENTATION

Jared is a basketball player and has a 70% chance of making a free throw. What is the probability that Jared will make three of his next four free throws?

SOLUTION

Jared has a 7 out of 10 chance of making a free throw. Let the seven digits 0, 1, 2, 3, 4, 5, and 6 represent a free throw made by Jared, and let the digits 7, 8, and 9 represent a free throw missed by Jared. The digits properly represent the probabilities of 70% and 30%, respectively. An experiment consists of randomly selecting four digits from a table of random digits. The event occurs when a sequence of four digits has exactly three digits from 0 to 6. We repeat the experiment 30 times ($n = 30$) and count the number of times (f) the event occurs. We select 30 sequences of four digits from the following portion of Table 9.6.

	1	2	3	4
1	10480	15011	01536	02011
	22368	46573	25595	85393
	24130	48360	22527	97265
	42167	93093	06243	61680
5	37570	39975	81837	16656
	77921	06907	11008	42751

The following shows the 30 sequences of four digits. The sequences in blue represent that Jared made exactly three free throws.

1048	0150	1101	5360	2011
2236	8465	7325	5958	5383
2413	0483	6022	5279	7625
4216	7930	9306	2436	1680
3757	0399	7581	8371	6656
7792	1069	0711	0084	2751

The 30 experimental results show 12 experiments resulted in three free throws made, so $f = 12$, $n = 30$, and $f/n = 12/30 = 0.40$. The experimental probability that Jared makes three of his next four free throws is 40%.

▲

TABLE 9.6 **Table of Random Digits**

	1	2	3	4	5	6	7	8	9	10
1	10480	15011	01536	02011	81647	91646	69179	14194	62590	36207
	22368	46573	25595	85393	30995	89198	27982	53402	93965	34095
	24130	48360	22527	97265	76393	64809	15179	24830	49340	32081
	42167	93093	06243	61680	07856	16376	39440	53537	71341	57004
5	37570	39975	81837	16656	06121	91782	60468	81305	49684	60672
	77921	06907	11008	42751	27756	53498	18602	70659	90655	15053
	99562	72905	56420	69994	98872	31016	71194	18738	44013	48840
	96301	91977	05463	07972	18876	20922	94595	56869	69014	60045
	89579	14342	63661	10281	17453	18103	57740	84378	25331	12566
10	85475	36857	53342	53988	53060	59533	38867	62300	08158	17983
	28918	69578	88231	33276	70997	79936	56865	05859	90106	31595
	63553	40961	48235	03427	49626	69445	18663	72695	52180	20847
	09429	93969	52636	92737	88974	33488	36320	17617	30015	08272
	10365	61129	87529	85689	48237	52267	67689	93394	01511	26358
15	07119	97336	71048	08178	77233	13916	47564	81056	97735	85977
	51085	12765	51821	51259	77452	16308	60756	92144	49442	53900
	02368	21382	52404	60268	89368	19885	55322	44819	01188	65255
	01011	54092	33362	94904	31273	04146	18594	29852	71585	85030
	52162	53916	46369	58586	23216	14513	83149	98736	23495	64350
20	07056	97628	33787	09998	42698	06691	76988	13602	51851	46104
	48663	91245	85828	14346	09172	30168	90229	04734	59193	22178
	54164	58492	22421	74103	47070	25306	76468	26384	58151	06646
	32639	32363	05597	24200	13363	38005	94342	28728	35806	06912
	29334	27001	87637	87308	58731	00256	45834	15398	46557	41135

Now we describe the steps for designing a simulation.

How to Conduct a Simulation to Approximate the Probability of an Event

1. Select a model (for example, a table of random digits).
2. Define an experiment (for example, randomly selecting a group of five digits).
3. Define the event (for example, determining that the event occurs when three of the five digits are 0, 1, or 2).
4. Conduct n trials using the model (for example, randomly picking $n = 70$ groups of five digits).
5. Record the frequency f of the number of times the event occurred (for example, marking the groups of digits that indicate the event occurred and then counting the number of marks).
6. Compute the ratio f/n as an estimate of the probability of the event.

The steps for conducting a simulation to approximate a probability can be modified for other situations, as demonstrated in the next problem. The key is to make sure that the model represents the probabilities accurately.

EXAMPLE 9.40

COMMUNICATION
CONNECTION
PROBLEM SOLVING
REASONING
REPRESENTATION

Maria has a 42% chance of winning a prize in a carnival game. She plays the game until she wins two prizes for her brother and sister. Use a simulation to estimate the number of games she needs to play to win two prizes.

SOLUTION

We can use a table of random digits to simulate this experiment. An experiment consists of randomly selecting pairs of digits. Each pair of digits represented a game played. The pairs 00, 01, . . . , 41 represent that Maria won a prize. The other possibilities 42, 43, . . . , 99 represent that Maria did not win a prize. The pairs of digits properly represent the probabilities of 42% and 58%, respectively. We pick pairs of digits until two prizes are won (using Table 9.6). Nine results of 27 repetitions of the experiment as shown below.

10 48 01	(three games)	50 11 01	(three games)	53 60 20 11	(four games)
81 64 79 16 46 69 17	(seven games)	91 41 94 62 59 03	(six games)	22 36	(two games)
. . .		. . .		. . .	
19 17	(two games)	82 60 46 88 13 05	(six games)	77 92 10 69 07	(five games)

Then we average the number of games: $(3 + 3 + 4 + 7 + 6 + 2 + \ldots + 2 + 6 + 5)/27 = 116/27 \approx 4.3$. On average, Maria needs to play 4.3 games to win two prizes. (We could have used 25, 42, or 58 repetitions, but we chose 27.)

▲

The following student page illustrates how a simulation could be used to estimate the number of boxes of cereal you could expect to buy to win a prize.

Simulations

MATH LAB

Explore how to use a simulation to model an experiment.

QUICK REVIEW
Find the mean.
1. 4, 5, 4, 6, 6   2. 2, 3, 1, 2, 3, 1
3. 10, 9, 17, 10   4. 15, 10, 14
5. 250, 200, 150

You need a 5-section spinner and a calculator.

A cereal company is having a contest. To win a prize, you have to collect five cards that spell *PRIZE*. One of the five letters is put into each cereal box when the cereal is produced. The letters are divided equally among the cereal boxes.

You can conduct an experiment to simulate how many boxes of cereal you have to buy to get all five letters.

Activity 1

- Use a spinner to generate random numbers. Each of the numbers 1 to 5 will represent one of the letters.

P	R	I	Z	E
1	2	3	4	5

- Spin the pointer on the spinner, and tally the numbers you get.

- Continue to spin the pointer until you get every number at least once.

- Repeat the experiment.

NUMBER	TALLY
1	///
2	///
3	/
4	/
5	///

Think and Discuss
- How many spins did it take in the first experiment to get all five numbers? in the second experiment?

- What is the mean of the spins in your two experiments?

- How many boxes of cereal do you expect you will have to buy to get all five letters? If you bought this many boxes, would you be sure to win? Explain.

Practice
- Repeat the experiment three more times.

- Combine your data with data from 5 classmates. Find the mean of the spins from all five sets of data.

- How many boxes of cereal do you expect you will have to buy to get all five letters? How does this differ from what you expected after the first two experiments?

(Harcourt *Math*, Student Edition, Grade 5, p. 424)

Odds in Favor and Odds Against

CONNECTION   The probability of an event is a part-to-whole comparison. For example, if the probability of event E occurring is 0.24, then ideally event E would occur 24 out of 100 times. So $P(E) = \frac{24}{100}$ and $P(\sim E) = \frac{76}{100}$. The ratio $P(E){:}P(\sim E)$ has a simpler form: $\frac{24}{100}{:}\frac{76}{100} = 24{:}76$ (by multiplying both terms in the ratio by 100). So the ratio 24:76 compares the number of "favorable outcomes" to the number of "unfavorable outcomes" for E. There are 24 outcomes that favor E, and there are 76 outcomes that do not favor E. In this example, we say the "odds in favor of E" are 24:76, and the "odds against E" are 76:24. Odds are more comprehensible with simpler ratios, so we should report 24:76 and 76:24 as "the odds in favor of E are 6:19" and "the odds against E are 19:6."

> **Definition**
>
> Let E be an event with the probability $P(E)$.
>
> - The **odds in favor of** E occurring is the ratio $P(E){:}P({\sim}E)$.
> - The **odds against** E occurring is the ratio $P({\sim}E){:}P(E)$.

EXAMPLE 9.41

COMMUNICATION
CONNECTION
PROBLEM SOLVING
REASONING
REPRESENTATION

A card is randomly drawn from a standard deck of 52 cards. What are the odds

a. in favor of drawing a 10?

b. against drawing a face card?

SOLUTION

a. Let E be the event of drawing a 10. There are four 10s in the deck, and the probability of drawing a 10 is $P(E) = 4/52$. Then the probability of not drawing a 10 is $P({\sim}E) = 48/52$. Then we have the following.

$$\text{odds in favor of drawing a 10} = P(E){:}P({\sim}E)$$

$$= \frac{4}{52}{:}\frac{48}{52}$$

$$= 4{:}48 \qquad \textbf{Multiply both terms by 52.}$$

$$= 1{:}12 \qquad \textbf{Divide both terms by 4.}$$

This means that for every 1 chance of drawing a 10, there are 12 chances of drawing a card that is not a 10.

b. There are 12 face cards in the deck, so the probability of drawing a face card is $12/52$ and the probability of not drawing a face card is $1 - 12/52 = 40/52$. Then we have the following.

$$\text{odds against drawing a face card} = P(E){:}P({\sim}E)$$

$$= \frac{40}{52}{:}\frac{12}{52}$$

$$= 40{:}12 \qquad \textbf{Multiply both terms by 52.}$$

$$= 10{:}3 \qquad \textbf{Divide both terms by 4.}$$

This means that for every 10 chances of drawing a nonface card, there are 3 chances of drawing a face card.

▲

EXAMPLE 9.42

CONNECTION

According to the CDC, 80% of adult smokers in the United States started smoking before the age of 18. What are the odds that an adult smoker started smoking before the age of 18?

SOLUTION

Because 80% of adult smokers started smoking before age 18, 20% of adult smokers started smoking at age 18 or later. The odds (in favor of) an adult smoker starting to smoke before the age of 18 are 0.80:0.20, 80:20, 8:2, or 4:1. This means that for every four adult smokers who started smoking before the age of 18, there is one adult smoker who started smoking at age 18 or later.

▲

The next example illustrates how to convert odds to probability.

EXAMPLE 9.43

CONNECTION

REASONING

Patients seek care at the outpatient department of a hospital for a variety of reasons, such as medical treatment, counseling, weight management, nutrition, or asthma education. According to the National Hospital Ambulatory Medical Care Survey for outpatient department visits by CDC, the odds were 2 to 3 that a male patient visited the outpatient department for medical treatment. What is the probability that a male patient visited the outpatient department for medical treatment?

SOLUTION

Let E be the event that a randomly selected male visited the outpatient department for medical treatment. The ratio 2:3 is equivalent to $P(E):P(\sim E)$.

$$P(E):P(\sim E) = 2:3$$

$$\frac{P(E)}{P(\sim E)} = \frac{2}{3}$$

$$3P(E) = 2P(\sim E)$$

$$3P(E) = 2(1 - P(E))$$

$$3P(E) = 2 - 2P(E)$$

$$5P(E) = 2$$

$$P(E) = \frac{2}{5}$$

The probability that a randomly selected male visited the outpatient department for medical treatment is 2/5, or 40%.

▲

In the preceding example, the odds were 2:3 and $P(E) = \dfrac{2}{5} = \dfrac{2}{2+3}$. Then $P(\sim E) = 1 - \dfrac{2}{5} = \dfrac{3}{5} = \dfrac{3}{2+3}$.

This suggests the following rule for converting odds to probability.

Definition

If the odds in favor of E occurring are $a{:}b$, then $P(E) = \dfrac{a}{a+b}$ and $P(\sim E) = \dfrac{b}{a+b}$.

EXAMPLE 9.44

The odds are 4:21 that a victim of identity theft will incur expenses of $5000 to $15,000 (for example, paying legal fees), according to *Forbes* magazine. What is the probability that a victim of identity theft incurs expenses of $5000 to $15,000?

SOLUTION

The probability is $\dfrac{4}{4+21} = \dfrac{4}{25} = 16\%$. There is a 16% chance that a victim of identity theft incurs expenses of $5000 to $15,000.

▲

QUESTIONS FOR SECTION 9.3

REPRESENTATION

Refresher: Representations (language, diagrams, tables, symbols, algebra, manipulatives, and contextualized situations) are important because we use them to organize, record, and communicate mathematical ideas and to make them more comprehensible.

1. The Venn diagram represents events A and B for a sample space S with equally likely outcomes. Explain why the odds of A occurring are 2:3.

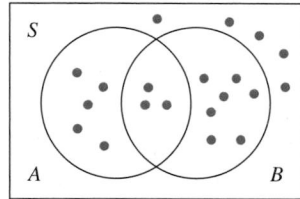

2. Determine the expected value of the spinner.

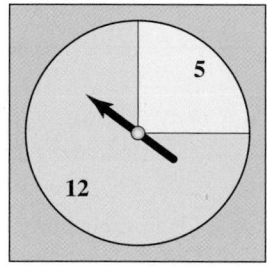

3. Determine the expected value of the spinner.

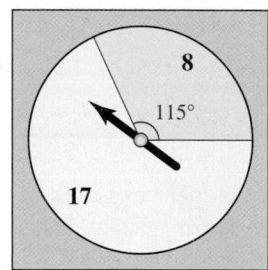

4. A teacher created the histogram shown of weights of boxes of cereal. What reasonable assumption can you make about the variable?

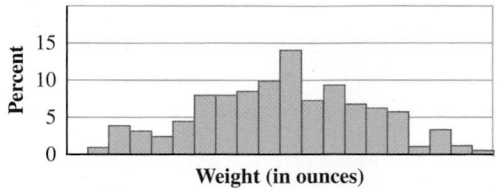

5. The three histograms L8, 4U, and 2B display data taken from the same normal distribution. The histograms summarize 50, 200, and 500 values.

   a. Which histogram summarizes 50 values? Explain your answer.

   b. Which histogram summarizes 500 values? Explain your answer.

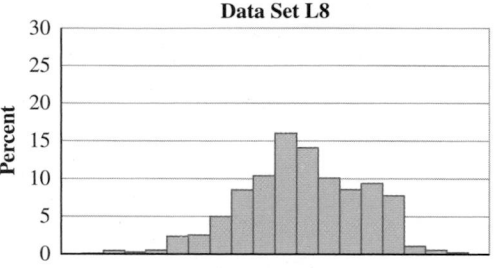

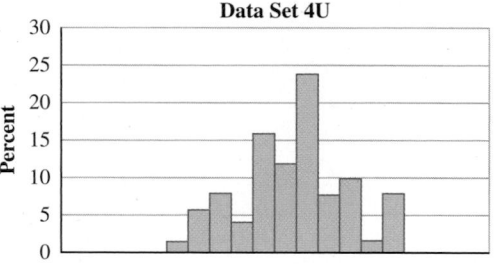

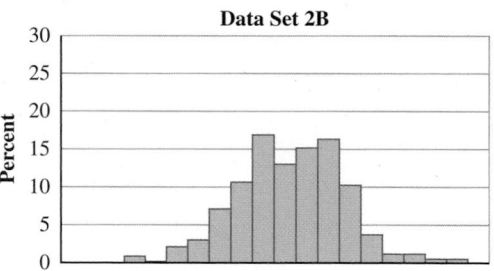

6. A teacher created the histogram shown. Estimate the mean of the data. Assume the numbers on the horizontal axis represent the right endpoint b of the interval (a, b) for the rectangle.

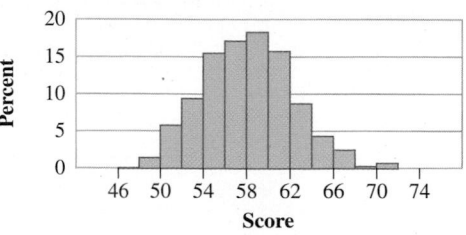

7. Identify the graph with the larger standard deviation.

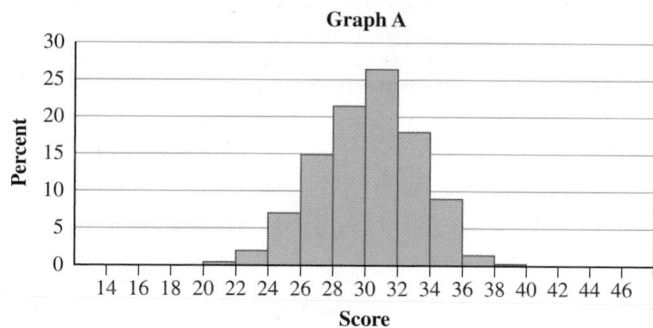

Graph A

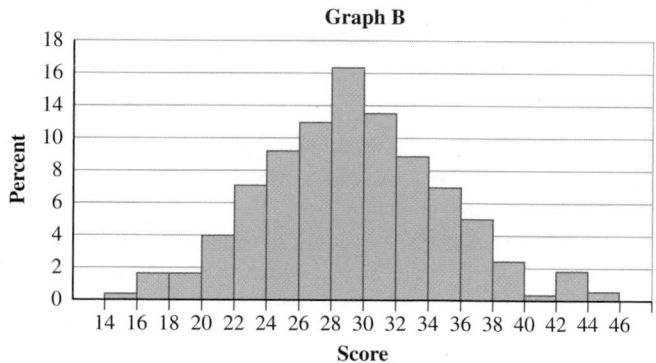

Graph B

8. Mario took a history test, and Jennifer took a math test. The mean of the math test was 74, and the mean of the history test was 78. The z-score for Mario was 1.7, and the z-score for Jennifer was 1.54. Who scored relatively higher on his or her test? Explain your answer.

PROBLEM SOLVING

Refresher: Problem solving (reaching a goal that is not immediately attainable) is important because it helps students think more deeply about what they know and deal with unfamiliar situations.

9. Answer the following for the spinner shown.

a. Is the expected value less than 3 or greater than 3?

b. Is the expected value less than 6 or greater than 6?

c. What is the expected value of the spinner?

10. Gary scored an 82 on a quiz in his math class, which had a mean of 78 points and standard deviation of 10 points. Dan scored 68 points on a quiz in a history class, which had a mean of 60 points and standard deviation of 4 points. Who scored relatively better on the test?

11. Joey took a quiz in his math class. The mean was 72 points, and the standard deviation was 10 points. Mitchell scored 86 points on a quiz in his history class, which had a mean of 74 points and standard deviation of 5 points. What is the minimum score that Joey should have earned to score relatively higher than Mitchell? Show your work.

12. Ben scored 82 on a history test, which had a mean of 74. Molly scored 88 on a math test, which had a mean of 80. The z-score for Ben was 1.4, and the z-score for Molly was 0.8. Which class had test scores with more variation? Show your work.

13. A game consists of tossing three coins. If all three coins land on heads, then the player wins $75. If all three coins land on tails, then the player wins $45. Otherwise, the player wins nothing. On average, how much should a player expect to win each game?

14. The probability that a person in the United States dies between 40 and 45 years of age is 0.011506, according to a life table for the total population in a National Vital Statistics Report based on the 2000 U.S. Census. Suppose a 40-year-old purchases a 5-year, $250,000 life insurance policy. Then the insurance company pays either $0 or $250,000.

a. Use the data to determine the "expected payout" for the policy.

Payout	$0	$250,000
Probability	0.988494	0.011506

b. Suppose the insurance company charges $3000 for each policy. How much profit should it expect to make for each policy?

c. How much should the insurance company charge to make a profit of $600?

REASONING AND PROOF

Refresher: Reasoning and proof (thinking and justifying) are important because they help students make sense of mathematics.

15. Each set of numbers has the same mean: 80. Rank the sets in the order of increasing standard deviation, without calculating the standard deviation.

$$A = \{80, 70, 80, 90\}$$
$$B = \{40, 90, 78, 88, 87, 97\}$$
$$C = \{75, 77, 83, 85\}$$

16. Consider a spinner with a payoff based on where the arrow stops.

Payoff	$1	$4
Probability	40%	60%

a. Ideally, in 10 spins we expect to land on $4 exactly _____ times.

b. Ideally, in 10 spins we expect to land on $1 exactly _____ times.

c. Ideally, in 10 spins we expect a total payoff of $____.

d. Ideally, we expect the total payoff per spin to be $___.

e. Use the definition of expected value to calculate the expected payout per spin.

17. The table shows the outcomes and probabilities for a four-sided die. What is the expected value of the die?

Outcome	3	4	6	7
Probability	0.20	0.15	0.35	0.30

18. Suppose you plan to use software to generate a list of 250 numbers from a distribution that is normally distributed with a mean of 80 and standard deviation of 5. Estimate the maximum and minimum values that you would expect to see in the list. Explain your answer.

19. The manager of a hotel wants to accept more daily reservations than the number of rooms in the hotel to minimize loss of revenue because of empty rooms caused by cancellations and no-shows. Past data show that each day the mean number of cancellations and no-shows was 10.5, with a standard deviation of 3.4. A histogram of the data is approximately bell shaped. How many additional reservations should the manager allow to remain confident that he honors most reservations? Explain your answer.

20. The teacher announced to her class that the mean of test 1 was 74.5 with a standard deviation of 8.2 and the mean of test 2 was 68.1 with a standard deviation of 3.5. Then she told the class that the scores for both tests were normally distributed. She said that a student scored a 60 on one of these tests but that she could not "remember" if the score was for test 1 or test 2. She asked her students whether they could use probability reasoning to help her decide which test the score was for. The students thought about this for a few minutes. Then Maria said, "The score was more likely to be for test 1." Explain how Maria could be correct.

CONNECTIONS

Refresher: Connections (linking and applying mathematical ideas) are important because they deepen student understanding and make mathematics more meaningful, flexible, and useful.

21. $P(A) = 0.42$. What are the odds for A?

22. The odds in favor of A are 4 to 7. What is the chance that A occurs?

23. A dart is randomly thrown at the dartboard shown. Assume the dart will hit the dartboard. The radius of the inner circle is 14 inches, and the radius of the outer circle is 24 inches. Verify the odds that the dart lands in the shaded region is about 33:17.

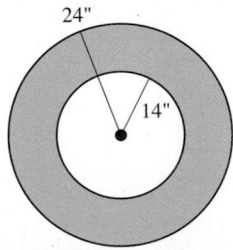

24. A dart is randomly thrown at the dartboard shown. Assume the dart will hit the dartboard. The radius of the inner circle is 14 inches, and the radius of the outer circle is 24 inches. Verify that the odds that the dart lands in the shaded region are about 11:39.

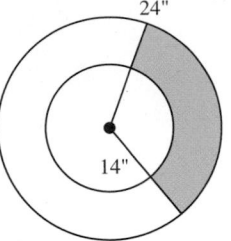

25. According to the American Cancer Society,

a. 30% of those who did not graduate from high school are current smokers. What are the odds that a randomly chosen person who did not graduate from high school is a current smoker? Explain your answer.

b. 72% of youth aged 11 to 18 get sunburned at least once during the summer months. What are the odds that a randomly chosen person aged 11 to 18 was not sunburned during the summer months? Explain your answer.

26. A game consists of tossing two standard dice. What are the odds of rolling a sum of 8?

27. In the game of Monopoly, you are on Pacific Avenue and your opponent has hotels on Park Place and Boardwalk. You move your piece the number of spaces indicated by the sum of two standard dice. If you roll a sum of 6 or 8, you will be charged rent to stay at Park Place or Boardwalk. What are the odds that you will land on one of these expensive hotels on the next roll? Explain your answer.

28. According to the American Cancer Society,

a. the odds that an adult achieves the daily recommended physical activity level (exercise 30 minutes or more per day at least 5 days per week) are 9:10. What is the probability that a randomly chosen adult achieves the daily recommended physical activity level?

b. the odds are 1:3 that a state does not require tobacco use prevention to be taught in elementary school. What is the probability that a randomly chosen state requires tobacco use prevention to be taught in elementary school?

COMMUNICATION

Refresher: Communication (written and verbal explanations using representations and proper mathematical vocabulary) is important because it helps students refine and strengthen their understanding.

29. Suppose the number of hours that people spend on the computer is "normally distributed." What does this mean?

30. Does the spinner have an expected value? Explain your answer.

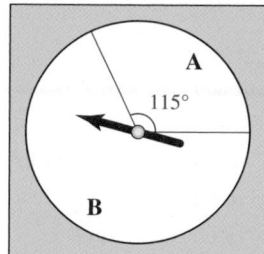

31. A cereal company puts one prize in every cereal box. There are five prizes (say, A, B, C, D, and E), and each prize has the same chance of being in any box. Maria wants to get two identical prizes for her younger twin brothers. Explain how you would use a table of random digits to estimate the number of boxes she should expect to buy to get two identical prizes.

More practice with the ideas of the section

32. Fill in the blank. Choose one of the following words, phrases, numbers, or equations: *2, 3, 68%, 95%, 99.7%, a/(a + b), b/(a + b), distribution, expected value, normally distributed, P(E):P(~E), simulation, table of random digits,* or *z-scores.*

   a. A(n) _____ is a sum obtained by multiplying outcomes and their probabilities.

   b. The odds in favor of E occurring is the ratio _____.

   c. If the odds in favor of E occurring are $a{:}b$, then $P(E) =$ _____.

   d. The _____ can be used to measure relative standings so that we can compare apples and oranges.

   e. The _____ of a variable essentially tells you possible values and how often these values occur.

   f. Data that have a histogram that is symmetric in the shape of a bell are said to be _____.

   g. Approximately _____ of the data values fall within 2 standard deviations of the mean.

   h. Approximately 99.7% of the data values fall within _____ standard deviations of the mean.

   i. A(n) _____ is a representation of an experiment that provides an estimate of a theoretical probability.

33. The probability that a 50-year-old person in the United States lives an additional year is 0.995587, according to a life table for the total population in a National Vital Statistics Report. Suppose a 50-year-old purchases a 1-year $250,000 life insurance policy. Then the insurance company pays either $0 or $250,000.

   a. Complete the table.

Payout	$0	$250,000
Probability		

   b. Determine the "expected payout" for each policy.

   c. How much should the insurance company charge to make a profit of $1200 per policy?

34. A radio station is having a contest. There is a vacation package worth $15,000. Three prizes are gift cards to a coffee shop worth $1000 each. Five prizes provided tutoring for your math course, worth $500 each.

   a. Compute the expected value for this contest, assuming 10,000 people enter this contest.

   b. What are the odds for winning the vacation package?

35. In the game of Monopoly, a player must move his piece 40 squares from the start position to the Pass Go square or beyond to collect $200 from the bank. On average, how many rolls of a pair of dice does the player need to make it from the start position to collect $200 from the bank? (Hint: Determine the expected value of a fair die.)

36. The chances that an amateur golfer hits a hole-in-one are approximately 1 in 13,000. What is the probability that an amateur golfer hits a hole-in-one?

37. A cash sweepstakes is offered. In a random drawing, 100 winners will be selected from among all eligible entries received by an independent judging organization, whose decisions are final. The prize values are $1000, $500, $100, and $25. The prize values, the number of prizes, and the estimated odds of winning are 1 prize of $1000 at 1:6.8 million, 1 prize of $500 at 1:6.8 million, 1 prize of $100 at 1:6.8 million, and 97 prizes of $25 at 1:70,000.

   a. Estimate the expected value of the sweepstakes.

   b. Are the expected winnings more or less than the cost of a postage stamp to mail a standard envelope, assuming a stamp currently costs $0.44?

38. Use a table of random digits to estimate the probability that a baseball player with a batting average of 0.280 will get two hits in his next three at-bats. (Hint: Consider representing an at-bat with two digits. For example, 02 and 46 could each represent one at-bat. Which pairs of digits should you choose to represent that the batter gets a hit? How many pairs of digits should you choose to represent three at-bats?)

39. A player pays $2 to play a dice game. The player rolls two dice. If the difference between the two dice is 1, 4, or 5, then the player is given $x worth of prizes. If the difference between the two dice is 3, 0, or 2, then the player loses and the game is over. How much should the player be given when the difference between the two dice is 1, 4, or 5 so that, on the average, the player wins a prize worth the money he paid to play the game (the player breaks even)?

40. An automobile insurance company sells an annual insurance policy. Based on data from past claims, the company has calculated that

   • 1 in 40 policyholders will file a claim of $1500.
   • 1 in 25 policyholders will file a claim of $800.
   • 4 in 15 policyholders will file a claim of $300.

   a. Verify that the insurance company can expect to pay out $149.50 per policy each year, on average.

   b. How much should the insurance company charge for each policy if it wants to make a profit of $500 for each policy each year?

41. Jack and Jill went up the hill to play tennis. Their history shows that, on average, Jack wins three out of the seven games they play.

   a. What is the probability that Jack wins a game against Jill? Explain your answer.

   b. Use a table of random digits to estimate the probability that Jack wins exactly two out of three games played against Jill.

42. A physician sees many patients every day. The office manager knows that each day some patients fail to keep their appointment or reschedule at the last minute. Based on past records, the office manager notices that every hour one out of five patients will not show or will cancel at the last minute; therefore, the manager schedules six patients each hour. Use a simulation to estimate the probability that all six scheduled patients will show up during the hour.

43. Two baseball teams, Westrikeout and Werunslow, miraculously reach the World Series. It was an odd year indeed. The World Series has a best four-out-of-seven format. During the regular season, Westrikeout won 75% of the games against Werunslow. Use a table of random digits to estimate the number of games you would expect to be played before a winner is determined.

44. A cereal company puts one prize in every cereal box. There are seven prizes, and each prize has the same chance of being in any box. Maria wants to get two identical prizes for her younger twin brothers. Use a table of random digits to estimate the number of boxes she should expect to buy to get two identical prizes.

45. Misha has an 80% chance of winning a prize in a carnival game. She plays the game until she wins three prizes for friends. Use a table of random digits to estimate the number of games she should expect to play to win three prizes.

46. Kelly is a basketball player and has an 80% chance of making a free throw. Use a table of random digits to estimate the probability that she will make all three of her next three free throws.

47. The school nurse measures the heights of fifth-grade students at his school. A histogram of the data suggests the heights are normally distributed because of the symmetry in the shape of a bell. The histogram does not suggest there are any outliers. The lowest measurement is 130 cm, and the highest measurement is 163 cm. Estimate the mean and standard deviation of the measurements.

48. The data set consists of the scores 42, 58, 60, and 52.
  a. Calculate the mean.   **b.** Calculate the standard deviation.
  c. Is 36 a usual or unusual value?
  d. Is 45 a usual or unusual value?

49. The data set consists of the scores 105, 145, 150, and 130.
  a. Calculate the mean.   **b.** Calculate the standard deviation.
  c. Is 100 a usual or unusual value?
  d. Is 180 a usual or unusual value?

50. Suppose the life span of a brand of lightbulbs is normally distributed with a mean of 2000 hours and standard deviation of 320 hours. What percentage of lightbulbs have a life span
  a. between 1360 and 2000 hours?
  b. between 1680 and 2640 hours?
  c. less than 2320 hours?   **d.** more than 2640 hours?

51. The mean SAT score for high school students on the writing portion of the test in 2010 was 492, with a standard deviation of 111. What percentage of students have the following scores?
  a. more than 714   **b.** less than 381
  c. between 381 and 714   **d.** between 270 and 492

52. The manager of a security company told concert organizers that the company would provide one security guard for every 500 people at the concert. Past data show that 7400 people attend the concert on average, with a standard deviation of 650 people. A histogram of the data is approximately bell shaped. How many security guards should the manager schedule for the concert? Explain your answer.

CHAPTER 9 REVIEW

CHAPTER 9 Organizer

Section	What You Should Learn	Review Problems
9.1	**1.** Use qualitative phrases such as "likely to occur" and "unlikely to occur" to characterize the level of uncertainty in a situation.	1
	2. Use the language of probability, such as experiment, outcome, sample space, and event.	2–3
	3. List the sample space and probability of each outcome in an experiment.	4–5
	4. Use a frequency table to determine experimental probabilities.	6
	5. Demonstrate an understanding of the law of large numbers.	7–10
	6. Use probability to make decisions or predictions.	11–13
	7. Compute a probability using the complement of an event.	14
	8. Know the connection between experimental probability and theoretical probability.	15
	9. Determine the probability of an event when the outcomes are equally likely.	16–17
	10. Compare probabilities using the terms "more likely" and "less likely."	18–19

Section	What You Should Learn	Review Problems
9.2	**1.** Explain why events are mutually exclusive, independent, or dependent.	20–23
	2. Apply basic probability formulas.	24
	3. Determine the probabilities $P(A \text{ or } B)$ and $P(A \text{ and } B)$.	25–27
	4. Use data in two-way tables to answer probability questions.	28–30
	5. Solve problems involving conditional probability.	31–34
	6. Use a tree diagram to represent and analyze experiments.	35–36
	7. Solve multi-stage probability problems using probability theory.	37–39
9.3	**1.** Compute the expected value of a probability experiment.	40–43
	2. Relate odds and probability.	44–45
	3. Calculate the standard deviation.	46
	4. Explain what it means for a variable to have a normal distribution.	47–49
	5. Apply the 68-95-99.7 rule.	50–51
	6. Compare two scores using the z-score.	52
	7. Estimate a probability using a simulation.	53–54

Key Terms and Concepts

probability 489

qualitative phrases in probability 490

experiment 491

outcome 491

sample space 491

event 491

simple event 491

compound event 491

$P(E)$ 492

experimental probability 492

short-term behavior 494

long-term behavior 494

theoretical probability 494

Law of Large Numbers 494

interpreting probability 495

equally likely 496

sum of probabilities 499

complementary event 499

complement of $E(\sim E)$ 500

mutually exclusive events 509

$P(A \text{ or } B)$ for mutually exclusive events 510

$P(A \text{ or } B)$ for any events 511

independent events 512

dependent events 512

with replacement 512

without replacement 512

$P(A \text{ and } B)$ for independent events 513

conditional probability 514

$P(B|A)$ 514

$P(A \text{ and } B)$ for any events 515

probability tree diagram 518

expected value 527

standard deviation 528

z-score 529

distribution 530

normal distribution 531

68-95-99.7 rule 531

usual values 534

unusual values 534

minimum usual value 534

maximum usual value 534

simulations 535

odds in favor 540

odds against 540

relating odds and probability 540

Review Questions

1. A teacher shows her class a bag of marbles. It contains 20 blue marbles, 15 yellow marbles, and 68 green marbles. The teacher randomly selects a marble from the bag. Use the words *impossible, unlikely, likely,* or *certain* to describe the chance that the teacher will draw a marble with the specified color.

   a. The teacher selects a blue marble.

   b. The teacher selects a green marble.

2. List the sample space for each experiment.

   a. An experiment consists of rolling two standard dice and adding the results of each die.

   b. An experiment consists of rolling two standard dice and subtracting the lower number from the higher number so that the result is nonnegative.

3. The probability of an event E is 32%. Explain what this means.

4. An experiment consists of rolling two standard dice and recording the maximum number of the two dice. For example, if the dice land on a 3 and a 5, then the outcome is 5.

   a. Complete the table.

	1	2	3	4	5	6
1						
2		2				
3					5	
4						
5						
6						

   b. List the sample space for this experiment.

   c. Complete the table to list each outcome and corresponding probability.

Outcome			3		6	
Probability						

5. An experiment consists of spinning the spinner shown and recording the letter to which the arrow points.

   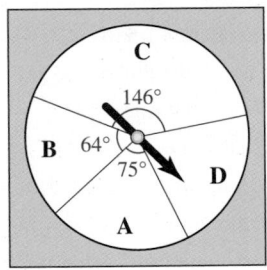

   a. List the sample space for this experiment.

   b. Use a table to display the probability of each outcome.

6. A student conducted an experiment and recorded the frequency table shown.

Outcome	0	1	2	3	4	5
Frequency	5	2	8	2	1	4

   Find the experimental probability of each event.

   a. $A = \{0\}$ b. $B = \{2, 3, 0\}$

7. The table shows data for Maria, Ken, and Leila.

Name	Times E occurred	n
Maria	21	50
Ken	100	200
Leila	301	500

   a. For each student, determine the experimental probability that E will occur.

   b. Which experimental probability seems like the best estimate of $P(E)$? Why?

   c. How could these results be combined in some way to obtain a potentially better estimate of $P(E)$?

8. Describe how your fifth-grade students can estimate the probability of flipping a bent coin and getting tails three times in a row.

9. An experiment consists of randomly drawing a marble, with replacement, from a bag containing three yellow marbles, two blue marbles, and four green marbles. We cannot foretell the outcome of a single draw. Therefore, we cannot predict the next term in the sequence GGYGG . . . , where G represents that the marble was green and Y represents that the marble was yellow.

   a. What aspect of the sequence is predictable if we repeat the experiment many times, say, 10,000 times?

   b. What aspect of the sequence is unpredictable, besides the result of the next draw, if we repeat the experiment a small number of times, say, 12 times?

10. Ron flipped a fair coin 720 times. Valerie flipped the same coin 40 times. One of these students observed that he or she obtained tails 35% of the times. Which student do you think it was? Explain your answer.

11. Bag A contains 6 blue marbles and 3 yellow marbles. Bag B contains 30 blue marbles and 18 yellow marbles. If you wanted to draw a blue marble, which bag would you choose? Explain your answer.

12. Suppose $P(E) = 0.55$. How many times do you expect E to occur when the experiment is repeated 200 times? Explain your answer.

13. Two players play a dice game rolling two standard dice. The outcome is the sum of the two numbers. For example, if the two dice show a 2 and a 5, then the outcome is $7 (5 + 2 = 7)$. Player A wins if the outcome is a 3, a 7, an 8, or a 9. Otherwise, player B wins. Which player would you rather be?

14. The doctor tells a patient that there is a 5% chance the disease will return. What is the probability that the disease will not return? Explain your answer.

15. The graph shows the experimental probabilities of an event E for different values of n, the number of repetitions of the experiment. Estimate the theoretical probability of E occurring.

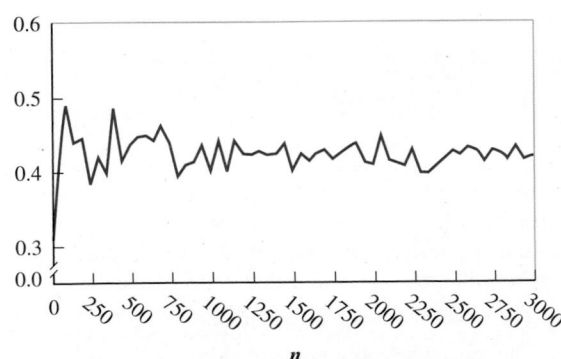

16. An experiment consists of randomly drawing a card from a standard deck of 52 cards. Find the probability of drawing a 4 or a 7.

17. Two players play a dice game rolling two standard dice. The outcome is the difference of the larger number and the smaller number. For example, if the two dice show a 2 and a 5, then the outcome is 3 ($5 - 2 = 3$). Player A wins if the difference is 0, 1, or 5. Player B wins if the difference is 2, 3, or 4. Which player would you rather be?

18. Suppose a survey posed the question "Which is your favorite sport?" to students who like bowling, tennis, soccer, or football. Here are the data.

18% bowling   42% tennis
25% soccer   15% football

  a. Verify that a randomly selected student is about 2.33 times as likely to prefer tennis as bowling.

  b. Verify that a randomly selected student is about 1.67 times as likely to prefer soccer as football.

  c. Verify that a randomly selected student is 2.8 times less likely to prefer football than tennis.

  d. Verify that a randomly selected student is 68% more likely to prefer tennis than soccer.

  e. Verify that a randomly selected student is 16.7% less likely to prefer football than bowling.

19. Find $P(B)$.

  a. $P(A) = 0.042$, and B is 12 times as likely as A.

  b. $P(A) = 0.06$, and B is five times less likely than A.

  c. $P(A) = 0.15$, and B is 24% more likely than A.

  d. $P(A) = 0.24$, and B is 15% less likely than A.

20. Consider the events $A = \{3, 5, 6\}$ and $B = \{1, 3, 6, 4\}$ and the sample space $S = \{1, 2, 3, 4, 5, 6\}$. Explain why events A and B are not mutually exclusive.

21. Consider the events $A = \{3, 5, 6\}$ and $B = \{1, 2\}$ and sample space $S = \{1, 2, 3, 4, 5, 6\}$. Explain why events A and B are mutually exclusive.

22. A jar contains two pennies, four dimes, and five quarters. An experiment consists of selecting a coin from the jar. The coin is replaced after it is selected, before the next selection.

  a. B is the event that the coin is a penny. Determine the probability that B will occur.

  b. A is the event that the coin is a dime. Determine the probability that B will occur, given that A has already occurred.

  c. Show why event A and event B are independent events.

23. Do the following.

  a. B is the event of drawing a queen from a standard deck of cards. Determine $P(B)$.

  b. An experiment consists of drawing two cards from a standard deck of cards, without replacement. Let A be the event of drawing a 5. What is the probability of B, given that event A occurred?

  c. Show why event A and event B are dependent events.

24. Do the following.

  a. Suppose A and B are independent events. Complete the equation: $P(A \text{ and } B) = \underline{\quad} \times \underline{\quad}$.

  b. Suppose A and B are independent events. Complete the equation: $P(A \mid B) = \underline{\quad}$.

  c. Suppose A and B are mutually exclusive events. Complete the equation: $P(A \text{ or } B) = \underline{\quad} + \underline{\quad}$.

  d. Suppose A and B are any events. Complete the equation: $P(A \text{ or } B) = \underline{\quad} + \underline{\quad} - \underline{\quad}$.

  e. Suppose A and B are any events. Complete the equation: $P(A \text{ and } B) = \underline{\quad} \times \underline{\quad}$.

25. According to a study published by the *BBC News* in April 2003, approximately two-fifths of the U.S. population does not use the Internet. About half of those people do not expect to use the Internet, because they have no interest in using e-mail or browsing the web. What is the probability that a person does not use the Internet and has no interest in using e-mail or browsing the web?

26. An experiment consists of drawing two cards from a standard deck of cards. What is the probability that the first card is a king and the second card is a spade? Assume you draw the cards one at a time

  a. with replacement.   **b.** without replacement.

27. A card is randomly chosen from an ordinary deck of 52 cards. Find the probability of selecting

  a. a face card.   **b.** a face card or a 3.   **c.** a 10 or an ace.

  d. a red card and a face card.   **e.** a red card or a face card.

  f. a diamond or a club.   **g.** a heart and a 10.

The following table is based on the 2002 population survey by the U.S. Census Bureau. The table shows the number of survey respondents (in thousands, 25 years or older) by region and highest level of education attainment (for example, high school graduates have a high school diploma as their highest level of education attainment). Surveys by the U.S. Census Bureau reflect characteristics of the population of the United States, so we consider randomly selecting a person who lives in the United States. The total is 182,216, in thousands. Use the data in the table to answer Review Questions 28–30.

	Not a HS graduate	HS graduate	≤2 years of college	Bach. degree	Advan. degree
NE	5268	12,520	7721	6711	3933
MW	5357	14,933	11,137	7214	3544
S	11,895	20,446	15,624	10,994	5336
W	6452	10,569	11,598	7362	3602

NE = Northeast, MW = Midwest, S = South, W = West, HS = high school, advan. = advanced.

28. Answer each question regarding the highest level of education attainment.

   a. What is the probability that a randomly selected person is from the South?

   b. What is the probability that a randomly selected person had a bachelor's degree?

   c. What is the probability that a randomly selected person was from the South and had a bachelor's degree?

29. Answer the following questions regarding the highest level of education attainment.

   a. What is the probability that a randomly selected person who was from the South earned a bachelor's degree?

   b. What is the probability that a randomly selected person who earned a bachelor's degree was from the South?

30. Answer the following questions regarding the highest level of education attainment.

   a. What is the probability that a randomly selected person was from the South or earned a bachelor's degree?

   b. What is the probability that a person who was from the West did not graduate from high school?

31. An experiment consists of drawing two cards from a standard deck of cards. Determine the probability that the first card is a 2 and the second card is a face card. Assume the cards are drawn

   a. without replacement.   b. with replacement.

32. Two marbles are drawn, without replacement, from a bag containing five blue marbles, four red marbles, and three green marbles. Determine the probability that the second marble is blue, given that the first one is green.

33. The Venn diagram represents events *A* and *B* for a sample space *S* with equally likely outcomes. A teacher spilled coffee

on the diagram, and as a result, the Venn diagram is partially obscured. What is the probability that event *B* will occur, given that event *A* has occurred?

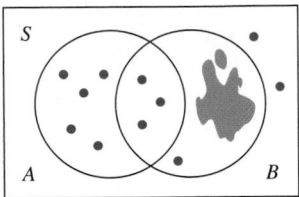

34. The Venn diagram represents events *A* and *B* for a sample space *S* with equally likely outcomes.

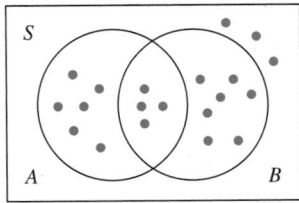

   a. What is the probability that event *A* will occur?

   b. What is the probability that event *B* will occur?

   c. What is the probability that event *A* will occur, given that event *B* has occurred?

   d. What is the probability that event *B* will occur, given that event *A* has occurred?

   e. What is the probability event that *B* will occur, given that event *A* did not occur?

   f. What is the probability that event "*A* and *B*" will occur?

   g. What is the probability that event "*A* or *B*" will occur?

35. A multistage experiment has the following tree diagram. Write the outcomes and their corresponding probabilities.

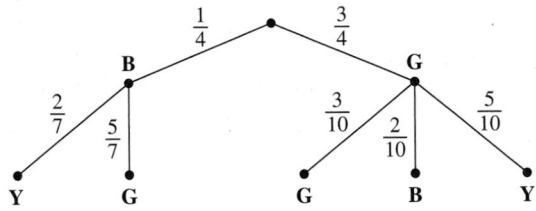

36. According to a report called "Mathematics Equals Opportunity" released in the late 1990s, approximately two-thirds of all U.S. high school students take introductory algebra and geometry courses, and approximately four-fifths of those students go on to college. Approximately seven-20ths of students who did not take introductory algebra and geometry courses went to college.

   a. Make a tree diagram for this probability situation.

   b. What is the probability that a high school student goes on to college, given that the student took introductory algebra and geometry courses?

   c. What is the probability that a high school student goes on to college, given that the student did not take introductory algebra and geometry courses?

d. What is the probability that a high school student took introductory algebra and geometry courses and went to college?

e. What is the probability that a high school student did not take introductory algebra and geometry courses and went to college?

f. What is the probability that a high school student goes on to college?

37. Player A and player B are playing a dice game. Two dice are rolled. Player A wins if the dice differ by 1 or 5 (for example, a 1 and a 2, a 4 and a 3, or a 6 and a 1). Player B wins if the sum is 8 or the dice differ by 3. The dice are rolled until one of the players wins.

a. The probability that the game will end on the first roll is 23/36. Verify this calculation.

b. The probability that the game ends on the third roll is about 8%. Verify this calculation.

38. A box contains eight blue marbles, five red marbles, and two green marbles. A marble is drawn from the box, without replacement, until a green marble is picked. Determine the probability of each event.

a. Two draws are needed.   **b.** Three draws are needed.

39. A box contains 20 blue marbles, 8 red marbles, and 12 green marbles. You draw 3 marbles randomly. What is the probability that none of the marbles are green? Assume you draw the marbles one at a time

a. with replacement.   **b.** without replacement.

40. Consider a spinner with a payoff based on where the arrow stops.

Outcome	$3	$5
Probability	20%	80%

a. Ideally, in 10 spins we expect to land on $5 exactly _____ times.

b. Ideally, in 10 spins we expect to land on $3 exactly _____ times.

c. Ideally, in 10 spins we expect a total payoff of $___.

d. Ideally, we expect the total payoff per spin to be $___.

e. Use the definition of expected value to calculate the expected payout per spin.

f. Ideally, what would the charge to play the game need to be so that the game is considered "fair"?

41. A radio station is having a contest. One prize is a computer worth $2000. Two prizes are $500 gift cards to a clothing store. Three prizes are $300 worth of tutoring for your math course. Assuming 8000 people enter this contest. Compute the expected value for this contest, and interpret your result.

42. Suppose a standard die is rolled and you receive the amount of money, in dollars, equal to the number showing on the top face of the die.

a. How many dollars do you expect to receive each roll?

b. How many rolls would it take, on average, to earn $73?

43. A jar contains three blue marbles and two yellow marbles. Marbles are randomly drawn, one at a time without replacement, until a yellow marble is chosen.

a. What is the minimum number of marbles that must be selected?

b. What is the maximum number of marbles that must be selected?

c. Let an outcome be the number of draws required. Complete the table.

Outcome	1	2	3	4
Probability				

d. On average, how many draws are required to select a yellow marble?

44. The Venn diagram represents events A and B for a sample space S with equally likely outcomes.

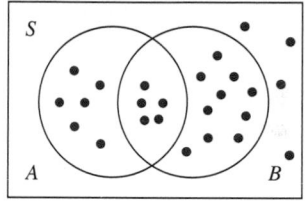

a. What are the odds that A occurs? Explain your answer.

b. What are the odds against B occurring? Explain your answer.

45. Answer the following, explaining your answers.

a. The probability that event A occurs is 0.38. What are the odds that A occurs?

b. The probability that event B occurs is 0.28. What are the odds against B occurring?

46. The data set consists of the scores 126, 174, 180, and 156.

a. Calculate the mean ($\bar{x}$).

b. Calculate the standard deviation (s).

c. Is 130 a usual or unusual value?

d. Is 205 a usual or unusual value?

47. Suppose the weight of brand X boxes of cereal is "normally distributed." What does this mean?

48. The histogram summarizes the life span of a type of tree. What reasonable assumption can you make about the variable?

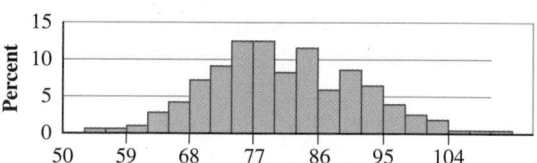

49. Suppose the numbers in your data set are normally distributed with a mean of 55 and standard deviation of 8. What are the maximum and minimum values that you might expect?

50. A publisher determined that the number of pages that could be printed with an ink cartridge was normally distributed, with a mean of 2000 pages and standard deviation of 258 pages. What is the probability that a randomly chosen ink cartridge prints

    a. between 1484 and 2258 pages?

    b. between 1742 and 2774 pages?

    c. fewer than 2258 pages?   d. more than 2774 pages?

51. Students in a class summarized some measurements with a histogram. The histogram of the data suggests the measurements are normally distributed because of the symmetry in the shape of a bell. The histogram does not suggest there are any outliers. The lowest measurement is 8.6 g, and the highest measurement is 15.2 g. Estimate the mean ($\bar{x}$) and standard deviation (s) of the measurements.

52. Laura scored an 85 on a quiz in her math class, which had a mean of 73 points and standard deviation of 8 points. Charlie scored 70 points on a quiz in a history class, which had a mean of 62 points and standard deviation of 4 points. Who scored relatively better?

53. According to a CNN survey, about 20% of parents say lack of funding is the biggest problem their schools face (next was lack of discipline, followed by overcrowding). Use a simulation to estimate the probability that exactly two out of five randomly selected parents will say that lack of funding is the biggest problem at their school. Explain your answer.

54. A jar contains three blue marbles and two yellow marbles. Marbles are drawn randomly, one at a time without replacement, until a yellow marble is chosen. Use a simulation to estimate the average number of draws that are needed to get a yellow marble.

Chapter 9 Test

1. *Demonstrate an understanding of the law of large numbers.* The table shows data for Lennie, Gina, and Taylor.

Name	Times E occurred	Repetitions
Lennie	44	95
Gina	155	250
Taylor	270	400

   a. For each student, determine the experimental probability that E will occur.

   b. Which experimental probability seems like the best estimate of $P(E)$? Why?

   c. How could these results be combined in some way to obtain a potentially better estimate of $P(E)$?

2. *Demonstrate an understanding of the law of large numbers.* An experiment consists of randomly picking a marble from a bag containing three blue marbles, four green marbles, and eight yellow marbles; noting the color; and replacing the marble. We know that we cannot foretell the color of the marble that we will draw. Therefore, we cannot identify the next term in the sequence YBGBGB . . . , where B represents a blue marble was drawn, G represents a green marble was drawn, and Y represents a yellow marble was drawn.

   a. What aspect of the sequence is predictable if we repeat the experiment a large number of times, say, 3000 times?

   b. What aspect of the sequence is unpredictable, besides the result of the next draw, if we repeat the experiment a few times, say, 24 times?

3. *Use probability to make decisions or predictions.*

   a. Bag A contains 8 blue marbles and 5 yellow marbles. Bag B contains 45 blue marbles and 30 yellow marbles. If you wanted to draw a blue marble, which bag would you choose?

   b. Suppose $P(E) = 0.28$. How many times do you expect E to occur when the experiment is repeated 250 times? Explain your answer.

4. *Use probability to make decisions or predictions.* Two players play a dice game by rolling two standard dice. The outcome is the sum of the two numbers. For example, if the two dice show a 2 and a 5, then the outcome is 7 (5 + 2 = 7). Player A wins if the outcome is a 5, a 6, a 7, or a 9. Otherwise, player B wins. Which player would you rather be? Explain your answer.

5. *Determine the probability of an event when the outcomes are equally likely.*

   a. What is the probability of drawing a king or an ace from a regular deck of 52 cards?

   b. A marble is drawn from a bag containing three blue marbles, four red marbles, and five green marbles. Find the probability that the marble is blue or green.

6. *Explain why events are mutually exclusive, independent, or dependent.* A bag contains the following marbles: three green marbles, eight yellow marbles, and four blue marbles. An experiment consists of drawing a marble, without replacement.

   a. A is the event of drawing a yellow marble. Determine $P(A)$.

   b. Let B be the event of drawing a green marble. What is the probability of A, given that event B occurred?

   c. Explain why event A and event B are dependent events.

7. *Explain why events are mutually exclusive, independent, or dependent.* An experiment consists of drawing a card from a standard deck of cards, with replacement.

   a. B is the event of drawing a queen from a standard deck of cards. Determine $P(B)$.

   b. An experiment consists of drawing two cards from a standard deck of cards, with replacement. Let A be the event of drawing a 4. What is the probability of B, given that event A occurred?

   c. Explain why event A and event B are independent events.

8. *Determine the probabilities P(A or B) and P(A and B).*

   a. Suppose $P(A) = 0.43$, $P(B) = 0.62$, and $P(B \mid A) = 0.38$. Compute $P(A$ and $B)$.

   b. Suppose $P(A) = 0.62$, $P(B) = 0.37$, and $P(B \mid A) = 0.25$. Compute $P(A$ or $B)$.

9. *Solve problems involving conditional probability.* The Venn diagram represents events A and B for a sample space S with equally likely outcomes.

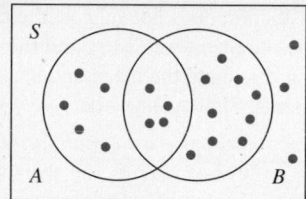

   a. What is the probability that event A will occur?

   b. What is the probability that event B will occur?

   c. What is the probability that event A will occur, given that event B has occurred?

   d. What is the probability that event B will occur, given that event A has occurred?

   e. What is the probability that event B will occur, given that event A did not occur?

   f. What is the probability that event "A and B" will occur?

   g. What is the probability that event "A or B" will occur?

10. *Solve problems involving conditional probability.* Two marbles are drawn, without replacement, from a box containing 12 blue marbles, 7 red marbles, and 6 green marbles. Verify that the probability that the second marble is blue is 48%.

11. *Solve problems involving conditional probability.* Player A and player B are playing a dice game. Two dice are rolled. Player A wins if the sum is 3 or 8. Player B wins if the sum is 7. The dice are rolled until one of the players win. The probability of the game ending on the third roll is 14.7%. Verify this calculation.

12. *Use a tree diagram to represent and analyze experiments.* A probability experiment consists of drawing two marbles, one at a time, without replacement. There are B blue marbles, G green marbles, and Y yellow marbles. The probability tree diagram is shown.

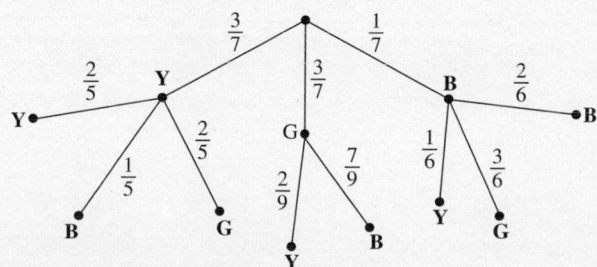

   a. Determine the probability that the second marble is yellow, given that the first marble is green.

   b. Determine the probability that the second marble is yellow, given that the first marble is yellow.

   c. Determine the probability that the first marble is blue and the second marble is green.

   d. Determine the probability that the first marble is yellow and the second marble is blue

13. *Use a tree diagram to represent and analyze experiments.* An experiment consists of randomly selecting two numbered chips from the jar shown, one at a time without replacement, and multiplying the results. For example, if chips 2 and 3 are chosen, then the outcome is 6.

   a. Draw a tree diagram for this experiment.

   b. Make a table to display the probability of each outcome.

14. *Solve multistage probability problems using probability theory.* A box contains 15 blue marbles, 3 red marbles, and 7 green marbles. A marble is drawn from the box, with replacement, until a green marble is picked. Determine the probability of each event.

   a. Two draws are needed.   **b.** Three draws are needed.

15. *Compute the expected value of a probability experiment.* Consider a spinner with just two outcomes: 4 points and 7 points.

Outcome	4	7
Probability	34%	66%

   a. Ideally, in 100 spins we expect to land on 4 exactly _____ times.

   b. Ideally, in 100 spins we expect to land on 7 exactly _____ times.

   c. Ideally, in 100 spins we expect a total of _____ points.

   d. Ideally, we expect the total number of points per spin to be _____.

   e. Use the definition of expected value to calculate the expected value (average number of points per spin).

16. *Relate odds and probability.*

   a. The probability that event A occurs is 0.42. What are the odds that A occurs?

   b. The probability that event B occurs is 0.32. What are the odds against B occurring?

17. *Explain what it means for a variable to have a normal distribution.* Suppose the height of females is "normally distributed." What does this mean?

18. *Explain what it means for a variable to have a normal distribution.* The histogram summarizes the measurements made by an engineer to calibrate a machine. What reasonable assumption can you make about the variable?

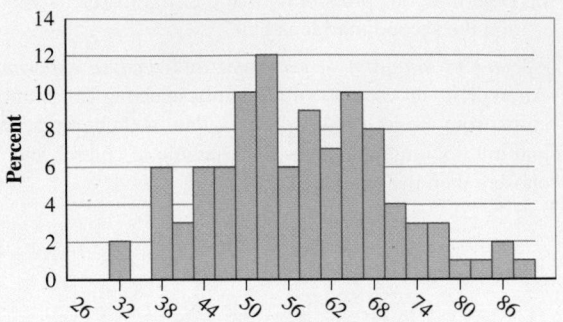

19. *Apply the 68-95-99.7 rule.* Suppose the weight of a bag of cement is normally distributed with a mean of 94 pounds and standard deviation of 2.5 pounds. What is the probability that a randomly chosen bag of cement weighs

   a. between 89 and 96.5 pounds?

   b. between 91.5 and 101.5 pounds?

   c. less than 91.5 pounds?   **d.** more than 99 pounds?

20. *Apply the 68-95-99.7 rule.* A tea producer used a histogram to summarize some measurements of the amount of caffeine in a cup of green tea. The graph suggests the measurements are normally distributed because of the symmetry in the shape of a bell. The histogram does not suggest there are any outliers. The lowest measurement was 28 g, and the highest measurement was 44 g. Estimate the mean and standard deviation of the measurements. Show your work.

21. *Estimate a probability using a simulation.* According to a *USA Today* snapshot, 80% of parents say their kids ask "Are we there yet?" on trips. Use a simulation to estimate the probability that three out of five parents will say their kids ask them that question on a trip.

10

Introduction to Geometry

Where Are We Going?

In **Section 10.1,** we introduce geometric language, diagrams, and symbolic notation that students need to describe, compare, and contrast geometric shapes and their properties. We also discuss point and line relationships. In **Section 10.2,** we discuss various angle relationships: vertical angles, complementary angles, supplementary angles, and angles created by a transversal. We also discuss attributes of triangles and parallelograms. In **Section 10.3,** we categorize objects in three dimensions.

How Did Ancient Cultures Use Geometry?

Geometry is the study of shapes and their patterns and properties. Ancient cultures used geometry in different ways according to their needs. The ancient Chinese used geometry to calculate heights and distances of objects in land surveys and to construct buildings and canals. The Mayans applied geometry in the construction of pyramids, temples, terraces, and reservoirs, as well as in their spiritual thinking. Geometry appears in their fabulous symmetric mosaic designs on ceramics and weavings. The ancient Egyptians used geometry to survey land and restore property boundaries after periodic flooding of the Nile and to construct religious temples and public buildings. They also cared about mathematical relationships between geometric figures, such as placing two right triangles together to form a rectangle, but some of their rules were inexact, such as the rule for the area of a circle ($A = 3.11r^2$).

What Is the Greek Influence on Geometry?

Although ancient cultures used geometry for religious, educational, and practical purposes, geometry progressed as an unorganized collection of results. The ancient Greeks, who learned geometry from the Egyptians, changed that by adding structure and logical reasoning, making geometry a subject to study from a mathematical and an abstract point of view. The word *geometry* stems from the Greek word *geometria,* which means "Earth measure." The Greeks' remarkable discoveries, methodical inquiry, and scholarly books led to the understanding and development of geometry in a systematic and organized way.

The step pyramid El Castillo ("the Castle"), built by the Mayans between the 900s and the 1300s.

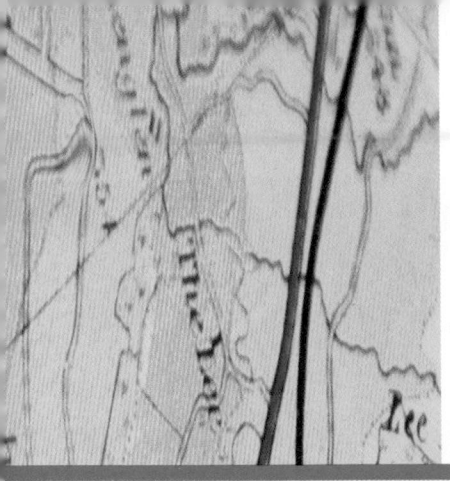

Today, geometry is an important branch of mathematics because it provides tools to represent and understand the world in an abstract way using notation and diagrams. For example, modern architects and engineers use computer-aided software to model objects such as robotic arms, electric saws, and gasoline engines.

The Greeks added structure and logical reasoning to geometry.

SECTION 10.1 | Representation of Building Blocks of Geometry

Terminology Helps Students Advance Their Geometrical Learning

Young children enjoy playing in playhouses. Parents love them too, because they help children develop their imagination and learn social skills as they play in a safe environment. Children tend to see a playhouse as a solitary building structure, much like they see a rectangle as a solitary shape. Eventually, children see the playhouse differently when they examine the individual components, such as the beams and rafters, much like students eventually see a rectangle with individual components, such as congruent opposite sides and four right angles.

In geometry, students begin with imprecise language to describe shapes. The precise use of language is a critical factor in progressing through geometric learning. NCTM's *Principles and Standards for School Mathematics* states:

> Pre-K–2 geometry begins with describing and naming shapes. Young students begin by using their own vocabulary to describe objects, talking about how they are alike and how they are different. Teachers must help students gradually incorporate conventional terminology into their descriptions of two- and three-dimensional shapes. However, terminology itself should not be the focus of the Pre-K–2 geometry program. The goal is that early experiences with geometry lay the foundation for more-formal geometry in later grades. Using terminology to focus attention and clarify ideas during discussions can help students build that foundation. (© NCTM Standards 2011 by National Council of Teachers of Mathematics)

Terminology is important for focusing attention on parts of diagrams and geometric shapes, clarifying and articulating ideas, saying what you mean, and meaning what you say. In this section, we discuss language, basic relationships, and representations so that you can help your elementary school students replace their invented terminology with the standard language of geometry as they (1) define shapes, (2) describe properties of shapes, and (3) clarify and articulate ideas for informal and formal geometric reasoning. Terminology also provides a foundation for guided instruction.

The Undefined Building Blocks of Geometry: Points, Lines, and Planes

Points, lines, and planes are undefined building blocks of geometry, much like the letters *a, b, c, . . . , z* of the alphabet are undefined building blocks of written words. We cannot formally define them to avoid circular reasoning (try to define them!), but we can attempt to *describe* the objects anyway.

Table 10.1 gives graphical and symbolic representations of each building block. A **point** has neither size nor shape; it simply has location. We draw a dot to represent a point, although the representation makes it appear to have size and shape. We think of a **line** as a collection of infinitely many closely spaced points, extending forever in opposite directions without width, in the shape of an uncooked spaghetti noodle. Lastly, we think of a **plane** as a collection of infinitely many closely spaced lines, side by side, extending in two directions without thickness. Students should be able to "draw points, lines, line segments, rays, angles (right, acute, obtuse), and perpendicular and parallel lines" and "identify these in two-dimensional figures" (CCSS, Gr. 4) (© 2010. National Governors Association Center for Best Practices and Council of Chief State School Officers. All rights reserved.).

CONNECTION
REPRESENTATION

TABLE 10.1 **Representations of the Building Blocks**

Building blocks of geometry	Diagram	Notation	Contextualized situation
point	• A	A	© Goran Bogicevic/Shutterstock.com
line	←—•——•—→ n A B	line n or $\overleftrightarrow{AB}$ (read as "line AB")	Cousin_Avi/Shutterstock.com
plane	• A • C • B	ABC (read as "plane ABC")	Coprid/Shutterstock.com

EXAMPLE 10.1

CONNECTION
COMMUNICATION
REASONING

a. Why must a plane have infinitely many points?

b. Imagine a plane has 35 labeled points, including *A, B,* and *C* such that no group of three points are collinear. Although a plane has infinitely many points, how many names can you write for the plane using the 35 labeled points?

SOLUTION

a. We think of a plane as a collection of infinitely many closely spaced lines, side by side. We also think of a line as a collection of infinitely many closely spaced points. So we can think of a plane as a collection of infinitely many points.

b. Some examples of names for the plane using the labeled points are *ABC* and *BAC*. There are 35 ways to choose the first point, 34 ways to choose the second point, and 33 ways to choose the third point. By the fundamental counting principle, there are $35 \cdot 34 \cdot 33 = 39{,}270$ ways to name the plane using the labeled points.

■ **Historical Note**

- Historians credit the Greeks with using letters to label points, lines, and planes. The earliest known occurrence was made by Hippocrates, about 440 BCE.
- Bonaventura Cavalieri (1598–1647) assumed a line consisted of infinitely many points and a plane consisted of infinitely many lines in his 1635 publication *Geometria Indivisibilibus Continuorum Nova Quadam Ratione Promota* (translated *A Certain Method for the Development of a New Geometry of Continuous Indivisibles*).

Definitions and Representations

Definitions ensure some uniformity in ideas, and making definitions is an engaging mathematical activity. Teachers need to supply some definitions to their students, but some definitions of geometric concepts are worth exploring as a classroom activity. Think about the object you are defining, draw a representation of the relationship, draft a definition, and then make sure your definition describes examples of similar objects.

Point Relationships

Figure 1 illustrates representations of point relationships: collinear points, noncollinear points, coplanar points, and noncoplanar points. How would you define these terms?

COMMUNICATION
REPRESENTATION

A, B, and C are *collinear points*.
A, B, and D are *noncollinear points*.

E, F, and G are *coplanar points*.
E, F, G, and H are *noncoplanar points*.

FIGURE 1
Point relationships.

We define terms to make sure we share a common language, using the undefined association *contains*.

A set of points is **collinear** if there is a line that contains all of the points. A set of points is **noncollinear** if there is no line that contains all of the points. A set of points is **coplanar** if there is plane that contains all of the points. A set of points is **noncoplanar** if there is no plane that contains all of the points.

Line Relationships

Figure 2 illustrates representations of line relationships: concurrent, parallel, transversal, and skew lines. How would you define these terms?

COMMUNICATION
REPRESENTATION

Lines *s, t,* and *v* are *concurrent lines.*
Lines *u, v,* and *w* are not concurrent lines.
Lines *u* and *s* are *parallel lines.*
Line *v* is a *transversal* for lines *u* and *s.*
Lines *t* and *w* are *skew lines.*
Lines *t* and *u* are not skew lines.
Lines *u* and *v* are not *parallel lines.*

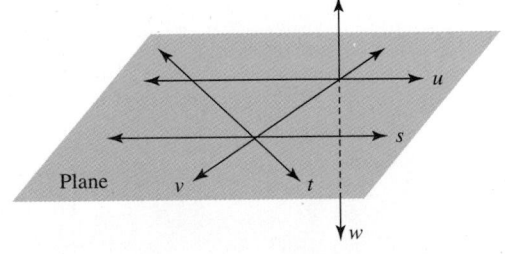

FIGURE 2
Line relationships.

Concurrent lines are three or more coplanar lines that intersect at one point. **Parallel lines** are coplanar lines that do not intersect. The symbol $\parallel$ in $\overleftrightarrow{AB} \parallel \overleftrightarrow{CD}$, read as "line AB is parallel to line CD," indicates line AB is parallel to line CD. A **transversal** is a line that intersects two or more coplanar lines at different points. **Skew lines** are two noncoplanar lines.

EXAMPLE 10.2 Write three statements for the diagram.

CONNECTION
COMMUNICATION
REASONING
REPRESENTATION

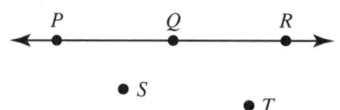

SOLUTION

Answers vary. For example,

P, Q, and R are collinear.
$\overleftrightarrow{PQ}$ and $\overleftrightarrow{RS}$ are not parallel lines.
$\overleftrightarrow{PS}$ is a transversal for lines $\overleftrightarrow{PR}$ and $\overleftrightarrow{RT}$.

▲

Historical Note

William Oughtred (1575–1660) used the symbol $\parallel$ to represent parallel lines in his 1657 publication *Trigonometria* (translated *Trigonometry*).

Distance, Line Segments, Congruence, and Rays

XY represents the **distance** between points X and Y in appropriate measurement units. If $X = Y$, then $XY = 0$, and if $X \neq Y$, then $XY > 0$. The expression ***A-B-C*** means all three of the following: A, B, and C are collinear; B is *between* A and C; and $AB + BC = AC$. The concept of "betweenness" is useful for describing line segments and rays. Line segment PQ, denoted $\overline{PQ}$, is the set of points containing P, Q, and all points between P and Q. Points P and Q on $\overline{PQ}$ are called endpoints. The symbol PQ represents the length of $\overline{PQ}$ or distance between P and Q. PQ is a number (in measurement units such as centimeters or feet), whereas $\overline{PQ}$ is a geometric object. Ray PQ, denoted $\overrightarrow{PQ}$, is the subset of line $\overleftrightarrow{PQ}$ that begins at P and extends through Q. Point P on ray PQ is called the endpoint of ray PQ. Table 10.2 summarizes representations of these geometric relationships or objects.

CONNECTION
REPRESENTATION

TABLE 10.2   Representation of Geometric Relationships or Objects

Words	Diagram	Notation	Contextualized situation
C is between A and B.	A C B	A-C-B or B-C-A	*(photo of birds on a wire)* christos_photo/Shutterstock.com
line segment with the endpoints P and Q	P Q	$\overline{PQ}$ or $\overline{QP}$	*(photo of a ladder)* Robert Spriggs/Shutterstock.com
ray from P through Q	P Q	$\overrightarrow{PQ}$	*(photo of light beams over a city at night)* gary yim/Shutterstock.com

EXAMPLE 10.3

REPRESENTATION

Draw a diagram for each situation.
a. Point Y is between points X and Z.
b. A line segment with the endpoints M and N.

SOLUTION

Answers vary.

a.

b.

EXAMPLE 10.4

CONNECTION

REASONING

REPRESENTATION

$AB = 6$ ft, $AC = 4$ ft, and $BC = 3$ ft. Determine whether C is between A and B.

SOLUTION

C is between A and B if and only if $AC + CB = AB$. The distance between B and C is the same as the distance between C and B, so $BC = CB$. Then $AC + CB = 4 + 3 = 7$ ft. $AB = 6$ ft, so $AC + CB \neq AB$. So C is not between A and B.

■ Historical Note

Bonaventura Cavalieri (1598–1647) used the symbol $\overline{AB}$ to represent the line segment with the endpoints A and B in his 1635 publication *Geometria Indivisibilibus Continuorum Nova Quadam Ratione Promota* (translated *A Certain Method for the Development of a New Geometry of Continuous Indivisibles*).

The following Classroom Connection shows that elementary school students should know how to relate symbolic representations and geometric figures.

◆ Classroom Connection

● Harcourt *Math*, Student Edition, Grade 6, p. 456

Draw and label a figure for each. (© by Harcourt, Inc. Reproduced by permission of the publisher, Houghton Mifflin Harcourt Publishing Company.)

a. $\overline{LM}$ **b.** $\overleftrightarrow{CD}$ **c.** point P

Postulates

We already listed, represented, and characterized the building blocks of geometry, along with a few point relationships and line relationships. Concept Map 10.1 lists basic relationships about points, lines, and planes that are useful for geometric reasoning. These relationships are stated as postulates. Postulates are properties we accept because they are intuitive and cannot be proved or because they are assumed to be true without proof. In this textbook, we assume all points and lines are coplanar unless stated otherwise.

> **Concept Map 10.1** Postulates for Points, Lines, and Planes

POSTULATE 1
Given two points, there is exactly one line containing the two points.

POSTULATE 2
Given three noncollinear points, there is exactly one plane containing the three points.

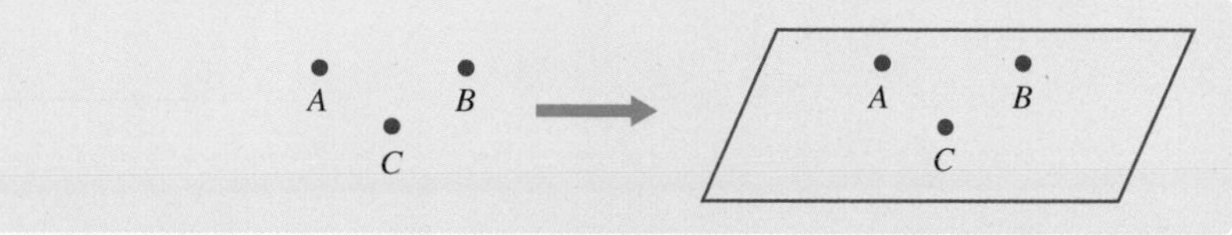

POSTULATE 3
Given two points in a plane, the line containing the two points lies in the plane.

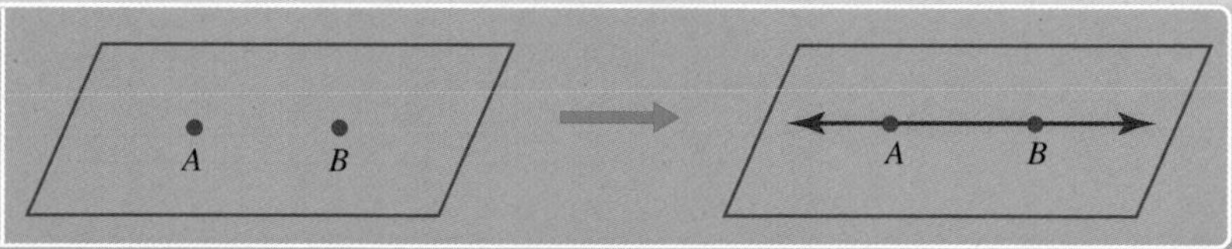

POSTULATE 4
Given two intersecting planes, their intersection is a line.

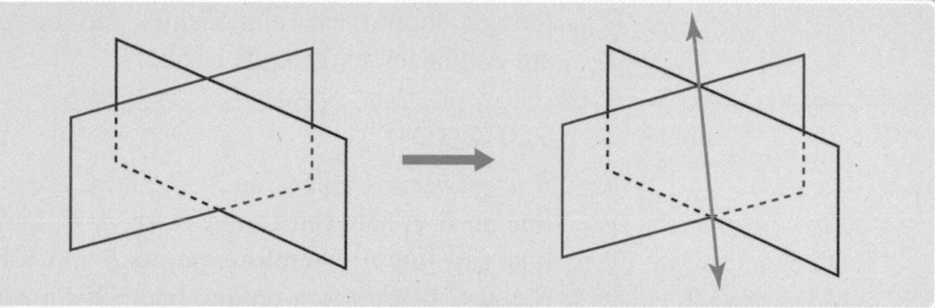

POSTULATE 5
There is a one-to-one correspondence between the points on a line and the points on the real number line.

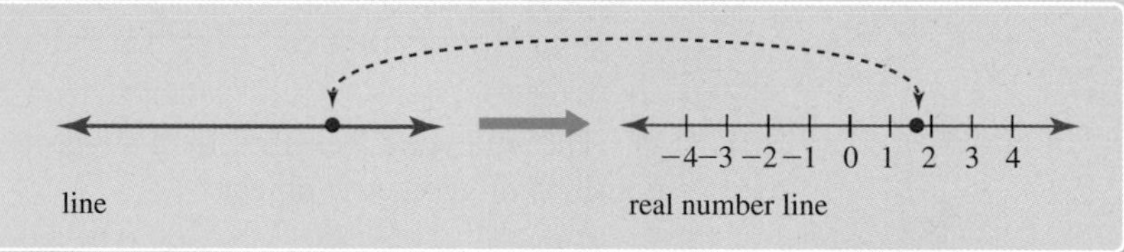

line

real number line

Undefined terms and postulates arise from necessity (for example, try defining *point*). Undefined terms, definitions, and postulates are starting points for geometric reasoning (as shown in Figure 3). We draw upon them to validate properties of geometrical objects. Theorems are noteworthy properties or statements that are to be proved using undefined terms, postulates, and definitions. Some properties are captured in postulates, whereas other properties are captured in theorems.

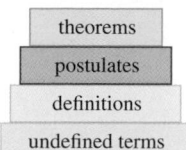

FIGURE 3
Undefined terms, definitions, and postulates are used to prove theorems.

EXAMPLE 10.5

COMMUNICATION

REASONING

REPRESENTATION

You are given a line and a point not on the line. Why is there one plane containing the point and the line?

SOLUTION

A line has infinitely many points, as indicated by Postulate 5 in Concept Map 10.1. Suppose points A and B are two particular points on the line and point C is not on the line. Let's draw a diagram to represent the situation.

Points A, B, and C are noncollinear points. There is a unique plane containing the three points, as indicated by Postulate 2. The plane also contains the line through A and B, as indicated by Postulate 3. So there is one plane that contains the given line and the given point not on the line. ▲

EXAMPLE 10.6

COMMUNICATION

REASONING

The teacher told the class that B is between A and C and B is between C and D. Yolanda thought about these relationships and the postulates, and then exclaimed, "A, B, C, and D are collinear!" Is Yolanda correct?

SOLUTION

B is between A and C, so A, B, and C are collinear. This means they belong to a line, say, line m. B is between C and D, so B, C, and D are collinear. This means they belong to a line, say, line n. Therefore, points B and C belong to lines m and n. By Postulate 1, points B and C belong to a unique line. This means $m = n$. Then A, B, C, and D belong to the same line. So A, B, C, and D are collinear. Yolanda is correct. ▲

The following Released Item suggests students should be able to reason about relationships of geometric objects.

> **▶ RELEASED ITEM**
>
> ● NAEP, 1996
>
> Jaime knows the following facts about points A, B, and C.
>
> • Points A, B, and C are on the same line but might not be in that order.
>
> • Point C is twice as far from point A as it is from point B.
>
> Jaime concluded that point C is always between points A and B. Is Jaime's conclusion correct?
>
> 23% of eighth-grade students gave the correct answer. (U.S. Department of Education, Institute of Education Sciences, National Center for Education Statistics, NAEP)

Angle and Its Parts

An **angle** is the union of two rays with a common endpoint, such as the one in Figure 4.

The symbol $\angle ABC$ represents the angle formed by $\overrightarrow{BA}$ and $\overrightarrow{BC}$. Each ray of an angle is called a **side.** The middle letter B in $\angle ABC$ designates the common endpoint of the rays, called the **vertex.** We can represent an angle simply by its vertex when there is no risk of

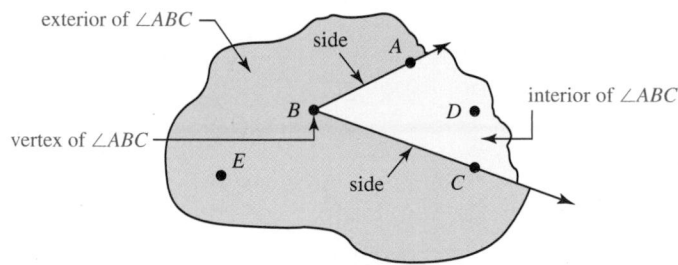

FIGURE 4
The parts of $\angle ABC$.

confusion. For example, $\angle B$ also represents the angle in Figure 4. Each angle separates the plane containing it into three nonoverlapping regions: the angle itself (two rays), the interior of the angle, and the exterior of the angle. Point D lies in the interior of $\angle ABC$, and point E lies in the exterior of $\angle ABC$.

Using a Wedge to Measure the Openness of an Angle

We can use the idea of a wedge (also called a sector) to quantify the openness of an angle. Figure 5 shows a wedge and $\angle A$. The measure of the angle is the number of wedges with the same shape and size that fit in the angle. The symbol $m\angle A$ represents the measure of $\angle A$. We see four wedges fit in $\angle A$, so $m\angle A = 4$ wedges.

REPRESENTATION

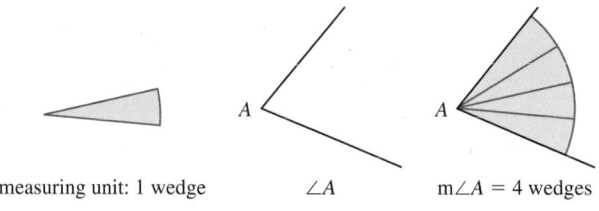

measuring unit: 1 wedge $\angle A$ $m\angle A = 4$ wedges

FIGURE 5
Measuring the openness of an angle.

Measuring an Angle with a Protractor

One degree (1°) represents a wedge when a circle is subdivided into 360 equal-sized wedges. Just as we use a ruler to quantify the length of a line segment, we use a measuring tool called a **protractor,** shown in Figure 6 on the next page, to quantify the *openness* of an angle.

Figure 7 on the next page shows a close-up of a portion of the protractor. The marks on the protractor reveal the number of degrees that fit in an angle. To measure the openness of an angle, place the center mark of the protractor at the vertex of the angle and the zero line of the protractor along one side of the angle. Then record the measurement associated with the hash mark indicated by the other side of the angle. In Figure 6, the measure of $\angle ABC$ is 58°, represented by $m\angle ABC = 58°$, and the measure of $\angle DBC$ is 135°, represented by $m\angle DBC = 135°$. There are two "zeros" on the protractor, so you can measure from the left zero line or the right zero line, depending on how you place the protractor. The measure of an angle using a semicircular protractor is at most 180°. $m\angle ABC$ is a number (in units of degrees), whereas $\angle ABC$ is a geometric object.

How could you find $m\angle DBA$ in Figure 6? One way is to reposition the zero line of the protractor along $\overrightarrow{BA}$ and then examine the mark on the protractor indicated by $\overrightarrow{BD}$. The following angle postulate offers an indirect way to find $m\angle DBA$.

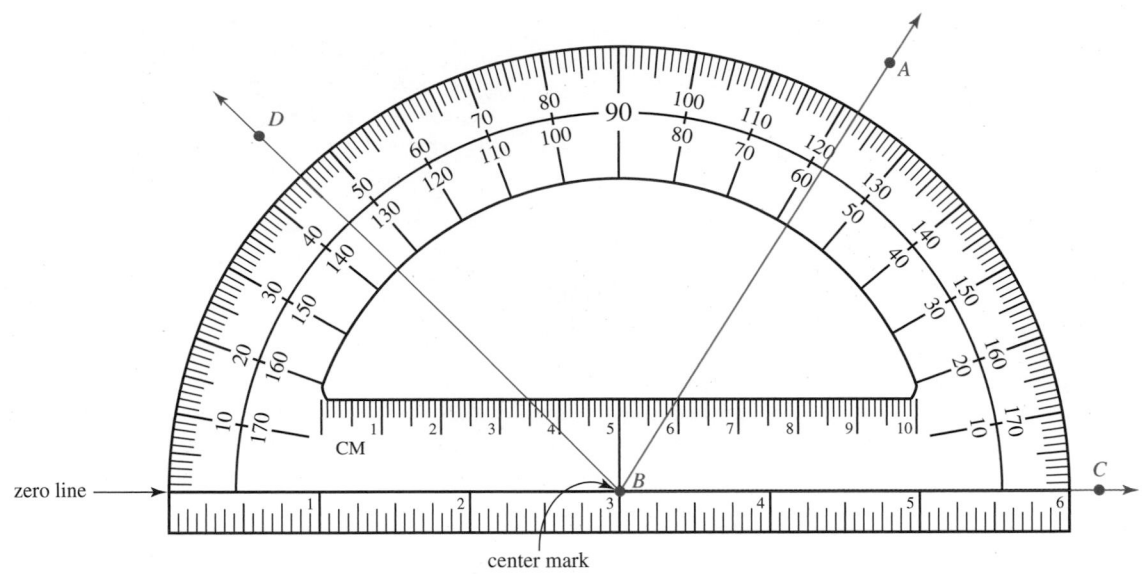

FIGURE 6
Semicircular protractor.

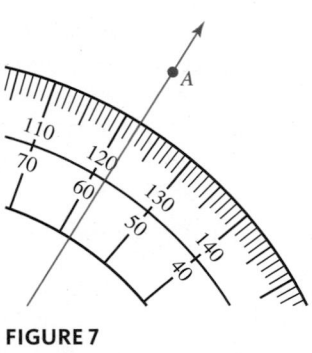

FIGURE 7
Close-up of protractor.

Angle Addition Postulate

If a point W lies in the interior of $\angle XYZ$, then m$\angle XYZ$ = m$\angle XYW$ + m$\angle WYZ$.

EXAMPLE 10.7

COMMUNICATION

CONNECTION

REASONING

In Figure 6, $\angle ABC$ = 58° and m$\angle DBC$ is 135°. Use the angle addition postulate to find m$\angle DBA$.

SOLUTION

The point A lies in the interior of $\angle DBC$. By the angle addition postulate, m$\angle DBC$ = m$\angle DBA$ + m$\angle ABC$. Then 135° = m$\angle DBA$ + 58°. Then m$\angle DBA$ = 135° − 58° = 77°. ▲

■ Historical Note

Oughtred used the symbol $\angle$ to represent angle in his 1657 publication *Trigonometria*.

Classifying Angles

Students should be able to look at angles and classify them as acute, right, obtuse, straight, or reflex. Figures 8–12 show examples of these types of angles.

Figure 8 shows some angles that are acute and some that are not. How would you define an acute angle?

Figure 9 shows some angles that are right and some that are not. How would you define a right angle?

Figure 10 shows some angles that are obtuse and some that are not. How would you define an obtuse angle?

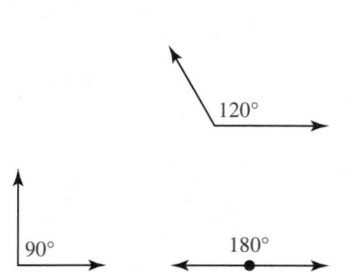

(a) acute angles that measure
62°, 28°, 18°, and 73°

(b) angles that are not acute

FIGURE 8

Examples and counterexamples
of acute angles.

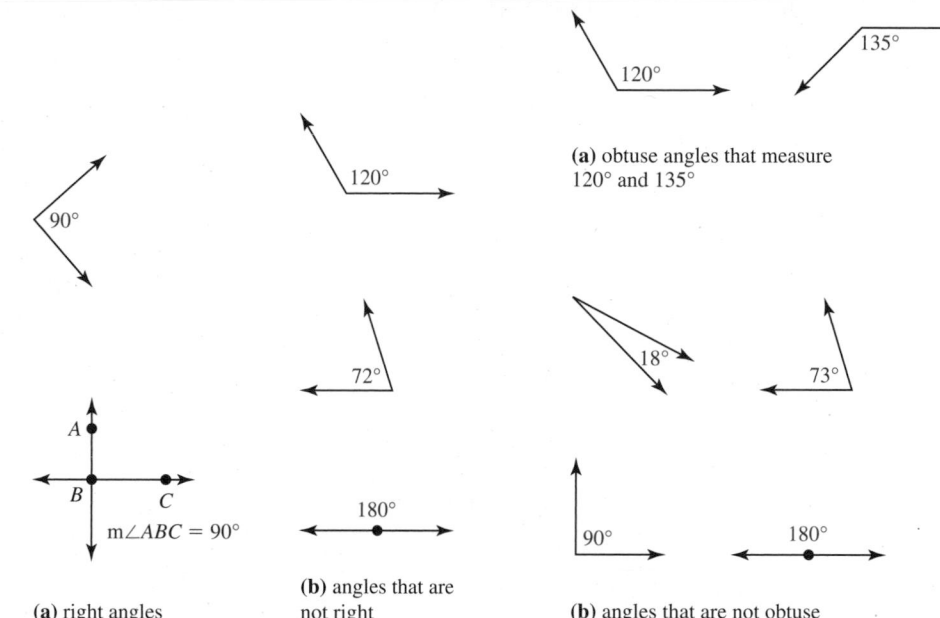

(a) right angles

(b) angles that are
not right

FIGURE 9

Examples and counterexamples of right angles.

(a) obtuse angles that measure
120° and 135°

(b) angles that are not obtuse

FIGURE 10

Examples and counterexamples of obtuse
angles.

The following Released Item asked students to draw an angle that measures more than 90°.

▶ RELEASED ITEM

● NAEP, 2003

In the space below, draw an angle that is <u>larger</u> than 90°.

32% of fourth graders and 74% of eighth graders answered the question correctly.

Figure 11 on the next page shows an angle that is straight and some that are not. How would you define a straight angle?

Figure 12 on the next page shows some angles that are reflex and some that are not. How would you define a reflex angle?

Now we define the terms to make sure we share a common language. An **acute angle** is an angle that measures between 0° and 90°. A **right angle** is an angle that measures 90°. An **obtuse angle** is an angle that measures between 90° and 180°. A **straight angle** is an angle that measures 180°. A **reflex angle** is an angle that measures between 180° and 360°.

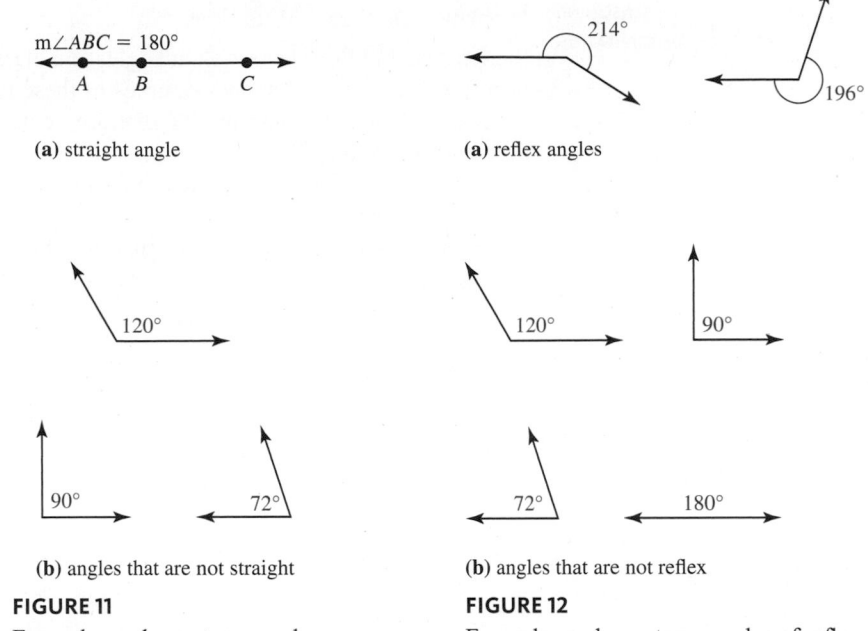

(a) straight angle

(a) reflex angles

(b) angles that are not straight

(b) angles that are not reflex

FIGURE 11
Examples and counterexamples of straight angles.

FIGURE 12
Examples and counterexamples of reflex angles.

Special Markings: Tick Marks, Arcs, and Arrowheads

Figure 13 shows how we use special markings (tick marks, arcs, and arrowheads) to represent a common relationship between pairs of line segments, angles, and lines.

REPRESENTATION

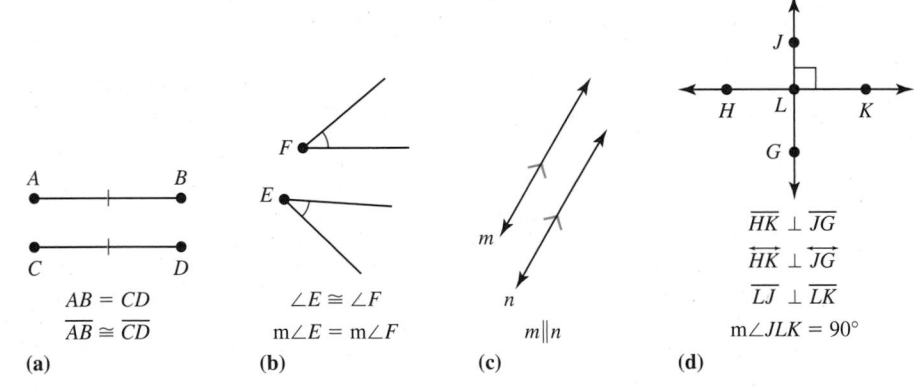

FIGURE 13
Markings that indicate relationships between pairs of basic geometric objects.

- The expression $\overline{AB} \cong \overline{CD}$, read as "line segment AB is congruent to line segment CD," means $\overline{AB}$ and $\overline{CD}$ have the same length, that is, $AB = CD$. The tick mark $|$ in the diagram means the two line segments are congruent.

- The expression $\angle E \cong \angle F$, read as "angle E is congruent to angle F," means $m\angle E = m\angle F$. The arc symbols $\backslash$ and $/$ in the angles symbolize the two angles are congruent.

- The arrowhead mark $>$ on lines m and n symbolizes that line m is parallel to line n, or $m \parallel n$.

- Multiple kinds of marks may be used in the same figure to represent two different congruencies of the same type. For example, two line segments could have two tick marks each, and two congruent angles can have two arcs each.

• Two intersecting line segments, rays, or lines (in any combination) are said to be perpendicular if the lines containing them form a right angle. We use the symbols ⊥ (upside-down T) and ⌐ (corner) to represent a right angle relationship in expressions and diagrams, respectively. For example, the expression $\overline{HK} \perp \overline{JG}$ means $\overline{HK}$ and $\overline{JG}$ are perpendicular. Students should be able to "draw perpendicular and parallel lines" (Gr. 4, CCSS).

Midpoint of a Line Segment

The midpoint of the line segment $\overline{PQ}$ is a point M on $\overline{PQ}$ such that $PM = MQ$. Then $PM = \frac{1}{2}PQ$. Every line segment has a unique midpoint. The midpoint M belongs to $\overline{PQ}$, which means P-M-Q and $PQ = PM + MQ$.

EXAMPLE 10.8

COMMUNICATION
CONNECTION
PROBLEM SOLVING
REASONING
REPRESENTATION

A, B, C, and D are collinear points. C is the midpoint of $\overline{AB}$, $AB = 60$ cm, and $AD = 42$ cm. Find possible values for CD.

SOLUTION

We draw a diagram to represent the situation. The midpoint C is between A and B such that $AC = CB$.

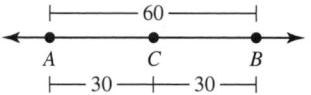

The point D is 42 cm from A, and $42 = 30 + 12$. The following diagram shows two possible locations for D.

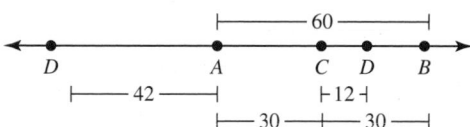

The diagram shows CD may be 12 cm or 72 cm ($72 = 30 + 42$).

▲

EXAMPLE 10.9

COMMUNICATION
REASONING

A plane contains points A and B. The teacher asked the class to think of another point on the plane. Teresa thinks about the point relationship and the postulates for a few minutes, and then she shouts, "The plane contains the midpoint of $\overline{AB}$!" Do you agree or disagree?

SOLUTION

Teresa is correct. By definition, the midpoint of $\overline{AB}$ belongs to $\overline{AB}$, so the midpoint belongs to $\overleftrightarrow{AB}$. By Postulate 3, the plane containing A and B also contains $\overleftrightarrow{AB}$. So the plane contains the midpoint of $\overline{AB}$.

▲

QUESTIONS FOR SECTION 10.1

REPRESENTATION

Refresher: Representations (language, diagrams, tables, symbols, algebra, manipulatives, and contextualized situations) are important because we use them to organize, record, and communicate mathematical ideas and make them more comprehensible.

1. Use the diagram to do the following.

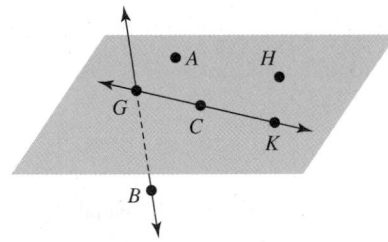

  a. Identify three coplanar points.

  b. Identify four noncoplanar points.

  c. Identify three collinear points in the plane.

  d. Identify a line not contained in the plane.

  e. Identify a line contained in the plane.

2. Suppose ∠*ABC* is congruent to ∠*DEF*. Which statements are correct?

  a. m∠*ABC* ≅ m∠*DEF*   b. m∠*ABC* = m∠*DEF*

  c. ∠*ABC* ≅ ∠*DEF*   d. ∠*ABC* = ∠*DEF*

3. Express each situation using mathematical notation (not a diagram).

  a. the line segment with the endpoints *A* and *K*

  b. the line containing the points *Q* and *R*

  c. ∠*ABC* is congruent to ∠*DEF*

  d. ∠*ABC* as an acute angle

  e. the plane containing *Q* and $\overleftrightarrow{HW}$

4. Describe the expressions with words (and symbols as necessary).

  a. *AB* = *CD*   b. m∠*ABC* = 90°

  c. m∠*A* = m∠*B*   d. *X-Y-Z*

5. Let *C* denote the set of coplanar lines, *S* the set of skew lines, and *P* the set of parallel lines. Make a Venn diagram for the given sets.

  a. *C* and *S*   b. *C* and *P*   c. *S* and *P*   d. *C, S,* and *P*

6. Draw a diagram to represent the following line relationships.

  a. two coplanar lines   b. three noncollinear points

  c. three collinear points   d. three concurrent lines

  e. two parallel lines

7. Draw a diagram to represent each expression or relationship.

  a. *AQ* = 2 · *AB*   b. ∠*ABC*   c. $\overrightarrow{AB}$ d. a right angle

8. Mark the diagram so that

  a. the two lines are parallel.

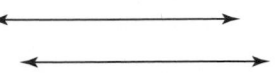

  b. the two line segments are congruent.

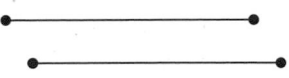

  c. the two angles are congruent.

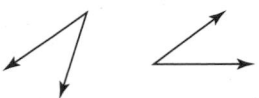

9. Trace and cut out the wedge drawn here.

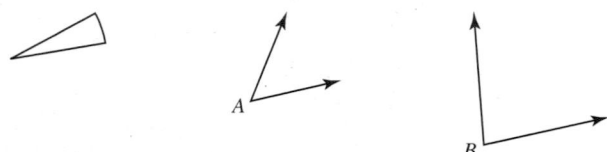

  a. Estimate how many wedges fit in each angle.

  b. Measure each of the angles shown. Write your answers as "m∠*A* = ___ wedges" or "m∠*B* = ___ wedges." Round your answer to the nearest whole number.

PROBLEM SOLVING

Refresher: Problem solving (reaching a goal that is not immediately attainable) is important because it helps students think more deeply about what they know and deal with unfamiliar situations.

10. The measure of ∠*A* is 15° more than three times the measure of ∠*B*. The sum of their measures is 155°. Find m∠*A* and m∠*B*.

11. There are 56 labeled points in a plane, and no collection has three points that are collinear.

  a. Using these 56 labeled points, how many names are there for lines in the plane? (For example, $\overleftrightarrow{AB}$ and $\overleftrightarrow{BA}$ are different names.)

  b. Of these names, how many of them represent different lines? (For example, $\overleftrightarrow{AB}$ and $\overleftrightarrow{BA}$ represent the same line, but $\overleftrightarrow{AB}$ and $\overleftrightarrow{BC}$ represent different lines.)

12. Use the given measurements m∠*ABC* = 160°, m∠*DBC* = 120°, and m∠*ABE* = 105° and the angle addition postulate to determine m∠*ABD*, m∠*DBE*, and m∠*EBC*. The diagram is not drawn to scale, so do not use a protractor to measure the angles.

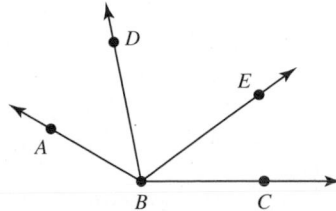

REASONING AND PROOF

Refresher: Reasoning and proof (thinking and justifying) are important because they help students make sense of mathematics.

13. Suppose you know *GH* = 32 cm, *GK* = 40 cm, and *HK* = 10 cm. Is *K* between *G* and *H*? Show your work.

14. *Q*, *W*, and *K* are collinear. *WQ* = 8 cm, and *WK* = 30 cm. Determine *QK*.

15. *A*, *B*, *C*, and *D* are collinear points. *C* is the midpoint of $\overline{AB}$, *A* is between *D* and *C*, *AB* = 20 cm, and *BD* = 24 cm. Find *AD*. (Hint: Draw a diagram.)

16. In the illustration that follows, assume m∠*APB* = 48°, m∠*CPE* = 102°, and m∠*DPE* = 34°.

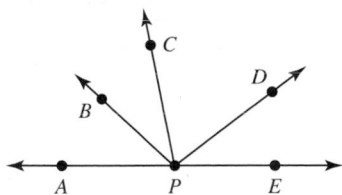

Use the angle addition postulate to calculate the measure of each angle.

   a. m∠*CPD*   **b.** m∠*APC*   **c.** m∠*BPC*

17. Mr. Smith draws the following diagram on the board.

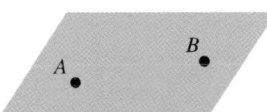

Then he asks his class, "Does the plane contain the line through *A* and *B*?" Some students quickly said, "No." Lisa thought about this and exclaimed, "Yes, the plane contains the line through *A* and *B*!" Why is Lisa correct?

18. The distinct lines *m* and *n* intersect at one point *A*. Use postulates to justify why there is a plane containing the two lines.

CONNECTIONS

Refresher: Connections (linking and applying mathematical ideas) are important because they deepen student understanding and make mathematics more meaningful, flexible, and useful.

19. m∠*A* = 28°, and m∠*B* = 175°. Which statements adequately compare the measures of the angles?
   a. m∠*A* is 140° less than m∠*B*.
   b. m∠*A* is three times m∠*B*.   **c.** m∠*A* is 16% of m∠*B*.
   d. m∠*B* is about 6.3 times m∠*A*.
   e. m∠*B* is 7° more than six times m∠*A*.

20. Using the protractor shown here, find m∠*ABC*, m∠*DBC*, and m∠*ABD*.

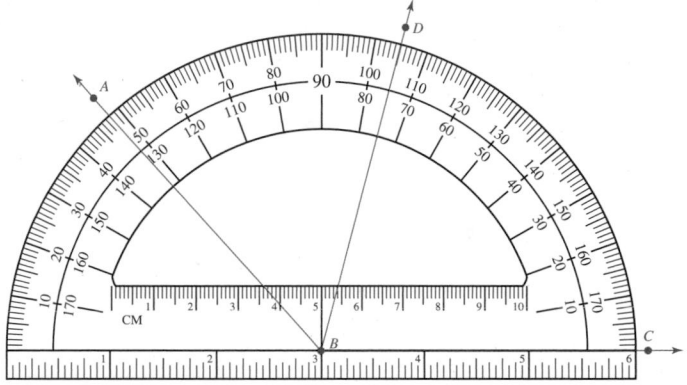

21. How many different names are there for each line using only the labeled points?

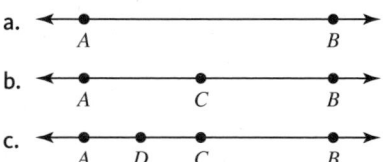

   d. a line with *n* points that are labeled

22. When you use a protractor to measure an angle, the reported measurement is rounded to the nearest degree. However, some measurements must be more precise. You can make more precise measurements using smaller units of measure. For example, 1° equals 60 minutes (60′), and 1′ equals 60 seconds (60″). The measurement 75°20′48″ represents 75 degrees, 20 minutes, and 48 seconds, or 75 + 20/60 + 48/3600 ≈ 75.347 degrees. Express each measurement in degrees, rounded to the nearest thousandth.

   a. 21°15′30″   **b.** 30°40′50″   **c.** 5°20′35″

23. A bearing is a direction relative to a north–south orientation. Measurements for bearing report the direction (north or south), an acute angle with one side of the angle belonging to the north–south line, and another direction (west or east). For example, in the illustration, suppose you are at point *A* and heading toward point *B*. The bearing for $\overrightarrow{AB}$ would be N 65° W. Suppose you are at point *A* and heading toward point *C*. The

bearing for $\overline{AC}$ would be S 50° E. Draw a line segment with the given bearing.

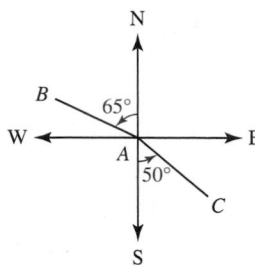

a. N 30° E   **b.** N 20° W   **c.** S 40° E   **d.** S 75° W

24. Azimuth, often used in astronomy, is an angle measured from the north–south line in a clockwise direction. The diagram shows the azimuth of line segment $\overline{PQ}$ is 135°. The azimuth of east is 90°, and the azimuth of south is 180°. Draw a line segment that has the given azimuth.

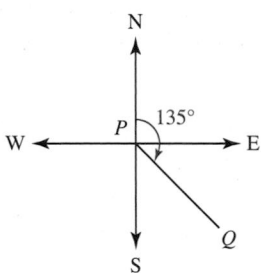

a. 30°   **b.** 138°   **c.** 225°

COMMUNICATION

Refresher: Communication (written and verbal explanations using representations and proper mathematical vocabulary) is important because it helps students refine and strengthen their understanding.

25. What is the relationship between points and lines?

26. What words do we use to describe relationships among points?

27. What words can we use to describe the relationship between points and planes?

28. What words can we use to describe the relationship between two coplanar lines?

29. Describe a physical model (example) for each.

a. perpendicular lines   **b.** line segment   **c.** acute angle

d. obtuse angle   **e.** right angle   **f.** parallel line segments

30. How are pairs of parallel and skew lines

a. similar?   **b.** different?

31. How are the names $\angle ABC$ and $\overrightarrow{DE}$ alike?

32. Draw a geometric figure that pertains to ideas in this section. Describe the geometric figure to a student in the class. As you describe the geometric figure, have the student draw the figure. Compare the two figures. How well did they match?

33. Do the following.

a. The endpoints of a line segment are A and B. Write a geometric expression that represents the line segment. Does the order of the points A and B matter?

b. A line contains points A and B. Write a geometric expression that represents the line. Does the order of the points A and B matter?

c. A plane contains points A, B, and C. Write a geometric expression that represents the plane. Does the order of the points A, B, and C matter?

34. Answer the following.

a. A ray contains points A and B. What do you need to know about A and B to write a geometric expression that represents the ray in terms of the points A and B?

b. An angle contains points A, B, and C. Point C is the vertex. What do you need to know about A and B to write a geometric expression that represents the angle in terms of the points A, B, and C?

35. Answer the following.

a. How many points are needed to determine a unique line?

b. What is the minimum number of points needed to create a set of noncollinear points?

36. Answer the following.

a. How many points are needed to determine a unique plane?

b. What is the minimum number of points needed to create a set of noncoplanar points?

More practice with the ideas of the section

37. Fill in the blank. Choose one of the following words or phrases: *acute angle, between, collinear points, compass, coplanar points, degree, endpoint, line, noncoplanar points, obtuse angle, one degree, openness, parallel lines, perpendicular, plane, postulates, protractor, ray, transversal,* or *vertex.*

a. _____ are points that belong to the same line.

b. _____ are points that belong to the same plane.

c. _____ are coplanar lines that do not intersect.

d. A(n) _____ is a line that intersects two or more coplanar lines.

e. _____ represents the openness of a wedge when a circle is subdivided into 360 equal-sized wedges.

f. We say B is _____ A and C if and only if $AB + BC = AC$.

g. _____ are properties we accept because they are intuitive and cannot be proved.

h. We use a(n) _____ to quantify the openness of an angle.

i. A(n) _____ is an angle that measures between 0° and 90°.

j. A(n) _____ is an angle that measures between 90° and 180°.

k. Two intersecting line segments, rays, or lines are said to be _____ if they form a right angle.

l. A protractor is a tool that we can use to measure the _____ of an angle.

38. In the illustration that follows, assume m∠APB = 25°, m∠CPE = 82°, and m∠BPD = 102°.

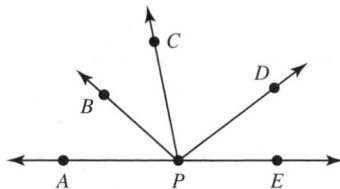

Use the angle addition postulate to calculate each angle.

a. m∠DPE **b.** m∠CPD **c.** m∠BPC

39. Use the measurements m∠DBE = 40°, m∠FBD = 80°, and m∠ABE = $\frac{1}{2}$ · m∠DBC and the angle addition postulate to determine each angle.

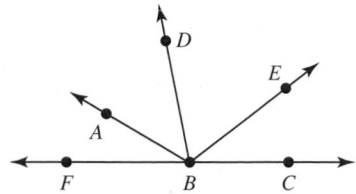

a. m∠EBC **b.** m∠ABD **c.** m∠FBA

40. Express each situation using mathematical notation.

a. a ray with the endpoint O and containing the point K

b. the distance between point H and point I

c. line m parallel to line y

d. ∠ABC is a right angle

e. line m perpendicular to line y

41. Draw a diagram for each of the following. If it is not possible, then explain why.

a. two perpendicular line segments

b. ∠ABC with the vertex C

c. ∠ABC and ∠DEF such that the interior of ∠DEF is in the interior of ∠ABC

42. Draw the following.

a. m∠ABC = 40° **b.** m∠DEF = 125°

43. A line divides a plane into two regions.

Two intersecting lines divide a plane into four regions.

a. Three concurrent lines divide the plane into how many regions?

b. Four concurrent lines divide the plane into how many regions?

c. Twenty-three concurrent lines divide the plane into how many regions?

44. Represent each expression with a diagram. Use appropriate markings.

a. Y-Q-B **b.** point C and $\overrightarrow{AB}$ such that A-B-C

c. point Q in the interior of ∠ABC **d.** $\overleftrightarrow{PQ} \perp \overleftrightarrow{AB}$

45. Do the following.

a. Given $\overline{AB}$, draw all points P such that m∠PAB = 60°.

b. Given $\overline{CD}$, draw all points Q such that m∠QCD = 135°.

46. Label the statement as *correct* or *incorrect* for the figure.

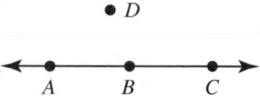

a. A is between B and C. **b.** A, B, and C are collinear.

c. A, B, and D are noncollinear. **d.** $\overleftrightarrow{AB} = \overleftrightarrow{CB}$.

47. Suppose P belongs to the interior of ∠ABC. Prove m∠PBC < m∠ABC.

48. You are given that m∠ABC = m∠DBE. ∠ABE is a straight angle. ∠CBD is an obtuse angle. Find possible measurements for m∠ABC.

49. State two reasons $\overleftrightarrow{CD}$ and EFG are alike.

50. A carpenter is not sure whether two walls he constructed form a 90° angle at their intersection. Unfortunately, he left his tools at home. However, there is a pile of wood scraps in the room containing triangular wedges, and he recalls that each has an angle of 18°. Explain how the carpenter can use the wood scraps to verify that the angle between the two walls is 90°.

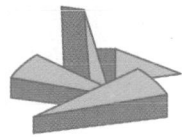

51. How many names can you find for the plane using the labeled points?

a. Three points are shown.

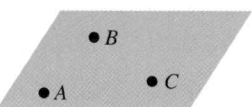

b. Four points are shown.

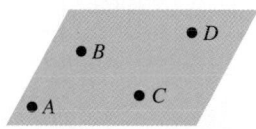

c. Five points are shown.

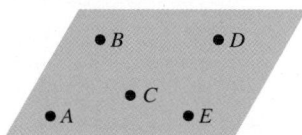

52. Use a protractor to find the angle measures.

a. 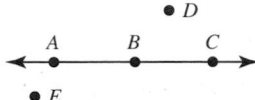 b.

53. Use the diagram to determine three concurrent lines.

• D

A   B   C

• E

54. $m\angle A = 55°$, and $m\angle B = 170°$. Fill in the blanks.

    a. $m\angle A$ is ___° less than $m\angle B$.

    b. $m\angle B$ is ___ times larger than $m\angle A$.

    c. $m\angle A$ is ___% of $m\angle B$.

    d. $m\angle B$ is ___° more than three times $m\angle A$.

    e. $m\angle A$ is ___% less than $m\angle B$.

55. There are 32 labeled points in a plane, and no collection has three points that are collinear. How many ways can you name the plane using the labeled points?

Pairs of Angles and Types of Polygons

Why We Need a Thorough Understanding of Pairs of Angles

In this section, we build on terminology from the previous section and introduce new language to describe, represent, and categorize pairs of angles and types of shapes. We classify angles formed by intersecting lines and identify properties of angles created by a transversal that cuts parallel lines. Students should be able to "use facts about supplementary, complementary, vertical, and adjacent angles in a multi-step problem to write and solve simple equations for an unknown angle in a figure" (Gr. 7, CCSS). A thorough understanding of angles provides students a foundation for understanding polygons, especially properties of quadrilaterals. The NCTM's *Principles and Standards for School Mathematics* states:

> In the early grades, students will have classified and sorted geometric objects such as triangles or cylinders by noting general characteristics. In grades 3–5, they should develop more-precise ways to describe shapes, focusing on identifying and describing the shape's properties and learning specialized vocabulary associated with these shapes and properties. (2000, p. 165)

Complementary and Supplementary Angles

Figure 14 shows pairs of angles. How would you define complementary angles?

COMMUNICATION
REASONING
REPRESENTATION

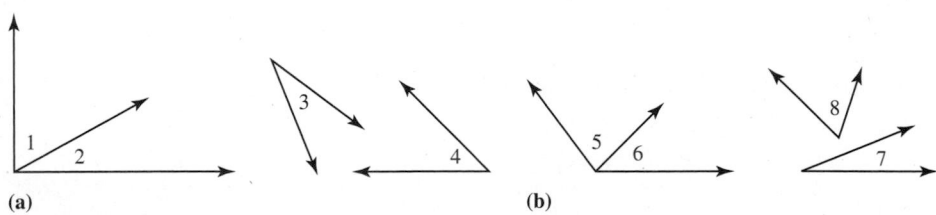

(a)   (b)

FIGURE 14

Examples and counterexamples of complementary angles.

$m\angle 1 = 35°$	$m\angle 3 = 18°$	$m\angle 5 = 80°$	$m\angle 7 = 15°$
$m\angle 2 = 55°$	$m\angle 4 = 72°$	$m\angle 6 = 60°$	$m\angle 8 = 32°$
$m\angle 1 + m\angle 2 = 90°$	$m\angle 3 + m\angle 4 = 90°$	$m\angle 5 + m\angle 6 \neq 90°$	$m\angle 7 + m\angle 8 \neq 90°$

pairs of complementary angles   pairs of noncomplementary angles
$\angle 1$ and $\angle 2$ $\angle 5$ and $\angle 6$
$\angle 3$ and $\angle 4$ $\angle 7$ and $\angle 8$

Figure 15 shows pairs of angles. How would you define supplementary angles?

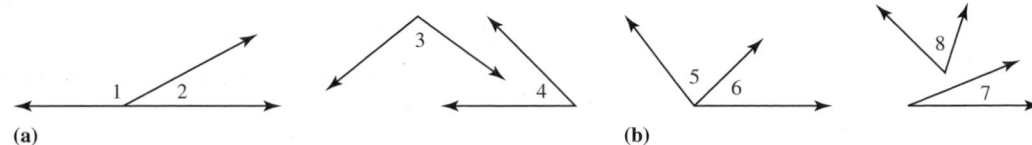

(a)   **(b)**

FIGURE 15

Examples and counterexamples of supplementary angles.

$m\angle 1 = 146°$ $m\angle 3 = 109°$ $m\angle 5 = 80°$ $m\angle 7 = 15°$

$m\angle 2 = 34°$ $m\angle 4 = 71°$ $m\angle 6 = 60°$ $m\angle 8 = 32°$

$m\angle 1 + m\angle 2 = 180°$ $m\angle 3 + m\angle 4 = 180°$ $m\angle 5 + m\angle 6 \neq 180°$ $m\angle 7 + m\angle 8 \neq 180°$

pairs of supplementary angles   pairs of nonsupplementary angles

$\angle 1$ and $\angle 2$ $\angle 5$ and $\angle 6$

$\angle 3$ and $\angle 4$ $\angle 7$ and $\angle 8$

$\angle A$ and $\angle B$ are **complementary angles** if and only if $m\angle A + m\angle B = 90°$. $\angle A$ and $\angle B$ are **supplementary angles** if and only if $m\angle A + m\angle B = 180°$. The terms *supplementary* and *complementary* apply to *pairs* of angles; for example, three angles measuring 50°, 60°, and 70° are not supplementary.

The following Classroom Connection is a problem involving complementary angles.

Classroom Connection

● *Math*, Grade 6, p. 464

Find the unknown measure.

The measure of an angle is twice the measure of a complementary angle. What is the measure of each angle? (© 2000 Macmillan/McGraw Hill. Reprinted by permission.)

EXAMPLE 10.10

CONNECTION

REASONING

a. The measure of a complementary angle of $\angle A$ is 42°. What is the measure of $\angle A$?

b. $m\angle Q = 58°$. What is the measure of a supplementary angle of $\angle Q$?

SOLUTION

a. The two angles are complementary, so $42° + m\angle A = 90°$. Then $m\angle A = 90° - 42° = 48°$.

b. The two angles are supplementary, and $180° - 58° = 122°$. A supplementary angle of $\angle Q$ has the measure 122°.

▲

EXAMPLE 10.11

PROBLEM SOLVING

REASONING

REPRESENTATION

An angle measures 14° more than three times the measure of a complementary angle. What is the measure of each angle?

SOLUTION

METHOD 1. Use the Draw a Diagram strategy. The measure of the larger angle is slightly more than three times the measure of the smaller angle. The sum of two angles is 90°. The rectangle in Figure 16 represents the measure of the smaller angle.

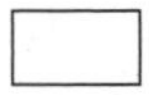

FIGURE 16

Representation of the measure of the smaller angle.

(continued)

Figure 17 displays the relationship between the two angles.

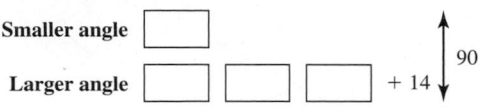

FIGURE 17
Representation of the two angles and their
relationship as complementary angles.

Then we get Figure 18.

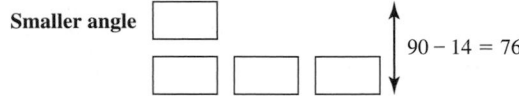

FIGURE 18
Simplifying the angle relationship.

Now split 76° into four equal-sized groups, which calls for division: $76° \div 4 = 19°$. This means each rectangle in Figure 18 represents 19°. The measure of the smaller angle is 19°, and the measure of the larger angle is $3 \cdot 19 + 14 = 71°$.

METHOD 2. Apply the Solve an Equation strategy. Let the variable s represent the measure of the smaller angle. The algebraic expression $3s + 14$ represents the measure of the larger angle. The sum of two expressions is 90°. Then

$$s + (3s + 14) = 90$$
$$4s + 14 = 90$$
$$4s = 76$$
$$s = 19$$

Then $3 \cdot 19 + 14 = 57 + 14 = 71$. The measures of the two angles are 19° and 71°. ▲

Vertical and Adjacent Angles

We consider two intersecting lines that form four related angles. In Figure 19, angles $\angle 1$ and $\angle 2$ are adjacent angles because they have a common side. Can you identify the three remaining pairs of adjacent angles?

In addition to the adjacent angles, $\angle 1$ and $\angle 3$ are vertical angles, as are $\angle 2$ and $\angle 4$, in Figure 19.

COMMUNICATION

REASONING

REPRESENTATION

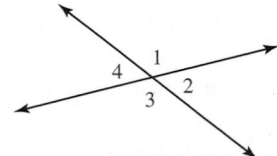

FIGURE 19
Two intersecting lines form adjacent and vertical angles.

Adjacent angles are two angles that have a common side (and therefore have the same vertex and do not have overlapping interiors). **Vertical angles** are two nonadjacent angles formed by two intersecting lines. Students should know that all pairs of vertical angles are congruent. The following example shows this result using inductive reasoning and then proves it using deductive reasoning.

EXAMPLE 10.12 Two intersecting lines are shown.

COMMUNICATION

REASONING

REPRESENTATION

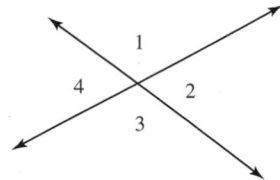

a. Identify all pairs of vertical angles.

b. Measure the angles.

c. Make a conjecture about vertical angles.

d. Prove your conjecture.

SOLUTION

a. $\angle 1$ and $\angle 3$ are vertical angles, as are $\angle 2$ and $\angle 4$.

b. $m\angle 1 = 115°$, $m\angle 2 = 65°$, $m\angle 3 = 115°$, and $m\angle 4 = 65°$.

c. The example supports the conjecture that vertical angles are congruent.

d. Let m and n be intersecting lines, as shown. We then show $\angle 1 \cong \angle 3$. $\angle 1$ and $\angle 2$ are supplementary angles, so $m\angle 1 + m\angle 2 = 180°$. $\angle 2$ and $\angle 3$ are supplementary angles, so $m\angle 2 + m\angle 3 = 180°$. Then

$$m\angle 1 = 180° - m\angle 2$$
$$m\angle 3 = 180° - m\angle 2$$
$$m\angle 1 = m\angle 3$$
$$\angle 1 \cong \angle 3$$

The line of reasoning is the same for $\angle 2$ and $\angle 4$. This proves the conjecture that vertical angles are congruent.

▲

Classifying Angles Formed by a Transversal

We turn our attention to classifying angles formed by a line that intersects two other lines. Later, this helps us derive some key properties about triangles and parallelograms.

In Figure 20, line k is a transversal for lines m and n. In Figure 21, line t is a transversal for lines p and q. As explained in Section 10.1, a transversal is any line that intersects two or more lines in a plane at different points. Both figures include labels for the angles formed by two lines cut by a transversal. Table 10.3 lists special pairs of angles: alternate interior angles, alternate exterior angles, and corresponding angles.

REPRESENTATION

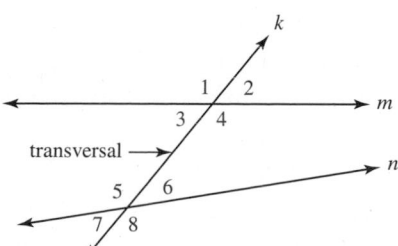

FIGURE 20
Angles formed by transversal k.

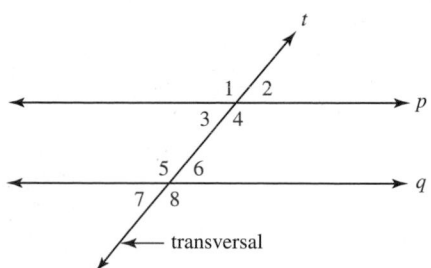

FIGURE 21
Angles formed by transversal t.

TABLE 10.3   **Types of Angles Created By a Transversal that Cuts Two Lines**

Interior angles	$\angle 3, \angle 4, \angle 5, \angle 6$
Alternate interior angles	$\angle 4$ and $\angle 5$, $\angle 3$ and $\angle 6$
Exterior angles	$\angle 1, \angle 2, \angle 7, \angle 8$
Alternate exterior angles	$\angle 1$ and $\angle 8$, $\angle 2$ and $\angle 7$
Corresponding angles	$\angle 2$ and $\angle 6$, $\angle 4$ and $\angle 8$, $\angle 1$ and $\angle 5$, $\angle 3$ and $\angle 7$

EXAMPLE 10.13

COMMUNICATION

REASONING

Two lines are cut by a transversal.

a. What do corresponding angles have in common?

b. What do alternate interior angles and alternate exterior angles have in common?

SOLUTION

a. They are always on the same side of the transversal.

b. They are always on the opposite sides of the transversal.

▲

EXAMPLE 10.14

COMMUNICATION

REASONING

REPRESENTATION

What is the relationship between the paired angles in the diagram regarding the transversal?

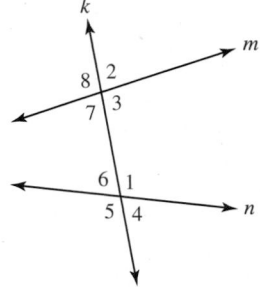

a. $\angle 8$ and $\angle 6$

b. $\angle 3$ and $\angle 6$

c. $\angle 2$ and $\angle 5$

d. $\angle 7$ and $\angle 6$

e. $\angle 8$ and $\angle 5$

SOLUTION

a. $\angle 8$ and $\angle 6$ are corresponding angles.

b. $\angle 3$ and $\angle 6$ are alternate interior angles.

c. $\angle 2$ and $\angle 5$ are alternate exterior angles.

d. $\angle 7$ and $\angle 6$ are interior angles.

e. $\angle 8$ and $\angle 5$ are exterior angles.

▲

The following Classroom Connection challenges elementary school students to think about corresponding angles formed by a transversal that cuts two nonparallel lines.

> ◆◆ **Classroom Connection**
>
> ● *Math*, Grade 6, p. 465
>
> Draw a transversal that cuts two lines that are not parallel. Measure the corresponding angles. Are they congruent? Explain. (© 2000 Macmillan/McGraw Hill. Reprinted by permission.)

EXAMPLE 10.15

COMMUNICATION

REASONING

Maria drew two lines cut by a transversal such that the corresponding angles $\angle 1$ and $\angle 2$ were congruent. She labeled the angles as shown. Prove that all pairs of corresponding angles are congruent.

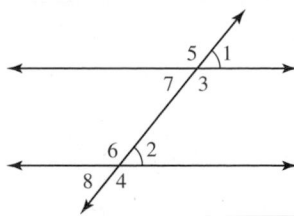

SOLUTION

We are given $\angle 1 \cong \angle 2$. We need to show $\angle 3 \cong \angle 4$, $\angle 5 \cong \angle 6$, and $\angle 7 \cong \angle 8$.

- $m\angle 1 + m\angle 3 = 180°$, and $m\angle 2 + m\angle 4 = 180°$. Then $m\angle 1 + m\angle 3 = m\angle 2 + m\angle 4$. But $m\angle 1 = m\angle 2$, so by subtracting $m\angle 2$ from both sides, we get $m\angle 3 = m\angle 4$. Then $\angle 3 \cong \angle 4$.

- $\angle 3$ and $\angle 5$ are vertical angles, so $\angle 3 \cong \angle 5$. $\angle 4$ and $\angle 6$ are vertical angles, so $\angle 4 \cong \angle 6$. But $\angle 3 \cong \angle 4$, so $\angle 3 \cong \angle 5$ and $\angle 3 \cong \angle 6$. Then $\angle 5 \cong \angle 6$.

- $\angle 1$ and $\angle 7$ are vertical angles, so $\angle 1 \cong \angle 7$. $\angle 2$ and $\angle 8$ are vertical angles, so $\angle 2 \cong \angle 8$. But $\angle 1 \cong \angle 2$, so $\angle 1 \cong \angle 7$ and $\angle 1 \cong \angle 8$. Then $\angle 7 \cong \angle 8$.

▲

The moral of the story is that once we know one pair of corresponding angles are congruent, we can be sure that all pairs of corresponding angles are congruent. It can easily be shown that all pairs of alternate interior angles and all pairs of alternate exterior angles are also congruent.

Properties of Angles Formed by a Transversal That Cuts Parallel Lines

Return to Figures 20 and 21. Each displays a transversal that intersects two lines. Which figure looks like it contains parallel lines? Identify and measure all corresponding angles in the figures before continuing. Which figure contains congruent corresponding angles? From Example 10.15, we learned that if two lines cut by a transversal create two congruent corresponding angles, then we can be sure that all pairs of corresponding angles are congruent.

Students should be able to "use informal arguments to establish facts about the angles created when parallel lines are cut by a transversal" (Gr. 8, CCSS). The following postulate provides a practical way to decide whether two lines are parallel based on angle measure.

F Postulate

Two lines cut by a transversal are parallel if and only if any two corresponding angles created by the transversal are congruent.

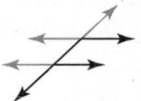 If a transversal cuts two lines and you identify two congruent corresponding angles, then you know those two lines are parallel. On the other hand, if you know a transversal cuts two parallel lines, then you know any two corresponding angles are congruent. The following two examples apply the F Postulate.

EXAMPLE 10.16

COMMUNICATION

REASONING

Luis drew two parallel lines cut by a transversal, as shown in the diagram. After studying the diagram, Kelly shouted, "The alternate interior angles created by the transversal are congruent!" Prove that Kelly is correct.

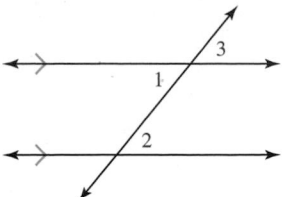

SOLUTION

The two lines are parallel, so any two corresponding angles are congruent by the F Postulate. So $m\angle 2 = m\angle 3$. But $\angle 1$ and $\angle 3$ are vertical angles, so $m\angle 1 = m\angle 3$. Then $m\angle 2 = m\angle 3$ and $m\angle 1 = m\angle 3$. Therefore, $m\angle 1 = m\angle 2$. The argument for the other alternate interior angles is similar. Kelly is correct: The alternate interior angles created by the transversal are congruent. ▲

EXAMPLE 10.17

COMMUNICATION

REASONING

Kelly drew two lines cut by a transversal such that the alternate interior angles were congruent, as shown in the diagram. After studying the diagram, Luis exclaimed, "The two lines are parallel!" Prove that Luis is correct.

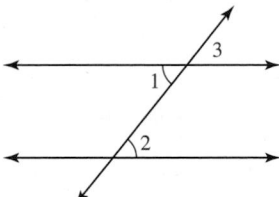

SOLUTION

$\angle 1$ and $\angle 2$ are congruent alternate interior angles, so $m\angle = m\angle 2$. Angles $\angle 1$ and $\angle 3$ are vertical angles, so $m\angle 1 = \angle 3$. Then $m\angle 1 = m\angle 2$ and $m\angle 1 = m\angle 3$. Therefore, $m\angle 2 = m\angle 3$. So $\angle 2$ and $\angle 3$ are congruent corresponding angles. By the F Postulate, the two lines cut by the transversal are parallel. Luis is correct: The two lines are parallel. ▲

Together, Examples 10.16 and 10.17 lead us to conclude that two lines cut by a transversal are parallel if and only if any two alternate interior angles created by the transversal are congruent.

Polygons

Figure 22 shows various types of curves. A **curve** is a drawing that you can make without lifting your pencil and without retracing portions of the drawing, except for possibly isolated points. A simple curve is a curve that does not retrace any points, except possibly the "start" and "stop" points. A closed curve is a curve in which the start and stop points coincide. A convex curve is a simple closed curve with the property that for any two points in the interior of the curve, the line segment joining the two points also belongs to the interior of the curve. Otherwise, the simple closed curve is a concave curve. A polygonal curve is a curve that consists solely of line segments. A **polygon** is a simple closed polygonal curve.

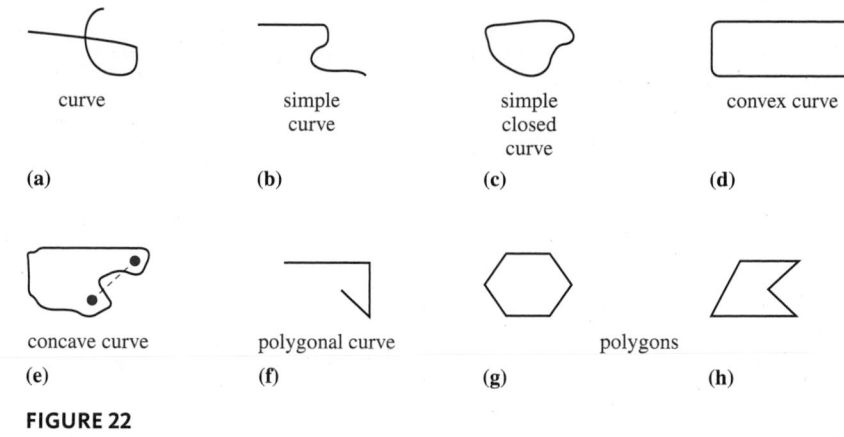

FIGURE 22
Types of curves.

EXAMPLE 10.18 Draw a curve with the given properties.
a. a simple curve that is not closed

b. a closed curve that is not simple

c. a concave polygon

SOLUTION

Answers vary.

a.  b. 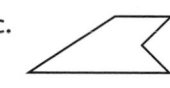 c.

The Released Item illustrates that students should be able to draw polygons with certain properties.

> **RELEASED ITEM**
>
> ● NAEP, 2003
> In the space below, draw a closed figure with 5 sides. Make 2 of the angles right angles.
>
> 27% of fourth-grade students provided a suitable drawing.

Anatomy of a Polygon

Figure 23 on the next page shows the anatomy of a polygon. A polygon separates the plane into three disjoint regions: the curve itself, the interior of the polygon, and the exterior of the polygon. Every line segment that forms the polygon is called a **side.** A **vertex** of a polygon is a point on the polygon that is the intersection of two adjacent sides. A **diagonal** of a polygon is a line segment joining two nonconsecutive vertices. An **interior angle** of a polygon is an angle formed by two adjacent sides of the polygon. An **exterior angle** of a convex polygon is the angle formed by extending a side of the polygon. Each vertex of a convex polygon has two exterior angles, because there are two sides that can be extended at each vertex. An interior angle and an exterior angle of a convex polygon are supplementary angles.

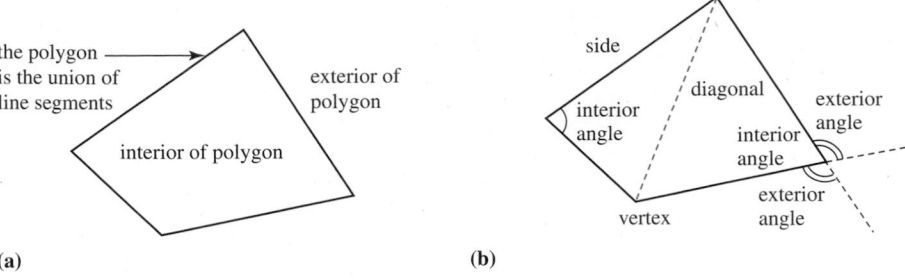

(a)   **(b)**

FIGURE 23
Anatomy of a polygon.

TABLE 10.4   Types of Polygons

Number of sides	Name
3	triangle
4	quadrilateral
5	pentagon
6	hexagon
7	heptagon
8	octagon
9	nonagon
10	decagon
11	undecagon
12	dodecagon
n	n-gon

Naming Polygons

We name (classify) polygons according to the number of sides they have. The word *polygon* originates from the Greek words *poly* (meaning "many") and *gonia* (meaning "angles"). Table 10.4 lists the names of common polygons. As early as second grade, students should be able to "identify triangles, quadrilaterals, pentagons, and hexagons" (Gr. 2, CCSS).

The shapes of most traffic signs are polygons. Some shapes are restricted to specific purposes, making them more recognizable to give motorists more time to comprehend and react to the situation. The trapezoidal shape is reserved for recreational and cultural interest signs and for National Forest route signs. The pentagonal shape with an upward point is reserved for school advance warning signs and county route signs. The octagon shape is reserved exclusively for stop signs. Rectangular shapes, including squares, are reserved for warning signs.

L. Kragt Bakker/Shutterstock.com

Classifying Triangles by Their Angles

A **triangle** is a polygon with exactly three sides. We can classify triangles according to their interior angles. Figure 24 shows an acute triangle, an obtuse triangle, and a right triangle.

REPRESENTATION

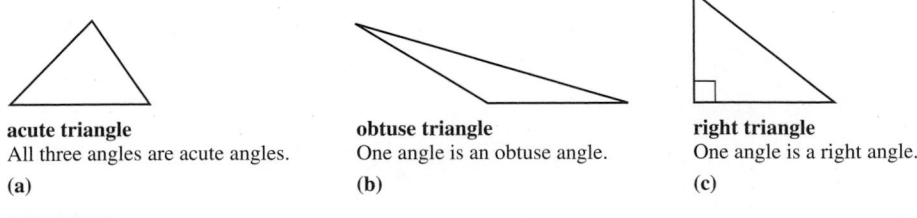

acute triangle
All three angles are acute angles.
(a)

obtuse triangle
One angle is an obtuse angle.
(b)

right triangle
One angle is a right angle.
(c)

FIGURE 24
Classifying triangles according to their interior angles.

Classifying Angles by Their Sides

We can also classify triangles according to the lengths of their sides. Figure 25 shows a scalene triangle, isosceles triangle, and equilateral triangle.

REPRESENTATION

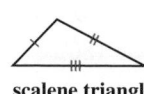

scalene triangle
All three sides have different lengths.
(a)

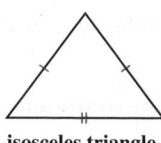

isosceles triangle
Exactly two sides have the same length.
(b)

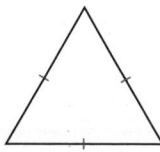

equilateral triangle
All three sides have the same length.
(c)

FIGURE 25
Classifying triangles according their sides.

The following Released Item illustrates students should be able to classify a triangle according to its sides.

> ▶ **RELEASED ITEM**
>
> ● NAEP, 2003
>   A triangle that has sides with lengths 6, 6, and 10 is called
>   **a.** acute   **b.** right   **c.** scalene   **d.** isosceles   **e.** equilateral
>
>   43% of eighth-grade students gave the correct answer.

In the next example, we use identifying marks to indicate relationships among lengths of sides of a triangle.

EXAMPLE 10.19 List possible names for the triangle.

COMMUNICATION
REASONING
REPRESENTATION

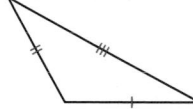

SOLUTION
scalene triangle, obtuse triangle, and obtuse scalene triangle ▲

The Sum of the Measures of Angles of a Triangle Is 180°

Use a straightedge to draw a triangle. Then tear the three corners and put them together as shown in the diagram.

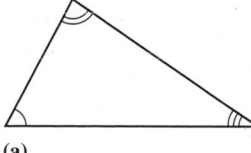

(a)

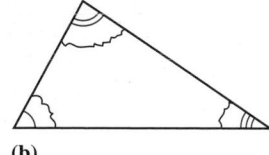

(b)

(c)

We "see" that the sum of the interior angles of a triangle is 180°. The following example proves this elementary fact.

EXAMPLE 10.20 Prove that the sum of the interior angles of a triangle is 180°.

COMMUNICATION
REASONING
REPRESENTATION

SOLUTION

Figure 26(a) shows a triangle with interior angles $a°$, $b°$, and $c°$. We need to find the sum $a° + b° + c°$.

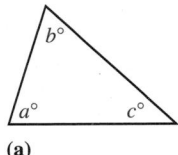

FIGURE 26
A triangle with angle measures $a°$, $b°$, and $c°$.

As shown in Figure 26(b), we draw a line segment through a vertex that is parallel to its opposite side.

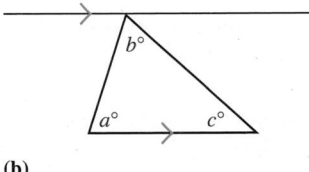

(b)

FIGURE 26
A line through a vertex and parallel to a side.

As indicated in Figure 26(c), each transversal that cuts the parallel line segments creates congruent alternate interior angles.

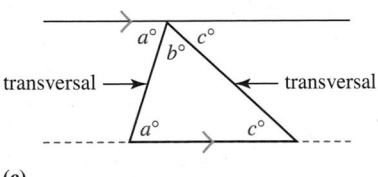

(c)

FIGURE 26
Two sides of the triangle are transversals for parallel lines.

We see that $a° + b° + c° = 180°$. Therefore, the sum of the interior angles of a triangle is 180°.

▲

Students should be able to "use informal arguments to establish facts about the angle sum and exterior angle of triangles" (Gr. 8, CCSS). The following Released Item expects students to recognize that the sum of the angles of a triangle is 180° and relate this to the measure of an exterior angle.

RELEASED ITEM

● NAEP, 2003

In the triangle, what is the degree measure of $\angle ABC$?

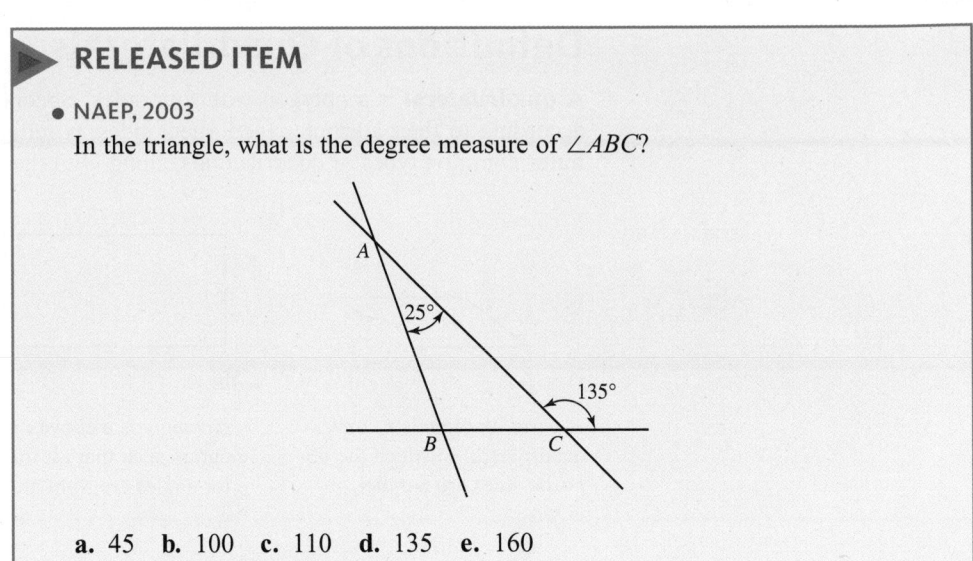

a. 45 **b.** 100 **c.** 110 **d.** 135 **e.** 160

33% of eighth-grade students gave the correct answer.

In the next example, we illustrate how to use two strategies to solve a typical problem involving angle relationships.

EXAMPLE 10.21 In $\triangle ABC$, the measure of $\angle B$ is twice the measure of $\angle A$ and the measure of $\angle C$ is three times the measure of $\angle B$. Find the measure of each angle.

PROBLEM SOLVING

REASONING

REPRESENTATION

SOLUTION

METHOD 1. Use the Draw a Diagram strategy. $m\angle B$ depends on $m\angle A$, and $m\angle C$ depends on $m\angle B$. So let each rectangle in Figure 27 represent $m\angle A$. The sum of the three angles is 180°.

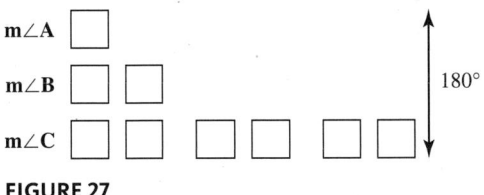

FIGURE 27

Now split 180° into nine equal-sized groups, which calls for division: $180° \div 9 = 20°$. This means each rectangle in Figure 27 represents 20°. Then $m\angle A = 20°$, $m\angle B = 2 \cdot m\angle A = 2 \cdot 20° = 40°$, and $m\angle C = 3 \cdot m\angle B = 3 \cdot 40° = 120°$. Let's check our work: $m\angle A + m\angle B + m\angle C = 20° + 40° + 120° = 180°$. The answer checks.

METHOD 2. Use the Solve an Equation strategy. We know that $m\angle B = 2 \cdot m\angle A$ and $m\angle C = 3 \cdot m\angle B = 3 \cdot (2 \cdot m\angle A) = 6 \cdot m\angle A$. Then

$$m\angle A + m\angle B + m\angle C = 180°$$
$$m\angle A + 2 \cdot m\angle A + 6 \cdot m\angle A = 180°$$
$$9 \cdot m\angle A = 180°$$
$$m\angle A = 20°$$

Then $m\angle A = 20°$, $m\angle B = 2 \cdot m\angle A = 2 \cdot 20° = 40°$, and $m\angle C = 3 \cdot m\angle B = 3 \cdot 40° = 120°$. Let's check our work: $m\angle A + m\angle B + m\angle C = 20° + 40° + 120° = 180°$. The answer checks.

Definitions of Quadrilaterals

A **quadrilateral** is a polygon with four sides. Special types of quadrilaterals are named according to their attributes (congruent sides, parallel sides, and so on). Figure 28 illustrates common types of quadrilaterals, along with their definitions.

REPRESENTATION

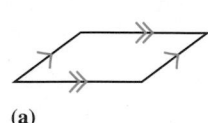

(a)

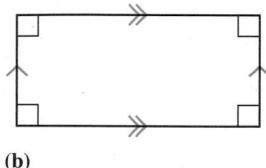

(b)

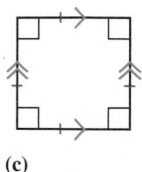

(c)

A *parallelogram* is a convex quadrilateral in which the opposite sides are parallel.

A *rectangle* is a convex parallelogram such that all four interior angles are right angles.

A *square* is a rectangle in which all four sides are congruent.

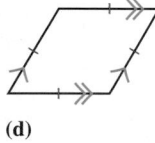

(d)

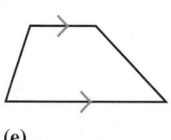

(e)

(f)

A *rhombus* is a convex parallelogram in which all four sides are congruent.

A *trapezoid* is a convex quadrilateral with exactly one pair of sides that are parallel.

A *kite* is a convex quadrilateral such that the four sides can be divided into exactly two pairs of congruent consecutive sides.

FIGURE 28

Common types of convex quadrilaterals.

As students draw shapes and use precise language (for example, vertex, vertical angles, parallel, and angles) to describe shapes, they begin to consider relationships within shapes (for example, opposite angles of a parallelogram are congruent) and between shapes (for example, all squares are rectangles). In time, teachers help them justify these properties using deductive reasoning.

Some shapes may have multiple names. For example, the geometric shape in Figure 29 is a parallelogram, rhombus, rectangle, and square. We generally choose the name that is most specific—in this case, square. However, if someone asks whether a square is a parallelogram, then the answer is "yes."

Our definition of a trapezoid is the same as most definitions of trapezoids seen in elementary mathematics textbooks. With this definition, a rectangle is not a trapezoid. A few textbooks define a trapezoid as a quadrilateral with at least one set of opposite sides that are parallel. With this alternative definition, a rectangle would be a trapezoid.

In the following example, the measure of an angle of a parallelogram is given, and we learn that opposite angles in a parallelogram are congruent.

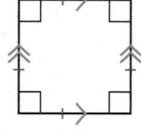

FIGURE 29

The quadrilateral is a parallelogram, rhombus, rectangle, and square.

EXAMPLE 10.22

CONNECTION
PROBLEM SOLVING
REASONING
REPRESENTATION

Leila drew the parallelogram *ABCD* such that m∠*A* = 65°.

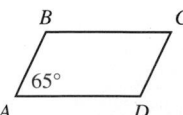

Gina studied the diagram. Then she exclaimed, "the measure of ∠*C* is 65° too!" Why is Gina correct?

SOLUTION

We extend each side of the parallelogram. We see that $\overleftrightarrow{AB}$ is a transversal for the parallel lines $\overleftrightarrow{AD}$ and $\overleftrightarrow{BC}$. Then corresponding angles are congruent, and we obtain the diagram shown.

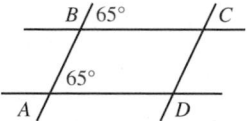

We also see that $\overleftrightarrow{BC}$ is a transversal for the parallel lines $\overleftrightarrow{AB}$ and $\overleftrightarrow{CD}$. Then alternate interior angles are congruent, and we obtain the diagram shown. This shows m∠C = 65°. So Gina is correct.

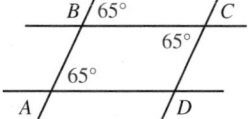

The Sum of the Measures of the Interior Angles of a Polygon

Earlier we proved the sum of the measures of the interior angles of a triangle is 180°. The next example shows how to apply this fact to find the sum of the measures of the interior angles of a quadrilateral.

EXAMPLE 10.23 Find m∠A + m∠B + m∠C + m∠D for the quadrilateral $ABCD$ shown here.

COMMUNICATION

CONNECTION

PROBLEM SOLVING

REASONING

REPRESENTATION

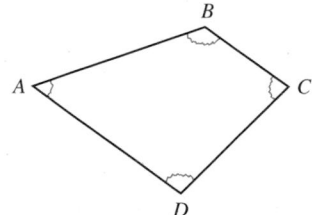

SOLUTION

As shown in Figure 30, we draw a diagonal and split the quadrilateral into two triangles.

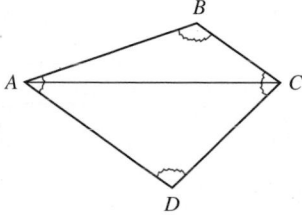

FIGURE 30
Finding the sum of measures of the interior angles of a quadrilateral.

The sum of the angles of the quadrilateral equals the sum of the angles of the two triangles, and 2 · 180° = 360°. Then m∠A + m∠B + m∠C + m∠D = 360°.

As shown in Figure 31, you can use the pentagon *ABCDE* to reason that the sum of the angles in a pentagon is $3 \cdot 180° = 540°$.

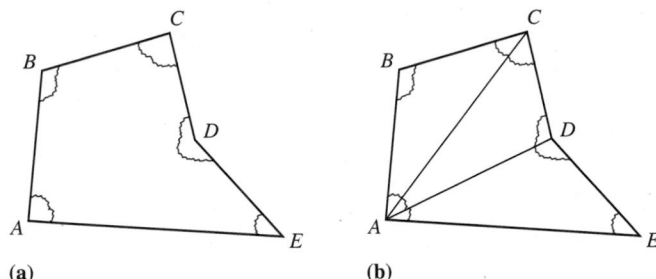

(a) (b)

FIGURE 31
Finding the sum of the interior angles of a pentagon.

We can extend these ideas to polygons with *n* sides.

Sum of Measures of the Interior Angles in a Polygon

The sum of the measures of the interior angles of a polygon with *n* sides is $(n - 2) \cdot 180$ degrees.

Angles of Regular Polygons

A **regular polygon** is a polygon such that

- The sides are congruent line segments.
- The interior angles of the polygon are congruent.

Figure 32 shows some regular polygons.

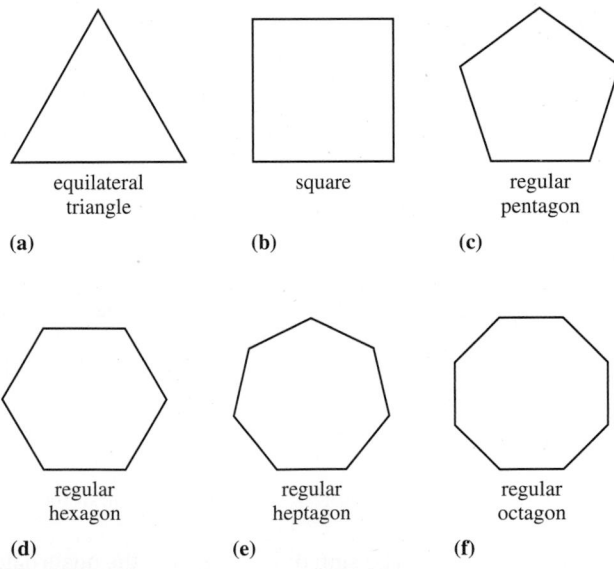

equilateral triangle
(a)

square
(b)

regular pentagon
(c)

regular hexagon
(d)

regular heptagon
(e)

regular octagon
(f)

FIGURE 32
Regular polygons.

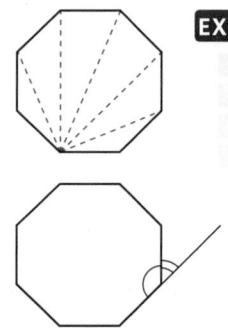

EXAMPLE 10.24 Find the measure of each interior and exterior angle of a regular octagon.

COMMUNICATION
CONNECTION
REASONING
REPRESENTATION

SOLUTION

We can draw a regular octagon and decompose it into six triangles. $6 \cdot 180° = 1080°$, so the sum of the interior angles is $1080°$. Each interior angle has the same measure: $1080°/8 = 135°$. The interior angle and the exterior angle are supplementary angles, and $180° - 135° = 45°$. So each exterior has the measure $45°$. ▲

Measures of Angles in a Regular Polygon

- The sum of the measures of the interior angles of a regular polygon with n sides is $(n - 2) \cdot 180$ degrees.

- Each interior angle of a regular polygon with n sides has the measure $\dfrac{(n - 2) \cdot 180}{n}$ degrees.

- Each exterior angle of a regular polygon with n sides has the measure $180 - \dfrac{(n - 2) \cdot 180}{n}$ degrees, which equals $\dfrac{360}{n}$ degrees.

van Hiele Learning Theory for Spatial Thinking

Pierre van Hiele and Dina van Hiele-Geldof taught students at secondary schools in the Netherlands. Their widely accepted learning theory, first presented in 1959 and based on two decades of empirical research, states that students learn geometry in stages that depend more on instruction and learning opportunities than age. Students proceed through five sequential and hierarchical levels of reasoning as they learn geometry concepts. They move from inductive reasoning to deductive reasoning. The van Hieles proposed the following levels of thought.

Level 1: Visualization
Students judge geometric shapes by their appearances and orientation without paying attention to properties or individual components. They identify, cut, compare, draw, and sort shapes. They associate shapes with physical objects, such as squares and boxes. They use invented words (for example, *round* and *pointy*) and sometimes correct language (for example, *square* and *rectangle*).
Level 2: Description
Students distinguish, classify, and measure shapes. They discover, examine, recognize, and list their properties. For example, they see the opposite sides of a parallelogram are congruent. Their sketches of shapes reflect properties. Students use correct language (for example, *sides, diagonals,* and *vertex*) and representations. They use inductive reasoning as the basis for developing and validating properties, so a formal proof is pointless to them. They use properties to solve some problems.
Level 3: Analysis
Students perceive relationships between shapes (for example, a square is a special rectangle). They can create possible shapes from a list of properties. Definitions are meaningful at this level, because they require some underlying knowledge of the concept defined, so making and explaining definitions reflect a degree of understanding. Students can solve multistep geometry problems. They can supply some missing explanations or rationale in proofs.

> **Level 4: Abstraction**
>
> Students reproduce and develop proofs using undefined terms, definitions, postulates, given information, and diagrams in sound logical arguments (for example, prove the diagonals of a kite are perpendicular), including contraposition and contradiction. They focus on Euclidean geometry.
>
> **Level 5: Proof**
>
> Students study geometry from an axiomatic point of view and focus on non-Euclidean geometry, such as the Poincaré model, spherical model, and taxicab model.

Students begin at level 1 and generally pass from one level to another without skipping levels. Each level includes a collection of vocabulary and representations, so the students' level of thought affects how they respond to geometry questions or problems. A student may be at one level for a particular geometric concept but at a different level for a different geometric concept. A student who understands most of one level is ready to transition to the next level. Teachers who teach at a higher level than that of their students make it difficult for their students to understand the material and complete assignments. Teachers are more effective when they recognize the level of thought of their students and adjust their instruction and learning opportunities accordingly to steer students to the next level. Ideally, elementary school teachers help their students through the first two levels; middle-school teachers gradually introduce their students to level 3; high school teachers help their students progress through levels 3 and 4; and college teachers help their students progress through level 5 in an abstract geometry course. Here is a brief description of how the van Hieles theory applies to the three grade bands (elementary, middle, and secondary):

- Students in elementary schools primarily engage in geometry tasks that ask them to compare, sketch, measure, represent, identify, describe, label, and classify geometric figures, as well as objects around them. They tend to think about individual figures and shapes. Along the way, teachers introduce and reinforce correct language and provide instructive activities to help them clarify and communicate ideas.

- Students in middle schools discover, infer, analyze, recognize, and list properties of shapes. They tend to think about collections of similar objects. They also think of shapes in terms of their properties, rather than their appearance. Their experiences include reflections and explanations of relationships, beginning the gradual transition from informal reasoning to formal reasoning in their study of geometry and preparing them for the next stage in secondary school.

- Students in secondary schools combine undefined terms, definitions, postulates, theorems, and formal reasoning. They give formal proofs to verify geometric relationships.

QUESTIONS FOR SECTION 10.2

REPRESENTATION

Refresher: Representations (language, diagrams, tables, symbols, algebra, manipulatives, and contextualized situations) are important because we use them to organize, record, and communicate mathematical ideas and make them more comprehensible.

1. Answer the following.
   a. *ABCD* and *BCDA* are valid names for the rectangle shown. Is *ACDB* a valid name? Explain your answer.

   b. How many names can you write for the rectangle using the vertices? Give the names.

   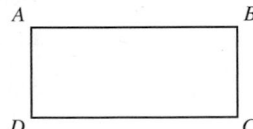

2. What is wrong with this diagram?

   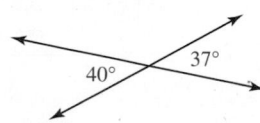

3. Trace $\overline{BC}$ onto your paper. Then sketch or shade the portion of the plane that contains all points A such that $\angle ABC$ is

   a. an obtuse angle.   **b.** a right angle.   **c.** an acute angle.

4. Tell how $\angle 1$ and $\angle 2$ are related.

   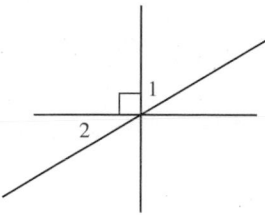

5. Sketch a quadrilateral with two right angles, one obtuse angle, and exactly one pair of opposite sides that are parallel.

6. Sketch two distinct lines that divide the plane into the given number of regions (without counting the lines as regions).

   a. four regions   **b.** three regions

7. On the dot paper, draw each of the following.

   a. scalene triangle   **b.** isosceles triangle

   c. congruent line segments   **d.** parallelogram

   e. obtuse triangle

8. Sketch an obtuse isosceles triangle.

9. Do the following.

   a. Find the measure of $\angle 1$.

   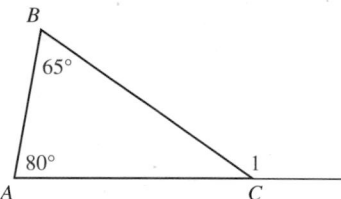

   b. Find the measure of $\angle 2$.

   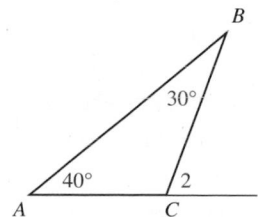

PROBLEM SOLVING

Refresher: Problem solving (reaching a goal that is not immediately attainable) is important because it helps students think more deeply about what they know and deal with unfamiliar situations.

10. In $\triangle ABC$, m$\angle B$ is 5° more than three times m$\angle A$, and m$\angle C$ is 5° less than m$\angle B$. Find the measures of all three angles. Solve this problem using the Draw a Diagram strategy.

11. In $\triangle ABC$, m$\angle B = n$ degrees, m$\angle A = 2n + 3°$, and m$\angle C = n + 5°$. Find the measures of all three angles.

12. $\angle T$ and $\angle Q$ are complementary angles. m$\angle T$ is 6° less than twice m$\angle Q$. Find m$\angle T$ and m$\angle Q$.

13. $\angle A$ and $\angle B$ are supplementary angles. m$\angle A$ is 6° less than twice m$\angle B$. Find m$\angle A$ and m$\angle B$.

14. Two angles are supplementary angles. The measure of the larger angle is 5° more than three times the measure of the smaller angle. Find the measures of the two angles.

REASONING AND PROOF

Refresher: Reasoning and proof (thinking and justifying) are important because they help students make sense of mathematics.

15. Suppose $\triangle ABC$ is a right triangle, where $\angle A$ is the right angle. Prove that $\angle B$ and $\angle C$ are complementary angles.

16. Indicate whether each sentence is true or false.

   a. Every square is a trapezoid.

   b. Every rectangle is a parallelogram.

   c. Every rhombus is a rectangle.

   d. Every square is a rhombus.

   e. Some rectangles are squares.

   f. Some squares are rectangles.

   g. Some trapezoids are parallelograms.

   h. Every rectangle is a trapezoid.

17. In the quadrilateral $ABCD$, $\angle A$ and $\angle C$ are opposite angles and $\angle B$ and $\angle D$ are opposite angles. Suppose $\angle A \cong \angle C$ and $\angle B \cong \angle D$.

   a. Find m$\angle A$ + m$\angle B$ + m$\angle C$ + m$\angle D$.

   b. Use part (a) and $\angle A \cong \angle C$ and $\angle B \cong \angle D$ to find m$\angle A$ + m$\angle B$.

   c. Let E be a point such that A-B-E. Compare m$\angle A$ and m$\angle EBC$. What does this imply about $\overleftrightarrow{AD}$ and $\overleftrightarrow{BC}$?

   d. Let F be a point such that D-C-F. Compare m$\angle B$ and m$\angle BCF$. What does this imply about $\overleftrightarrow{AB}$ and $\overleftrightarrow{CD}$?

   e. Write a descriptive name for quadrilateral $ABCD$.

18. Do the following.

a. Randy drew two lines cut by a transversal, as shown, such that $\angle 5 \cong \angle 8$. After studying the diagram, Sandra shouted, "Hey! Lines m and n are parallel lines." Prove that Sandra is correct.

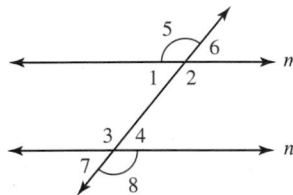

b. Crista drew two lines cut by a transversal, as shown, such that $\angle 6 \cong \angle 7$. After studying the diagram, Carlo shouted, "Hey! Lines m and n are parallel lines." Prove that Carlo is correct.

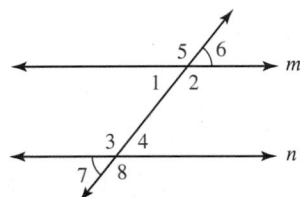

c. Use the results in part (a) to complete the following conjecture: If alternate exterior angles in any pair formed by a transversal that cuts two lines are congruent, then _____.

19. Sandra drew two parallel lines cut by a transversal, as shown.

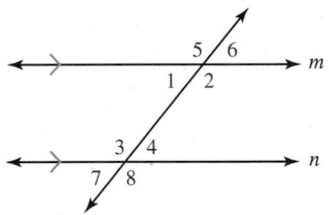

a. Pam studied the diagram for a few minutes, focusing on the alternate exterior angles $\angle 5$ and $\angle 8$. Then she shouted, "$\angle 5$ is congruent to $\angle 8$!" Prove that Pam is correct.

b. Cindy studied the diagram for a few minutes, focusing on the alternate exterior angles $\angle 6$ and $\angle 7$. Then she exclaimed, "$\angle 6$ is congruent to $\angle 7$!" Prove that Cindy is correct.

c. Use the result in part (a) to complete the following conjecture: If two parallel lines are cut by a transversal, then _____.

20. An interior angle of a parallelogram has the measure 35°. What are the measures of the other three interior angles in a clockwise order?

21. Complete the table for regular polygons. (Hint: Draw the regular polygon and decompose it into triangles.)

Type of polygon	Number of angles	Sum of the interior angles for the polygon	Measure of each interior angle for a *regular* polygon
triangle	3	180°	180°/3 = 60°
quadrilateral	4	2 · 180° = 360°	360°/4 = 90°
pentagon	5		
hexagon	6		
heptagon	7		
n-gon	n		

22. Verify each statement.

a. The sum of the measures of the interior angles of a heptagon is 900°.

b. In a regular heptagon, each interior angle has the measure 128.57°, to the nearest hundredth.

c. In a regular heptagon, each exterior angle has the measure 51.43°, to the nearest hundredth.

23. Verify each statement.

a. The sum of the measures of the interior angles of a nonagon is 1260°.

b. In a regular nonagon, each interior angle has the measure 140°.

c. In a regular nonagon, each exterior angle has the measure 40°.

CONNECTIONS

Refresher: Connections (linking and applying mathematical ideas) are important because they deepen student understanding and make mathematics more meaningful, flexible, and useful.

24. As seen in the given illustrations, a triangle has no diagonals, a quadrilateral has two diagonals, and a pentagon has five diagonals.

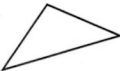 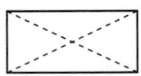 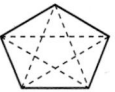

a. How many diagonals does a hexagon have?

b. How many diagonals does a heptagon have?

c. How many diagonals does an octagon have?

d. Look for a pattern to predict how many diagonals a dodecagon (a polygon with 12 sides) has.

e. Use algebraic notation to write an expression that tells how many diagonals an n-gon has.

25. Two angles are said to be linear pairs if they are supplementary and adjacent angles. Two lines can create four linear pairs. Three lines can create eight linear pairs.

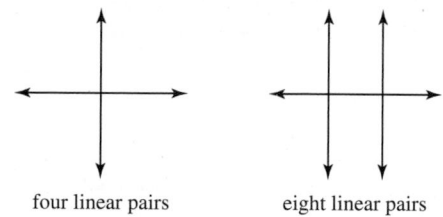

four linear pairs   eight linear pairs

The following table lists the number of lines and the maximum number of possible linear pairs that can be created with the lines. Complete the table.

Number of lines	2	3	4	5	6	7	8
Maximum possible linear pairs	4	8					

26. A line divides the plane into two regions, and two lines can divide a plane into four regions, without counting the lines themselves as regions.

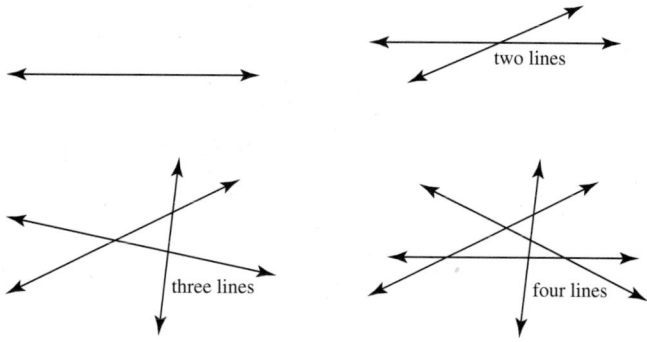

two lines

three lines   four lines

Use patterns to complete the table.

Number of lines	1	2	3	4	5	6	7	8
Maximum regions	2	4						

27. Draw a Venn diagram illustrating the relationship between the two shapes.
   a. squares and rectangles
   b. rectangles and parallelograms
   c. parallelograms and trapezoids
   d. rhombuses and rectangles

COMMUNICATION

Refresher: Communication (written and verbal explanations using representations and proper mathematical vocabulary) is important because it helps students refine and strengthen their understanding.

28. Explain why a triangle does not have any diagonals.

29. Explain why lines m and n in the given diagram are not parallel.

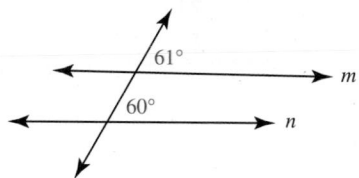

30. Explain why a triangle cannot have two obtuse angles.

More practice with the ideas of the section

31. Fill in the blank. Choose one of the following words, phrases, or angles: *180°, 360°, acute, alternate, complementary, corresponding, equilateral, hexagon, heptagon, isosceles, nonagon, obtuse, parallel, perpendicular, polygon, scalene, skew, straight,* or *supplementary.*

   a. In a(n) _____ triangle, all three sides have different lengths.
   b. _____ angles are two angles such that the sum of their measures is 90°.
   c. In a(n) _____ triangle, there is one obtuse angle.
   d. The sum of the interior angles of a quadrilateral is _____.
   e. A(n) _____ is a polygon that has nine sides.
   f. A(n) _____ is a simple closed curve consisting of line segments.
   g. _____ angles lie on the same side of the transversal.
   h. _____ are two angles such that the sum of their measures is 180°.
   i. _____ angles lie on the opposite side of the transversal.
   j. In a(n) _____ triangle, exactly two sides have the same length.

32. Is it possible to draw a quadrilateral so that one line can be drawn such that it intersects all four sides and no vertices? If it is, draw the quadrilateral. If it is not, explain your answer.

33. On the dot paper, draw each of the following.

   a. trapezoid   b. pentagon   c. concave quadrilateral
   d. isosceles triangle

34. In $\triangle ABC$ and $\triangle DEF$, $\angle A$ is congruent to $\angle D$ and $\angle B$ is congruent to $\angle E$. Prove $\angle C$ is congruent to $\angle F$.

35. Describe the pair of angles as complementary, supplementary, adjacent, or vertical. List all terms that apply.

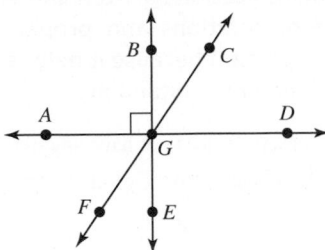

a. ∠BGC and ∠CGD   b. ∠FGE and ∠BGC

c. ∠AGC and ∠FGA   d. ∠AGB and ∠BGC

e. ∠EGD and ∠BGA   f. ∠BGC and ∠AGF

36. △ABC is an equilateral triangle. Use a protractor to measure each interior angle of the triangle. Make a conjecture about the relationships among the interior angles.

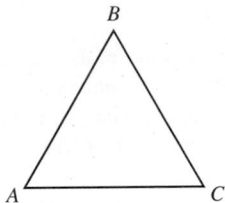

37. Suppose lines *m* and *n* are cut by a transversal and m∠1 = m∠2. What can you conclude about lines *m* and *n*? The diagram may not be drawn to scale.

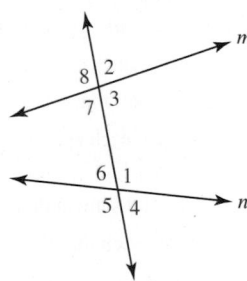

38. What is wrong with this diagram?

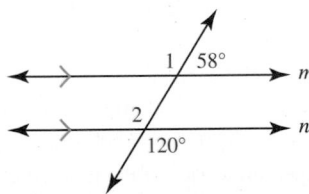

39. Rafael drew the diagram below with two lines cut by a transversal such that ∠5 ≅ ∠8. After studying the diagram, Susan shouted, "Hey! ∠2 and ∠3 are congruent!" Then Maria exclaimed, "The two lines cut by the transversal are parallel!"

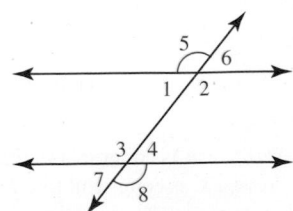

a. Why is Susan correct?   b. Why is Maria correct?

40. Sheila drew the given diagram with two lines cut by a transversal such that ∠2 and ∠4 are supplementary angles on the same side of the transversal. After studying the diagram, Gail exclaimed, "The two lines cut by the transversal are parallel!"

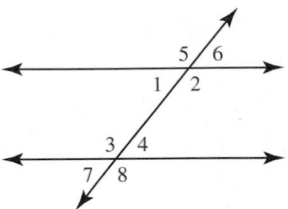

a. ∠2 and ∠4 are called consecutive interior angles. Identify another pair of consecutive interior angles.

b. Complete the following conjecture: If two lines cut by a transversal form consecutive interior angles that are supplementary, then _____.

c. Why is Gail correct?

41. Indicate whether each sentence is true or false.

a. Every quadrilateral is convex.

b. Some squares are convex.   c. Every kite is a trapezoid.

d. Some trapezoids are kites.   e. All squares are rectangles.

f. Some trapezoids are nonconvex.

g. Some kites are rectangles.   h. Some kites are squares.

i. Some squares are kites.

42. △ABC is a right isosceles triangle. ∠A is a right angle. Draw △ABC. Use appropriate markings.

43. How would you classify the quadrilateral ABCD? Justify your answer.

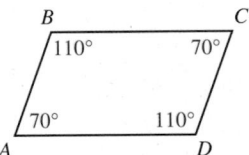

44. Marion drew two lines *m* and *n*. Then she drew line *k* so that it was perpendicular to each line. She studied the diagram, and then shouted, "Lines *m* and *n* are parallel!" Why is Marion correct?

45. Kelly drew the parallel lines *m* and *n*. Then he drew line *k* so that it was perpendicular to line *m*. Marion studied the diagram, and then exclaimed, "Lines *n* and *k* are perpendicular!" Why is Marion correct?

46. △ABC is a right triangle. m∠A is 10° less than three times m∠B. Find m∠A and m∠B, assuming ∠A is an acute angle.

47. A trapezoid is a quadrilateral with exactly one pair of sides that are parallel. ABCD is a trapezoid.

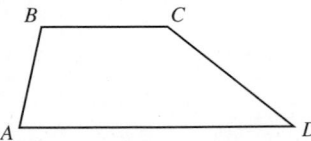

The sides that are parallel are called the bases. The sides that are not parallel are called the legs. Identify the bases and legs of trapezoid ABCD.

48. Suppose a textbook defines a rectangle as "a convex quadrilateral such that all four interior angles are right angles."

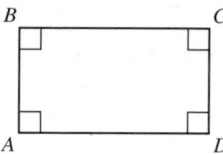

Prove that *ABCD* is a parallelogram.

49. *ABCD* is a right trapezoid, as shown. Find m∠*D*.

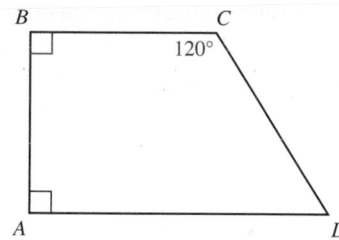

50. Find m∠1.

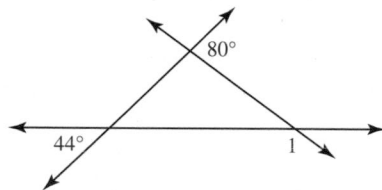

51. Measure the lengths of each side of each triangle. Then measure the interior angles of each triangle.

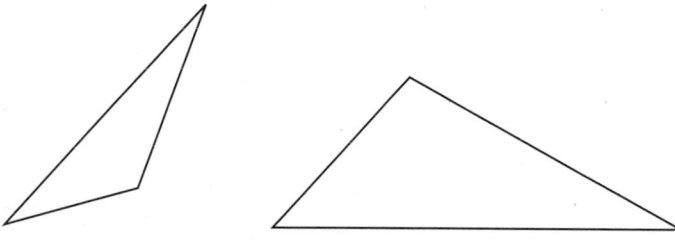

Make a conjecture about the side opposite the

a. largest interior angle of the triangle.

b. smallest interior angle of the triangle.

52. Identify the labeled angles that have the given property. Write "none" if there are no angles that have the given property.

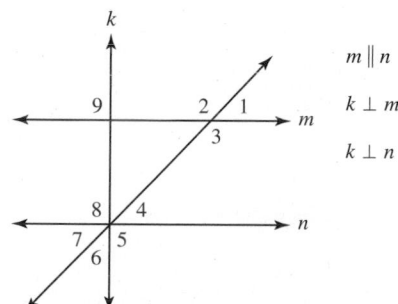

a. complementary angles   **b.** supplementary angles

c. vertical angles   **d.** right angle   **e.** obtuse angle

f. acute angle   **g.** alternate interior angles

h. alternate exterior angles   **i.** corresponding angles

53. Find *n*.

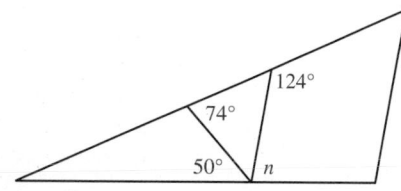

54. In a regular polygon with 14 sides, what is the measure of each

a. interior angle?   **b.** exterior angle?

55. In a regular polygon with 32 sides, what is the measure of each

a. interior angle?   **b.** exterior angle?

56. Each interior angle of a regular polygon has the measure 165.6°. How many sides does the polygon have?

57. Each exterior angle of a regular polygon has the measure 8°. How many sides does the polygon have?

58. Each interior angle of a regular polygon has the measure 175.5°. How many sides does the polygon have?

59. The sum of the measures of the interior angles of a polygon is 6840°. How many sides does the polygon have?

Multiple choice questions

Choose the correct answer for each multiple choice question.

60. Which phrase does not belong to the group?

a. obtuse angle   **b.** complementary angle

c. vertical angle   **d.** supplementary angle

61. What must corresponding angles have in common?

a. They are congruent.

b. They are on the same side of the transversal.

c. They are on opposite sides of the transversal.

d. They are complementary.

e. The answer is not listed here.

62. Suppose ∠*A* and ∠*B* are supplementary angles of ∠*C*. Then

a. m∠*A* + m∠*B* = 180°.

b. m∠*A* + m∠*B* + m∠*C* = 180°.

c. ∠*A* + ∠*B* = 180°.   **d.** ∠*A* ≅ ∠*B*.

63. We classify polygons by the number of

a. congruent sides.   **b.** diagonals.   **c.** sides.

d. parallel sides.

SECTION 10.3	Three-Dimensional Shapes

Common Three-Dimensional Shapes

We can think of a plane as a flat tablecloth without thickness that extends forever in all directions. A plane is a geometric object that is considered a two-dimensional space. In this section, we introduce the vocabulary for common three-dimensional shapes (prisms, pyramids, cylinders, cones, and spheres) and explore their properties. Precise terminology makes it easier to describe, compare, and contrast three-dimensional shapes. The NCTM's *Principles and Standards for School Mathematics* (2000) states that students in grades 3–5 should be able to "classify two- and three-dimensional shapes according to their properties and develop definitions of classes of shapes such as triangles and pyramids."

Simple Closed Surfaces and Solids

Convex curves, such as circles and polygons, separate the plane into exactly three sets of points: the curve itself, the interior of the curve, and the exterior of the curve. We can extend this idea to objects in space. A **simple closed surface** is a geometric object that is hollow, without holes, and separates space into three sets of points: the surface itself, the interior of the surface that is enclosed by the surface and consists of one set of points rather than a union of sets of points, and the exterior of the surface. A popular example is a sphere, which consists of all points in space that are a fixed distance from a given point in space. Figure 33 shows some clarifying examples.

REPRESENTATION

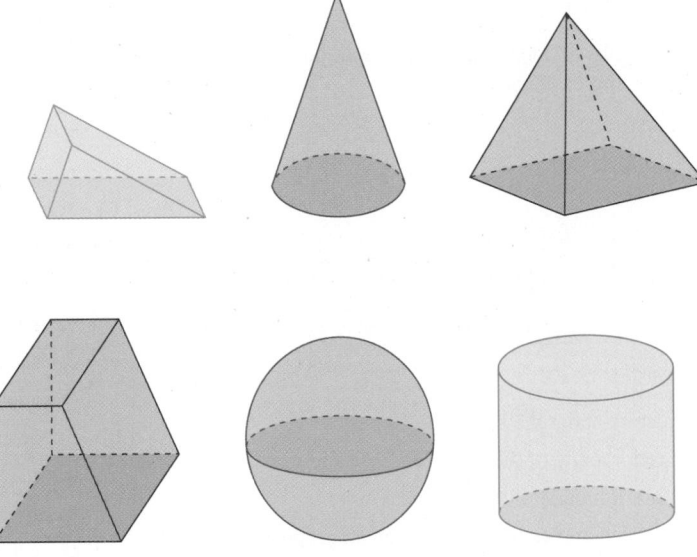

(a) shapes that are simple closed surfaces

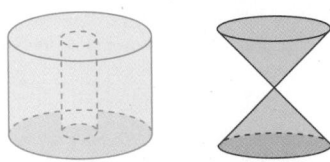

(b) shapes that are not simple closed surfaces

FIGURE 33

Examples and counterexamples of simple closed surfaces.

A solid is the union of the simple closed surface and the interior region it encloses. A billiard ball is an example of a solid. In the next chapter, we measure the surface area and volume of common solids.

Polyhedrons

A **polyhedron** is a simple closed surface that consists of polygonal regions. Concept Map 10.2 shows examples of polyhedrons and nonpolyhedrons, and it illustrates and defines the three parts (vertex, face, and edge) of a polyhedron. The shapes of many molecules and crystals are polyhedrons.

> **Concept Map 10.2** Concept Map for a Polyhedron

nonpolyhedrons

polyhedron: a simple closed surface that consists of polygonal regions.

polyhedrons

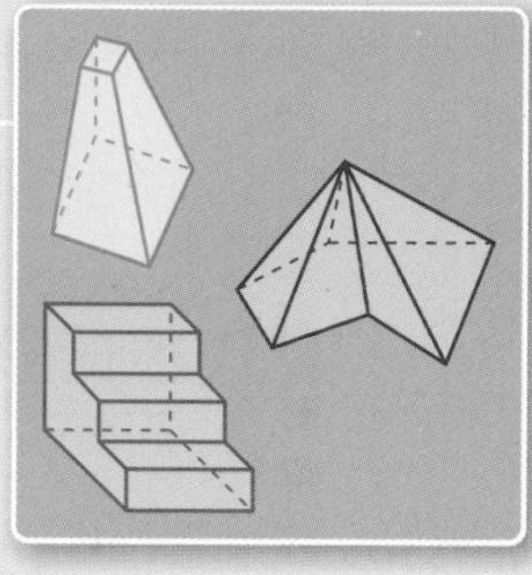

The word *polyhedron* is based on the Greek words *poly*, which means "many," and *hedra*, which means "faces."

three parts of a polyhedron:
vertex
face
edge

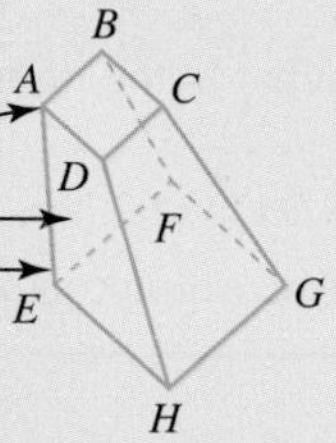

A **face** of a polyhedron is the union of a polygon and the interior region the polygon encloses. For example, *ABCD* and *ADHE* are faces.

A **vertex** of a polyhedron is the intersection of three or more faces. For example, *A* and *E* are vertices.

An **edge** of a polyhedron is the intersection of two adjacent faces. For example, $\overline{AE}$ and $\overline{FG}$ are edges.

EXAMPLE 10.25 What is the minimum number of faces that intersect to form a vertex of a polyhedron?

COMMUNICATION
REASONING

SOLUTION

A single face cannot form a closed surface. Two faces form a V-shaped figure and cannot form a closed surface. Then a vertex of a polyhedron must be the intersection of more than two faces. Each vertex in the polyhedron shown is formed by the intersection of three or more faces.

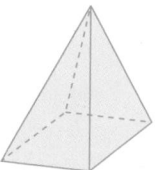

Therefore, a vertex of a polyhedron is the intersection of three or more faces.

How to Name a Polyhedron

In Section 10.2, we named a polygon according to its number of sides. For example, a polygon with five sides is a pentagon, and a polygon with eight sides is an octagon. We name a polyhedron according to its number of faces. Table 10.5 shows the names of a few polyhedrons.

TABLE 10.5 **Names of Polyhedrons**

Number of faces	Name	Number of faces	Name
4	tetrahedron	9	nonahedron
5	pentahedron	10	decahedron
6	hexahedron	11	undecahedron
7	heptahedron	12	dodecahedron
8	octahedron	20	icosahedron

EXAMPLE 10.26 What is the name of a polyhedron with 10 faces?

SOLUTION

According to Table 10.5, a polyhedron with 10 faces is called a decahedron. ▲

Polyhedrons Called Prisms

Figure 34 illustrates polyhedrons called prisms.

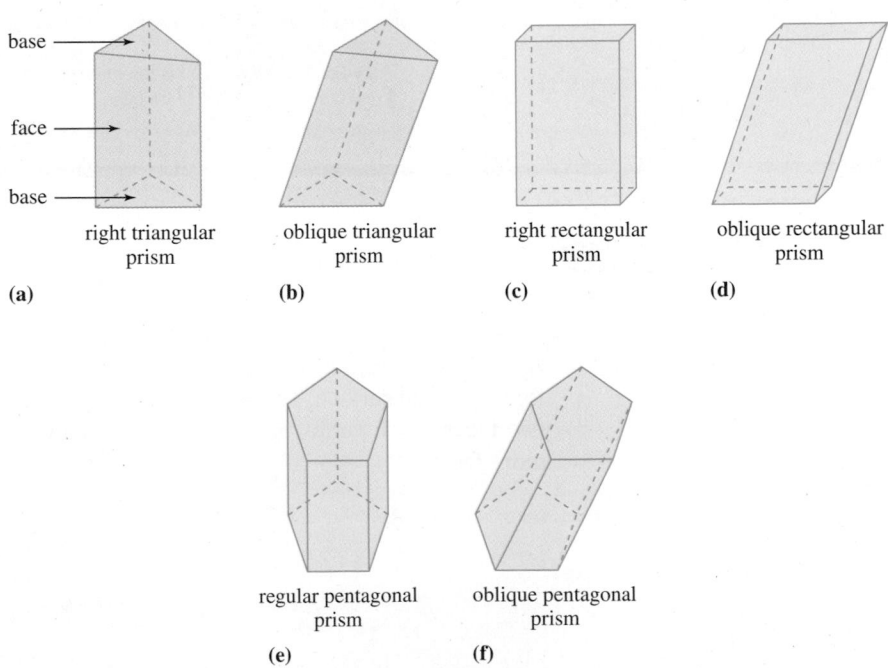

base
face
base

right triangular prism
(a)

oblique triangular prism
(b)

right rectangular prism
(c)

oblique rectangular prism
(d)

regular pentagonal prism
(e)

oblique pentagonal prism
(f)

FIGURE 34
Polyhedrons called prisms.

> **Definition**
>
> A **prism** is a polyhedron with two congruent polygonal faces that lie in parallel planes; the other faces are parallelograms.

Prisms form a family of polyhedral shapes.

- The **bases** are two faces that are parallel and congruent.
- All other faces are called **lateral faces,** and they have the shape of parallelograms.
- A **right prism** is a prism in which the shape of each lateral face is a rectangle. Each angle formed by a lateral face and a base is a right angle.
- An **oblique prism** is a prism that has at least one lateral face that is not a rectangle. This means at least one angle formed by a face and a base is a nonright angle.
- A **regular prism** is a right prism with a base that is a regular polygon.
- We name a prism according to the base and the shape of the lateral faces.

EXAMPLE 10.27   Identify the shape of the bases and the other faces in the prism. Then name the prism.

CONNECTION

REPRESENTATION

a. 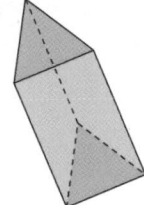   **b.**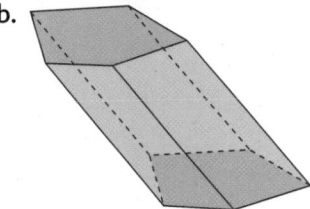

SOLUTION

a. The bases are equilateral triangles, and the lateral faces are rectangles. It is a regular triangular prism.

b. The bases are pentagons, and the lateral faces are parallelograms without right angles. It is an oblique pentagonal prism.

▲

REPRESENTATION   # Polyhedrons Called Pyramids

Figure 35 shows some examples of polyhedrons called pyramids.

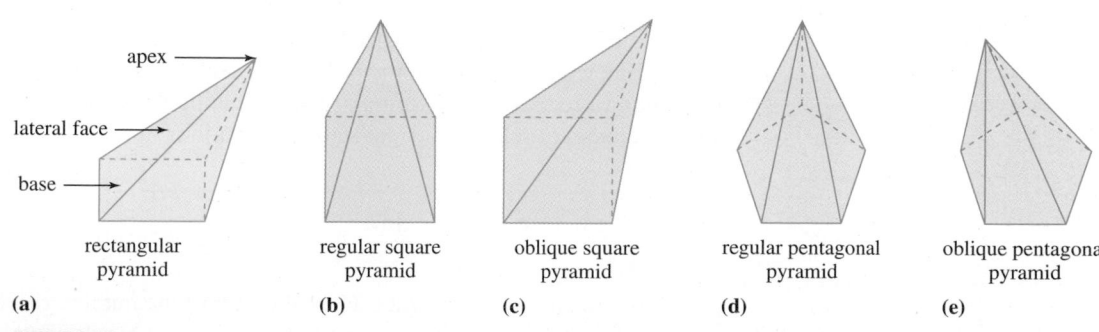

FIGURE 35
Polyhedrons called pyramids.

> **Definition**
>
> A **pyramid** is a polyhedron such that one face is a polygonal region and the other faces are triangular regions with a common vertex.

Pyramids form a family of polyhedral shapes.

- Each pyramid has a face called the **base.** The base is a polygon.
- Each pyramid has **lateral faces,** each of which is a triangle.
- The **apex** is a vertex in the pyramid formed by the intersection of the lateral faces. The apex cannot belong to the plane that contains the base.
- In a **regular pyramid,** the base is a regular polygon and all lateral faces have the same size and shape (congruent isosceles triangles or congruent equilateral triangles).
- In an **oblique pyramid,** the base is a regular polygon but all lateral faces do not have the same size and shape.
- The name of the pyramid is influenced by the shape of the base.

EXAMPLE 10.28   Identify the shape of the base and the other faces in the pyramid. Then name the pyramid.

CONNECTION

REPRESENTATION

a. 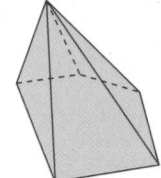   b. 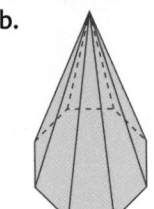   c.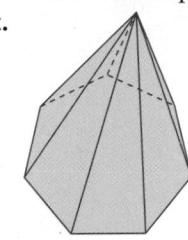

SOLUTION

a. The base is a pentagon, but it is not a regular pentagon. The polyhedron is a pentagonal pyramid.

b. The base is a regular octagon. The lateral faces have the shape of congruent isosceles triangles. The polyhedron is a regular octagonal pyramid.

c. The base is a regular heptagon. The lateral faces do not have the shape of congruent isosceles triangles or congruent equilateral triangles. The polyhedron is an oblique heptagonal pyramid.

Euler's Formula

CONNECTION

REASONING

Leonhard Euler (1707–1783) discovered an interesting relationship among the number of vertices V, the number of faces F (the number of bases and lateral faces), and the number of edges E of any convex polyhedron. The resulting equation is called **Euler's formula.** Some homework questions at the end of this section ask you to use patterns and inductive reasoning to rediscover the formula. The following Classroom Connection illustrates how some elementary school students learn the relationship.

> ◆◆ **Classroom Connection**
>
> ● *Math,* Grade 6, p. 539
>
> What pattern do you notice about the sum of the number of faces, F, and vertices, V, in a polyhedron compared to the number of edges, E? (© 2000 Macmillan/McGraw Hill. Reprinted by permission.)

Some homework questions at the end of this section will help you discover other relationships, such as the relationship between the number of edges of a prism and the number of vertices of a prism, or between the number of faces of a pyramid and the number of edges of the pyramid.

The following Historical Note suggests a relationship between language and notation.

 Historical Note

Mathematicians typically used the first letter of the key word to represent the number of vertices, faces, and edges in a convex polyhedron. They chose abbreviations in the language in which they were writing, and Latin was a common language known by mathematicians and scientists. For example, Euler used S = *numerus angulorum solidorum* (vertices), H = *numerus hedrarum* (faces), and A = *numerus acierum* (edges), whereas German writers usually use the letters k = *kanten* (vertices), f = *flächen* (faces), and e = *ecken* (edges).

The Five Regular Polyhedrons (Platonic Solids)

Figure 36 shows regular polygons and their interior angles.

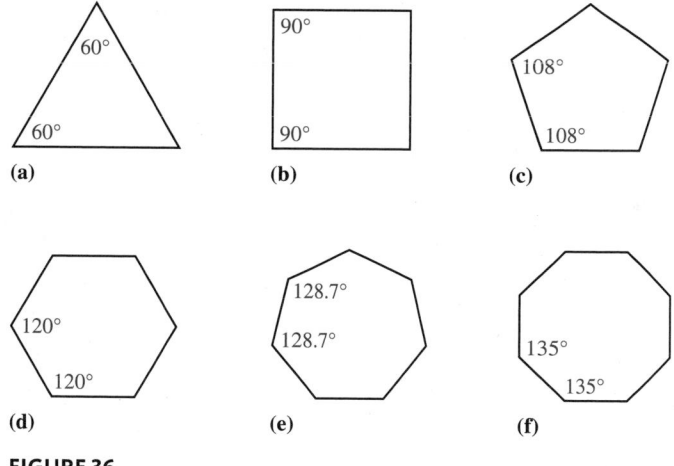

FIGURE 36
Some regular polygons.

A **regular polyhedron** (also called a **Platonic solid**) is a convex polyhedron such that
- the faces are congruent regular polygonal regions.
- each vertex is formed by the intersection of the same number of faces.

There are exactly five regular polyhedrons. Figure 37 illustrates the possibilities and their corresponding nets. A **net** is a two-dimensional figure that can be folded to make a three-dimensional object. The polygonal regions are joined by their edges in the net. The regular tetrahedron consists of 4 congruent triangular faces. The regular hexahedron (cube) consists of 6 congruent square faces. The regular octahedron consists of 8 congruent triangular faces. The regular dodecahedron consists of 12 congruent pentagonal faces. The regular icosahedron consists of 20 congruent triangular faces.

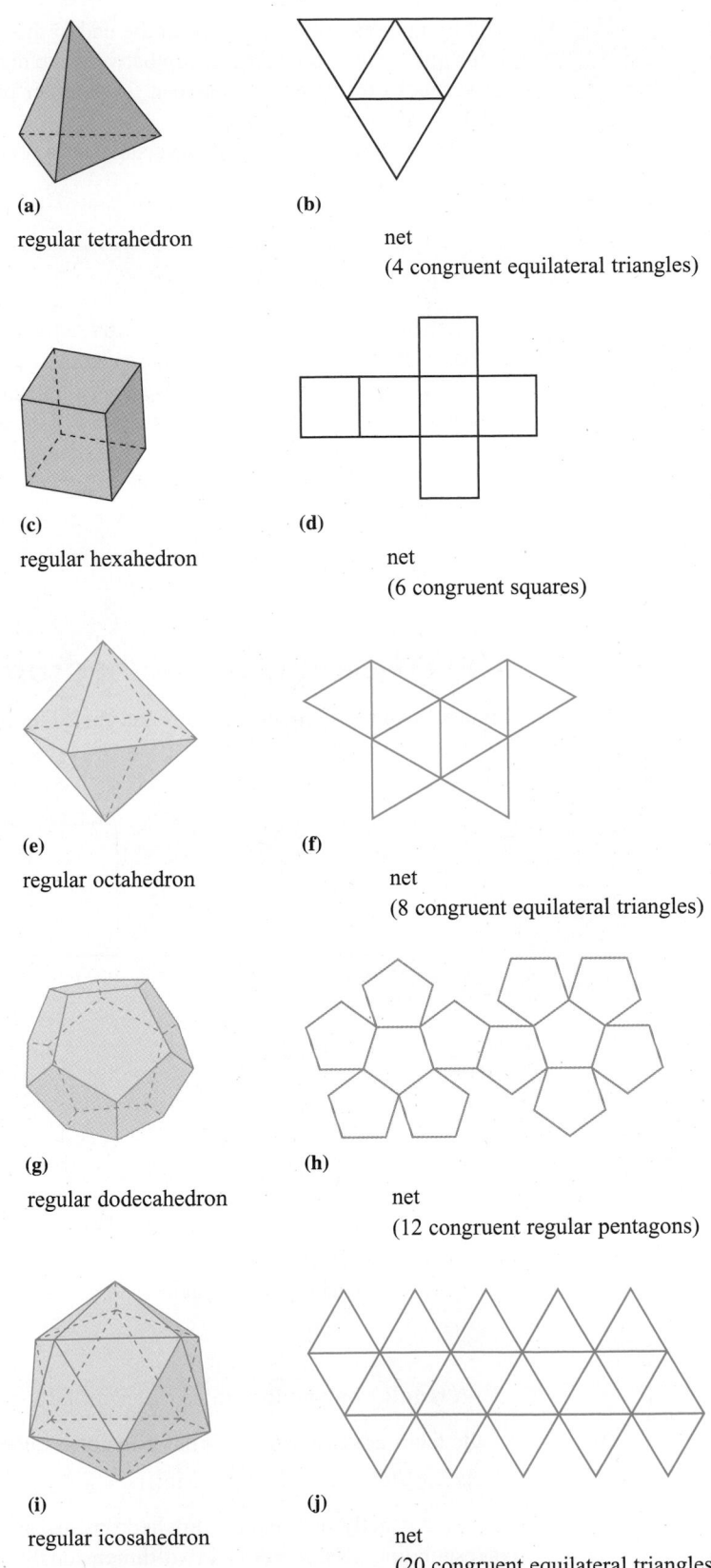

(a)
regular tetrahedron

(b)
net
(4 congruent equilateral triangles)

(c)
regular hexahedron

(d)
net
(6 congruent squares)

(e)
regular octahedron

(f)
net
(8 congruent equilateral triangles)

(g)
regular dodecahedron

(h)
net
(12 congruent regular pentagons)

(i)
regular icosahedron

(j)
net
(20 congruent equilateral triangles)

FIGURE 37
There are exactly five regular polyhedrons.

Why There Are Exactly Five Regular Polyhedrons

The ancient Greeks studied regular polyhedrons with faces that have the shape of equilateral triangles (tetrahedron, octahedron, and icosahedron), squares (hexahedron), and pentagons (dodecahedron). Could there be a regular polyhedron composed of faces that have the shape of regular n-gons for $n \geq 6$? To answer this question, let's build on what we know. Study the shaded regions in the nets of the regular octahedron and dodecahedron in Figure 38. They suggest the *sum* of the interior angles that share a common vertex must be *less* than 360° because of the "missing" wedge. Our informal answer to the question hinges on this informal observation.

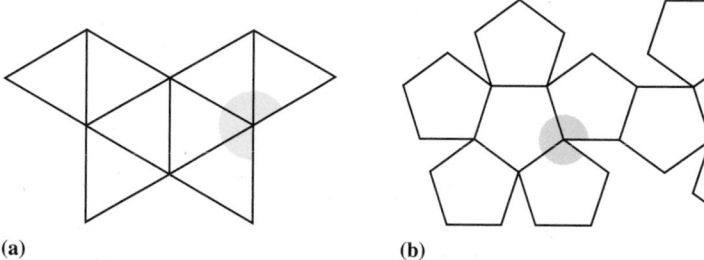

(a)   (b)

FIGURE 38
The sum of the interior angles that share a common vertex is less than 360°.

Here's why there are no regular polyhedrons with regular hexagonal faces. Figure 39 shows a regular hexagon *ABCDEF* with diagonals from vertex *B*.

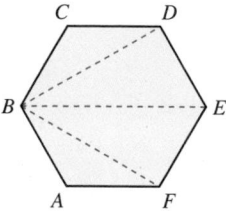

FIGURE 39
The diagonals decompose the regular hexagon into four triangles.

As we learned in Section 10.2, the sum of the interior angles of a regular hexagon $(n = 6)$ is $(6 - 2) \cdot 180° = 4 \cdot 180°$. The interior angles of a regular hexagon are congruent, so each interior angle must have the measure $4 \cdot 180°/6$, which equals 120°. Each vertex of a polyhedron is formed by the intersection of at least three faces (see Example 10.25). This means that the sum of the interior angles that share a common vertex in a regular polyhedron with hexagonal faces must be *at least* $120° + 120° + 120° = 360°$. But we observed in Figure 38 that the sum of the measures of the angles at a vertex in a regular polyhedron must be *less* than 360°. This suggests a regular polyhedron with hexagonal faces cannot exist. The measure of the interior angles in a regular polygon increases as the number of sides increases, so regular polyhedrons composed of heptagonal faces cannot exist either. A homework question at the end of this section asks you to follow this line of reasoning to confirm that a regular polyhedron with heptagonal faces cannot exist.

Cones, Cylinders, and Spheres

The surface of polyhedral solids is composed of polygonal regions. The surface of non-polyhedral solids, such as the examples in Figures 40 and 41, includes nonpolygonal (curved) regions.

A **cylinder** is a solid that consists of two circular bases that lie in parallel planes, a lateral surface, and the region they enclose (see Figure 40). The bases of a cylinder are congruent, circular regions that lie in parallel planes. The lateral surface of a cylinder is the set of parallel line segments that connect points from one base to corresponding points in the other base. In a right cylinder, the line segments are perpendicular to the bases. Otherwise, the cylinder is called an oblique cylinder. A cylinder is similar to a prism.

REPRESENTATION

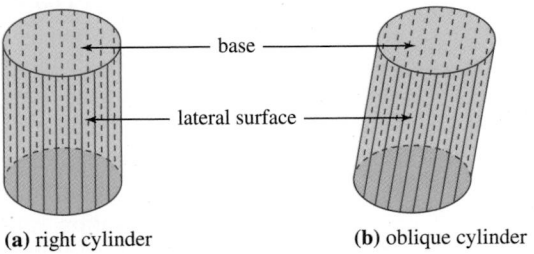

(a) right cylinder   **(b)** oblique cylinder

FIGURE 40
Examples of cylinders.

A **cone** is a solid that consists of a circular base, an apex, and a lateral surface (see Figure 41). The base of a cone is the union of a circle and the region it encloses. The apex is a point that lies outside the plane containing the base. The lateral surface of the cone is the set of line segments that connect the apex to all points on the boundary of the base. In a right cone, the line segments in the lateral surface extending from the apex to the base have the same length. Otherwise, the cone is called an oblique cone. A cone is similar to a pyramid. A **sphere** consists of all points that are a fixed distance (radius) from a given point (center).

REPRESENTATION

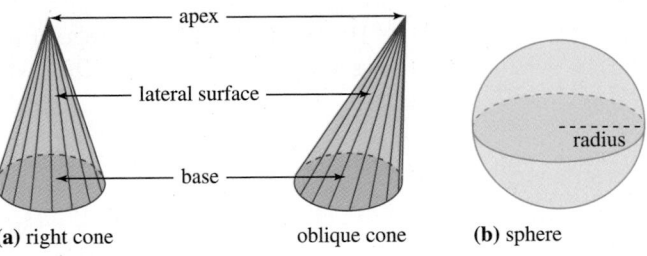

(a) right cone   oblique cone   **(b)** sphere

FIGURE 41
Examples of cones and spheres.

Although these solids are not polyhedrons, they still have many real-life applications.

QUESTIONS FOR SECTION 10.3

REPRESENTATION

Refresher: Representations (language, diagrams, tables, symbols, algebra, manipulatives, and contextualized situations) are important because we use them to organize, record, and communicate mathematical ideas and make them more comprehensible.

1. Name the bases of the prism.

   a.

   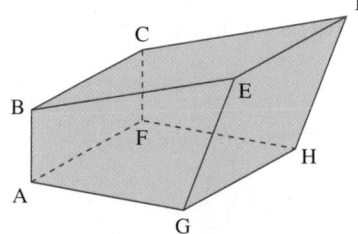

   b.

   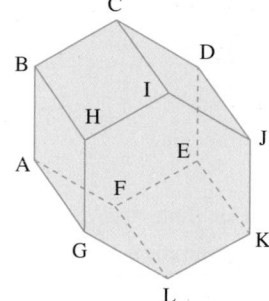

2. Use the given labels to answer the questions about the right prism.

   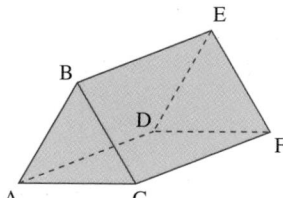

   a. Name the vertices.
   b. Name the vertices hidden from view.
   c. Name the lateral faces.
   d. Name the lateral faces hidden from view.
   e. Name the edges.
   f. Name the edges hidden from view.
   g. Name the bases.
   h. Write a descriptive name of the prism (without using the labels).

3. The diagram shows two right prisms. What do their lateral faces have in common?

   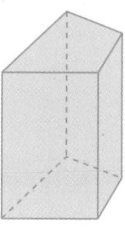 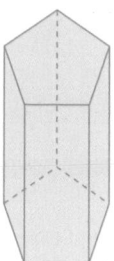

4. The diagram shows two regular prisms.

   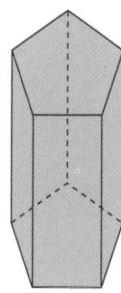 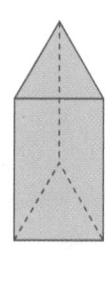

   a. What do their bases have in common?
   b. What do their lateral faces have in common?

5. Follow these steps to draw a triangular prism.

   1. Draw a base.

   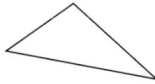

   2. Draw another copy of the base slightly lower than the first one.

   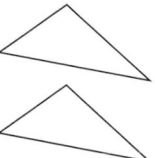

   3. Draw the edges by connecting corresponding vertices.

   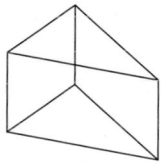

   4. Use dashed lines to indicate hidden edges.

   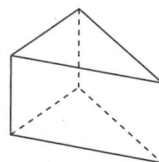

Apply these steps to draw the following prisms.

   a. regular hexagonal prism   **b.** right pentagonal prism

6. Study the diagrams of the regular pyramids.

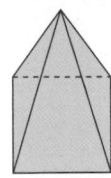
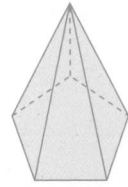

   regular square   regular pentagonal
      pyramid   pyramid

   a. What type of triangle do the lateral faces form?

   b. What do the bases have in common?

7. Explain why the polyhedron is not a regular pyramid.

   a.   **b.**

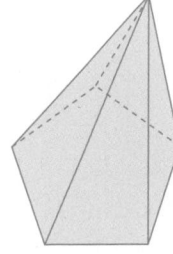
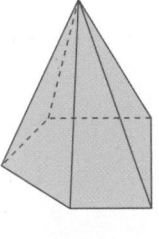

8. Follow these steps to draw a triangular pyramid.

   1. Draw the base.

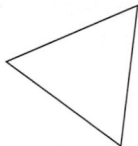

   2. Draw the apex.

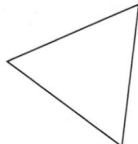

   3. Draw the edges by connecting the apex to the vertices of the base.

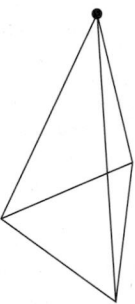

   4. Use dashed lines to indicate hidden edges.

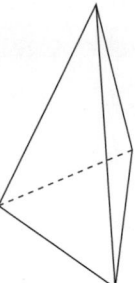

Apply these steps to draw the following pyramids.

   a. rectangular pyramid   **b.** pentagonal pyramid

9. Use the given labels to answer the questions about the oblique pyramid.

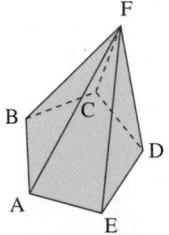

   a. Name the vertices.

   b. Name the vertices hidden from view.

   c. Name the lateral faces.

   d. Name the lateral faces hidden from view.

   e. Name the edges.   **f.** Name the edges hidden from view.

   g. Name the base.

   h. Write a descriptive name of the pyramid (without using the labels).

10. Identify the polyhedron corresponding to the net.

   a.   **b.**

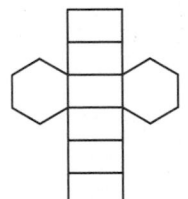
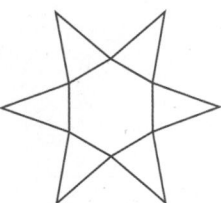

11. A teacher asked his students to think about what the name of a regular polyhedron refers to. After a few minutes, Kendra exclaimed, "The name refers to the number of faces!" Daniel shouted, "The name refers to the number of vertices!" Explain who is correct.

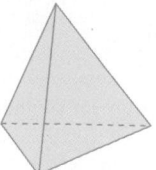
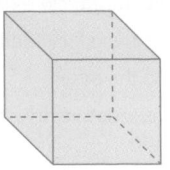

     regular   regular
   tetrahedron   hexahedron

PROBLEM SOLVING

Refresher: Problem solving (reaching a goal that is not immediately attainable) is important because it helps students think more deeply about what they know and deal with unfamiliar situations.

12. Let F represent the number of faces (base and lateral faces), let V represent the number of vertices, and let E represent the number of edges of the pyramid.

    a. Complete the table.

Type of pyramid	F	V	$F + V$	E
triangular	4	4	8	6
square				
pentagonal				
hexagonal				

    b. Write an equation (called Euler's formula) that relates F, V, and E for pyramids.

13. Let F represent the number of faces (bases and lateral faces), let V represent the number of vertices, and let E represent the number of edges of the prism.

    a. Complete the table.

Type of prism	F	V	$F + V$	E
triangular	5	6	11	9
square				
pentagonal				
hexagonal				

    b. Write an equation (called Euler's formula) that relates F, V, and E for prisms.

REASONING AND PROOF

Refresher: Reasoning and proof (thinking and justifying) are important because they help students make sense of mathematics.

14. A teacher showed her class three solids: a cone, a pyramid, and a prism. Then she asked her students to identify the solid that does not belong. After a few minutes, Olivia shouted, "The cone does not belong!" Then Leon exclaimed, "The prism does not belong!"

    a. Explain how Olivia could be correct.

    b. Explain how Leon could be correct.

15. A teacher showed her class three solids: a cone, a prism, and a cylinder. Then she asked her students to identify the solid that does not belong. After a few minutes, Pedro shouted, "The cone does not belong!" Then Leila exclaimed, "The prism does not belong!"

    a. Explain how Pedro could be correct.

    b. Explain how Leila could be correct.

16. What do all oblique pyramids have in common?

17. What do regular prisms and regular pyramids have in common?

18. What do the regular tetrahedron, octahedron, and icosahedron have in common?

CONNECTIONS

Refresher: Connections (linking and applying mathematical ideas) are important because they deepen student understanding and make mathematics more meaningful, flexible, and useful.

19. Fill in the blank: We name a polygon according to the number of _____. We name a polyhedron according to the number of _____.

20. Let F represent the number of faces (bases and lateral faces), let V represent the number of vertices, and let E represent the number of edges of the prism. Let n represent the number of sides of a polygonal base.

    a. Use the prisms shown to complete the table.

    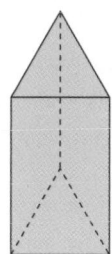 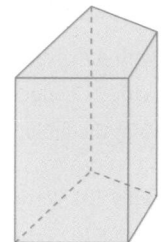 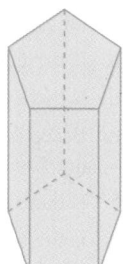

n	V	E	F
3	6	9	5
4			
5			

    b. Based on the pattern in the table, write an equation involving E and n.

    c. Is there a prism with 456 edges? Show your work.

    d. Is there a prism with 314 edges? Show your work.

    e. Based on the pattern in the table, write an equation involving V and n.

    f. Is there a prism with 217 vertices? Show your work.

    g. Is there a prism with 826 vertices? Show your work.

    h. Based on the pattern in the table, write an equation involving F and n.

    i. Is there a prism with 419 faces? Show your work.

    j. Is there a prism with 628 faces? Show your work.

k. Suppose a prism has 678 edges. How many vertices does it have?

l. Suppose a prism has 742 vertices. How many edges does it have?

21. Let F represent the number of faces (bases and lateral faces), let V represent the number of vertices, and let E represent the number of edges of the pyramid. Let n represent the number of sides of the polygonal base.

a. Use the pyramids shown to complete the table.

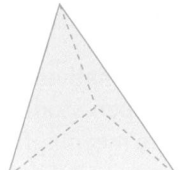 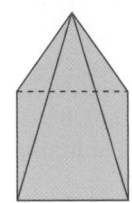 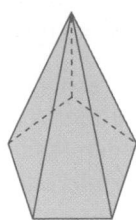

n	V	E	F
3	4	6	4
4			
5			

b. Based on the pattern in the table, write an equation involving E and n.

c. Is there a pyramid with 456 edges? Show your work.

d. Is there a pyramid with 777 edges? Show your work.

e. Based on the pattern in the table, write an equation involving V and n.

f. Is there a pyramid with 201 vertices? Show your work.

g. Is there a pyramid with 826 vertices? Show your work.

h. Based on the pattern in the table, write an equation involving F and n.

i. Is there a pyramid with 419 faces? Show your work.

j. Is there a pyramid with 628 faces? Show your work.

k. Suppose a pyramid has 678 edges. How many vertices does it have?

l. Suppose a pyramid has 742 vertices. How many edges does it have?

22. Answer the following.

a. A pyramid has 28 faces. How many lateral faces does it have?

b. A pyramid has 403 faces. How many edges does it have?

23. Determine whether the polyhedron could be a prism, pyramid, both, or neither: The number of edges of the polyhedron is always a multiple of

a. 2.   **b.** 3.   **c.** 5.

COMMUNICATION

Refresher: Communication (written and verbal explanations using representations and proper mathematical vocabulary) is important because it helps students refine and strengthen their understanding.

24. Answer the following.

a. What is a regular polygon?

b. What is a regular polyhedron?

25. Ancient Romans played dice games with dice in the shape of regular polyhedrons.

a. Why do you think they preferred regular polyhedrons?

b. Why are many dice games played with dice in the shape of a regular hexahedron rather than a regular tetrahedron?

26. Use appropriate vocabulary to describe the intersection of

a. two faces of a prism.   **b.** three faces of a prism.

27. Use appropriate vocabulary to describe the intersection of

a. two faces of a pyramid.   **b.** three faces of a pyramid.

28. Explain how prisms and cylinders are alike.

29. Explain how pyramids and cones are alike.

30. How are the lateral faces of a regular prism and regular pyramid

a. alike?   **b.** different?

31. Explain why a sphere is not a polyhedron.

32. Explain why a cylinder is not a polyhedron.

More practice with the ideas of the section

33. Fill in the blank. Choose one of the following words or phrases: *acute, apex, base, baseball, cone, cylinder, edges, faces, fences, irregular polygon, lateral faces, left, net, oblique, oblique pyramid, obtuse, parallelogram, pentagon, polygon, polyhedron, prism, rectangle, regular polygon, regular prism, regular pyramid, right, sides, square, triangle, triangles,* or *vertices.*

a. The three main parts of a polyhedron are faces, vertices, and _____.

b. We can name a polyhedron according to the number of _____.

c. A(n) _____ is similar to a pyramid, because each has an apex.

d. The name of a pyramid is influenced by the shape of the _____.

e. The lateral faces of a(n) _____ prism are rectangles.

f. In a regular pyramid, the lateral faces are congruent _____.

g. The _____ is the intersection of all lateral faces of the pyramid.

h. In a(n) _____, the base is a regular polygon but the lateral faces do not have the same size and shape.

i. In a(n) _____, the lateral faces have the shapes of congruent isosceles triangles or congruent equilateral triangles.

j. The bases of a(n) _____ are congruent, circular regions that lie in parallel planes.

k. The lateral faces of a(n) _____ prism are parallelograms without any right angles.

l. A(n) _____ is a two-dimensional model of the surface of a three-dimensional object.

34. Answer the following questions.

   a. What is a polygon?   **b.** What is a polyhedron?

35. The base of a pyramid has *n* sides.

   a. How many lateral faces does the pyramid have?

   b. How many faces does the pyramid have?

36. The base of a prism has *n* sides.

   a. How many lateral faces does the prism have?

   b. How many faces does the prism have?

37. What is the shape of each lateral face of

   a. an oblique prism?   **b.** a right prism?

38. What is the shape of each lateral face of

   a. an oblique pyramid?   **b.** a regular pyramid?

39. Face *ABHG* and face *EDJK* in the given diagram are congruent polygonal regions that lie in parallel planes. A teacher asks the class whether these faces could be bases of the prism. After a few moments, Maria says, "Yes, because they are congruent polygons that lie in parallel planes." How would you respond?

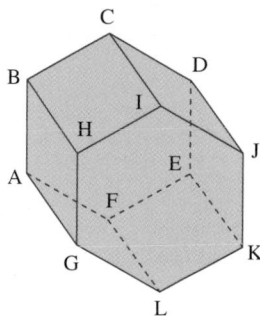

40. Fill in the blanks to complete the argument that a regular polyhedron with heptagonal faces cannot exist.

regular
heptagon

   a. The measure of each interior angle of a regular _____ with *n* sides is $\dfrac{(n-2)\cdot 180}{n}$ degrees.

   b. The measure of each interior angle of a regular heptagon is about _____.

   c. Each vertex of a polyhedron is formed by the intersection of at least _____ faces.

   d. This means the sum of the interior angles that share a common vertex in a regular polyhedron with heptagonal faces must be *at least* _____.

   e. But we initially observed the sum must be _____ than 360°. This suggests a regular polyhedron with heptagonal faces cannot exist.

41. Explain why a soccer ball is not a regular polyhedron.

42. Name the solid.

   a. It has parallel bases, and the lateral faces are rectangles.

   b. The lateral faces are congruent isosceles triangles, and the base is a regular polygon.

43. Name the solid.

   a. It has parallel bases, and the lateral faces are parallelograms.

   b. The base is a polygon, the faces are triangles, and the triangles meet at a point.

44. Two students were gazing at a geometric object the teacher drew on the board. Then she asked her students to use vocabulary they had discussed to describe it. Ken exclaimed, "It is an example of a pentagonal pyramid!" The teacher asked if there was another way to describe the object. Fred said, "It is an example of a hexahedron." Could both students be correct? Explain your answer.

45. A teacher announces to the class that two faces of a polyhedron are face *ABCD* and face *CDEF*. Then she asks her students what they can say about the polyhedron. Luis thinks about this for a few minutes and then says, "The polyhedron cannot be a pyramid." Why is Luis correct?

46. A teacher announces to the class that two faces of a polyhedron are face *ABCD* and face *EFGH*. Then she asks her students what they can say about the polyhedron. Kyla thinks about this for a few moments and then shouts, "The polyhedron could be a prism!" Why is Kyla correct?

47. A teacher announces to the class that two faces of a polyhedron are face *ABC* and face *DEF*. Then she asks her students what they can say about the polyhedron. Pedro thinks about this for a few moments and then exclaims, "The polyhedron cannot be a pyramid!" Why is Pedro correct?

48. Explain why a regular tetrahedron is a pyramid.

49. How many faces intersect to form a vertex in the given polyhedron?

   a. regular tetrahedron   **b.** regular hexahedron

   c. regular octahedron   **d.** regular dodecahedron

   e. regular icosahedron

Multiple choice questions

Choose the correct answer for each multiple choice question.

50. What is the minimum number of faces that intersect to form a vertex of a polyhedron?

   a. one   **b.** two   **c.** three   **d.** four

   e. a number not listed here

51. A polyhedron with seven faces is called

   a. a heptagon.   **b.** a heptahedron.   **c.** a nonahedron.

   d. an octahedron.   **e.** a shape not listed here.

52. A pyramid has four lateral faces. The pyramid is also an example of a

   a. pentahedron.   **b.** hexahedron.   **c.** heptahedron.

   d. tetrahedron.   **e.** shape not listed here.

53. How many faces does a hexagonal prism have?

   a. 6   **b.** 7   **c.** 8   **d.** 18   **e.** a number not listed here

54. The base of a prism is a polygon with 125 sides. How many edges does the prism have?

a. 125   **b.** 250   **c.** 500   **d.** 750

e. a number not listed here

55. The base of a pyramid is a polygon with 200 sides. How many faces does the pyramid have?

a. 199   **b.** 200   **c.** 201   **d.** 600

e. a number not listed here

CHAPTER 10 REVIEW

CHAPTER 10 Organizer

Section	What You Should Learn	Review Problems
10.1	**1.** Be familiar with the vocabulary and notation for geometric objects or situations.	1
	2. Describe or recognize point relationships or line relationships.	2–4
	3. Classify angles as acute, right, straight, obtuse, or reflex.	5–6
	4. Solve problems involving angle relationships.	7–8
	5. Determine the measure of angles using the angle addition postulate or a protractor.	9–11
10.2	**1.** Identify pairs of angles and know their relationships.	12–14
	2. Solve problems involving complementary and supplementary angles.	15–16
	3. Know and apply the *F* Postulate: Two lines cut by a transversal are parallel if and only if any two corresponding angles created by the transversal are congruent.	17–19
	4. Classify triangles according to their angles or sides.	20–21
	5. Know that the sum of the angles of a triangle is 180°.	22–23
	6. Know that the sum of the angles of a quadrilateral is 360°.	24
	7. Calculate the sum of the angles of a polygon or the measure of an interior or exterior angle of a regular polygon.	25–27
	8. Identify the parts of a polygon: side, vertex, diagonal, interior angle, and exterior angle.	28
	9. Identify and draw common quadrilaterals, and know how they are related.	29–30
	10. Characterize curves using terms such as closed curve, simple curve, polygonal curve, and polygon.	31
10.3	**1.** Label the parts of a prism and pyramid.	32–33
	2. Classify polyhedrons.	34–36
	3. Know the relationship between the number of sides of a base of a prism (*n*) and its number of faces (*F*), edges (*E*), or vertices (*V*).	37–38
	4. Know the relationship between the number of sides of the base of a pyramid (*n*) and its number of faces (*F*), edges (*E*), or vertices (*V*).	39–40
	5. Know there are exactly five regular polyhedrons (or Platonic solids).	41
	6. Classify cylinders and cones.	42
	7. Identify or draw possible nets of prisms, pyramids, cylinders, and cones.	43–46
	8. Relate real-world three-dimensional objects and geometric terminology	47

Key Terms and Concepts

geometry 555	supplementary angles 573	simple closed surface 594
point 557	adjacent angles 574	polyhedron 595
line 557	vertical angles 574	face 595
plane 557	transversal 575	vertex 595
collinear 558	corresponding angles 576	edge 595
noncollinear 558	alternate interior angles 576	prism 597
coplanar 558	alternate exterior angles 576	bases 597
noncoplanar 558	curve 578	lateral faces 597
concurrent lines 559	polygon 578	right prism 597
parallel lines 559	side 579	oblique prism 597
transversal 559	vertex 579	regular prism 597
skew lines 559	diagonal 579	pyramid 598
line segment 559	interior of a polygon 580	base 598
endpoints 559	exterior of a polygon 580	lateral faces 598
distance 559	interior angle 580	apex 598
ray 559	exterior angle 580	regular pyramid 598
postulates 560	triangle 580	oblique pyramid 598
angle 562	acute triangle 580	Euler's formula 598
side 562	obtuse triangle 580	regular polyhedron 599
vertex 562	right triangle 580	Platonic solid 599
interior of an angle 563	scalene triangle 581	net 599
exterior of an angle 563	isosceles triangle 581	cylinder 602
degree 563	equilateral triangle 581	cone 602
protractor 563	quadrilateral 584	lateral surface of a cylinder 602
measure of an angle 563	parallelogram 584	bases of a cylinder 602
acute angle 565	rectangle 584	right cylinder 602
right angle 565	square 584	oblique cylinder 602
obtuse angle 565	rhombus 584	apex of a cone 602
straight angle 565	trapezoid 584	lateral surface of a cone 602
reflex angle 565	kite 584	right cone 602
perpendicular lines 566	regular polygon 586	oblique cone 602
congruent line segments 566	measures of angles in a regular polygon 587	sphere 602
midpoint 567		
complementary angles 573		

Review Questions

1. Express each situation using mathematical notation.

   a. $\overline{XY}$ is congruent to $\overline{DE}$.

   b. $\overleftrightarrow{RT}$ and $\overleftrightarrow{UV}$ are parallel.

   c. $\angle A$ is congruent to $\angle X$.

2. Determine whether the phrase is associated with a point relationship, a line relationship, or both.

   a. collinear   **b.** skew   **c.** concurrent   **d.** parallel

   e. coplanar   **f.** between   **g.** perpendicular

3. Identify the point relationship indicated by the diagram.

   a. 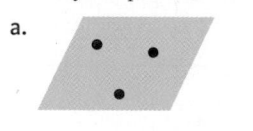   **b.**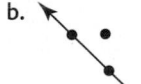

   c. 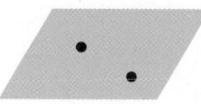   **d.**

4. Identify the line relationship indicated by the diagram.

   a.

   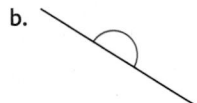

   b.

   c.

5. Classify the angle as acute, right, straight, obtuse, or reflex.

   a. m∠ABC = 145°   b. m∠ABC = 90°

   c. m∠ABC = 23°   d. m∠ABC = 180°

   e. m∠ABC = 225°

6. Classify the angle as acute, right, straight, obtuse, or reflex.

   a.   b.

   c.   d.

   e.

7. ∠A and ∠B are supplementary angles. m∠A is 12° more than three times m∠B. Find m∠A and m∠B. Solve this problem using the

   a. Draw a Diagram strategy.

   b. Solve an Equation strategy.

8. The measure of ∠A is 8° fewer than four times the measure of ∠B. The sum of their measures is 202°. Find m∠A and m∠B.

9. Measure ∠ABC and ∠DBA.

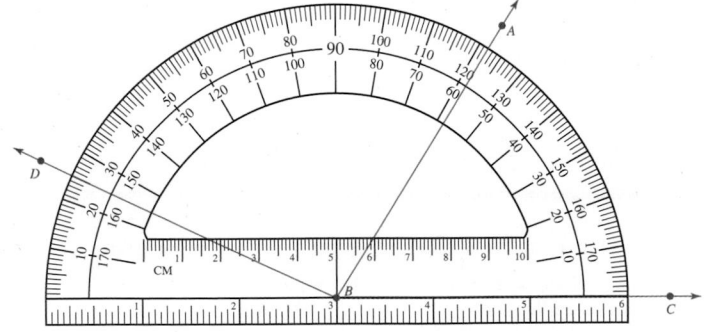

10. In the given illustration, assume m∠APB = 50°, m∠CPE = 95°, and m∠BPD = 102°. Use the angle addition postulate to calculate each angle.

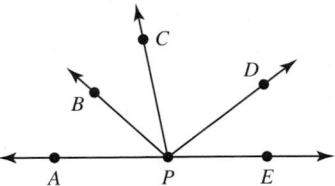

    a. m∠DPE   b. m∠BPC

11. Use the measurements m∠DBE = 60°, m∠FBD = 100°, and m∠ABE = m∠DBC and the given diagram to determine m∠ABD and m∠FBA. The diagram is not drawn to scale, so do not use a protractor to measure the angles.

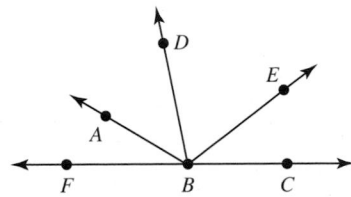

12. Write an appropriate name for each pair of marked angles.

    a.   b.

    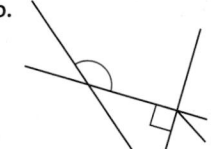

    c.   d.

    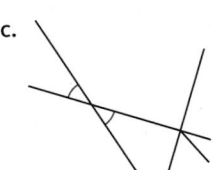   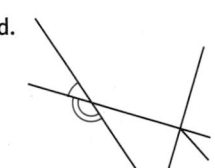

    e.   f.

    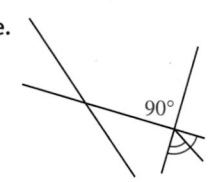   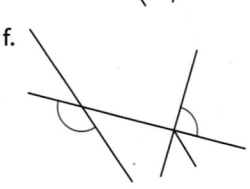

13. In the given diagram, m∠CFE = 140°, m∠AFB = 35°, and B, F, and E are collinear. Find m∠CFD.

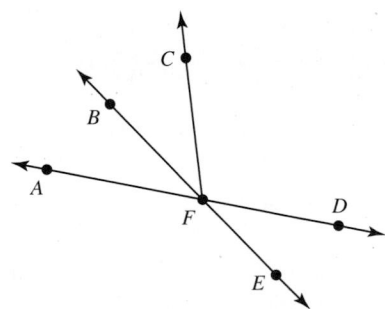

14. What is wrong with this diagram?

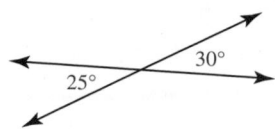

15. ∠T and ∠Q are complementary angles. m∠T is 6° less than five times m∠Q. Find m∠T and m∠Q. Solve this problem using the Solve an Equation strategy.

16. Two angles are supplementary angles. One angle is 21° more than twice the other angle. Find the measure of the larger angle. Solve this problem using the Solve an Equation strategy.

17. Are the horizontal lines parallel? Explain your answer. The diagrams may not be drawn to scale.

a.

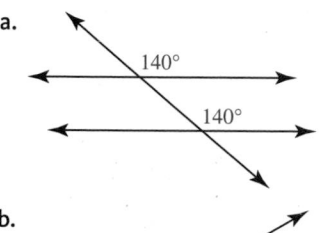

b.

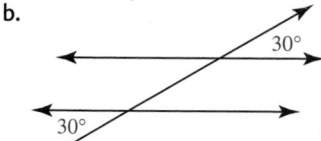

c.

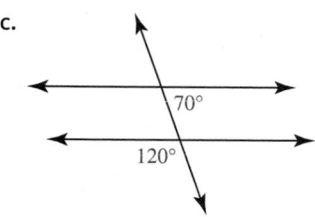

18. Why are $\overleftrightarrow{AC}$ and $\overleftrightarrow{DB}$ parallel?

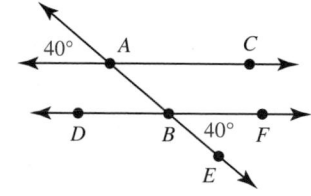

19. *ABCD* is a parallelogram.

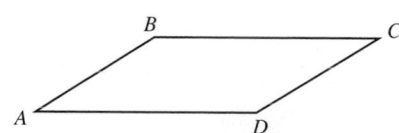

    a. Prove ∠A and ∠B are supplementary.

    b. Prove ∠B is congruent to ∠D.

20. Classify the triangle. Choose all that apply: *acute triangle, obtuse triangle, right triangle, scalene triangle, isosceles triangle,* or *equilateral triangle.*

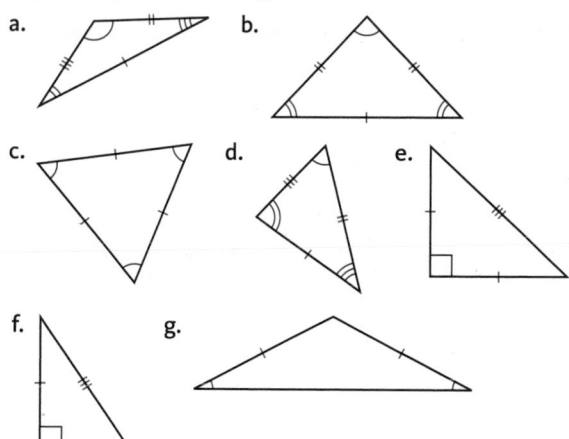

21. On the dot paper, draw the specified triangle.

    a. acute isosceles triangle   **b.** right isosceles triangle

    c. acute scalene triangle

22. Find m∠1.

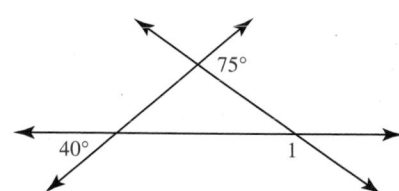

23. Suppose ΔABC is a right triangle, where ∠A is the right angle. What is the relationship between ∠B and ∠C?

24. Determine the measure of ∠1.

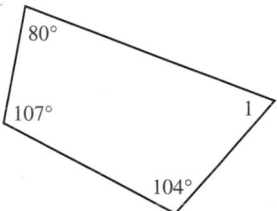

25. Do the following.

    a. Verify that the sum of the interior angles in a polygon with 40 sides is 6840°.

    b. Verify that in a regular polygon with 40 sides, each interior angle has the measure 171°.

26. What is the sum of the interior angles in each polygon?

a.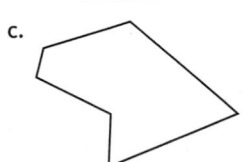
b.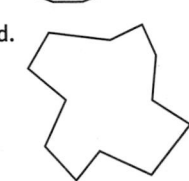

c.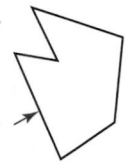
d.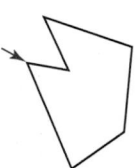

27. I am thinking of a regular polygon. The measure of each interior angle is 162°. How many sides does the regular polygon have? Show your work.

28. Name the indicated geometric object associated with the polygon.

a.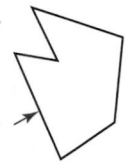
b.
c.

d.
e.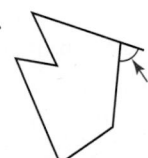
f.

29. The Venn diagram shows the relationships among polygons with four sides. Identify the regions marked with letters (choose from the following: *kite, parallelogram, quadrilateral, rectangle, rhombus, square,* or *trapezoid*).

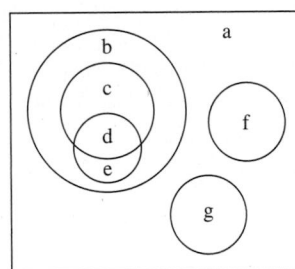

30. Draw the specified quadrilateral on the dot paper.

    a. parallelogram   **b.** trapezoid   **c.** rhombus

31. Explain why the curve is not a polygon.

a.   b.   c.

32. Name the indicated part of the prism.

a.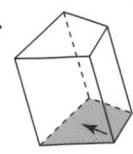
b.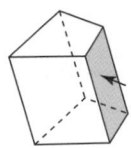

c.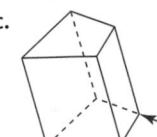
d.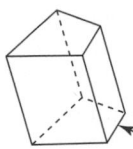

33. Name the indicated part of the pyramid.

a.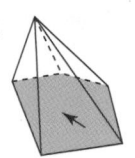
b.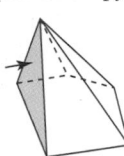
c.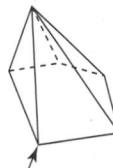

d.
e.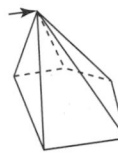

34. Name the pyramid.

a.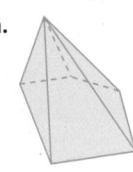
b.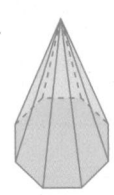
c.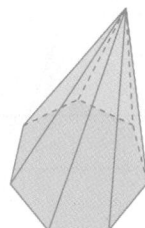

35. Explain why the polyhedron is not a regular pyramid.

a.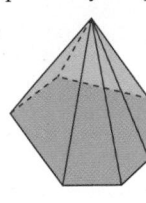
b.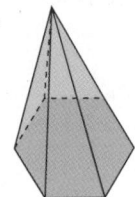

36. Name the prism.

a.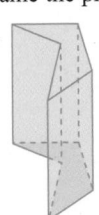
b.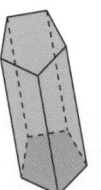
c.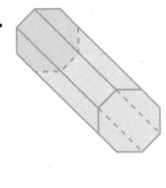

37. For a prism with a base that is an *n*-gon, let F represent the number of faces, E represent the number of edges, and V represent the number of vertices of the prism.

    a. Which equation expresses the relationship between n and F? Choose $F = n - 2$, $F = n + 2$, $F = n - 1$, $F = n + 1$, $F = 2n - 2$, $F = 2n$, $F = 2n + 2$, or $F = 3n$.

b. Which equation expresses the relationship between n and E? Choose $E = n - 2$, $E = n + 2$, $E = n - 1$, $E = n + 1$, $E = 2n - 2$, $E = 2n$, $E = 2n + 2$, or $E = 3n$.

c. Which equation expresses the relationship between n and V? Choose $V = n - 2$, $V = n + 2$, $V = n - 1$, $V = n - 1$, $V = 2n - 2$, $V = 2n$, $V = 2n + 2$, or $V = 3n$.

38. Consider a pentagonal prism.

a. How many faces does it have?

b. How many edges does it have?

c. How many vertices does it have?

39. For a pyramid with a base that is an n-gon, let F represent the number of faces, E represent the number of edges, and V represent the number of vertices of the pyramid.

a. Which equation expresses the relationship between n and F? Choose $F = n - 2$, $F = n - 1$, $F = n + 1$, $F = 2n - 2$, $F = 2n$, $F = 2n + 2$, or $F = 3n$.

b. Which equation expresses the relationship between n and E? Choose $E = n - 2$, $E = n - 1$, $E = n + 1$, $E = 2n - 2$, $E = 2n$, $E = 2n + 2$, or $E = 3n$.

c. Which equation expresses the relationship between n and V? Choose $V = n - 2$, $V = n - 1$, $V = n + 1$, $V = 2n - 2$, $V = 2n$, $V = 2n + 2$, or $V = 3n$.

40. Answer the following questions about a hexagonal pyramid.

a. How many faces does it have?

b. How many edges does it have?

c. How many vertices does it have?

41. Answer the following.

a. What is a regular polygon?

b. How many regular polygons are there?

c. What is a regular polyhedron?

d. How many regular polyhedrons are there?

42. Name the solid.

a. 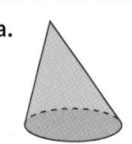   b.

c. 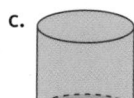   d.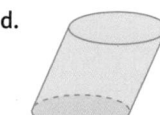

43. The diagram shows the net of a solid. What is the type of the solid?

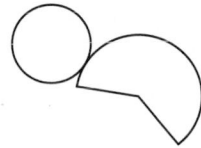

44. The diagram shows the net of a solid. What is the type of the solid?

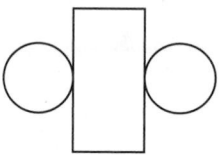

45. Explain why the given diagram cannot be the net of a solid.

46. A net for a quadrilateral pyramid is shown. Explain why $AH = AE$. The net is not drawn to scale.

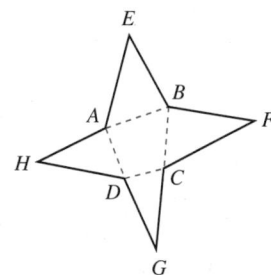

47. The first list contains real-world objects. The second list contains names of geometric shapes. Which geometric terminology best describes the given object? Some geometric shapes may not be matched to a given real-world object, and some may be used more than once.

Real-world object	Geometric shape
a. sun	(i) rectangular prism
b. book	(ii) triangular prism
c. doorstop	(iii) cube
d. can of soup	(iv) pentagonal prism
e. pup tent	(v) octagonal pyramid
f. die	(vi) sphere
g. coin	(vii) cylinder
h. Quonset hut	(viii) cone
i. house	(ix) square pyramid
j. Egyptian pyramid	(x) hemisphere
k. soap bubbles on water	(xi) simple closed curve
l. teepee	(xii) semi-cylinder

Chapter 10 Test

1. *Be familiar with the vocabulary and notation for geometric objects or situations.*

   a. How many names can you find for the line using only the labeled points?

   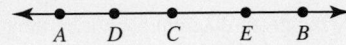

   b. How many names can you find for the plane using the labeled points?

   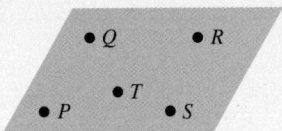

2. *Be familiar with the vocabulary and notation for geometric objects or situations.*

   a. How are $\overleftrightarrow{PQ}$ and *ABC* alike?

   b. How are $\overrightarrow{PQ}$ and $\angle ABC$ alike?

3. *Classify angles as acute, right, straight, obtuse, or reflex.* Trace $\overline{BC}$ onto your paper. Then sketch or shade the portion of the plane that contains all points *A* such that $\angle ABC$ is

   a. an obtuse angle.   **b.** an acute angle.

4. *Classify angles as acute, right, straight, obtuse, or reflex.* The dot grid shows $\overline{YZ}$. How many ways can you choose *X* such that $\triangle XYZ$ is

   a. an obtuse triangle?   **b.** an acute triangle?

   c. a right triangle?

   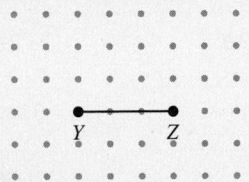

5. *Solve problems involving angle relationships.* Draw a triangle. Create an external angle for one of the vertices of the triangle. Then measure the two angles in the triangle that are not adjacent to the exterior angle you created. Determine the sum of the two measured angles in the triangle. Then measure the exterior angle. How are the sum of the two measured angles in the triangle and the measure of the exterior angle related?

6. *Solve problems involving angle relationships.* Choose the correct answer for each multiple choice question.

   a. How are $\angle 1$ and $\angle 2$ related?

   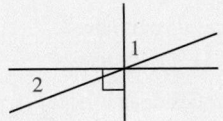

   (i)   They are right angles.
   (ii) They are vertical angles.
   (iii) They are supplementary angles.
   (iv) They are not related.
   (v)   They are complementary angles.

   b. What do all pairs of corresponding angles have in common?
   (i)   They are congruent.
   (ii) They are on the same side of the transversal.
   (iii) They are on opposite sides of the transversal.
   (iv) They are complementary.

   c. Which statement is *false*?
   (i)   The sum of the measures of the interior angles of a triangle is 180°.
   (ii) Vertical angles are congruent.
   (iii) The sum of the measures of the interior angles of a quadrilateral is 360°.
   (iv) If two lines are cut by a transversal, then the corresponding angles must be congruent.

7. *Solve problems involving angle relationships.* Find the measures of $\angle 1$, $\angle 2$, and $\angle 3$.

   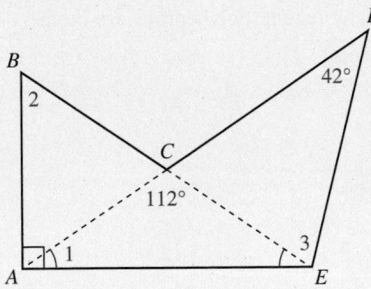

8. *Determine the measure of angles using the angle addition postulate or a protractor.* In the given illustration, assume $m\angle APB = 46°$, $m\angle CPE = 78°$, and $m\angle BPD = 110°$. Use the angle addition postulate to calculate each angle.

   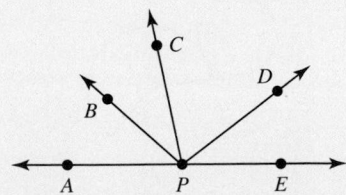

   a. $m\angle DPE$ **b.** $m\angle CPD$ **c.** $m\angle BPC$

9. *Solve problems involving complementary and supplementary angles.* ∠A and ∠B are supplementary angles. m∠A is 4° less than three times m∠B. Find m∠A and m∠B.

10. *Know and apply the F Postulate (Two lines cut by a transversal are parallel if and only if two corresponding angles created by the transversal are congruent).* Do the coplanar lines *m* and *n* intersect? Explain your answer.

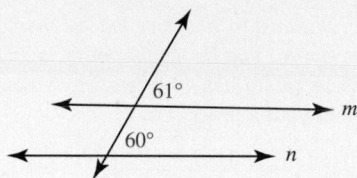

11. *Know and apply the F Postulate (Two lines cut by a transversal are parallel if and only if two corresponding angles created by the transversal are congruent).* What is wrong with this diagram?

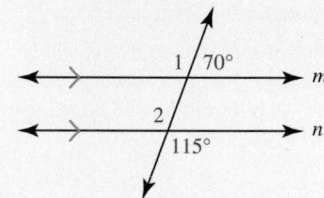

12. *Know that the sum of the angles of a triangle is 180°.* Find m∠1.

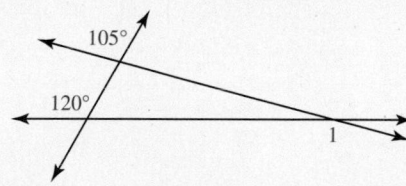

13. *Know that the sum of the angles of a triangle is 180°.* Suppose ΔABC is a right triangle, where ∠C is a right angle. What is the relationship between ∠A and ∠B?

14. *Calculate the sum of the angles of a polygon or the measure of an interior or exterior angle of a regular polygon.* Answer the following.

    a. What is the measure of an interior angle and an exterior angle of the regular polygon?

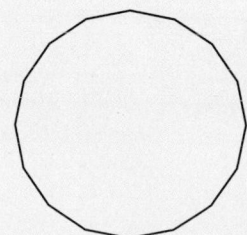

b. What is the sum of the measures of the interior angles of the polygon?

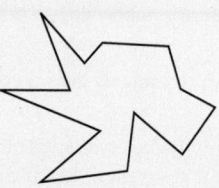

15. *Calculate the sum of the angles of a polygon or the measure of an interior or exterior angle of a regular polygon.* What is the sum of the measures of the marked angles of the polygon?

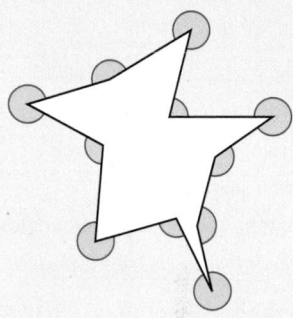

16. *Calculate the sum of the angles of a polygon or the measure of an interior or exterior angle of a regular polygon.* I am thinking of a regular polygon. The measure of each interior angle is 165°. How many sides does the regular polygon have? Show your work.

17. *Identify the parts of a polygon: side, vertex, diagonal, interior angle, and exterior angle.*

    a. Name the indicated geometric object associated with the polygon.

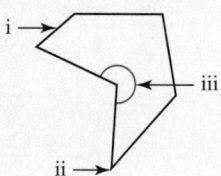

b. The pentagonal numbers are whole numbers that can be represented by the pentagonal shapes shown. The first four pentagonal numbers are 1, 5, 12, and 22. Predict the next two pentagonal numbers.

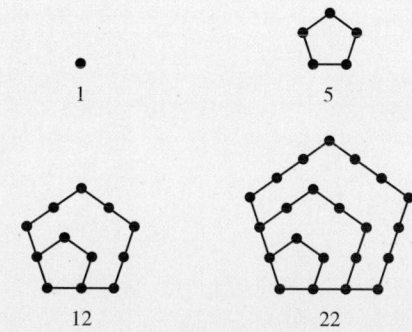

18. *Identify the parts of a polygon: side, vertex, diagonal, interior angle, and exterior angle.*

   a. How many interior angles does a convex polygon with *n* sides have?

   b. How many exterior angles does a convex polygon with *n* sides have?

19. *Identify and draw common quadrilaterals, and know how they are related.* On the dot paper, sketch each of the following.

   a. a rhombus that is not a square

   b. a scalene triangle with a right angle

   c. an isosceles triangle

   d. a parallelogram without any right angles

20. *Classify polyhedrons or classify cylinders and cones.* Name each solid.

   a. 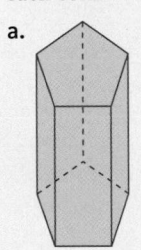   **b.** 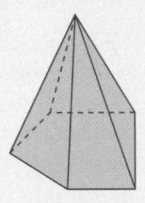   **c.**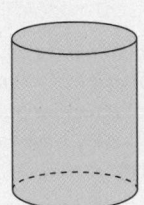

   d. 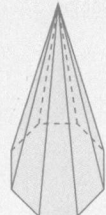   **e.** 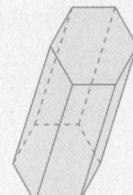   **f.**

21. *Know the relationship between the number of sides of the base of a prism (n) and its number of faces (F), edges (E), or vertices (V).* Answer the following questions about a prism with a base that has 47 sides.

   a. How many faces does it have?

   b. How many edges does it have?

   c. How many vertices does it have?

22. *Know the relationship between the number of sides of the base of a prism (n) and its number of faces (F), edges (E), or vertices (V).* A prism has 48 edges. How many faces does it have? Explain your answer.

23. *Know the relationship between the number of sides of the base of a pyramid (n) and its number of faces (F), edges (E), or vertices (V).* Answer the following questions about a heptagonal pyramid.

   a. How many faces does it have?

   b. How many edges does it have?

   c. How many vertices does it have?

24. *Know the relationship between the number of sides of the base of a pyramid (n) and its number of faces (F), edges (E), or vertices (V).* A pyramid has 58 edges. How many vertices does it have?

11

Measurement

Where Are We Going?

In **Section 11.1,** we consider measurable attributes, define measurement, outline the process of measurement, and define and apply the concepts of precision and greatest possible error. We also present the U.S. customary and the metric measurement systems and use proportions and dimensional analysis to convert units of measurement. In **Section 11.2,** we define area and derive and apply formulas for the area of common shapes. In **Section 11.3,** we discuss the Pythagorean theorem, along with triangle inequalities, and derive the formula for the area of a regular polygon. In **Section 11.4,** we define volume and use dimensional analysis to convert units of volume. We derive and apply formulas for the volume of common solids.

How Old Is Measurement?

Measurement is a mathematical activity common to all civilizations, because it answers fundamental questions such as "How much?" "How far?" and "How heavy?" Ancient Egyptians measured short distances, such as the lengths of stones to build temples and pyramids, using the *cubit,* which is the distance from the end of the middle finger to the tip of the elbow. Ancient Romans measured some distances in terms of *pace,* or two walking steps. Ancient Greeks measured land area by the *aroura,* the amount of land a yoke of oxen can plow in a day. Ancient Babylonians measured the weight of a bag of coins using the *talent,* the equivalent of roughly 75 pounds. Ancient Mayans were accurate timekeepers and used the *kin* to represent the length of a day.

Why Do We Need a Common Measurement System?

Measurement systems as recent as those used just a few hundred years ago typically varied from one country to another, from one town to another, and even from one occupation to another. Differing standards of measure created frustration and confusion for consumers, merchants, manufacturers, and scientists. France, for example, had so many different measurement systems in the late 1780s that an agricultural scientist named Arthur Young wrote: "In France, the infinite complexity of the measures exceeds all

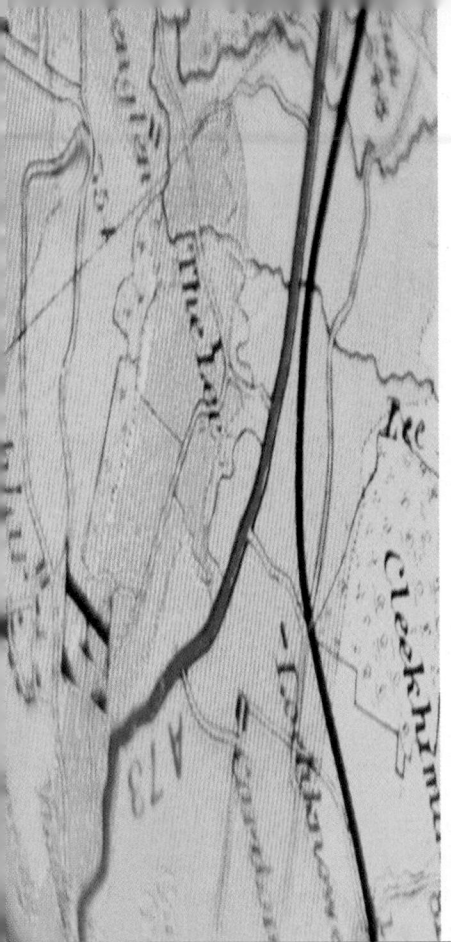

comprehension. They differ not only in every province, but in every district, and almost in every town; and these tormenting variations are found equally in the denominations and contents of the measures of land and corn" (Young, pp. 406–407). The need for a common system of measurement increased as interaction between and within societies increased. A uniform system of measurements makes it easier for consumers to compare similar items, for merchants to trade products fairly and competitively, for manufacturers to design and build products, and for international scientists to share advances in medicine and technology.

Because of a long and gradual evolution of measurement systems, we now have an international system of measurement (commonly known as the metric system) that makes it easier for everyone to apply and communicate measurements. Measurement has widespread use in daily life and hence a significant role in the mathematics curriculum. The NCTM's *Principles and Standards for School Mathematics* states:

> Measurement is one of the most widely used applications of mathematics. It bridges two main areas of mathematics—geometry and number. Measurement activities can simultaneously teach important everyday skills, strengthen students' knowledge of other important topics in mathematics, and develop measurement concepts and processes that will be formalized and expanded in later years. (© NCTM Standards 2011 by National Council of Teachers of Mathematics)

SECTION 11.1 | **Concept of Measurement and Measurement Systems**

The NCTM's *Principles and Standards for School Mathematics* states, "Prior to grade 3, students should have begun to develop an understanding of what it means to measure an object, that is, identifying an attribute to be measured, choosing an appropriate unit, and comparing that unit to the object being measured" (2000, p. 171). What is an attribute? What is measurement? What is the process of measurement? We answer these questions in this section.

Measurable Attributes

There are many factors to consider before purchasing a door, such as cost, appearance, material, height, and degree of security provided. In measurement, an **attribute** of an object is a characteristic that we can quantify, that is, represent in terms of a number. Some examples of attributes are brightness, speed, temperature, conductivity, and duration. The list of attributes of a cereal box includes length, width, height, weight, surface area, and volume.

EXAMPLE 11.1

COMMUNICATION
REASONING

List some measurable attributes of a person.

SOLUTION

Answers vary. Some possible attributes are height, weight, and blood pressure. ▲

What Is Measurement?

We cannot quantify the appearance of a door, because beauty is in the eye of the beholder, but we can quantify its height. The following situation illustrates the process of measurement. First, we choose a measurable attribute: the height of the door, as shown in Figure 1(a). Second, we choose a **measurement unit** to serve as a frame of reference, that is, something to compare the height of the door to. Let's use the paint bucket in Figure 1(b) as the measurement unit. We see the door is much taller than the bucket. But how tall is the door?

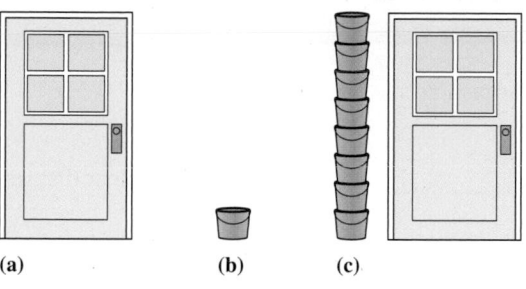

(a)   (b)   (c)

FIGURE 1
Measurement is a comparison.

Third, we stack buckets in a vertical column, as shown in Figure 1(c). This illustrates a vital aspect of measurement called **iteration** or repetition, which is the process of placing the measurement unit end to end to cover the attribute without gaps or overlaps. The number of repetitions of the bucket quantifies the height of the door. Finally, we report the measurement: the height of the door is "eight buckets," which means it is eight times the height of the bucket. Students should be able to "express the length of an object as a whole number of length units by laying multiple copies of a shorter object (the length unit) end to end; understand that the length measurement of an object is the number of same-size length units that span it with no gaps or overlaps" and "limit to contexts where the object being measured is spanned by a whole number of length units with no gaps or overlaps" (Gr. 1, CCSS).

> **Definition**
>
> A **measurement** is a quantitative comparison of an attribute of an object to the chosen measurement unit. For example, if the height of a door is "eight buckets," then we are saying the door is eight times as tall as one bucket.

The following example reinforces the meaning of measurement.

EXAMPLE 11.2   A student reports the length of a pen is three paper clips. What does this mean?

COMMUNICATION

REASONING

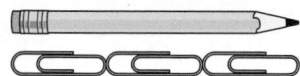

SOLUTION

One reasonable answer is that the length of the pen equals the cumulative length of three individual paper clips, placed end to end, covering the pen without gaps or overlaps. Alternatively, we could say that the pen is three times as long as one paper clip.

▲

EXAMPLE 11.3

COMMUNICATION
REASONING

A teacher points to a backpack and tells the class that it weighs 4 oobas, a contrived unit of weight. She asks her students to explain what this means. Sally says, "It means the backpack weighs four times as much as 1 ooba!" Pedro says, "It means the backpack weighs the same as the combined weight of 4 oobas." Which student is correct?

SOLUTION

Both students are correct. ▲

EXAMPLE 11.4

CONNECTION
REASONING
REPRESENTATION

A teacher draws a line segment on the board and says it has a length of 3 lunas, a contrived unit of length, as shown.

Draw a line segment that represents the unit of measurement.

SOLUTION

The luna was repeated three times, so we divide the line segment into three equal-sized parts.

The line segment shown represents 1 luna. ▲

The Process of Measurement

Now we summarize the sequence of steps involved in the process of measurement in the elementary mathematics classroom that applies to measuring length, area, and volume.

The Process of Measurement

1. Choose an attribute of an object to measure.
2. Choose an appropriate measurement unit.
3. Place the measurement unit end to end to cover the attribute without gaps or overlaps, and then count the number of repetitions.
4. Report the measurement with a numerical value and a unit of measurement.

Major Principle of Measurement

Figure 2 illustrates a major principle of measurement.

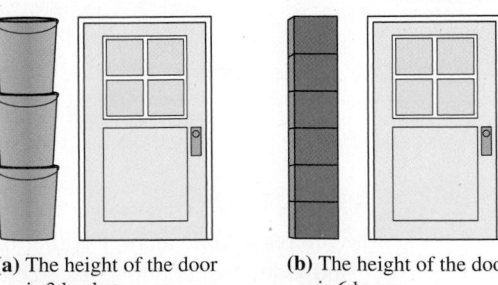

(a) The height of the door is 3 buckets.   **(b)** The height of the door is 6 boxes.

FIGURE 2
Illustrating a major principle of measurement.

If you use a smaller unit of measurement, then you increase the number of repetitions. It is common for students to "measure the length of an object twice, using length units of different lengths for the two measurements" and "describe how the two measurements relate to the size of the unit chosen" (Gr. 2, CCSS).

Two Common Ways to Determine a Measurement

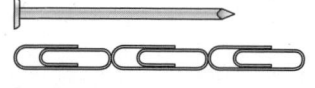

FIGURE 3

Using paper clips to measure length.

In Figure 3, we measure the length of a nail using a paper clip as the measurement unit. The NCTM's *Principles and Standards for School Mathematics* (2000) states that students should understand how to measure with nonstandard units, "such as paper clips laid end to end" (Pre-K–2). We see the true (but unknown) length in Figure 3 is between two and three paper clips.

We could estimate the length of the nail as 2.3 paper clips. Estimation leads to inconsistent results, because others could easily arrive at different estimates, such as 2.4 paper clips. Estimation is still valuable when approximations are acceptable. But we are mainly interested in measurement methods that lead to consistent results.

The first strategy is to round to the nearest paper clip. In this case, the length of the nail is two paper clips. Students apply this strategy, for example, when they measure the length of an object to the nearest millimeter, centimeter, inch, or foot.

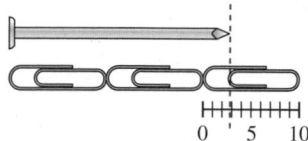

FIGURE 4

Partitioning the paper clip into tenths.

The second strategy is to partition the paper clip and then round to the nearest part. In Figure 4, we partition the paper clip into 10 equal-sized parts.

We now see the length of the nail is 2.3 paper clips, rounded to the nearest tenth of a paper clip. Students apply this strategy, for example, when they measure the length of an object to the nearest sixteenth, eighth, fourth, or half of an inch.

Rulers

We often use a **ruler,** as shown Figure 5, or tape measure to measure short distances. The distance between two consecutive whole numbers on a ruler represents one unit of measurement, and the whole numbers represent the number of repetitions of the measurement unit.

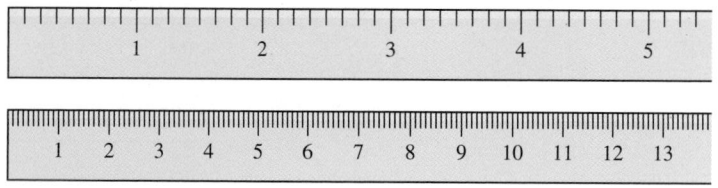

FIGURE 5

Examples of rulers.

The next example illustrates how to measure the length of a nail that is not placed at the zero mark of a ruler.

EXAMPLE 11.5

REASONING

REPRESENTATION

What is the length of the nail shown?

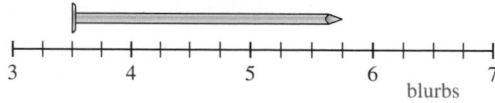

SOLUTION

The left endpoint of the nail is at $3\frac{1}{2}$ blurbs, and the right endpoint of the nail is at $5\frac{3}{4}$ blurbs. Let n be the length of the nail. Then $3\frac{1}{2} + n = 5\frac{3}{4}$. Then $n = 5\frac{3}{4} - 3\frac{1}{2} = 2\frac{1}{4}$. The length of the nail is $2\frac{1}{4}$ blurbs. ▲

The following Released Item suggests elementary school students should know how to properly use a ruler.

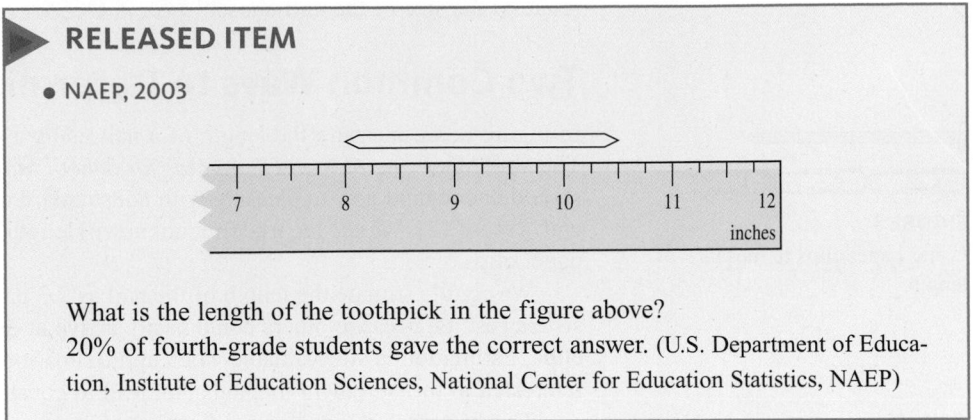

> **▶ RELEASED ITEM**
>
> ● NAEP, 2003
>
> What is the length of the toothpick in the figure above?
> 20% of fourth-grade students gave the correct answer. (U.S. Department of Education, Institute of Education Sciences, National Center for Education Statistics, NAEP)

Precision

In Figure 6, we use three different "inch rulers," or rulers where the measurement unit is the inch, to measure the length of a nail. Measurements are generally inexact because of unavoidable rounding, and the reported measurement depends on the ruler used.

REASONING
REPRESENTATION

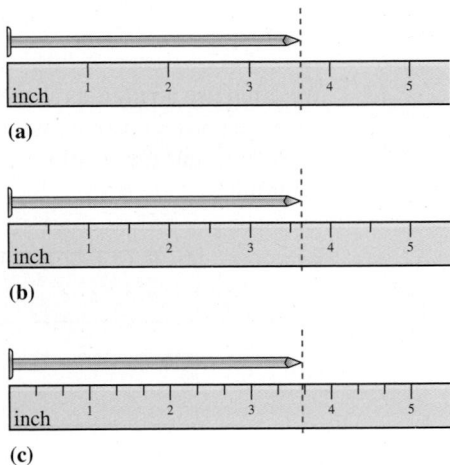

FIGURE 6
Measuring the length of a nail using different rulers.

- In Figure 6(a), we see the actual length of the nail is between 3 and 4 inches. We round to the nearest inch to obtain the measurement 4 inches.

- In Figure 6(b), we see the actual length of the nail is between $3\frac{1}{2}$ and 4 inches. We round to the nearest $\frac{1}{2}$ inch to obtain the measurement $3\frac{1}{2}$ inches.

- In Figure 6(c), we see the actual length of the nail is between $3\frac{1}{3}$ and $3\frac{2}{3}$ inches. We round to the nearest $\frac{1}{3}$ inch to obtain the measurement $3\frac{2}{3}$ inches.

The **precision** of a ruler with uniformly spaced marks is the distance between two consecutive marks. We see the ruler in Figure 6(a) has a precision of 1 inch, the ruler in Figure 6(b) has a precision of $\frac{1}{2}$ inch, and the ruler in Figure 6(c) has a precision of $\frac{1}{3}$ inch. The ruler in Figure 6(c) has greater precision than the rulers in Figures 6(a) and 6(b) and more accurately estimates the true, but unknown, length of the nail.

EXAMPLE 11.6

CONNECTION

What is the precision of the ruler?

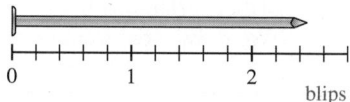

0   1   2

blips

SOLUTION

The precision of the ruler is 1/5 blip.

▲

Accuracy

The terms *accuracy* and *precision* have different meanings in the context of measurement. **Accuracy** is the difference between your reported measurement and the true (but unknown) measurement. It's generally impossible to calculate the accuracy of a measurement, because it requires us to know the true measurement. Precision refers to the perceived level of accuracy of a measuring tool. We generally assume a measurement tool, such as a ruler, with a greater degree of precision (that is, smaller units or more closely spaced marks) results in a measurement with a greater degree of exactness (because we perceive there will be less rounding error). For example, we *expect* a ruler with a precision of 0.1 cm to produce a more accurate measurement than a ruler with a precision of 0.5 cm. The following example requires you to choose the more precise measurement.

EXAMPLE 11.7

COMMUNICATION

REASONING

Jenny and Marco measure the height of a chair. Jenny records the measurement as 3.4 feet, and Marco records the measurement as 3.42 feet.

a. Which measurement is more precise?

b. Which measurement is more accurate?

SOLUTION

a. The measurement 3.42 is more precise.

b. Without further information, it is impossible to determine which measurement is more accurate in this situation. However, we *expect* 3.42 feet to be more accurate than 3.4 feet, because it may involve less rounding error.

▲

Improving Accuracy

CONNECTION

One way to possibly obtain more accurate measurements is to use higher precision. Scientists often use another approach: once you choose a measurement unit, take several measurements and report the *average value*. The average measurement of several measurements may be more accurate than any individual value, because positive and negative rounding errors offset each other (see Section 8.2).

Possible Values of a True (but Unknown) Measurement

The next example illustrates that if we know the *precision* of a measurement instrument (such as a ruler, tape measure, scale, protractor, gauge, or thermometer), then we could find an interval of measurements that captures the *true* (but unknown) measurement.

EXAMPLE 11.8

COMMUNICATION

CONNECTION

REASONING

REPRESENTATION

Olivia measured the weight of a statue using a scale with a precision of 0.1 pound. She recorded her measurement as 2.7 pounds. What are all possible values of the actual weight of the statue?

SOLUTION

The precision is 0.1 pound, which means the scale rounds to the nearest tenth of a pound. We draw a diagram to represent the situation.

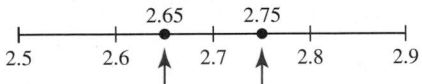

Then we get $2.7 - 0.05 = 2.65$ and $2.7 + 0.05 = 2.75$. So the true weight of the statue is somewhere between 2.65 and 2.75 pounds. ▲

In the context of measurement, it's easier to say a measurement of 2.7 pounds has a true measurement somewhere "from 2.65 to 2.75 pounds" rather than bother with rounding rules and think that 2.75 must be rounded to 2.8, especially because rounding 2.75 to 2.8 is a "choice." Some people or software programs round 2.75 to 2.7.

Greatest Possible Error

Concept Map 11.1 shows a nail, along with a ruler with a precision of $\frac{1}{5}$ inch. When we measure the length of the nail, we round to the nearest tick mark on the ruler, so the **greatest possible error (GPE)** between the true (unknown) measurement and the reported (known) measurement is half of the precision: GPE $= \frac{1}{10}$ inch, because $\frac{1}{2} \cdot \frac{1}{5} = \frac{1}{10}$.

> **Concept Map 11.1** Visualizing Precision and GPE

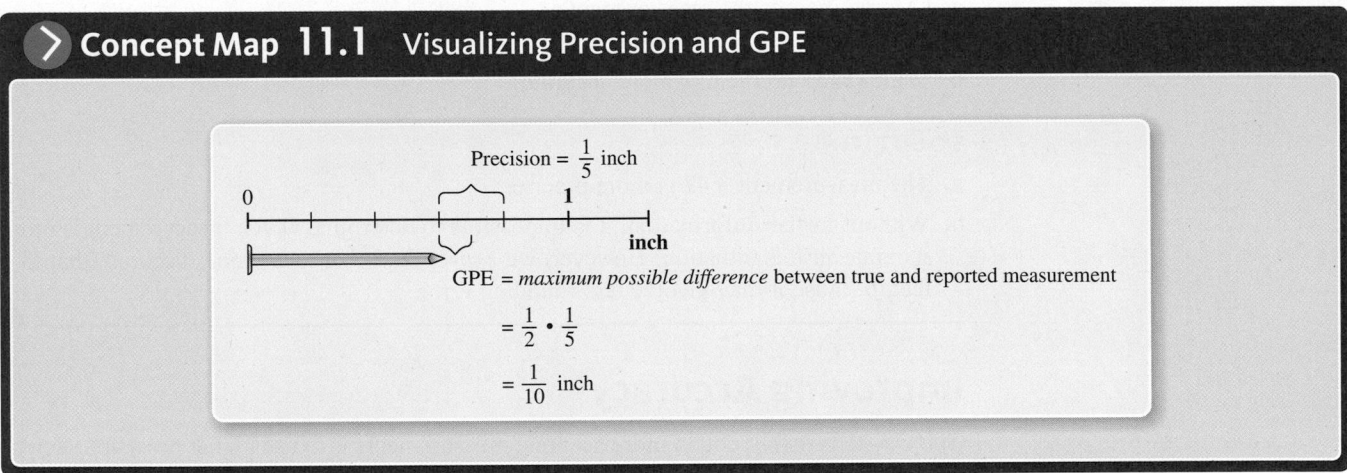

REPRESENTATION

A ruler with a precision of 0.5 inch has a GPE of 0.25 inch $\left(\text{GPE} = \frac{1}{2} \cdot 5 = 0.25\right)$. A scale with a precision of 0.1 pound has a GPE of 0.05 pound $\left(\frac{1}{2} \cdot 0.1 = 0.05\right)$. The GPE of a measurement tool represents the maximum possible difference between your reported measurement and the true (but unknown) measurement.

EXAMPLE 11.9

CONNECTION

Find the precision and GPE associated with each measurement.
a. 62.3 mi
b. 62.30 mi

SOLUTION

a. The precision is 0.1 mile, because 62.3 is rounded to the nearest tenth. $\frac{1}{2} \cdot 0.1 = 0.05$, so the GPE is 0.05 mile.

b. The precision is 0.01 mile, because 62.30 is rounded to the nearest hundredth. $\frac{1}{2} \cdot 0.01 = 0.005$, so the GPE is 0.005 mile. ▲

COMMUNICATION   As measurements, 62.3 and 62.30 are different, because 62.3 (6.23×10^1) has three
REASONING   significant digits, whereas 62.30 (6.230×10^1) has four significant digits. They are also different because the interval of numbers that round to 62.3 is wider than the interval of numbers that round to 62.30. The Classroom Connection illustrates that middle school students should know how to infer the GPE of a measurement and relate the precision and the GPE.

Classroom Connection

- *Middle Grades Math Tools for Success* (Course 3), p. 447

  Find the greatest possible error of each measurement.
  a. 225 ft   **b.** 5 3/8 gal

  How does the precision of a measurement relate to the greatest possible error of a measurement? (From Suzanne H. Chapin. © 1999 by Pearson Education, Inc. or its affiliates. Used by permission. All rights reserved.)

The following Released Item shows that students should be able to synthesize the concepts of measurement and GPE to make a judgment about the actual measurement.

RELEASED ITEM

- NAEP, 2003

  Length can be measured to within 0.05 centimeter accuracy by using a certain type of measuring instrument.

  A reading of 3.7 centimeters on this instrument means that the actual length is at least
  a. 3.20 centimeters   **b.** 3.65 centimeters   **c.** 3.69 centimeters
  d. 3.70 centimeters   **e.** 3.75 centimeters

  22% of eighth-grade students gave the correct answer.

Measurement Systems

A **measurement system** is a collection of units of measurement and rules for relating the various units. We can use a table to represent a measurement system. Table 11.1 shows a contrived measurement system, with units of measurement and rules for relating them.

REPRESENTATION

TABLE 11.1   **Contrived Measurement System**

Measurement unit	Relationship
zip	3 zips = 4 thors
thor	
leed	5 leeds = 8 zips

History shows that early measurement systems throughout the world not only depended on location and time but also lacked simple ways to relate units of measurement within a system and between systems, making trade and science prone to confusion, error, and fraud. Today, the U.S. customary system and the International System of Units are the two most common measurement systems. The NCTM's *Principles and Standards for School Mathematics* (2000) states that students should "understand the need for measuring with standard units and become familiar with standard units in the customary and metric systems" (Gr. 3–5) and "understand both metric and customary systems of measurement" (Gr. 6–8).

U.S. Customary System

The **U.S. customary system** is the standardized system most commonly used in daily life in the United States. Table 11.2 shows typical U.S. customary system units of linear measurement. The inch is the smallest unit of length in this system. One inch, roughly the width of an adult male's thumb, was once defined as the length of three barleycorns. The word *inch* stems from the Latin word *uncia,* which means "one twelfth part." The foot is the second smallest unit of measurement composed of 12 inches. One foot is roughly the length of an adult male's foot.

TABLE 11.2 **U.S. Customary System Units of Linear Measurement**

Unit	Symbolic representation	Relationship to feet
inch	in	$12 \text{ in} = 1 \text{ ft}$ or $1 \text{ in} = \dfrac{1}{12} \text{ ft}$
foot	ft	1 ft
yard	yd	1 yd = 3 ft
mile	mi	1 mi = 5280 ft

Metric System

Le Système international d'unités
The International System of Units

© BIPM, Photography courtesy of the BIPM

The **metric system** is a decimal system of weights and measures adopted by France in 1795. The word *meter* stems from the Greek word *metron,* which means "a measure." The metric system spread across Europe in the 1800s, when the need for an international system of weights and measures grew as commerce increased between continents and scientific achievements changed the world. Eventually, leading industrialized countries, including the United States, created an organization in 1875 called the International Bureau of Weights and Measures (IBWM) located in Sevres, France, to manage and oversee an international system of weights and measures. The measurement system is known today as the International System of Units (SI). SI is the modern version of the metric system, so we commonly refer to it as the metric system. Table 11.3 lists a few SI units of measurement for some attributes. The IBWM is responsible for creating new SI units of measurement as the scientific need arises.

TABLE 11.3 **Standard SI Units of Measurement**

Attribute	length	time	force	voltage	energy	power
Unit of measurement	meter	second	newton	volt	joule	watt
Symbolic representation	m	s	N	V	J	W

A prefix is a phrase that appears at the beginning of a word to alter the original meaning of the word. We form multiples (for example, *giga-*) and fractions (for example, *centi-*) of the standard units in Table 11.3 by joining a prefix and a standard unit of measurement. Table 11.4 lists symbols and numerical values of prefixes.

TABLE 11.4 **Examples of Prefixes**

Prefix	*giga-*	*mega-*	*kilo-*	*hecto-*	*deca-*	none	*deci-*	*centi-*	*milli-*	*micro-*	*nano-*
Symbolic representation	G	M	k	h	da	none	d	c	m	μ	n
Factor	10^9	10^6	10^3	10^2	10^1	$10^0 = 1$	10^{-1}	10^{-2}	10^{-3}	10^{-6}	10^{-9}

Each prefix represents a certain integer power of ten ($\ldots, 10^2, 10^1, 10^0, 10^{-1}, 10^{-2}, \ldots$). The following example illustrates how we join prefixes and standard units to form additional units of measurement.

EXAMPLE 11.10

CONNECTION

The meter is the SI unit of measurement of length. Use prefixes to create two additional metric units.

SOLUTION

We join a prefix to the word *meter.* Some possible metric units of length are kilometer and micrometer.

▲

The following example illustrates how to represent the SI units with symbols.

EXAMPLE 11.11

REPRESENTATION

a. What abbreviation do we use to represent a kilowatt?

b. What does the symbol GN represent?

c. What does 4.6 ms represent?

SOLUTION

a. *k* represents the prefix *kilo-, W* represents the unit *watt,* so *kW* represents *kilowatt.*

b. *G* represents the prefix *giga-* and *N* represents the unit *newton,* so *GN* represents *giganewton.*

c. *m* represents the prefix *milli-* and *s* represents the unit *second,* so 4.6 ms represents 4.6 milliseconds.

▲

The examples illustrate how the combination of a prefix and a unit of measurement produces a single word or symbol, without spaces or commas, to produce a new unit of measurement. SI also accepts non-SI units of measurement, such as minute (min), hour (h), day (d), liter (L or l), decibel (dB), knot (kn), hectare (ha), and millimeter of mercury (mm Hg). However, the advantage of the prefix may be lost with non-SI units. For example, megaminute is not a valid SI unit of measurement (but milliliter is a valid one).

SI uses prefixes to form multiples (for example, *kilo-, hecto-,* and *deca-*) and fractions (for example, *deci-, centi-,* and *milli-*) of a unit of measurement (for example, *meter*). Because there is a ubiquitous need to measure length, in Table 11.5 we relate some SI linear measurement units.

> ■ **Historical Note**
>
> Historians generally regard Gabriel Mouton (1618–1694), a clergyman of St. Paul's Church in Lyons, France, as the founder of the metric system. His simple and scientific measurement system, which he proposed in 1670, relied on the decimal system. The metric system later became the foundation of the global measurement system known as SI.

TABLE 11.5 **SI Units of Length**

Unit	Symbolic representation	Relationship to next smaller unit	Relationship to meter
megameter	Mm	1 Mm = 1000 km	1 Mm = 1,000,000 m
kilometer	km	1 km = 10 hm	1 km = 1000 m
hectometer	hm	1 hm = 10 dam	1 hm = 100 m
decameter	dam	1 dam = 10 m	1 dam = 10 m
meter	m	1 m = 10 dm	1 m
decimeter	dm	1 dm = 10 cm	1 dm = 0.1 m
centimeter	cm	1 cm = 10 mm	1 cm = 0.01 m
millimeter	mm	1 mm = 1000 μm	1 mm = 0.001 m

CONNECTION

Here are some classic benchmark measurements. A millimeter is about the thickness of a standard paper clip, a centimeter is about the width of the fingernail on your pinky finger, and a meter is about the distance from the floor to the doorknob on a door.

The following example illustrates how to relate different units of measurement within the metric system. Students should be able to "carry out simple unit conversions, such as from centimeters to meters, within a system of measurement" (Gr. 3–5, NCTM).

EXAMPLE 11.12 Convert the unit of measurement: 83.0527 hW = ___ W

SOLUTION

We use a diagram for the conversion. One hectowatt equals 100 watts.

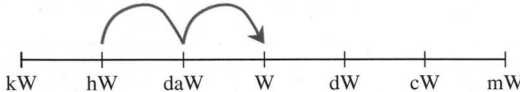

There are more watts than hectowatts, so 83.0527 hW = 8305.27 W.

▲

Prefixes make it convenient to convert SI units of measurement—we simply shift the decimal point to the left or right according to the prefix.

Dimensional Analysis

Suppose our goal is to convert 276 ounces to pounds using two different approaches. We can express 276 ounces in pounds using proportional reasoning. We need to find n such that n lb = 276 oz. There is 1 pound for every 16 ounces, so we have the following proportion:

$$\frac{n \text{ lb}}{276 \text{ oz}} = \frac{1 \text{ lb}}{16 \text{ oz}} \qquad \textbf{Line up the units.}$$

$$\frac{n}{276} = \frac{1}{16} \qquad \textbf{Write without the units.}$$

$$16n = 276 \cdot 1 \qquad \textbf{Cross-multiply.}$$

$$n = \frac{276 \cdot 1}{16} \qquad \textbf{Divide both sides by 16.}$$

$$n = 17.25 \qquad \textbf{Simplify.}$$

So 276 oz = 17.25 lb.

Proportional reasoning is the foundation of another approach called dimensional analysis. **Dimensional analysis** (also called **unit analysis**) is a structured process of using conversion factors to convert a unit of measurement to another unit of measurement. This is especially helpful in the U.S. customary system measurements, because the system lacks simple ways to convert from one unit to another. Dimensional analysis is also helpful in converting between measurement systems. To see how dimensional analysis works, let's again express 276 ounces in pounds. We treat pounds and ounces as variables, although they are really labels: divide both sides of the equation 16 oz = 1 lb by 16 ounces. Then we get $1 = \frac{1 \text{ lb}}{16 \text{ oz}}$. Then

$$276 \text{ oz} = 276 \text{ oz} \cdot \frac{1 \text{ lb}}{16 \text{ oz}} \qquad \frac{\textbf{1 lb}}{\textbf{16 oz}} \textbf{ is a unit factor.}$$

$$= 276 \,\cancel{\text{oz}} \cdot \frac{1 \text{ lb}}{16 \,\cancel{\text{oz}}} \qquad \textbf{Treat the units as variables, although the units are really labels.}$$

$$= \frac{276 \cdot 1}{16} \text{ lb} \qquad \textbf{Simplify.}$$

$$= 17.25 \text{ lb} \qquad \textbf{Simplify.}$$

This is the same result we obtained using proportional reasoning. A factor such as $\frac{1 \text{ ft}}{12 \text{ in}}$ or $\frac{12 \text{ in}}{1 \text{ ft}}$ is often called a *conversion factor* or *unit factor*. Multiplying by a unit factor is like multiplying by 1.

Some students are unsure of when to multiply or divide during conversion. Dimensional analysis is powerful, because *it tells you what and when to multiply and divide.*

Students should be able to "understand relationships among units and convert from one unit to another within the same system" (Gr. 6–8, NCTM).

EXAMPLE 11.13

CONNECTION

REASONING

Use dimensional analysis to convert each measurement.

a. 549 in = ___ yd

b. 55 mph = ___ ft per sec

SOLUTION

a. $549 \text{ in} = 549 \text{ in} \cdot \dfrac{1 \text{ ft}}{12 \text{ in}} \cdot \dfrac{1 \text{ yd}}{3 \text{ ft}} = \dfrac{549}{12 \cdot 3} \text{ yd} = 15.25 \text{ yd}$

b. $55 \dfrac{\text{mi}}{\text{h}} = 55 \dfrac{\text{mi}}{\text{h}} \cdot \dfrac{5280 \text{ ft}}{1 \text{ mi}} \cdot \dfrac{1 \text{ h}}{60 \text{ min}} \cdot \dfrac{1 \text{ min}}{60 \text{ sec}} = \dfrac{55 \cdot 5280}{60 \cdot 60} \dfrac{\text{ft}}{\text{sec}} \approx 80.7 \dfrac{\text{ft}}{\text{sec}}$

The following Classroom Connection indicates students should know how to convert units using dimensional analysis.

 Classroom Connection

● *Middle Grades Math Tools for Success* (Course 3), p. 284

Use dimensional analysis to convert each measure. (From Suzanne H. Chapin.
© 1999 by Pearson Education, Inc. or its affiliates. Used by permission. All rights reserved.)

a. 32 in = ___ ft   **b.** $1\frac{1}{2}$ mi = ___ ft

In the next example we convert U.S. customary system units to SI units using the *exact* relationship 1 in = 2.54 cm.

EXAMPLE 11.14

CONNECTION

REASONING

Change the unit of measurement. 1500 ft per hour = ___ m per sec

SOLUTION

$1500 \dfrac{\text{ft}}{\text{h}} = 1500 \dfrac{\text{ft}}{\text{h}} \cdot \dfrac{12 \text{ in}}{1 \text{ ft}} \cdot \dfrac{2.54 \text{ cm}}{1 \text{ in}} \cdot \dfrac{1 \text{ m}}{100 \text{ cm}} \cdot \dfrac{1 \text{ h}}{60 \text{ min}} \cdot \dfrac{1 \text{ min}}{60 \text{ s}} = \dfrac{1500 \cdot 12 \cdot 2.54}{100 \cdot 60 \cdot 60} \dfrac{\text{m}}{\text{s}} = 0.127 \dfrac{\text{m}}{\text{s}}$

 Historical Note

In 1999, the $125 million Mars Climate Orbiter spacecraft was destroyed as it sped too close to the Martian atmosphere. An investigation revealed that one team of engineers used the U.S. customary system and another team used the metric system in navigation software.

The standard unit of mass in the metric system is the kilogram (kg). We also use it to measure weight. Students should be able to explain the difference between weight and mass. A contextualized example clarifies the difference between mass and weight. The mass of a certain rock is the amount of physical matter that forms the rock. The weight of the rock is the heaviness of the rock, which depends on the force of gravitational attraction (the same force that pulls you down after you jump up). The force of gravitational attraction is stronger on Earth than on the Moon. Thus, the rock has the same mass on Earth and on the Moon but has greater weight on Earth than on the Moon.

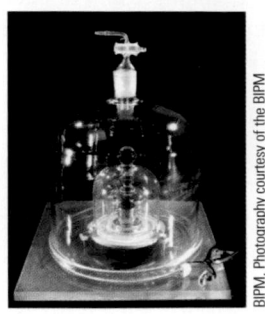

BIPM. Photography courtesy of the BIPM

Uniqueness of the Kilogram

The kilogram is unique for two reasons. First, the kilogram is the only remaining basic SI unit of measurement defined by a physical object. It is a durable metal alloy in the shape of a cylinder, with a height of 39 mm and a diameter of 39 mm, consisting of 90% platinum and 10% iridium. The cylinder is known as Le Grand K and is kept in a vault in France that requires three keys, each held by different officials, to open it. Second, the kilogram is the only standard SI unit of measurement that contains a prefix (the standard SI units in Table 11.3 do not contain prefixes). SI rules state that metric units cannot contain two prefixes, so we cannot attach a prefix to kilogram. Multiples (such as *deca-* and *hecto-*) and fractions (such as *centi-* and *milli-*) of mass are formed by attaching a prefix to the word *gram* (g). Thus, decagram (dag) and milligram (mg) are valid metric units. The kilogram survived historical efforts to change the standard unit to gram, because it was easier to build a prototype for 1 kg (roughly the weight of a baseball bat) than for 1 g (roughly the weight of a dollar bill).

> ### ■ Historical Note
>
> Long ago, physical prototypes were used to represent standard metric units. France created and distributed prototypes to physically represent the meter—metal bars with two marks. The definition of the meter evolved through the years. Today, scientists define 1 m as the distance light travels in space (or a vacuum) in 1/299,792,458 of a second. We define all U.S. customary and SI units in terms of physical constants (with the exception of the kilogram) measurable by accurate scientific instruments. The kilogram is the only SI unit that is defined in terms of a physical object (in the shape of a cylinder), but scientists are actively looking for ways to redefine it in terms of a physical constant or property of nature. The cylinder is stored in three nested jars in a vault.

QUESTIONS FOR SECTION 11.1

REPRESENTATION

Refresher: Representations (language, diagrams, tables, symbols, algebra, manipulatives, and contextualized situations) are important because we use them to organize, record, and communicate mathematical ideas and make them more comprehensible.

1. Determine the precision of each ruler.

a.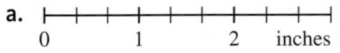

b.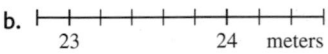

2. The diagram shows three rulers that can be used to measure the length of a line segment.

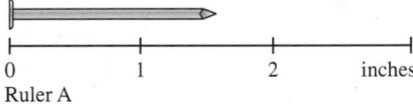
Ruler A

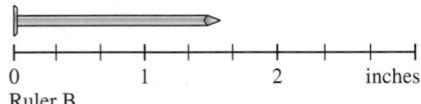
Ruler B

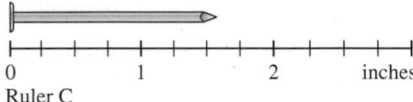
Ruler C

a. What is the precision of each ruler?

b. What is the length of the nail for each ruler?

c. Which ruler provides the most accurate measurement of the nail? Explain your answer.

d. Does a higher-precision ruler always lead to a more accurate measurement? Explain your answer.

3. Do the following.

   a. Determine the precision of the ruler.

   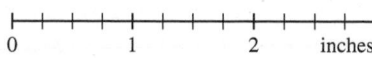

   b. Trace the ruler on a sheet of paper. Draw two different line segments that would have a length of 1.75 inches using this ruler.

4. Use the given line segment.

   _____

   The length of the line segement is exactly 4 zippos, a contrived length. Draw a line segement that has a length of 1 zippo.

5. Write in words the following SI units.

   a. kW   b. mJ   c. J/s   d. nm   e. s   f. MV

PROBLEM SOLVING

Refresher: Problem solving (reaching a goal that is not immediately attainable) is important because it helps students think more deeply about what they know and deal with unfamiliar situations.

6. What are the precision and GPE associated with each measurement?

   a. 14.32 lb   b. 37.8 m   c. 57.623 mi   d. 40 cm

7. Convert the contrived measurements given here to the indicated units using dimensional analysis. Round your final answer to the nearest hundredth.

Measurement unit	Relationship
flop	4 flops = 3 hats
bit	2 bits = 0.4 den
hat	
den	1.7 dens = 5 hats

   a. ___ flops = 5.4 hats   b. 3 bits = ___ hats

   c. 0.15 den = ___ bit   d. 5 flops = ___ bits

REASONING AND PROOF

Refresher: Reasoning and proof (thinking and justifying) are important because they help students make sense of mathematics.

8. A teacher shows the class a piece of string and tells them the length is 4 glops, a contrived length.

   a. What does 4 tell you?

   b. What does the word *glops* tell you?

9. Use this line segment to do the following.

   . . . .
   . _____ .
   . . . .

a. Suppose the contrived length is 2 snerds. Sketch a "snerd."

b. Suppose the length is 3 tullies. Sketch a "tully."

c. Suppose the length is 6 blips. Sketch a "blip."

d. Determine what happens to the length of the unit as the number of units in the length increases.

10. A ruler has a precision of 0.25 m.

    a. Both 3.25 and 0.75 m are possible measurements using this ruler. Give two more examples.

    b. Both 0.15 and 4.001 m are measurements that are not possible using this ruler. Give two more examples.

11. Tamisha reports the weight of a book is 3.2 pounds. What are possible values for the true weight of the book?

12. A measurement system consists of blips, lugs, and gifs. In this contrived system, 15 blips equal 4 lugs and 7 lugs equal 13 gifs.

    a. How many blips equal 3 gifs?

    b. What is the smallest unit of measurement?

13. The line segment shown has the exact contrived measurement 1.25 zippos.

    _____

    Draw a suitable ruler that would give this measurement.

CONNECTIONS

Refresher: Connections (linking and applying mathematical ideas) are important because they deepen student understanding and make mathematics more meaningful, flexible, and useful.

14. The actual length of a certain pencil is 14.5 cm. Three students obtain the following measurements: 14.3, 14.2, and 14.7 cm. The differences in the measurements may be because of how the students placed the pen along the ruler and how they rounded.

    a. Calculate the mean of the measurements.

    b. Which of the four values, including the mean, is the most accurate? Explain your answer.

15. Which measurement would be more appropriate for the given attribute of a typical minivan?

    a. length: 201 cm, 201 m, 201 in, 201 ft

    b. height: 68 cm, 68 m, 68 in, 68 ft

    c. weight: 4500 tons, 4500 g, 4500 kg, 4500 lb

16. What is the connection between the precision of a ruler and the GPE of a measurement?

17. People typically round their height to the nearest inch. John is 5 feet 9 inches. What is the shortest and tallest actual height that John could be?

18. Convert the given measurements to the indicated units using proportional reasoning.

    a. 285 ft = ___ yd   b. 3.4 mi = ___ ft

    c. 7 ft = ___ in   d. 45 cm = ___ mm

19. Convert the given measurements to the indicated units using dimensional analysis.

    a. 340 ft = ___ yd   **b.** 2.5 mi = ___ ft

    c. 60 in = ___ ft   **d.** 2400 yd = ___ mi

20. The Qinghai–Tibet railway is 1956 km long and stretches over frozen tundra amid high elevation. What is this distance in miles?

21. What is the connection between the following measurements?

    a. meter and kilometer

    b. second and millisecond

22. List some measurable attributes of a yacht.

23. What is the length of the nail?

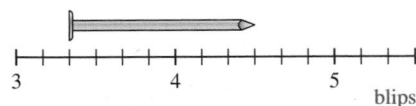

24. One light-year is the distance that light travels in 1 year. This unit of measurement is used to measure distances in space, such as the distances between stars or from Earth to a star. The speed of light is 299,792,458 meters per second.

    a. Convert the speed of light to feet per second.

    b. Determine how far light will travel in a year in miles (1 year = 365 days).

COMMUNICATION

Refresher: Communication (written and verbal explanations using representations and proper mathematical vocabulary) is important because it helps students refine and strengthen their understanding.

25. **a.** What is a measurement?

    b. What is a measurement system?

26. What are the two most common measurement systems?

27. Why are common measurement systems needed?

28. List two reasons the kilogram is unique.

29. If you are comparing the lengths of two species of ants, which of these would be the best units to use, and why? *millimeter, centimeter,* or *meter*

30. List some measurable attributes of each object.

    a. automobile   **b.** box   **c.** coin

31. Lilia was converting 20 yards to feet. Lilia wrote $20 \text{ yd} = 20 \times \frac{1}{3} \text{ ft} = \frac{20}{3} \text{ ft}$. What advice would you give Lilia to correct her thinking?

32. Explain how you could use a single yardstick to measure the length of a 20-foot room.

33. Devise your own measurement system. Represent it with a table and rules for relating units of measurement. Create some unit conversion problems. Then solve them.

More practice with the ideas of the section

34. Fill in the blank. Choose one of the following acronyms, words, numbers, or phrases: *2.45, 2.54, accuracy, attribute, decision, dimensional analysis, expect, GPE, gram, guarantee, hope, incision, iteration, kilogram, measurement system, precision, postfix, prefix, psychoanalysis, ruler,* or *table.*

    a. In measurement, a(n) _____ of an object is a characteristic of that object that we can quantify, that is, represent in terms of a number.

    b. _____ is the process of placing the measurement unit end to end to cover the attribute without gaps or overlaps.

    c. The _____ of a ruler with uniformly spaced marks is the distance between two consecutive marks, which is also the least positive measurable length.

    d. _____ refers to how close the reported measurement is to the actual measurement.

    e. We _____ a ruler with a precision of 0.1 unit to produce a more accurate measurement than a ruler with a precision of 0.25 unit.

    f. One inch is defined as exactly ___ cm.

    g. The _____ of a measurement tool represents the maximum possible difference between your reported measurement and the actual (but unknown) measurement.

    h. A(n) _____ is a collection of units of measurement and rules for relating the various units.

    i. A(n) _____ is a phrase that appears at the beginning of a word to alter the original meaning of the word.

    j. _____ is a structured process of using conversion factors to convert a unit of measurement to another unit of measurement.

    k. The standard unit of mass in the metric system is the _____.

35. Louie measured the height of a bottle using a tape measure with a precision of 0.25 cm. He recorded his measurement as 14.75 cm. What are the lowest and highest possible values of the actual height of the bottle?

36. Measure the following line segment to the nearest unit.

    ──────────────────────

    a. mile   **b.** foot   **c.** inch   **d.** millimeter

37. Use the following contrived measurement system and dimensional analysis to convert units. Round the final answer to the nearest hundredth.

Measurement unit	Relationship
zippo	3.1 zippos = 5 thors
thor	
leed	4.5 leeds = 6 zippos
pen	2 pens = 4.8 leeds

    a. 2 leeds = ___ zippos   **b.** 1.8 thors = ___ pens

    c. ___ leeds = 5.7 thors   **d.** ___ pens = 0.57 zippos

38. Convert the given measurements to the indicated units using proportional reasoning.

    a. 35 ft = ___ yd

    b. 60 ft = ___ in

    c. 28 in = ___ cm

    d. 420 m = ___ km

39. Use the following representation of prefixes to convert the measurements.

    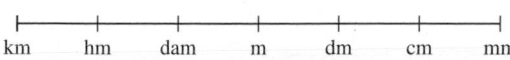

    a. 1 km = ___ m   b. 1 m = ___ km

    c. 7.8 hm = ___ dm   d. 81.3 cm = ___ hm

40. All space aliens on Planet Same have a height of 7 yups and 5 peps, and 12 peps equals 1 yup.

    a. If you stacked 25 aliens from head to toe, how tall would the stack be?

    b. If you stacked 42 aliens from head to toe, how tall would the stack be?

41. One way to visualize the size of a meter is that it is approximately the distance from an adult's nose to the end of his or her outstretched arm. Using this approach, estimate the length, in meters, of a typical

    a. skateboard.   b. bicycle.   c. sport utility vehicle.

42. An electronic scale for weighing fruit indicates weights in increments of 0.01 lb.

    a. What is the precision of the scale?

    b. According to this scale, a bunch of grapes weighs 1.72 pounds. What are the minimum and maximum possible actual weights of the bunch of grapes?

43. What are the precision and GPE associated with each measurement?

    a. 500 m (rounded to the nearest 100 m)

    b. 500 m (rounded to the nearest meter)

44. What are the precision and GPE for the following gauges?

    a.    b.

45. Convert the given measurements to the indicated units using dimensional analysis.

    a. 53 yd = ___ in   b. 6.8 mi = ___ ft

    c. 0.4 ft = ___ cm   d. 46 ft per second = ___ mi per day

46. Match the items on the left side to the nearest approximations on the right side, without using calculations. Then explain how you made your choices.

Item	Approximation
a. 5 cm	(i) 3 m
b. 2.3 mi	(ii) 1.97 in
c. 10 ft	(iii) 4048 yd

47. What are the symbolic representations of the following units of measurement of time?

    a. day   b. hour   c. minute   d. second

48. Convert the measurement to the indicated units using dimensional analysis: 2.5 mi per week = ___ m per h.

49. Draw a ruler. State the unit, precision, and GPE.

50. A student reports the length of the given line segment is 2 cm. How would you respond?

    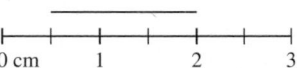

51. The price of a fish is proportional to the length of the fish.

    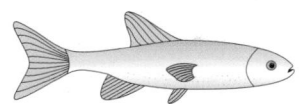

    a. How would a grocer measure the length to increase profits?

    b. How would a consumer measure the length to reduce costs?

52. Measure the dimensions of the playing card shown below using a metric ruler. What are the dimensions?

53. Do the following.

    a. Determine the precision of the ruler.

    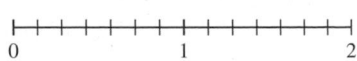

    b. Trace the ruler on a sheet of paper. Draw two different line segments that would have the length $1\frac{3}{7}$ units for the ruler shown.

54. Measure the height of this page using the two paper clips of the different sizes shown.

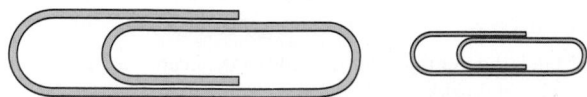

    a. If the units are "small paper clip," what is the height of the page?

    b. If the units are "large paper clip," what is the height of the page?

    c. Which measurement involves more repetitions? Why?

    d. Make a conclusion about the relationship between the length of a unit and the number of repetitions in a measurement.

55. What are the precision and GPE for each gauge?

    a.

    b.

56. Measure the length of the paper clip using the ruler.

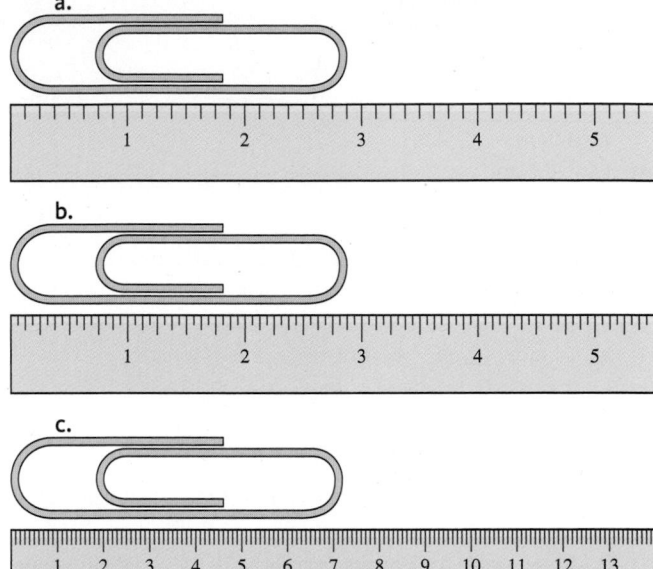

57. The GPE of a ruler is 0.5 cm. Determine which measurements, if any, are not possible using this ruler: 3.5 cm, 7.25 cm, and 14.0 cm.

58. What are the precision and GPE associated with each measurement?

    a. 62.04 lb   **b.** 41.52 cm   **b.** 17.567 mi

59. Convert units. Round to the nearest hundredth.

    a. ___ in = 3.2 m   **b.** 10 yd = ___ m

    c. 1 m = ___ ft   **d.** ___ cm = 59 ft   **e.** 3 ft = ___ m

    f. 25 yd = ___ cm

SECTION 11.2   Perimeter and Area

Irregular Shapes and Conceptualization

In this section, we focus on two attributes of simple closed figures: perimeter and area. We use irregular shapes to conceptualize these attributes but then emphasize common geometric shapes such as triangles, squares, rectangles, parallelograms, and circles, because (1) we can represent their perimeter and area with words or formulas, and (2) they are the building blocks for finding the perimeter and area of similar or complex geometric shapes.

Perimeter

The **perimeter** of a simple closed figure is a measure of the length of the boundary of the figure. The word *perimeter* is based on the Greek word *perimetros,* which means "around measure." Perimeter is a special application of length. We report the perimeter with both a number and a measurement unit (such as 18 inches, 6 feet, or 2 m). The following example gives one question that you can ask to assess whether your students understand the concept of perimeter.

EXAMPLE 11.15

COMMUNICATION

REASONING

FIGURE 7
Irregular shape.

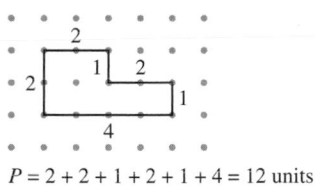

$P = 2 + 2 + 1 + 2 + 1 + 4 = 12$ units

FIGURE 8
Perimeter of an irregular polygon.

How could you measure the perimeter of the irregular shape in Figure 7?

SOLUTION

The earlier definition tells you what perimeter is but not how to calculate it. To find the perimeter of the shape, we could trace its entire boundary with a piece of string, being careful to avoid gaps or overlaps, and then straighten the string and use a ruler to measure the length of the string needed to cover the edge of the shape.

▲

Perimeter of a Polygon

A dot grid is a rectangular array of dots in which the distance between two adjacent dots in the same row or column is defined to be 1 unit (the unit could be inch or centimeter, for example). The dot grid is useful for drawing polygons and illustrating geometric principles. The perimeter P of the polygon in Figure 8 is 12 units.

Perimeter problems that involve irregular polygonal shapes help students conceptualize the concept of perimeter without the risk of applying formulas incorrectly or meaninglessly.

> **Definition**
>
> The perimeter of a polygon is the sum of the lengths of the sides.

Perimeter of a Rectangle

In Figure 9(a), we see a rectangle. In Figure 9(b), we use a dot grid to determine the measurements of the sides. The perimeter is the sum of the measurements, and we obtain $P = 3 + 5 + 3 + 5 = 16$ units.

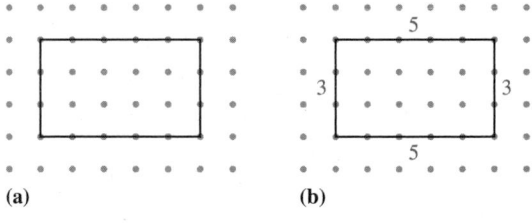

(a)   (b)

FIGURE 9
The perimeter of a rectangle.

By regrouping the measurements, we also obtain $P = 2 \cdot 3 + 2 \cdot 5$ units, which suggests a formula for the perimeter of a rectangle.

> **Definition of the Perimeter of Rectangles and Squares**
>
> - The perimeter P of a rectangle with a length of l units and width of w units is given by $P = 2l + 2w$ units.
> - The perimeter P of a square with sides of length s units is given by $P = 4s$ units.

Some elementary school students use formulas without paying attention to their conceptual basis, making them susceptible to applying incorrect formulas or using incorrect units. The following Released Item indicates students should understand how to apply formulas when they are given a perimeter.

> **RELEASED ITEM**
>
> ● NAEP, 2005
> A rectangular playground has a perimeter of 390 feet. The width of the playground is 75 feet. What is its length?
> **a.** 5.2 feet **b.** 97.5 feet **c.** 120 feet **d.** 130 feet **e.** 240 feet
>
> 40% of eighth-grade students answered the question correctly.

The following problem illustrates the use of the Solve an Equation strategy to solve a problem involving the perimeter of a rectangle.

EXAMPLE 11.16

CONNECTION
PROBLEM SOLVING
REASONING
REPRESENTATION

The perimeter of a rectangle is 100 feet. The width of the rectangle is 2 feet more than three times the length of the rectangle. Determine the width of the rectangle.

SOLUTION

The perimeter is 100 feet. Let l and w represent the length and the width of the rectangle. Then $w = 3l + 2$. Then

$$P = 2w + 2l$$
$$100 = 2(3l + 2) + 2l$$
$$100 = 6l + 4 + 2l$$
$$100 = 8l + 4$$
$$96 = 8l$$
$$96 \div 8 = l$$
$$12 = l$$

Then $w = 3 \cdot 12 + 2 = 36 + 2 = 38$. The length is 12 feet, and the width is 38 feet. ▲

Properties of rectangles are useful for finding the perimeter of irregular polygonal shapes with some unlabeled measurements. This type of problem requires coordinating properties, spatial skills, and measurement.

EXAMPLE 11.17

CONNECTION
PROBLEM SOLVING
REASONING

Find the perimeter of the polygon.

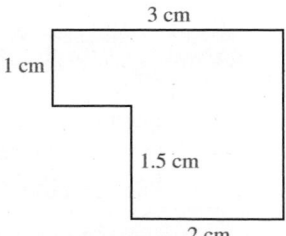

SOLUTION

We partition the polygon into squares and rectangles and use our knowledge that their opposite sides are congruent to find the missing lengths.

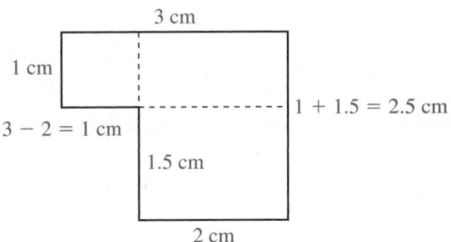

Beginning from the upper left and moving in a clockwise direction, the perimeter is
$P = 1 + 3 + 2.5 + 2 + 1.5 + 1 = 11$ cm.

▲

The perimeter of a rectangle depends on the length and width. Students should be able to "explore what happens to measurements of a two-dimensional shape such as its perimeter and area when the shape is changed in some way" (Gr. 3–5, NCTM).

EXAMPLE 11.18

CONNECTION

A rectangle has a length of 3 cm and width of 7 cm. Increase each measurement by 2 cm. Fill in the blank with a number:

a. The perimeter increased by ___ cm.

b. The perimeter increased by ___%.

SOLUTION

The perimeter of the first rectangle is $2 \cdot 3 + 2 \cdot 7 = 20$ cm. The perimeter of the second rectangle is $2(3 + 2) + 2(7 + 2) = 28$ cm.

a. $28 - 20 = 8$ cm. The perimeter increased by 8 cm.

b. $(28 - 20)/20 = 8/20 = 0.40 = 40\%$. The perimeter increased by 40%.

▲

Circumference of a Circle

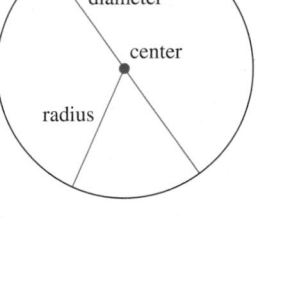

A **circle** is a set of points that are equidistant from a given point. The given point is called the **center.** A **radius** of a circle is a line segment from the center of the circle to any point on the circle. A **diameter** of a circle is a line segment that passes through the center and has endpoints that belong to the circle. Radius and diameter also refer to the lengths of these line segments.

The circumference is another measurement associated with a circle. **Circumference** is the conventional name for the perimeter of the circle. Students should be able to "develop and use formulas to determine the circumference of circles" (Gr. 6–8, NCTM) and should "know the formulas for the circumference of a circle and use them to solve problems" (© 2010. National Governors Association Center for Best Practices and Council of Chief State School Officers. All rights reserved.). In Figure 10 we show how to approximate the circumference C and diameter d of a circle with a rope. We traced the boundary of one of grandma's plates with a rope, being careful to cover the boundary without gaps or overlap. The length of this rope C is the circumference. Then we cut another piece of rope to represent the diameter d of the plate.

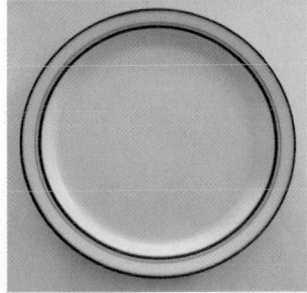  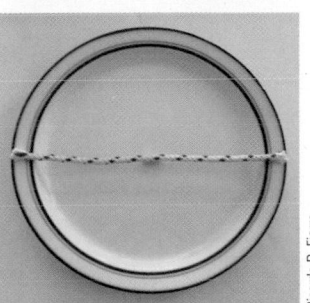

FIGURE 10
Measuring the circumference and diameter.

Ricardo D. Fierro

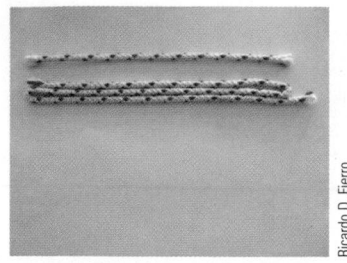

FIGURE 11

Comparing the circumference
and diameter.

In Figure 11, we compare the circumference (see the folded rope) to the diameter. We "see" the circumference is slightly more than three times the diameter, that is, $C \approx 3d$, or $C/d \approx 3$. In Table 11.6, we gather more empirical evidence by measuring circular objects and comparing the results.

TABLE 11.6   Actual Measurements of Some Circular Objects

Object	Circumference C	Diameter d	C/d
plate	31.75 in	10.0 in	3.2
bottle cap	5.0 in	1.5 in	3.3
wastebasket	23.0 in	7.5 in	3.1

CONNECTION

REASONING

The quotient C/d, the symbol for the circumference divided by the diameter, is a fixed number independent of the circle considered. The values of C/d in Table 11.6 differ because of unavoidable human and measurement errors. In the early 1700s, mathematicians replaced the fixed number C/d with the lone symbol π (pi). This type of activity gives students the opportunity to make sense of π through experimentation.

Definition

Let C and d represent the circumference and diameter of a circle, respectively.

The symbol π, read as "pie" but spelled "pi," represents the constant $\dfrac{C}{d}$, that is, $\pi = \dfrac{C}{d}.$

The number π is an irrational number, which means it has infinitely many digits after the decimal point without any repeating pattern. Here are a few leading digits of π: $\pi \approx 3.14159265358979323846$. The definition of π leads to the following theorem. Students who know the circumference is about three times the diameter seem to understand the equation $C = \pi d$.

Theorem

The circumference C of a circle with diameter d units and radius r units is given by $C = \pi d$ units or $C = 2\pi r$ units.

In calculations, an acceptable approximation of π is 3.1416.

EXAMPLE 11.19   a. A circle has a circumference of 30 cm. Determine the radius of the circle.

b. Express the circumference as a function of the radius using function notation.

SOLUTION

a. The formula is $C = 2\pi r$. Then $r = C/(2\pi) = 30/(2\pi) \approx 4.8$ cm. The radius is about 4.8 cm.

b. $C(r) = 2\pi r$ (This means that given the radius of a circle, its circumference can be uniquely determined.)

EXAMPLE 11.20

CONNECTION

A circle has a radius of 10 cm. Increase the radius by 2 cm. Fill in the blank with a number:
a. The circumference increased by ___ cm.
b. The circumference increased by ___%.

SOLUTION

The circumference of a circle with a radius of 10 cm is $2\pi r = 2 \cdot \pi \cdot 10 = 20\pi$ cm. The circumference of a circle with a radius of 12 cm is $2\pi r = 2 \cdot \pi \cdot 12 = 24\pi$ cm.
a. $24\pi - 20\pi = 4\pi \approx 12.57$. The circumference increased by approximately 12.6 cm.
b. $4\pi/20\pi = 20\%$. The circumference increased by 20%.

▲

■ **Historical Note**

Archimedes, a Greek mathematician in 250 BCE, developed the first numerical procedure to estimate π. He inscribed a regular polygon with 96 sides in a circle with circumference C and then circumscribed the circle with a regular polygon with 96 sides. The perimeter of the inscribed polygon is less than C, whereas the perimeter of the circumscribed polygon is greater than C. He calculated the perimeters of the polygons by solving simpler problems (using polygons with $n = 6$, 12, 24, and 48 sides) and applying formulas he developed. Archimedes determined $3.14085 < \pi < 3.14286$ (rounded to five decimal digits), a remarkable achievement for that period. The current record for calculating the digits of π is nearly 2.7 trillion decimal digits (January 2010), requiring nearly 1 terabyte of hard disk space to store. This record may soon be eclipsed by a recent claim (August 2010) of calculating the digits of π to 5 trillion decimal digits.

Arc Length

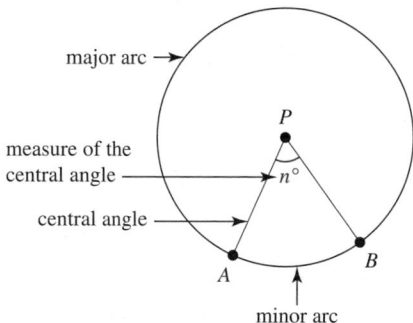

Arc length, another measurement associated with a circle, is the distance from one point on a circle to another point on the circle as we travel along the circle. The symbol $\overset{\frown}{AB}$ represents the arc with endpoints A and B. Each arc is associated with a **central angle,** which is an angle where the vertex is the center of the circle and both sides of the angle intersect the circle. There are two arcs associated with the points A and B. The arc with a central angle less than or equal to 180° is called the *minor arc*. The other arc is called the *major arc*. In the following example, we express arc lengths as a fraction of the circumference to infer a general formula.

EXAMPLE 11.21

CONNECTION

REASONING

Use the diagram to express the arc length of $\overset{\frown}{AB}$ as a fraction of the circumference C of a circle with the center P. Then express each arc length in terms of the measure of the central angle.

a.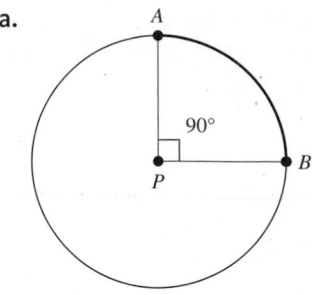

b.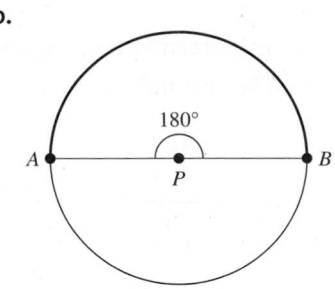

c.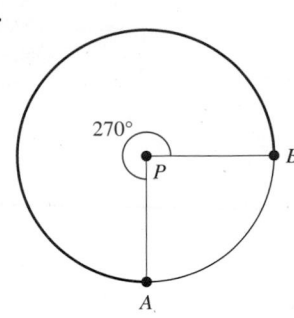

SOLUTION

We see that for each part the arc length equals one-quarter, one-half, and three-quarters of the circumference, respectively.

a. The arc length of $\overset{\frown}{AB} = \dfrac{1}{4}C$; $\frac{1}{4} = \dfrac{90}{360}$, so the arc length of $\overset{\frown}{AB} = \dfrac{90}{360}C$.

b. The arc length of $\overset{\frown}{AB} = \dfrac{1}{2}C$; $\dfrac{1}{2} = \dfrac{180}{360}$, so the arc length of $\overset{\frown}{AB} = \dfrac{180}{360}C$.

c. The arc length of $\overset{\frown}{AB} = \dfrac{3}{4}C$; $\dfrac{3}{4} = \dfrac{270}{360}$, so the arc length of $\overset{\frown}{AB} = \dfrac{270}{360}C$.

▲

This example establishes a pattern to help us find the length of any arc. Let $\overset{\frown}{AB}$ be a 42° arc in a circle with a radius of 5 cm. Then the arc length of $\overset{\frown}{AB}$ is $\frac{42}{360}C = \frac{42}{360}(2\pi \cdot 5) \approx$ 3.67 cm. This leads to the following result.

Theorem

Let $\overset{\frown}{AB}$ represent an arc on a circle with center P and circumference C units that determines a central angle with the measure $n°$. The arc length of $\overset{\frown}{AB}$ is $\dfrac{n}{360}C$ units.

The theorem states that the arc length is a fraction of the circumference. There is no standard notation for arc length.

> **RELEASED ITEM**

● NAEP, 2007

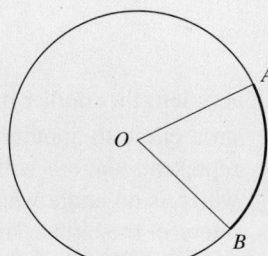

The circle above has center O. If the length of the darkened arc is 1/6 of the circumference, what is the degree measure of $\angle AOB$?
a. 75° **b.** 60° **c.** 45° **d.** 36° **e.** 30°

34% of eighth-grade students answered the question correctly.

Area

The concept of area for elementary school students begins with counting units of measurement. This leads to the familiar formula for the area of a rectangle. Later, they use this formula to develop formulas for other shapes, either by cutting a figure and rearranging the parts or putting two copies of the figure together, to make a figure whose area they know. We follow this strategy to develop formulas for the areas of parallelograms, triangles, trapezoids, and circles. Students should be able to "develop, understand, and use formulas to find the area of rectangles and related triangles and parallelograms" (Gr. 3–5, NCTM) and "the area of triangles, parallelograms, trapezoids, and circles and develop strategies to find the area of more complex shapes" (Gr. 6–8, NCTM).

Area is a measure of the region enclosed by a simple closed figure. Area is a comparison of the region and a measurement unit. We apply the concept of iteration (repetition) and cover the region with copies of a measurement unit without gaps or overlaps. Let's find the area of the hexagon in Figure 12 and consider two possible measurement units: the triangular unit and the trapezoidal unit.

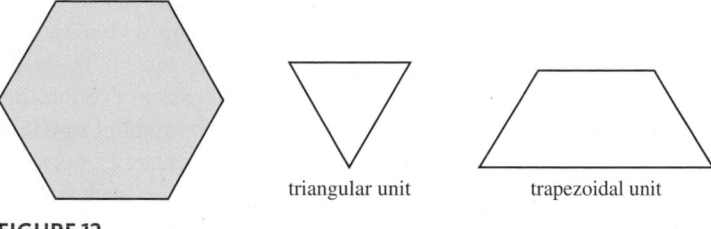

triangular unit   trapezoidal unit

FIGURE 12
Area of hexagon and measurement units.

We need to determine the number of measurement units that cover the hexagon, without gaps or overlaps. Figure 13 shows that the reported measurement of the area depends on the choice of the measurement unit. By counting the number of units, we see the area of the hexagon is six triangular units, but also two trapezoidal units.

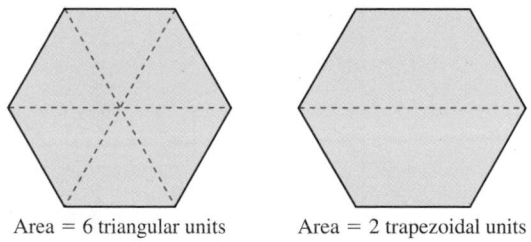

Area = 6 triangular units   Area = 2 trapezoidal units

FIGURE 13
The measurement of area depends on the measurement unit.

Square Units

We often use units of measurement with a square shape, because as we show, they simplify estimation and calculation of area because of their close connection to linear measurement. A **unit square** is a square that has sides of the length 1 unit. Table 11.7 shows representations of unit squares. A unit square that has sides of the length 1 cm is defined to have an area of 1 cm², or square centimeter. A unit square that has sides of the length 1 inch is defined to have an area of 1 in², or square inch. Both "square centimeter" and "square inch" are units of area measurement.

CONNECTION **TABLE 11.7** **Representations of Two Common Square Units**

Diagram of a unit square	Area of a unit square	Symbol
⊢1 cm⊣ ▢	1 square centimeter	cm^2
⊢———1 inch———⊣ ▢	1 square inch	in^2

We typically define the area of a region enclosed by a simple closed figure as the number of unit squares that can fit in the figure without any gaps or overlaps. Students should know that "a square with side length 1 unit, called 'a unit square,' is said to have 'one square unit' of area, and can be used to measure area" and that "a plane figure which can be covered without gaps or overlaps by n unit squares is said to have an area of n square units" (Gr. 3, CCSS). The symbol **unit²** represents a "square unit," but some students mistakenly read it as "unit squared," because they read n^2 as "n squared." For example, in^2 represents "square inch," not "inch squared."

The following Released Item illustrates that students should be able to find the area of an irregular shape on a grid.

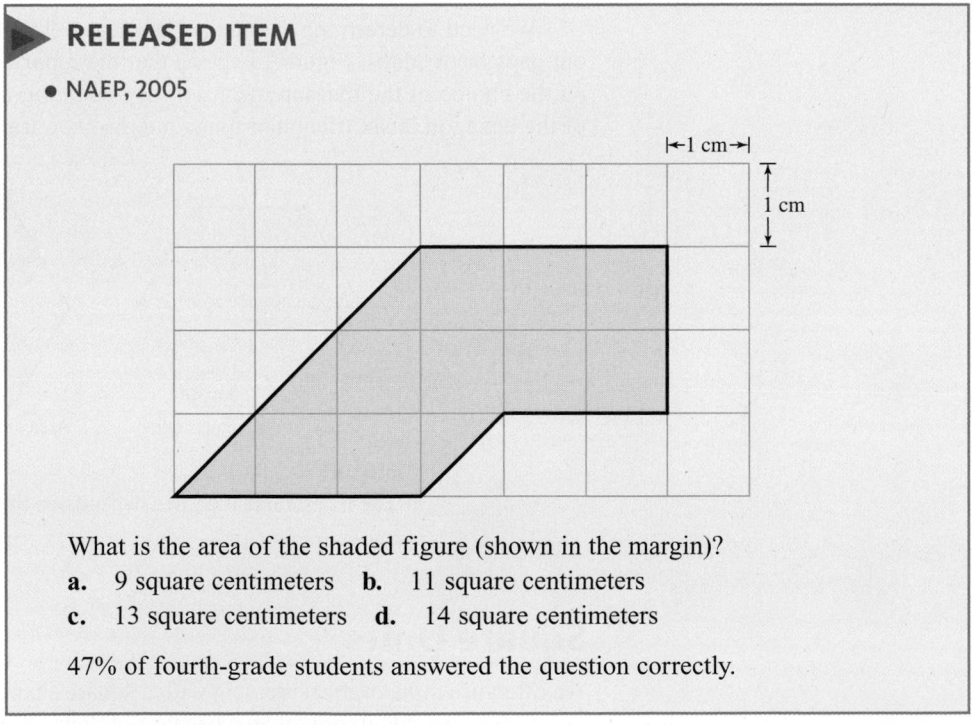

▶ **RELEASED ITEM**

● NAEP, 2005

What is the area of the shaded figure (shown in the margin)?
a. 9 square centimeters   b. 11 square centimeters
c. 13 square centimeters   d. 14 square centimeters

47% of fourth-grade students answered the question correctly.

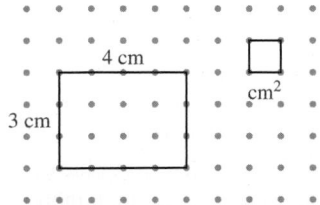

FIGURE 14
Rectangle on a dot grid.

Area of a Rectangle

Let's find the area of a rectangle with a length of 3 cm and width of 4 cm, as shown in the dot grid in Figure 14. The unit of area measurement is the *square centimeter (cm²)*.

CONNECTION

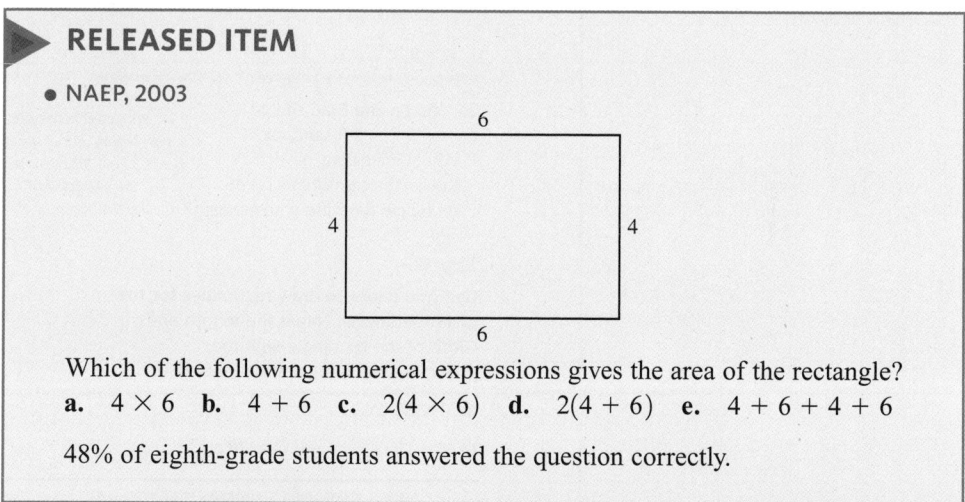

FIGURE 15

The area of the rectangle is 12 cm².

By counting the number of unit squares in Figure 15, we see that the area of the rectangle is 12 cm² (sometimes written as 12 sq. cm).

The rectangle is covered by a 3-by-4 array of unit squares without gaps or overlaps. In general, the length and width tell you how many rows and how many columns are in the array structure in the rectangle. The product tells you the number of unit squares that cover the rectangle without gaps or overlaps. The array structure of these unit squares makes it possible to determine the area of a rectangle by multiplying the width and length of the rectangle without counting the unit squares. This leads to the following formula.

> ### Formula for the Area of a Rectangle
>
> The area A of a rectangle with a length of l units and width of w units is given by $A = l \cdot w$ square units.

Students should be able to "partition a rectangle into rows and columns of same-size squares and count to find the total number of them" (Gr. 2, CCSS) and "measure areas by counting unit squares (square cm, square m, square in, square ft, and improvised units)" (Gr. 3, CCSS). The two most common mistakes students make in applying perimeter and area formulas are choosing the wrong formula (because they learn perimeter and area as procedures) and writing the wrong unit of measurement (for example, centimeter versus square centimeter). Some students use this formula correctly but later forget the conceptual basis for the formula and as a result forget how the linear measurements relate to the array structure embedded in the rectangle.

The following Released Item challenges students to apply the formula for the area of a rectangle.

> ### ▶ RELEASED ITEM
>
> • NAEP, 2003
>
> ```
>           6
>   ┌───────────────┐
>   │               │
> 4 │               │ 4
>   │               │
>   └───────────────┘
>           6
> ```
>
> Which of the following numerical expressions gives the area of the rectangle?
> **a.** 4×6 **b.** $4 + 6$ **c.** $2(4 \times 6)$ **d.** $2(4 + 6)$ **e.** $4 + 6 + 4 + 6$
>
> 48% of eighth-grade students answered the question correctly.

The following example probes student understanding of area measurement.

EXAMPLE 11.22

CONNECTION

Draw a diagram that shows the area of a rectangle with a length of 2 units and width of 5 units is 10 square units.

SOLUTION

By drawing grid lines in the rectangle at 1-unit intervals, we see the length reveals the number of rows and the width reveals the number of columns of an array of square units in the rectangle. Using the array model of multiplication, the number of square units in the array is $2 \cdot 5$, or 10. The area is 10 unit². The 10 tells "how many," and the unit² tells what we are counting.

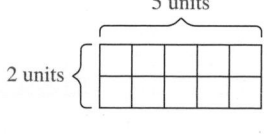

5 units
2 units

Some homework questions at the end of this section are designed to help you think about "exhibiting rectangles with the same perimeter and different areas or with the same area and different perimeters" (Gr. 3, CCSS). The following student page is an example of an activity that relates the perimeter and area of a rectangle.

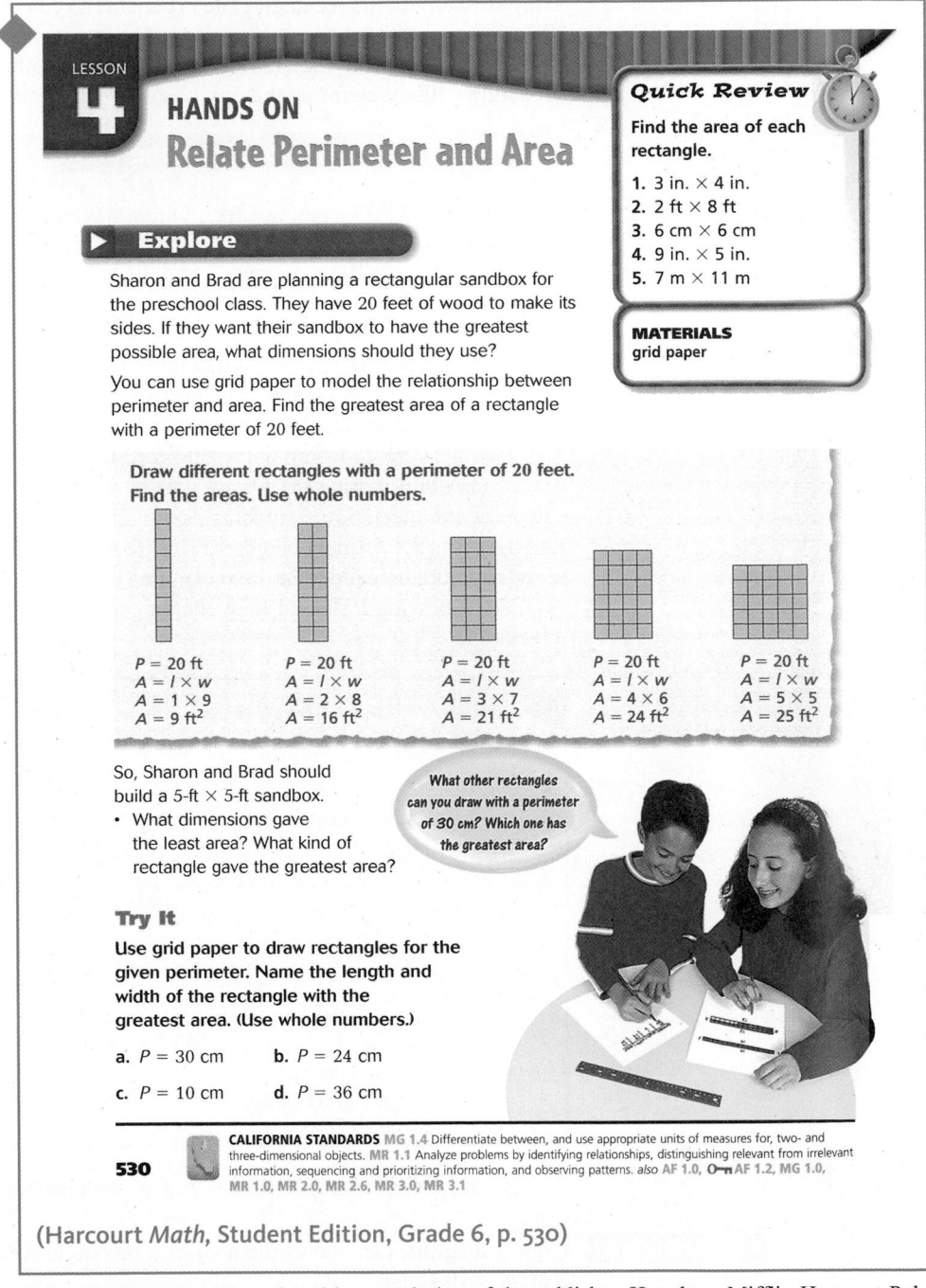

LESSON **4**

HANDS ON
Relate Perimeter and Area

▶ Explore

Sharon and Brad are planning a rectangular sandbox for the preschool class. They have 20 feet of wood to make its sides. If they want their sandbox to have the greatest possible area, what dimensions should they use?

You can use grid paper to model the relationship between perimeter and area. Find the greatest area of a rectangle with a perimeter of 20 feet.

Draw different rectangles with a perimeter of 20 feet. Find the areas. Use whole numbers.

$P = 20$ ft	$P = 20$ ft	$P = 20$ ft	$P = 20$ ft	$P = 20$ ft
$A = l \times w$	$A = l \times w$	$A = l \times w$	$A = l \times w$	$A = l \times w$
$A = 1 \times 9$	$A = 2 \times 8$	$A = 3 \times 7$	$A = 4 \times 6$	$A = 5 \times 5$
$A = 9$ ft²	$A = 16$ ft²	$A = 21$ ft²	$A = 24$ ft²	$A = 25$ ft²

So, Sharon and Brad should build a 5-ft × 5-ft sandbox.

- What dimensions gave the least area? What kind of rectangle gave the greatest area?

What other rectangles can you draw with a perimeter of 30 cm? Which one has the greatest area?

Try It

Use grid paper to draw rectangles for the given perimeter. Name the length and width of the rectangle with the greatest area. (Use whole numbers.)

a. $P = 30$ cm   **b.** $P = 24$ cm

c. $P = 10$ cm   **d.** $P = 36$ cm

Quick Review

Find the area of each rectangle.

1. 3 in. × 4 in.
2. 2 ft × 8 ft
3. 6 cm × 6 cm
4. 9 in. × 5 in.
5. 7 m × 11 m

MATERIALS
grid paper

530   **CALIFORNIA STANDARDS** MG 1.4 Differentiate between, and use appropriate units of measures for, two- and three-dimensional objects. MR 1.1 Analyze problems by identifying relationships, distinguishing relevant from irrelevant information, sequencing and prioritizing information, and observing patterns. also AF 1.0, O—n AF 1.2, MG 1.0, MR 1.0, MR 2.0, MR 2.6, MR 3.0, MR 3.1

(Harcourt *Math*, Student Edition, Grade 6, p. 530)

(© by Harcourt, Inc. Reproduced by permission of the publisher, Houghton Mifflin Harcourt Publishing Company.)

The following example illustrates how we can use representation to multiply two algebraic expressions.

EXAMPLE 11.23 Use a diagram to simplify the product $(a + 1)(2a + 3)$.

CONNECTION

REASONING

REPRESENTATION

SOLUTION

In the diagram, $a + 1$ units represent the length and $2a + 3$ units represent the width of the rectangle. The area of the rectangle is $(a + 1)(2a + 3)$ square units, which is the sum of the four areas: $a \cdot 2a$, $a \cdot 3$, $1 \cdot 2a$, and $1 \cdot 3$. Then $(a + 1)(2a + 3) = a \cdot 2a + a \cdot 3 + 1 \cdot 2a + 1 \cdot 3$. Then $(a + 1)(2a + 3) = 2a^2 + 5a + 3$.

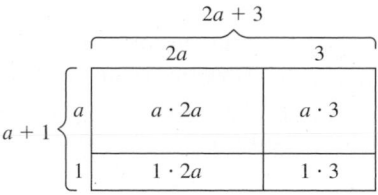

You should think about how to use a diagram to simplify the products $(a - 2)3a$ and $(a - 2)(3a + 1)$.

Dimensional Analysis and Area

Table 11.8 lists common units of area in the U.S. customary system, along with contextualized situations that might use these measurements.

TABLE 11.8 Common Units of Area in the U.S. Customary System

Unit	Symbol	Contextualized situation
square inch	in^2	A carpenter charges customers by the square inch to determine how much to charge for a hardwood cabinet door.
square foot	ft^2	Real estate agents report the size of a house in square feet.
square yard	yd^2	A carpet company may sell carpet by the square yard, such as $15 to $35 per square yard.
square mile	mi^2	The area of Texas is 261,797 square miles, but 70% of the population of Texas lives within 200 miles of the capital, Austin.

An acre is another unit of area, with 640 acres = 1 square mile.

How many square feet are in 1 square yard? We can answer this question using a diagram. Figure 16(a) is a representation of a square with area 1 square yard. The length of each side is 1 yard, or 3 feet. In Figure 16(b), we "see" $1 \text{ yd}^2 = 9 \text{ ft}^2$.

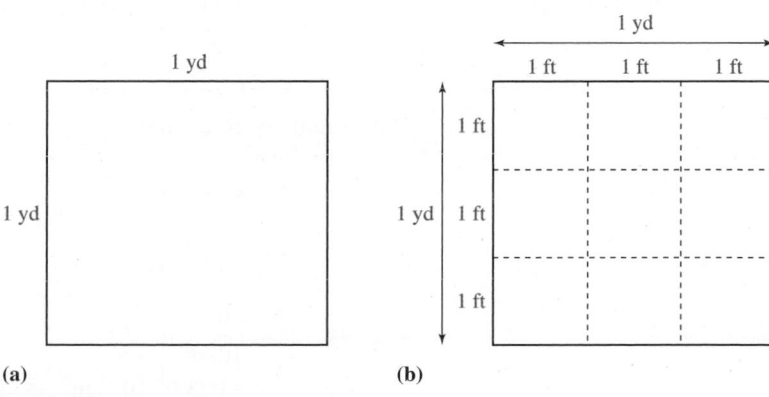

(a)   **(b)**

FIGURE 16

Relating yd^2 and ft^2.

In dimensional analysis, we treat the measurement unit as a variable, as in the equation $(3a)^2 = 3^2a^2$, although it is a label. In this example, we get

$$1 \text{ yd}^2 = 1 \text{ yd}^2 \cdot \left(\frac{3 \text{ ft}}{1 \text{ yd}}\right)^2 = 1 \text{ yd}^2 \cdot \frac{3^2 \text{ ft}^2}{1^2 \text{ yd}^2} = 1 \cancel{\text{yd}^2} \cdot \frac{3^2 \text{ ft}^2}{1^2 \cancel{\text{yd}^2}} = \frac{1 \cdot 9}{1} \text{ ft}^2 = 9 \text{ ft}^2.$$

This agrees with the equation $1 \text{ yd}^2 = 9 \text{ ft}^2$ obtained from Figure 16(b).

EXAMPLE 11.24

CONNECTION

REASONING

Use dimensional analysis.

a. How many square feet of carpet are needed for a room with an area of 54 square yards?

b. Convert 765 square feet to square yards.

SOLUTION

a.

$$54 \text{ yd}^2 = 54 \text{ yd}^2 \cdot \left(\frac{3 \text{ ft}}{1 \text{ yd}}\right)^2 = 54 \text{ yd}^2 \cdot \frac{3^2 \text{ ft}^2}{1^2 \text{ yd}^2} = 54 \cancel{\text{yd}^2} \cdot \frac{9 \text{ ft}^2}{1 \cancel{\text{yd}^2}} = 54 \cdot 9 \text{ ft}^2 = 486 \text{ ft}^2$$

b.

$$765 \text{ ft}^2 = 765 \text{ ft}^2 \cdot \left(\frac{1 \text{ yd}}{3 \text{ ft}}\right)^2 = 765 \text{ ft}^2 \cdot \frac{1^2 \text{ yd}^2}{3^2 \text{ ft}^2} = 765 \cancel{\text{ft}^2} \cdot \frac{1 \text{ yd}^2}{9 \cancel{\text{ft}^2}} = \frac{765}{9} \text{ yd}^2 = 85 \text{ yd}^2$$

Table 11.9 lists common square units of measurement of area in the metric system, along with contextualized situations that might use these measurements.

TABLE 11.9 **Standard Units of Measurement of Area in the Metric System**

Unit	Symbol	Contextualized situation
square millimeter	mm²	The shipping industry uses inexpensive microchips of the size 0.4 mm² embedded in labels and barcodes to keep track of packages.
square centimeter	cm²	A study showed there were 100 million germs per square centimeter on kitchen sponges but only 300 germs per square centimeter on kitchen countertops.
square meter	m²	Real estate agents typically report the area of commercial properties in square meters.
square kilometer	km²	Population density is the number of people per square kilometer.

EXAMPLE 11.25

CONNECTION

Use dimensional analysis to convert 50.23 mm² to m².

SOLUTION

$$50.23 \text{ mm}^2 = 50.23 \text{ mm}^2 \cdot \left(\frac{1 \text{ m}}{1000 \text{ mm}}\right)^2$$

$$= 50.23 \text{ mm}^2 \cdot \frac{1^2 \text{ m}^2}{1000^2 \text{ mm}^2}$$

$$= 50.23 \cancel{\text{mm}^2} \cdot \frac{1 \text{ m}^2}{1000^2 \cancel{\text{mm}^2}}$$

$$= \frac{50.23}{1000^2} \text{ m}^2$$

$$= 5.023 \times 10^{-5} \text{ m}^2 \qquad \textbf{Use scientific notation to represent very large or very small numbers}$$

Base and Height

The terms *base* and *height* apply to parallelograms and triangles. The base, represented by the symbol *b*, is a side. The **height** (or **altitude**), represented by the symbol *h*, is the perpendicular line segment extending from a vertex of the polygon to the line containing the base. The terms *base* and *height* also refer to lengths. We illustrate these concepts in the following example.

EXAMPLE 11.26

CONNECTION

REPRESENTATION

Draw an altitude for each triangle or parallelogram for the given base.

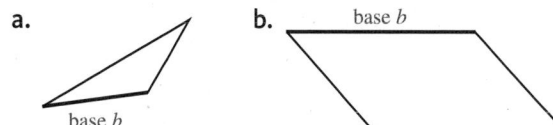

SOLUTION

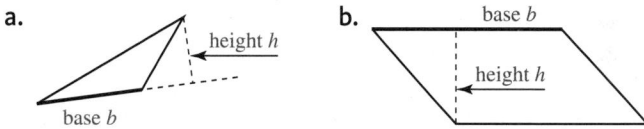

In both cases, the base is a side of the polygon, the height (or altitude) and a line containing the base are perpendicular, and the height (or altitude) can be chosen so that it contains at least one vertex of the polygon. ▲

A triangle could have any side designated as the base. Each base then has a corresponding height. The height is usually not the same as one of the sides, unless the side meets the base at a right angle. This is a source of confusion for some students, because they mistakenly think the base and height are adjacent sides.

Area of a Parallelogram, Triangle, and Trapezoid

Now we are ready to find the area of a parallelogram, triangle, and trapezoid. Your students can easily follow along with a cutout of a parallelogram and scissors to derive the area of a parallelogram. Figure 17 shows a parallelogram. Cut the parallelogram along the dotted line, and move the triangle to the other side to form a rectangle.

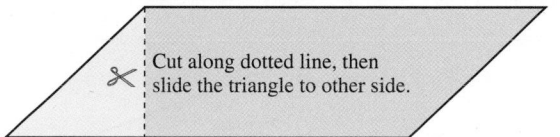

FIGURE 17
Visualizing the formula for the area of a parallelogram.

The area of parallelogram equals the area of the rectangle. What do we need to know about the rectangle in Figure 18 to find its area? We need to know its *length* and *width*. That is the same as needing to know the *base* and *height* of the parallelogram.

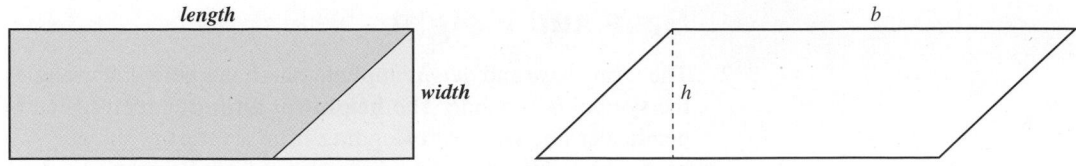

FIGURE 18

The area of a parallelogram depends on the base and height of the parallelogram.

This leads to the following general formula.

> ### Formula for the Area of a Parallelogram
>
> The area A of a parallelogram with a base of b units and a height of h units is given by $A = bh$ square units.

EXAMPLE 11.27 Use a formula to find the area of the parallelogram.

CONNECTION

REPRESENTATION

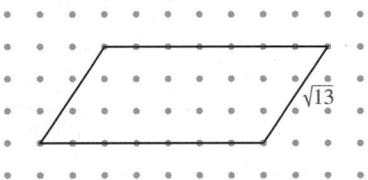

SOLUTION

The horizontal side has a length of 7 units. By choosing this to be the base, we observe the height is 3 units. Then the area of the parallelogram is $A = bh = 7 \cdot 3 = 21$ square units.

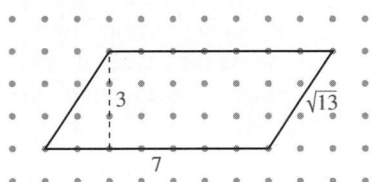

Your students could easily follow along to understand the formula for the area of a triangle. First, draw a triangle on a sheet of paper and mark the base and height of the triangle with b and h, respectively, as shown in Figure 19. Then trace the triangle on another sheet of paper. Use scissors to cut out the second triangle, and then place it along the original triangle until you form a parallelogram.

CONNECTION

REASONING

REPRESENTATION

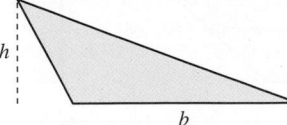 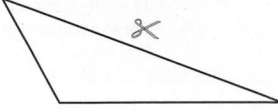 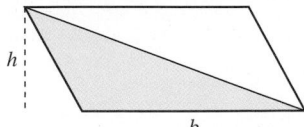

FIGURE 19

Visualizing the formula for the area of a triangle.

The diagram reveals the result: the area of the triangle is half the area of the parallelogram. This leads to the following general formula.

Formula for the Area of a Triangle

The area A of a triangle with a base of b units and corresponding height of h units is given by $A = \frac{1}{2}bh$ square units.

EXAMPLE 11.28 Use a formula to find the area of the triangle.

CONNECTION

REPRESENTATION

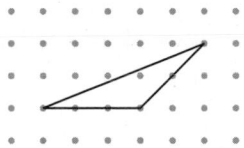

SOLUTION

The horizontal side has a length of 3 units. By choosing this to be the base, we observe the height is 2 units. Then the area of the triangle is $A = \frac{1}{2}bh = \frac{1}{2}(3 \cdot 2) = 3$ square units.

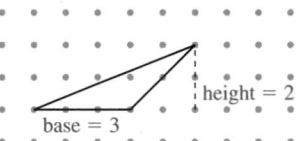

CONNECTION

REPRESENTATION

Your students could easily follow along with manipulatives to understand the formula for the area of a trapezoid. The terms *base* and *height* also apply to trapezoids. The parallel sides are bases. First, draw a trapezoid on a sheet of paper and mark the bases a and b and the height h, as shown in Figure 20. Then trace the trapezoid on another sheet of paper. Use scissors to cut out the second trapezoid, and then place it along the original trapezoid until you form a parallelogram.

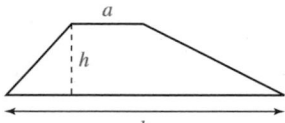 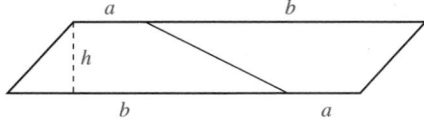

FIGURE 20
Visualizing the formula for the area of a trapezoid.

The diagram reveals that the area A of the trapezoid is half the area of the parallelogram with a base of $a + b$ units and height of h units: $A = \frac{1}{2}(a + b)h$ square units. This leads to the following area formula for trapezoids.

Formula for the Area of a Trapezoid

The area A of a trapezoid with bases of a and b units and a height of h units is given by $A = \frac{1}{2}(a + b)h$ square units.

The number $\frac{1}{2}(a + b)$ is the average of the two bases. It may help to think of the area of a trapezoid as the average base times the height.

Area of a Circle

A **sector** of a circle is the region bounded by two radii of the circle and the arc of the circle that is intercepted by the radii. A sector looks like a slice of apple pie. We can motivate the formula for the area of a circle as follows. Partition a shaded circle with a radius of r units into thin sectors that look like triangles, as shown in Figure 21(a). Figure 21(b) shows how to cut the sectors, and Figure 21(c) shows how to put them together.

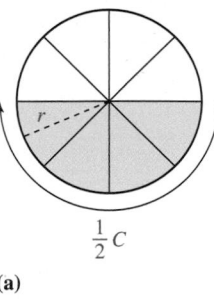

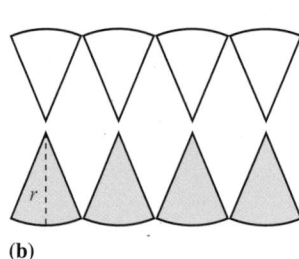

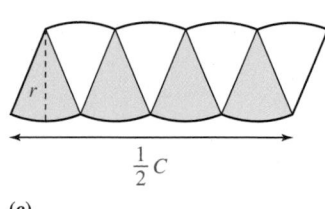

(a)   (b)   (c)

FIGURE 21
Visualizing the formula for the area of a circle.

The bumpy shape in Figure 21(c) resembles a parallelogram with a base of $\frac{1}{2}C$ units, height of r units, and area $A \approx (\frac{1}{2}C)r = (\frac{1}{2}2\pi r)r = \pi r^2$ square units. The shape looks increasingly like a parallelogram as sectors become thinner. Students should "know the formulas for the circumference of a circle and use them to solve problems" (Gr. 7, CCSS). Now we give the exact formula for the area of a circle.

Formula for the Area of a Circle

The area A of a circle with a radius of r units is given by $A = \pi r^2$ square units.

EXAMPLE 11.29

REPRESENTATION

a. Find the area of a circle with a radius of 3.52 feet.

b. The area of a circle is 48 square feet. Find the circumference of the circle.

SOLUTION

a. $A = \pi(3.52)^2 = \pi(12.3904) \approx 38.93$ ft^2

b. $A = \pi r^2$, so $48 = \pi r^2$. Then $r^2 = 48/\pi$. Then $r = \sqrt{48/\pi}$. Then $C = 2\pi r = 2\pi\sqrt{48/\pi}$
≈ 24.6 ft.

▲

EXAMPLE 11.30

CONNECTION

REASONING

Fill in the blank with a number: The area of a circle with the radius $3r$ is _____ times the area of a circle with the radius r.

SOLUTION

$$A = \pi(3r)^2 \text{ square units}$$
$$= \pi \cdot 9r^2 \text{ square units}$$
$$= 9 \cdot \pi r^2 \text{ square units}$$

This means the area of a circle with the radius $3r$ is nine times the area of a circle with the radius r.

▲

The following Classroom Connection illustrates that students should be able to use the circle area formula to solve problems.

> ### Classroom Connection
>
> ● (Harcourt *Math*, Student Edition, Grade 5, p. 479
>
> A Ferris wheel at the local amusement park has a circumference of 800 ft. This is the same distance as one complete revolution. Find the radius of the Ferris wheel. (© by Harcourt, Inc. Reproduced by permission of the publisher, Houghton Mifflin Harcourt Publishing Company.)

Area of a Sector

In the following example, we report the areas of sectors as fractions of the area of the circle.

EXAMPLE 11.31

CONNECTION

REASONING

Express each area of a sector with the given central angle as a fraction of the area of a circle with a radius of r units.

a.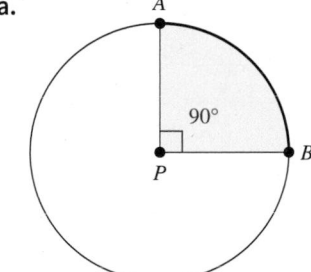

b.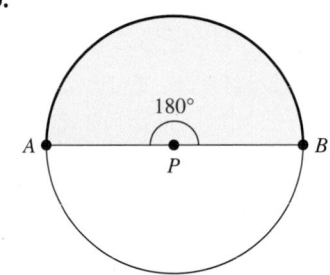

c.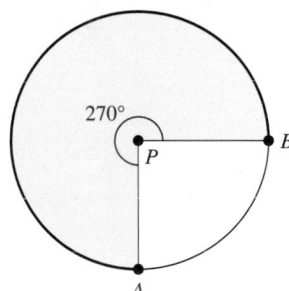

SOLUTION

We see the shaded regions equal one-quarter, one-half, and three-quarters of the area of the circle.

a. The area of the sector $= \frac{1}{4}\pi r^2$. $\frac{1}{4} = \frac{90}{360}$, so the area of the sector $= \frac{90}{360}\pi r^2$.

b. The area of the sector $= \frac{1}{2}\pi r^2$. $\frac{1}{2} = \frac{180}{360}$, so the area of the sector $= \frac{180}{360}\pi r^2$.

c. The area of the sector $= \frac{3}{4}\pi r^2$. $\frac{3}{4} = \frac{270}{360}$, so the area of the sector $= \frac{270}{360}\pi r^2$.

This example establishes a pattern to help us find the area of any sector of a circle. Let $\overset{\frown}{AB}$ be a 42° arc on a circle with a radius of 5 cm. Then the area of the sector is $\frac{42}{360}\pi \cdot 5^2 \approx 9.2$ cm².

> ### Theorem
>
> Let $\overset{\frown}{XY}$ be an arc on a circle with a radius of r units. Let A be the area of the sector, and let the central angle of the sector be $n°$. Then $A = \dfrac{n}{360}\pi r^2$.

The result states that the area of a sector is a fraction of the area of its circle. As you may have guessed, there is no standard notation for the area of a sector.

EXAMPLE 11.32 The radius of the circle is 4 cm, and the area of the sector is 9.8 cm².

CONNECTION

REASONING

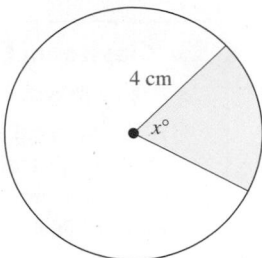

What is the measure of the central angle? Round your result to the nearest degree.

SOLUTION

The radius of the circle is 4 cm, so the area of the circle is 16π cm². Let x be the measure of the central angle for the arc. Then

$$\text{area of the sector} = \frac{x}{360} \cdot \text{area of circle}$$

$$9.8 \text{ cm}^2 = \frac{x}{360} \cdot 16\pi \text{ cm}^2$$

$$x = \frac{9.8 \cdot 360}{16\pi}$$

$$x \approx 70$$

The measure of the central angle is approximately 70°.

▲

We develop formulas for the area of regular polygons in the next section (after we discuss the Pythagorean theorem).

QUESTIONS FOR SECTION 11.2

REPRESENTATION

Refresher: Representations (language, diagrams, tables, symbols, algebra, manipulatives, and contextualized situations) are important because we use them to organize, record, and communicate mathematical ideas and make them more comprehensible.

1. Use this rectangle to do the following.

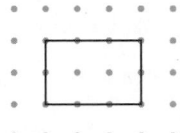

a. Suppose the area is 2 "tullies." Sketch a possible tully.

b. Suppose the area is 3 "snerds." Sketch a possible snerd.

c. Suppose the area is 6 "blips." Sketch a possible blip.

d. Determine what happens to the size of the measurement unit as the number of measurement units increases.

2. The diagram shows a polygon on a centimeter dot grid.

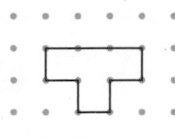

a. Calculate the perimeter and area of the polygon.

b. Where could you place another square centimeter to increase the area by 1 cm² and keep the perimeter the same?

c. If you increase the area of a polygon, does the perimeter automatically increase?

3. Draw on the dot grid a triangle with an area of 15 square units of the given type.

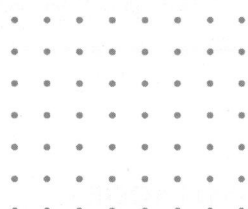

   a. obtuse triangle   **b.** acute triangle   **c.** right triangle

4. Do the following.

   a. Draw a picture of a unit square with an area of 1 square inch.

   b. Draw a picture of a unit square with an area of 1 cm^2.

5. Use a formula to find the area of the triangle.

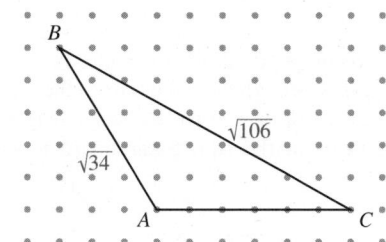

6. Use a formula to find the area of the parallelogram.

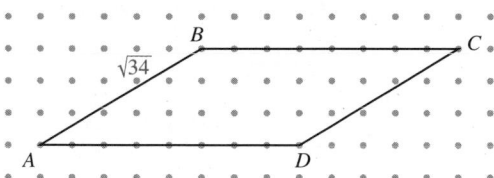

7. Use a formula to find the area of the polygon.

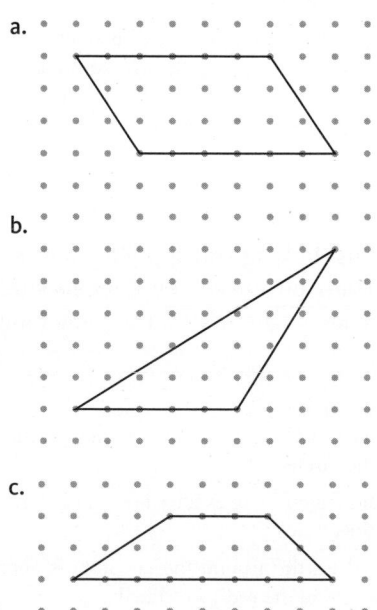

8. Find the area of each polygon shown.

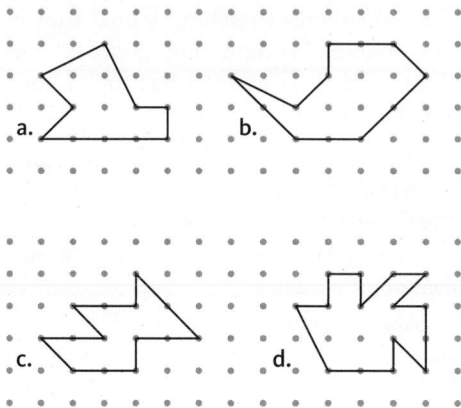

9. Use the following representation of prefixes to convert the measurements.

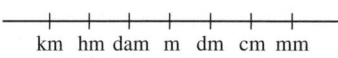

   a. 4 km^2 = ___ m^2 **b.** 1 m^2 = ___ km^2

   c. 0.5 hm^2 = ___ m^2 **d.** 567 cm^2 = ___ dm^2

10. Find the area of the polygon in terms of each measurement unit shown.

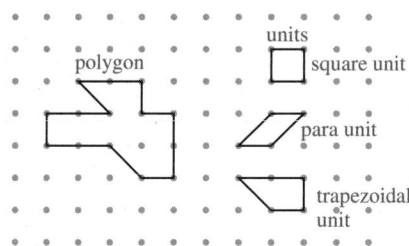

   a. square unit   **b.** para unit   **c.** trapezoidal unit

11. Rectangle *ABCD* is partitioned into rectangles *ABFE* and *EFCD*.

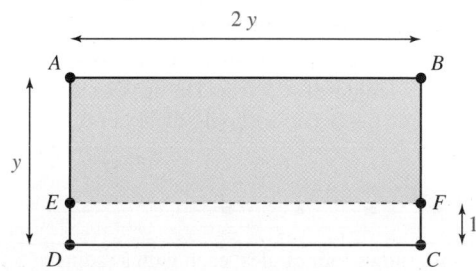

   a. What does $y \times (2y)$ represent?

   b. What does $1 \times 2y$ represent?

   c. What does $(y - 1)(2y)$ represent?

   d. Complete the equation: $y \times (2y) =$ ___ + ___.

   e. Use the equation in part (d) to complete the following equation: $(y - 1)(2y) =$ ___ − ___.

12. Use a diagram to simplify $(a + 1)(3a + 4)$.

13. Use a diagram to simplify $(a - 3)(3a + 4)$.

PROBLEM SOLVING

Refresher: Problem solving (reaching a goal that is not immediately attainable) is important because it helps students think more deeply about what they know and deal with unfamiliar situations.

14. The width of a rectangle is 3 cm more than four times the length of the rectangle. The perimeter is 945 cm. Find the width and length of the rectangle. Show your work.

15. A rectangle has a perimeter of 32 cm and area of 48 cm². Find the dimensions of the rectangle.

16. A spa in the shape of a circle has a radius of 15 feet. The deck of the spa that surrounds the pool also has the shape of a circle and is 3 feet wide.

    a. Draw a diagram that represents the situation.

    b. Determine the area of the deck.

17. Tim plans to retile the living room floor, which has the shape of a rectangle with the dimensions 30 by 14 feet. The tiles are 3-by-3-inch squares. There are 24 tiles in each box. How many boxes of tiles does Tim need? Show your work.

18. The area of $\triangle ABC$ is 15 cm². What is the area of the trapezoid? Show your work.

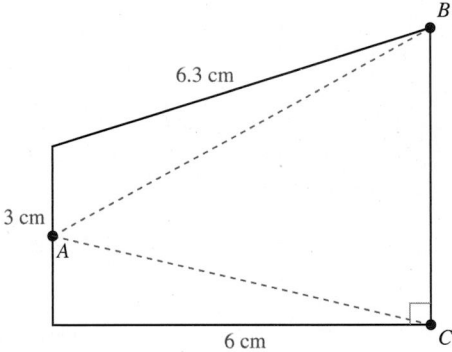

19. A small bucket of paint covers 145 square feet. How many buckets of paint would you need to paint a rectangular wall that is 44 by 17 feet? Show your work.

20. A security company plans to place sensors every 8 feet along a fence with a length of 425 feet. The sensors are sold in packs of three. How many packs should the security company manager order?

21. The figure shows four circles, each with a radius of 5 cm. Find the area of the region between the circles.

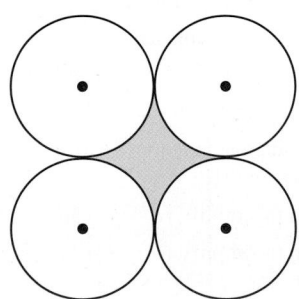

22. The parallelogram has sides of the contrived length 4 and 2 jobes. The parallelogram can be covered with 8 equal-sized pieces without overlaps or gaps. What could 1 jobe look like?

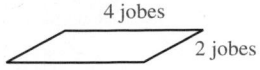

REASONING AND PROOF

Refresher: Reasoning and proof (thinking and justifying) are important because they help students make sense of mathematics.

23. Use a centimeter dot grid to do the following.

    a. Draw two rectangles, each with an area of 12 cm² but different perimeters.

    b. Draw two rectangles, each with a perimeter of 12 cm but different areas.

24. A student cuts out a circle from a square piece of cardboard. The circle passes through the midpoints of the sides of a square as shown. Each side of the square has a length of 12 units. What percentage of the square cardboard is wasted? Show your work.

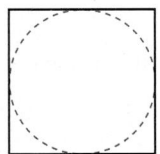

25. A rectangle has a length of 4 cm and width of 6 cm. Now increase each measurement by 3 cm. Fill in the blank with a number. Show your work.

    a. The perimeter increased by ___ cm.

    b. The perimeter increased by ___%.

26. A sign at a fabric store gives the following directions for determining the square yardage of your quilt: Measure the length, measure the width, multiply the length and width, and then divide by 1296. Explain these directions.

CONNECTIONS

Refresher: Connections (linking and applying mathematical ideas) are important because they deepen student understanding and make mathematics more meaningful, flexible, and useful.

27. Answer the following.

    a. The distance around a circle is about how many times the distance across the circle?

    b. The distance around a circle is exactly how many times the distance across the circle?

28. The circumference of Earth (around the equator) is approximately 40,074.87 km. Find the radius of Earth.

29. Consider Heron's formula: Let $s = (a + b + c)/2$ denote the *semiperimeter* of a triangle with sides of the lengths

a units, b units, and c units. The area of the triangle is $A = \sqrt{s(s-a)(s-b)(s-c)}$ square units. Find the area of the triangle with sides of the given lengths.

a. 7, 12, and 8 cm   **b.** 5, 3, and 4 cm

c. 15, 20, and 18 cm

30. Convert the measurements. Round to two decimal places as appropriate.

a. 15 cm² = ___ in²   **b.** 2.75 ft² = ___ mm²

c. 3 m² = ___ ft²   **d.** 1527.56 yd² = ___ mi²

31. The Large Hadron Collider is a power particle accelerator. It sends protons smashing into each other, and the resulting collision creates new particles that scientists study. At full speed, the protons travel 0.999999991 times the speed of light. The protons travel in the path of a circle with a circumference of 17 miles, making 11,000 revolutions per second. How far do the protons travel in 1 second?

32. The front wheel of a tricycle has a circumference of 54 inches, and the back wheels have a circumference of 36 inches. If points P and Q are both touching the sidewalk when Jose starts to ride, when will P and Q first touch the sidewalk at the same time again? Explain your answer.

33. The base of a triangle is decreased by 20%. How much must you increase the height to keep the area of the triangle the same? Express your answer as a percent.

34. Calculate the area of $\triangle ABC$ in three ways, using each side of the triangle as the base. Use a metric ruler to measure each base and corresponding height in millimeters.

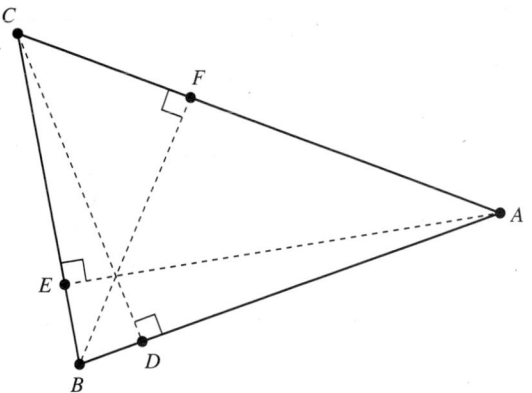

a. Organize your results in a table. Use appropriate symbolic representations and measurement units.

b. Discuss your results.

COMMUNICATION

Refresher: Communication (written and verbal explanations using representations and proper mathematical vocabulary) is important because it helps students refine and strengthen their understanding.

35. What is π?

36. Rectangle A has the dimensions 9 by 12 feet, and rectangle B has the dimensions 340 by 400 feet. Which rectangle looks more like a square? Explain your answer.

37. A teacher showed the following diagram on a centimeter dot grid to her students. She asked her class, "What is the perimeter of the rectangle?" The students wrote their answers on paper. Samantha wrote, "The perimeter is 20 cm." Luis wrote, "The perimeter is 18."

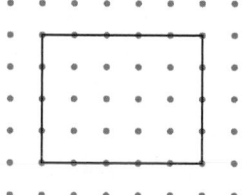

a. What error did Samantha make?

b. What error did Luis make?

38. What effect does multiplying a radius by 4 have on the

a. circumference?   **b.** area?

39. What effect does multiplying the sides of a rectangle by 4 have on the

a. perimeter?   **b.** area?

More practice with the ideas of the section

40. Fill in the blank. Choose one of the following words or phrases: *altitude, attitude, centimeter dot grid, correct formulas, customized, incorrect formulas, meter, metric, perimeter, rectangle, section, sector, slice of pie, square, square unit, unit of measurement, unit squared,* or *U.S. customary.*

a. The _____ of a simple closed figure is a measure of the length of the boundary of the figure.

b. A(n) _____ is a rectangular array of dots in which the distance between two adjacent dots in the same row or column is 1 cm.

c. The perimeter P of a _____ with a length of l units and width of w units is $P = 2l + 2w$ units.

d. The perimeter P of a _____ with sides of the length s units is $P = 4s$ units.

e. Some elementary-school students use formulas without paying attention to their conceptual basis, making them susceptible to applying _____ or using incorrect units.

f. The symbol unit² represents _____.

g. The two most common mistakes students make in applying perimeter and area formulas are that students choose the wrong formula and write the wrong _____ (for example, centimeter versus square centimeter).

h. Measurement units such as feet and miles belong to the _____ system.

i. Measurement units such as meters and volts belong to the _____ measurement system.

j. The _____ of a triangle or parallelogram is the perpendicular line segment extending from a line containing the base to another side of the polygon such that the altitude contains at least one vertex of the polygon.

k. A(n) _____ of a circle is the region between two radii of the circle.

41. Determine the area of the trapezoid.

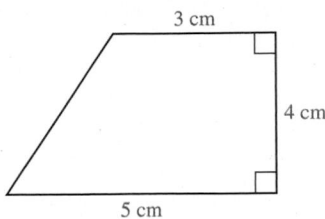

42. Draw each polygon on a dot grid.

a. A trapezoid with an area of 12 cm². Label the bases and height.

b. An obtuse triangle with an area of 6 cm². Label the base and height.

c. A parallelogram with an area of 8 cm². Label the base and height.

43. A dog chases a cat around a circular table. They run 43 laps around the table for a total of 645 feet. What is the radius of the table?

44. Do the following.

a. Earth's equatorial radius (the distance from its center to the equator) is 6378.135 km. Convert this measurement to miles.

b. A satellite revolves in a circular orbit around Earth. The satellite is 4300 miles from the center of Earth. How far does it travel during 18 revolutions?

c. A satellite revolves in a circular orbit around Earth. The satellite is 250 miles from the surface of Earth. How far does it travel during 5 revolutions?

45. A spa in the shape of a circle has a radius of 15 feet. The deck that surrounds the spa also has the shape of a circle and is 4 feet wide.

a. Draw a diagram that represents the situation.

b. Determine the area of the deck.

46. Use a metric ruler to find the circumference of the circle.

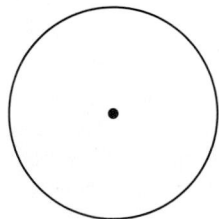

47. Use a metric ruler to find the perimeter and area of the rectangle.

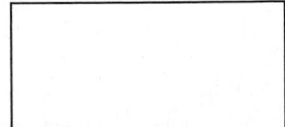

48. Use a metric ruler to find the area of the triangle.

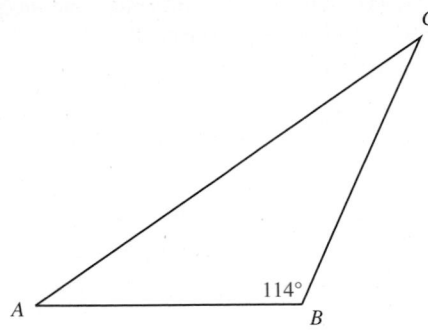

49. Use a metric ruler to find the area of the parallelogram.

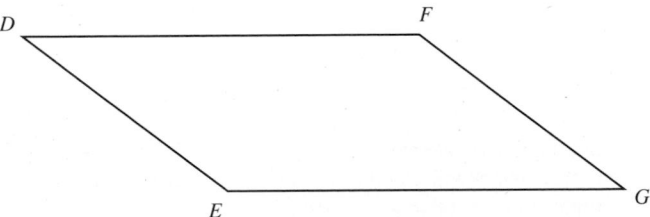

50. Use a protractor to find each measurement.

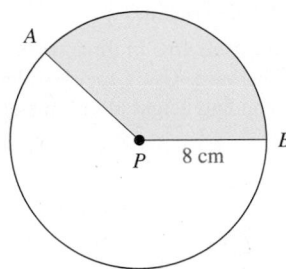

a. The area of the sector determined by $\overarc{AB}$.

b. The arc length of $\overarc{AB}$.

51. Two squares have the same area. Justify why they must have the same perimeter using algebra. (Hint: Use the variables A_1, P_1, s_1, A_2, P_2, and s_2.)

52. Two circles have the same circumference. Justify why they must have the same area using algebra. (Hint: Use the variables A_1, C_1, r_1, A_2, C_2, and r_2.)

53. How many square feet are in a rectangle with the dimensions 3 by 2 yards? Use

a. a diagram.   b. dimensional analysis.

54. If you increase the perimeter of a rectangle, must the area of the rectangle also increase? Support your answer with examples.

55. The radius of circle P is eight times the radius of circle Q. Fill in the blank with a number: The area of a circle with the radius $8r$ is _____ times as large as the area of a circle with the radius r.

56. A triangle has a base of 3 cm and height of 5 cm. Now increase each measurement by 4 cm. Fill in the blank with a number. Show your work.

a. The area increased by ___ cm².

b. The area increased by ___%.

57. If you roll a quarter around the edge of the rectangle until it returns to its original position, about how many revolutions will the coin have turned? (Hint: The diameter of a quarter is 24.26 mm, and 1 in = 2.54 cm.)

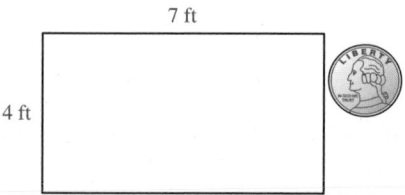

7 ft

4 ft

58. The base of a parallelogram is 3 cm more than four times the height. Write the area of the parallelogram as a function of height.

59. Draw a rectangle with a perimeter of 24 m. Calculate the area of the rectangle. Do all rectangles with a perimeter of 24 m have the same area? Explain your answer.

60. Draw a rectangle with an area of 24 m². Calculate the perimeter of the rectangle. Do all rectangles with an area of 24 m² have the same perimeter? Explain your answer.

61. Do the following. Round each measurement to the nearest tenth. Assume $\overline{BC} \perp \overline{AE}$ and $\overline{CD} \perp \overline{AB}$.

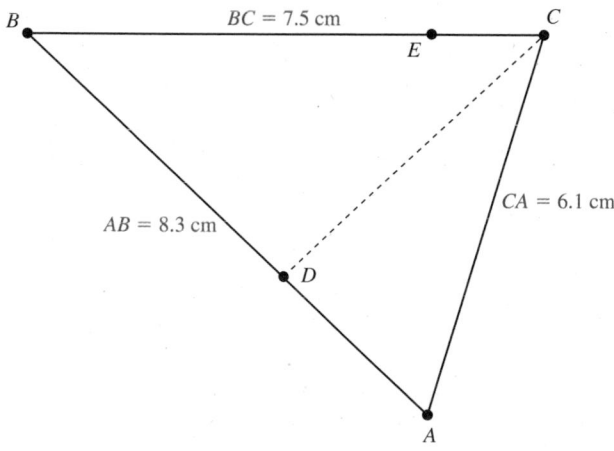

BC = 7.5 cm

E

CA = 6.1 cm

AB = 8.3 cm

D

A

a. Find the perimeter of △ABC.

b. Find the area of △ABC. (Hint: Use Heron's formula in Problem 29.)

c. Find CD.

62. Find the missing measurement AC. Assume $\overline{BD} \perp \overline{AC}$ and $\overleftrightarrow{CE} \perp \overline{AB}$.

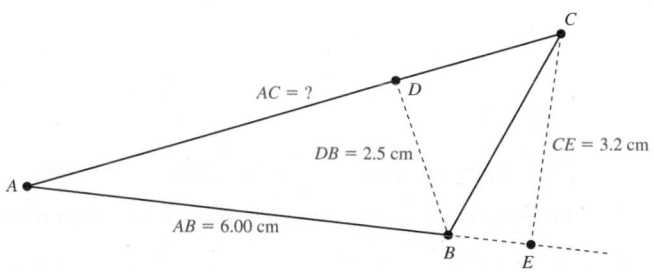

C

AC = ?

D

DB = 2.5 cm

CE = 3.2 cm

A

AB = 6.00 cm

B   E

63. Answer the following.

a. If the area of a square is 30 m², what must the perimeter be?

b. If the area of a rectangle is 30 m², what can the perimeter be?

c. If the area of a circle is 30 m², what must the circumference be?

64. A spa in the shape of a circle has a radius of 12 feet. The deck that surrounds the spa also has the shape of a circle and is x feet wide.

a. Draw a diagram that represents the situation.

b. Express the area of the deck as a function of x.

65. Write the formula for the perimeter of a regular polygon with the following number of sides, each of the length s units.

a. three sides   b. four sides   c. five sides   d. n sides

66. The diagram shows a kite. Discuss the measurements you would need to calculate the area A of the kite. Then write a formula for A. Let d_1 and d_2 denote the diagonals of the kite.

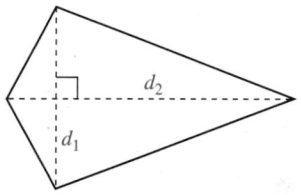

d_2

d_1

67. Do the following, using the diagram shown.

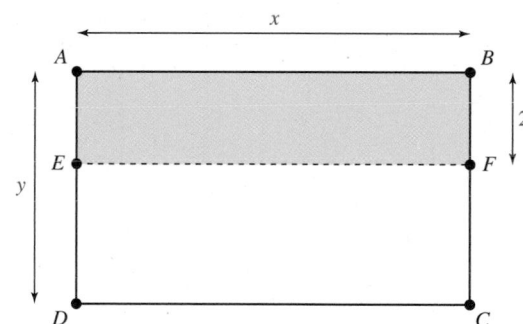

x

A   B

2

E   F

y

D   C

a. What does xy represent?   b. What does 2x represent?

c. What does x(y − 2) represent?

d. Complete the equation: xy = ___ + ___.

e. Use the equation in part (d) to complete the following equation: x(y − 2) = ___ − ___.

68. The directions for pancake mix say that one large scoop of mix makes 12 circular pancakes, each with a diameter of 4 inches. Samantha plans to make the pancakes in a circular pan with a diameter of 6 inches. How many whole pancakes can she make, each with a diameter of 6 inches?

69. Let A be the area of a rectangle with a length of l and width of w. How much must you decrease the width of the rectangle to keep the area constant if you increase the length by 15%?

70. Let A be the area of a rectangle with a length of l and width of w. How much must you increase the width of the rectangle to keep the area constant if you decrease the length by 12%?

71. The base of a triangle is decreased by 40%. How much must you increase the height to keep the area the same?

72. The radius of circle P is 120% of the radius of circle Q. So the area of circle P is how many times the area of circle Q?

SECTION 11.3 The Pythagorean Theorem and Triangle Inequalities

The Pythagorean Theorem

A right triangle is a triangle with an angle of 90°. The **hypotenuse** of a right triangle is the side of the triangle opposite the right angle. The word *hypotenuse* stems from the Greek word *hypoteinousa*, which means "to stretch." The legs of the triangle are the two other sides. Similar to the term *radius,* the words *hypotenuse* and *leg* dually refer to both the sides and their measurements.

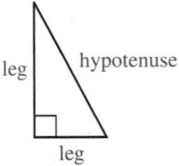

Now we state the **Pythagorean theorem,** which relates the sides of a right triangle, using words and a diagram.

> ### Pythagorean Theorem
>
> If a right triangle has legs of a units and b units and a hypotenuse of c units, then $a^2 + b^2 = c^2$.
>
>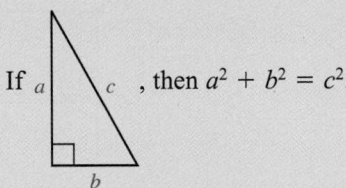
> If [triangle], then $a^2 + b^2 = c^2$.

This result states that if you know the length of two sides of a right triangle, then you can calculate the length of the third side. The following examples apply the Pythagorean theorem to obtain measurements indirectly.

EXAMPLE 11.33 A right triangle has the given measurements. Find the missing measurement to the nearest tenth.

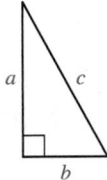

a. $a = 5$ cm, and $b = 7$ cm

b. $b = 3$ cm, and $c = 8$ cm

SOLUTION

a. $c^2 = a^2 + b^2$, so $c^2 = 5^2 + 7^2 = 25 + 49 = 74$. Then $c = \sqrt{74}$. Then $c \approx 8.6$ cm.

b. $c^2 = a^2 + b^2$, so $a^2 = c^2 - b^2 = 8^2 - 3^2 = 64 - 9 = 55$. Then $a = \sqrt{55}$. Then $a \approx 7.4$ cm.

> ► **RELEASED ITEM**
>
> • NAEP, 2009
>
>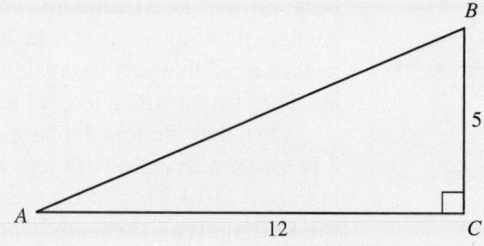
>
> In the right triangle above, what is the length of $\overline{AB}$?
> **a.** 8.5 **b.** 12 **c.** 13 **d.** 17 **e.** 30
>
> 40% of eighth-grade students gave the correct answer.

EXAMPLE 11.34   Determine the perimeter of the triangle. Round to the nearest tenth.

CONNECTION
PROBLEM SOLVING
REASONING

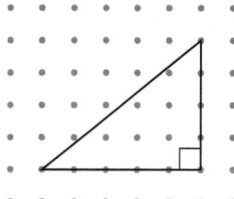

SOLUTION

The triangle is a right triangle. The legs are 5 units and 4 units. The hypotenuse is c units, where $c^2 = 5^2 + 4^2$. Then $c^2 = 25 + 16$. Then $c^2 = 41$. Then we obtain the indirect measurement $c = \sqrt{41}$ units. So the perimeter is $5 + 4 + \sqrt{41} \approx 15.4$ units. ▲

> ■ **Historical Note**
>
> Ancient clay tablets indicate the Babylonians knew of the Pythagorean relationship for right triangles. For example, an ancient tablet contains the following problem: "A reed stands against the wall. If the top slides down three units when the lower end slides away nine units, how long is the reed?" (Boyer, 1991, p. 40). If you let n represent the length of the reed, then this leads to a right triangle having legs of length $n - 3$ and 9 units, and a hypotenuse of length n units. The equation $(n - 3)^2 + 9^2 = n^2$ leads to the correct answer: 15 units.

EXAMPLE 11.35   Draw a line segment with a length of $\sqrt{34}$ units.

CONNECTION
PROBLEM SOLVING
REASONING
REPRESENTATION

SOLUTION

Our goal is to express 34 as the sum of two perfect squares. With some trial and error, we get $25 + 9 = 34$. Then $5^2 + 3^2 = 34$. Then $5^2 + 3^2 = (\sqrt{34})^2$. Then a right triangle with legs of 5 and 3 units has a hypotenuse with a length of $\sqrt{34}$ units, as shown in Figure 22.

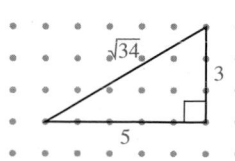

FIGURE 22

Using a dot grid to represent $\sqrt{34}$. ▲

The approach in the previous example using a dot grid fails for some numbers, such as $\sqrt{24}$.

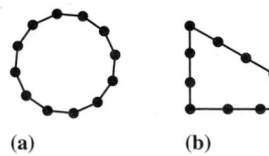

FIGURE 23

Using a knotted rope to form a 3-4-5 triangle.

The Converse of the Pythagorean Theorem

The ancient Egyptians built their civilization near the Nile River, a continual source of water in the desert climate. They often divided their property into rectangular shapes. Annual flooding of the Nile River destroyed many property boundaries, so surveyors needed a reliable way to create right angles in the rectangular shapes of property boundaries. They began with a loop of rope with 12 equally spaced knots, as shown in Figure 23(a).

Then they stretched the rope in the shape of a triangle and put stakes at knots 1, 4, and 8 to create a triangle with legs of 3 and 4 spaces and a hypotenuse of 5 spaces, as shown in Figure 23(b). They knew this triangle was a right triangle. Now we state the **converse of the Pythagorean theorem,** which establishes a condition for the sides of a right triangle.

Converse of the Pythagorean Theorem

If $a^2 + b^2 = c^2$, then a triangle with sides of lengths a units, b units, and c units is a right triangle with a hypotenuse of length c units.

If $a^2 + b^2 = c^2$, then a ⟋ c .

The following example applies this result.

EXAMPLE 11.36

CONNECTION

REASONING

Do the line segments of the given lengths form a right triangle?
a. 6, 8, and 10 m
b. 5, 7, and 9 m

SOLUTION

We must determine whether the measurements satisfy the Pythagorean equation $a^2 + b^2 = c^2$. The line segment with the greatest length would be the hypotenuse of the right triangle.

a. $6^2 + 8^2 \stackrel{?}{=} 10^2$

$36 + 64 \stackrel{?}{=} 100$

$100 = 100$

Yes, the line segments form a right triangle.

b. $5^2 + 7^2 \stackrel{?}{=} 9^2$

$25 + 49 \stackrel{?}{=} 81$

$74 \neq 81$

No, the line segments do not form a right triangle.

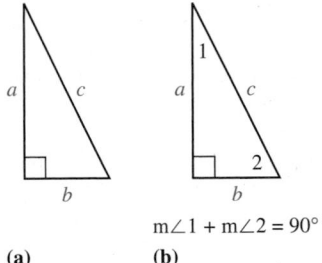

(a)   **(b)**

FIGURE 24

A right triangle with sides of length a, b, and c units.

CONNECTION

REASONING

REPRESENTATION

Students should be able to "understand the statement of the Pythagorean Theorem and its converse" (Gr. 8, CCSS) and "explain a proof of the Pythagorean Theorem and its converse" (Gr. 8, CCSS). There are several hundred proofs of the Pythagorean theorem, but we provide an accessible proof based on a diagram, algebra, and basic area principles. We begin with a right triangle, in Figure 24(a), with sides of the lengths a, b, and c units.

The sum of measures of the interior angles of the right triangle is 180°, so m∠1 + m∠2 = 90°, as shown in Figure 24(b). In Figure 25, we arrange copies of the triangle to form a square with sides of the length $a + b$ units. The newly created angles are labeled 3, 4, 5, and 6. The area of the square is $(a + b)^2$ square units.

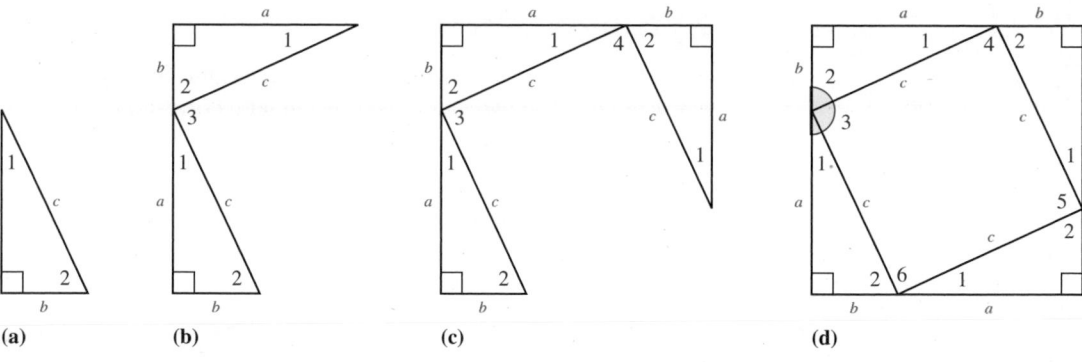

FIGURE 25

Four right triangles are assembled to form a square with sides of length $a + b$ units.

Each side of the quadrilateral with angles $\angle 3$, $\angle 4$, $\angle 5$, and $\angle 6$ has sides of the length c units. As explained in Section 12.1, a quadrilateral with opposite sides that are congruent must be a parallelogram. In this case, all four sides of the parallelogram equal c units, so the parallelogram is a rhombus. Now we establish that the rhombus is a square. In Figure 25(d), we see $m\angle 1 + m\angle 2 + m\angle 3 = 180°$. But $m\angle 1 + m\angle 2 = 90°$ (see Figure 24), so

$$m\angle 1 + m\angle 2 + m\angle 3 = 180°$$
$$90° + m\angle 3 = 180°$$
$$m\angle 3 = 90°$$

Applying the same reasoning, we can show $m\angle 4$, $m\angle 5$, and $m\angle 6$ are right angles too. Each angle of the rhombus is a right angle. Then the rhombus is a square with an area of c^2 square units. Then we have:

area of the square = area of the four triangles + area of the quadrilateral

$$(a + b)^2 = 4(\tfrac{1}{2}ab) + c^2$$
$$a^2 + 2ab + b^2 = 2ab + c^2$$
$$a^2 + b^2 = c^2$$

This proves the Pythagorean theorem. A proof of the converse of the Pythagorean equation requires the SSS triangle congruence axiom given in Chapter 12.

■ Historical Note

Pythagoras (about 569–475 BCE), a mystic, musician, and mathematician who lived in Greece, traveled to the Middle East to learn religion and mathematics. Eventually, he created and led a school on the coast of southern Italy that focused on philosophy, religion, and mathematics. The students at the Pythagorean school regarded their leader highly and followed a strict code of conduct (for example, "that at its deepest level, reality is mathematical in nature" and "that all brothers of the order should observe strict loyalty and secrecy"). The motto of the school was "All is number." To the Pythagoreans, whole numbers and rational numbers were sufficient to explain nature. But imagine their shock when the Pythagoreans later discovered the existence of irrational numbers such as the square root of 2. Although the Babylonians and Chinese applied the theorem at least 1000 years before Pythagoras, scholars named it the "Pythagorean theorem" hundreds of years after his death, because Pythagoras probably gave the first proof of the theorem. No writings of Pythagoras or his contemporary biographers exist today, so we are uncertain of his precise contributions to mathematics. But historians generally agree Pythagoras and his followers were crucial in the development of mathematical thought in Western civilization (Boyer, 1991).

Konovalikov Andrey/Shutterstock.com

Pythagorean Inequalities

Classify the triangles in Figure 26 as acute, right, or obtuse. For each triangle, let a and b correspond to the two shorter sides, and let c correspond to the longest side. Calculate a^2, b^2, and c^2, and then compare the two numbers $a^2 + b^2$ and c^2 and look for a pattern. What do you notice?

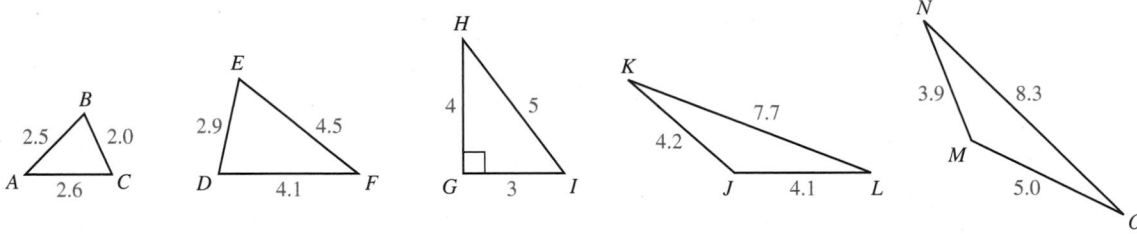

FIGURE 26

Triangles can be classified as acute, right, or obtuse based on the lengths of the sides of the triangle.

You likely noticed that the inequality $c^2 < a^2 + b^2$ holds for acute triangles and the inequality $a^2 + b^2 < c^2$ holds for obtuse triangles. These are called **Pythagorean inequalities.** You already know the Pythagorean equation $a^2 + b^2 = c^2$ holds for right triangles. Therefore, you can use the sides to classify a triangle as acute, right, or obtuse. Verify these relationships for the triangles in Figure 27.

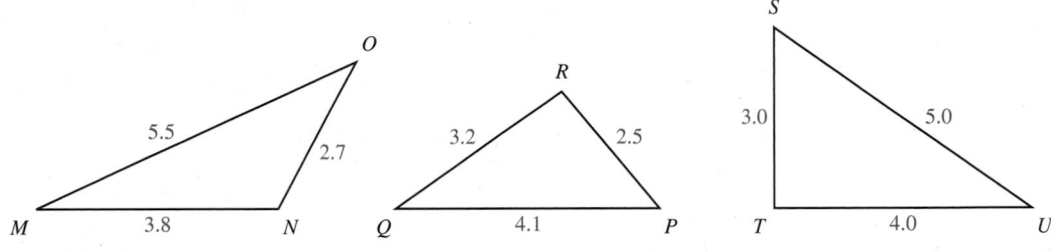

FIGURE 27

Compare the numbers $a^2 + b^2$ and c^2 to classify a triangle, where c is the length of the longest side of the triangle.

Now we state the side relationships using algebra.

> ## Pythagorean Inequalities
>
> For any triangle with sides of the lengths a, b, and c units (longest side),
>
> - $c^2 < a^2 + b^2$ if and only if the triangle is an acute triangle.
> - $a^2 + b^2 < c^2$ if and only if the triangle is an obtuse triangle.

EXAMPLE 11.37

CONNECTION

REASONING

A triangle has sides of the lengths 17, 20, and 30 cm. Classify the triangle as acute, right, or obtuse.

SOLUTION

The longest side is 30 cm. To apply the Pythagorean inequalities, we need to compare $17^2 + 20^2$ and 30^2. Because $17^2 + 20^2 = 689$ and $30^2 = 900$, we have $17^2 + 20^2 < 30^2$. The triangle is an obtuse triangle. ▲

> ### ■ Historical Note
>
> The ancient Chinese used the word *kou* (meaning "leg") to name the base of a right triangle, *ku* (meaning "thigh") to name the height or altitude, and *hsian* (meaning "bowstring") to name the side opposite the right angle in a triangle.

Relating the Sides and Angles of a Triangle

Draw several triangles using a straightedge. Measure the angles of each triangle. Identify the largest angle in each triangle. Where is the longest side of each triangle? Now draw several more triangles using a straightedge. Measure the lengths of the sides of each triangle. Identify the longest side of each triangle. Where is the largest angle of each triangle?

As you may have noticed, the longest side of a triangle is always opposite the largest angle. Verify this angle–side relationship for the triangles in Figure 28.

CONNECTION
REASONING
REPRESENTATION

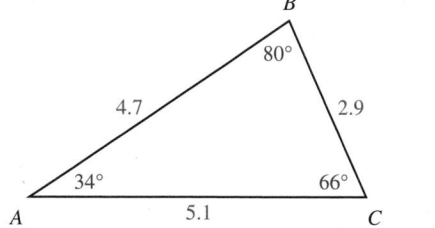 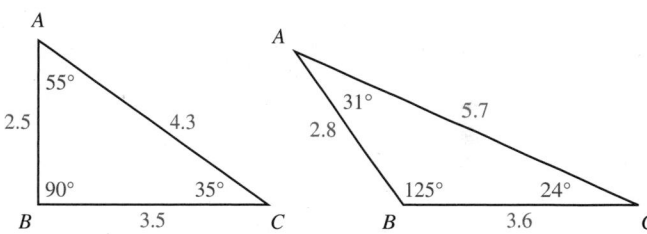

FIGURE 28
Exploring angle-side relationships. (Note: The measurements are approximate.)

Now we represent these angle–side relationships using words.

> ### Angle–Side Triangle Inequalities Theorem
>
> - The longest side of a triangle is opposite the largest angle of the triangle.
> - The shortest side of a triangle is opposite the smallest angle of the triangle.
> - The largest angle of a triangle is opposite the longest side of the triangle.
> - The smallest angle of a triangle is opposite the shortest side of the triangle.

EXAMPLE 11.38

REASONING
CONNECTION

a. $m\angle A = 63°$, and $m\angle B = 25°$. Identify the longest and the shortest side of $\triangle ABC$.
b. $DE = 3.2$ cm, $EF = 2.7$ cm, and $FD = 2.2$ cm. Identify the largest and the smallest angle of $\triangle DEF$.

SOLUTION

a. $m\angle C = 180° - 63° - 25° = 92°$. The largest angle is $\angle C$, so the opposite side $\overline{AB}$ is the longest side. The smallest angle is $\angle B$, so the opposite side $\overline{AC}$ is the shortest side.

b. $\overline{DE}$ is the longest side, so the opposite angle $\angle F$ is the largest angle. $\overline{FD}$ is the shortest side, so the opposite angle $\angle E$ is the smallest angle.

▲

The Triangle Inequality

The **triangle inequality** is a statement that helps you determine whether three line segments can be used to form a triangle.

Triangle Inequality Theorem

Line segments with lengths of a, b, and c units can be used to form a triangle, if and only if, all three inequalities hold:

$$a < b + c,$$
$$b < a + c, \text{ and}$$
$$c < a + b.$$

The triangle inequality states conditions on lengths of three line segments. If one of the three conditions is violated, then you have three line segments that are incapable of being the three sides of a triangle, much like the figure shown here.

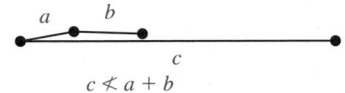

$c \not< a + b$

EXAMPLE 11.39
CONNECTION

Can you form a triangle with the given line segments? Explain your answer.
a. 6, 8, and 10 cm
b. 5, 7, and 19 cm

SOLUTION

We must determine whether the measurements satisfy the triangle inequality.
a. Yes, because $6 < 8 + 10$, $8 < 6 + 10$, and $10 < 6 + 8$.
b. No, because $19 \not< 5 + 7$.

The following example illustrates the triangle inequality and provides boundaries for the length of a third side.

EXAMPLE 11.40
CONNECTION
PROBLEM SOLVING
REASONING

A triangle has sides of the lengths 18 and 23 cm. What are possible lengths of the third side?

SOLUTION

The third side has a length of n cm. The triangle inequality implies $n < 18 + 23$, $18 < n + 23$, and $23 < n + 18$. Then $n < 41$, $-5 < n$, and $5 < n$. The inequality $-5 < n$ is useless, but the two inequalities $n < 41$ and $5 < n$ can be combined to give $5 < n < 41$. The length of the third side is between 5 and 41 cm.

CONNECTION
REASONING

The triangle inequality says the shortest distance between X and Z in Figure 29 is achieved by walking along the line segment with the endpoints X and Z. If you stray from the line segment and walk from X to Y to Z, then the distance will be greater $(c < a + b)$.

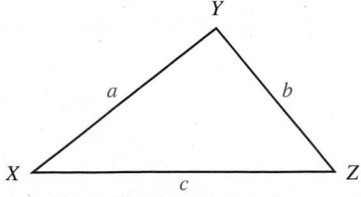

FIGURE 29
According to the triangle inequality, the distance from
x to z is shorter than the distance from x to y to z.

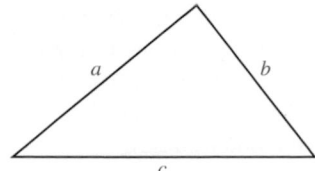

FIGURE 30

A triangle with longest side
c units, so $a \leq c$ and $b \leq c$.

Here's a proof of the triangle inequality. Consider a triangle with sides of lengths a, b, and c units. One of the sides is the longest, say the side with a length of c units, as shown in Figure 30. Then $a \leq c$ and $b \leq c$.

Construct the altitude for the side with a length of c units, and label the resulting segments as shown in Figure 31. The altitude creates two right triangles, with hypotenuses of a and b cm.

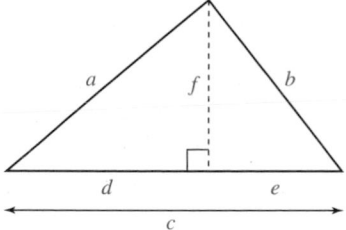

FIGURE 31

A triangle with $d < a$, $e < b$, so $d + e < a + b$, or $c < a + b$.

We know $d < a$ and $e < b$, because a leg is shorter than the hypotenuse of a right triangle. Then $d + e < a + b$. But $c = d + e$, so $c < a + b$. We know $a \leq c$, so $a < b + c$ (we simply added the nonzero number b to c). Also, we know $b \leq c$, so $b < a + c$ (we simply added the nonzero number a to c).

Area of a Regular Polygon

Recall that a regular polygon is a polygon with congruent sides and congruent interior angles. Figure 32 shows how to sketch a regular pentagon: (a) draw a circle with a center C; (b) draw a radius; (c) calculate $360/5 = 72$ and use a protractor to create a $72°$ angle; (d) create more $72°$ angles to partition the circle; and (e) draw a pentagon by drawing line segments joining consecutive points on the circle. The center of the circle that circumscribes the regular pentagon is defined as the center of the regular pentagon.

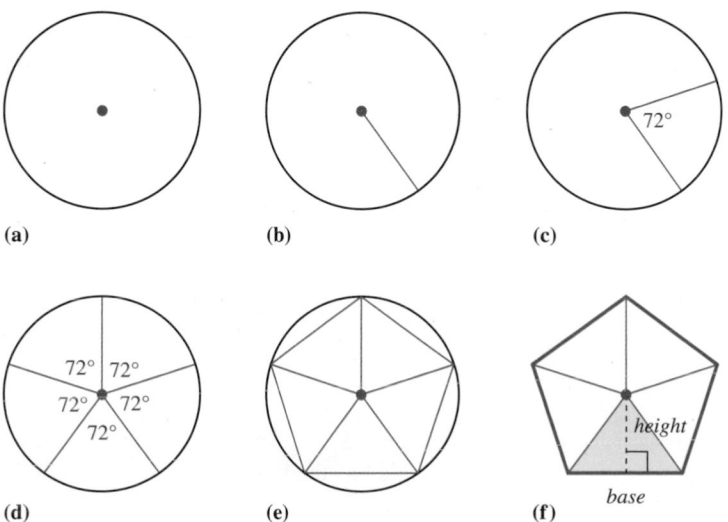

FIGURE 32

Sketching a regular pentagon.

How could we find the area of the regular pentagon? We could split the pentagon into five triangles, each with the same shape and size. We see that the area of the regular pentagon is five times the area of one of the triangles. So we need to know the base and height of each triangle, as indicated in Figure 32(f). Figure 33 illustrates three line segments (side, apothem, and radius) associated with every regular polygon. A side (denoted *s*) is a line segment of the polygon. The **apothem** (denoted *a*) is a line segment that extends from the center of the polygon to the midpoint of a side (the radius of the inner circle). The apothem is perpendicular to the side. The radius (denoted *r*) is a line segment that extends from the center of the polygon to a vertex of the polygon (the radius of the outer circle).

CONNECTION

REPRESENTATION

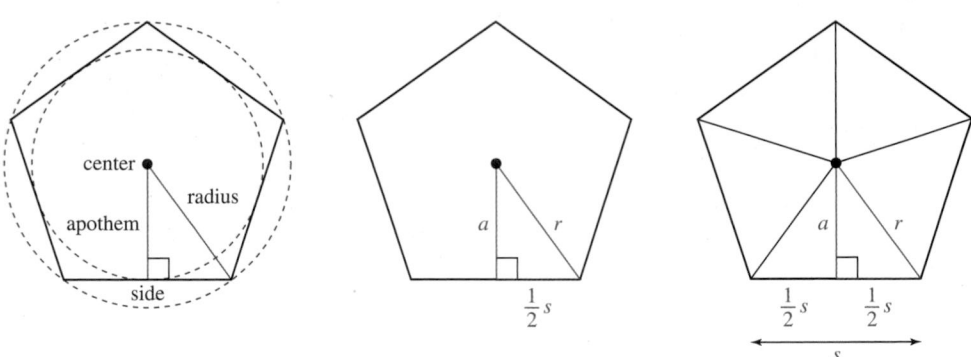

FIGURE 33
Regular pentagon and its side, apothem, and radius.

In Figure 34, the five triangles in a regular pentagon have the same shape and size, and each triangle has the height *a* and base *s*. Each height is also the apothem of the pentagon.

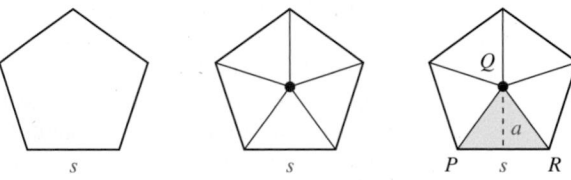

FIGURE 34
The area of a regular pentagon.

The area *A* of the regular pentagon is

$$A = 5 \cdot \text{area of } \triangle PQR$$

$$= 5 \cdot \left(\frac{1}{2} \cdot \text{base} \cdot \text{height} \right)$$

$$= 5 \cdot \frac{1}{2} \cdot sa$$

$$= \frac{1}{2} 5sa$$

$$= \frac{1}{2} Pa \qquad \textbf{\textit{P} is the perimeter of the pentagon } (P = 5s)$$

In Figure 35, the six triangles in a regular hexagon have the same shape and size, and each triangle has the height *a* and base *s*. Each height is also the apothem of the hexagon.

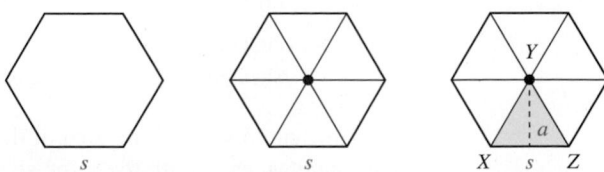

FIGURE 35
The area of a regular hexagon.

The area A of the regular hexagon is

$$A = 6 \cdot \text{area of } \triangle XYZ$$

$$= 6 \cdot \left(\frac{1}{2} \cdot \text{base} \cdot \text{height} \right)$$

$$= 6 \cdot \frac{1}{2} sa$$

$$= \frac{1}{2} 6sa$$

$$= \frac{1}{2} Pa, \quad \textbf{\textit{P} is the perimeter of the hexagon } (\textbf{\textit{P} = 6\textit{s}})$$

This leads to the following general formula.

> ### Area of a Regular *n*-gon
>
> The area A of a regular n-gon with an apothem of a units and a perimeter of P units is given by $A = \frac{1}{2}Pa$ square units.

Students should be able to "find the area of right triangles, other triangles, special quadrilaterals, and polygons by decomposing into rectangles or decomposing into triangles and other shapes" (Gr. 6, CCSS).

CONNECTION
As the number of sides of a regular polygon increases, the polygon increasingly looks like a circle. The perimeter P of the polygon approximates the circumference $2\pi r$ of the circle. Then the area A of the polygon approximates the area of the circle and $A = \frac{1}{2}Pa \approx \frac{1}{2}(2\pi r)r = \pi r^2$.

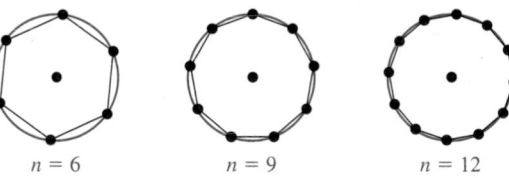

$n = 6$ $\qquad$ $n = 9$ $\qquad$ $n = 12$

EXAMPLE 11.41 A regular octagon has sides of the length 12 cm and an apothem of 14.5 cm. Determine the area of the octagon.

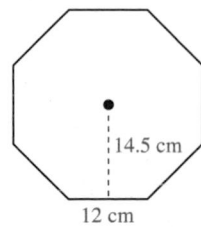

14.5 cm

12 cm

SOLUTION

The perimeter of the octagon is $8 \cdot 12 = 96$ cm. The area A of the octagon is

$$A = \frac{1}{2}Pa$$

$$= \frac{1}{2} \cdot 96 \cdot 14.5$$

$$= 696 \text{ cm}^2$$

▲

The Pythagorean theorem relates the apothem, side, and radius of any regular polygon

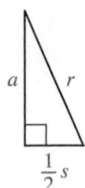

where $a^2 + \left(\frac{1}{2}s\right)^2 = r^2$.

EXAMPLE 11.42 A regular pentagon has a perimeter of 75 cm and radius of 12.8 cm. Find the apothem of the pentagon.

CONNECTION

PROBLEM SOLVING

REPRESENTATION

SOLUTION

We are given $r = 12.8$ cm and $P = 75$ cm. We need to find s and then a. $P = 5s$, so $75 = 5s$. Then $s = 75/5 = 15$ cm. Then

$$a^2 + \left(\frac{1}{2}s\right)^2 = r^2$$

$$a^2 + \left(\frac{1}{2}\cdot 15\right)^2 = 12.8^2$$

$$a^2 + 56.25 = 163.84$$

$$a^2 = 163.84 - 56.25$$

$$a^2 = 107.59$$

$$a \approx 10.4$$

The apothem is approximately 10.4 cm.

QUESTIONS FOR SECTION 11.3

REPRESENTATION

Refresher: Representations (language, diagrams, tables, symbols, algebra, manipulatives, and contextualized situations) are important because we use them to organize, record, and communicate mathematical ideas and make them more comprehensible.

1. Find the distance between B and C.

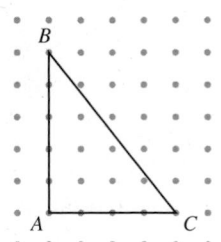

2. A square has a diagonal of the length 12 cm.
   a. Represent the situation with a diagram.
   b. Find the length of each side of the square.

3. A little birdie leaves the nest. It flies 2 miles north and then 5 miles east.
   a. Represent the situation with a diagram.
   b. How far from the nest was the birdie?

4. Identify the longest side of the triangle. Justify your answer.

a.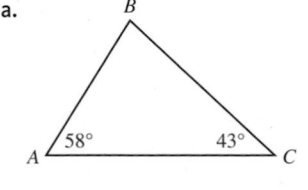

b.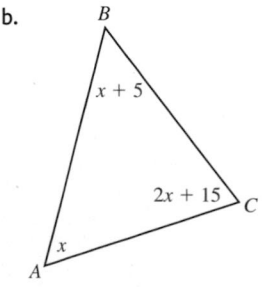

5. Find the area of each regular polygon.

a.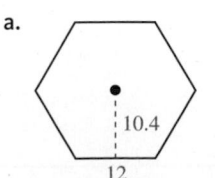

b.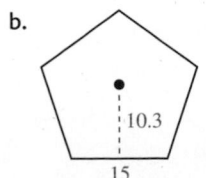

PROBLEM SOLVING

Refresher: Problem solving (reaching a goal that is not immediately attainable) is important because it helps students think more deeply about what they know and deal with unfamiliar situations.

6. A rectangle has an area of 112 m². The length is 12 m more than four times the width. What is the length of a diagonal of the rectangle?

7. A painter leans a 20-foot ladder against a wall. The top of the ladder is 16 feet above the ground. How far is the bottom of the ladder from the wall? Show your work.

8. A painter leans a 25-foot ladder against the wall. The bottom of the ladder is 15 feet from the base of the wall. The painter then moves the bottom of the ladder 8 feet closer to the wall. How much higher is the top of the ladder on the wall? Show your work.

9. Two buses depart Hypotenuse Station at the same time. Bus A travels due west at a constant rate of 52 mph. Bus B travels due south at a constant rate of 40 mph. How far apart are the two buses

   a. 30 minutes later?   b. 21 minutes later?

REASONING AND PROOF

Refresher: Reasoning and proof (thinking and justifying) are important because they help students make sense of mathematics.

10. A triangle has sides with lengths of 17, 10, and 21 cm. Classify the triangle as acute, right, or obtuse. Explain your answer.

11. $\triangle ABC$ has the measurements $AB = 10$ cm, $BC = x$ cm, and $AC = 12$ cm.

   a. What are possible values for x?

   b. If $\overline{BC}$ is the *shortest* side of the triangle, what are possible values for x that guarantee $\triangle ABC$ is an acute triangle?

12. $\triangle ABC$ has measurements $AB = 15$ cm, $BC = 23$ cm, and $AC = x$ cm.

   a. What are possible values for x?

   b. What are possible values for x that guarantee $\triangle ABC$ is a right triangle?

13. $\triangle ABC$ has measurements $AB = 15$ cm, $BC = x$ cm, and $AC = 32$ cm.

   a. What are possible values for x?

   b. If $\overline{BC}$ is the *longest* side of the triangle, what are possible values for x that guarantee $\triangle ABC$ is an obtuse triangle?

14. Is it possible to construct a triangle from line segments with the following lengths? Explain your answer.

   a. 4, 10, and 13 cm   b. 45, 38, and 92 m
   c. 21, 17, and 8 cm   d. 1720, 1600, and 5 cm

15. Find the area of a square with a diagonal measuring 18 feet.

CONNECTIONS

Refresher: Connections (linking and applying mathematical ideas) are important because they deepen student understanding and make mathematics more meaningful, flexible, and useful.

16. Identify the shortest side or sides of $\triangle ABC$.

   a. $m\angle A = 40°$, and $m\angle B = 35°$

   b. $m\angle B = 71°$, and $m\angle C = 42°$

   c. $m\angle A = m\angle B$, and $m\angle C = 80°$

   d. $m\angle A = 3 \cdot m\angle B + 8°$, and $m\angle C = 36°$

17. Classify the triangles as acute, obtuse, or right.

   a. $AB = 5$ cm, $BC = 4$ cm, and $AC = 8$ cm

   b. $AB = 12$ cm, $BC = 16$ cm, and $AC = 20$ cm

   c. $AB = 7$ cm, $BC = 24$ cm, and $AC = 25$ cm

   d. $AB = 5$ cm, $BC = 7$ cm, and $AC = 6$ cm

18. Three whole numbers a, b, and c that satisfy the equation $a^2 + b^2 = c^2$ is called a Pythagorean triple. The Greeks gave the following formula for generating a Pythagorean triple: $a = v^2 - u^2$, $b = 2uv$, and $c = v^2 + u^2$, where u and v are any counting numbers such that $v > u$. Use this formula to generate a Pythagorean triple for a, b, and c. Verify that the three whole numbers a, b, and c form a Pythagorean triple.

19. An aspect ratio is a ratio that compares the horizontal dimension to the vertical dimension of a rectangular image. Two common aspect ratios of televisions are 4:3 and 16:9. The size of a television is the diagonal measurement of the television screen.

   a. The aspect ratio of a 32-inch television screen is 16:9. Find the horizontal and vertical dimensions of the screen.

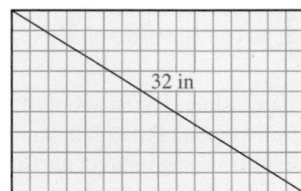

   b. The aspect ratio of a 40-inch standard television screen is 4:3. What is the area of the screen?

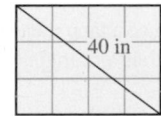

20. The perimeter of the polygonal shape is 126 cm. Find AB.

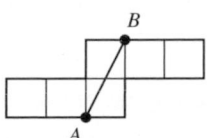

21. Let $ABCD$ represent a rectangle with sides of the lengths w and l units. Use the Pythagorean theorem to prove that the diagonals of the rectangle have the same length.

22. Three circles each with a diameter of 5 cm are in a stack, as shown in the diagram. What is the height of the stack? Round to the nearest tenth of a centimeter.

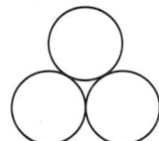

23. The diagram shows the dimensions of "home plate" in Major League Baseball.

    a. Based on the diagram, what is the distance from B to D?

    b. Based on the Pythagorean theorem, what is the distance from B to D?

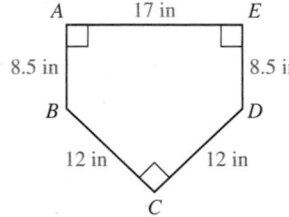

COMMUNICATION

Refresher: Communication (written and verbal explanations using representations and proper mathematical vocabulary) is important because it helps students refine and strengthen their understanding.

24. Someone tells you the lengths of the sides of a triangle. Explain how you can determine the largest angle in the triangle.

25. Someone tells you the measure of two interior angles of a triangle. Explain how you can determine the shortest side of the triangle.

26. Fiona and Kim are fishing on the shore of a lake. Fiona is at point A, and Kim is at point B. Explain how you could find the distance between them using indirect measurement.

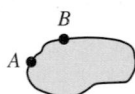

27. Explain how you can use a tape measure, rather than a protractor, to determine whether a triangle is a right triangle.

28. What is a hypotenuse?

29. What is the Pythagorean equation?

30. Is it possible to classify a triangle as acute, right, or obtuse based solely on the measurements of the three sides of the triangle? Explain your answer.

More practice with the ideas of the section

31. Fill in the blank. Choose one of the following words or phrases: *acute, arm, hypotenuse, largest angle, left, leg, longest side, Monty Python equation, obtuse, opposite, Pythagorean equation, right, same, shortest side, smallest angle,* or *triangle.*

a. The _____ of a triangle is opposite the longest side of the triangle.

b. A triangle with sides of the lengths 8, 20, and 15 cm is a(n) _____ triangle.

c. A triangle with sides of the lengths 12, 20, and 18 cm is a(n) _____ triangle.

d. The _____ is the side of a right triangle that is opposite the right angle.

e. The equation $a^2 + b^2 = c^2$ is called the _____.

f. The _____ of a triangle is opposite the smallest angle of the triangle.

32. The diagonal of a rectangle is $\sqrt{1664}$ cm. The length is 5 times the width. Find the length and width of the rectangle.

33. Identify the largest angle in $\triangle ABC$.

a. $AB = 5$ cm, $BC = 4$ cm, and $AC = 8$ cm

b. $AB = 12$ cm, $BC = 15$ cm, and $AC = 9$ cm

c. $AB = 20$ cm, $BC = 13$ cm, and $AC = 12$ cm

34. Find the unknown length.

a.    b.

35. A rectangle has a width of 5 units and diagonal of $\sqrt{89}$ units. Find the length.

36. The width of a rectangle is 1 cm less than two times the length of the rectangle. The diagonal of the rectangle is 17 cm. What are the dimensions of the rectangle?

37. Is it possible to construct a triangle from line segments with the following lengths?

a. 6, 15, and 8 cm   b. 42, 58, and 96 m

c. 4, 8, and 7 yards   d. 72 cm, 60 cm, and 145 cm

38. A regular heptagon has an area of 817.6 cm² and an apothem of 15.6 cm. What is the length of each side of the heptagon?

39. Use the dot grid to draw a line segment with a length of $\sqrt{20}$ units.

40. Determine the exact length of each side of $\triangle DEF$.

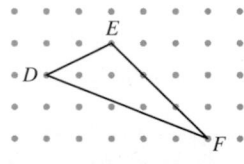

41. Do the following, using the dot grid shown.

  a. Draw an obtuse triangle with an area of 12 square units.

  b. Determine the exact length of each side.

42. A regular octagon has a radius of 15.7 cm and perimeter of 96 cm.

  a. What is the apothem of the octagon?

  b. What is the area of the octagon?

43. A regular hexagon has an apothem of 8.7 cm and perimeter of 60 cm.

  a. What is the area of the hexagon?

  b. What is the radius of the hexagon?

44. A regular pentagon has a radius of 9.36 cm and perimeter of 55 cm. What is the area of the pentagon?

45. A regular pentagon has a radius of 11.9 cm and sides of the length 14 cm. What is the area of the pentagon?

46. $\triangle ABC$ has the measurements $AB = 8$ cm, $BC = 12$ cm, and $AC = x$ cm.

  a. What are possible values for x?

  b. If $\overline{AC}$ is the *shortest* side and $\triangle ABC$ is an obtuse triangle, what are possible values for x?

47. Identify the longest side of the triangle. Justify your answer.

  a.

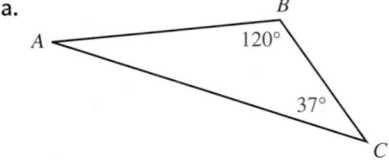

  b.

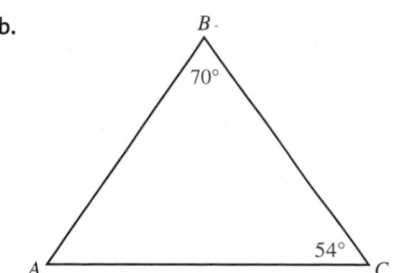

48. A homeowner plans to cover a 14-by-20-foot floor with rectangular shapes of wood of the dimensions 3.5 by 7.5 inches, as shown in the diagram. The homeowner has an electric saw to cut any rectangular pieces along the edges that need trimming.

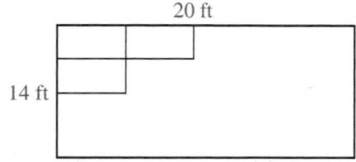

  a. How many rectangular pieces of wood would be needed?

  b. How many rectangular pieces of wood must be trimmed?

49. A painter leans a 25-foot ladder against the wall. When the painter lowers the top of the ladder by 9 feet, the bottom of the ladder is 20 feet from the wall.

  a. Represent the situation with a diagram.

  b. How far from the wall was the bottom of the ladder originally?

50. Two buses depart Hypotenuse Station at the same time. Bus A travels due east at a constant rate of 48 mph. Bus B travels due north at a constant rate of 36 mph. How far apart are the two buses 20 minutes later? Show your work.

SECTION 11.4   Volume and Surface Area

Similarity and Difference between Volume and Capacity

Imagine a bucket of water. The bucket itself takes up space, and the volume of the bucket tells you how much material is needed to make the bucket. The volume of water in the bucket tells you how much water is actually in the bucket, but the capacity of the bucket tells you how much water it can hold. **Volume** is the amount of space that a three-dimensional object occupies. The **capacity** of a container tells you the amount of material that the container can hold.

Cubic Units of Volume

The cubic centimeter and cubic inch are units of volume. A **cubic centimeter (cm³)** is the space occupied by a cube with a length of 1 cm, width of 1 cm, and height of 1 cm. A **cubic inch (in³)** is the space occupied by a cube with a length of 1 inch, width of 1 inch, and height of 1 inch. "A cube with side length 1 unit, called a 'unit cube,' is said to have 'one cubic unit' of volume, and can be used to measure volume" (Gr. 5, CCSS). Figure 36 shows two unit cubes. One unit cube has sides of the length 1 cm and a volume of 1 cm³. The other has sides of the length 1 inch and a volume of 1 cubic inch.

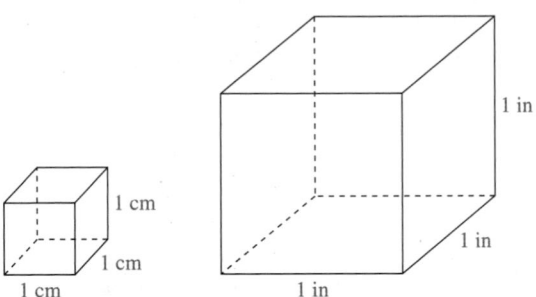

FIGURE 36
Unit cubes with the volumes 1 cubic centimeter (1 cm³) and 1 cubic inch (1 in³).

REPRESENTATION
CONNECTION
REASONING
REPRESENTATION

More generally, the symbol **unit³** is a measurement of volume represented by the space occupied by a cube with dimensions of length = 1 unit, width = 1 unit, and height = 1 unit. Students should know that "a solid figure which can be packed without gaps or overlaps using *n* unit cubes is said to have a volume of *n* cubic units" (Gr. 5, CCSS). Students also should be able to "measure volumes by counting unit cubes, using cubic cm, cubic in, cubic ft, and improvised units" (Gr. 5, CCSS).

EXAMPLE 11.43 Each cube has sides with a length of 1 cm. Find the volume of each solid.

CONNECTION
REPRESENTATION

a.

b.

SOLUTION

a. 6 cm³

b. 8 cm³

▲

We use the cubic centimeter, for example, to measure the

- volume of cancer tumors.
- density of material, such as 5 g/cm³ or 400 photons per cubic centimeter.
- quantity of powder needed to make a bullet with a certain explosive discharge.

We use the cubic inch, for example, to measure the

- volume of an electrical box.
- interior space of a microwave oven.
- shipping charges for packages, such as $0.15 per cubic inch.

EXAMPLE 11.44   How many cubic centimeters equal 1 cubic inch?

CONNECTION

REASONING   SOLUTION

REPRESENTATION   We use the equation 1 in = 2.54 cm and treat cm as a variable, similar to the variable a in the equation $(2a)^3 = 8a^3$, even though cm is a label.

$$1 \text{ in}^3 = 1 \text{ in}^3 \cdot \left(\frac{2.54 \text{ cm}}{1 \text{ in}}\right)^3 = 1 \text{ in}^3 \cdot \frac{2.54^3 \text{ cm}^3}{1^3 \text{ in}^3} = 1 \text{ in}^3 \cdot \frac{2.54^3 \text{ cm}^3}{1^3 \text{ in}^3} \approx 16.4 \text{ cm}^3$$

▲

Tables 11.10 and 11.11 list some common cubic units of volume.

TABLE 11.10   Common Cubic Units of Volume or Capacity in the U.S. Customary System

Unit	Symbol	Contextualized situation
cubic inch	in^3	The cost to mail a box often depends on its size, measured in cubic inches.
cubic feet	ft^3	The volume of air per hour that a fan moves is typically reported in cubic feet.
cubic yard	yd^3	Soil for landscaping is typically sold in bags holding 2 to 3 cubic yards.
cubic mile	mi^3	Scientists report the volume of ice that melts at the North Pole using cubic miles.

TABLE 11.11   Common Cubic Units of Volume or Capacity in the Metric System

Unit	Symbol	Contextualized situation
cubic millimeter	mm^3	Researchers often measure the number of T cells per cubic millimeters of blood to monitor the effect of a drug for the treatment of a disease.
cubic centimeter	cm^3	The size of an engine measured in units of cubic centimeters is the volume of air the engine displaces with one cycle of the cylinders.
cubic meter	m^3	Governments typically estimate natural gas deposits using cubic meters.
cubic kilometer	km^3	Scientists report the volume of large bodies of water such as the Great Lakes using cubic kilometers.

EXAMPLE 11.45   **a.** Convert 1 cubic yard to cubic feet.

CONNECTION   **b.** Convert 1 km^3 to cubic meters.

REASONING

REPRESENTATION   SOLUTION

a. $1 \text{ yd}^3 = 1 \text{ yd}^3 \cdot \left(\frac{3 \text{ ft}}{1 \text{ yd}}\right)^3 = 1 \text{ yd}^3 \cdot \frac{3^3 \text{ ft}^3}{1^3 \text{ yd}^3} = 1 \text{ yd}^3 \cdot \frac{27 \text{ ft}^3}{1 \text{ yd}^3} = \frac{1 \cdot 27}{1} \text{ft}^3 = 27 \text{ ft}^3$

b. $1 \text{ km}^3 = 1 \text{ km}^3 \cdot \left(\frac{1000 \text{ m}}{1 \text{ km}}\right)^3 = 1 \text{ km}^3 \cdot \frac{1000^3 \text{ m}^3}{1^3 \text{ km}^3} = 1 \text{ km}^3 \cdot \frac{1000^3 \text{ m}^3}{1^3 \text{ km}^3} = 10^9 \text{ m}^3$

▲

EXAMPLE 11.46

CONNECTION

REASONING

Scientists estimate that part of a Greenland ice sheet loses approximately 108 km³ of ice per year. Express this measurement in cubic miles per month.

SOLUTION

$$108 \, \frac{km^3}{yr} = 108 \, \frac{km^3}{yr} \cdot \frac{1 \, yr}{12 \, mo} \cdot \left(\frac{1000 \, m}{1 \, km} \right)^3 \cdot \left(\frac{100 \, cm}{1 \, m} \right)^3 \cdot \left(\frac{1 \, in}{2.54 \, cm} \right)^3 \cdot \left(\frac{1 \, ft}{12 \, in} \right)^3 \cdot \left(\frac{1 \, mi}{5280 \, ft} \right)^3$$

$$= 108 \, \frac{km^3}{yr} \cdot \frac{1 \, yr}{12 \, mo} \cdot \frac{1000^3 \, m^3}{1^3 \, km^3} \cdot \frac{100^3 \, cm^3}{1^3 \, m^3} \cdot \frac{1^3 \, in^3}{2.54^3 \, cm^3} \cdot \frac{1^3 \, ft^3}{12^3 \, in^3} \cdot \frac{1^3 \, mi^3}{5280^3 \, ft^3}$$

$$= 108 \, \frac{\cancel{km^3}}{\cancel{yr}} \cdot \frac{1 \, \cancel{yr}}{12 \, mo} \cdot \frac{1000^3 \, \cancel{m^3}}{1\cancel{km^3}} \cdot \frac{100^3 \, \cancel{cm^3}}{1 \, \cancel{m^3}} \cdot \frac{1 \, \cancel{in^3}}{2.54^3 \, \cancel{cm^3}} \cdot \frac{1 \, \cancel{ft^3}}{12^3 \, \cancel{in^3}} \cdot \frac{1 \, mi^3}{5280^3 \, \cancel{ft^3}}$$

$$= \frac{108 \cdot 1000^3 \cdot 100^3}{12 \cdot 2.54^3 \cdot 12^3 \cdot 5280^3} \, \frac{mi^3}{mo} \approx 2.2 \, \frac{mi^3}{mo}$$

The ice sheet loses approximately 2.2 cubic miles per month.

Noncubic Units of Volume

Noncubic units of volume or capacity are everyday units of measurement, such as the teaspoon, tablespoon, fluid ounce, cup, pint, quart, and gallon. Table 11.12 summarizes noncubic units of volume in the U.S. customary system, as well as their relationships.

TABLE 11.12 Noncubic Units of Volume or Capacity in the U.S. Customary System

Unit	Abbreviation	Connection to preceding unit
teaspoon	tsp	
tablespoon	tbsp	1 tbsp = 3 tsp
fluid ounce	fl oz	1 fl oz = 2 tbsp
cup	c	1 c = 8 fl oz
pint	pt	1 pt = 2 c
quart	qt	1 qt = 2 pt
gallon	gal	1 gal = 4 qt

Keep in mind that an *ounce* is a measure of weight (16 oz = 1 lb), whereas a *fluid ounce* is a measure of volume (8 fl oz = 1 c). Concept Map 11.2 relates the units of volume to powers of 2 (gallon and 2^0, 1/2 gallon and 2^1, quart and 2^2, pint and 2^3, and cup and 2^4).

EXAMPLE 11.47

CONNECTION

REASONING

Choose the appropriate measurement unit.

a. Felix needs to measure flour to make a birthday cake for his sister. Should he measure in cups or tablespoons?

b. Kelly is estimating the amount of water the washer uses for one load of laundry. Should she estimate in pints or gallons?

SOLUTION

a. cups

b. gallons

> **Concept Map 11.2**   Relating Gallon, Quart, Pint, and Cup

gallon															2^0
1/2 gallon							1/2 gallon								2^1
quart				quart				quart				quart				2^2
pint		pint		pint		pint		pint		pint		pint		pint		2^3
cup	cup	cup	cup	cup	cup	cup	cup	cup	cup	cup	cup	cup	cup	cup	cup	2^4

In some cases, students use multiplication or division, based on the relative sizes of the units, to convert from one unit to another unit of measurement within a measurement system.

EXAMPLE 11.48   Convert the following measurement units.

CONNECTION
REASONING

a. 12 pt = ___ c

b. 11 qt = ___ gal

SOLUTION

a. There are more cups than pints, so we multiply: $2 \cdot 12 = 24$, so 12 pt = 24 c.

b. There are fewer gallons than quarts, so we divide: $11 \div 4 = 2$ R3, so 11 qt = $2\frac{3}{4}$ gal. ▲

As we have seen, dimensional analysis is a robust method for converting units. It is especially useful when the conversions require multiple steps.

EXAMPLE 11.49   Fill in the blank:

CONNECTION
REASONING
REPRESENTATION

a. 3 qt = ___ c

b. 12 c = ___ gal

SOLUTION

a. $3 \text{ qt} = 3 \text{ qt} \cdot \dfrac{2 \text{ pt}}{1 \text{ qt}} \cdot \dfrac{2 \text{ c}}{1 \text{ pt}} = 3 \cancel{\text{ qt}} \cdot \dfrac{2 \cancel{\text{ pt}}}{1 \cancel{\text{ qt}}} \cdot \dfrac{2 \text{ c}}{1 \cancel{\text{ pt}}} = 3 \cdot 2 \cdot 2 \text{ c} = 12 \text{ c}$

b. $12 \text{ c} = 12 \text{ c} \cdot \dfrac{1 \text{ pt}}{2 \text{ c}} \cdot \dfrac{1 \text{ qt}}{2 \text{ pt}} \cdot \dfrac{1 \text{ gal}}{4 \text{ qt}} = 12 \cancel{\text{ c}} \cdot \dfrac{1 \cancel{\text{ pt}}}{2 \cancel{\text{ c}}} \cdot \dfrac{1 \cancel{\text{ qt}}}{2 \cancel{\text{ pt}}} \cdot \dfrac{1 \text{ gal}}{4 \cancel{\text{ qt}}} = \dfrac{12}{2 \cdot 2 \cdot 4} \text{ gal} = \dfrac{3}{4} \text{ gal}$ ▲

Table 11.13 summarizes noncubic units of volume in the metric system and their relationships.

TABLE 11.13   Noncubic Units of Volume or Capacity in the Metric System

Unit	Abbreviation	Connection to preceding unit
milliliter	mL or ml	
liter	L or l	1 L = 1000 mL
kiloliter	kL or kl	1 kL = 1000 L

EXAMPLE 11.50

CONNECTION

REASONING

Choose the appropriate measurement unit.

a. Medicine for children should be measured by the milliliter or by the cup?

b. The amount of water stored in a local lake should be measured in cubic inches or in kiloliters?

SOLUTION

a. milliliter

b. kiloliters

▲

Connection within and between Metric and U.S. Customary Units of Volume

Table 11.14 shows relationships within and between metric and U.S. customary units of volume.

CONNECTION

TABLE 11.14   Relationships within and between Metric and U.S. Customary Units of Volume

1 L = 1000 cm^3
1 L = 1.056688 qt (rounded to the nearest millionth)
1 L = 33.8140227 fl oz (rounded to the nearest ten-millionth)
1 mL = 1 cm^3
1 qt = 32 fl oz
1 gal = 231 in^3

EXAMPLE 11.51

CONNECTION

REASONING

REPRESENTATION

A biosand water filter is a water purifier that removes bacteria using layers of sand and gravel through natural processes. A particular biosand filter contains 5800 cubic inches of water. How many gallons of water does the water filter contain?

SOLUTION

$$5800 \text{ in}^3 = 5800 \text{ in}^3 \cdot \frac{1 \text{ gal}}{231 \text{ in}^3} = 5800 \text{ in}^3 \cdot \frac{1 \text{ gal}}{231 \text{ in}^3} = \frac{5800}{231} \text{ gal} \approx 25.1 \text{ gal}.$$

The filter contains approximately 25.1 gallons of water.

▲

Volume of a Rectangular Prism

We can use a unit cube as a measurement unit for volume. Remember, the length of each side of a unit cube (unit^3) is 1 unit. With this measurement unit, the volume of a solid is the number of unit cubes that fit within the solid, without gaps or overlaps. Figure 37 shows several solids composed of unit cubes. For these solids, the volume is easily obtained by counting the number of unit cubes.

CONNECTION

REASONING

REPRESENTATION

Volume = 1 unit^3

Volume = 3 unit^3

Volume = 6 unit^3

FIGURE 37
The volume of each solid equals the number of unit cubes.

Many three-dimensional objects have the shape of a right rectangular prism, such as a box of cereal or a refrigerator. Figure 38(a) shows a right rectangular prism. What is the volume of the prism? To help you determine this, Figure 38(b) shows the prism disassembled into four slices.

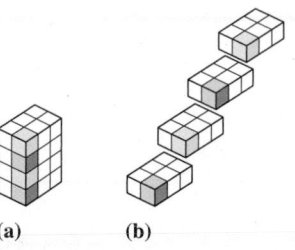

(a)   (b)

FIGURE 38
Disassembling a right
rectangular prism into four slices.

The cubes in each slice are arranged in a 2-by-3 rectangular array, so the volume of each slice is $2 \cdot 3$ cubic units. There are four slices, so the volume of the right rectangular prism is $2 \cdot 3 \cdot 4 = 24$ cubic units. The dimensions of the right rectangular prism in Figure 38(a) are length = 2 units, width = 3 units, and height = 4 units. The expression $l \cdot w$ tells us the number of cubic units in each slice, and h tells us the number of slices in the right rectangular prism. Students should be able to "find the volume of a right rectangular prism with whole-number side lengths by packing it with unit cubes, and show that the volume is the same as would be found by multiplying the edge lengths, equivalently by multiplying the height by the area of the base" (Gr. 5, CCSS).

Figure 39(a) shows a standard deck of cards, which is a model of a rectangular prism with the volume V of the card paper given by $V = lwh$ in^3. In Figure 39(b), the same deck of cards is slightly pushed to the side and represents a model of an oblique prism. The volume of card paper remains the same, because the volume of the paper is the same, so the volume V of the card paper in the new stack is still given by $V = lwh$ in^3. Both decks of cards have the same height.

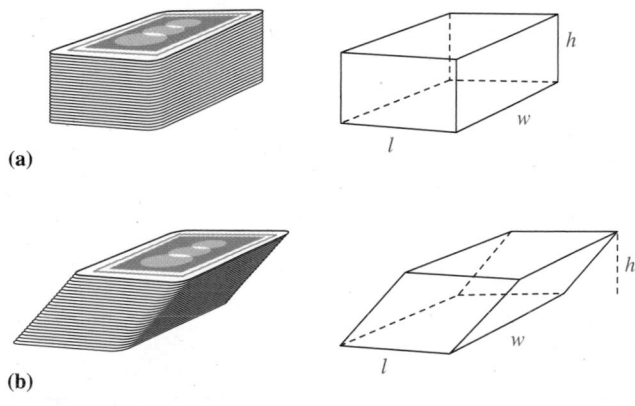

(a)

(b)

FIGURE 39
The volume of paper in both decks of cards is the same.

Now we state the formula for the volume of a right or oblique rectangular prism.

The Volume of a Right or Oblique Rectangular Prism

The volume V of a right or oblique rectangular prism with the linear dimensions of length = l units, width = w units, and height = h units is given by $V = lwh$ cubic units.

EXAMPLE 11.52

COMMUNICATION
PROBLEM SOLVING
REASONING
REPRESENTATION

A landscaper is spreading soil to make a new rectangular lawn with the dimensions 20 by 45 feet. The soil will be 3 inches deep. The soil costs $15 per cubic yard. What is the total cost of the soil?

SOLUTION

First, let's convert the measurements to yards: 20 ft = 20/3 yd, 45 ft = 45/3 yd, and 3 in = 1/12 yd. The volume V of soil in the new lawn is $V = lwh = (20/3)(45/3)(1/12) = 8.333$ yd^3. Then $15 \cdot 8.333 = \$125$. The total cost of the soil is $125.

▲

CONNECTION
REASONING
REPRESENTATION

Volume of a Prism

Figure 40 shows a pentagon and polyhedron. B unit squares cover the pentagon without any gaps or overlaps, so the area of the pentagon is B square units. The polyhedron is composed of unit cubes, and every unit square (or fraction of one) in the pentagon has a corresponding face in a unit cube (or fraction of one) in the polyhedron. This means there are B unit cubes in the polyhedron, so it has a volume of B cubic units.

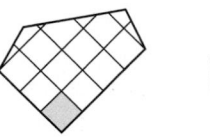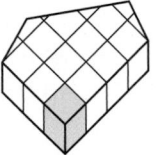

FIGURE 40
The area of the polygon is B square units, so
the volume of the polyhedron is B cubic units.

Our immediate goal is to develop a formula for the volume of a right prism that has a base with an area of B square units and height of $h = 6$ units, as shown in Figure 41(a). As shown in Figure 40, the volume of the layer (or slice) that has a height of 1 unit, as shown in Figure 41(b), is B cubic units. In Figure 41(c), we see there are 6 slices in the right prism.

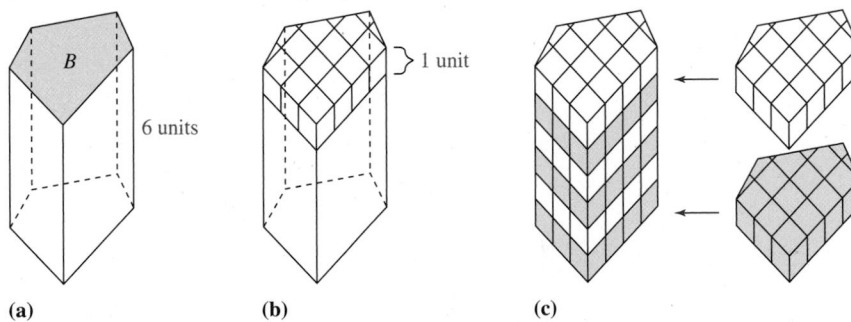

B

6 units

1 unit

(a)   (b)   (c)

FIGURE 41
Visualizing the volume of a right prism that has a base with area B square units and height 6 units.

There are B unit cubes in each layer and 6 layers, so there are $B \cdot 6$ unit cubes altogether. More generally, the formula for the volume V of a right prism is $V = Bh$ cubic units. Figures 40 and 41 help justify why we multiply the area B of a base and height h of the prism to find the volume of the prism. This is the same formula for the volume of an oblique prism, in the same way as explained with the "leaning" deck of cards in Figure 39. The height of a prism is the distance between the parallel planes that contain the bases.

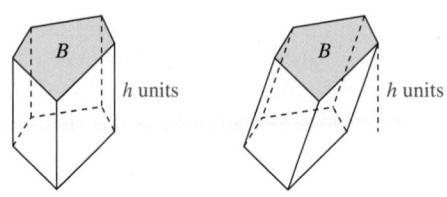

> ### The Volume of a Right or Oblique Prism
>
> The volume V of a right or oblique prism that has a base with an area of B square units and height of h units is given by $V = Bh$ cubic units.

EXAMPLE 11.53

COMMUNICATION
PROBLEM SOLVING
REASONING
REPRESENTATION

A hexagonal aquarium provides multiple viewpoints and is suited for desktops or small places. A hexagonal aquarium with a height of 15 inches has sides with a length of 14 inches and an apothem of 12.1 inches. One guideline for determining the number of small community fish in an aquarium is 1 inch of fish per gallon of water. The average length of adult neon tetras is approximately 2 inches. According to this guideline, what is the maximum number of neon tetra fish this aquarium can support? (Hint: 1 gal = 231 in³.)

SOLUTION

The maximum volume of water in the aquarium is

$$V = Bh \ = \frac{1}{2}Pa \cdot h \ = \frac{1}{2}(6 \cdot 14) \cdot 12.1 \cdot 15 \ = 7623 \text{ in}^3 \ = 7623 \text{ in}^3 \cdot \frac{1 \text{ gal}}{231 \text{ in}^3} \ = 33 \text{ gal}$$

An adult tetra that is 2 inches long requires 2 gallons of water. Then 33 gallons ÷ 2 gallons per fish = 16.5 fish. Under these guidelines, the aquarium can support 16 adult neon tetras. ▲

CONNECTION
REASONING
REPRESENTATION

Volume of a Cylinder

Figure 42 shows a circle that has a radius of r units and a cylinder with a base that has a radius of r units and height of 1 unit. Because πr^2 unit squares cover the circle without any gaps or overlaps, the area of the circle is πr^2 square units. Every unit square in the circle (or fraction of one) corresponds to a face in a unit cube (or fraction of one) in the cylinder. This means there are πr^2 unit cubes in the cylinder, so the volume of the solid is πr^2 cubic units.

FIGURE 42

The area of the circle is πr^2 square units, so the area of the cylinder is πr^2 cubic units.

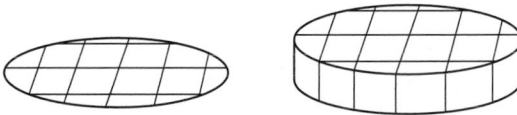

Our goal is to develop a formula for the volume of a right cylinder that has a base with a radius of r units and height of $h = 4$ units, as shown in Figure 43(a). As shown in Figure 42, the volume of the layer (or slice) in Figure 43(b) is πr^2 cubic units. There are 4 slices, as shown in Figure 43(c).

FIGURE 43

Visualizing the volume of a cylinder that has a base with radius r units and a height of 4 units.

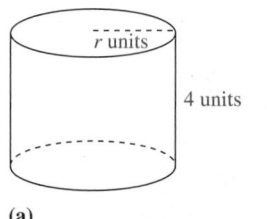

(a)

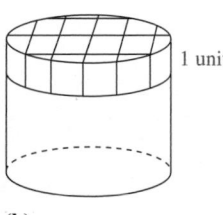

(b)

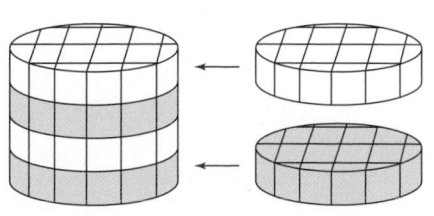

(c)

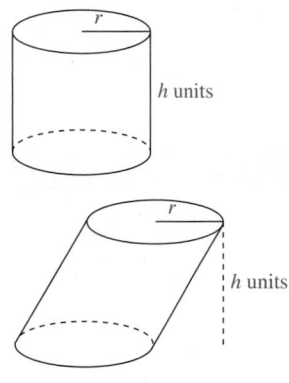

There are πr^2 unit cubes in each layer and 4 layers, so there are $\pi r^2 h \cdot 4$ unit cubes altogether. More generally, the formula for the volume V of a right cylinder is $V = \pi r^2 h$ cubic units. This is also the formula for the volume of an oblique cylinder, in the same way as explained with the "leaning" deck of cards in Figure 39. The height of a cylinder is the distance between the parallel planes that contain the bases.

The Volume of a Right or Oblique Cylinder

The volume V of a right or oblique cylinder with a radius of r units and height of h units is given by $V = \pi r^2 h$ cubic units.

Suppose the radius and height of a cylinder are each doubled. What happens to the volume? Let r and h be the original radius and height, and let R and H be the new radius and height. Then $R = 2r$ and $H = 2h$. Then $V = \pi R^2 H = \pi(2r)^2(2h) = \pi \cdot 4r^2 \cdot 2h = 8(\pi r^2 h)$. This means the new volume is eight times the original volume.

Volume of an Irregularly Shaped Object

Archimedes's principle states that the volume of an object is equal to the volume of water displaced when you submerge the object in water. This allows us to find the volume of an irregularly shaped object using a procedure called the displacement method, which we illustrate in Figure 44. We begin with a volume of water in a container. Then we submerge the object in the water. Finally, we measure the volume of water displaced by the object. The volume of water displaced equals the volume of the object. The displacement method is straightforward to apply for right rectangular prisms or right cylinders, because the volume of water displaced is easy to measure.

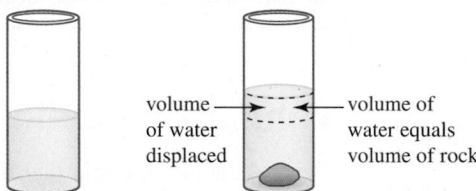

FIGURE 44
Visualizing Archimedes's Principle.

EXAMPLE 11.54

CONNECTION

A graduated cylinder is a right cylinder with a marked scale to make accurate liquid volume measurements. In Figure 45, a graduated cylinder initially contains 200 cm^3 of water. A rock is dropped into the cylinder. Find the volume of the rock.

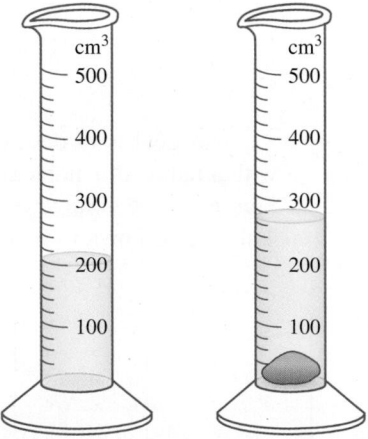

FIGURE 45
Applying Archimedes's Principle.

SOLUTION

The volume of water is 200 cm³. The combined volume of rock and water is 260 cm³, and $260 - 200 = 60$. The rock displaces 60 cm³ of water. Therefore, the volume of the rock is 60 cm³.

▲

Volume of Pyramids and Cones

Our goal is to derive a formula for the volume of a rectangular pyramid. Let's begin with a prism with the same rectangular base and height as the pyramid, as shown in Figure 46. You could follow along with pyramids and a prism made from thin cardboard. We fill three such pyramids with rice and empty them into the prism.

CONNECTION

REASONING

REPRESENTATION

Step 1. Begin with a pyramid.

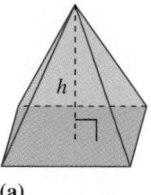

(a)

Step 2. Create a prism with an open top with the same base and height as the pyramid.

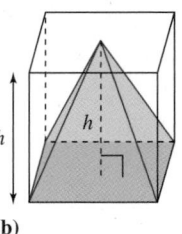

(b)

Step 3. Fill three pyramids with rice.

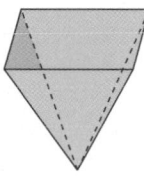 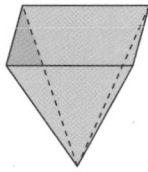 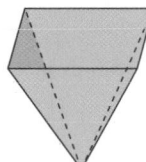 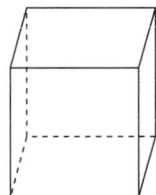

(c)

Step 4. Empty the three pyramids into the prism.

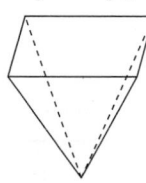 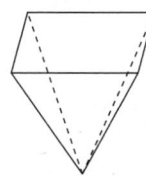 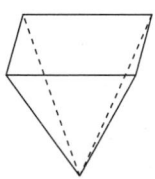 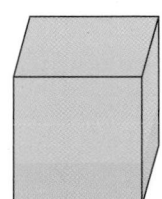

(d)

FIGURE 46
Relating the volumes of a pyramid and prism.

Then the volume of one pyramid equals one-third times the volume of the prism. As you might expect, this result holds for *any* pyramid.

To arrive at a formula for the volume of a cone, begin with a cylinder with the same base and height as the cone. Then, add rice to the cone and pour it into the cylinder. Do this three times altogether. Then you will learn that the volume of one cone equals one-third times the volume of the cylinder.

> ### The Volume of a Pyramid or Cone
>
> The volume V of a pyramid that has a base with an area of B square units and height of h units is given by $V = \frac{1}{3}Bh$ cubic units.
>
> The volume V of a cone that has a base with a radius of r units and height of h units is given by $V = \frac{1}{3}\pi r^2 h$ cubic units.

EXAMPLE 11.55

CONNECTION
PROBLEM SOLVING
REASONING

A regular pentagonal pyramid has a height of 10 cm, sides of the length 12 cm, and an apothem of 8.3 cm. Find the volume of the pyramid.

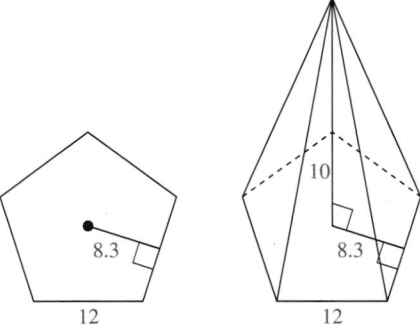

SOLUTION

The base is a regular pentagon with sides of the length 12 cm and an apothem of 8.3 cm.

$$V = \frac{1}{3}Bh$$

$$= \frac{1}{3}\left(\frac{1}{2}Pa\right)h$$

$$= \frac{1}{3}\left(\frac{1}{2}(5 \cdot 12) \cdot 8.3\right) \cdot 10$$

$$= 830 \text{ cm}^3$$

Then the volume of the pyramid is 830 cm³.

EXAMPLE 11.56

CONNECTION
PROBLEM SOLVING
REASONING

A cone with a radius of 5 cm holds 700 cm³ of water. Find the height of the cone.

SOLUTION

The formula for the volume of a circular cone of radius r and height h is $V = \frac{1}{3}\pi r^2 h$ cubic units. Then $700 = \frac{1}{3}\pi 5^2 h$, so $2100 = \pi 25h$. Then $h = 2100/(25\pi) \approx 26.7$ cm. The height of the cone is approximately 26.7 cm.

The following student page shows some problems that middle school students may see for the volume of prisms and pyramids.

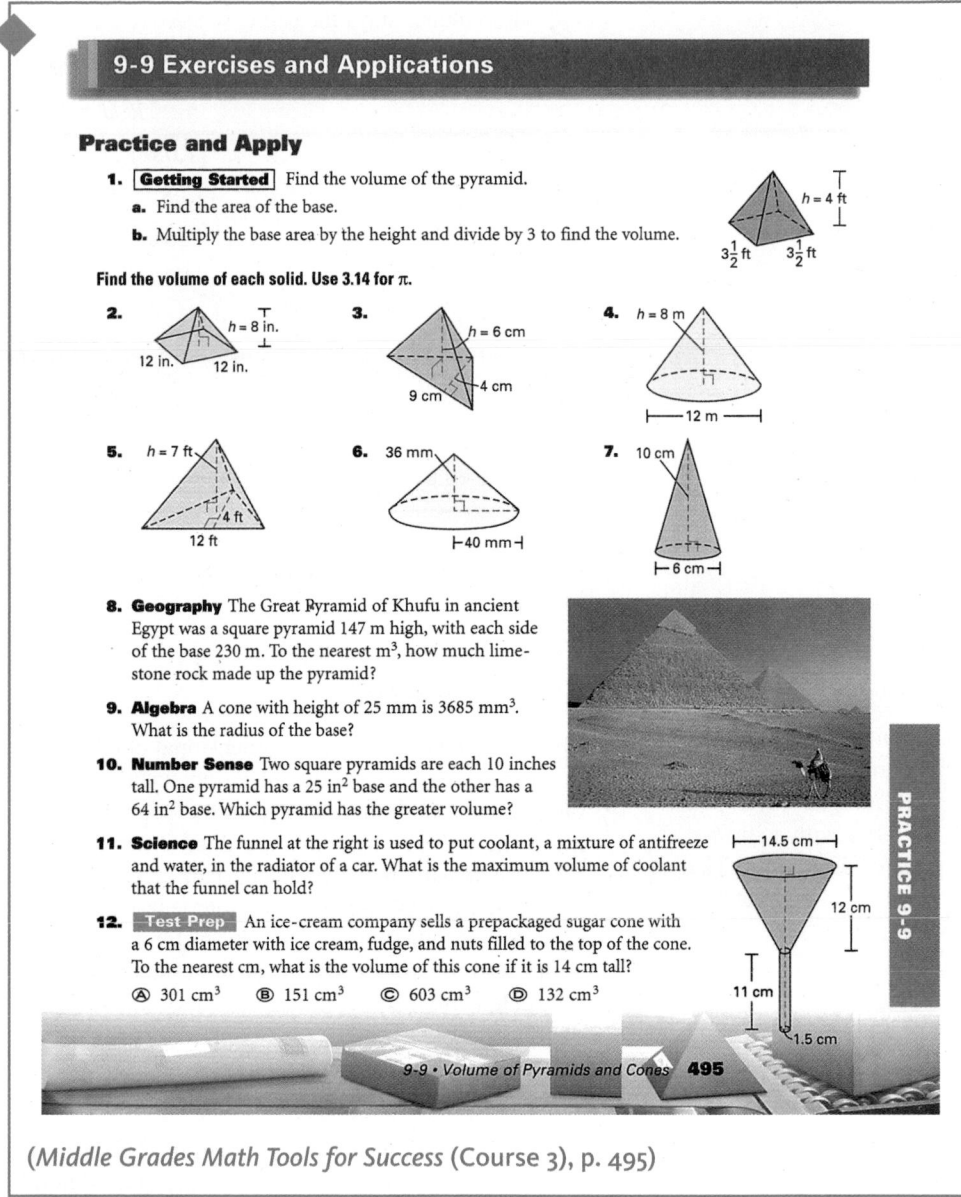

9-9 Exercises and Applications

Practice and Apply

1. **Getting Started** Find the volume of the pyramid.
   a. Find the area of the base.
   b. Multiply the base area by the height and divide by 3 to find the volume.

   $h = 4$ ft, $3\frac{1}{2}$ ft, $3\frac{1}{2}$ ft

Find the volume of each solid. Use 3.14 for π.

2. $h = 8$ in. 12 in. 12 in.

3. $h = 6$ cm, 9 cm, 4 cm

4. $h = 8$ m, 12 m

5. $h = 7$ ft, 4 ft, 12 ft

6. 36 mm, 40 mm

7. 10 cm, 6 cm

8. **Geography** The Great Pyramid of Khufu in ancient Egypt was a square pyramid 147 m high, with each side of the base 230 m. To the nearest m^3, how much limestone rock made up the pyramid?

9. **Algebra** A cone with height of 25 mm is 3685 mm^3. What is the radius of the base?

10. **Number Sense** Two square pyramids are each 10 inches tall. One pyramid has a 25 in^2 base and the other has a 64 in^2 base. Which pyramid has the greater volume?

11. **Science** The funnel at the right is used to put coolant, a mixture of antifreeze and water, in the radiator of a car. What is the maximum volume of coolant that the funnel can hold?

    14.5 cm, 12 cm, 11 cm, 1.5 cm

12. **Test Prep** An ice-cream company sells a prepackaged sugar cone with a 6 cm diameter with ice cream, fudge, and nuts filled to the top of the cone. To the nearest cm, what is the volume of this cone if it is 14 cm tall?
    Ⓐ 301 cm^3 Ⓑ 151 cm^3 Ⓒ 603 cm^3 Ⓓ 132 cm^3

9-9 • Volume of Pyramids and Cones **495**

PRACTICE 9-9

(*Middle Grades Math Tools for Success* (Course 3), p. 495)

(From Suzanne H. Chapin. © 1999 by Pearson Education, Inc. or its affiliates. Used by permission. All rights reserved.)

The next example illustrates how a change in one variable affects another variable. These types of questions are more easily answered using algebra.

EXAMPLE 11.57

CONNECTION
PROBLEM SOLVING
REASONING
REPRESENTATION

A company sells its oatmeal product in right cylinders. It decided to redesign the container and increased the radius by 8%. How much should it decrease the height to maintain the same volume?

SOLUTION

Let r and h denote the radius and height, respectively, of the original cylinder, and let R and H denote the radius and height, respectively, of the new container. The radius r is increased by 8%, so

$$\begin{aligned}R &= r + 0.08r \\ &= 1 \cdot r + 0.08r \\ &= (1 + 0.08)r \\ &= 1.08r\end{aligned}$$

The volume stays the same, so $\pi R^2 H = \pi r^2 h$. Then

$$\pi R^2 H = \pi r^2 h$$
$$R^2 H = r^2 h$$
$$(1.08r)^2 H = r^2 h$$
$$(1.08^2 r^2)H = r^2 h$$
$$(1.1664 r^2)H = r^2 h$$
$$1.1664 H = h$$
$$H = \frac{1}{1.1664}h$$
$$H \approx 0.86h.$$

The new height is approximately 86% of the original height, so the new height must be decreased by approximately 14%.

As an example, the equation $H = 1.45h$ would mean the height must be increased by 45%.

■ Historical Note

Scientists at a research group at the University of Michigan developed material with a surface area of 5200 m²/g. That would be like stretching a dime to cover a football field.

Surface Area

The **surface area** of a three-dimensional object is the total area of the surface of the object. A painter would be interested in the surface area of a room, rather than the volume. An oncologist would be interested in the body surface area of a cancer patient to help determine the proper chemotherapy dose. Manufacturers often use scientific instruments to measure density, porosity, and surface area of material to understand and use raw products efficiently. For example, an environmental company produced iron powder with a greater surface area, allowing the powder to bind to more toxic soil and water contaminants that could lead to various adverse health effects. We focus on the surface area of common solids such as prisms, pyramids, cylinders, and cones.

Surface Area of a Right Prism and Right Cylinder

We use the right quadrilateral prism in Figure 47 to motivate the formula for the surface area of a right prism. The two bases are quadrilaterals, and the lateral faces are rectangles. Let B represent the area of a base, P represent the perimeter of a base, and h represent the height of the right prism. We see the lateral surface area of the prism is the same as the area of a rectangle with the dimensions P and h units, or Ph square units. Then the surface area *S.A.* of the right prism is *S.A.* $= 2B + Ph$ square units.

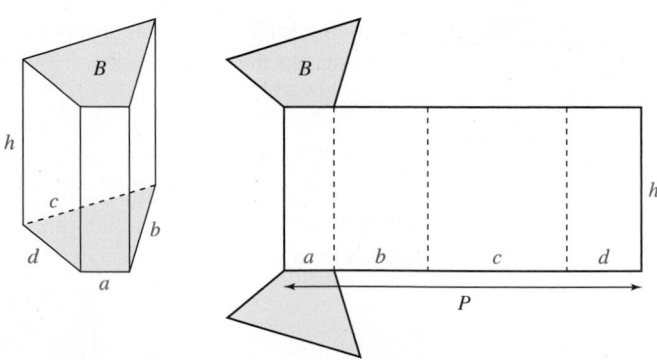

FIGURE 47
The surface area of a right prism is *S.A.* $= 2B + Ph$ square units.

Figure 48 shows the surface area of cylinder is straightforward to compute by considering a net for the cylinder. The bases of the cylinder are circles with a radius of r units. If we cut along the edge of the bases and unfold the lateral side, we obtain a rectangle with the dimensions h units (the height of the cylinder) and $2\pi r$ units (the circumference of a base).

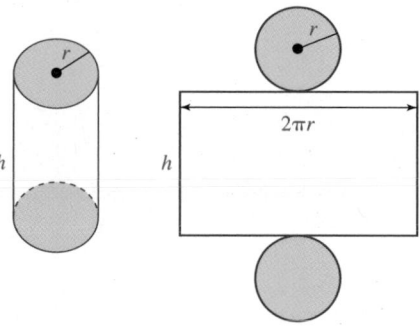

FIGURE 48
The surface area of a cylinder is $S.A. = 2\pi r^2 + 2\pi rh$ square units.

The Surface Area of a Right Prism and a Right Cylinder

- If the base of a right prism has a perimeter of P units and area of B square units and the prism has a height of h units, then the surface area is $S.A. = 2B + Ph$ square units.
- If a right cylinder has a radius of r units and height of h units, then the surface area is $S.A. = 2\pi r^2 + 2\pi rh$ square units.

EXAMPLE 11.58

CONNECTION

REPRESENTATION

A regular hexagonal prism has a base with sides of the length 15 cm and an apothem of 13 cm. The height of the prism is 20 cm.
a. What is the area of the base?
b. What is the lateral surface area?
c. What is the surface area of the prism?

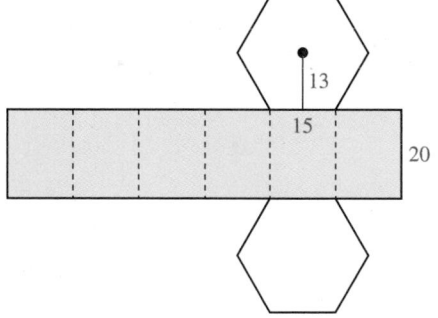

SOLUTION

The diagram is a net for the hexagonal prism.

a. $B = \dfrac{1}{2}Pa = \dfrac{1}{2}(6 \cdot 15) \cdot 13 = 585$ cm^2

b. $Ph = (6 \cdot 15) \cdot 20 = 1800$ cm^2

c. $S.A. = 2B + Ph$
$= 2 \cdot 585 + 1800$
$= 2970$ cm^2

Surface Area of a Regular Pyramid and Right Cone

The lateral faces of a regular pyramid are congruent isosceles or equilateral triangles. The **slant height** of a regular pyramid, denoted l, is the line segment from the apex of the pyramid to the midpoint of a side of the regular polygon. The slant height does not exist for nonregular pyramids, because the lateral faces are nonidentical.

Figure 49 illustrates a regular pentagonal pyramid with a slant height of l, sides of the length s, a height of h, and an apothem of a. The surface area of the regular pentagonal pyramid is easier to visualize by forming a net from unfolding the lateral faces. The lateral surface area of a pyramid is the combined area of the lateral faces.

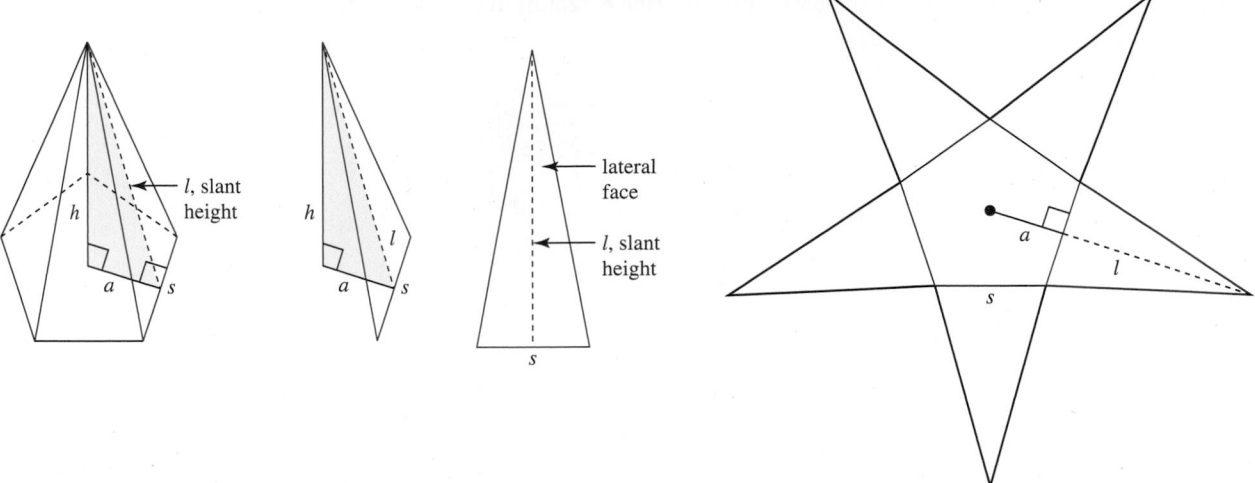

FIGURE 49

Visualizing the surface area and lateral surface area of a regular pyramid.

CONNECTION

REPRESENTATION

The surface area of a regular pyramid with a slant height of l, sides of the length s, a height of h, an apothem of a, and a base that is a regular polygon with n sides is

$$S.A. = \text{area of base} + \text{lateral surface area}$$

$$= \frac{1}{2} \cdot \text{perimeter} \cdot \text{apothem} + n \cdot \frac{1}{2} \cdot \text{base of triangle} \cdot \text{height of triangle}$$

$$= \frac{1}{2}Pa + n \cdot \frac{1}{2}sl$$

$$= \frac{1}{2}Pa + \frac{1}{2}(ns)l$$

$$= \frac{1}{2}Pa + \frac{1}{2}Pl \text{ square units}$$

Figure 50 shows a regular hexagonal pyramid. The surface area of the hexagonal pyramid is the area of the base plus the lateral surface area: $S.A. = \left(\frac{1}{2}\right)Pa + \left(\frac{1}{2}\right)Pl$, where a is the apothem of the hexagon and l is the slant height of the pyramid.

CONNECTION

REPRESENTATION

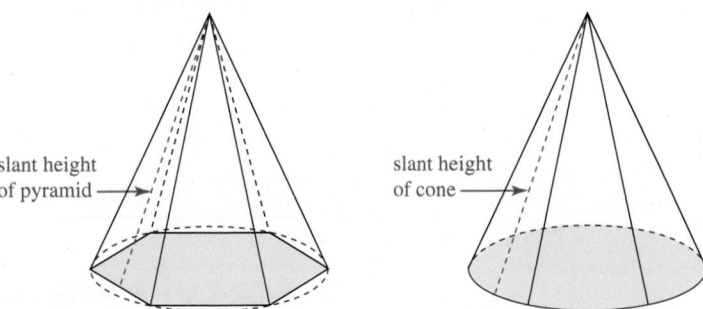

slant height of pyramid

slant height of cone

FIGURE 50

Regular hexagonal pyramid and cone.

As the number of sides of the base of the pyramid increases, the shape of the base becomes more circular, the apothem a more closely resembles the radius r of a circle, the perimeter P of the polygon more closely resembles the circumference C of a circle, and the shape of the pyramid more closely resembles a cone. The slant height l of a cone is the length of a line segment from the apex of the cone to any point on the circle. The surface area of the regular pyramid is

$$S.A. = \frac{1}{2}Pa + \frac{1}{2}Pl \text{ square units}$$

Now we replace P with $2\pi r$ and a with r to get the surface area of a cone:

$$S.A. = \frac{1}{2}(2\pi r)r + \frac{1}{2}(2\pi r)l$$
$$= \pi r^2 + \pi rl \text{ square units}$$

We now summarize the results.

The Surface Area of a Regular Pyramid and Right Cone

- The surface area $S.A.$ of a regular pyramid with a slant height of l units and a base that is a regular polygon with an apothem of a units, perimeter of P units, and area of B units is given by $S.A. = \frac{1}{2}Pa + \frac{1}{2}Pl$ square units.

- The surface area $S.A.$ of a right cone with a radius of r units and slant height of l units is given by $S.A. = \pi r^2 + \pi rl$ square units.

EXAMPLE 11.59

CONNECTION
REASONING
REPRESENTATION

A regular pentagonal pyramid has a height of 12 cm and a base with sides that are 10 cm and an apothem of 7 cm.

a. Find the slant height of the pyramid.

b. Find the area of the base.

c. Find the lateral surface area of the pyramid.

d. Find the surface area of the pyramid.

SOLUTION

We draw a diagram to visualize the relationships.

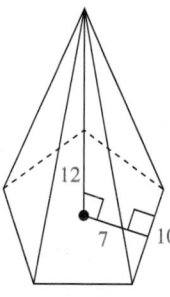 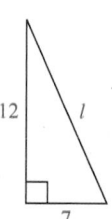

a. The slant height l is the hypotenuse of the triangle with the legs 12 cm and 7 cm. Then
$l^2 = 12^2 + 7^2 = 193$, so $l = \sqrt{193}$ cm.

b. $B = \frac{1}{2}Pa = \frac{1}{2}(5 \cdot 10)7 = 175$ cm²

c. $\frac{1}{2}Pl = \frac{1}{2}(5 \cdot 10)\sqrt{193} \approx 347.3$ cm²

d. $S.A.$ = area of base + lateral surface area
$\approx 175 + 347.3$
$= 522.3$ cm²

Surface Area and Volume of a Sphere

Recall that a circle is a set of points in the plane that are a fixed distance (r units) from a point (called the center). A **sphere** is a set of points in *space* that are a fixed distance (r units) from a point (called the center). A baseball or billiard ball is a model of a sphere. We derive the formula for the surface area of a sphere and then apply that formula to derive the formula for the volume of the sphere. The derivations that we describe are informal but accessible; formal methods require mathematics (calculus) beyond the scope of this book.

Imagine, as shown in Figure 51(a), a sphere resting on a rectangular piece of wrapping paper that has a width of $2r$ and length of C, where r is the radius of the sphere and C is the circumference of the sphere, with $C = 2\pi r$. Figure 51(b) shows the ends of the paper wrapped to form a cylinder without bases. Figure 51(c) shows how you can fold the lower and upper portions of the cylinder onto the surface of the sphere. Some unavoidable overlapping of the wrapping paper occurs when you initially fold in the paper, so you need to cut or tear the paper to remove overlaps and cover gaps. Figure 51(d) shows that the rectangular wrapping paper covers the sphere without gaps or overlaps. The area of the rectangular wrapping paper is $2r \cdot C = 2r \cdot 2\pi r = 4\pi r^2$. Then the surface area of the sphere is $4\pi r^2$ square units.

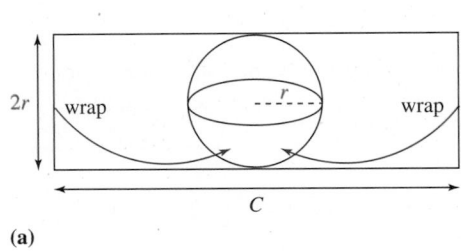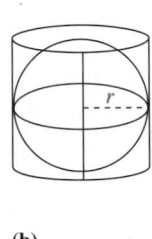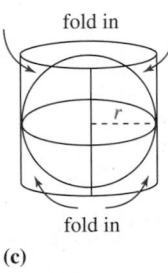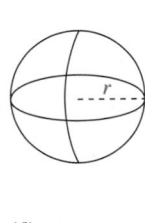

(a)   (b)   (c)   (d)

FIGURE 51

Visualizing the surface area of a sphere.

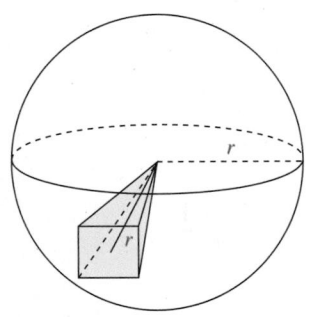

FIGURE 52

Right pyramid with a base of B_1 square units and height of r units in a sphere with a radius of r units.

Figure 52 makes it easier to motivate the formula for the volume of a sphere with a radius of r units. Imagine that we carve a regular pyramid with a base of B_1 square units and height r units so that the base of the pyramid is a tiny piece of the surface of the sphere. The pyramid has a volume of $V_1 = \frac{1}{3}B_1 r$ cubic units.

Imagine that we partition the sphere into n regular pyramids such that their bases B_1, B_2, ..., B_n cover the surface of the sphere without gaps or overlaps. Then the sum $B_1 + B_2 + \ldots + B_n$ equals the surface area of $4\pi r^2$ of the sphere. Then the volume V of the sphere is

$$V = V_1 + V_2 + \cdots + V_n$$

$$= \frac{1}{3}B_1 r + \frac{1}{3}B_2 r + \cdots + \frac{1}{3}B_n r$$

$$= \frac{1}{3}(B_1 + B_2 + \cdots + B_n)r$$

$$= \frac{1}{3}(4\pi r^2)r$$

$$= \frac{4}{3}\pi r^3$$

We now summarize the results.

The Surface Area and Volume of a Sphere

- The surface area *S.A.* of a sphere with a radius of r units is given by $S.A. = 4\pi r^2$ square units.
- The volume V of a sphere with a radius of r units is given by $V = \frac{4}{3}\pi r^3$ cubic units.

QUESTIONS FOR SECTION 11.4

REPRESENTATION

Refresher: Representations (language, diagrams, tables, symbols, algebra, manipulatives, and contextualized situations) are important because we use them to organize, record, and communicate mathematical ideas and make them more comprehensible.

1. Each cube represents 1 cm³. Determine the volume of each solid. The cubes are placed on a flat surface, so some cubes are hidden.

a.   **b.**   **c.**

2. Do the following.

   a. Estimate the total number of square units in the circle shown.

   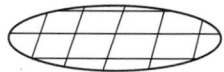

   b. Using the previous result, estimate the total number of cubic units in the cylinder shown.

   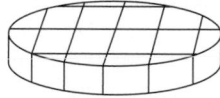

   c. Using the previous result, estimate the volume of the cylinder shown.

   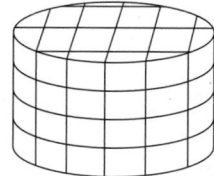

3. Refer to the diagram of the regular octagonal pyramid and use appropriate geometric notation for each part. Assume D is the midpoint of $\overline{CE}$.

   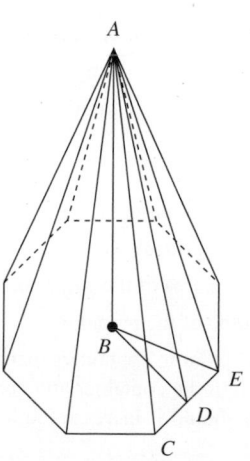

a. apothem   **b.** slant height   **c.** height   **d.** side
e. radius   **f.** m∠ABE   **g.** m∠ABD   **h.** m∠BDE

4. The diagram shows a regular heptagonal pyramid.

   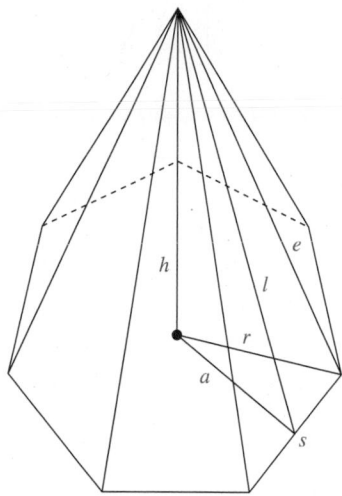

   a. Write an equation involving the side s, apothem a, and radius r.

   b. Write an equation involving the slant height l, apothem a, and height h.

   c. Write an equation involving the lateral edge e, radius r, and height h.

5. The diagram represents a regular pentagonal pyramid. The measurements unit is centimeters.

   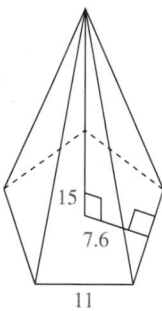

   a. Find the area of the base.

   b. Find the lateral surface area of the pyramid.

   c. Find the surface area of the pyramid.

   d. Find the volume of the pyramid.

6. The diagram represents a regular pentagonal pyramid. The measurements unit is feet.

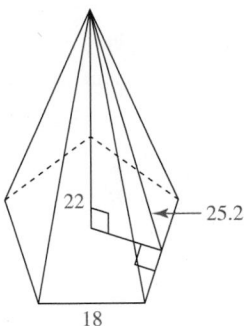

22 ← 25.2

18

a. Find the area of the base.

b. Find the lateral surface area of the pyramid.

c. Find the surface area of the pyramid.

d. Find the volume of the pyramid.

7. The diagram represents a right pentagonal prism. The measurements unit is feet.

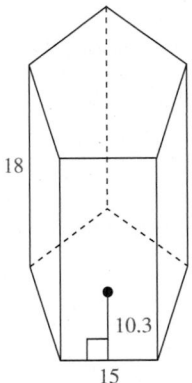

18

10.3

15

a. Find the area of the base.

b. Find the lateral surface area.

c. Find the surface area of the prism.

d. Find the volume of the prism.

8. The formula for the surface area of a circular cylinder is $V = 2\pi r^2 + 2\pi rh$ cubic units.

a. What does $2\pi r^2$ represent?

b. What does $2\pi rh$ represent?

9. Do the following.

a. Draw a representation of a cubic centimeter.

b. Draw a representation of a cubic inch.

PROBLEM SOLVING

Refresher: Problem solving (reaching a goal that is not immediately attainable) is important because it helps students think more deeply about what they know and deal with unfamiliar situations.

10. A farmer plans to cover a 70-by-125-yard rectangular field with enriched soil 3 inches deep. Each truckload of soil costs $280 and has a volume of 85 cubic yards.

a. How many truckloads of soil does the farmer need?

b. What is the total cost of the soil?

11. A painter plans to paint the exterior of a cargo container. The cargo container has a length of 55 feet, width of 8 feet, and height of 10 feet. The paint is sold by the gallon, and each gallon of paint covers 275 square feet. How many gallons of paint are needed? Assume the painter will not paint the bottom of the container.

12. A manufacturing company plans to coat the entire exterior of a cylindrical shipping container with a 0.075-mm layer of special rustproof paint. The cylinder has a radius of 5 cm and height of 12 cm. The paint costs $0.35 per cubic centimeter. What is the cost of the paint for each cylinder?

13. The surface area of a right rectangular prism is 856 cm². The height is 14 cm. The length of the base is 2 cm more than the width of the base. Find the volume of the prism.

14. The dimensions of the edges in a right rectangular prism have the ratio 3:5:12. The volume of the prism is 1350 cm³. What is the length of the shortest side?

REASONING AND PROOF

Refresher: Reasoning and proof (thinking and justifying) are important because they help students make sense of mathematics.

15. What is the length of each side of the cube?

a. The volume of a cube is 421.875 cm³.

b. The surface area of a cube is 150 cm².

16. A rectangular prism filled with water has a length of 12.5 cm, width of 10.1 cm, and height of 8.4 cm. The water is poured into a cylinder with a radius of 7.0 cm and height of 6.6 cm. Will the water overflow? Explain your answer.

17. A rectangular aquarium with a height of 60 cm, length of 40 cm, and width of 35 cm contains 52 L of water. What is the height of the water? (Hint: 1 L = 1000 cm³).

18. A regular pyramid has a pentagonal base with sides of the length 15 cm, an apothem of 10.3 cm, and a height of 20 cm.

a. Find the area of the base.

b. Find the lateral surface area of the pyramid.

c. Find the surface area of the pyramid.

d. Find the volume of the pyramid.

19. A regular pyramid has a pentagonal base with sides of the length 22 cm, a slant height of 33.6 cm, and a height of 30 cm.

a. Find the area of the base.

b. Find the lateral surface area of the pyramid.

c. Find the surface area of the pyramid.

d. Find the volume of the pyramid.

20. A regular pyramid has a square base with sides of the length 5 cm and a height of 12 cm.

a. Find the area of the base.

b. Find the lateral surface area of the pyramid.

c. Find the surface area of the pyramid.

d. Find the volume of the pyramid.

21. A company sells paint in containers that are right cylinders. It decided to redesign the container and decreased the radius by 5%. How much should it increase the height to maintain the same volume?

22. Convert the following measurements.
    a. $567 \text{ in}^3 = $ ___ ft^3 b. $789 \text{ in}^3 = $ ___ yd^3
    c. $400 \text{ cm}^3 = $ ___ in^3 d. $567 \text{ m}^3 = $ ___ ft^3

CONNECTIONS

Refresher: Connections (linking and applying mathematical ideas) are important because they deepen student understanding and make mathematics more meaningful, flexible, and useful.

23. A graduated cylinder has a radius of 3.5 cm. An object is dropped into a graduated cylinder with water, and the water rises 0.25 cm.
    a. What is the volume of water displaced by the object?
    b. What is the volume of the object?

24. A student drops an object into a water-filled right rectangular prism with a width of 40 cm, length of 28 cm, and height of 20 cm. The water rises 3 cm. What is the volume of the object?

25. The height of a cylinder is three times its radius. Express the volume V of a cylinder using function notation.

26. The table shows a contrived measurement system for length. Use dimensional analysis to convert the measurements. Round the final answer to the nearest hundredth.

Measurement unit	Relationship
zippo	3.1 zippos = 5 thors
thor	
leed	4.5 leeds = 0.25 zippo

    a. 810.5 cubic leeds to cubic zippos
    b. 4.8 cubic thors to cubic leeds

27. One guideline for determining the number of small community fish in an aquarium is 1 inch of fish per gallon of water $(231 \text{ in}^3 = 1 \text{ gal})$. The average length of a marigold swordtail is 5 inches. According to this guideline, what is the maximum number of marigold swordtails an aquarium can support if
    a. the capacity of the aquarium is 248 gallons?
    b. the aquarium is a rectangular prism with a height of 14 inches, length of 40 inches, and width of 15 inches?

28. Oxygen diffuses into the surface water in an aquarium. The larger the surface area, the more fish the aquarium can support. The surface method is a guideline to determine the number of slender fish an aquarium can support. It states that an aquarium can support 1 inch of fish per 12 square inches of surface area. The average length of a tiger barb is 3 inches. What is the maximum number of tiger barbs an aquarium can support if
    a. the base is rectangular with a length of 22 inches and width of 14 inches?
    b. the base is hexagonal with sides of length of 12 inches and an apothem of 10.4 inches?

COMMUNICATION

Refresher: Communication (written and verbal explanations using representations and proper mathematical vocabulary) is important because it helps students refine and strengthen their understanding.

29. The diagram shows two solids.

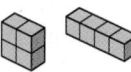

    a. Find the volume of each solid.
    b. Find the surface area of each solid.
    c. What did you learn?

30. The diagram shows two solids.

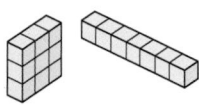

    a. Find the surface area of each solid.
    b. Find the volume of each solid. c What did you learn?

31. A teacher wrote the following four words on the board in alphabetical order: *capacity, container, solid, volume*. She asked the class: "Which two words go together?" The students pondered the question. Then Liza excitedly exclaimed, "*Capacity* and *container* go together, and *solid* and *volume* go together!" Then Mario proclaimed, "*Capacity* and *volume* go together, and *container* and *solid* go together." Explain how each student could be correct.

32. A cylinder has a diameter of 5 units and height of 10 units. A prism has a square base with sides of the length 5 units, and a height of 10 units.
    a. Draw the shape of their bases.
    b. Without calculating the volumes, can you determine which of them has the greater volume? Explain your answer.
    c. Calculate the volume of each.
    d. Without calculating surface areas, can you determine which of them has the greater surface area? Explain your answer.
    e. Calculate the surface area of each.

33. Each notation is an incorrect volume or weight measurement. Give the correct notation.
    a. mLs b. grs c. ci d. oz

More practice with the ideas of the section

34. Fill in the blank. Choose one of the following words or phrases: *capacity, cone, cubic centimeter, cubic inch, cylinder, prism, pyramid, standard measures of volume,* or *volume.*
    a. _____ is the amount of space that a three-dimensional object occupies.
    b. The _____ of a container, such as a box or jar, tells us the amount of material the container can hold.
    c. _____ refer to units of volume within the U.S. customary system (for example, cubic inch, cubic feet, or gallon) or the metric system (for example, cubic centimeter, cubic meter, or liter).

d. A _____, abbreviated cm³, is the space occupied by a cube with a length of 1 cm, width of 1 cm, and height of 1 cm.

e. A _____, abbreviated in³, is the space occupied by a cube with a length of 1 inch, width of 1 inch, and height of 1 inch.

f. A formula for the volume of a polyhedron is $V = (1/3)Bh$ cubic units. The polyhedron is a _____.

g. A formula for the volume of a polyhedron is $V = lwh$ cubic units. The polyhedron is a _____.

h. A formula for the volume of a solid is $V = \pi r^2 h$. The solid is a _____.

35. Match the amount of water needed for a task to the quantity (www.epa.gov/safewater).

Task	Water needed
a. taking a shower	(i) 4–7 gal
b. watering the lawn	(ii) 15–30 gal
c. brushing teeth	(iii) 62,600 gal
d. drinking	(iv) 180 gal
e. flushing the toilet	(v) 1/2 gal
f. producing 1 ton of steel	(vi) 1 gal

36. The diagram shows a regular square pyramid. Do the following, rounding the final answer to the nearest tenth.

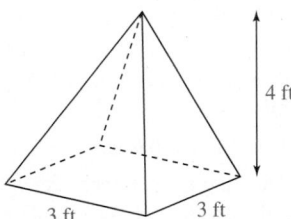

a. Find the area of the base.

b. Find the lateral surface area of the pyramid.

c. Find the surface area of the pyramid.

d. Find the volume of the pyramid.

37. The diagram shows a right cylinder. Do the following, rounding the final answer to the nearest tenth.

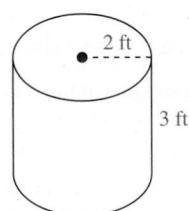

a. Find the area of each base.

b. Find the lateral surface area of the cylinder.

c. Find the surface area of the cylinder.

d. Find the volume of the cylinder.

38. The diagram shows a cone. Do the following, rounding the final answer to the nearest tenth.

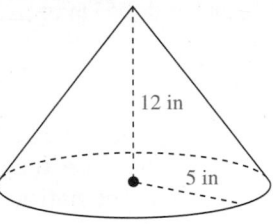

a. Find the area of the base.

b. Find the lateral surface area of the cone.

c. Find the surface area of the cone.

d. Find the volume of the cone.

39. The diagram shows a cone. Do the following, rounding the final answer to the nearest tenth.

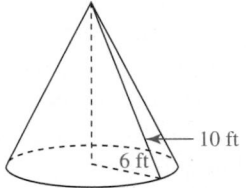

a. Find the area of the base.

b. Find the lateral surface area of the cone.

c. Find the surface area of the cone.

d. Find the volume of the cone.

40. A regular pyramid has a height of 20 cm, with a pentagonal base with a perimeter of 48 cm and an apothem of 6.6 cm.

a. Find the area of the base.

b. Find the lateral surface area of the pyramid.

c. Find the surface area of the pyramid.

d. Find the volume of the pyramid.

41. A regular hexagonal pyramid has a height of 14 cm. The base has a radius of 8 cm and sides of the length 8 cm.

a. Find the area of the base.

b. Find the lateral surface area of the prism.

c. Find the surface area of the prism.

d. Find the volume of the prism.

42. In a right pentagonal prism, each side of the base has a length of 7.5 cm, the apothem of the base is 5.2 cm, and the height is 13.1 cm.

a. Find the area of each base.

b. Find the lateral surface area of the prism.

c. Find the surface area of the prism.

d. Find the volume of the prism.

43. A regular square pyramid has a slant height of 16.25 cm. The length of each side of the base is 12.5 cm.

a. Find the lateral surface area of the pyramid.

b. Find the apothem of the base.

c. Find the height of the pyramid.

d. Find the area of the base of the pyramid.

e. Find the surface area of the pyramid.

44. Start with a cube with sides of the length 3 units.

   a. What is its surface area?

   b. If you double the length of the sides of the cube, what is the new surface area?

   c. If you triple the length of the sides of the cube, what is the new surface area?

   d. If you multiply the length of the sides of the cube by n, where n is any positive integer, what is the surface area of the new cube?

   e. Make a conjecture about the relationship between how you change the length of the sides of a cube and the resulting surface area, as follows: Assume that a cube has sides of the length s. Then its surface area is $6s^2$. If the sides are multiplied by a positive integer n, then the surface area of the resulting cube is _____.

   f. Prove your conjecture.

45. Start with a cube with sides of the length 4 m.

   a. What is its volume?

   b. If you double the length of the sides of the cube, what is the new volume?

   c. If you triple the length of the sides of the cube, what is the new volume?

   d. If you multiply the length of the sides of the cube by n, where n is any positive integer, what is the volume of the new cube?

   e. Make a conjecture about the relationship between how you change the length of the sides of a cube and the resulting volume, as follows: Assume that a cube has sides of the length s. Then its volume is s^3. If the sides are multiplied by a positive integer n, then the volume of the resulting cube is

   _____.

   f. Prove your conjecture.

46. An acre-foot is a measurement unit often used to measure large volumes of water, such as in lakes or reservoirs. Thus, 1 acre-foot is the volume of water covering 1 acre to a depth of 1 foot.

   a. Convert 1 acre-foot to cubic feet. (Hint: 1 acre = 43,560 ft^2.)

   b. Convert 1 acre-foot to gallons. (Hint: 1 gal = 231 in^3.)

   c. An average swimming pool has 20,000 gallons of water. How many pools can be filled with 1 acre-foot of water?

47. An acre-foot of water is 325,851 gallons, which is enough to meet the water needs of three families for 1 year. At this rate, how much water would each family use per day? (Hint: 1 year = 365 days.)

48. The ratio of the diameter to the height of a cylinder is 3:5. The volume of the cylinder is 151.875π cubic inches. What is the radius of the cylinder? Show your work.

49. One guideline for determining the number of large fish in an aquarium is 1 inch of fish per 6 gallons of water. The average length of a Chinese algae eater is approximately 7.5 inches. According to this guideline, what is the maximum number of Chinese algae eaters an aquarium can support? (Hint: 231 in^3 = 1 gal.)

   a. Assume the capacity of the aquarium is 420 gallons.

   b. Assume the aquarium is rectangular with a height of 4 feet, length of 7 feet, and width of 2 feet and 4 inches.

50. Ornamental rocks in aquariums provide fish with shelter from other fish. An ornamental rock is placed in a rectangular aquarium. The aquarium has a height of 14 inches, width of 9 inches, and length of 12 inches. The volume of water displaced by the rock is 43.2 cubic inches.

   a. What is the volume of the ornamental rock?

   b. How much did the water rise?

51. Find the slant height of a cone with a radius of 10 cm and height of 18 cm.

52. Find the height of a cone with a radius of 8 cm and slant height of 17 cm.

53. Sandra has a coffee mug in the shape of a cylinder with a radius of 3.5 inches and a height of 5 inches. She pours 4 cups of water in the coffee mug. What is the height of the water in the coffee mug? (Hint: 231 in^3 = 16 c.)

54. Find the surface area and volume of the given solid.

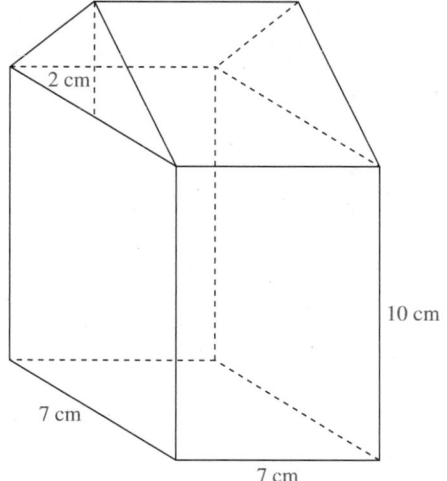

CHAPTER 11 REVIEW

CHAPTER 11 Organizer

Section	What You Should Learn	Review Problems
11.1	1. Understand major principles of measurement.	1–3
	2. Determine the precision and greatest possible error (GPE).	4–6
	3. Determine the range of values of the actual measurement.	7
	4. Use dimensional analysis to convert linear measurements.	8–10
	5. Solve problems involving linear measurement.	11–13
11.2	1. Determine the perimeter or area of a polygon.	14–16
	2. Describe the relationship between the size of the unit and the number of units needed to measure the area of an object.	17
	3. Find the area, circumference, radius, or diameter of a circle.	18–19
	4. Know what happens to the circumference or area of a circle when you change the radius.	20
	5. Explore what happens to the perimeter or area of a rectangle when you change the dimensions.	21–22
	6. Use dimensional analysis to convert area measurements.	23–24
	7. Relate the area of a sector and angle measure of a sector.	25–27
	8. Solve problems involving area measurement	28–32
11.3	1. Apply the Pythagorean theorem and its converse.	33–37
	2. Use the Pythagorean inequalities to classify a triangle as acute, right, or obtuse.	38
	3. Use the Triangle Inequality to determine whether line segments of given lengths can be used to form a triangle.	39–40
	4. Use angle-side triangle inequalities for a triangle.	41
	5. Relate the perimeter, area, apothem, and radius of a regular polygon.	42–45
11.4	1. Find the volume of a solid consisting of cubes.	46
	2. Find the surface area and volume of a right prism, regular pyramid, cylinder, or cone.	47–52
	3. Apply Archimedes' principle to find the volume of an irregularly shaped object.	53–54
	4. Use dimensional analysis to convert volume measurements.	55–56
	5. Solve problems involving volume measurement.	57–58

Key Terms and Concepts

measurement unit 619	precision 622	prefix 626
iteration (repetition) 619	accuracy 623	dimensional analysis 628
measurement 619	greatest possible error (GPE) 624	unit factor 628
process of measurement 620	measurement system 625	uniqueness of kilogram 630
major principle of measurement 620	U.S. customary system 626	perimeter 634
ruler 621	metric system 626	perimeter of rectangle 635

Key Terms and Concepts

circle 637	area of a circle 650	dimensional analysis and volume 673
center 637	area of a sector 651	noncubic units 674
radius 637	hypotenuse 658	volume of a rectangular prism 676
diameter 637	leg 658	volume of a prism 678
circumference 637	Pythagorean theorem 658	volume of a cylinder 679
π 638	converse of the Pythagorean theorem 660	Archimedes's principle 680
arc length 639	Pythagorean inequalities 662	volume of a pyramid 681
central angle 639	angle–side inequalities 663	volume of a cone 681
area 641	triangle inequality 663	surface area 684
unit square 641	area of a regular polygon 665	surface area of a right prism 684
square unit 642	apothem 666	surface area of a right cylinder 684
area of a rectangle 643	radius of a regular polygon 666	surface area of a right pyramid 685
dimensional analysis and area 645	volume 671	slant height 685
base 647	capacity 671	surface area of a right cone 686
height (altitude) 647	cubic centimeter (cm³) 672	sphere 688
area of a parallelogram 648	cubic inch (in³) 672	surface area of a sphere 688
area of a triangle 649	unit cube 672	volume of a sphere 688
area of a trapezoid 649		

Review Questions

1. List two attributes of a coin that you can measure.

2. The four steps of measurement are listed here. Organize them in their proper order: (i) Place the measurement unit end to end to cover the attribute without gaps or overlaps, and then count the number of repetitions. (ii) Determine an attribute of an object to measure. (iii) Report the measurement with a numerical value and a unit of measurement. (iv) Choose an appropriate measurement unit.

3. Use this line segment to do the following and learn a major principle of measurement.

   a. Suppose the length is 3 pins. Sketch a pin.
   b. Suppose the length is 4 lops. Sketch a lop.
   c. Suppose the length is 6 wans. Sketch a wan.
   d. What happens to the length of the unit as the number of units in the length increases?

4. What are the precision and GPE of each ruler?

   a.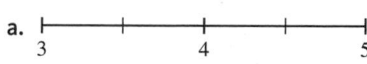

   b.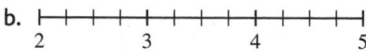

   c.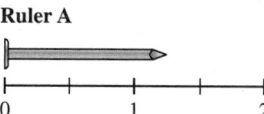

5. Find the GPE of each measurement.
   a. 17.8 yd   b. 15 ft   c. 24.3 m   d. 72.78 mi
   e. 4.0 lb

6. The diagram shows three rulers used to measure the length of a nail.

   Ruler A

   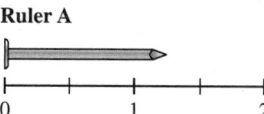

   Ruler B

   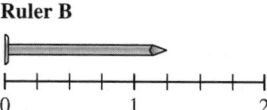

   Ruler C

   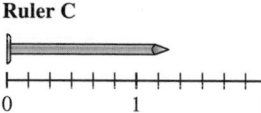

   a. What is the precision of each ruler?
   b. What is the length of the nail for each ruler?
   c. Which ruler provides the most accurate measurement of this nail?
   d. Does a higher-precision ruler always lead to a more accurate measurement?
   e. In general, which ruler would you expect to provide the most accurate measurement of a nail?

7. Fill in the blank.

   a. A reading of 12.32 pounds on a weighing scale means that the true weight is at least _____ pounds and at most _____ pounds.

   b. A measurement of 26.4 feet means that the true distance is at least _____ feet, and the true distance is at most _____ feet.

8. The table shows a contrived measurement system.

Measurement unit	Relationship
cap	3 caps = 5 inks
pen	7 pens = 4 caps
ink	

   Convert the measurements to the indicated units using dimensional analysis.

   a. ___ caps = 2 inks   b. 5 pens = ___ caps

   c. 8 inks = ___ pens   d. 4 pens = ___ caps

9. Convert the following measurements using dimensional analysis.

   a. 5 in = ___ mi   b. 16 ft = ___ yd

   c. 0.25 mi = ___ ft   d. 475 in = ___ mi

   e. 67 mi per hour = ___ ft per sec

10. The Trans-Siberian Railroad in Russia is the longest railroad in the world, at 9289 km. What is this distance in miles, rounded to the nearest mile?

11. The table shows a contrived measurement system. Which measurement unit (cap, pen, or ink) is the smallest?

Measurement unit	Relationship
cap	2 caps = 5 inks
pen	4 pens = 3 caps
ink	

12. Fill in the blanks with metric units of length (to create benchmarks). A _____ is about the thickness of a standard paper clip. A _____ is about the width of the fingernail on your pinky finger. A _____ is about the distance from the floor to the doorknob on a door.

13. A single paper denomination of U.S. money ($1, $5, $20, and $100 note) weighs 1 g. How much would $1 million weigh, in pounds? (Hint: 1 kg = 2.2046 lb)

   a. Assume the bills are $1 notes.

   b. Assume the bills are $5 notes.

14. Determine the perimeter and area of each shape.

   a. 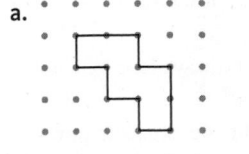   b.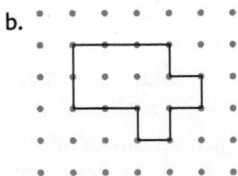

15. Determine the area of a parallelogram, in terms of para units, as shown.

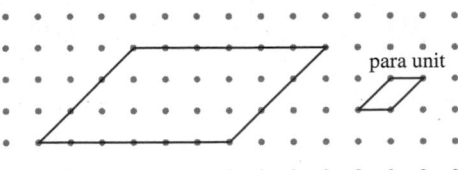

16. Use a formula to determine the area of each shape.

   a.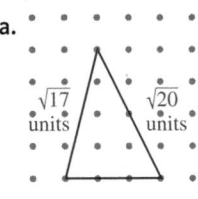

   b.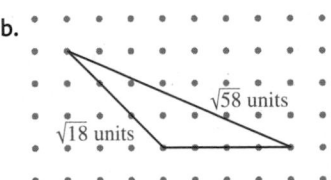

   c.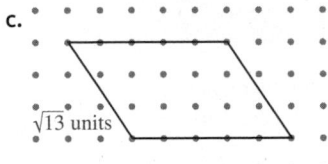

   d.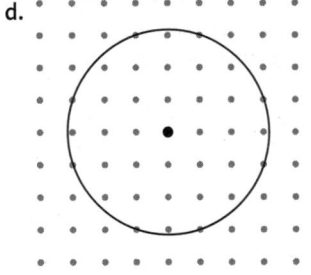

17. Do the following using the contrived measurements given.

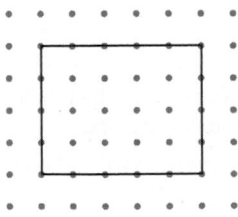

   a. Suppose the area is 5 pins. Sketch a possible pin.

   b. Suppose the area is 10 wans. Sketch a possible wan.

   c. What happens to the size of the unit as the number of units in the area increases?

18. A circle has a circumference of 38 cm. Determine the diameter of the circle. Round to the nearest tenth.

19. Do the following. Use a protractor or ruler as needed.

    a. Determine the circumference of circle *H*.

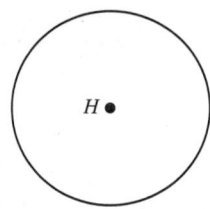

    b. Determine the area of circle *K*.

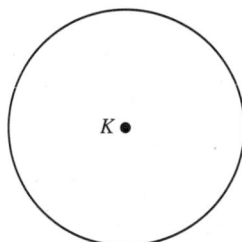

20. What effect does multiplying the radius of a circle by 4 have on the

    a. circumference?   b. area?

21. What effect does multiplying the sides of a rectangle by 5 have on the

    a. perimeter?   b. area?

22. A rectangle has a length of *l* units and width of *w* units. How much must you increase the width of the rectangle to keep the area constant if you decrease the length by 40%?

23. Do the following.

    a. Determine the number of square feet of carpet needed for a room with an area of 75 square yards.

    b. Determine the number of square yards of carpet needed for a room with an area of 328 square feet.

    c. Use dimensional analysis to convert 12,708 square feet to square miles.

    d. Use dimensional analysis to convert 1234 square inches to square yards.

24. Convert the measurements. Round the final answer to two decimal places.

    a. $18 \text{ cm}^2 =$ ___ in^2 b. $4 \text{ ft}^2 =$ ___ cm^2

    c. $7 \text{ m}^2 =$ ___ ft^2 d. $20{,}500 \text{ yd}^2 =$ ___ mi^2

25. What is the area of the sector that is shaded?

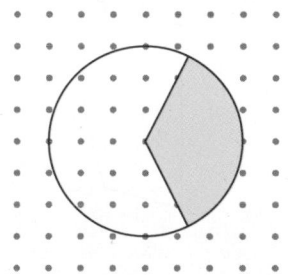

26. The radius of a circle is 8 cm, and a sector has the angle measure of 72°. What is the area of the sector?

27. The radius of a circle is 5 cm, and the area of a sector is 10.47 cm^2. What is the measure of the central angle of the sector? Round your result to the nearest degree.

28. A pool in the shape of a rectangle has a length of 12 m and a width of 5 m. The deck around the pool also has a rectangular shape and is 2 m wide.

    a. Draw a diagram that represents the situation.

    b. Determine the area of the deck.

29. A triangle has sides of the lengths 17, 20, and 25 cm. Determine the lengths of the sides of a square that has the same perimeter.

30. Store A sells five rolls of wrapping paper in a package that costs $4.25. Each roll is 18 inches wide and 35 feet long. Store B sells three rolls of wrapping paper in a package that costs $2.25. Each roll is 15 inches wide and 37 feet long. Which store offers the better buy?

31. A landscaper is spreading soil to make a new rectangular lawn with the dimensions 18 by 30 feet. The soil will be 2 inches deep. The total cost for the soil is $380. What is the cost of each cubic yard of soil?

32. Lead-based paint is any paint that has at least 1 mg of lead per square centimeter. Determine whether each situation indicates lead-based paint. Show your work.

    a. A lab determines there are 30 mg of lead in a 14-by-5-cm rectangular sample of paint.

    b. A lab determines there are 50 mg of lead in a 4-by-3-cm rectangular sample of paint.

33. Determine whether line segments of the given lengths form a right triangle. Explain your answer.

    a. 6, 8, and 10 m   b. 7, 9, and 12 m

34. A 289-inch ladder leans against a wall. The bottom of the ladder is 240 inches from the base of the wall. The ladder is moved 50 inches closer to the wall. How much higher is the ladder? Round your answer to the nearest inch.

35. The area of the polygonal shape is 576 cm^2. Find *AB*.

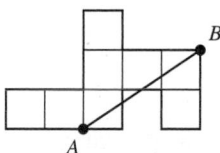

36. An aspect ratio of a rectangular image is a ratio that compares the horizontal dimension to the vertical dimension. Two common aspect ratios of televisions are 4:3 and 16:9. The size of a television is the diagonal measurement of the television screen. Do the following. Show your work.

    a. The aspect ratio of a 37-inch screen television is 16:9. Find the horizontal and vertical dimensions of the television, rounded to the nearest inch.

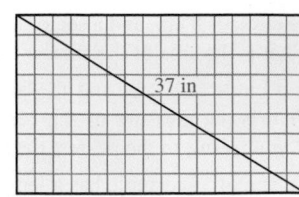

b. The aspect ratio of a 46-inch standard screen is 4:3. What is the area of the television screen, rounded to the nearest square inch?

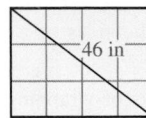

37. Trapezoid *ABCD* has the dimensions shown in the diagram. Find the area of the trapezoid, rounded to the nearest square cm. Show your work.

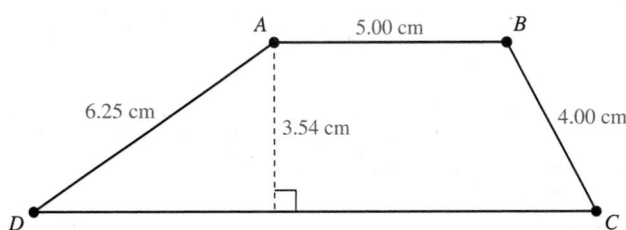

38. Classify the triangle as acute, right, or obtuse. Explain your answer.

  a. This triangle has sides of the lengths 15, 18, and 24 cm.

  b. This triangle has sides of the lengths 13, 17, and 20 cm.

  c. This triangle has sides of the lengths 15, 20, and 25 cm.

39. Can you form a triangle with the given line segments?

  a. 2, 15, and 35 cm   **b.** 15, 7, and 19 cm

  c. 12, 22, and 10 cm   **d.** 7, 9, and 18 cm

40. A triangle has sides of the lengths 16 cm and 25 cm. What are possible lengths of the third side?

41. Identify the shortest side or sides of $\triangle ABC$.

  a. $m\angle A = 25°$, $m\angle B = 75°$

  b. $m\angle B = 68°$, $m\angle C = 52°$

  c. $m\angle A = m\angle B$, $m\angle C = 70°$

  d. $m\angle A = 3m\angle B - 4°$, $m\angle C = 44°$

42. A regular pentagon has an apothem of 28.9 cm, and each side has a length of 42 cm.

  a. What is the area of the pentagon?

  b. What is the radius of the pentagon?

43. A regular octagon has a radius of 28.7 cm and perimeter of 176 cm.

  a. What is the apothem of the octagon?

  b. What is the area of the octagon?

44. A regular hexagon has an apothem of 27.7 cm and perimeter of 192 cm.

  a. What is the area of the hexagon?

  b. What is the radius of the hexagon?

45. A regular hexagon has a perimeter of 108 cm and area of 841.8 cm².

  a. What is the apothem of the hexagon?

  b. What is the radius of the hexagon?

46. Each cube represents 1 cm³. Determine the volume of each solid. The cubes are placed on a flat surface, so some cubes are hidden.

a.    **b.**

47. In a right pentagonal prism with a height of 20.7 cm, each side of the base has a length of 8.5 cm, and the apothem of the base is 5.8 cm. Find the

  a. lateral surface area of the prism.

  b. area of the base.   **c.** surface area of the prism.

  d. volume of the prism.

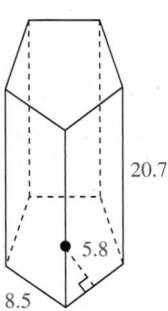

48. In a right hexagonal prism with a height of 33 cm, each side of the base has a length of 14 cm, and the radius of the base is 14 cm. Find the

  a. lateral surface area of the prism.

  b. area of the base.   **c.** surface area of the prism.

  d. volume of the prism.

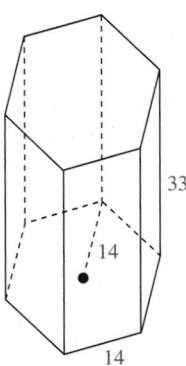

49. The diagram shows a regular square pyramid with a height of 6 cm and sides with a length of 4.8 cm. Find the

 a. area of the base.   b. slant height of the pyramid.

 c. lateral surface area of the pyramid.

 d. surface area of the pyramid.

 e. volume of the pyramid.

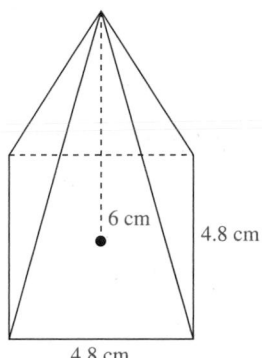

50. The diagram shows a regular hexagonal pyramid with a height of 8 cm, radius of 3.6 cm, and base with sides of the length 3.6 cm. Find the

 a. apothem of the pyramid.   b. area of the base.

 c. slant height of the pyramid.

 d. lateral surface area of the pyramid.

 e. surface area of the pyramid.   f. volume of the pyramid.

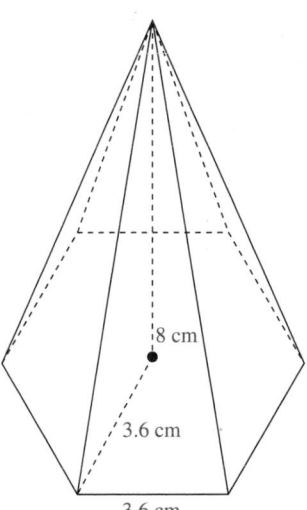

51. The diagram shows a right cylinder. Find the

 a. area of each base.

 b. lateral surface area of the cylinder.

 c. surface area of the cylinder.   d. volume of the cylinder.

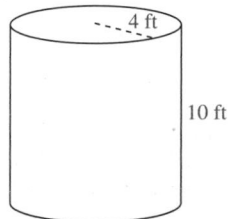

52. Find the surface area and volume of each cone.

 a.

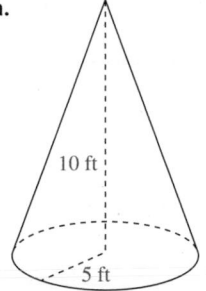

 b.

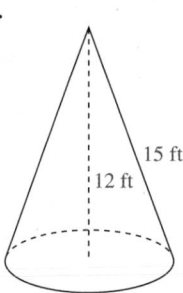

53. A graduated cylinder has a radius of 8 cm. An object is dropped into a graduated cylinder holding water, and the water rises 0.40 cm.

 a. What is the volume of water displaced by the object?

 b. What is the volume of the object?

54. A student drops an object into a right rectangular prism with a width of 25 cm, length of 30 cm, and height of 42 cm. The water in the prism rises 12 cm. What is the volume of the object?

55. Convert the volume measurements.

 a. $7685 \text{ yd}^3 = \_\_\_ \text{ mi}^3$ b. $6789 \text{ cm}^3 = \_\_\_ \text{ km}^3$

 c. $567 \text{ cm}^3 = \_\_\_ \text{ in}^3$ d. $876 \text{ cm}^3 = \_\_\_ \text{ ft}^3$

 e. $2345 \text{ cm}^3 = \_\_\_ \text{ yd}^3$ f. $5 \text{ gal} = \_\_\_ \text{ qt}$

56. Convert the measurements. Round the final answer to the nearest tenth.

$$1 \text{ L} = 1000 \text{ cm}^3$$
$$1 \text{ L} = 33.8140227 \text{ fl oz}$$
$$1 \text{ qt} = 32 \text{ fl oz}$$
$$1 \text{ gal} = 231 \text{ in}^3$$

 a. $15 \text{ L} = \_\_\_ \text{ qt}$ b. $500 \text{ in}^3 = \_\_\_ \text{ gal}$

 c. $22 \text{ gal} = \_\_\_ \text{ L}$ d. $1.5 \text{ qt} = \_\_\_ \text{ cm}^3$

57. A rectangular aquarium with a height of 42 cm, length of 50 cm, and width of 36 cm contains 30 L of water. What is the height of the water, rounded to the nearest tenth? (Hint: $1 \text{ L} = 1000 \text{ cm}^3$.)

58. What is the length of each side of the cube?

 a. The volume of the cube is 614.125 cm^3.

 b. The surface area of the cube is 1350 cm^2.

Chapter 11 Test

1. *Understand major principles of measurement.* List two attributes of a jar that you can measure.

2. *Understand major principles of measurement.*

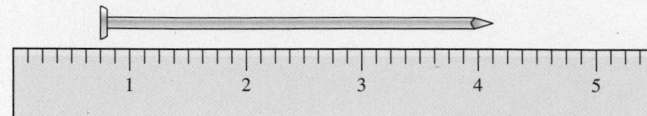

   a. Explain how an elementary school student could mistakenly report the length of the nail as $4\frac{1}{8}$ inches.

   b. Determine the correct length of the nail. Show your work.

3. *Determine the precision and greatest possible error (GPE).* Part of a ruler is shown. Determine the precision and GPE of the ruler.

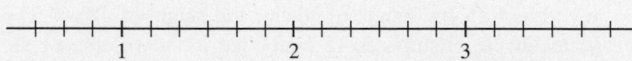

4. *Determine the precision and greatest possible error (GPE).* Lewis and Clark measure the circumference of a tree. Lewis records the measurement as 2.3 feet, and Clark records the measurement as 2.38 feet.

   a. Which measurement is more precise?

   b. Which measurement is more accurate?

   c. Which measurement do you expect would be more accurate?

5. *Determine the range of values of the actual measurement.* A student reports that the length of a pipe is 46.7 feet. The true length of the pipe is between ___ and ___ feet.

6. *Use dimensional analysis to convert linear measurements.* Convert the following measurements using dimensional analysis. Round the final answer to the nearest hundredth.

   a. 800 yd = ___ mi

   b. 32 ft = ___ cm

7. *Determine the perimeter or area of a polygon.* Use formulas to find the area of each polygon.

   a.
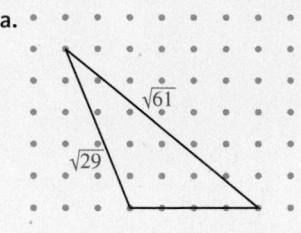

   b.
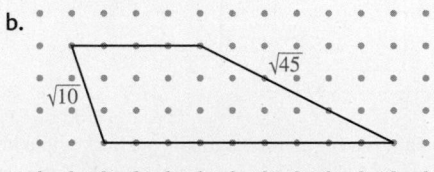

   c.
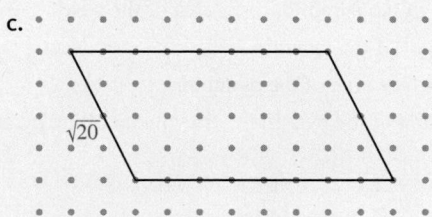

8. *Find the area, circumference, radius, or diameter of a circle.*

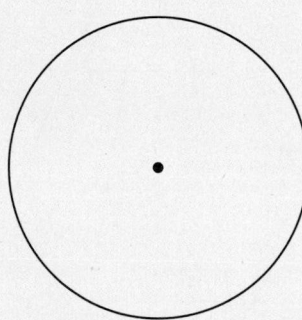

   a. Find the circumference of the circle, rounding to the nearest mm.

   b. Find the area of the circle, rounding to the nearest mm^2.

9. *Find the area, circumference, radius, or diameter of a circle.* A circle has a circumference of 55.8 cm. Determine the diameter of the circle. Round to the nearest hundredth.

10. *Solve problems involving area measurement.*

  a. The radius of a circle is 8 cm, and a sector has the angle measure 72°. What is the area of the sector?

  b. What is the area of the sector that is shaded? (Use a protractor.)

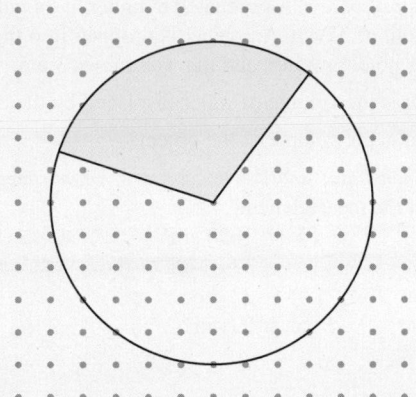

11. *Explore what happens to the perimeter or area of a polygon when you change the dimensions.* What effect does multiplying the sides of a rectangle by 7 have on the

  a. perimeter?   **b.** area?

12. *Use dimensional analysis to convert area measurements.* Convert the following measurement using dimensional analysis. Round the final answer to the nearest tenth.

  a. 846 cm = ___ ft   **b.** 7.8 m = ___ yd

  c. 9500 ft = ___ mi

13. *Relate the area of a sector and angle measure of a sector.* The radius of a circle is 8 cm, and the area of a sector is 65 cm². What is the measure of the central angle of the sector? Round your result to the nearest degree.

14. *Solve problems involving area measurement.* Lead-based paint is any paint that has at least 1 mg of lead per square centimeter. Determine whether each situation indicates lead-based paint. Explain your answer.

  a. A lab determines there are 7 mg of lead in a 3-by-5-cm rectangular sample of paint.

  b. A lab determines there are 14 mg of lead in a 4-by-3-cm rectangular sample of paint.

15. *Apply the Pythagorean theorem and its converse.* Find the perimeter of the trapezoid. Round to the nearest tenth.

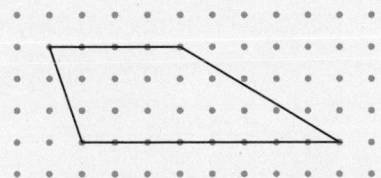

16. *Apply the Pythagorean theorem and its converse.* The area of the polygon shown is 330 square units. Find *AB*.

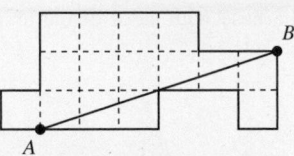

17. *Use the triangle inequality to determine whether line segments of given lengths can be used to form a triangle.* A triangle has sides of the lengths 20 and 32 cm. What are possible lengths of the third side?

18. *Use angle–side triangle inequalities for a triangle.* Classify the triangle as acute, right, or obtuse.

  a. This triangle has sides of the lengths 14, 18, and 28 cm.

  b. This triangle has sides of the lengths 25, 40, and 32 cm.

  c. This triangle has sides of the lengths 39, 89, and 80 cm.

19. *Relate the perimeter, area, apothem, and radius of a regular polygon.*

  a. Find the area of the regular polygon.

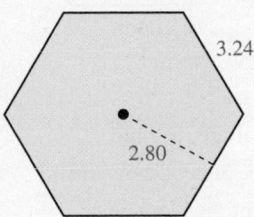

  b. A regular octagon has a perimeter of 112 cm and area of 946.37 cm². Find the apothem and radius of the octagon.

20. *Find the surface area or volume of a solid consisting of cubes.* Each cube has volume 1 cm³. Determine the volume of each solid. The cubes are placed on a flat surface, so some cubes are hidden.

  a.    **b.**

21. *Find the surface area or volume of a solid consisting of cubes.* Each cube has volume 1 cm³. Determine the surface area of the solid. The cubes are placed on a flat surface, so some faces are hidden.

22. *Find the surface area and volume of a right prism, regular pyramid, cylinder, or cone.* The diagram shows a regular octagonal pyramid with a height of 15.03 cm, a radius of 4.21 cm, and a base with sides of the length 3.22 cm. Find each measurement.

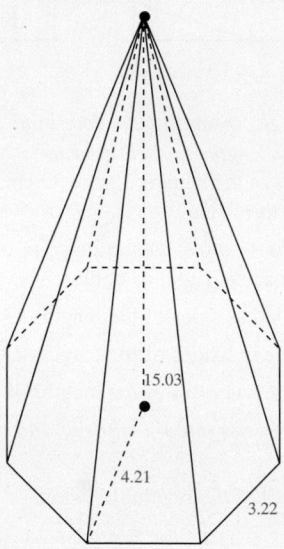

   a. apothem of the pyramid
   b. area of the base
   c. slant height of the pyramid
   d. lateral surface area of the pyramid
   e. surface area of the pyramid
   f. volume of the pyramid

23. *Find the surface area and volume of a right prism, regular pyramid, cylinder, or cone.* Find the volume and surface area of the rectangular prism.

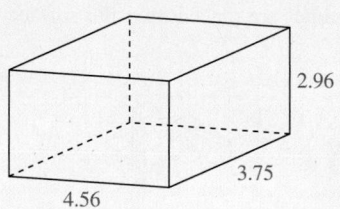

24. *Find the surface area and volume of a right prism, regular pyramid, cylinder, or cone.* A rectangular aquarium with a height of 60 cm, length of 55 cm, and width of 42 cm contains 28 L of water. What is the height of the water, rounded to the nearest centimeter? (Hint: 1 L = 1000 cm^3.)

25. *Apply Archimedes's principle to find the volume of an irregularly shaped object.* A graduated cylinder has a radius of 7 cm and height of 32 cm. An object is dropped into the graduated cylinder holding water, and the water rises 3 cm.

   a. What is the volume of water displaced by the object?
   b. What is the volume of the object?

26. *Use dimensional analysis to convert volume measurements.* Convert the measurements.
$$1 \text{ L} = 1000 \text{ cm}^3$$
$$1 \text{ L} = 33.8140227 \text{ fl oz}$$
$$1 \text{ qt} = 32 \text{ fl oz}$$
$$1 \text{ gal} = 231 \text{ in}^3$$

   a. 20 L = ___ qt
   b. 200 in^3 = ___ gal
   c. 15 gal = ___ L
   d. 3 qt = ___ cm^3

27. *Solve problems involving volume measurement.* Convert the volume measurements.

   a. 6789 yd^3 = ___ mi^3
   b. 420 cm^3 = ___ in^3
   c. 4846 cm^3 = ___ ft^3

12

Triangles and Quadrilaterals

Where Are We Going?

In **Section 12.1,** we discuss triangle congruence axioms and demonstrate how to use them to prove properties of common quadrilaterals. Although you may already be familiar with many of these properties, the proofs give you a chance to see *why* properties of quadrilaterals are true. The proofs also give you a glimpse of the geometry that middle school students will study extensively in high school. In **Section 12.2,** we build on familiarity with properties of circles, triangles, and quadrilaterals and use a compass and straightedge to construct basic geometric figures, such as an angle bisector, perpendicular lines, and parallel lines. Straightedge and compass constructions can help students establish or reinforce properties and spatial relationships. In **Section 12.3,** we focus on similarity of triangles. Similar polygons are polygons that have the same shape and possibly different sizes. Similar geometric figures occur, for example, when we magnify or shrink an image using a photocopy machine, fiddle with the zoom features on a camera, or paint a picture of objects. A terrific application of similar triangles is indirect measurement, such as measuring the distance across a pond or the height of a tree.

How Do Triangles Hold Up the Eiffel Tower?

The Eiffel Tower, completed in 1889 by the French structural engineer Alexandre-Gustave Eiffel as a monument to the French Revolution of 1789, soars approximately 1000 feet. You can reach the viewing platform at the top by climbing 1665 steps. It is considered an architectural wonder because it withstands the deforming and sheering stresses of wind, swaying merely 4.75 inches in high winds (the John Hancock Tower in Boston stands 790 feet tall and can sway up to 36 inches in high winds). An astonishing fact about the Eiffel Tower is that the air within a cylinder containing the tower would have more weight than the iron tower itself. Part of the success of the design of the sturdy tower results from the incorporation of triangles in the structure. One of the things you will learn in this chapter is that triangles have a rigid shape, which means the lengths of the sides uniquely determine the shape of the triangle.

Triangles stabilize and strengthen the Eiffel Tower.

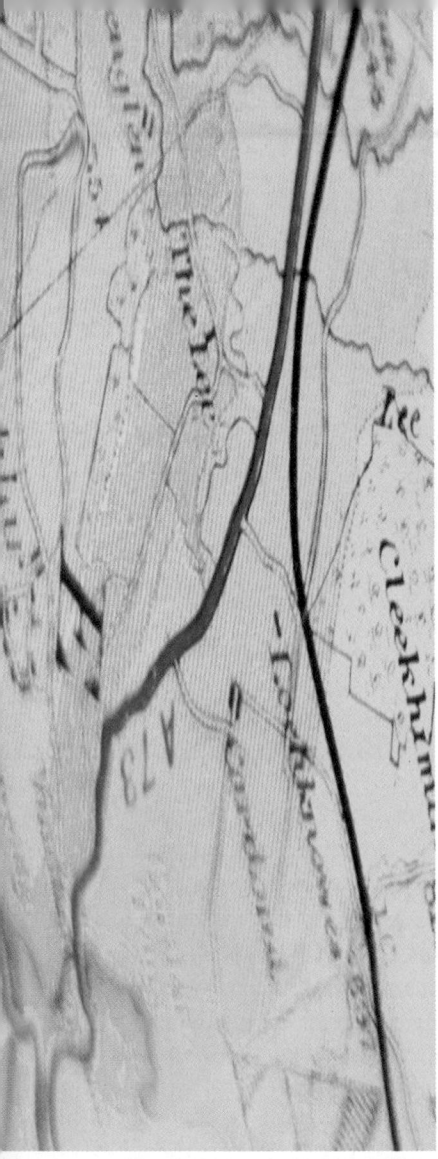

Why Do We Study Triangle Axioms?

Axioms are statements we accept as true. We begin this chapter by studying triangle axioms that relate two triangles that have the same shape and size. Then we apply triangle properties to establish properties of quadrilaterals, such as parallelograms, rectangles, squares, rhombuses, and kites.

We could study a few rectangles, without relating them to triangles, by using a ruler and protractor to infer a property of all rectangles. Inductive reasoning provides an interesting and gradual way for elementary and middle school students to learn. Although exploration leads to discovery, such as that the opposite sides of a rectangle are congruent and the diagonals of a rectangle are congruent, this approach does not answer the question of *why* the opposite sides are congruent or *why* the diagonals are congruent. A **proof** using deductive reasoning explains *why* a statement is true.

Prospective teachers should know the content at a more advanced level than they are expected to teach so that they have a better idea of what their students need to know in later grades. The Math Panel Report (2008) which focuses on improving mathematics education, supports this assertion: "Teachers must know in detail and from a more advanced perspective the mathematical content they are responsible for teaching and the connections of that content to other important mathematics, both prior to and beyond the level they are assigned to teach" (p. 38). Keep in mind that many of the proofs we explore were proved 2000 years ago by Euclid in his masterpiece called *The Elements,* a compilation of 13 books.

The proofs we consider consist of a collection of simple statements and can be organized in paragraph or two-column form. After our experiences with proofs, we use a compass and straightedge to construct some geometric shapes. Then we explore the concept of similarity, in particular two polygons that have the same shape but possibly different sizes.

Before we continue, take a few moments to identify the properties of the listed quadrilaterals in Table 12.1. Place a "Y" for "yes" in a box if every quadrilateral of that type has the given property. Otherwise, leave the box blank. The word *bisect* means to partition into two equal-sized parts. We prove some of these properties in worked examples and homework questions in this chapter.

TABLE 12.1 Identify the Attributes

Attribute	Parallelogram	Rectangle	Square	Rhombus	Kite
1. Opposite sides are always congruent.					
2. Diagonals are always congruent.					
3. Diagonals are always perpendicular.					
4. Diagonals always bisect the angles.					
5. Diagonals always bisect each other.					
6. Opposite sides are always parallel.					
7. Exactly one diagonal is bisected.					
8. Opposite angles are congruent.					

SECTION 12.1 # Congruence Axioms for Triangles

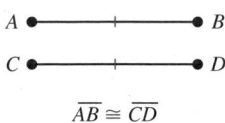

$$\overline{AB} \cong \overline{CD}$$

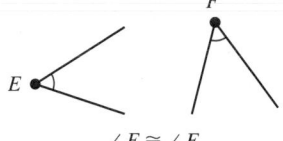

$$\angle E \cong \angle F$$

Throughout this section, we draw diagrams to represent relationships and evoke thought in geometry. Diagrams are widely accepted as legitimate tools in supporting an explanation; however, they do not take the place of proofs.

Congruent Figures and Congruence Properties

We have already used the idea of congruence for line segments and angles. Two line segments are congruent if and only if they have the same length ($\overline{AB} \cong \overline{CD}$ if and only if $AB = CD$). Two angles are congruent if and only if they have the same angle measure ($\angle E \cong \angle F$ if and only if m$\angle E$ = m$\angle F$).

Table 12.2 summarizes some useful congruence properties of line segments and angles. We use them periodically in the chapter.

TABLE 12.2 Congruence Properties

Reflexive property of congruence	Symmetric property of congruence	Transitive property of congruence
$\overline{AB} \cong \overline{AB}$ and $\overline{AB} \cong \overline{BA}$. $\angle ABC \cong \angle ABC$ and $\angle ABC \cong \angle CBA$.	If $\overline{AB} \cong \overline{CD}$, then $\overline{CD} \cong \overline{AB}$. If $\angle ABC \cong \angle DEF$, then $\angle DEF \cong \angle ABC$.	If $\overline{AB} \cong \overline{CD}$ and $\overline{CD} \cong \overline{EF}$, then $\overline{AB} \cong \overline{EF}$. If $\angle ABC \cong \angle DEF$ and $\angle DEF \cong \angle GHI$, then $\angle ABC \cong \angle GHI$.

FIGURE 1

Congruent figures have the same shape and size.

Intuitively, two figures are said to be congruent if and only if they have the same shape and size. Consider the two shapes shown in Figure 1. We can use scissors to cut one of the shapes along its boundary and then place it directly over the other figure to verify the two figures are congruent.

In mathematical expressions, we use the symbol $\cong$ to indicate two figures are congruent, as explained in Chapter 10. The following definition defines what it means to say two triangles are congruent. We use tick marks on the sides and arcs on the angles of polygons to signify congruent corresponding parts.

> **Definition of Congruent Triangles**
>
> **Using Words**
>
> Two triangles are **congruent** if and only if there is a correspondence between the vertices such that all pairs of corresponding sides are congruent and all pairs of corresponding angles are congruent.
>
> **Using Symbols**
>
> $\triangle ABC \cong \triangle DEF$ if and only if $\overline{AB} \cong \overline{DE}$, $\overline{BC} \cong \overline{EF}$, $\overline{AC} \cong \overline{DF}$, $\angle A \cong \angle D$, $\angle B \cong \angle E$, and $\angle C \cong \angle F$.
>
> **Using a Diagram**
>
> $\triangle ABC \cong \triangle DEF$ if and only if
>
>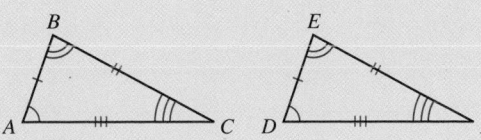
>
> **Notes**
>
> * The congruence statement $\triangle ABC \cong \triangle DEF$ tells us the correspondence between vertices (for example, $A \leftrightarrow D$) and implies the correspondences between sides (for example, $\overline{AC} \approx \overline{DF}$) and between angles (for example, $\angle B \cong \angle E$).
> * The acronym **CPCTC** stands for "corresponding parts of congruent triangles are congruent."

EXAMPLE 12.1

CONNECTION
COMMUNICATION
REASONING

A teacher writes $\triangle OLD \cong \triangle NEW$. Explain why $\overline{OD} \cong \overline{NW}$.

SOLUTION

We are given $\triangle OLD \cong \triangle NEW$. The definition of congruent triangles means corresponding parts are congruent. $\overline{OD}$ and $\overline{NW}$ are corresponding parts, so $\overline{OD} \cong \overline{NW}$.

▲

EXAMPLE 12.2

CONNECTION
REASONING

A teacher writes $\triangle EDP \cong \triangle WAG$. Fill in each blank, and explain your reasoning.

a. $\overline{EP} \cong$ ___

b. $\angle P \cong$ ___

c. ___ $\cong \triangle AGW$

SOLUTION

a. $\overline{EP} \cong \overline{WG}$, because CPCTC.

b. $\angle P \cong \angle G$, because CPCTC.

c. $\triangle DPE \cong \triangle AGW$, because the corresponding vertices must be written in the same order.

▲

The definition of congruent triangles naturally extends to congruent polygons.

What Is an Axiom?

Recall that an axiom is a useful mathematical statement that we accept as true. How do we decide that a statement should be an axiom? The statement should be reasonable, lead to interesting consequences, and be independent from existing knowledge (that is, we cannot derive the statement from existing knowledge). In some grades, a statement that can actually be proved from existing knowledge is designated as an axiom simply because the proof of the statement is beyond expectations for that grade level, even though technically it is a theorem. In an advanced college geometry class, students typically begin with one triangle congruence axiom and then use it to prove the other triangle congruence statements as "theorems." In this textbook, all triangle congruence statements are axioms because of the scope of mathematics for elementary school teachers' courses.

Before continuing, consider the following: If the six corresponding parts of two triangles are congruent, then the two triangles are congruent. If we know a few corresponding parts of two triangles are congruent, then does that provide enough information to conclude that the two triangles are congruent?

EXAMPLE 12.3

COMMUNICATION
REASONING
REPRESENTATION

A teacher asked her class the following question: "If you know that two sides of one triangle are congruent to the corresponding sides of another triangle, then can you automatically conclude the two triangles are congruent?" What is your answer?

SOLUTION

Figure 2 shows two possible triangles, $\triangle ABC$ and $\triangle DEF$, that satisfy the conditions.

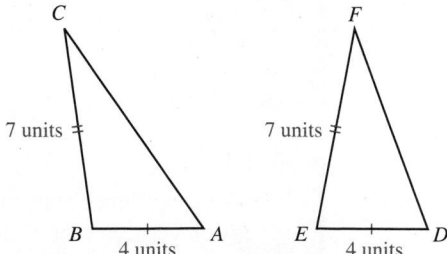

FIGURE 2
$\triangle ABC$ and $\triangle DEF$ satisfy the two conditions. Are the triangles congruent?

△*ABC* is an obtuse triangle, and △*DEF* is an acute triangle. In particular, ∠*B* is an obtuse angle, and all angles of △*DEF* are acute angles. This means we cannot possibly establish a one-to-one correspondence between ∠*B* and an angle of △*DEF.* Therefore, all six corresponding parts cannot be congruent. So the two triangles are not congruent.

REASONING   If you know two sides of one triangle are congruent to the corresponding sides of another triangle, then you cannot automatically conclude the two triangles are congruent. Try to answer these questions (and explain each answer):

- If you know one side of a triangle is congruent to the corresponding side of another triangle, then can you automatically conclude the two triangles congruent?

- If you know one angle of a triangle is congruent to the corresponding angle of another triangle, then can you automatically conclude the two triangles congruent?

- If you know two angles of one triangle are congruent to the corresponding angles of another triangle, then can you automatically conclude the two triangles congruent?

- If you know a side and an angle of one triangle are congruent to the corresponding side and angle of another triangle, then can you automatically conclude the two triangles congruent?

Now we explore axioms that say that if you know a few corresponding parts of two triangles are congruent, then you have enough information to conclude that the two triangles are congruent. These axioms could also help you answer the question in the following Classroom Connection.

> ### ◆ Classroom Connection
>
> ● *Middle Grades Math Tools for Success* (Course 3), p. 572
>
> If you are checking two triangles for congruency, do you need to measure every side and every angle? If not, how many measurements do you need? (From Suzanne H. Chapin. © 1999 by Pearson Education, Inc. or its affiliates. Used by permission. All rights reserved.)

Side-Side-Side Congruence Axiom

We now introduce the **side-side-side (SSS) congruence axiom.** Figure 3 shows three line segments with lengths 4, 6, and 8 units.

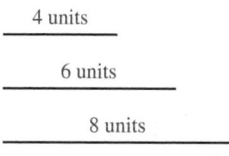

4 units

6 units

8 units

FIGURE 3
Three sides of a triangle.

Trace the arrays in Figure 4 with lengths 4, 6, and 8 units onto a piece of paper, and then cut them out to make a triangle as shown. The arrays should only touch at the corners. Then compare your triangle to the one shown.

FIGURE 4
Arrays for sides of a triangle.

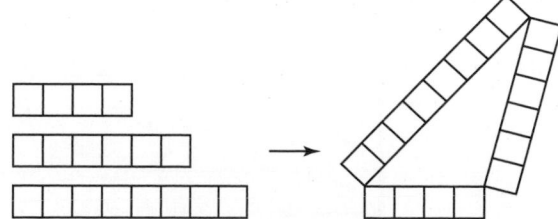

All six corresponding parts between your triangle and the triangle shown should be congruent. Is it possible to use the same arrays to create a triangle with a different shape? The answer is "No." This means that the three sides of a triangle uniquely determine the triangle. We summarize this result using words, symbols, and a diagram.

Side-Side-Side (SSS) Congruence Axiom

Using Words

If three sides of one triangle are congruent to the corresponding sides of another triangle, then the two triangles are congruent.

Using Symbols

If $\overline{AB} \cong \overline{DE}$, $\overline{BC} \cong \overline{EF}$, and $\overline{AC} \cong \overline{DF}$, then $\triangle ABC \cong \triangle DEF$.

Using a Diagram

If _____ and _____ then $\triangle ABC \cong \triangle DEF$.

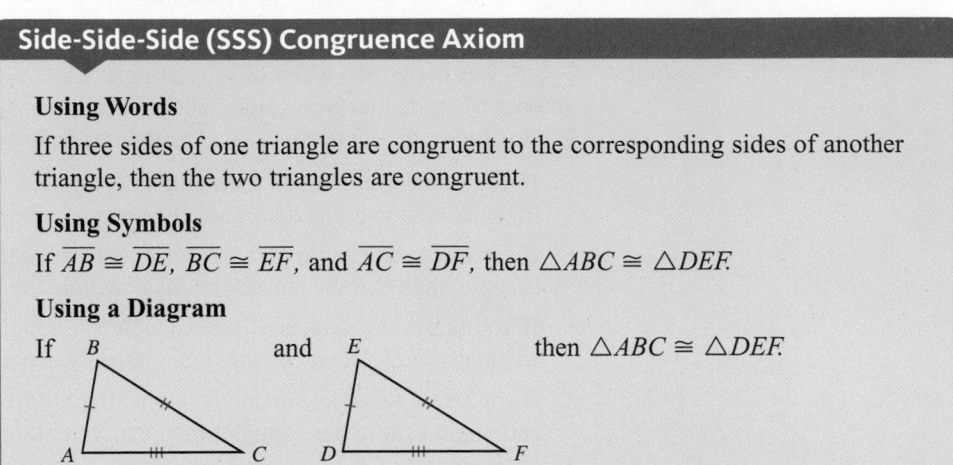

Angle-Side-Angle Congruence Axiom

CONNECTION

REASONING

REPRESENTATION

Next is the **angle-side-angle (ASA) congruence axiom.** Use a protractor and ruler to draw $\triangle ABC$ such that $m\angle A = 40°$, $m\angle B = 70°$, and the line segment joining A and B has a length of 22 mm, as shown in Figure 5. A side between two given angles is called the **included side.** Then compare your triangle to the one shown.

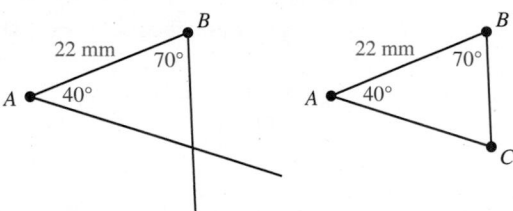

FIGURE 5

Drawing a triangle with angle-side-angle measurements.

    All six corresponding parts between your triangle and the one shown should be congruent. Is it possible to use the same angle measures and included side to create a triangle with a different shape? The answer is "No." This means that two angles and an included side of a triangle uniquely determine the triangle. We summarize this result using words, symbols, and a diagram.

Angle-Side-Angle (ASA) Congruence Axiom

Using Words

If two angles and the included side of one triangle are congruent to the corresponding two angles and included side of another triangle, then the two triangles are congruent.

Using Symbols

If $\angle B \cong \angle E$, $\overline{BC} \cong \overline{EF}$, and $\angle C \cong \angle F$, then $\triangle ABC \cong \triangle DEF$.

Using a Diagram

If _____ and _____ then $\triangle ABC \cong \triangle DEF$.

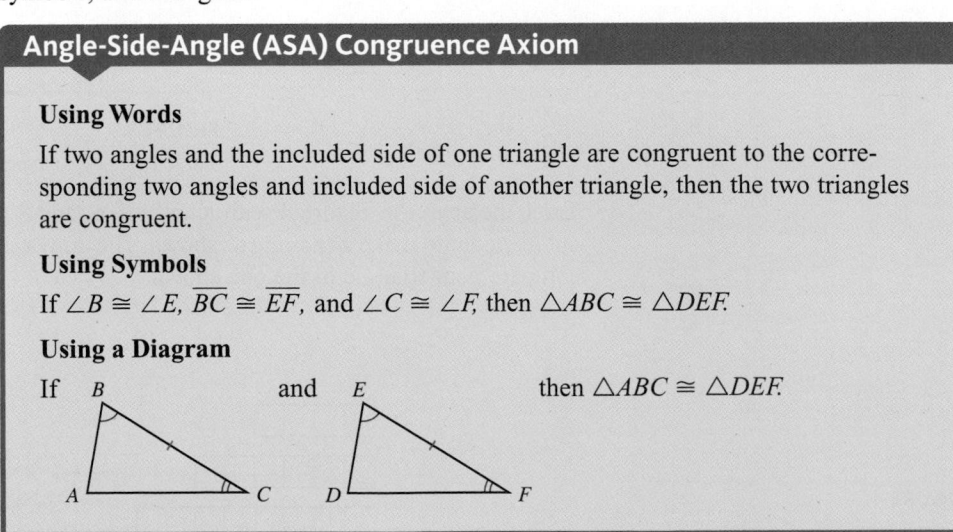

Side-Angle-Side Congruence Axiom

CONNECTION
REASONING
REPRESENTATION

Next is the **side-angle-side (SAS) congruence axiom.** Use a protractor and ruler and draw $\triangle ABC$, in which $\overline{AB}$ has a length of 13 mm and $\overline{AC}$ has a length of 22 mm such that the angle between $\overline{AB}$ and $\overline{AC}$ is 70°. The angle between two given line segments is called the **included angle.** Then compare your triangle to a triangle formed by another student in your class.

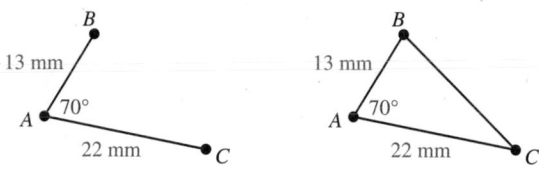

FIGURE 6
Drawing a triangle with side-angle-side measurements.

All six corresponding parts between your triangle and the one shown should be congruent. Is it possible to use the same line segments and included angle to create a triangle with a different shape? The answer is "No." This means that two sides and an included angle of a triangle uniquely determine the triangle. We summarize this result using words, symbols, and a diagram.

Side-Angle-Side (SAS) Congruence Axiom

Using Words

If two sides and the included angle of one triangle are congruent to the corresponding two sides and included angle of another triangle, then the two triangles are congruent.

Using Symbols

If $\overline{AB} \cong \overline{DE}$, $\angle B \cong \angle E$, and $\overline{BC} \cong \overline{EF}$, then $\triangle ABC \cong \triangle DEF$.

Using a Diagram

If   *B*   and   *E*   then $\triangle ABC \cong \triangle DEF$.

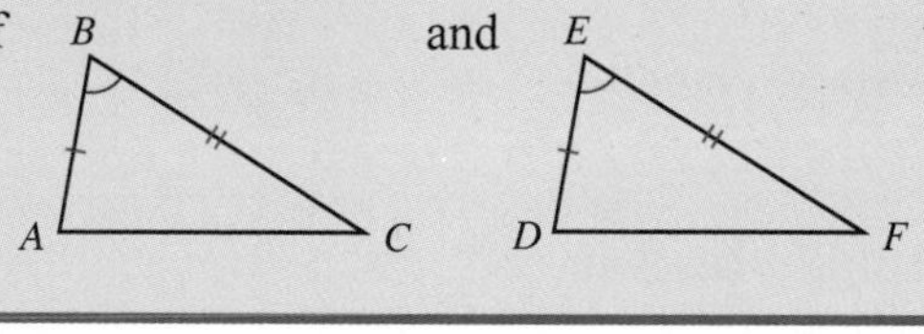

A   *C*   *D*   *F*

Angle-Angle-Side Congruence Axiom

Finally, consider the **angle-angle-side (AAS) congruence axiom.** Let's draw a triangle with a side having length 4 units, as shown in Figure 7, and two angles with measures 60° and 80°.

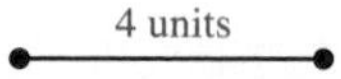

4 units

FIGURE 7
The length of a non-included side of a triangle with two given angle measurements.

The first step is draw a line segment with length 4 units. The next step is to draw a 60° angle with the given line segment as one side of the angle as shown in Figure 8. Then draw an 80° angle so that the given line segment of 4 units is a non-included side of the triangle with 60° and 80° angles. Then compare your triangle to the one shown.

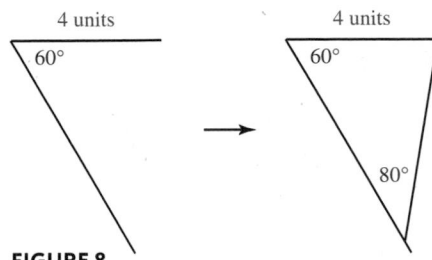

FIGURE 8
Drawing a triangle with two angles with measures 80° and 60°, and a non-included side with length 4 units.

All six corresponding parts between your triangle and the one shown should be congruent. Is it possible to use the same angle measures and non-included side to create a triangle with a different shape? The answer is "No." This means that two angles and a non-included side of a triangle uniquely determine the triangle. We summarize this result using words, symbols, and a diagram.

Angle-Angle-Side (AAS) Congruence Axiom

Using Words

If two angles and a nonincluded side of one triangle are congruent to the corresponding two angles and nonincluded side of another triangle, then the two triangles are congruent.

Using Symbols

If $\angle A \cong \angle D$, $\angle B \cong \angle E$, and $\overline{BC} \cong \overline{EF}$, then $\triangle ABC \cong \triangle DEF$.

Using a Diagram

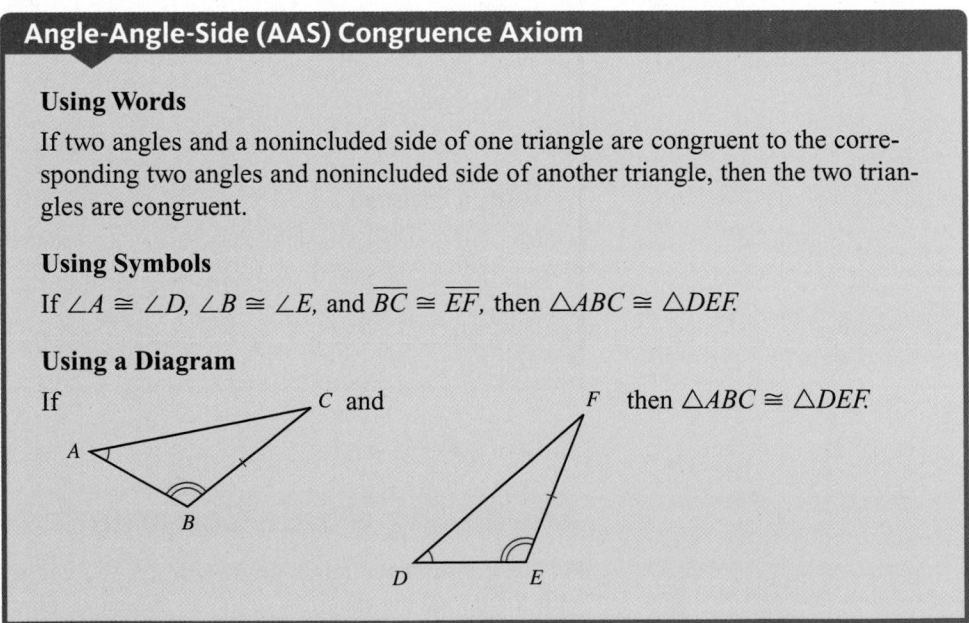

If [diagram] and [diagram] then $\triangle ABC \cong \triangle DEF$.

The following page from a middle school textbook illustrates that students should be able to interpret congruence statements and identify congruence axioms.

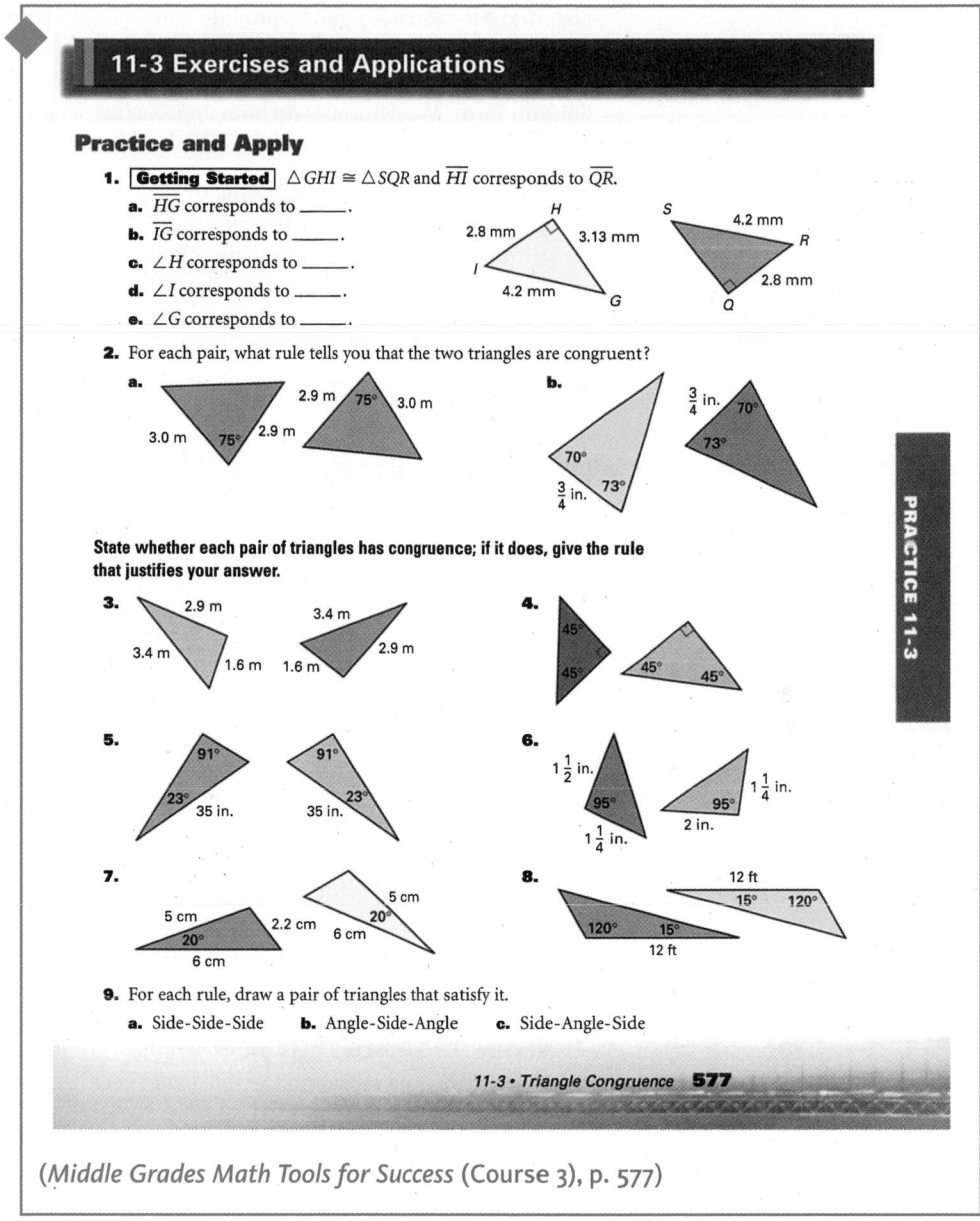

(*Middle Grades Math Tools for Success* (Course 3), p. 577)

The Nature and Purpose of Proof

A conjecture is a statement that seems true, usually based on specific examples. Once we make a conjecture, we usually think about *why* the conjecture is true. A proof of a conjecture is a collection of true statements such that the statements logically lead to the conjecture. A geometry proof usually begins with definitions, axioms, given assumptions, and a statement to prove. We often include diagrams, which are widely used as means of displaying and visualizing information and properties in support of an explanation. Then we use logical reasoning and write a collection of statements that convinces the reader that the statement is true.

The purpose of the proofs we consider in this textbook is to explain *why* a property of a geometric figure is true. The proofs we explore are basic; they were even known to Euclid and his students 2000 years ago. They help us organize, link, and solidify knowledge. They also make it easier for you to provide and evaluate your students' explanations about properties of geometric figures.

You will encounter two ways to present geometric proofs: paragraph form or two-column form. We demonstrate both approaches. The NCTM's *Principles and Standards for School Mathematics* states:

> Students should see the power of deductive proof in establishing the validity of general results from given conditions. The focus should be on producing logical arguments and presenting them effectively with careful explanation of the reasoning, rather than on the form of proof used (e.g., paragraph proof or two-column proof). (© NCTM Standards 2011 by National Council of Teachers of Mathematics)

Applying the Triangle Congruence Axioms

The reflexive property is especially useful for problems that involve triangles with a common side, because it generates a congruence statement to consider.

EXAMPLE 12.4

CONNECTION
COMMUNICATION
REASONING
REPRESENTATION

Triangles named $\triangle RUN$ and $\triangle FUN$ are shown in the diagram. Prove $\triangle RUN \cong \triangle FUN$.

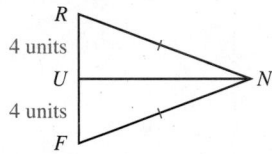

SOLUTION

According to the diagram, $\overline{RU} \cong \overline{FU}$ and $\overline{RN} \cong \overline{FN}$. By the reflexive property of congruence, $\overline{UN} \cong \overline{UN}$. The sides of $\triangle RUN$ are congruent to the corresponding sides of $\triangle FUN$, so $\triangle RUN \cong \triangle FUN$ by the SSS congruence axiom. ▲

Figure 9 shows two isosceles triangles. The two congruent sides in an isosceles triangle are called the legs, and the third side is called the base. The angle formed by the legs is called the apex angle, and the other two angles are called base angles. How are the base angles of an isosceles triangle related? Measure the base angles (which are opposite the congruent sides) of each triangle with a protractor, and compare the measurements. After identifying a pattern in the observations, make a statement about your observations that seems true.

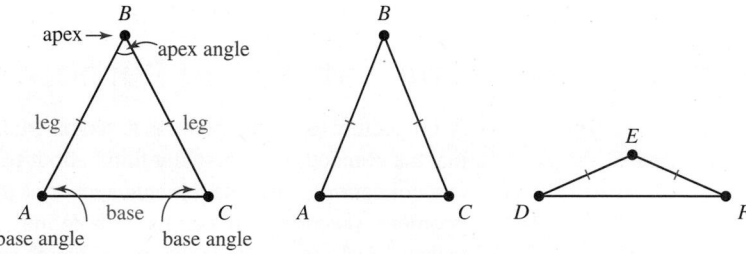

FIGURE 9

Anatomy of an isosceles triangle with examples of isosceles triangles.

Your observations should have led you to conclude that the base angles of an isosceles triangle are congruent. In the next example, we prove this famous property for *any* isosceles triangle, using the SSS congruence axiom. We follow the given steps to apply the axiom.

How to Apply the SSS Congruence Axiom

1. Identify two triangles.

2. Use the given information and reasoning to show that corresponding sides are congruent.

3. Use the SSS congruence axiom to conclude that the two triangles are congruent and write a congruence statement.

Our justification is written in paragraph form with diagrams as needed to help convey ideas.

EXAMPLE 12.5

CONNECTION

COMMUNICATION

REASONING

REPRESENTATION

$\triangle ABC$ is an isosceles triangle, with $\overline{AB} \cong \overline{BC}$.

a. Prove $\angle A \cong \angle C$ using the SSS congruence axiom.

b. Write a sentence that summarizes what you proved in part (a).

SOLUTION

a. Draw a diagram to represent the given information, as shown in Figure 10. (Our goal is to prove the base angles named $\angle A$ and $\angle C$ of the isosceles triangle are congruent. To apply the SSS congruence axiom, we need to identify two triangles. Sometimes this requires creating points and line segments with certain properties.)

FIGURE 10

Representation of an isosceles triangle.

Let M be the midpoint of $\overline{AC}$, as shown in Figure 11. According to the definition of a midpoint of a line segment, $AM = MC$. Then $\overline{AM} \cong \overline{MC}$, which is indicated by the double tick marks.

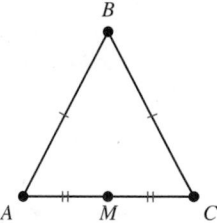

FIGURE 11

M is the midpoint of the base $\overline{AC}$.

Then we draw the line segment named $\overline{BM}$, as shown in Figure 12. This produces two triangles with a common side.

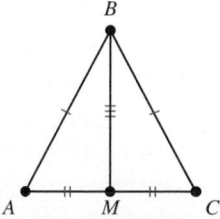

FIGURE 12

Two triangles with a common side.

(continued)

If the triangles are named $\triangle ABM$ and $\triangle CBM$, then the corresponding sides are $\overline{AB}$ and $\overline{BC}$, $\overline{MA}$ and $\overline{MC}$, and $\overline{BM}$ and $\overline{BM}$. Now $\overline{AB} \cong \overline{BC}$ (given), $\overline{BM} \cong \overline{BM}$ (reflexive property), and $\overline{MA} \cong \overline{MC}$ (M is the midpoint of $\overline{AC}$). So the sides of $\triangle ABM$ are congruent to the corresponding sides of $\triangle CBM$. Then $\triangle ABM \cong \triangle CBM$ by the SSS congruence axiom. Then $\angle A \cong \angle C$ by CPCTC.

b. The base angles of an isosceles triangle are congruent. ▲

Many proofs of mathematical statements are written in paragraph form, such as in the previous example, much in the same way you would tell someone why a statement is true. Proofs involving triangle axioms may also be written in a two-column format, where we list the statements in the first column and the reason for each statement in the second column. The two-column format may be easier to follow than the paragraph form.

EXAMPLE 12.6 Suppose $\overline{AB} \cong \overline{CD}$. Prove $\overline{AB} \cong \overline{DC}$.

COMMUNICATION

REASONING   SOLUTION

Statement	Reason
1. $\overline{AB} \cong \overline{CD}$	1. Given
2. $\overline{CD} \cong \overline{DC}$	2. Reflexive property of congruence
3. $\overline{AB} \cong \overline{DC}$	3. Transitive property of congruence

▲

In the next example, we apply the ASA congruence axiom to prove a famous property of parallelograms. We follow these steps to apply the axiom.

How to Apply the ASA Congruence Axiom

1. Identify two triangles.
2. Use the given information and reasoning to show that two angles and the included side of one triangle are congruent to the corresponding angles and included side of the other triangle.
3. Use the ASA congruence axiom to conclude that the two triangles are congruent and write a congruence statement.

EXAMPLE 12.7 $ABCD$ is a parallelogram.

CONNECTION   a. Prove $\overline{AB} \cong \overline{CD}$ and $\overline{AD} \cong \overline{BC}$ using the ASA congruence axiom.

COMMUNICATION   b. Write a sentence that summarizes what you proved in part (a).

PROBLEM SOLVING

REASONING

REPRESENTATION   SOLUTION

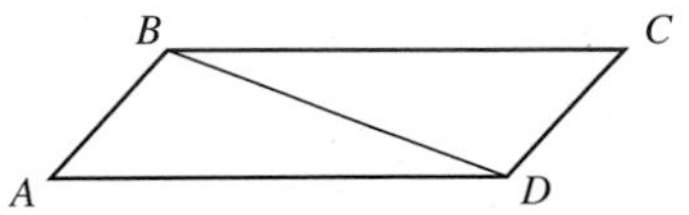

FIGURE 13

The diagonal of the parallelogram creates two triangles.

a. We begin with a picture to visualize relationships, and then we organize a proof once the picture becomes clearer. Draw the parallelogram $ABCD$. We need to identify two triangles to apply the ASA congruence axiom. Draw the parallelogram $ABCD$ with a diagonal $\overline{BD}$. This creates two triangles, as shown in Figure 13. The opposite sides of a parallelogram are parallel, and any transversal that cuts opposite sides creates pairs of congruent alternate interior angles.

In Figure 14, we see that $\overline{BD}$ is a transversal for $\overline{AB}$ and $\overline{CD}$, so we use single arcs to label congruent alternate interior angles. We also see that $\overline{BD}$ is a transversal for $\overline{AD}$ and $\overline{BC}$, so we use double arcs to label congruent alternate interior angles. The diagonal is congruent to itself, so we can put a mark on diagonal $\overline{BD}$. Diagrams are valid parts of a proof in geometry.

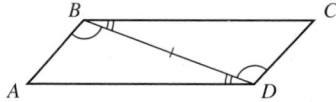

FIGURE 14

The diagonal of the parallelogram is a transversal that cuts parallel sides.

Now that we have our bearings, we are ready for a proof. The proof begins with a diagram.

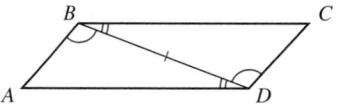

Statement	Reason
1. *ABCD* is a parallelogram	1. Given
2. $\angle ABD \cong \angle CDB$	2. $\overline{BD}$ is a transversal for the parallel sides $\overline{AB}$ and $\overline{CD}$, creating congruent alternate interior angles
3. $\overline{BD} \cong \overline{BD}$	3. Reflexive property of congruence
4. $\angle ADB \cong \angle CBD$	4. $\overline{BD}$ is a transversal for the parallel sides $\overline{AD}$ and $\overline{BC}$, creating congruent alternate interior angles
5. $\triangle BDA \cong \triangle DBC$	5. ASA congruence axiom (statements 2, 3, and 4)
6. $\overline{AB} \cong \overline{CD}$	6. CPCTC
7. $\overline{AD} \cong \overline{BC}$	7. CPCTC

b. The opposite sides of a parallelogram are congruent.

▲

In statement 5 of the two-column proof in Example 12.7, we have full freedom to name the first triangle in a congruence statement, so let's name the first triangle $\triangle BDA$ to take advantage of the markings of the single arc, single tick mark, and double arc in the order of the letters: *B, D, A.* Then the name of the second triangle is $\triangle DBC$. Then $\triangle BDA \cong \triangle DBC$.

Before reading further, can you explain why the opposite sides of a rectangle are congruent?

In the next example, we apply the SAS congruence axiom to prove a famous property of rectangles. We follow these steps to apply the axiom.

> ### How to Apply the SAS Congruence Axiom
>
> **1.** Identify two triangles.
> **2.** Use the given information and reasoning to show that two sides and the included angle of one triangle are congruent to the corresponding sides and included angle of another triangle.
> **3.** Use the SAS congruence axiom to conclude the two triangles are congruent and write a congruence statement.

EXAMPLE 12.8

CONNECTION

COMMUNICATION

PROBLEM SOLVING

REASONING

REPRESENTATION

ABCD is a rectangle.

a. Prove $\overline{AC} \cong \overline{BD}$ using the SAS congruence axiom.

b. Write a sentence that summarizes what you proved in part (a).

SOLUTION

a. The interior angles of a rectangle are right angles, and the opposite sides of a rectangle are congruent because a rectangle is a special type of parallelogram. We draw a diagram of the rectangle with two diagonals and mark sides and angles to visualize relationships, as shown in Figure 15. We also pull apart the triangles to see the correspondences and relationships more clearly.

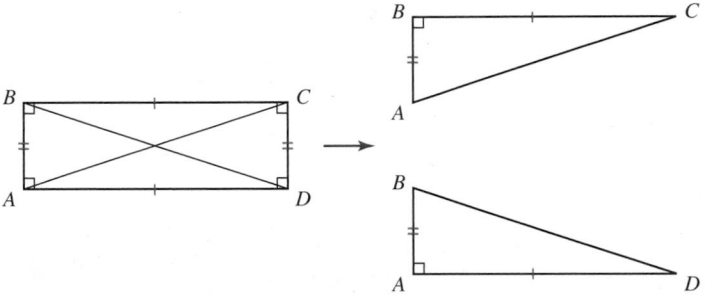

FIGURE 15

The diagonals of a rectangle create two triangles with a common side.

The two triangles are right triangles with the common side $\overline{AB}$. The right angles are included angles. Now we are ready to write the proof in the two-column format.

Statement	Reason
1. *ABCD* is a rectangle	1. Given
2. $\overline{CB} \cong \overline{DA}$	2. Because the opposite sides of a parallelogram are congruent, and a rectangle is a parallelogram
3. $\angle CBA$ and $\angle DAB$ are right angles	3. Because the interior angles of a rectangle are right angles
4. $\angle CBA \cong \angle DAB$	4. Because right angles are congruent
5. $\overline{BA} \cong \overline{AB}$	5. Reflexive property of congruence
6. $\triangle CBA \cong \triangle DAB$	6. SAS congruence axiom (statements 2, 4, and 5)
7. $\overline{AC} \cong \overline{BD}$	7. CPCTC

b. The diagonals of a rectangle are congruent.

▲

EXAMPLE 12.9

CONNECTION

COMMUNICATION

PROBLEM SOLVING

REASONING

REPRESENTATION

ABCD is a convex quadrilateral such that opposite sides are congruent. Prove *ABCD* is a parallelogram.

SOLUTION

As before, we begin with a picture to visualize relationships, and then we organize a proof once the picture becomes clearer. In Figure 16, we draw the parallelogram *ABCD,* with tic marks to indicate the given conditions, and then draw the diagonal $\overline{BD}$ to create two triangles. We quickly see that we can use the SSS congruence axiom to prove the two triangles are congruent.

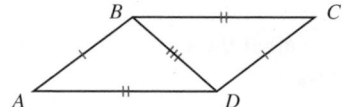

FIGURE 16

The diagonal of the quadrilateral creates two triangles.

To prove that the opposite sides of the quadrilateral are parallel, we just need to prove alternate interior angles created by the diagonal are congruent, as shown in Figure 17. This would establish that the opposite sides of the quadrilateral are parallel.

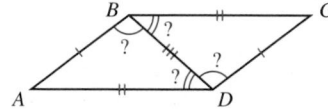

FIGURE 17

If the alternate interior angles are congruent, then the opposite sides of the quadrilateral would be parallel.

Now we are ready to write the proof in the two-column format.

Statement	Reason
1. $\overline{AB} \cong \overline{CD}$	1. Given
2. $\overline{AD} \cong \overline{BC}$	2. Given
3. $\overline{BD} \cong \overline{BD}$	3. Reflexive property of congruence
4. $\triangle ABD \cong \triangle CDB$	4. SSS congruence axiom (statements 1, 2, and 3)
5. $\angle ABD \cong \angle CDB$	5. CPCTC
6. $\overline{AB} \parallel \overline{CD}$	6. Because $\overline{BD}$ is a transversal for $\overline{AB}$ and $\overline{CD}$, with congruent alternate interior angles named $\angle ABD$ and $\angle CDB$
7. $\angle ADB \cong \angle CBD$	7. CPCTC
8. $\overline{AD} \parallel \overline{BC}$	8. Because $\overline{BD}$ is a transversal for $\overline{AD}$ and $\overline{BC}$, with congruent alternate interior angles named $\angle ADB$ and $\angle CBD$

Then $\overline{AB}$ and $\overline{CD}$ are parallel and $\overline{AD}$ and $\overline{BC}$ are parallel, so $ABCD$ is a parallelogram. This proves that if the opposite sides of a convex quadrilateral are congruent, then the quadrilateral is a parallelogram. ▲

The four congruence axioms for triangles are SSS, ASA, SAS, and AAS. It turns out that AAA and SSA are not triangle congruence axioms. Some mathematicians refer to SSA as the "donkey theorem" because only a "fool" would use it.

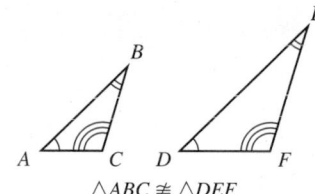

$\triangle ABC \not\cong \triangle DEF$

AAA is not a triangle congruence axiom.

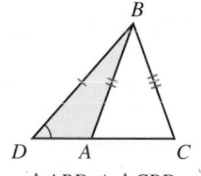

$\triangle ABD \not\cong \triangle CBD$

SSA is not a triangle congruence axiom.

Congruence Axioms for Right Triangles

The SSS, AAS, and SAS congruence axioms apply to all triangles. These axioms can be specialized for right triangles.

• $\triangle CAB$ and $\triangle EDF$ in Figure 18 are right triangles. The corresponding legs are congruent. Explain why the two triangles are congruent. This is called the LL theorem (because of the SAS congruence axiom), where LL means "leg-leg."

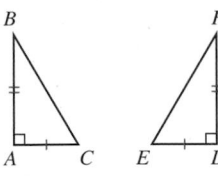

FIGURE 18
LL theorem.

• $\triangle CAB$ and $\triangle EDF$ in Figure 19 are right triangles. The corresponding legs are congruent, and the hypotenuses are congruent. Explain why the two triangles are congruent. This is called the HL theorem (because of an application of the Pythagorean theorem and the SSS congruence axiom), where it means "hypotenuse-leg."

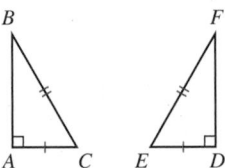

FIGURE 19
HL theorem.

• $\triangle CAB$ and $\triangle EDF$ in Figure 20 are right triangles. Corresponding nonright angles are congruent, and the hypotenuses are congruent. Explain why the two triangles are congruent. This is called the HA theorem (because of an application of the AAS congruence axiom), where HA means "hypotenuse-angle."

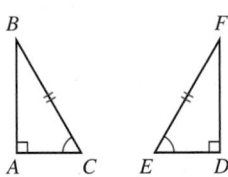

FIGURE 20
HA theorem.

QUESTIONS FOR SECTION 12.1

REPRESENTATION

Refresher: Representations (language, diagrams, tables, symbols, algebra, manipulatives, and contextualized situations) are important because we use them to organize, record, and communicate mathematical ideas and make them more comprehensible.

1. A student writes $\triangle ABC \cong \triangle DEF$.

   a. Explain why $\angle B \cong \angle E$.   **b.** Explain why $\overline{AC} \cong \overline{DF}$.

   c. Fill in the blank: $\triangle EFD \cong$ ___.

2. The two quadrilaterals shown are congruent.

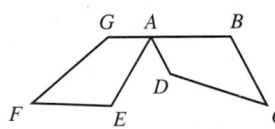

   a. $ABCD \cong$ ___   **b.** $\angle B \cong$ ___   **c.** $DC =$ ___

3. Do the following.

   a. $\overline{GH}$ and $\overline{HK}$ are two sides of a triangle. Identify the included angle for these two sides.

   b. Illustrate the SAS congruence axiom for triangles with a diagram and write a congruence statement.

4. Do the following.

   a. A triangle has the vertices Q, W, and E. Identify the included side for $\angle Q$ and $\angle W$.

   b. Illustrate the ASA congruence axiom for triangles with a diagram and write a congruence statement.

5. Use the given diagram of the rectangle to indicate whether the following statements are true or false.

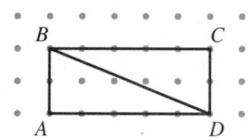

   a. $\triangle ABD = \triangle BAD$ b. $\triangle ABD \cong \triangle CDB$

   c. $\angle ABD \cong \angle CDB$ d. $\triangle ABD = \triangle CDB$

   e. $\triangle ABD \cong \triangle DCB$

PROBLEM SOLVING

Refresher: Problem solving (reaching a goal that is not immediately attainable) is important because it helps students think more deeply about what they know and deal with unfamiliar situations.

6. Mr. Butler drew a circle with a center O and diameter $\overline{AB}$ that bisects $\overline{CD}$ at point E. Then he asked his class, "What can you say about the line segments $\overline{AB}$ and $\overline{CD}$?" After a few minutes, Coco shouted, "$\overline{AB}$ is perpendicular to $\overline{CD}$!" Prove Coco is correct.

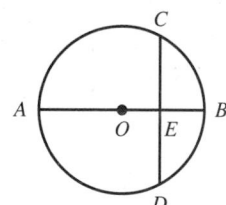

7. The diagram shows a circle with the center B. Find each angle's measure.

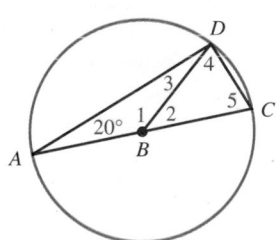

8. $ABCD$ and $AEFG$ are congruent quadrilaterals.

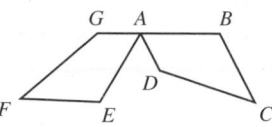

   a. Prove $\overline{AF} \cong \overline{AC}$.   b. Prove $\angle DAG \cong \angle BAE$.

9. $\triangle SUN$ and $\triangle TEA$ are isosceles triangles as shown. Prove $\triangle SUN \cong \triangle TEA$.

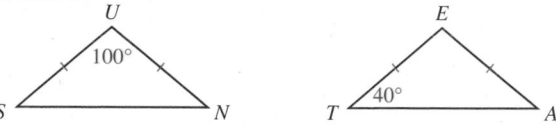

REASONING AND PROOF

Refresher: Reasoning and proof (thinking and justifying) are important because they help students make sense of mathematics.

10. $ABCD$ is a convex quadrilateral such that all four sides are congruent: $\overline{AB} \cong \overline{BC} \cong \overline{CD} \cong \overline{AD}$. Prove $ABCD$ is a rhombus.

11. A student is writing a proof to show that two triangles $\triangle AHQ$ and $\triangle BID$ are congruent using the ASA congruence axiom. A student writes the following two congruence statements: $\angle H \cong \angle I$ and $\overline{HQ} \cong \overline{ID}$. Determine what additional congruence statement the student needs to apply the axiom.

12. Determine whether the given information is enough to conclude $\triangle ABC \cong \triangle DEF$. Explain your answer.

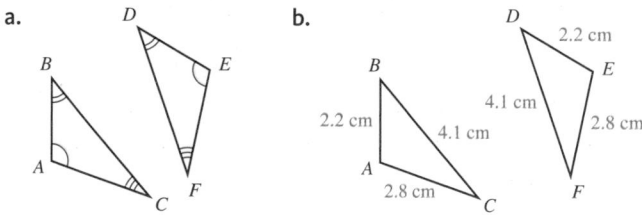

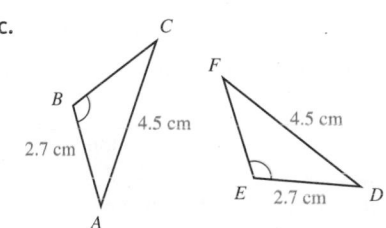

13. Let $\triangle RST$ be an isosceles triangle with a base of $\overline{RT}$. Let M be a point on $\overline{RT}$ such that R-M-T and that $\overline{SM}$ bisects the apex angle $\angle S$.

   a. Draw a diagram to represent the relationships.

   b. Prove $\overline{SM} \perp \overline{RT}$.   c. Prove M is the midpoint of $\overline{RT}$.

14. Let $\triangle RST$ be an isosceles triangle with a base of $\overline{RT}$. Let M be the midpoint of $\overline{RT}$.

    a. Draw a diagram to represent the relationships.

    b. Prove $\overline{SM}$ bisects the apex angle $\angle S$.

    c. Prove $\overline{SM} \perp \overline{RT}$.

15. Let $\triangle RST$ be an isosceles triangle with a base of $\overline{RT}$. Draw a line l through the apex S that is perpendicular to $\overline{RT}$. Let M be the intersection of l and $\overline{RT}$.

    a. Prove $\overline{SM}$ bisects $\angle S$.

    b. Prove M is the midpoint of $\overline{RT}$.

16. $ABCD$ is a convex quadrilateral such that the opposite sides are congruent: $\overline{AB} \cong \overline{DC}$ and $\overline{AD} \cong \overline{BC}$.

    a. Prove $\overline{AB} \| \overline{DC}$.   b. Prove $\angle D \cong \angle B$.

    c. Prove $\overline{AD} \| \overline{BC}$.   d. Prove $\angle A \cong \angle C$.

17. $ABCD$ is a rhombus.

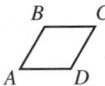

    a. Prove $\triangle DAB \cong \triangle DCB$.   b. Prove $\angle A \cong \angle C$.

    c. Prove $\angle B \cong \angle D$.

    d. Make a statement that describes the relationship between opposite angles in a rhombus.

18. $ABCD$ is a rhombus.

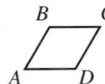

    a. Prove $\triangle ABC \cong \triangle ADC$.

    b. Prove the diagonal $\overline{AC}$ bisects $\angle A$ and $\angle C$.

    c. Prove the diagonal $\overline{BD}$ bisects $\angle B$ and $\angle D$.

    d. Make a statement that describes a property of the diagonals of a rhombus.

CONNECTIONS

Refresher: Connections (linking and applying mathematical ideas) are important because they deepen student understanding and make mathematics more meaningful, flexible, and useful.

19. A hat contains two letters, A and S. A student randomly selects a letter, records the result, and puts the letter back in the hat. The student makes three selections in all. How many different arrangements of three letters can be formed?

20. In an example in this section, we proved that if a triangle is an isosceles triangle, then the base angles are congruent. Now prove the converse of that statement: If a triangle has exactly two congruent angles, then the triangle is an isosceles triangle. Suppose $\triangle ABC$ has exactly two congruent angles: $\angle A \cong \angle C$. Prove $\triangle ABC$ is an isosceles triangle. (Hint: Consider $\triangle ABC$ and $\triangle CBA$.)

21. $\triangle ABC$ and $\triangle DEF$ are right triangles, with $\overline{AB} \cong \overline{DE}$, $\overline{BC} \cong \overline{EF}$, and right angles $\angle A$ and $\angle D$.

    a. Represent the given information with a diagram.

    b. Prove $\triangle ABC \cong \triangle DEF$. (Hint: Use the Pythagorean theorem, and then use a congruence axiom for triangles.)

    c. Complete the statement (HL theorem): If a leg and hypotenuse of a right triangle are congruent to the corresponding leg and hypotenuse of another right triangle, then _____.

22. $\triangle ABC$ and $\triangle DEF$ are right triangles, with $\overline{AB} \cong \overline{DE}$, $\overline{AC} \cong \overline{DF}$, and right angles $\angle A$ and $\angle D$.

    a. Represent the given information with a diagram.

    b. Prove $\triangle ABC \cong \triangle DEF$.

    c. Complete the statement (LL theorem): If two legs of a right triangle are congruent to the corresponding legs of another right triangle, then _____.

23. $\triangle ABC$ and $\triangle DEF$ are right triangles, with $\angle B \cong \angle E$, $\overline{BC} \cong \overline{EF}$, and right angles $\angle A$ and $\angle D$.

    a. Represent the given information with a diagram.

    b. Prove $\triangle ABC \cong \triangle DEF$.

    c. Complete the statement (HA theorem): If the hypotenuse and a nonright angle of a right triangle are congruent to the corresponding hypotenuse and nonright angle of another right triangle, then _____.

24. State why the pairs of triangles are congruent using the HL theorem, LL theorem, HA theorem.

a. 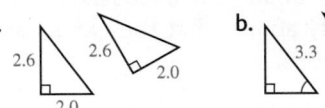   b. 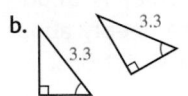   c.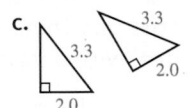

25. Triangles are important in the design of building structures, because with proper design they withstand normal tension and compression forces without changing their shape. Which triangle congruence axiom would best explain this?

COMMUNICATION

Refresher: Communication (written and verbal explanations using representations and proper mathematical vocabulary) is important because it helps students refine and strengthen their understanding.

26. A teacher drew a triangle on a piece of paper that he kept hidden from his students. He told his students that they could ask him questions about the triangle and their goal was to draw a triangle that is congruent to the one that he drew. What is the minimum number of questions that the students can ask to guarantee they could draw a congruent triangle?

27. The diagram shows two triangles and some angle congruencies. What additional information would you need to conclude $\triangle HOT \cong \triangle AET$? Explain.

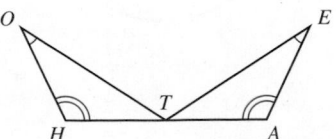

28. Mrs. Dugger drew △*CAT* and △*COW* on the board, as shown in the diagram.

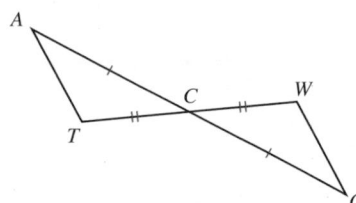

Then she asked her class, "What can you say about the relationship between $\overleftrightarrow{AT}$ and $\overleftrightarrow{OW}$?" After a few minutes, Lilly exclaimed, "$\overleftrightarrow{AT}$ and $\overleftrightarrow{OW}$ are parallel!" Explain why Lilly is correct.

29. Could AAA be a triangle congruence axiom? Justify your answer.

30. Explain why SSS is not a congruence axiom for quadrilaterals.

31. Answer the following.

a. Do you prefer writing a proof in paragraph form or two-column format?

b. Do you prefer reading a proof in paragraph form or two-column format?

More practice with the ideas of the section

32. Fill in the blank. Choose one of the following words or phrases: *axiom, congruence, congruent parts, corresponding parts, no, paragraph form, proof, three, two-column format*, or *yes*.

a. A proof may be sentences written in _____.

b. A proof may be written as statements in a(n) _____, where one column contains the statements and the other column contains the reasons.

c. A(n) _____ of a conjecture is a collection of true statements such that the conjecture logically follows from the statements.

d. A(n) _____ is a useful mathematical statement that we accept as true.

e. If you know three parts of one triangle are congruent to the corresponding parts of another triangle, then you automatically know the two triangles are congruent. Your answer (yes or no): _____

f. If you know four parts of one triangle are congruent to the corresponding parts of another triangle, then you automatically know the two triangles are congruent. Your answer (yes or no): _____

g. In the acronym CPCTC, the initial letters CP stand for _____.

33. *CATS* and *BIRD* are quadrilaterals, and *CATS* ≅ *BIRD*.

a. Fill in the blank: ∠*TSC* ≅ ___.

b. Fill in the blank: $\overline{IR}$ ≅ ___.

c. Explain why △*CAT* ≅ △*BIR*.

34. Is the pair of triangles congruent? Explain your answer.

a.

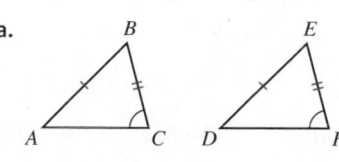

b.

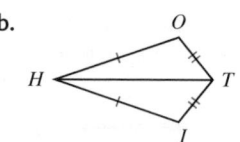

c.

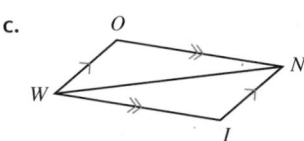

35. A rectangle is a parallelogram with four right angles. Based on Example 12.7, we also know that the opposite sides of a rectangle are congruent. Let *ABCD* be a rectangle as shown, with the diagonals $\overline{AC}$ and $\overline{BD}$. Let *E* be the point of intersection of the diagonals.

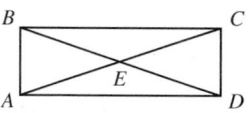

a. Prove △*AED* ≅ △*CEB*.   b. Prove $\overline{BD}$ bisects $\overline{AC}$.

c. Prove $\overline{AC}$ bisects $\overline{BD}$.

36. Suppose $\overline{AB}$ ≅ $\overline{CD}$. Using the two-column format, prove $\overline{DC}$ ≅ $\overline{AB}$.

37. Suppose $\overline{AC}$ and $\overline{BD}$ are two line segments such that $\overline{AC}$ ⊥ $\overline{BD}$ and $\overline{BD}$ bisects $\overline{AC}$. Let *E* be the intersection of $\overline{BD}$ and $\overline{AC}$.

a. Represent the given information with a diagram, labeling the points in alphabetical order.

b. Prove $\overline{BD}$ bisects ∠*ABC*.   c. Prove $\overline{AB}$ ≅ $\overline{BC}$.

d. Prove ∠*BAD* ≅ ∠*BCD*.

38. *KITE* is a convex quadrilateral with *KI* = *IT* and *KE* = *TE*, as shown in the diagram. Let *S* be the intersection of the diagonals.

a. Prove the diagonal $\overline{IE}$ bisects ∠*I*.

b. Prove the diagonal $\overline{IE}$ bisects ∠*E*.

c. Prove the diagonals are perpendicular.

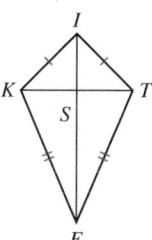

39. $\overline{AN}$ ≅ $\overline{AP}$ and $\overline{AT}$ ≅ $\overline{AE}$. Prove △*ANT* ≅ △*APE*.

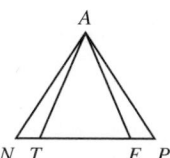

40. Figure *ABCD* is a square. Draw the midpoints of each side of the square, and then connect the midpoints with line segments to form a convex quadrilateral.

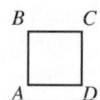

a. Complete the conjecture: If you form a convex quadrilateral using the midpoints of the sides of a square, then _____.

b. Prove your conjecture.

41. What does CPCTC mean?

42. Explain why the diagram is impossible.

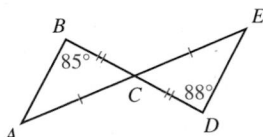

43. A *median* of a triangle is a line segment from one vertex of the triangle to the midpoint of the opposite side of that vertex. Let $\overline{OW}$ be a median for $\triangle DON$ and $\overline{EA}$ be a median for $\triangle SET$. Suppose $\overline{OW} \cong \overline{EA}$, $\overline{ON} \cong \overline{ET}$, and $\overline{DN} \cong \overline{ST}$.

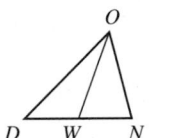 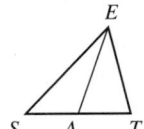

a. Prove $\triangle NOW \cong \triangle TEA$.   b. Prove $\triangle DON \cong \triangle SET$.

44. $BETA$ is a trapezoid with $\overline{AB} \| \overline{ET}$ and $\triangle BET \cong \triangle ATE$. Prove $BETA$ is an isosceles trapezoid (that is, prove $\overline{BE} \cong \overline{AT}$).

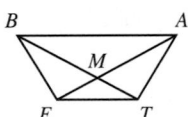

45. Do the following.

a. Draw two parallel lines m and n cut by a transversal t. Let A be the intersection of t and m, and let B be the intersection of t and n. Let X be the midpoint of the line segment $\overline{AB}$. Draw any line segment with one endpoint C on line m and the other endpoint D on line n such that X belongs to the line segment $\overline{CD}$.

b. Prove $\triangle AXC \cong \triangle BXD$.

46. In the diagram, $\angle 2 \cong \angle 3$ and $\angle 5 \cong \angle 6$. Prove $\overline{AB} \cong \overline{BC}$.

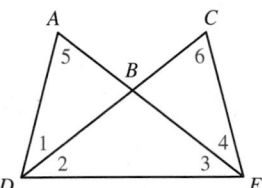

47. $ABCD$ is a convex quadrilateral, with $AB = CD$ and $\overline{AB} \| \overline{CD}$.

a. Prove $ABCD$ is a parallelogram.

b. Complete the statement: If a convex quadrilateral has at least one pair of sides that are congruent and parallel, then _____.

48. Let $\overline{BD}$ be a diagonal of quadrilateral $ABCD$ that bisects $\angle B$ and $\angle D$ as shown in the diagram. Let E be the point of inter-

section of the diagonals. Prove that the diagonals are perpendicular.

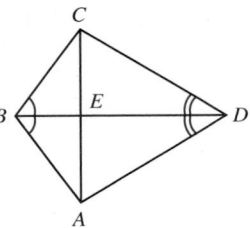

49. $ABCD$ is a rhombus with the midpoints of the sides as shown.

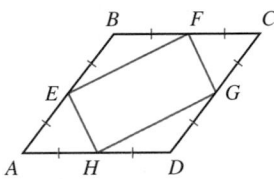

a. Complete the conjecture: If you form a quadrilateral using the midpoints of the sides of a rhombus, then the quadrilateral is a(n) _____.

b. How are $\angle A$ and $\angle C$ related?

c. How are $\angle B$ and $\angle D$ related?

d. Prove $\triangle HAE \cong \triangle GCF$.   e. Prove $\triangle HDG \cong \triangle EBF$.

f. Prove $EFGH$ is a parallelogram. (Hint: See Example 12.9.)

g. The following diagram is useful for showing the interior angles of the parallelogram $EFGH$ are congruent.

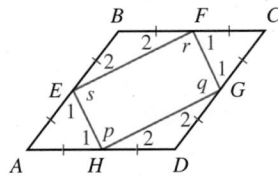

Here, $m\angle 1 + m\angle p + m\angle 2 = 180°$ and $m\angle 1 + m\angle q + m\angle 2 = 180°$. Then $m\angle p = 180° - m\angle 1 - m\angle 2$ and $m\angle q = 180° - m\angle 1 - m\angle 2$. Then $\angle p \cong \angle q$. You can use the same reasoning to prove $\angle p \cong \angle r$ and $\angle p \cong \angle s$. What is the measure of each angle of parallelogram $EFGH$?

h. Prove $EFGH$ is a rectangle.

50. The diagram shows a circle with the center B, a circle with the center E, and line segments. F is the intersection of $\overrightarrow{AB}$ and $\overline{CD}$.

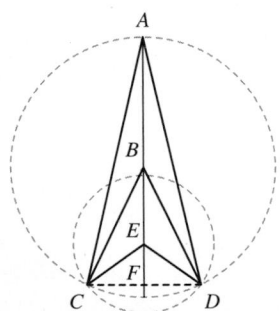

a. Show $\triangle BCE \cong \triangle BDE$.   b. Show $\triangle CEF \cong \triangle DEF$.

SECTION 12.2 Euclidean Constructions

What Is a Construction?

A **construction** is a geometric drawing using only a compass and straightedge. In this section, we focus on constructing geometric figures using these two tools and justifying each construction.

- We use a compass to create points that are equidistant from a fixed point. The result is a circle or a portion of a circle, defined as an arc. A compass has two legs and two points called the center point and pencil point. The *center point* determines the center of the circle (or arc), and the *pencil point* draws the circle (or arc) when we swing the compass, as shown in Figure 21. The leg of the compass with the center point stays in one position, while the leg of the compass with the pencil point changes position. The *radius* is the distance between the center point and the pencil point on the compass. A compass provides a functional meaning of a circle as a set of points that are equidistant from a given point.

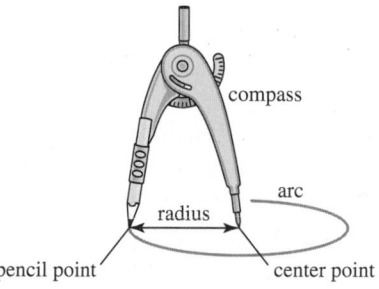

FIGURE 21

A compass creates a set of points that are equivalent from a given point.

- We use a straightedge to guide the pencil as we draw a line segment or line, such as the line containing two given points *A* and *B,* as shown in Figure 22.

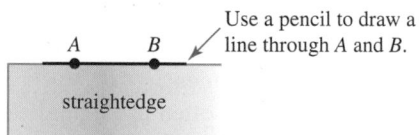

FIGURE 22

A straightedge is used to create a line segment or line.

Three Basic Skills of Construction

Constructions give students a dynamic chance to think about spatial relationships in geometric figures such as triangles and quadrilaterals. Constructions depend on the following three simple skills.

1. For any given points *A* and *B,* we can use a compass to construct a circle or arc with the center *A* and radius *AB* so that the circle or arc contains *B.*

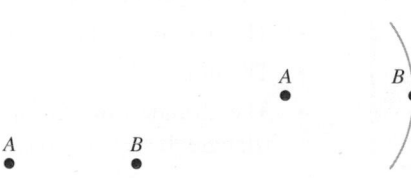

2. For any given points *A, B,* and *C,* we can use a compass to construct a circle or arc with the center *A* and radius *BC.*

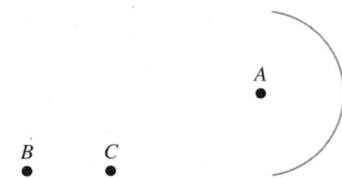

3. For any given points A and B, we can use a straightedge to construct the line segment $\overline{AB}$, ray $\overrightarrow{AB}$, or line $\overleftrightarrow{AB}$.

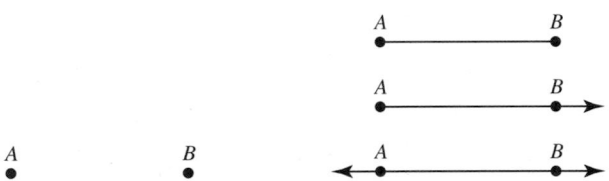

Constructions do not involve measuring distances using rulers or measuring angles using protractors. If you use a ruler as a straightedge, then ignore the markings on the ruler. We can use the compass to "measure" the distance between two given points by placing the compass points at the two points. The distance is the radius. The phrase **Euclidean tools** refers to the compass and straightedge.

With basic construction skills, we can construct additional points from intersections of geometric figures (for example, line segments and arcs) and use any two points to draw line segments, rays, or lines. The basic constructions are copying a segment, bisecting a segment, copying an angle, bisecting an angle, constructing a line through a given point that is perpendicular to a given line, and constructing a line through a given point that is parallel to a given line. The basic constructions we show you form the building blocks for more complex constructions, such as constructing a triangle that has sides with given lengths, constructing an altitude of a triangle, constructing a circle that circumscribes a triangle, or constructing a rhombus with sides that are congruent to a given line segment.

We often use triangle axioms to justify constructions. The justifications are based on properties of parallel lines cut by a transversal, triangle congruence axioms, and the properties of quadrilaterals we already studied. Your knowledge of properties of angles, circles, triangles, quadrilaterals, and intersecting lines empowers you to construct geometric figures and understand why your construction is truly what you intended.

The following list summarizes important geometric properties we apply in this chapter:

- Two corresponding angles created by a transversal that cuts two lines are congruent if and only if the two lines are parallel.
- If the opposite sides of a quadrilateral are parallel, then the quadrilateral is a parallelogram.
- If all sides of a quadrilateral are congruent, then the quadrilateral is a rhombus.
- The diagonals of a rhombus are perpendicular.
- The diagonals of a rhombus bisect each other.
- The diagonals of a rhombus bisect the interior angles of the rhombus.
- The altitude from the apex of an isosceles triangle is perpendicular to the base of the triangle, bisects the base, and bisects the apex angle.

■ **Historical Note**

Euclidean tools played an important role in the development of geometry. Ancient Greeks, including Euclid and his colleagues and students, experimented with these tools, made conjectures about spatial relationships, and then attempted to prove the conjectures using deductive reasoning. Euclidean tools give students a way to follow in the ancient Greeks' footsteps to visualize and apply spatial relationships.

Constructing a Line Segment Congruent to a Given Line Segment

Given a line segment, our goal is to construct a congruent line segment.

EXAMPLE 12.10

CONNECTION

COMMUNICATION

REASONING

REPRESENTATION

a. Given the line segment $\overline{AB}$, construct $\overline{CD}$ so that $\overline{CD} \cong \overline{AB}$.

b. Justify the construction.

SOLUTION

a. Follow these steps.

Step 1. Draw a point C, and use a straightedge to construct a line segment through C.

Step 2. Open the compass to create an arc with radius AB.

Step 3. Maintaining the same compass opening, place the point of the compass at C and swing an arc so that the arc intersects the line segment. Label the point of intersection D.

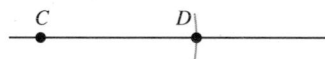

Then $\overline{CD} \cong \overline{AB}$.

b. The point D belongs to a circle with the center C and radius AB, so $CD = AB$. Then $\overline{CD} \cong \overline{AB}$.

▲

Constructing an Angle Congruent to a Given Angle

Given an angle, our goal is to construct a congruent angle (that is, copy an angle).

EXAMPLE 12.11

CONNECTION

COMMUNICATION

REASONING

REPRESENTATION

a. Given $\angle A$, construct $\angle B$ so that $\angle B \cong \angle A$.

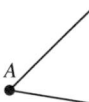

b. Justify the construction.

SOLUTION

a. Follow these steps.

Step 1. Draw a point B, and use the straightedge to construct a ray with the endpoint B.

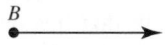

Step 2. Place the point of the compass at A, and swing an arc of any radius that intersects both sides of $\angle A$. Label the points of intersection X and Y.

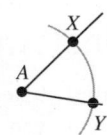

Step 3. Maintaining the same compass opening, place the point of the compass at B and swing an arc so that it intersects the ray. Label the point of intersection U.

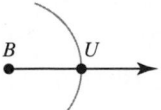

Step 4. Place the point of the compass at Y, and open the compass so that you can swing an arc that belongs to a circle with the center Y and radius XY.

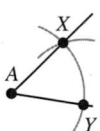

Step 5. Maintaining the same compass opening from step 4, place the point of the compass at U and swing an arc that intersects the arc containing U. Let V be the point of intersection of the arcs.

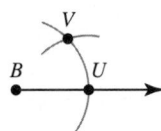

Step 6. Use the straightedge to construct ray $\overrightarrow{BV}$. Then $\angle B \cong \angle A$.

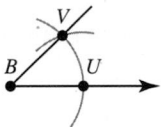

b. Think about $\triangle XAY$ and $\triangle VBU$ in Figure 23.

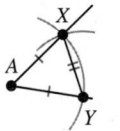 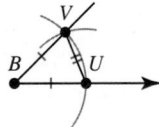

FIGURE 23
A visual summary of the relationships in the construction.

From step 2 of part (a), we know X and Y lie on the same circle with center A and radius r units, where r depends on how much we opened the compass. So $r = AX = AY$. From step 3, we maintained the same opening of the compass, so U and V lie on a circle with the center B and radius r; thus, $r = BV = BU$. Then $AX = BV$ (side) and $AY = BU$ (side). In step 4, we opened the compass so that X lies on a circle with the center Y and radius XY. In step 5, we maintained the same opening of the compass and constructed a point V that lies on a circle with the center U and radius XY; thus, $XY = VU$ (side). Then $\triangle XAY \cong \triangle VBU$ by the SSS congruence axiom. Then $\angle B \cong \angle A$ by CPCTC. ▲

Constructing an Angle Bisector

An **angle bisector** is a line segment, ray, or line that divides an angle into two congruent angles. Given an angle, our goal is to construct a ray that bisects the angle.

EXAMPLE 12.12

CONNECTION

COMMUNICATION

REASONING

REPRESENTATION

a. Construct an angle bisector for $\angle A$.

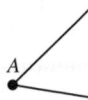

b. Justify the construction.

SOLUTION

a. Follow these steps.

Step 1.   Place the point of the compass at A, and swing an arc of any radius that intersects both sides of $\angle A$. Label the points of intersection X and Y.

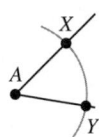

Step 2.   Maintaining the same compass opening, place the point of the compass at Y and swing an arc. Then place the point of the compass at X and swing another arc with the same radius.

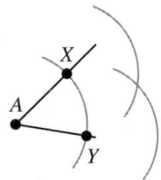

Step 3.   Label the point of intersection of the new arcs B.

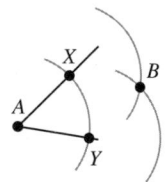

Step 4.   Use a straightedge to construct a line segment or ray from A through B. Then $\angle XAB \cong \angle YAB$.

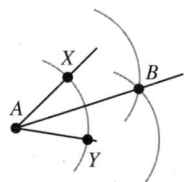

b. Think about quadrilateral $AXBY$ in Figure 24.

From step 1 of part (a), we know X and Y lie on the circle with center A and radius r units, where r depends on how much we opened the compass. So $r = AX = AY$. In step 2, we maintained the same opening of the compass, so B lies on a circle with the center X and radius r and on a circle with the center Y and radius r. Then $r = XB = YB$. So $AX = AY = XB = YB$. The opposite sides of quadrilateral $AXBY$ are congruent, so $AXBY$ is a parallelogram (see Example 12.9). The four sides are congruent, so $AXBY$ is a rhombus. The diagonals of a rhombus bisect the vertex angles, so $\angle XAB \cong \angle YAB$. This means the diagonal $\overline{AB}$ bisects $\angle A$.

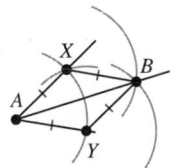

FIGURE 24
Bisecting an angle.

▲

Constructing the Perpendicular Bisector of a Line Segment

A **perpendicular bisector** of a given line segment is a line segment, ray, or line that forms a right angle with the line segment and divides the line segment into two congruent line segments. Given line segment $\overline{AB}$, our goal is to construct a line segment or line that bisects $\overline{AB}$ and forms a right angle with $\overline{AB}$.

EXAMPLE 12.13

CONNECTION
COMMUNICATION
REASONING
REPRESENTATION

a. Construct the perpendicular bisector of line segment $\overline{AB}$.

b. Justify the construction.

SOLUTION

a. Follow these steps.

Step 1. Open the compass so that it is wider than one-half the distance from A to B. Place the point of the compass at A, and swing an arc that extends from one side of $\overleftrightarrow{AB}$ to the other side.

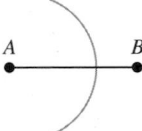

Step 2. Maintaining the same compass opening, place the point of the compass at B and swing an arc that extends from one side of $\overleftrightarrow{AB}$ to the other side, making sure it intersects the arc with the center A in two locations.

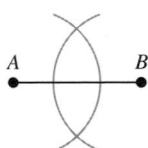

Step 3. Label the points of intersection of the arcs C and D. Use a straightedge to draw a line segment through C to D. Then $\overline{CD}$ is perpendicular to $\overline{AB}$ and bisects $\overline{AB}$.

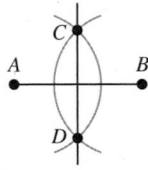

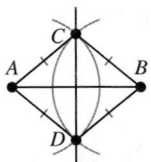

FIGURE 25
A visual summary of the relationships in the construction.

b. Think about quadrilateral $ACBY$ in Figure 25.

From step 1 of part (a), we know C and D lie on the circle with center A and radius r units, where r depends on how much we opened the compass. So $r = AC = AD$. In step 2, we maintained the same opening of the compass, so C and D lie on a circle with the center B and radius r. Then $r = CB = DB$. So $AC = AD = DB = CB$. The opposite sides of quadrilateral $ACBD$ are congruent, so $ACBD$ is a parallelogram (see Example 12.9). The four sides are congruent, so parallelogram $ACBD$ is a rhombus. The diagonals of a rhombus are perpendicular and bisect each other, so $\overline{CD}$ is the perpendicular bisector of $\overline{AB}$.

Constructing a Line through a Given Point and Perpendicular to a Given Line

Given a point and a line, construct a line that contains the point and is perpendicular to the given line. We examine two possibilities: the point belongs to the line and the point does not belong to the line.

EXAMPLE 12.14

CONNECTION

COMMUNICATION

REASONING

REPRESENTATION

a. Suppose P is a point on line l. Construct a line through P that is perpendicular to l.

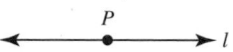

b. Justify the conclusion.

SOLUTION

a. Follow these steps.

Step 1. Put the point of the compass at P and swing an arc that intersects line l at two points. Label the constructed points A and B.

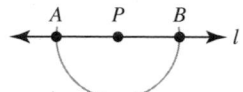

Step 2. Open the compass so that it is wider than one-half the distance from A to B. Place the point of the compass at A, and swing an arc that extends over point P.

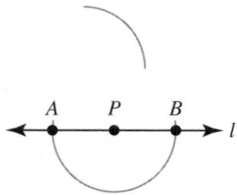

Step 3. Maintaining the same compass opening, place the point of the compass at B and swing an arc that intersects the arc with the center A.

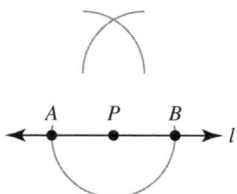

Step 4. Let C be the point of intersection of the two arcs. Use a straightedge to construct a line through C and P. Then $\overleftrightarrow{CP}$ is perpendicular to $\overleftrightarrow{AB}$.

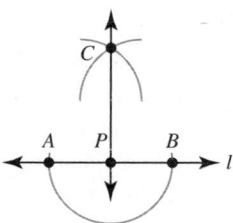

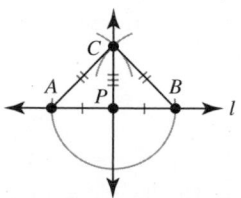

FIGURE 26

A visual summary of the relationships in the construction.

b. Think about $\triangle CAP$ and $\triangle CBP$ in Figure 26.

From step 1 of part (a), we know A and B lie on the circle with the center P and a radius of r units, where r depends on how much we opened the compass. So $r = AP = BP$ (side). In steps 2 and 3, we created arcs with the same radius greater than $(1/2)AB$, so $AC = BC$ (side). Then $PC = PC$ by the reflexive property (side). So $\triangle CAP \cong \triangle CBP$ by the SSS congruence axiom. $\angle APC$ and $\angle BPC$ are congruent by CPCTC. Because they are supplementary and congruent, each must be 90°. So $\overleftrightarrow{CP}$ is perpendicular to $\overleftrightarrow{AB}$. ▲

EXAMPLE 12.15

CONNECTION

COMMUNICATION

REASONING

REPRESENTATION

a. Suppose point P does not belong to line l. Construct a line through P that is perpendicular to l.

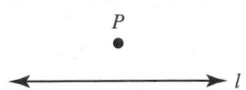

b. Justify the conclusion.

SOLUTION

a. Follow these steps.

Step 1. Open a compass wide enough to construct an arc with the center P and intersecting the given line at two points. Label the constructed points A and B.

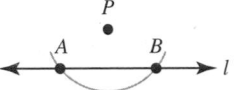

Step 2. Maintaining the same compass opening, place the point of the compass at A and swing an arc on the side opposite of P of the given line.

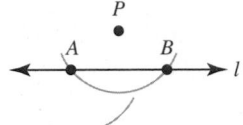

Step 3. Maintaining the same compass opening, place the point of the compass at B and swing an arc on the side opposite of P of the given line so that it intersects the arc with the center A.

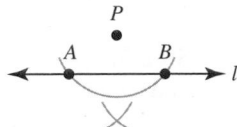

Step 4. Let C be the point of intersection of the two arcs. Use a straightedge to construct a line through C and P. Then $\overleftrightarrow{CP}$ is perpendicular to $\overline{AB}$.

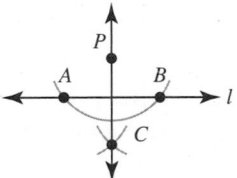

b. The points A and B lie on a circle with center P and radius r units, where r depends on how much we opened the compass. So $r = AP = BP$. The point C lies on a circle with the center A and radius r, so $r = AC$. The point C also lies on a circle with the center B and radius r, so $r = BC$. So $AP = BP = AC = BC$. The opposite sides of quadrilateral $APBC$ are congruent, so $APBC$ is a parallelogram (see Example 12.9). The four sides are congruent so parallelogram $APBC$ is a rhombus. The diagonals of a rhombus are perpendicular, so $\overline{PC} \perp \overline{AB}$. So $\overleftrightarrow{PC}$ is perpendicular to the given line l.

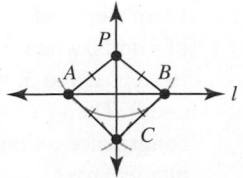

Constructing a Line through a Given Point and Parallel to a Given Line

Given a point P and a line l that does not contain P, our goal is to construct a line that contains P and is parallel to l.

EXAMPLE 12.16

CONNECTION
COMMUNICATION
REASONING
REPRESENTATION

a. Suppose point P does not belong to line l. Construct a line through P that is parallel to l.

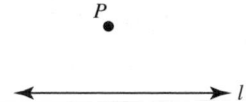

b. Justify the conclusion.

SOLUTION

a. Follow these steps.

> **Step 1.** Use a straightedge to construct a line through P and intersecting line l. Label the point of intersection A.

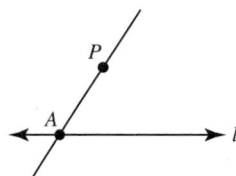

> **Step 2.** Follow the steps for copying $\angle A$ to an angle with the vertex P: Put the point of a compass at A, and swing an arc of any radius that intersects both lines. Label the points of intersection B and C. Maintaining the same compass opening, place the point of the compass at P and swing an arc so that it intersects the line containing P. Label the point of intersection X.

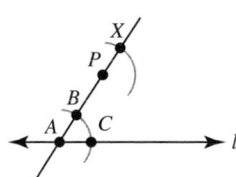

> **Step 3.** Place the point of the compass at B, and open the compass so that you can swing an arc that belongs to a circle with the center B and radius BC. Maintaining the same compass opening, place the point of the compass at X and swing an arc that intersects the arc containing X.

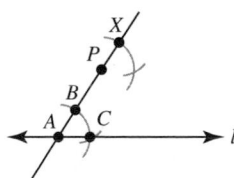

> **Step 4.** Label the point of intersection Y, and use the straightedge to draw a line through X and Y. Then $\overleftrightarrow{PY}$ is parallel to line l.

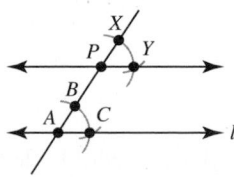

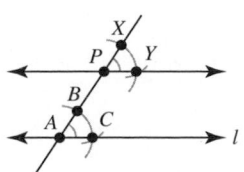

b. Steps 2–4 of part (a) are the same steps given earlier for copying an angle. $\angle BAC$ and $\angle XPY$ are congruent corresponding angles for the transversal $\overleftrightarrow{AP}$ that cuts lines l and $\overleftrightarrow{PY}$. So $\overleftrightarrow{PY}$ contains point P and is parallel to line l.

▲

Historical Note

There are three famous construction problems of antiquity: squaring the circle (given any circle, construct a square that has the same area as the circle), trisecting an angle (given any angle, use construction techniques to divide the angle into three congruent angles), and doubling the cube (given any cube, construct a cube that has twice the volume). In the 1800s, mathematicians proved these constructions were impossible using just a compass and straightedge.

The student page shows some constructions that sixth graders may encounter in geometry studies.

CHECK ✓ *For another example, see Set 9-4 on p. 532.*

Trace $\overline{MP}$ and ∠V at the right.

1. Construct a segment congruent to $\overline{MP}$.
2. Construct an angle congruent to ∠V.

Make another tracing of $\overline{MP}$ and ∠V.

3. Construct the perpendicular bisector of $\overline{MP}$.
4. Construct the bisector of ∠V.
5. **Reasoning** $\overleftrightarrow{NQ}$ is the perpendicular bisector of $\overline{XY}$. What is the measure of ∠NOY? Which segments are congruent?

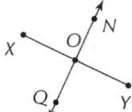

PRACTICE *For more practice, see Set 9-4 on p. 537.*

A Skills and Understanding

Trace $\overline{HG}$ and ∠C at the right.

6. Construct a segment congruent to $\overline{HG}$.
7. Construct an angle congruent to ∠C.

Make another tracing of $\overline{HG}$ and ∠C.

8. Construct the perpendicular bisector of $\overline{HG}$.
9. Construct the bisector of ∠C.
10. **Reasoning** $\overrightarrow{QB}$ bisects ∠PQR. If m∠PQR = 82°, find m∠PQB.

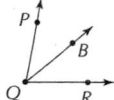

B Reasoning and Problem Solving

Math and Art

Beautiful designs can be created using a straightedge and a compass. The design shown here includes construction of a perpendicular bisector and four angle bisectors. Many of these design elements are used by people of many cultures to decorate such objects as pottery, eggs, jewelry, and window glass.

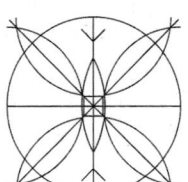 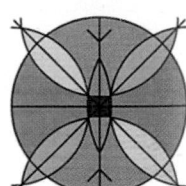

11. Create and color your own geometric design using a straightedge and a compass.
12. Which constructions did you include in your art?

486

(*Mathematics*, Grade 6, p. 486)

Constructible Regular Polygons

A regular polygon is a polygon such that all sides have the same length and all interior angles have the same measure. Figure 27 displays the construction of a regular triangle (equilateral triangle, $n = 3$), regular quadrilateral (square, $n = 4$), and regular pentagon ($n = 5$, complicated to explain but still possible to construct; we do not expect you to know how to construct a regular pentagon).

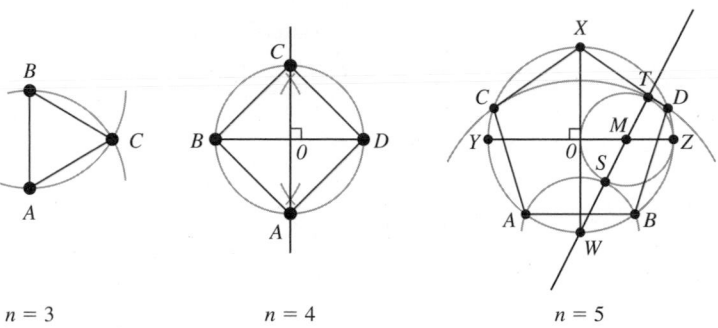

$n = 3$ $n = 4$ $n = 5$

FIGURE 27
Constructions of regular polygons.

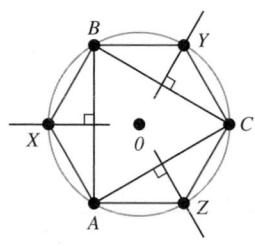

FIGURE 28
Bisect the sides of the equilateral triangle $\triangle ABC$ to construct regular hexagon $AXBYCZ$.

Figure 28 suggests the following way to construct a regular hexagon ($n = 6$): Begin with an equilateral triangle and a circle that circumscribes the triangle. Construct a perpendicular bisector for each side of the triangle. The intersection of the circle and a perpendicular bisector creates a vertex of the hexagon. This process creates three points of the hexagon (points X, Y, and Z in Figure 28). Then $AXBYCZ$ is a regular hexagon.

Can you visualize how to construct a regular polygon with 12 sides? 24 sides? 48 sides? Or, beginning with a regular pentagon ($n = 5$), can you visualize how to construct a regular polygon with 10 sides? 20 sides? 40 sides?

The ancient Greeks attempted to use construction techniques to construct a regular heptagon ($n = 7$) but failed. There's a good reason: only some regular polygons can be constructed using a compass and straightedge, as mathematicians proved in the 1800s. The formal proof is beyond the scope of this class, so we instead discuss which regular polygons are constructible and which are not.

CONNECTION   A Fermat number is a number of the form $1 + 2^{2^k}$, where k is a whole number. A Fermat prime is a Fermat number that is a prime number. The known Fermat prime numbers are 3, 5, 17, 257, and 65,537 ($1 + 2^{2^0} = 3$, $1 + 2^{2^1} = 5$, $1 + 2^{2^2} = 17$, $1 + 2^{2^3} = 257$, and $1 + 2^{2^4} = 65,537$). There could be other Fermat prime numbers, but it is unlikely because so far these are the only ones mathematicians have discovered (for example, the next Fermat number $1 + 2^{2^5} = 4,294,967,297$ is a composite with a nontrivial factor 641). Mathematicians have proved a theorem stating that you can use a compass and straightedge alone to construct a regular polygon with n sides if and only if the only prime factors of n are any power of 2 (such as 2^0, 2^1, 2^2, ...) and Fermat prime numbers, as long as the Fermat prime numbers are repeated at most once. For example, the prime factorizations of 6, 8, 9, and 15 are $6 = 2 \cdot 3$, $8 = 2 \cdot 2 \cdot 2$, $9 = 3 \cdot 3$, and $15 = 3 \cdot 5$, respectively. So you can use Euclidean tools to construct a regular polygon with 6 sides, 8 sides, and 15 sides but not one with 9 sides, because the Fermat prime 3 repeats more than once. The theorem tells you which regular polygons are constructible but not how to construct them.

EXAMPLE 12.17   Can you use a compass and straightedge to construct a regular polygon with n sides?

CONNECTION   **a.** $n = 7$

COMMUNICATION   **b.** $n = 50$

REASONING   **c.** $n = 24$

SOLUTION

The known Fermat prime numbers are 3, 5, 17, 257, and 65,537.

a. No; 7 is a prime number, but it is not a Fermat prime number (which explains why the ancient Greeks were doomed in their attempts).

b. No; the prime factorization of 50 is $50 = 2 \cdot 5 \cdot 5$. Although 5 is a Fermat prime number, it is repeated more than once as a prime factor in the factorization.

c. Yes; the prime factorization of 24 is $24 = 2^3 \cdot 3$. There are no restrictions on how many times the prime number 2 can be repeated (exponent 3), and 3 is a Fermat prime number that is repeated at most once.

▲

A Legal Case Involving the Center of a Circle

We close this section with an interesting legal case. An employee of a packaging company signed an employment contract. The employee agreed to a noncompete clause that said he would not work for a competitor within a 150-mile radius of the company while employed with the company and within 12 months of employment. The employee worked from home while the company investigated locations to establish a place of business. Months later, the employee resigned and was hired by a local competitor. The packaging company sued the former employee, claiming he breached the noncompete clause by working for a competitor within a 150-mile radius and within 12 months of employment. A judge ruled in favor of the employee, saying that because the company never established a place of business, there was no established center to create a circle with a 150-mile radius.

QUESTIONS FOR SECTION 12.2

REPRESENTATION

Refresher: Representations (language, diagrams, tables, symbols, algebra, manipulatives, and contextualized situations) are important because we use them to organize, record, and communicate mathematical ideas and make them more comprehensible.

1. A student begins with two given points. Then the student creates the following construction.

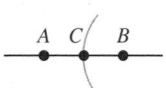

   a. Identify the given points.
   b. Identify all constructed geometric objects.

2. A student begins with a given point. Then the student creates the following construction. Identify the constructed object.

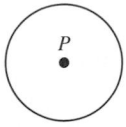

3. A student begins with a given point and given line. Then the student creates the following construction.

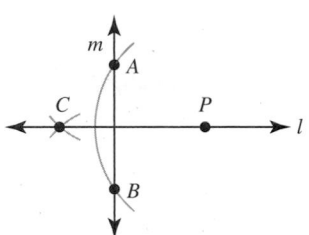

   a. Identify all given points in the construction.
   b. Identify the given line.
   c. Identify the constructed points.
   d. Identify the constructed line.
   e. Explain what the student constructed.

4. A student constructs a right triangle. Both legs have the length n units. What is the length of the hypotenuse?

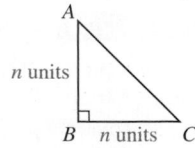

5. Sketch (that is, draw by hand) a representation of each situation.

 a. C lying on the perpendicular bisector of $\overline{AB}$

 b. the midpoint of $\overline{AB}$ c. an angle bisector

 d. the angle relationship between the diagonals of a rhombus

 e. a circle with center C and radius r

 f. the equation $a^2 + b^2 = c^2$

6. Construct a copy of $\angle K$.

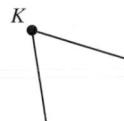

7. Construct the angle bisector of $\angle F$.

8. Construct the perpendicular bisector of $\overline{PQ}$.

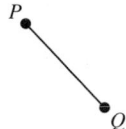

9. Construct a line through W that is parallel to h.

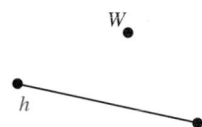

PROBLEM SOLVING

Refresher: Problem solving (reaching a goal that is not immediately attainable) is important because it helps students think more deeply about what they know and deal with unfamiliar situations.

10. $AB = 3$ units. Construct a line segment that has a length of 4.5 units.

11. Construct an equilateral triangle with sides congruent to $\overline{AB}$.

12. Construct an angle with the measure 90°.

13. Construct an angle with the measure 45°.

14. Construct an angle with the measure 60°.

15. Construct an angle with the measure $2 \cdot m\angle A$.

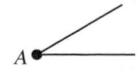

16. Construct an angle with the measure 120°.

17. The line segment has a length of r units.

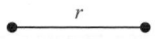

 a. Construct a square that has diagonals with the length r units.

 b. Use your compass to verify that the sides of the quadrilateral have the same length.

18. Use the following line segment.

 Construct a rectangle $ABCD$ that has diagonal $\overline{AC}$.

19. The line segment $\overline{AC}$ is a diagonal of a rhombus.

 a. What angle is formed by the diagonals of a rhombus?

 b. Construct rhombus $ABCD$ with a diagonal of the length AC.

20. Construct a right triangle with legs that have the lengths a and b units.

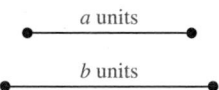

REASONING AND PROOF

Refresher: Reasoning and proof (thinking and justifying) are important because they help students make sense of mathematics.

21. Do the following.

 a. Suppose C lies on the perpendicular bisector of $\overline{AB}$. Prove $\overline{AC} \cong \overline{BC}$.

 b. Suppose $\overline{AC} \cong \overline{BC}$. Prove C lies on the perpendicular bisector of $\overline{AB}$.

22. a. Construct a triangle with sides of the lengths a, b, and c units.

 b. Justify your construction.

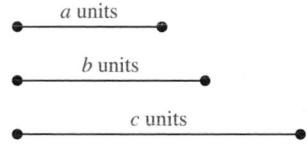

23. The diagram shows the two points B and X. Point B is a vertex of square $ABCD$, and point X is the intersection of the diagonals of the square.

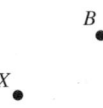

 a. What are the various ways the diagonals of a square are related?

 b. Construct square $ABCD$.   c. Justify your construction.

24. Do the following.

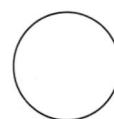

   a. Construct a line segment with a length of $\sqrt{2}$ units.
   b. Justify your construction.

CONNECTIONS

Refresher: Connections (linking and applying mathematical ideas) are important because they deepen student understanding and make mathematics more meaningful, flexible, and useful.

25. A *chord* is a line segment that joins two points on a circle.

   a. Construct a chord for the circle shown. Label the endpoints of the chord A and B.
   b. Construct the perpendicular bisector for $\overline{AB}$.
   c. Construct another chord for the circle. Label the endpoints of the chord C and D.
   d. Construct the perpendicular bisector for $\overline{CD}$.
   e. Locate the center of the circle.
   f. Justify why the point you chose in part (e) is the center of the circle.

26. Do the following.

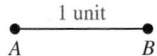

   a. Construct a circle that contains the three given points A, B, and C. (Hint: Refer to the previous question.)
   b. Justify your construction.

27. Construct a line segment that has a length of $\sqrt{5}$ units.

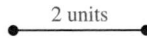

28. Construct a triangle with sides that have a ratio 2:2:3.

29. Construct a circle with diameter $\overline{AB}$.

   A   B

30. Can you use a compass and straightedge to construct a regular polygon with n sides? (Hint: Recall the Fermat prime numbers.)

   a. $n = 2^7 \cdot 3 \cdot 5$ b. $n = 40$ c. $n = 19$ d. $n = 33$
   e. $n = 2^4 \cdot 3^7 \cdot 5$

COMMUNICATION

Refresher: Communication (written and verbal explanations using representations and proper mathematical vocabulary) is important because it helps students refine and strengthen their understanding.

31. A tangent line to a circle is a line that intersects the circle at exactly one point. It has the property that is perpendicular to the radius of the circle. A teacher constructs a circle and a point Q on the circle. Then she asks whether anyone can construct a tangent line that contains the point Q. Martin says, "That's easy! All you need to do is place your straightedge so that it touches the circle only at the point Q and then draw a line." What mistake did Martin make?

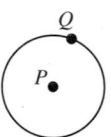

32. Explain the steps needed to construct a parallelogram with sides of the lengths a and b units and an angle congruent to ∠X.

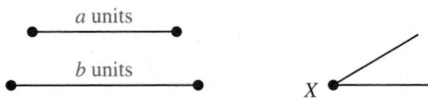

33. Explain why you cannot use Euclidean tools to construct a regular polygon with 140 sides.

   A constructible number is a number that equals the length of a line segment with endpoints constructed from a compass and straightedge.

34. Given two line segments of the lengths a and b units, explain how you can construct a + b.

35. Given two line segments of the lengths a and b units with b > a, explain how you can construct a line segment with a length of b − a.

36. The line segments shown have the lengths a and b units.

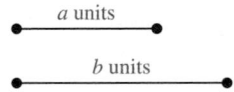

   Construct line segments with the following lengths.

   a. a + b units   b. b − a units

More practice with the ideas of the section

37. Fill in the blank. Choose one of the following words or phrases: *center, center point, compass, constructed, construction, Euclidean, given, impossible, intersection, pencil, pencil point, point, straightedge, radius, ruler, perpendicular bisector, possible,* or *useful.*

   a. A(n) _____ is a tool to construct a circle or arc.
   b. We use a(n) _____ to construct a line segment.
   c. The _____ of a compass is the distance between the two points of the compass.

d. A(n) _____ point is the intersection of two lines, two arcs, or a line and an arc.

e. The _____ of the compass draws the arcs.

f. The _____ of a compass determines the center of the circle or arc.

g. Any point C that satisfies the equation $AC = BC$ must belong to the _____ of $\overline{AB}$.

h. Together, the compass and straightedge are called _____ tools.

i. The prime factorization of 336 is $336 = 2^4 \cdot 3 \cdot 7$. It is _____ to construct a regular polygon with 336 sides.

38. Construct the perpendicular bisector of $\overline{AB}$.

39. Construct an isosceles triangle with an altitude $\overline{AB}$ and apex B.

40. Construct the angle bisector of the given angle.

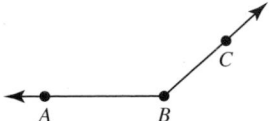

41. You are given $m\angle A = 50°$. Construct an angle whose measure is 20°.

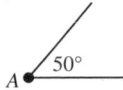

42. Construct an isosceles triangle $\triangle ABC$ with the apex angle $\angle A$ and legs of the length k units. Justify your construction.

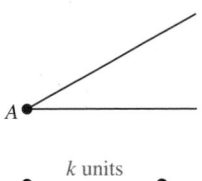

43. Construct a triangle that is congruent to $\triangle ABC$.

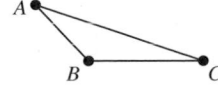

44. Construct an obtuse triangle that has an area of 3 square units.

45. The following line segments are two sides of a right triangle.

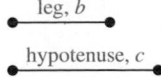

a. Construct a triangle that is congruent to the right triangle with two of the sides as shown.

b. Justify your construction.

46. Construct an angle with the measure 30°.

47. Explain how you could construct a 75° angle.

48. Construct a kite with diagonals of the lengths a and b units.

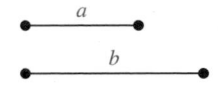

49. Do the following.

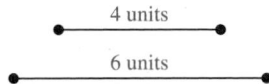

a. Construct a line segment with a length of $\sqrt{52}$ units.

b. Justify your construction.

50. Our goal in this problem is to learn how to inscribe a circle in a triangle. An *inscribed circle* is a circle that touches each side at exactly one point on each side. The center of this circle is called the *incenter* of the triangle, and the circle itself is called the *incircle*.

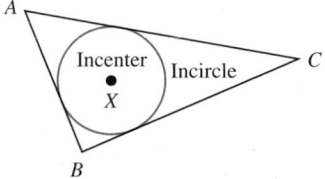

a. Construct the angle bisector for each interior angle of the triangle just shown.

b. Describe what you notice about the angle bisectors.

c. Construct a line that contains the incenter X and is perpendicular to a side (pick any side) of the triangle shown. Let Y be the point of intersection of the perpendicular line and the side of the triangle you chose. Open your compass so that it has the radius XY. Construct a circle with the center X and radius XY. Describe what you notice.

51. Use the triangle shown.

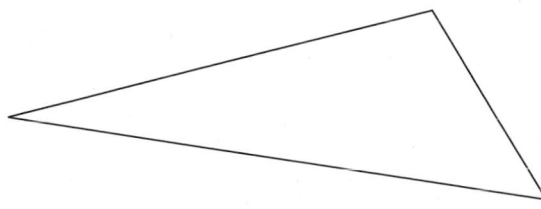

a. Construct the incenter for the triangle.

b. Construct the incircle for the triangle.

52. A *median* of a triangle is a line segment that connects a vertex and the midpoint of the side that is opposite the vertex. The three medians of a triangle intersect at a single point, and the point of intersection is called the *centroid*. Construct the centroid of the triangle shown. The centroid is the "balance point" or "center of mass" of the triangle. If the triangle were made of wood of uniform thickness, then you could conceivably balance the triangle with a pencil point.

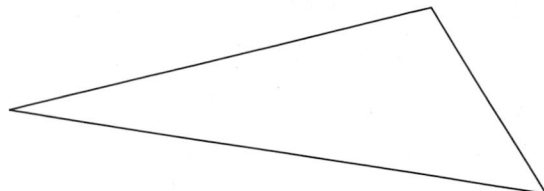

53. Our goal in this problem is to learn how to circumscribe a triangle with a circle. A *circumscribed circle* is a circle that touches each vertex of the triangle. The center of this circle is called the *circumcenter* of the triangle, and the circle itself is called the *circumcircle*.

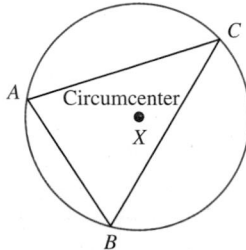

a. Construct the perpendicular bisector for each side of the triangle.

b. Describe what you notice about the bisectors.

c. Open your compass so that it has radius AX. Construct a circle with the center X and radius AX. Describe what you notice.

54. Construct the circumcenter and circumcircle for the triangle.

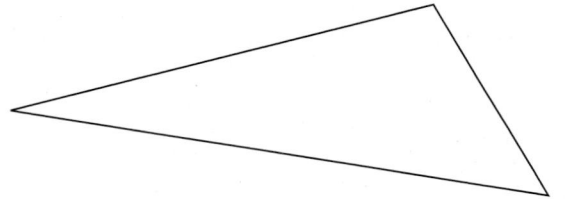

55. The goal of this question is to prove the circumcenter X is equidistant from the vertices of $\triangle ABC$ (that is, $AX = BX = CX$).

a. Prove $AX = BX$.

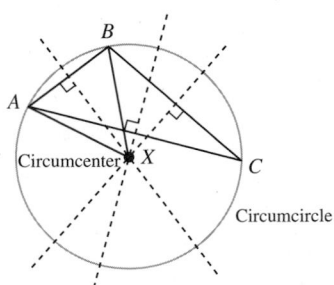

b. Prove $BX = CX$.

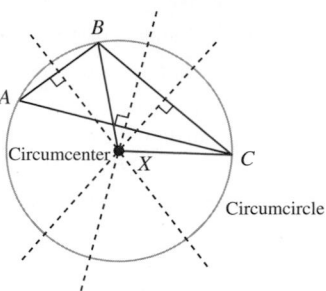

c. Prove $AX = CX$.

d. Explain how the circumcenter is related to the vertices of a triangle.

56. Recall that an altitude from a vertex of a triangle is a line segment such that (i) the vertex is one endpoint and the other endpoint belongs to the line containing the side opposite the vertex and (ii) the line segment is perpendicular to the line containing the side opposite the vertex. The three altitudes of a triangle intersect at a single point, and the point of intersection is called the *orthocenter* of the triangle. Trace the triangle shown on a piece of paper. Then construct the orthocenter of the triangle.

57. Construct the orthocenter of the triangle.

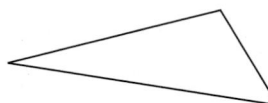

58. Do the following.

a. A rectangle is shown. Construct the midpoints of each side.

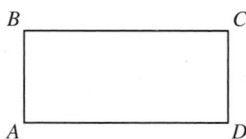

b. Classify the polygon formed by the midpoints.

c. Determine how the diagonals of the polygon and the sides of the rectangle are related.

59. How are the points on an arc and the points on the perpendicular bisector of a line segment alike?

60. Use a compass to construct a circle. Then construct a second circle that has twice the area of the first circle. Describe your steps and justify why the second circle has twice the area of the first circle.

61. Given a square, outline a method to circumscribe the square with a circle. Give an example.

62. Given a circle with the center O, construct a square $ABCD$ whose vertices lie on the circle.

63. You are given point Q and line l, as shown.

a. Sketch a line m through Q that is perpendicular to line l (you do not have to construct m).

b. Sketch a line n through Q that is perpendicular to line m (you do not have to construct n).

c. What is the relationship between lines l and n? (Hint: Refer to Section 10.2.)

64. $ABCD$ is an isosceles trapezoid. Construct the perpendicular bisector of $\overline{AB}$ and $\overline{CD}$.

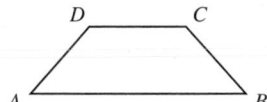

SECTION 12.3 Similarity

What Is Similarity?

Similarity is a relationship between two geometric figures that have the same shape and possibly different sizes. For polygons, it specifies the relationship between corresponding angles and corresponding sides. In this section, we learn how to identify similar triangles, discuss the connection between similarity and ratios, apply similarity to solve indirect measurement problems, and explore how similarity affects perimeter and area. The NCTM's *Principles and Standards for School Mathematics* states, "It is important that middle-grades students understand similarity, which is closely related to their more general understanding of proportionality and to the idea of correspondence" (2000, p. 245).

Uses of Similarity

According to tradition, Thales (about 624–584 BCE) of Miletus (located on the coast of modern-day Turkey) proved basic geometric results such as vertical angles are congruent and base angles of an isosceles triangle are congruent. He is credited with measuring heights of pyramids by applying concepts of similarity to measurements of sticks and shadows. Some forest scientists use formulas based on similarity axioms to estimate the volume of usable lumber in trees that have tapering diameters. Pathologists use a microscope to magnify and study images of specimens to diagnose diseases. The images represent enlargements of the specimens. Artists use concepts of similarity to paint pictures of actual objects, such as a basket of fruit.

Photographers often shrink or enlarge pictures. In Figure 29, the second image is an enlargement of the first image. The two images seem to have the same shape. A and D are corresponding points. $\triangle ABC$ and $\triangle DEF$ seem to have the same shape. How are the triangles related?

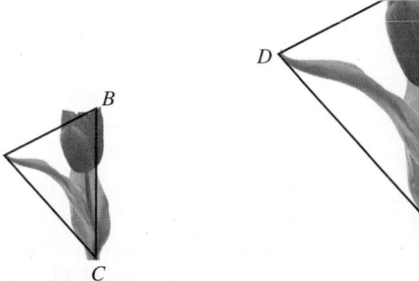

FIGURE 29
The second image is an enlargement of the first image.

Table 12.3 shows the measurements of the interior angles and lengths of the sides of triangles. We rounded all angle measurements to the nearest degree (equal to the precision of the protractor), and rounded all linear measurements to the nearest millimeter (equal to the precision of the ruler).

TABLE 12.3   **Measurements and Relationships**

$\triangle ABC$	$\triangle DEF$	Corresponding parts	Relationship
m$\angle A = 76°$	m$\angle D = 76°$	$\angle A$ and $\angle D$	$\angle A \cong \angle D$
m$\angle B = 63°$	m$\angle E = 63°$	$\angle B$ and $\angle E$	$\angle B \cong \angle E$
m$\angle C = 41°$	m$\angle F = 41°$	$\angle C$ and $\angle F$	$\angle C \cong \angle F$
$AB = 14$ mm	$DE = 28$ mm	$\overline{AB}$ and $\overline{DE}$	$\dfrac{DE}{AB} = 2$
$BC = 20$ mm	$EF = 40$ mm	$\overline{BC}$ and $\overline{EF}$	$\dfrac{EF}{BC} = 2$
$AC = 18$ mm	$DF = 36$ mm	$\overline{AC}$ and $\overline{DF}$	$\dfrac{DF}{AC} = 2$

CONNECTION

The data in Table 12.3 suggest the corresponding angles are congruent and the corresponding sides have identical ratios. In this section, the term *ratio,* which has multiple meanings, refers to a *quotient* ($a \div b$, or a/b, for $b \neq 0$), which is a number. We write the quotient in decimal form or the fraction form a/b.

Definition of Similar Triangles

The following example provides experience with finding ratios associated with corresponding sides, a key skill in learning similarity. We always refer to the same triangle for the first term (or numerator) in the ratios.

EXAMPLE 12.18   The diagram shows $\triangle OLD$ and $\triangle NEW$.

CONNECTION

REASONING

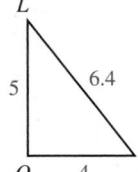
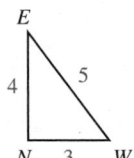

Assume vertices *O, L,* and *D* correspond to vertices *N, E,* and *W,* respectively. Find the ratios of the corresponding sides.

SOLUTION

$\overline{OL}$ corresponds to $\overline{NE}$, and the ratio is $OL/NE = 5/4$. $\overline{LD}$ corresponds to $\overline{EW}$, and the ratio is $LD/EW = 6.4/5 = 32/25$. $\overline{OD}$ corresponds to $\overline{NW}$, and the ratio is $OD/NW = 4/3$. The ratios of the corresponding sides are 5/4, 32/25, and 4/3. ▲

We can obtain another possible answer by comparing sides of $\triangle NEW$ to corresponding sides of $\triangle OLD$ to obtain the reciprocal ratios 4/5, 25/32, and 3/4.

When we say two geometric figures are similar, we mean the figures look alike in the sense that one looks like a contraction (reduction), dilation (enlargement), or exact copy (duplicate) of the other so that they have the same shape but possibly different sizes.

Corresponding angles are congruent, and the lengths of corresponding sides have identical ratios. We use the symbol $\sim$ to indicate similarity. The wiggly marks on the sides of triangles indicate the corresponding sides have identical ratios.

Definition of Similar Triangles

Using Words

Two triangles are **similar** if and only if there is a correspondence between the vertices such that all pairs of corresponding angles are congruent and all pairs of corresponding sides have identical ratios.

Using Symbols

$\triangle ABC \sim \triangle DEF$ if and only if $\angle A \cong \angle D$, $\angle B \cong \angle E$, $\angle C \cong \angle F$, and $\dfrac{AB}{DE} = \dfrac{BC}{EF} = \dfrac{AC}{DF}$.

Using a Diagram

$\triangle ABC \sim \triangle DEF$ if and only if

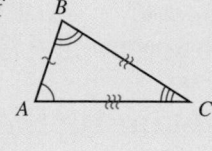 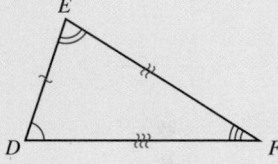

Notes

The similarity statement $\triangle ABC \sim \triangle DEF$

- tells us the correspondence between vertices (for example, $A \leftrightarrow D$).
- implies corresponding angles are congruent (for example, $\angle B \cong \angle E$).

- implies there is a number k (called the *scale factor*) such that
$$\frac{AB}{DE} = k, \frac{BC}{EF} = k, \text{ and } \frac{AC}{DF} = k.$$

The following example is an opportunity to identify corresponding parts of similar triangles.

EXAMPLE 12.19

CONNECTION

REASONING

$\triangle CUP$ and $\triangle TEA$ are similar triangles.

a. Write expressions that tell how the corresponding angles are related.

b. Write expressions that tell how the corresponding sides are related.

SOLUTION

a. $\angle C \cong \angle T$, $\angle U \cong \angle E$, and $\angle P \cong \angle A$.

b. $\dfrac{CU}{TE} = \dfrac{UP}{EA} = \dfrac{CP}{TA}$, or there is a number k such that $\dfrac{CU}{TE} = k$, $\dfrac{UP}{EA} = k$, and $\dfrac{CP}{TA} = k$.

▲

EXAMPLE 12.20

CONNECTION

REASONING

$\triangle ABC$ and $\triangle XYZ$ are similar triangles.

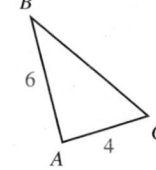 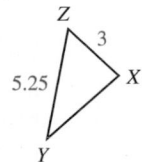

a. Determine the scale factor.

b. Determine BC

c. Determine XY

SOLUTION

a. $\triangle ABC \sim \triangle XYZ$, so $\dfrac{AB}{XY} = \dfrac{BC}{YZ} = \dfrac{AC}{XZ}$. Then $\dfrac{6}{XY} = \dfrac{BC}{5.25} = \dfrac{4}{3}$. The scale factor is $\dfrac{4}{3}$.

b. $\dfrac{BC}{5.25} = \dfrac{4}{3}$, so $3 \cdot BC = 5.25 \cdot 4$. Then $BC = \dfrac{5.25 \cdot 4}{3} = 7$ units.

c. $\dfrac{6}{XY} = \dfrac{4}{3}$, so $4 \cdot XY = 6 \cdot 3$. Then $XY = \dfrac{6 \cdot 3}{4} = 4.5$ units.

When we write a statement such as $\triangle ABC \sim \triangle DEF$, the vertices could be written in any order, as long as A and D are in corresponding locations, B and E are in corresponding locations, and C and F are in corresponding locations. For example, you could also write $\triangle BAC \sim \triangle EDF$. When we write a proportion such as $\frac{ML}{TU} = \frac{LN}{US}$, we could also write the proportion $\frac{LM}{TU} = \frac{LN}{US}$ or $\frac{TU}{ML} = \frac{US}{LN}$.

Naming Similar Scalene Triangles

The diagram in the definition of similar triangles indicates that (i) corresponding angles are congruent, and (ii) sides that are opposite corresponding angles are corresponding sides.

We already know that the longest side of a triangle is opposite the angle with the largest measure. For similar scalene triangles, this means that (i) the angles with the largest measure in each triangle must be corresponding angles, and (ii) the two longest sides must be corresponding sides because they are opposite corresponding angles.

We already know that the shortest side of a triangle is opposite the angle with the smallest measure. For similar scalene triangles, this means that (i) the angles with the smallest measure in each triangle must be corresponding angles, and (ii) the two shortest sides must be corresponding sides because they are opposite corresponding angles.

These observations could help you write correct similarity statements more easily in problems based on a diagram or given measurements.

EXAMPLE 12.21 The two triangles shown are similar triangles drawn to scale. Write a similarity statement.

CONNECTION
COMMUNICATION
REASONING

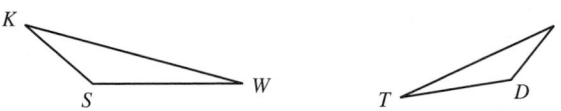

SOLUTION

The diagram indicates that $\overline{SK}$ and $\overline{KW}$ are the shortest and longest sides, respectively, of one triangle. They have the corresponding sides $\overline{DL}$ and $\overline{LT}$, respectively. Then a possible similarity statement is $\triangle SKW \sim \triangle DLT$.

Similarity Axioms

If you wanted to check whether two triangles $\triangle ABC$ and $\triangle DEF$ are similar by applying the definition of similar triangles, you would need to identify a correspondence between the vertices, verify that corresponding angles are congruent, and verify that the three ratios of corresponding sides are identical. As with triangle congruence axioms, a few triangle similarity axioms are more efficient than the definition: the **side-side-side (SSS) similarity axiom,** the **angle-angle (AA) similarity axiom,** and the **side-angle-side (SAS) similarity axiom.**

Side-Side-Side Similarity Axiom

The following similarity axiom applies to all three corresponding sides of a pair of triangles.

Side-Side-Side (SSS) Similarity Axiom

Using Words

If all three pairs of corresponding sides in two triangles have identical ratios, then the two triangles are similar.

Using a Diagram

If and then $\triangle ABC \sim \triangle DEF$.

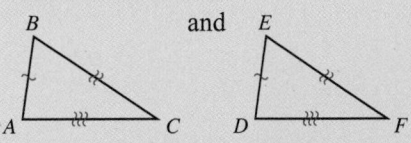

Using Symbols

If $\dfrac{AB}{DE} = \dfrac{BC}{EF} = \dfrac{AC}{DF}$, then $\triangle ABC \sim \triangle DEF$.

EXAMPLE 12.22

CONNECTION

PROBLEM SOLVING

REASONING

The length of each side of $\triangle DEF$ is three times the length of the corresponding side of $\triangle ABC$. Show that $\triangle ABC \sim \triangle DEF$.

SOLUTION

The length of a side of $\triangle DEF$ is three times the length of the corresponding side of $\triangle ABC$. So $DE = 3 \cdot AB$, $EF = 3 \cdot BC$, and $DF = 3 \cdot AC$. Then $\frac{DE}{AB} = 3$, $\frac{EF}{BC} = 3$, and $\frac{DF}{AC} = 3$. Then $\frac{DE}{AB} = \frac{EF}{BC} = \frac{DF}{AC}$. The ratios of the corresponding sides of $\triangle ABC$ and $\triangle DEF$ are identical, so $\triangle ABC \sim \triangle DEF$ by the SSS similarity axiom.

▲

Angle-Angle Similarity Axiom

The following similarity axiom applies to two corresponding angles in a pair of triangles.

Angle-Angle (AA) Similarity Axiom

Using Words

If two angles in a triangle are congruent to the corresponding angles in another triangle, then the two triangles are similar.

Using a Diagram

If and then $\triangle ABC \sim \triangle DEF$.

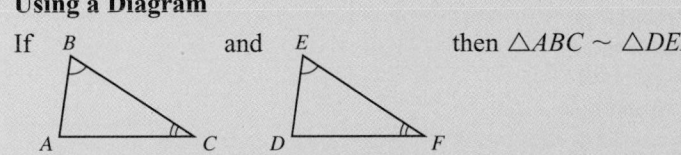

Using Symbols

If $\triangle ABC$ and $\triangle DEF$ are two triangles such that $\angle B \cong \angle E$ and $\angle C \cong \angle F$, then $\triangle ABC \sim \triangle DEF$.

EXAMPLE 12.23 Identify two similar triangles in each diagram. Explain why they are similar.

COMMUNICATION

REASONING

a.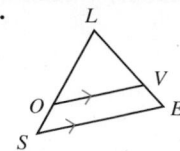

b.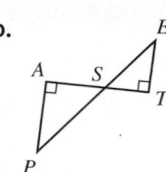

SOLUTION

a. $\overleftrightarrow{OV}$ and $\overleftrightarrow{SE}$ are parallel lines cut by the transversal $\overrightarrow{SO}$, and $\angle LOV$ and $\angle S$ are corresponding angles, so $\angle LOV \cong \angle S$. $\angle L \cong \angle L$ by the reflexive property. Therefore, $\angle LOV$ and $\angle L$ in $\triangle LOV$ are congruent to the corresponding angles $\angle S$ and $\angle L$ in $\triangle LSE$. Then $\triangle LOV \sim \triangle LSE$ by the AA similarity axiom.

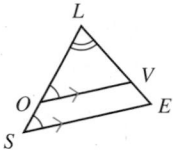

b. $\angle ASP$ and $\angle TSE$ are vertical angles, so they are congruent. $\angle A$ and $\angle T$ are right angles, so they are congruent. $\angle A$ and $\angle ASP$ in $\triangle PAS$ are congruent to the corresponding angles $\angle T$ and $\angle TSE$ in $\triangle ETS$. Then $\triangle PAS \sim \triangle ETS$ by the AA similarity axiom.

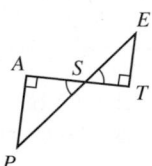

The previous example illustrates the general property of triangles illustrated in Figure 30. Suppose line segment $\overline{DE}$ joins two sides of $\triangle ABC$ and $\overline{DE}$ is parallel to the third side. Then the resulting triangles $\triangle ABC$ and $\triangle DBE$ are similar. Here's why: $\angle B \cong \angle B$, and $\angle BAC \cong \angle BDE$, because parallel lines cut by a transversal create congruent corresponding angles. Then $\triangle ABC \sim \triangle DBE$ by the AA similarity axiom.

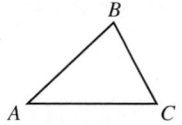 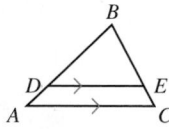

FIGURE 30

If $\overline{DE} \| \overline{AC}$, then $\triangle ABC \sim \triangle DBE$ because of the AA similarity axiom.

EXAMPLE 12.24 Find BC.

CONNECTION

COMMUNICATION

REASONING

REPRESENTATION

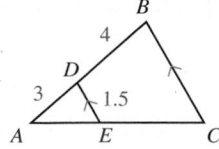

SOLUTION

$\overline{DE}$ joins two sides of $\triangle ABC$ and is parallel to the third side $\overline{BC}$. So $\triangle ABC \sim \triangle ADE$ by the AA similarity axiom. Then the ratios of corresponding sides are identical, so $\frac{AD}{AB} = \frac{DE}{BC}$. Then $\frac{3}{7} = \frac{1.5}{BC}$. Then $3 \cdot BC = 7 \cdot 1.5$, and $BC = (7 \cdot 1.5)/3 = 3.5$. So $BC = 3.5$ units.

The following Released Item suggests students should be able to apply the AA similarity axiom to help them solve problems involving two right triangles that share a common angle.

▶ RELEASED ITEM

● NAEP, 2007

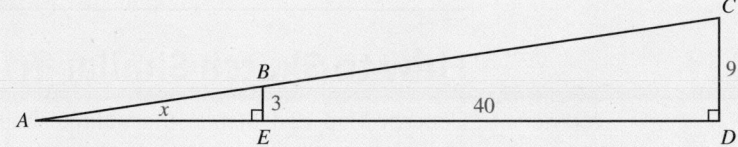

The figure above shows two right angles. The length of *AE* is *x* and the length of *DE* is 40. Show all of the steps that lead to finding the value of *x*. Your last step should give the value of *x*.

1% of eighth graders gave the correct answer, and 12% gave a partially correct answer. (U.S. Department of Education, Institute of Education Sciences, National Center for Education Statistics, NAEP)

Side-Angle-Side Similarity Axiom

The following similarity axiom applies to two corresponding sides and their included angle in a pair of triangles.

Side-Angle-Side (SAS) Similarity Axiom

Using Words

If two pairs of corresponding sides have identical ratios and their included angles are congruent, then the two triangles are similar.

Using a Diagram

If and then $\triangle ABC \sim \triangle DEF$.

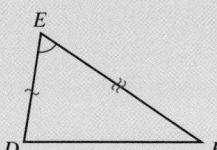

Using Symbols

If $\dfrac{AB}{DE} = \dfrac{BC}{EF}$ and $\angle B \cong \angle E$, then $\triangle ABC \sim \triangle DEF$.

EXAMPLE 12.25 The diagram shows two triangles.

COMMUNICATION

REASONING

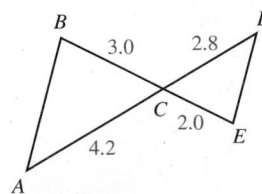

a. Explain why the two triangles are similar.

b. Write a similarity statement.

SOLUTION

a. $\angle BCA \cong \angle ECD$, because vertical angles are congruent. The two triangles with the common vertex C are named $\triangle ACB$ and $\triangle DCE$, so their longest sides are corresponding parts. Now let's compare ratios. $\frac{AC}{DC} = \frac{4.2}{2.8} = 1.5$ and $\frac{BC}{EC} = \frac{3.0}{2.0} = 1.5$, so the ratios of two pairs of corresponding sides are identical and their included angles of the sides are congruent. Then the two triangles are similar by the SAS similarity axiom.

b. $\triangle ACB \sim \triangle DCE$

▲

How to Sketch Similar Triangles

CONNECTION
REASONING
REPRESENTATION

Concept Map 12.1 demonstrates three simple ways to sketch triangles that are similar to an arbitrary triangle $\triangle ABC$. Each method hinges on the ability to draw parallel lines. Because the idea is to "sketch" similar triangles, you just need to draw parallel lines to the best of your ability. To create precise drawings, you could use the construction techniques we discussed in Section 12.2. Students should be able to show that "various configurations of lines give rise to similar triangles because of the angles created when a transversal cuts parallel lines" (Gr. 8, CCSS) (© 2010. National Governors Association Center for Best Practices and Council of Chief State School Officers. All rights reserved.).

> **Concept Map 12.1** Three Simple Ways to Sketch a Triangle That Is Similar to a Given Triangle

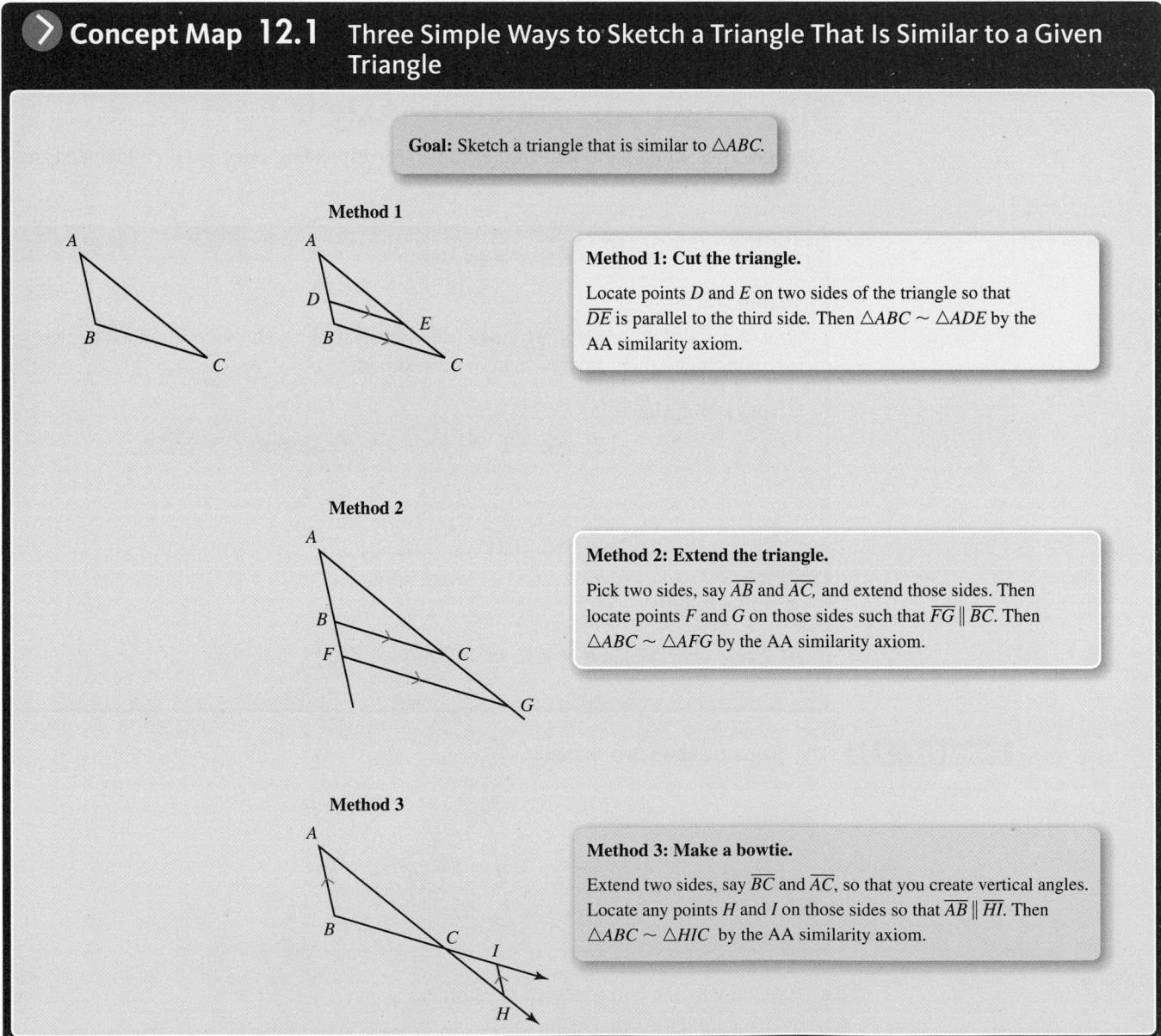

Goal: Sketch a triangle that is similar to $\triangle ABC$.

Method 1

Method 1: Cut the triangle.

Locate points D and E on two sides of the triangle so that $\overline{DE}$ is parallel to the third side. Then $\triangle ABC \sim \triangle ADE$ by the AA similarity axiom.

Method 2

Method 2: Extend the triangle.

Pick two sides, say $\overline{AB}$ and $\overline{AC}$, and extend those sides. Then locate points F and G on those sides such that $\overline{FG} \parallel \overline{BC}$. Then $\triangle ABC \sim \triangle AFG$ by the AA similarity axiom.

Method 3

Method 3: Make a bowtie.

Extend two sides, say $\overline{BC}$ and $\overline{AC}$, so that you create vertical angles. Locate any points H and I on those sides so that $\overline{AB} \parallel \overline{HI}$. Then $\triangle ABC \sim \triangle HIC$ by the AA similarity axiom.

Indirect Measurement

Early uses of similarity involved **indirect measurement,** or measuring a distance using other measurements that are easier to obtain. The following Classroom Connection is one example that uses similar right triangles. The legs of the right triangles are formed by the heights and shadows of the objects.

> **Classroom Connection**
>
> • *Pre-Algebra,* California Edition, p. 292
>
> A tree casts a shadow 8 ft long. A 6-ft man casts a shadow 4 ft long. The triangle formed by the tree and its shadow is similar to the triangle formed by the man and his shadow. How tall is the tree? (From David M. Davidson. © 2001 by Pearson Education, Inc. or its affiliates. Used by permission. All rights reserved.)

Figure 31 represents the information provided in the preceding Classroom Connection. These types of indirect measurement problems reasonably assume that the Sun's rays strike the tree and person at the same angle, which explains the arcs that indicate congruent angles. Then the two triangles are similar because of the AA similarity axiom.

CONNECTION
PROBLEM SOLVING
REASONING

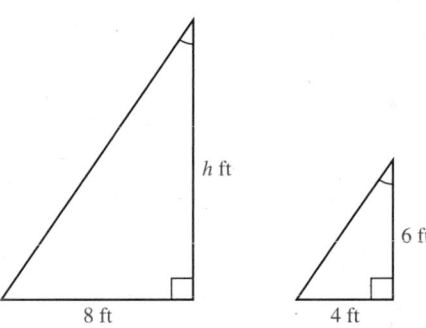

FIGURE 31
Indirect measurement of the height of a tree.

This leads to the proportion $\frac{h}{8} = \frac{6}{4}$, which helps us find the height of the tree: $h = 12$ feet.

Now, suppose you wish to measure the distance between points B and C on the shore of the pond in Figure 32. How could you use land measurements to determine BC?

We could draw similar triangles, measure the lengths of their sides, and set up a proportion involving the unknown measurement BC. We need to create sides that can be measured on "land" to indirectly find the distance BC across the water.

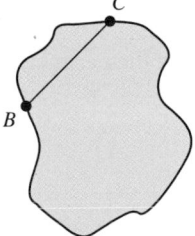

FIGURE 32
$BC = ?.$

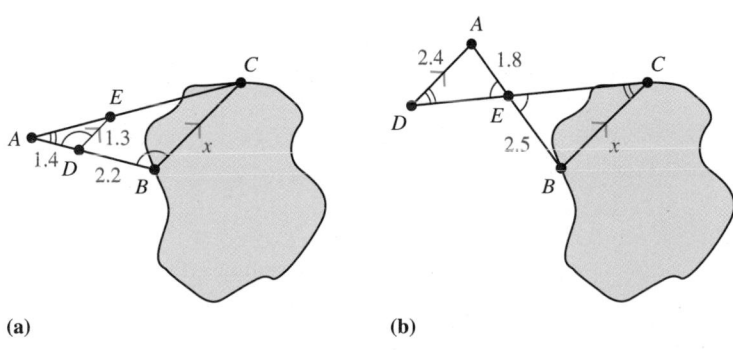

(a)   (b)

FIGURE 33
Indirect measurement of distance across a pond.

• In Figure 33(a), we create two triangles $\triangle ADE$ and $\triangle ABC$ such that $\overline{DE}$ and $\overline{BC}$ are parallel. This creates corresponding angles that are congruent. The two triangles also have a common vertex. Then $\triangle ADE \sim \triangle ABC$ because of the AA similarity axiom. We can now set up a proportion to find BC indirectly using the measurable parts: $\frac{x}{1.3} = \frac{3.6}{1.4}$. Then $x = \frac{1.3 \cdot 3.6}{1.4}$. Then $x \approx 3.3$ units.

- In Figure 33(b), we create two triangles $\triangle EAD$ and $\triangle EBC$ such that $\overline{AD}$ is parallel to $\overline{BC}$. This creates alternate interior angles that are congruent. The two triangles also have vertical angles. Then $\triangle EAD \sim \triangle EBC$ because of the AA similarity axiom. We can now set up a proportion to find BC indirectly using the measurable parts: $\frac{x}{2.4} = \frac{2.5}{1.8}$. Then $x = \frac{2.4 \cdot 2.5}{1.8}$. Then $x \approx 3.3$ units.

Impact of Similarity on Perimeter

The next two examples illustrate the connection between the sides and perimeters of two similar triangles.

EXAMPLE 12.26

CONNECTION
COMMUNICATION
REASONING

A teacher draws $\triangle DEF$, as shown in Figure 34(a). She informs the class that $\triangle ABC$ and $\triangle DEF$ are similar triangles. A student represents $\triangle ABC$ with the diagram in Figure 34(b). Explain why this is a valid representation of $\triangle ABC$.

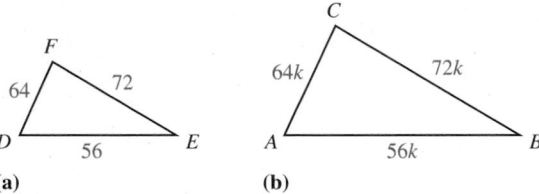

(a)   **(b)**

FIGURE 34
Connection between the sides of two similar triangles.

SOLUTION

$\triangle ABC \sim \triangle DEF$, so corresponding angles are congruent and $\frac{AB}{56} = \frac{BC}{72} = \frac{AC}{64}$. These ratios are identical numbers, so this means there is a number k such that $\frac{AB}{56} = k$, $\frac{BC}{72} = k$, and $\frac{AC}{64} = k$. Then $AB = 56k$, $BC = 72k$, and $AC = 64k$. ▲

The previous example highlights the relationship of the corresponding sides of two similar triangles.

We can generalize these results and examine the impact of similarity on the perimeter. Suppose $\triangle ABC \sim \triangle DEF$. Then there is a number k such that $\frac{AB}{DE} = k$, $\frac{CD}{EF} = k$, and $\frac{AD}{DF} = k$. Then $AB = k \cdot DE$, $BC = k \cdot EF$, and $AC = k \cdot DF$. Then

$$\frac{\text{perimeter of } \triangle ABC}{\text{perimeter of } \triangle DEF} = \frac{AB + BC + AC}{DE + EF + DF}$$

$$= \frac{k \cdot DE + k \cdot EF + k \cdot DF}{DE + EF + DF}$$

$$= \frac{k(DE + EF + DF)}{DE + EF + DF}$$

$$= k.$$

For two similar triangles, the ratio of the perimeters equals the common ratio of the sides. For example, suppose $\triangle ABC \sim \triangle DEF$ and each side of $\triangle ABC$ has a length that is three times the length of the corresponding side of $\triangle DEF$. Then $AB = 3 \cdot DE$ and the perimeter of $\triangle ABC$ is three times the perimeter of $\triangle DEF$.

For two similar triangles, knowing the perimeter of one triangle and a ratio of two corresponding sides provides enough information to determine the perimeter of the other triangle.

EXAMPLE 12.27

CONNECTION

PROBLEM SOLVING

REASONING

The diagram shows $\triangle DEF.$ $\triangle ABC$ and $\triangle DEF$ are similar triangles. The perimeter of $\triangle ABC$ is 36 units. Determine lengths of the sides of $\triangle ABC$.

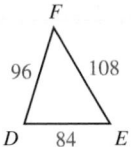 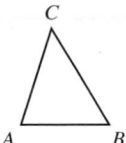

SOLUTION

We need to determine AB, BC, and AC. $\triangle ABC \sim \triangle DEF$, so we can represent $\triangle ABC$ with the diagram shown.

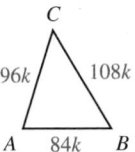

The perimeter of $\triangle ABC$ is 36 units, so

$$36 = AB + BC + AC$$
$$= 84k + 108k + 96k$$
$$= 288k$$

So the scale factor is $k = 36/288 = 0.125$. Then $AB = 84k = 84 \cdot 0.125 = 10.5$ units, $BC = 108k = 108 \cdot 0.125 = 13.5$ units, and $AC = 96k = 96 \cdot 0.125 = 12$ units. To check our work, $10.5 + 13.5 + 12 = 36$ units, which equals the perimeter of $\triangle ABC$. ▲

EXAMPLE 12.28

CONNECTION

PROBLEM SOLVING

REASONING

$\triangle RUN$ and $\triangle JOG$ shown in the diagrams are similar triangles. The perimeter of $\triangle RUN$ is 24 units. Determine the perimeter of $\triangle JOG$.

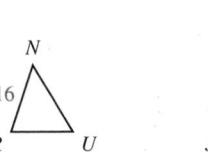 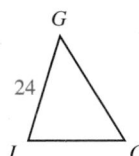

SOLUTION

$\triangle RUN \sim \triangle JOG$, and $\dfrac{\text{perimeter of } \triangle JOG}{\text{perimeter of } \triangle RUN} = \dfrac{JO}{RU} = \dfrac{OG}{UN} = \dfrac{JG}{RN}$. We know the perimeter of $\triangle RUN$ is 24 units and the ratio $\dfrac{JG}{RN} = \dfrac{24}{16} = \dfrac{3}{2}$. Then $\dfrac{\text{perimeter of } \triangle JOG}{24} = \dfrac{3}{2}$. Then the perimeter of $\triangle JOG$ equals $\dfrac{3}{2} \cdot 24 = 36$ units. ▲

Impact of Similarity on Area

The following example illustrates the connection between the ratio of altitudes and the ratio of two corresponding sides of two similar triangles. Think about this and predict the relationship before continuing your reading.

EXAMPLE 12.29

CONNECTION

COMMUNICATION

PROBLEM SOLVING

REASONING

REPRESENTATION

The length of any side of $\triangle DEF$ is three times the length of the corresponding side of $\triangle ABC$. Verify the length of the altitude of $\triangle DEF$ from vertex E is three times the length of the altitude of $\triangle ABC$ from vertex B.

SOLUTION

First, we draw the two triangles and altitudes. $\overline{BX}$ is the altitude of $\triangle ABC$ from vertex B, and $\overline{EY}$ is the altitude of $\triangle DEF$ from vertex E. Each altitude forms a right angle with the side opposite the vertex. Right angles are congruent, so $\angle BXC \cong \angle EYF$. The length of any side of $\triangle DEF$ is three times the length of the corresponding side of $\triangle ABC$, so $\triangle ABC \sim \triangle DEF$ by the SSS similarity axiom. Then $\angle C \cong \angle F$ because corresponding angles of similar triangles are congruent.

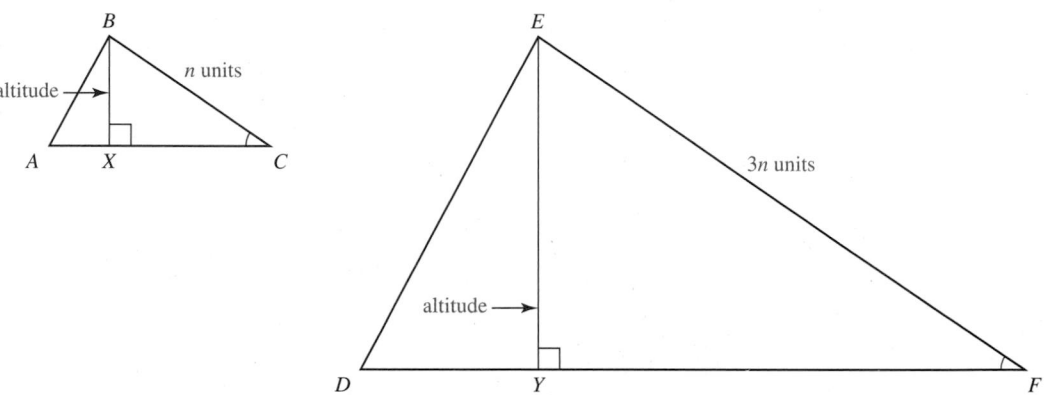

Then $\angle BXC \cong \angle EYF$ and $\angle C \cong \angle F$, which leads to $\triangle BXC \sim \triangle EYF$ by the AA similarity axiom. Then $\frac{EY}{BX} = \frac{YF}{XC} = \frac{EF}{BC}$. The length of any side of $\triangle DEF$ is three times the length of the corresponding side of $\triangle ABC$, so $EF = 3 \cdot BC$. Then $\frac{EF}{BC} = 3$. But $\frac{EF}{BC} = \frac{EY}{BX}$, so $\frac{EY}{BX} = 3$. Then $EY = 3 \cdot BX$. The altitude of $\triangle DEF$ from vertex E is three times the altitude of $\triangle ABC$ from vertex B.

▲

In similar triangles, the ratio of the altitudes equals the scale factor.
The next example illustrates the impact of similarity on area.

EXAMPLE 12.30

CONNECTION

COMMUNICATION

PROBLEM SOLVING

REASONING

REPRESENTATION

The length of any side of $\triangle DEF$ is three times the length of the corresponding side of $\triangle ABC$. Verify that the area of $\triangle DEF$ is nine times the area of $\triangle ABC$.

SOLUTION

The length of any side of $\triangle DEF$ is three times the length of the corresponding side of $\triangle ABC$. Then $\triangle ABC \sim \triangle DEF$ by the SSS similarity axiom. Let b represent the base and h represent the altitude in $\triangle ABC$. Let B represent the base and H represent the altitude in $\triangle DEF$. Then, $B = 3b$ and by Example 12.29, $H = 3h$. The area of $\triangle ABC$ is $\frac{1}{2}bh$, and the area of $\triangle DEF$ is $\frac{1}{2}BH$. Then

$$\text{area of } \triangle DEF = \frac{1}{2}BH$$

$$= \frac{1}{2}(3b)(3h)$$

$$= 9 \cdot \left(\frac{1}{2}bh\right)$$

$$= 9 \cdot \text{area of } \triangle ABC$$

So the area of $\triangle DEF$ is nine times the area of $\triangle ABC$.

▲

Similar Polygons

The following definition defines what it means for two polygons to be similar.

> ### Definition of Similar Polygons
>
> Two polygons are similar if and only if there is a correspondence between the vertices such that all pairs of corresponding angles are congruent and all pairs of corresponding sides have identical ratios.

EXAMPLE 12.31 The diagrams show two rectangles.

CONNECTION

REASONING

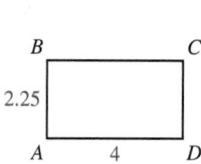
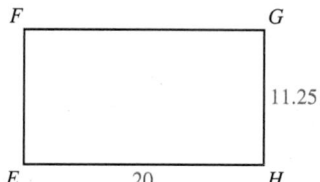

a. Explain why rectangles *ABCD* and *EFGH* are similar.

b. Write a similarity statement.

SOLUTION

a. Each angle in a rectangle is a right angle, and all right angles are congruent angles. Now we check the ratio of corresponding sides:

$$\frac{AB}{EF} = \frac{2.25}{11.25} = 0.2, \frac{BC}{FG} = \frac{4}{20} = 0.2, \frac{CD}{GH} = \frac{2.25}{11.25} = 0.2, \frac{AD}{EH} = \frac{2.25}{11.25} = 0.2$$

So the ratios of corresponding sides are identical. In rectangles *ABCD* and *EFGH,* the corresponding angles are congruent and the ratios of corresponding sides are identical, so the two rectangles are similar.

b. $ABCD \sim EFGH$.

▲

The following example explores the relationship between the perimeters of two similar rectangles.

EXAMPLE 12.32 Rectangles *ABCD* and *EFGH* are similar. The dimensions of *ABCD* are 6 by 15 feet. The perimeter of *EFGH* is 189 feet. Find the dimensions of *EFGH*.

CONNECTION

COMMUNICATION

PROBLEM SOLVING   SOLUTION

REASONING   We draw representations of the rectangles.

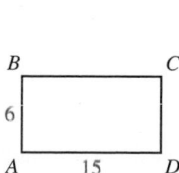
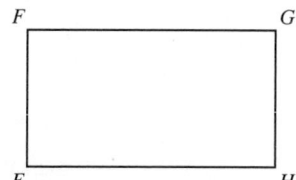

The two rectangles are similar, so $\frac{EF}{6} = \frac{FG}{15} = \frac{GH}{6} = \frac{EH}{15}$. Because the ratios are identical, there is a number k (the scale factor) such that each ratio equals k: $\frac{EF}{6} = k, \frac{FG}{15} = k,$

$\frac{GH}{6} = k$, and $\frac{EH}{15} = k$. Then $EF = 6k$, $FG = 15k$, $GH = 6k$, and $EH = 15k$. The perimeter of $EFGH$ is 189 feet, so

$$189 = EF + FG + GH + EH$$
$$= 6k + 15k + 6k + 15k$$
$$= 42k$$

So the scale factor is $k = 189/42 = 4.5$. $EF = 6 \cdot 4.5 = 27$ feet, and $FG = 15 \cdot 4.5 = 67.5$ feet. $EFGH$ is a 27-by-67.5-foot rectangle.

▲

The previous example illustrates that we could represent the two similar rectangles with a variable.

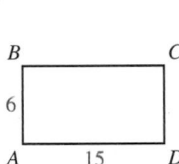
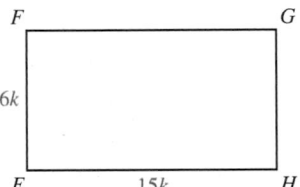

The NCTM's *Principles and Standards for School Mathematics* states that "students need to understand that the perimeters of pairs of similar shapes are proportional to their corresponding side lengths but that the areas are proportional to the squares of the corresponding side lengths" (2000, p. 245).

EXAMPLE 12.33

CONNECTION
PROBLEM SOLVING
REASONING
REPRESENTATION

Rectangles $STUV$ and $WXYZ$ are similar. Suppose $\frac{ST}{WX} = 5$. Fill in the blank and show your work.

a. The perimeter of $STUV$ is _____ times the perimeter of $WXYZ$.

b. The area of $STUV$ is _____ times the area of $WXYZ$.

SOLUTION

$\frac{ST}{WX} = 5$ means $ST = 5 \cdot WX$. Rectangles $STUV$ and $WXYZ$ are similar. Each side of $STUV$ is five times the length of the corresponding side of $WXYZ$. We draw diagrams to represent the situation.

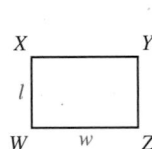
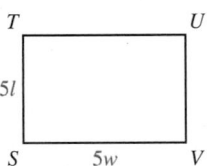

a. The perimeter of $WXYZ$ is $2l + 2w$ units. The perimeter of $STUV$ is $2(5l) + 2(5w) = 5(2l + 2w)$ units. The perimeter of $STUV$ is five times the perimeter of $WXYZ$.

b. The area of $WXYZ$ is lw square units. The area of $STUV$ is $(5l)(5w) = 25(lw)$ square units. The area of $STUV$ is 25 times the area of $WXYZ$.

▲

Students should "understand relationships among the angles, side lengths, perimeters, areas, and volumes of similar objects" (Gr. 6–8, NCTM). In general,

- the ratio of any two corresponding lengths associated with two similar figures equals the scale factor.

- the ratio of the areas of two similar figures equals the square of the scale factor.

- the ratio of the volumes of two similar figures equals the cube of the scale factor.

Here are some examples.

- Suppose each side of polygon A is five times the length of the corresponding side of polygon B. Then the perimeter of polygon A is five times the perimeter of polygon B, and the area of polygon A is 25 times the area of polygon B.

- Suppose each edge of polyhedron A is 5 times the length of the corresponding edge of polyhedron B. Then the surface area of polyhedron A is 25 times the surface area of polyhedron B, and the volume of polyhedron A is 125 times the volume of polyhedron B.

QUESTIONS FOR SECTION 12.3

REPRESENTATION

Refresher: Representations (language, diagrams, tables, symbols, algebra, manipulatives, and contextualized situations) are important because we use them to organize, record, and communicate mathematical ideas and make them more comprehensible.

1. Does the diagram show two similar triangles?

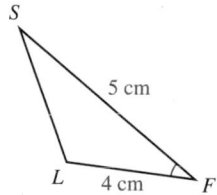

2. Refer to the diagram. Write three proportions.

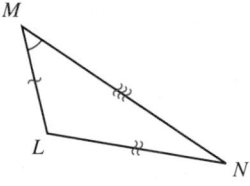

3. The equation represents relationships between two triangles:
$$\frac{WI}{OH} = \frac{FI}{HA} = \frac{FW}{AO}.$$

   a. Draw an appropriate diagram.

   b. Write a similarity statement.

   c. Identify the similarity axiom that justifies the similarity statement.

4. The equations represent relationships between two triangles:
$$\angle A \cong \angle X \text{ and } \frac{GA}{BX} = \frac{MA}{XT}.$$

   a. Draw an appropriate diagram.

   b. Write a similarity statement.

   c. Identify the appropriate similarity axiom that justifies the similarity statement.

5. The equations represent relationships between two triangles: $\angle PQR \cong \angle STU$ and $\angle QPR \cong \angle TSU$.

   a. Draw an appropriate diagram.

   b. Write a similarity statement.

   c. Identify the similarity axiom that justifies the similarity statement.

6. Represent the SAS similarity axiom using a diagram.

7. Draw a triangle that is similar to $\triangle ABC$ with an area larger than $\triangle ABC$.

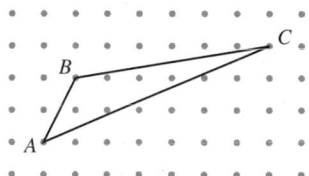

8. Draw a triangle that is similar to $\triangle ABC$ with an area smaller than $\triangle ABC$.

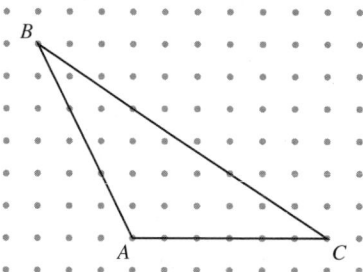

9. The diagram shows $\triangle ABC$.

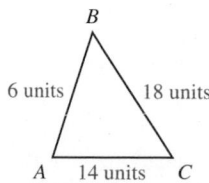

   Which representation indicates $\triangle DEF$ is similar to $\triangle ABC$?

a.

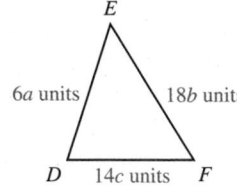

6*a* units   18*b* units

D   14*c* units   F

b.

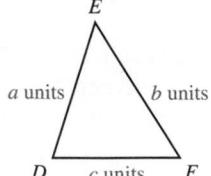

a units   *b* units

D   *c* units   F

c.

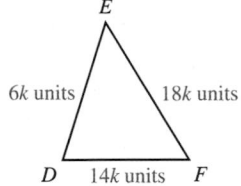

6*k* units   18*k* units

D   14*k* units   F

10. The diagram shows two similar triangles. The variable *k* represents a positive number.

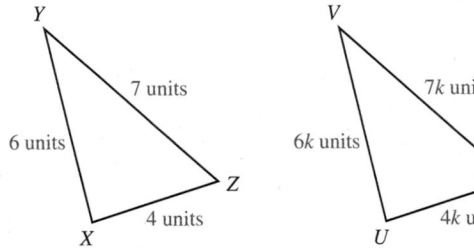

Y   7 units   6 units   4 units   Z   X

V   7*k* units   6*k* units   4*k* units   W   U

a. Write a similarity statement.

b. Justify the similarity statement.

PROBLEM SOLVING

Refresher: Problem solving (reaching a goal that is not immediately attainable) is important because it helps students think more deeply about what they know and deal with unfamiliar situations.

11. △*OLD* and △*NEW* are similar triangles. The perimeter of △*NEW* is 48 units.

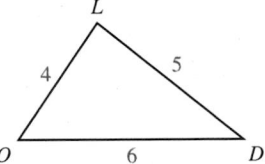

L   4   5   O   6   D

a. Draw a diagram that includes a variable to help represent the lengths of the sides of △*NEW*.

b. Determine the length of each side of △*NEW*.

12. Ernie, who is 6 feet tall, wants to measure the height of a tree. He measures that his shadow is 3.5 feet long and at the same time determines the tree casts a 24-foot-long shadow. Because the Sun is so far away, the Sun's rays reach Ernie and the tree at the same angle.

a. Represent this situation with two right triangles, with appropriate measurements and angle markings, and write an appropriate similarity axiom.

b. What is the height of the tree?

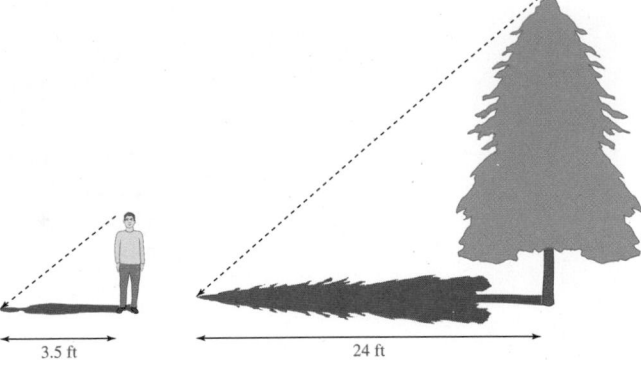

3.5 ft   24 ft

13. Points *A* and *B* are on the edge of a lake. A hiker wants to know the distance from point *A* to point *B*. The hiker determines lengths of segments of triangles in such a way that two similar triangles are created and known distances can be used to determine *AB*. The hiker paces distances as shown in the diagram. Determine *AB* to the nearest tenth.

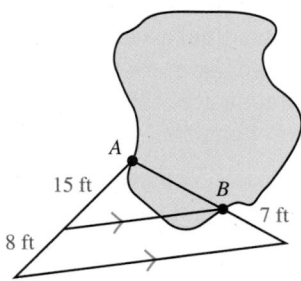

A   15 ft   B   7 ft   8 ft

REASONING AND PROOF

Refresher: Reasoning and proof (thinking and justifying) are important because they help students make sense of mathematics.

14. △*ABC* and △*DEC* are similar triangles, and $\frac{BC}{EC} = 2.8$. Indicate whether the following measurements are possible or not, and explain your answer.

a. *AC* = 4.0 units and *DC* = 11.2 units

b. *AB* = 7.3 units and *DE* = 3.2 units

c. *BC* = 8.2 units and *EC* = 3.8 units

d. *AC* = 9.8 units and *DC* = 3.5 units

15. Do the following.

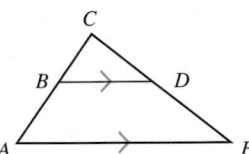

C   B   D   A   E

a. Identify a pair of similar triangles.

b. Justify your answer in part (a).

16. A right triangle has an angle with the measure 18°, and another right triangle has an angle with the measure 72°. Are the two triangles similar? Explain.

17. $\triangle OLD \sim \triangle NEW.$ Find each measure.

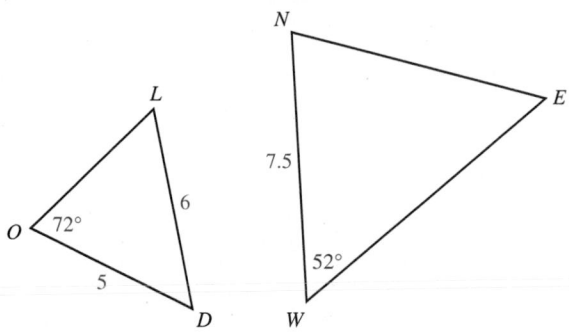

    a. $m\angle L$ **b.** EW

18. $\triangle ABC$ and $\triangle DEF$ are similar triangles. $\triangle ABC$ has a base of b_A units and a height of h_A units. $\triangle DEF$ has a base of b_D units and a height of h_D units. Suppose $\dfrac{AB}{DE} = 5.$

    a. Fill in the blank: The area of $\triangle ABC$ is _____ times the area of $\triangle DEF.$

    b. Justify your answer in part (a).

19. Suppose $\dfrac{AB}{BC} = \dfrac{DE}{EF}.$ Prove $\dfrac{AB}{AC} = \dfrac{DE}{DF}.$

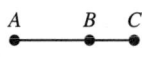

20. The teacher told his class, "The corresponding angles of two polygons are congruent." Then Kelly said, "The two polygons must be similar!" Draw a counterexample to help Kelly see that two polygons with congruent corresponding angles do not need to be similar.

21. The teacher told her class that the corresponding sides of two polygons have the same ratio. Kyle said, "The two polygons must be similar." Draw a counterexample to help Kyle see that two polygons with corresponding sides that have the same ratio do not need to be similar.

CONNECTIONS

Refresher: Connections (linking and applying mathematical ideas) are important because they deepen student understanding and make mathematics more meaningful, flexible, and useful.

22. $\triangle KIT$ and $\triangle WON$ are isosceles triangles with congruent apex angles $\angle I$ and $\angle O.$ Prove $\triangle KIT$ and $\triangle WON$ are similar triangles.

23. $\triangle RUN \sim \triangle HOP.$ Find the values for x and y that make the triangles similar.

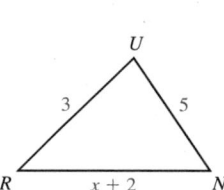

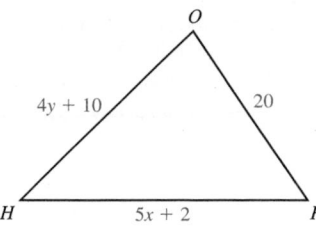

24. Suppose $\triangle ABC \sim \triangle DEC$ and $AB = 14$ units, $BC = 10$ units, and $AC = 8$ units. For each side of $\triangle DEC,$ write an equation involving its length.

25. Refer to the figure.

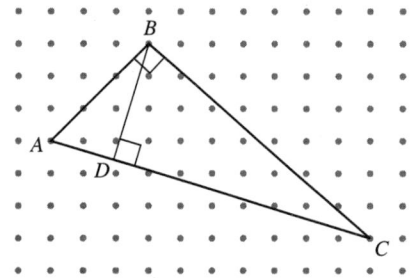

    a. Determine $AC.$ **b.** Determine $AB.$

    c. Justify the statement $\triangle ADB \sim \triangle ABC.$

    d. Verify $AD \approx 1.7$ units, rounded to the nearest tenth.

26. $\triangle ABC$ and $\triangle DEF$ are similar triangles. Suppose $\dfrac{AB}{DE} = 5.$

    a. Draw a diagram that represents the relationship.

    b. What is the ratio of the perimeter P_A of $\triangle ABC$ to the perimeter P_D of $\triangle DEF?$ (That is, $\dfrac{P_A}{P_D} =$ ___.) Show your work.

27. Rectangle $ABCD$ has a length of $BC = 3$ units and a width of $AB = 4$ units. Rectangle $EFGH$ has a length of $FG = 9$ units and a width of $EF = 12$ units.

    a. Prove the rectangles are similar.

    b. Using a straightedge, draw both rectangles on the given dot grid. For each rectangle, draw the longer side along the horizontal axis. Place the lower left corner of each rectangle where the axes meet. Then draw a diagonal for each rectangle, from the lower left corner to the upper right corner. Describe what you notice about the diagonals.

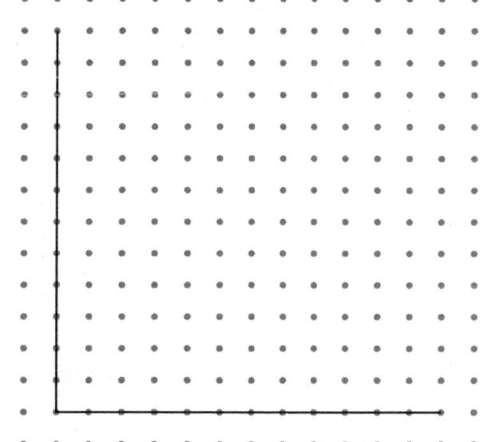

28. Rectangle *ABCD* has a length of *AB* = 3 units and a width of *BC* = 4 units. Rectangle *EFGH* has a length of *EF* = 7 units and a width of *FG* = 8 units.

a. Prove the rectangles are not similar.

b. Using a straightedge, draw both rectangles on the given dot grid. For each rectangle, draw the longer side along the horizontal axis. Place the lower left corner of each rectangle where the axes meet. Then draw a diagonal for each rectangle, from the lower left corner to the upper right corner. Describe what you notice about the diagonals.

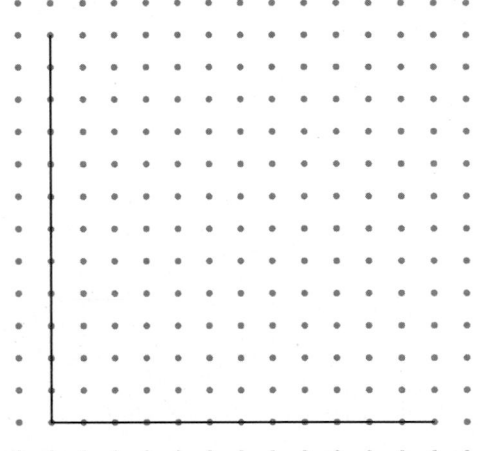

COMMUNICATION

Refresher: Communication (written and verbal explanations using representations and proper mathematical vocabulary) is important because it helps students refine and strengthen their understanding.

29. Two triangles are similar. What is the relationship between their corresponding sides?

30. Two triangles are similar. What is the relationship between their corresponding angles?

31. Mitchell claims that two right triangles are similar if each triangle has an acute angle with the same measure. Explain why this claim is true.

32. Discuss how you can use parallel lines to draw two similar triangles. Draw a diagram to support your answer. Be sure to include appropriate markings on the diagram.

33. Explain how you can prove two triangles are similar without measuring any angles.

34. Explain how you can prove two triangles are similar without measuring any sides.

More practice with the ideas of the section

35. Fill in the blank. Choose one of the following words, phrases, or symbols: ≅, ~, ≈, *14, 49, angles, congruence, congruent, different, direct, identical, indirect, ratio, proportional reasoning, shape, seven, sides,* or *similarity.*

a. Similar triangles have _____ angles.

b. The ratios of corresponding sides of similar triangles are _____.

c. If △*ABC* is similar to △*DEC* and the length of each side of △*ABC* is seven times the length of each corresponding side of △*DEC*, then the perimeter of △*ABC* is _____ times the perimeter of △*DEC*.

d. If △*ABC* is similar to △*DEC* and the length of each side of △*ABC* is seven times the length of each corresponding side of △*DEC*, then the area of △*ABC* is _____ times the area of △*DEC*.

e. _____ is a relationship between two geometric figures that have the same shape and possibly different sizes.

f. We use the symbol _____ to indicate similarity.

g. _____ measurement involves measuring a distance, such as the height of a tree, using simpler and accessible measurements and similarity axioms.

h. In this section, you learned how to calculate measurements of lengths of sides of two similar triangles using _____.

36. $\overline{EP}$ is parallel to $\overline{XZ}$.

a. Identify two similar triangles.

b. Explain why they are similar.

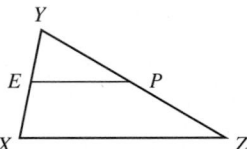

37. Write a similarity statement for two triangles that satisfy the compound equation $\dfrac{AT}{NH} = \dfrac{TP}{EN} = \dfrac{PA}{HE}$.

38. Represent the relationships with a diagram. ∠*A* ≅ ∠*H* and $\dfrac{HL}{AB} = \dfrac{HM}{AC}$.

39. Explain how you know the two given triangles are congruent, and write a similarity statement.

a.

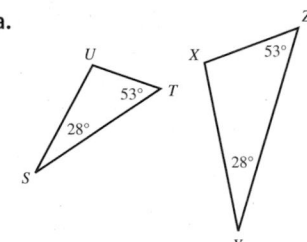

b.

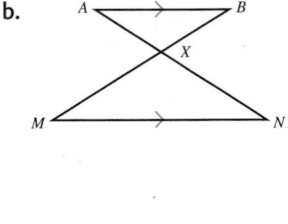

c.

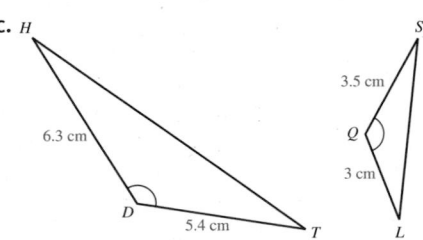

40. Suppose $\triangle ABC \sim \triangle DEC$. Prove $\overline{AB} \parallel \overline{DE}$.

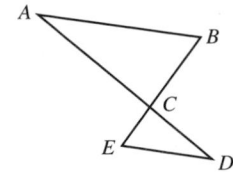

41. Do the following.

   a. List two triangles that are similar.

   b. Justify your answer in part (a).

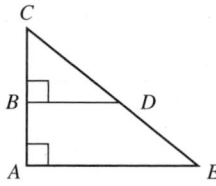

42. $\triangle OLD$ and $\triangle NEW$ are similar triangles. The area of $\triangle NEW$ is 720 square units. Determine the area of $\triangle OLD$.

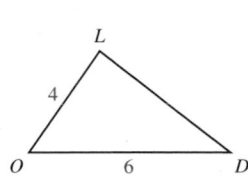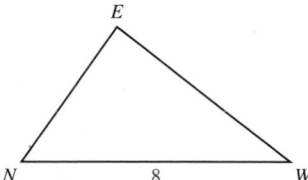

43. Mr. Smith draws two triangles on the board. His students agree that the two triangles are similar. Then he asks his students to justify the similarity. After a few minutes of thinking, Lenna exclaims, "The two triangles are similar by the SAS similarity axiom!" Explain why Lenna is correct.

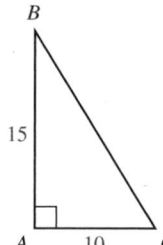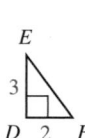

44. The diagram shows two triangles. Prove the two triangles are similar.

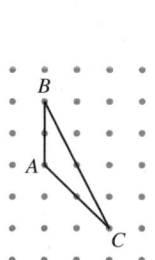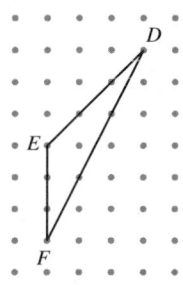

45. Prove $\triangle TUY \sim \triangle VXZ$.

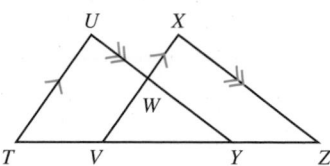

46. The two triangles shown are similar.

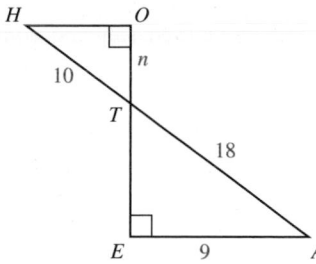

   a. Write a similarity statement.   **b.** Find n.

47. The diagram shows $\triangle XYZ$. $\triangle UVW$ and $\triangle XYZ$ are similar triangles. The perimeter of $\triangle UVW$ is 255 units. Determine the lengths of the sides of $\triangle UVW$.

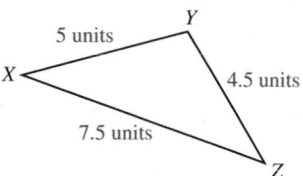

48. The two triangles shown are similar.

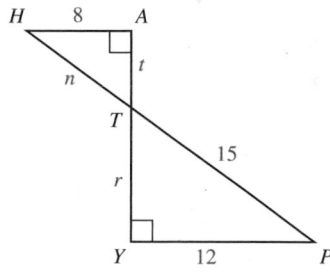

   a. Write a similarity statement.

   b. Find the missing lengths.

49. Mrs. Dugger tells her class, "Each length of each side of rectangle A is five times the length of the corresponding side of rectangle B." She asks her students to tell what else they know about the rectangles. Luis shouts, "The rectangles are similar!" Peter exclaims, "The area of the larger rectangle is 25 times the area of the smaller rectangle."

   a. Prove Luis is correct.   **b.** Prove Peter is correct.

50. The length of each side of rectangle $EFGH$ is three times the length of the corresponding side of rectangle $ABCD$. Prove the length of diagonal $\overline{EG}$ is three times the length of diagonal $\overline{AC}$.

51. *ABCD* and *EFGH* are similar rectangles. The perimeter of *ABCD* is 340 units. Determine the area of *ABCD,* rounded to the nearest whole number.

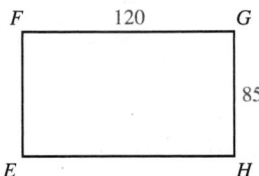

52. Suppose *ABCD* and *EFGH* are similar quadrilaterals and $\frac{AB}{EF} = 8$. What is the ratio of the perimeter P_A of quadrilateral *ABCD* to the perimeter P_E of quadrilateral *EFGH*? (That is, $\frac{P_A}{P_E} = \underline{\quad}$.) Show your work.

53. Are the rectangles similar?

   a. Rectangle A has a length of 4 cm and a width of 3 cm. Rectangle B has a length of 8 cm and a width of 12 cm.

   b. Rectangle A has a length of 4 cm and a width of 3 cm. Rectangle B has a length of 4 in and a width of 3 in.

   c. Rectangle A has a length of 4 cm and a width of 3 cm. Rectangle B has a length of 8 cm and a width of 6 cm.

   d. Rectangle A has a length of *l* units and a width of *w* units. Rectangle B has a length of 2*l* units and a width of 2*w* units.

54. Suppose *ABCDE* and *FGHIJ* are similar pentagons and *AB/FG* = 4.5. Suppose the perimeter of *FGHIJ* is 20 cm. What is the perimeter of *ABCDE*?

55. Suppose *ABCDE* and *FGHIJ* are similar pentagons and *BC/GH* = 6. Suppose the area of *ABCDE* is 180 cm². What is the area of *FGHIJ*?

56. Suppose $\triangle ABC \sim \triangle DEF$ and $\triangle DEF \sim \triangle GHI$. Prove $\triangle ABC \sim \triangle GHI$.

57. Suppose $\triangle SPT \sim \triangle SAK$. Prove $\frac{SP}{PT} = \frac{SA}{AK}$.

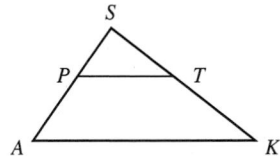

58. $\triangle DOG$ and $\triangle RUN$ are similar triangles. Determine the perimeter of each triangle.

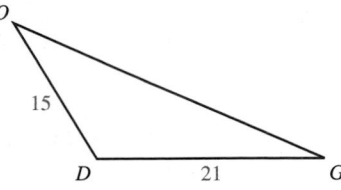

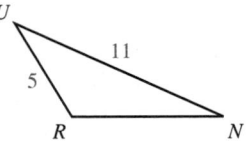

59. Determine *x*.

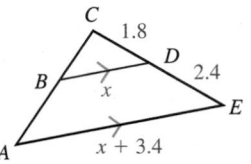

60. Points *C* and *D* are on the edge of a lake, as shown in the diagram. A hiker wants to determine the distance between *C* and *D* using similar triangles and measurable distances to determine *CD*.

   a. Draw possible similar triangles that would help the hiker indirectly measure *CD*.

   b. Set up a proportion that follows from the diagram that could be used to determine *CD*.

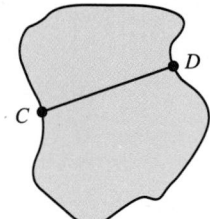

CHAPTER 12 REVIEW

CHAPTER 12 Organizer

Section	What You Should Learn	Review Problems
12.1	**1.** Identify corresponding parts, included sides, and included angles of congruent figures.	1–5
	2. Apply triangle congruence axioms and properties of triangles to justify statements.	6–15
12.2	**1.** Be familiar with vocabulary and ideas of construction.	16
	2. Describe and justify constructions.	17–26
	3. Given that the known Fermat primes are 3, 5, 17, 257, and 65,537, determine whether or not you can use Euclidean tools to construct a regular polygon with a given number of sides.	27
12.3	**1.** Identify similar triangles and write a similarity statement.	28–32
	2. Apply triangle similarity axioms.	33–36
	3. Find missing angle measures or lengths of similar polygons.	37–40
	4. Relate the perimeters and areas of similar polygons.	41–44
	5. Use similarity for indirect measurements.	45–46
	6. Sketch a triangle that is similar to a given triangle.	47

Key Terms and Concepts

axiom 704	purpose of proof 711	similarity 739
proof 704	construction 723	definition of similar triangles 740
congruent line segments 705	compass 723	similar 741
congruent angles 705	center point 723	SSS similarity axiom 743
definition of congruent triangles 705	pencil point 723	AA similarity axiom 743
CPCTC 705	radius 723	SAS similarity axiom 743
SSS congruence axiom 707	Euclidean tools 724	how to sketch similar triangles 746
ASA congruence axiom 708	angle bisector 726	indirect measurement 747
SAS congruence axiom 709	perpendicular bisector 728	impact of similarity on perimeter 748
included angle 709	Fermat number 733	impact of similarity on area 749
AAS congruence axiom 709	Fermat prime number 733	

Review Questions

1. The two triangles shown are congruent. Fill in the blanks.

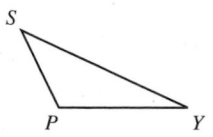

a. $\triangle WHO \cong$ ___   **b.** $\angle Y \cong$ ___   **c.** $PS =$ ___

2. The two quadrilaterals shown are congruent. Fill in the blanks.

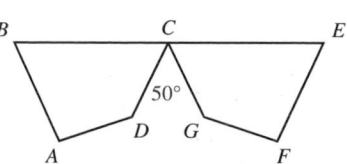

a. $\angle BAD \cong$ ___   **b.** $AB =$ ___   **c.** $m\angle BCD =$ ___

3. $\overline{KL}$ and $\overline{LW}$ are two line segments in a triangle. Identify the included angle for these two line segments.

   a. Name the angle using one letter.

   b. Name the angle using three letters.

4. A student writes $\triangle STU \cong \triangle VWX$.

   a. Explain why $\angle T \cong \angle W$.   **b.** Explain why $\overline{ST} \cong \overline{VW}$.

5. A triangle has vertices X, Y, and Z. Identify the included side for $\angle X$ and $\angle Z$.

6. Mrs. Smith drew a circle with a center O and $\overline{CD}$. The diameter $\overline{AB}$ is perpendicular to $\overline{CD}$. Then she asked her class, "What can you say about $\angle OCE$ and $\angle ODE$?" After a few minutes, Sam proclaimed, "They are congruent angles!" Prove Sam is correct.

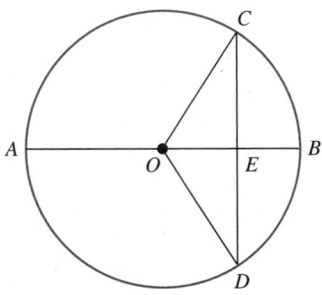

7. The diagram shows a circle with the center A. Find the measure of each angle.

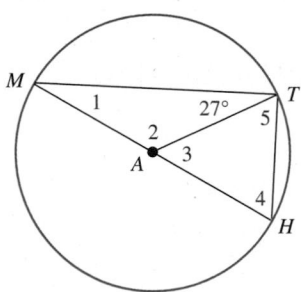

8. $ABCD$ is a parallelogram with area 360 square units. $\overline{BE}$ is the altitude from vertex B to $\overline{AD}$. Find ED.

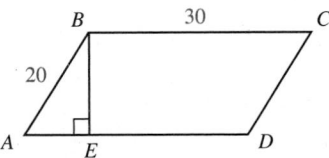

9. A student is writing a proof to show that two triangles are congruent using the SAS congruence axiom. A student writes the following two congruence statements: $\angle HDK \cong \angle EYL$ and $\overline{DH} \cong \overline{YE}$. What additional congruence statement does the student need to apply the SAS congruence axiom?

10. What is inaccurate about this diagram? Justify your answer.

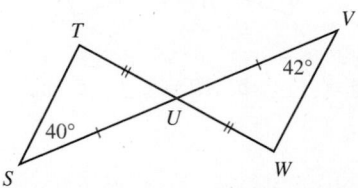

11. Determine whether the given information is enough to conclude the two triangles are congruent. Explain your answer.

   a.

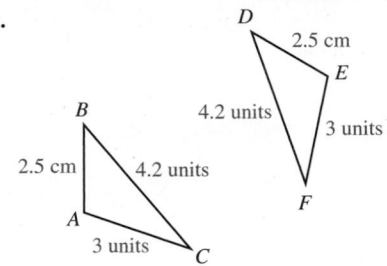

   b.

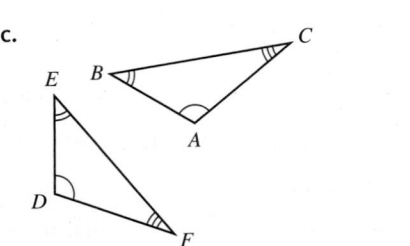

   c.

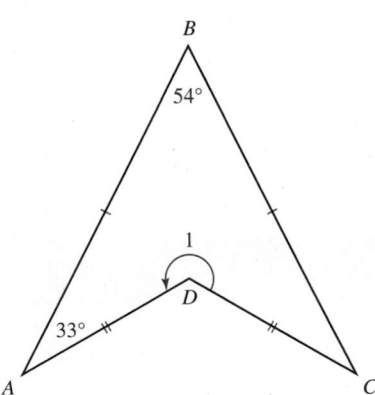

12. Let E be the intersection of the diagonals of parallelogram $ABCD$.

   a. Prove $\triangle BCE \sim \triangle DAE$.

   b. Prove E is the midpoint of diagonal $\overline{BD}$.

   c. Prove E is the midpoint of diagonal $\overline{AC}$.

13. The diagram shows a concave quadrilateral $ABCD$ with properties and angles marked. Find the measure of $\angle 1$.

14. $\triangle ABC$ is an equilateral triangle. Let X be the midpoint of $\overline{AB}$, Y be the midpoint of $\overline{BC}$, and Z be the midpoint of $\overline{AC}$.

   a. Draw a diagram to represent the situation.

   b. Use congruence axioms to prove $\triangle XYZ$ is an equilateral triangle.

15. *ABCD* is a rhombus. We know the diagonals bisect the interior angles and opposite sides are parallel. Based on this information, we can represent a rhombus with the following diagram.

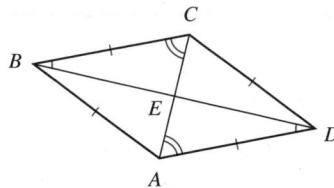

a. Prove △*BCE* ≅ △*DAE*. **b.** Prove △*BCE* ≅ △*DCE*.

c. Use part (b) to prove the diagonals of a rhombus are perpendicular.

16. Fill in the blanks with the most appropriate word: *center, compass, construction, equidistant, pencil, radius,* or *straightedge.*

a. A(n) _____ is a geometric drawing based only on a compass and straightedge.

b. We use a(n) _____ to draw a line, such as a line containing the two given points *A* and *B*.

c. A(n) _____ provides a functional meaning of a circle as a set of points that are equidistant from a given point.

d. Use a compass to create points that are _____ from a fixed point.

e. A compass has two legs and two points. The _____ point determines the center of the circle (or arc).

f. A compass has two legs and two points. The _____ point draws the circle (or arc) when we swing the compass.

g. The _____ is the distance between the center point and the pencil point on the compass.

17. Construct rhombus *ABCD* with sides of the length *a*.

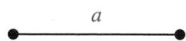

18. Construct an equilateral triangle △*ABC* with sides of the length *a*.

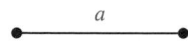

19. Construct an isosceles triangle with legs that have a length of *a* units and a base of *b* units.

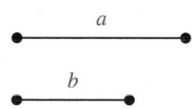

20. Construct a right triangle with legs of length *a* and *b* units.

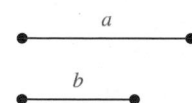

21. Do the following.

a. Construct a triangle with legs of length *a* and *b* units.

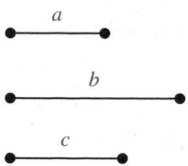

b. Justify your construction.

22. Do the following.

a. Construct the center *W* of a circle that contains the three given points *A, B,* and *C*.

b. Justify your construction.

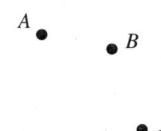

23. Construct the apothem, a line segment that extends from the center of the polygon to the midpoint of a side, of the regular hexagon.

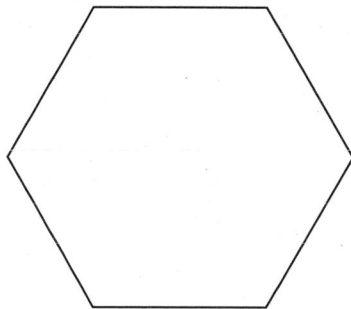

24. Construct a line *m* containing *P* and parallel to *l*.

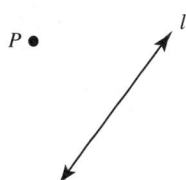

25. Do the following.

a. Determine the length of the hypotenuse of a right triangle with legs of the lengths 1 and 2 units.

b. Construct a circle with a radius of $\sqrt{5}$ units.

1 unit

26. Describe how you can construct a triangle that has an area that is twice the area of △*ABC*.

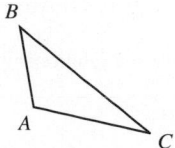

27. Can you use a compass and straightedge to construct a regular polygon with *n* sides?

   a. $n = 2^3 \cdot 3 \cdot 5$ **b.** $n = 2^3 \cdot 3^4 \cdot 5$ **c.** $n = 2^4 \cdot 5 \cdot 17$

   d. $n = 90$ **e.** $n = 16$ **f.** $n = 37$ **g.** $n = 27$

   h. $n = 1050$

28. Are the triangles similar? Explain your answer, and write a similarity statement if possible.

   a.

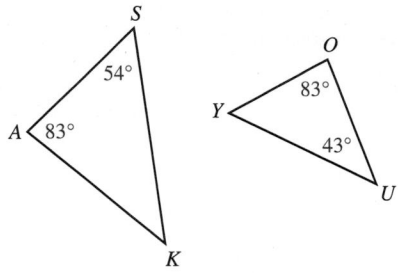

   b.

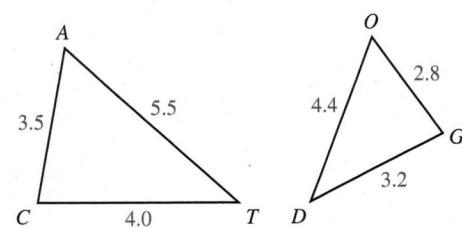

   c.

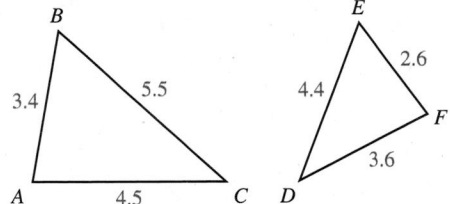

29. Do the following.

   a. Label all corresponding parts for the two similar triangles.

   b. Write a similarity statement for the triangles.

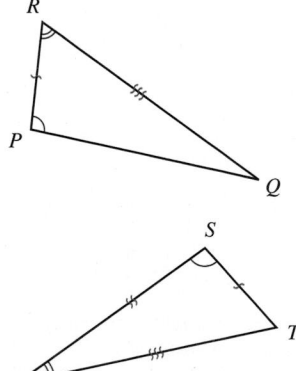

30. The equation represents a relationship between two triangles:

$$\frac{TN}{OP} = \frac{TE}{OH} = \frac{EN}{PH}.$$

   a. Draw an appropriate diagram.

   b. Write a similarity statement.

   c. Identify the similarity axiom that justifies the similarity statement.

31. The equations represent relationships between two triangles:

$$\angle T \cong \angle B \text{ and } \frac{BU}{AT} = \frac{SB}{CT}.$$

   a. Draw an appropriate diagram.

   b. Write a similarity statement.

   c. Identify the similarity axiom that justifies the similarity statement.

32. The equations represent relationships between two triangles: $\angle MNO \cong \angle DFE$ and $\angle NMO \cong \angle EDF.$

   a. Draw an appropriate diagram.

   b. Write a similarity statement.

   c. Identify the similarity axiom that justifies the similarity statement.

33. A right triangle has an angle with the measure 20°, and another right triangle has an angle with the measure 68°. Are the two triangles similar? Explain.

34. $\triangle ABC$ and $\triangle DEF$ are isosceles triangles. One of the angles of $\triangle ABC$ has the measure 47°, and one of the angles of $\triangle DEF$ has the measure 130°. Could $\triangle ABC$ and $\triangle DEF$ be similar triangles? Explain.

35. $\triangle XYZ$ and $\triangle MNO$ are similar triangles, and $\frac{XZ}{MO} = 2.8$.

   Which of the following measurements are possible? Explain your answer.

   a. $XY = 4.2$ units and $MN = 1.5$ units

   b. $YZ = 6.5$ units and $NO = 2.6$ units

36. The length of each side of rectangle $ABCD$ is five times the length of the corresponding side of rectangle $WXYZ$. Prove the length of diagonal $\overline{AC}$ is five times the length of diagonal $\overline{WY}$.

37. Do the following.

   a. Explain why the two triangles shown are similar.

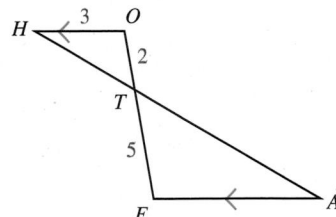

   b. Write a similarity statement.   **c.** Find *EA*.

38. $\triangle MET \sim \triangle OPH$. Find each measure.

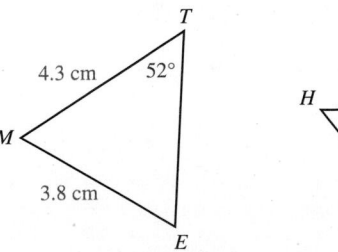

   a. $m\angle M$ **b.** OP

39. Find *BC*.

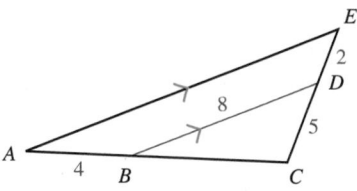

40. Let △*ABC* be any triangle. Suppose *D* is the midpoint of $\overline{AB}$ and *E* is the midpoint of $\overline{AC}$.

   a. Prove △*BAC* ~ △*DAE*.

   b. Prove $\overline{DE}$ is parallel to $\overline{BC}$.

41. If the ratio of a side of figure A to the corresponding side of figure B is *k*, then the ratio of the perimeter of figure A to the perimeter of figure B is _____ and the ratio of the area of figure A to the area of figure B is _____.

42. We are given that △*OLD* ~ △*NEW* and the perimeter of △*NEW* is 72 units.

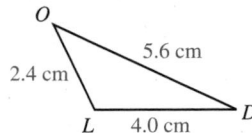

   a. Draw a diagram that includes a variable to represent the lengths of the sides of △*NEW*.

   b. Determine the length of each side of △*NEW*.

43. △*ABC* ~ △*XYZ*, and the perimeter of △*XYZ* is 45 cm. Determine the perimeter of △*ABC*.

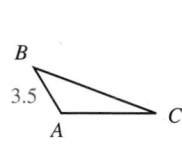 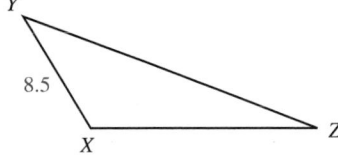

44. △*ABC* ~ △*XYZ*. Determine the area of △*ABC*.

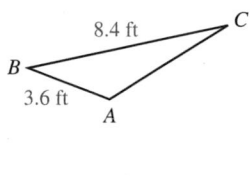

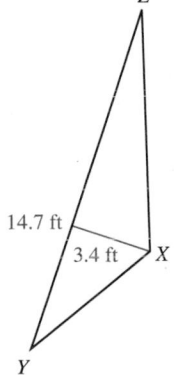

45. Points *A* and *B* are on the edge of a lake. A hiker wants to know the distance from point *A* to point *B*. The hiker determines lengths of segments of triangles in such a way that two similar triangles are created and known distances can be used to determine *AB*. The hiker paces distances as shown in the diagram. Determine *AB* to the nearest foot.

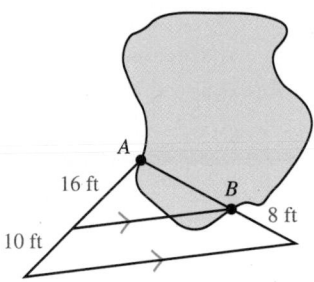

46. Michael is 6 feet tall and is standing next to a flag pole. He casts a shadow that is 8 feet long, while the flag pole casts a shadow that is 28 feet long. How tall is the flag pole?

47. Do the following.

   a. Locate a point *E* such that △*ABC* ~ △*DEC*.

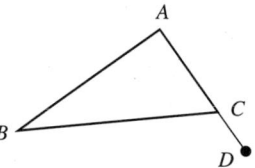

   b. Locate a point *E* such that △*ABC* ~ △*AED*.

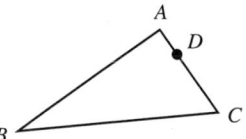

   c. Locate a point *E* such that △*ABC* ~ △*AED*.

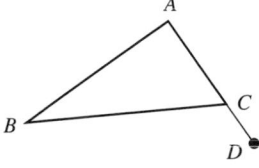

Chapter 12 Test

1. *Apply triangle congruence axioms and properties of triangles to justify statements.* A circle has the center D. Suppose $\overline{AB}$ is a diameter of the circle that is perpendicular to $\overline{CE}$, where C and E lie on the circle.

a. Draw a diagram to represent the situation.

b. Prove the diameter bisects $\overline{CE}$.

2. *Apply triangle congruence axioms and properties of triangles to justify statements.* $\triangle PQR$ is an isosceles triangle with the apex Q and a base of $\overline{PR}$. S and T are points on $\overline{PR}$ such that $\angle PQS \cong \angle RQT$ as shown. Prove $\overline{QS} \cong \overline{QT}$.

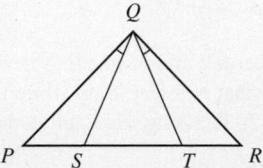

3. *Apply triangle congruence axioms and properties of triangles to justify statements.* Suppose $ABCD$ is a rhombus. Prove diagonal $\overline{AC}$ bisects $\angle A$ and $\angle C$.

4. *Apply triangle congruence axioms and properties of triangles to justify statements.* The diagram shows a circle with the center E. Find the measure of each angle.

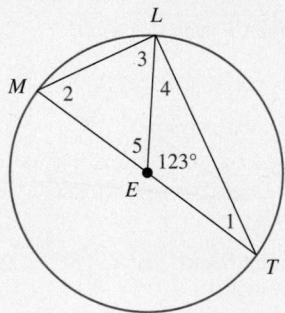

5. *Apply triangle congruence axioms and properties of triangles to justify statements.* The diagram shows a concave quadrilateral $ABCD$, with the properties and angles marked as shown.

a. Explain why m$\angle BCD = 30°$. **b.** Find m$\angle 1$.

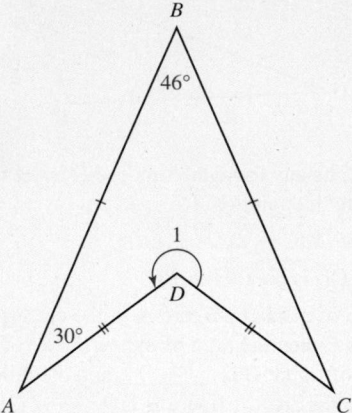

6. *Apply triangle congruence axioms and properties of triangles to justify statements.* $KITE$ is a convex quadrilateral with $KI = IT$ and $KE = TE$. Prove $\angle K \cong \angle T$.

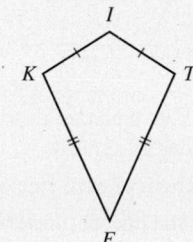

7. *Describe, apply, and justify constructions.*

a. Use construction techniques to locate a point M such that $\triangle PQR \sim \triangle PMT$.

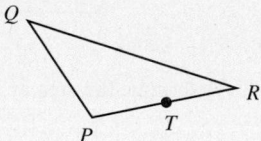

b. Justify the similarity statement in part (a).

8. *Describe, apply, and justify constructions.* Construct the point H such that $AH = BH = CH$.

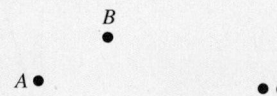

9. *Describe, apply, and justify constructions.* Do the following.

   a. Construct a triangle with sides of the lengths *a*, *b*, and *c* units.

   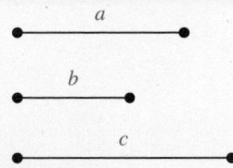

   b. Justify your construction.

10. *Describe, apply, and justify constructions.* You are given an angle with the measure 24°. Describe how you can construct an angle with the measure 33°.

    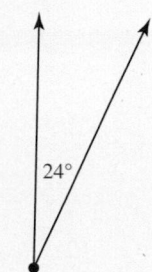

11. *Describe, apply, and justify constructions.* Construct an obtuse triangle that has an area of 6 square units.

12. *Given that the known Fermat primes are 3, 5, 17, 257, and 65,537, determine whether or not you can use Euclidean tools to construct a regular polygon with a given number of sides. Can you use a compass and straightedge to construct a regular polygon with n sides?*

    a. $n = 2^5 \cdot 3 \cdot 17$ **b.** $n = 2^3 \cdot 3 \cdot 5^4$ **c.** $n = 2^{10} \cdot 5 \cdot 17$

    d. $n = 255$ **e.** $n = 54$ **f.** $n = 22{,}282{,}580$

13. *Identify similar triangles, and write a similarity statement.* Suppose two scalene triangles are similar. Then the longest sides of the two triangles must be corresponding parts. Explain why.

14. *Find missing angle measures or lengths of similar polygons.* The two triangles are similar. Find each measure.

    a. m∠*A*   **b.** *AC*

    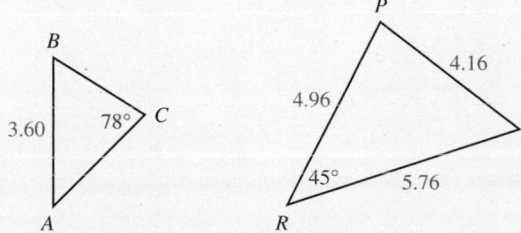

15. *Find missing angle measures or lengths of similar polygons.* Two similar triangles are shown.

    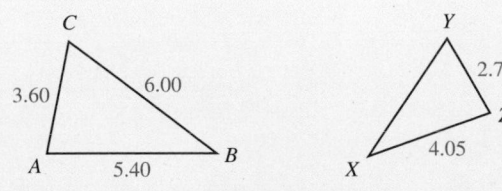

a. Determine the scale factor.

b. Write a similarity statement.   **c.** Determine *XY*.

16. *Find missing angle measures or lengths of similar polygons.* The two triangles shown are similar.

    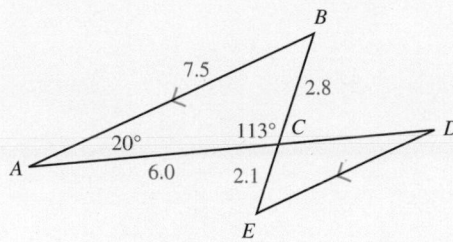

    a. Write a similarity statement.   **b.** Find *CD*.

17. *Relate the perimeters and areas of similar polygons.* Rectangles *STUV* and *WXYZ* are similar. Suppose $\dfrac{ST}{WX} = 12$. Fill in the blank.

    a. The perimeter of *STUV* is _____ times the perimeter of *WXYZ*.

    b. The area of *STUV* is _____ times the area of *WXYZ*.

18. *Relate the perimeters and areas of similar polygons.* Suppose △*HEN* ~ △*CUB*, the perimeter of △*CUB* is 72 cm, and $\dfrac{CB}{HN} = 12$. Find the perimeter of △*HEN*.

19. *Relate the perimeters and areas of similar polygons.* Suppose △*OLD* ~ △*NEW*, the area of △*NEW* is 1008 square units, and $\dfrac{OL}{NE} = 6$. Find the area of △*OLD*.

20. *Use similarity for indirect measurements.* The engineers of a town want to build a bridge from point *A* to point *B*. They begin at point *A* and walk 42 m to point *C*. Then they continue walking another 18 m to point *D*. Then they turn at a right angle until points *B* and *C* are in their line of sight at point *E*, which is 14 m from point *D*. How long is the bridge? Explain your answer.

    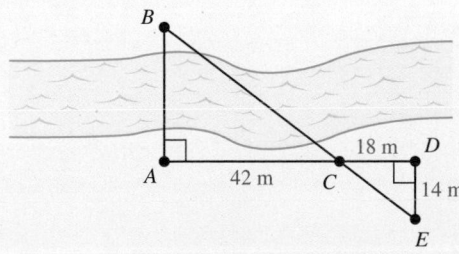

21. *Use similarity for indirect measurements.* A student is 5 feet tall and casts a shadow that is 8 feet long. At the same time, a flag pole casts a shadow that is 36 feet long.

    a. Draw a diagram to represent the situation.

    b. What axiom allows you to conclude the two triangles are similar?

    c. Find the height of the flag pole.

13

Coordinate Geometry and Plane Transformations

Where Are We Going?

In **Section 13.1,** we focus on connections between algebraic and graphical representation of lines. In **Section 13.2,** we discuss the distance formula, equation of a circle, and midpoint formula. We show how to use coordinate geometry to examine properties of triangles and quadrilaterals. In **Section 13.3,** we discuss transformations of the plane such as translations, rotations, reflections, and size transformations. We also include symmetries (line, rotational, and point) and tessellations.

What Is the First Use of a Coordinate System?

Cartography is the art and science of making maps. The ancient Greek philosopher and mathematician Eratosthenes (about 275–195 BCE) invented the first coordinate system, using it to locate positions on maps. Mapmakers refined that coordinate system from the 1500s to the 1800s, leading to the present system.

How Is a Location Determined on a Map?

The map system begins with two imaginary circles, called the equator and prime meridian, as frames of reference or axes, as shown in Figure 1. The equator is equidistant from the North Pole and the South Pole, while the prime meridian goes

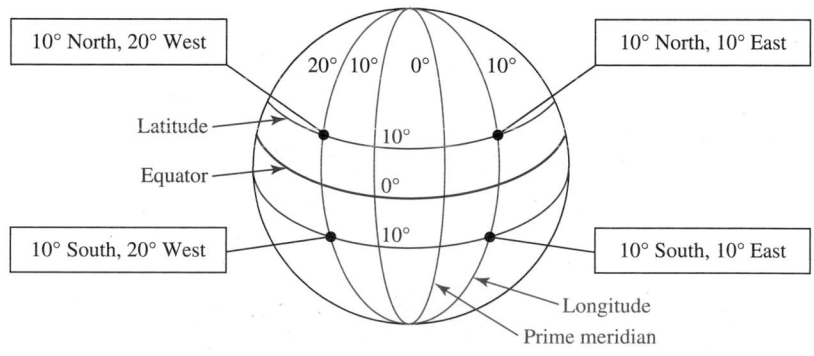

FIGURE 1

Latitudes tell you distances north or south from the equator. Longitudes tell you distances west or east of the prime meridian.

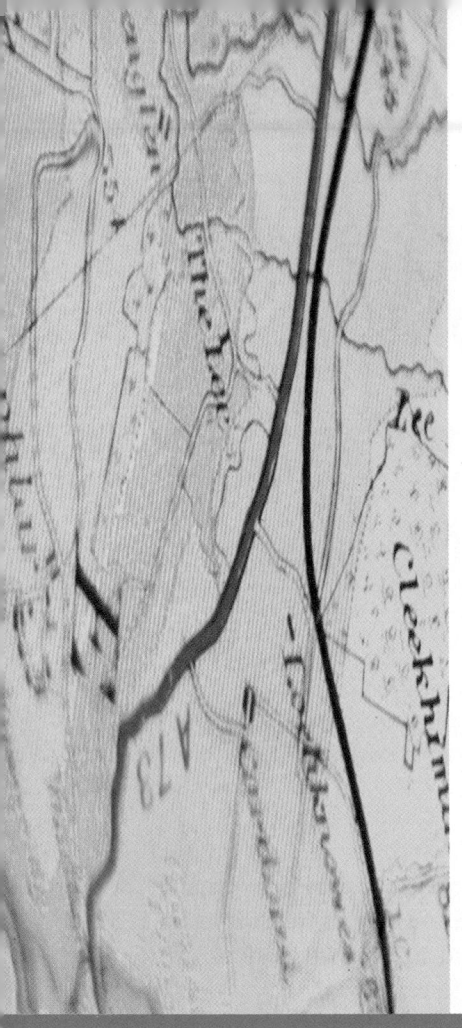

through the North Pole, South Pole, and Greenwich, England. A **parallel** is a circle on a map that is parallel to the equator. Meridians are circles on a map that pass through the poles. Every position on the map depends on an ordered pair of numbers, which is the intersection of a parallel and a meridian. The latitude is the first number of the ordered pair (e.g., 48° N or 34° S) and tells you how far north or south you are from the equator, measured along the prime meridian. Latitudes vary from 0° to 90°. The longitude is the second number of the ordered pair (e.g., 11° E or 58° W) and tells you how far east or west you are from the prime meridian, measured along the equator. Longitudes vary from 0° to 180°.

The coordinates of the Statue of Liberty are (to the nearest degree) 41° N, 74° W (read as "41 degrees north, 74 degrees west"). This means it is 41 degrees north of the equator and 74 degrees west of the prime meridian.

The ordered pair 41° N, 74° W for the Statue of Liberty may also be written 41°, −74°. Positive values of latitude indicate north, and negative values of latitude indicate south; positive values of longitude indicate east, and negative values of longitude indicate west. With this representation, the latitude can vary from −90° to 90° and the longitude can vary from −180° to 180°. You can go to the website www.itouchmap.com/latlong.html and enter your address to find its representation as latitude and longitude coordinates. A global positioning system (GPS) uses a third number called altitude, which indicates elevation above or below sea level.

Coordinate geometry provides a link between geometric and algebraic representations in geometry. This chapter will be easier to follow if you have pencil, blank paper, graph paper, straightedge, protractor, and compass ready and if you follow the proofs and steps discussed.

| SECTION 13.1 | # Representations of Lines |

What Is a Coordinate System?

A coordinate system is a tool used to locate positions. By the middle 1600s, mathematicians—namely, René Descartes, Pierre de Fermat, Isaac Newton, and Gottfried Leibniz—provided the foundation for displaying geometric objects using a coordinate system and thus created a new branch of mathematics called **coordinate geometry,** which merges the fields of algebra and geometry. It provides a way to visualize equations and represent geometric figures. For example, Figure 2 shows how we could represent the point A on line l (as explained in Chapter 10). Figure 3 shows how the same point and line could appear using coordinate geometry.

REPRESENTATION

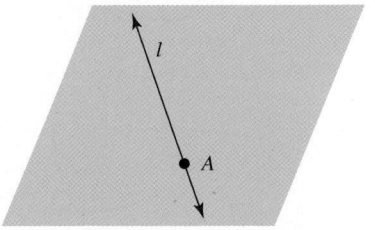

FIGURE 2
Point A on line l in the plane.

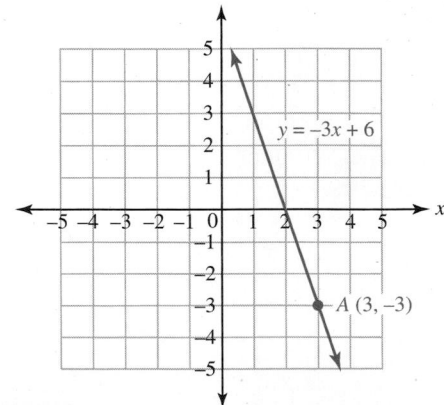

FIGURE 3
Point A on a line in the coordinate plane.

A **coordinate plane** (also known as the **Cartesian plane**) is a plane that contains two perpendicular number lines. The horizontal number line is called the **x-axis,** and the vertical number line is called the **y-axis.** Their intersection is called the **origin.** The axes serve as a reference for how far horizontally and how far vertically you are from the origin. The coordinate plane lets us prescribe the *location* of a point using two numbers called an **ordered pair.** Each ordered pair has the form (a, b). The first number a, commonly called the x-coordinate, tells you how far to move left or right from the vertical axis, and the second number b, commonly called the y-coordinate, tells how far to move above or below the horizontal axis. The ordered pair $(0, 0)$ is the location of the origin.

Three Types of Lines

CONNECTION

REPRESENTATION

There are three types of lines in the coordinate plane: vertical, horizontal, and oblique. We represent the lines using tables, graphs, and algebra. Students should "explore relationships between symbolic expressions and graphs of lines, paying particular attention to the meaning of intercept and slope" (NCTM, Gr. 6–8) (© NCTM Standards 2011 by National Council of Teachers of Mathematics). In the xy-plane, we often interchange the terms *ordered pair* and *point*.

Two points determine a unique line. If two different points satisfying the equation of the line have been determined, then you can use a straightedge to draw a line through the two points, resulting in the graph of the equation.

Vertical Line

CONNECTION

REPRESENTATION

Table 13.1 shows a few solutions (x, y) to the equation $x = 3$. If $x = 3$, then y can be any number.

TABLE 13.1   **Some Solutions to the Equation $x = 3$**

x	3	3	3	3
y	-1	0	1	2

The graph of $x = 3$, shown in Figure 4, is the set of all points (x, y) that satisfy the equation $x = 3$. We "see" the x-coordinate of any point on the vertical line is 3 and the x-intercept is $(3, 0)$. A **vertical line** has an equation of the form $x = a$ for some number a.

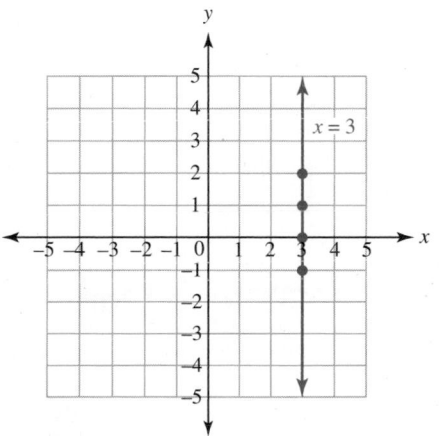

FIGURE 4

Graph of $x = 3$.

Table 13.1 and Figure 4 suggest the following general result.

> ### Equation of a Vertical Line
>
> Let a represent any number. The graph of the equation $x = a$ is a vertical line that passes through the point $(a, 0)$.

Horizontal Line

CONNECTION
REPRESENTATION

Table 13.2 shows a few solutions (x, y) to the equation $y = 2$. If $y = 2$, then x can be any number.

TABLE 13.2 Some Solutions to the Equation $y = 2$

x	-2	0	2	3
y	2	2	2	2

The graph of $y = 2$, shown in Figure 5, is the set of all points (x, y) that satisfy the equation $y = 2$. We see the y-coordinate of any point on the horizontal line is 2 and the y-intercept is $(0, 2)$. A **horizontal line** has an equation of the form $y = b$ for some number b.

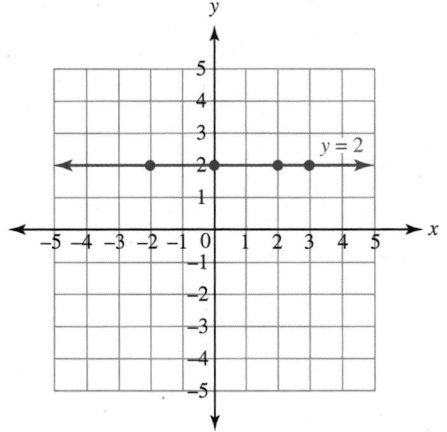

FIGURE 5
Graph of $y = 2$.

Table 13.2 and Figure 5 suggest the following result.

> ### Equation of a Horizontal Line
>
> Let b represent any number. The graph of the equation $y = b$ is a horizontal line that passes through the point $(0, b)$.

Oblique Line

CONNECTION
REPRESENTATION

Table 13.3 shows a few solutions to $y = 2x + 1$.

TABLE 13.3 Some Solutions to the Equation $y = 2x + 1$

x	-1	0	1	2
y	-1	1	3	5

The graph of $y = 2x + 1$, shown in Figure 6, is the set of all points (x, y) that satisfy the equation $y = 2x + 1$. An **oblique line** is a line that is neither vertical nor horizontal.

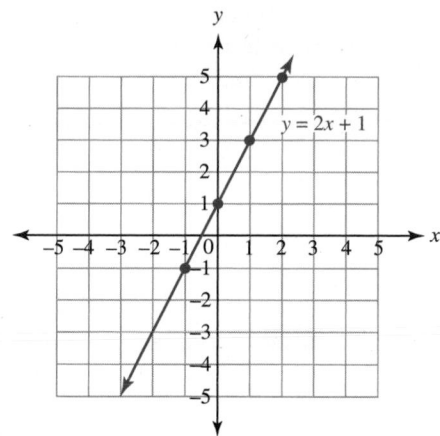

FIGURE 6

Graph of $y = 2x + 1$.

Table 13.3 and Figure 6 suggest the following result.

> ## Equation of an Oblique Line
>
> Suppose $m \neq 0$ and b is any real number. The graph of the equation $y = mx + b$ is an oblique line.

The following Classroom Connection illustrates that students should know how to graph lines.

> ### ◆◆ Classroom Connection
>
> ● *Math*, Grade 5, p. 465
>
> A scientist finds that the temperature increase in a valley is related by the number of hours of sunlight by the equation $y = 4x + 2$. Graph this equation. (© 2000 Macmillan/McGraw Hill. Reprinted by permission.)

Measuring How Quickly a Line Rises or Falls: Slope

The slope (steepness) of a line is the number of units the graph rises or falls vertically for every unit we move to the right (in the same direction that we read a number line, from left to right). In Figure 7, we illustrate how students can informally determine the slope of a line from a graph. In Figure 7(a), the graph of the line rises 3 units for each unit we move to the right. So we say the slope of the line $y = 3x + 1$ is 3. In Figure 7(b), the graph of the line falls 2 units for each unit we move to the right. So we say the slope of the line $y = -2x + 8$ is -2.

CONNECTION

REASONING

REPRESENTATION

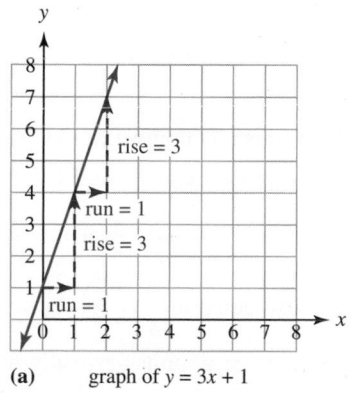

(a)   graph of $y = 3x + 1$

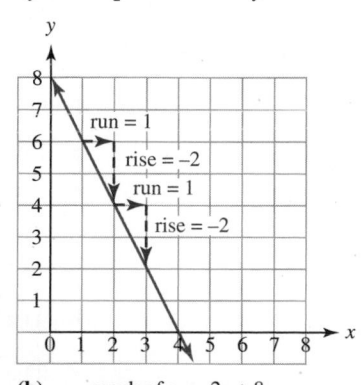

(b)   graph of $y = -2x + 8$

FIGURE 7

Determining the slope of a line from the graph.

Whenever the slope is determined from a graph, the "run" is positive and moves from left to right, whereas the "rise" is positive or negative and moves up or down accordingly.

EXAMPLE 13.1 Calculate the slope of the line.

CONNECTION

REASONING

REPRESENTATION

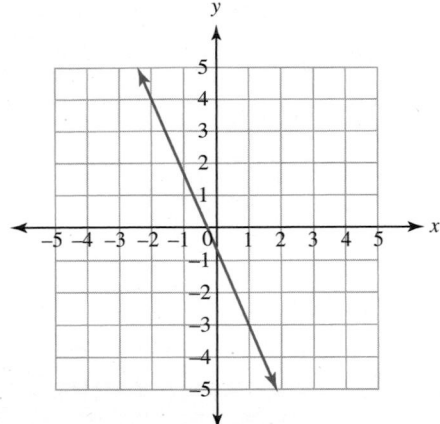

SOLUTION

We need to determine the rise and run of the line. We locate two points on the line that make the calculation of the rise and run possible.

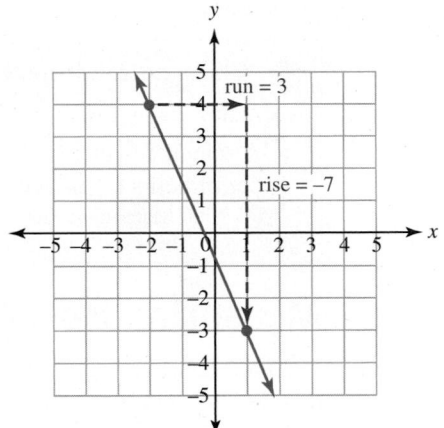

The slope is $-\dfrac{7}{3}$.

Here's how we measure the slope of a nonvertical line based on the coordinates of two points on the line.

- Begin with two distinct points (x_1, y_1) and (x_2, y_2) on a nonvertical line (i.e., $x_1 \neq x_2$).
- Calculate the numbers $y_2 - y_1$ and $x_2 - x_1$.
- $\dfrac{y_2 - y_1}{x_2 - x_1}$ is the slope of the nonvertical line containing the points (x_1, y_1) and (x_2, y_2).
- The slope is also equal to $\dfrac{y_1 - y_2}{x_1 - x_2}$, because $\dfrac{y_2 - y_1}{x_2 - x_1} = \dfrac{-1 \cdot (y_2 - y_1)}{-1 \cdot (x_2 - x_1)} = \dfrac{y_1 - y_2}{x_1 - x_2}$.
- The line moves $y_2 - y_1$ units vertically for every $x_2 - x_1$ units it moves horizontally.

This leads to the following definition of slope.

> **Definition**
>
> Suppose the points (x_1, y_1) and (x_2, y_2) lie on the nonvertical line l. Then the
> **slope** of the line l is $\dfrac{y_2 - y_1}{x_2 - x_1}$.
>
> - The vertical change (also called the rise) is $y_2 - y_1$.
> - The horizontal change (also called the run) is $x_2 - x_1$.

The slope of a vertical line is "undefined" because $x_2 - x_1 = 0$ and $\dfrac{y_2 - y_1}{0}$ is unde-fined. This means a vertical line does not have a slope.

EXAMPLE 13.2   Calculate the slope of the line through the points $(-4, 3)$ and $(2, -5)$.

CONNECTION

SOLUTION

The line is a nonvertical line because the x-coordinates are different. We use the formula for the slope:

$$\text{slope} = \frac{y_2 - y_1}{x_2 - x_1} = \frac{3 - (-5)}{-4 - 2} = \frac{8}{-6} = \frac{-8}{6}, \text{ or } -\frac{4}{3}$$

▲

Connection between the Slope and the Equation of an Oblique Line

The following example helps students "explore relationships between symbolic expressions and graphs of lines, paying particular attention to the meaning of intercept and slope" (Gr. 6–8, NCTM).

EXAMPLE 13.3   The equation of a line is $y = 3x + 2$.

CONNECTION

REASONING

REPRESENTATION

a. Calculate the slope of the line.

b. Calculate the y-intercept of the line.

SOLUTION

a. $y = 3x + 2$ is a nonvertical line. To calculate the slope, we must determine two ordered pairs (x_1, y_1) and (x_2, y_2) with different x-coordinates that satisfy the equation $y = 3x + 2$. Let $x = 1$. Then $y = 3 \cdot (1) + 2 = 5$. So $(x_1, y_1) = (1, 5)$ belongs to the line. Let $x = 6$. Then $y = 3 \cdot 6 + 2 = 20$. So $(x_2, y_2) = (6, 20)$ belongs to the line. The slope of the line is

$$\text{slope} = \frac{y_2 - y_1}{x_2 - x_1} = \frac{20 - 5}{6 - 1} = \frac{15}{5} = 3.$$

The order of the two points does not matter, because $\dfrac{5 - 20}{1 - 6} = \dfrac{-15}{-5} = 3.$

b. We must calculate y when $x = 0$. Then $y = 3 \cdot 0 + 2 = 2$. So the y-intercept is $(0, 2)$.

▲

Using the same approach in this example, you can verify that the equation of the line $y = -2x + 4$ has a slope of -2 and a y-intercept of $(0, 4)$ and that the equation of the line $y = 6x - 5$ has a slope of 6 and a y-intercept of $(0, -5)$. These observations suggest the following result.

> ### Meaning of the Constants m and b in the Equation $y = mx + b$
>
> For the nonvertical line $y = mx + b$, the coefficient m is the slope of the line and the point $(0, b)$ is the y-intercept of the line.

If a nonvertical line has slope m and y-intercept $(0, b)$, then the **slope-intercept form** of the line is $y = mx + b$. The following problem illustrates the steps that can be followed to write the slope-intercept form of a line, given two points that belong to the line.

EXAMPLE 13.4   Write the slope-intercept form of the line passing through the points $(5, 8)$ and $(3, 14)$.

CONNECTION

REASONING

REPRESENTATION   **SOLUTION**

The slope-intercept form of a nonvertical line is $y = mx + b$. The slope of the line through $(5, 8)$ and $(3, 14)$ is $\dfrac{14 - 8}{3 - 5} = \dfrac{6}{-2} = -3$, so the equation becomes $y = -3x + b$. The point $(5, 8)$ lies on the line, so we must choose b such that $8 = -3 \cdot 5 + b$. Then $8 = -15 + b$. Then $23 = b$. So the slope-intercept form of the line is $y = -3x + 23$.

▲

The following problem illustrates the steps that can be followed to write the slope-intercept form of a line, given the slope of the line and a point on the line.

EXAMPLE 13.5   Write the slope-intercept form of the line with a slope of -4 and passing through the point $(5, 8)$.

CONNECTION

REASONING

REPRESENTATION   **SOLUTION**

The slope-intercept form of a nonvertical line is $y = mx + b$. The slope is -4, so the equation becomes $y = -4x + b$. The point $(5, 8)$ lies on the line, so we must choose b such that $8 = -4 \cdot 5 + b$. Then $8 = -20 + b$. Then $28 = b$. So the equation of the line with a slope of -4 and passing through the point $(5, 8)$ is $y = -4x + 28$.

▲

The following Classroom Connection illustrates that the two previous worked examples reflect problems middle school students should know how to solve.

> ### ◆ Classroom Connection
>
> ● Holt *Mathematics*, Student Edition, p. 641
>
> Write the equation of the line that passes through each pair of points in slope-intercept form. $(-2, -7)$ and $(3, 8)$; $(0, 3)$ and $(2, -5)$.
>
> ● Holt *Mathematics*, Student Edition, p. 646
>
> Write the point-slope form of the equation with the given slope that passes through the indicated point: the line with a slope of -5 passing through the point $(-3, -5)$. (© 2007 by Holt, Rinehart, and Winston. All rights reserved. Reprinted with permission of the publisher, Houghton Mifflin Harcourt Publishing Company.)

An equation of the form $f(x) = mx + b$ is sometimes called a linear function. We use the adjective *linear* because the graph of the equation is a straight line. The following example requires an interpretation of the slope in a situation.

EXAMPLE 13.6

CONNECTION

COMMUNICATION

PROBLEM SOLVING

The manager of a deli determined his daily profit P from selling x pastrami sandwiches could be modeled by the linear function $P(x) = 4x - 7$ dollars.

a. Interpret the slope.

b. Interpret the y-intercept.

SOLUTION

a. The slope of the line determined by the equation $P(x) = 4x - 7$ is 4. The graph of the line rises 4 units for each unit you move to the right. The measurement unit of the vertical scale is dollars. The measurement unit of the horizontal scale is the number of pastrami sandwiches sold. Then

$$\text{slope} = \frac{\text{vertical change}}{\text{horizontal change}} = \frac{4}{1} = 4.$$

This means the daily profit increases at a rate of $4 per pastrami sandwich sold.

b. We obtain the y-intercept by calculating $P(0)$: $P(0) = 4(0) - 7 = -7$. This means if the deli does not sell any pastrami sandwiches, then the deli loses $7 for that day because of the unsold pastrami sandwiches.

▲

EXAMPLE 13.7

CONNECTION

COMMUNICATION

REASONING

The equation of a line is $y = 4x - 5$.

a. Suppose the x value increases by 3 units. By how much does the y value increase or decrease?

b. Suppose the y value decreases by 7 units. By how much does the x value increase or decrease?

SOLUTION

The slope of the line $y = 4x - 5$ equals 4.

a. The slope is 4, and the x value increases by 3 units. Then

$$\text{slope} = \frac{\text{vertical change}}{\text{horizontal change}}$$

$$4 = \frac{\text{vertical change}}{3}$$

$$\text{vertical change} = 4 \cdot 3$$

$$\text{vertical change} = 12$$

This means that if the x value increases by 3 units, then the y value increases by 12 units.

b. The slope is 4, and the y value decreases by 7 units. Then

$$\text{slope} = \frac{\text{vertical change}}{\text{horizontal change}}$$

$$4 = \frac{-7}{\text{horizontal change}}$$

$$\text{horizontal change} = \frac{-7}{4}$$

$$\text{horizontal change} = -1.75$$

This means that if the y value decreases by 7 units, then the x value decreases by 1.75 units.

▲

The following Released Item challenges students to determine the effect of changing the value of one variable in a linear equation.

> ### RELEASED ITEM
>
> ● NAEP, 2005
>
> In the equation $y = 4x$ if the value of x is increased by 2, what is the effect on the value of y?
> a. It is 8 more than the original amount.
> b. It is 6 more than the original amount.
> c. It is 2 more than the original amount.
> d. It is 16 times the original amount.
> e. It is eight times the original amount.
>
> 34% of eighth-grade students gave the correct answer. (U.S. Department of Education, Institute of Education Sciences, National Center for Education Statistics, NAEP)

Connection between Slopes of Parallel Lines

Lines in the same plane are said to be *parallel* if and only if they do not intersect. Suppose you know two lines are parallel. The following example explains why both lines must be vertical lines, horizontal lines, or oblique lines. When two lines are parallel, there's no mixing of the types of lines.

EXAMPLE 13.8

CONNECTION

COMMUNICATION

REASONING

a. Explain why the vertical line $x = a$ must intersect the oblique line $y = mx + b$.
b. Explain why the horizontal line $y = c$ must intersect the oblique line $y = mx + b$.
c. Explain why the vertical line $x = a$ must intersect the horizontal line $y = c$.

SOLUTION

a. Let $x = a$ and $y = mx + b$ represent the equations for horizontal and oblique lines, respectively. If we replace x with a in the equation $y = mx + b$, then $y = ma + b$. The point $(a, ma + b)$ belongs to both lines. So a horizontal line must intersect an oblique line.

b. Let $y = c$ and $y = mx + b$ represent the equations for vertical and oblique lines, respectively. If we replace y with c in the equation $y = mx + b$, then $c = mx + b$. Solving for x, we get $x = (c - b)/m$. The point $((c - b)/m, c)$ belongs to both lines. So a vertical line must intersect an oblique line.

c. Let $x = a$ and $y = c$ represent horizontal and vertical lines, respectively. The point (a, c) belongs to both lines. So a vertical line must intersect a horizontal line.

▲

CONNECTION

COMMUNICATION

REASONING

Two vertical lines are parallel. To see this, let's consider the vertical lines $x = a$ and $x = b$ such that $a \neq b$. If a point (p, q) belongs to the vertical lines $x = a$ and $x = b$, then $p = a$ (because (p, q) belongs to $x = a$) and $p = b$ (because (p, q) belongs to $x = b$). Then $a = b$ (because $p = a$ and $p = b$). But we chose a and b such that $a \neq b$. So it follows there cannot be a point (p, q) that belong to the vertical lines $x = a$ and $x = b$. So the vertical lines $x = a$ and $x = b$ are parallel.

Figure 8 shows the slopes of graphs of two nonvertical lines in the same coordinate plane. When the slopes of nonvertical lines are identical, do the lines intersect or are the lines parallel? Think about this and complete the conjecture: If the slopes of two nonvertical lines are equal, then _____.

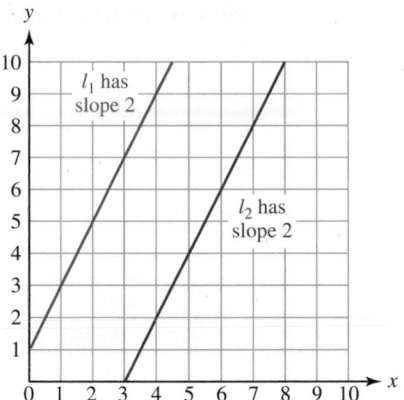

FIGURE 8

l_1 and l_2 have the same slope.

CONNECTION

COMMUNICATION

REASONING

Now suppose two nonvertical lines are parallel. What can we say about their slopes? Calculate the slopes of the parallel lines in Figure 9. How are the slopes related? Think about this and complete the conjecture: If two nonvertical lines are parallel, then _____.

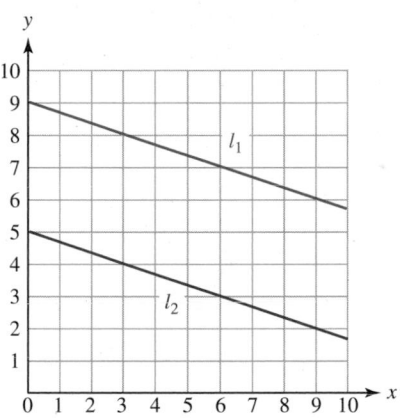

FIGURE 9

l_1 and l_2 are parallel lines.

Hopefully, Figures 8 and 9 helped you conclude the following:

- If the slopes of two nonvertical lines are equal, then the two lines are parallel.
- If two nonvertical lines are parallel, then their slopes are equal.

EXAMPLE 13.9

CONNECTION

REASONING

Two lines are parallel.

a. The slope of one line is $\frac{3}{2}$. What is the slope of the other line?

b. The equation of one line is $y = 5x + 2$. Write a possible equation of the other line.

SOLUTION

a. The two lines are parallel lines, so they must have the same slope. Therefore, the slope of the other line is $\frac{3}{2}$.

b. The slopes must be the same, so all equations must have the form $y = 5x + b$, where b is any number. One possible answer is $y = 5x + 8$.

▲

EXAMPLE 13.10

CONNECTION

REASONING

The equation of line n is $y = 2x + 7$. Write the equation of a line parallel to line n and passing through $(4, -1)$.

SOLUTION

The equation has the form $y = 2x + b$. The line passes through $(4, -1)$, so b must satisfy the equation $-1 = 2 \cdot 4 + b$. Then $-1 = 8 + b$, so $b = -9$. The equation is $y = 2x - 9$.

▲

Now we summarize the connection between slopes and parallel nonvertical lines.

Theorem 1

If the slopes of two nonvertical lines are equal, then the two lines are parallel.

Theorem 2

If two nonvertical lines are parallel, then their slopes are equal.

The proofs of Theorems 1 and 2 are given in Appendix C.

Connection between Slopes of Perpendicular Lines

CONNECTION

REASONING

Figure 10 shows pairs of perpendicular lines. What is the connection between the slopes of two perpendicular lines? For each pair of lines, calculate the slopes and find the product of slopes. Then complete the conjecture: If two lines are perpendicular, then the product of their slopes is _____, or _____.

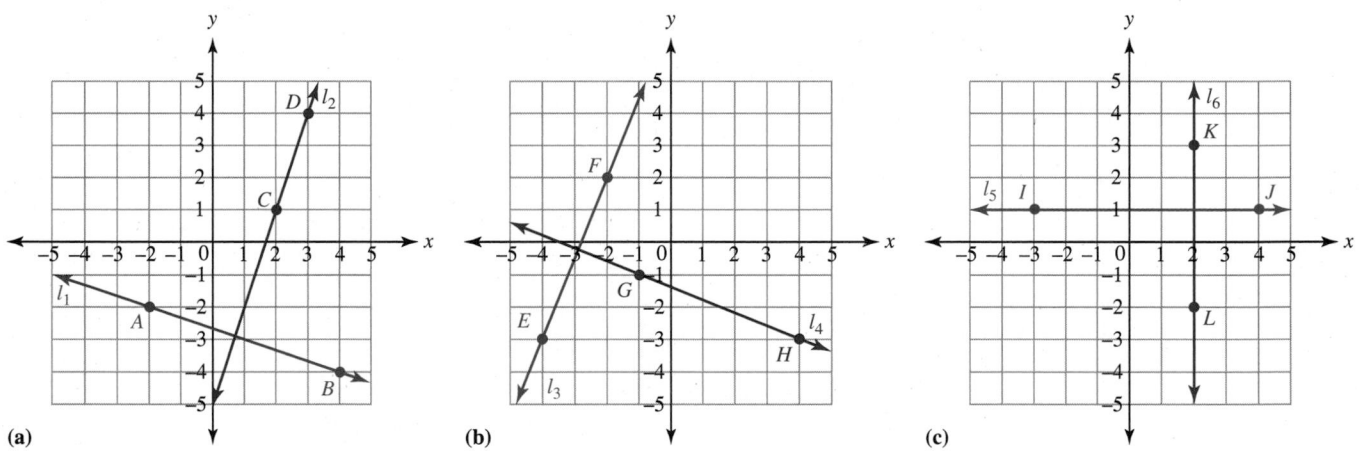

FIGURE 10
Relating the slopes of two perpendicular lines.

Hopefully, you concluded the following: If two lines are perpendicular, then the product of their slopes is -1, or one line is horizontal and the other line is vertical.

EXAMPLE 13.11

CONNECTION

REASONING

Two lines are perpendicular.
a. The slope of one line is $\frac{3}{2}$. What is the slope of the other line?
b. The slope of one line is 0. What is the slope of the other line?

SOLUTION

a. The two lines are oblique lines. The slope of the other line equals the negative reciprocal of $\frac{3}{2}$, which is $-\frac{2}{3}$.

b. The slope of one line is 0, so it is a horizontal line. The other line must be vertical, so its slope is undefined (it does not have a slope).

EXAMPLE 13.12 What is the slope of a line perpendicular to the line with the equation $y = \frac{2}{5}x + 4$?

CONNECTION

REASONING   SOLUTION

The slope of the given line is $\frac{2}{5}$. The slope of any line perpendicular to that line equals the negative reciprocal of $\frac{2}{5}$, which is $-\frac{5}{2}$.

▲

EXAMPLE 13.13 Find the equation of the line passing through the point $(4, 2)$ and perpendicular to the line with the equation $y = 3x + 1$.

CONNECTION

REASONING

SOLUTION

The slope of any line perpendicular to $y = 3x + 1$ equals the negative reciprocal of 3, which is $-\frac{1}{3}$. So the line must have an equation of the form $y = -\frac{1}{3}x + b$. The line passes through $(4, 2)$, so b must satisfy the equation $2 = -\frac{1}{3} \cdot 4 + b$. Then $2 = -\frac{4}{3} + b$, so $b = \frac{10}{3}$. The equation of the line is $y = -\frac{1}{3}x + \frac{10}{3}$.

▲

CONNECTION

REASONING

REPRESENTATION

Now suppose that the slopes of two oblique lines are m_1 and m_2 and that $m_1 \cdot m_2 = -1$, or one line is horizontal and the other line is vertical. Are the two lines perpendicular? Use a protractor to measure the angle formed by the two lines in Figure 11 for which the product of their slopes is equal to -1. Then complete the conjecture: If the product of the slopes of two lines is -1, or one line is horizontal and the other line is vertical, then _____.

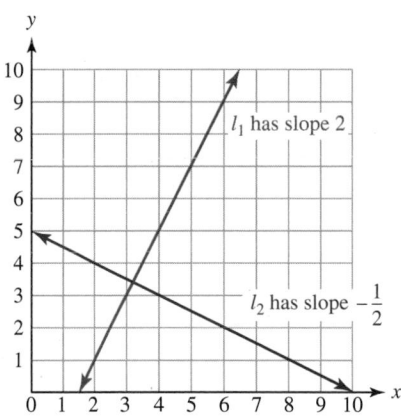

FIGURE 11
The product of the slopes is -1.

Hopefully, you concluded the following: If the product of the slopes of two lines is -1, or one line is horizontal and the other line is vertical, then the two lines are perpendicular.

EXAMPLE 13.14 Determine whether the graphs of the lines with the given equations are perpendicular.

CONNECTION   **a.** $y = -\frac{3}{5}x + 1$ and $3y - 5x = -36$

REASONING   **b.** $y = -7x + 1$ and $y = 2x + 8$

REPRESENTATION

SOLUTION

a. The slope-intercept forms of the lines are $y = -\frac{3}{5}x + 1$ and $y = \frac{5}{3}x - 12$. The slopes of the lines are $-\frac{3}{5}$ and $\frac{5}{3}$. The product of the slopes is $-\frac{3}{5} \cdot \frac{5}{3} = -1$. So the two lines are perpendicular.

b. The slopes of the lines are -7 and 2. The product of the slopes is $(-7) \cdot 2 = -14$, and $-14 \neq -1$. So the two lines are not perpendicular.

▲

Now we summarize the connection between slope and perpendicular lines.

Theorem 3

If two lines are perpendicular, then the product of their slopes is -1, or one line is horizontal and the other line is vertical.

Theorem 4

If the product of the slopes of two lines is -1, or one line is horizontal and the other line is vertical, then the two lines are perpendicular.

The proofs of Theorems 3 and 4 are given in Appendix C.

QUESTIONS FOR SECTION 13.1

REPRESENTATION

Refresher: Representations (language, diagrams, tables, symbols, algebra, manipulatives, and contextualized situations) are important because we use them to organize, record, and communicate mathematical ideas and make them more comprehensible.

1. Determine whether the line is vertical, horizontal, or oblique.
   a. $x = 0$ b. $y = 7.2$ c. $3x = 4$ d. $y = -2$
   e. $3x - y = 1$ f. $y = -3$ g. $x = -5$

2. Determine the x-intercept, y-intercept, and the slope of the line shown.

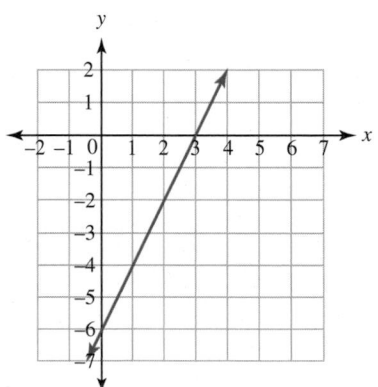

3. Lines l_1, l_2, l_3, and l_4, are shown in the graph. Which line has
   a. a positive slope?   b. a negative slope?
   c. a zero slope?   d. an undefined slope?

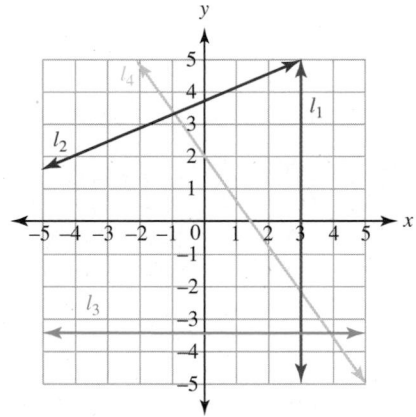

PROBLEM SOLVING

Refresher: Problem solving (reaching a goal that is not immediately attainable) is important because it helps students think more deeply about what they know and deal with unfamiliar situations.

4. The owner of a local movie theater determined the number of tickets S sold for the movie *Scary Fractions* could be modeled by the linear function $S(t) = -24t + 384$, where t is the number of days after the movie's release.
   a. Find and interpret the slope.
   b. Find and interpret the t-intercept.
   c. Find and interpret the S-intercept.

5. Pressure p increases linearly as a function of the depth d of the water. At the surface of ocean water ($d = 0$), the pressure is 15 pounds per square inch. At a depth of 11 feet ($d = 11$), the pressure is 20 pounds per square inch.

   a. Express the pressure p in terms of the depth d.

   b. Verify that $(22, 25)$ is a solution to your equation.

   c. Interpret the ordered pair $(22, 25)$.

REASONING AND PROOF

Refresher: Reasoning and proof (thinking and justifying) are important because they help students make sense of mathematics.

6. Suppose y is the number of tables produced, x is the number of hours required to make a table, and x and y are related by the linear equation $y = mx + b$. Also suppose y increases by 3 units when x increases by 2 units.

   a. What is the value of m?

   b. Interpret the slope within the context of the problem.

7. Suppose two distinct points (x_1, y_1) and (x_2, y_2) belong to the nonvertical line $y = mx + b$. Prove that m is the slope. (Hint:

   Prove $m = \dfrac{y_2 - y_1}{x_2 - x_1}$.)

8. l_1, l_2, and l_3 are distinct oblique lines with the slopes m_1, m_2, and m_3, respectively.

   a. Suppose l_1 and l_2 are parallel, and l_1 and l_3 are perpendicular. Prove l_2 and l_3 are perpendicular.

   b. Suppose l_1 and l_2 are perpendicular, and l_1 and l_3 are perpendicular. Prove l_2 and l_3 are parallel.

CONNECTIONS

Refresher: Connections (linking and applying mathematical ideas) are important because they deepen student understanding and make mathematics more meaningful, flexible, and useful.

9. Do the following.

   a. Use the definition of a slope to calculate the slope of the line $y = 4x + 5$.

   b. Use the definition of a slope to calculate the slope of the line $y = -8x + 2$.

   c. Use the definition of a slope to calculate the slope of the line $y = 3x - 4$.

   d. Make a conjecture about the significance of the parameter m in the equation $y = mx + b$.

10. Do the following.

    a. Determine the y-intercept of the line $y = 4x + 5$.

    b. Determine the y-intercept of the line $y = -8x + 2$.

    c. Determine the y-intercept of the line $y = 3x - 4$.

    d. Make a conjecture about the significance of the parameter b in the equation $y = mx + b$.

11. Determine whether the lines are parallel, perpendicular, or neither.

    a. $y = 5x - 2$ and $y = 10x - 4$

    b. $y = -2x - 6$ and $2y + 4x = 12$

    c. $y = 10x - 2$ and $y + 10x = 0$

    d. $4y + 3x = -18$ and $3y = 4x + 7$

    e. $5y = 7x + 2$ and $y = \frac{5}{7}x + 12$

12. Write the equation of a line that passes through the point $(3, 5)$ and is perpendicular to the line with the equation $y = 4x - 1$.

13. Determine the equation of a line that is parallel to $y = 3x + 4$ and passes through $(5, 2)$.

14. Determine the equation of a line that is perpendicular to $3y = -8x - 5$ and passes through $(1, 4)$.

15. Archeologists often study unearthed artifacts, such as pottery and bones, to learn about ancient civilizations. An unearthed bone may contain clues of diet, disease, cause of death, and population characteristics. The table shows recorded measurements of bones from unearthed skeletons of adult males.

Length of femur L (in.)	12.5	16.4	21.7
Height of adult male H (in.)	55.75	63.16	73.23

The variable L represents the length of the femur (thigh) bone, the longest and strongest bone in the human body, and the variable H represents the height of an adult male.

   a. What does the ordered pair $(12.5, 55.75)$ mean?

   b. Write an equation for the height H of an adult male that depends on the length L of the femur. Express the height as a linear function of the length of femur.

   c. Suppose archeologists unearth a femur bone of the length 18.2 inches. Predict the height of the adult male.

   d. Suppose the height of an adult male is 70 inches. Predict the length of the femur.

16. A student uses the function notation $f(n) = 4n - 5$ to represent the arithmetic sequence $-1, 3, 7, 11, \ldots$.

   a. What does n represent?

   b. What does $f(n)$ represent?

17. Suppose y and x have the linear relationship $y = 7x + 10$ and x increases by 2 units. By how much does the y value increase or decrease?

18. Suppose y and x have the linear relationship $-2y - 5x = 12$ and y increases by 3 units. By how much does the x value increase or decrease?

19. Draw a line that has a slope of $\frac{3}{2}$ and passes through the point $(-4, -3)$.

20. Do the following.

   a. A nonvertical line with the slope m contains the points (x, y) and (x_1, y_1). Use algebra to show that the equation of that line is $y - y_1 = m(x - x_1)$. This form is called the point-slope form of a line.

   b. Find the point-slope form of a line with a slope of 3 containing the point $(2, 5)$.

c. Find the point-slope form of a line with a slope of -4 containing the point $(3, -5)$.

d. Find the point-slope form of the line with a slope of 5 containing the point $(-4, 1)$.

COMMUNICATION

Refresher: Communication (written and verbal explanations using representations and proper mathematical vocabulary) is important because it helps students refine and strengthen their understanding.

21. Suppose $(4, w)$ and $(4, k)$ are distinct points that belong to the same line. Is the line oblique, horizontal, or vertical? Explain.

22. Suppose $(2, w)$ and $(5, k)$ are distinct points that belong to the same line. Is the line oblique, horizontal, or vertical? Explain.

23. Do the following.

a. Draw the graph of each line on graph paper: $y = 0.5x$, $y = 1.5x$, and $y = 3x$.

b. Discuss how the positive slope influences the graphs of the lines.

24. Do the following.

a. Draw the graph of each line on graph paper: $y = 2x - 3$, $y = 2x + 1$, and $y = 2x + 4$.

b. Discuss how the constant influences the graphs of the lines.

25. Do the following.

a. Graph the functions: $y = 3x - 2$ and $y = |3x| - 2$.

b. Graph the functions: $y = -2x + 1$ and $y = |-2x| + 1$.

c. Discuss the effect of the absolute value.

26. Do the following.

a. Graph the functions: $y = 3x - 2$ and $y = |3x - 2|$.

b. Graph the functions: $y = -2x - 3$ and $y = |-2x - 3|$.

c. Discuss the effect of the absolute value.

27. Do the following.

a. Explain why the horizontal line $y = 3$ is perpendicular to the y-axis.

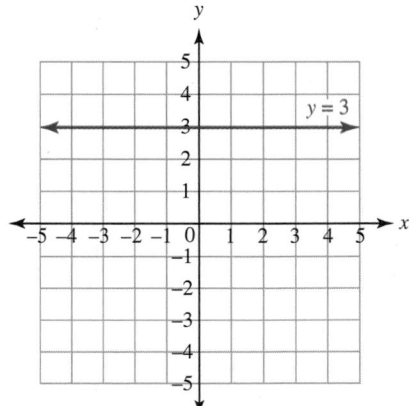

b. Explain why the vertical line $x = 2$ is perpendicular to the x-axis.

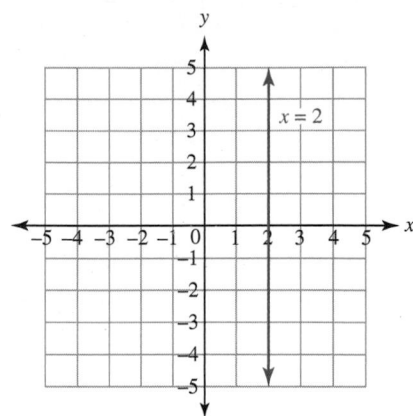

More practice with the ideas of the section

28. Fill in the blank. Choose one of the following words, phrases, numbers, or symbols: (a, b), (b, a), $\frac{2}{5}$, $-\frac{2}{5}$, $\frac{5}{2}$, $-\frac{5}{2}$, 2, -2, *axis, horizontal, horizontal change, linear, negative, nonlinear, non-vertical, oblique, positive, slope, undefined, vertical, vertical change, x-axis, x-intercept, y-axis, y-intercept,* or *zero.*

a. Given two points (x_1, y_1) and (x_2, y_2) on a line, the number $x_2 - x_1$ is the _____ as you move from (x_1, y_1) and (x_2, y_2).

b. Given two points (x_1, y_1) and (x_2, y_2) on a line, the number $y_2 - y_1$ is the _____ as you move from (x_1, y_1) and (x_2, y_2).

c. The slope of a horizontal line is _____.

d. The slope of a vertical line is _____.

e. The graph of $x = 5$ is a(n) _____ line.

f. The graph of $y = 3$ is a(n) _____ line.

g. The graph of $y = -2x - 7$ is a(n) _____ line.

h. The slope of the graph of the line $5y + 2x = 8$ is _____.

29. Is the ordered pair a solution to the equation $y = -3x + 5$?

a. $(3, 4)$ **b.** $(6, -13)$

30. In this problem, we will calculate the slope of the line through the points $(3, 7)$ and $(-1, -5)$ using the formula slope = $\dfrac{y_2 - y_1}{x_2 - x_1}$.

a. Let $(x_1, y_1) = (3, 7)$ and $(x_2, y_2) = (-1, -5)$. Calculate the slope.

b. Let $(x_1, y_1) = (-1, -5)$ and $(x_2, y_2) = (3, 7)$. Calculate the slope.

c. Tell what you learned.

31. Is the ordered pair a solution to both of the equations: $3y + 2x = 18$ and $2x^2 + 5y = 38$?

a. $(-3, 8)$ **b.** $(3, 4)$

32. The equation of a line is $-5y = 4x - 6$.

a. Suppose the x value decreases by 3 units. By how much does the y value increase or decrease?

b. Suppose the y value increases by 2 units. By how much does the x value increase or decrease?

33. Draw the graph of the equation $2y - 6x = 4$ over the specified domain.

   a. $\{-1, 0, 1\}$ **b.** the real numbers

34. Find the slope of the line through the given points.

   a. $(4, 3)$ and $(0, 6)$ **b.** $(2, 7)$ and $(7, 7)$

   c. $(-2, 6)$ and $(3, 8)$

35. Determine the equation of the line through the given points.

   a. $(5, 3)$ and $(-1, -9)$ **b.** $(3, 5)$ and $(-9, -1)$

   c. $(8, -1)$ and $(6, 5)$

36. Graph each equation for the domain of nonnegative numbers.

   a. $y = -2x + 3$ **b.** $y = -3$ **c.** $x = 3$

37. Use algebra to find the x- and y-intercepts of each line.

   a. $y = -4x + 7$ **b.** $3x - 4y = 24$ **c.** $y = 4$

38. Write an equation of an oblique line with the following properties.

   a. The slope is -4, and the x-intercept is $(3, 0)$.

   b. The slope is 2, and the y-intercept $(0, -1)$.

   c. The slope is 3, and the line passes through $(4, 2)$.

39. Find an equation of the line with the given slope and y-intercept.

   a. The slope is -4, and the y-intercept is $(0, 5)$.

   b. The slope is 3, and the y-intercept is $(0, -8)$.

40. Find an equation of the line with the given slope and y-intercept.

   a. The slope is 5, and the y-intercept is $(0, 7)$.

   b. The slope is -2, and the y-intercept is $(0, -3)$.

41. Find a number u such that a line through $(2, 3)$ and $(4, u)$ has a slope of

   a. 5.   **b.** 0.2.   **c.** -3.

42. A taxi charges an initial fee of $2.00, as well as $0.34 for each one-fifth or part of a mile.

   a. Write an equation for the cab fare f that depends on the mileage m driven.

   b. Verify that the cab fare for a 3-mile ride is $7.10.

   c. What is the cab fare for an 8-mile ride?

   d. Does this function have an m-intercept?

   e. Suppose the cab fare was $29.20. How many miles was the taxi ride? Show your work.

43. Suppose y is the number of books sold when the price is x dollars and x and y are related by the linear equation $y = mx + b$. Suppose y decreases by 5 units when x increases by 2 units.

   a. What is the slope of the line?

   b. Interpret the slope using the given units in the problem.

44. If the slope of the line through (a, b) and (c, d) is the number k, what is the slope of the line through (b, a) and (d, c) in terms of k?

45. An arithmetic sequence is given in the table.

Position	1	2	3	4
Term	4	7	10	13

   a. Determine a linear function that relates the position to the term in the sequence.

   b. Using your function, verify that the second term is 7.

   c. Use your function to find the 15th term in the sequence.

46. What point belongs to both lines?

   a. the vertical line $x = k$ and the oblique line $y = mx + b$

   b. the horizontal line $y = k$ and an oblique line $y = mx + b$

47. A rental car company charges $125 to rent a car for 1 week plus $0.30 per mile.

   a. Write a function for the cost C that depends on the mileage m driven.

   b. What is the domain for this function?

   c. Does this function have an m-intercept?

   d. What is the cost to rent the car for 1 week and drive it 257 miles?

   e. Interpret the ordered pair $(23, 131.90)$.

   f. Suppose your budget for renting a car for 1 week is $391. What is the maximum number of miles you can drive the rental car?

48. An athlete eats a lunch consisting of one small order of fries and some pieces of chicken. A small order of fries has 230 calories. Each small piece of chicken has 45 calories. How many pieces of chicken should the athlete eat to consume a lunch that has 995 calories?

49. Draw a line that has a slope of $\frac{-2}{3}$ and passes through the point $(-3, -1)$.

50. Draw a line that has a slope of 1.5 and passes through the point $(-1, -2)$.

51. A contractor is building a ramp to a doorway that is 3.5 feet above the street. How far from the edge of the dock (x feet) should the ramp be placed so that the ramp will have a slope of $-\frac{5}{8}$?

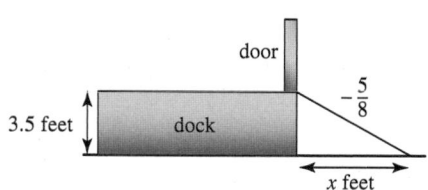

52. The following graph shows the distance y Mary is from home as a function of the time x. Identify the part of the graph that corresponds to each of the following statements: Mary left her friend's house and went home; Mary stayed at her friend's house for a while; After school, Mary walked to her friend's house.

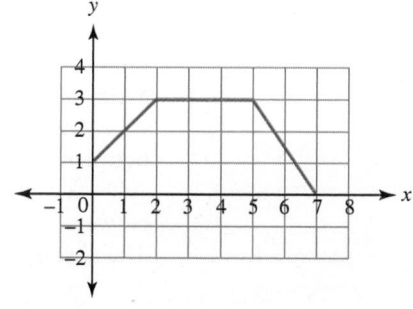

SECTION 13.2 Properties of Polygons Using Coordinate Geometry

The Pythagorean Theorem and the Distance Formula

Our goal is to derive a formula for the distance AB between two points $A(x_1, y_1)$ and $B(x_2, y_2)$. To achieve this, we combine our knowledge about vertical lines, horizontal lines, and the Pythagorean theorem.

EXAMPLE 13.15

CONNECTION

a. Figure 12 shows two points $P(3, 2)$ and $Q(3, -4)$ on the vertical line $\overleftrightarrow{PQ}$ given by the equation $x = 3$. Determine the distance between P and Q. How did you arrive at your answer?

b. Figure 12 shows two points $S(-3, 4)$ and $T(2, 4)$ on the horizontal line given by the equation $y = 4$. Determine the distance between S and T. How did you arrive at your answer?

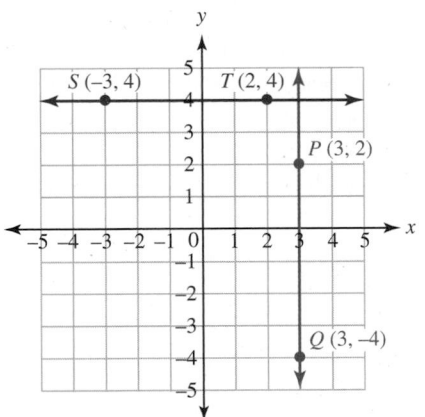

FIGURE 12

Distance between two points on a nonoblique line.

SOLUTION

a. 6 units, by counting the units

b. 5 units, by counting the units

The distance between P and Q on the vertical line $x = 3$ is the length of $\overline{PQ}$, which is the positive difference in their y-coordinates. So $PQ = |2 - (-4)| = |2 + 4| = |6| = 6$ units or $PQ = |-4 - 2| = |-6| = 6$ units. The distance between S and T on the horizontal line $y = 4$ is the length of $\overline{ST}$, which is the positive difference in their x-coordinates. So $ST = |2 - (-3)| = |2 + 3| = |5| = 5$ units or $ST = |-3 - 2| = |-5| = 5$ units.

More generally, if $P(k, y_1)$ and $Q(k, y_2)$ lie on the vertical line $x = k$, then the distance between P and Q is the positive difference between the y-coordinates, that is, $PQ = |y_2 - y_1|$. If $S(x_1, h)$ and $T(x_2, h)$ lie on the horizontal line $y = h$, then the distance between S and T is the positive difference between the x-coordinates, that is, $ST = |x_2 - x_1|$. The absolute value signs ensure the distance is nonnegative.

EXAMPLE 13.16 Determine the distance between $V(1, 5)$ and $W(6, 2)$.

CONNECTION

COMMUNICATION

PROBLEM SOLVING

REASONING

REPRESENTATION

SOLUTION

We plot $V(1, 5)$ and $W(6, 2)$, as shown in Figure 13. We can draw a horizontal line segment through W and a vertical line segment through V and then let U be the intersection of these line segments. The coordinates of U are $(1, 2)$. This creates a right triangle $\triangle UVW$ such that $\overline{VW}$ is the hypotenuse. The lengths of the legs are simple to find because they are horizontal and vertical distances, which we already know how to calculate. Then we can use the Pythagorean theorem to find VW.

$$(VW)^2 = (VU)^2 + (UW)^2 = |5 - 2|^2 + |1 - 6|^2 = 3^2 + 5^2 = 9 + 25 = 34$$

So $VW = \sqrt{34}$ units, or approximately 5.8 units.

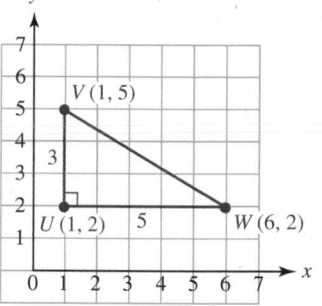

FIGURE 13

Distance between two points on an oblique line.

The **distance formula** is an equation for expressing the length of the line segment that joins points $A(x_1, y_1)$ and $B(x_2, y_2)$, as shown in Figure 14(a). The point C is the intersection of the horizontal line through A and the vertical line through B, as shown in Figure 14(b). We see that C has the coordinates (x_2, y_1). $\triangle ACB$ is a right triangle, and the distance AB between A and B is the length of the hypotenuse.

CONNECTION

REPRESENTATION

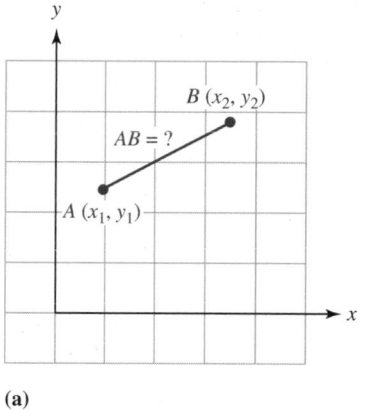

(a)

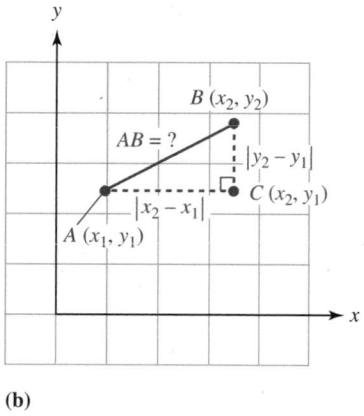

(b)

FIGURE 14

Distance between points $A(x_1, y_1)$ and $B(x_2, y_2)$.

So

$$(AB)^2 = (AC)^2 + (CB)^2$$
$$= |x_2 - x_1|^2 + |y_2 - y_1|^2$$
$$= (x_2 - x_1)^2 + (y_2 - y_1)^2$$
$$AB = \sqrt{(x_2 - x_1)^2 + (y_2 - y_1)^2}$$

This leads to the following formula to calculate distance.

Formula for the Distance between Two Points

The **distance** AB between points $A(x_1, y_1)$ and $B(x_2, y_2)$ in the coordinate plane is $AB = \sqrt{(x_2 - x_1)^2 + (y_2 - y_1)^2}$.

Students should be able to "apply the Pythagorean theorem to find the distance between two points in a coordinate system" (Gr. 8, CCSS) (© 2010. National Governors Association Center for Best Practices and Council of Chief State School Officers. All rights reserved.).

EXAMPLE 13.17

CONNECTION

Find the distance between $P(3, -7)$ and $Q(5, 1)$.

SOLUTION

We use the distance formula:

$$PQ = \sqrt{(3 - 5)^2 + (-7 - 1)^2} = \sqrt{(-2)^2 + (-8)^2} = \sqrt{4 + 64} = \sqrt{68} \approx 8.2 \text{ units.}$$

▲

EXAMPLE 13.18

CONNECTION

PROBLEM SOLVING

REASONING

REPRESENTATION

$\triangle LRN$ has the vertices $L(1, -6)$, $R(5, 2)$, and $N(-3, 4)$. Identify the angle of $\triangle LRN$ with the

a. largest measure.

b. smallest measure.

SOLUTION

The angle of $\triangle LRN$ with the largest measure is opposite the longest side, and the angle of $\triangle LRN$ with the smallest measure is opposite the shortest side (see Section 11.3). So let's calculate the lengths of the sides: $LR = \sqrt{(1 - 5)^2 + (-6 - 2)^2} = \sqrt{80} \approx 8.9$ units, $RN = \sqrt{(5 - (-3))^2 + (2 - 4)^2} = \sqrt{68} \approx 8.2$ units, and $LN = \sqrt{(1 - (-3))^2 + (-6 - 4)^2} = \sqrt{116} \approx 10.8$ units.

a. $\angle R$ is the largest angle.

b. $\angle L$ is the smallest angle.

▲

EXAMPLE 13.19

CONNECTION

REASONING

$\triangle LRN$ has the vertices $L(2, -7)$, $R(1, 3)$, and $N(-5, 8)$. Use the distance formula to help you classify the triangle as acute, right, or obtuse.

SOLUTION

In Section 11.3, we learned how to use the lengths of the sides of a triangle to classify a triangle as acute, right, or obtuse. Let c represent the length of the longest side, and let a and b represent the lengths of the other two sides. If $c^2 < a^2 + b^2$, then $\triangle LRN$ is an acute triangle. If $c^2 = a^2 + b^2$, then $\triangle LRN$ is a right triangle. If $c^2 > a^2 + b^2$, then $\triangle LRN$ is an obtuse triangle. Let's calculate the lengths of the sides of the triangle: $LR = \sqrt{(2 - 1)^2 + (-7 - 3)^2} = \sqrt{101}$, $RN = \sqrt{(1 - -5)^2 + (3 - 8)^2} = \sqrt{61}$, and $LN = \sqrt{(2 - -5)^2 + (-7 - 8)^2} = \sqrt{274}$. Then $c = \sqrt{274}$. Let $a = \sqrt{101}$ and $b = \sqrt{61}$. Then $c^2 = 274$, $a^2 + b^2 = 101 + 61 = 162$, and $c^2 > a^2 + b^2$. So $\triangle LRN$ is an obtuse triangle.

▲

EXAMPLE 13.20

CONNECTION

PROBLEM SOLVING

REASONING

$\triangle ABC$ is a right triangle with the vertices $A(4, 19)$, $B(20, 15)$, and $C(14, -9)$. Identify the right angle.

SOLUTION

Method 1. We see that there are no vertical or horizontal line segments in the triangle. We could use slopes to determine the right angle by identifying the slopes that are negative reciprocals.

$$\text{slope of } \overline{AB} = \frac{19 - 15}{4 - 20} = \frac{4}{-16} = -\frac{1}{4}$$

$$\text{slope of } \overline{BC} = \frac{15 - (-9)}{20 - 14} = \frac{24}{6} = 4$$

$$\text{slope of } \overline{AC} = \frac{19 - (-9)}{4 - 14} = \frac{28}{-10} = -\frac{14}{5}.$$

The slopes $-\frac{1}{4}$ and 4 are negative reciprocals, and B is the common endpoint of $\overline{AB}$ and $\overline{BC}$, so $\angle B$ is the right angle.

Method 2. We could use the distance formula. The right angle in a triangle is always opposite the hypotenuse, which is the longest side of a right triangle. The lengths of the sides are as follows:

$$AB = \sqrt{(4-20)^2 + (19-15)^2} = \sqrt{(-16)^2 + 4^2} = \sqrt{256 + 16} = \sqrt{272}$$
$$BC = \sqrt{(20-14)^2 + (15--9)^2} = \sqrt{6^2 + 24^2} = \sqrt{36 + 576} = \sqrt{612}$$
$$AC = \sqrt{(4-14)^2 + (19--9)^2} = \sqrt{(-10)^2 + 28^2} = \sqrt{100 + 784} = \sqrt{884}$$

Then $\overline{AC}$ is the hypotenuse and $\angle B$ is the right angle. ▲

The following Classroom Connection illustrates that in some situations, students need to relate multiple ideas to answer questions about the vertices of a polygon.

Classroom Connection

- Holt *Mathematics*, Student Edition, p. 350

Square $ABCD$ has the vertices at $(1, 2)$ and $(1, -2)$. Find the possible coordinates of the two missing vertices to create the square with the least area. Justify your solution. (© 2007 by Holt, Rinehart, and Winston. All rights reserved. Reprinted with permission of the publisher, Houghton Mifflin Harcourt Publishing Company.)

The Distance Formula and the Standard Equation of a Circle

We can use the distance formula to derive an equation satisfied by every point on a circle.

EXAMPLE 13.21

CONNECTION

REASONING

A circle has a center of $A(h, k)$ and a radius of r. Verify that all points $B(x, y)$ on the circle satisfy the equation $(x - h)^2 + (y - k)^2 = r^2$.

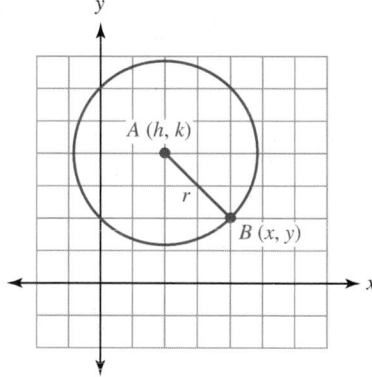

SOLUTION

Let $B(x, y)$ represent any point on the circle with center $A(h, k)$. Every point B on the circle satisfies the equation $BA = r$. Applying the distance formula, we get the following:

$$BA = r$$
$$\sqrt{(x-h)^2 + (y-k)^2} = r$$
$$(x-h)^2 + (y-k)^2 = r^2$$

▲

Standard Equation of a Circle

The **standard equation** of the circle with center (h, k) and radius r units is
$(x - h)^2 + (y - k)^2 = r^2$.

EXAMPLE 13.22 The points on a circle satisfy the equation $(x + 3)^2 + (y - 5)^2 = 30$.

CONNECTION

a. Write the equation in standard form.

REASONING

b. Determine the center and radius of the circle.

SOLUTION

a. The standard form of the equation is $(x - (-3))^2 + (y - 5)^2 = (\sqrt{30})^2$.

b. The center of the circle is $(-3, 5)$, and the radius is $\sqrt{30}$ units.

▲

Similarity, Distance Formula, and the Midpoint Formula

Our goal is to derive a formula for coordinates of the midpoint M of the line segment that joins points $A(x_1, y_1)$ and $B(x_2, y_2)$, as shown in Figure 15(a). To achieve this, we combine our knowledge about determining horizontal and vertical distances, similar triangles, and proportions. It's one example where students should be able to "show that various configurations of lines give rise to similar triangles because of the angles created when a transversal cuts parallel lines" (Gr. 8, CCSS).

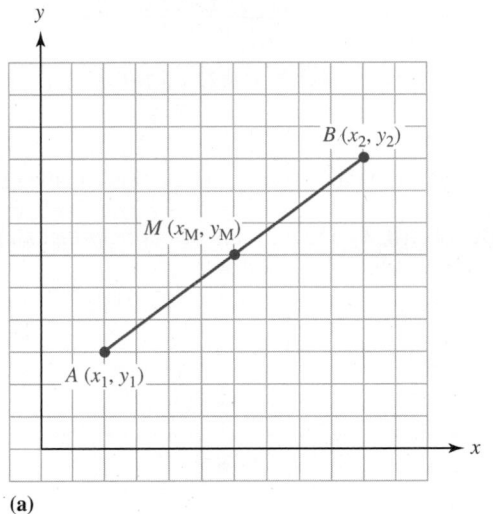

(a)

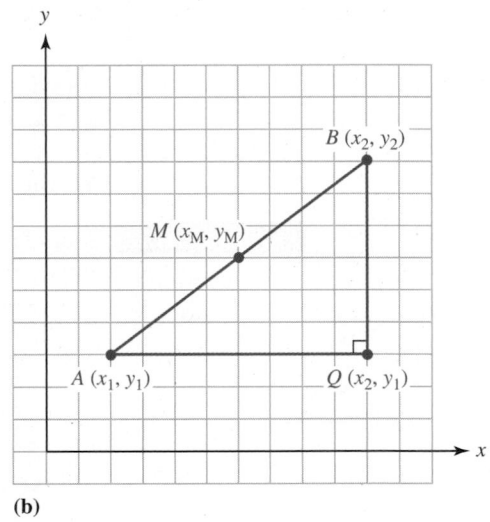

(b)

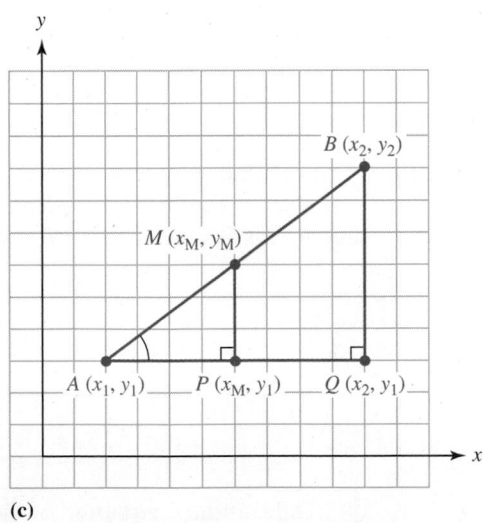

(c)

FIGURE 15
Deriving the Midpoint Formula.

CONNECTION
COMMUNICATION
REASONING
REPRESENTATION

The point Q is the intersection of the horizontal line segment through A and the vertical line segment through B, as shown in Figure 15(b). We see that Q has the coordinates (x_2, y_1). $\triangle ABQ$ is a right triangle, and the distance AB between A and B is the length of the hypotenuse. We also draw a perpendicular line segment from M to $\overline{AQ}$, as shown in Figure 15(c). The point $P(x_M, y_1)$ is the intersection of these two line segments.

This creates two right triangles, $\triangle AMP$ and $\triangle ABQ$. Then $\triangle AMP \sim \triangle ABQ$ by the AA similarity axiom. Then

$$\frac{AM}{AB} = \frac{AP}{AQ} = \frac{MP}{BQ}$$
Because the ratio of corresponding sides is identical

$$\frac{1}{2} = \frac{AP}{AQ} = \frac{MP}{BQ}$$
Because $\dfrac{1}{2} = \dfrac{AM}{AB}$ by definition of the midpoint

$$\frac{1}{2} = \frac{AP}{AQ} \text{ and } \frac{1}{2} = \frac{MP}{BQ}$$
Because each ratio must equal $\dfrac{1}{2}$

$$\frac{1}{2} = \frac{x_M - x_1}{x_2 - x_1} \text{ and } \frac{1}{2} = \frac{y_M - y_1}{y_2 - y_1}$$
Substitution

$$x_M = \frac{x_1 + x_2}{2} \text{ and } y_M = \frac{y_1 + y_2}{2}$$
Solving for x_M and y_M

This result is summarized here.

Formula for the Midpoint of a Line Segment

The **midpoint** $M(x_M, y_M)$ of the line segment that joins $A(x_1, y_1)$ and $B(x_2, y_2)$ has the x-coordinate $x_M = \dfrac{x_1 + x_2}{2}$ and the y-coordinate $y_M = \dfrac{y_1 + y_2}{2}$.

EXAMPLE 13.23   Determine the midpoint M of $\overline{PQ}$ with the endpoints $P(5, -4)$ and $Q(7, 15)$.

CONNECTION

SOLUTION

The midpoint has the x-coordinate $x_M = \dfrac{x_1 + x_2}{2} = \dfrac{5 + 7}{2} = \dfrac{12}{2} = 6$ and the y-coordinate $y_M = \dfrac{y_1 + y_2}{2} = \dfrac{-4 + 15}{2} = \dfrac{11}{2} = 5.5$. The midpoint of $\overline{PQ}$ is $M(6, 5.5)$.

▲

EXAMPLE 13.24   Find the equation of the perpendicular bisector of the line segment joining $A(-6, 1)$ and $B(2, 4)$.

CONNECTION
COMMUNICATION
PROBLEM SOLVING
REASONING
REPRESENTATION

SOLUTION

The perpendicular bisector of $\overline{AB}$ passes through the midpoint of $\overline{AB}$ and has a slope that is the negative reciprocal of the slope of $\overline{AB}$.

- The midpoint has the x-coordinate $x_M = \dfrac{x_1 + x_2}{2} = \dfrac{-6 + 2}{2} = -2$ and the y-coordinate $y_M = \dfrac{y_1 + y_2}{2} = \dfrac{1 + 4}{2} = \dfrac{5}{2}$. The midpoint of $\overline{AB}$ is $M\left(-2, \dfrac{5}{2}\right)$.

- The slope of $\overline{AB}$ is $\dfrac{\text{rise}}{\text{run}} = \dfrac{4 - 1}{2 - (-6)} = \dfrac{3}{8}$.

(continued)

The slope of the perpendicular bisector is the negative reciprocal of $\frac{3}{8}$, or $-\frac{8}{3}$. The perpendicular bisector has the equation $y = -\frac{8}{3}x + b$ and passes through $\left(-2, \frac{5}{2}\right)$. We need to choose b such that $\frac{5}{2} = -\frac{8}{3} \cdot (-2) + b$, so $b = -\frac{17}{6}$. Then the equation of the perpendicular bisector is $y = -\frac{8}{3}x - \frac{17}{6}$.

▲

Coordinate Proofs

One of the main goals in this section is to learn how to use coordinate geometry to verify some properties of polygons. Students should be able to "use coordinate geometry to represent and examine properties of geometric shapes and use coordinate geometry to examine special geometric shapes, such as regular polygons or those with pairs of parallel or perpendicular sides" (Gr. 6–8, NCTM). We should be ready to apply the following tools: the midpoint formula, distance formula, slope, and definitions of polygons.

In coordinate geometry, each vertex of a polygon corresponds to an ordered pair. If we use ordered pairs with numbers, then the properties hold for that particular polygon. For example, Figure 16 shows rectangle $ABCD$ with the given points $A(2, 4)$, $B(2, 8)$, $C(9, 8)$, and $D(9, 4)$.

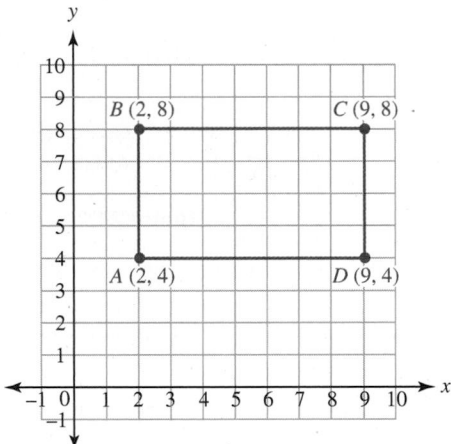

FIGURE 16
Rectangle $ABCD$.

We can use the distance formula to prove the diagonals of rectangle $ABCD$ are congruent:

$$AC = \sqrt{(9 - 2)^2 + (8 - 4)^2} = \sqrt{49 + 16} = \sqrt{65} \text{ units}$$
$$BD = \sqrt{(2 - 9)^2 + (8 - 4)^2} = \sqrt{49 + 16} = \sqrt{65} \text{ units}$$

The coordinate proof for showing the diagonals of rectangle $ABCD$ in Figure 16 are congruent only applies to rectangle $ABCD$. We have to use variables as coordinates in the ordered pairs to make generalizations to any rectangle $ABCD$. Assigning one of the vertices as the origin and positioning one of the sides of the polygon along an axis simplifies labeling the other vertices because some of the coordinates have a value of 0. The use of variables in the ordered pairs leads to generalizations with proofs that involve algebraic reasoning.

Let's use coordinate geometry to prove the diagonals of a rectangle are congruent. According to the definition of a rectangle, the opposite sides of a rectangle are parallel and it has four right angles. We have to use definitions, along with any given assumptions, to draw the diagram and assign coordinates to the vertices. Figure 17 shows rectangle $ABCD$. Here's how we arrived at this diagram.

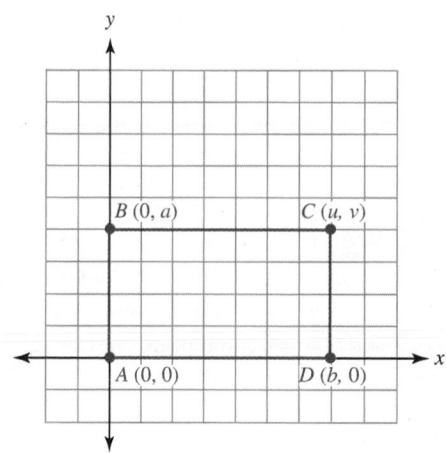

FIGURE 17
Position the sides of the rectangle along the axes.

1. We chose A to have the coordinates $(0, 0)$.

2. We placed B along the y-axis. $\overline{AB}$ can have any length, so we assigned B with the co-ordinates $(0, a)$.

3. $\overline{AB}$ and $\overline{AD}$ must be perpendicular, so we placed D along the x-axis. $\overline{AD}$ can have any length, so we assigned D with the coordinates $(b, 0)$.

4. We initially assigned the point C with the coordinates (u, v), but we need to use reasoning to rename the coordinates of C to ensure the opposite sides of the rectangle are parallel.

The sides $\overline{AB}$ and $\overline{CD}$ must be parallel and $\overline{AB}$ is a vertical line segment, so $\overline{CD}$ must be a vertical line segment. $\overline{CD}$ contains the point $(b, 0)$, so the x-coordinate of C must be b. Therefore, $u = b$.

The sides $\overline{AD}$ and $\overline{BC}$ must be parallel and $\overline{AD}$ is a horizontal line segment, so $\overline{BC}$ must be a horizontal line segment. $\overline{BC}$ contains the point $(0, a)$, so the y-coordinate of C must be a. Therefore, $v = a$. Then the point (b, a) is now C. This leads to the graph in Figure 18.

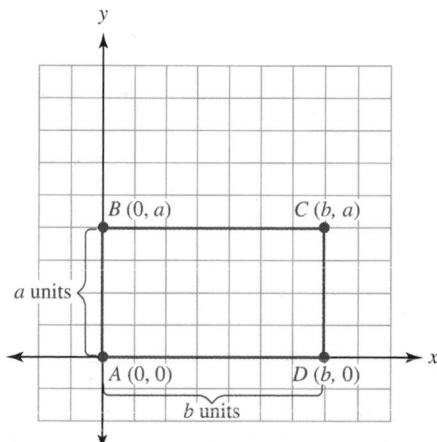

FIGURE 18
General graph of a rectangle in the coordinate plane.

EXAMPLE 13.25 Use coordinate geometry to prove the diagonals of a rectangle are congruent.

CONNECTION

REASONING **SOLUTION**

REPRESENTATION We position rectangle $ABCD$ as shown in Figure 18. We need to compute the length of each diagonal:

(continued)

$$AC = \sqrt{(b-0)^2 + (a-0)^2} = \sqrt{b^2 + a^2}$$
$$BD = \sqrt{(0-b)^2 + (a-0)^2} = \sqrt{(-b)^2 + a^2} = \sqrt{b^2 + a^2}$$

$AC = BD$, so $\overline{AC} \cong \overline{BD}$. The diagonals of a rectangle are congruent. ▲

EXAMPLE 13.26 *ABCD* is a parallelogram.

CONNECTION
COMMUNICATION
PROBLEM SOLVING
REASONING
REPRESENTATION

a. Draw *ABCD* and label the vertices in a coordinate geometry.

b. Verify that your choice for the coordinates of the vertices ensures *ABCD* is a parallelogram.

SOLUTION

a. We need to assign coordinates to the vertices of *ABCD*.

- We chose *A* to have the coordinates $(0, 0)$.

- We placed *B* in the first quadrant with the coordinates (a, b).

- We placed *D* on the *x*-axis. $\overline{AD}$ can have any length, so we assigned *D* with the coordinates $(c, 0)$.

- We initially assigned the point *C* with the coordinates (u, v), but we need to use reasoning to rename the coordinates of *C* to ensure that opposite sides of the parallelogram are parallel. This leads to the graph in Figure 19.

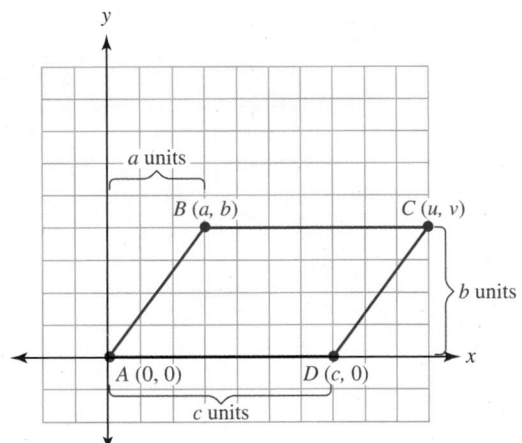

FIGURE 19
Initial placement and labeling of the parallelogram.

We know the opposite sides of a parallelogram are parallel. $\overline{AD}$ is a horizontal line segment, so $\overline{BC}$ must be a horizontal line segment. So *B* and *C* must have the same *y*-coordinate. Then *C* has the coordinates (u, b). $\overline{AB}$ and $\overline{CD}$ must be parallel, so their slopes must be equal. The slope of $\overline{AB}$ is $\frac{b}{a}$. The slope of $\overline{CD}$ is $\frac{b}{u-c}$. Then

$$\frac{b}{a} = \frac{b}{u-c}$$ **Because the slope of $\overline{AB}$ equals the slope of $\overline{CD}$**

$$b(u - c) = ba$$ **Because in a proportion, the cross-products are equal**

$$u - c = a$$ **Dividing both sides by *b***

$$u = a + c$$ **Definition of subtraction**

Figure 20 shows the labels of the vertices of the parallelogram with a minimal use of variables.

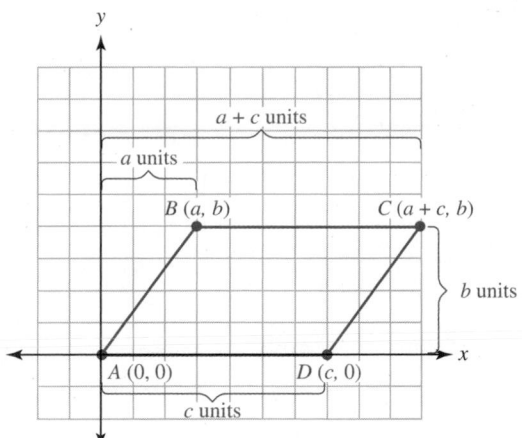

FIGURE 20
General graph of a parallelogram in the coordinate plane.

b. $\overline{AD}$ and $\overline{BC}$ each have a slope of 0, and $\overline{AB}$ and $\overline{DC}$ each have a slope of $\frac{b}{a}$. Opposite sides of $ABCD$ are parallel.

▲

A homework question asks you to use Figure 20 to prove the following theorems about parallelograms:

- The opposite sides of a parallelogram are congruent.
- The diagonals of a parallelogram bisect each other.

In the following example, we show how to strategically place an isosceles triangle in the coordinate plane and prove that the perpendicular bisector of the base of the isosceles triangle contains the apex of the triangle.

EXAMPLE 13.27

CONNECTION
COMMUNICATION
PROBLEM SOLVING
REASONING
REPRESENTATION

a. Draw an isosceles triangle in a coordinate plane. Verify that your choice for the coordinates of the vertices ensures the triangle is an isosceles triangle.

b. Prove that the perpendicular bisector of the base contains the apex of the isosceles triangle.

SOLUTION

a. We place the vertices A, B, and C as shown in Figure 21, with A and C along the x-axis. We must assign coordinates to C so that the legs are congruent; that is, $AB = BC$. Then

$$AB = \sqrt{(a - 0)^2 + (b - 0)^2} = \sqrt{a^2 + b^2}$$
$$BC = \sqrt{(a - u)^2 + (b - 0)^2} = \sqrt{(a - u)^2 + b^2}$$

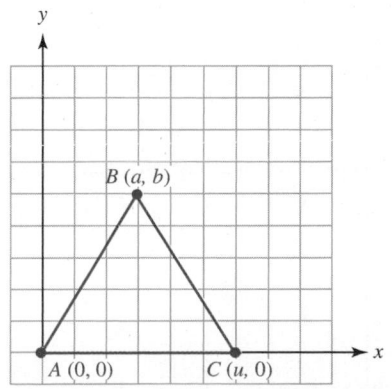

FIGURE 21
Initial placement and labeling of the isosceles triangle.

(continued)

So

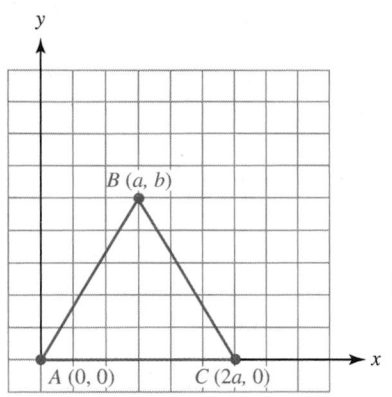

FIGURE 22

General graph of an isosceles triangle in the coordinate plane.

$AB = BC$	Because the legs of an isosceles triangle are congruent
$\sqrt{a^2 + b^2} = \sqrt{(a - u)^2 + b^2}$	Substitution
$a^2 + b^2 = (a - u)^2 + b^2$	Squaring both sides of the equation
$a^2 = (a - u)^2$	Subtracting b^2 from both sides
$a^2 = (u - a)^2$	Because $(n)^2 = (-n)^2$
$a = u - a$	Because $u - a$ is positive, taking the square root of both sides
$2a = u$	Solving for u

Then $u = 2a$. So the coordinates for C are $(2a, 0)$, and $AB = BC = \sqrt{a^2 + b^2}$.

b. Figure 22 shows the graph for the isosceles triangle. B is the apex of the isosceles triangle. We must show the perpendicular bisector of $\overline{AC}$ passes through B.

The midpoint of $\overline{AC}$ is $M(a, 0)$. The perpendicular bisector of $\overline{AC}$ must contain the midpoint $M(a, 0)$. $\overleftrightarrow{AC}$ is a horizontal line, so the perpendicular bisector must be a vertical line passing through $M(a, 0)$. Then the perpendicular bisector is a vertical line described by the equation $x = a$. The point $B(a, b)$ has the x-coordinate $x = a$, so the perpendicular bisector contains the apex B of the isosceles triangle. ▲

QUESTIONS FOR SECTION 13.2

REPRESENTATION

Refresher: Representations (language, diagrams, tables, symbols, algebra, manipulatives, and contextualized situations) are important because we use them to organize, record, and communicate mathematical ideas and make them more comprehensible.

1. *ABCD* is a parallelogram. Find the coordinates of each vertex: *A, B, C,* and *D.*

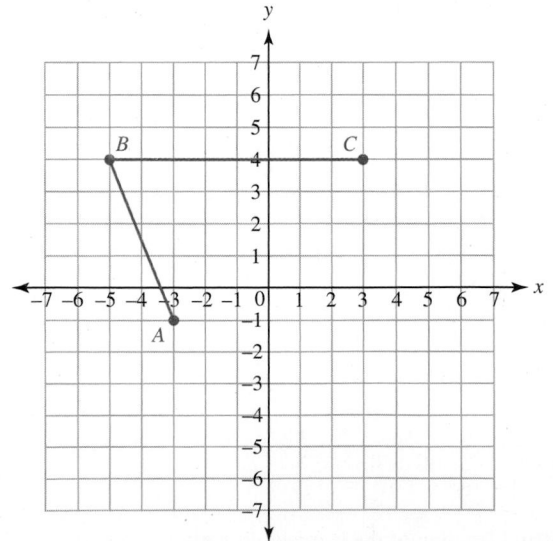

2. *ABCD* is a parallelogram. Find the coordinates of each vertex: *A, B, C,* and *D.*

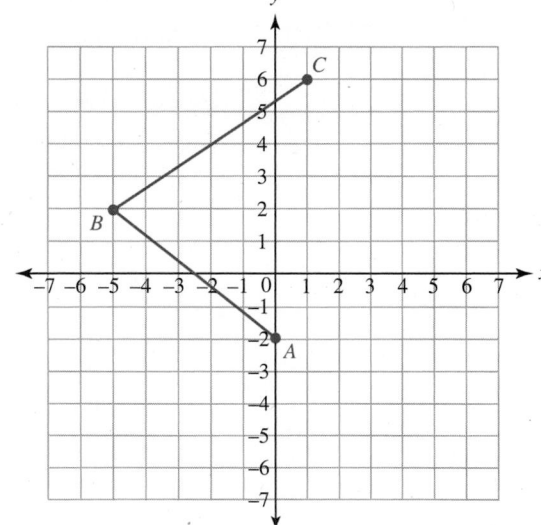

3. *ABCD* is a rectangle. Find the coordinates of each vertex: *A, B, C,* and *D.*

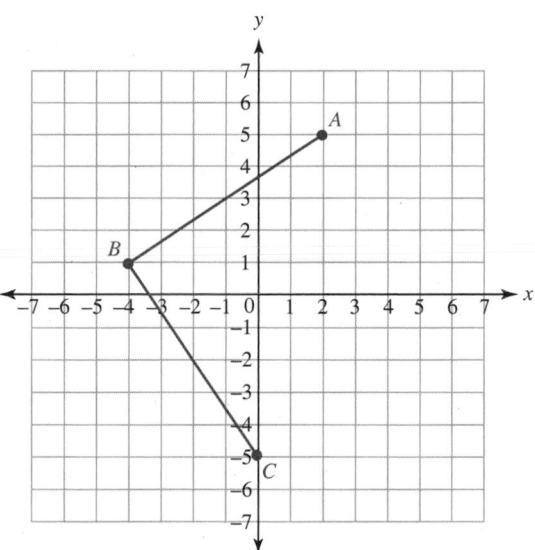

4. △*ABC* is a right triangle. Find the coordinates of *C.*

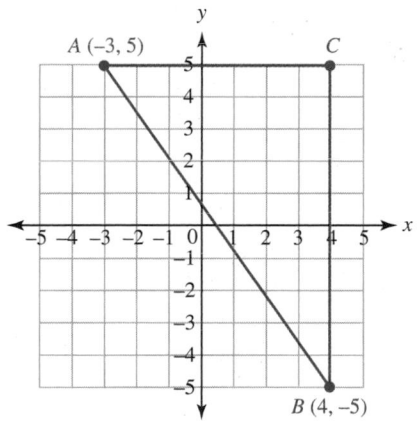

5. Write the standard form of the equation of the circle shown.

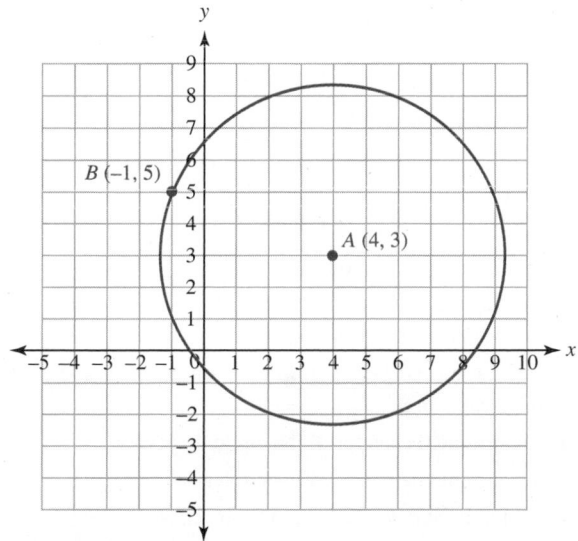

6. Rectangle *ABCD* in a coordinate system has the vertices shown. Use appropriate variables to represent the coordinates of *B* and *D.*

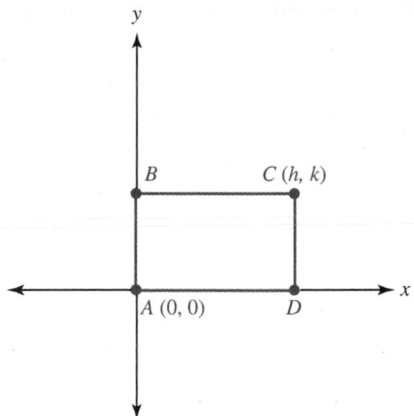

7. Isosceles trapezoid *ABCD* in a coordinate system has the vertices shown (where *AB* = *CD*). Use appropriate expressions to represent the coordinates of *B* and *D.*

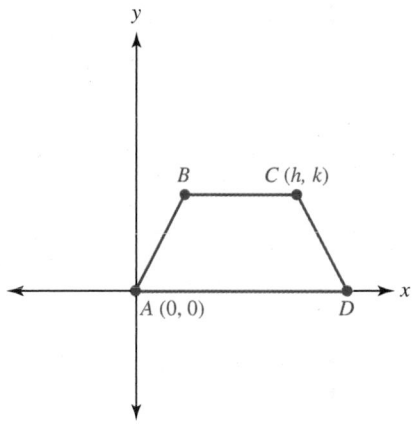

PROBLEM SOLVING

Refresher: Problem solving (reaching a goal that is not immediately attainable) is important because it helps students think more deeply about what they know and deal with unfamiliar situations.

8. Find a positive value for *k* such that $A(k, 3)$, $B(4, -3)$, and $C(7, -2)$ are vertices of a right triangle.

9. Do the following.

   a. Graph $R(4, 5)$ and the line segment with the endpoints $L(-5, 4)$ and $N(7, 2)$ in a coordinate system.

   b. Find the equation of line *k* through *R* and perpendicular to $\overleftrightarrow{LN}$.

10. △*LRN* has an area of 6 square units and a height of 3 units.

   a. What is the length of the base of the triangle for the given height?

   b. Give an example of coordinates of *L, R,* and *N* such that the area of the triangle is 6 square units, the height of the triangle is 3 units, and the base has the length found in part (a).

   c. Draw the triangle in the coordinate plane.

11. Find the area of the quadrilateral with the vertices $A(-2, 2)$, $B(3, 5)$, $C(10, 5)$, and $D(5, 2)$.

12. The width of a rectangle is 3 units more than four times the length of the rectangle. Draw the rectangle in a coordinate plane. Include the coordinates of each vertex of the rectangle.

REASONING AND PROOF

Refresher: Reasoning and proof (thinking and justifying) are important because they help students make sense of mathematics.

13. Parallelogram $ABCD$ has the vertices $A(-2, 4)$, $B(3, 7)$, $C(3, -2)$, and $D(-2, -5)$. Prove that the diagonals bisect each other.

14. Parallelogram $ABCD$ has the vertices $A(-2, 3)$, $B(3, -5)$, $C(-3, -7)$, and $D(-8, 1)$. Prove that the diagonals bisect each other.

15. Prove that the points $A(-4, 2)$, $B(2, 6)$, $C(-1, 0)$, and $D(-7, -4)$ are the vertices of a parallelogram.

16. $A(-2, 2)$, $B(3, -3)$, $C(6, 0)$, and $D(1, 5)$ are the vertices of a rectangle. Show that $\overline{AC}$ and $\overline{BD}$
    a. are congruent.   b. bisect each other.

17. $A(-1, 3)$, $B(2, -3)$, $C(9, -2)$, and $D(6, 4)$ are the vertices of a quadrilateral.
    a. Prove $\overline{AB} \cong \overline{CD}$.   b. Prove $\overline{AD} \cong \overline{BC}$.

18. Given the equation $\dfrac{1}{2} = \dfrac{x_M - x_1}{x_2 - x_1}$, solve for x_M to verify that $x_M = \dfrac{x_1 + x_2}{2}$.

19. Given the equation $\dfrac{1}{2} = \dfrac{y_M - y_1}{y_2 - y_1}$, solve for y_M to verify that $y_M = \dfrac{y_1 + y_2}{2}$.

CONNECTIONS

Refresher: Connections (linking and applying mathematical ideas) are important because they deepen student understanding and make mathematics more meaningful, flexible, and useful.

20. $\triangle CAT$ has the vertices $C(3, -2)$, $A(8, -1)$, and $T(10, 7)$. Identify the angle of $\triangle CAT$ with the
    a. largest measure.
    b. smallest measure.

21. Verify that $A(3, 5)$, $B(6, 1)$, and $C(10, 4)$ are the vertices of a right triangle using the converse of the Pythagorean theorem.

22. $P(0.5, 9.25)$, $Q(3.5, 8.75)$, and $R(2.25, 7.5)$ are the vertices of a right triangle. Which line segment is the hypotenuse? Explain your answer.

23. $A(3, 7)$, $B(8, 9)$, $C(6, 4)$, and $D(1, 2)$ are the vertices of a quadrilateral. Use slopes to verify that the quadrilateral is a parallelogram.

24. $A(3, 5)$, $B(6, 1)$, and $C(10, 4)$ are the vertices of a triangle. Use slopes to verify that the triangle is a right triangle.

25. Find the equation of the line that is a perpendicular bisector of $\overline{AB}$, with the endpoints $A(7, 3)$ and $B(4, -1)$.

26. $W(5, 7)$ is the center of a circle. A is a point on the circle with the coordinates $(-11, 18)$. Determine the coordinates of a point B on the circle so that $\overline{AB}$ is a diameter for the circle.

27. $\triangle FUN$ has the vertices $F(7, 5)$, $U(-8, 2)$, and $N(3, 1)$. Use the distance formula to classify the triangle as acute, right, or obtuse.

28. A circle has a center of $(0, 0)$ with a radius of r units.
    a. Write the equation of the circle.
    b. $\overline{PQ}$ is a diameter of the circle with endpoints on the x axis, and $R(b, c)$ is any other point on the circle, as shown. Prove that $\triangle PQR$ is a right triangle.

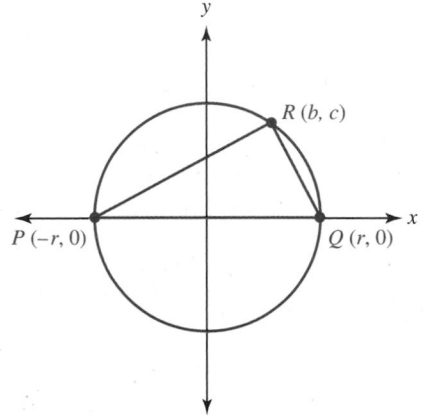

COMMUNICATION

Refresher: Communication (written and verbal explanations using representations and proper mathematical vocabulary) is important because it helps students refine and strengthen their understanding.

29. $A(2, 4)$, $B(6, -1)$, $C(10, 2)$, and $D(6, 7)$ are the vertices of a quadrilateral.
    a. Show that opposite sides are congruent.
    b. Show that opposite sides are parallel.
    c. Is $ABCD$ a rectangle?

More practice with the ideas of the section

30. Determine the midpoint of the line segment with the endpoints A and B.
    a. $A(4, -2), B(7, -6)$ b. $A(-6, 2), B(4, 3)$

31. M is the midpoint of $\overline{AB}$. Determine the coordinates of the missing endpoint of the line segment.
    a. $M(6, -13), A(4, -2)$
    b. $M(6, -13), B(6, 10)$

32. Prove that the points $A(1, 2)$, $B(2, 5)$, $C(8, 5)$, and $D(7, 2)$ are the vertices of a parallelogram.

33. $P(-3, 5)$ and $Q(11, 7)$ are points on a circle, and $\overline{PQ}$ is a diameter of a circle.
    a. Determine the center of the circle.
    b. Determine the radius of the circle.
    c. Write the standard equation of the circle.

34. $A(3, 5)$ and $B(9, 1)$ are points on a circle, and $\overline{AB}$ is a diameter of a circle.

   a. Determine the center of the circle.

   b. Determine the radius of the circle.

   c. Write the standard equation of the circle.

35. $\triangle KIT$ has the vertices $K(2, 5)$, $I(-3, 2)$, and $T(5, 7)$. Use the distance formula to classify the triangle as acute, right, or obtuse.

36. $\triangle RPM$ has the vertices $R(-5, 3)$, $P(-5, -5)$, and $M(4, -5)$. Use the distance formula to classify the triangle as acute, right, or obtuse.

37. $\triangle UPS$ has the vertices $U(-3, 4)$, $P(-4, -5)$, and $S(4, -2)$. Use the distance formula to classify the triangle as acute, right, or obtuse.

38. The width of a rectangle is 2 units more than three times the length of the rectangle. Draw the rectangle in a coordinate plane. Include the coordinates of each vertex of the rectangle.

39. $A(-1, 2)$, $B(3, -6)$, $C(7, -4)$, and $D(3, 4)$ are the vertices of a rectangle. Show that $\overline{AC}$ and $\overline{BD}$

   a. are congruent.   **b.** bisect each other.

40. The distance between $(x, 3)$ and $(2, 7)$ is 5. Find x.

41. A teacher drew the isosceles triangle $\triangle HAT$, as shown, with a base of $\overline{HT}$.

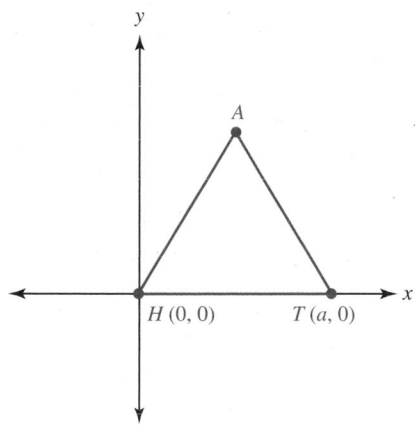

He asked his students to use variables to label the coordinates of A. Maria thought about this and claimed the coordinates of A are $(a/2, b)$. The teacher asked her to justify her answer. Maria said she began by observing that the y-coordinate of A is height of the triangle and that there was no restriction on the height, so she chose a new variable b to represent the y-coordinate of A. Then she said she considered the coordinates (u, b) for A and planned to choose u to ensure that $HA = AT$. Then the bell rang and the hungry class rushed to lunch.

   a. Assuming Maria is correct that A has the coordinates $(a/2, b)$, verify that $HA = AT$.

   b. Using the coordinates (u, b) for A, show how Maria used algebra and the equation $HA = AT$ to arrive at the equation $u = a/2$.

42. The diagram shows an isosceles trapezoid and the coordinates of its vertices. Verify the following properties of the given isosceles trapezoid.

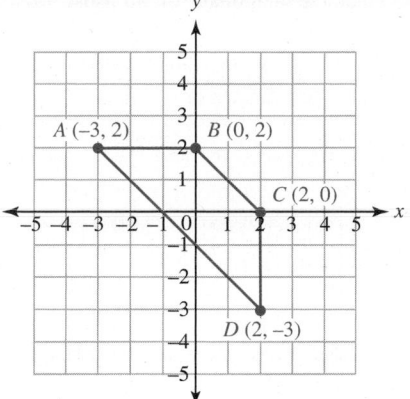

   a. The diagonals are congruent.

   b. The bases are parallel.   **c.** The legs are congruent.

43. The diagram shows an isosceles trapezoid and the coordinates of its vertices. Verify the following properties of the given isosceles trapezoid.

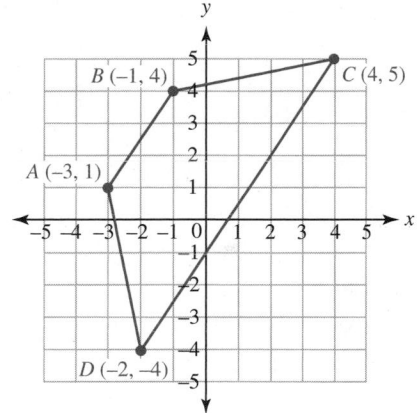

   a. The diagonals are congruent.

   b. The bases are parallel.   **c.** The legs are congruent.

44. Isosceles trapezoid $ABCD$ in a coordinate system has the vertices shown.

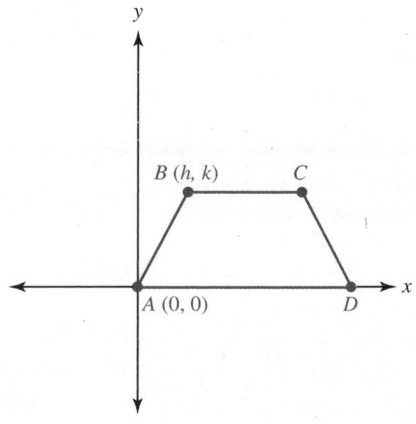

a. Use appropriate variables to represent the coordinates of C and D.

b. Using your answers in part (a), verify that $\overline{AB} \cong \overline{CD}$.

c. Verify that the diagonals of an isosceles trapezoid are congruent.

45. Rhombus $ABCD$ in a coordinate system has the vertices shown. Find the coordinates of B.

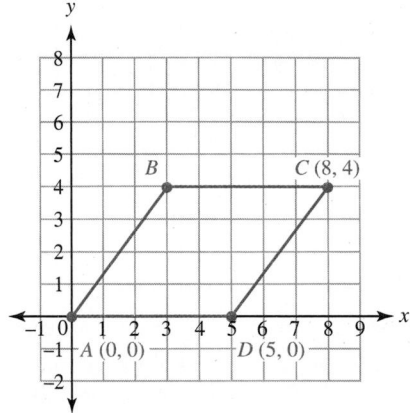

46. Rhombus $ABCD$ in a coordinate system has the vertices shown.

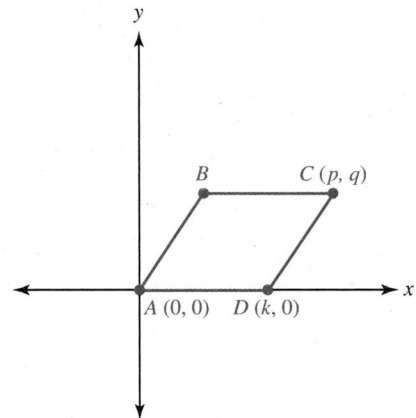

a. Express the coordinates of B in terms of k, p, and q.

b. Prove that k, p, and q are related by the equation $p^2 + q^2 = 2pk$.

c. Write a formula for the area A of the rhombus in terms of k, p, and q.

47. The diagram shows a rhombus and the coordinates of its vertices. Verify the following properties of the given rhombus.

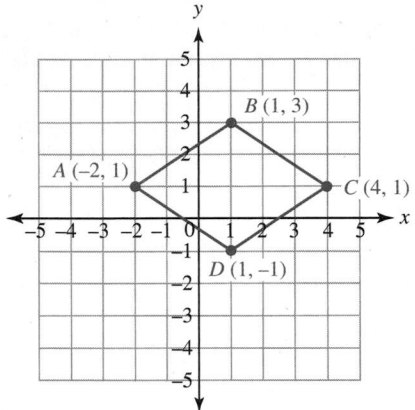

a. The diagonals are perpendicular.

b. The diagonals bisect each other.

c. The opposite sides are parallel.

48. The diagram shows a kite and the coordinates of its vertices. Verify the following properties of the given kite.

a. The diagonals of the kite are perpendicular.

b. One diagonal of the kite bisects the other diagonal.

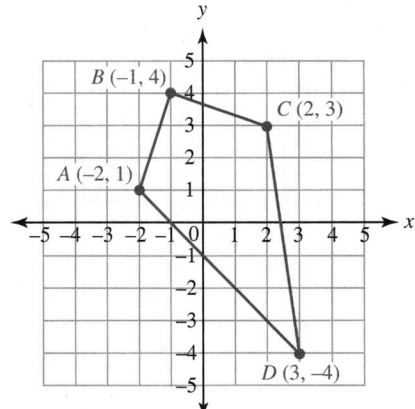

SECTION 13.3 Transformations of the Plane

What Is a Transformation?

Recall that a function relates two sets of objects. The element a in one set is associated with exactly one element $f(a)$ in the other set. We say the "image" of a is $f(a)$. We also say the "preimage" of $f(a)$ is a. A **mapping** relates two sets of points in the plane. In a mapping, the **image** of point P is the point P', and the **preimage** of P' is P.

transformation

A transformation of the plane is a special type of mapping.

Definition of a Transformation

A **transformation** maps the plane to itself such that every point in the plane has one image and every point in the plane has one preimage.

In a transformation, every point P in the plane corresponds to a unique point P' in the plane. A transformation maps the point (a, b) to the unique point (c, d). For example, in Figure 23, the point (a, b) is mapped to the point $(a + 2b, a + b)$. Here, the point $B(1, 2)$ is mapped to $B'(5, 3)$ because $1 + 2 \cdot 2 = 5$ and $1 + 2 = 3$.

REPRESENTATION

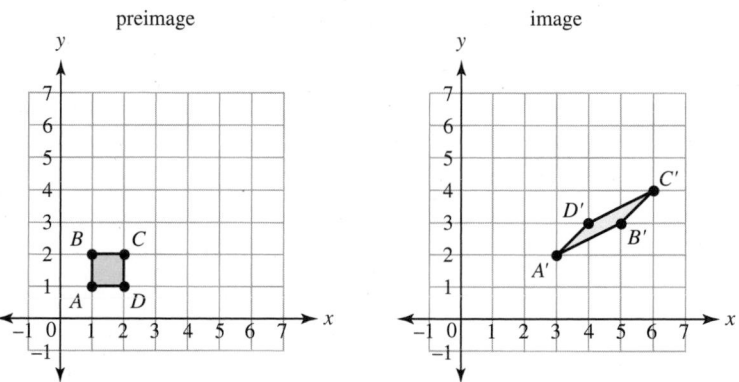

FIGURE 23
Visual example of a plane transformation.

The points $A(1, 1)$ and $B(1, 2)$ have the images $A'(3, 2)$ and $B'(5, 3)$. $AB = 1$ unit and $A'B' = \sqrt{5}$ units, but $AB \neq A'B'$. The plane transformation in Figure 23 does not preserve distances because there exist points A and B such that $AB \neq A'B'$.

A rigid motion is a transformation of the plane that preserves distances. Mathematically, this means that for any two points A and B in the plane, the distance between A and B equals the distance between A' and B' (i.e., $AB = A'B'$).

Definition of a Rigid Motion (Isometry)

Words

A **rigid motion** (also called an **isometry**) is a transformation of the plane that preserves distances.

Notation

A rigid motion is a transformation of the plane such that $AB = A'B'$ for any two points A and B.

Interpretation

A rigid motion does not distort, enlarge, or shrink images.

The word *isometry* has Greek roots: *iso* means "equal" and *metron* means "measure." A rigid motion preserves distances, so a triangle gets mapped to a triangle (by the SSS congruence axiom), and it preserves angles (by CPCTC). Furthermore, parallel lines get mapped to parallel lines because angles are preserved (just think of the F Postulate in Chapter 10).

There are exactly three basic rigid motions of the plane: translation (slide), reflection (flip), and rotation (turn). Every possible rigid motion of the plane can be expressed as some sequence of these three basic rigid motions, so we focus on these three types of movements. Figure 24 demonstrates their movements with △*ABC* and its image △*A'B'C'*.

REPRESENTATION

Translation (slide)

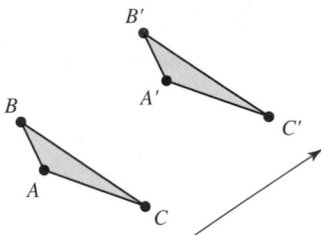

Reflection (flip)

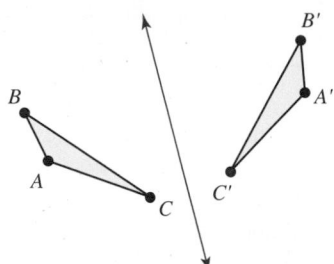

Rotation (turn)

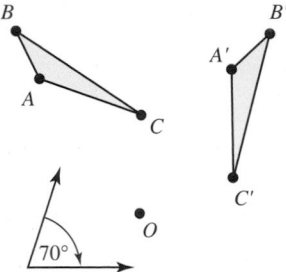

In a translation, every point moves the same direction and distance.

In a reflection, every point on one side of the mirror line has a corresponding point on the other side of the line the same distance from the line.

In a rotation, every point turns a certain number of degrees in the same direction (clockwise or counterclockwise) using a center of rotation.

FIGURE 24

Three basic rigid motions of the plane: translation, reflection, and rotation.

If two figures are congruent, then there is a sequence of translations, reflections, rotations, or some combination of these that maps one figure to another congruent figure. For example, a sequence may consist of one reflection. It may consist of two reflections. Or it may consist of two reflections followed by a rotation.

Translation

A translation shifts every point in the plane the same direction by the same distance. It involves a movement along a straight line. Figure 25 illustrates a translation. The **translation vector** tells us the direction, and the distance between the initial point and the terminal point of the translation vector tells us how far the points in the plane move.

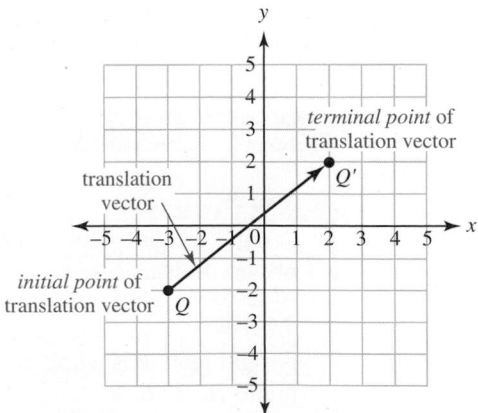

FIGURE 25

Visual representation of a translation.

EXAMPLE 13.28 A translation point maps point A to the point A' in the coordinate system, as shown.

CONNECTION

COMMUNICATION

REASONING

REPRESENTATION

a. Describe how points move under the translation.

b. Locate the image of B.

c. Compare AA' and BB'.

d. Draw a translation vector.

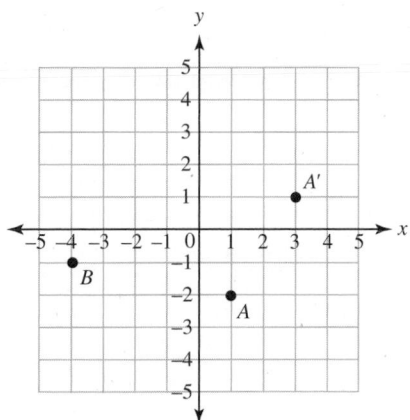

SOLUTION

a. To move from A to A', we need to move 2 units to the right and 3 units upward. The translation moves every point 2 units to the right and 3 units upward.

b. The diagram shows the location of B'.

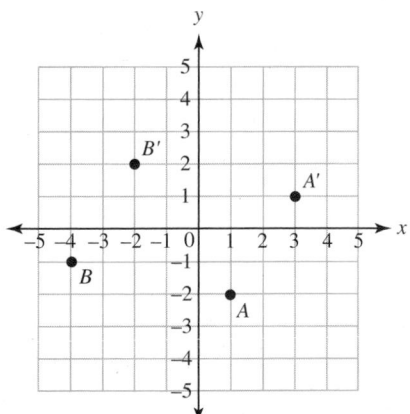

c. The distance between $A(1, -2)$ and $A'(3, 1)$ is $AA' = \sqrt{(1-3)^2 + (-2-1)^2} = \sqrt{(-2)^2 + (-3)^2} = \sqrt{13}$ units. The distance between $B(-4, -1)$ and $B'(-2, 2)$ is $BB' = \sqrt{(-4--2)^2 + (-1-2)^2} = \sqrt{(-2)^2 + (-3)^2} = \sqrt{13}$ units. So $AA' = BB'$. This means A and B moved the same distance.

d. A translation vector for this translation is any vector with the property that you can move from the initial point to the terminal point by moving 2 units to the right and 3 units upward. The diagram shows a possible translation vector.

(continued)

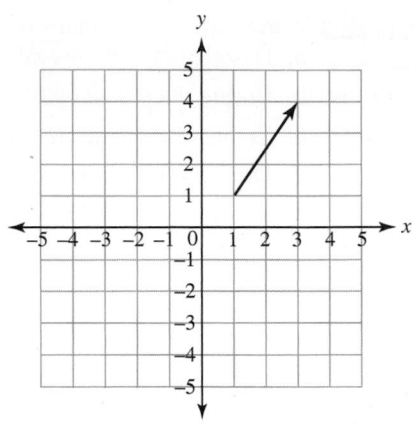

Definition of a Translation

A **translation** is a transformation of the plane such that every point moves the same distance in the same direction.

The length of a translation vector equals the distance between a point and its image. If a translation moves A to A' and B to B', then $AA' = BB'$ by definition. (Shortly, we show that $AB = A'B'$ for any two points A and B.)

EXAMPLE 13.29

CONNECTION
COMMUNICATION
REASONING
REPRESENTATION

A translation moves every point 4 units horizontally to the right and 5 units downward. How far does each point move?

SOLUTION

We represent the translation vector with a diagram. We can apply the Pythagorean theorem to find the distance: $\sqrt{4^2 + 5^2} = \sqrt{16 + 25} = \sqrt{41}$.

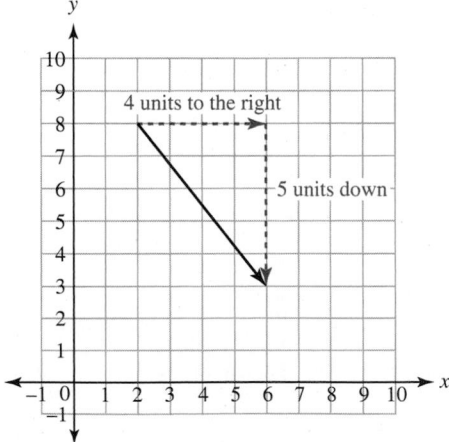

Therefore, each point moves $\sqrt{41}$ units.

Now we prove that a translation preserves distances and therefore is a rigid motion of the plane. This means a translation does not distort, enlarge, or shrink images.

EXAMPLE 13.30 A translation maps A to A' and B to B', as shown. Prove $AB = A'B'$.

CONNECTION
COMMUNICATION
REASONING
REPRESENTATION

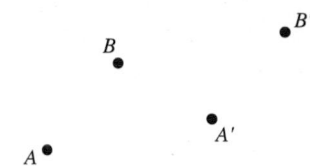

SOLUTION

A translation moves all points the same distance in the same direction, so $\overline{AA'}$ and $\overline{BB'}$ are congruent and parallel line segments. $\angle BB'A$ and $\angle A'AB$ are alternate interior angles formed by a transversal that cuts parallel line segments, so $\angle BB'A \cong \angle A'AB'$. $\overline{AB'} \cong \overline{B'A}$ by the reflexive property of congruence.

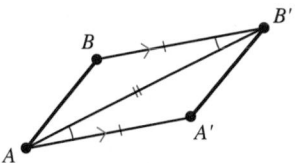

Then $\triangle BB'A \cong \triangle A'AB'$ by the SAS congruence axiom. Consequently, $\overline{AB} \cong \overline{A'B'}$ by CPCTC. Thus, $AB = A'B'$, by definition of congruent line segments. ▲

Reflection

A reflection requires a line called a **mirror line** (also called a line of reflection). It is similar to reflecting an image in a mirror. The diagram in Figure 26 illustrates a reflection with the mirror line l.

REPRESENTATION

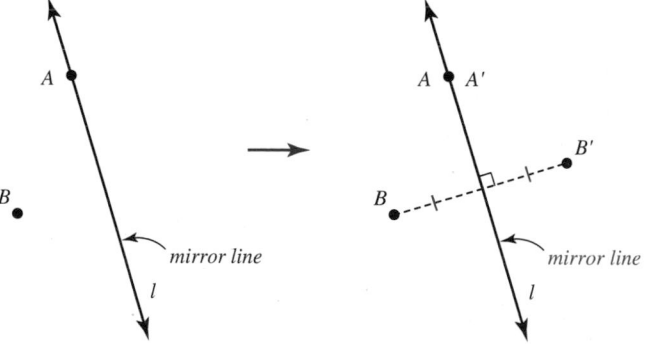

FIGURE 26
Representation of a reflection about line l.

Every point A on line l is mapped to itself so that $A = A'$, and every point B that does not belong to l is mapped to a point B' such that l is the perpendicular bisector of the line segment that joins B and B'.

> **Definition of a Reflection**
>
> A **reflection** is a transformation of the plane such that there is a line l, called the mirror line, with the following properties:
>
> **1.** If point A belongs to l, then $A = A'$.
> **2.** If point A does not belong to l, then l is the perpendicular bisector of $\overline{AA'}$.

EXAMPLE 13.31

CONNECTION
COMMUNICATION
REASONING
REPRESENTATION

Sketch an image of point Q under the reflection with the mirror line l, as shown.

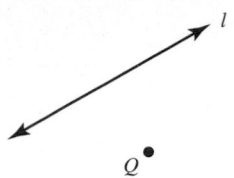

SOLUTION

Q does not belong to the line, so the mirror line l is the perpendicular bisector of $\overline{QQ'}$.

Step 1. Draw a line through Q and perpendicular to l, and let point M be the intersection of the lines.

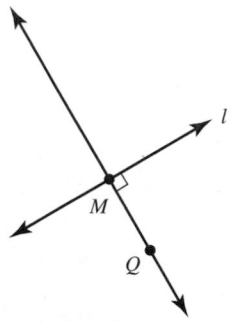

Step 2. Locate point Q' on $\overleftrightarrow{QM}$ so that M is the midpoint of $\overline{QQ'}$ (you can use a compass).

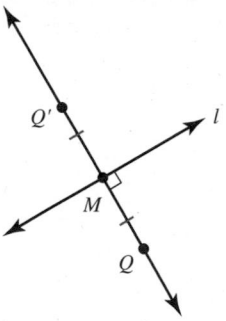

EXAMPLE 13.32

CONNECTION
COMMUNICATION
REASONING
REPRESENTATION

The diagram shows point A and its image A' under a reflection about line l. Sketch the mirror line l.

$A \bullet$

$\bullet A'$

SOLUTION

$A \neq A'$, so point A does not belong to the line. This means the mirror line l is the perpendicular bisector of $\overline{AA'}$.

Step 1. Draw a line segment joining A and A', and locate the midpoint M of the line segment.

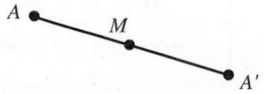

STEP 2. Draw the perpendicular bisector of $\overline{AA'}$ through the midpoint M. The mirror line is perpendicular to $\overline{AA'}$.

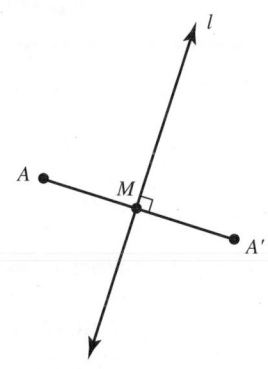

The following example suggests that a reflection preserves distances and therefore is a rigid motion of the plane. This means a reflection does not distort, enlarge, or shrink images.

EXAMPLE 13.33

CONNECTION
COMMUNICATION
REASONING
REPRESENTATION

A reflection maps A to A' and B to B', as shown. Prove $AB = A'B'$.

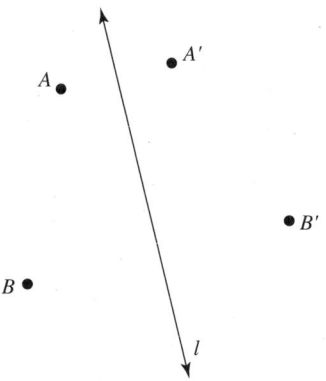

SOLUTION

Figure 27(a) shows the images of A and B and the midpoints M and K of line segments $\overline{AA'}$ and $\overline{BB'}$, respectively. Figure 27(b) shows two triangles, $\triangle BKM$ and $\triangle B'KM$.

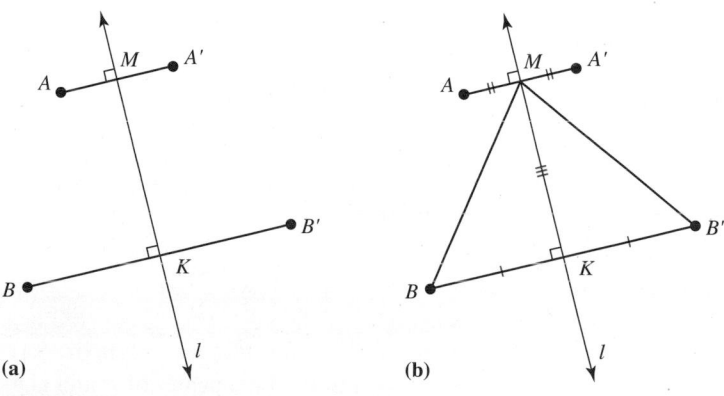

FIGURE 27
Creating triangles $\triangle BKM$ and $\triangle B'KM$.

$\triangle BKM \cong \triangle B'KM$ by the SAS congruence axiom. Then $\angle KMB \cong \angle KMB'$ and $\overline{MB} \cong \overline{MB'}$ by CPCTC, as marked in Figure 28(a). Now we form two new triangles, $\triangle BMA$ and $\triangle B'MA'$, in Figure 28(b).

(continued)

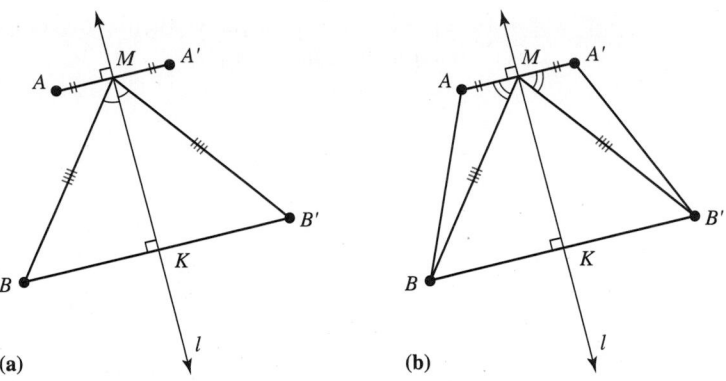

FIGURE 28
Creating triangles $\triangle BAM$ and $\triangle B'A'M$.

$\mathrm{m}\angle BMA = 90° - \mathrm{m}\angle KMB = 90° - \mathrm{m}\angle KMB' = \mathrm{m}\angle B'MA'$, so $\angle BMA \cong \angle B'MA'$. Then $\triangle BMA \cong \triangle B'MA'$ by the SAS congruence axiom. Consequently, $\overline{AB} \cong \overline{A'B'}$ by CPCTC. Thus, $AB = A'B'$ by definition of congruent line segments. ▲

Rotations

A rotation requires a center of rotation and an angle with direction. It involves a movement along an arc of a circle. Figure 29 shows $\overline{AB}$ is rotated 75° in a clockwise direction, pivoting about point P. It also focuses on the effect of the rotation on points A and B.

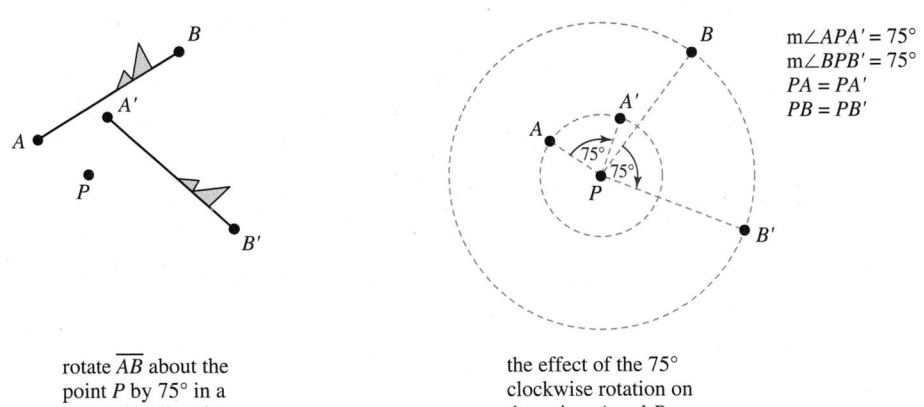

rotate $\overline{AB}$ about the
point P by 75° in a
clockwise direction

the effect of the 75°
clockwise rotation on
the points A and B

$\mathrm{m}\angle APA' = 75°$
$\mathrm{m}\angle BPB' = 75°$
$PA = PA'$
$PB = PB'$

FIGURE 29
Rotation that turns a geometric figure by 75° in a clockwise direction, about the center of rotation P.

Definition of a Rotation

A **rotation** with a center of P and angle of rotation with a measurement of n degrees (either clockwise or counterclockwise) is a transformation of the plane such that

1. $P' = P$.

2. if $Q \neq P$, then $PQ = PQ'$ and $\mathrm{m}\angle QPQ' = n$ degrees.

EXAMPLE 13.34

Find the image of $\overline{AB}$ under a rotation with a center of P and counterclockwise rotation of 40°.

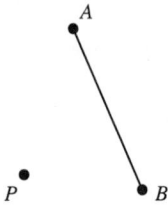

SOLUTION

Step 1. Use a straightedge to construct $\overrightarrow{PB}$. Then use a compass to draw a circle (or arc) with a center of P and a radius of PB.

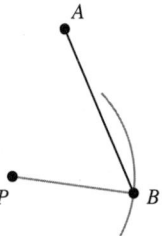

Step 2. Use a protractor to draw a 40° angle with the vertex P and side $\overrightarrow{PB}$ in a counterclockwise direction. Label the intersection of the circle (or arc) and the second side of the angle as B'. Then m$\angle BPB' = 40°$ and $PB = PB'$.

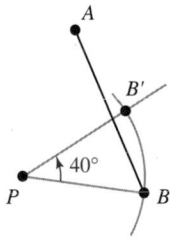

Step 3. Use a straightedge to construct $\overrightarrow{PA}$. Then use a compass to draw a circle (or arc) with a center of P and a radius of PA.

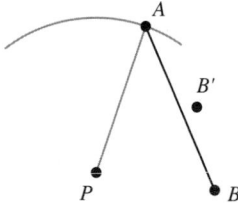

Step 4. Use a protractor to draw a 40° angle with the vertex P and side $\overrightarrow{PA}$ in a counterclockwise direction. Label the intersection of the circle (or arc) and the second side of the angle as A'. Then m$\angle APA' = 40°$ and $PA = PA'$.

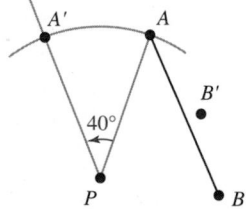

Step 5. Use the straightedge to construct a line segment with the endpoints A' and B'. Then $\overline{A'B'}$ is the image of $\overline{AB}$.

(continued)

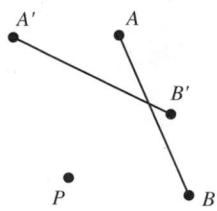

EXAMPLE 13.35

CONNECTION
REASONING
REPRESENTATION

A rotation maps A to A' and B to B', as shown.
a. Find the center of rotation.
b. Determine the degree of rotation.

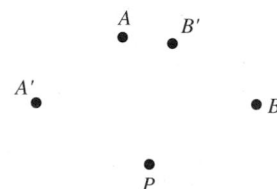

SOLUTION

a. $A \neq A'$ and $B \neq B'$, so we know the center of rotation is neither A nor B. The center of rotation is a point P such that $PA = PA'$ and $PB = PB'$. The equation $PA = PA'$ means P is the same distance from A and A', so P lies on the perpendicular bisector of $\overline{AA'}$. The equation $PB = PB'$ means P is the same distance from B and B', so P lies on the perpendicular bisector of $\overline{BB'}$. The center of rotation P is the intersection of the two perpendicular bisectors, as shown.

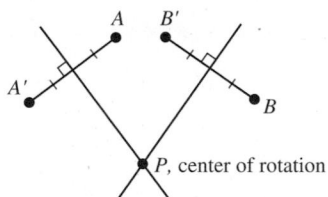

b. The rotation maps point A to A', so the degree of rotation is $m\angle APA'$. We use a protractor to measure $\angle APA'$, and the result is $m\angle APA' = 50°$. So all points turn $50°$ in a counterclockwise direction.

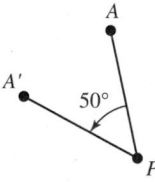

The following example suggests that a rotation preserves distances and therefore is a rigid motion of the plane. This means a rotation does not distort, enlarge, or shrink images.

EXAMPLE 13.36

CONNECTION
COMMUNICATION
REASONING
REPRESENTATION

A rotation with the center of rotation P and a counterclockwise turn angle with the measure n degrees maps A to A' and B to B', as shown. Prove $AB = A'B'$.

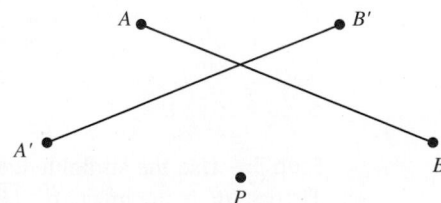

SOLUTION

We can draw some line segments to create $\triangle APB$ and $\triangle A'PB'$, where $\overline{AB}$ and $\overline{A'B'}$ are corresponding sides. The diagram incorporates the counterclockwise turn angle with the measure of n degrees. Let k degrees represent the measure of $\angle APB'$.

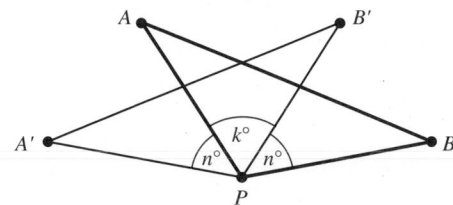

If we can prove $\triangle APB \cong \triangle A'PB'$, then we can use corresponding parts of congruent triangles to conclude $\overline{AB} \cong \overline{A'B'}$ and in turn conclude $AB = A'B'$.

$AP = A'P$ and $BP = B'P$ by the definition of a rotation. So far, two corresponding sides of $\triangle APB$ and $\triangle A'PB'$ are congruent. The included angles are $\angle APB'$ and $\angle A'PB'$. By the angle addition postulate, m$\angle A'PB' = n° + k°$ and m$\angle APB = n° + k°$. Therefore, m$\angle APB = $ m$\angle A'PB'$, showing the included angles are congruent. It follows that $\triangle APB \cong \triangle A'PB'$ by the SAS congruence axiom. Consequently, $\overline{AB} \cong \overline{A'B'}$ by CPCTC. Thus, $AB = A'B'$, by definition of congruent line segments. ▲

▶ **RELEASED ITEM**

- NAEP, 2009

   For this question, you may want to use your pieces labeled X. The given figure shows two triangles, labeled 1 and 2.

   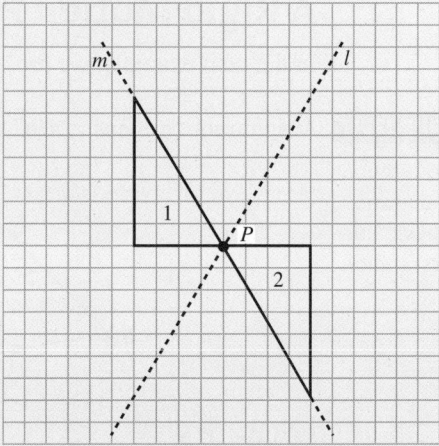

   Which one of the following describes a way to move triangle 1 so that it completely covers triangle 2?

   a. Turn (rotate) 180 degrees about point P.
   b. Flip (reflect) over line l.
   c. Slide (translate) 5 units to the right followed by 8 units down.
   d. Flip (reflect) over line m.
   e. Slide (translate) 10 units to the right followed by 16 units down.

   65% of eighth graders answered the question correctly.

Order of Rigid Motions May Matter

In Figure 30, we show $\overline{AB}$. We apply a combination of two transformations: a translation from P to Q and a reflection with the mirror line k. Here, the translation vector and mirror line are not parallel. When we apply the translation followed by the reflection, we obtain the blue line segment $\overline{A''B''}$. But when we apply the reflection followed by the translation, we obtain the red line segment $\overline{A''B''}$.

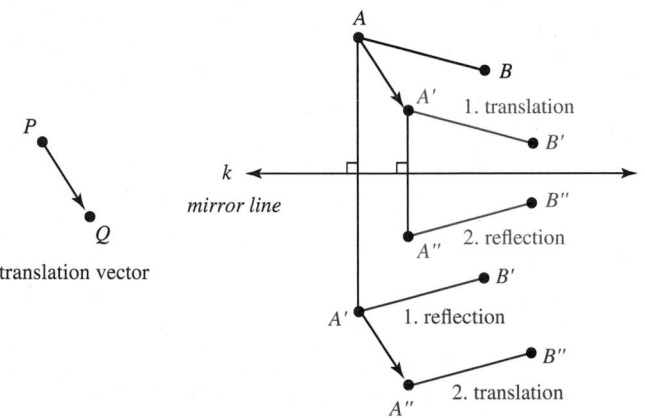

FIGURE 30
The order of rigid motions may affect the results.

REPRESENTATION   In this simple example, the final result $(\overline{A''B''})$ depends on the order in which the translation and reflection are applied. In general, the order of the rigid motions in a sequence may affect the results because they do not necessarily produce figures in the same locations. This simple example proves the order of transformations is not commutative because it is a counterexample.

A Rigid Motion Preserves Angles

In the next example, we prove that a rigid motion preserves angles.

EXAMPLE 13.37 A rigid motion maps $\angle ABC$ to $\angle A'B'C'$. Prove $\angle ABC \cong \angle A'B'C'$.

CONNECTION
COMMUNICATION
REASONING
REPRESENTATION

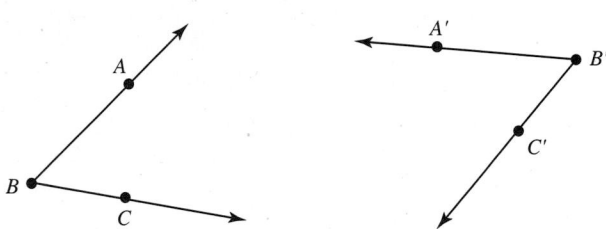

SOLUTION
Let's consider $\triangle ABC$ and $\triangle A'B'C'$.

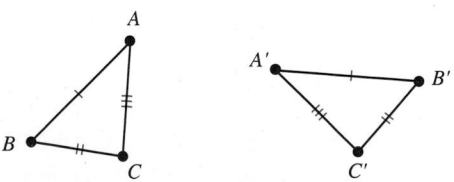

An isometry preserves distances, so $\overline{AB} \cong \overline{A'B'}$, $\overline{BC} \cong \overline{B'C'}$, and $\overline{AC} \cong \overline{A'C'}$. Then $\triangle ABC \cong \triangle A'B'C'$ by the SSS congruence axiom for triangles. Then $\angle ABC \cong \angle A'B'C'$ by CPCTC. ▲

A sequence of rigid motions is another rigid motion. Remember that a rigid motion is any transformation of the plane that preserves distances $(AB = A'B')$. Some worked examples illustrate that a translation, reflection, and rotation preserve distances for some possible choices of A and B. The following basic theorem states that these rigid motions preserve distances for all possible choices of A and B (the proof is omitted).

Theorem 5

1. A translation (slide) is a rigid motion.

2. A reflection (flip) is a rigid motion.

3. A rotation (turn) is a rigid motion.

To assess your understanding of transformations, several homework problems ask you to identify a rigid motion (slide, flip, or turn) that maps one figure to another or to find a translation vector, line of reflection, or center of rotation.

COMMUNICATION

REASONING

Suppose a transformation consists of a sequence of two rigid motions, such as a rotation followed by a translation. Although the order of the rigid motions may affect the location of the final image, the following example proves that a sequence of two rigid motions still produces another rigid motion (preserves distances).

EXAMPLE 13.38 A transformation consists of two rigid motions. The first rigid motion maps the point P to P', and the second one maps P' to P''. Prove the combination is a rigid motion.

REASONING

SOLUTION

To prove the sequence of transformations is a rigid motion, we must prove it preserves distances, that is, prove $AB = A''B''$ for any two points A and B in the plane.

$AB = A'B'$	**Because the first transformation is an isometry**
$A'B' = A''B''$	**Because the second transformation is an isometry**
$AB = A''B''$	**Because of the transitive property of equality**

This means $AB = A''B''$ for any two points A and B in the plane. Therefore, a transformation consisting of two rigid motions is a rigid motion.

▲

This leads to the following theorem on two rigid motions.

Theorem 6

A sequence of two rigid motions is a rigid motion.

Now, suppose a transformation consists of a combination of three rigid motions, T_1, T_2, and T_3, in that order. Then this combination is a rigid motion, too. Here's why: T_1 and T_2 produce a rigid motion (say T) by Theorem 6. T and T_3 produce a rigid motion too by Theorem 6. This means the combination of three rigid motions T_1, T_2, and T_3 is a rigid motion. Using the same line of reasoning, *any* sequence of rigid motions produces a rigid motion.

This leads to the following theorem on two or more rigid motions.

Theorem 7

A sequence of two or more rigid motions is a rigid motion.

Every sequence of rigid motions is a rigid motion. In Figures 31(a) through (e), we describe a possible sequence that maps $\triangle ABC$ to $\triangle DEF$ that meets the following standard: "given two congruent figures, describe a sequence that exhibits the congruence between them" (Gr. 8, CCSS).

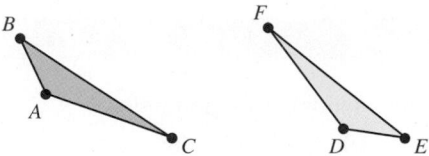

(a) Initial positions of $\triangle ABC$ and $\triangle DEF$ are shown.

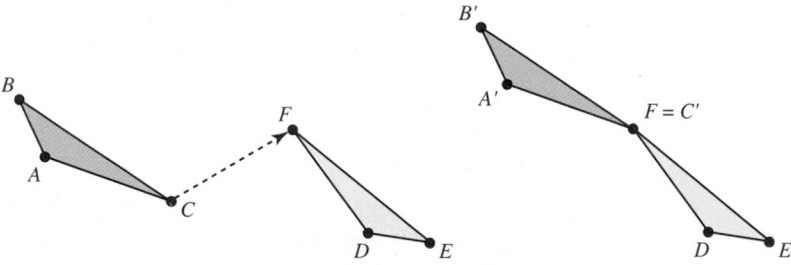

(b) Use a translation to move all points in the direction from C to F.

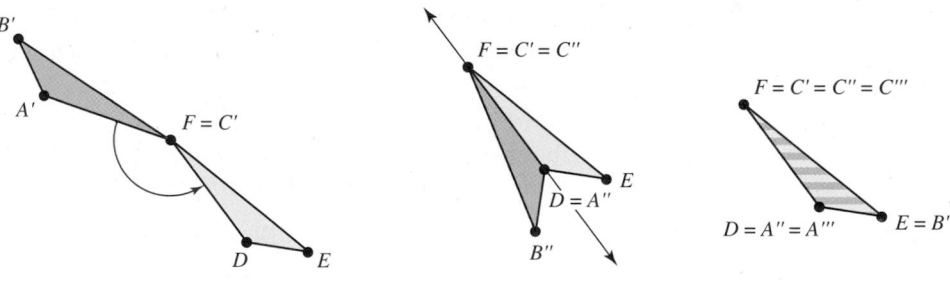

(c) Rotate $\triangle A'B'C'$ in a counterclockwise direction by the amount $m\angle A'C'D$ about the center of rotation C'.

(d) Reflect $\triangle A''B''C''$ about the mirror line $\overleftrightarrow{A''C''}$.

(e) The result is $\triangle A''B''C'' \cong \triangle DEF$.

FIGURE 31
Describing a possible sequence of rigid motions that maps $\triangle ABC$ to $\triangle DEF$.

According to Figures 31(a) through (e), one possible sequence of rigid motions that maps $\triangle ABC$ to $\triangle DEF$ is a translation, rotation, and reflection. This sequence is a rigid motion, so $\triangle ABC \cong \triangle DEF$.

CONNECTION   In general, two figures are congruent if and only if there is a sequence of translations, reflections, and rotations that maps one of the figures to the other figure. Student should "understand that a two-dimensional figure is congruent to another if the second can be obtained from the first by a sequence of rotations, reflections, and translations" (Gr. 8, CCSS). But we can define what it means for two figures to be congruent in simpler terms—just keep reading.

Mapping Congruent Figures Using a Single Rigid Motion

We just learned that translations, reflections, and rotations are rigid motions of the plane. This means they preserve distances (i.e., for any two points A and B in the plane, $AB = A'B'$). We also learned that a sequence of rigid motions results in another rigid motion of the plane. For example, a translation, followed by a reflection, then followed by a rotation results in another rigid motion.

We also demonstrated that if two figures are congruent, then there exists a sequence of translations, reflections, and rotations that maps one figure to the other figure (Figure 31). It turns out that a sequence of rigid motions (translations, reflections, and rotations) is equivalent to a single translation, reflection, rotation, or glide reflection. A **glide reflection** is a combination of a translation and a reflection such that the translation vector is parallel to the mirror line. Figure 32 illustrates a glide reflection.

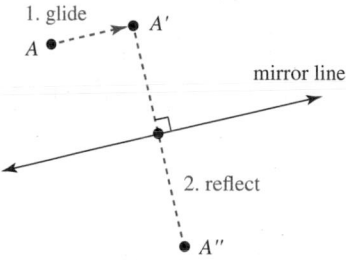

FIGURE 32

A glide reflection is a combination of a translation and reflection. The translation vector and the mirror line must be parallel.

Figure 33 suggests the order of the transformations does not affect the result. Either way, we see the final image A'' has the same location.

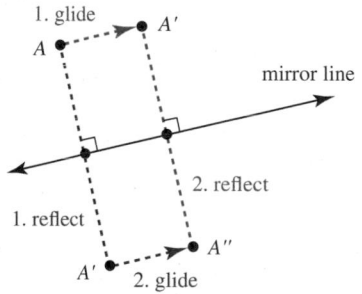

FIGURE 33

In a glide reflection, the order of the transformations does not matter.

Definition of a Glide Reflection

A **glide reflection** is a transformation such that

1. the transformation consists of a translation and a reflection, in any order.

2. the translation vector is parallel to the mirror line.

A sequence of two or more rigid motions results in another rigid motion of the plane, so it follows that a glide reflection is also a rigid motion.

CONNECTION   Now we consider a sequence of two reflections. In the first case, their mirror lines are parallel. In the second case, their mirror lines intersect. We use this simple example to illustrate a major point: a sequence of rigid motions produces the same result as exactly one of the following rigid motions: translation, reflection, rotation, or glide reflection.

Let's consider a sequence of two reflections with parallel mirror lines. Figure 34 shows $\triangle ABC$ that will be reflected about mirror line p to obtain $\triangle A'B'C'$, which will then be reflected about mirror line q to obtain $\triangle A''B''C''$. Does this result in a new rigid motion? The distance between lines p and q is 7.5 units.

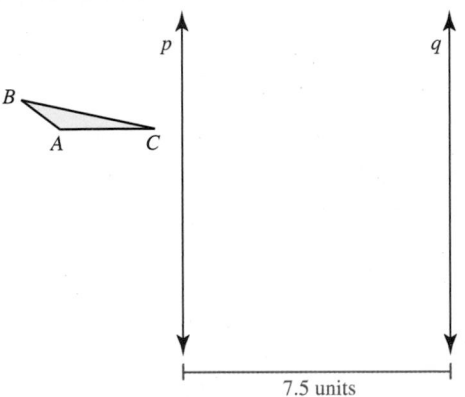

FIGURE 34

Two parallel mirror lines, p and q.

Figure 35 shows the result of $\triangle ABC$ after two reflections. We reflect $\triangle ABC$ about mirror line p to obtain $\triangle A'B'C'$ and then reflect $\triangle A'B'C'$ about mirror line q to obtain $\triangle A''B''C''$. Figure 35 also shows that we can transform $\triangle ABC$ to $\triangle A''B''C''$ with one translation by moving $\triangle ABC$ 15 units in a direction perpendicular to the mirror lines. In general, a sequence of two reflections with parallel mirror lines is equivalent to one reflection.

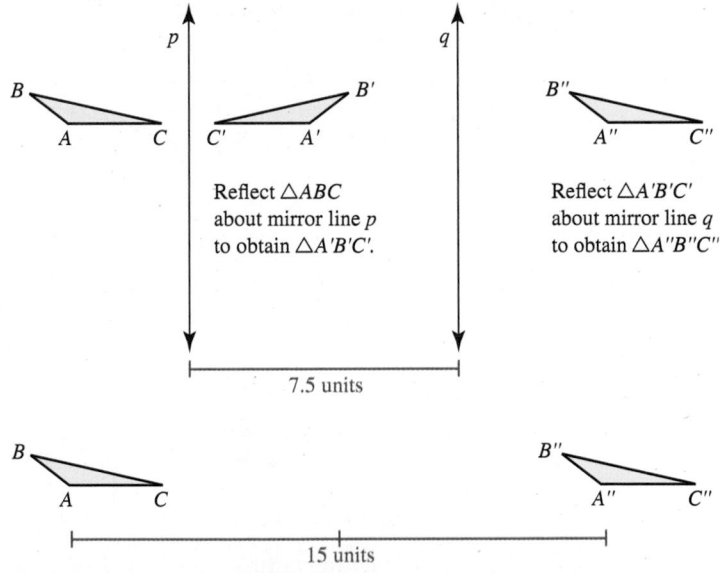

The direction of the translation vector is perpendicular to the mirror lines. The length of the translation is twice the distance between the parallel mirror lines.

FIGURE 35

Two reflections with parallel mirror lines is equivalent to one translation.

CONNECTION Now, let's consider a sequence of two reflections with intersecting mirror lines. Figure 36 shows $\triangle ABC$ that will be reflected about mirror line p to obtain $\triangle A'B'C'$, which will then be reflected about mirror line q to obtain $\triangle A''B''C''$. Does this result in a new rigid motion? The angle between lines p and q is 35°.

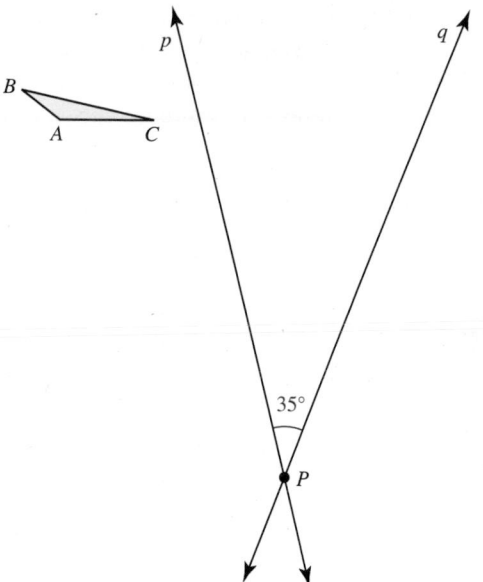

FIGURE 36

Two intersecting mirror lines, p and q.

Figure 37 shows the result of $\triangle ABC$ after two reflections. We reflect $\triangle ABC$ about mirror line p to obtain $\triangle A'B'C'$ and then reflect $\triangle A'B'C'$ about mirror line q to obtain $\triangle A''B''C''$. Figure 37 also shows that we can transform $\triangle ABC$ to $\triangle A''B''C''$ with one rotation, with the center at the intersection of the mirror lines and a rotation angle that is twice the angle formed by the intersecting mirror lines. In general, a sequence of two reflections with intersecting mirror lines is equivalent to one rotation.

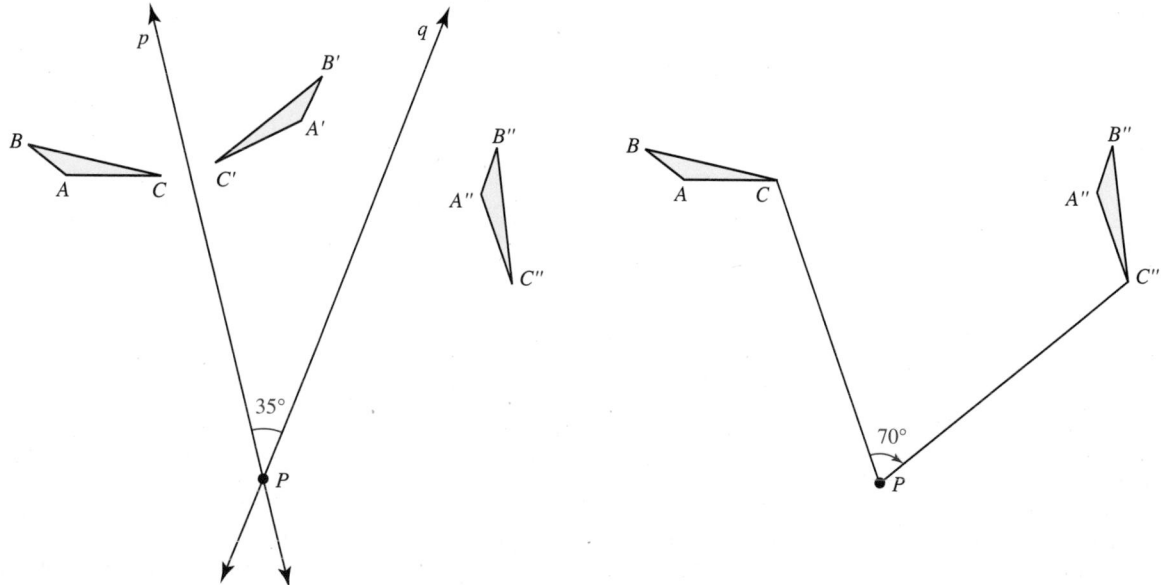

FIGURE 37

Two reflections with intersecting mirror lines is equivalent to one rotation.

This leads to the following general result: If $\triangle A'B'C'$ is mapped to $\triangle A''B''C''$ by two consecutive reflections, then the sequence can be accomplished by a single translation or rotation.

CONNECTION   Now we consider the result of a sequence of two rigid motions consisting of translations, reflections, rotations, or glide reflections. Table 13.4 displays the possible results. We see that two consecutive translations, reflections, rotations, or glide reflections result in a translation, reflection, rotation, or glide reflection. For example, the table shows that a reflection followed by a reflection results in a translation or rotation. In addition, a rotation followed by a rotation is equivalent to a translation or rotation.

TABLE 13.4   The Effect of Two Rigid Motions

		Second Rigid Motion		
		Translation	**Reflection**	**Rotation**	**Glide reflection**
First Rigid Motion	**Translation**	Translation	Glide reflection	Rotation	Reflection or glide reflection
	Reflection	Glide reflection	Translation or rotation	Glide reflection	Translation or rotation
	Rotation	Rotation	Glide reflection	Translation or rotation	Glide reflection
	Glide reflection	Reflection or glide reflection	Translation or rotation	Glide reflection	Translation or rotation

We can apply Table 13.4 to any sequence of rigid motions consisting of translations, reflections, and rotations (the three basic rigid motions) and conclude that the sequence is equivalent to a single translation, reflection, rotation, or glide reflection. This leads to the following definition of congruent figures.

> **Definition**
>
> Two figures F_1 and F_2 are congruent, written $F_1 \cong F_2$ if and only if F_1 can be mapped to F_2 using a single translation, reflection, rotation, or glide reflection.

Any figure is automatically congruent to itself by a rotation of 360° about any point. In a nutshell:

1. There are three basic rigid motions of the plane: translation, reflection, and rotation.

2. If two figures in the plane are congruent, then there is a sequence of rigid motions consisting of translations, reflections, and rotations that maps one figure to the other one.

3. A glide reflection is a combination of a translation and a reflection such that the translation vector and mirror line are parallel.

4. Any sequence that maps one figure to another congruent figure can be expressed more compactly as exactly one of the following rigid motions: translation, reflection, rotation, or glide reflection.

5. This leads to the following equivalent definitions of congruent figures:

   • Two figures F_1 and F_2 are congruent if and only if F_1 can be mapped to F_2 using a sequence of translations, reflections, and rotations.

   • Two figures F_1 and F_2 are congruent if and only if F_1 can be mapped to F_2 using exactly one of the following rigid motions: translation, reflection, rotation, or glide reflection.

Symmetry

There are three types of symmetry: line symmetry, rotational symmetry, and point symmetry.

The **line symmetry** of a geometric figure is a line such that a reflection that has the line as a mirror line maps the geometric figure to itself. Line symmetry arises naturally, as in the butterfly and tarantula shown. Figure 38 shows the line symmetry for an isosceles

triangle, rectangle, and square. You can fold paper to help identify line symmetry: fold the figure along a crease in the paper and see whether the figure folds onto itself.

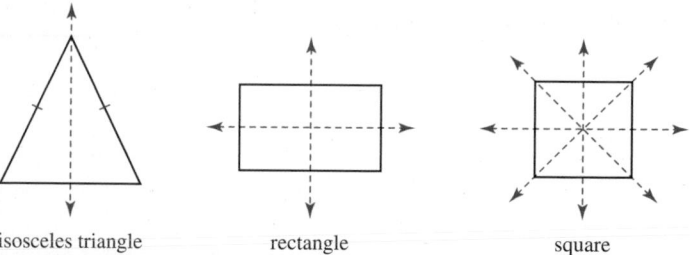

isosceles triangle   rectangle   square

FIGURE 38

Reflections about a line of symmetry map a figure to itself.

Students should be able to "recognize a line of symmetry for a two-dimensional figure as a line across the figure such that the figure can be folded along the line into matching parts and identify line-symmetric figures and draw lines of symmetry" (Gr. 4, CCSS).

Some students incorrectly think that a line through the midpoints of two opposite sides of a parallelogram is a line of symmetry. To correct that misconception, think about the image of C under a reflection with a mirror line that goes through the midpoints of opposite sides. Some students also incorrectly think that a line through the opposite vertices of a parallelogram is a line of symmetry. To correct that misconception, think about the image of the vertex C of a reflection with the mirror line $\overleftrightarrow{BD}$.

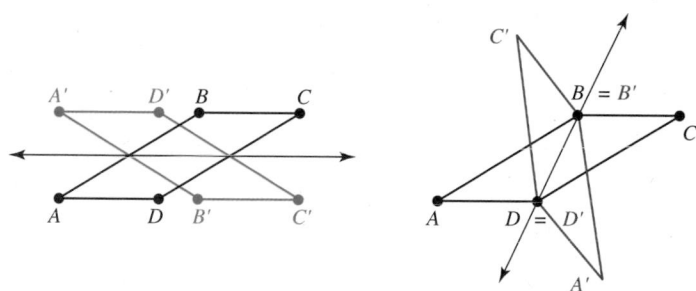

All figures automatically appear the same after rotating the figure about a center of rotation through an angle of 0° or 360°. A geometric figure has **rotational symmetry** (also called **turn symmetry**) if the figure looks exactly the same after rotating the figure about a center of rotation through an angle between 0° and 360°. Any figure that looks the same after rotating it 60° also looks the same after rotating it 120°, 180°, 240°, or 300°. The **angle of symmetry** is the smallest angle between 0° and 360° that preserves the geometric figure. The angle of symmetry of the hubcap and quilt pattern shown here are 360/6 = 60° and 90°, respectively. A figure may have no rotational symmetry, such as the American flag.

hubcap   quilt pattern

EXAMPLE 13.39 What is the angle of symmetry of each design?

CONNECTION   **a.**   **b.**

REASONING

SOLUTION

a. The angle of symmetry is 40°, because 360 ÷ 9 = 40.

b. The angle of symmetry is 30°, because 360 ÷ 12 = 30.

▲

A figure is said to have **point symmetry** if there is a point on the figure such that a 180° rotation (also called a **half turn**) of the figure about that point results in the same figure. For example, a parallelogram has point symmetry (where the point is the intersection of the diagonals).

The British flag has point symmetry. Some capital letters of the English alphabet also have point symmetry.

Size Transformation

An isometry preserves the shape and size of a geometric figure. A size transformation (also called a *dilation*) is a transformation that maps a geometric figure to a *similar* figure in the plane. This means that the geometric figure and its image have the same shape but possibly different sizes without distortion (such as similar triangles). This happens, for example, when we use the reduction/enlargement feature on a printer or copy machine. Figure 39 illustrates a size transformation. Each size transformation has a center and scale factor.

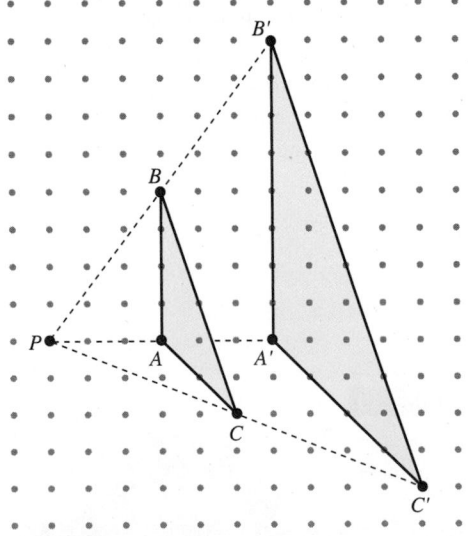

FIGURE 39

The size transformation with a center of P and a scale factor of 2 maps $\triangle ABC$ to $\triangle A'B'C'$.

P, A, and A' are collinear.	P, B, and B' are collinear.	P, C, and C' are collinear.
$PA = 3$ units	$PB = 5$ units	$PC = \sqrt{29}$ units
$PA' = 6$ units	$PB' = 10$ units	$PC' = \sqrt{116}$ units
$PA' = 2 \cdot PA$	$PB' = 2 \cdot PB$	$PC' = 2 \cdot PC$

Here's the definition of a size transformation.

> ### Definition of Size Transformation
>
> A **size transformation** (also called a **dilation**) is a transformation with a center of P and a positive number k (called the **scale factor**) such that
>
> **1.** the point P is mapped to itself.
>
> **2.** if $Q \neq P$, then Q is mapped to the point Q' on $\overrightarrow{PQ}$ with $PQ' = k \cdot PQ$.

The points P, Q, and Q' are collinear, and $\overrightarrow{PQ} = \overrightarrow{PQ'}$. If $0 < k < 1$, then the size transformation is called a **contraction.** If $1 < k$, then the size transformation is called an **expansion.**

EXAMPLE 13.40

CONNECTION

REASONING

REPRESENTATION

A size transformation has a center of P and a scale factor of 3, with A and B', as shown in the diagram.

a. Sketch A'.

b. Sketch B.

SOLUTION

a. We need to draw a point A' on $\overrightarrow{PA}$ so that $PA' = 3 \cdot PA$. Given $PA = 12$ mm, A' is the point on $\overrightarrow{PA}$ such that $PA' = 3 \cdot PA$. Then $PA' = 3 \cdot 12 = 36$ mm. Draw a ray from P through A. Using a ruler with the zero mark at P and aligned along $\overrightarrow{PA}$, we let A' be the point corresponding to 36 mm.

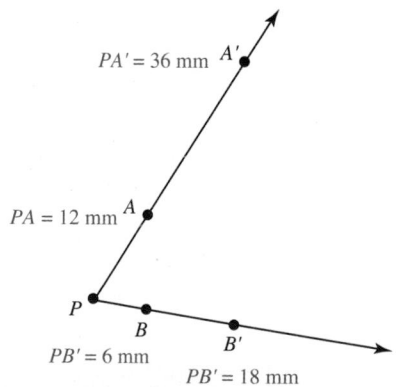

b. P, B, and B' lie on a ray with the endpoint P such that $PB' = 3 \cdot PB$. Then $PB = \frac{1}{3}PB'$. Using a ruler, we find $PB' = 18$ mm. Then $PB = \frac{1}{3} \cdot 18 = 6$ mm. Using the ruler with the zero mark at P and aligned along $\overrightarrow{PB'}$, we let B be the point corresponding to 6 mm.

▲

EXAMPLE 13.41

CONNECTION

REASONING

A size transformation has a center of $Q(2, 7)$ and maps $A(5, 16)$ to $A'(9, 28)$. Find the scale factor, rounding the final answer to the nearest hundredth.

SOLUTION

The scale factor must satisfy the equation $QA' = k \cdot QA$. Then $k = QA'/QA$. Using the distance formula, we get $QA' = \sqrt{490}$ units and $QA = \sqrt{90}$ units. Then $k = QA'/QA = \sqrt{490}/\sqrt{90} \approx 2.33$.

▲

EXAMPLE 13.42

CONNECTION

COMMUNICATION

REASONING

REPRESENTATION

A size transformation with a center of P and a scale factor of k maps A to A' and B to B'. Prove that $A'B' = k \cdot AB$.

SOLUTION

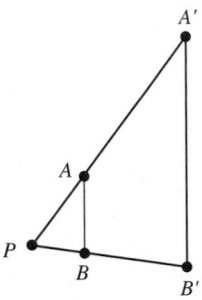

FIGURE 40

A size transformation with scale factor k maps $\overrightarrow{AB}$ to $\overrightarrow{A'B'}$.

Figure 40 is a representation of the size transformation. Then

$PA' = k \cdot PA$	**By the definition of a size transformation**
$\dfrac{PA'}{PA} = k$	**By solving for k**
$PB' = k \cdot PB$	**By the definition of a size transformation**
$\dfrac{PB'}{PB} = k$	**By solving for k**
$\angle APB \cong \angle A'PB'$	**Because $\overrightarrow{PA} = \overrightarrow{PA'}$ and $\overrightarrow{PB} = \overrightarrow{PB'}$**

Then two corresponding sides of $\triangle APB$ and $\triangle A'PB'$ have the same ratio ($PA'/PA = k$ and $PB'/PB = k$), and their included angles are congruent ($\angle APB \cong \angle A'PB'$). So $\triangle APB \sim \triangle A'PB'$ by the SAS similarity axiom. This means all corresponding sides have a common ratio. Then $\frac{PA'}{PA} = \frac{PB'}{PB} = \frac{A'B'}{AB}$. We know $k = \frac{PA'}{PA}$, so $k = \frac{A'B'}{AB}$. Therefore, $A'B' = k \cdot AB$.

▲

Although size transformations do not preserve distances for $k \neq 1$, the previous example can be summarized in a theorem.

Theorem 8

A size transformation with a center of P and a scale factor of k maps X to X' and Y to Y'. The distances $X'Y'$ and XY are related by the equation $X'Y' = k \cdot XY$.

EXAMPLE 13.43

CONNECTION
REASONING
REPRESENTATION

A size transformation has a center of Q and a scale factor of 5. Suppose the length of $\overline{AB}$ is 7 units. What is the length of $\overline{A'B'}$?

SOLUTION

We are given $k = 5$ and $AB = 7$ units and must find $A'B'$. We know k satisfies the equation $A'B' = k \cdot AB$. Then $A'B' = k \cdot AB = 5 \cdot 7 = 35$. So $A'B' = 35$ units. ▲

In a size transformation with a scale factor of 5, a line segment is mapped to another line segment that is five times longer.

EXAMPLE 13.44

CONNECTION
REASONING
REPRESENTATION

A size transformation with a center of P and a scale factor of k maps $\triangle ABC$ to $\triangle A'B'C'$. Prove $\triangle ABC$ and $\triangle A'B'C'$ are similar triangles.

SOLUTION

We draw a diagram to represent the situation. In general, we know the distances $X'Y'$ and XY are related by the equation $X'Y' = k \cdot XY$. So $\frac{X'Y'}{XY} = k$.

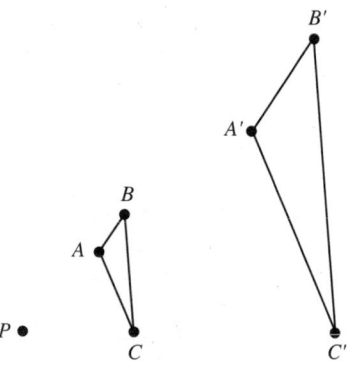

Then $\frac{A'B'}{AB} = k$, $\frac{B'C'}{BC} = k$, and $\frac{A'C'}{AC} = k$. This means corresponding sides of $\triangle ABC$ and $\triangle A'B'C'$ have the same ratio. Then $\triangle ABC \sim \triangle A'B'C'$ by the SSS similarity axiom. ▲

In terms of triangles, a size transformation maps $\triangle ABC$ to $\triangle A'B'C'$ with $\triangle ABC \sim \triangle A'B'C'$. As a consequence, $\angle ABC$ is mapped to the congruent angle $\angle A'B'C'$, because corresponding angles of similar triangles are congruent. In general, a size transformation maps an angle to a congruent angle.

In general, a size transformation with scale factor k maps figure F_1 to a similar figure F_2. In Section 12.3, we learned how the perimeters and areas of similar figures are related. The perimeter of image F_2 is k times the perimeter of F_1, and the area of image F_2 is k^2 times the area of F_1.

EXAMPLE 13.45

CONNECTION
COMMUNICATION
REASONING

A size transformation with a scale factor of 2 maps $\triangle ABC$ to $\triangle A'B'C'$.

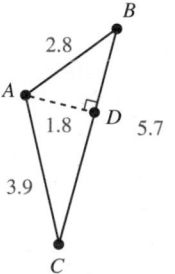

a. Determine the perimeter of $\triangle A'B'C'$.

b. Determine the area of $\triangle A'B'C'$.

SOLUTION

a. The perimeter of $\triangle ABC$ is $2.8 + 5.7 + 3.9 = 12.4$ units. Therefore, the perimeter of $\triangle A'B'C'$ is $2 \cdot 12.4 = 24.8$ units.

b. The area of $\triangle ABC$ is $\frac{1}{2}(5.7 \cdot 1.8) = 5.13$ square units. Therefore, the area of $\triangle A'B'C'$ is $2^2 \cdot 5.13 = 20.52$ square units.

▲

The following Classroom Connection illustrates a problem for middle school students that requires relating the scale factor with the sides, perimeter, and area of a polygon.

> ### ◀◀◆ Classroom Connection
>
> ● Holt *Mathematics*, Student Edition, p. 247
>
> A square has a side of the length 4.8 feet. If the square is dilated by a factor of 4, what is the length of a side of the new square? What is its perimeter? What is its area? (© 2007 by Holt, Rinehart, and Winston. All rights reserved. Reprinted with permission of the publisher, Houghton Mifflin Harcourt Publishing Company.)

Students should "understand that a two-dimensional figure is similar to another if the second can be obtained from the first by a sequence of rotations, reflections, translations, and dilations" (Gr. 8, CCSS). A **similarity transformation** is any combination of a size transformation and rigid motions. Now we are able to provide a general definition of two similar figures.

> ### Definition of Similar Figures
>
> Two geometric figures F_1 and F_2 in a plane are similar, written $F_1 \sim F_2$, if and only if there is a similarity transformation that maps one geometric figure to the other.

Tessellations

CONNECTION A **tessellation** is a repetition of a shape that covers the plane without any gaps or overlaps. The repeating shape is called a tile. A **tile** is a simple closed curve and its interior. Any tile that has the shape of a triangle tessellates the plane. The idea hinges on rotating the triangle 180° about the midpoint of a side of the triangle, as shown in Figure 41. The interior angles always meet at a common vertex.

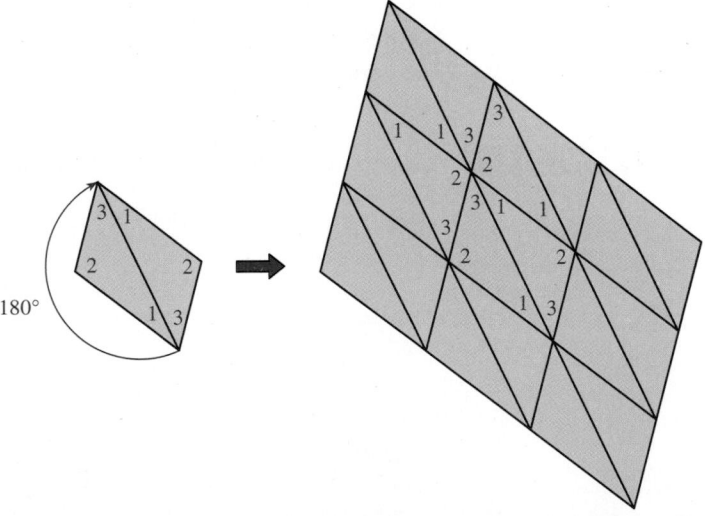

FIGURE 41
Any triangle tessellates the plane.

Figure 42 suggests that any rectangle or parallelogram tessellates the plane.

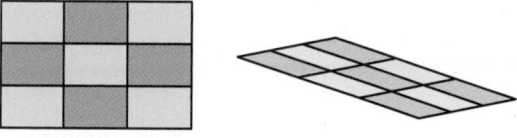

FIGURE 42

Any rectangle or parallelogram tessellates the plane.

Figure 43 shows how to tessellate a plane using any convex quadrilateral (the procedure also works for any concave quadrilateral). Pick a side of the quadrilateral. Then rotate the quadrilateral 180° about the midpoint of the side. Trace the image. Then pick a side of the image and rotate the image 180° about the midpoint of the side. Trace the new image. By repeating this process, the quadrilateral tessellates the plane. Every vertex of the tessellation is formed by the four interior angles of the quadrilateral.

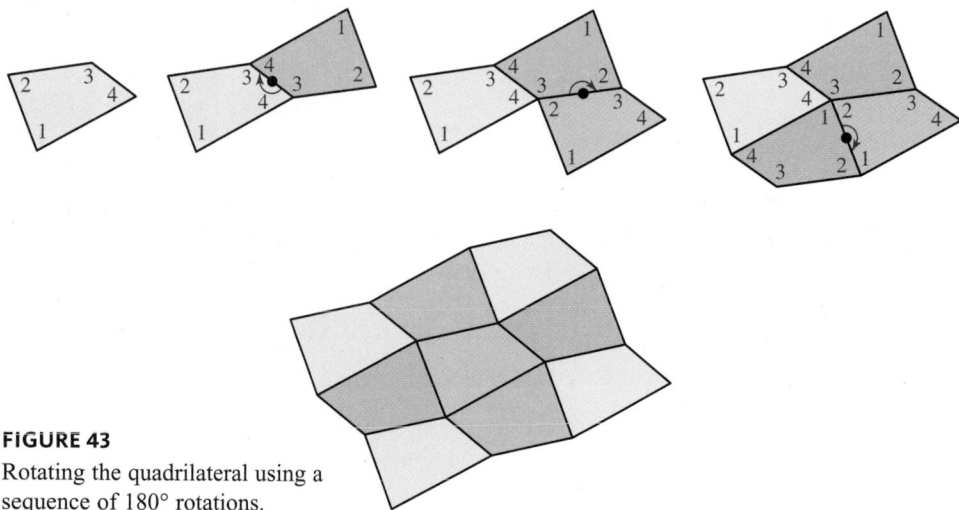

FIGURE 43

Rotating the quadrilateral using a sequence of 180° rotations.

Some convex pentagons are tiles, but some convex pentagons do not tile the plane. Similarly, some convex hexagons are tiles, but some convex hexagons do not tile the plane. It turns out that no convex polygons with seven or more sides tessellate the plane.

Regular and Semiregular Tessellations

CONNECTION   A **regular tessellation** is a tessellation in which the tile is a regular polygon. Regular polygons are often used to make wallpaper or borders of stationery paper, for example. Each section of wallpaper in Figure 44 has a tile in the shape of a regular polygon; can you identify the tiles? A homework problem deals with using regular polygons (such as a square) to tessellate the plane, and you should learn why there are only three regular polygons that tessellate the plane.

FIGURE 44

Artwork based on a square tile.   equilateral triangle   square   regular hexagon

A **semiregular tessellation** is a tessellation in which

a. the tile is composed of two or more different regular polygons.

b. the sides of all regular polygons in the tile have a common length.

c. every vertex in the tile looks identical.

There are only eight semiregular tessellations, as shown in Figure 45. Each tile requires three or more regular polygons meeting at a vertex, because the interior angle of any regular polygon is less than 180°. They use a combination of equilateral triangles, squares, regular hexagons, regular octagons, and regular dodecagons. These regular polygons make it possible for the sum of the angles at a vertex to be 360°.

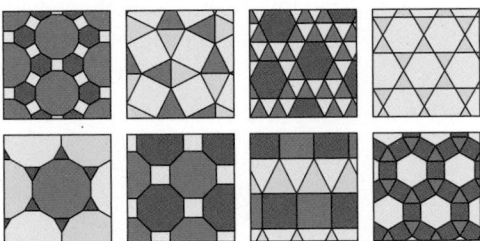

FIGURE 45
There are exactly eight semiregular tessellations.

Create an Escher-like Tessellation with Interlocking Figures

The tile in Figure 46(a) is a cat, the tile in Figure 46(b) is a lion, and the tile in Figure 46(c) is a face. Figure 46 illustrates that a tessellation can be a combination of art and mathematics.

(a)   (b)   (c)

Joshua Stanley/Shutterstock.com   Mark Grenier/Shutterstock.com   Mark Grenier/Shutterstock.com

FIGURE 46
Tesselations based on interlocking tiles.

CONNECTION   The Dutch artist Maurits Cornelis Escher (1898–1972) studied architecture and created pictures on paper and in woodcuts. He integrated geometry, illusion, and mathematics into his work, even though he had no formal training in mathematics. In 1922 and 1936, he visited the fourteenth century Alhambra Palace in Spain, which is famous for its artwork and architecture. The stylish and patterned designs in the palace inspired him to create interlocking tiles using familiar figures, such as insects, frogs, and birds, rather than abstract geometric shapes.

Now we describe how to apply translations to create an Escher-like tessellation with interlocking figures. The idea is to create a curve, copy and translate it, and repeat this process, forming a closed figure. Then we decorate the figure, assemble copies of the tile, and place them together without gaps or overlaps.

How To Create an Original Escher-like Tessellation Using Translations

STEP 1. Begin with a rectangle, and draw a curve from one corner to an adjacent corner of the rectangle.

STEP 2. Translate the curve to the opposite side of the rectangle.

STEP 3. Draw a curve on the other side of the rectangle.

STEP 4. Translate the curve to the opposite side of the rectangle.

STEP 5. Erase the parts of the rectangle that you do not need to produce the shape of the tile.

STEP 6. Decorate the tile, and make several copies.

STEP 7. Assemble the interlocking tiles.

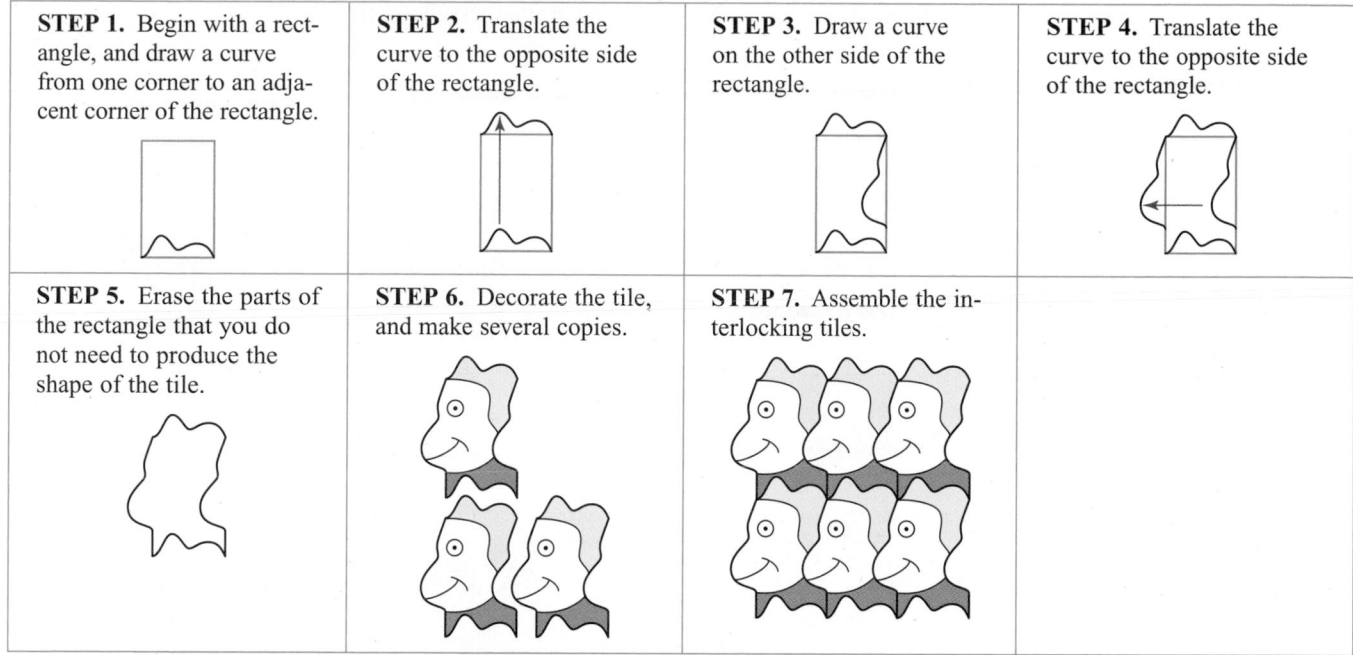

Now we describe how to create an original Escher-like tessellation with interlocking figures by applying reflections and translations to a rectangle. The idea is to create a curve, copy it, and reflect it and then create a second curve, copy it, and translate it, forming a closed figure. Then we decorate it, copy it, and reflect that figure. Then we assemble copies of the tiles and place them together without gaps or overlaps.

How To Create an Original Escher-like Tessellation Using Reflections and Translations

STEP 1. Begin with a rectangle, and draw any curve from one corner to an adjacent corner of the rectangle.

STEP 2. Reflect the curve using a horizontal mirror line. Translate the reflected curve to the opposite side of the rectangle.

STEP 3. Draw a curve on the other side of the parallelogram.

STEP 4. Translate the curve to the opposite side of the parallelogram.

STEP 5. Erase the parts of the rectangle you do not need to produce the shape of the tile.

STEP 6. Decorate the tile.

STEP 7. Reflect the tile.

STEP 8. Make multiple copies of the tile and its reflection.

STEP 9. Assemble the interlocking tiles.

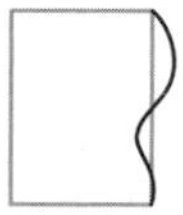

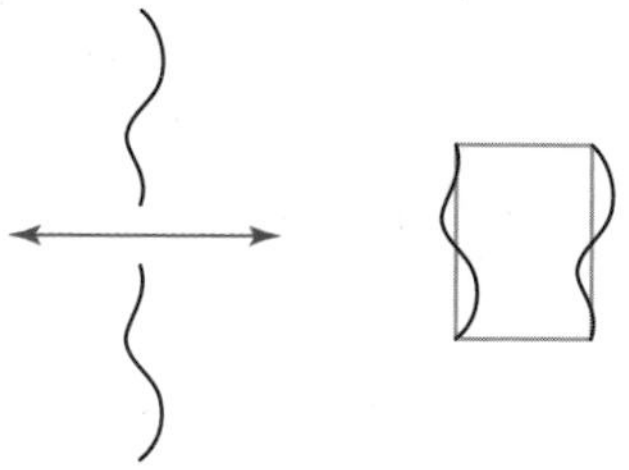

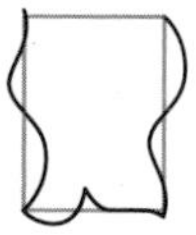

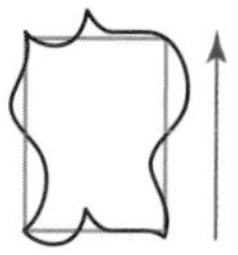

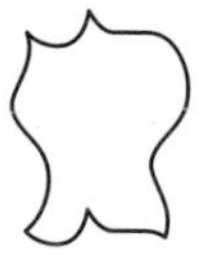

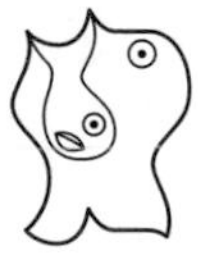

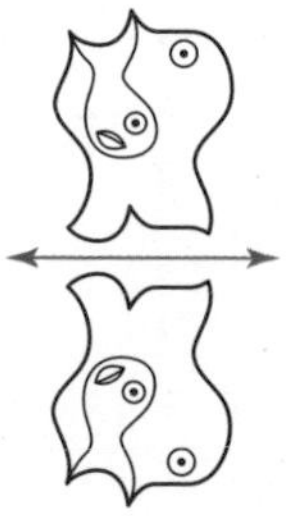

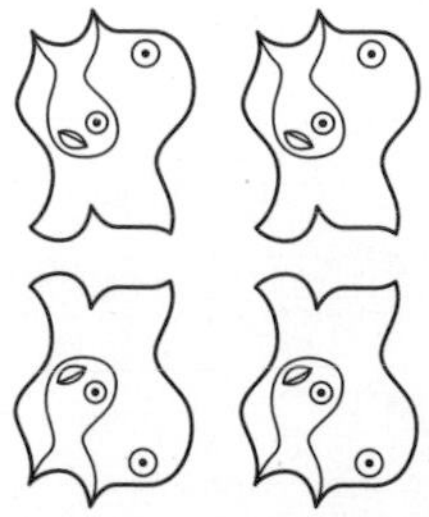

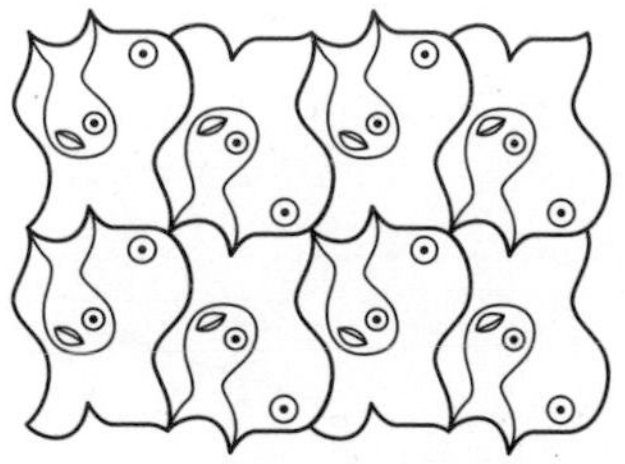

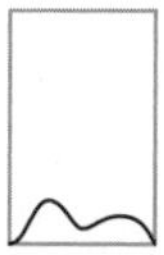

The student page from an elementary mathematics textbook shows how you can apply rotations to create an interlocking figure that tessellates the plane.

PRACTICE

C Extensions

20. Follow these steps to change a square into a shape that tessellates the plane.

a. Cut out a square piece of paper about 8 cm on a side. Label the sides and vertices as shown.

b. Draw and cut any shape out of side 1. Do <u>not</u> cut off a corner.

c. Rotate the piece about point A and tape it to side 2. Be sure to tape the piece the same distance from point A as it was before you cut it.

d. Similarly, cut into side 3, rotate the piece about point B, and tape the piece to side 4.

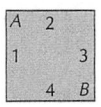 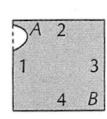 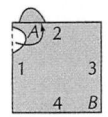 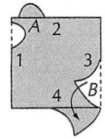

e. Repeat the process a few more times, cutting into any <u>unaltered</u> part of the square except a corner. Remember this plan:

- Rotate pieces from side 1 onto side 2, and from side 2 onto side 1. (Be sure to tape the piece the same distance from A.)

- Rotate pieces from side 3 onto side 4, and from side 4 onto side 3. (Be sure to tape the piece the same distance from B.)

f. Add artistic details and draw the tessellation.

(*Mathematics*, Grade 6, p. 519)

QUESTIONS FOR SECTION 13.3

REPRESENTATION

Refresher: Representations (language, diagrams, tables, symbols, algebra, manipulatives, and contextualized situations) are important because we use them to organize, record, and communicate mathematical ideas and make them more comprehensible.

1. In a transformation of the plane, which point is mapped to A'?

2. In a transformation of the plane, which point is B mapped to?

3. Draw the image of the triangle under the translation with a translation vector that takes P to Q.

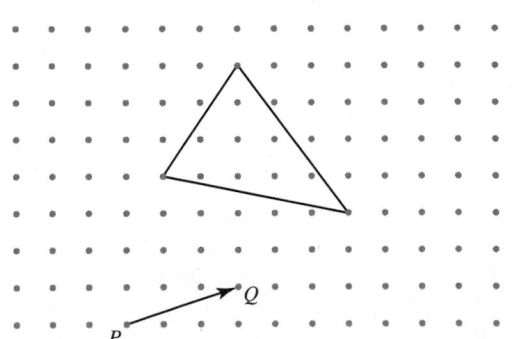

4. Draw a translation vector that takes $\overline{AB}$ to $\overline{A'B'}$.

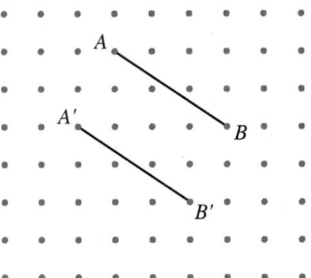

5. Find the image of the line segment under a reflection with the mirror line l.

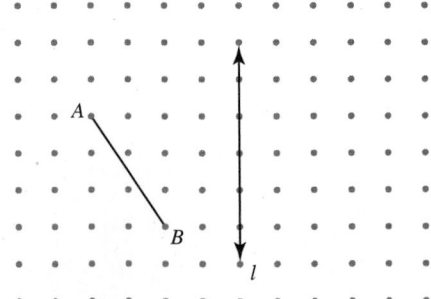

6. Draw the mirror line for the reflection.

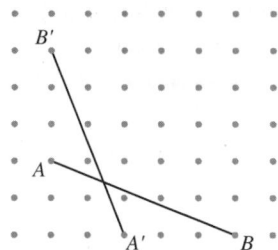

7. Sketch the image of the triangle under a reflection about line *l*.

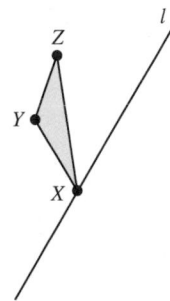

8. Under a reflection, the point *P* is mapped to *P′*, as shown. Trace these points on a piece of paper, and then sketch the mirror line for the reflection.

P

P′

9. Under a reflection, the point *P* is mapped to *P′* (with *P* = *P′*) and *Q* is mapped to *Q′* (with *Q* = *Q′*), as shown. Trace these points on a piece of paper, and then sketch the mirror line for the reflection.

P ● *P′*

Q ● *Q′*

10. Trace *Q* and $\overline{AB}$ on a sheet of paper. Use a protractor to help you sketch the image of $\overline{AB}$ under a rotation with a center of *Q* and clockwise rotation of 35°.

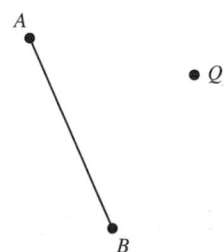

11. Trace *Q* and $\overline{AB}$ on a sheet of paper. Then draw the image of $\overline{AB}$ under a size transformation with a center of *Q* and a scale factor of 3.

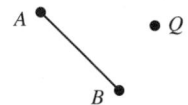

12. Trace the rectangle and its lines of symmetry. Fold the rectangle along a line of symmetry and observe how the line segments interact. What properties of rectangles does it confirm?

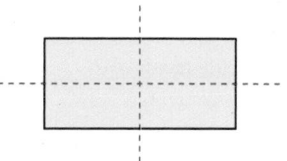

13. Discuss the symmetry in the design.

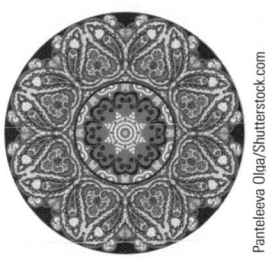

Panteleeva Olga/Shutterstock.com

14. What types of symmetry do these flags have in common?

Macedonia

Atlaspix/Shutterstock.com

Jamaica

pdesign/Shutterstock.com

Switzerland

adam.golabek/Shutterstock.com

15. A rotation with a center of P maps $\overline{AB}$ to $\overline{A'B'}$. What is the degree and direction of rotation?

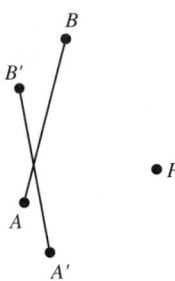

16. Find the image of A and B under a size transformation with a center of P and a scale factor of 2.

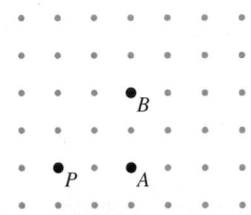

17. Find A and B' under a size transformation with a center of P and a scale factor of 1/2.

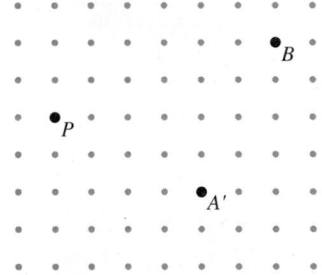

18. Find the image of $\overline{AB}$ under a size transformation with a center of Q and a scale factor of 2.

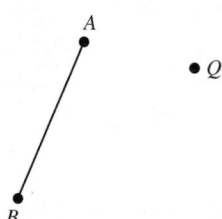

PROBLEM SOLVING

Refresher: Problem solving (reaching a goal that is not immediately attainable) is important because it helps students think more deeply about what they know and deal with unfamiliar situations.

19. A translation maps football B to football A.

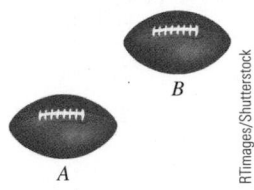

RTimages/Shutterstock

a. Sketch a translation vector.

b. Suppose the length of the football is 4 cm. How far was the football moved?

20. A scale transformation maps $\overline{AB}$ to $\overline{A'B'}$.

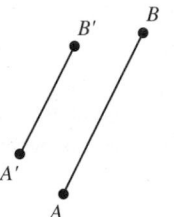

a. Is scale factor k or less than or greater than 1?

b. Use a ruler to help estimate scale factor k.

21. Figure 2 is mapped to Figure 1 using a similarity transformation. Use a ruler to estimate the scale factor of the scale transformation. Explain the process you used.

Larysa Diachenko/Shutterstock

REASONING AND PROOF

Refresher: Reasoning and proof (thinking and justifying) are important because they help students make sense of mathematics.

22. Under a rotation, the point A is mapped to A' and B is mapped to B', as shown. Trace the figure on a piece of paper.

a. Locate the center Q of rotation.

b. Determine the angle of rotation.

c. Is the rotation clockwise or counterclockwise?

23. A rotation maps $\triangle ABC$ to $\triangle A'B'C'$. Locate the center of rotation.

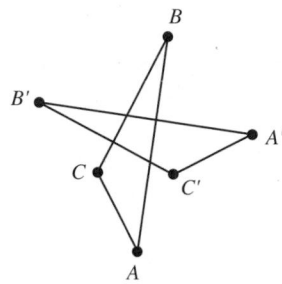

24. A size transformation has a center of Q and a scale factor of 2.

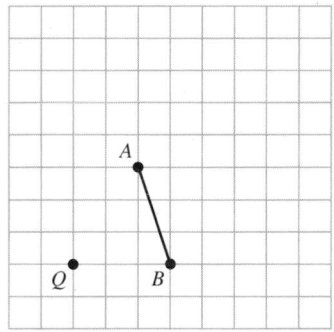

a. Sketch the image $\overline{A'B'}$ of $\overline{AB}$.

b. Prove $\overline{AB}$ and $\overline{A'B'}$ are parallel.

25. A size transformation has a center of Q and a scale factor of 4.

a. Suppose $QA = 5$ ft. What is QA'?

b. Suppose $AB = 6$ ft. What is $A'B'$?

c. Suppose $W'K' = 32$ ft. What is WK?

d. Given that $AB = 12$ ft, $BC = 8$ ft, and $AC = 5$ ft, determine the perimeter of $\triangle A'B'C'$.

26. A size transformation has a center of Q and a scale factor of 5.

a. Suppose $QA = 3$ cm. What is QA'?

b. Suppose $AB = 7$ cm. What is $A'B'$?

c. Suppose $W'K' = 10$ cm. What is WK?

d. Suppose $\triangle ABC$ has an altitude of 3 cm and a base of 4 cm. Determine the area of $\triangle A'B'C'$.

CONNECTIONS

Refresher: Connections (linking and applying mathematical ideas) are important because they deepen student understanding and make mathematics more meaningful, flexible, and useful.

27. Lines l and m are parallel. A reflection with the mirror line l maps A to A'. Then another reflection with the mirror line m maps A' to A''.

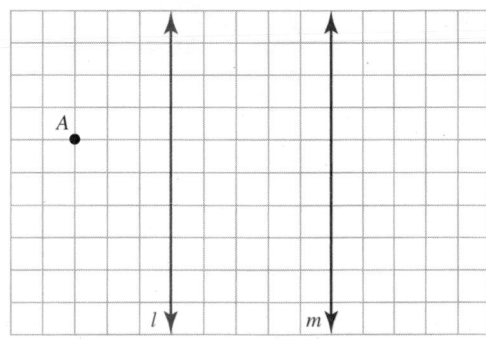

a. Plot A' and A''.

b. The distance between l and m is 5 units. What is the distance between A and A''?

c. Suppose Q is mapped to Q'' using a sequence of two reflections, and their mirror lines are parallel and n units apart. Make a conjecture about the distance between Q and Q''.

28. Some regular polygons are shown here.

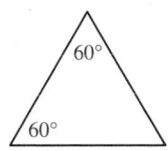
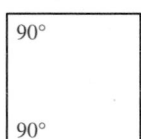
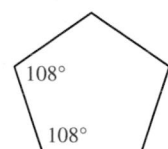

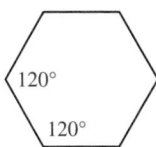
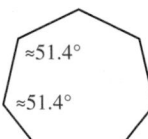
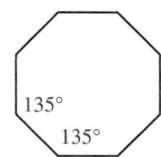

A regular tessellation is a tessellation of a regular polygon. Only three regular polygons tessellate the plane.

a. Identify the three regular polygons based on the figures shown here.

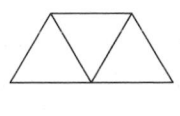
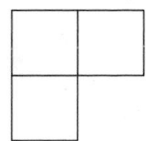
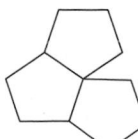

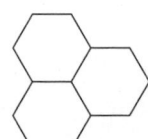

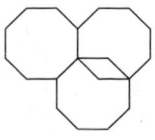

b. Discuss how the interior angles of the three regular polygons that you identified are alike.

29. *l* and *m* are two intersecting mirror lines of reflections. The points *A* and *B* and the letter F are reflected through line *l*, and then their images are reflected through line *m*. Let *Q* be the intersection of the two mirror lines.

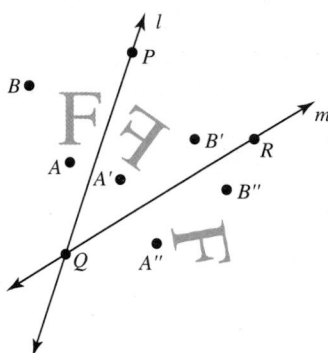

a. Measure $\angle AQA''$ and $\angle BQB''$ using a protractor.

b. Measure $\angle PQR$ using a protractor.

c. A transformation consisting of two reflections with intersecting mirror lines is the same as a rotation. If the intersecting mirror lines form an angle of *n* degrees, what is the angle of rotation?

d. If the intersecting mirror lines form an angle of *n* degrees, which point is the center of rotation?

30. A size transformation maps eyeglasses 1 to eyeglasses 2.

zirconicusso/Shutterstock.com

a. Locate the center of the size transformation.

b. Is the scale factor less than or greater than 1?

c. Use a ruler to help estimate the scale factor.

31. Figure 1 is mapped to Figure 2 using a similarity transformation. Use a ruler to estimate the scale factor of the size transformation. Explain the process you used.

Memo Angeles/Shutterstock.com

COMMUNICATION

Refresher: Communication (written and verbal explanations using representations and proper mathematical vocabulary) is important because it helps students refine and strengthen their understanding.

32. Explain why an isometry maps $\triangle ABC$ to a congruent triangle $\triangle A'B'C'$.

33. Explain why an isometry maps $\angle ABC$ to a congruent angle $\angle A'B'C'$.

34. How are rigid motions of the plane used to define congruence?

35. Mrs. Dugger reads the following problem to her class: "I am thinking of a plane transformation that maps $A(2, 5)$ to $A'(4, 7)$ and $B(-3, 1)$ to $B'(6, 2)$. Could this mapping be an isometry?" Her students think about this for a few minutes. Then Alicia exclaims, "The mapping cannot be an isometry!" Explain why Alicia is correct.

36. A transformation maps *P* to *P'* and *Q* to *Q'*, as shown. Explain why the transformation cannot be a reflection.

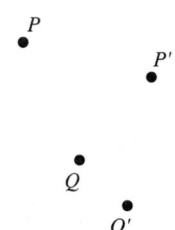

37. A transformation maps *P* to *P'* and *Q* to *Q'*, as shown. Explain why the transformation cannot be a rotation.

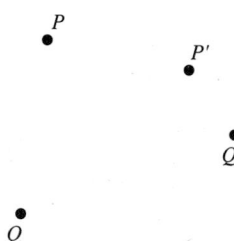

38. A reflection maps helmet 1 to helmet 2. Sketch the helmets on a piece of paper. Then sketch the mirror line for the reflection.

Tribalium/Shutterstock.com

39. Identify the type of transformation for each part: *translation, reflection, rotation, glide reflection, size transformation.*

a.

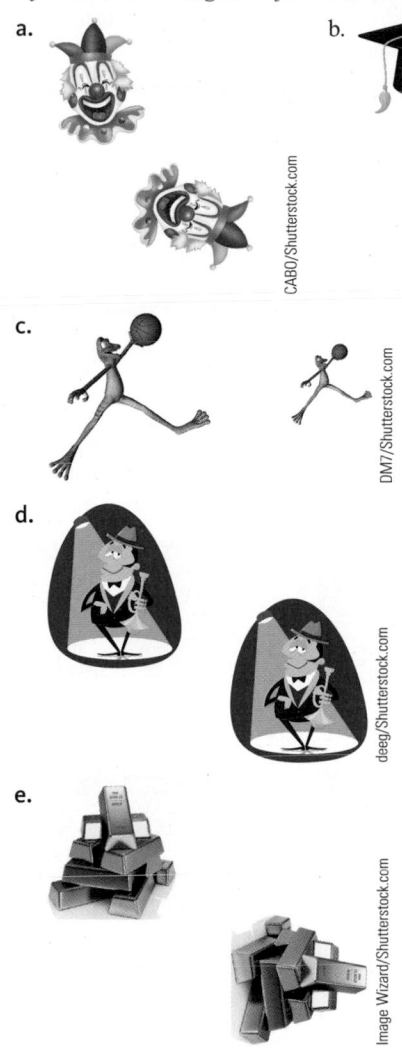

b.

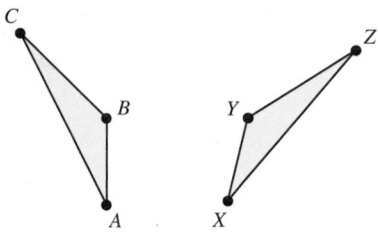

c.

d.

e.

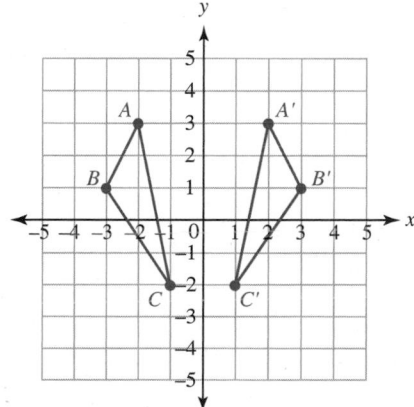

40. An isometry maps △*ABC* to △*A'B'C'*.

a. Identify the isometry.

b. Using coordinates, verify that *A'B'* = *AB*.

41. Describe a sequence of isometries that maps △*ABC* to △*XYZ*.

42. Apply translations to create an original Escher-like tessellation with interlocking figures.

43. Applying reflections and translations to create an original Escher-like tessellation with interlocking figures.

More practice with the ideas of the section

44. Fill in the blank. Choose one of the following words, phrases, or equations: *AB* = *A'B'*, *AB* ≠ *A'B'*, *angle, congruent, congruence, direction, flip, flipper, flop, image, left turn, mapping, mirror, paper folding, preimage, right turn, rigid motion, similar, similarity, similarity transformation, slip, slide, straight, transformation,* or *turn.*

a. We can use _____ to verify that a two-dimensional shape has line symmetry.

b. We can generate _____ figures using size transformations.

c. An isometry is a transformation such that _____ for any two points *A* and *B*.

d. A(n) _____ maps the plane to itself such that every point in the plane has one image and every point in the plane has one preimage.

e. The point *A* is called the _____ of *A'*.

f. Two figures *F₁* and *F₂* are said to be congruent if and only if there is a(n) _____ that maps *F₁* to *F₂*.

g. Two figures *F₁* and *F₂* are said to be similar if and only if there is a(n) _____ that maps *F₁* to *F₂*.

h. Every rotation has a center of rotation and a(n) _____ angle.

i. A reflection is also called a(n) _____.

j. A translation is also called a(n) _____.

k. In a translation, every point moves the same distance and the same _____.

l. A line of reflection is often called a(n) _____ line.

m. The point *A'* is called the _____ of *A*.

n. A(n) _____ relates two sets of points in the plane.

o. A(n) _____ is a transformation of the plane that preserves distances.

45. Find the image of each point under a reflection with the given mirror line.

a.

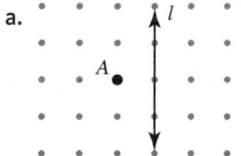

b. 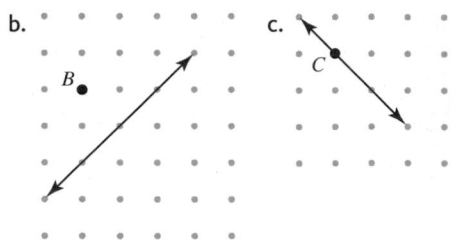 **c.**

46. A size transformation with a center of Q and a scale factor of 2 maps $\triangle ABC$ to $\triangle A'BC'$. Sketch the diagram on a piece of paper, and then sketch $\triangle A'B'C'$.

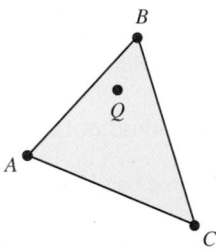

47. A size transformation maps $\triangle ABC$ to $\triangle A'B'C'$.

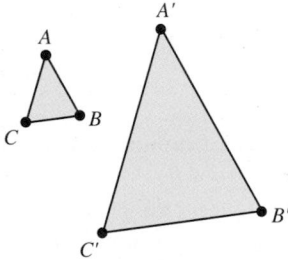

a. Locate the center of the size transformation.

b. Is the scale factor less than or greater than 1?

c. Use a ruler and a calculator to help estimate the scale factor.

48. A rotation maps one piano to the other one.

lem/Shutterstock.com

a. Locate the center of rotation.

b. Use a protractor and straightedge to determine the angle of rotation.

49. Trace the isosceles triangle (shown with the midpoint of the base) on a piece of paper. Fold the triangle so that points A and C overlap; make sure you create a crease in the paper. Observe how the line segments and angles interact.

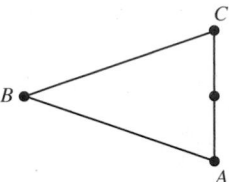

a. How are angles $\angle A$ and $\angle C$ related? Explain your answer.

b. What angle does the paper crease form with $\overline{AC}$?

c. Does the paper crease pass through B?

d. Does the paper crease pass through the midpoint of $\overline{AC}$?

50. How many lines of symmetry does each flag have?

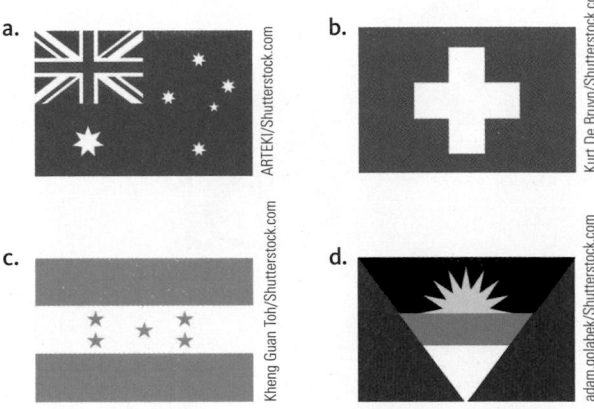

a. ARTEKI/Shutterstock.com

b. Kurt De Bruyn/Shutterstock.com

c. Kheng Guan Toh/Shutterstock.com

d. adam.golabek/Shutterstock.com

51. A size transformation with a center of Y and a scale factor of k maps P to Q. What is the scale factor of a size transformation with a center of Y that maps Q to P?

52. In an example in this section, we proved that if a rotation with a center of rotation P and counterclockwise turn angle that has the measure n degrees maps A to A' and B to B' such that P, A, and B are noncollinear, then $AB = A'B'$. Now, suppose P, A, and B are collinear, as represented in the diagram, so that P, A', and B' are collinear, as shown. Prove $AB = A'B'$.

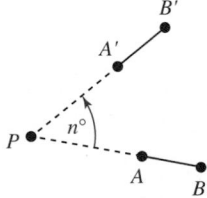

53. The diagram shows a parallelogram with lines k and h through the midpoints of opposite sides. Are they lines of symmetry? Why or why not?

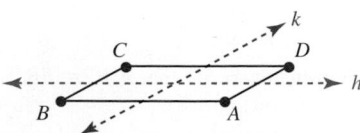

54. Which capital letters of the alphabet have line symmetry?

A B C D E F G H I J K L M N O P Q R S T U V W X Y Z

55. Which capital letters of the alphabet have point symmetry?

A B C D E F G H I J K L M N O P Q R S T U V W X Y Z

56. Draw a quadrilateral with

  a. one line of symmetry.

  b. two lines of symmetry.

  c. four lines of symmetry.

57. Draw a hexagon with

  a. one line of symmetry.

  b. two lines of symmetry.

  c. six lines of symmetry.

58. A size transformation with a center of $Q(1, -1)$ maps $B(3, -7)$ to $B'(7, -19)$. Find the scale factor.

59. A size transformation with a center of $P(3, 9)$ maps $C(2, 5)$ to $C'(5, 17)$. Find the scale factor.

60. A size transformation has a center of Q and a scale factor of $\frac{3}{4}$. Suppose the length of $\overline{AB}$ is 72 units. What is the length of $\overline{A'B'}$?

61. A size transformation has a center of Q and a scale factor of 3. Suppose the length of $\overline{A'B'}$ is 72 units. What is the length of $\overline{AB}$?

62. A size transformation maps $\triangle ABC$ to $\triangle A'B'C'$.

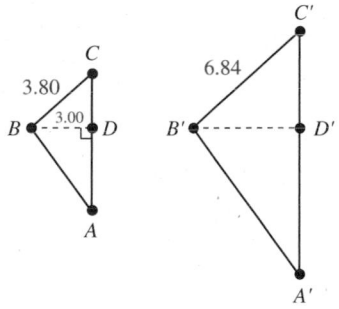

  a. Determine the scale factor of the size transformation.

  b. Determine the distance $B'D'$.

  c. Suppose the area of $\triangle ABC$ is 9.50 cm². Determine the area of $\triangle A'B'C'$.

63. A size transformation maps $\triangle ABC$ to $\triangle A'B'C'$.

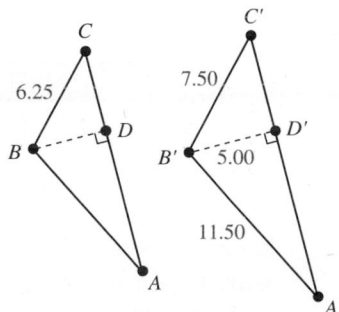

  a. Determine the scale factor of the size transformation.

  b. Determine the perimeter of $\triangle ABC$.

64. Each line segment is reflected about the y-axis.

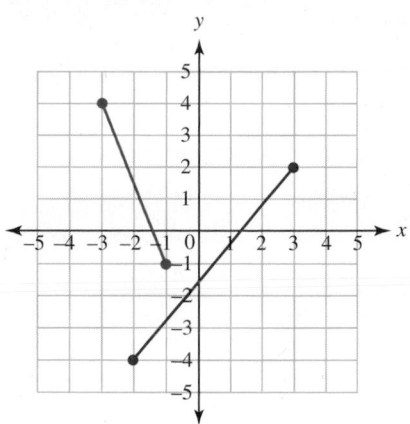

  a. Draw the image of each line segment.

  b. Compare the slopes of each line segment and image.

  c. Make a conjecture about the relationships of the slopes of nonvertical line segments reflected about the y-axis.

65. Each line segment is reflected about the x-axis.

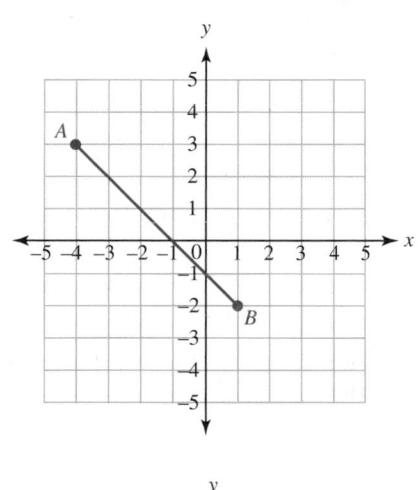

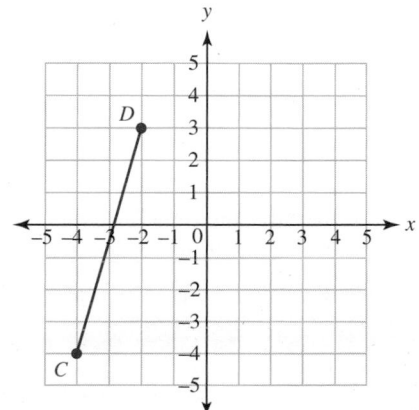

  a. Draw the image of each line segment.

  b. Compare the slopes of each line segment and image.

  c. Make a conjecture about the relationships of the slopes of nonvertical line segments reflected about the x-axis.

CHAPTER **13 REVIEW**

CHAPTER **13** Organizer

Section	What You Should Learn	Review Problems
13.1	**1.** Use algebra or graphs to represent horizontal, vertical, and oblique lines.	1–5
	2. Write or graph the equation of a line given the slope and any point on the line.	6–9
	3. Determine and interpret the slope of a line.	10–11
	4. Calculate the intercepts of a line.	12–13
	5. Determine the effect of changing the value of one variable in a linear equation.	14–15
	6. Know the relationships between the slopes of two lines and of perpendicular or parallel lines.	16–22
	7. Apply concepts of linear equations.	23–24
13.2	**1.** Apply the distance formula (e.g., to classify triangles, or identify the largest angle of a triangle).	25–28
	2. Determine the midpoint of the line segment with given endpoints and write the equation of the perpendicular bisector of the line segment joining two given points.	29–31
	3. Relate an equation of a circle to its standard form $(x - h)^2 + (y - k)^2 = r^2$, center, and radius.	32–35
	4. Sketch graphs of polygons in the coordinate plane with given properties.	36–40
	5. Use coordinate geometry to apply or prove properties of a polygon.	41–44
13.3	**1.** Know basic information about four transformations of the plane: translation, reflection, rotation, and size transformation.	45–46
	2. Determine the image, preimage, or component of a rigid motion.	47–56
	3. Describe the symmetry, if any, in a figure.	57–58
	4. Describe a sequence of rigid motions that maps one geometric figure to a congruent figure.	59
	5. Given a size transformation, sketch the image or preimage, determine a distance, or locate the center and estimate the scale factor.	60–67
	6. Know the impact of a similarity transformation on perimeter and area.	68–69
	7. Identify the transformation as a reflection, translation, rotation, or size transformation.	70
	8. Explain how a particular tessellation is constructed.	71

Key Terms and Concepts

parallel 768	origin 769	linear function 774
coordinate system 768	ordered pair 769	slopes and parallel lines 776
coordinate geometry 768	vertical line 769	slopes and perpendicular lines 778
coordinate plane (Cartesian plane) 769	horizontal line 770	distance formula 785
	oblique line 770	standard equation of a circle 787
x-axis 769	slope 773	formula for the midpoint 789
y-axis 769	slope-intercept form 774	coordinate proofs 790

Key Terms and Concepts

mapping   798

image   798

preimage   798

transformation   799

rigid motion (isometery)   799

translation vector   800

translation   802

mirror line   803

reflection   803

rotation   806

glide reflection   813

definition of congruent figures   816

line symmetry   816

rotational symmetry (turn
   symmetry)   817

angle of symmetry   817

point symmetry (half turn)   818

size transformation (dilation)   819

scale factor   819

contraction   819

expansion   819

similarity transformation   822

definition of similar figures   822

tessellation   822

tile   822

regular tessellation   823

semiregular tessellation   824

Escher-like tessellation   824

Review Questions

1. Determine whether the graph is of a vertical, horizontal, or oblique line.

   a. $x = 0$ **b.** $y = -4.3$ **c.** $5x = 2$ **d.** $y = -15$

   e. $4x - 5y = 8$ **f.** $x = -3$

2. Do the following.

   a. Draw a horizontal line that passes through the point $(-2, 3)$.

   b. Draw a vertical line that passes through the point $(4, -2)$.

3. Graph the set of solutions to the equation $y = 4x - 3$.

4. Write the equation of each line.

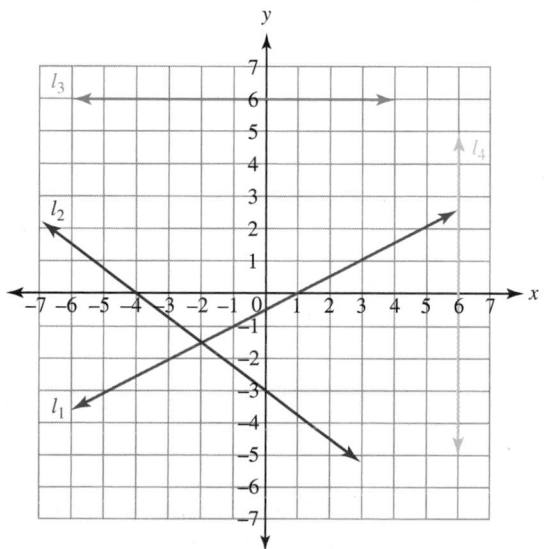

5. A line passes through $(3, 5)$. Write an equation such that the line is

   a. vertical.   **b.** horizontal.   **c.** oblique.

6. Draw a line that has a slope of 3 and an x-intercept of $(4, 0)$.

7. Draw a line that has a slope of $-\dfrac{2}{3}$ and a y-intercept of $(0, 3)$.

8. Write the equation of the line in slope-intercept form with a

   a. slope of 3 and a y-intercept of $(0, 2)$.

   b. slope of 2 and an x-intercept of $(-3, 0)$.

9. A line passes through $A(4, -1)$ and $B(5, 2)$.

   a. What is the slope of the line?

   b. What is the equation of the line? Write it in the form $y = mx + b$.

10. A phone company charges a monthly fee plus an additional fee for every minute of phone use. Suppose the cost C is given by the equation $C = 25 + 0.06m$ dollars for m minutes of monthly phone usage.

    a. What is the monthly fee?

    b. Interpret the slope of the equation in the context of the problem.

11. Determine the slope of each line.

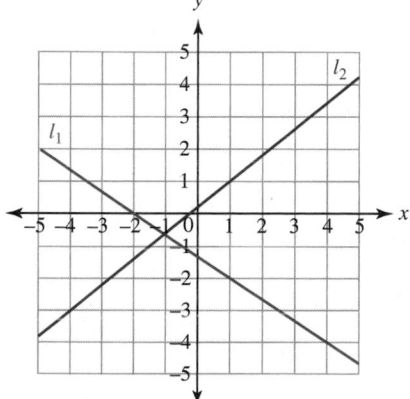

12. Determine the x- and y-intercepts of the line shown.

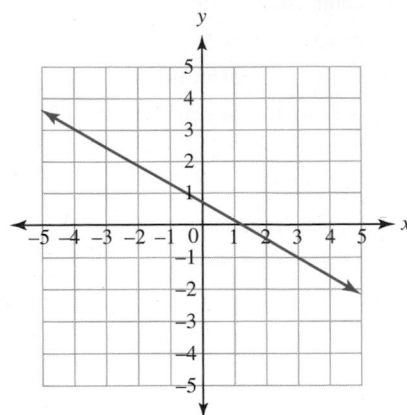

13. The equation of a line is $4y + 3x = 7$. Find the
    a. slope of the line.   b. x-intercept of the line.
    c. y-intercept of the line.

14. The equation of a line is $-3y = 5x - 7$.
    a. Suppose the x value decreases by 2 units. By how much does the y value increase or decrease?
    b. Suppose the y value increases by 3 units. By how much does the x value increase or decrease?

15. Suppose y is the number of tires sold for a given brand of tires, x is the price of a tire, and they are related by the equation $y = -2x + 300$.
    a. The price of a tire increases by $5. What will be the change in the number of tires sold?
    b. The price of a tire decreases by $3. What will be the change in the number of tires sold?

16. Fill in the blank.
    a. The slope of a horizontal line is _____.
    b. The slope of a vertical line is _____.
    c. If the slopes of two nonvertical lines are equal, then the two lines are _____.
    d. If two nonvertical lines are parallel, then their _____ are equal.
    e. If two lines are perpendicular, then the product of their slopes is _____, or one line is horizontal and the other line is vertical.
    f. If the product of the slopes of two lines is equal to -1, then the two lines are _____.
    g. If one line is horizontal and the other line is _____, then the two lines are perpendicular.

17. Determine whether the lines are parallel, perpendicular, or neither.
    a. $y = 3x - 5$ and $y = 18x - 30$
    b. $y = -2x - 6$ and $10y + 20x = 6$
    c. $y = 5x - 1$ and $y + 10x = 1$
    d. $12y + 9x = -1$ and $3y = 4x + 7$
    e. $8y = 3x + 5$ and $y = \dfrac{8}{3}x + 2$

18. Two lines are perpendicular.
    a. The slope of one line is $-\frac{3}{5}$. What is the slope of the other line?

    b. The slope of one line is undefined. What is the slope of the other line?

19. Do the following.

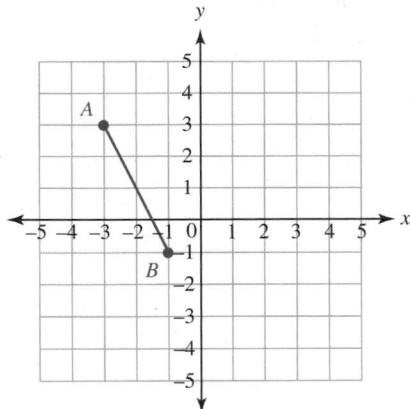

    a. Locate a point C on the graph so that $\triangle ABC$ is a right triangle.
    b. Explain how you located C.
    c. Verify that $\triangle ABC$ is a right triangle.

20. The equation of line l is $y = \dfrac{6}{5}x - 4$.
    a. What is the slope of a line perpendicular to line l?
    b. What is the slope of a line parallel to line l?

21. Write the equation of a line that passes through the point $(1, -5)$ and is perpendicular to a line with the equation $y = 8x - 3$.

22. Write the equation of a line that passes through the point $(-2, 3)$ and is parallel to a line with the equation $y = 4x + 3$.

23. A rental car company charges $115 to rent a car for 1 week plus $0.25 per mile.
    a. Write the cost C for one week as a function of the mileage m.
    b. What is the cost to rent the car for 1 week and drive it 250 miles?
    c. Interpret the ordered pair $(50, 127.5)$.
    d. Suppose your budget for renting a car for 1 week is $260. What is the maximum number of miles you can drive the rental car?

24. Forensic scientists often need to estimate height based on an incomplete set of human bones or a decomposing body. One study showed that there is a strong correlation between the hand length (as measured by the distance between the wrist crease and the tip of the middle finger) and the height of a person belonging to a particular group of people. The formulas for the relationship between hand length and height could vary from one group to another group of people due to different physical activity levels and diet. Suppose the researchers recorded measurements for adult males in the table shown.

Hand length L (cm)	19.4	21.3	22.8
Height of adult male H (cm)	171.6	178.25	183.5

The variable L represents the hand length, and the variable H represents the height of the adult male.

  a. What does the ordered pair $(21.3, 178.25)$ mean?

  b. Express the adult male height as a linear function of the length of a hand.

  c. Suppose archeologists unearth a hand of the length 17 cm. Predict the height of the adult male.

  d. Suppose the height of an adult male is 175.3 cm. Predict the length of the hand.

25. Find the distance between $P(5, -3)$ and $Q(2, 5)$.

26. Use the distance formula to identify the angle of $\triangle PQR$ with the largest measure. Explain your answer.

  a. $\triangle PQR$ has the vertices $P(10, -7)$, $Q(1, 3)$, and $R(-2, 5)$.

  b. $\triangle PQR$ has the vertices $P(1, -2)$, $Q(3, 5)$, and $R(2, 8)$.

27. Use the distance formula to identify the right angle in each right triangle $\triangle ABC$. Explain your answer.

  a. $A(2, 3)$, $B(6, 7)$, and $C(4, 1)$

  b. $A(3, -2)$, $B(-1, -6)$, and $C(-3, -4)$

28. Verify that $\triangle ABC$ is a right triangle using the converse of the Pythagorean theorem.

  a. $A(-3, 2)$, $B(-1, 4)$, $C(1, -2)$

  b. $A(-3, 3)$, $B(-1, -2)$, $C(4, 0)$

29. Determine the midpoint M of $\overline{PQ}$ with the endpoints $P(2, -7)$ and $Q(-3, 4)$.

30. $M(-1, 6)$ and $P(3, 7)$ are points such that M is the midpoint of $\overline{PQ}$. Determine the coordinates of Q.

31. Find the equation of the perpendicular bisector of the line segment joining $A(-3, 2)$ and $B(1, 4)$.

32. The standard form of the equation of a particular circle is $(x - 2)^2 + (y - (-1))^2 = (\sqrt{10})^2$.

  a. Determine the center of the circle.

  b. Determine the radius of the circle.

33. The points on a circle satisfy the equation $(x - 4)^2 + (y + 7)^2 = 22$.

  a. Write the equation in standard form.

  b. Determine the center of the circle.

  c. Determine the radius of the circle.

34. Write the standard form of the equation of the circle shown.

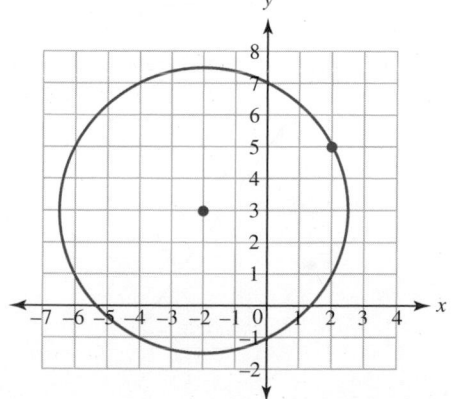

35. $A(2, 7)$ and $B(3, -5)$ are points on a circle, and $\overline{AB}$ is a diameter of a circle.

  a. Determine the center of the circle.

  b. Determine the radius of the circle.

  c. Write the standard equation of the circle.

36. $ABCD$ is a parallelogram. Find the coordinates of D.

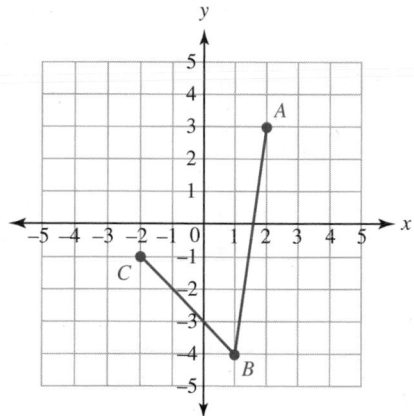

37. $ABCD$ is a rectangle. Find the coordinates of D.

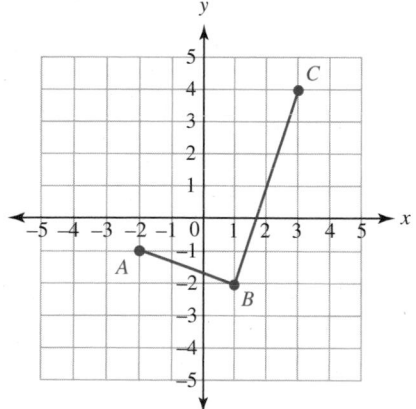

38. Draw a rectangle in a coordinate plane such that the width of a rectangle is 2 units less than five times the length of the rectangle. Include the coordinates of each vertex.

39. Draw an obtuse triangle in the coordinate plane with an area of 10 square units. Include the coordinates of each vertex.

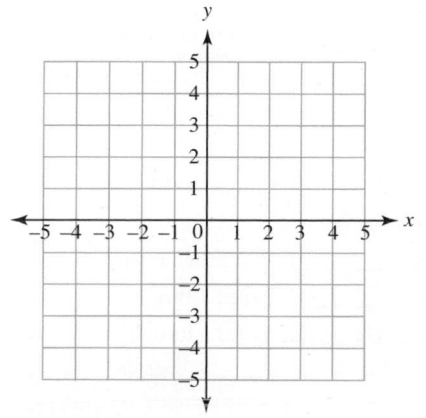

40. Draw a parallelogram in the coordinate plane with an area of 10 square units. Include the coordinates of each vertex.

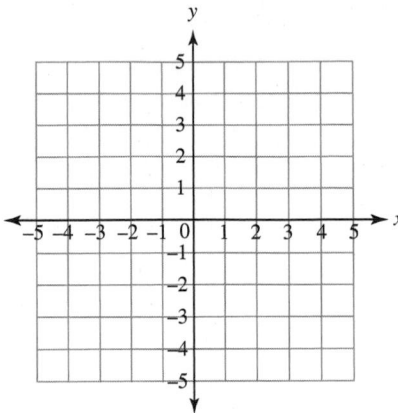

41. Prove that the points $A(-3, -2)$, $B(-2, 1)$, $C(3, 2)$, and $D(2, -1)$ are the vertices of a parallelogram.

42. $A(-3, -1)$, $B(-3, 2)$, $C(2, 2)$, and $D(2, -1)$ are the vertices of a rectangle. Show that $\overline{AC}$ and $\overline{BD}$

   a. are congruent.

   b. bisect each other.

43. $A(-1, 0)$, $B(1, -5)$, $C(3, 0)$, and $D(1, 3)$ are the vertices of a convex quadrilateral.

   a. Verify that the quadrilateral is a kite.

   b. Verify that the diagonals of the kite are perpendicular.

44. $\triangle WHY$ is a triangle in the coordinate plane.

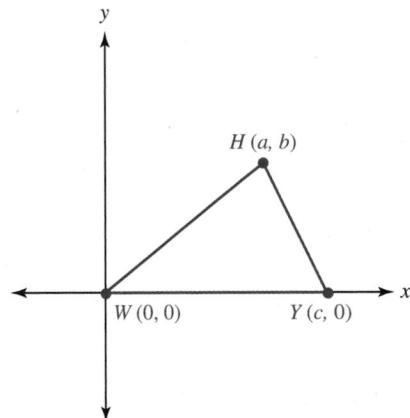

   a. Find the coordinates of the midpoint A of $\overline{WH}$.

   b. Find the coordinates of the midpoint B of $\overline{HY}$.

   c. Verify that $AB = \dfrac{1}{2}WY$.

   d. Prove that $\overline{AB}$ is parallel to $\overline{WY}$.

45. Fill in the blank.

   a. A(n) _____ is also called a slide.

   b. A(n) _____ is called a flip.

   c. A(n) _____ is called a turn.

   d. A(n) _____ is a transformation of the plane such that $AB = A'B'$ for any two points A and B.

   e. A line of _____ of a geometric figure is a line such that a reflection maps the geometric figure to itself.

   f. A(n) _____ maps a geometric figure to a similar figure using a center and scale factor.

46. Suppose a rigid motion maps A to A' such that $A = A'$. What can you say about A if you know the rigid motion is a

   a. reflection? **b.** rotation?

47. A translation point maps point Q to the point Q' in the coordinate system, as shown.

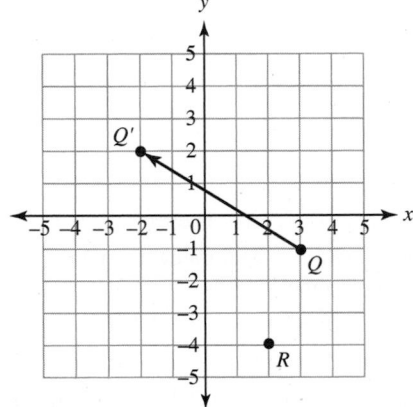

   a. Describe how points move under the translation.

   b. Locate the image of R.

48. A translation maps $A(5, 2)$ to $A'(3, -7)$. Find the image of $B(6, 4)$.

49. A translation maps $A(1, -3)$ to $A'(4, 8)$. Find the preimage of $B'(-7, 2)$.

50. Find the image of $\overline{DE}$ under a rotation with a center of F and clockwise turn of $75°$.

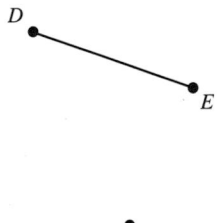

51. Sketch the preimage of A' under a reflection about line l.

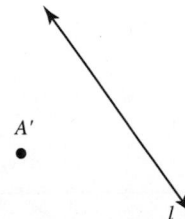

52. Sketch the mirror line for the reflection that takes A to A'.

A

A'

53. Identify the rigid motion that relates the two pictures.

Gorelova/Shutterstock.com

54. Sketch the image of the triangle under a reflection about the mirror line l.

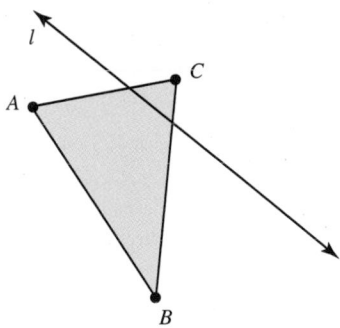

l

C

A

B

55. A rotation maps A to A' and B to B', as shown.

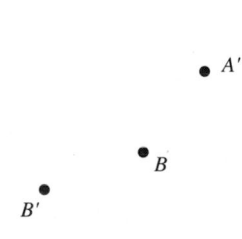

A

A'

B

B'

a. Find the center of rotation.

b. Determine the degree of rotation.

56. A rotation maps one figure to the other. Determine the degree of rotation.

Involved Channel/Shutterstock.com

57. Identify the angle of symmetry of each hubcap. If there is no angle of symmetry, explain why.

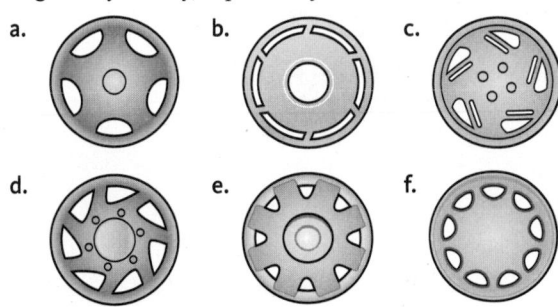

a.   **b.**   **c.**

d.   **e.**   **f.**

58. How many lines of symmetry does the flag have?

a. Cambodia   **b.** Scotland

c./Shutterstock.com   pdesign/Shutterstock.com

c. Macedonia   **d.** Panama

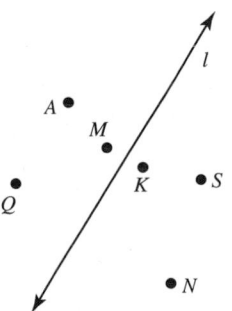

Michael Roeder/Shutterstock.com   Kheng Guan Toh/Shutterstock.com

59. Isometry 1 consists of a reflection with the mirror line l, followed by a clockwise rotation of 35° with a center of Q. Isometry 2 consists of a clockwise rotation of 35° with a center of Q, followed by a reflection with the mirror line l.

l

A

M

K S

Q

N

a. What are the two points that A is mapped to in isometry 1? List the points in order.

b. What are the two points that A is mapped to in isometry 2? List the points in order.

c. Explain what this problem illustrates.

60. Do the following.

a. Sketch the image of $\triangle STU$ under a scale transformation with a center of C and a scale factor of 2.

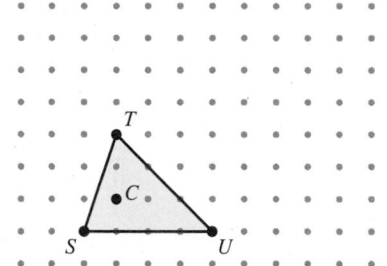

b. Calculate $S'T'$, ST, and the quotient $S'T'/ST$.

c. Calculate $T'U'$, TU, and the quotient $T'U'/TU$.

d. Calculate $S'U'$, SU, and the quotient $S'U'/SU$.

e. Let P' and P denote the perimeters of $\triangle S'T'U'$ and $\triangle STU$. Calculate the quotient P'/P.

f. Let A' and A denote the areas of $\triangle S'T'U'$ and $\triangle STU$. Calculate A', A, and the quotient A'/A.

61. Sketch the image of $\triangle ABC$ under a scale transformation with a center of Q and a scale factor of $\frac{1}{3}$.

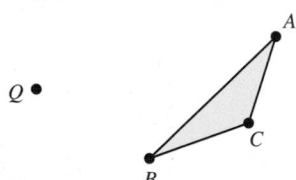

62. The diagram shows the image $\triangle A'B'C'$ of $\triangle ABC$ under a size transformation with a center of Q and a scale factor of 2. Sketch the preimage $\triangle ABC$.

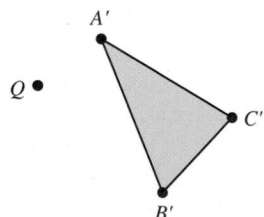

63. Trace the given diagram on a piece of paper. A size transformation has a center of Q and a scale factor of $k = 1.5$, with A and B' as shown in the diagram. Sketch A' and B.

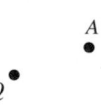

64. A size transformation has a center of Q and a scale factor of 4.

a. Suppose $QA = 5$ cm. What is QA'?

b. Suppose $AB = 6$ cm. What is $A'B'$?

65. A size transformation has a center of $Q(3, -5)$ and maps $A(5, -13)$ to $A'(14, -49)$. Find the scale factor, rounding the final answer to the nearest hundredth.

66. A size transformation maps $\triangle ABC$ to $\triangle A'B'C'$, as shown.

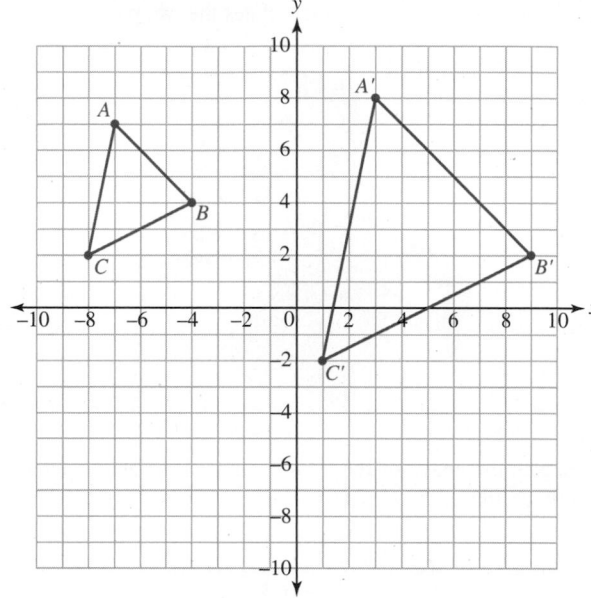

a. Determine the scale factor.

b. Which quadrant (I, II, III, or IV) contains the center of the size transformation?

67. Use a ruler to estimate the scale factor for the size transformation that maps Figure 1 to Figure 2.

68. A size transformation has a center of Q and a scale factor of 3.

a. Suppose the perimeter of $\triangle ABC$ is 25 cm. What is the perimeter of $\triangle A'B'C'$?

b. Suppose the area of $\triangle ABC$ is 8 cm². What is the area of $\triangle A'B'C'$?

69. Do the following.

a. A size transformation has a center of Q and a scale factor of 4. Suppose the perimeter of $\triangle A'B'C'$ is 5 cm. What is the perimeter of $\triangle ABC$?

b. A size transformation has a center of Q and a scale factor of 5. Suppose the area of $\triangle A'B'C'$ is 80 cm². What is the area of $\triangle ABC$?

70. Identify the each of the given transformations as a reflection, translation, rotation, or size transformation.

a.

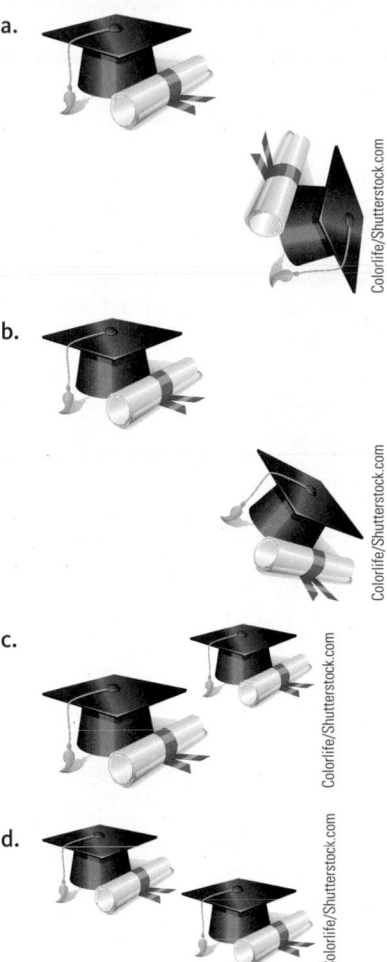

Colorlife/Shutterstock.com

b.

c.

d.

Colorlife/Shutterstock.com   Colorlife/Shutterstock.com

Colorlife/Shutterstock.com

71. The following diagram is constructed from a single shape (tile) that tessellates the plane.

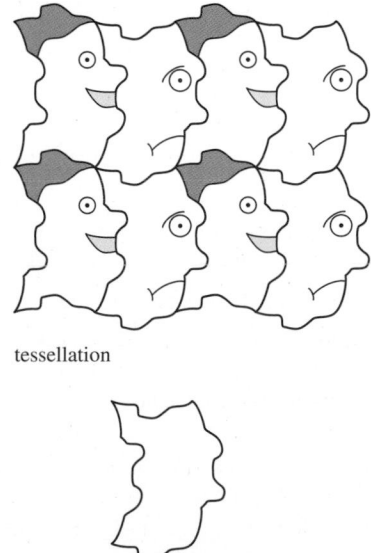

tessellation

tile for the tessellation

Explain each step needed to construct the tessellation.

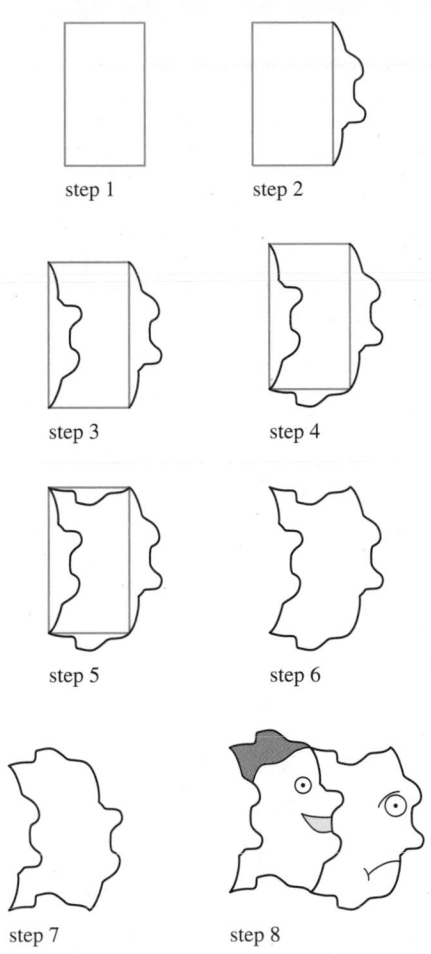

step 1   step 2

step 3   step 4

step 5   step 6

step 7   step 8

Chapter 13 Test

1. *Use algebra or graphs to represent horizontal, vertical, and oblique lines.* Write the equation for the graph of each line.

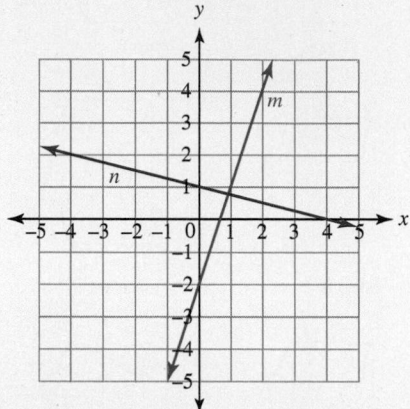

   a. *m* **b.** *n*

2. *Write or graph the equation of a line given the slope and any point on the line.* Write the equation for each line.

   a. The slope is -12, and $(4, -10)$ is a point on the line.

   b. The slope is 7, and $(4, 25)$ is a point on the line.

3. *Determine and interpret the slope of a line.* A company has determined that its daily cost C to make n chairs is given by the equation $C(n) = 40n + 500$ dollars.

   a. What is the cost to manufacture 60 chairs?

   b. Suppose the company manufacturers k chairs. What is the additional cost to manufacture one more chair?

4. *Calculate the intercepts of a line.* The monthly cost C of a cell phone plan is given by $C(n) = 0.04n + 20$ dollars, where n is the number of minutes the phone was used.

   a. Find the C-intercept.

   b. Interpret the C-intercept.

5. *Determine the effect of changing the value of one variable in a linear equation.* Suppose y is the cost (in dollars) to paint n linear feet of fence and the variables are related by the equation $y = 6.50n + 200$. What will be the change in the number of feet of fence painted if

   a. the cost increases by $94.25?

   b. the cost decreases by $24.70?

6. *Know the relationships between the slopes of two lines and of perpendicular or parallel lines.* Determine whether the lines are parallel, perpendicular, or neither.

   a. $y = 7x - 4$ and $8y = 56x + 32$

   b. $6x - 10y = 18$ and $y = -\frac{3}{5}x - 8$

   c. $y = 4x - 1$ and $3x + 12y = 15$

7. *Know the relationships between the slopes of two lines and of perpendicular or parallel lines.* Two lines are perpendicular.

   a. The slope of one line is $\frac{5}{8}$. What is the slope of the other line?

   b. The slope of one line is 0. What is the slope of the other line?

8. *Know the relationships between the slopes of two lines and of perpendicular or parallel lines.* Write the equation of a line that passes through the point $(-5, 4)$ and is perpendicular to a line with the equation $y = 10x + 7$.

9. *Apply the distance formula.* $\triangle PQR$ has the vertices $P(4, -3)$, $Q(7, 4)$, and $R(-2, 6)$. Use the distance formula to identify the angle of $\triangle PQR$ with the largest measure.

10. *Apply the distance formula.* $P(-3, 3)$, $Q(3, -1)$, and $R(8, 1)$ are the vertices of a triangle. Use the distance formula to help classify the triangle as acute, right, or obtuse.

11. *Determine the midpoint of the line segment with given endpoints, and write the equation of the perpendicular bisector of the line segment joining two given points.* Write the equation of the perpendicular bisector of the line segment with the endpoints $A(4, 9)$ and $B(2, 15)$.

12. *Relate an equation of a circle to its standard form $(x - h)^2 + (y - k)^2 = r^2$, center, and radius.* The points on a circle satisfy the equation $(x + 8)^2 + (y - 3)^2 = 21$.

    a. Write the equation in standard form.

    b. Determine the center of the circle.

    c. Determine the radius of the circle.

13. *Use coordinate geometry to apply or prove properties of a polygon.* A rhombus is placed in the coordinate system, as shown.

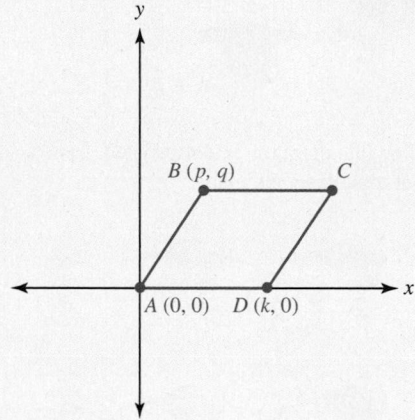

    a. Express the coordinates of C, using the variables k, p, and q as needed.

    b. Write an equation that relates k, p, and q. (Hint: Use the equation $AD = DC$.)

    c. Use the equation in part (b) to verify that the diagonals of the rhombus are perpendicular.

14. *Use coordinate geometry to apply or prove properties of a polygon.* Parallelogram $ABCD$ has the vertices $A(1, 4)$, $B(6, -4)$, $C(0, -6)$, and $D(-5, 2)$. Prove that the diagonals bisect each other.

15. *Know basic information about four transformations of the plane: translation, reflection, rotation, and size transformation.* Do the following.

    a. Explain what it means for a plane transformation to be a rigid motion.

b. Suppose F_1 and F_2 are figures in the plane. Define $F_1 \cong F_2$ (congruence) in terms of plane transformations.

c. Suppose F_1 and F_2 are figures in the plane. Define $F_1 \sim F_2$ (similarity) in terms of plane transformations.

16. *Know basic information about four transformations of the plane: translation, reflection, rotation, and size transformation.* Isometry 1 consists of a reflection with the mirror line l followed by a translation that moves Q to R. Isometry 2 consists of a translation that moves Q to R followed by a reflection with the mirror line l.

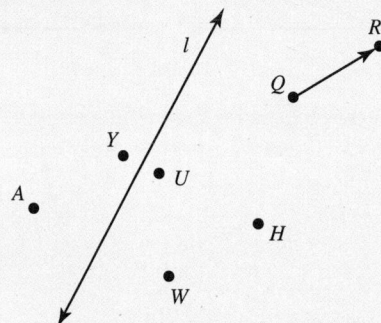

a. List, in order, the points that A is mapped to in isometry 1.

b. List, in order, the points that A is mapped to in isometry 2.

c. Explain what this problem illustrates.

17. *Determine the image, preimage, or component of a rigid motion.* Sketch the image of $\triangle ABC$ under a rotation with a center of P and clockwise rotation of $50°$.

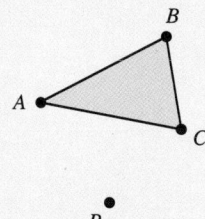

18. *Determine the image, preimage, or component of a rigid motion.* $A(7, 3)$, $B(2, 5)$, and $C(-2, 4)$ are the vertices of a triangle. Find the coordinates of the vertices of $\triangle ABC$ when you move the triangle 5 units to the left and 7 units upward.

19. *Determine the image, preimage, or component of a rigid motion.* A rotation with a center of P and clockwise rotation maps $\overline{AB}$ to $\overline{A'B'}$.

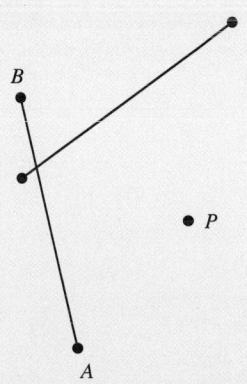

a. Label the endpoints of $\overline{A'B'}$.

b. Determine the angle of rotation.

20. *Describe the symmetry, if any, in a figure.* Answer the following.

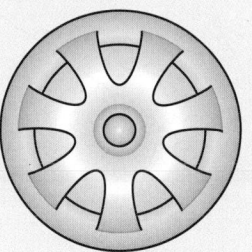

a. How many lines of symmetry does the design have?

b. What is the angle of symmetry of the design?

21. *Given a size transformation, sketch the image or preimage, determine a distance, or locate the center and estimate the scale factor.* A scale transformation maps $\overline{AB}$ to $\overline{A'B'}$.

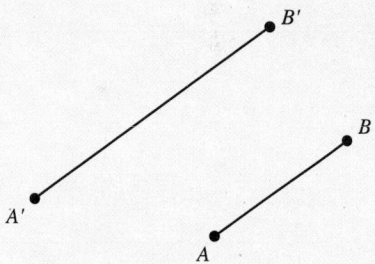

a. Is the scale factor k less than or greater than 1?

b. Use a ruler to help estimate the scale factor k.

c. Locate the center P of the size transformation.

22. *Given a size transformation, sketch the image or preimage, determine a distance, or locate the center and estimate the scale factor.* A size transformation has a center of $Q(-4, -2)$ and maps $A(-2, 1)$ to $A'(4, 10)$. Find the scale factor, rounding the final answer to the nearest hundredth.

23. *Know the impact of a similarity transformation on perimeter and area.* Do the following.

a. A size transformation has a center of Q and a scale factor of 4.5. Suppose the perimeter of $\triangle ABC$ is 540 cm. What is the perimeter of $\triangle A'B'C'$?

b. A size transformation has a center of Q and a scale factor of 6. Suppose the area of $\triangle A'B'C'$ is 972 cm^2. What is the area of $\triangle ABC$?

24. *Know the impact of a similarity transformation on perimeter and area.* A size transformation maps △ABC to △A'B'C'.

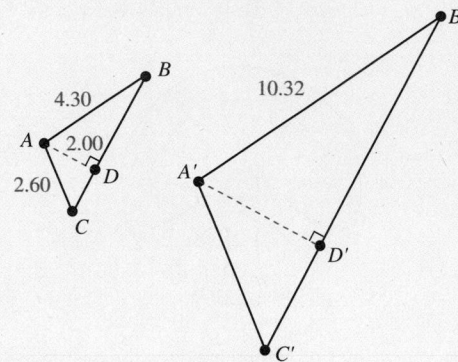

a. Determine the scale factor of the size transformation.

b. Determine the area of △A'B'C'.

25. *Identify the transformation as a reflection, translation, rotation, glide reflection, or size transformation.* Identify the plane transformation that maps △ABC to

  a. △DEF

  b. △GHI

  c. △JKL

  d. △MNO

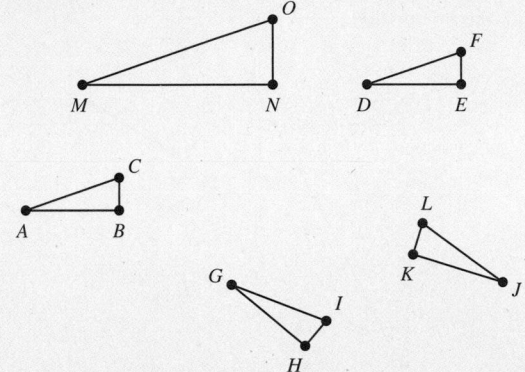

TI-73 Graphing Calculator

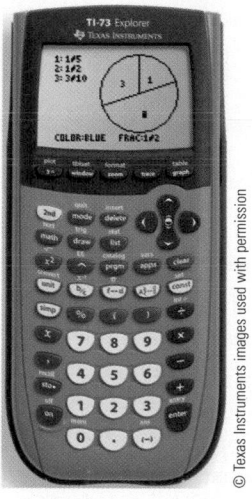

© Texas Instruments images used with permission

USING THE TI-73 EXPLORER CALCULATOR

The TI-73 Explorer calculator was designed by Texas Instruments for students in grades 6–8. This graphing calculator allows you to display multiple lines of text, graphs of functions, and statistical plots such as pie graphs, histograms, and box plots. The TI-73 can display eight lines, with up to 16 characters in each line. It has the same capabilities as a scientific calculator, which typically allows you to work with only one or two lines. The TI-73 has a large screen, called the **Home screen.** This is the interface between the user and the calculator.

The TI-73 has keys for entering fractions and mixed numbers and converting them to decimal form. It has other capabilities, such as converting units, working with tables, solving equations, and calculating statistics such as the mean, standard deviation, and five-number summary (lowest value, 25th percentile, median, 75th percentile, and highest value) of a list of numbers. A user's manual for the TI-73 is freely available at education .ti.com/downloads/guidebooks/graphing/73/73$book-eng.pdf.

The purpose of this appendix is to help you develop essential skills for using the TI-73 for basic entry, editing, and execution of calculator expressions that are often needed for this course. It would be helpful for you to follow along with the instructions. Take some time to experiment with the calculator. Some of the ideas presented here apply to other graphing calculators, such as the TI-83 or TI-83 Plus.

BASIC KEYS

The table summarizes some commonly used keys.

DEL	Deletes the character at the cursor
INS	Sets the cursor to the insertion mode to modify an entry
ENTER	Executes a command or selects an option
2nd	Provides a way to access green keys and turns the cursor into an ↑ arrow
MATH	Provides access to a few math functions, such as LCM and GCF
CLEAR	Clears the command or screen
◄, ►, ▲, and ▼	Move the cursor left, right, up, and down, respectively
QUIT	Exits a menu or screen
Y =	Allows the user to enter formulas for functions

You can clear the Home screen using the CLEAR key. The ◄, ►, ▲, and ▼ keys allow you to move the cursor. The 2nd key allows you to access the green keys, which are indicated by square brackets [ ]. For example, 2nd [QUIT] exits a menu. The ENTER key tells the calculator to evaluate an expression or select an option.

OPERATIONS WITH INTEGERS

Use the negative sign $\boxed{(-)}$ key instead of the subtraction $\boxed{-}$ key for negative integers.

1. Use a calculator to evaluate each expression.
   a. $-3 + 8$
   b. $-3 - 8$

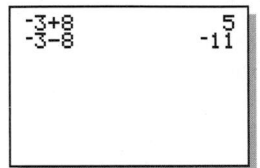

2. Use a calculator to evaluate each expression.
   a. $5(-2)$
   b. $-8 \div 6$

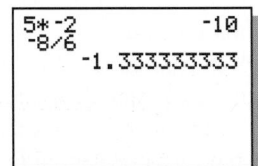

3. Use the calculator to multiply $6 \cdot (-2)$ by using the minus sign instead of the negative sign.

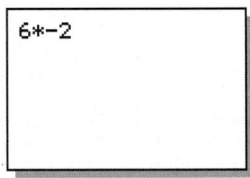

Notes The result of using the minus sign instead of the negative sign could be an error.

By default, the selection 1:Quit is highlighted. But, if you scroll down to 2:Goto and press $\boxed{\text{ENTER}}$, you will be taken back to the previous home screen and the cursor will blink at the location of the first error in the expression. Then you can repair the expression.

ORDER OF OPERATIONS

The following examples demonstrate how to evaluate expressions with multiple operations. Graphing calculators obey the order of operations: parentheses, exponents, multiplication,

and division in the order that they appear from left to right and addition and subtraction in the order that they appear from left to right.

1. Use a calculator to evaluate each expression.
   a. $4 + 5 \cdot 6$
   b. $24 \div 4 \cdot 2$

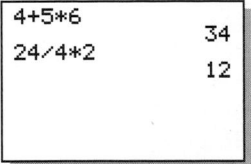

Notes
- A graphing calculator will follow the order of operations. The expression $4 + 5 \cdot 6$ is evaluated as $4 + (5 \cdot 6)$, so you do not need parentheses.
- Some students incorrectly multiply before dividing in the expression $24 \div 4 \cdot 2$ to get 3 rather than the correct answer, 12. The order of operations assumes that multiplication and division are performed from left to right in the absence of parentheses and exponents. So here is how the correct answer is found: $24 \div 4 \cdot 2 = (24 \div 4) \cdot 2 = 6 \cdot 2 = 12$.

2. Use a calculator to evaluate each expression.
   a. $42 \div 3 \cdot 2$
   b. $42 \div (3 \cdot 2)$

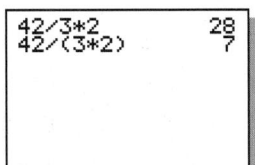

EVALUATING EXPRESSIONS WITH EXPONENTIAL NOTATION

Some examples of expressions with exponential notation are 3^5 and $(-2)^3$. The expression 3^5 has the base 3 and the exponent 5, and $(-2)^3$ has the base -2 and the exponent 3. Most graphing calculators have a $\boxed{\wedge}$ key that can be used to evaluate expressions written with exponential notation.

1. Use a calculator to evaluate each expression.
   a. 3^4
   b. $7^2 \cdot 4^3 + 1$

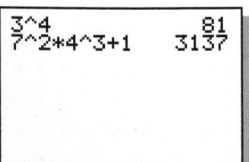

2. Use a calculator to evaluate each expression.

   a. $24 \div 3 \cdot 2^{3+1} + 12$

   b. $5^3 \cdot (18 - 14)^4$

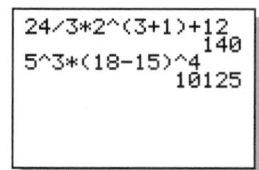

3. Use a calculator to evaluate each expression.

   a. $(-2)^4$

   b. -2^4

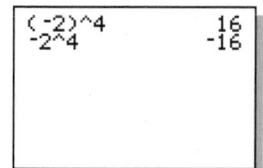

EVALUATING EXPRESSIONS WITH FRACTION NOTATION

Use parentheses for numerators and denominators with operations.

1. Use a calculator to evaluate each expression.

   a. $\dfrac{72}{3 + 6}$

   b. $\dfrac{19 \cdot 30 + 6}{7 + 5^2}$

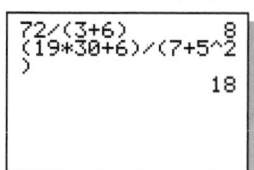

Notes For denominators with operations, be sure to use parentheses. Some students may incorrectly evaluate $\frac{72}{3+6}$ using the keystrokes $72/3 + 6$. This is evaluated as $72/3 + 6 = 24 + 6 = 30$. But $\frac{72}{3+6}$ is really $72/(3 + 6) = 8$.

For numerators and denominators with operations, be sure to use parentheses for both parts.

MIXED NUMBERS AND FRACTIONS

The calculator can convert mixed numbers and fractions.

1. Follow the directions to enter fractions and mixed numbers.

   a. Enter a fraction, such as $\frac{3}{5}$, as follows: $\boxed{3}$ $\boxed{b\%c}$ $\boxed{5}$ $\boxed{\blacktriangleright}$ $\boxed{\text{ENTER}}$.

b. Enter a mixed number, such as $5\frac{6}{7}$, as follows: $\boxed{5}$ $\boxed{\text{UNIT}}$ $\boxed{6}$ $\boxed{b\%c}$ $\boxed{7}$ $\boxed{\blacktriangleright}$ $\boxed{\text{ENTER}}$.

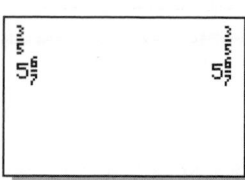

Notes There are two **mode** settings for how fractions are *displayed* or *simplified*. The two display settings are A‿b/c and b/c:

- The A‿b/c setting displays improper fractions as mixed numbers. This is the default setting.

- The b/c setting displays all fractions in the fraction form.

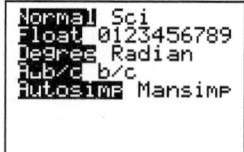 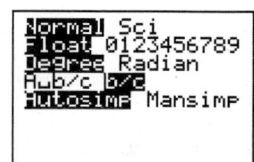

Here are the steps to select a mode setting for displaying fractions: $\boxed{\text{MODE}}$ (move the cursor to A‿b/c or b/c) $\boxed{\text{ENTER}}$. The two simplification settings are Autosimp and Mansimp. The Autosimp setting automatically simplifies fractions. For example, the result of $\frac{1}{6} + \frac{2}{6}$ would be $\frac{1}{2}$. The Mansimp setting does not automatically simplify a fraction. For example, the result of $\frac{17}{36} + \frac{13}{36}$ would be $\frac{30}{36}$, with an arrow $\downarrow$ next to it. Let's choose the mode setting as b/c and the simplification setting as Mansimp, as shown, by pressing the following keys: $\boxed{\text{MODE}}$ $\boxed{\blacktriangledown}$ $\boxed{\blacktriangledown}$ $\boxed{\blacktriangledown}$ $\boxed{\blacktriangleright}$ $\boxed{\text{ENTER}}$ $\boxed{\blacktriangledown}$ $\boxed{\blacktriangleright}$ $\boxed{\text{ENTER}}$ $\boxed{\text{2nd}}$ [QUIT].

With the Mansimp setting, we can manually simplify a fraction. For example, enter the sum $\frac{17}{36} + \frac{13}{36}$ to get the following screen.

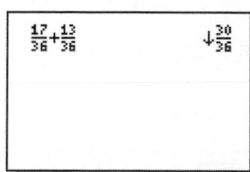

The arrow $\downarrow$ next to the sum $\frac{30}{36}$ indicates that we can simplify the sum. The whole number 3 is a factor of both 30 and 36. Press the $\boxed{\text{SIMP}}$ key, followed by the $\boxed{3}$ key, and then press ENTER. This has the effect of dividing the numerator and denominator by 3: $\frac{30}{36} = \frac{30 \div 3}{36 \div 3} = \frac{10}{12}$.

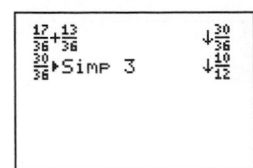

The arrow ↓ indicates the fraction can be further simplified. In this example, any common factor of 30 and 36 could have been used as the simplification factor, such as 6. The arrow disappears when the simplest form of the fraction is displayed.

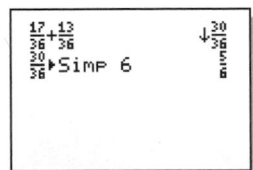

2. Follow these directions to convert between fractions and mixed numbers.

  a. Convert the improper fraction $\frac{16}{7}$ to a mixed number, as follows: 16 ⌐b/c⌐ 7 ⌐A b/c ↔ d/e⌐ ENTER.

  b. Convert $5\frac{6}{7}$ to an improper fraction, as follows: 5 UNIT 6 ▼ 7 ⌐A b/c ↔ d/e⌐ ENTER.

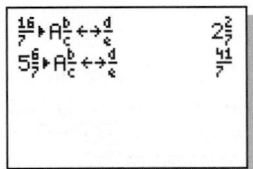

FRACTIONS AND DECIMAL NUMBERS

F↔D converts fractions to decimals.

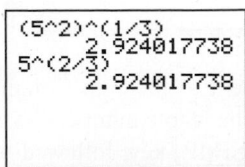

EVALUATING EXPRESSIONS WITH RADICAL SIGNS

The expression $\sqrt[c]{a^b}$ is the same as $(a^b)^{\frac{1}{c}}$ and $a^{\frac{b}{c}}$.

1. Use a calculator to express $\sqrt[3]{5^2}$ in decimal form.

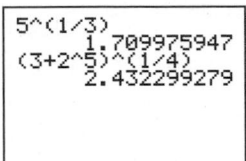

2. Use a calculator to express each expression in decimal form.

  a. $\sqrt[3]{5}$

  b. $\sqrt[4]{3 + 2^5}$

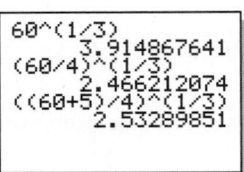

SOLVE AN EQUATION

Suppose n and a are nonnegative numbers. The nonnegative solution to an equation of the form $x^n = a$ is $x = a^{\frac{1}{n}}$.

1. Use a calculator to write the nonnegative solution to the equation in decimal form.

  a. $3^n = 60$

  b. $4 \cdot 3^n = 60$

  c. $4 \cdot 3^n - 5 = 60$

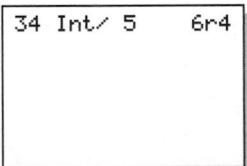

FIND THE QUOTIENT AND REMAINDER IN A WHOLE NUMBER DIVISION PROBLEM

Whole number division is performed using the 2nd [INT÷] key of the calculator.

1. Use the calculator to verify the equation $34 \div 5 = 6$ R4, as follows: 3 4 2nd [INT÷] 5 ENTER.

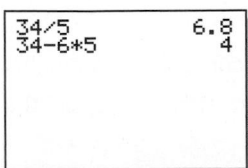

2. Use arithmetic operations to find the quotient and remainder in $34 \div 5$.

Notes Arithmetic operations can be used to find the quotient and remainder in whole number division problems, such as 34 ÷ 5. First, calculate 34 ÷ 5 = 6.8. The quotient is 6. Second, calculate $34 - 6 \cdot 5 = 4$. Then the remainder is 4. So 34 ÷ 5 = 6 R4.

EDITING AN EXPRESSION

We can edit an expression by deleting characters or inserting characters.

1. The ⎡DEL⎤ key is useful for deleting entries in an expression. It erases the character at the cursor. For example, suppose we want to Evaluate 245 ÷ 37, but inadvertently entered 2456 ÷ 37. Use the ⎡◄⎤ key to move the cursor to the left of 6. Then press the ⎡DEL⎤ key, thereby erasing the 6. Finally, press ⎡ENTER⎤ to evaluate the expression 245 ÷ 37.

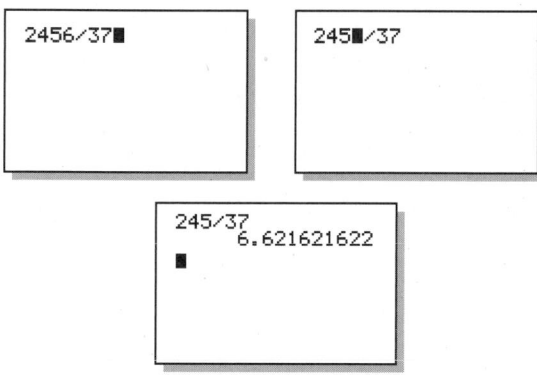

2. The ⎡2nd⎤ [INS] key is useful for inserting entries in an expression. Pressing ⎡2nd⎤ [INS] causes the cursor to change from a blinking square to a blinking underscore. The new characters that are inserted appear to the left of the blinking cursor. Use the left and right arrow keys to move the cursor to the position where you want to enter new characters.

Suppose we entered the expression $85 \cdot 42 + 3$, but meant to enter $85 \cdot 142 + 3$. Use the arrow keys to move the cursor to the left. Put the cursor at 6, and then press ⎡2nd⎤ [INS]. The cursor turns into a blinking underscore, and new characters will appear to the left of the blinking cursor. Press ⎡1⎤. Then press ⎡ENTER⎤ to evaluate the expression $85 \cdot 142 + 3$.

If you are inserting characters, then pressing ⎡2nd⎤ [INS] again terminates the insertion of characters. Then you can use the arrows keys to move the cursor or press ⎡ENTER⎤ to evaluate the expression. Experiment with these keys to understand them.

RETRIEVING THE LAST EXPRESSION

2nd [ENTRY] recalls the last expression evaluated in the Home screen. Enter the expression $5 \cdot 3^2 \cdot 8$ in the calculator and then press the ⎡ENTER⎤ key. Then your Home screen will look like the following.

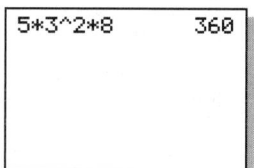

The Home screen can display the previous expression through ⎡2nd⎤ [ENTRY]. This is especially useful when you want to modify a previous expression.

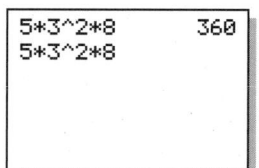

RETRIEVING A PREVIOUS EXPRESSION

There are two ways to retrieve previous expressions that have been evaluated in the Home screen. One way is through the repeated use of ⎡2nd⎤ [ENTRY]. This displays previous expressions, one each time ⎡2nd⎤ [ENTRY] is pressed. Another way is to use the arrow key ⎡▲⎤ to scroll up the Home screen. Then move the cursor to the expression you want to appear on the command line in the Home screen, and press ⎡ENTER⎤.

ENTERING AND EVALUATING FUNCTIONS

A function can be entered using the ⎡Y=⎤ key, which can then be used to evaluate the function at various inputs, such as $x = 4$ and $x = 7$, to find $f(4)$ and $f(7)$, respectively. The ⎡Y=⎤ key allows you to define and edit functions of the independent variable x. The possible names of functions (dependent variables) are Y1, Y2, Y3, and Y4.

1. Suppose $f(x) = 2x^2 + 3$. Use the calculator to enter the function.

Notes First, press the ⎡Y=⎤ key.

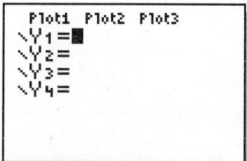

Second, enter the function on the first line, as shown. Use the $\boxed{x}$ key (which is adjacent to the $\boxed{7}$ key), as needed. If a function already appears in Y1, then you can press $\boxed{\text{CLEAR}}$ to erase it and then enter the function.

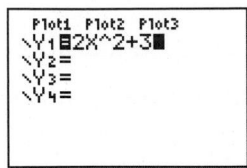

Then return to the Home screen by pressing $\boxed{\text{2nd}}$ [QUIT].

2. Suppose $f(x) = 2x^2 + 3$. Use the calculator to evaluate the function for $x = 4$ and $x = 7$.

Notes Using the function you just entered, follow these steps to evaluate the function: Press $\boxed{\text{2nd}}$ [VARS], and then press the arrow key $\boxed{\blacktriangledown}$ to select 2:Y-Vars. The cursor will be at 1:Y1, so press $\boxed{\text{ENTER}}$. Then Y1 will appear on the Home screen. Then press $\boxed{(4)}$ $\boxed{\text{ENTER}}$.

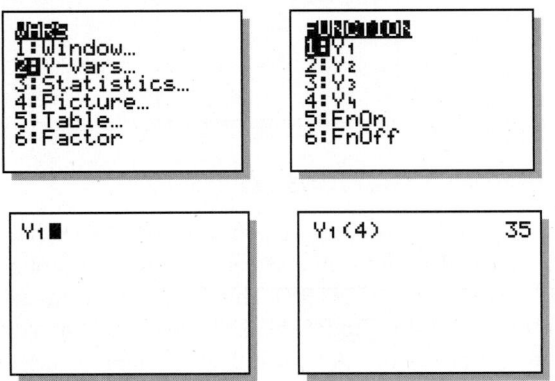

Y1(4) is the value of $f(4)$. So $f(4) = 35$.

We already know how to recall the previous expression that was evaluated, so press $\boxed{\text{2nd}}$ [ENTRY] to recall the expression Y1(4) in the command line of the Home screen. Then use the arrow key $\boxed{\blacktriangleleft}$ and replace the 4 with a 1 and press $\boxed{\text{ENTER}}$. Y1(7) is the value of $f(7)$. So $f(7) = 101$.

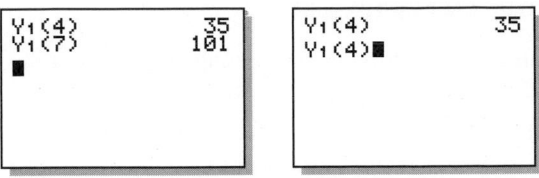

You can store four functions and evaluate expressions involving the functions. Use the arrow keys to navigate the lines for storing expressions in Y1 and Y2. Use the $\boxed{\text{2nd}}$ [VARS] key to call Y2 in the same way you called Y1.

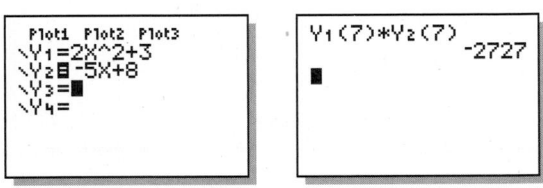

Geometer's Sketchpad

INTRODUCTION TO GEOMETER'S SKETCHPAD

Courtesy of Key Curriculum Press

Key Curriculum Press

Geometer's Sketchpad (by Key Curriculum Press) is a dynamic software program for drawing geometric shapes using straightedges and circles. It allows students to observe, explore, and discover properties of geometric shapes. For example, suppose a rhombus is constructed such that the shape remains a rhombus as the student changes the lengths of the sides of the rhombus. How do the size and shape of the rhombus affect the angles formed by the diagonals? The student could measure the angles formed by the diagonals and observe that they always form a right angle as the student dynamically changes the size and shape of the rhombus and use inductive reasoning to make the conjecture that the diagonals of a rhombus are perpendicular.

The **Help menu** offers a variety of electronic resources to help you learn the various capabilities of Geometer's Sketchpad. To access this resource, click on the Help menu, and then scroll down to the particular resource you would like to explore. During your exploration, we recommend that you choose the **Reference Center,** where a browser window will pop up with links to information on topics such as objects (for example, points, lines, and circles and measurements such as length and area), tools (for example, to create geometric objects), and menus (for example, to set display settings, to construct objects such as the perpendicular bisector of a line segment, and to transform objects using translations, reflections, rotations, or dilations). These electronic resources are stored on your hard drive when you install Geometer's Sketchpad. The Reference Center has exceptional descriptions for every object, tool, and menu and is especially useful for users with limited experience with Geometer's Sketchpad.

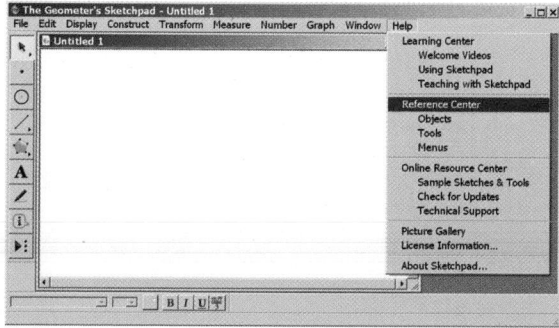

Key Curriculum Press also offers an online resource (learningcenter.dynamicgeometry .com/x14.xml) that describes the tools and menus in Geometer's Sketchpad. The tutorials can be viewed in a comic-strip or a video format.

The purpose of this appendix is to provide a convenient overview of the basics of Geometer's Sketchpad. So launch Geometer's Sketchpad on your computer and follow the directions given in the illustrative examples.

THE GEOMETER'S SKETCHPAD WINDOW

When you launch Geometer's Sketchpad, you will see a window similar to the one shown. The three main components are the menu bar, the sketch plane, and the toolbox:

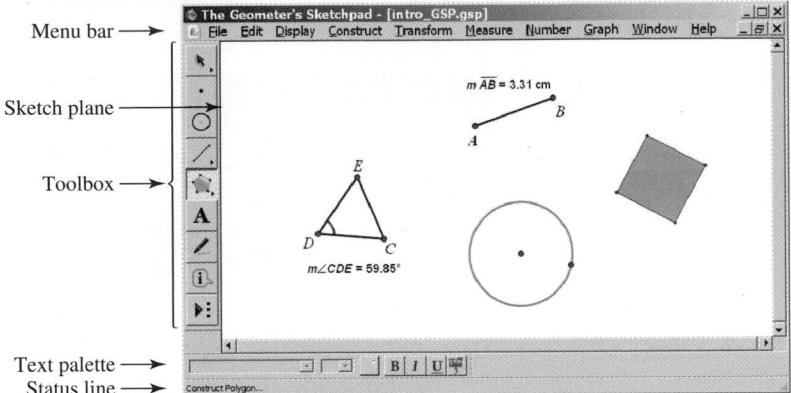

- The **menu bar** contains groups of commands. For example, the Display menu allows you to change the appearance of objects, such as the point size (for example, medium), line style (for example, thick), and color (for example, blue). The Measure menu allows you to measure numerical properties of objects, such as perimeter, angle, and area.

- The **sketch plane** is the location where objects, such as text, points, line segments, polygons, and measurements, are placed. All objects in the sketch plane can be saved to a single file.

- The **toolbox** contains tools to create points, line segments, circles, and captions in the sketch plane.

The window has additional components:

- The **text palette** allows you to change the font and size of the text and choose from a suite of mathematical symbols.

- The **status line** indicates the current tool selected or the current action being taken.

THE TOOLBOX

The toolbox has nine main features:

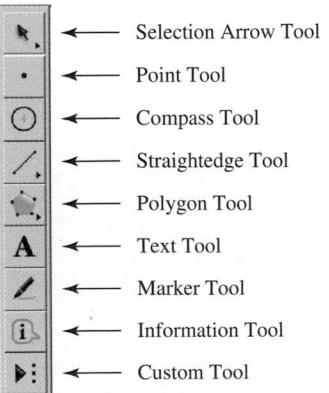

- The **selection arrow tool** is used to select objects in the sketch plane and drag them to translate, rotate, or resize the objects.

- The **point tool** is used to create a point in the sketch plane or a point on an object in the sketch plane.
- The **compass tool** is used to create a circle with a center.
- The **straightedge tool** is used to create a line segment, ray, or line.
- The **polygon tool** is used to create the interior of a polygon, the interior of a polygon and the polygon, or just the polygon.
- The **text tool** is used to create text in the sketch plane. The text can be used to label objects or simply provide some narration to the drawing.
- The **marker tool** is used to mark a line segment with tick marks, mark angles with arcs, or create hand-drawn objects in the sketch plane.
- The **information tool** provides information about the relationships among parts of a geometric object. The information appears in a dialog balloon. To display the information, click on the information tool. Then move the cursor to the sketch plane and click on a part of a geometric object. A dialog balloon will appear, describing how the part selected is related to other parts. For example, if a line is selected, the information could be, "Line #40 is perpendicular to Segment #39 passing through Point #74."
- The **custom tool** is a way for you to create your own tools, much like the built-in tools for the software. Then you can re-create one of your drawings in a few steps, rather than starting from scratch. The custom tool is an advanced feature that allows you to extend the functionality of Geometer's Sketchpad.

USING BASIC TOOLS

In the following examples, you will learn how to activate and use tools. The selection arrow tool (shown here) allows you to select objects in the sketch plane. The ability to select objects in the sketch plane is a simple but important skill for using Geometer's Sketchpad.

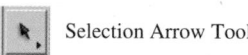 Selection Arrow Tool

The selection arrow tool also allows you to deselect objects in the sketch plane or deactivate a tool by clicking on the selection arrow tool and then clicking on a blank area of the sketch plane. Another way to deactivate the current tool is to simply click on another tool.

Once you select objects in the sketch plane, you can drag the objects (to translate, rotate, or dilate them).

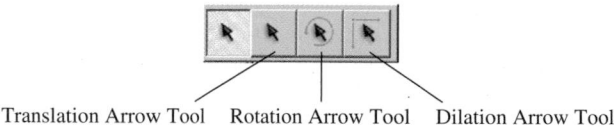

Translation Arrow Tool   Rotation Arrow Tool   Dilation Arrow Tool

As we show, once you select objects in the sketch plane, you can also change their appearance by using the Display menu. Let's get started.

Example 1. Placing Points in the Sketch Plane. Click on the point tool from the toolbox, move the cursor to the sketch plane, and then click the mouse. Each click creates a point in the sketch plane. These are "independent points," because they can be moved anywhere in the sketch plane.

Example 2. Labeling a Point. Place a point in the sketch plane. Click on the text tool, and then move the cursor to the sketch plane and click on the point. A label for the point will appear. Double-click on the label to open the Properties box that allows you to change the label. You can also click on the label and move the cursor to reposition the label.

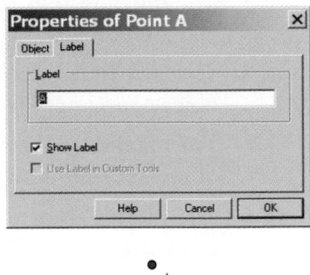

$\bullet$
A

Example 3. Drawing a Circle. Click on the compass tool from the toolbox, and then move the cursor to the sketch plane. Click the mouse to create the center of the circle, and drag the cursor to adjust the radius of the circle. The second click of the mouse will set the radius. After you deactivate the tool (for example, click on the selection arrow tool, and then click on a blank area of the sketch plane), you can click on the point on the circle and drag the point to readjust the radius of the circle. The point on the circle is a "dependent point," because it must stay on the circle when it is moved. The two points of the circle shown are control points that allow you to change the size of the circle.

Example 4. Drawing a Line Segment, Ray, or Line. Click on the straightedge tool from the toolbox and drag the cursor to the right. Three options will appear that can be used to draw a line segment, ray, and line: the **segment tool, ray tool,** and **line tool,** respectively. Move the cursor to select one of these options.

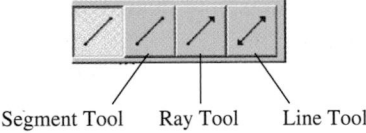

Segment Tool   Ray Tool   Line Tool

    Move the cursor to the sketch plane, click the mouse, move the cursor to drag the second point, and then click the mouse again. The two clicks define your straightedge (line segment, ray, or line). After you deactivate the tool, you can click on one of the control points of the straightedge and change its orientation.

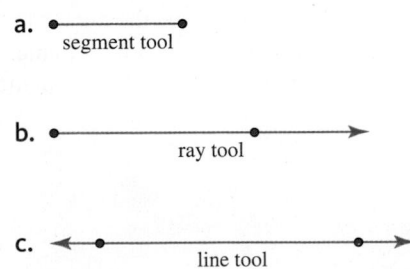

a. segment tool

b. ray tool

c. line tool

Example 5. Drawing a Polygon. Click on the polygon tool from the toolbox, and drag the cursor to the right. Three options will appear that can be used to draw the vertices of a polygon with preferences: the interior of a polygon, the interior of a polygon and the polygon, and just the polygon. Pick one of these options.

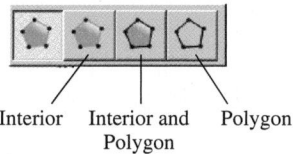

Interior   Interior and   Polygon
            Polygon

Move the cursor to the sketch plane, and then click the mouse. Move the cursor again, and click the mouse again. Each click results in a vertex of the polygon. Double-click the mouse on a point to complete the selection of the vertices of the polygon. After you deactivate the tool, you can click on any vertex and change the location of that vertex.

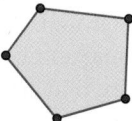

Example 6. Entering Text. Click on the text tool from the toolbox, move the cursor to the sketch plane, and then double-click the mouse. Begin typing your text in the box.

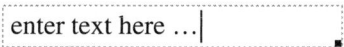

enter text here ...|

Then click on the selection arrow tool to deactivate the text tool. You can move the text box to another location in the sketch plane by moving the cursor over the box, clicking and holding the button on the mouse, and then moving the cursor.

Example 7. Marking a Line Segment. Draw a polygon in the sketch plane. Click on the marker tool. Move the cursor to the sketch plane and then to a side of the polygon. The orientation of the marker changes as the marker moves from the sketch plane to the side of the polygon. Click on a side of the polygon. Without moving the cursor, click the mouse a few more times. The number of tick marks should change.

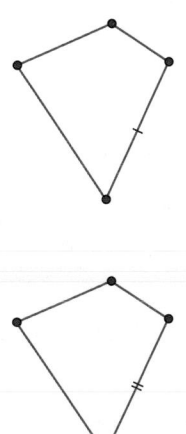

Try this: Right-click on the tick mark to generate a pop-up menu. This allows you to change the attributes of the tick mark. For example, you can change the tick mark to an arrow. You can even change its color.

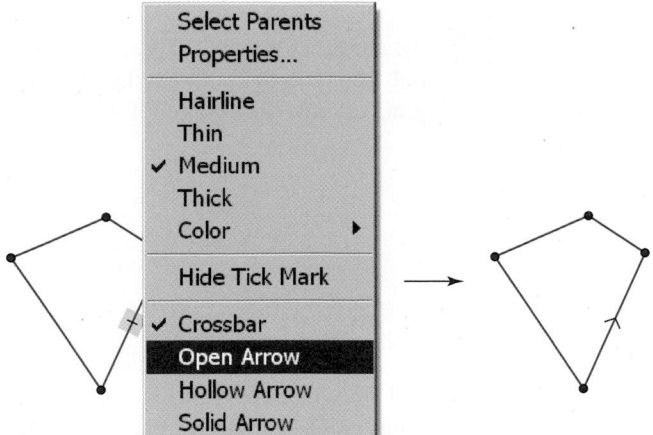

Example 8. Marking an Angle. Draw a polygon in the sketch plane. Click on the marker tool. Move the cursor to the sketch plane and then to a vertex. The orientation of the marker changes as the marker moves from the sketch plane to the vertex. Click on a vertex, and drag the cursor to the interior of the polygon. Click on the arc a few times. The number of arcs should change.

Try this: Right-click on the arc to generate a pop-up menu. This allows you to change the attributes of the arc. For example, you can change the opacity of the arc or show the angle direction. Select the Properties option, select the Marker tab, and then choose the counterclockwise button. Set the number of strokes equal to 1, click on the box next to Show Angle Direction, and then click on the OK button.

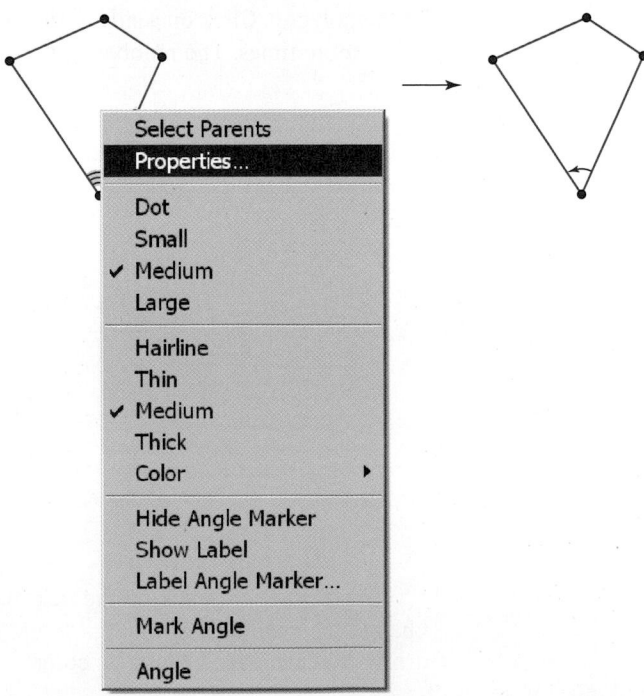

Example 9. Selecting an Object. Draw a polygon in the sketch plane. Click on the selection arrow tool. To select an object, you can (1) move the cursor to the sketch plane and click on all parts of the object or (2) click on a blank area in the sketch plane and drag the cursor to select the whole object. The selected objects should have a "glow" to them.

Example 10. Moving an Object or Part of an Object. Draw and select a polygon in the sketch plane. Click on the selection arrow tool, and choose the **translation arrow tool.** Select the whole object. Then click on one part of the selected object and move the cursor. The whole object should move. If you initially choose one part of the object, then that part (and its related parts) will move.

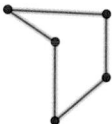

Deactivate the tool by clicking on a blank area of the sketch plane.

Notes
- If you click on the selection arrow tool and choose the **rotation arrow tool,** then dragging the polygon will rotate it rather than slide it in the direction of the cursor.
- If you click on the selection arrow tool and choose the **dilation arrow tool,** then dragging the polygon will change the size rather than slide it in the direction of the cursor.

Example 11. Removing an Object from the Sketch Plane. The most recent object created can be removed by simultaneously pressing the two keyboard keys [Ctrl] and [Z] (Ctrl-Z). Or, select the object with the cursor and press the [Delete] (Delete) key.

Example 12. Hide an Object. You can hide an object, such as a point, line, or circle, by selecting the object and simultaneously pressing the two keyboard keys [Ctrl] and [H]. Try this: Draw a circle in the sketch plane. Then select the circle and simultaneously press the [Ctrl] and [H] keys. Did the circle disappear? No, just the selected objects disappear.

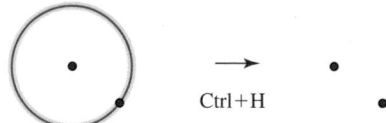

USING THE MENUS

In the following examples, you will learn how to activate and use some features of the following menus: Edit, Display, Construct, Transform, Measure, Number, and Graph. When you choose a menu, some of the options may be faded. This means those options are unavailable for the selected figure. For example, if you select a line segment and click on the Measure menu, the Length option will appear prominently to indicate you can measure the length of the line segment, whereas the Area option will be faded to indicate that you cannot measure the area of a line segment.

Example 13. Use the Edit Menu To Set Preferences. Click on the Edit menu to set preferences for units (for example, distance in pixels, centimeters, or inches and precision in tenths or hundredths), color (for example, color of points, lines, and circles), text, and tools. The default setting is typically sufficient, but you should be aware of the preferences available.

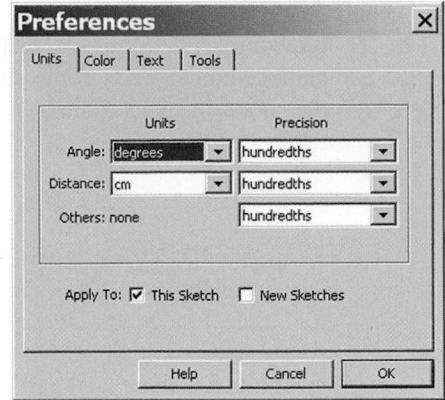

Example 14. Use the Display Menu To View and Reset the Line Style Settings for a Curve. Draw and select a line segment in the sketch plane. Click on the Display menu to view the current Line Style settings for the line segment. Experiment with the line settings, for example, choose **Thick** and **Solid,** or choose **Thin** and **Dashed.** Then draw a circle in the sketch plane, select the circle, and reset the Line Style setting for the circle.

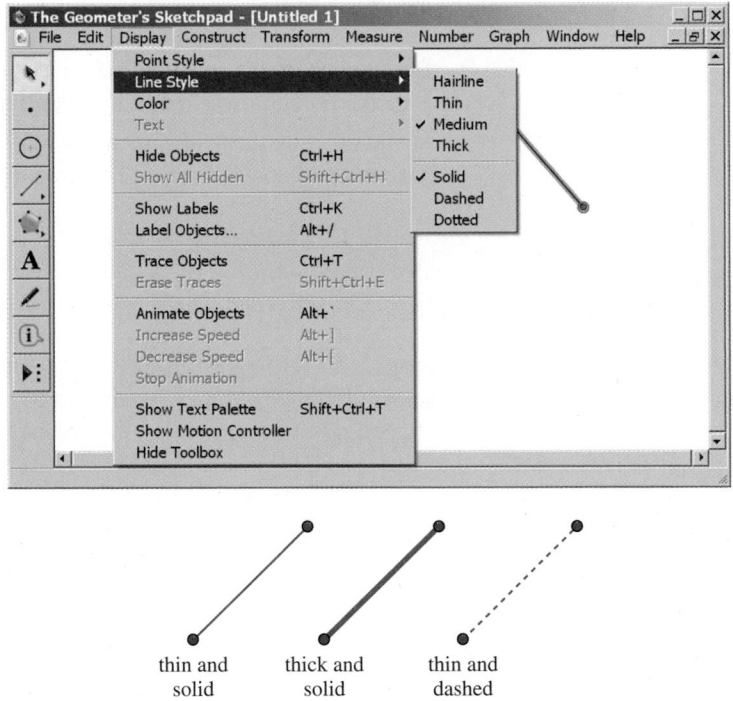

thin and solid   thick and solid   thin and dashed

Example 15. Use the Display Menu To View and Reset the Point Style Settings for Points. Draw a line segment on the sketch plane. Then select the endpoints of the line segment. Click on the Display menu to view the Point Style settings for the endpoints. Experiment with the settings; for example, choose Medium or Large.

medium   large

Example 16. Use the Construct Menu To Construct a Line Segment, Ray, or Line through Two Points. Draw and select two points in the sketch plane. Click on the Construct menu to see a menu of options. The options that are faded cannot be executed, because they do not apply to the selected objects (in this case, the two points). Choose the **Segment** option to construct a line segment through the two selected points.

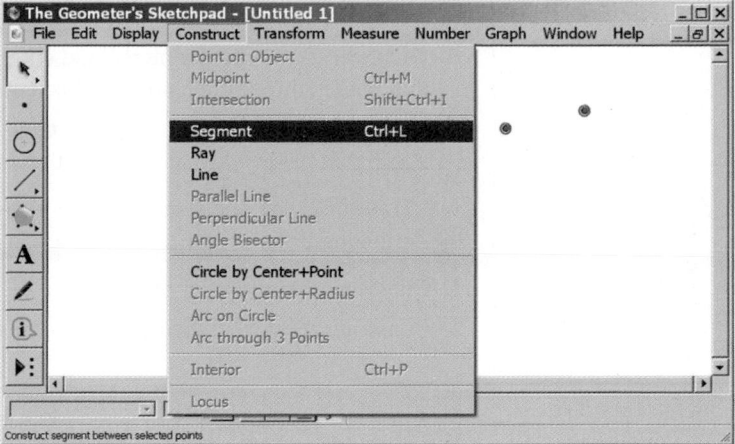

Experiment with the other options for two selected points: **Ray** (the first point selected is the endpoint of the ray, and the ray passes through the second point), **Line** (the selected points determine the line), and **Circle by Center+Point** (the first point selected is the center of the circle, and the second point selected is a point on the circle).

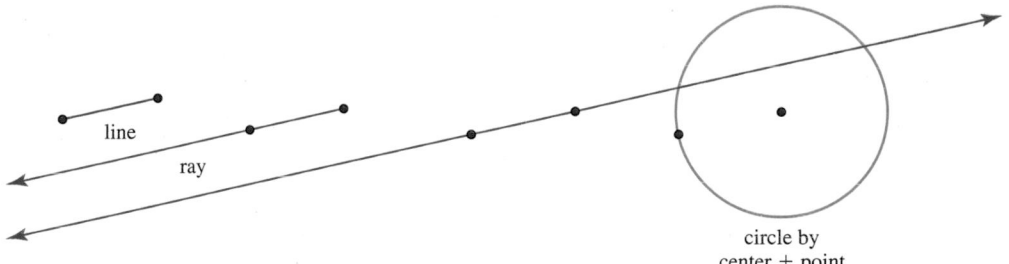

Example 17. Use the Construct Menu To Construct the Intersection of Two Curves. Use the tools to draw an intersecting circle and line segment in the sketch plane. Then use the selection arrow tool to select the circle and line segment (without including the center of the circle, point on the circle, and endpoints of the line segment). Click on the Construct menu, and choose the **Intersection** option to construct the intersection of the two selected objects.

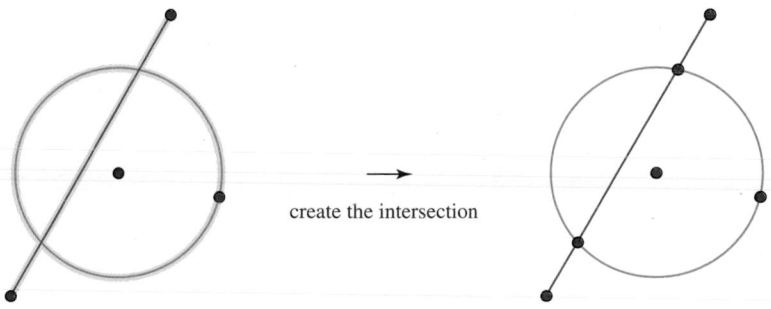

create the intersection

Example 18. Use the Construct Menu To Construct the Midpoint of a Line Segment. Draw and select a line segment in the sketch plane. Click on the Construct menu, and choose the **Midpoint** option to construct the midpoint of the line segment. Select and drag one of the endpoints of the line segment, and observe the behavior of the midpoint.

Example 19. Use the Construct Menu To Construct a Line through a Point that Is Parallel or Perpendicular To a Given Line. Draw a line in the sketch plane and a point that does not belong to the line. Select the point and the line. Then do one of the following:

• Click on the Construct menu, and choose the **Parallel Line** option to construct a line that passes through the point and is parallel to the selected line.

• Click on the Construct menu, and choose the **Perpendicular Line** option to construct a line that passes through the point and is perpendicular to the selected line.

Try this. Draw line segment in the sketch plane. Use the Construct menu, and then do the following:

1. Construct the midpoint of the line.

2. Construct the perpendicular bisector of the line segment.

Example 20. Use the Construct Menu To Construct a Circle with a Given Center and Radius Equal To a Given Line Segment. Draw a point and a line segment in the sketch plane. Now construct a circle such that the point is the center and the radius is equal to the length of the line segment. Select the point and the line segment (but do not select the endpoints of the line segment). Click on the Construct menu, and choose the **Circle by Center+Radius** option to construct a circle such that the point is the center and the radius is equal to the length of the line segment.

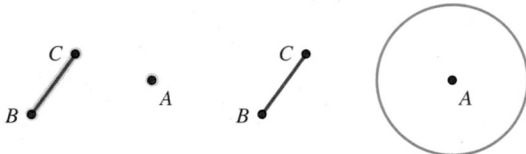

Select one of the endpoints of the line segment, and drag the point in the sketch plane. What happens to the circle?

Example 21. Use the Construct Menu To Construct an Arc through Three Given Points. Draw three points in the sketch plane. Select the three points. The first and last point selected will serve as the endpoints of the arc. Click on the Construct menu, and choose the **Arc through 3 Points** option to construct an arc through the three points.

Experiment with the arc by moving one of the points on the arc.

Example 22. Use the Transform Menu To Translate an Object. Click on the polygon tool, and draw a triangle in the sketch plane. Click on the text tool, and then click on each vertex to label the vertices. Draw two points in the sketch plane. Click on the two points, one point at a time. Click on the Transform menu, and select the **Mark Vector** option. A translation will move the triangle in the direction from the first point to the second point in the order clicked, and the triangle will move the same distance as the distance between the two points.

Select the triangle. Click on the Transform menu, and select **Translate.** Click on the text tool, and then click on the vertices of the new triangle to label the vertices.

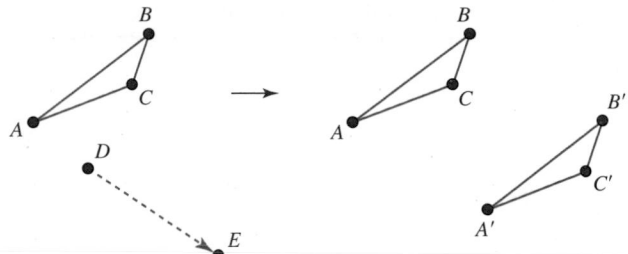

Experiment with the translation by dragging one of the two points of the translation vector or by dragging a vertex or side of the triangle.

Notes
- When you mark the translation vector, an animation will briefly appear to show you the direction of the translation.
- You can copy and paste to place a picture in the sketch plane and then translate it using the Translate option of the Transform menu.

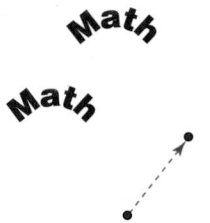

Example 23. Use the Transform Menu To Reflect an Object. Click on the polygon tool, and draw a triangle in the sketch plane. Click on the text tool, and then click on each vertex to label the vertices. Click on the straightedge tool, and draw a line segment, ray, or line. The straightedge that you drew should be highlighted (selected). Click on the Transform menu, and select the **Mark Mirror** option. The straightedge will be the mirror line for the reflection. Click on the translation arrow tool, and then select the triangle. Click on the Transform menu, and select the **Reflect** option. Click on the text tool, and then click on the vertices of the new triangle to label the vertices.

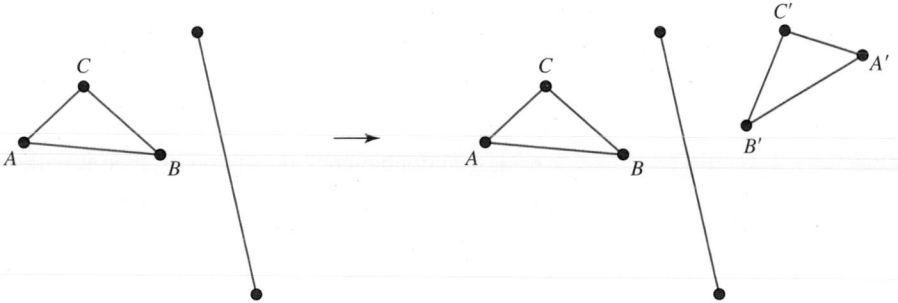

Try this: Move a vertex of the triangle closer to the mirror line. Observe the effect on the image of the vertex. Select a control point of the straightedge, and move it in the sketch plane. Observe the effect on the image.

Notes

- If you double-click on any straightedge, then it will be marked as the mirror.
- You can copy and paste to place a picture in the sketch plane and then reflect it using the Reflect option of the Transform menu.

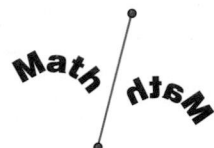

Example 24. Use the Transform Menu To Rotate an Object. Click on the polygon tool, and draw a triangle in the sketch plane. Click on the text tool, and then click on each vertex to label the vertices. Click on the point tool, and draw a point in the sketch plane. The point should be highlighted (selected). Click on the Transform menu, and select the **Mark Center** option. The point will be the center of rotation. Click on the translation arrow tool, and then select the triangle. Click on the Transform menu, and select the **Rotate** option. Enter the degree of rotation in the field (for example, "30" will rotate the triangle 30° in a counterclockwise direction, and "−30" will rotate the triangle 30° in a clockwise direction). Then click on the Rotate button. Finally, click on the text tool and then each vertex of the new triangle to label the vertices.

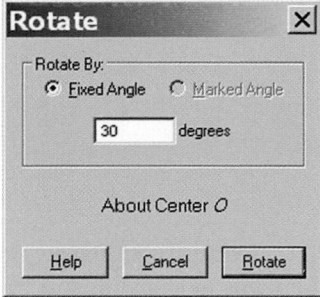

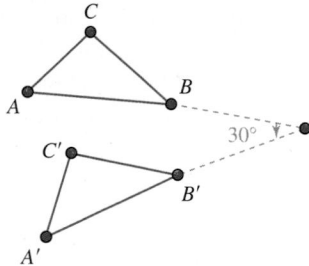

Notes

- If you double-click on any point, then it will be marked as the center of rotation.
- You can copy and paste to place a picture in the sketch plane and then rotate it using the Rotate option of the Transform menu.

Example 25. Use the Transform Menu To Dilate an Object. Click on the polygon tool, and draw a triangle in the sketch plane. Click on the text tool, and then click on each vertex to label the vertices. Click on the point tool, and draw a point in the sketch plane. The point should be highlighted (selected). Click on the Transform menu, and select the Mark Center option. The point will be the center of the dilation. Click on the translation arrow tool, and then select the triangle. Click on the Transform menu, and select the **Dilate** option. Enter a fraction in the field (for example, fractions less than 1 will shrink the triangle, whereas fractions more than 1 will enlarge the triangle). Then click on the Dilate button. Finally, click on the text tool and then each vertex of the new triangle to label the vertices.

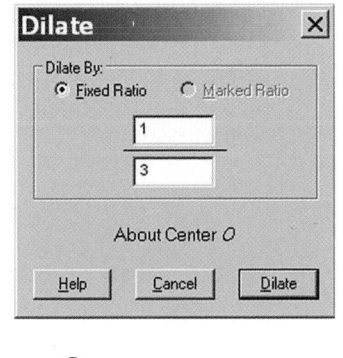

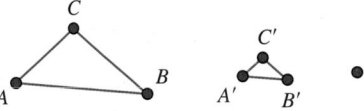

Notes
- If you double-click on any point, then it will be marked as the center of the dilation.
- You can copy and paste to place a picture in the sketch plane and then dilate it using the Dilate option of the Transform menu.

Example 26. Use the Measure Menu To Measure the Length of a Line Segment. Draw a line segment in the sketch plane. Click on the selection arrow tool, and then select the line segment. Click on the Measure menu, and choose the **Length** option.

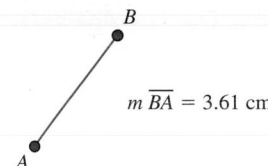

$m\,\overline{BA} = 3.61$ cm

Experiment with the results by changing the labels of the endpoints of the line segment or by dragging an endpoint of the line segment.

Example 27. Measure the Distance Between Two Points. Draw two points in the sketch plane, and select both points. Click on the Measure menu, and choose the **Distance** option.

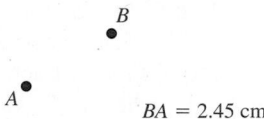

Experiment with the results by changing the labels of the points or by dragging one of the points.

Example 28. Measure an Angle. Draw an angle formed by two line segments with a common endpoint. Click on the three points, making sure the vertex of the angle is the second point that you click on. Then click on the Measure menu and choose the **Angle** option.

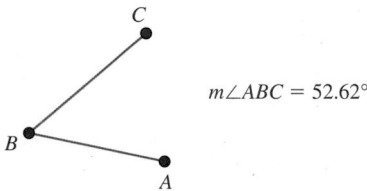

Experiment with the results by dragging one of the endpoints of the line segments. You could also click on any three points in the sketch plane and measure the angle determined by the three points, where the vertex of the angle is the second point you click on.

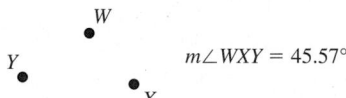

Experiment with the results by dragging one of the points.

Example 29. Measure the Perimeter of a Polygon. Use the polygon tool to draw a polygon in the sketch plane. Choose the option that draws the polygon and its interior. Click on the interior of the polygon (because the software requires that you click on the interior of the polygon to measure the perimeter). Then click on the Measure menu and choose the **Perimeter** option.

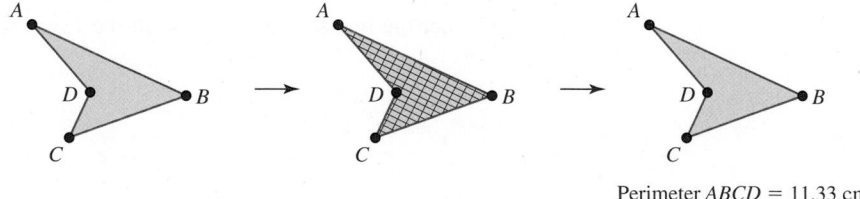

Experiment with the results by dragging one of the vertices of the polygon.

Example 30. Measure the Area of a Polygon. Use the polygon tool to draw a polygon in the sketch plane. Choose the option that draws the polygon and its interior. Click on the interior of the polygon so that you can measure the area. Then click on the Measure menu and choose the **Area** option.

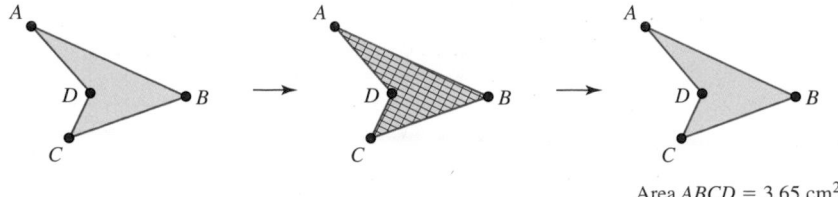

Area $ABCD = 3.65 \text{ cm}^2$

Experiment with the results by dragging one of the vertices of the polygon.

Example 31. Use the Number Menu To Create a Numerical Value Based on Existing Measurements. Draw a circle in the sketch plane. Draw a diameter for the circle (for example, use the Construct menu to construct a line through the center and point on the circle and to construct the intersection of the line and the circle, and then use the Display menu to hide the line. Next, use the Construct menu to construct a line segment, with the two points on the circle as the endpoints of the line segment). Use the text tool to label the three points. Use the Measure menu options to measure the length of the diagonal and the circumference of the circle. The number of decimal digits that appear after the decimal point depends on your Preference settings under the Edit menu.

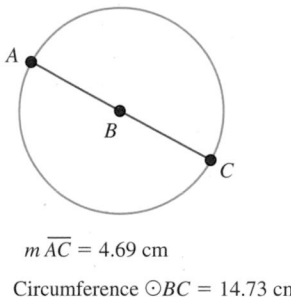

$m\,\overline{AC} = 4.69 \text{ cm}$

Circumference $\odot BC = 14.73 \text{ cm}$

Click on the **Number** menu, and select the **Calculate** option. Then click on the circumference measurement in the sketch plane, the division key in the pop-up window, and finally the diameter measurement in the sketch plane. Then click on the OK button in the pop-up window. The calculation will appear in the sketch plane in the form of an equation.

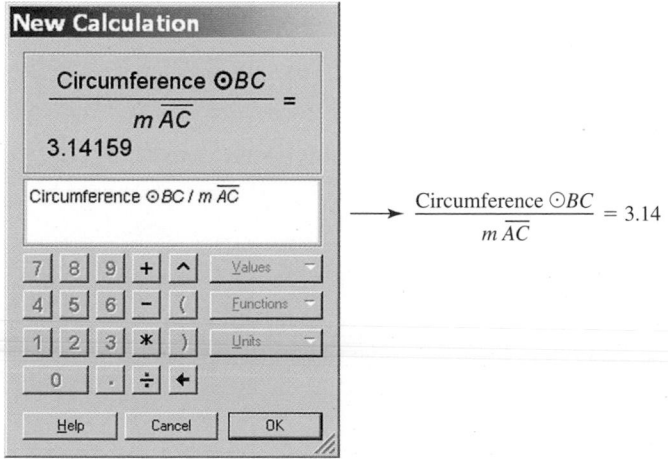

Experiment with the results by dragging one of the points on the circle to change the size of the circle. Observe how the measurements change, and observe the calculation. Does the quotient depend on the size of the circle?

The quotient of the circumference and diameter will be 3.14, which is the value of π to two decimal digits. It confirms that the circumference is approximately three times longer than the diameter and that the quotient of the circumference and diameter is constant.

THEOREM 1

If the slopes of two nonvertical lines are equal, then the two lines are parallel.

PROOF OF THEOREM 1

Suppose the slopes of two nonvertical lines are equal. We already know that a horizontal line and an oblique line must intersect. Therefore, both lines are horizontal or both lines are oblique. Let's handle each situation separately.

Suppose both lines are horizontal, with equations of the form $x = a$ and $x = b$ and with $a \neq b$. Every point on line $x = a$ has the form (a, h), and every point on line $x = b$ has the form (b, k). Because $a \neq b$, it follows that $(a, h) \neq (b, k)$ for all possible values of h and k. So the horizontal lines cannot have any points in common. Therefore, the horizontal lines must be parallel.

Now, suppose the two lines are oblique lines with the same slope m. Then $y = mx + c$ and $y = mx + d$ are the equations of the lines, with $c \neq d$. The lines intersect, or the lines are parallel. For the moment, assume the lines intersect (we will show this is impossible). Then there would be a point (u, v) that belongs to both lines. This would mean $v = mu + c$ and $v = mu + d$. In turn, this would mean $c = y - mu$ and $d = y - mu$. It then follows that $c = d$. But this is impossible, because $c \neq d$. So the two lines do not have a point in common. Therefore, the oblique lines are parallel.

THEOREM 2

If two nonvertical lines are parallel, then their slopes are equal.

PROOF OF THEOREM 2

Suppose two nonvertical lines are parallel. We already know that a horizontal line and an oblique line must intersect. Therefore, the parallel lines are both horizontal lines or both oblique lines. Let's handle each situation separately.

Suppose both lines are horizontal lines. All horizontal lines have a slope of 0. Therefore, their slopes are equal.

Now, suppose the two lines l_1 and l_2 shown in Figure 1 are parallel oblique lines with the slopes m_1 and m_2. We must prove their slopes are equal. Pick any two points $P(x_1, y_1)$ and $Q(x_2, y_2)$ on line l_1, as shown in Figure 1.

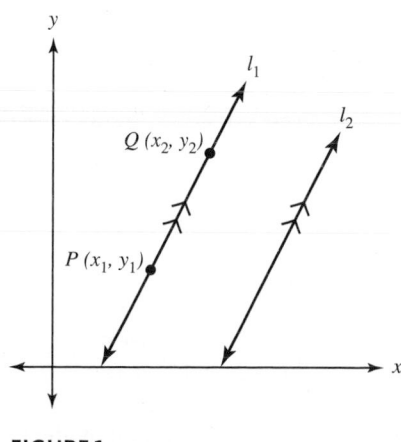

FIGURE 1

Next, create a horizontal line segment that extends from P to the other line at point A and a horizontal line segment that extends from Q to the other line at point B, as shown in Figure 2. We can see that the two line segments are parallel.

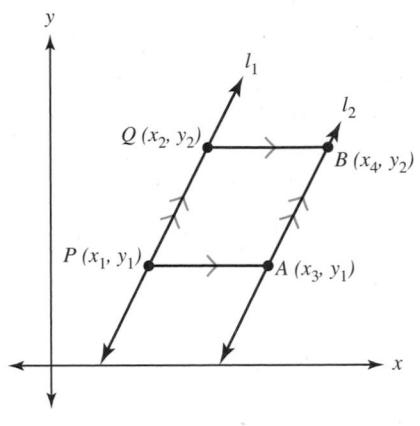

FIGURE 2

Then the quadrilateral $PQBA$ is a parallelogram. We know that opposite sides of a parallelogram are congruent, so $PA = QB$, which means $x_3 - x_1 = x_4 - x_2$. But $x_3 = x_1 + PA$, and $x_4 = x_2 + QB = x_2 + PA$.

Now, let's calculate the slope of each line:

- The slope of $\overleftrightarrow{PQ}$ is $\dfrac{y_2 - y_1}{x_2 - x_1}$.

- The slope of $\overleftrightarrow{AB}$ is $\dfrac{y_2 - y_1}{x_4 - x_3} = \dfrac{y_2 - y_1}{(x_2 + PA) - (x_1 + PA)} = \dfrac{y_2 - y_1}{x_2 - x_1}$.

Therefore, the slope of $\overleftrightarrow{PQ}$ equals the slope of $\overleftrightarrow{AB}$. Thus, if two oblique lines are parallel, then their slopes are equal.

We just proved two things:

- If two horizontal lines are parallel, then their slopes are equal.
- If two oblique lines are parallel, then their slopes are equal.

Together, this proves that if two nonvertical lines are parallel, then their slopes are equal.

THEOREM 3

If two lines are perpendicular, then the product of their slopes is -1, or one line is a horizontal line and the other line is a vertical line.

PROOF OF THEOREM 3

Assume the two lines are perpendicular and that they are neither horizontal nor vertical lines. Then the two lines are oblique lines l_1 and l_2. Suppose their respective slopes are m_1 and m_2. We must prove $m_1 \cdot m_2 = -1$. Let Q be the intersection of the two perpendicular lines l_1 and l_2 as shown in Figure 3. Let $\overline{PR}$ be a line segment with endpoints on l_1 and l_2 such that $\overline{PR}$ is parallel to the horizontal axis as shown in Figure 3. Then $\triangle PQR$ is a right triangle with right angle $\angle Q$. Let S be the point on $\overline{PR}$ such that $\overline{QS}$ is the altitude from Q to the hypotenuse of $\triangle PQR$. Label the *lengths* of the line segments a, b, and c as shown.

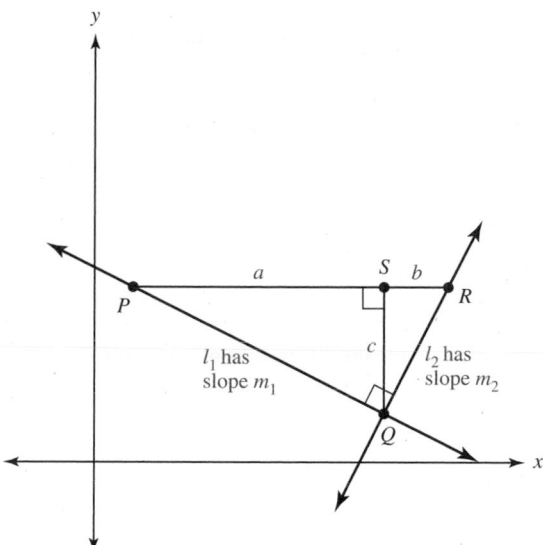

FIGURE 3

Then $m_1 = \dfrac{\text{rise}}{\text{run}} = \dfrac{-c}{a}$ and $m_2 = \dfrac{\text{rise}}{\text{run}} = \dfrac{c}{b}$.

$\triangle PQR \sim \triangle PSQ$ by the AA similarity axiom, and $\triangle PQR \sim \triangle QSR$ by the AA similarity axiom, so $\triangle PSQ \sim \triangle QSR$. The relation $\triangle PSQ \sim \triangle QSR$ implies the proportion $\dfrac{a}{c} = \dfrac{c}{b}$, or $\dfrac{c^2}{ab} = 1$. Then $m_1 \cdot m_2 = \dfrac{-c}{a} \cdot \dfrac{c}{b} = -\left(\dfrac{c^2}{ab}\right) = -(1) = -1$.

THEOREM 4

If the product of the slopes of two lines is -1 or one line is a horizontal line and the other line is a vertical line, then the two lines are perpendicular.

PROOF OF THEOREM 4

There are two possible situations.

- Suppose one line is a horizontal line and the other line is a vertical line. Any horizontal line and vertical line are perpendicular.

- Suppose the product of the slopes of the two lines in Figure 4 is -1. Let m_1 and m_2 be the slopes of the lines. Then $m_1 \cdot m_2 = -1$. Our goal is to show the two lines are perpendicular. To accomplish this, we create two triangles $\triangle RQP$ and $\triangle TSR$ and apply the SAS similarity axiom to show $\triangle RQP \sim \triangle TSR$, and eventually show $\angle PRT$ is a right angle.

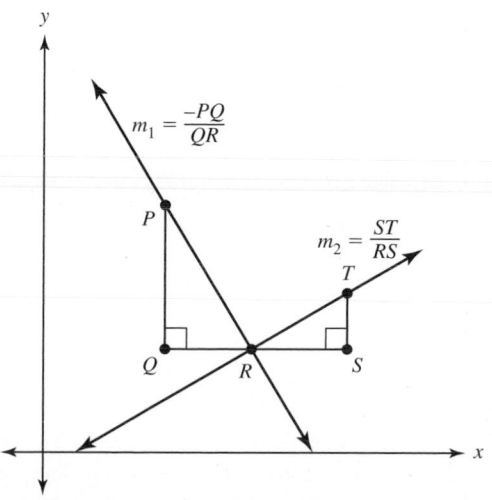

FIGURE 4

Note that m_1 is negative. Then $m_1 = \dfrac{-PQ}{QR}$ and $m_2 = \dfrac{ST}{RS}$. Then

$$m_1 \cdot m_2 = -1$$

$$\frac{-PQ}{QR} \cdot \frac{ST}{RS} = -1$$

$$\frac{PQ}{RS} = \frac{QR}{ST}.$$

This means the legs of the two right triangles have a common ratio. Also, $\angle Q \cong \angle S$, because right angles are congruent. Then $\triangle RQP \sim \triangle TSR$ by the SAS similarity axiom. By the definition of similar triangles, all corresponding angles are congruent, so $\angle QPR \cong \angle SRT$ and $\angle QRP \cong \angle STR$, as indicated by the arcs in Figure 5.

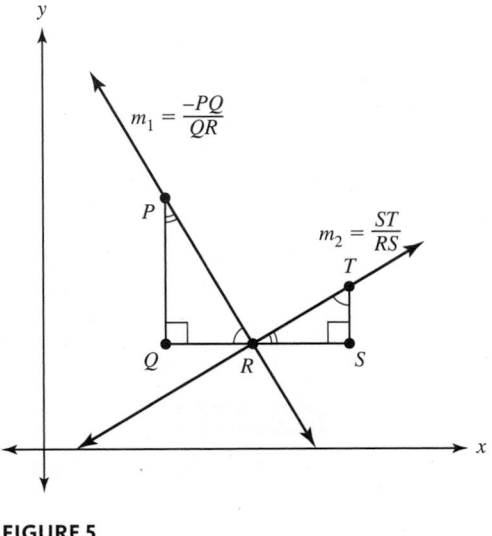

FIGURE 5

$\angle QRP$ and $\angle TRS$ are complementary angles (because $\angle QRP$ and $\angle QPR$ are complementary angles in $\triangle RQP$) and $\angle QRS$ is a straight angle, so $\angle PRT$ is a right angle. Therefore, the two lines are perpendicular.

CHAPTER 1

SECTION 1.1

1. a. Beginning with 1, obtain the next term by adding 3 to the previous term.

b.

n	1	2	3	4
y	1	4	7	10

c. $y = 3n - 2$, where y is the nth term

d.

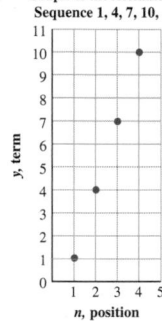

Graph of the Arithmetic Sequence 1, 4, 7, 10, ...

2. a. arithmetic sequence **b.** geometric sequence
c. neither   **d.** arithmetic sequence
e. both ($a = 4, d = 0$ and $a = 4, r = 1$)

3. a. -5 **b.** 7
c.

n	1	2	3	4
y	-5	2	9	16

4. a.

n	1	2	3	4
y	5	9	13	17

b. There is a straight line through the points on the graph.

5. a. 4   **b.** 3   **c.** $y = 3n + 1$
d. Graph of the Arithmetic Sequence 4, 7, 10, 13, ...   **e.** Graph of the Line Through the Points   **f.** 3

g. The slope is 3, and the common difference is 3. They are the same. Thus, the common difference is the slope of the line through the points on the graph that represents the arithmetic sequence.

6. 1

7. a. 80 students   **b.** 90 tables

8. Answers vary. Find values of d and n such that $11 + d(n - 1) = 195$, where d is the fixed amount depos-

ited each month. For example, he could have deposited $92 each month ($d = 92, n = 3$).

9. cell D

10. Multiply the sum $2 + 3 + 4 + 5$ by 3.

11. 253 games

12. 564

13. $3333337^2 = 11,111,135,555,569$

14. a. The product is an even number.
b. The product of two consecutive numbers is an even number.
c. inductive reasoning

15. a. $9 = 4 + 5, 11 = 5 + 6, 13 = 6 + 7$
b. An odd number can be written as the sum of two consecutive numbers.
c. inductive reasoning

16. 41

17. a. 34, 35, 36 has 3 terms ($36 - 34 + 1 = 3$)
34, 35, 36, 37 has 4 terms ($37 - 34 + 1 = 4$)
b. 588 ($621 - 34 + 1 = 588$)

18. a. $a = 8, d = 8, y = 8n$
b. $a = 10, d = 10, y = 10n$
c. A skip-counting sequence is an arithmetic sequence in which the initial term equals the common difference.

19. The right-hand side of the equations forms a geometric sequence 64, 16, 4, 1, . . . with common ratio 1/4.
$4^3 = 64$
$4^2 = 16$
$4^1 = 4$
$4^0 = 1$

20. The right-hand side of the equations forms an arithmetic sequence with common difference $- 4$.
$3 \times 4 = 12$
$2 \times 4 = 8$
$1 \times 4 = 4$
$0 \times 4 = 0$
$-1 \times 4 = -4$
$-2 \times 4 = -8$

21. $n - 7 = 16$ $n - 16 = 7$ $\boxed{7 + 16 = n}$ $\boxed{16 + 7 = n}$

22. a.

Fourth staircase

b.

position (n)	1	2	3	4
perimeter (P)	4	8	12	16

c. $P = 4n$ units, for $n = 1, 2, 3, 4, . . .$ **d.** 56 units

23. a. 20, 40, 60, 80; $85 - 80 = 5$; $85 \div 20 = 4\ R5$
  b. 15, 30, 45; $52 - 45 = 7$; $52 \div 15 = 3\ R7$
  c. 12, 24, 36, 48, 60; $64 - 60 = 4$; $64 \div 12 = 5\ R4$

24. a. $3 \div 3 = 1\ R0$
    $4 \div 3 = 1\ R1$
    $5 \div 3 = 1\ R2$
    $6 \div 3 = 2\ R0$
    $7 \div 3 = 2\ R1$
    $8 \div 3 = 2\ R2$
  b. The remainders follow a repeating pattern:
    0, 1, 2, 0, 1, 2, 0, 1, 2, . . .

25. $1 + 3 + 5 + 7 + 9 = 5^2$
  $1 + 3 + 5 + 7 + 9 + 11 = 6^2$
  (The sum of the first n odd numbers is n^2.)

26. $2 + 4 + 6 + 8 + 10 = 5 \times 6$
  $2 + 4 + 6 + 8 + 10 + 12 = 6 \times 7$

27. a. A pattern is similarity or regularity in observations that allows you to predict the behavior in the observations or what comes next.
  b. A conjecture (or claim) is a general statement that seems to be true.
  c. Inductive reasoning is the process of using patterns to make a conjecture.
  d. A limitation of inductive reasoning is that the conjecture you make may not be true.

28. a. Yes. The initial term is 1, and the common difference is 1.
  b. No. It does not have a common ratio.

29. a. Yes. The 7 repeats.
  b. Yes. The initial term is 7, and the common difference is 0.
  c. Yes. The initial term is 7, and the common ratio is 1.

30. a. exercises   **b.** problem solving   **c.** pattern
  d. inductive reasoning   **e.** representations   **f.** arithmetic
  g. skip counting   **h.** generalize

31. a. 20, 23, 26   **b.** 216, 343, 512   **c.** 320, 640, 1280
  d. 34, 55, 89   **e.** 17, 12, 19

32. 120, 720, 5040

33. a. Answers vary. For example, $3 \times 5 = 15$, $4 \times 5 = 20$, $5 \times 5 = 25$, $6 \times 5 = 30$.
  b. The ones digit of the product is 0 or 5.
  c. The ones digit of a multiple of 5 is 0 or 5.
  d. inductive reasoning

34. a. Beginning with -3, obtain the next term by adding 4 to the previous term.
  b.

n	1	2	3	4
y	-3	1	5	9

  c.
  Graph of the Line Through the Points

y, term vertical axis, *n*, position horizontal axis

d. $y = -3 + 4(n - 1)$ or $y = 4n - 7$
  e. Solve the inequality $4n - 7 < 513$ to get $n < 130$. So 129 terms are less than 513.

35. a. 133,225
  b. You can easily predict $472 \times 473 = 223,256$

36. The constant terms may follow the pattern 5, 10, 30, 120, ... The variable terms may follow the pattern: $2a$, $3a$, $4a$, $5a$.

37. 8

38. a. $64^2 = 4096$
      $664^2 = 440,896$
     $6664^2 = 44,408,896$
    $66664^2 = 4,444,088,896$
  b. $666664^2 = 44,444,408,888,896$

39. a. 31,928   **b.** 15,184

40. a. 1, 6, 11, 16, . . . $y = 5n + 1$
    5, 10, 15, 20, . . . $y = 5n$
  b. 5, 8, 11, 14, . . . $y = 3n + 2$
    3, 6, 9, 12, . . . $y = 3n$

41. a.

n	1	2	3	4
y	5	9	13	17

  b. $y = 5 + 4(n - 1)$ or $y = 4n + 1$

42. a. 768   **b.** 1/4   **c.** $y = 768 \times (1/4)^{n-1}$

43. Answers vary. Find a and r such that $62,500 = a \cdot r^{5-1}$. Replace r with 2, and then solve for a. One possible geometric sequence is described by the equation $y = 3906.25 \cdot 2^{n-1}$.

44. 4

45. a. 27   **b.** 270   **c.** 2700   **d.** 27,000

46. $15 + 21 = 6^2$
  $21 + 28 = 7^2$
  $28 + 36 = 8^2$

47. a.

year (n)	0	1	2	3
value (y)	25,000	21,250	18,062.5	15,353.125

  b. The car depreciates the most in the first year.   **c.** 0.85

48. a.
  b. 15
  c. no, because each shape needs an odd number of cotton swabs
  d. $y = 2n + 1$, where y is the number of cotton swabs to make the nth shape

49. 54 toothpicks

50. a. 1 4 6 4 1   row 4   **b.** Most likely, $11^4 = 14,641$.
  c. Using a calculator, $11^4 = 14,641$. This answer matches the prediction.
  d. No. The 5th row of Pascal's triangle is
    1 5 10 10 5 1
    but a calculator shows 161,051.

51. a.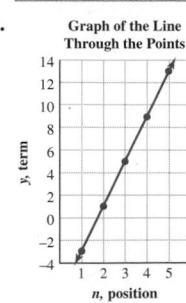
  fourth shape   fifth shape

b. $y = 2n - 1$, where y is the number of dots in the nth shape
  $y = 2(1) - 1 = 1$, which agrees with the given shape
  $y = 2(2) - 1 = 3$, which agrees with the given shape
  $y = 2(3) - 1 = 5$, which agrees with the given shape

52. a. sequence A
  b. You can draw a straight line through the points.

SECTION 1.2

1. a.

	add 5	square result	add 15	divide by 4	
☐	→	☐	→ ☐	→ ☐	→ 46

b. 8

	subtract 5	square root	subtract 15	multiply by 4	
8	←	13	← 169	← 184	← 46

2. 3093 cuts

3. 854 in

4. 236 people

5. nine ways

6. 709 pages

7. 0

8. Tonya likes vanilla, Rosa likes pistachio, and Naomi likes chocolate chip.

9. 21 min

10. 19 or 39 students

11. 4 cm

12. a. The product is an even number.
  b. The product of two consecutive numbers is an even number.
  c. inductive reasoning

13. 13 boxes

14. a. Put four marbles on each side of the balance scale. One side will be heavier. Weigh the four marbles from the heavier side by placing two marbles on each side of the scale. One side will be heavier. Now weigh the two marbles from the heavier side by placing one marble on each side of the scale. The third weighing will determine the heavier marble.
  b. Put three marbles on each side of the balance scale. Case 1. One side will be heavier. The heavier marble must be one the three marbles on the heavier side of the scale. Weigh two marbles from the heavier side by placing one marble on each side of the scale, set aside the third marble. If the scale balances, then the heavier marble is the one set aside. If the scale does not balance, then the heavier marble is identified. Either way, the heavier marble is identified with two weighings.
  Case 2. The scale balances. The heavier marble is not on the scale, so it must be one of the two marbles not on the scale. Weigh the two marbles by placing one marble on each side of the scale. The heavier marble will be identified in two weighings.

15. two weighings

16. six children, because the four daughters each have the same brothers

17. pages 464 and 465

18. Barrel A is filled with water; barrel B is empty. Fill the 8-quart pail with water, and dump it into barrel B. Fill the 5-quart pail with water from barrel B, and pour the water in the 5-quart pail into barrel A. This sequence of action adds 3 quarts of water to barrel B. If we repeat this sequence again, then barrel B will have 6 quarts of water. If we repeat this sequence one more time, then barrel B will have 9 quarts of water.

19. $4842

20. a. There are 360 degrees in one revolution of the hour hand. Each hour, the hour hand rotates 1/12 of the revolution. There are 60 minutes in 1 hour.
$$\frac{360 \text{ deg}}{1 \text{ rev}} \times \frac{1 \text{ rev}}{12 \text{ hr}} \times \frac{1 \text{ hr}}{60 \text{ min}} = 0.5 \text{ degree/min}$$
  b. There are 360 degrees in one revolution of the minute hand. Each hour, the minute hand makes one full revolution. There are 60 minutes in 1 hour.
$$\frac{360 \text{ deg}}{1 \text{ hr}} \times \frac{1 \text{ hr}}{60 \text{ min}} = 6 \text{ deg/min}$$

21. $111

22. a. 13, because $13 \div 9 = 1$ R4
  b. 22, because $22 \div 9 = 2$ R4   **c.** 1678

23. a.

b. $y = 8 + 4(n - 1)$ or $y = 4n + 4$, where y is the number of white tiles needed for the nth shape
  c. The number of black tiles needed for the nth shape is n^2. We need to find the smallest value of n such that $n^2 > 3(4n + 4)$ or $n^2 > 12n + 12$. The number of black tiles needed is 169.

24. 397 sandwiches

25. ≈ 10.73 cm^2

26. So that they can apply different strategies to solve a problem. Problem-solving strategies are tools to solve problems.

27. Every multiple of 6 must be an even number.

28. a. She subtracted: $851 - 143 = 708$.
  b. Solve a simpler problem, such as a chapter begins on page 2 and ends on page 4. How many pages are in the chapter? It has pages 2, 3, 4, so it has 3 pages. We quickly see that subtracting $(4 - 2 = 2)$ gives the incorrect answer. Polly needs to add 1 to the difference. $708 + 1 = 709$.

29. Plan A

30. a. 42×4 Horses have 4 legs, so there are 42 horses.
  $+ \underline{15 \times 2}$ Ducks have 2 legs, so there are 15 ducks.
  198
  The solution 57 is obtained by adding: $42 + 15 = 57$. The number of legs, 198, is the result of the calculation.
  b. From the equation $(25 \times 4) + (43 \times 2) = 186$ and the sum $25 + 43 = 68$, we can pose the following barnyard problem: "A farmer wants to know how many horses and ducks are on the farm. He counts 186 legs and 68 animals. How many of each animal are on the farm?"

31. a. Solve a Simpler Problem   **b.** Guess and Check
   c. Think of a Similar Problem   **d.** *How to Solve It*
   e. questions

32. a. 20 pieces   **b.** 80 min

33. $48

34. 55 cuts; the last cut created two slices of meat

35. 18 raffle tickets

36. 24 videos

37. O = 8¢, X = 25¢

38. 14 coins

39. 9

40. 62 cars and 23 motorcycles

41. 9 and 15 ft

42. a. 5 cards   **b.** 9 cards

43. from first to fifth place: Last Chance, You Betcha, Boomer, Happy-Go-Lucky, and You-Too-Slow

44. 0

45. 6 × 11 ft

46. 10 pieces

47. Zed takes 14.17 hours and Iggy takes 13.75 hours to cross the finish line.

48. 15

SECTION 1.3

1.

$n \div 3$	algebraic expr.	n
$(4 + x) \times 5$	algebraic expr.	x
$(3 + 9) \div 2 = 6$	equation	
$a \times 8 = 25$	equation	a
$(7 + 2) \times 3$	numerical expr.	
$(b - 3) \div m = 8$	equation	m and b

2. the number of books Mary has

3. the number of coins Tanya has

4. a.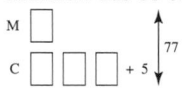

   b. Let c represent the number of pencils Cory has. Then Veronica has $3c + 5$ pencils.

5. a.

(cost) c	12	24	36	48
(gallons) g	5	10	15	20

   b. $\dfrac{c}{g} = \dfrac{12}{5}$, so $5c = 12g$, so $c = 2.4g$

6. Answers vary.
   a. Ken has three more stamps than Lana. Write a variable expression to represent the relationship.
   b. Ken has five fewer stamps than Lana. Write a variable expression to represent the relationship.
   c. Ken has four more than three times as many stamps as Lana. Write a variable expression to represent the relationship.

   d. Ken has three fewer than four times as many stamps as Lana. Write a variable expression to represent the relationship.

7. a. 15 stamps   **b.** 13 marbles

   c. 23 beads

8. Matthew has 18 coins. Courtney has 59 coins.

9. Carol scored 45. Marty scored 59. Solve the equation $2c - 31 + c = 104$.

10. Matthew has 40 coins. Courtney has 76 coins. Solve the equation $m + 2m - 4 = 116$, where m is the number of coins Matthew has.

11. a. Answers vary. Sums: $5 + 7 = 12$, $3 + 5 = 8$, $23 + 31 = 54$. Conjecture: The sum of two odd numbers is an even number.
   b. An even number has the form 2 × (whole number), or $2n$ for some whole number n. An odd number has the form 2 × (whole number) + 1, or $2n + 1$ for some whole number n. Let a and b represent any two odd numbers. Then $a = 2m + 1$ and $b = 2n + 1$ for some whole numbers m and n. Then
   $$a + b = 2m + 1 + 2n + 1$$
   $$= 2m + 2n + 2$$
   $$= 2(m + n + 1).$$
   $m + n + 1$ is a whole number, so $a + b$ equals 2 times a whole number. Therefore, $a + b$ is an even number.

12. a.

number of marbles Judy has (j)	5	6	7
number of marbles Mary has (m)	8	9	10

   b. $j + 3$ **c.** $m = j + 3$

13. a.

number of books Cheryl has (c)	10	11	12
number of books Mike has (m)	2	3	4

   b. $c - 8$ **c.** $m = c - 8$

14. a.

number of coins Fred has (f)	5	6	7
number of coins Mark has (m)	15	18	21

   b. $3f$ **c.** $m = 3f$

15. a.

number of pencils Sara has (s)	1	2	3
number of pencils Martin has (m)	5	8	11

  b. $3s + 2$ **c.** $m = 3s + 2$

16. The new area is four times as large as the original area of the circle.

17. a. 2   **b.** 4   **c.** $y = 2 + 4(n - 1)$ or $y = 4n - 2$

  d.

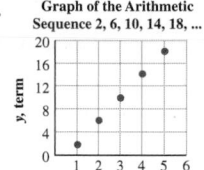

Graph of the Arithmetic Sequence 2, 6, 10, 14, 18, ...

  e.

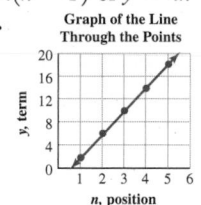

Graph of the Line Through the Points

  f. 4

  g. The common difference is the slope of the line through the points that represent the arithmetic sequence.

18. To have "2 more than n" means we need to have n objects in the first place. So "2 more than n" is appropriately represented by $n + 2$, rather than $2 + n$.

19. To have "4 fewer than n" means we need to have n objects in the first place. So "4 fewer than n" is appropriately represented by $n - 4$ rather than $4 - n$.

20. a. Brian has seven times as many pencils as Sandra.
  b. Brian has three fewer pencils than Sandra.
  c. Brian has five more pencils than Sandra.
  d. Brian has two more than three times as many pencils than Sandra.
  e. Brian has three fewer than five times as many pencils than Sandra.

21. a. $48 - 5 = 43$. Melanie has \$43 more than Steve.
  b. $9 - 4 = 5$. Aaron sold five more books than Marty.

22. a. $23 \div 7 = 3$ R2
    Kate collected two more than three times as many butterflies as Ellen.
  b. $13 \div 4 = 3$ R1
    Bob has one more than three times as many marbles as Carrie.

23. a. Cindy added $(2 + 3 = 5)$, and Andy multiplied $(2 \times 3 = 6)$.
  b. 6
  c.

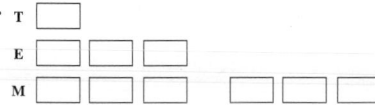

  The diagram shows that Mark has six times as many coins as Tom.
  d. Let T be the number of coins Tom has. Then Elijah has $3T$ coins. Mark has twice as many coins as Elijah, so Mark has $2(3T)$ coins, which equals $6T$ coins.

24. Let n represent the original number. Simplify
$$\frac{(n - 3) \times 6 + 10}{2} = \frac{6n - 18 + 10}{2} = \frac{6n - 8}{2} = 3n - 4.$$
To determine the original number n, just add 4 to her final result and divide by 3.

25. a. Pick a number. Add 5 to it. Multiply the result by 9. Add 3. Subtract the original number. Divide the result by 4.
  b. $[9(n + 5) + 3 - n] \div 4$ equals $2n + 12$. To determine the original number n, just subtract 12 from the final result and divide by 2.

26. a. numerical   **b.** algebraic   **c.** algebra   **d.** variable
  e. evaluate   **f.** equation   **g.** additive   **h.** multiplicative

27. a. n = the number of socks Sam has
  b. $3n - 4$ = the number of socks Max has

28. a. n = the number of coins Jon has
  b. $5n + 3$ = the number of coins Caitlyn has

29. a. F ▢
    M ▢ ▢ ▢
  b. Let f represent the number of stamps Fred has. Then $3f$ represents the number of stamps Mark has.

30. a. A ▢
    P ▢ ▢ ▢ ▢ ▢ - 4
  b. Let a represent the number of beads Amy has. Then $5a - 4$ represents the number of beads Pam has.

31. \$130 each month

32. Answers vary. Maddy has 3 fewer than three times as many coins as Ken. Altogether, they have 73 coins. How many coins does Maddy have?

33. a. $a = j + 3$, where a represents the age of Amanda and j represents the age of Jerry
  b. $k = 3c$, where c represents how fast Carlos can run and k represents how fast Krista can run
  c. $s = 3c + 4$, where c represents how many coins Cory has and s represents how many coins Sam has
  d. $r + 6 = 4d$, where r represents how many stamps Ralph has and d represents how many stamps Dorothy has

34. a. $d + (3d - 2) = 26$, so $d = 7$. There are seven dimes and 19 nickels, which is \$1.65.

35. a. $8p + 2$ **b.** $3m - 5$ **c.** $5f + 8$ **d.** $a + 18$

36. 11, by solving $n + (n + 1) + (n + 2) + \ldots + (n + 27) = 686$ for n.

37. a. \$2805   **b.** $n + 410 = 3215$
  c. n represents the original balance of the bank account.

38. They sold 37 raffle tickets for the golf clubs and 14 raffle tickets for the Disneyland pass.

39. \$2520

40. a. Answers vary. Pick 5 and 6. Then $6^2 - 5^2 = 36 - 25 = 11$. Pick 3 and 4. Then $4^2 - 3^2 = 7$. Pick 7 and 8. Then $8^2 - 7^2 = 15$.
  b. The difference of two consecutive squares is the sum of the two numbers that are squared.
  c. $(n + 1)^2 - n^2 = n^2 + 2n + 1 - n^2$
$$= 2n + 1$$
$$= n + (n + 1)$$
  So $(n + 1)^2 - n^2$ is the sum of the two consecutive numbers $n + 1$ and n.
  d. 426 and 427

41. Neal earned $0.15g + 0.03c + 3.75$ dollars, where g is the number of bottles and c is the number of cans he delivered to the center.

42. a. Answers vary. Pick 1, 2, and 3.
Then $2^2 = 4$. $4 - 1 \cdot 3 = 4 - 3 = 1$.
Pick 4, 5, and 6. Then $5^2 = 25$. $25 - 4 \cdot 6 = 25 - 24 = 1$.
Pick 7, 8, and 9. Then $8^2 = 64$. $64 - 7 \cdot 9 = 64 - 63 = 1$.
b. The three consecutive numbers are n, $n + 1$, and $n + 2$.
c. $(n + 1)^2 - n(n + 2) = n^2 + 2n + 1 - (n^2 + 2n)$
$= n^2 + 2n + 1 - n^2 - 2n$
$= 1$

43. Answers vary.
a. Tariq had 37 marbles. He gave some away. Write an expression that tells how many marbles he had left.
b. There are apples in a bin. Lisa puts two more apples in the bin. Write an expression that tells how many apples are now in the bin.
c. Maria has six fewer than three times as many beads as Victoria. Write an expression that tells how many beads Maria has.

44. a. $5, 10, 15, 20, \ldots$ $y = 5n$
$7, 12, 17, 22, \ldots$ $y = 5n + 2$
$73, 78, 83, 88, \ldots$ $y = 5n + 68$
b. Each sequence has a common difference of 5.

45. a. $2 \cdot 5 - 5 = 5$
$2 \cdot 6 - 6 = 6$
$2 \cdot 7 - 7 = 7$
b. $2n - n = n$ **c.** yes

46. There are 17 horses and 11 chickens.

47. 227 coins

48. You could ask them whether different values of a solve the equation. For example, "Does $a = 3$ solve the equation $a + 5 = 12$? Does $a = 7$ solve the equation $a + 5 = 12$?"

49. a. $336,400 - 149,505 = 186,895$
Napoleon's memoir sold for $186,895 more than an early draft of his will.
b. $336,400 \div 149,505 = 2$ R37,390
Napoleon's memoir sold for $37,390 more than twice the amount of an early draft of his will.

50. a. Answers vary. Pick 2 and 3. Then $2 + 3 = 5$.
Pick 3 and 4. Then $3 + 4 = 7$.
Pick 5 and 6. Then $5 + 6 = 11$.
b. The sum of two consecutive numbers is an odd number.
c. inductive

51. Let n be any whole number. Then, n and $n + 1$ are consecutive whole numbers. Then, $n + (n + 1) = 2n + 1$. So the sum of two consecutive whole numbers is an odd number.

52. a. Answers vary. Pick 3 and 5. Then $3 \times 5 = 15$.
Pick 7 and 3. Then $7 \times 3 = 21$.
Pick 5 and 9. Then $5 \times 9 = 45$.
The examples support the claim that the product of two odd numbers is an odd number.
b. An odd number can be written in the form $2a + 1$ for some whole number a. Let m and n represent any two odd numbers. Then $m = 2x + 1$ for some whole number x and $n = 2y + 1$ for some whole number y. Then
$mn = (2x + 1)(2y + 1)$
$= 2x2y + 2x + 2y + 1$
$= 2(2xy + x + y) + 1$
$2xy + x + y$ is a whole number, so mn has the form $2q + 1$, where q is a whole number. So mn is an odd number.

53. a.

		Is the equation $2p = 7n$ true?		Is the equation $2n = 7p$ true?	
p	n	Yes	No	Yes	No
2	7		X	X	
4	14		X	X	
6	21		X	X	

b. $2n = 7p$ or $n = (7/2)p$ or $n = 3.5p$

54. a. students   **b.** 2
c.

P	1	2	3
S	12	24	36

d. $S = 12P$

55. The sum of three consecutive odd numbers is 159.
a. $50 + 51 + 52 = 153$ is too low. $52 + 53 + 54 = 159$.
b. Let n represent the least whole number of the three consecutive numbers. Then the three consecutive numbers are n, $n + 1$, and $n + 2$. Then
$n + (n + 1) + (n + 2) = 159$
$3n + 3 = 159$
$3n = 156$
$n = 52$
This means the smallest whole number is 52. The three consecutive numbers are 52, 53, and 54.

SECTION 1.4

1. a. III   **b.** IV   **c.** I   **d.** III

2. a.

b.

c.

d.

3. a.

b.

c. The statements have different diagrams, so they are not logically equivalent.

4. The Euler diagram shows that Lisa's reasoning is incorrect. The conclusion that Mike is a mathematician does not automatically follow.

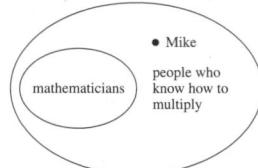

5. The Euler diagram shows that the argument is valid. The symbol for Fred must be outside of the ring of birds and therefore cannot be in the ring for people who read newspapers.

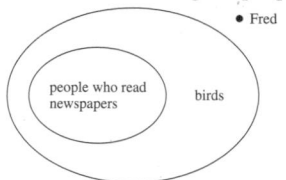

6. Let n be any even number. Then $n = 2k$ for some whole number k. Then $n + 2 = 2k + 2 = 2(k + 1)$. We know $k + 1$ is a whole number, so $n + 2$ can be expressed as 2 times a whole number. Therefore, $n + 2$ is an even number.

7. Let n be any odd number. Then $n = 2k + 1$ for some whole number k. Then
$$n + 4 = (2k + 1) + 4$$
$$= 2k + 4 + 1$$
$$= 2(k + 2) + 1$$
We know $k + 2$ is a whole number, so $n + 4$ can be expressed as 2 times a whole number plus 1.
Therefore, $n + 4$ is an odd number.

8. Let n be any odd number. Then $n = 2k + 1$ for some whole number k. Then
$$n^2 = (2k + 1)^2$$
$$= 4k^2 + 4k + 1$$
$$= 2(2k^2 + 2k) + 1.$$
We know $2k^2 + 2k$ is a whole number, so n^2 can be expressed as 2 times a whole number plus 1.
Therefore, n^2 is an odd number.

9. We know 5 divides the number n. Then $n = 5k$ for some whole number k. Then $6n = 6(5k) = 30k = 10(3k)$. The equation $6n = 10(3k)$ reveals that 10 divides the number $6n$.

10. Suppose n is a multiple of 5. Then $n = 5k$ for some whole number k. Then $n^2 = (5k)^2 = 5k \times 5k = 25k^2$. Then n^2 is a multiple of 25.

11. The argument is invalid. The conclusion does not necessarily follow from the premises as shown in the diagram.

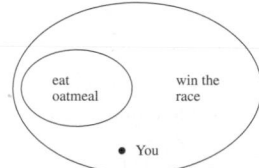

12. The argument is valid; it has the form of the chain rule.

13.

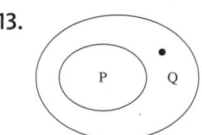

The Euler diagram satisfies the premises, but the conclusion $\sim Q$ does not inescapably follow.

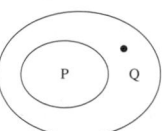

The Euler diagram satisfies the premises, but the conclusion P does not inescapably follow.

14. a. fallacy of the inverse   **b.** fallacy of the converse
     c. fallacy of the converse   **d.** fallacy of the inverse

15. Answers vary. For example, the conclusion "Jenna is not rich" must follow, or the conclusion "Jenna does not subscribe to the *Wall Street Journal*" must follow.

16. Statements (a) and (d) are equivalent because they are contrapositive statements. Statements (b) and (c) are equivalent because they are contrapositive statements.
a. If P, then Q.   **b.** If Q, then P.
c. If not P, then not Q.   **d.** If not Q, then not P.

17. a. Answers vary, but make sure Q is true, such as "8 is an even number."
b. Answers vary, but make sure Q is false, such as "3 is an even number."

18. Dan's reasoning is incorrect, as shown in the Euler diagram. The premises are represented, but the conclusion does not inescapably follow.

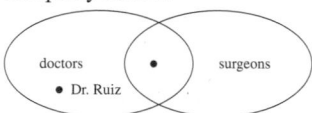

19. The first Euler diagram supports the conclusion, but the second diagram does not because there is no guarantee of a bird that belongs to all three rings. So Taylor's reasoning is incorrect.

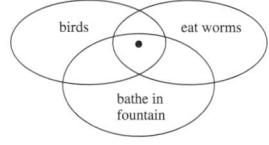

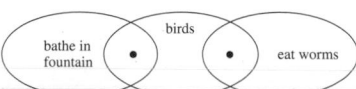

20. a. If your homework is late, then it will not be accepted.
b. If the person is a mathematician, then the person uses calculators.

21. Answers vary.
a. Draw a rectangle where the perpendicular sides do not have the same length.

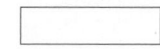

b. Pick any whole number less than or equal to 10, say 5.
c. Find three numbers that satisfy the Pythagorean equation, say $a = 3$, $b = 4$, and $c = 5$.

d. Find one solution: $x = 3$.

e. Find one odd factor, say 3.

22. To prove a conditional statement is false, we need the hypothesis to be true and the conclusion to be false. Answers vary.

   a. Let $n = 4$. Then $5n = 5(4) = 20$, which is not an odd number.

   b. Pick $a = 5$ and $b = 1$. Then $(a - b)^2 = (5 - 1)^2 = 4^2 = 16$ and $a^2 - b^2 = 5^2 - 1^2 = 25 - 1 = 24$. So $(a - b)^2 \neq a^2 - b^2$.

   c. Pick the even number $x = 5000$. Then $2x + 6 = 2 \cdot 5000 + 6 = 10,006$, which is not less than 1000.

   d. Pick $a = 100$ and $b = 50$. Then $a > b$, but $ab \not< 500$ because $100 \cdot 50 \not< 500$.

   e. Pick $x = 10$. Then x is greater than 5, but x is not an odd number.

23. Answers vary. The Euler diagram is shown (just use your own versions of A and B).

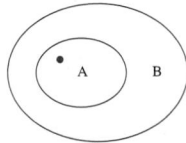

   If your conclusion has the form "x is a B," then your argument is valid.

   If your conclusion has the form "x is not a B," then your argument is invalid, because the x must be contained in the ring for B.

24. **a.** P is true and Q is true, so the statement is true.

   b. P is false, so the statement is true.

   c. P is true and Q is false, so the statement is false.

   d. P is false, so the statement is true.

25. The statement "If 6 is an odd number, then 4 is an even number" is true because the hypothesis "6 is an odd number" is false. If we know that if the statement P is false, then the statement P → Q is automatically true.

26. Answers vary. Suppose the conclusion is "x is A." Then, the argument is invalid because the conclusion does not follow due to the Venn diagram shown.

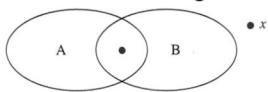

27. Answers vary. The justification should include an Euler diagram that shows why the conclusion does not inescapably follow.

28. **a.** The passengers did not board the train and they found a taxi.

   b. He did not send an email or he did not purchase stamps at the post office.

   c. Mark has a job or he does not walk to school.

   d. Mary did not call her mother and Jim rode his bike.

29. **a.** Converse: Q → P
   Inverse: ~P → ~Q
   Contrapositive: ~Q → ~P

   b. Converse: R → (P and Q)
   Inverse: (~P or ~Q) → ~R
   Contrapositive: ~R → (~P or ~Q)

   c. Converse: R → (P or Q)
   Inverse: (~P and ~Q) → ~R
   Contrapositive: ~R → (~P and ~Q)

   d. Converse: (Q or R) → P
   Inverse: ~P → (~Q and ~R)
   Contrapositive: (~Q and ~R) → ~P

30. **a.** universal   **b.** argument   **c.** existential   **d.** valid
   e. statement   **f.** invalid   **g.** Euler   **h.** converse
   i. inverse   **j.** contrapositive   **k.** conditional   **l.** Q
   m. ~P   **n.** P → R

31. **a.** No. It is an exclamation.

   b. Yes. It is either true or false (although we may not know its truth value).

   c. No. It is an open sentence.

   d. Yes. The statement is true (choose $n = 38$).

   e. Yes. The statement is false (choose $n = -2$).

32. **a.** There are some computers in the library.

   b. The lights in the office never flicker.

   c. Some dogs do not chase cats.

   d. Some rats play football.

   e. There are some fleas on the cat.

   f. No whole numbers are negative integers.

   g. Some cars do not require fuel.

33. Answers vary.

   a. Choose statements P and Q that are both true or both false. For example, P could be $3 + 5 = 8$ and Q could be $7 \times 4 = 28$.

   b. Choose P that is false and Q that is true. For example, P could be $3 + 5 = 10$ and Q could be $7 \times 4 = 28$.

34. Answers vary.

   a. Choose P that is true and Q that is true. For example, P could be $3 + 5 = 8$ and Q could be $7 \times 4 = 28$. Then the inverse ~P → ~Q will be true because ~P is false.

   b. Choose P that is false and Q that is true. For example, P could be $3 + 5 = 1$ and Q could be $7 \times 4 = 28$. Then the inverse ~P → ~Q will be false because ~P is true and ~Q is false.

35. The argument is invalid.

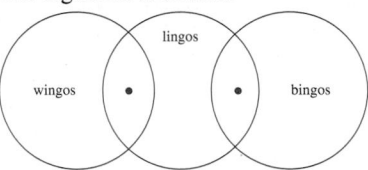

36. Answers vary.

   a. Pick any statement Q that is true, such as $3 + 2 = 5$.

   b. Pick any statement Q that is false, such as $3 + 2 = 10$.

37. **a.** If n is a whole number, then $n > -12$.

   b. If a is a whole number, then $a + 5 < a + 8$.

   c. If a geometric figure is a square, then the geometric figure is a rectangle.

38. We know m is an odd number and n is an even number. Then $m = 2a + 1$ and $n = 2b$ for some whole numbers a and b. Then $m + n = 2a + 1 + 2b = 2(a + b) + 1$.

   We know $a + b$ is a whole number. This means $m + n$ can be expressed in the form 2 times a whole number plus 1. So $m + n$ is an odd number.

39. The argument is invalid. The Euler diagram shows the conclusion does not necessarily follow.

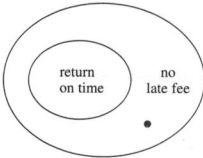

40. The argument is valid due to the chain rule.

41. The argument is valid due to the law of detachment.

42. The argument is valid due to the law of contraposition.

43. The argument is invalid. The Euler diagram shows the conclusion does not inescapably follow.

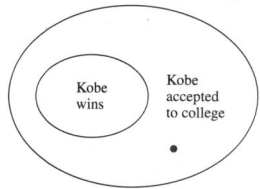

44. The argument is invalid. The Euler diagram shows the conclusion does not inescapably follow.

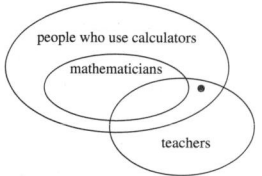

REVIEW QUESTIONS

1. Conjecture: If n is an even number, then n^2 is an even number.

2. The product of an even number and an odd number is an even number.

3. a. $1551 \times 13 = 20{,}163$
      $15{,}551 \times 13 = 202{,}163$
      $155{,}551 \times 13 = 2{,}022{,}163$
   b. $1{,}555{,}551 \times 13 = 20{,}222{,}163$
      $15{,}555{,}551 \times 13 = 202{,}222{,}163$

4. a. W   **b.** N

5. 6

6. a. 20   **b.** 48   **c.** $4(n-1)$
   d. A 7-by-7 patio has more white bricks than dark bricks.

7. 164

8. a. 15, 30, 45, 60; $74 - 60 = 14$; $74 \div 15 = 4$ R14
   b. 32, 64, 96, 128; $145 - 128 = 17$; $145 \div 32 = 4$ R17
   c. 12, 24, 36, 48, 60, 72, 84; $94 - 84 = 10$;
      $94 \div 12 = 7$ R10

9. Organize the equations vertically:
   $5^3 = 125$
   $5^2 = 25$
   $5^1 = 5$
   $5^0 = 1$

10. $2 \times 5 = 10$
   $1 \times 5 = 5$
   $0 \times 5 = 0$
   $-1 \times 5 = -5$
   $-2 \times 5 = -10$

11. a. 11   **b.** 4
   c.

position (n)	1	2	3	4
term (y)	11	15	19	23

   d. $y = 11 + 4(n - 1)$ or $y = 4n + 7$ **e.** 910

12. a.

shape (n)	1	2	3	4
number of corners on the perimeter (y)	4	6	8	10

   c. $y = 2n + 2$, where y is the number of corners on the perimeter in the nth shape

13. a. 3   **b.** 4
   c.

position (n)	1	2	3	4
term (y)	3	12	48	192

   d. $y = 3 \times 4^{n-1}$ **e.** 7

14. 236

15. twice

16. The next three likely terms are 12,600, 100,800, and 907,200. Multiply by 3, then multiply by 4, then multiply by 5, ...

17. a. 5   **b.** -3
   c.

position (n)	1	2	3	4
term (y)	5	2	-1	-4

18. a. 4   **b.** -4

19. A pattern is a similarity or regularity in observations that allows you to predict what comes next or allows you to form a relationship. Inductive reasoning is the process of using observations to make a conjecture. A limitation of inductive reasoning is that the conjecture may not be true.

20. They finished in the following order: Mr. Brown, Mrs. Smith, and Mrs. Grady.

21. 214 and 215

22. 202.5 min

23. a. 8 hamburgers   **b.** 548 hamburgers

24. 43 cards

25. 110 cookies

26. -9

27. 11 boxes

28. $416

29. a. use in formulas **b.** describe properties
c. represent relationships

30. 272 stamps

31. 64 marbles

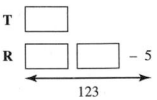

32. 426 beads

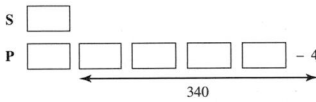

33. a. n tells her the number of coins Mike has.
b. $5n - 4$ tells her the number of coins Paul has.

34. "n = Cindy" suggests n is a person. An improvement would be "n = the number of marbles Cindy has."

35. a. $4n - 3$ = the number of marbles David has
b. n tells you the number of marbles Ann has.

36. a. Mitchell has 34 more coins than Joey.
b. Mitchell has 6 more than three times as many coins as Joey.

37. 100 min

38. a. the number of hours Nick worked
b. the number of packages Nick delivered
c. the number of packages Mathew delivered
d. $4(m + 5) + 6m = 390$
e. Mathew worked 37 hours. Nick worked 42 hours.
f. Mathew delivered 222 packages. Nick delivered 168 packages.

39. $1191

40. $2.97

41. a. true **b.** true **c.** true **d.** false

42. a. Some birds do not eat worms.
b. All skiers drink hot chocolate.
c. Some of the cats meowed when the cow appeared.
d. All elephants are pink.

43. a. Some A are B. **b.** No A are B. **c.** All A are B.
d. Some A are not B.

44. valid

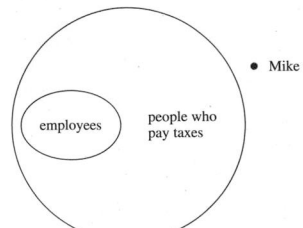

45. invalid

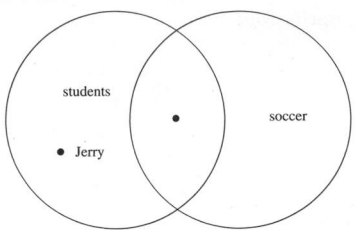

46. invalid

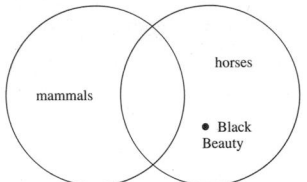

47. valid

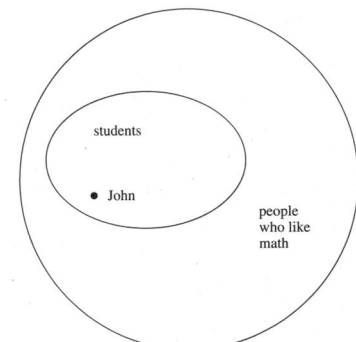

48. invalid

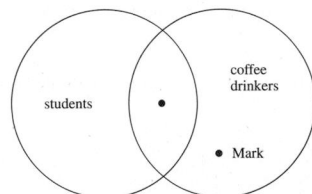

49. Diagram C is the correct Euler diagram.

50. a. false **b.** true **c.** true **d.** true

51. a. P → Q is false for P true and Q false. So any true statement P will work, such as "3 + 5 = 8."
b. P → Q is true for P true and Q true. So any true statement Q will work, such as "3 + 5 = 8."

52. a. If you are smart, then you read the newspaper.
b. If you do not read the newspaper, then you are not smart.
c. If you are not smart, then you do not read the newspaper.

53. invalid

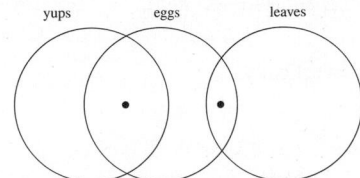

54. valid by the chain rule

55. valid by the law of detachment

56. invalid

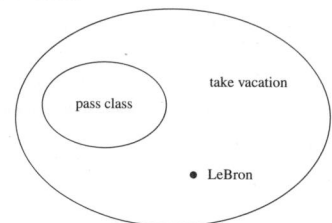

CHAPTER 1 TEST

1. a. A pattern is a similarity or regularity in observations that allows you to predict what comes next or allows you to form a relationship.
   b. A conjecture is a statement that seems true.
   c. Inductive reasoning is the process of using observations to make a conjecture.

2. The sum of three consecutive numbers is divisible by 3.

3. a. 3   **b.** 4
   c. Beginning with 3, obtain the next term by adding 4 to the previous term.
   d.

position (n)	1	2	3	4
term (y)	3	7	11	15

4. a. $y = 1 + 3(n - 1)$ or $y = 3n - 2$ **b.** no
   c.   **d.**

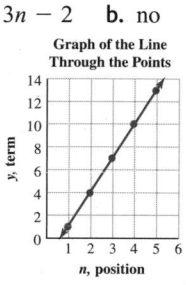

   e. slope = 3
   f. The slope of the line through the points equals the common difference.

5. a. $56^2 = 3136$
   $566^2 = 320,356$
   $5666^2 = 32,103,556$
   $56,666^2 = 3,211,035,556$
   b. $566,666^2 = 321,110,355,556$

6. a. $2445 \times 13 = 31,785$
   $24,445 \times 13 = 317,785$
   $244,445 \times 13 = 3,177,785$
   b. $2,444,445 \times 13 = 31,777,785$
   $24,444,445 \times 13 = 317,777,785$

7. Problem solving is the process of finding a solution to a problem, where the process requires that you think about what you know and apply one of the many problem strategies, such as draw a diagram or write an equation.

8. H

9. a. $y = 3n - 1$, where y is the number of dark bricks used to make an n-by-$(n + 1)$ patio.
   b. no

10. 116

11. 17 tables

12. 64 min

13. 115 beads

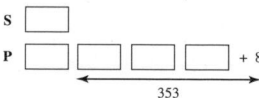

14. a. Algebra is the use of variables to represent unknowns or relationships and manipulate the variables.
   b. A variable is a letter or symbol.
   c. An equation is a statement that says two expressions are equal.

15. a. n represents the number of coins Dan has. $4n + 3$ represents the number of coins Gary has.
   b. $3n - 2$ represents the number of marbles Mario has. n represents the number of marbles Jennifer has.

16. a. $3n + 5$ **b.** 62   **c.** $2473

17. a. Mitchell has 29 more coins than Joey.
   b. Mitchell has five more than three times as many coins as Joey.

18. a. In logical reasoning, a premise is a statement that we accept as true.
   b. A valid argument is a collection of premises and a conclusion such that the conclusion inescapably follows from the premises.
   c. An invalid argument is a collection of premises and a conclusion such that the conclusion does not necessarily follow from the premises.
   d. A simple argument is an argument that consists of two premises and a conclusion.

19. valid argument, because the conclusion must follow from the premises

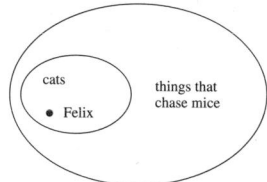

20. invalid argument, because the conclusion does not necessarily follow from the premises.

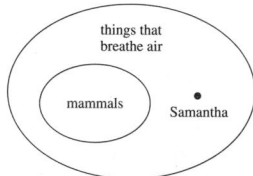

21. invalid argument, because the conclusion does not necessarily follow from the premises

22. valid argument, because the conclusion must follow from the premises.

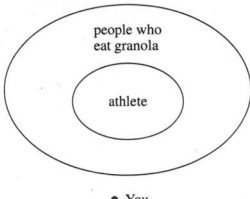

• You

23. invalid argument, because the conclusion does not necessarily follow from the premises.

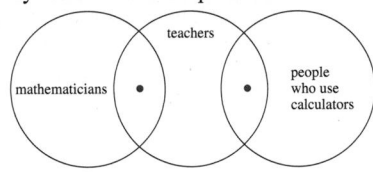

CHAPTER 2

SECTION 2.1

1.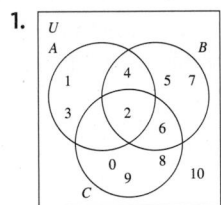

2. **a.** $x \in A$ **b.** $\sim B = \{3, 4, 5\}$ **c.** $A \cap B = \varnothing$
   d. $C \neq \varnothing$ **e.** $n(A \cup B) = 3$ **f.** $G \not\subseteq H$

3. **a.** 4 **b.** $9 + 14 = 23$

4. 5 students

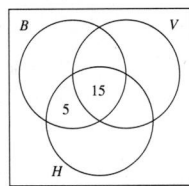

5. **a.** the set of students who like history and math
   b. the set of students who only like history and math
   c. the set of students who only like math
   d. the set of students who only like chemistry or only like history

6. **a.** 4 students **b.** 15 students **c.** 26 students

7. No. The Venn diagram represents the responses and suggests there were $11 + 5 + 20 = 36$ people surveyed, which exceeds the number of people actually surveyed.

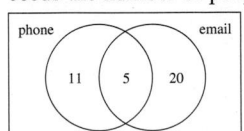

8. 14 students

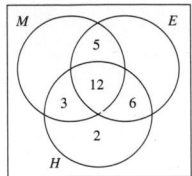

9. **a.** $A \cup B = \{a, e, d, 1\}$ and $B \cup A = \{a, e, d, 1\}$
   b. $A \cup B = \{1, 2, 3, 4\}$ and $B \cup A = \{1, 2, 3, 4\}$
   c. $A \cup B = \{4, a, y, 5\}$ and $B \cup A = \{4, a, y, 5\}$
   d. $A \cup B = B \cup A$ for any sets A and B

10. **a.** $A \cap B = \{e, d\}$ and $B \cap A = \{e, d\}$
    b. $A \cap B = \{2, 5, 6\}$ and $B \cap A = \{2, 5, 6\}$
    c. $A \cap B = \varnothing$ and $B \cap A = \varnothing$
    d. $A \cap B = B \cap A$ for any sets A and B

11. **a.** $A - B = \{a, f, c\}$ and $B - A = \{1\}$
    b. $A - B = \{1, 3, 4\}$ and $B - A = \{7\}$
    c. $A - B = \{4, a, y, 1, 7, 8\}$ and $B - A = \varnothing$

12. Answers vary. $A = \{3, 4, 5\}$ and $B = \{4, 5, 6, 7\}$.

13. No, because as the Venn diagram suggests, there would be 20 students enrolled in history or math rather than 25 students in both combined, as stated in the problem.

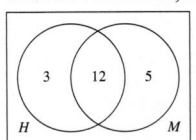

14. Yes, as the following Venn diagram illustrates. In this situation, there could be 3 students who did not see either movie.

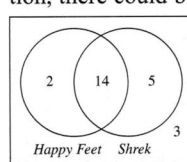

15. The conditions in the problem lead to the following Venn diagram. We need to determine the sum $c + 4$.

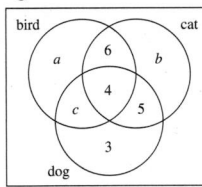

Because 8 people said they owned exactly one pet, we know $a + b + 3 = 8$. Then $a + b = 5$. There are 27 people who owned a bird, cat, or dog, so
$$a + b + c + 6 + 4 + 5 + 3 = 27$$
$$5 + c + 6 + 4 + 5 + 3 = 27$$
$$c = 4.$$
Then $c + 4 = 4 + 4 = 8$. So 8 people owned a bird and dog.

16.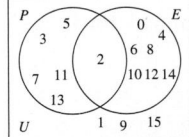

17.

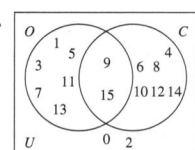

18.

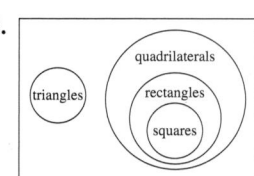

19. Yes. For example, $A = \{n\}$ and $B = \{1, 2, 3, 4, 5\}$.

20. Yes. Match the element x in N with the element $x + 5$ in S. Each element of N corresponds to exactly one element in S, and each element in S corresponds to exactly one element in S. So $N \sim S$.

21. a. Both A and B are the empty sets.
   b. A and B are disjoint (they do not have any elements in common).
   c. A is a subset of B (every element of A is also an element of B).
   d. A is the universal set.

22. The symbol $\cup$ looks like the first letter of the word *union*.

23. The hotel manager has the pigeon in hole n move to hole $n + 1$. Then he puts the pigeon that just arrived in hole 1.

24. a. cardinal **b.** set **c.** universal **d.** equivalent
   e. $A \cup B$ **f.** $A \cap B$ **g.** $\sim B$ **h.** $B - A$

25. a. $A \cup B = \{1, 2, 3, 4, 6, 7\}$, $A \cap B = \{3, 4\}$,
   $A - B = \{6\}$, and $\sim A = \{1, 2, 5, 7, 8\}$
   b. $A \cup B = \{1, 2, 3, 4, 5, 6\}$, $A \cap B = \varnothing$,
   $A - B = \{2, 4, 6\}$, and $\sim A = \{1, 3, 5, 7, 8\}$

26. a. $A \cup B = \{1, 2, 3, 5\}$, $A \cap B = \{1, 3\}$,
   $A - B = \{5\}$, $\sim A = \{2, 4, 6, 7\}$
   b. $A \cup B = \{1, 2, 3, 4, 5\}$, $A \cap B = \{1, 4, 5\}$,
   $A - B = \varnothing$, and $\sim A = \{2, 3, 6, 7\}$
   c. $A \cup B = \{1, 2, 3, 4\}$, $A \cap B = \varnothing$,
   $A - B = \varnothing$, and $\sim A = \{1, 2, 3, 4, 5, 6, 7\}$

27. a. true **b.** true **c.** true **d.** true **e.** false **f.** true

28. a. Answers vary. $\{2\}$ and 8
   b. Answers vary. $\{\{2\}, 8\}$ and $\{\{2\}, \{4, 6\}, 8\}$

29. a. 4 **b.** 1 **c.** 1

30. a. 37 **b.** 22

31. a. At least one of the sets is nonempty.
   b. They have at least one element in common.
   c. A is not a subset of B.
   d. A is not the universal set.

32. a. $\{\ \}$ **b.** $\varnothing, \{1\}$ **c.** $\varnothing, \{1\}, \{2\}, \{1, 2\}$
   d. $\varnothing, \{1\}, \{2\}, \{3\}, \{1, 2\}, \{2, 3\}, \{1, 3\}, \{1, 2, 3\}$
   e. $\{1, 2, 3, \ldots, k\}$ has 2^k subsets.

33. We organize the information in the following Venn diagram:

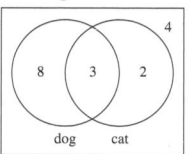

   a. 4 students **b.** 10 students $(8 + 2 = 10)$

34. 10 saw both movies. Let S be the set of students who saw Scary Fractions and D be the set of students who saw Dr. Venn and Mr. Diagram. Then

$$n(S \cup D) = n(S) + n(D) - n(S \cap D)$$
$$40 = 18 + 32 - n(S \cap D)$$
$$40 = 50 - n(S \cap D)$$
$$n(S \cap D) = 10$$

35. Let C equal the set of students who read *Charlotte's Web* and T equal the set of students who read *Trumpet of the Swan*. Then $n(C) = 15$ and $n(T) = 20$. The number of students who read *Charlotte's Web* or *Trumpet of the Swan* must be less than or equal to the total number of students in the class, so $n(C \cup T) \leq 23$. We know $n(C \cup T) = n(C) + n(T) - n(C \cap T)$. Then $n(C) + n(T) - n(C \cap T) \leq 23$. Then $15 + 20 - n(C \cap T) \leq 23$. Then $35 - n(C \cap T) \leq 23$. Then $12 \leq n(C \cap T)$. At the least, 12 students have read both books.

36. Let M equal the number of students who play a musical instrument and S equal the number of students who belong to a sports team. Then $n(M) = 16$ and $n(S) = 18$. The number of students who play a musical instrument or belong to a sports team is less than or equal to 25, so $n(M \cup S) \leq 25$. We know $n(M \cup S) = n(M) + n(S) - n(M \cap S)$. Then $n(M) + n(S) - n(M \cap S) \leq 25$. Then $16 + 18 - n(<M \cap S) \leq 25$. Then $34 - n(M \cap S) \leq 25$. Then $9 \leq n(M \cap S)$. So the number of students who participate in both activities must be greater or equal to 9. The following Venn diagram meets the conditions: 16 students play a musical instrument and 18 students belong to a sports team. In addition, 7 students neither play a musical instrument nor belong to a sports team.

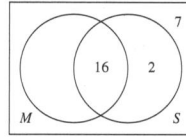

Any other arrangement reduces the number of students who neither play a musical instrument nor belong to a sports team (try it). So the maximum number of students who neither play a musical instrument nor belong to a sports team is 7.

37. a. $A = \{a, d\}$, $\sim A = \{b, c, e\}$, and $\sim(\sim A) = \{a, d\}$.
   So $A = \sim(\sim A)$.
   b. $A = \{a, b, c\}$, $\sim A = \{d, e\}$, and $\sim(\sim A) = \{a, b, c\}$.
   So $A = \sim(\sim A)$.
   c. $A = \varnothing$, $\sim A = U$, and $\sim(\sim A) = \varnothing$. So $A = \sim(\sim A)$.
   d. $A = \sim(\sim A)$ for any set A.

38. a. A **b.** $\sim B$

39. a. $A - B = \{2\}$ **b.** $A \cap B = \{4, 6\}$
   c. $B - A = \{5, 7, 8\}$

d. $(A - B) \cup (B - A)$
$A - B = \{2, 4, 6\} - \{4, 5, 6, 7, 8\}$
$\quad = \{2\}$
$B - A = \{4, 5, 6, 7, 8\} - \{2, 4, 6\}$
$\quad = \{5, 7, 8\}$
So $(A - B) \cup (B - A) = \{2, 5, 7, 8\}$.

40. Yes. The element a of A corresponds to the element $(5/2)a$ of B. Then $2 \leftrightarrow 5$, $4 \leftrightarrow 10$, and $6 \leftrightarrow 15$.

41. a. $B \cup \varnothing = B$ **b.** $B - \varnothing = B$
c. $n + 0 = n$ and $n - 0 = n$

42. a. $B \cap \varnothing = \varnothing$ **b.** $n \cdot 0 = 0$

43. a. $A \times B = \{(x, a), (x, b)\}$, $n(A \times B) = 2$, and
$n(A) \times n(B) = 2$
b. $A \times B = \{(x, a), (x, b), (y, a), (y, b)\}$, $n(A \times B) = 4$,
and $n(A) \times n(B) = 4$
c. $A \times B = \{(x, a), (x, b), (y, a), (y, b), (z, a), (z, b)\}$,
$n(A \times B) = 6$, and $n(A) \times n(B) = 6$
d. $n(A \times B) = n(A) \times n(B)$ for any sets A and B.

44. Answers vary. $A = \{1, 2, 3\}$ and $B = \{1, 2, 3, 4, 5\}$.

45. 13 gamblers $(6 + 4 + 3 = 13)$
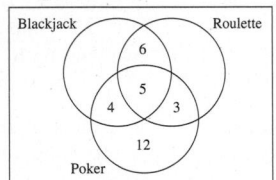

46. a. 22
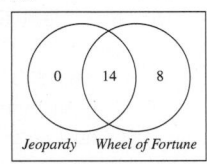

b. 36
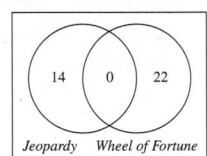

47.
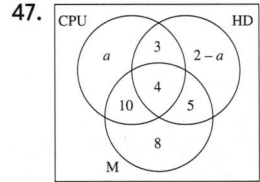
a. 10 people $(a + 2 - a + 8 = 10)$
b. 18 people $(3 + 5 + 10 = 18)$

SECTION 2.2

1. c

2. a. 20 billion, 390 million
b. twenty billion, three hundred ninety million

3. a. 40
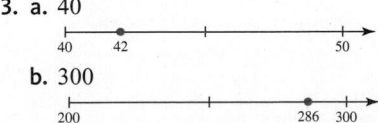
b. 300

c. 0

4. a. 23,087   **b.** 145,241,083   **c.** 373,058,000,216

5. a.

b. ꡁꡁꡁ∩∩∩∩∩IIIIIIII

6. a.   **b.**   **c.**

7. a.

b.

c.

8. a. 2001_{five} **b.** 3133_{five}

9. a. 10000_{three} **b.** 2202_{three}

10. a.

b.

c.

11.

12. a. The sum $b + c$ must be a single digit: $b + c = a$.
b. Answers vary. $b = 4$, $c = 3$, and $a = 7$.

13. 51, 73, 95

14. Answers vary.
a. 168   **b.** 267

15. 27 digits; use the strategies of solve simpler problems and look for a pattern.

16. 19; use the strategies of solve simpler problems (e.g., $332^2 = 110{,}224$ and $3332^2 = 11{,}102{,}224$) and look for a pattern.

17. 48,000 rounded to the nearest *one* equals 48,000.
48,002 rounded to the nearest *ten* equals 48,000.
48,031 rounded to the nearest *hundred* equals 48,000.
48,287 rounded to the nearest *thousand* equals 48,000.
We could have rounded to the nearest one, ten, hundred, or thousand.

18. a. 250   **b.** 349   **c.** 100

19. Think round(4258) + round(n) = 12,000.
  a. Answers vary. n could be 8200.
  b. 7500   **c.** 8499   **d.** 1000

20. a. $7 \cdot 20 + 13 \cdot 1 = 153$
  b. $1 \cdot 360 + 2 \cdot 20 + 3 \cdot 1 = 403$
  c. $5 \cdot 360 + 0 \cdot 20 + 19 \cdot 1 = 1819$
  d. $1 \cdot 360 + 0 \cdot 20 + 0 \cdot 1 = 360$
  e. $3 \cdot 360 + 9 \cdot 20 + 15 \cdot 1 = 1275$
  f. $6 \cdot 7200 + 10 \cdot 360 + 0 \cdot 20 + 8 \cdot 1 = 46{,}808$

21. a. $2 \cdot 20 + 14$

  b. $17 \cdot 20 + 8$

  c. $2 \cdot 360 + 11 \cdot 20 + 2$

  d. $1 \cdot 360 + 13 \cdot 20 + 7$

  e. $2 \cdot 7200 + 8 \cdot 360 + 3 \cdot 20 + 5$

22. a. $11 \cdot 60^2 + 0 \cdot 60^1 + 1 \cdot 60^0 = 39{,}601$
  b. $30 \cdot 60^2 + 1 \cdot 60^1 + 12 \cdot 60^0 = 108{,}072$
  c. $5 \cdot 60^1 + 12 \cdot 60^0 = 312$
  d. $30 \cdot 60^2 + 0 \cdot 60^1 + 8 \cdot 60^0 = 108{,}008$
  e. $1 \cdot 60^4 + 0 \cdot 60^3 + 10 \cdot 60^2 + 0 \cdot 60^1 + 25 \cdot 60^0$
     $= 12{,}996{,}025$

23. a. $54 = $
  b. $348 = 5 \cdot 60 + 48 = $
  c. $942 = 15 \cdot 60 + 42 \cdot 1$
  d. $627 = 10 \cdot 60 + 27 \cdot 1$
  e. $17{,}345 = 4 \cdot 3600 + 49 \cdot 60 + 5 \cdot 1$

24. a. 60, but could be 1   **b.** 720

25. They are alike because they are place value number systems. They are different because the Babylonian number system uses two symbols to form nonzero digits (1 to 59) whereas the Hindu-Arabic number system uses nine symbols to form nonzero digits (1–9).

26. a. three   **b.** four   **c.** fifteen

27. a. $1_{\text{five}} \cdot 10^2{}_{\text{five}} + 3_{\text{five}} \cdot 10^1{}_{\text{five}} + 4_{\text{five}} \cdot 10^0{}_{\text{five}}$
  b. $7_{\text{eight}} \cdot 10^2{}_{\text{eight}} + 2_{\text{eight}} \cdot 10^1{}_{\text{eight}} + 5_{\text{eight}} \cdot 10^0{}_{\text{eight}}$
  c. $A \cdot 10^3{}_{\text{twelve}} + 4_{\text{twelve}} \cdot 10^2{}_{\text{twelve}} + 7_{\text{twelve}} \cdot 10^1{}_{\text{twelve}} +$
     $B \cdot 10^0{}_{\text{twelve}}$

28. a. 25   **b.** 36   **c.** 49

29. a. 107   **b.** 7643   **c.** 829

30. a. 3142   **b.** 3B19   **c.** 12345

31. a. 100_{five}, 101_{five} **b.** 65_{seven}, 66_{seven} **c.** 10_{twelve}, 11_{twelve}

32. A collection of symbols to represent quantities, or numbers, using a prescribed set of rules

33. The numeration system must have a set of symbols, and it must have a framework that determines how a sequence of those symbols, called a numeral, represents the number of objects counted.

34. A place value numeration system has a set of symbols called digits. Each numeral is a sequence of digits. Each digit has a place value within a numeral that determines the size of a grouping, and each digit in a numeral conveys a value that depends on the digit itself and the place value of the digit. Finally, one digit, called zero, signifies the absence of the grouping associated with its place value.

35. The answer "the underlined digits have different values," because values take into account both the place value of the digit and the digit itself

36. The place values are powers of 10. Adjacent place values differ by a factor of 10.

37. They are alike because they are place value number systems. They are different because the Mayan number system has many more digits (the Hindu–Arabic system has digits that represent 0 to 9, whereas the Mayan system has digits that represent 0 to 19).

38. Answers vary.

39. a. place value   **b.** value   **c.** digits   **d.** numeral
  e. number   **f.** short word form   **g.** expanded form
  h. standard form

40. a. 328,052,000,211   **b.** 78,013,000,007,789
  c. 639,003

41. a. hundreds   **b.** ten millions   **c.** hundreds

42. a. thousands   **b.** tens   **c.** hundred millions

43. a. 8000   **b.** 0   **c.** 400,000

44. a. 40   **b.** 600,000   **c.** 0

45. a. Each represents two groups of something.
  b. They have different values.
  c. They make it easier to read the number.

46. a. 227 million, 936 thousand, 640
  b. two hundred twenty-seven million, nine hundred thirty-six thousand, six hundred forty

47. a. 72,084
  b. 53,128,421
  c. 21,000,012,089

48. a. 45 thousand, 36
  b. forty-five thousand, thirty-six
  c. $40{,}000 + 5000 + 0 + 30 + 6$
  d. $4 \cdot 10{,}000 + 5 \cdot 1000 + 0 \cdot 100 + 3 \cdot 10 + 6 \cdot 1$
  e. $4 \cdot 10^4 + 5 \cdot 10^3 + 0 \cdot 10^2 + 3 \cdot 10^1 + 6 \cdot 10^0$

49. a. 5   **b.** 0   **c.** 3

50. a. millions   **b.** ten billions   **c.** ten thousands

51. a. b, ac, abc **b.** c, ab, cba

52. Answers vary.
  a. 3, 15, 6 or 2, 25, 6   **b.** 623, 50, 1 or 623, 49, 11
  c. 678, 5 or 677, 15   **d.** 7, 4, 12 or 6, 14, 12

53. a. 47, 8 **b.** 13, 0, 4 **c.** 2, 562 **d.** 89, 0, 5

54. a. 5 **b.** 13 **c.** 19 **d.** 9

55. a. 1000

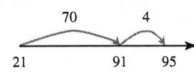

  b. 400

  c. 4 million

  d. 10 billion

56. a. 12,000,000 **b.** 8,500,000 **c.** 985,383,000

57. a. $842 \div 15 \approx 56.13$, so 842 is between 56×15 and 57×15; $0.13 < 0.5$ and $56 \times 15 = 840$, so 842 rounded to the nearest multiple of 15 is 840
  b. $5924 \div 23 \approx 257.56$, so 5924 is between 257×23 and 258×23; $0.56 > 0.5$ and $258 \times 23 = 5934$, so 5924 rounded to the nearest multiple of 23 is 5934
  c. $72,950 \div 41 \approx 1779.26$, so 72,950 is between 1779×41 and 1779×41; $0.26 < 0.5$ and $1779 \times 41 = 72,939$, so 72,950 rounded to the nearest multiple of 41 is 72,939

58. a. ∩∩∩‖

  b. ℓℓ૭૭૭∩∩∩∩∩∩∩‖

  c. ∭∭ℓℓℓℓ∩∩‖‖

  d. ꝏꝏℓ૭૭૭૭∩∩∩∩∩∩∩∩‖‖‖‖‖

59. a. $10 \cdot 60^2 + 0 \cdot 60^1 + 11 \cdot 60^0 = 36,011$
  b. $30 \cdot 60^2 + 0 \cdot 60^1 + 12 \cdot 60^0 = 108,012$
  c. $13 \cdot 60^2 + 0 \cdot 60^1 + 1 \cdot 60^0 = 46,801$
  d. $10 \cdot 60^5 + 0 \cdot 60^4 + 0 \cdot 60^3 + 21 \cdot 60^2 + 0 \cdot 60^1 + 3 \cdot 60^0$
    $= 7,776,075,603$
  e. $12 \cdot 60^2 + 0 \cdot 60^1 + 14 \cdot 60^0 = 43,214$

60. a. $600_{nine} + 70_{nine} + 8_{nine}$
  b. $1000_{five} + 200_{five} + 0_{five} + 3_{five}$
  c. $A000_{twelve} + 200_{twelve} + B0_{twelve} + 8_{twelve}$

61. a. 10203 **b.** A3B2 **c.** 5056

62. a. 194 **b.** 2011 **c.** 19,006 **d.** 13,539

63. a. base twelve **b.** base eight **c.** base six

64. a. 99 **b.** 44_{five} **c.** 66_{seven} **d.** BB_{twelve}

SECTION 2.3

1. a. $5 + 2 = 7$

•••• •• → •••••••

  b. $3 + 6 = 9$

••• •••••• → •••••••••

2. a. $6 - 2 = 4$

  b. $8 - 5 = 3$

3. a. $2 + 6 = 8$

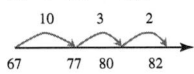

  b. $4 + 3 = 7$

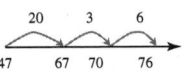

4. Answers vary, but the diagrams should involve breaking apart or decomposing an addend to form easy combinations. Here are possibilities:
  a. $21 + 74 = 95$

  b. $67 + 15 = 82$

  c. $47 + 29 = 76$

5. a.

M ☐ – 8
V ☐
  70

  b. Let m equal the number of coins Maria has. Then $m = 70 - 8 = 62$. So Maria has 62 coins.

6. $n + 1$

7. Answers vary.
  (i) Juan has 24 coins. He gave 6 to his brother. How many does he have left?
  (ii) Juan needs 24 pennies to complete a roll of pennies. He found 6 pennies in a jar. How many more pennies does he need?
  (iii) Juan has 24 coins. His brother has 6 coins. How many more coins does Juan have?

8. a. 100 **b.** 1010

9. a. $13 - 4 = 9$ **b.** $20 - 5 = 15$ **c.** $19 - 7 = 12$
  d. $18 - 2 = 16$ **e.** $a + b - b = a$

10. a. $5 + 4 = 9$ **b.** $10 + 5 = 15$ **c.** $5 + 7 = 12$
  d. $14 + 2 = 16$ **e.** $a - b + b = a$

11. a. $k - 15 = 22$
    $k - 15 + 15 = 22 + 15$
    $k = 22 + 15$
    $k = 37$
  b. $n + 6 = 14$
    $n + 6 - 6 = 14 - 6$
    $n = 14 - 6$
    $n = 8$

12. Yes. The third number is $a + b$ by the closure property of addition.

13. a. $12 = n + 3$ **b.** $12 = n - 3$

14. identity property of whole number addition (use the facts $7 + 0 = 7$, $6 + 0 = 6$, and $5 + 0 = 5$)

15. $a \leq b$, so there is a whole number k such that $a + k = b$.
$b \leq c$, so there is a whole number h such that $b + h = c$.
Then

$$a + k = b$$
$$(a + k) + h = b + h \quad \textbf{by the addition property}$$
$$\textbf{of equality}$$
$$(a + k) + h = c \quad \textbf{because } c = b + h$$
$$a + (k + h) = c. \quad \textbf{by the associative property}$$
$$\textbf{of addition}$$

Because k and h are whole numbers, $k + h$ is a whole number. So a plus a whole number equals c. By the definition of $\leq$, $a \leq c$.

16. a. $n - 18 = 25$
$\qquad n = 25 + 18$
$\qquad n = 43$

b. $\qquad n - 18 = 25$
$\quad n - 18 + 18 = 25 + 18$
$\qquad\qquad n = 25 + 18$
$\qquad\qquad n = 43$

c. $n - 18 = 25 \quad n = 18 + 25$
$\quad n - 25 = 18 \quad n = 25 + 18$
The equation $n = 18 + 25$ leads to $n = 43$.

17. a. $n + 14 = 52$
$\quad n = 52 - 14$
$\quad n = 38$

b. $\qquad n + 14 = 52$
$\quad n + 14 - 14 = 52 - 14$
$\qquad\qquad n = 52 - 14$
$\qquad\qquad n = 38$

c. $n + 14 = 52 \quad 14 + n = 52$
$\quad n = 52 - 14 \quad 14 = 52 - n$
The equation $n = 52 - 14$ leads to $n = 38$.

18. Suppose $a + c = b + c$.   **given**
Then $a + c - c = b + c - c$.   **addition property**
$\qquad\qquad\qquad\qquad\qquad$ **of equality**
Then $a = b + c - c$.   **+ and − are inverse**
$\qquad\qquad\qquad\qquad\qquad$ **operations**
Then $a = b$.   **+ and − are inverse**
$\qquad\qquad\qquad\qquad\qquad$ **operations**

19. $n = 4 + 13$ and $n = 13 + 4$

20. identity property of addition

21. The polygon is decomposed into two rectangles.

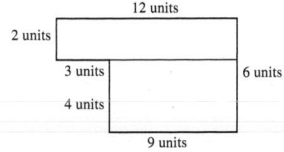

$A = 2 \times 12 + 4 \times 9 = 24 + 36 = 60$ square units.

22. John has 6 fewer trading cards than Bob. Bob has 6 more cards than John.

23. a. $6 + 3 = 9$, $9 - 3 = 6$, and then $6 + 3 - 3 = 6$.
b. Answers vary. Begin with eight coins. Add two coins.
Then take away two coins:
$8 + 2 = 10$
$10 - 2 = 8$
$8 + 2 - 2 = 8$

c. $a + b - b = a$, which illustrates subtraction is the inverse operation of addition

24. a. $5 - 2 = 3$, $3 + 2 = 5$, and then $5 - 2 + 2 = 5$.
b. Answers vary. Begin with eight coins. Take away six coins. Then add six coins:
$8 - 6 = 2$
$2 + 6 = 8$
$8 - 6 + 6 = 6$
c. $a - b + b = a$, which shows addition is the inverse operation of subtraction

25. Answers vary.
(i) Use a fact family and look for the equation that helps you solve for the unknown.
(ii) Use addition and subtraction as inverse operations.
(iii) Use the definition of subtraction.

26. Addition is commutative. Subtraction is not commutative, so we have different names for the numbers involved.

27. The two addends can switch places in the sum. The two addends are also subtracted.

28. The word problems vary, but their structure should be similar to that of these examples:
a. Marco had 14 pieces of candy. He gave some candy to his friends. He had 5 pieces of candy remaining. How many pieces of candy did he give to his friends?
b. Marco had some candy. He gave 7 pieces of candy to his friends. He had 10 pieces of candy remaining. How many pieces of candy did he have altogether?

29. a. subtrahend   **b.** minuend   **c.** missing addend
d. difference   **e.** sum   **f.** decomposing
g. joining   **h.** difference   **i.** number sense

30. a. $3 + 5$
••• ••••• $\longrightarrow$ •••••••• $3 + 5 = 8$
b. $2 + 7$
•• ••••••• $\longrightarrow$ ••••••••• $2 + 7 = 9$

31. a. $4 + 7 = 11$

$$\begin{array}{c} \overset{4}{\longrightarrow} \quad \overset{7}{\longrightarrow} \\ \mid \ \mid \ \mid \ \mid \ \mid \ \mid \ \mid \ \mid \ \mid \ \mid \ \mid \ \mid \\ 0 \ 1 \ 2 \ 3 \ 4 \ 5 \ 6 \ 7 \ 8 \ 9 \ 10 \ 11 \end{array}$$

b. $2 + 5 = 7$

$$\begin{array}{c} \overset{2}{\longrightarrow} \quad \overset{5}{\longrightarrow} \\ \mid \ \mid \ \mid \ \mid \ \mid \ \mid \ \mid \ \mid \ \mid \ \mid \ \mid \\ 0 \ 1 \ 2 \ 3 \ 4 \ 5 \ 6 \ 7 \ 8 \ 9 \ 10 \end{array}$$

32. a. $5 - 2 = 3$ **b.** $9 - 4 = 5$

33. a. ○ ○ ○ ○
$\uparrow\ \uparrow\ \uparrow\ \uparrow$
X X X X X X
b. ○ ○ ○
$\uparrow\ \uparrow\ \uparrow$
X X X X X X X

34. $5 + 4 = 9$, and because 4 is a positive number, $5 < 9$

35. The number to the left is less than the number to the right.
a. $\mid\ \mid\ \bullet\ \mid\ \mid\ \mid\ \bullet\ \mid\ \mid\ \mid$
$\quad$ 0 1 2 3 4 5 6 7 8 9 10
So $2 < 6$.
b. $\mid\ \mid\ \mid\ \mid\ \mid\ \bullet\ \mid\ \mid\ \bullet\ \mid\ \mid$
$\quad$ 0 1 2 3 4 5 6 7 8 9 10
So $5 < 8$.
c. $\mid\ \mid\ \mid\ \mid\ \bullet\ \mid\ \mid\ \bullet\ \mid\ \mid\ \mid$
$\quad$ 0 1 2 3 4 5 6 7 8 9 10
So $4 < 7$.

36. a.

So $5 - 2 = 3$.

b.

So $9 - 3 = 6$.

37. a.

b.

c.

38. a. comparison model of subtraction
b. missing addend model of subtraction
c. take-away model of subtraction

39. a. 15 coins **b.** 25 coins

40. a. $3 + n = 21$ **b.** $n + 3 = 21$

41. a. $15 - n = 3$ **b.** $n - 3 = 15$

42. a. $8 - 5 = 3$

b. $6 - 2 = 4$

43. Answers vary.
a. Maria has eight coins. Frankie has seven coins. How many coins do they have altogether?
b. Ned has some coins. He gave Amy 4 coins. He has 12 coins remaining. How many coins did he have?
c. Sheila has $7. She is saving her money to buy a CD that costs $13. How much more money does she need to save?

44. a. number of marbles Alley has
b. number of marbles Ken has

45. a. $7 - 2 = 5$ and $7 - 5 = 2$
b. $E - L = Y$ and $E - Y = L$

46. a. $345 - 5 = w$ **b.** $X - Y = 4$

47. a. $Y + 2 = 9, 2 + Y = 9, 9 - 2 = Y, 9 - Y = 2$
b. $13 - K = 3, 13 - 3 = K, 13 = K + 3, 13 = 3 + K$
c. $4 + 6 = 10, 6 + 4 = 10, 10 - 4 = 6, 10 - 6 = 4$

48. a. Both can be solved using subtraction: $n = 7 - 2$ and $n = 15{,}831 - 943$.
b. A student could solve $2 + n = 7$ using an addition fact, while a student would use subtraction to solve $943 + n = 15{,}831$.

49. a. $4 + 7 + 6 = 10 + 7 = 17$
b. $14 + 7 + 13 = 14 + 20 = 34$
c. $12 + 38 + 15 = 50 + 15 = 65$

50. $k + 5 = 11$ $\quad$ $5 + k = 11$
$11 - k = 5$ $\quad$ $\boxed{11 - 5 = k}$

51. $57 - m = 29$ $\quad$ $\boxed{57 - 29 = m}$
$57 = 29 + m$ $\quad$ $57 = m + 29$

52. a. associative property **b.** commutative property
c. identity property **d.** commutative property

53. Answers vary.
a. $5 + 9 = (4 + 1) + 9 = 4 + (1 + 9) = 4 + 10 = 14$
b. $24 + 8 = 24 + (6 + 2) = (24 + 6) + 2 = 30 + 2 = 32$
c. $18 + 5 = 18 + (2 + 3) = (18 + 2) + 3 = 20 + 3 = 23$
d. $15 + 13 = (8 + 7) + 13 = 8 + (7 + 13) = 8 + 20 = 28$

54. 15 and 4

55. a. Here are two possible ways to solve the problem.
(i) Using numerical examples: Suppose Samantha has 25 marbles. Then Amanda has $25 + 8 = 33$ marbles. Then Kyle has $33 + 4 = 37$ marbles. Because $37 - 25 = 12$, Kyle has 12 more marbles than Samantha.
(ii) Using algebra: Suppose Samantha has n marbles. Then Amanda has $n + 8$ marbles. Then Kyle has $(n + 8) + 4$ marbles. Because $(n + 8) + 4 = n + (8 + 4) = n + 12$, Kyle has 12 more marbles than Samantha.

b. Here are two possible ways to solve the problem.
(i) Using numerical examples: Suppose Taylor has 25 coins. Then Nick has $25 - 7 = 18$ coins. Then Gabby has $18 - 3 = 15$ coins. Because $25 - 15 = 10$, Gabby has 10 fewer coins than Taylor.
(ii) Using algebra: Suppose Taylor has n coins, where $n \geq 10$. Then Nick has $n - 7$ coins. Then Gabby has $(n - 7) - 3$ coins. Because $(n - 7) - 3$ is a whole number, $(n - 7) - 3 = k$, for some whole number k that represents the number of coins Gabby has. By the missing addend model of subtraction, $n - 7 = k + 3$. By the missing addend model of subtraction again, $n = (k + 3) + 7$. Then $n = k + (3 + 7)$. Then $n = k + 10$. Then $n - 10 = k$. So Gabby has 10 fewer coins than Taylor.

56. a. 1 **b.** 1 **c.** 1 **d.** 1
e. To subtract 9, first subtract 10 and then add 1.

57. associative property of addition
a. $14 + 8 = 14 + 6 + 2 = 20 + 2 = 22$
b. $27 + 5 = 27 + 3 + 2 = 30 + 2 = 32$
c. $17 + 6 = 17 + 3 + 3 = 20 + 3 = 23$
d. $18 + 15 = 18 + 2 + 13 = 20 + 13 = 33$

58. a. $4 + 7 = 4 + (4 + 3) = (4 + 4) + 3 = 8 + 3 = 11$
b. $6 + 5 = (1 + 5) + 5 = 1 + (5 + 5) = 1 + 10 = 11$
c. $9 + 7 = (2 + 7) + 7 = 2 + (7 + 7) = 2 + 14 = 16$

59. a. $18 - 5 = 13 + 5 - 5 = 13$
b. $27 - 5 = 22 + 5 - 5 = 22$
c. $17 - 6 = 11 + 6 - 6 = 11$

60. Yes. $5547 - 2108 = 3439$. The challenger would have won by 3439 votes.

61. 62%

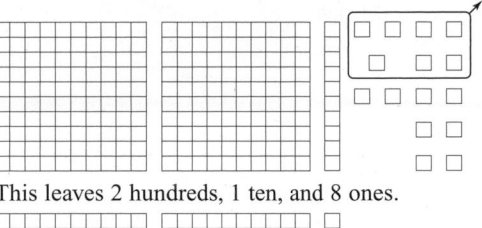

62. a. no, because 5 + 5 does not belong to {5}
   b. no, because 1 + 1 does not belong to {0, 1}
   c. yes
   d. no, because 3 + 5 = 8 and 8 is not an odd number
   e. yes

63. The set of whole numbers is {0, 1, 2, 3, 4, 5, . . .}. Because
5 − 3 = 2, 5 − 3 belongs to the set of whole numbers. But
3 − 5 = −2, and −2 does not belong to the set of whole
numbers. Thus, the set of whole numbers is not closed under
subtraction.

SECTION 2.4

1. a. Step 1. Build the minuend.

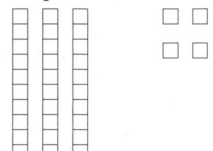

Step 2. Regroup 1 ten as 10 ones.

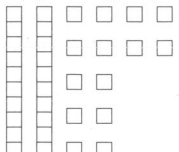

Step 3. Take away 8 ones.

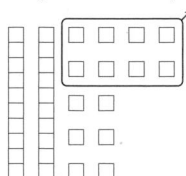

Then 34 − 8 = 26.
b. Step 1. Build the minuend.

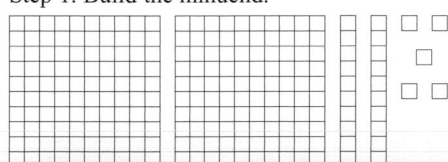

Step 2. We have 5 ones and we need to take away 7 ones.
There are not enough ones, so we regroup one of the tens
as 10 ones. Instead of having 2 tens and 5 ones, we now
have 1 ten and 15 ones.

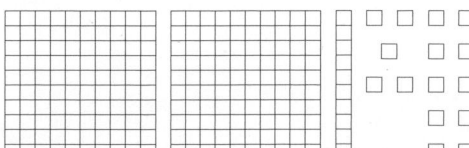

Step 3. Take away 7 ones.

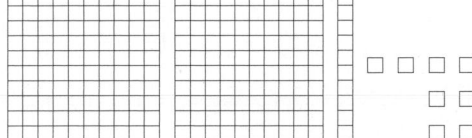

This leaves 2 hundreds, 1 ten, and 8 ones.

Step 4. We have 1 ten and we need to take away 4 tens.
There are not enough tens, so we need to regroup 1 hundred as 10 tens. Then 10 tens + 1 ten = 11 tens.

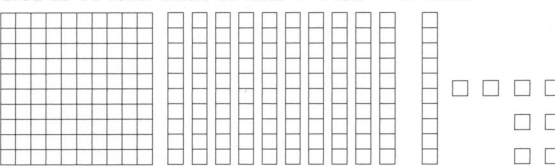

Step 5. Take away 4 tens.

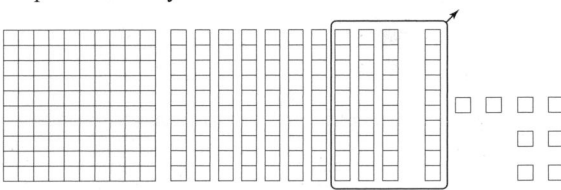

Step 6. This leaves 1 hundred, 7 tens, and 8 ones.

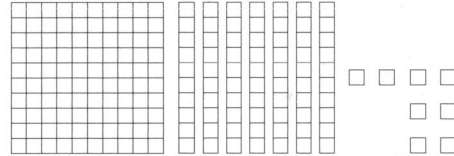

So 225 − 47 = 178.
c. Step 1. Build each addend.

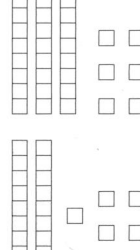

Step 2. There are 11 ones. We need to regroup the 11 ones as 1 ten and 1 one.

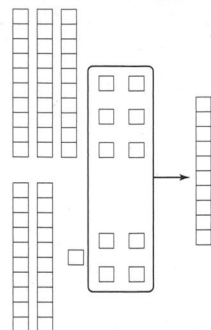

No more regrouping is possible, so 36 + 25 = 61.

d. Step 1. Build each addend.

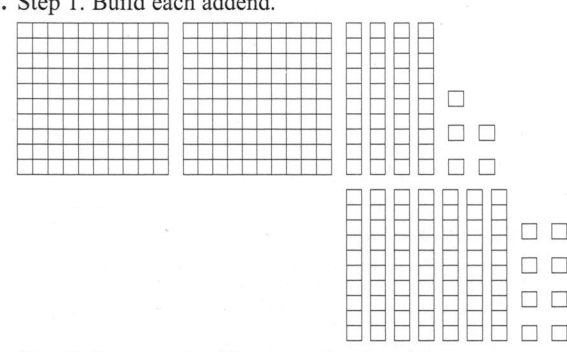

Step 2. Regroup the 13 ones as 1 ten and 3 ones.

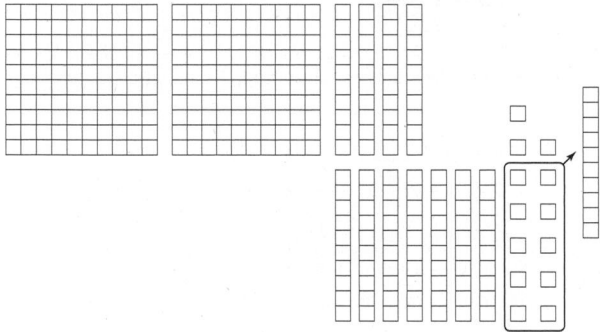

Step 3. Then there are 2 hundreds, 12 tens, and 3 ones. Regroup the 12 tens as 1 hundred and 2 tens.

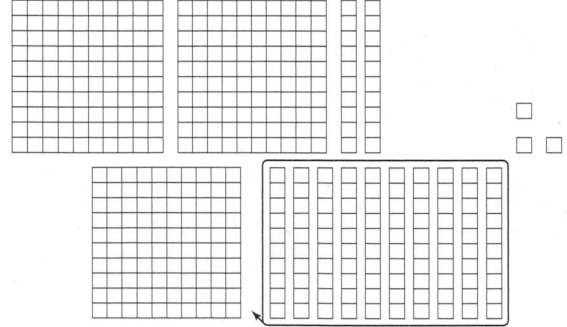

Step 4. That leaves 3 hundreds, 2 tens, and 3 ones. There is no more regrouping.

Then 245 + 78 = 323.

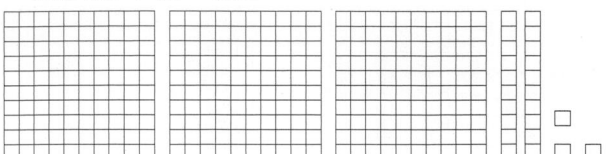

2. 7 ones + 8 ones = 15 ones = 1 ten, 5 ones. The 1 above the 3 represents the 1 ten from regrouping 15 ones as 1 ten and 5 ones.

3. We have 3 ones and we need to take away 9 ones. There are not enough ones, so we regroup one of the tens as 10 ones. Instead of having 6 tens, we now have 5 tens.

4. There are 4 ones, and we need to take away 8 ones. There are not enough ones, so we regroup 1 ten as 10 ones. Then 10 ones + 4 ones = 14 ones. The 14 above the 4 represents the 14 ones.

5. Answers vary. 537 + 56.

6. Answers vary. 897 + 645.

7. Answers vary. 197 + 265.

8. Answers vary. 269 + 345.

9. a. 532   b. 932   c. 992

10. a. 3 (for example, 45 + 888)
    b. 5 (for example, 456 + 99,999)   c. 160

11. a. $a = 8, b = 5$ b. 1

12. identity property of addition

13.
$$
\begin{array}{r}
\overset{1}{3}\,4,\,2\,1\,6 \\
+\quad\ \ 3\,7\,5 \\
\hline
3\,4,\,5\,9\,1
\end{array}
$$

14. a.
$$
\begin{array}{r}
64 \\
+\ 58 \\
\hline
12 \\
110 \\
\hline
122
\end{array}
$$

   b.
$$
\begin{array}{r}
6\qquad 4 \\
+\ 5\qquad 8 \\
\end{array}
$$

   c.
$$
\begin{array}{r}
\overset{1\ 1}{\ } \\
64 \\
+58 \\
\hline
122
\end{array}
$$

   d.
$$
\begin{array}{c|c|c}
 & 6 & 4 \\
+ & 5 & 8 \\
\hline
 & 11 & 12 \\
 & 12 & 2 \\
1 & 2 & 2
\end{array}
$$

15. a.
```
   345
 +938
   13
   70
 1200
   83
 1200
 1283
```

b.

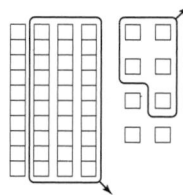

```
      3    4    5
  +   9    3    8
```
lattice with 1/2, 0/7, 1/3
```
  1    2    8    3
```

16. a. 8 hrs 7 min 1 sec   **b.** 1 day 13 hrs 48 min 20 sec

17. a. 7 hrs 28 min 11 sec   **b.** 6 hrs 47 min 53 sec

18. When n is rounded to the nearest 1000, it must equal 42,000 − 18,000 = 24,000.
   a. The smallest n could be is 23,500.
   b. The largest n could be 24,499.
   c. 1000, because the arithmetic sequence 23,500, 23,501, . . . , 24,499 has 1000 terms (24,499 − 23,500 + 1 = 1000)

19. Consider the subtraction problem 34 − 18 using the standard subtraction algorithm. Then 34 = 3 tens, 4 ones would be regrouped as 34 = 2 tens, 14 ones to have enough ones to take away 8 ones.

20. Consider the addition problem 174 + 282. It involves 7 tens + 8 tens = 15 tens, which is regrouped as 15 tens = 1 hundred, 5 tens.

21. The diagonals of the lattice represent place values.

22. In the first step, we add the values of digits in the same column. For example, in the problem 345 + 987, the partial sums are 5 + 7 = 12, 40 + 80 = 120, and 300 + 900 = 1200.

23. In the first step, we add the digits in the same column, which have the same place values. So we add the ones with the ones, the tens with the tens, the hundreds with the hundreds, and so on. Then we regroup.

24. a. Build each addend. Put the ones together and the tens together. Then regroup the 12 ones as 1 ten and 2 ones. Then there are 4 tens and 2 ones. Then 34 + 8 = 42.

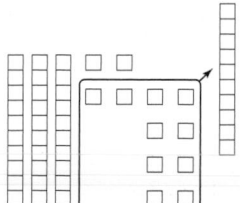

b. Build each addend. Put the ones together and the tens together. Regroup the 12 tens as 1 hundred and 2 ones. Then there are 1 hundred, 2 tens, and 6 ones. Then 74 + 52 = 126.

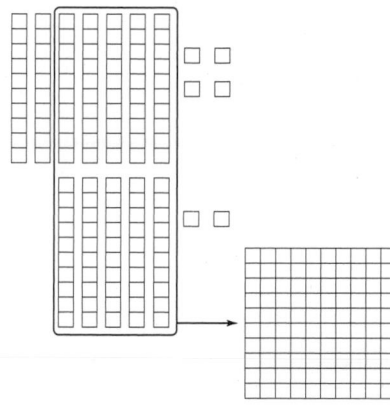

c. Build the minuend. Then take away 5 ones and 3 tens. There are 1 ten and 3 ones remaining. Then 48 − 35 = 13.

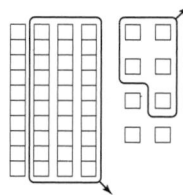

d. Step 1. Build the minuend.

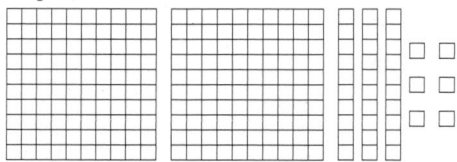

Step 2. There are 6 ones, and we need to take away 7 ones. There are not enough ones, so regroup 1 ten as 10 ones. Then there are enough ones to take away 7 ones.

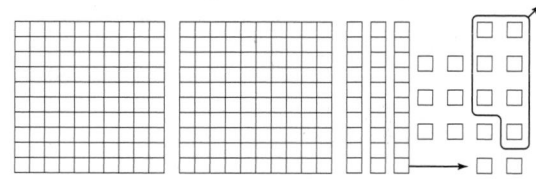

Step 3. There are now 2 hundreds, 2 tens, and 9 ones. We need to take away 5 tens. There are not enough tens to take away, so we regroup 1 hundred as 10 tens and then take away 5 tens.

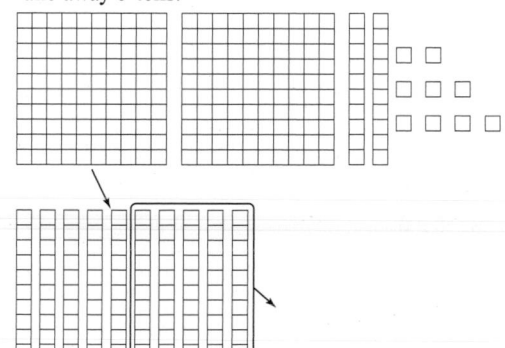

That leaves 1 hundred, 7 tens, and 9 ones. Then $236 - 57 = 179$.

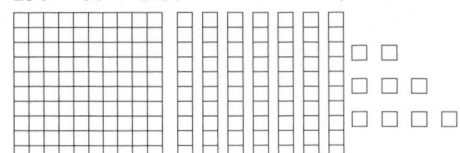

25. a. 834 **b.** 1085

26. a.

	5	7	8
+	8	3	7
	13	10	15
1	3	10	15
1	4	0	15
1	4	1	5

b.

	5	7	8
+	8	3	7
	13	10	15
	13	11	5
	14	1	5
1	4	1	5

27. a. 617 **b.** 917 **c.** 997

28. a. 738 **b.** 729 **c.** 699

29. 7 tens + 5 tens = 12 tens = 1 hundred, 2 tens. The 1 above the 2 represents the 1 hundred from regrouping 12 tens as 1 hundred and 2 tens.

30. a. 5 ones + 7 ones = 12 ones = 1 ten, 2 ones. The 1 above the 8 represents the 1 ten from regrouping 12 ones as 1 ten and 2 ones.

  b. 1 ten + 8 tens + 6 tens = 15 tens = 1 hundred, 5 tens. The 1 above the 4 represents the 1 hundred from regrouping 15 tens as 1 hundred and 5 tens.

31. a.

```
        5   7
    +   7   2
            9
    1   2   0
    1   2   9
```

  b.

```
    3   2   1
    +       3   6
                7
        5   0
    3   0   0
        5   7
    3   0   0
    3   5   7
```

32. a.

```
        3       4
    +   5       5
```

/	0 /	0 /
	8	9
	8	9

b.

```
        3   2   1
    +       7   6
```

/	0 /	0 /	0 /
	3	9	7
	3	9	7

c.

```
    2   3   6   7
    +   4   8   7
```

/	0 /	0 /	1 /	1 /
	2	7	4	4
	2	8	5	4

33. a.

	3	4
+	5	5
	8	9

  b.

	3	2	1
+		7	6
	3	9	7

  c.

	2	3	6	7
+		4	8	7
	2	7	14	14
	2	7	15	4
	2	8	5	4

34. $a = 6, b = 7, c = 8$

35. a.

```
      1   2
      2   5
      6₀  7₂
      3   9₁
    + 4   2
    1 7   3
```

  b.

```
    2   2
        8₀  5
    2   3   3
    5   4   6₄
  + 7₄  9₃
  9 4   3
```

36. Answers vary.
  a. $34 - 8 = 36 - 10 = 26$
  b. $567 - 24 = 563 - 20 = 543$
  c. $5003 - 635 = 5000 - 632$
  $\qquad\qquad = 4400 - 32$
  $\qquad\qquad = 4370 - 2$
  $\qquad\qquad = 4368$

37. Answers vary.
  a. $43 + 879 \approx 40 + 880 = 920$
  b. $124 + 68 \approx 130 + 70 = 200$
  c. $87 + 325 \approx 75 + 325 = 400$

38. First build 345, and then regroup to take away.

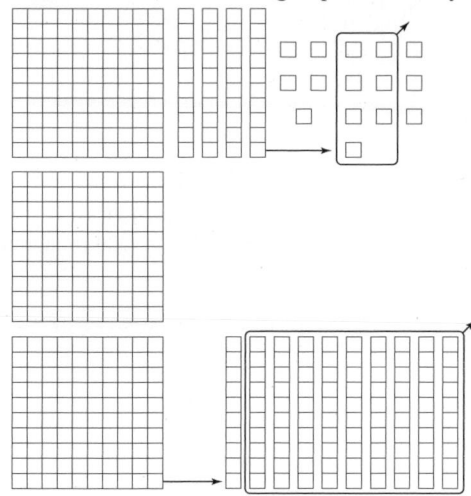

So 345 − 97 = 248.

39. a. $527 + 62 \approx 500 + 60 = 560$
  b. $745 - 97 \approx 700 - 90 = 610$
  c. $731 + 398 \approx 700 + 300 = 1000$

40. a.
$$
\begin{array}{r}
79 \\
-15 \\
\hline
4 \\
60 \\
\hline
64
\end{array}
$$

  b.
$$
\begin{array}{r}
757 \\
-83 \\
\hline
4 \\
-30 \\
700 \\
\hline
4 \\
670 \\
\hline
674
\end{array}
$$

41. a.
$$
\begin{array}{r}
\overset{3}{\cancel{4}}\ \overset{15}{\cancel{5}}\ 6 \\
-\ 2\ 7\ 3 \\
\hline
1\ 8\ 3
\end{array}
$$

  b.
$$
\begin{array}{r}
\overset{7}{\cancel{8}}\ \overset{\overset{12}{\cancel{13}}}{\cancel{3}}\ \overset{14}{\cancel{4}} \\
-\ 4\ 6 \\
\hline
7\ 8\ 8
\end{array}
$$

  c.
$$
\begin{array}{r}
\overset{7}{\cancel{8}}\ \overset{10}{\cancel{0}}\ 3 \\
-\ 5\ 1 \\
\hline
7\ 5\ 2
\end{array}
$$

42. a. $57 - 43 = 57 - 40 - 3 = 17 - 3 = 14$
  b. $65 - 28 = 65 - 20 - 8$
    $= 45 - 8$
    $= 45 - 5 - 3$
    $= 40 - 3 = 37$
  c. $131 - 63 = 1 + 130 - 60 - 3$
    $= 1 + 70 - 3$
    $= 1 + 67$
    $= 68.$

43. a. $57 + 43 = 50 + 7 + 43 = 50 + 50 = 100$
  b. $65 + 28 = 65 + 20 + 8 = 85 + 8 = 85 + 5 + 3$
    $= 90 + 3 = 93$
  c. $72 + 25 = 75 - 3 + 25 = 100 - 3 = 97$

44.
$$
\begin{array}{r}
367 \\
+487 \\
\hline
14 \\
140 \\
700 \\
\hline
154 \\
700 \\
\hline
854
\end{array}
$$

45. Answers vary.
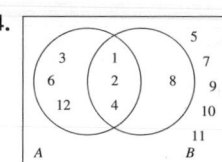

46. a. $345 + 687 \approx 300 + 700 = 1000$
  b. $345 + 687 \approx 350 + 690 = 1040$

47. a. $868 - 532 \approx 900 - 500 = 400$
  b. $868 - 532 \approx 870 - 530 = 340$

48. a. 600 and 699   **b.** 900 and 999

49. n must be equal to 4700 after you round n to the nearest hundred.
  a. 4650   **b.** 4749
  c. All numbers in the sequence 4650, 4651, 4652, . . . , 4749 equal 4700 when rounded to the nearest hundred. There are $4749 - 4650 + 1 = 100$ numbers in this sequence. So there are 100 possible values for n.

50. a. 1222_{five} **b.** 1122_{five} **c.** 1352_{twelve} **d.** $79B_{\text{twelve}}$

51. a. 214_{five} **b.** 111_{five} **c.** 363_{twelve} **d.** 575_{twelve}

REVIEW QUESTIONS

1. Answers vary.
  a. $A = \{1, 2, 3\}, 1 \in A$
  b. $A = \{1, 2\}, B = \{1, 2, 3\}, A \subseteq B$
  c. $U = \{1, 2, 3, 4\}, A = \{1, 2, 3\}, {\sim}A = \{4\}$
  d. $A = \{1, 2, 3\}, B = \{1, 4\}, A \cap B = \{1\}$
  e. $X = \{1, 2, 3\}, Y = \{2, 4\}, X \cup Y = \{1, 2, 3, 4\}$

2. a. true   **b.** false   **c.** false   **d.** true   **e.** true   **f.** true

3. a. $n(A) = 4$
  b. $n(A) = 37$
  c. 3
  d. 3
  e. 1

4.

```
 ┌─────────────────────────┐
 │        ⎛   ⎞    5        │
 │     3  ⎜ 1 ⎟      7      │
 │     6  ⎜ 2 ⎟  8    9     │
 │    12  ⎝ 4 ⎠      10     │
 │                 11       │
 │  A              B        │
 └─────────────────────────┘
```

5. a. $\{a, d, f, h\}$ **b.** $\{b, d, e, h, k\}$ **c.** $\{a, b, d, e, f, h, k\}$
  d. $\{d, h\}$ **e.** $\{a, f\}$ **f.** $\{b, e, k\}$ **g.** $\{c, g, m, b, e, k\}$
  h. $\{a, c, f, g, m\}$ **i.** $\{a, b, c, d, e, f, g, h, k, m\}$

6. a. 8   b. 10   c. 15   d. 3   e. 5   f. 7   g. 10
   h. 8   i. 18

7. a. {1}   b. {0, 2, 3, 5, 6, 7, 11}   c. ∅

8. $n(A \cup B) \stackrel{?}{=} n(A) + n(B) - n(A \cap B)$
   $16 \stackrel{?}{=} 10+9-3$
   $16 \stackrel{?}{=} 19-3$
   $16 = 16$

9. a. 19 (if X and Y are disjoint)   b. 13 (if $X \subseteq Y$)

10. a. 5 (if $X \subseteq Y$)   b. 0 (if X and Y are disjoint)

11. a. 24   b. 4   c. 6   d. 24   e. 8   f. 8

12.
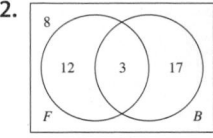
   a. 12   b. 32   c. 8   d. 17   e. 29

13. symbols, numerals

14. a. number   b. numeral   c. digits   d. digit
    e. place value   f. position   g. 200   h. 100 (hundreds)

15. a. 368   b. 36   c. 74

16. a.
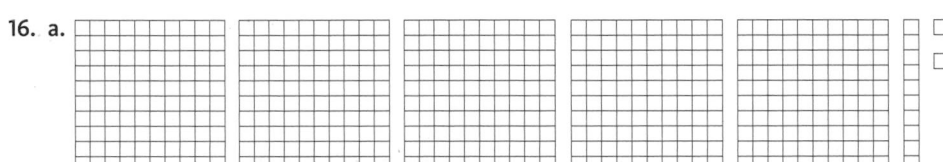

   b.
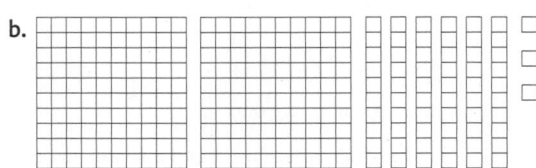

17. a. 2213_{four} b. 2202_{three}

18. a. 31, 6   b. 72, 0, 5   c. 4, 811   d. 5, 6, 2

19. a. 12   b. 354

20. a. hundreds   b. 4000   c. 3

21. $20 \times 144,000 = 2,880,000$

22. a. 71 thousand, 492
    b. seventy-one thousand, four hundred ninety-two
    c. $70,000 + 1,000 + 400 + 90 + 2$
    d. $7 \times 10,000 + 1 \times 1,000 + 4 \times 100 + 9 \times 10 + 2 \times 1$
    e. $7 \times 10^4 + 1 \times 10^3 + 4 \times 10^2 + 9 \times 10^1 + 2 \times 10^0$

23. a. 482,152,219   b. 79,506,304   c. 302,000,057,082

24. a. 2116   b. 217,156   c. 21,771,556
    d. 217,777,155,556

25. a. 1150   b. 1249

26. 4000

   3000 ———————— 3870 4000

27. 1400

   1400 ——— 1435 ——— 1500

28. Examples vary: ones place (1800 → 1800), tens place
    (1803 → 1800), hundreds place (1842 → 1800)

29. a. 47,962   b. 2897   c. 116,292   d. 20   e. 360

30. a.   b.   c.

31. a.   b.

32. a. ▼▼▼ ◄◄◄▼▼
       ▼▼▼   ◄
        ▼

    b. ◄▼▼ ∥ ▼▼▼ ◄◄◄▼
            ▼

    c. ◄◄▼ ▼▼▼ ∥ ◄◄◄▼▼▼
          ▼▼▼   ◄◄
           ▼▼

33. a. $8 \times 60^1 + 34 \times 60^0 = 514$
    b. $32 \times 60^2 + 0 \times 60^1 + 35 \times 60^0 = 115,235$
    c. $3 \times 60^3 + 0 \times 60^2 + 1 \times 60^1 + 21 \times 60^0 = 648,081$

34. a. ▼ ◄◄◄▼▼▼ ◄◄◄▼▼▼
           ▼   ▼▼▼
                      ▼▼

    b. ▼▼▼ ▼▼ ▼

35. a. 10423_{five} b. 214432_{five} c. 3406_{seven} d. 5181_{twelve}

36. a. 382   b. 967   c. 17,558   d. 10,318   e. 241

37. a. associative property of addition
    b. commutative property of addition
    c. identity property of addition
    d. commutative property of addition

38. a. $8 + 6 = (2 + 6) + 6 = 2 + (6 + 6) = 2 + 12 = 14$
    b. $9 + 5 = (4 + 5) + 5 = 4 + (5 + 5) = 4 + 10 = 14$

39. The student could make ten,
    $8 + 7 = 8 + (2 + 5) = (8 + 2) + 5 = 10 + 5 = 15,$
    or use doubles,
    $8 + 7 = (1 + 7) + 7 = 1 + (7 + 7) = 1 + 14 = 15.$

40. 28 and 8

41. $11 - 4 = 7$

42. a.

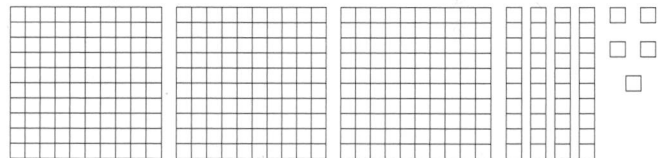

$12 - 4 = 8$

b.

$7 - 5 = 2$

43. a. $y + 3 = 22$

$y = 22 - 3$

$y = 19$

b. $y + 3 = 22$

$y + 3 - 3 = 22 - 3$

$y = 22 - 3$

$y = 19$

c. $y + 3 = 22 \qquad 3 + y = 22$

$y = 22 - 3 \qquad 3 = 22 - y$

The equation $y = 22 - 3$ leads to $y = 19$.

44. a. $n - 15 = 18$

$n = 18 + 15$

$n = 33$

b. $n - 15 = 18$

$n - 15 + 15 = 18 + 15$

$n = 18 + 15$

$n = 33$

c. $n - 15 = 18 \qquad n = 18 + 15$

$n - 18 = 15 \qquad n = 15 + 18$

The equation $n = 15 + 18$ leads to $n = 33$.

45. a. comparison model **b.** missing addend model
c. take-away model

46. Answers vary.

a. Marco gave 8 pieces of candy to his brother. Then Marco had 15 pieces of candy. How many pieces of candy did he originally have?

b. Manuel put four apples in a bucket. Then there were nine apples in the bucket. How many apples were in the bucket?

c. Marc had 12 paper clips. He used some for his paperwork. Then he had 5 paper clips remaining. How many paper clips did he use?

47. Bob has five more trading cards than John.
John has five fewer trading cards than Bob.

48. a. 52 oz **b.** 40 in **c.** 16 ft

49. a. $14 - h \leq 8$ **b.** $a + 5 = 3 + 7 = 10$
c. $k - 5$ **d.** $x \leq 14$ **e.** $12 \leq y$

50. a. 3 ones + 7 ones = 10 ones = 1 ten, 0 ones. The one above the 6 represents the 1 ten from regrouping the ones.
b. 4 hundreds + 9 hundreds = 13 hundreds = 1 thousand, 3 hundreds. The 1 above the + sign represents the 1 thousand from regrouping the hundreds.

51. a.
```
  857
 +67
 ----
   14
  110
  800
 ----
  924
```

b.
```
  678
 +365
 ----
   13
  130
  900
 ----
 1043
```

52. a.

| 3 | 6 | 4 |
| + | 7 | 5 |

0/3 1/3 0/9

| 4 | 3 | 9 |

b.

3	6	4
+	7	5
3	13	9
4	3	9

53. Answers vary; 492 and 83.

54. a. The addends vary.

	3	9	9
+	0	6	3
	3	15	12
	3	16	2
	4	6	2

b. The addends vary.

		9	5	7
+		7	8	5
		16	13	12
		16	14	2
		17	4	2
	1	7	4	2

55. a. Step 1. Build the minuend 345.

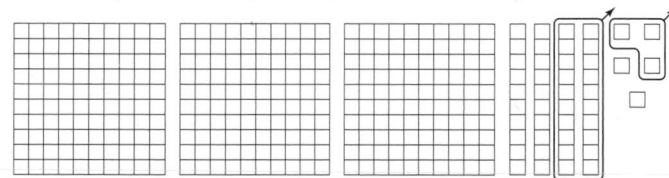

Step 2. Take away 3 ones, and then take away 2 tens.

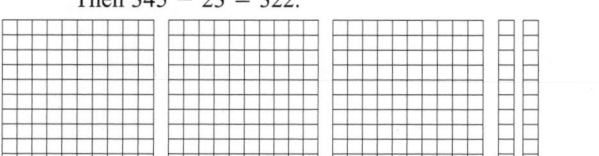

That leaves 3 hundreds, 2 tens, and 2 ones remaining.
Then $345 - 23 = 322$.

b. Step 1. Build the minuend 43.

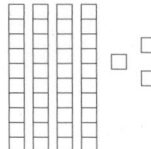

Step 2. There are 3 ones. We need to take away 8 ones. There are not enough ones, so regroup 1 ten as 10 ones.

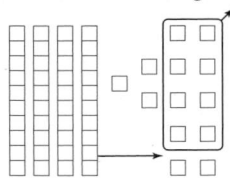

Step 3. This leaves 3 tens and 5 ones. Now we need to take away 1 ten.

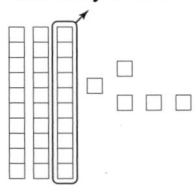

This leaves 2 tens and 5 ones. Then $43 - 18 = 25$.

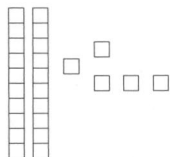

56. Answers vary.
   a. minuend = 732, subtrahend = 479.
   b. minuend = 785, subtrahend = 323.

57. a.

$$\begin{array}{r} 5 \ \overset{6}{\cancel{7}} \ \overset{13}{\cancel{3}} \\ - \quad 4 \ 8 \\ \hline 5 \ 2 \ 5 \end{array}$$

b.

$$\begin{array}{r} \ \ \overset{13}{} \\ 2 \ \overset{14}{\cancel{4}} \ \overset{15}{\cancel{5}} \ 6 \\ \cancel{3} \ \ \\ - \quad 7 \ 8 \ 2 \\ \hline 2 \ 6 \ 7 \ 4 \end{array}$$

58. a.

$$\begin{array}{r} 456 \\ -364 \\ \hline 2 \\ - \ 10 \\ \hline 100 \\ -8 \\ \hline 100 \\ \hline 92 \end{array}$$

b.

$$\begin{array}{r} 734 \\ -579 \\ \hline -5 \\ -40 \\ \hline 200 \\ \hline -5 \\ 160 \\ \hline 155 \end{array}$$

59. a. $573 - 85 \approx 580 - 80 = 500$
   b. $76,421 + 3872 \approx 76,000 + 4000 = 80,000$

60. a. $16,378 + 4632 \approx 16,000 + 5000 = 21,000$
   b. $63,234 + 14,732 \approx 63,000 + 15,000 = 78,000$

61. a. 432_{five} **b.** 311_{five} **c.** $\text{AA2}_{\text{twelve}}$ **d.** $99\text{B}_{\text{twelve}}$

62. a. 131_{five} **b.** 230_{five} **c.** $50\text{A}_{\text{twelve}}$ **d.** 349_{twelve}

CHAPTER 2 TEST

1. a. true **b.** false **c.** true **d.** true
   e. true **f.** false **g.** false

2. a. There is a one-to-one correspondence between $\{4, \{0, 1\}\}$ and $\{1, 2\}$: $4 \leftrightarrow 1, \{0, 1\} \leftrightarrow 2$.
   b. There is a one-to-one correspondence between $\{\{5, 2\}, \{1\}, \varnothing\}$ and $\{1, 2, 3\}$: $\{5, 2\} \leftrightarrow 1, \{1\} \leftrightarrow 2, \varnothing \leftrightarrow 3$.
   c. The set is finite. $\{4, 2\} \leftrightarrow 1, \{2, 1\} \leftrightarrow 2,$ $\{2, 4, 6, 8, \ldots\} \leftrightarrow 3$. So the cardinality of $\{\{4, 2\}, \{2, 1\}, \{2, 4, 6, 8, \ldots\}\}$ is 3.

3. a. $\{1, 2, 3, 5, 6, 7, 8\}$ **b.** $\{5, 6, 7, 8\}$ **c.** $\{1, 2\}$
   d. $\{3\}$ **e.** $\{1, 2, 4, 9, 10\}$ **f.** $\{4, 9, 10\}$

4. a. $\{1, 2, 3, 4, 5, 6\}$ **b.** $\{2, 3, 4\}$ **c.** $\{5\}$
   d. $\{1, 6\}$ **e.** $\{0, 1, 6, 7, 8\}$

5. a. 33 **b.** 4 **c.** 11 **d.** 3 **e.** 11 **f.** 2

6.

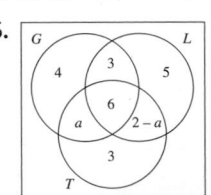

a. 3 **b.** 12 **c.** 6, 7, or 8

7. digits, numeral, number

8. a. hundreds **b.** 2000 **c.** 4 million, 52 thousand, 348
   d. four million, fifty-two thousand, three hundred forty-eight

9. $96^2 = 9216$
   $996^2 = 992,016$
   $9996^2 = 99,920,016$
   Then by inductive reasoning, $999,996^2 = 999,992,000,016$

10. a. $300,000 + 40,000 + 5000 + 600 + 70 + 8$
   b. $3 \cdot 100,000 + 4 \cdot 10,000 + 5 \cdot 1000 + 6 \cdot 100 + 7 \cdot 10 + 8 \cdot 1$
   c. $3 \cdot 10^5 + 4 \cdot 10^4 + 5 \cdot 10^3 + 6 \cdot 10^2 + 7 \cdot 10^1 + 8 \cdot 10^0$

11. a. 60

$$\begin{array}{c} \vdash\!\!-\!\!-\!\!-\!\!-\!\!-\!\!\!-\!\!\bullet\!\!-\!\!-\!\!-\!\!-\!\!\!\dashv\!\!-\!\!-\!\!-\!\!\rightarrow \\ {\scriptstyle 50 \qquad\qquad\quad 57 \qquad 60} \end{array}$$

   b. 400

$$\begin{array}{c} \vdash\!\!-\!\!-\!\!-\!\!-\!\!-\!\!\!-\!\!\bullet\!\!-\!\!-\!\!-\!\!-\!\!\!\dashv\!\!-\!\!-\!\!-\!\!\rightarrow \\ {\scriptstyle 300 \qquad\qquad 372 \qquad 400} \end{array}$$

   c. 4000

$$\begin{array}{c} \vdash\!\!\bullet\!\!-\!\!-\!\!-\!\!-\!\!\!\dashv\!\!-\!\!-\!\!-\!\!-\!\!-\!\!\!\dashv\!\!-\!\!-\!\!-\!\!\rightarrow \\ {\scriptstyle 4000 \quad 4278 \qquad\qquad 5000} \end{array}$$

12. ones place ($42,000 \rightarrow 42,000$)
   tens place ($42,003 \rightarrow 42,000$)
   hundreds place ($42,037 \rightarrow 42,000$)
   thousands place ($41,800 \rightarrow 42,000$)

13. a. Answers vary; 11,250. **b.** 10,500 **c.** 11,499

14. a. **b.** **c.**

   3124   100,902

   1,729,457

15. a.    **b.** ▼▼▼ ◄◄▼▼▼ ◄◄◄▼▼ ▼
                                           ▼▼▼
                                           ▼▼▼

   c. 115,221   **d.** 11133_{five} **e.** $2A4B_{\text{twelve}}$

16. a. $8 + 6 = 8 + 2 + 4 = 10 + 4 = 14$
   b. $7 + 9 = 7 + 7 + 2 = 14 + 2 = 16$
   c. $27 + 5 = 27 + 3 + 2 = 30 + 2 = 32$
   d. $12 + 37 + 8 = 20 + 37 = 57$

17. a. comparison model   **b.** take-away model

18. a. subtraction property of equality
   b. addition and subtraction are inverse operations
   c. addition property of equality
   d. addition and subtraction are inverse operations

19. a. $n + 3 = 8, 3 + n = 8, 8 - n = 3, 8 - 3 = n$. The equation $8 - 3 = n$ leads to the solution $n = 5$.
   b. $k - 26 = 84$
   $k = 26 + 84$
   $k = 110$
   c. $b + 18 = 45$
   $b = 45 - 18$
   $b = 27$

20. a. $m + 45 = 131$
   $m + 45 - 45 = 131 - 45$
   $m = 131 - 45$
   $m = 86$
   b. $h - 23 = 68$
   $h - 23 + 23 = 68 + 23$
   $h = 68 + 23$
   $h = 91$

21. The student would check his work by addition to see whether the sum is 65: $38 + 33 = 71$. So his answer of 33 is incorrect.

22. a.
$$
\begin{array}{r}
4\ \ 5\ \ 6 \\
+\ \ 3\ \ 2\ \ 8 \\
\hline
0\diagup 0\diagup 1 \\
7\diagup 7\diagup 4 \\
\hline
7\ \ 8\ \ 4
\end{array}
$$

   b.
$$
\begin{array}{r}
\ \ 4\ |\ 5\ |\ 6 \\
+\ \ 3\ |\ 2\ |\ 8 \\
\hline
7\ |\ 7\ |\ 14 \\
\hline
7\ |\ 8\ |\ 4
\end{array}
$$

23. a. 6 ones + 8 ones = 14 ones = 1 ten, 4 ones. The 1 above the 5 represents the 1 ten from regrouping the ones.
   b. 1 hundred + 4 hundreds + 7 hundreds = 12 hundreds = 1 thousand, 2 hundreds. The 1 above the + sign represents the 1 thousand from regrouping 12 hundreds as 1 thousand, 2 hundreds.

24. a. We have 6 ones, and we need to take away 7 ones. There are not enough ones, so we regrouped 1 ten as 10 ones. This leaves 7 tens instead of 8 tens.
   b. We regrouped one of the tens as 10 ones. Then 10 ones + 6 ones gives us 16 ones. So the 16 represents the 16 ones.

25. a. $567 + 215 \approx 570 + 220 = 790$ (rounded to the nearest 10)
   b. $52,820 + 7285 \approx 53,000 + 7000 = 60,000$ (rounded to the nearest thousand)

c. $73 - 37 \approx 70 - 40 = 30$ (rounded to the nearest ten)
   d. $12,350 - 4788 \approx 12,000 - 5000 = 7000$ (rounded to the nearest thousand)

26. a. 1140_{five} **b.** 114_{five} **c.** $69B_{\text{twelve}}$ **d.** 357_{twelve}

CHAPTER 3

SECTION 3.1

1. 2×4

2. a. ••• ••• ••• ••• •••

   b. ••••• ••••• •••••

3. a.
$$5 \times 3 = 15$$
   b.
$$3 \times 5 = 15$$

4. a. Maria is correct by viewing each column as a group, which leads to five groups of three dots.

   b. Lenny is correct by viewing each row as a group, which leads to three groups of five dots.

5. 4 = number of groups, 15 = number of objects in each group

6. a. The tree diagram shows four groups of three combinations. The student can order 12 possible lunches.

   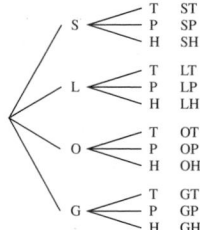

   b. The table shows a three-by-four array of possibilities. Because $3 \times 4 = 12$, the student can order 12 possible lunches.

	S	**L**	**O**	**G**
T	TS	TL	TO	TG
P	PS	PL	PO	PG
H	HS	HL	HO	HG

7.   Luis
   Martin
   Kyle

   two times as many
   three times as many

   Thus, Kyle has six times as many coins as Luis.

8. 45 accountants, 50 supervisors, and 150 mechanics

9. Use a pattern to solve this problem:
$456 \times 10^0 = 456$ 3 digits $(0 + 3 = 3)$
$456 \times 10^1 = 4560$ 4 digits $(1 + 3 = 4)$
456×10^{78} has $78 + 3 = 81$ digits.

10. two shirts and six hats

11. $5 \times 5 \times 5 = 125$

12. **a.** 19 **b.** 25 **c.** 31 **d.** 49

13. **a.** measurement model: $4 \times 12,000 = 48,000$
b. set model: $4 \times 8 = 32$
c. Cartesian product model: $7 \times 4 = 28$
d. comparison model: $5 \times 7 = 35$
e. array model: $2 \times 200 = 400$

14. **a.** $a(b + c + d) = a(b + c) + ad$
$$= ab + ac + ad$$
b. $(a + b)(c + d) = (a + b)c + (a + b)d$
$$= ac + bc + ad + bd$$
$$= ac + ad + bc + bd$$
The formula $(a + b)(c + d) = ac + ad + bc + bd$ is also called the FOIL method: first $= ac$, outer $= ad$, inner $= bc$, last $= bd$.

15. $12 \times 6 = (3 \times 4) \times 6 = 3 \times (4 \times 6) = 3 \times 24 = 72$

16. 5 and $3 + 4$

17. **a.** $b = 0$ **b.** $a = 0$ or $b = 0$

18. **a.** Suppose a, b, and c are whole numbers with $b \geq c$. Then $a(b - c) = ab - ac$.
b. $5a = 5b$
$5a - 5b = 0$
$5(a - b) = 0$
5 is not zero, so $a - b = 0$. Then $a = b$.
c. $na = nb$
$na - nb = 0$
$n(a - b) = 0$
n is a counting number, so $a - b = 0$. Then $a = b$.

19. Subtraction is not commutative, so we use two different words (minuend and subtrahend) to describe the numbers.

20. Use patterns in the exponents and right-hand side.
$2^3 = 8$ ⎫ Observe the multiple sequences:
$2^2 = 4$ ⎬ $2^3, 2^2, 2^1, 2^0$
$2^1 = 2$ ⎭ $8, 4, 2,$ ___
$2^0 = 1$

21. **a.** 3, 6, 9, 12, 15, so $5 \times 3 = 15$.
b. 5, 10, 15, 20, 25, 30, so $6 \times 5 = 30$.
c. 12, 24, 36, so $3 \times 12 = 36$.

22. Use patterns in the exponents and right-hand side.
$5^3 = 125$ ⎫ Observe the multiple sequences:
$5^2 = 25$ ⎬ $5^3, 5^2, 5^1, 5^0$
$5^1 = 5$ ⎭ $125, 25, 5,$ ___
$5^0 = 1$

23. **a.** $700 = 7 \times 100$ **b.** $80 = 8 \times 10$
c. $700 \times 80 = (7 \times 100) \times (8 \times 10) =$
$(7 \times 8)(100 \times 10) = 56 \times 1000 = 56,000$

24. $10^9 = 1,000,000,000 = 1$ billion

25. $26^5 = 11,881,376$

26. Disagree, because 3×4 represents $4 + 4 + 4$, not $3 + 3 + 3 + 3$.

27. There are five boxes, and each box contains eight oranges. Write an expression involving multiplication that tells how many oranges there are altogether.

28. Answers vary. For example, 101×42 is an amazing product because $101 \times 42 = 4242$, which is the juxtaposition of 42 and 42.

29. **a.** multiplicative reasoning **b.** repeated addition
c. repeated multiplication **d.** 4 **e.** factors
f. skip counting **g.** array **h.** number sense
i. distributive **j.** associative **k.** commutative

30. **a.**

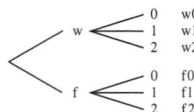

$2 \times 3 = 6$

b.

	0	**1**	**2**
w	w0	w1	w2
f	f0	f1	f2

$2 \times 3 = 6$

31. **a.** measurement model **b.** set model **c.** array model
d. comparison model **e.** Cartesian product model

32. Answers vary, but the solutions should look like the word problems in Question 31.

33. **a.** 12 miles **b.** 110 pounds per month

34. **a.** $7(4 + 8a) = 7 \cdot 4 + 7 \cdot (8a) = 28 + (7 \cdot 8)a = 28 + 56a$
b. $2n \cdot 7n = [(2n) \cdot 7]n$
$$= [7 \cdot (2n)]n$$
$$= [(7 \cdot 2)n]n$$
$$= [14n]n$$
$$= 14(n \cdot n)$$
$$= 14n^2$$

35. **a.** commutative property of multiplication
b. zero property of multiplication
c. commutative property of multiplication
d. commutative property of multiplication
e. zero property of multiplication
f. identity property of multiplication
g. distributive property of multiplication over addition

36. $10 \times (11 \times 9) = (10 \times 11) \times 9$ Associative property of multiplication
$= (11 \times 10) \times 9$ Commutative property of multiplication
$= 11 \times (10 \times 9)$ Associative property of multiplication
$= 11 \times (9 \times 10)$ Commutative property of multiplication

37. **a.** 7 **b.** 5 **c.** 1 **d.** 9 **e.** 3

38. $6 \times 10 = 6 \times (2 \times 5) = (6 \times 2) \times 5 = 12 \times 5$. There were 12 basketball teams (with 5 students on each team).

39. a. $3000 \times \$35 = \$105,000$
  b. $3000 \times 35 = (1000 \times 3) \times 35 = 1000 \times (3 \times 35) = 1000 \times 105 = 105,000$

40. a. $4 \times 3 + 5 \times 3 = (4 + 5) \times 3$
  b. $3 + w \times 3 = 1 \times 3 + w \times 3 = (1 + w) \times 3$
  c. $3 \times a - 3 \times b = 3 \times (a - b)$
  d. $(x + y) + (x + y) + (x + y) = 3 \times (x + y)$

41. a. $5 \times 13 = 5 \times (10 + 3) = 5 \times 10 + 5 \times 3 = 50 + 15 = 65$
  b. $23 \times 12 = 23 \times (10 + 2) = 23 \times 10 + 23 \times 2 = 230 + 46 = 276$
  c. $67 \times 9 = 67 \times (10 - 1) = 67 \times 10 - 67 \times 1 = 670 - 67 = 603$

42. a. $4 \times 125 = 4 \times (25 \times 5) = (4 \times 25) \times 5 = 100 \times 5 = 500$
  b. $15 \times 20 = (3 \times 5) \times 20 = 3 \times (5 \times 20) = 3 \times 100 = 300$
  c. $30 \times 90 = 30 \times (9 \times 10) = (30 \times 9) \times 10 = 270 \times 10 = 2700$
  d. $5 \times 140 = 5 \times (2 \times 70) = (5 \times 2) \times 70 = 10 \times 70 = 700$

43. a. 44   **b.** 39

44. a. $6 \times (5 + 4) + 3 = 57$ **b.** $(6 + 1) \times 5 + 3 = 38$

45. Answers vary.
  a. Mary saved her weekly allowance to buy a sewing kit for $32. She saved the same amount for 4 weeks. What is her weekly allowance? Write an equation that represents the situation.
  b. Mary plans to save her weekly allowance of $4 to buy a sewing kit for $32. How many weeks does she need to save her allowance?

46. a. 5^3 has the base 5 and the exponent 3. $5^3 = 5 \times 5 \times 5$.
  b. 23^4 has the base 23 and the exponent 4. $23^4 = 23 \times 23 \times 23 \times 23$.
  c. 2^3 has the base 2 and the exponent 3. $2^3 = 2 \times 2 \times 2$.
  d. 3^2 has the base 3 and the exponent 2. $3^2 = 3 \times 3$.

47. a. $5^4 \times 5^2 = 625 \times 25 = 15,625$ and $5^6 = 15,625$. So $5^4 \times 5^2 = 5^6$.
  b. $3^3 \times 3^2 = 27 \times 9 = 243$, and $3^5 = 243$. So $3^3 \times 3^2 = 3^5$.
  c. The examples support the conjecture $a^m \times a^n = a^{m+n}$.

48. 15 times as many beads

49. $(3^2)^3 = 9^3 = 729$, and $3^{2 \times 3} = 3^6 = 729$. $(5^4)^2 = 625^2 = 390,625$, and $5^{4 \times 2} = 5^8 = 390,625$. $(2^3)^4 = 8^4 = 4096$, and $2^{3 \times 4} = 2^{12} = 4096$. These examples support the conjecture $(a^m)^n = a^{m \times n}$.

50. The variable rate plan is cheaper provided $2n + 4 < 45$. If you plan to use fewer than 20 minutes each month, then the variable rate plan is the better deal. However, if you plan to use more than 20 minutes each month, then the fixed rate plan is the better deal.

51. The total price is $3h + 2s$ dollars, where h is the number of hot dogs sold and s is the number of sodas sold.

52. a. $8^{12} = (2^3)^{12} = 2^{3 \times 12} = 2^{36}$
  b. $20^8 = (4 \times 5)^8 = 4^8 \times 5^8 = (2^2)^8 \times 5^8 = 2^{2 \times 8} \times 5^8 = 2^{16} \times 5^8$

53. Answers vary.
  a. $15 \times 20 = 15 \times (2 \times 10) = (15 \times 2) \times 10$
        $= 30 \times 10$
        $= 300$
  b. $5 \times 18 \times 2 = 5 \times (18 \times 2)$
        $= 5 \times (2 \times 18)$
        $= (5 \times 2) \times 18 = 10 \times 18 = 180$
  c. $14 \times 6 = (10 + 4)6 = 10 \cdot 6 + 4 \cdot 6$
        $= 60 + 24$
        $= 84$

54. a. $3h + 5h = (3 + 5)h = 8h$
  b. $7d - 3d = (7 - 3)d = 4d$

55. $18 \times 35 = (20 - 2) \times 35 = 20 \times 35 - 2 \times 35 = 700 - 70 = 630$

56. $600 \times 40 = 6 \times 100 \times 4 \times 10 = 24 \times 1000 = 24,000$

57. $3000 \times 70 = 3 \times 1000 \times 7 \times 10 = 21 \times 10,000 = 210,000$

58. $4 \times 5 \times 5 = 100$

59. a. $5a + 3a = 8a$, and $3a$ is a counting number. By the definition of *less than*, $5a < 8a$.
  b. $a < b$, so there is a counting number c such that $a + c = b$. Then $5(a + c) = 5b$. Then $5a + 5c = 5b$. $5c$ is a counting number, so by the definition of *less than*, $5a < 5b$.

60. The patterns are easily described by an equation:
  a. $aa \times 1001 = aa0aa$ **b.** $abc \times 1001 = abcabc$
  c. $a0a \times 1001 = a0aa0a$

61. a. 5 and 6 belong to $\{5, 6, 7\}$, but 5×6 does not belong to $\{5, 6, 7\}$.
  b. 2 belongs to $\{0, 2\}$, but 2×2 does not belong to $\{0, 2\}$.

62. a. $2 \cdot 8 = 16$, $4 \cdot 6 = 24$, and $6 \cdot 10 = 60$.
     16, 24, and 60 are even numbers.
     These examples support the conjecture that the set of even numbers is closed under multiplication.
  b. $3 \cdot 5 = 15$, $7 \cdot 3 = 21$, and $1 \cdot 5 = 5$.
     15, 21, and 5 are odd numbers.
     These examples support the conjecture that the set of odd numbers is closed under multiplication.
  c. $3 \cdot 6 = 18$, $6 \cdot 9 = 54$, $9 \cdot 15 = 135$.
     18, 54, and 135 are multiples of 3.
     These examples support the conjecture that the set of multiples of 3 is closed under multiplication.

63. 45×67 is a whole number by the closure property of multiplication, and $45 \times 67 + 7531$ is a whole number by the closure property of addition.

SECTION 3.2

1. a. $18 \div 6 = 3$ **b.** $20 \div 4 = 5$

2. a. $18 \div 3 = 6$ **b.** $16 \div 2 = 8$ **c.** $0 \div 3 = 0$

3. a. ⊙⊙ ⊙⊙ ⊙⊙ ⊙⊙ ⊙   **b.** ⊙⊙⊙ ⊙⊙⊙ ⊙⊙⊙ ⊙

4.

M ☐

C ☐☐☐ | 60

$60 \div 4 = 15$
$3 \times 15 = 45$
Matthew has 15 coins. Courtney has 45 coins.

5.

$77 - 5 = 72$
$72 \div 4 = 18$
$3 \times 18 + 5 = 59$
Matthew has 18 coins. Courtney has 59 coins.

6.

$116 + 4 = 120$
$120 \div 3 = 40$
$2 \times 40 - 4 = 76$
$76 - 40 = 36$
Courtney has 36 more coins than Matthew.

7. a.

$20 \div 4 = 5$
Marco has five coins.
 b. Let M equal the number of coins Marco has. Then Tyson has $4M$ coins.
$4M = 20$
$M = 5$
Marco has five coins.

8. a. 2   **b.** 14
 c. The formula for the nth term is $2 + 12(n - 1)$. The 58th term is $2 + 12(58 - 1) = 686$.

9. a. $122 - 8 = 114$. The average blue whale weighs 114 more tons than a Hummer.
 b. $122 \div 8 = 15$ R2. The average blue whale weighs 2 more tons than 15 times as much as a Hummer.

10. a. $50 \div 6 = 8$ R2   **b.** $b \div 4 = (3y + 1)$ R1

11. a. $k \div 8 = 72$
$k \div 8 \times 8 = 72 \times 8$
$k = 72 \times 8$
$k = 576$
 b. $15 \times n = 105$
$15 \times n \div 15 = 105 \div 15$
$n = 105 \div 15$
$n = 7$

12. a. $(y + 1) \div 3 = q + 1$ **b.** $(y + 2) \div 3 = (q + 1)$ R1
 c. $(2y - 3) \div 3 = 2q$ R1

13. a. $5 \times 3 = 15$ **b.** $15 \div 3 = 5$ **c.** $15 \div 5 = 3$

14. B

15. $3 \times 7 + 2 = 21 + 2 = 23$, so $23 \div 3 = 7$ R2

16. a. $7 \times b = 21$
$b \times 7 = 21$
$\boxed{21 \div 7 = b}$
$21 \div b = 7$
 b. $72 \div n = 4$
$\boxed{72 \div 4 = n}$
$b \times 4 = 72$
$4 \times b = 72$

17. Answers vary.
 a. A teacher has 16 pieces of candy. He wants to split it evenly among three students. How many pieces of candy would be left over?
 b. A teacher has 16 pieces of candy. He wants split it evenly among three students. How many more pieces of candy would he need to give all of it away?
 c. A teacher has 16 pieces of chocolate. He wants to put 3 pieces in each bag to give to his colleagues. How many bags of chocolate can he make?

18. The remainder must be less than the divisor.

19. The student could write the fact family for the equation and select the equation that helps solve for n or use the fact that multiplication is the inverse operation of division.

20. a. $3 \times n = 12$ because the student would "know" n equals 4.
 b. Division could be used to solve for d in $d \times 543 = 225{,}345$ (by dividing 225,345 by 543).

21. As stated in the main text:
"We can express whole number division problems with zero or nonzero remainders, such as $20 \div 5 = 4$ and $17 \div 3 = 5$ R2. We can 'check our work.' For example, let's verify the equation $27 \div 4 = 6$ R3 using the quotient–remainder theorem: $4 \times 6 + 3 = 24 + 3 = 27$, so $27 \div 4 = 6$ R3. We can use the theorem to compare two quantities. For example, Mary has 14 apples and John has 3 apples. We know $14 \div 3 = 4$ R2. Then we can say, 'Mary has 2 more than four times as many apples as John.'"

22. a. The remainder is greater than the divisor.
 b. The divisor times the quotient is greater than the dividend.

23. Multiplicative comparison: $100{,}000 \div 15 = 6666$ R10 and $100{,}000 \div 45 = 2222$ R10. The candidate had 2222 to 6666 times the normal level of dioxin, which suggests the candidate was poisoned. Answers vary, but a sensational headline could read "Presidential candidate poisoned."

24. a. multiplicative reasoning   **b.** repeated subtraction
 c. fair share   **d.** missing factor
 e. quotient   **f.** division

25. a. dividend = 214, divisor = 12, quotient = 17, remainder = 10
 b. dividend = 322, divisor = 14, quotient = 23, remainder = 0

26. a.

$9 \div 4 = 2$ R1
 b.

$14 \div 3 = 4$ R2
 c.

$3 \div 5 = 0$ R3

27. a.

$9 \div 4 = 2$ R1
 b.

$14 \div 3 = 4$ R2
 c. •••

$3 \div 5 = 0$ R3

28. a. $24 - 8 = 16$, $16 - 8 = 8$, and $8 - 8 = 0$, so $24 \div 8 = 3$
   b. $15 - 3 = 12$, $12 - 3 = 9$, $9 - 3 = 6$, $6 - 3 = 3$,
   and $3 - 3 = 0$, so $15 \div 3 = 5$
   c. $20 - 4 = 16$, $16 - 4 = 12$, $12 - 4 = 8$, $8 - 4 = 4$,
   and $4 - 4 = 0$, so $20 \div 4 = 5$

29. a. $n \div 3 = 5$
   $n = 3 \times 5$
   $n = 15$
   b. $n \times 5 = 30$
   $n = 30 \div 5$
   $n = 6$
   c. $24 \div n = 8$
   $24 = n \times 8$
   $n = 24 \div 8$
   $n = 3$

30. Answers vary.
   a. Mrs. Litt has 38 pieces of candy. She wants to split the candy evenly among five students. How many pieces of candy does each student get?
   b. A class with 38 students is going on a field trip. Each van can hold 5 students. How many vans are needed?
   c. Mrs. Litt has 38 pieces of candy. She wants to split the candy evenly among five students. How many pieces of candy are left over?
   d. Mrs. Litt has 38 plastic roses. She wants to put 5 roses in each flower arrangement. How many more roses does she need so that she uses all of her plastic roses?

31. a. whole numbers from 0 to 6
   b. whole numbers from 0 to 8
   c. whole numbers from 0 to $b - 1$

32. a. $14 \div 3 = 4$ R2   **b.** $14 \div 4 = 3$ R2

33. a. 13 marbles   **b.** 17 beads

34. a.

   $453 - 6 = 447$
   $447 \div 3 = 149$
   Peter has 149 trading cards.
   b.

   $263 + 5 = 268$
   $268 \div 4 = 67$
   Amanda read 67 pages last week.

35. a.

   $160 \div 5 = 32$
   $4 \times 32 = 128$
   Michael has 32 coins. Elijah has 128 coins.
   b.

   $340 - 4 = 336$
   $336 \div 8 = 42$
   $7 \times 42 + 4 = 298$
   Michael has 42 coins. Elijah has 298 coins.

c.

   $110 + 5 = 115$
   $115 \div 5 = 23$
   $4 \times 23 - 5 = 87$
   Michael has 23 coins. Elijah has 87 coins.

36. a. $18 \div 7 = 2$ R4   **b.** $18 \div 5 = 3$ R3

37. a. 20   **b.** 32   **c.** 88   **d.** 94

38. a. $2 \times 8 + 1 = 16 + 1 = 17$, so $17 \div 2 = 8$ R1
   b. $1 \times 7 + 5 = 7 + 5 = 12$, so $12 \div 7 = 1$ R5
   c. $3 \times 5 = 15$, so $15 \div 3 = 5$

39. a. $28 \div 7 = 4$, $28 \div 4 = 7$, $4 \times 7 = 28$, $7 \times 4 = 28$
   b. $4 \times 5 = 20$, $5 \times 4 = 20$, $20 \div 4 = 5$, $20 \div 5 = 4$
   c. $a \times 6 = 150$, $6 \times a = 150$, $150 \div 6 = a$, $150 \div a = 6$

40. a. 23^5 **b.** 425^{15} **c.** 72^{68}

41. Answers vary. For example, there are 48 flower bulbs. Wally wants to plant 6 of them in each row. How many rows will he plant?

42. a. 2   **b.** 27   **c.** 2   **d.** 1   **e.** 7

43. No

44. C

45. 2 wheels

46. $140 million

47. a. 8   **b.** 15   **c.** 7

48. 18 pieces of candy

49. a. Saturn is 1,277,127,510 km farther from the Sun than Earth.
   b. Saturn is about 10 times as far from the Sun as Earth.
   c. Multiplicative reasoning is more appropriate because it is easier to comprehend "about 10 times" as far than to comprehend "1,277,127,510 km farther."

50. a. $288 - 48 = 240$. A person burns 240 more calories per hour moving boxes than watching TV.
   b. $288 \div 48 = 6$. A person burns six times as many calories per hour moving boxes as watching TV.

51. 7 is a multiple of 3 if and only if there is a counting number n such that $7 = 3n$. By the definition of division, then n must satisfy the equation $n = 7 \div 3$. But $7 \div 3 = 2$ R1, so n is not a counting number. So 7 is not a multiple of 3.

52. 2

53. 1

54. a. Rounding, because of the trailing zeros
   b. $35,000 - 800 = 34,200$. There are about 34,000 more products on shelves in a typical grocery today compared to the 1930s.
   c. $35,000 \div 800 = 43$ R600. There are nearly 44 times as many products on shelves in a typical grocery today compared to the 1930s.

55. a. $a = 14$ **b.** $b = 35$ **c.** $a = b$

56. a. $7,838,400 \div 28,400 = 276$. There were 276 audience members. The repeated subtraction model is more appropriate, because the number of groups is unknown.

b. $550,000 \div 20 = 27,500$. Each station was fined $27,500. The fair-share model of division is more appropriate, because the number of objects per group is unknown.

57. a. $108 \div d = k$ **b.** $y \div h = 17$

58. No. $8 \div 2 = 4$, but $2 \div 8 = 0$ R2. Then $8 \div 2 \neq 2 \div 8$.

59. No. $(24 \div 8) \div 2 = 3 \div 2 = 1$ R1, but $24 \div (8 \div 2) = 24 \div 4 = 6$. So $(24 \div 8) \div 2 \neq 24 \div (8 \div 2)$.

60. a. $(y + 4) \div 5 = (q + 1)$ R2 **b.** $(y - 1) \div 5 = q$ R2
c. $(y + 12) \div 5 = q + 3$

61. a. $(y - 2) \div 4 = k$ R3
b. $(2y + 1) \div 4 = (2k + 2)$ R3
c. $(3y - 2) \div 4 = (3k + 3)$ R1

62. a. $1002 \times 84 = 84,168$
b. $1002 \times a = 1000a + 2a$

63. a. $18 \times n = 90$
$18 \times n \div 18 = 90 \div 18$
$n = 90 \div 18$
$n = 5$
b. $18 \times n = 90$
$n = 90 \div 18$
$n = 5$

SECTION 3.3

1. Step 1. Build four copies of 37.

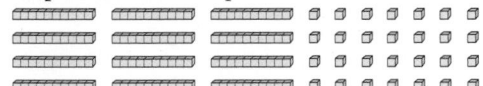

Step 2. Regroup the 28 ones as 2 tens and 8 ones.

Step 3. Regroup the 14 tens as 1 hundred and 4 tens. No more regrouping is needed.

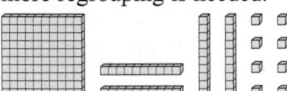

There are 1 hundred, 4 tens, and 8 ones. So $4 \times 37 = 148$.

2. a. $863 \div 4 \approx 800 \div 4 = 200$
b. Step 1. Build 863 using base ten blocks.

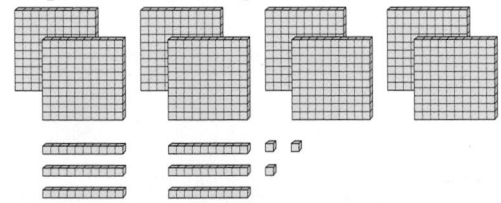

Step 2. Separate the hundreds and tens into four equal-sized groups.

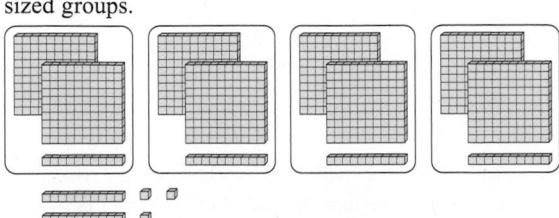

Step 3. Regroup the remaining 2 tens as 20 ones. Then 2 tens plus 3 ones equals 23 ones.

Step 4. Divide the 23 ones equally among the four groups. There are 3 ones left over.

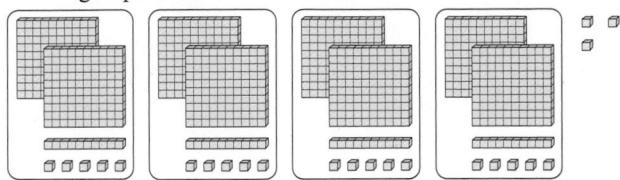

Each group gets 2 hundreds, 1 ten, and 5 ones, with 3 remaining. Then $863 \div 4 = 215$ R3.

3. a. The partial quotients are 3, 10, 1, and 13.
b. The quotient is 27. **c.** The remainder is 35.
d. The equation is $3302 \div 121 = 27$ R35

4. $212 \div 3 = 70$ R2 and $72 \div 2 = 36$. She can invite 36 people to the party.

5. Use the guess-and-check strategy.
a. 36 and 7 **b.** 63 and 41

6. a. 432×6 **b.** 644×6

7. 234×6 and 234×50

8. 345×48

9. a. 7 **b.** $3456 \div 7 = 493$ R5
c. $7 \times 493 + 5 = 3451 + 5 = 3456$

10. $38 \times 400 = 38 \times (4 \times 100) = (38 \times 4) \times 100 = 152 \times 100 = 15,200$

11. a. Answers vary. For example, $b = 30$ and $a = 30 \times 1553 + 25 = 46,615$.
b. No. For example, another possibility is $b = 40$ and $a = 62,145$.

12. $600, 601, 602, \ldots, 699$

13. a. We are regrouping 2 hundreds, 3 tens as 23 tens.

b. We are regrouping 1 ten, 7 ones as 17 ones.

14. mn partial products

15. a. $456 \times 82 = 37,392$
b.

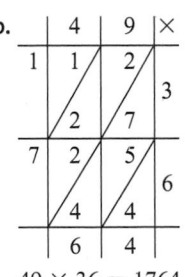

$49 \times 36 = 1764$

c.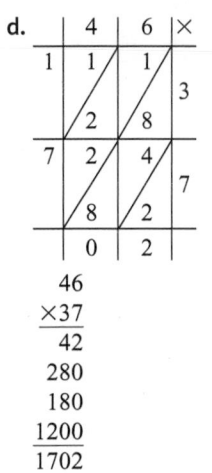

$724 \times 23 = 16,652$

d.

```
    46
  ×37
   42
  280
  180
 1200
 1702
```

$46 \times 37 = 1702$

e. The entries in the lattice method are the products 6×7, 4×7, 6×3, and 4×3. The partial products are 6×7, 40×7, 6×30, and 40×30.

f. Each diagonal is a place value. For example, the diagonal in the lower right-hand corner is the ones place. The diagonal above that is the tens place.

16. a. $(4x^2 + 8x + 3)(6x + 5) = 24x^3 + 68x^2 + 58x + 15$

	$4x^2$	$8x$	3	
	$24x^3$	$48x^2$	$18x$	$6x$
$24x^3$	$20x^2$	$40x$	15	5
	$68x^2$	$58x$	15	

b. $(2x^2 + 7x + 4)(8x - 3) = 16x^3 + 50x^2 + 11x - 12$

	$2x^2$	$7x$	4	
	$16x^3$	$56x^2$	$32x$	$8x$
$16x^3$	$-6x^2$	$-21x$	-12	-3
	$50x^2$	$11x$	-12	

c. $(3x^2 + 4x - 7)(5x - 2) = 15x^3 + 14x^2 - 43x + 14$

	$3x^2$	$4x$	-7	
	$15x^3$	$20x^2$	$-35x$	$5x$
$15x^3$	$-6x^2$	$-8x$	14	-2
	$14x^2$	$-43x$	14	

17. The product equals the sum of the partial products.

18. The quotient equals the sum of the partial quotients.

19. a. 8×3 ones $= 24$ ones $= 2$ tens, 4 ones. The 2 above the 4 represents the 2 tens from regrouping 24 ones as 2 tens, 4 ones.

   b. 8×4 tens $+ 2$ tens $= 34$ tens $= 3$ hundreds, 4 tens. The 3 appears in the hundreds place from regrouping 34 tens as 3 hundreds, 4 tens.

20. Monique is calculating the simpler product 30×7, which equals $(3 \times 7) \times 10$. The zero anticipates multiplying the product 3×7 by 10.

21. The student thought "6 goes into 7" once. The student seems to have written the 1 above the 4 instead of the 7. Then, when determining "6 goes into 14" twice, the student wrote the 2 above the 7 instead of the 4. That could be how the student arrived at the quotient 214 instead of the correct quotient 124.

22. a. partial products   b. partial quotients   c. long division

23. 1081

24. a.
```
   127
  ×45
   35
  100
  500
  280
  800
 4000
 5715
```

   b.
```
   602
  ×27
    14
     0
  4200
    40
     0
 12000
 16254
```

25. Answers vary. For example, 654 and 23.

26. Theus is calculating the simpler product 500×342, which equals $(5 \times 342) \times 100$. The two zeros anticipate multiplying the product 5×342 by 100.

27. 52

28. a. 92
   b. $3421 \div 92 = 37$ R17
   c. $92 \times 37 + 17 = 3404 + 17 = 3421$

29. a. 78
   b. $2329 \div 78 = 29$ R67
   c. $29 \times 78 + 67 = 2262 + 67 = 2329$

30. a. 3662
   b. $3662 \div 25 = 146$ R12
   c. $25 \times 146 + 12 = 3650 + 12 = 3662$

31. a. 7689
   b. $7689 \div 43 = 178$ R35
   c. $178 \times 43 + 35 = 7654 + 35 = 7689$

32. Estimates and partial quotients vary.

   a. $1841 \div 23 \approx 1800 \div 20 = 90$

```
    23)1841
       -230   10
       ────
       1611
       -460   20
       ────
       1151
       -920   40
       ────
        231
       -230   10
       ────
          1
```

   $1841 \div 23 = 80 \text{ R}1$

   b. $2194 \div 150 \approx 2100 \div 150 = 210 \div 15 = 14$

```
  150)2194
     -1500   10
     ────
       694
      -300    2
      ────
       394
      -300    2
      ────
        94
```

   $2194 \div 150 = 14 \text{ R}94$

33. Estimates and partial quotients vary.

   a. $2501 \div 30 \approx 2400 \div 30 = 80$ (underestimate)

```
   30)2501
      -300   10
      ────
      2201
     -1500   50
     ────
       701
      -600   20
      ────
       101
       -90    3
       ───
        11
```

   $2501 \div 30 = 83 \text{ R}11$

   b. $5182 \div 125 \approx 6000 \div 120 = 50$

```
  125)5182
     -1250   10
     ────
      3932
     -2500   20
     ────
      1432
     -1250   10
     ────
       182
      -125    1
      ────
        57
```

   $5182 \div 125 = 41 \text{ R}57$

34. Estimates vary.

   a. $4304 \div 30 \approx 4200 \div 30 = 140$

```
       143
   30)4304
     -30
     ───
      130
     -120
     ────
      104
      -90
      ───
       14
```

   $4304 \div 30 = 143 \text{ R}14$

   b. $2314 \div 22 \approx 2400 \div 24 = 100$

```
       105
   22)2314
     -22
     ───
      114
     -110
     ────
        4
```

   $2314 \div 22 = 105 \text{ R}4$

35. **a.** $358 \div 4 \approx 360 \div 4 = 90$

   b. $7718 \div 52 \approx 8000 \div 50 = 800 \div 5 = 160$

   c. $3105 \div 43 \approx 3200 \div 40 = 320 \div 4 = 80$

36. $300,000 \times 20 = 3 \times 100,000 \times 2 \times 10 = 6,000,000 =$ $6 million

37. 36 cartons

38. $133,000 \times 365 = 48,545,000$

39.

```
        1  [3] [7]
     ×  2  [5]
    ─────────────
           3  [5]
        1  5  0
        5  0  0
     [1] 4  0
        6  0  0
  [2] 0  0  0
  ─────────────
     3  4  2  5
```

40. Answers vary.

   a. $40 \times 50 = 2000$ **b.** $40 \times 700 = 28,000$

   c. $2000 \times 300 \times 100 = 60,000,000$

41. $80, 81, \ldots, 89$

42. Answers vary. For example, 83 and 96.

43. **a.** $6000 \leq 24 \times 365 \leq 12,000$

   b. $45,000 \leq 97 \times 547 \leq 60,000$

   c. $12,000 \leq 262 \times 67 \leq 21,000$

44. **a.** $98 \ (15 \times 100 = 1500)$ **b.** $21 \ (20 \times 18 = 360)$

   c. $9 \ (10 \times 45 = 450)$ **d.** $275 \ (10 \times 25 + 25)$

45. 9 quarters + 37 nickels = $2 + 25 cents + $2 − 15 cents $= \$4.10$

46. 13 shirts, as 10 shirts cost $160, and 3 more shirts cost $48, for a total of $208.

47. **a.** $2 \times 4 \times 6 \times 5 = 24 \times 10 = 240$

   b. $45 \times 8 \times 5 \times 2 = 45 \times 8 \times 10 = (320 + 40) \times 10 = 3600$

   c. $5 \times 4 \times 8 \times 6 \times 5 = 100 \times 48 = 4800$

   d. $13 \times 4 \times 2 \times 25 = 26 \times 100 = 2600$

48. **a.** $8 \times 12 = 80 + 16 = 96$

   b. $9 \times 35 = 270 + 45 = 315$

   c. $32 \times 41 = 32 \times 40 + 32 = 1280 + 32 = 1312$

   d. $234 \times 50 = 234 \times 100 \div 2 = 23,400 \div 2 = 11,700$

49. 1092 carrots, 728 radishes, and 1456 leaves of lettuce

50. **a.** $24 \times 13 = 312$ **b.** $12 \times 12 = 144$

51. 50×160, because it involves the least changes to the factors

52. 18 cartons

53. 810 blocks

54. No, because they could use rounding to different place values.

55. 1008 pavers

56. 808 items

57. **a.** $8lw + 6st$ square feet
    b. Answers vary. For example, each corn field could be 4 by 7 feet.
    c. Answers vary. For example, each wheat field could be 4 by 8 feet.

58. $94

59.

Number	300	320	11	40	43
\, /, or X	X	X	/	X	/

60. $234_{\text{five}} \times 2_{\text{five}}$ and $234_{\text{five}} \times 40_{\text{five}}$

61. $241_{\text{six}} \times 24_{\text{six}}$

62. **a.** $3_{\text{five}} \times 4_{\text{five}} = 22_{\text{five}} = 2_{\text{five}}$ longs, 2_{five} units. The 2 above the 4 represents the 2_{five} longs when 22_{five} is regrouped as 2_{five} longs, 2_{five} units.
    b. $43_{\text{five}} \times 4_{\text{five}} = 332_{\text{five}}$

63. 2121_{five}

64. The following are base five calculations.

    a.
    ```
       132
      ×24
      ----
        13
       220
       400
        40
      1100
      2000
      ----
      4323
    ```

    b.
    ```
       42
      ×31
      ----
        2
       40
      110
      ----
      2200
      ----
      2402
    ```

65. The following are base five calculations.

    a.
    ```
       11
      322
      ×23
      -----
      2021
     11440
     -----
     14011
    ```

    b.
    ```
       33
       22
      134
      ×43
      -----
      1012
     12010
     -----
     13022
    ```

66. **a.** The student regrouped 11_{five} flats and 2_{five} longs as 112_{five} longs.
    b. 112_{five} longs

67. **a.** 1_{five} flat   **b.** 4_{five} flats

68. **a.** 434_{five} **b.** $434_{\text{five}} \div 23_{\text{five}} = 14_{\text{five}} \text{ R}2_{\text{five}}$

69. **a.** $3320_{\text{five}} \div 12_{\text{five}} = 230_{\text{five}} \text{ R}10_{\text{five}}$
    b. $3323_{\text{five}} \div 12_{\text{five}} = 231_{\text{five}} \text{ R}1_{\text{five}}$
    c. $3330_{\text{five}} \div 12_{\text{five}} = 231_{\text{five}} \text{ R}3_{\text{five}}$
    d. $3332_{\text{five}} \div 12_{\text{five}} = 231_{\text{five}} \text{ R}10_{\text{five}}$

70.

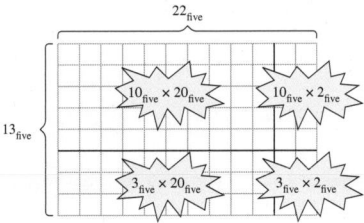

71. The following are base five calculations.
    ```
         30)4304
           -3000  100
           -----
            1304
            -300   10
            -----
            1004
            -300   10
            -----
             204
            -110    2
            -----
              44
             -30    1
             ----
              14
    ```
    $4304_{\text{five}} \div 30_{\text{five}} = 123_{\text{five}} \text{ R}14_{\text{five}}$

72. **a.** 233_{five}
    b. Solve the equation $23020_{\text{five}} = b \times 233_{\text{five}} + 3_{\text{five}}$ for b.

REVIEW QUESTIONS

1. **a.**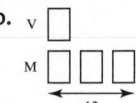

    b.

2. **a.** set model   **b.** comparison model
   c. measurement model   **d.** Cartesian product model
   e. set model   **f.** array model   **g.** measurement model

3. **a.** Answers vary. For example, 245.121.01.3.
   b. Answers vary. For example, 555.555.555.555.
   c. 256^4, or 4,294,967,296, IP addresses

4. 56 outfits

5. Answers vary.
   a. There are five boxes of pears, and each box has four pears. How many pears are in the boxes altogether?
   b. Joey had three boxes of books. Each box had the same number of books. There were 24 books in all. Write a number sentence for the problem.
   c. Tina has 15 beads in each bag. Altogether, there are 45 beads. How many bags of beads does she have?

6. **a.** four   **b.**
   $12 \div 3 = 4$. Verne has four coins.
   c. Let V equal the number of coins Verne has. Then Mary has $3V$ coins. Then $12 = 3V$. Then $V = 12 \div 3 = 4$. Verne has four coins.

d. Some elementary students see the word *times,* so they multiply the two numbers in the word problem.

7. 46 digits

8. a. 234 coins   **b.** 367 coins   **c.** 133 coins

9. a. 5, 10, 15, 20. Then $4 \times 5 = 20$.
   b. 4, 8, 12. Then $3 \times 4 = 12$.

10. a. $15 \times 11 = 15 \times (10 + 1) = 15 \times 10 + 15 \times 1 = 150 + 15 = 165$
   b. $7 \times 12 = 7 \times (10 + 2) = 7 \times 10 + 7 \times 2 = 70 + 14 = 84$

11. a. $4 \times 125 = 4 \times (25 \times 5) = (4 \times 25) \times 5 = 100 \times 5 = 500$
   b. $25 \times 20 = 25 \times (4 \times 5) = (25 \times 4) \times 5 = 100 \times 5 = 500$
   c. $5 \times 120 = 5 \times (12 \times 10) = (5 \times 12) \times 10 = 60 \times 10 = 600$

12. Answers vary. For example, $21 \times 481 = (7 \times 3) \times 481 = 7 \times (3 \times 481) = 7 \times 1443$. So $7 \times 1443 = 10,101$.

13. a. 4624   **b.** 446,224   **c.** 44,462,224
   d. The number of leading fours and the number of twos in the result equal the number of sixes in the original number.
   e. 44,444,462,222,224

14. a. $40 \times 6 = (10 \times 4) \times 6 = 10 \times (4 \times 6) = 10 \times 24 = 240$
   b. $300 \times 50 = (100 \times 3) \times (5 \times 10) = (3 \times 5) (100 \times 10) = 15 \times 10,000 = 15,000$

15. a. $3(5a) = (3 \times 5)a = 15a$
   b. $6n \times 8n = [(6n) \times 8]n = [6(n \times 8)]n = [6 \times (8 \times n)]n = [(6 \times 8) \times n]n = [48n]n = 48(n \times n) = 48n^2$

16. a. 22, because $396 = 360 + 36 = 20 \cdot 18 + 2 \cdot 18 = 22 \cdot 18$
   b. 13, because $156 = 144 + 12 = 12 \cdot 12 + 1 \cdot 12 = 13 \cdot 12$
   c. 98, because $1470 = 1500 - 30 = 100 \cdot 15 - 2 \cdot 15 = 98 \cdot 15$

17. a. base $= 7$, exponent $= 4$, $7^4 = 7 \times 7 \times 7 \times 7$
   b. base $= 16$, exponent $= 5$, $16^5 = 16 \times 16 \times 16 \times 16 \times 16$
   c. base $= 4$, exponent $= 3$, $4^3 = 4 \times 4 \times 4$

18. $3^3 = 27$
   $3^2 = 9$
   $3^1 = 3$
   $3^0 = 1$

19. a. $8^4 = (2^3)^4 = 2^{3 \times 4} = 2^{12}$
   b. $24^5 = (8 \times 3)^5 = 8^5 \times 3^5 = (2^3)^5 \times 3^5 = 2^{3 \times 5} \times 3^5 = 2^{15} \times 3^5$

20. a. ⊛ ⊛ ⊛ ⊛   **b.** ⊛ ⊛ ⊛ ⊛ ⊛ ⊛
   ⊛ ⊛ ⊛ ⊛   • • • •
   $24 \div 8 = 3$ $14 \div 5 = 2\,\text{R}4$

21. a. (••••) (••••) (••••)   **b.** ⊛ ⊛ ••
   $24 \div 8 = 3$ $14 \div 5 = 2\,\text{R}4$

22. a. repeated subtraction model of division
   b. 7 pennies

23. a. 21 packages   **b.** repeated subtraction model

24. a.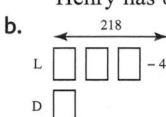
   Henry has 81 more coins than Kyle.
   b.

   $218 + 4 = 222$, $222 \div 3 = 74$. Diane read 74 pages.

25. C

26. Remind the student that multiplication and division are inverse operations.
   $$n \div 7 = 84$$
   $$n \div 7 \times 7 = 84 \times 7$$
   $$n = 84 \times 7$$
   $$n = 588$$

27. Remind the student that multiplication and division are inverse operations.
   $$510 \div n = 15$$
   $$510 \div n \times n = 15 \times n$$
   $$510 = 15 \times n$$
   $$510 \div 15 = 15 \times n \div 15$$
   $$510 \div 15 = n$$
   $$34 = n$$

28. One of two answers could be circled.
   $n \div 8 = 72$ $n \div 72 = 8$ ⟨$n = 8 \times 72$⟩ ⟨$n = 72 \times 8$⟩

29. Suppose $6 \div 0$ is the number n. Then n solves the equation $6 = 0 \times n$. Then $6 = 0$. This equation is false, so $6 \div 0$ is not a number.

30. Suppose $0 \div 0$ is the number n. Then $0 \div 0 = n$. Then n solves the equation $0 = 0 \times n$. The equation has many solutions, such as $n = 5$ and $n = 8$. Then $5 = 8$, which is false, so $0 \div 0$ cannot be a number.

31. The remainder is less than the divisor, and $15 \times 19 + 6 = 285 + 6 = 291$. So the student's work is correct.

32. a. 133   **b.** 2   **c.** 19

33. $46 \div 8 = 5.75$, $46 - 8 \times 5 = 6$, so $46 \div 8 = 5\,\text{R}6$

34. 20 bags

35. a. Percy has 85 more coins than Kenneth.
   b. Percy has 5 fewer than three times as many coins as Kenneth.

36. Answers vary.
   a. Kelly had some beads in a bag. She used five beads for each bracelet. She made three bracelets. She used all of the beads. How many beads did she have in the bag?
   b. Mr. Dugger had 14 raffle tickets. He wanted to split them equally among three students. How many raffle tickets does each student get?

37. a. 75   **b.** 5   **b.** 11

38. a. $(2 + 4) \div 2 \times 3 = 9$
   b. $(6 + 18) \div (3 \times 2) + 3 = 7$
   c. $9 \div 3 \times 3 + 20 \div (4 + 1) = 13$
   d. $14 \div (6 \div 3) \times 3 + 2 \times 4 = 29$

39. Step 1. Build three copies of 27.

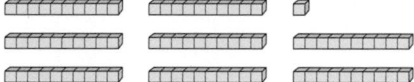

Step 2. Regroup the 21 ones as 2 tens, 1 one.

There are 8 tens and 1 one. No more regrouping is needed, so $27 \times 3 = 81$.

40. 456×30 and 456×2

41. The student is calculating the simpler product 456×30, which equals $(456 \times 3) \times 10$. The zero anticipates multiplication of 456×3 by 10.

42. Distributive property of multiplication over addition

43. First, multiply 5274×3 to get 15,822. Second, append the result with two zeros to get 1,582,200. Then $5274 \times 300 = 1,582,200$.

44. a. 37,568 **b.** 27,002

45.
```
        5  [7]
    ×   4  [3]
    ─────────
        2  [1]
     1  5  0
     2 [8] 0
   [2] 0  0  0
   ──────────
   2  4  5  1
```

46. $412_{\text{five}} \times 20_{\text{five}}$ and $412_{\text{five}} \times 3_{\text{five}}$

47. $523_{\text{six}} \times 32_{\text{six}}$

48. These are base five calculations.

a.
```
     213
    ×23
   ─────
    1144
    4310
   ─────
   11004
```

b.
```
      11
     312
    ×42
   ─────
    1124
   23030
   ─────
   24204
```

49. a.
```
      428
     ×73
   ──────
       24
       60
     1200
      560
     1400
    28000
   ──────
    31244
```

b.
```
      789
     ×48
   ──────
       72
      640
     5600
      360
     3200
    28000
   ──────
    37872
```

50. a.

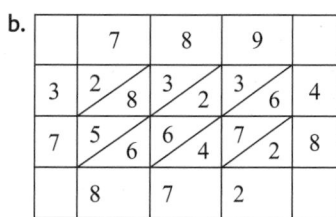

$428 \times 73 = 31,244$

b.

$789 \times 48 = 37,872$

51. a. These are base five calculations.
```
     213
    ×23
   ─────
      14
      30
    1100
     110
     200
    4000
   ─────
   11004
```

b.
```
     312
    ×42
   ─────
       4
      20
    1100
     130
     400
   22000
   ─────
   24204
```

52. a. $36 \times 198 \approx 36 \times 200 = 7200$
  b. $42 \times 305 \approx 40 \times 300 = 12,000$
  c. $486,367 \times 72 \approx 500,000 \times 70 = 35,000,000$

53. Step 1. Build the dividend 412.

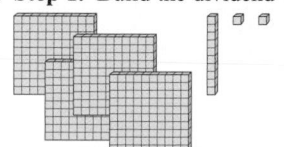

Step 2. Divide the hundreds equally among three groups.

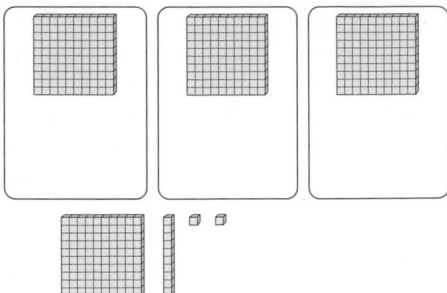

Step 3. Regroup the remaining 1 hundred as 10 tens.

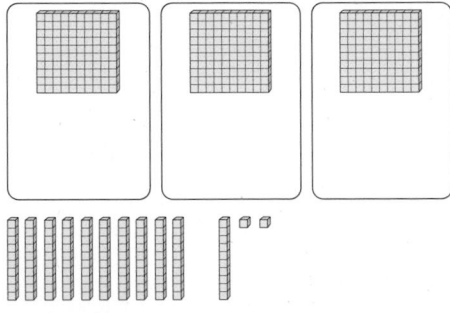

Step 4. Divide the tens equally among the three groups.

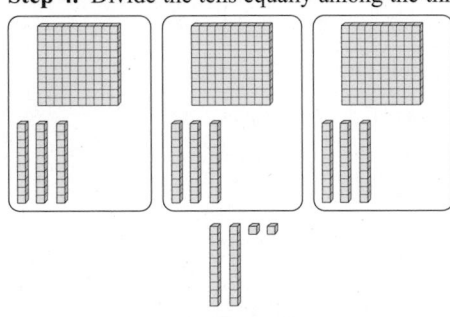

Step 5. Regroup the remaining 2 tens as 20 ones.

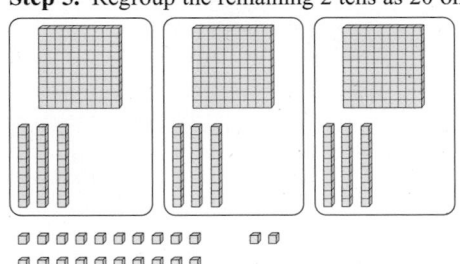

Step 6. Divide the ones equally among the three groups

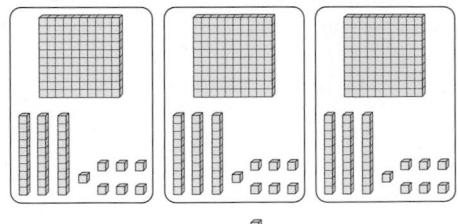

Then $412 \div 3 = 137 \text{ R}1$

54. **a.** The partial quotients vary, but the quotient is 37 and the remainder is 16.

$$
\begin{array}{r}
123\overline{)4567} \\
-1230 \quad 10 \\
\overline{3337} \\
-2460 \quad 20 \\
\overline{877} \\
-246 \quad 2 \\
\overline{631} \\
-246 \quad 2 \\
\overline{385} \\
-246 \quad 2 \\
\overline{139} \\
-123 \quad 1 \\
\overline{16}
\end{array}
$$

b. The partial quotients vary, but the quotient is 103_{five} and the remainder is 3_{five}.

$$
\begin{array}{r}
14\overline{)2010} \\
-1400 \quad 100 \\
\overline{110} \\
-14 \quad 1 \\
\overline{41} \\
-14 \quad 1 \\
\overline{22} \\
-14 \quad 1 \\
\overline{3}
\end{array}
$$

55. **a.** 1,898,331   **b.** $1,898,331 \div 450 = 4218 \text{ R}231$

56. **a.** $3460 \div 12 = 288 \text{ R}4$

$$
\begin{array}{r}
288 \\
12\overline{)3460} \\
-24 \\
\overline{106} \\
-96 \\
\overline{100} \\
-96 \\
\overline{4}
\end{array}
$$

b. $3401_{\text{five}} \div 21_{\text{five}} = 133_{\text{five}} \text{ R}3_{\text{five}}$

$$
\begin{array}{r}
133 \\
21\overline{)3401} \\
-21 \\
\overline{130} \\
-113 \\
\overline{121} \\
-113 \\
\overline{3}
\end{array}
$$

57. 1 hundred, 3 tens are regrouped as 13 tens.

CHAPTER 3 TEST

1. **a.** comparison model   **b.** measurement model
   c. set model   **d.** Cartesian product model
   e. array model

2. **a.** $38 \times 400 = 38 \times (4 \times 100) = (38 \times 4) \times 100 = 152 \times 100 = 15,200$
   b. $42 \times 103 = 42 \times (100 + 3) = 42 \times 100 + 42 \times 3 = 4200 + 126 = 4326$
   c. $35 \times 98 = 35 \times (100 - 2) = 35 \times 100 - 35 \times 2 = 3500 - 70 = 3430$
   d. $44 \times 25 = (11 \times 4) \times 25 = 11 \times (4 \times 25) = 11 \times 100 = 1100$

e. $11 \times 18 = (10 + 1) \times 18 = 10 \times 18 + 1 \times 18 = 180 + 18 = 198$

3. a. $C = 7n + 60$ **b.** $928   **c.** 214 shirts

4. a.

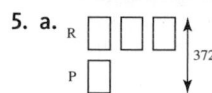

$15 \div 5 = 3$. Tony has three coins.

b. Let T equal the number of coins that Tony has. Then Daniel has $5T$ coins. Then $5T = 15$. Then $T = 15 \div 5$. Then $T = 3$. Tony has three coins.

5. a.

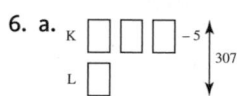

$372 \div 4 = 93$. $3 \times 93 = 279$. Pam has 93 coins, and Rachel has 279 coins.

b. Let P equal the number of coins Pam has. Then Rachel has $3P$ coins. Then $P + 3P = 372$. Then $4P = 372$. Then $P = 372 \div 4 = 93$ and $3 \times 93 = 279$. Pam has 93 coins, and Rachel has 279 coins.

6. a.

$307 + 5 = 312$. $312 \div 4 = 78$. $3 \times 78 - 5 = 229$. Kira has 229 coins, and Leo has 78 coins.

b. Let L equal the number of coins Leo has. Then Kira has $3L - 5$ coins. Then $L + 3L - 5 = 307$. Then $4L - 5 = 307$. Then $4L = 312$. Then $L = 312 \div 4 = 78$ and $3 \times 78 - 5 = 229$. Kira has 229 coins, and Leo has 78 coins.

7. a. 3^4 **b.** 7^{125}

8. a. $10^{12} = (2 \cdot 5)^{12} = 2^{12} \cdot 5^{12}$

b. $20^{25} \cdot 10^{31} = (10 \cdot 2)^{25} \cdot 10^{31} = 10^{25} \cdot 2^{25} \cdot 10^{31} = 10^{56} \cdot 2^{25} = (2 \cdot 5)^{56} \cdot 2^{25} = 2^{56} \cdot 5^{56} \cdot 2^{25} = 2^{81} \cdot 5^{56}$

9. a. repeated subtraction model, $28 \div 7 = 4$

b. fair share model, $20 \div 5 = 4$

10. a. $14 \div 4 = 3$ R2   **b.** $14 \div 3 = 4$ R2

11. a. division property of equality

b. Multiplication and division are inverse operations.

c. multiplication property of equality

d. Multiplication and division are inverse operations.

12. a. $n \div 24 = 120$
$n = 24 \times 120$
$n = 2880$

b. $n \div 24 = 120$
$n \div 24 \times 24 = 120 \times 24$
$n = 120 \times 24$
$n = 2880$

13. a. $n \times 24 = 120$
$n = 120 \div 24$
$n = 5$

b. $n \times 24 = 120$
$n \times 24 \div 24 = 120 \div 24$
$n = 120 \div 24$
$n = 5$

14. a. 8, 16, 24. Then $3 \times 8 = 24$.

b. $12 \times 8 = (10 + 2) \times 8 = 10 \times 8 + 2 \times 8 = 80 + 16 = 96$

15. 108 cubes

16. The student can check whether $6 \times 7 + 3$ equals 44. So $6 \times 7 + 3 = 42 + 3 = 45$. This does not equal the dividend 44, so the student made an error.

17. $20 \div 6 = 3$ R2. Ellen sold 2 more than three times as many rolls as Lenny.

18. The remainder is greater than the divisor.

19. P

20. Answers vary.

a. Lisa had 32 beads. She divided them into equal-sized piles. There were 8 beads in each pile. How many piles were there?

b. The gardener has 22 flowers. He wanted to plant 4 flowers in each row. How many rows of flowers did he plant?

21. a. 13   **b.** 96   **c.** 64   **d.** 30   **e.** 98

22. a. Distributive property of multiplication over addition

b. 482×57 **c.** 942×30 and 942×8

23. a.
$$
\begin{array}{r}
256 \\
\times 63 \\
\hline
18 \\
150 \\
600 \\
360 \\
3000 \\
12000 \\
\hline
16128
\end{array}
$$
The partial products are 18, 150, 600, 360, 3000, and 12,000.

b. $abc \times ef = 15{,}408$ and $abc \times fe = 26{,}964$

c. Lisa is calculating the simpler product 234×500, which equals $(234 \times 5) \times 100$. The two zeros anticipate multiplying 234×5 by 100.

24. a. 2 thousand, 0 hundreds = 20 hundreds. We can view this as splitting 20 hundreds into three groups. Each group gets 6 hundreds.

b. 3 groups of 6 hundreds = 18 hundreds. Of the 20 hundreds, we have given away 18 hundreds.

c. We regrouped 2 hundreds, 5 tens as 25 tens.

25. a.
$$
\begin{array}{r}
412\overline{)47937} \\
-41200 \quad 100 \\
\hline
6737 \\
-4120 \quad 10 \\
\hline
2617 \\
-2060 \quad 5 \\
\hline
557 \\
-412 \quad 1 \\
\hline
145
\end{array}
$$
The partial quotients are 100, 10, 5, and 1. $47{,}937 \div 412 = 116$ R145.

b. 731,395

c. 41

CHAPTER 4

SECTION 4.1

1. a.

a	4	7	10	13	16	19
$a \div 3$	1 R1	2 R1	3 R1	4 R1	5 R1	6 R1

b.

a	4	7	10	13	16	19
$a \div 5$	0 R4	1 R2	2 R0	2 R3	3 R1	3 R4

2. $18 \div 7 = 2$ R4

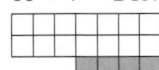

3. a.

  b. The array has 5 columns, and each column has the same number of rows, so the remainder of $15 \div 5$ is zero.

4. a.

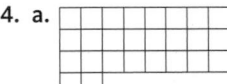

  b.

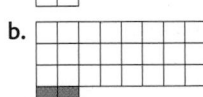

  c. Each row (or column) does not have the same number of cells or boxes.

5. 11 boxes

6. a. 9 **b.** 14 **c.** 284 (evaluate $5n - 1$ for $n = 57$)

7. 32 students

8. a. yes (because 6 divides 12 but not 32)
  b. yes (because 2 does not divide 4,509,231)
  c. yes (because 3 is not a factor)
  d. yes (because 6 divides each addend)

9. a. The number 3 is a factor of k, so $k = 3n$ for some whole number n. Then $k + 1 = 3n + 1$. Then $(k + 1) \div 3 = n$ R1. The nonzero remainder means 3 is not a factor of $k + 1$.
  b. The number 3 is a factor of k, so $k = 3n$ for some whole number n. Then $k + 2 = 3n + 2$. Then $(k + 2) \div 3 = n$ R2. The nonzero remainder means 3 is not a factor of $k + 2$.

10. a. $4 + 5 + 6 = 15$, which is divisible by 3.

    $18 + 19 + 20 = 57$, which is divisible by 3.

    $60 + 61 + 62 = 183$, which is divisible by 3.

    These examples support the claim that the sum of three consecutive numbers in divisible by 3.
  b. Let n represent the least of the three consecutive numbers. Then the three consecutive numbers are n, $n + 1$, and $n + 2$. Then the sum of the three consecutive numbers is $n + n + 1 + n + 2$, which equals $3n + 3$, or $3(n + 1)$. $3(n + 1)$ is divisible by 3. This proves that the sum of three consecutive numbers in divisible by 3.

11. a. no
  b. For any values of a and b, 3 divides the left-hand side of the equation but not the right-hand side of the equation. So there are no values of a and b that solve the equation.

12. a. 2 divides n if and only if 2 divides the rightmost digit of n.
  b. 2^2 divides n if and only if 2^2 divides the 2 rightmost digits of n.
  c. 2^3 divides n if and only if 2^3 divides the 3 rightmost digits of n.
  d. 2^4 divides n if and only if 2^4 divides the 4 rightmost digits of n.
  e. $2400 \div 16 = 150$, and $92{,}400 \div 16 = 5775$. $4987 \div 16 = 311$ R11, and $197{,}564{,}987 \div 16 = 12{,}347{,}811$ R11. The conjecture seems to be true, according to these limited examples.
  f. 2^k divides n if and only if 2^k divides the k rightmost digit of n.

13. 30 divides n, so $n = 30k$ for some whole number k. Then $n = 15(2k)$. Because $2k$ is a whole number, 15 divides n.

14. a. 1 **b.** 1 **c.** 1
  d. No, because the remainder is nonzero for each of these divisors.

15. a. 1 **b.** 4 **c.** 2
  d. $3 \cdot 8 = 6 \cdot 4$, so $3 \cdot 8 \cdot 7 = 6 \cdot 4 \cdot 7$
  e. Answers vary. For example, 7383 (because $4 \cdot 6 = 3 \cdot 8$).

16. Every counting number divides 0.

17. a. 6 **b.** 8 **c.** 0
  d. The other digits are specified by the type of industry, the language of publication, the publisher, and title of the work. So, the checksum digit is specified last to make a valid weighted sum.

18. $1 \cdot 9 + 3 \cdot 7 + 1 \cdot 8 + 3 \cdot 0 + 1 \cdot 7 + 3 \cdot 9 + 1 \cdot 1 + 3 \cdot 4 + 1 \cdot 1 + 3 \cdot 7 + 1 \cdot 6 + 3 \cdot 4 + 1 \cdot 5 = 130$, which is divisible by 10.

19. 2

20. 9

21. 8

22. $n = 7$ (find the digit n such that $79 + 3n$ is a multiple of 10)

23. The largest possible weighted sum is 225. There are more possible multiples of 3 than multiples of 10 when you think of all possible weighted sums, so the weighted sum could be the wrong multiple of 3 more easily than the wrong multiple of 10. So a weighted sum that needs to be divisible by 3 would be more prone to errors.

24. A multiple of the counting number k is any number of the form nk, where n is a whole number. Then we say that k is a factor of nk, k divides nk, or nk is divisible by k. For example, 24 is a multiple of 6, because $24 = 4 \cdot 6$. Thus, 6 is a factor of 24, 6 divides 24, or 24 is divisible by 6.

25. 4 divides 32, but 4 does not divide 7. By Theorem 3(a), 4 does not divide $32 + 7$.

26. Yes, because 3 divides 42 and 12.

27. $n = 5k$ for some counting number k. Then $n + 1 = 5k + 1$. Then $(n + 1) \div 5 = k$ R1. So 5 does not divide $k + 1$.

28. a. 41 and 28 are factors of 1148.
   b. 5481 is divisible by 27.   **c.** 6 does not divide 45.

29. 2 divides both $4a$ and $20b$, so $4a + 20b$ is an even number. But 901 is an odd number. So there are no whole numbers a and b such that $4a + 20b = 901$ since an even number cannot be an odd number.

30. a. number theory   **b.** does not   **c.** divisibility rules
   d. multiples   **e.** factor

31. a. 110 does not divide 5897.
   b. 580 is not a perfect square.
   c. 25 is a perfect square.

32. a. Yes, because 3 divides both 6 and 24.
   b. No, because 5 divides 15 but 5 does not divide 7.
   c. Yes, because 10 divides both 140 and 50.
   d. No, because 3 does not divide 130 but 3 divides 8220.
   e. Yes, because 4 divides both 836 and 724.
   f. No, because 4 divides 520 but 4 does not divide 311.

33. Answers vary.
   a. $a = 6$ and $b = 4$ **b.** $a = 6$ and $b = 7$

34. Answers vary.
   a. $a = 10$ and $b = 4$ **b.** $a = 10$ and $b = 5$

35. Suppose a is a divisor of b and b is a divisor of c. Then $b = ap$ and $c = bq$ for some whole numbers p and q. Then $c = bq = (ap)q = a(pq)$. By the closure property of multiplication of whole numbers, pq is a whole number. Then a is a divisor of c.

36. Suppose a is a divisor of b and c is a counting number. Then $b = aq$ for some counting number q. Then $bc = (aq)c$. Then $bc = (ac)q$. By the closure property of multiplication of whole numbers, ac is a whole number. Then ac divides bc.

37. 3 divides 27 and 9, so 3 divides $27a$ and $9b$. Then 3 divides the sum $27a + 9b$. If you could find values of a and b that satisfy the equation $27a + 9b = 1111$, then 3 would need to divide 1111. But $1111 \div 3 = 370$ R1, so 3 does not divide 1111. Thus, there cannot be any whole numbers a and b such that $27a + 9b = 1111$.

38. a. $n = 3, 6, 9, 12, \ldots$ **b.** none   **c.** none

39. a. $25 = 5^2$ **b.** $16 = 4^2$
   c. $a^6 = a^{3 \times 2} = (a^3)^2$, so a^6 is a perfect square

40. a. $27 = 3^3$ **b.** $125 = 5^3$
   c. $a^6 = a^{2 \times 3} = (a^2)^3$, so a^6 is a perfect cube

41. a. 4 divides 92, so 4 divides 2,296,492.
   b. 4 does not divide 58, so 4 does not divide 20,858.
   c. Answers vary. For example, 45,638 is an even number that is not divisible by 4 because 4 does not divide 38.

42. a. $656 \div 8 = 82$. 656 is divisible by 8, so 23,528,656 is divisible by 8.
   b. $348 \div 8 = 43$ R4. 348 is not divisible by 8, so 365,348 is not divisible by 8.
   c. three ways

43. a. 7410 is an even number, so 2 divides 7410. The sum of the digits of 7410 is 12, so 3 divides 7410. Then 2 and 3 divide 7410; therefore, 6 divides 7410.

   b. 3256 is an even number, so 2 divides 3256. The sum of the digits of 3256 is 16, which is not divisible by 3. So 3256 is not divisible by 6.
   c. An odd number is not divisible by 2. The divisibility test for 6 requires that 2 divide the number.

44. a. 54,230 is divisible by 5 because the ones digit is 0 or 5.
   b. 225,099,695 is divisible by 5 because the ones digit is 0 or 5.
   c. 843,021,024 is not divisible by 5 because the ones digit is neither 0 nor 5.

45. a. $3 \times 8 = 24$, and the only common factor of 3 and 8 is 1. Then 24 divides a number if and only if 3 and 8 divide the number.
   b. 8 divides 016, and 3 divides the sum of all digits: 15. Then 8 and 3 divide 125,016. Then 24 divides 125,016.
   c. 8 divides 608, but 3 does not divide the sum of all digits: 25. 74,608 is not a multiple of 24.

46. a. $3 \times 5 = 15$, and the only common factor of 3 and 5 is 1. 15 divides a number n if and only if 3 divides n and 5 divides n.
   b. Answers vary. For example, does 15 divide 495? 3 divides 495, and 5 divides 495. Then 15 divides 495. Check: $495 \div 15 = 33$.
   c. Answers vary. For example, does 15 divide 125? 3 does not divide 125, but 5 divides 125. Then 15 does not divide 125. Check: $125 \div 15 = 8$ R5.

47. a. $abcd = ab \cdot 100 + cd$. Any number can be written in the form $k \cdot 100 + xy$, where k is a counting number and x and y are digits. Because 25 divides 100, the following divisibility rule is suggested: 25 divides the whole number n if and only if 25 divides the number formed by two rightmost digits of n.
   b. No, because 89 is not divisible by 25.
   c. Yes, because 75 is divisible by 25.

48. a. one way   **b.** zero ways   **c.** 10 ways

49. a. $2 \div 4 = 0$ R2, $6 \div 4 = 1$ R2, $10 \div 2 = 2$ R2, $\ldots$. Divide each term by 4 (the common difference).
   b. $3 \div 5 = 0$ R3, $8 \div 5 = 1$ R3, $13 \div 5 = 2$ R3, $\ldots$. Divide each term by 5 (the common difference).

50. No. For example, 4 divides 48 and 8 divides 48. But 32 does not divide 48.

51. Suppose b divides a and n is any counting number. Then $a = bq$ for some counting number q. Then $an = (bq)n$. Then $an = b(qn)$. By the closure property of multiplication of whole numbers, qn is a whole number. Then b divides an.

52. a. $4 \times 5 = 20$, and the only common factor of 4 and 5 is 1. 20 divides a number n if and only if 4 divides n and 5 divides n.
   b. Answers vary. For example, does 20 divide 7180? 4 divides 7180, and 5 divides 7180. Then 20 divides 7180. Check: $7180 \div 20 = 359$.
   c. Answers vary. For example, does 20 divide 125? 4 does not divide 125, but 5 divides 125. Then 20 does not divide 125. Check: $125 \div 20 = 6$ R5.

53. a. 0   **b.** 1   **c.** 2

54. a.

a	2	6	10	14	18	22
$a \div 2$	1 R0	3 R0	5 R0	7 R0	9 R0	11 R0

The remainders form the repeating sequence 0, 0, 0, . . . , or all the remainders are 0.

b.

a	2	6	10	14	18	22
$a \div 3$	0 R2	2 R0	3 R1	4 R2	6 R0	7 R1

The remainders form the repeating sequence 2, 0, 1, 2, 0, 1, ...

c.

a	2	6	10	14	18	22
$a \div 4$	0 R2	1 R2	2 R2	3 R2	4 R2	5 R2

The remainders form the repeating sequence 2, 2, 2, 2, . . . , or all the remainders are 2.

55. a.

a	3	8	13	18	23	28
$a \div 2$	1 R1	4 R0	6 R1	9 R0	11 R1	14 R0

The remainders form the repeating sequence 1, 0, 1, 0, 1, ...

b.

a	3	8	13	18	23	28
$a \div 3$	1 R0	2 R2	4 R1	6 R0	7 R2	9 R1

The remainders form the repeating sequence 0, 2, 1, 0, 2, 1, ...

c.

a	3	8	13	18	23	28
$a \div 4$	0 R3	2 R0	3 R1	4 R2	5 R3	7 R0

The remainders form the repeating sequence 3, 0, 1, 2, 3, 0, 1, 2, ...

56. a. True
   b. False. Answers vary; for example, 14 is not a divisor of 21, but 7 is a divisor of 21.
   c. False. Answers vary; for example, $3 + 7$ is divisible by 5, but 5 is not a factor of 3.
   d. False. Answers vary; for example, $2 + 4$ is divisible by 3, but 9 is not a divisor of $2 + 4$.
   e. True

57. a. no **b.** yes **c.** yes

58. a. True. Assume n is divisible by 6. Then $n = 6q$ for some counting number q. Then $n = 3(2q)$. Then n is divisible by 3.
   b. False. Answers vary; for example, 15 is divisible by 5, but 15 is not divisible by 10.
   c. False. Answers vary; for example, 20 is divisible by 4, but 20 is not divisible by 8.
   d. True. Assume n is divisible by 100. Then $n = 100q$ for some counting number q. Then $n = 20(5q)$. Then n is divisible by 20.
   e. False. Answers vary; for example, 40 is divisible by 20, but 40 is not divisible by 100.

SECTION 4.2

1. The number 10 has two array representations.

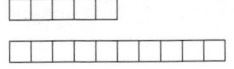

So 10 is a composite number.

2.

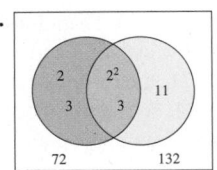

3. No, because 8 is not a prime number.

4. a. $\text{GCF}(90, 144) = 2 \cdot 3^2$
   b. $\text{LCM}(90, 144) = 2^4 \cdot 3^2 \cdot 5$

5. a.

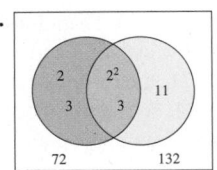

   b. $\text{GCF}(72, 132) = 2^2 \cdot 3 = 12$ and $\text{LCM}(72, 132) = (2 \cdot 3) \cdot (2^2 \cdot 3) \cdot 11 = 792$
   c. The GCF is a common factor, so the GCF is less than or equal to the LCM. Multiply the factors in the intersection of the rings to obtain the GCF.

6. $a = 7 \cdot 75 = 525$ and $b = 75 \cdot 2^3 = 600$

7. a. $\text{LCM}(a, b) = 2^4 \cdot 3^4 \cdot 5^4 \cdot 7^2 \cdot 11$
   b. $\text{GCF}(a, b) = 2^3 \cdot 3 \cdot 5^3$

8.

$$48 = 2^4 \cdot 3$$

9. a. $a = 120, b = 12\ c = 10, d = 4$
   b. $a = 2^3 \cdot 3 \cdot 5$

10. 16 flowers

11. 60 pieces, or $\text{LCM}(1, 2, 3, 4, 5)$

12. $960

13. five times

14. **a.** 60 years   **b.** 420 years   **c.** 420 years

15. 5 divides 35, so the ones digit of a multiple of 35 must be a 0 or 5. Then the LCM must have a ones digit equal to 0 or 5.

16. The LCM of two numbers cannot exceed the product of the two numbers. 102 is larger than $3 \cdot 17$.

17. $b = 548$

18. No. $n = 15b + 3 = 3(5b + 1)$, so n must be a composite number for all counting numbers b.

19. Answers vary. For example, $n = 2^2 \cdot 3 \cdot 5$.

20. The left-hand side of the equation has 5 as one of the prime factors. The right-hand side of the equation does not have 5 as one of the prime factors. The prime factors of $5n$ do not match the prime factors of 24. The prime factorization of a number is unique, so $5n \neq 24$ for any whole number n.

21. No. The number n would need to have the form $n = p^a \cdot q^b$ for some prime numbers p and q and counting numbers a and b. Then a and b would need to satisfy the equation $(a + 1) \cdot (b + 1) = 5$. Here, $(a + 1) \cdot (b + 1)$ is a product of two counting numbers greater than 1, and this would imply 5 is a composite number. 5 is a prime number.

22. **a.** $54 = 2 \cdot 3^3$ **b.** eight divisors
    c. Every common factor of a and b must divide the GCF (think of the intersection of the rings in the Venn diagram for finding the GCF of a and b). Because 54 has eight factors, a and b must have eight common factors.

23. **a.** 230 pages
    b. No. There are not enough periods (thousand, million, billion, trillion, and so on) for such a large number.

24. **a.** Multiples of 6: 6, 12, 18, 24, 30, . . .
    Multiples of 8: 8, 16, 24, 32, . . .
    Then $LCM(6, 8) = 24$.
    b. Factors of 28: 1, 2, 4, 7, 14, 28
    Factors of 98: 1, 2, 7, 14, 49, 98
    Then $GCF(28, 98) = 14$.
    c. Multiples of 42: 42, 84, 126, 168
    Multiples of 24: 24, 48, 72, 96, 120, 144, 168
    Then $LCM(42, 24) = 168$
    d. Factors of 42: 1, 42, 2, 21, 3, 14, 6, 7
    Factors of 78: 1, 78, 2, 39, 3, 26, 6, 13
    Then $GCF(42, 78) = 6$

25. $GCF(336, 1500) \times LCM(336, 1500) = 336 \times 1500$
    $12 \times LCM(336, 1500) = 504,000$
    $LCM(336, 1500) = 504,000/12$
    $LCM(336, 1500) = 42,000$

26. 1, 32, 2, 16, 4, 8

27. **a.** $24 + 32 = 8(3 + 4)$ **b.** $45x + 30xy = 15x(3 + 2y)$
    c. $124x^4y^2 + 42x^3y^5 = 2x^3y^2(62x + 21y^3)$

28. sieve of Eratosthenes

29. square root test

30. Any other pair of consecutive numbers would involve an even number n greater than 2, which would make n a composite number.

31. A prime number p has exactly two factors: 1 and p. Because 3 is a prime number, $3 = 1 \times 3$. But 1 is not a prime number, so 3 cannot be written as a product of prime numbers.

32. $p + 1$ is a composite number because $p > 2$ is an odd number and $p + 1$ must be an even number greater than 2.

33. a and b have no common prime factors.

34. a and b have at least one common prime factor.

35. Any counting number n greater than 5 that has a ones digit of 0, 2, 4, 6, or 8 must be a composite number, because n would be divisible by 2, as well as 1 and n. Any counting number n greater than 5 that has a ones digit of 5 must be a composite number, because n would be divisible by 5, as well as 1 and n.

36. **a.** number theory   **b.** 105   **c.** 3
    d. prime factorization   **e.** factorization   **f.** list
    g. composite   **h.** sieve of Eratosthenes
    i. GCF   **j.** $12 \cdot 16$

37. 1, 42, 2, 21, 3, 14, 6, 7

38. **a.**

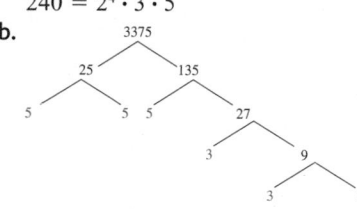

$240 = 2^4 \cdot 3 \cdot 5$
    b.

$3375 = 3^3 \cdot 5^3$

39. **a.** 48   **b.** 135   **c.** 70   **d.** 126

40. **a.** 3   **b.** 86

41. **a.** 4   **b.** 985

42. **a.** 3   **b.** 20

43. Answers vary. For example, $5^2 \times 7$ (175).

44. $4

45. Every common factor of a and b must divide the GCF (think of the intersection of the rings in the Venn diagram for finding the GCF of a and b). Because 24 has eight factors, a and b must have eight common factors.

46. **a.** 24 seconds later   **b.** 12 times

47. A prime number is a counting number that has 1 as the only proper divisor.

48. **a.** The number of factors is an odd number.
    b. A perfect square has an odd number of factors.
    c. p has $(2k_1 + 1)(2k_2 + 1) \cdots (2k_n + 1)$ factors. This is a product of odd numbers, so p has an odd number of factors.

49. **a.** yes   **b.** no   **c.** no

50. **a.** yes   **b.** no   **c.** no   **d.** yes

51. Answers vary, such as 5 and 7, 11 and 13, or 17 and 19.

52. a. yes   **b.** yes   **c.** no   **d.** no

53. Answers vary.
   a. $a = 2^3 \cdot 5^2$ **b.** $a = 2^6$ **c.** $a = 2 \cdot 7^4$

54. $7 \cdot 11 \cdot 13 = 1001$
Let xyz be any three-digit number. Then
$$\begin{aligned} xyz \cdot 7 \cdot 11 \cdot 13 &= xyz \cdot 1001 \\ &= xyz\,(1000 + 1) \\ &= xyz \cdot 1000 + xyz \\ &= xyz000 + xyz \\ &= xyzxyz \end{aligned}$$
Any six-digit number of the form $xyzxyz$ can be expressed as $xyz \cdot 7 \cdot 11 \cdot 13$. So dividing the number $xyzxyz$ by 7, 11, and 13 is like dividing $xyz \cdot 7 \cdot 11 \cdot 13$ by 7, 11, and 13. The result is xyz.

55. a. 126   **b.** 18,000   **c.** $\mathrm{LCM}(a, b) = 2^4 \cdot 3^2 \cdot 5^3 \cdot 7$
   d. $\mathrm{GCF}(a, b) = 2 \cdot 3^2$

56. No. $n = 12b + 4 = 4(3b + 1)$. So n has at least three factors: n, 1, and 4. So n is a composite number.

57. a. $\mathrm{LCM}(a, b) = 2^4 \cdot 3^4 \cdot 5^4 \cdot 7^2 \cdot 11$
   b. $\mathrm{LCM}(a, b) = 2^3 \cdot 3^4 \cdot 5^4 \cdot 7^4 \cdot 11^5 \cdot 13^2$
   c. $\mathrm{LCM}(a, b) = 120x^4y^3$

58. a. $13^2 < 173$. Prime, because none of the prime numbers 2, 3, 5, 7, 11, and 13 divide 173.
   b. $30^2 < 921$. Composite, because 3 divides 921.
   c. $26^2 < 719$. Prime, because none of the prime numbers 2, 3, 5, 7, 11, 13, 17, 19, and 23 divide 719.
   d. $14^2 < 221$. Composite, because 13 divides 221.

59. a. $\mathrm{GCF}(a, b) = 2^3 \cdot 3 \cdot 5^3$ **b.** $\mathrm{GCF}(a, b) = 5^2 \cdot 13$
   c. $\mathrm{GCF}(a, b) = 3x^3y^2$

60. Answers vary.
   a. $a = 2^3 \cdot 5^3 \cdot 7^8 \cdot 11$ and $b = 2^7 \cdot 5^2 \cdot 7^4 \cdot 11$
   b. $a = 2^3 \cdot 5^2 \cdot 7 \cdot 11$ and $b = 2 \cdot 7^4$

61. a. 1   **b.** $a \cdot b$

62. 1, 2, 4, 5, 10, 20

63. a.
$$\begin{array}{r} 3 \\ 2\overline{)6} \\ 2\overline{)12} \\ 2\overline{)24} \\ 2\overline{)48} \end{array}$$
Then $48 = 2^4 \cdot 3$.
   b.
$$\begin{array}{r} 5 \\ 5\overline{)25} \\ 3\overline{)75} \\ 2\overline{)150} \\ 2\overline{)300} \end{array}$$
Then $300 = 2^2 \cdot 3 \cdot 5^2$.

64. a. $\mathrm{LCM}(240, 372) = 7440$ **b.** $\mathrm{LCM}(336, 192) = 1344$

65. a.
$$\begin{aligned} \mathrm{GCF}(234, 420) &= \mathrm{GCF}(234, 186) \\ &= \mathrm{GCF}(48, 186) \\ &= \mathrm{GCF}(48, 42) \\ &= \mathrm{GCF}(6, 42) \\ &= 6 \end{aligned}$$
$$\mathrm{LCM}(234, 420) = \frac{234 \cdot 420}{\mathrm{GCF}(234, 420)} = 16{,}380$$

b.
$$\begin{aligned} \mathrm{GCF}(580, 18{,}300) &= \mathrm{GCF}(580, 320) \\ &= \mathrm{GCF}(260, 320) \\ &= \mathrm{GCF}(60, 320) \\ &= \mathrm{GCF}(60, 20) \\ &= 20 \end{aligned}$$
$$\mathrm{LCM}(580, 18{,}300) = \frac{580 \cdot 18{,}300}{\mathrm{GCF}(580, 18{,}300)} = 530{,}700$$

SECTION 4.3

1. a. 0   **b.** -4 **c.** 4   **d.** 3   **e.** -1

2. a. $-3 + -2 = -5$

••• ••

   b. $-2 + 4 = 2$

   c. $-1 + -3 = -4$

• •••

3. a. **STEP 1.** Represent the minuend.

•••

   STEP 2. Add zero pairs as needed.

••• ○○○○

   STEP 3. Take away the subtrahend.

••• ○○○○

   STEP 4. Subtract: $-3 - 4 = -7$.

   b. **STEP 1.** Represent the minuend.

○

   STEP 2. Add zero pairs as needed.

○ ○○○○
••••

   STEP 3. Take away the subtrahend.

○ ○○○○
••••

   STEP 4. Subtract: $1 - -4 = 5$.

   c. **STEP 1.** Represent the minuend.

••

   STEP 2. Add zero pairs as needed.

•• ○○○○○

   STEP 3. Take away the subtrahend.

•• ○○○○○

   STEP 4. Subtract: $-2 - 5 = -7$.

4. $4 + -7 = -3$

5. a. $-3 + -2 = -5$

   b. $-2 + 5 = 3$

   c. $2 + -5 = -3$

6. $-5 - -7 = 2$

7. a. $-3 - 4 = -7$

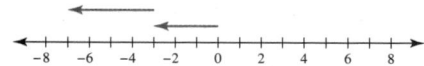

b. $3 - -4 = 7$

c. $-2 - -6 = 4$

8. a. $5 - -3 = 8$ **b.** $3 - -1 = 4$ **c.** $-3 - 2 = -5$

9. a. 0 **b.** 3 **c.** -4 **d.** -2 **e.** -2 **f.** 4

10. a. $7 + -4 = 3$

b. $5 - -3 = 8$

c. $-5 + 3 = -2$

d. $-4 - -3 = -1$

e. $-5 - 2 = -7$

11. $-4 < 3$

12. $70

13. 23 units

14. four dishes

15. a. They are non-negative integers.
b. They are nonpositive integers.

16. a. Addition property of equality
b. Associative property of addition
c. Additive inverse property
d. Additive identity property

17. a. definition of subtraction **b.** definition of subtraction
c. simplification

18. a. positive
b. If n is positive, then $n \cdot n \cdot n$ is positive. If n is negative, then $n \cdot n \cdot n$ is negative.

19. $4 \times 2 = 8$
$4 \times 1 = 4$
$4 \times 0 = 0$
$4 \times -1 = -4$
$4 \times -2 = -8$
$4 \times -3 = -12$

20. a. Addition property of equality
b. Additive inverse property
c. Associative property of addition
d. Additive inverse property
e. Additive identity property

21. a. Addition property of equality
b. Additive identity property
c. Associative property of addition
d. Additive inverse property
e. Additive identity property

22. a. No. For example, 5 and 3 are whole numbers, but $3 - 5$ (which equals -2) is not a whole number.
b. Yes. Here's why. $a - b = a + (-b)$ due to subtracting integers by adding the opposite. The additive inverse of an integer is an integer, so $-b$ is an integer. $a + (-b)$ is an integer because the set of integers is closed under addition, due to the closure property of addition. Then $a - b$ is an integer.

23. 189°F

24. 9250 m

25. a. negative **b.** positive **c.** negative **d.** positive
e. If there is an odd number of negative signs, then the number is negative. If there is an even number of negative signs, then the number is a positive number. You can tell whether the number is negative or odd by counting the number of negative signs and using the pattern described.

26. a. $-1 \cdot 4 = -4$ **b.** $3 \cdot -1 = -3$ **c.** $4^0 = 1$

27. a. $\varnothing$ **b.** $\{\ldots, -3, -2, -1, 1, 2, 3, \ldots\}$ or $I - \{0\}$
c. $\varnothing$ **d.** $\{0\}$ **e.** W **f.** W

28. Answers vary. For example, Terri owed her father $7. Then she paid her father $3. How much more money does she owe her father?

29. Answers vary. For example, the temperature was -3°F this morning. It dropped 7°F by 1 p.m. What was the temperature at 1 p.m.?

30. a. $-3 - 5 = -8$ and $5 - -3 = 8$
b. $-6 - -1 = -5$ and $-1 - -6 = 5$
c. If a and b are any two integers, then $a - b = -(b - a)$.

31. First, evaluate $32 \div 8$ to get 4. Because 32 and -8 have different signs, the quotient is negative. Then $32 \div -8 = -4$.

32. a. concrete **b.** pictorial **c.** symbolic **d.** positive
e. negative **f.** multiplicative identity
g. additive identity **h.** -3 **i.** 3 **j.** 0
k. sign rules **l.** debts and assets

33. a. -3 **b.** 5 **c.** $-b$ **d.** -8 **e.** 0 **f.** $-p + -q$

34. a. $4 < 10$ **b.** $-10 < 2$ **c.** $-5 > -100$

35. If you plot both numbers on the number line, then the number on the left is less than the number on the right. Negative integers are always to the left of zero, and positive integers are always to the right of zero. So any negative integer is always to the left of any positive integer. So any negative integer is less than any positive integer.

36.

$-(4 - 5n)$	**Original equation**
$(-1)(4 - 5n)$	**Since $-a = (-1)a$**
$(-1)(4 + -5n)$	**Subtract by adding the opposite**
$(-1)(4) + (-1)(-5n)$	**Distributive property of multiplication over addition**
$(-1)(4) + [(-1)(-5)]n$	**Associative property of multiplication**
$-4 + 5n$	**Sign rules for multiplication**

37. a. $-4 - 3 = -7$

$\bullet\bullet\bullet\bullet$ $\;\;$ $\boxed{\circ\,\circ\,\circ}\nearrow$

b. $-4 - 3 = -7$

38. a. $n - -3 = 8$ $\qquad$ Original equation
$\quad$ $n = 8 + -3$ $\qquad$ Definition of subtraction
$\quad$ $n = 5$ $\qquad\qquad$ Simplification

b. $4n + 3 = -21$ $\qquad$ Original equation
$\quad$ $4n = -21 - 3$ $\qquad$ Definition of subtraction with integers
$\quad$ $4n = -24$ $\qquad\quad$ Simplification
$\quad$ $n = -24 \div 4$ $\qquad$ Definition of division with integers
$\quad$ $n = -6$ $\qquad\qquad$ Simplification

39. a. $3 - -5 = 3 + 5 = 8$
b. $-2 - 8 = -2 + -8 = -10$
c. $-5 - -11 = -5 + 11 = 6$
d. $10 - 14 = 10 + -14 = -4$

40. $-\$350$

41. a. $3 + -2 = 1$
$\quad$ $3 + -3 = 0$
$\quad$ $3 + -4 = -1$
b. $-4 + 2 = -2$
$\quad$ $-4 + 1 = -3$
$\quad$ $-4 + 0 = -4$

42. a. Build on known facts (sum of two whole numbers).
$\quad$ $2 + 4 = 6$
$\quad$ $1 + 4 = 5$
$\quad$ $0 + 4 = 4$
$\quad$ $-1 + 4 = 3$
$\quad$ $-2 + 4 = 2$
$\quad$ $-3 + 4 = 1$
b. Build on known facts (difference of two whole numbers).
$\quad$ $3 - 3 = 0$
$\quad$ $3 - 2 = 1$
$\quad$ $3 - 1 = 2$
$\quad$ $3 - 0 = 3$
$\quad$ $3 - -1 = 4$
$\quad$ $3 - -2 = 5$

43. a. Build on known facts (products of whole numbers).
$\quad$ $2 \cdot 4 = 8$
$\quad$ $1 \cdot 4 = 4$
$\quad$ $0 \cdot 4 = 0$
$\quad$ $-1 \cdot 4 = -4$
$\quad$ $-2 \cdot 4 = -8$
$\quad$ $-3 \cdot 4 = -12$
b. Build on known facts (products of whole numbers).
$\quad$ $3 \cdot 2 = 6$
$\quad$ $3 \cdot 1 = 3$
$\quad$ $3 \cdot 0 = 0$
$\quad$ $3 \cdot -1 = -3$
$\quad$ $3 \cdot -2 = -6$

44. Assume the student already knows how to multiply a negative integer and a positive integer.
$\quad$ $-3 \cdot 2 = -6$
$\quad$ $-3 \cdot 1 = -3$
$\quad$ $-3 \cdot 0 = 0$
$\quad$ $-3 \cdot -1 = 3$
$\quad$ $-3 \cdot -2 = 6$

45. a. 3 and -9 have different signs, so 3×-9 is negative. $3 \times 9 = 27$, so $3 \times -9 = -27$.
b. -4 and 7 have different signs, so -4×7 is negative. $4 \times 7 = 28$, so $-4 \times 7 = -28$.
c. 12 and 5 have the same signs, so the product is positive: $12 \times 5 = 60$.
d. -4 and -9 have the same sign, so the product is positive: $4 \times 9 = 36$, so $-4 \times -9 = 36$.

46. a. 36 and -9 have different signs, so $36 \div -9$ is negative. $36 \div 9 = 4$, so $36 \div -9 = -4$.
b. -42 and 7 have different signs, so $-42 \div 7$ is negative. $42 \div 7 = 6$, so $-42 \div 7 = -6$.
c. 20 and 5 have the same sign, so $20 \div 5$ is positive: $20 \div 5 = 4$.
d. -24 and -4 have the same sign, so $-24 \div -4$ is positive. $24 \div 4 = 6$, so $-24 \div -4 = 6$.

47. a. $-2n - 6n = -2n + -6n = (-2 + -6)n = -8n$
b. $4n - 7n = n4 - n7 = n(4 - 7) = n(-3) = -3n$

48. a. -6 $\quad$ **b.** $2h - 7$ $\quad$ **c.** -3 $\quad$ **d.** 6

49. a. -15 $\quad$ **b.** 2 $\quad$ **c.** 7

50. a. 1 $\quad$ **b.** -5 $\quad$ **c.** 4

51. $-\$31$

52. 7 L

53. a. No. For example, 8, 3, and 2 are whole numbers. $(8 - 3) - 2 = 5 - 2 = 3$ and $8 - (3 - 2) = 8 - 1 = 7$.
b. No. For example, 8, 3, and 2 are integers. $(8 - 3) - 2 = 5 - 2 = 3$ and $8 - (3 - 2) = 8 - 1 = 7$.

54. a. $4(-3x + 2y)$ $\quad$ **b.** $6x^2y^2(3y^3 - 2x^5)$

55. a. $|-3 - 5| = |-8| = 8$ $\quad$ **b.** $|4 - -9| = |13| = 13$
c. $|-12 - -5| = |-7| = 7$ $\quad$ **d.** $|8 - 5| = |3| = 3$

56. a. -6 $\quad$ **b.** -7 $\quad$ **c.** $y = -7n + 1$, where y is the nth term
d. -370 $\quad$ **e.** no

57. a. -1586 $\quad$ **b.** 2240

58. The sequence is generalized by the equation $y = -4n + 34$, where y is the nth term.

59. a. 8 $\quad$ **b.** 44 $\quad$ **c.** $31 - a$

60. a. $n - 7 = 10$ and $n - 7 = -10$ $\quad$ **b.** $|7 - -3|$

61. a. -6 and 10 $\quad$ **b.** -43 and 31 $\quad$ **c.** 59 and 11

62. a. $a \times -b = -(a \times b)$ $\quad$ **b.** $-a \times -b = a \times b$
c. $-a \div -b = a \div b$ $\quad$ **d.** $-a \div b = -(a \div b)$

63. a. false $\quad$ **b.** false $\quad$ **c.** false $\quad$ **d.** true
e. false $\quad$ **f.** true

64. Conjecture: Suppose a and b are integers such that $a < b$. If n is a positive integer, then $an < bn$.

65. Conjecture: Suppose a and b are integers such that $a < b$. If n is a negative integer, then $an > bn$.

REVIEW QUESTIONS

1.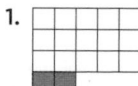

2.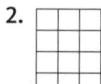

Each row (or column) has the same number of cells or squares.

3. a.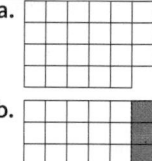

b.

c. Each column does not have the same number of rows.

4. a. yes **b.** no **c.** no **d.** yes **e.** yes **f.** no

5. Answers vary.
   a. $a = 6$ and $b = 10$ **b.** $a = 7$ and $b = 4$

6. a. Yes, since 2 divides 712 and 2 divides 930.
   b. No, since 2 does not divide 811 and 2 divides 538.
   c. Yes, since 10 divides 120 and 10 divides 30.
   d. No, since 10 does not divide 81 and 10 divides 720.

7. Answers vary.
   a. $a = 11$ and $b = 3$ **b.** $a = 7$ and $b = 6$

8. a. No, since 5 does not divide 1532 and 5 divides 120.
   b. Yes, since 5 divides 7320 and 5 divides 810.
   c. Yes, since 10 divides 1620 and 10 divides 730.
   d. No, since 10 does not divide 7263 and 10 divides 620.

9. a. 78 and 382 are factors of 29,796, and 29,796 is a composite number.
   b. 285 does not divide 10,300.
   c. 456 is not a perfect square.
   d. 2296 is divisible by 56, or 2296 is a composite number.
   e. n is a composite number, or n has four prime factors.
   f. 125 is a perfect cube.

10. a. yes **b.** no **c.** yes **d.** no **e.** yes **f.** yes

11. If 12 is a factor of n, then $n = 12a$. Then $n = 3(4a)$. Then 3 is a factor of n. So 12 cannot be the smallest factor of n.

12. Suppose 4 is a factor of n. Then $n = 4k$ for some counting number k. Then $n + 3 = 4k + 3$. Then $(n + 3) \div 4 = k\,R3$. The remainder of $(n + 3) \div 4$ is nonzero, so $n + 3$ is not divisible by 4.

13. a. Yes; $M = 49 \cdot (3^{250} \cdot 7^{48} \cdot 11^{14})$.
   b. Yes; $Q = 10 \cdot (2^{139} \cdot 7^{168} \cdot 5^2)$.
   c. Yes; $R = 5^2 \cdot 6^3 \cdot (5^2 \cdot 6^4 \cdot 11^2)$.

14. a. 3 does not divide 2356.   **b.** 2 does not divide 6987.

15. a. 9 **b.** 9 **c.** 9 **d.** 6

16. a. 9 **b.** 8 **c.** 7

17. A possible answer is the six-digit number $abcabc$, or $aabbcc$.

18. a. 14 divides n if and only if 2 and 7 both divide n.
   b. 2 divides 43,848 by the divisibility test and 7 divides 43,848 by division. Then 14 divides 43,848.
   c. 7 does not divide 10,140, so 14 does not divide 10,140.

19. a. 22 divides n if and only if 2 and 11 both divide n.
   b. 2 and 11 both divide 2706 by the divisibility tests. So 22 divides 2706.
   c. 11 does not divide 928, so 22 does not divide 928.

20. a. A counting number that has exactly two factors
   b. There is only one way to represent 3 as an array (ignoring orientation).
   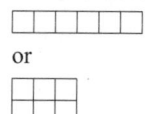

21. a. A counting number that has more than two factors
   b. There is more than one way to represent 6 as an array.

   or

22. a. composite **b.** prime **c.** composite **d.** prime

23. Use divisibility tests or the square root test.
   a. Composite, since 3 divides the sum of digits.
   b. Prime, since $13^2 \leq 193$ and no primes from 2 to 13 divide 664.
   c. Composite, since $14^2 \leq 203$ and 7 divides 203.
   d. Prime, since $20^2 \leq 401$ and no primes from 2 to 20 divide 181.
   e. Composite, since 5 divides 1375.

24. No. $B = 8(3A + 1)$, which makes B a composite number.

25. Yes. Consider $A = 3$.

26. No. A^2 has at least three factors: 1, A, and A^2.

27. Answers vary.
   a. $72 = 8 \times 3^2$ **b.** $90 = 2 \times 3^2 \times 5$

28. a. $1485 = 3^3 \times 5 \times 11$
   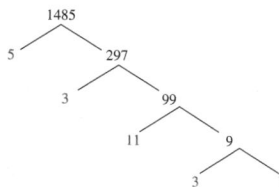

   b. $600 = 2^3 \times 3 \times 5^2$
   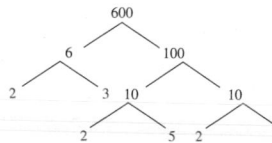

   c. $225 \times 12 = 2^2 \times 3^3 \times 5^2$
   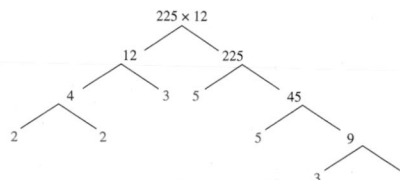

29. a. 1, 60, 2, 30, 3, 20, 4, 15, 5, 12, 6, 10
   b. 1, 42, 2, 21, 3, 14, 6, 7

30. a. $76 = 2^2 \times 19$

$$\begin{array}{r} 19 \\ 2\overline{)38} \\ 2\overline{)76} \end{array}$$

b. $354 = 2 \times 3 \times 59$

$$\begin{array}{r} 59 \\ 3\overline{)177} \\ 2\overline{)354} \end{array}$$

31. a. 84; 3; 80   **b.** 56; 3; 52   **c.** 432; 4; 427
    d. 8; 3; 4   **e.** 12; 3; 8

32. a. 4   **b.** 3

33. $378 = 2 \times 3^3 \times 7$

34. mn factors

35. a. Composite, since $21^2 \le 451$ and 11 divides 451.
    b. Prime, since $17^2 \le 311$ and no prime numbers from 2 to
      17 divide 311.
    c. Prime, since $23^2 \le 563$ and no primes from 2 to 23 divide
      563.
    d. Composite, since $18^2 \le 341$ and 11 divides 341.

36. GCF$(6300, 12{,}500) = 2^2 \times 5^2$ and LCM$(6300, 12{,}500) =$
    $2^2 \times 3^2 \times 5^5 \times 7$

37. a. GCF$(12, 15) = 3$ and LCM$(12, 15) = 60$
    b. GCF$(18, 24) = 6$ and LCM$(18, 24) = 72$
    c. GCF$(5, 8) = 1$ and LCM$(5, 8) = 40$

38. a. $2^3 \cdot 3^4 \cdot 5^2 \cdot 7 \cdot 13$
    b. $2^3 \cdot 5^3 \cdot 7^2 \cdot 11^4 \cdot 13^2$
    c. $2^3 \cdot 3^6 \cdot 7^2 \cdot 11 \cdot 13^3 \cdot 17^3$

39. a. $2^3 \cdot 5^2$ **b.** 11   **c.** $11 \cdot 13 \cdot 17$

40. a. GCF$(346, 68) =$ GCF$(6, 68) =$ GCF$(6, 2) =$
    GCF$(0, 2) = 2$
    b. GCF$(1232, 64) =$ GCF$(16, 64) =$ GCF$(16, 0) = 16$
    c. GCF$(1044, 300) =$ GCF$(144, 300) =$ GCF$(144, 12) =$
    GCF$(0, 12) = 12$

41. a. LCM$(15, 36) = \dfrac{15 \times 36}{\text{GCF}(15, 36)} = \dfrac{15 \times 36}{3} = 180$
    b. LCM$(330, 260) = \dfrac{330 \times 260}{\text{GCF}(330, 260)} = \dfrac{330 \times 260}{10} = 8580$
    c. LCM$(312, 124) = \dfrac{312 \times 124}{\text{GCF}(312, 124)} = \dfrac{312 \times 124}{4} = 9672$

42. LCM$(70, 90, 110) = 6930.$

43. Answers vary.

    ⦾ and ⦾⦾

44. Answers vary.

    ●●● and ●●●●◦

45. a.
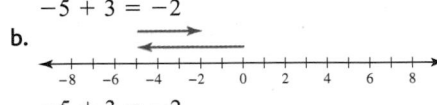
    $-5 + 3 = -2$
    b.
    $-5 + 3 = -2$

46. a. ●●●   ●●●●●
    $-5 + -3 = -8$
    b.
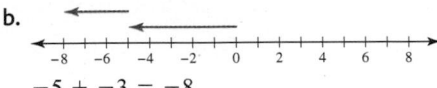
    $-5 + -3 = -8$

47. a. ●●▭▭▭↗
    $-5 - -3 = -2$
    b.
    $-5 - -3 = -2$

48. a. ●●●● ▭▭▭↗
    $-4 - 3 = -7$
    b.
    $-4 - 3 = -7$

49. a. $4 - -7 = 4 + 7 = 11$
    b. $-5 - 12 = -5 + -12 = -17$
    c. $-3 - -21 = -3 + 21 = 18$

50. a. $2 + -2 = 0$ **b.** $-3 + 1 = -2$
    $2 + -3 = -1$ $-3 + 0 = -3$

51. a. Build on known facts (multiplication with whole
    numbers).
      $2 \cdot 5 = 10$
      $1 \cdot 5 = 5$
      $-1 \cdot 5 = -5$
      $-2 \cdot 5 = -10$
    b. Build on known facts (multiplication with whole
    numbers).
      $4 \cdot 2 = 8$
      $4 \cdot 1 = 4$
      $4 \cdot 0 = 0$
      $4 \cdot -1 = -4$
      $4 \cdot -2 = -8$
      $4 \cdot -3 = -12$

52. a. The factors have different signs, so the product is nega-
    tive. $2 \cdot 8 = 16$, so $2 \cdot (-8) = -16$.
    b. The factors have different signs, so the product is nega-
    tive. $5 \cdot 9 = 45$, so $(-5) \cdot 9 = -45$.
    c. The factors have the same signs, so the product is positive.
    $15 \cdot 3 = 45$.
    d. The factors have the same signs, so the product is positive.
    $8 \cdot 5 = 40$, so $(-8) \cdot (-5) = 40$.

53. a. The factors have different signs, so the quotient is nega-
    tive. $18 \div 6 = 3$, so $18 \div -6 = -3$.
    b. The factors have different signs, so the quotient is nega-
    tive. $24 \div 6 = 4$, so $-24 \div 6 = -4$.
    c. The factors have the same sign, so the quotient is positive.
    $42 \div 7 = 6$, so $-42 \div -7 = 6$.

54. negative

55. a. Addition property of equality
    b. Addition property of equality
    c. Associative property of addition
    d. Additive inverse property   **e.** Additive identity property

56.

$a - 5 = -12$	**Original equation**
$a - 5 + 5 = -12 + 5$	**Addition property of equality**
$a = -12 + 5$	**Addition and subtraction are inverse operations**
$a = -7$	**Simplification**

57. 9°F

58. $45

CHAPTER 4 TEST

1. **a.** yes **b.** no **c.** no **d.** yes

2. One of the following answers may be given for each equation.
   a. 45 and 123 are factors of 5535, or the number 5535 is a composite number.
   b. 17 is not a factor of 57.
   c. 32 divides 1856, 32 is a factor of 1856, 58 divides 1856, or 58 is a factor of 1856.
   d. n has four prime divisors or n is a composite number.

3. 560

4. **a.** Suppose 15 is a factor of the number n. Then $n = 15k$ for some counting number k. Then $n = (3 \cdot 5)n = 3(5n)$. Then 3 divides n. Then 15 cannot be the smallest factor of n.
   b. Answers vary. The digits a and d are nonzero. Then $acb + de$ is divisible by 9.

5. **a.** Yes, since $175 = 5^2 \cdot 7$ and $B = (5^2 \cdot 7)(5^{212} \cdot 7^{42} \cdot 11^{10})$.
   b. Yes, since $112 = 2^4 \cdot 7$ and $K = (2^4 \cdot 7)(2^{171} \cdot 5^{38} \cdot 7^{367})$.

6. **a.** 9 **b.** 7 **c.** 8

7. **a.** 18 divides n if and only if 2 and 9 divide n.
   b. 2 divides 9972, and 9 divides 9972. Also, $9972 \div 18 = 554$. So the divisibility rule works.
   c. 2 divides 12,082, but 9 does not divide 12,082. Also, $12,082 \div 18 = 671$ R4. So the divisibility rule works.

8. $2520 = 2^3 \times 3^2 \times 5 \times 7$

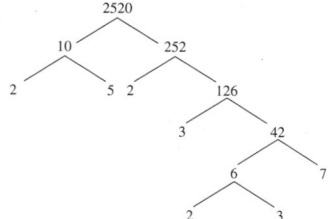

9. **a.** A counting number that has exactly two factors
   b. A counting number that has more than two factors
   c. 51 is divisible by 3, because its sum of digits is 6. Then 51 has at least three factors: 1, 3, and 51. So 51 is a composite number.

10. No. $B = 3(2n + 5)$, so B has at least three factors: 1, B, and 3.

11. 1, 140, 2, 70, 4, 35, 5, 28, 7, 20, 10, 14

12. **a.** 540 **b.** 3 **c.** 536

13. 2240

14. **a.** Composite, since $14^2 \le 217$ and 7 divides 217.
    b. Prime, since $16^2 \le 257$ and no prime numbers from 2 to 16 divide 257.

15. $\text{GCF}(43{,}094, 54{,}432) = 2^4 \times 7$ and $\text{LCM}(43{,}094, 54{,}432) = 2^8 \times 3^5 \times 7^3$

16. **a.** factors of 18; 1, 2, $\boxed{3}$, 6, 9, 18
       factors of 15: 1, $\boxed{3}$, 5, 15
       $\text{GCF}(18, 15) = 3$
    b. multiples of 18: 18, 36, 54, 72, $\boxed{90}$, 108
       multiples of 15: 15, 30, 45, 60, 75, $\boxed{90}$, 105
       $\text{LCM}(18, 15) = 90$

17. **a.** $\text{LCM}(a, b) = 2^4 \cdot 3^7 \cdot 7^2 \cdot 13$
    b. $\text{LCM}(a, b) = 2^3 \cdot 5^4 \cdot 11^2 \cdot 13$
    c. $\text{LCM}(a, b) = 2^6 \cdot 5^6 \cdot 7^2 \cdot 11 \cdot 13^3 \cdot 17$

18. **a.** $\text{GCF}(a, b) = 2^2 \cdot 3^4$ **b.** $\text{GCF}(a, b) = 5^3 \cdot 11^2$
    c. $\text{GCF}(a, b) = 5^3 \cdot 11 \cdot 13$

19. **a.** $\text{GCF}(7520, 1728) = \text{GCF}(608, 1728)$
    $$\begin{aligned} &= \text{GCF}(608, 512) \\ &= \text{GCF}(96, 512) \\ &= \text{GCF}(96, 32) \\ &= \text{GCF}(0, 32) \\ &= 32 \end{aligned}$$
    b. $\text{GCF}(1068, 72) = \text{GCF}(60, 72)$
    $$\begin{aligned} &= \text{GCF}(60, 12) \\ &= \text{GCF}(0, 12) \\ &= 12 \end{aligned}$$

20. $\text{LCM}(12, 42) \times \text{GCF}(12, 42) = 12 \times 42$
    $$\text{GCF}(12, 42) = \frac{12 \times 42}{\text{LCM}(12, 42)} = \frac{12 \times 42}{84} = 6$$

21. The addends have opposite signs, so compare the absolute values of the addends: $|24| < |-40|$. Then the sum will be negative. Next, perform a whole number subtraction problem: $40 - 24 = 16$. Then $24 + -40 = -16$.

22. **a.** $-5 - 3 = -5 + -3 = -8$
    b. $145 - -24 = 145 + 24 = 169$
    c. $24 - 42 = 24 + -42 = -18$

23.
$$\begin{aligned} 2 \times 6 &= 12 \\ 1 \times 6 &= 6 \\ 0 \times 6 &= 0 \\ -1 \times 6 &= -6 \\ -2 \times 6 &= -12 \end{aligned}$$

24. **a.** 2 and -8 have different signs, so the product is negative. $2 \times 8 = 16$, so $2 \times (-8) = -16$.
    b. -3 and -7 have the same sign, so the product is positive. $3 \times 7 = 21$, so $(-3) \times (-7) = 21$.
    c. 24 and -4 have opposite signs, so the quotient is negative. $24 \div 4 = 6$, so $24 \div -4 = -6$.
    d. -48 and -8 have the same sign, so the quotient is positive. $48 \div 8 = 6$, so $-48 \div -8 = 6$.

25. **a.** Addition property of equality
    b. Associative property of addition
    c. Additive inverse property
    d. Additive identity property

26. Answers vary.
    a. Marco borrowed $7 from his parents to buy lunch each week for 5 weeks. How much money did he owe them altogether?
    b. Marco owes his parents $42. He planned to repay them the same amount each week over a period of 6 weeks. How much should he pay them each week?

CHAPTER 5

SECTION 5.1

1. a. The collection consists of three equal-sized parts.
b. Each equal-sized part is called one-fifth.
c. Answers vary. The diagram is one representation.

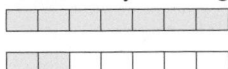

2. a. The collection consists of nine equal-sized parts.
b. Each equal-sized part is called one-seventh.
c. Answers vary. The diagram is one representation.

3. a.   **b.** ○○○ ○○○ **c.**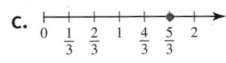

4. $\dfrac{8}{3}$

5. a. $\dfrac{3}{5}$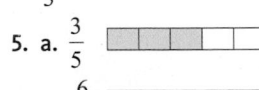

$\dfrac{6}{10}$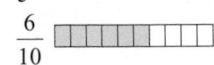

b.

c. $\dfrac{3}{5}$ [number line 0 to 1 marked in fifths, 3/5 shaded]

$\dfrac{6}{10}$ [number line 0 to 1 marked in tenths, 6/10 shaded]

6. a. $\dfrac{10}{8}$ **b.** $1\frac{2}{8}$ or $1\frac{1}{4}$

7. a. $\dfrac{31}{7}$ **b.** $4\frac{3}{7}$

8.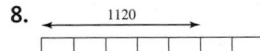
1120

$1120 \div 5 = 224$, and $7 \cdot 224 = 1568$. So 1568 people voted in the election.

9. birds flew away
 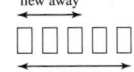
240 birds

$240 \div 5 = 48$, and $2 \cdot 48 = 96$. So 96 birds remained.

10. boys   girls
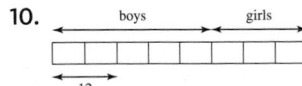
12

$12 \div 2 = 6$, and $8 \cdot 6 = 48$. There are 48 students in the class.

11. n is the number of green marbles to be added. Solve $\dfrac{6+n}{48+n} = \dfrac{3}{5}$ for n. Then $n = 57$. Latifah added 57 green marbles.

12. Each phrase tells how many (3 and four) and what is being counted (pencils and fifths).

13. The fraction $\frac{2}{5}$ indicates two equal-sized parts. Split the rectangle into two equal-sized parts.

[rectangle split into two parts]

Each part is a fifth. We know five-fifths equal a whole.

[rectangle split into five parts]

Then a whole can be shown as follows:

[whole rectangle]

Split the whole into four equal-sized parts.

[rectangle split into four parts]

Shade three of the equal-sized parts.

[rectangle with three of four parts shaded]

14. The whole for Molly is the entire rectangle.

The whole for Ben is one entire row.

[row with one of four parts shaded]

15. $\dfrac{18}{42} = \dfrac{n}{112}$
$42n = 18 \cdot 112$
$42n = 2016$
$n = 48$

16. spilled   300
[bar diagram]
$300 \div 2 = 150$, and $5 \cdot 150 = 750$. There were 750 beads in the jar.

17. a. ○○○○○○ **b.** [rectangle with one part shaded] **c.** [number line 0 to 3/5 in fifths]

18. a. 300,000
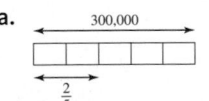
$\frac{2}{5}$
$300,000 \div 5 = 60,000$ and $2 \cdot 60,000 = 120,000$. So 120,000 Americans will select the new procedure each year.
b. 360,000 days

19. $\dfrac{440}{760} = \dfrac{44}{76} \approx \dfrac{45}{75} = \dfrac{3}{5}$

20. a. yes **b.** yes **c.** no **d.** no

21. a. $\dfrac{1}{5}$ (58 g) **b.** $\dfrac{1}{10}$ (123 g)

22. $\frac{1}{7}$ is more than $\frac{1}{8}$, so $\frac{3}{7}$ is more than $\frac{3}{8}$.

23. $\frac{3}{7}$ is less than $\frac{1}{2}$, which is less than $\frac{5}{8}$. So $\frac{3}{7}$ is less than $\frac{5}{8}$.

24. a. $11 \div 4 = \frac{11}{4}$ or $2\frac{3}{4}$. Each student gets $\frac{11}{4}$ (or $2\frac{3}{4}$) cookies.
b. $11 \div 4 = 2$ R3. Each student gets two marbles.
c. Each problem requires $11 \div 4$ using the fair share model of division.
d. There are no leftovers when we divide cookies, because we can break them into equal-sized parts, but there are leftovers when we divide marbles, because we cannot break them into equal-sized parts.

25. a. $\dfrac{8}{5}$ **b.** 1 R3

26. Answers vary.
   a. $7 \div 3 = 2$ R1. Mrs. Roberts has seven pencils. She wants to split them evenly among three students. How many pencils does each student get?
   b. $7 \div 3 = \frac{7}{3}$. Mrs. Roberts has 3 pounds of clay. She wants to split the clay evenly among three students. How much clay does each student get?

27. $\frac{10}{15} = \frac{2 \times 5}{3 \times 5} = \frac{2}{3}$ by the fundamental law of fractions.

28. $\frac{2}{7}$ is less than $\frac{1}{2}$, but $\frac{4}{5}$ is more than $\frac{1}{2}$.

29. **a.** quotient   **b.** division   **c.** numerator
   d. denominator   **e.** improper   **f.** proper

30. **a.** Seven-thirds is a collection of seven equal-sized parts.
   b. Each equal-sized part is called one-third.
   c.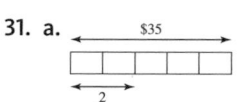

31. **a.**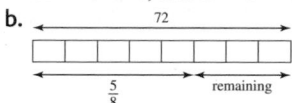

$35 \div 5 = 7$, and $2 \times 7 = 14$. He spent $14.
   b.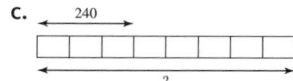

$72 \div 8 = 9$, and $3 \times 9 = 27$. He has 27 g of sugar left.
   c.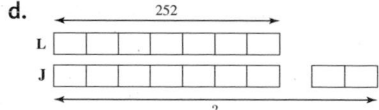

$240 \div 3 = 80$, and $8 \times 80 = 640$. Fred has 640 coins.
   d.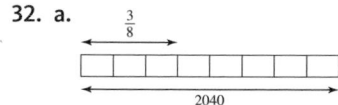

$252 \div 7 = 36$, and $9 \times 36 = 324$. Jeremy ran 324 m.

32. **a.**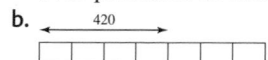

$2040 \div 8 = 255$, and $3 \times 255 = 765$. Yvonne spends $765 per month on housing.
   b.

$420 \div 4 = 105$, and $7 \times 105 = 735$. Jasmine has 735 coins in the piggy bank.

33. Answers vary.
   a. $\frac{3}{4} = \frac{3 \cdot 6}{4 \cdot 6} = \frac{18}{24}$ and $\frac{3}{4} = \frac{3 \cdot 5}{4 \cdot 5} = \frac{15}{20}$
   b. $\frac{7}{3} = \frac{7 \cdot 6}{3 \cdot 6} = \frac{42}{18}$ and $\frac{7}{3} = \frac{7 \cdot 5}{3 \cdot 5} = \frac{35}{15}$
   c. $\frac{12}{5} = \frac{12 \cdot 6}{5 \cdot 6} = \frac{72}{30}$ and $\frac{12}{5} = \frac{12 \cdot 5}{5 \cdot 5} = \frac{60}{25}$

34. Answers vary.
   a. $\frac{24}{32} = \frac{24 \div 2}{32 \div 2} = \frac{12}{16}$ and $\frac{24}{32} = \frac{24 \div 4}{32 \div 4} = \frac{6}{8}$
   b. $\frac{42}{14} = \frac{42 \div 2}{14 \div 2} = \frac{21}{7}$ and $\frac{42}{14} = \frac{42 \div 7}{14 \div 7} = \frac{6}{2}$

c. $\frac{120}{200} = \frac{120 \div 10}{200 \div 10} = \frac{12}{20}$ and $\frac{120}{200} = \frac{120 \div 40}{200 \div 40} = \frac{3}{5}$

35. **a.** The cross-products are 44 and 42. The fractions are not equivalent.
   b. The cross-products are 18,468 and 18,468. The fractions are equivalent.
   c. The cross-products are 28 and 27. The fractions are not equivalent.

36. multiplication: $\frac{6}{4} = \frac{6 \times 2}{4 \times 2} = \frac{12}{8}$

   division: $\frac{12}{8} = \frac{12 \div 2}{8 \div 2} = \frac{6}{4}$

   cross-products: $6 \times 8 = 48$ and $4 \times 12 = 48$

37. **a.** $1\frac{1}{3}$ **b.** $6\frac{1}{3}$ **c.** $\frac{6}{7}$ **d.** $\frac{4}{5}$ **e.** $8\frac{2}{3}$

38. OOO

39. **a.** $1543 \div 35 = 44$ R3   **b.** $990 \div 42 = 23$ R24

40. **a.** $41 \div 12 = 3\frac{5}{12}$ **b.** $398 \div 15 = 26\frac{8}{15}$

41. **a.** **STEP 1.** $2 - \frac{2}{3} = \frac{4}{3}$. Split the interval on the number line from $\frac{2}{3}$ and 2 into four equal-sized parts. Then we obtain

   STEP 2. Split the interval from 1 to 2 into two equal-sized parts. Then we obtain

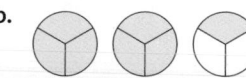

   The dot represents $1\frac{1}{2}$.
   b. **STEP 1.** Convert the mixed number $1\frac{2}{3}$ to the fraction $\frac{5}{3}$. Then split the interval on the number line from 0 to $\frac{5}{3}$ into five equal-sized pieces.

   STEP 2. $\frac{3}{3} = 1$, so locate 1.

   STEP 3. Divide the interval on the number line from 0 to 1 into four equal-sized pieces.

   The dot represents $\frac{3}{4}$.

42. Answers vary. For example, one circle represents the whole unit.
   a.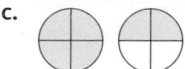

   b.

   c.

43. **a.**
   b.
   c.
   d. We can repeat this process of dividing the interval from 0 to 1. The diagrams illustrate the density property of fractions.

44. STEP 1. The fraction $\frac{5}{4}$ represents five equal-sized parts. Split the rectangle into five equal-sized parts.

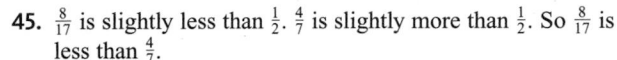

STEP 2. Each equal-sized part is called one-fourth. There are four-fourths in a whole. So select four of the equal-sized parts to represent a whole.

STEP 3. There are three-thirds in a whole. Split the rectangle into three equal-sized parts. Then shade two equal-sized parts. The shaded region represents $\frac{2}{3}$.

45. $\frac{8}{17}$ is slightly less than $\frac{1}{2}$. $\frac{4}{7}$ is slightly more than $\frac{1}{2}$. So $\frac{8}{17}$ is less than $\frac{4}{7}$.

46. a. $1\frac{1}{3}$ batches   **b.** $\frac{4}{8}$ or $\frac{1}{2}$ bag   **c.** $\frac{4}{5}$ box

47. a. $\frac{298}{408} \approx \frac{300}{400} = \frac{3}{4}$ **b.** $\frac{435}{821} \approx \frac{400}{800} = \frac{1}{2}$

c. $\frac{425}{1340} \approx \frac{400}{1200} = \frac{1}{3}$

48. a. 112   **b.** 11   **c.** 10

49. a. $\frac{1}{8}, \frac{1}{6}, \frac{1}{2}$ **b.** $\frac{1}{15}, \frac{1}{12}, \frac{1}{10}$

c. If $0 < m < n$, then $\frac{1}{n} < \frac{1}{m}$.

50. a. $\frac{9}{25}, \frac{12}{25}, \frac{18}{25}$ **b.** $\frac{12}{32}, \frac{27}{32}, \frac{108}{32}$

c. If $0 < a < b$, then $\frac{a}{c} < \frac{b}{c}$.

51. $\frac{m-2}{m}, \frac{n-2}{n}$

52. a. $\frac{27}{80} \approx \frac{27}{81} = \frac{3}{9} = \frac{1}{3}$ **b.** $\frac{23}{99} \approx \frac{25}{100} = \frac{1}{4}$

c. $\frac{64}{131} \approx \frac{64}{128} = \frac{1}{2}$ **d.** $\frac{88}{260} \approx \frac{90}{270} = \frac{1}{3}$

53. a. $\frac{9}{5}$ because of the large numerator

b. $\frac{12}{7}$, because the fractions have the same number of equal-sized parts, so we compare the size of the equal-sized parts

c. $\frac{7}{6}$, because $\frac{4}{5}$ is less than 1 and 1 is less than $\frac{7}{6}$

54. Answers vary.

a. $\frac{6}{20}$ and $\frac{8}{20}$ **b.** $\frac{22}{33}$ and $\frac{23}{33}$ **c.** $\frac{106}{56}$ and $\frac{107}{56}$

55. $\frac{48}{72} = \frac{2 \times 2 \times 2 \times 2 \times 3}{2 \times 2 \times 2 \times 3 \times 3} = \frac{2}{3}$

56. Acme because 5 million is more than 4 million. Widget because $\frac{5}{20} < \frac{4}{6}$.

57. a. 446   **b.** 46   **c.** no largest number

58. a. no   **b.** yes   **c.** no   **d.** no

59. a. $\frac{n+3}{2}$ **b.** Simplification is not possible.

c. 3   **d.** $\frac{35}{37}$

60. $120 \div 3 = 40$, $5 \times 40 = 200$. The length of the race is 200 meters.

61. a. $480 \div 8 = 60$, and $5 \times 60 = 300$. Angela has 300 stamps.

b. $84 \div 4 = 21$, and $7 \times 21 = 147$. The gift costs $147.

c. $30 \div 3 = 10$, $5 \times 10 = 50$. There are 50 pages in the book.

d. $420 \div 5 = 84$, $3 \times 84 = 252$. Natalie has 252 beads.

62. a. 540 mph   **b.** 972 mph   **c.** 432 mph

63. a. $\frac{5}{2} = \frac{25}{10}, \frac{5}{2} = \frac{30}{12}$ nth term $= \frac{5(n+1)}{2(n+1)}$

b. $\frac{3}{4} = \frac{27}{36}, \frac{3}{4} = \frac{33}{44}$ nth term $= \frac{3(2n+1)}{4(2n+1)}$

c. There are infinitely many fractions equivalent to a given fraction.

64. a. $3\frac{4}{5}, 4\frac{3}{5}, 5\frac{2}{5}$

b. $y = \frac{3}{5} + \frac{4}{5}(n-1)$. If $n = 23$, then $y = 18\frac{1}{5}$.

SECTION 5.2

1. $\frac{2}{4} + \frac{3}{4} = \frac{5}{4}$

2. $\frac{1}{4} + \frac{3}{8} = \frac{5}{8}$

3. $\frac{7}{5} - \frac{3}{5} = \frac{4}{5}$

4. $\frac{6}{4} - \frac{5}{8} = \frac{7}{8}$

5. a. sum $\approx 6 + 4 = 10$, sum $= 9\frac{5}{12}$
 b. sum $\approx 8\frac{1}{2} + 5\frac{1}{2} = 14$, sum $= 14\frac{1}{8}$
 c. sum $\approx 2 + 7 = 9$, sum $= 9\frac{43}{100}$

6. a. difference $\approx 9 - 4 = 5$, difference $= 5\frac{1}{12}$
 b. difference $\approx 9 - 5 = 4$, difference $= 4\frac{6}{8}$ or $4\frac{3}{4}$
 c. difference $\approx 7 - 2 = 5$, difference $= 4\frac{47}{100}$

7. $5\dfrac{1}{12}$ cups

8. $2\frac{1}{4}$ yd

9. $\frac{5}{32}$ of the employees

10. a. $\dfrac{3}{4}$ **b.** $\dfrac{7}{8}$ **c.** $\dfrac{1023}{1024}$

11. $\frac{x}{y}$ is the additive inverse of $\frac{a}{b}$, so $\frac{a}{b} + \frac{x}{y} = 0$. Then $-\frac{a}{b} = \frac{x}{y}$. $\frac{u}{v}$ is the additive inverse of $\frac{a}{b}$, so $\frac{a}{b} + \frac{u}{v} = 0$. Then $-\frac{a}{b} = \frac{u}{v}$. Then $-\frac{a}{b} = \frac{x}{y}$ and $-\frac{a}{b} = \frac{u}{v}$. Then $\frac{x}{y} = \frac{u}{v}$.

12. a. Answers vary.

$$\frac{3}{4} + \frac{2}{5} = \frac{3 \cdot 5}{4 \cdot 5} + \frac{4 \cdot 2}{4 \cdot 5} = \frac{15}{20} + \frac{8}{20} = \frac{15 + 8}{20} = \frac{23}{20}$$

$$\frac{2}{5} + \frac{3}{4} = \frac{2 \cdot 4}{5 \cdot 4} + \frac{5 \cdot 3}{5 \cdot 4} = \frac{8}{20} + \frac{15}{20} = \frac{23}{20}$$

 b. Suppose a, b, c, and d are integers and $ad \neq 0$. Then $\frac{a}{b} + \frac{c}{d} = \frac{ad}{bd} + \frac{bc}{bd} = \frac{ad + bc}{bd}$. $ad + bc$ is an integer, and bd is a nonzero integer. So $\frac{ad + bc}{bd}$ is a fraction. Therefore, if $\frac{a}{b}$ and $\frac{c}{d}$ are fractions, then $\frac{ad + bc}{bd}$ is a fraction.

13. $\frac{a}{b} = \frac{e}{f} + \frac{c}{d}$. Then $\frac{a}{b} + \frac{-c}{d} = \left(\frac{e}{f} + \frac{c}{d}\right) + \frac{-c}{d}$. Then $\frac{a}{b} - \frac{c}{d} = \left(\frac{e}{f} + \frac{c}{d}\right) + \frac{-c}{d}$. Then $\frac{a}{b} - \frac{c}{d} = \frac{e}{f} + \left(\frac{c}{d} + \frac{-c}{d}\right)$. Then $\frac{a}{b} - \frac{c}{d} = \frac{e}{f} + 0$. Then $\frac{a}{b} - \frac{c}{d} = \frac{e}{f}$.

14. a. $<$ **b.** $>$ **c.** $<$ **d.** $<$

15. a. not possible, because $\frac{3}{5} + \frac{4}{7} > 1$
 b. possible, because $\frac{5}{8} + \frac{2}{7} < 1$

16. a. $n - \dfrac{3}{8} = \dfrac{5}{6}$

$$n = \frac{5}{6} + \frac{3}{8}$$
$$n = \frac{20}{24} + \frac{9}{24}$$
$$n = \frac{29}{24}$$
$$n = 1\frac{5}{24}$$

 b. $n - \dfrac{3}{8} = \dfrac{5}{6}$

$$n - \frac{3}{8} + \frac{3}{8} = \frac{5}{6} + \frac{3}{8}$$
$$n = \frac{5}{6} + \frac{3}{8}$$
$$n = \frac{20}{24} + \frac{9}{24}$$
$$n = \frac{29}{24}$$
$$n = 1\frac{5}{24}$$

c. $n - \dfrac{3}{8} = \dfrac{5}{6}$

$$n + \frac{-3}{8} = \frac{5}{6}$$
$$\left(n + \frac{-3}{8}\right) + \frac{3}{8} = \frac{5}{6} + \frac{3}{8}$$
$$n + \left(\frac{-3}{8} + \frac{3}{8}\right) = \frac{5}{6} + \frac{3}{8}$$
$$n + 0 = \frac{5}{6} + \frac{3}{8}$$
$$n = \frac{5}{6} + \frac{3}{8}$$
$$n = \frac{20}{24} + \frac{9}{24}$$
$$n = \frac{29}{24}$$
$$n = 1\frac{5}{24}$$

17. $1\frac{5}{12} - \frac{2}{3} = \frac{17}{12} - \frac{2}{3} = \frac{17}{12} - \frac{8}{12} = \frac{9}{12}$. The distance between $\frac{2}{3}$ and $1\frac{5}{12}$ is $\frac{9}{12}$. We must split $\frac{9}{12}$ into three equal-sized parts. So $\frac{9}{12} \div 3 = \frac{9}{12} \times \frac{1}{3} = \frac{1}{4}$. So the distance between each hash mark is $\frac{1}{4}$. So A $= \frac{2}{3} + \frac{1}{4} + \frac{1}{4} = \frac{7}{6} = 1\frac{1}{6}$.

18. a. 12 **b.** 12 **c.** 12 **d.** 12

19. $\frac{1}{4}$ in.

20. a. $3 \div 8 = \dfrac{3}{8} = \dfrac{2 + 1}{8} = \dfrac{2}{8} + \dfrac{1}{8} = \dfrac{1}{4} + \dfrac{1}{8}$
 b. $5 \div 8 = \dfrac{5}{8} = \dfrac{4 + 1}{8} = \dfrac{4}{8} + \dfrac{1}{8} = \dfrac{1}{2} + \dfrac{1}{8}$
 c. $5 \div 6 = \dfrac{5}{6} = \dfrac{3 + 2}{6} = \dfrac{3}{6} + \dfrac{2}{6} = \dfrac{1}{2} + \dfrac{1}{3}$

21. $4\dfrac{2}{5} - 2\dfrac{4}{5} = 1\dfrac{3}{5}$ in.

22. A fraction is a collection of equal-sized parts. The sum of the two fractions with common denominators means we are combining two collections of equal-sized parts, with each collection having the same equal-sized part. Then the sum is straightforward to find, because it builds on counting with whole numbers.

23. Answers vary. For example, Samantha is baking a cake. She put $\frac{3}{4}$ cup of sugar and $2\frac{1}{2}$ cups of flour in a bowl. How many cups of ingredients did she use so far?

24. Answers vary. Samantha is baking a cake. She added $2\frac{1}{2}$ cups of flour in a bowl. She realized she added too much flour, so she removed $\frac{3}{4}$ cup of flour. How much flour remained in the bowl?

25. a. Answers vary. For example, let $\frac{1}{4}$ be one fraction and $\frac{5}{7} - \frac{1}{4} = \frac{13}{28}$ be the other. Then $\frac{13}{28} + \frac{1}{4} = \frac{5}{7}$.
 b. Answers vary. For example, let $\frac{17}{20}$ be one fraction and $\frac{17}{20} - \frac{3}{5} = \frac{1}{4}$ be the other. Then $\frac{17}{20} - \frac{1}{4} = \frac{3}{5}$.

26. a. additive inverse **b.** rename **c.** unlike **d.** denominator **e.** fraction strips **f.** adding the opposite

27. a. 4 **b.** 4 **c.** 6 **d.** 6

28. a. $21\frac{1}{2}$ **b.** $5\frac{3}{16}$

29. a. 6 **b.** 6 **c.** 7 **d.** 7 **e.** 4 **f.** 4 **g.** 15 **h.** 15

30. a. $\dfrac{5}{6} + \dfrac{7}{8} = \dfrac{5 \cdot 4}{6 \cdot 4} + \dfrac{7 \cdot 3}{8 \cdot 3}$

$\qquad = \dfrac{20}{24} + \dfrac{21}{24}$

$\qquad = \dfrac{41}{24}$

$\qquad = 1\dfrac{17}{24}$

b. $\dfrac{5}{6} + \dfrac{7}{8} = \dfrac{5 \cdot 8 + 6 \cdot 7}{6 \cdot 8}$

$\qquad = \dfrac{40 + 42}{48}$

$\qquad = \dfrac{82}{48}$

$\qquad = \dfrac{41}{24}$

$\qquad = 1\dfrac{17}{24}$

31. a. $\dfrac{7}{8} - \dfrac{5}{6} = \dfrac{7 \cdot 3}{8 \cdot 3} - \dfrac{5 \cdot 4}{6 \cdot 4}$

$\qquad = \dfrac{21}{24} - \dfrac{20}{24}$

$\qquad = \dfrac{1}{24}$

b. $\dfrac{7}{8} - \dfrac{5}{6} = \dfrac{7 \cdot 6 - 8 \cdot 5}{8 \cdot 6}$

$\qquad = \dfrac{42 - 40}{48}$

$\qquad = \dfrac{2}{48}$

$\qquad = \dfrac{1}{24}$

c. $\dfrac{7}{8} - \dfrac{5}{6} = \dfrac{7}{8} + \dfrac{-5}{6}$

$\qquad = \dfrac{7 \cdot 6 + -5 \cdot 8}{86}$

$\qquad = \dfrac{42 + -40}{48}$

$\qquad = \dfrac{2}{48}$

$\qquad = \dfrac{1}{24}$

32. a. $\dfrac{4}{3} + n = \dfrac{9}{5}$

$\qquad n = \dfrac{9}{5} - \dfrac{4}{3}$

$\qquad n = \dfrac{27}{15} - \dfrac{20}{15}$

$\qquad n = \dfrac{7}{15}$

b. $\dfrac{4}{3} + n = \dfrac{9}{5}$

$\qquad \dfrac{4}{3} + n - \dfrac{4}{3} = \dfrac{9}{5} - \dfrac{4}{3}$

$\qquad n = \dfrac{9}{5} - \dfrac{4}{3}$

$\qquad n = \dfrac{27}{15} - \dfrac{20}{15}$

$\qquad n = \dfrac{7}{15}$

c. $\dfrac{4}{3} + n$

$\qquad \dfrac{-4}{3} + \left(\dfrac{4}{3} + n\right) = \dfrac{9}{5}$

$\qquad \left(\dfrac{-4}{3} + \dfrac{4}{3}\right) + n = \dfrac{-4}{3} + \dfrac{9}{5}$

$\qquad 0 + n = \dfrac{-4}{3} + \dfrac{9}{5}$

$\qquad n = \dfrac{-4}{3} + \dfrac{9}{5}$

$\qquad n = \dfrac{-20}{15} + \dfrac{27}{15}$

$\qquad n = \dfrac{7}{15}$

33. a. $\dfrac{3}{4} - y = \dfrac{5}{6}$

$\qquad \dfrac{3}{4} = y + \dfrac{5}{6}$

$\qquad \dfrac{3}{4} - \dfrac{5}{6} = y$

$\qquad \dfrac{9}{12} - \dfrac{10}{12} = y$

$\qquad \dfrac{9 - 10}{12} = y$

$\qquad \dfrac{-1}{12} = y$

b. $\dfrac{3}{4} - y = \dfrac{5}{6}$

$\qquad \dfrac{3}{4} - y + y = \dfrac{5}{6} + y$

$\qquad \dfrac{3}{4} = \dfrac{5}{6} + y$

$\qquad \dfrac{3}{4} - \dfrac{5}{6} = \dfrac{5}{6} + y - \dfrac{5}{6}$

$\qquad \dfrac{3}{4} - \dfrac{5}{6} = y$

$\qquad \dfrac{9}{12} - \dfrac{10}{12} = y$

$\qquad \dfrac{-1}{12} = y$

34. The distance between $\frac{3}{4}$ and $1\frac{11}{20}$ is $1\frac{11}{20} - \frac{3}{4} = \frac{31}{20} - \frac{15}{20} = \frac{16}{20}$. We can split $\frac{16}{20}$ into four equal-sized parts: $\frac{16}{20} \div 4 = \frac{16}{20} \times \frac{1}{4} = \frac{4}{20} = \frac{1}{5}$. Then $A = \frac{3}{4} + \frac{1}{5} + \frac{1}{5} = \frac{23}{20} = 1\frac{3}{20}$.

35. a. $1\frac{2}{3} + n = 5\frac{3}{4}$ **b.** $n + 2\frac{1}{3} = 4\frac{1}{5}$

36. a. $3\frac{4}{5} = n + 1\frac{2}{3}$ **b.** $3\frac{4}{5} = n - 1\frac{2}{3}$

37. a. $4\frac{2}{3} - 1\frac{1}{4} = n$ **b.** $4\frac{2}{3} - n = 1\frac{1}{4}$ **c.** $n - 1\frac{1}{4} = 4\frac{2}{3}$

38. $1\frac{1}{4}$ in.

39. a. $-\dfrac{5}{7}$ **b.** $-\dfrac{11}{3}$ **c.** $\dfrac{5}{4}$

40. a. $\dfrac{4}{3} + -\dfrac{4}{3} = \dfrac{4 + -4}{3} = \dfrac{0}{3} = 0$

  b. $\dfrac{4}{3} + -\dfrac{8}{6} = \dfrac{8}{6} + -\dfrac{8}{6} = \dfrac{8 + -8}{6} = \dfrac{0}{6} = 0$

  c. $\dfrac{4}{3} + -\dfrac{12}{9} = \dfrac{12}{9} + -\dfrac{12}{9} = \dfrac{12 + -12}{9} = \dfrac{0}{9} = 0$

41. a. $\dfrac{39}{7}$ **b.** $\dfrac{-77}{6}$ or $-\dfrac{77}{6}$

42. a. $2\frac{3}{20}$ **b.** $3\frac{9}{11}$ **c.** $-3\frac{7}{16}$ **d.** $-5\frac{2}{3}$

43. Both approaches lead to the same difference.

  a. $\dfrac{2}{3} - \dfrac{8}{3} = \dfrac{2 - 8}{3} = \dfrac{-6}{3} = -2$

  $\dfrac{2}{3} - \dfrac{8}{3} = \dfrac{2}{3} + \dfrac{-8}{3} = \dfrac{2 + -8}{3} = \dfrac{-6}{3} = -2$

  b. $\dfrac{4}{7} - \dfrac{-3}{4} = \dfrac{16}{28} - \dfrac{-21}{28} = \dfrac{16 - -21}{28} = \dfrac{37}{28}$

  $\dfrac{4}{7} - \dfrac{-3}{4} = \dfrac{4}{7} + \dfrac{3}{4} = \dfrac{16}{28} + \dfrac{21}{28} = \dfrac{16 + 21}{28} = \dfrac{37}{28}$

44. a. $n = 14$ **b.** $n < 14\frac{3}{8}$

45. $70 - 20 = 50$. $\dfrac{5}{11} < \dfrac{9}{16}$, so $70\frac{5}{11} - 20\frac{9}{16} < 50$.

46. a. $\dfrac{3}{5}$ **b.** $\dfrac{7}{5}$

47. a. 20 **b.** 21 **c.** 96 **d.** 48 **e.** 74 **f.** 80

48. $\dfrac{6}{10}$ or $\dfrac{3}{5}$

49. a. $n = 16$ **b.** $n = 7$

50. $\dfrac{9}{28}$

51. a. yes **b.** yes

52. $2\frac{1}{2}$ cups

53. $1\frac{11}{12}$ cups

54. a. The numerator and denominator have a common factor of 4.
  b. The fractional part $\frac{4}{3}$ is an improper fraction.
  c. The fractional part $\frac{8}{8}$ is an improper fraction.
  d. The numerator and denominator of $\frac{4}{10}$ have a common factor of 2.

55. a. $\dfrac{18}{5}, \dfrac{22}{5}, \dfrac{26}{5}$ **b.** $\dfrac{9}{10}, \dfrac{11}{12}, \dfrac{13}{14}$

SECTION 5.3

1. a. $\dfrac{3}{5} \times \dfrac{4}{6} = \dfrac{12}{30}$

  b. $\dfrac{4}{6} \times \dfrac{3}{5} = \dfrac{12}{30}$

2. a.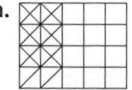

$\dfrac{3}{4} \times \dfrac{2}{5} = \dfrac{6}{20}$

  b.

$\dfrac{2}{5} \times \dfrac{3}{4} = \dfrac{6}{20}$

3. a. $\dfrac{13}{4} \times \dfrac{7}{5}$ **b.** $\dfrac{10}{3} \times \dfrac{9}{4}$

4. $500 - 4 = 496$, $496 \div 8 = 62$, and $3 \times 62 + 4 = 190$. Ellie has 190 coins.

5. $105 + 3 = 108$, $108 \div 9 = 12$, and $2 \times 12 - 3 = 21$. Neal has 21 coins.

6. a. $\dfrac{2}{5}$ **b.** $\dfrac{2}{3}$ **c.** $\dfrac{3}{5}$ **d.** $1\frac{2}{3}$

7. a.

27 ÷ 3 = 9, and 4 × 9 = 36. She solved 36 problems in the morning.

  b. Let n equal the number of math problems in the chapter review. Then $\frac{3}{7}n = 27$, $n = \frac{7}{3} \times 27$, $n = 63$. Then $63 - 27 = 36$. She solved 36 problems in the morning.

8. a.

536 ÷ 8 = 67, and 3 × 67 = 201. David has 201 beads.

  b. Let n equal the number of beads Erin has. Solve the equation $n + \frac{3}{5}n = 536$ to get $n = 335$. Then, $\frac{3}{5}n = \frac{3}{5} \cdot 335 = 201$. David has 201 beads.

9. a.

671 − 6 = 665, 665 ÷ 7 = 95, 5 × 95 = 474, and 2 × 95 + 6 = 196. David has 196 beads.

  b. Let n equal the number of beads Erin has. Solve $n + \frac{2}{5}n + 6 = 671$ to get $n = 475$. Then, $\frac{2}{5}n + 6 = \frac{2}{5} \cdot 475 + 6 = 196$. David has 196 beads.

10. a.

401 + 5 = 406, 406 ÷ 7 = 58, and 4 × 58 = 232. Erin has 232 beads.

  b. Let n equal the number of beads Erin has. Solve the equation $n + \frac{3}{4}n - 5 = 401$ to get $n = 232$. Erin has 232 beads.

11. Suppose $\frac{a}{b}$ and $\frac{c}{d}$ are any two fractions. Then $\frac{a}{b} \times \frac{c}{d} = \frac{ac}{bd}$ and $\frac{c}{d} \times \frac{a}{b} = \frac{ca}{db} = \frac{ac}{bd} = \frac{a}{b} \times \frac{c}{d}$. Then $\frac{a}{b} \times \frac{c}{d} = \frac{c}{d} \times \frac{a}{b}$.

12. Suppose $\frac{a}{b}$, $\frac{c}{d}$, and $\frac{e}{f}$ are any three fractions. Then $\left(\frac{a}{b} \times \frac{c}{d}\right) \times \frac{e}{f} = \frac{ac}{bd} \times \frac{e}{f} = \frac{ace}{bdf}$ and $\frac{a}{b} \times \left(\frac{c}{d} \times \frac{e}{f}\right) = \frac{a}{b} \times \frac{ce}{df} = \frac{ace}{bdf}$. Then $\left(\frac{a}{b} \times \frac{c}{d}\right) \times \frac{e}{f} = \frac{a}{b} \times \left(\frac{c}{d} \times \frac{e}{f}\right)$.

13. $\dfrac{4}{5} \times \dfrac{2}{3}$

14. The sunflower grew $5 - 2 = 3$ cm taller, while the tomato plant grew $8\frac{1}{4} - 4\frac{1}{2} = 3\frac{3}{4}$ cm taller. So Linda could be correct. $3 \div 2 = 1\frac{1}{2}$ and $3\frac{3}{4} \div 4\frac{1}{2} = \frac{15}{18}$, which means the sunflower grew $1\frac{1}{2}$ times its original height and the tomato plant grew $\frac{15}{18}$ times its original height. So Barry could be correct.

15. **a.** quotient **b.** Fundamental **c.** Multiplicative inverse **d.** any number divided by 1 is the number itself.

16. **a.**
$$y \times \frac{5}{6} = 24$$
$$\left(y \times \frac{5}{6}\right) \times \frac{6}{5} = 24 \times \frac{6}{5}$$
$$y \times \left(\frac{5}{6} \times \frac{6}{5}\right) = 24 \times \frac{6}{5}$$
$$y \times 1 = 24 \times \frac{6}{5}$$
$$y = 24 \times \frac{6}{5}$$
$$y = \frac{144}{5}$$
$$y = 28\frac{4}{5}$$

b. $y \times \dfrac{5}{6} = 24$
$$y = 24 \div \frac{5}{6}$$
$$y = 24 \times \frac{6}{5}$$
$$y = \frac{144}{5}$$
$$y = 28\frac{4}{5}$$

c. $y \times \dfrac{5}{6} = 25$
$$y \times \frac{5}{6} \div \frac{5}{6} = 25 \div \frac{5}{6}$$
$$y = 25 \div \frac{5}{6}$$
$$y = 24 \times \frac{6}{5}$$
$$y = \frac{144}{5}$$
$$y = 28\frac{4}{5}$$

17. **a.** $y \div \dfrac{7}{3} = 65$
$$y \div \frac{7}{3} \times \frac{7}{3} = 65 \times \frac{7}{3}$$
$$y = 65 \times \frac{7}{3}$$
$$y = \frac{455}{3}$$
$$y = 151\frac{2}{3}$$

b. $y \div \dfrac{7}{3} = 65$
$$y = \frac{7}{3} \times 65$$
$$y = \frac{455}{3}$$
$$y = 151\frac{2}{3}$$

c. $y \div \dfrac{7}{3} = 65$
$$y \times \frac{3}{7} = 65$$
$$\left(y \times \frac{3}{7}\right) \times \frac{7}{3} = 65 \times \frac{7}{3}$$
$$y \times \left(\frac{3}{7} \times \frac{7}{3}\right) = 65 \times \frac{7}{3}$$
$$y \times 1 = 65 \times \frac{7}{3}$$
$$y = 65 \times \frac{7}{3}$$
$$y = \frac{455}{3}$$
$$y = 151\frac{2}{3}$$

18. **a.**

126,000

$126,000 \div 3 = 42,000$, and $4 \times 42,000 = 168,000$. So 168,000 signatures are needed.

b. Let n equal the total number of signatures needed. Solve $\frac{3}{4}n = 126,000$ for n. It shows 168,000 signatures are needed.

19. **a.** The number of city miles driven is $\frac{1}{6} \times 12,000 = 2000$ miles. The number of gallons of gasoline to drive 2000 miles is $2000 \div 24 \approx 83$ gallons. The number of highway miles driven is $\frac{5}{6} \times 12,000 = 10,000$ miles. The number of gallons of gasoline to drive 10,000 miles is $10,000 \div 42 \approx 238$ gallons. Then $83 + 238 = 321$ and $321 \times 3.50 = \$1123$. The total cost is approximately $1100.

b. $2800

20. **a.** The number of city miles driven is $\frac{2}{3} \times 24,000 = 16,000$ miles. The number of gallons of gasoline to drive 16,000 miles is $16,000 \div 16 = 1000$ gallons. The number of highway miles driven is $\frac{1}{3} \times 24,000 = 8000$ miles. The number of gallons of gasoline to drive 8000 miles is $8000 \div 28 \approx 286$ gallons. Then $1000 + 286 = 1286$ and $1286 \times 3 = 3858$. The total cost is approximately $3900.

b. $6800

21. **a.** no **b.** yes **c.** yes **d.** no

22. The reciprocal would be $\frac{3}{0}$, which equals $3 \div 0$. Division by 0 is undefined. So $\frac{0}{3}$ does not have a reciprocal.

23. Answers vary. For example, $\frac{3}{4}$ of voters supported Proposition A. Of these voters, $\frac{2}{3}$ were female. What fraction of voters supported Proposition A and were female?

24. Answers vary. For example, the cook has $4\frac{1}{3}$ cups of sugar. Each batch of cookies requires $\frac{3}{4}$ cup of sugar. How many batches of cookies can be made?

25. a. $8 \times 6 = 48$ and $\frac{3}{5} \times \frac{2}{7} = \frac{6}{35}$
   b. No. $8\frac{3}{5} \times 6\frac{2}{7} = (8 + \frac{3}{5})(6 + \frac{2}{7}) =$
   $8 \times 6 + \frac{3}{5} \times \frac{2}{7} + (8 \times \frac{2}{7} + 6 \times \frac{3}{5}) =$
   $48\frac{6}{35} + (8 \times \frac{2}{7} + 6 \times \frac{3}{5})$

26. Answers vary.
   a. $\frac{5}{7} \div \frac{4}{9}$ and $\frac{4}{9}$. Then $\frac{5}{7} \div \frac{4}{9} \times \frac{4}{9} = \frac{5}{7}$.
   b. $\frac{3}{5} \times \frac{4}{7}$ and $\frac{4}{7}$. Then $\frac{3}{5} \times \frac{4}{7} \div \frac{4}{7} = \frac{3}{5}$.

27. Answers vary. For example, Maria has $6\frac{2}{3}$ feet of ribbon. She is making bows. Each bow requires $\frac{3}{4}$ feet of ribbon. How many bows can she make?

28. a.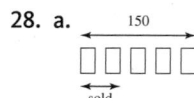
   $150 \div 5 = 30$, and $2 \times 30 = 60$. He sold 60 lollipops.
   b.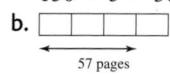
   $57 \div 3 = 19$
   $4 \cdot 19 = 76$
   There were 76 pages in the book.
   c.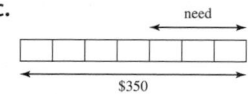
   $350 \div 7 = 50$
   $3 \cdot 50 = 150$
   Erika needs $150.

29. a. $\frac{2}{3} \div \frac{3}{4} = \frac{2}{3} \times \frac{4}{3} = \frac{8}{9}$
   b. $\frac{14}{20} \div \frac{7}{45} = \frac{14}{20} \times \frac{45}{7} = \frac{18}{4} = 4\frac{1}{2}$
   c. $8\frac{3}{4} \div 3\frac{2}{5} = \frac{35}{4} \div \frac{17}{5} = \frac{35}{4} \times \frac{5}{17} = \frac{175}{68} = 2\frac{39}{68}$

30. a. $\frac{4}{7} \times y = 12$
   $\frac{4}{7} \times y \div \frac{4}{7} = 12 \div \frac{4}{7}$
   $y = 12 \div \frac{4}{7}$
   $y = 12 \times \frac{7}{4}$
   $y = \frac{12 \times 7}{4}$
   $y = 21$

   b. $\frac{4}{7} \times y = 12$
   $y = 12 \div \frac{4}{7}$
   $y = 12 \times \frac{7}{4}$
   $y = \frac{12 \times 7}{4}$
   $y = 21$

c. $\frac{4}{7} \times y = 12$
   $\frac{7}{4} \times (\frac{4}{7} \times y) = \frac{7}{4} \times 12$
   $(\frac{7}{4} \times \frac{4}{7}) \times y = \frac{7}{4} \times 12$
   $1 \times y = \frac{7}{4} \times 12$
   $y = \frac{7}{4} \times 12$
   $y = \frac{7 \times 12}{4}$
   $y = 21$

31. a. $y \div \frac{2}{5} = \frac{3}{4}$
   $y \div \frac{2}{5} \times \frac{2}{5} = \frac{3}{4} \times \frac{2}{5}$
   $y = \frac{3}{4} \times \frac{2}{5}$
   $y = \frac{6}{20}$
   $y = \frac{3}{10}$

   b. $y \div \frac{2}{5} = \frac{3}{4}$
   $y = \frac{3}{4} \times \frac{2}{5}$
   $y = \frac{6}{20}$
   $y = \frac{3}{10}$

32.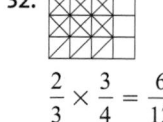
   $\frac{2}{3} \times \frac{3}{4} = \frac{6}{12}$

33. a. $\frac{2}{6} \times \frac{2}{5}$
   b. $\frac{3}{5} \times \frac{2}{3}$

34. a. G ☐☐☐ B ☐ whole class
   Three-fourths of the class consists of girls.
   b. B ☐☐☐ G ☐☐ whole class
   Two-fifths of the class consists of girls.

35. a. B ☐☐☐☐ G ☐ whole class
   Four-fifths of the class consists of boys.
   b. B ☐☐☐ G ☐☐☐☐ whole class
   Three-sevenths of the class consists of boys.

36.

18 ÷ 3 = 6, and 8 × 6 = 48. The remote car cost $48.

37.

3 × 6 = 18, 18 ÷ 2 = 9, and 5 × 9 = 45. Originally, there were 45 ounces of milk in the container.

38. a. M
       G   135

135 ÷ 9 = 15, and 4 × 15 = 60. Martha planted 60 apple trees.

  b. Let m equal the number of apple trees Martha planted. Then $1\frac{1}{4}m$ equals the number of apple trees George planted. Solve $m + 1\frac{1}{4}m = 135$ to get $m = 60$. Martha planted 60 apple trees.

39. a. M
       G   +5   432

432 − 5 = 427, 427 ÷ 7 = 61, and 4 × 61 + 5 = 249. George plants 249 apple trees.

  b. Let m equal the number of apple trees Martha planted. Then $1\frac{1}{3}m + 5$ equals the number of apple trees George planted. Solve $m + 1\frac{1}{3}m + 5 = 432$ to get $m = 183$. Then $1\frac{1}{3} \times 183 + 5 = 249$. George planted 249 apple trees.

40. a. M
       G   −8   172

172 + 8 = 180, 180 ÷ 5 = 36, and 3 × 36 − 8 = 100. George planted 100 apple trees.

  b. Let m equal the number of apple trees Martha planted. Then $1\frac{1}{2}m - 8$ equals the number of apple trees George planted. Solve $m + 1\frac{1}{2}m - 8 = 172$ to get $m = 72$. Then $1\frac{1}{2} \times 72 - 8 = 100$. George planted 100 apple trees.

41. Answers vary. For example, $\frac{2}{3}$ of the students played basketball. $\frac{4}{7}$ of these students also played baseball. What fraction of the students played basketball and baseball?

42.
$$4\frac{2}{3}y + 5 = 17$$
$$4\frac{2}{3}y = 12$$
$$\frac{14}{3}y = 12$$
$$\frac{3}{14} \times \frac{14}{3}y = \frac{3}{14} \times 12$$
$$y = \frac{3}{14} \times 12$$
$$y = \frac{36}{14}$$
$$y = 2\frac{4}{7}$$

43. a. 140°F   **b.** 14°F   **c.** 185°F   **d.** −4°F

44. a. $C = \frac{5}{9}(F - 32)$ **b.** 10°C   **c.** −25°C

45. a. Rule for subtracting fractions
  b. Rule for multiplying fractions

c. Distributive property of multiplication over subtraction
d. Rule for subtracting fractions
e. Rule for multiplying fractions

46. 4800 cm

47. a. $\frac{3}{4} \times 456$ **b.** 342 bus drivers

48. a.

$$\frac{9}{4} \div \frac{5}{4} = 1\frac{4}{5}$$

  b.

$$\frac{3}{2} \div \frac{5}{2} = \frac{3}{5}$$

49. a. $\frac{c}{d}$ is equivalent to $\frac{6}{5}$.   **b.** $\frac{c}{d}$ is equivalent to $\frac{5}{6}$.

50. a. $\frac{7}{6} \times \frac{5}{3} = \frac{35}{18}$, so the student's answer checks.
  b. $2\frac{3}{5} \times \frac{2}{3} = \frac{13}{5} \times \frac{2}{3} = \frac{26}{15} = 1\frac{11}{15} \neq \frac{8}{5}$, so the student's answer is incorrect.

51. B
      T

  a. $\frac{3}{8}$ **b.** $1\frac{3}{5}$ **c.** $\frac{5}{8}$

52. J
      S

  a. $1\frac{2}{5}$ **b.** $\frac{5}{7}$ **c.** $\frac{2}{5}$

53. a. $\frac{8}{36}$ or $\frac{2}{9}$
  b. $\frac{7}{9}$ **c.** $\frac{2}{7}$ **d.** $1\frac{2}{7}$

54. a. $\frac{12}{30}$ or $\frac{2}{5}$ **b.** $\frac{18}{30}$ or $\frac{3}{5}$ **c.** $\frac{12}{18}$ or $\frac{2}{3}$ **d.** $\frac{30}{18}$ or $1\frac{2}{3}$

55. a. $\frac{43}{8} \div \frac{5}{8} = \frac{43}{5}$ **b.** $\frac{17}{8} \div \frac{5}{3} = \frac{51}{40}$

56. a. Multiplication property of equality
  b. Multiplication and division are inverse operations.
  c. Rule for multiplying fractions   **d.** Simplification

57. a. Jenny walked $6\frac{3}{4}$ times as far as Hillary.
  b. Ken spent $3\frac{1}{19}$ times as many hours on his project as Larry.
  c. A compact car gets $56\frac{2}{3}$ times as many miles per gallon as a heavily armed tank.

58. 60 cups

59.

84 ÷ 7 = 12, 3 × 12 = 36, and 36 + 24 = 60. Tyler paid $60.

60. a. base = 8, exponent = 5
  b. base = −3, exponent = 4
  c. base = $\frac{2}{3}$, exponent = −4
  d. base = −5a, exponent = 7

61. a. product rule **b.** power of a product rule
c. power of a quotient rule **d.** quotient rule

62. a. $8x^{12}$ **b.** $\dfrac{1}{9x^2}$ **c.** $\dfrac{x^7}{y^6}$ **d.** $\dfrac{-1}{x^{12}y^{15}}$

63. a. $25x^{11}$ **b.** $64a$ **c.** $\dfrac{a^6c}{b^7}$

SECTION 5.4

1. 4 to 5, 4:5, and $\dfrac{4}{5}$

2.

BBB	BBB	BBB
GGGG	GGGG	GGGG

3. $3{:}4 = 3\cdot 3{:}4\cdot 3 = 9{:}12$

4. $12{:}15 = 12 \div 3{:}15 \div 3 = 4{:}5$

5.

Number of pens (x)	3	6	9	12
Number of pencils (y)	7	14	21	28

6. Answers vary; for example, 3:5 and 6:10.

7. a. J □□□ ↑
A □□□□□ 480↓
480 ÷ 8 = 60. Ann has 300 beads.
b. $\frac{5}{8} = \frac{n}{480}$, and $n = 300$. Ann has 300 beads.
c. $3n + 5n = 480$, $8n = 480$, $n = 60$, and $5n = 5 \times 60 = 300$. Ann has 300 beads.

8. a. 4500
S □□□□□
J □□□
4500 ÷ 2 = 2250, 5 × 2250 = 11,250, and 3 × 2250 = 6750. Smith spent \$11,250, and Jones spent \$6750.
b. $5n - 3n = 4500$, $2n = 4500$, and $n = 2250$. Then $5n = 5 \times 2250 = 11{,}250$ and $3n = 3 \times 2250 = 6750$. Smith spent \$11,250, and Jones spent \$6750

9. Solve $5n - 2n = 840$ to get $n = 280$. Then $2 \times 280 = 560$. Acme spent \$560 on postage.

10. Solve $7n - 4n = 258$ to get $n = 86$. $7 \times 86 = 602$. Mark saved \$602.

11. Both expressions could represent a ratio. But $a{:}b$ is not a number, while $\frac{a}{b}$ could be a number or a ratio.

12. a. 3 **b.** $x = y$

13. a.

Blue paint (oz)	7	14	21
Yellow paint (oz)	5	10	15
Additive comparison	$7 - 5 = 2$	$14 - 10 = 4$	$21 - 15 = 6$
Multiplicative comparison	$7 \div 5 = 1\frac{2}{5}$	$14 \div 10 = 1\frac{2}{5}$	$21 \div 15 = 1\frac{2}{5}$

b. 5 **c.** $1\frac{2}{5}$ **d.** multiplication and division

14. a. $a = b$ **b.** There are no restrictions on a and b.

15. a. 54 **b.** $1\frac{2}{3}$ **c.** 8

16. Answers vary. For example, 2:3, 4:1, or 3:7.

17. a.

No. of cats	3	6	9	12	15
No. of mice	7	14	21	28	35

There are 35 mice.

b. 15
C □□□
M □□□□□□□
$15 \div 3 = 5$, so each box in the diagram is worth five cats or 5 mice. $7 \cdot 5 = 35$. There are 35 mice.

c. $3{:}7 = 1{:}\frac{7}{3} = 15 \cdot 1{:}15 \cdot \frac{7}{3} = 15{:}35$. There are 35 mice.

d.

No. of cats	3	15
No. of mice	7	n

$\frac{3}{7} = \frac{15}{n}$, $3n = 7 \cdot 15$, $3n = 105$, and $n = 35$. There are 35 mice.

e.

No. of cats	3	$3n$
No. of mice	7	$7n$

$3n = 15$, so $n = 5$. $7n = 7 \cdot 5 = 35$. There are 35 mice.

18. $1\frac{2}{7}$ gal or $10\frac{2}{7}$ pt

19. a. \$3000 to \$45,000
b. 1:15. It costs \$1 for every \$15 raised.

20. two-fifths

21.

b	7
n	3

$b = \dfrac{7}{3}n$

22. a. 72 cents per gallon of fuel **b.** \$1.32 per gallon of fuel

23. a. 5:2 **b.** $\dfrac{5}{7}$ **c.** 5:7 **d.** $\dfrac{3}{5}$

24. a. The student used addition or subtraction rather than multiplication or division.
b. Drawing a diagram helps the student see that multiplication or division is appropriate, not addition or subtraction, for generating equivalent ratios.
BBB GGGGG
BBB GGGGG
BBB GGGGG
BBB GGGGG
c. 20 girls

25. The fraction $\frac{a}{b}$ is a number, but the ratio $\frac{a}{b}$ is not a number. In the ratio $\frac{a}{b}$ the second term b can be zero, but in the fraction $\frac{a}{b}$ the denominator b cannot be zero.

26. $5{:}2 = 2\frac{1}{2}{:}1$
$8{:}3\frac{1}{2} = 2\frac{2}{7}{:}1$
The lemonade made by Tom is slightly sourer.

27. **a.** There are two As for every five Bs (or five Bs for every two As).
   b. Two out of every seven letters are As (or five out of every seven letters are Bs).
   c. There are seven letters for every two As (or there are seven letters for every five Bs).

28.

2	4	6	8
5	10	15	20

29. $\frac{3}{7} = \frac{n}{28}$, and $n = 12$. There are 12 pennies.

30. $1\frac{1}{3}$ tsp

31. **a.** 108 oz   **b.** 117 oz   **c.** 124 oz

32. **a.** $11:4 = \frac{11}{4}:1 = \frac{11}{4} \cdot 30:1 \cdot 30 = 82\frac{1}{2}:30$. He burns $82\frac{1}{2}$ calories.
   b. $\frac{11}{4} = \frac{n}{30}$, $n = 82\frac{1}{2}$. He burns $82\frac{1}{2}$ calories.

33. 20,500 people

34. 6:4 or 3:2

35. grocer B

36. $2:1:\frac{1}{2} = 6:3:1\frac{1}{2}$. He should add 2 cups of sugar and 1 cup of lemon juice.

37. 41 teachers

38. **a.**

   $252 \div 3 = 84$ and $2 \cdot 84 = 168$. Kyle has 168 marbles.
   b. Solve $5n - 2n = 252$ to get $n = 84$. Then $2 \cdot 84 = 168$. Kyle has 168 marbles.
   c. $2:3 = \frac{2}{3}:1 = \frac{2}{3} \cdot 252:1 \cdot 252 = 168:252$. Kyle has 168 marbles.

39. $\frac{5}{12}$

40. $m = \frac{5}{8}c$

41. less than $1.23 per pack

42. The proportion $\frac{2}{5} = \frac{n}{24}$ does not have a whole number solution.

43. $\frac{3}{7} \times 420 = 180$

   $\frac{180 + n}{420 + 600} = \frac{1}{2}$

   $n = 330$
   $330:600 = 11:20$

44. Mitchell has 960 pennies, and Joey has 352 pennies.

45. 250 million hydrogen atoms

46. 8:6, 23:42, and 12:23

47. 75 channels

48. **a.** There were four pennies for every seven coins.
   b. There were three boys for every girl.

49. Answers vary. For example, Maria has 14 fewer stamps than Arnold. Maria has 3 stamps for every 5 stamps Arnold has. How many stamps does each have? (Maria has 21 stamps, and Arnold has 35 stamps.)

50. Answers vary. Leila has 2 beads for every 5 beads Lakisha has. Altogether, they have 210 beads. How many beads does each have? (Leila has 60 beads, and Lakisha has 150 beads.)

REVIEW QUESTIONS

1. five, one-third

2. **a.** one-eighth   **b.** three

3. **a.** 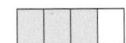   **b.**
   c.

4. The shaded area is $\frac{3}{4}$.

5. **a.**

   $364 \div 7 = 52$, and $2 \times 52 = 104$. David has 104 coins.
   b. Let n equal the number of coins Erin has. Then David has $\frac{2}{5}n$ coins. Solve the equation $n + \frac{2}{5}n = 364$ to get $n = 260$. Then $\frac{2}{5} \times 260 = 104$. David has 104 coins.

6. **a.**

   $243 \div 3 = 81$ and $2 \times 81 = 162$. David has 162 coins.
   b. Let n equal the number of coins Erin has. Then David has $\frac{2}{5}n$ coins. Solve the equation $n - \frac{2}{5}n = 243$ to get $n = 405$. Then $\frac{2}{5} \times 405 = 162$. David has 162 coins.

7. **a.**

   $302 + 8 = 310$, $310 \div 5 = 62$, and $2 \times 62 - 8 = 116$. David has 116 coins.
   b. Let n equal the number of coins Erin has. David has $\frac{2}{3}n - 8$ coins. Solve the equation $n + \frac{2}{3}n - 8 = 302$ to get $n = 186$. Then $\frac{2}{3} \times 186 - 8 = 116$. David has 116 coins.

8. **a.** $7 \div 3 = 2$ R1   **b.** $7 \div 3 = \frac{7}{3}$

9. Answers vary.
   a. The teacher has nine pencils. She wants to divide them equally among four students. How many pencils should each student get?
   b. The teacher has nine cookies. She wants to divide them equally among four students. How much cookie should each student get?

10. **a.**

b.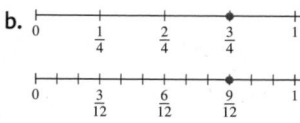

c. $3 \cdot 12 = 36$, and $4 \cdot 9 = 36$.

11. Answers vary.

$$\frac{210}{672} = \frac{210 \div 3}{672 \div 3} = \frac{70}{224}$$

$$\frac{210}{672} = \frac{210 \div 2}{672 \div 2} = \frac{105}{336}$$

12. Answers vary.

$$\frac{7}{9} = \frac{7 \times 5}{9 \times 5} = \frac{35}{45}$$

$$\frac{7}{9} = \frac{7 \times 4}{9 \times 4} = \frac{28}{36}$$

13. a. ad and bc **b.** $ad < bc$

14. Answers vary. For example, $\frac{3}{4} = \frac{6}{8}$ and $\frac{6}{8} > \frac{5}{8}$.
Then $6 > 5$, so $\frac{6}{8} > \frac{5}{8}$.

15. Mark could be correct because 3 cups of raisins is more than 2 cups of raisins. Lisa could be correct because $\frac{2}{7}$ of her mixture is raisins, while $\frac{3}{11}$ of Mark's mixture is raisins, and $\frac{2}{7} > \frac{3}{11}$.

16. tenths

17. a. model of $\frac{2}{3}$

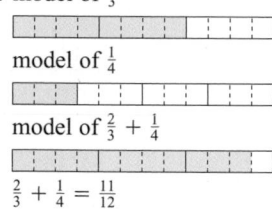

model of $\frac{1}{4}$

model of $\frac{2}{3} + \frac{1}{4}$

$\frac{2}{3} + \frac{1}{4} = \frac{11}{12}$

b. model of $\frac{2}{3}$

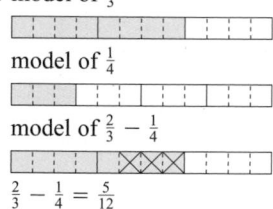

model of $\frac{1}{4}$

model of $\frac{2}{3} - \frac{1}{4}$

$\frac{2}{3} - \frac{1}{4} = \frac{5}{12}$

18. $\frac{3}{4}$ in

19.
$$y + \frac{5}{3} = \frac{9}{4}$$
$$\left(y + \frac{5}{3}\right) + -\frac{5}{3} = \frac{9}{4} + -\frac{5}{3}$$
$$y + \left(\frac{5}{3} + -\frac{5}{3}\right) = \frac{9}{4} + -\frac{5}{3}$$
$$y + 0 = \frac{9}{4} + -\frac{5}{3}$$
$$y = \frac{9}{4} + -\frac{5}{3}$$
$$y = \frac{7}{12}$$

20.
$$y + \frac{5}{3} = \frac{9}{4}$$
$$y = \frac{9}{4} - \frac{5}{3}$$
$$y = \frac{27}{12} - \frac{20}{12}$$
$$y = \frac{27 - 20}{12}$$
$$y = \frac{7}{12}$$

21.
$$y - \frac{5}{3} = \frac{9}{4}$$
$$y - \frac{5}{3} + \frac{5}{3} = \frac{9}{4} + \frac{5}{3}$$
$$y = \frac{9}{4} + \frac{5}{3}$$
$$y = \frac{47}{12}$$
$$y = 3\frac{11}{12}$$

22.
$$y - \frac{5}{3} = \frac{9}{4}$$
$$y = \frac{9}{4} + \frac{5}{3}$$
$$y = \frac{47}{12}$$
$$y = 3\frac{11}{12}$$

23. a. 2   **b.** $-6\frac{1}{2}$ **c.** $23\frac{1}{2}$

24. a. $12\frac{3}{10}$ **b.** $6\frac{7}{12}$

25. a. $\frac{21}{8}$ **b.** $-\frac{53}{6}$ **c.** $6\frac{3}{7}$ **d.** $-5\frac{2}{3}$

26. a. $\frac{3}{4} \times \frac{3}{5}$ **b.** $\frac{2}{4} \times \frac{2}{3}$

27. a.

$$\frac{4}{7} \times \frac{2}{3} = \frac{8}{21}$$

b.

$$\frac{2}{5} \times \frac{3}{4} = \frac{6}{20}$$

28.
$$\frac{4}{5} \times y = 32$$
$$\frac{5}{4} \times \left(\frac{4}{5} \times y\right) = \frac{5}{4} \times 32$$
$$\left(\frac{5}{4} \times \frac{4}{5}\right) \times y = \frac{5}{4} \times 32$$
$$1 \times y = \frac{5}{4} \times 32$$
$$y = \frac{5}{4} \times 32$$
$$y = \frac{160}{4}$$
$$y = 40$$

29. $\frac{3}{5} \times y = 45$
$$y = 45 \div \frac{3}{5}$$
$$y = 45 \times \frac{5}{3}$$
$$y = \frac{225}{3}$$
$$y = 75$$

30. $n \div \frac{3}{5} = 28$
$$n \div \frac{3}{5} \times \frac{3}{5} = 28 \times \frac{3}{5}$$
$$n = 28 \times \frac{3}{5}$$
$$n = \frac{84}{5}$$
$$n = 16\frac{4}{5}$$

31. a.

$18 \div 3 = 6$, and $2 \times 6 - 2 = 10$. Carlos has 10 coins.

b.

$420 \div 4 = 105$, and $3 \times 105 + 2 = 317$. 317 people could not purchase tickets and $420 - 317 = 103$, so 103 people purchased tickets.

32. 402 people

33. $72,000

34. a. $\frac{3}{4}$ **b.** $1\frac{3}{4}$ **c.** $\frac{3}{7}$ **d.** $\frac{4}{7}$

35. a. $\frac{2}{5}, 1\frac{2}{5}$ **b.** $\frac{2}{3}, 1\frac{2}{3}$ **c.** $\frac{3}{7}, 1\frac{3}{7}$

36. a. $\frac{92}{147}$ **b.** $2\frac{32}{49}$ **c.** 16

37.
$$\frac{a}{b} \div \frac{c}{d} = \frac{\frac{a}{b}}{\frac{c}{d}}$$
$$= \frac{\frac{a}{b} \times \frac{d}{c}}{\frac{c}{d} \times \frac{d}{c}}$$
$$= \frac{\frac{a}{b} \times \frac{d}{c}}{1}$$
$$= \frac{a}{b} \times \frac{d}{c}$$

38. Answers vary.
  a. Samantha frosted two-thirds of the batch of cookies. Of these cookies, she put sprinkles on three-fourths of the cookies. What fraction of the batch of cookies had frosting and sprinkles?
  b. JoAnne has $4\frac{2}{5}$ pounds of ground beef. Each batch of chili requires $\frac{3}{4}$ pounds of chili. How many batches of chili can she make?

39. a. $\frac{1}{16}$ **b.** $\frac{17}{36}$

40. a. $\frac{3b^3}{16a^3c^5}$ **b.** $\frac{3^6}{a^3}$ **c.** $\frac{a^{12}}{b^{15}}$ **d.** $\frac{1}{3^2a^3b}$

41. 3:7, 3 to 7, $\frac{3}{7}$

42.

There are four circles for every six squares. There are two circles for every three squares.

43. a. 45 dogs **b.** 105 dogs

44. a. $1.68 **b.** $7\frac{7}{8}$ days **c.** 11 mi

45. store B

46. no, because the ratios 3:7 and 5:9 are not equivalent

47. a.

Cement (bags)	2	4	6	8	10
Water (gal)	5	10	15	20	25

Shehan needs 20 gallons of water.

b.

$8 \div 2 = 4$, and $5 \times 4 = 20$. Shehan needs 20 gallons of water.

c. $2:5 = 1:\frac{5}{2} = 8 \times 1:8 \times \frac{5}{2} = 8:20$

Shehan needs 20 gallons of water.

d. The number of bags of cement is $2n$, and the number of gallons of water needed is $5n$. $2n = 8$, so $n = 4$. Then $5n = 5 \times 4 = 20$. Shehan needs 20 gallons of water.

e.

Cement (bags)	2	8
Water (gal)	5	w

$\frac{2}{5} = \frac{8}{w}$. Then $2w = 5 \cdot 8$. Then $w = \frac{5 \cdot 8}{2}$. Then $w = 20$. Shehan needs 20 gallons of water.

48. The student used additive reasoning: $7 - 4 = 3$, so $12 + 3 = 15$. Ratios require multiplication and/or division for writing equivalent ratios.

49. a. $\frac{2}{3}$ **b.** $\frac{2}{5}$ **c.** $1\frac{2}{3}$ **d.** $\frac{3}{5}$

50. a. $\frac{4}{5}$ **b.** $\frac{4}{9}$ **c.** $1\frac{4}{5}$ **d.** $\frac{5}{9}$

51. a. 100 pounds of feed produces 35 more pounds of cricket than of beef.
   b. 100 pounds of feed produces $4\frac{1}{2}$ times as many pounds of cricket as beef.

CHAPTER 5 TEST

1. a. sixths   **b.** 8

2. $\frac{9}{4}$ or $2\frac{1}{4}$

3. a.

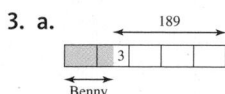

   b. $189 - 3 = 186$, $186 \div 3 = 62$, and $2 \times 62 - 3 = 121$. Benny has 121 marbles.

4. a.

J ▢▢▢▢▢▢▢
B ▢▢▢ −2   578

   b. $578 + 2 = 580$, $580 \div 10 = 58$, and $3 \times 58 - 2 = 172$. Bill has 172 coins.

5. a. $11 \div 4 = 2$ R3   **b.** $11 \div 4 = \frac{11}{4} = 2\frac{3}{4}$

6. Answers vary.
   a. A teacher has 17 pencils. She wants to divide them equally among five students. How many pencils should each person get?
   b. A teacher has 17 cookies. She wants to divide them equally among five students. How much cookie should each person get?

7. Yes, because their cross-products, $59 \times 11{,}648$ and $32 \times 21{,}476$, are equal.

8. a. $19\frac{8}{35}$ **b.** $-8\frac{6}{35}$

9. a. $\frac{34}{5}$ **b.** $-\frac{38}{5}$ or $\frac{-38}{5}$ **c.** $13\frac{1}{18}$ **d.** $-4\frac{3}{8}$

10.

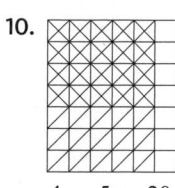

$\frac{4}{7} \times \frac{5}{6} = \frac{20}{42}$

11. $\frac{2}{7} \times \frac{3}{5}$

12. $y - \frac{7}{5} = \frac{2}{3}$

$y = \frac{2}{3} + \frac{7}{5}$

$y = \frac{31}{15}$

$y = 2\frac{1}{15}$

13.
$$y + \frac{5}{8} = \frac{4}{3}$$
$$y + \frac{5}{8} - \frac{5}{8} = \frac{4}{3} - \frac{5}{8}$$
$$y = \frac{4}{3} - \frac{5}{8}$$
$$y = \frac{17}{24}$$

14.
$$\frac{7}{5}y = \frac{2}{3}$$
$$\frac{7}{5}y \div \frac{7}{5} = \frac{2}{3} \div \frac{7}{5}$$
$$y = \frac{2}{3} \div \frac{7}{5}$$
$$y = \frac{2}{3} \times \frac{5}{7}$$
$$y = \frac{10}{21}$$

15. $\frac{8}{3} \times y = 60$ Original equation

$y = 60 \div \frac{8}{3}$ Definition of division

$y = 60 \times \frac{3}{8}$ Invert and multiply rule

$y = 22\frac{1}{2}$ Simplification

16. $n \div \frac{3}{5} = 45$

$n = 45 \times \frac{3}{5}$

$n = 27$

17.
$$\frac{3}{4} \times n = 6$$
$$\frac{4}{3} \times \left(\frac{3}{4} \times n\right) = \frac{4}{3} \times 6$$
$$\left(\frac{4}{3} \times \frac{3}{4}\right) \times n = \frac{4}{3} \times 6$$
$$1 \times n = \frac{4}{3} \times 6$$
$$n = \frac{4}{3} \times 6$$
$$n = \frac{24}{3}$$
$$n = 8$$

18. a. $\frac{3}{8}$ **b.** $\frac{5}{8}$ **c.** $\frac{3}{5}$ **d.** $1\frac{3}{5}$

19. a. $\frac{7}{9}$ **b.** $1\frac{7}{9}$ **c.** $\frac{7}{16}$ **d.** $\frac{9}{16}$

20. a. $\frac{42}{15} \div \frac{12}{5} = \frac{42}{15} \times \frac{5}{12} = \frac{7}{6} = 1\frac{1}{6}$

   b. $14\frac{5}{7} \div 3\frac{3}{4} = \frac{103}{7} \div \frac{15}{4} = \frac{103}{7} \times \frac{4}{15} = \frac{412}{105} = 3\frac{97}{105}$

21. a. $\frac{3a^2bc^6}{4}$ **b.** $\frac{16}{b^8}$ **c.** $\frac{b^{16}}{a^{20}}$ **d.** $\frac{a^2c^2}{25b}$

22. a. $924 \div 11 = 84$, and $7 \cdot 84 = 588$ trucks
b. $420 \div 3 = 140$, and $4 \cdot 140 = 560$ cars

23.
$$\frac{5}{9} = \frac{n}{60}$$
$$9n = 5 \times 60$$
$$n = \frac{5 \times 60}{9}$$
$$n = 33\frac{1}{3}$$
Kerry should add $33\frac{1}{3}$ cups of pineapple juice.

24. $3:5 = 1:\frac{5}{3} = 12 \times 1:12 \times \frac{5}{3} = 12:20$; so yes, because 3:5 and 12:20 are equivalents ratios

25. $7n - 4n = 924$, $3n = 924$, and $n = 308$. Then $7n = 7 \times 308 = 2156$. There are 2156 cans of green beans.

CHAPTER 6

SECTION 6.1

1. a. 0.52   **b.** 0.73

2. a.
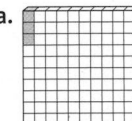
b.
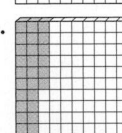
c.
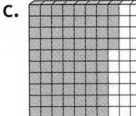

3. a. 35 and 8, and $35 > 8$
b.
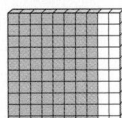
0.8
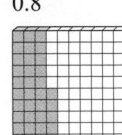
0.35
So $0.35 < 0.8$.

4.

```
  ├──┼──┼──┼──►
 0.4 0.5 0.6 0.7
```

5.

```
 ├┼┼┼┼┼┼┼┼┼┼►
0.40              0.50
```

6. a. 347.423   **b.** 28,374.00235   **c.** 58.0013

7. a. 9 and 5 hundredths
b. 56 thousand, 835 and 708 thousandths
c. 14 and 37 ten-thousandths

8. a. three and eighty-four thousand, one hundred twenty-three hundred-thousandths
b. sixty-two and four thousand, twenty-one hundred-thousandths
c. thirty-six ten-thousandths

9. a. 7   **b.** 1

10. a. 2063 minutes of local calls
b. 755 minutes of state-to-state calls
c. $0.0349x + 0.049y$
d. t is the total number of minutes.
$$x = \frac{5}{8}t \text{ and } y = \frac{3}{8}t$$
$$51.04 = 0.0349 \cdot \frac{5}{8}t + 0.049 \cdot \frac{3}{8}t$$
$$t \approx 1270, x \approx 794, y \approx 476$$

11. Solve simpler problems of $0.8 - 0.5^k$, and look for a pattern. The tenths digit is 7.

12. $73.33

13. $800

14. $(365.2425 - 365.24220) \times 100 = 0.03$ days

15. a. $34.12 \cdot 10^1 = 341.2$, $34.12 \cdot 10^2 = 3412$, and $34.12 \cdot 10^3 = 34{,}120$
b. Multiplying a number by 10^n shifts the decimal point n place values to the right.

16.
$$2.345 \times 100 = 2.345 \times 10^2$$
$$= (2 \cdot 10^0 + 3 \cdot 10^{-1} + 4 \cdot 10^{-2} + 5 \cdot 10^{-3}) \times 10^2$$
$$= 2 \cdot 10^2 + 3 \cdot 10^1 + 4 \cdot 10^0 + 5 \cdot 10^{-1}$$
$$= 234.5$$

17. a. $456.12 \div 10^1 = 45.612$, $456.12 \div 10^2 = 4.5612$, $456.12 \div 10^3 = 0.45612$, $456.12 \div 10^4 = 0.045612$
b. Dividing a number by 10^n shifts the decimal point n place values to the left.

18.
$$567.8 \div 100 = 567.8 \times \frac{1}{100}$$
$$= 567.8 \times 10^{-2}$$
$$= (5 \cdot 10^2 + 6 \cdot 10^1 + 7 \cdot 10^0 + 8 \cdot 10^{-1}) \times 10^{-2}$$
$$= 5 \cdot 10^0 + 6 \cdot 10^{-1} + 7 \cdot 10^{-2} + 8 \cdot 10^{-3}$$
$$= 5.678$$

19. 348×23

20. $222.31 \div 43$

21. a. $5.55 \le n < 5.65$ **b.** $7.225 \le n < 7.235$
c. $14.9995 \le n < 15.0005$

22. a. $12 \div 3 = 4$, so $13.845 \div 3.25 = 4.26$
b. $80 \div 4 = 20$, so $88.5495 \div 4.75 = 18.642$
c. $500 \times 10 = 5000$, so $487.24 \times 9.38 = 4570.3112$
d. $75 \div 3 = 25$, so $75.7341 \div 3.45 = 26.1282645$

23. $20 \div 1.25 = 16$
$20 \div 0.625 = 32$

24. a. Additive reasoning: $27{,}448 - 19{,}989 = 7459$. On the average, a high school graduate earns $7459 more than a high school dropout. Multiplicative reasoning: $27{,}448 \div 19{,}989 \approx 1.4$. On the average, a high school graduate earns 1.4 times as much as a high school dropout.
b. Additive reasoning: $47{,}853 - 27{,}448 = 20{,}405$. On the average, a college graduate with a bachelor's degree earns $20,405 more than a high school graduate. Multiplicative

reasoning: $47{,}853 \div 27{,}448 \approx 1.7$. On the average, a college graduate with a bachelor's degree earns 1.7 times as much as a high school graduate.

25. 450×32

26. When we multiply two decimal numbers, the first step is to ignore the decimal points. Then we get the whole number multiplication problem 820×5216.

27. $4350 \div 75$

28. 28 mpg

29. **a.** The ratio of the sides of a square is 1:1. $4:3 \approx 1.3{:}1$, and $16:9 \approx 1.8{:}1$. Therefore, the screen with the aspect ratio 4:3 looks more like a square.
    b. $4:3 \approx 1.3{:}1$, so landscape image
    $5:9 \approx 0.6{:}1$, so portrait image

30. **a.** $\frac{2}{200} = \frac{n}{710.25}$, $n \approx 7.10$ tons of ice
    b. $\frac{0.1}{200} = \frac{0.15}{n}$, $n = 300$ L of air

31. **a.** \$26.6667   **b.** \$1.5749

32. **a.** $\frac{0.27}{0.33} = \frac{n}{90}$, $n \approx 74$ lb of water
    b. $\frac{0.27}{0.33} = \frac{60}{n}$, $n \approx 73$ lb of cement
    c. Solve $0.27n + 0.33n = 90$ to get $n = 150$. Then $0.27 \times 150 = 40.5$ and $0.33 \times 150 = 49.5$, or 40.5 pounds of water and 49.5 pounds of cement.

33. The closest place values near the ones place are tens and tenths. The second closest place values are hundreds and hundredths. The third closest place values are thousands and thousandths, and so on. The place values are symmetric about the ones place.

34. Answers vary. For example, 0.4 and 0.40 have the same model.

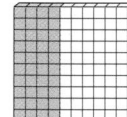

35. $6 \div 0.2$ is greater than 6 because there are 5 groups of 0.2 in 1 and therefore 30 groups of 0.2 in 6.

36. **a.** The student may be comparing 32 and 7, and $32 > 7$.

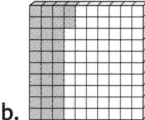

    b.
    0.32

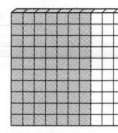

    0.7
    So $0.32 < 0.7$.

37. **a.** We are regrouping 1 one and 2 tenths as 12 tenths.
    b. 0   **c.** 8

38. **a.** decimal fractions or fractions   **b.** terminating
    c. hundredths   **d.** 0.002   **e.** .23

39. **a.** 278.0305   **b.** 36.000213

40. **a.** 0   **b.** 4   **c.** 8

41. **a.** 52 and 24 hundredths
    b. 38 and 24 ten-thousandths
    c. 15 thousand, 349 and 349 millionths

42. **a.** 10   **b.** 0.2   **c.** 40   **d.** 30

43. **a.** hundredths   **b.** ten-thousandths
    c. ten-millionths   **d.** billionths

44. **a.** 0.3 or 3/10   **b.** 50   **c.** 0   **d.** 0.008 or 8/1000

45. **a.** 8 and 15 thousandths
    b. 801 and 450 hundred-thousandths
    c. 82 hundred-thousandths

46. **a.** $3\frac{84{,}123}{100{,}000}$
    b. $62\frac{4021}{100{,}000}$
    c. $\frac{36}{10{,}000}$

47. **a.** $0.45 = \frac{45}{100} = \frac{9}{20}$
    b. $0.450 = \frac{450}{1000} = \frac{45}{100} = \frac{9}{20}$

48. **a.** forty-five hundredths
    b. four hundred fifty thousandths

49. **a.** 34.57   **b.** 600   **c.** 7341.004   **d.** 9000

50. **a.** $12.65 \le n < 12.75$ **b.** $12.695 \le n < 12.705$

51. **a.** \$0.50   **b.** \$0.75   **c.** \$1.20

52. **a.** 8 thousandths and 4 thousandths = 12 thousandths = 1 hundredth, 2 thousands. The 1 above the 5 represents the 1 hundredth from regrouping 12 thousandths as 1 hundredth, 2 thousandths.
    b. 6 tenths and 7 tenths = 13 tenths = 1 one, 3 tenths. The 1 above the 2 represents 1 one from regrouping 13 tenths as 1 one, 3 tenths.

53. **a.** There were 3 ones. We regrouped 1 one as 10 tenths, and that leaves 2 ones remaining. The 2 above the 3 represents the 2 ones remaining.
    b. We have 6 tenths and need to take away 7 tenths. There are not enough tenths, so we regrouped 1 one as 10 tenths. Then 10 tenths + 6 tenths = 16 tenths.

54. **a.** We are regrouping 1 one and 6 tenths as 16 tenths.
    b. 0   **c.** 9

55. [number line marked 1.2, 1.4, 1.5 with a point between 1.4 and 1.5]

56. Split the interval from 7.7 to 8.3 into six equal-sized regions to help you locate 8.1 and 8.2 on the number line. Then 8.15 is halfway between 8.1 and 8.2.
    [number line marked 7.7, 8.1, 8.2, 8.3 with a point between 8.1 and 8.2]

57. **a.** 35.7   **b.** 0.0053   **c.** 208.0305

58. **a.**
    $$\begin{array}{r} \overset{2\ 2}{434} \\ \times\ 26 \\ \hline 2604 \\ 8680 \\ \hline 11{,}284 \end{array}$$

So $434 \times 26 = 11{,}284$. The fractional parts of the factors 4.34 and 2.6 have three place values altogether. So 4.34×2.6 has three place values in the fractional part: $4.34 \times 2.6 = 11.284$. The answer is reasonable, because $4.34 \times 2.6 \approx 4 \times 3 = 12$.

b.
$$
\begin{array}{r}
^{1\ 4}\\
127\\
\times\ \ 6\\
\hline
762
\end{array}
$$

So $127 \times 6 = 762$. The fractional parts of the factors 12.7 and 0.06 have three place values altogether. So 12.7×0.06 has three place values in the fractional part: $12.7 \times 0.06 = 0.762$. The answer seems reasonable, because $12.7 \times 0.06 \approx 13 \times 6/100 = 78/100 = 0.78$.

c.
$$
\begin{array}{r}
^{3}\\
34\\
\times\ 28\\
\hline
272\\
680\\
\hline
952
\end{array}
$$

So $34 \times 28 = 952$. The fractional parts of the factors 0.034 and 0.28 have five place values altogether. So 0.034×0.28 has five place values in the fractional part: $0.034 \times 0.28 = 0.00952$. The answer seems reasonable, because $0.034 \times 0.28 \approx 0.03 \times 0.3 = 0.009$.

59. a. $7.8 \div 2.4 = 78 \div 24$. Then

$$
\begin{array}{r}
3.25\\
24\overline{)78.00}\\
-72\ \downarrow\downarrow\\
\hline
6\ 0\downarrow\\
-4\ 8\downarrow\\
\hline
1\ 20\\
-1\ 20\\
\hline
0
\end{array}
$$

So $7.8 \div 2.4 = 3.25$.

b. $3.144 \div 0.6 = 31.44 \div 6$. Then

$$
\begin{array}{r}
5.24\\
6\overline{)31.44}\\
-30\ \downarrow\downarrow\\
\hline
1\ 4\downarrow\\
-1\ 2\downarrow\\
\hline
24\\
-24\\
\hline
0
\end{array}
$$

So $3.144 \div 0.6 = 5.24$.

c. $0.6152 \div 0.04 = 61.52 \div 4$. Then

$$
\begin{array}{r}
15.38\\
4\overline{)61.52}\\
-4\downarrow\downarrow\downarrow\\
\hline
21\ \downarrow\downarrow\\
-20\ \downarrow\downarrow\\
\hline
1\ 5\downarrow\\
-1\ 2\downarrow\\
\hline
32\\
-32\\
\hline
0
\end{array}
$$

So $0.6152 \div 0.04 = 15.38$.

60. $3 + \frac{4}{10} + \frac{8}{100}$, because the expression is written in expanded form

61. Answers vary. For example, $0.47 = \frac{47}{100}$ and $0.8 = \frac{8}{10}$.

62. a. $(10a) \div b = 17.5$ b. $a \div (10b) = 0.175$

63. a. Yes. $\frac{5}{8}$ is simplified and the prime factors of 8 belong to $\{2, 5\}$.
    b. No. The fraction is simplified, and the prime factors $\{7, 5\}$ of the denominator do not all belong to $\{2, 5\}$.
    c. Yes. $\frac{33}{15} = \frac{11}{5}$. $\frac{11}{5}$ is simplified and the prime factors of 5 belong to $\{2, 5\}$.
    d. No. $\frac{105}{72} = \frac{35}{24}$. $\frac{35}{24}$ is simplified and the prime factors $\{2, 3\}$ of the denominator do not all belong to $\{2, 5\}$.

64. a. 0.75   b. 0.47   c. 0.19

65. 32 cents

66. a. yes
    b. Add 1.98 to each entry in the question's magic square, because $0.1 + 1.98 = 2.08$.

67. 46 reams

68. $(6.00 - 4.25) + 4(5.25 - 4.25) + (6.50 - 4.25) = \$8$

69. Answers vary. For example, $0.05 \cdot 1.7 = 0.085$ (insert 1 zero) and $0.0003 \cdot 4.8 = 0.00144$ (insert 2 zeros).

70. Answers vary.

SECTION 6.2

1. $0.2\overline{36}$

2. Draw a right triangle with legs whose lengths are 2 units and 1 unit. Then the hypotenuse has a length of c units, where $c^2 = 2^2 + 1^2$. Then $c^2 = 5$. Then $c = \sqrt{5}$.

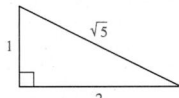

3. $x = 42^{\frac{1}{3}}$

4. Answers vary. For example, $x^3 = 25$ or $4x^3 = 100$ or $4x^3 - 2 = 98$.

5. The simplified fraction has a denominator with prime factors of just 2 and 5.

6. The simplified fraction has a denominator with a prime factor other than 2 or 5.

7. a. $0.\overline{35} = \frac{35}{99}$ b. $0.2\overline{182} = \frac{2161}{9900}$ c. $\frac{679{,}661}{99{,}900}$

8. 14 is between two consecutive perfect squares: $9 < 14 < 16$. So by Theorem 3, $\sqrt{14}$ is an irrational number.

9.

	Two significant digits	Three significant digits	Four significant digits
87,291	8.7×10^4	8.73×10^4	8.729×10^4
0.0045063	4.5×10^{-3}	4.51×10^{-3}	4.506×10^{-3}

10. 9

11. 000000003 (Look for a pattern in the repetends of $\frac{1}{3}, \frac{1}{33}, \frac{1}{333}$, and so on).

12. Answers vary.
    a. $a = 3\sqrt{2}$ and $b = 2\sqrt{2}$
    b. $a = 4 - \sqrt{2}$ and $b = \sqrt{2}$ c. $a = \sqrt{2}$ and $b = \sqrt{3}$
    d. $a = \sqrt{2}$ and $b = \sqrt{8}$ e. $a = \sqrt{6}$ and $b = \sqrt{2}$
    f. $a = \sqrt{8}$ and $b = \sqrt{2}$

13. no, because it is a repeating decimal, which makes it a rational number

14. a. all   b. some   c. all   d. some   e. some   f. no
    g. all   h. no   i. some   j. no   k. no   l. all
    m. no   n. all   o. no   p. all

15. The simplified fraction has a denominator with a prime factor other than 2 or 5.

16. $\sqrt{12}$ is an irrational number, because 12 is not a perfect square.

17. a. $\frac{154}{99} = 1.\overline{5}$, $\frac{155}{99} = 1.\overline{56}$, and $\frac{156}{99} = 1.\overline{57}$
    b. $\frac{157}{99} = 1.\overline{58}$

18. 9

19. Answers vary. For example, $x^5 = -38$, $4x^5 = -152$, or $2x^5 + 3 = -73$.

20. a. $\sqrt{3}$ is an irrational number because 3 is not a perfect square.
    b. 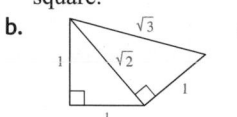   c.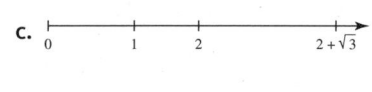

21. a. $\sqrt{2} \cdot \sqrt{3}$ and $\sqrt{6}$ have the same decimal representations.
    b. $\sqrt{5} \cdot \sqrt{7}$ and $\sqrt{35}$ have the same decimal representations.
    c. Conjecture: If m and n are whole numbers, then $\sqrt{m} \cdot \sqrt{n} = \sqrt{m \cdot n}$.

22. a. $\frac{\sqrt{8}}{\sqrt{5}}$ and $\sqrt{\frac{8}{5}}$ have the same decimal representations.
    b. $\frac{\sqrt{10}}{\sqrt{4}}$ and $\sqrt{\frac{10}{4}}$ have the same decimal representations.
    c. Conjecture: If m and n are counting numbers, then $\frac{\sqrt{m}}{\sqrt{n}} = \sqrt{\frac{m}{n}}$.

23. We assume a and b are positive integers. Suppose (a, b) lies on the graph of the equation $y = \sqrt{2}x$ (we show this is impossible). Then $b = \sqrt{2} \times a$. Then $\sqrt{2} = b/a$. Then $\sqrt{2}$ is a rational number, because b and a are integers. Then $\sqrt{2}$ is a rational number. This is impossible, because we know $\sqrt{2}$ is an irrational number. So there are no integers a and b such that (a, b) lies on the graph of the equation $y = \sqrt{2}x$.

24. Suppose a is an irrational number such that $(a, 14)$ lies on the graph of $y = 5x$ (we show that this is impossible). Then $14 = 5a$. Then $a = \frac{14}{5}$. Then a is a rational number, because 14 and 5 are integers. This is impossible, because we assumed a is an irrational number.

25. Answers vary. For example, it means the decimal representation of $\sqrt{5}$ is neither terminating nor repeating.

26. The positive solution is $x = \sqrt{65}$. 65 is not a perfect square, so $\sqrt{65}$ is an irrational number.

27. x^2 is non-negative and -54 is negative, so $x^2 \neq -54$ for any real number x.

28. 2 and 2.0 are alike because they have the same location on a number line. They are different because all numbers in the interval $[1.5, 2.5)$ are rounded to 2 when rounding to the nearest whole number, while all numbers in the interval $[1.95, 2.05)$ are rounded to 2.0 when rounding to the nearest tenth.

29. a. $x = 10$ and $x = -10$.
    b. $\sqrt{100}$ is a positive number, so $\sqrt{100} \neq -10$.

30. The decimal number neither terminates nor repeats, so it must be an irrational number.

31. yes, because it is a simplified fraction that has a denominator such that all its primes belong to $\{2,5\}$

32. yes, because it is a simplified fraction that has a denominator with prime factors other than 2 or 5

33. a. irrational number   b. rational number   c. period
    d. repetend   e. 4   f. principal square root   g. $\sqrt[3]{21}$

34. a. rational   b. rational   c. irrational
    d. irrational   e. rational

35. a. The number a must be a multiple of 3, for example, $a = 12$.
    b. a cannot be a multiple of 3, for example, $a = 4$.

36. Answers vary.
    a. 4.56   b. 4.565656…   c. 4.564564456444564444…

37. a. $1.\overline{48}$ b. $0.\overline{147}$ c. $0.0\overline{147}$

38. a. 5   b. 6   c. 2   d. 4

39. a. 5.1×10^{-4} b. 5.06×10^{-4} c. 5.061×10^{-4}

40. a. $\frac{254}{99} = 2.\overline{56}$, $\frac{255}{99} = 2.\overline{57}$, and $\frac{256}{99} = 2.\overline{58}$
    b. $\frac{257}{99} = 2.\overline{59}$

41. Answers vary.
    a. $8.9\overline{254}$ b. $0.125 = \frac{1}{8} = \frac{7}{56}$ c. 3.28567 d. $0.\overline{34}$
    e. $5.0\overline{027}$ f. $\sqrt{5}$ g. 3π

42. a. 18 is between two consecutive squares: $16 < 18 < 25$, so 18 is not a perfect square. So $\sqrt{18}$ is an irrational number.
    b. $\sqrt{1800} = \sqrt{100 \cdot 18} = \sqrt{100} \cdot \sqrt{18} = 10\sqrt{18}$, so $\sqrt{1800}$ is the product of a rational number and irrational number. Therefore, $\sqrt{1800}$ is an irrational number.

43. a. 317 is between two perfect squares: $17^2 < 317 < 18^2$, so 317 is not a perfect square. Then $\sqrt{317}$ is an irrational number.
    b. $\sqrt{3.17} = \sqrt{317 \times 10^{-2}} = \sqrt{317} \times \frac{1}{100}$, so $\sqrt{3.17}$ is the product of an irrational number and a rational number. Therefore, $\sqrt{3.17}$ is an irrational number.

44. a. 3.7×10^9 b. 3.67×10^9 c. 3.660×10^9
    d. 3.6600×10^9

45. **a.** 125   **b.** $9\sqrt[3]{9}$ **c.** 16

46. **a.** $4\sqrt{3}$ **b.** $10\sqrt{7}$ **c.** $15\sqrt{6}$

47. **a.** $x = \frac{1}{2}\sqrt[3]{12}$ **b.** $x = 3\sqrt{7}$ and $x = -3\sqrt{7}$
    c. $x = 6\sqrt{5}$ and $x = -6\sqrt{5}$

48. Answers vary.
    a. $x^3 = 5$ or $4x^3 + 2 = 22$ **b.** $(x - 1)^5 = 8$

49. **a.** $1.\overline{515}$ **b.** $1.\overline{516}$ **c.** $1.\overline{517}$

50. Suppose a and b are integers such that (a, b) lies on the graph of $y = \sqrt{3}x$. Then $b = \sqrt{3}a$. Then $\sqrt{3} = \frac{b}{a}$. Then $\sqrt{3}$ is a rational number, because a and b are integers. This is impossible, because we already know $\sqrt{3}$ is an irrational number. So Maria is correct.

51. 0225

52. 4

53. **a.** 19   **b.** 4

54. rational number, because $\frac{\sqrt{48}}{\sqrt{12}} = \frac{\sqrt{4} \cdot \sqrt{12}}{\sqrt{12}} = 2$

55. Yes, for example, $a = \sqrt{2}$ and $b = 3\sqrt{2}$.

56. Answers vary. $\sqrt[5]{8}$ is a real number that solves the equation $x^5 = 8$.

57.

	Rational	**Irrational**
-7.8	X	
$3/7$	X	
$43.26787878\ldots$		X
-689	X	
0.00079	X	
$5.242442444\ldots$		X
$\sqrt{27}$		X
$-\dfrac{15}{3}$	X	

58. **a.** irrational   **b.** irrational   **c.** rational   **d.** rational

59. Answers vary; for example, $4.0200200020002\ldots$.

60. Answers vary; for example, $\sqrt{5}$.

61. **a.** irrational   **b.** irrational   **c.** rational

62. **a.** yes   **b.** no   **c.** yes   **d.** no

63. **a.** $\sqrt[5]{28}$ **b.** $\sqrt[4]{12}$ **c.** $\sqrt[18]{35}$ and $-\sqrt[18]{35}$ **d.** $x^9 = 20$

64. $x = \sqrt[7]{10}$

65. $x = \sqrt[24]{95}$ or $x = -\sqrt[24]{95}$

66. **a.** $70{,}092 \times 4058 \approx (7 \times 10^4) \cdot (4 \times 10^3) = 2.8 \times 10^8$
    b. $7{,}500{,}821.32 \div 5082 \approx (7.5 \times 10^6) \div (5 \times 10^3) = 1.5 \times 10^3$

67. We know $\sqrt{3}$ is an irrational number. Suppose $8\sqrt{3}$ is a rational number. Then $8\sqrt{3} = \frac{a}{b}$ for some integers a and b. Then $\sqrt{3} = \frac{a}{8b}$. a and $8b$ are integers. This suggests $\sqrt{3}$ is a rational number, which is impossible. So $\sqrt{3}$ cannot be a rational number. So $\sqrt{3}$ is an irrational number.

68. We know $\sqrt{3}$ is an irrational number. Suppose $6 + \sqrt{3}$ is a rational number. Then $6 + \sqrt{3} = \frac{a}{b}$ for some integers a and b. Then $\sqrt{3} = \frac{a}{b} - 6$. We know $\frac{a}{b} - 6$ equals $\frac{a}{b} + (-6)$, so $\frac{a}{b} - 6$ is a rational number by the closure property of addition with rational numbers. This implies $\sqrt{3}$ is a rational number. But this is impossible, because we know $\sqrt{3}$ is an irrational number. So $6 + \sqrt{3}$ cannot be a rational number. So $6 + \sqrt{3}$ must be an irrational number.

69. **a.** $16w^{\frac{2}{3}}$ **b.** $a^6 b^{\frac{3}{2}}$ **c.** $\dfrac{b^2}{a^6}$

SECTION 6.3

1. **a.**

First graders:

n	250

Percent	48	100

Solve the proportion $\frac{n}{48} = \frac{250}{100}$ to get $n = 120$. Then 120 of the first graders are boys.
   b. Let n represent the number of first graders who are boys. Then $n = 48\% \cdot 250$. Then $n = 120$. So 120 of the first graders are boys.

2. **a.**

Beads:

126	n

Percent	45	100

Solve the proportion $\frac{126}{45} = \frac{n}{100}$ to get $n = 280$. There are 280 beads.
   b. Let n represent the number of beads. Then $126 = 45\% \cdot n$. Then $n = 280$. There are 280 beads.

3. **a.**

People:

45	125

Percent	p	100

Solve the proportion $\frac{45}{p} = \frac{125}{100}$ to get $p = 36$. Then 36% of the people in the survey liked the movie.
   b. $45 = p\% \cdot 125$
   $$45 = \frac{p}{100} \cdot 125$$
   Then $p = 36$. So 36% of the people in the survey liked the movie.

4. 45%

5. 513%

6. 20%

7. 36%

8. The price of the shirt must be $45 after the discount ($45 − $35 = $10 profit). Let R equal the regular price of the shirt. $R - 15\%R = 45$. $R = 52.94$ (to the nearest cent). The regular price of the shirt should be $52.94.

9. $15\% \cdot 450{,}000 = 67{,}500$, the number of ants at the annual picnic this year who preferred bread crumbs. Let n equal the number of ants who preferred bread crumbs last year. Solve the equation $67{,}500 = n - 25\%n$ to get $n = 90{,}000$.

10. $B = 0.86A$, because in the first year the stock lost 14% of its value. We want to verify that $B + 16.28\%B \approx A$.
    Then $B + 16.28\%B = B + 0.1628B$
    $$= 1.1628B$$
    $$= 1.1628(0.86A)$$
    $$= (1.1628 \times 0.86)A$$
    $$= 1.000008A$$
    $$\approx A.$$

11. a. $3n + 11n = 392$, $14n = 392$, $n = 28$, and $3 \times 28 = 84$. He used 84 L of oil.

 b. $392 - 84 = 308$, so he used 308 L of gasoline.

 c. The cost of the mixture is $84 \cdot \$0.75 + 308 \cdot \$1.60 = \$555.80$. Then $555.80 + 15\% \cdot 555.80 = 555.80 + 0.15 \cdot 555.80 = \$639.17$. Then $639.17 \div 392 \approx 1.63$. The mechanic should charge at least $1.63 for each liter of the mixture to guarantee at least 15% profit.

12.

Children	3	5
Percent	p	100

Solve the proportion $\frac{3}{p} = \frac{5}{100}$ to get $p = 60$.

 a. 40%   **b.** 60%

13.

Children	3	5
Percent	100	p

Solve the proportion $\frac{3}{100} = \frac{5}{p}$ to get $p \approx 166.67$.

 a. 66.67%   **b.** 166.67%

14.

Children	10	14
Percent	p	100

Solve the proportion $\frac{10}{p} = \frac{14}{100}$ to get $p \approx 71.43$.

 a. 28.57%   **b.** 71.43%

15.

Children	10	14
Percent	100	p

Solve the proportion $\frac{10}{100} = \frac{14}{p}$ to get $p = 140$.

 a. 40%   **b.** 140%

16. a. 2   **b.** 3   **c.** 3.5   **d.** 2.28   **e.** 1.15

17. $70 + 70 + 35 = 175$

18. a. $28 + 52 = 80$. There are 28 nickels for every 80 coins.

Coins	28	80
Percent	p	100

Then $\frac{28}{p} = \frac{80}{100}$, so $80p = 100 \cdot 28$. Then $p = \frac{100 \cdot 28}{80}$. Then $p = 35$. Then 35% of the coins are nickels.

 b. There are 28 nickels for every 80 coins. So if there 28k nickels, then there are 80k coins. Then $28k = p\% \cdot 80k$, $28 = p\% \cdot 80$, and $28 = \frac{p}{100} \cdot 80$. Then $p = \frac{28 \cdot 100}{80}$. Then $p = 35$. Then 35% of the coins are nickels.

19. 134°F

20. a.

Duck population (millions)	32.2	n
Percent	89	100

11% decrease

Solve the proportion $\frac{32.2}{89} = \frac{n}{100}$ to get $n = 36.2$ (rounded). The duck population in 2003 was 36.2 million.

 b. Let n equal the duck population in 2003. Then
$32.2 = n - 11\% \cdot n$ (percent change equation)
$32.2 = n - 0.11n$
$32.2 = 0.89n$
$n = 36.2$ (rounded)
The duck population in 2003 was 36.2 million.

21. a.

Complaints	76	225
Percent	p	100

Solve the proportion $\frac{76}{p} = \frac{225}{100}$ to get $p = 33.8$. The Lexus had 66.2% fewer complaints.

 b. Solve the equation $76 = 225 - p\% \cdot 225$, or $76 = 225 - \frac{p}{100} \cdot 225$, to get $p = 66.2$. The Lexus had 66.2% fewer complaints.

22. a. 64.3   **b.** 44.4   **c.** 80   **d.** 55.6

23. Answers vary. For example, inflation is measured using a percentage, and it serves as a minimum baseline in negotiations.

24. Yes; for example, three times as many is the same as 200% more.

25. No.

26. The janitor divided the difference 26,000 by 88,000 rather than 62,000.

27. a. The change is $51,000 - 57,600 = -6600$. The population of San Marcos decreased by 6600 from 2007 to 2010.

 b. The percent change is $\frac{-6600}{57,600} \approx -11.5\%$. The population of San Marcos decreased by 11.5% from 2007 to 2010.

28. a. The change is $442 - 520 = -78$. There were 78 fewer registered vehicles in Winkler this year compared to last year.

 b. The percent change is $\frac{-78}{520} = -15\%$. The number of registered vehicles this year dropped by 15% compared to last year.

29. Say your annual salary is $100. Option B: $100 + 12\% \times \$100 = \$112$, $\$112 + 5\% \times \$112 = \$117.60$. Option A: $\$100 + 5\% \times \$100 = \$105$, $\$105 + 12\% \times \$105 = \$117.60$. When the second annual pay raise takes effect, both options pay the same amount. But option B pays you $7 more during the first year. So option B is better.

30. a. additive   **b.** multiplicative   **c.** percent equation
 d. finding a percent of a number
 e. finding a number when the percent of that number is known
 f. representing one number as a percent of another number
 g. additive   **h.** multiplicative

31. a.

Calories	n	350
Percent	78	100

22% decrease

 b. $\frac{n}{78} = \frac{350}{100}$. Then $n = 273$. Kendall consumed 273 calories at lunch.

32. a.

Pages	80	n
Percent	100	135

35% increase

 b. $\frac{80}{100} = \frac{n}{135}$. Then $n = 108$. Lennie read 108 pages.

33. a. The change is $1650 - 1200 = 450$. The company spent $450 more on advertising this year compared to last year.

 b. The percent change is $\frac{450}{1200} = 37.5\%$. The company spent 37.5% more on advertising this year than last year.

34. a.

Children	n	42
Percent	100	120

20% more

Solve the proportion $\frac{n}{100} = \frac{42}{120}$ to get $n = 35$. There are 35 girls.

b. Let n equal the number of girls. Then

$42 = n + 20\% \cdot n$

$42 = n + 0.20n$

$42 = 1.20n$

$n = 42 \div 1.20$

$n = 35$

There are 35 girls.

35. a.

Charges n 7605

Percent   100   164.4

64.4% more

Solve the proportion $\frac{n}{100} = \frac{7605}{164.4}$ to get $n \approx 4626$. The tuition and fee charges were \$4626 in 2000–2001.

b. Let n equal the tuition and fee charges in 2000–2001. Then

$7605 = n + 64.4\% \cdot n$

$7605 = n + 0.644n$

$7605 = 1.644n$

$n = 7605 \div 1.644$

$n \approx 4626$

The tuition and fee charges were \$4626 in 2000–2001.

36. a.

HEVs   290,271 n

Percent   92.92   100

7.08% decrease

Solve the proportion $\frac{290,271}{92.92} = \frac{n}{100}$ to get $n \approx 312,388$. There were 312,388 HEVs sold in 2008.

b. Let n equal the number of HEVs sold in 2008. Then

$290,271 = n - 7.08\% \cdot n$

$290,271 = n - 0.0708n$

$7605 = 0.9292n$

$n = 7605 \div 0.9292$

$n \approx 312,388$

There were 312,388 HEVs sold in 2008.

37. a.

Mpg   20   35

Percent   100 p

Increase

Solve the proportion $\frac{20}{100} = \frac{35}{p}$ to get $p = 175$. The hybrid SUV gets 75% more miles per gallon than a conventional SUV.

b. $35 = 20 + p\% \cdot 20$

$35 = 20 + \frac{p}{100} \cdot 20$

$p = 75$

The hybrid SUV gets 75% more miles per gallon than a conventional SUV.

38. a.

Salary   3800 n

Percent   9   100

b. Solve the proportion $\frac{3800}{9} = \frac{n}{100}$ to get $n \approx \$42,222$. Her salary was \$42,222.

39. a. \$42,400   **b.** \$40,566

40. a. 226   **b.** 8   **c.** 27   **d.** 12

41. a. $16 \cdot 94 = 1504$ and $16\% \cdot 94 = 15.04$

    b. $23 \cdot 35 = 805$ and $23\% \cdot 35 = 8.05$

    c. $a\% \times b = \dfrac{(a \times b)}{100}$

42. Answers vary.

$a = b + 35\% \cdot b$. Pick $b = 120$. Then

$a = 120 + 0.35 \cdot 120$

$a = 120 + 42$

$a = 162$

So 162 is 35% more than 120.

43. Answers vary.

$a = b - 22\% \cdot b$. Pick $b = 50$. Then

$a = 5 - 0.22 \cdot 50$

$a = 50 - 11$

$a = 39$

So 39 is 22% less than 50.

44. a. 15%   **b.** 0.5%   **c.** 134.5%   **d.** 140%

45. a. Shift the decimal point one place value to the left.

    b. Divide the number by 4.

    c. Find 10% of the number, and then multiply by 4.

    d. Divide the number by 2.

46. a. 457%   **b.** 0.256%   **c.** 15,860%

47. a. 85%   **b.** 1280%   **c.** $566\frac{2}{3}\%$

48. a. 36   **b.** 125   **c.** 0.7

49. a. 73%   **b.** \$23   **c.** 335%

50. a. 0.014 m   **b.** $347\frac{2}{9}\%$ **c.** $15\frac{85}{121}\%$

51. \$981,600

52. a. 63   **b.** 20   **c.** 4

53. The change is $1419 - 748 = 671$. There were 671 more complaints about airline service in June 2010 than June 2009.

The percent change is $\frac{671}{748} = 0.897 \approx 90\%$. There were 90% more complaints about airline service in June 2010 than June 2009.

54. a. no   **b.** yes   **c.** 1460 to 1582 steps

    d. 3145 to 3273 steps

55. a. The change is $245 - 280 = -35$. There were 35 fewer people at the Calculator parade this year, compared to last year.

    b. The percent change is $\frac{-35}{280} = -0.125 = -12.5\%$. There were 12.5% fewer people at the Calculator parade this year, compared to last year.

56. 32. Suppose you purchase \$100 worth of stock. After the first year, it will be worth \$76, because the stock lost 24% of its value. To recover the losses, we need to solve the equation $76 + p\% \times 76 = 100$. Then, $76 + \frac{p}{100} \times 76 = 100$. Then, $\frac{p}{100} \times 76 = 24$. Then $\frac{p}{100} \times \frac{24}{76}$. Then, $p \approx 32$.

57. a. monthly payment $= 486.82$ (rounded)

      interest paid $= 60 \cdot 486.82 - 25,000 \approx \$4209$

    b. monthly payment $= \$249.81$

      interest paid $= 48 \cdot 249.81 - 10,000 \approx \$1991$

58. Solve $7\% \cdot n = 3\% \cdot n + 18$ to get $n = 450$.

59. $42\% \times 380 = \$159.60$

60. \$980

61. \$28.86

62. \$2.50

63. \$3.37

REVIEW QUESTIONS

1. a.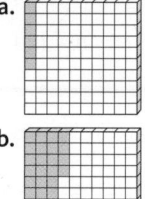

b.

2. a. 30 **b.** 1.4 **c.** 230 **d.** 20

3. a. hundredths **b.** ten-thousandths
c. hundred-thousandths **d.** ten-millionths

4. a. 432.045 **b.** 205.000098

5. a. $700 + 10 + 6 + 0 + 0.03 + 0.004$
b. $700 + 10 + 6 + \dfrac{0}{10} + \dfrac{3}{100} + \dfrac{4}{1000}$
c. $7 \cdot 100 + 1 \cdot 10 + 6 \cdot 1 + 0 \cdot 0.1 + 3 \cdot 0.01 + 4 \cdot 0.001$
d. $7 \cdot 10^2 + 1 \cdot 10^1 + 6 \cdot 10^0 + 0 \cdot 10^{-1} + 3 \cdot 10^{-2} + 4 \cdot 10^{-3}$

6. a. 17 thousand, 432 and 82 thousandths
b. 17 thousand, 432 and 82 ten-thousandths
c. 17 thousand, 432 and 82 hundred-thousandths

7. $5 \cdot 10 + 4 \cdot 1 + 3 \cdot 0.1 + 0 \cdot 0.01 + 2 \cdot 0.001$

8. a. 28 and 4
b.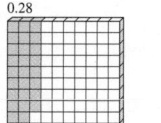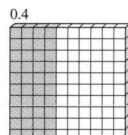

9. a. 83.0 **b.** 72.93 **c.** 416.348 **d.** 872.0

10. a. $2.965 \le n < 2.975$ **b.** $67.0345 \le n < 67.0355$

11. 0.38, 0.4, 7.000999, 7.0021, 8.004, 32.84, 46.1

12. a. $4.72 \times 10 = (4 \times 10^0 + 7 \times 10^{-1} + 2 \times 10^{-2}) \times 10^1 = 4 \times 10^1 + 7 \times 10^0 + 2 \times 10^{-1} = 47.2$. The decimal point shifts one place value to the right.
b. $4.72 \div 10 = (4 \times 10^0 + 7 \times 10^{-1} + 2 \times 10^{-2}) \times 10^{-1} = 4 \times 10^{-1} + 7 \times 10^{-2} + 2 \times 10^{-3} = 0.472$. The decimal point shifts one place value to the left.

13. a. So that we can add similar place values, such as tenths with tenths, hundredths with hundredths, ones with ones, and so on.
b. 5 hundredths + 8 hundredths = 13 hundredths = 1 tenth, 3 hundredths. The 1 above the 3 represents the 1 tenth from regrouping 13 hundredths as 1 tenth, 3 hundredths.

14. a. So that we can subtract hundredths from hundredths, tenths from tenths, ones from ones, and so on.
b. There are 4 hundredths. We need to take away 9 hundredths. There are not enough hundredths, so we regroup 1 tenth as 10 hundredths. Then 10 hundredths + 4 hundredths = 14 hundredths.

15. $0.0053 \times 32.7 = (53 \times 10^{-4}) \times (327 \times 10^{-1}) = (53 \times 327) \times 10^{-5}$. Once we compute 53×327, we shift the decimal point five place values to the left.

16. $567.3 \div 4.02 = \dfrac{5673}{10} \div \dfrac{402}{100}$
$= \dfrac{5673}{10} \times \dfrac{100}{402}$
$= \dfrac{56{,}730}{402}$

17. a. $30 \times 5 = 150$, so $27.15 \times 4.88 = 132.492$
b. $28 \div 4 = 7$, so $28.815 \div 4.25 = 6.78$

18. a. yes **b.** yes **c.** no

19. a. 627 **b.** 3

20. a. $0.\overline{34}$ **b.** $0.8\overline{57}$

21. a. $\dfrac{1240}{99}$ **b.** $\dfrac{1{,}582{,}539}{99{,}900}$

22. a. terminating decimal **b.** terminating decimal
c. repeating decimal **d.** repeating decimal
e. terminating decimal **f.** repeating decimal

23. 12 is not a perfect square.

24. a. irrational **b.** rational **c.** rational
d. rational **e.** irrational

25.

	Two significant digits	Three significant digits
185.73	1.9×10^2	1.86×10^2
0.0004561	4.6×10^{-4}	4.56×10^{-4}

26. a. $\sqrt{24}$ **b.** $\sqrt{24}$ and $-\sqrt{24}$
c. $x = \sqrt{24}$ and $x = -\sqrt{24}$

27. a. 1 **b.** 1 **c.** 2 **d.** 0

28. a. $256\sqrt[3]{25}$ **b.** $945\sqrt{7}$ **c.** $2ab\sqrt[3]{3ab^2}$
d. $a^4 b^3$ **e.** $\dfrac{1}{8}$

29. a. a^3 **b.** $a^4 b^3$ **c.** $\dfrac{b^{\frac{21}{4}}}{a^{\frac{11}{3}}}$ **d.** $\dfrac{b^3}{a^7}$

30. a. $\sqrt{15}$ **b.** 25 **c.** $3\sqrt{2}$

31. Answers vary, but 35% means 0.35, 35/100, or 35 parts of this to 100 parts of that.

32. 62.5%, because $5{:}8 = \frac{5}{8}{:}1 = \frac{5}{8} \cdot 100{:}1 \cdot 100 = 62.5{:}100$.

33. a. 10% = 10/100 = 1/10. Move the decimal point one place value to the left.
b. 15% = 15/100 = 10/100 + 5/100 = 1/10 + (1/2)(1/10). Find 10% of the number, and then add half of the result to that.
c. 20% = 20/100 = 2/10 = 2(1/10). Find 10% of the number, and then double the result.
d. 30% = 30/100 = 3/10 = 3(1/10). Find 10% of the number, and then triple the result.

34. a. 117

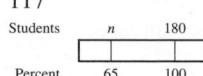

b. 80%

c. 300

35. a.

Solve the proportion $\frac{n}{55} = \frac{200}{100}$ to get $n = 110$. Then, 110 of the first graders are boys.

b. Let n equal the number of boys. Then, $n = 55\% \cdot 200 = 0.55 \cdot 200 = 110$. So, 110 of the first graders are boys.

36. a.

Solve the proportion $\frac{360}{45} = \frac{n}{100}$ to get $n = 800$. She has 800 beads.

b. Let n equal the number of beads. Then,
$360 = 45\% \times n$
$360 = 0.45n$
$n = 360 \div 0.45$
$n = 800$
She has 800 beads.

37. a.

Solve the proportion $\frac{72}{p} = \frac{400}{100}$ to get $p = 18$. Then, 18% of the people surveyed liked the movie.

b. $72 = p\% \cdot 400$

$72 = \frac{p}{100} \cdot 400$

$\frac{72}{400} = \frac{p}{100}$

$p = \frac{72}{400} \cdot 100$

$p = 18$

Then, 18% of the people surveyed liked the movie.

38. a.

Solve the proportion $\frac{450}{68} = \frac{n}{100}$ to get $n = 661.76$. Ken spent $661.76 last month.

b. Let n equal the utility bill from last month. Then,
$450 = n - 0.32 \cdot n$
$450 = 0.68n$
$n = 450 \div 0.68$
$n = 661.76$
Ken spent $661.76 last month.

39. a.

Solve the proportion $\frac{n}{100} = \frac{330}{165}$ to get $n = 200$. Pam read 200 pages.

b. Let n equal the number of pages Pam read. Then,
$330 = n + 0.65n$
$330 = 1.65n$
$n = 330 \div 1.65$
$n = 200$
Pam read 200 pages.

40. a.

Solve the proportion $\frac{400,000}{66} = \frac{n}{100}$ to get $n \approx 606,061$. $606,061 - 400,000 = 206,061$. There are about 206,000 wild chimpanzees remaining today.

b. Let n equal the number of wild chimpanzees 30 years ago. Then,
$400,000 = 66\% \cdot n$
$400,000 = 0.66 \cdot n$
$n = 400,000 \div 0.66$
$n = 606,061$
Then, $606,061 - 400,000 = 206,061$. There are about 206,000 wild chimpanzees remaining today.

41. a. The change is -1.7 billion. The number of Internet searches decreased by 1.7 billion from 2009 to 2010.

b. The percentage change is -16.2%. The number of Internet searches decreased by 16.2% from 2009 to 2010.

42. a. $48,837 **b.** $144,480

43. $20\% \cdot 28 = 5.6$. Let R be the regular price of the shirt. Solve the equation $0.75R - 28 = 5.6$ to get $R = 44.80$. The regular price of the shirt should be $44.80.

44.

Percentage	Fraction	Decimal
20%	$\frac{20}{100}$	0.20
172%	$\frac{172}{100}$	1.72
62.5%	$\frac{15}{24}$	0.625
0.42%	$\frac{42}{10,000}$	0.0042

45. a. 1.6 **b.** 8:5 **c.** 61.5 **d.** 37.5 **e.** 60 **f.** 62.5

46. a. 122 **b.** 55

CHAPTER 6 TEST

1. a. 2 **b.** 0 **c.** 4

2. a. hundredths **b.** ten-thousandths **c.** tens

3. 602.00083

4. 305 thousand, 632 and 4237 hundred-thousandths

5. a. $70 + 3 + 0.1 + 0 + 0.005$

b. $70 + 3 + \frac{1}{10} + \frac{0}{100} + \frac{5}{1000}$

c. $7 \cdot 10 + 3 \cdot 1 + 1 \cdot 0.1 + 0 \cdot 0.01 + 5 \cdot 0.001$

d. $7 \cdot 10^1 + 3 \cdot 10^0 + 1 \cdot 10^{-1} + 0 \cdot 10^{-2} + 5 \cdot 10^{-3}$

6. a. $34,708 \times 142$ **b.** $34,726.8 \div 4205$

7. a. There are 5 hundredths and we need to take away 8 hundredths. There are not enough hundredths, so we regroup 1 tenth as 10 hundredths. Then 10 hundredths + 5 hundredths = 15 hundredths.

b. 7 hundredths + 6 hundredths = 13 hundredths. The 13 hundredths is regrouped as 1 tenth and 3 hundredths. The 1 above the 4 represents the 1 tenth when 13 hundredths is regrouped as 1 tenth and 3 hundredths.

8. a. $\dfrac{617,283}{9900}$ **b.** $0.4\overline{60}$

9. a. terminating decimal **b.** terminating decimal **c.** terminating decimal **d.** repeating decimal

10. **a.** The number 15 is not a perfect square, so $\sqrt{15}$ is an irrational number.
   b. The product of a nonzero rational number and an irrational number is an irrational number.
   c. The decimal number is neither a terminating decimal nor a repeating decimal.

11. **a.** 4   **b.** 5.75×10^6 **c.** -4

12. **a.** $\sqrt[6]{18}$ and $-\sqrt[6]{18}$
   b. $\sqrt[5]{4}$

13. **a.** $x = \sqrt[12]{8.5}$ and $x = -\sqrt[12]{8.5}$
   b. Answers vary. For example, $x^7 = 15$ or $3x^7 + 2 = 47$.
   c. Answers vary. For example, $x^7 = 2^7 \cdot 15$.

14. $\sqrt[6]{-10}$ would be the solution to the equation $x^6 = -10$. The left-hand side of the equation is non-negative for any value of x, whereas the right-hand side of the equation is always negative. $x^6 = -10$ does not have a solution because a non-negative number cannot equal a negative number. So $\sqrt[6]{-10}$ is not a real number.

15.

Governors	28	50

Percent	p	100

Solve the proportion $\frac{28}{p} = \frac{50}{100}$ to get $p = 56$. Then 56% of the governors belonged to the Democratic Party.

16. Solve the equation $245 = n - 18\% \cdot n$ for n to get $n \approx 298.78$. Taylor spent about $298.78 last year on car repairs.

17. 240 books

18. **a.**

Students	14,507	n

Percent	100	131.7

31.7% increase

   b. Solve the proportion $\frac{14{,}507}{100} = \frac{n}{131.7}$ for n to get $n = 19{,}106$. There were 19,106 thousand students in 2008.

19. **a.**

Marriages	n	162,000

Percent	80.6	100

19.4% decrease

   b. Solve the proportion $\frac{n}{80.6} = \frac{162{,}000}{100}$ to get $n = 130{,}572$. There were 130,572 marriages in New York in 2007.

20. **a.** The change is $3634 - 3138 = 496$. The number of elementary and secondary teachers increased by 496 thousand teachers from 1997 to 2007.
   b. The percent change is $496/3138 \approx 0.158$. The number of elementary and secondary teachers increased by 15.8% from 1997 to 2007.

21. **a.** $0.0046 = \dfrac{0.0046 \times 100}{100} = \dfrac{0.46}{100} = 0.46\%$
   b. $586.3 = \dfrac{586.3 \times 100}{100} = \dfrac{58{,}630}{100} = 58{,}630\%$

22. **a.** $\dfrac{4}{7} = \dfrac{\frac{4}{7} \times 100}{100} = \dfrac{57\frac{1}{7}}{100} = 57\frac{1}{7}\%$
   b. $\dfrac{5}{8} = \dfrac{\frac{5}{8} \times 100}{100} = \dfrac{62.5}{100} = 62.5\%$

23. **a.** $312\% = \dfrac{312}{100} = 3.12$
   b. $18.4\% = \dfrac{18.4}{100} = 0.184$

24. **c.** $0.0024\% = \dfrac{0.0024}{100} = 0.000024$

24. **a.** 61.3 (38/62)   **b.** 36.8 (14/38)   **c.** 58.3 (14/24)
   d. 63.2 (24/38)   **e.** 158.3 (38/24)

CHAPTER 7

SECTION 7.1

1. $y(x) = 2x - 3$

2. $y(x) = 3x + 2$ or $f(x) = 3x + 2$

3. **a.** The output is four fewer than five times the input.
   b.

x	-2	-1	0	1	2
y	-14	-9	-4	1	6

   c. $\{(-2, -14), (-1, -9), (0, -4), (1, 1), (2, 6)\}$
   d.

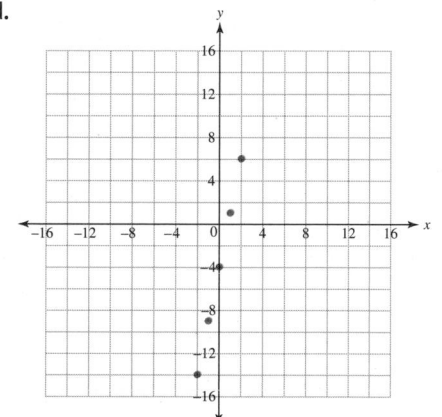

4. **a.** The charge to mail 3 pounds of clay is $11.   **b.** $14
   c. 4 pounds   **d.** $2   **e.** $65

5. **a.** $y(x) = 0.04x + 1985$, where x is the monthly sales and y is the monthly salary.
   b. $y(x) = 5x + 3$, where x is the number of coins Amber has and y is the number of coins Fred has.
   c. $y(x) = x - 248$, where x is the larger number and y is the smaller number.
   d. $c(t) = \dfrac{4}{7}t$ or $t(c) = \dfrac{7}{4}c$, where c is the number of cars and t is the number of trucks.
   e. $y(x) = 0.80x$, where x is the number of people surveyed and y is the number of people who supported the proposition.

6. **a.** $y(x) = 4x - 5$ **b.** $y(x) = 2x^2 + x - 3$
   c. $y(x) = -3\dfrac{1}{3}x + 2$ **d.** $A(l, w) = l \times w$

7. **a.** $2.80   **b.** $4.30
   c. $C(m) = 1.60 + 0.30 \times (5m - 1)$ dollars
   d. $12.40   **e.** 17 mi

8. **a.** $b(n) = (n - 2)^2$ **b.** 256 black tiles
   c. Yes. $2401 = (n - 2)^2$, $\sqrt{2401} = n - 2$, $49 = n - 2$, and $n = 51$, so a 51-by-51 patio is possible.
   d. No. The number of black tiles must be a perfect square, and 346 is not a perfect square.
   e. the number of white tiles in an n-by-n patio

9. **a.** $R(w) = 25w$ **b.** \$3625   **c.** 36 widgets
   d. $P(w) = 25w - 0.05w^2 - 3$ **e.** \$937.95
   f. 58 widgets (use the Guess and Check strategy or the quadratic formula to solve $1278 = 25w - 0.05w^2$)
   g. $0.05w^2 + 3 > 25w$ when 500 widgets are produced

10. **a.** yes, because each input has exactly one output
    b. no, because the input 3 has two outputs: 1 and −4

11. **a.** yes   **b.** no   **c.** no   **d.** no

12. **a.** no   **b.** no   **c.** yes   **d.** no

13. **a.** The formula for the area is correct for the given diagram.

    x ☐ x
    $600 - 2x$

    b. The formula for the area is correct for the given diagram.

    x
    $300 - 0.5x$ ☐ $300 - 0.5x$

14. **a.** 380 m²   **b.** 7 m

15. **a.** $S(x) = 2x^2 + \dfrac{320}{x}$ square units

    b. $S(10) = 2 \cdot 10^2 + \dfrac{320}{10} = 232$ cm².

16. **a.** $A(w) = (3w + 4)w$ or $A(w) = 3w^2 + 4w$ square units
    b. $P(l) = \dfrac{8}{3}(l - 1)$

17. **a.** 1 atm   **b.** 2 atm   **c.** 3 atm
    d. $d = 33(P - 1)$, so $P = \dfrac{d}{33} + 1$. Then $P(d) = \dfrac{d}{33} + 1$.
    e. 1.6 atm   **f.** 46.2 ft

18. h is a function of x, so each input x corresponds to exactly one output.

19. **a.** x **b.** k
    c. The decisions are based on the definition of function notation.

20. **a.** y **b.** x
    c. The decisions are based on the definition of function notation.

21. y decreases

22. y doubles

23. **a.** the position of a term in the sequence
    b. the term in the sequence

24. **a.** h **b.** y **c.** horizontal   **d.** vertical   **e.** relation
    f. function   **g.** equation

25. **a.** no   **b.** yes   **c.** no   **d.** no   **e.** yes   **f.** no

26. **a.** The output is two more than three times the input.
    b. $y(x) = 3x + 2$

27. **a.** The output is three more than two times the input.
    b. $T(n) = 2n + 3$

28. **a.** The output is three more than the square of the input.
    b.

x	0	1	−1	2
y	3	4	4	7

    c. $\{(0,3), (1,4), (-1,4), (2,7)\}$

d.

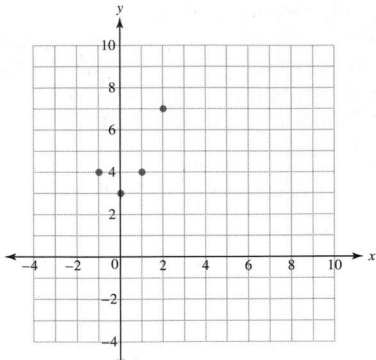

29. **a.**

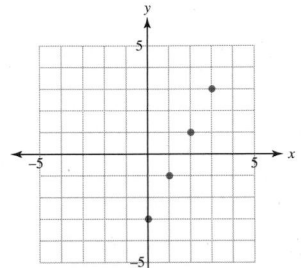

b.

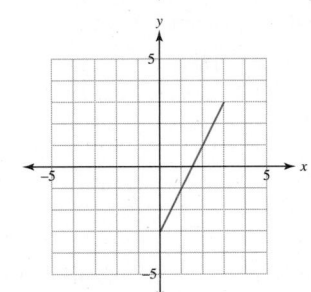

30. **a.** w **b.** h **c.** h, w

31. **a.** $j(a) = 4a + 5$ **b.** 277 stamps
    c. no, because the solution to the equation $135 = 4a + 5$ is not a whole number

32. the discount

33. **a.** the discount for the customer's merchandise
    b. the sales price of merchandise that regularly costs x dollars

34. **a.** $T = 4n - 5$ **b.** 76 coins
    c. no, because the solution to the equation $568 = 4n - 5$ is not a whole number

35. **a.** $T(n) = -2 + 0.5n$
    b. You could verify that $T(2)$ equals −1 and $T(4)$ equals 0.
    c. $T(33) = -2 + 0.5 \times 33 = 14.5$
    d. yes, because the solution to $90.5 = -2 + 0.5n$ is a whole number

36. $A(x) = x(400 - 0.5x)$

37. **a.** the number of tiles needed to build an n-by-$(n + 1)$ patio
    b. the number of black tiles in an n-by-$(n + 1)$ patio
    c. $b(n) = (n - 2)(n - 1)$ **d.** 1056 black tiles
    e. $w(n) = n(n + 1) - (n - 2)(n - 1) = 4n - 2$
    f. 134 white tiles   **g.** 57-by-58
    h. no, because the solution to $419 = 4n - 2$ is not a whole number

38. a. $A(l) = 24l$ **b.** $A(P) = 12P - 576$

39. a. $A(w) = (4w - 3)w$ or $A(w) = 4w^2 - 3w$

  b. $P(l) = \dfrac{1}{2}(5l + 3)$

40. $P(w) = \dfrac{72}{w} + 2w$

41. a.

x	1	2	3	4
y	-4.25	-3.50	-2.75	-2.00

  b. $p(n) = 0.75n - 5$ **c.** $85

42. a. 200 mph   **b.** 2100 mi   **c.** $S(t) = \dfrac{400}{t}$

43. a. ≈ 198 cm^3 **b.** $h(V, r) = \dfrac{V}{\pi r^2}$

44. a. $I(r) = 0.06r + \$100{,}000$ **b.** $145,000
  c. $1,900,000

45. a. $C(n) = 0.07n + 0.50$ **b.** 39 min

46. a. $140   **b.** $184

47. a. $d(c) = 48 + c$ **b.** 52 mph, 104 mi
  c. $u(c) = 48 - c$ **d.** 42 mph, 84 mi
  e. 12 mph, by solving $3(48 + c) = 5(48 - c)$ for c

48. a. $6   **b.** $9   **c.** $y(n) = 6n + 9$ **d.** $189

49. No; f and g do not have the same domain. For example, $(f + g)(5)$ is not defined, because $g(5)$ is not defined.

50.

$f + g$	Input	1	2	3	4	5
	Output	-3	0	4	9	12

$f - g$	Input	1	2	3	4	5
	Output	9	-8	0	3	4

$f \cdot g$	Input	1	2	3	4	5
	Output	-18	-16	4	18	32

f/g	Input	1	2	3	4	5
	Output	$-\dfrac{1}{2}$	-1	1	2	2

51. a. -18 **b.** 7/5   **c.** -2 **d.** 77

52. a. 13   **b.** 4   **c.** -5 **d.** $\dfrac{5}{8}$

53. Answers vary.

f	Input	1	2	3	4	5
	Output	4	1	2	0	3

g	Input	1	2	3	4	5
	Output	1	-1	1	8	1

54.

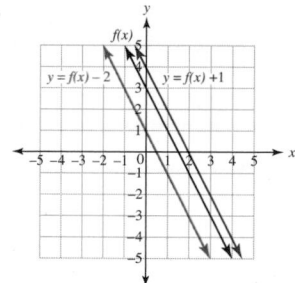

SECTION 7.2

1. $(2.3, -3.1)$ or $x = 2.3$ and $y = -3.1$

2. $(3, -2)$

3. a. $(2, 0)$ and $(-3, 0)$ **b.** $(0, 3)$
  c. We need to solve $4 = y(x)$, so $x = 1$.

4. a. 7   **b.** 2   **c.** -2 **d.** 4   **e.** -3

5. a. $a = c + 5, a + c = 29$ **b.** $k = l - 20, k + l = 112$
  c. $d = 3h - 8, d + h = 112$

6.

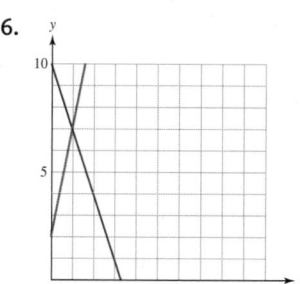

  The solution is $(1, 7)$.

7. a. $2m + 5y = 18.50, 4m + 2y = 17$
  b. $d = 2h - 9, d + h = 375$

8. a. $690   **b.** $40

9. a. When the driver has driven 5 hours, he is 200 miles from his destination.
  b. 320 mi   **c.** 60 mi

10. a. $2d + 3t = 183, d = 2t + 4$, where d and t are the number of dinner and tour tickets sold, respectively.
  b. $d = 54$ and $t = 25$. The class sold 54 raffle tickets for the fancy dinner and 25 raffle tickets for the sightseeing tour.

11. Each ream of paper costs $4.50, and each DVD costs $3.

12. $12 + 0.05n < 18 + 0.03n, n < 300$. Plan A is preferable if you make fewer than 300 minutes of long-distance calls.

13. a.

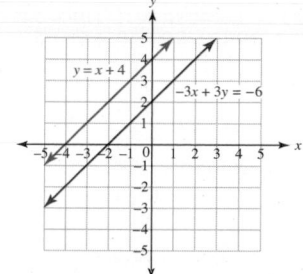

  b. The graphs of the equations do not intersect.
  c. Replace y with $x + 4$ to get $12 = 6$.

d. The equations $y = x + 4$ and $-3x + 3y = 6$ are equivalent to $3x - 3y = -12$ and $-3x + 3y = 6$. Adding these two equations leads to $0 = -6$.

14. a. Answers vary, but each system should lead to an equation of the form $a = b$, where a and b are different integers.

   b. If you solve a system of two linear equations and the process results in an equation of the form $a = b$, where a and b are different numbers (for example, $3 = 5$ or $7 = -2$), then the system of two linear equations does not have a solution.

15. a.

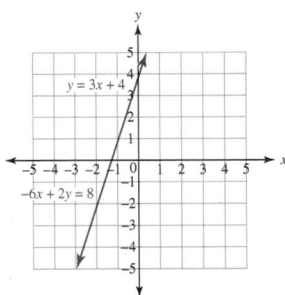

   b. The graphs of the two lines are identical.
   c. Replace y with $3x + 4$ in the equation $-6x + 2y = 8$ to get $8 = 8$.
   d. The equations $y = 3x + 4$ and $-6x + 2y = 8$ are equivalent to $6x - 2y = -8$ and $-6x + 2y = 8$. Adding these equations leads to $0 = 0$.

16. a. Each system leads to an equation of the form $a = a$, where a is a real number.

   b. If you solve a system of two linear equations and the process results in an equation of the form $a = b$, where a and b are identical numbers (for example, $0 = 0$ or $4 = 4$), then the system of two linear equations has infinitely many solutions.

17. a. no   **b.** yes

18. a. no   **b.** yes   **c.** yes   **d.** no

19. a. System I: $y = 2x + 5$ and $y = 2x - 1$

   System II: $y = 4x - \dfrac{2}{3}$ and $y = 4x + 7$

   System III: $y = \dfrac{5}{7}x - \dfrac{3}{7}$ and $y = \dfrac{5}{7}x - \dfrac{8}{7}$

   b. The system of two linear equations $y = mx + a$ and $y = mx + b$, where a and b are different numbers, does not have a solution.

20. $A = -6/7$

21. $70 = l \times w$ and $38 = 2l + 2w$. Replace l with $70/w$ to get $19 = 70/w + 2w$. Then $w^2 - 19w + 70 = 0$, $(w - 5)$ $(w - 14) = 0$. Then $w = 5$ and $l = 14$ or $w = 14$ and $l = 5$.

22. a. $44 = l \times w$, $l = 3w - 1$

   b. Methods vary. Using substitution, $44 = (3w - 1)w$, $3w^2 - w - 44 = 0$, and $(3w + 11)(w - 4) = 0$, so $w = 4$ and $l = 11$.

23. Answers vary. For example, $3x - 2 = 4$ is equivalent to $3x - 6 = 0$, so the student could graph the function $f(x) = 3x - 6$ and then look for x-intercepts of the function. Alternatively, the student could graph the two functions $f(x) = 3x - 2$ and $g(x) = 4$ and use the intersection method to find a solution.

24. $(0, f(0))$ is the y-intercept. $f(0)$ can have at most one value.

25. a. Maria is finding the y-intercept, if it exists.
   b. Nicole is finding the x-intercepts, if any exist.

26. $(0, f(0))$ is the y-intercept. The input 0 does not belong to the domain $[3, 12]$.

27. Answers vary.

28. Answers vary.

29. The student is using substitution.

30. a. (b, a) **b.** system of linear equations
   c. y-intercept   **d.** $f(a) = b$ **e.** x-intercept   **f.** solve

31. a. -1.5 **b.** -3.2 **c.** 1.8

32. $f + m = 240$, $m = 3f$

33. $f + m = 200$, $m = 3f + 8$

34. Yes; set $x = 0$, and then solve for y to get the solution $(0, -2)$.

35. Yes; set $y = 0$, and then solve for x to get the solution $(8/5, 0)$.

36. a. $d + t = 386$, $d = 2t + 8$
   b. $d = 260$ and $t = 126$. The class sold 260 raffle tickets for the fancy dinner and 126 raffle tickets for the sightseeing tour.

37. Answers vary.

38. a. $(1, 7)$

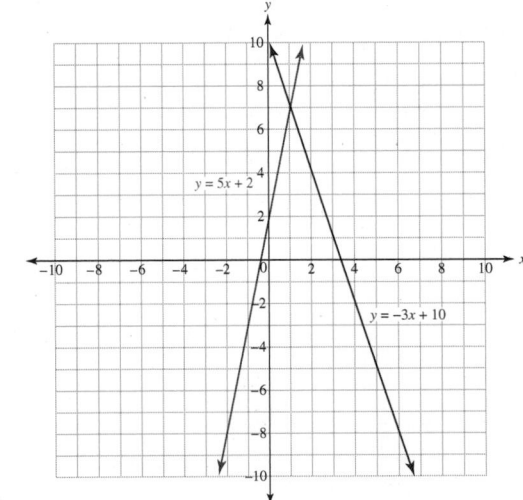

b. $(4, 1)$

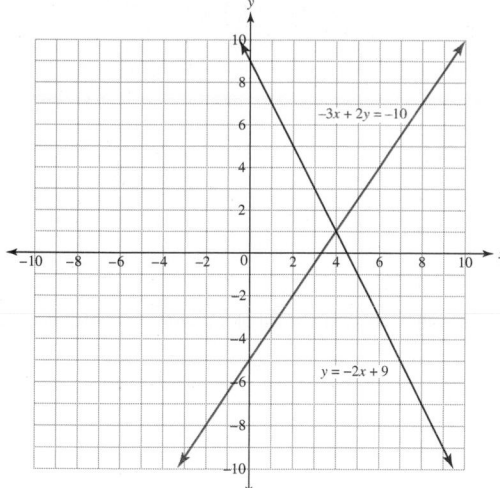

c. $(4, 3)$

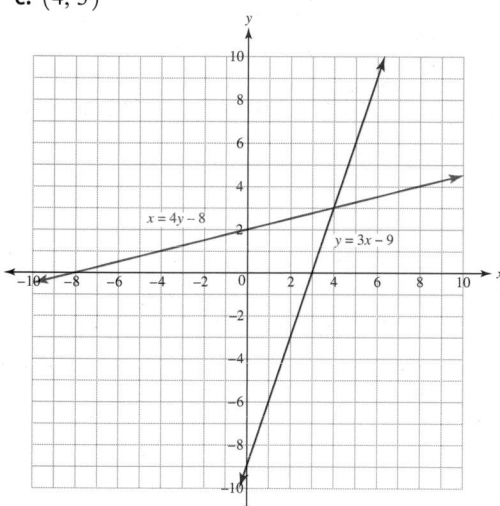

39. $(-2, 4)$

40. $(3, 5)$

41. $(4, -1)$

42. $(5, 2)$

43. $(4, 2)$

44. $(-1, 4)$

45. $(3, 5)$

46. $(3, -2)$

47. $d = 2n$, and $10d + 5n = 100$, so $d = 8$ and $n = 4$. Elliot has eight dimes and four nickels.

48. Answers vary.

49. Answers vary.

50. a. $d + q = 21$, $10q + 25d = 10d + 25q + 135$
(or $15d - 0.15q = 1.35$)
  b. Use the substitution method or elimination method to obtain $d = 15$ and $q = 6$.

51. a. $n + q = 11$, $5q + 25n = 5n + 25q + 60$
(or $20n - 20q = 60$)
  b. seven nickels   **c.**   four quarters

SECTION 7.3

1. a. $2n + 3 = n + 7$ **b.** $2n = 6$

2. a.

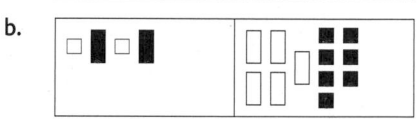

b.

3. a. $2n - 2 = -n - 8$ **b.** $-4n + 6 = n - 4$

4. a.   **b.**   **c.**

5. a.

b.

6. Solve $5n + 3 = 23$ to get $n = 4$. The number is 4.

7. Solve $2q + 4 = 5q - 8$ to get $q = 4$. There are four quarters.

8. a. $3 \cdot 1 \div 3 = 3 \div 3 = 1$, $3 \cdot 2 \div 3 = 6 \div 3 = 2$, $3 \cdot 3 \div 3 = 9 \div 3 = 1$, and $3 \cdot 4 \div 3 = 12 \div 3 = 4$. Then, we obtain the following table:

1	$3 \cdot 1 \div 3 = 1$
2	$3 \cdot 2 \div 3 = 2$
3	$3 \cdot 3 \div 3 = 3$
4	$3 \cdot 4 \div 3 = 4$

  b. $3n \div 3 = n$ for any counting number n.

9. a. $3n + 7 = 4n + 4$ **b.** $3n + 7 - 3n = 4n + 4 - 3n$
  c. $7 = n + 4$ **d.** $7 - 4 = n + 4 - 4$ **e.** $3 = n$

10.

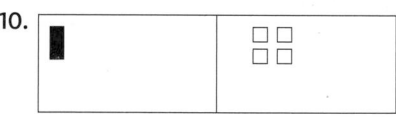

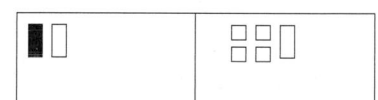

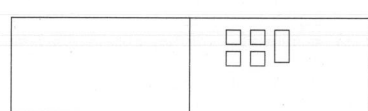

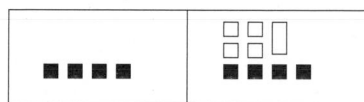

So $-n = 4$ is equivalent to $n = -4$.

11.

So $4n = 8$ is equivalent to $n = 2$.

12. a.
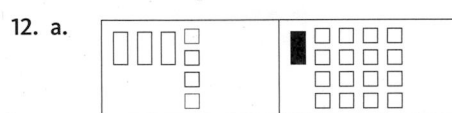

b. $y = 3n + 4$, so substitute y in the equation $y = -n + 16$ with $3n + 4$ to get $3n + 4 = -n + 16$. This equation can be solved using the tile mat in part (a).

13.

14.
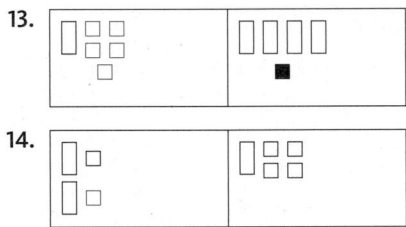

15. an equation that involves one inverse operation to solve the equation, such as $3x = 12$ and $x - 5 = 12$

16. an equation that involves two inverse operations to solve the equation, such as $8x - 4 = 12$ and $-4x + 2 = 8$

17. an equation that involves procedures such as combining like terms, applying the distributive property, and using inverse operations, such as $-3n - 2n = 20$ and $2(n + 2) = 30$

18. $2(3n - 5) = 8$, $6n - 10 = 8$, $6n - 10 + 10 = 8 + 10$, $6n = 18$, $6n \div 6 = 18 \div 6$, $n = 3$

19. Place three copies of $2x - 1$ on the left side of the mat, where $2x - 1$ requires two n-tiles and one -1-tile. Place nine 1-tiles on the right side of the mat. Then there are six n-tiles and three -1-tiles on the left side. Add three 1-tiles to each side of the mat. Then the left side has six n-tiles and the right side has twelve 1-tiles. Divide each side into six equal-sized groups. Then one n-tile equals two 1-tiles.

20. a. one-step   **b.** two-step   **c.** algebra tiles

21. a. $4n = 8$ **b.** $2n + 3 = 7$

22. a. two-step   **b.** one-step   **c.** one-step
d. multistep   **e.** multistep

23.

So $n = 2$.

24.

So $n = 2$.

25.

So $n = 4$.

26.

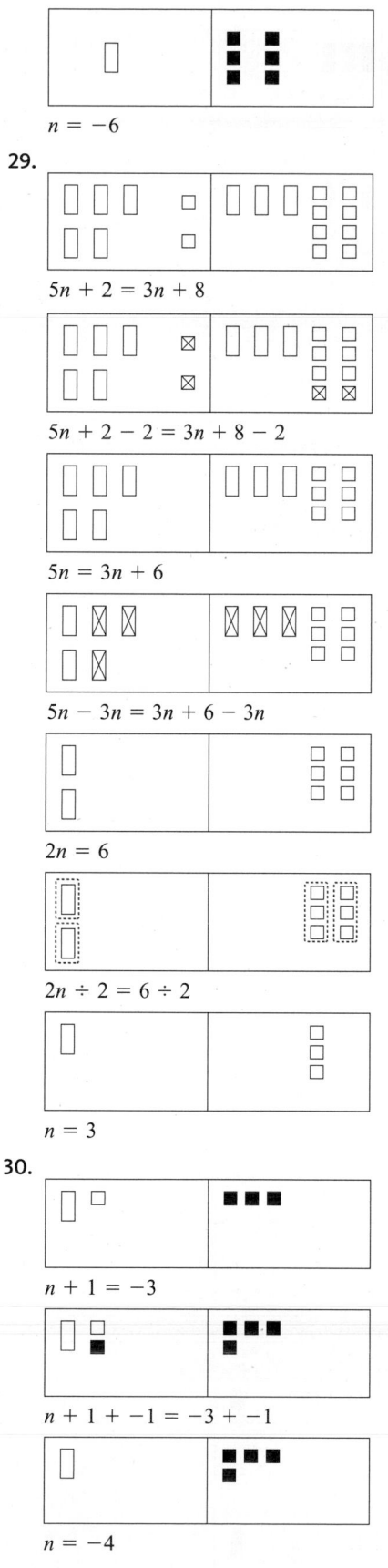

So $n = 2$.

27.

So $n = -2$.

28.

$2n + 3 = -9$

$2n + 3 + -3 = -9 + -3$

$2n = -12$

$2n \div 2 = -12 \div 2$

$n = -6$

29.

$5n + 2 = 3n + 8$

$5n + 2 - 2 = 3n + 8 - 2$

$5n = 3n + 6$

$5n - 3n = 3n + 6 - 3n$

$2n = 6$

$2n \div 2 = 6 \div 2$

$n = 3$

30.

$n + 1 = -3$

$n + 1 + -1 = -3 + -1$

$n = -4$

31.

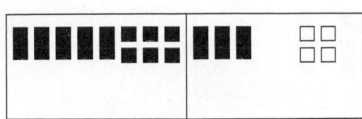

$$-5n - 6 = 4 - 3n$$

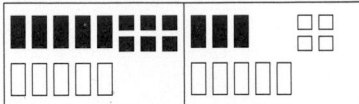

$$-5n - 6 + 5n = 4 - 3n + 5n$$

 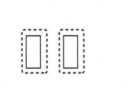

$$-6 = 4 + 2n$$

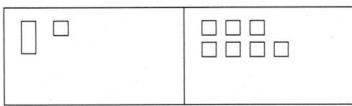

$$-6 + -4 = 4 + 2n + -4$$

$$-10 = 2n$$

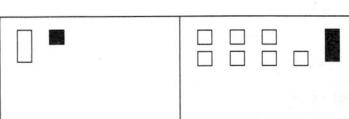

$$-10 \div 2 = 2n \div 2$$

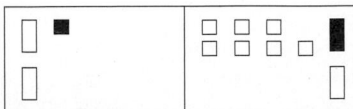

$$-5 = n$$

32.

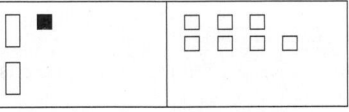

$$n + 1 = 7$$

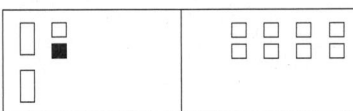

$$n + 1 + -1 = 7 + -1$$

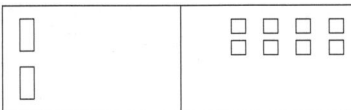

$$n = 6$$

33.

$$n - 1 = 7 - n$$

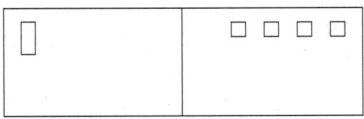

$$n - 1 + n = 7 - n + n$$

$$2n - 1 = 7$$

$$2n - 1 + 1 = 7 + 1$$

$$2n = 8$$

$$2n \div 2 = 8 \div 2$$

$$n = 4$$

34. Answers vary.

35. Answers vary.

36. a. n equals Bella's age now, and $n + 28$ equals Miguel's age now. Then $(n + 28) + 5 = 3(n + 5)$.
   b. $(n + 28) + 5 = 3(n + 5)$
   $$n + 33 = 3n + 15$$
   $$n + 18 = 3n$$
   $$18 = 2n$$
   $$9 = n$$
   Bella is 9 years old.

37. a. n equals Bella's age now, and $4n$ equals Miguel's age now. Then $4n + 8 = 3(n + 8)$.
   b. $4n + 8 = 3(n + 8)$
   $$4n + 8 = 3n + 24$$
   $$n + 8 = 24$$
   $$n = 16$$
   Then $4n = 4 \cdot 16 = 64$. Miguel is 64 years old.

REVIEW QUESTIONS

1. a. yes
   b. no, because the input 2 has two different outputs, 0 and 1

2. a. yes **b.** no

3. a. (iv) **b.** (iii) **c.** (i) **d.** (ii)

4. a. dependent **b.** function **c.** words **d.** ordered pair
   e. x-coordinate (or first coordinate)
   f. y-coordinate (or second coordinate)

5. a. yes **b.** no **c.** no **d.** no

6. a. $k(b) = b - 5$, where k is the number of marbles Kamran has and b is the number of marbles Bob has.
   b. $w(l) = 4l + 3$, where w and l are the width and the length of the rectangle, respectively.

c. $c(b) = \frac{2}{7}b$, where c is the number of cats and b is the number of birds.

d. $n(c) = \frac{3}{4}c$, where n is the number of nickels and c is the number of coins in the piggy bank.

7.

Input	A	B	B
Output	1	6	1

8. a. y **b.** x
   c. The decisions are based on the definition of function notation.

9. a.

n	1	2	3	4
C	14	22	30	38

b. $\{(1, 14), (2, 22), (3, 30), (4, 38)\}$

c.

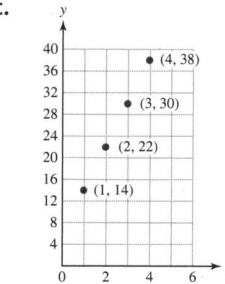

d. $C(x) = 8x + 6$ or $(C = 8x + 6)$ dollars to order n books $(n = 1, 2, 3, 4)$

10. a. $k = 0.024$ **b.** 5.4 ft **b.** 21.6 ft
   d. The stopping distance is four times as much as before.
   e. A car traveling at 70 mph has a stopping distance of 117.6 feet.

11. $y = -3x + 7$

12. $A = l(4l - 3)$

13. The elevation increases.

14. a. A job that lasts 5 hours costs $400.
   b. $C(h) = 30h + 250$, and $C(10) = 550$. The cost for a job that lasts 10 hours is $550.
   c. 7.5 hours, by solving the equation $30h + 250 = 475$ for h
   d. $250 **e.** $30

15. a. 470 mi **b.** 40 mi

16. a. $2.35 $(1.45 + 3 \times 0.30 = 2.35)$
   b. $F(m) = 1.45 + 0.30(4m - 1)$ dollars for an m-mile cab ride, where $m \geq 1$.
   c. $F(1) = 1.45 + 0.30(4 \times 1 - 1) = 1.45 + 3 \times 0.30 = 2.35, which agrees with part (a).
   d. $F(8.5) = $11.35 **e.** 15 mi

17. a. 460 mph, 1380 mi **b.** $T(w) = 420 + w$ mph
   c. 360 mph, 1080 mi **d.** $H(w) = 420 - w$ mph

18. a. 152 bags **b.** 167 bags **c.** 15 bags
   d. 407 bags **e.** 15 bags

19. a. $24 **b.** $15 (from the y-intercept)
   c. $3 (the y values increase $3 each hour)
   d. $C = 3h + 15$

20. y increases.

21. y increases.

22. y decreases.

23. a.

x	1	2	3	4	5	6
$g(x) + 2$	7	1	4	2	6	3

b.

x	1	2	3	4	5	6
$3 \times g(x)$	15	-3	6	0	12	3

24. $R(n) - C(n)$ or $(R - C)(n)$

25. a. no **b.** yes

26. All solutions to the equation lie on the graph of the equation.

27. Answers vary. For example, set $y = 0$, then solve for x. $(-1, 0)$

28. Answers vary. $(0, -4)$

29. The point lies on the graph of the function.

30. Yes; the obvious solution is $(5, 2)$.

31. $(1.68, 2.97)$ or $x = 1.68, y = 2.97$

32. a. x-intercept $= (10, 0)$, y-intercept $= (0, 10)$
   b. x-intercept $= (-2.5, 0)$ **c.** y-intercept $= (0, 6.5)$
   d. x-intercept $= (-4.5, 0)$, y-intercept $= (0, 9)$

33. a. x-intercepts $= (-2.5, 0), (-0.5, 0), (3.25, 0)$; y-intercept $= (0, -1)$ **b.** y-intercept $= (0, 3.5)$

34. a. 20
   b. The p-intercept is $(0, 40)$, which means 40 moviegoers watched the end of the movie.
   The t-intercept is $(30, 0)$, which means all moviegoers were gone 30 minutes after the movie ended.

35. $(2, -2)$

36. $(2, -3)$

37. $(1, 6)$

38. $(3, -2)$

39. $(2, -5)$

40. $(2, 9)$

41. $m + f = 417$ and $m = 2f - 6$, so $m = 276$ and $f = 141$. Mark had 276 coins, and Fred had 141 coins.

42. With plan A, $y = 0.03x + 5$. With plan B, $y = 0.05x + 2$. Solve $0.03x + 5 < 0.05x + 2$ to get $150 < x$. Plan A is cheaper for monthly long-distance calls totaling more than 150 minutes. Otherwise, plan B is cheaper.

43. a. ▯▯▯▯▯ **b.** ▮▮▮▮ **c.** ▮▮▮▯▯▯
   d. ▮▯▯▯

44. $-3n + 7 = n + 3$

45. a. [diagram]

   b. [diagram]

c.

46.

The solution is $n = 4$.

47.

The solution is $n = -4$.

48.

$9 + 2n = 6n - 3$

$9 + 2n - 2n = 6n - 3 - 2n$

$9 = 4n - 3$

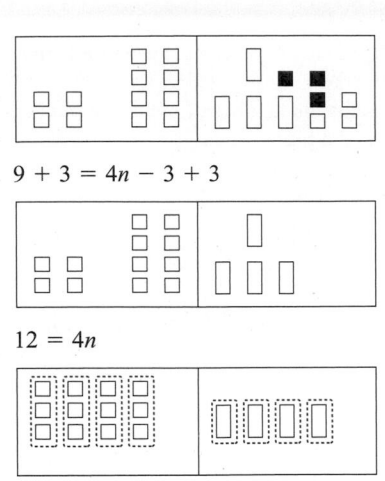

$9 + 3 = 4n - 3 + 3$

$12 = 4n$

$12 \div 4 = 4n \div 4$

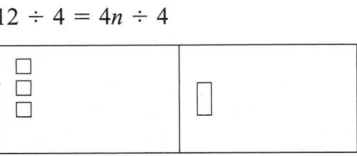

$3 = n$

CHAPTER 7 TEST

1. **a.** yes, because each input has one corresponding output
   b. no, because the input 1 has two possible outputs, 2 and 8

2. **a.** yes, because each input has one corresponding output
   b. no, because the input -3 has two possible outputs, 1 and 4

3. **a.** yes   **b.** no   **c.** no   **d.** yes

4. **a.** y **b.** x

5. **a.** After 4 hours or work, the company cleaned 180 windows.   **b.** $W(3.5) = 120$

6. **a.** function   **b.** independent   **b.** dependent
   d. function

7. **a.** $l(w) = 3w - 5$, where l is the length of the rectangle and w is the width of the rectangle.
   b. $c(m) = (3/5)m$ or $m(c) = (5/3)c$, where c is the number of cats and m is the number of mice.

8. **a.** 2150 $(5 \cdot 400 + 150 = 2150)$
   b. $C(d) = 400d + 150$ dollars   **c.** $\{1, 2, 3, 4, \ldots\}$

9. **a.**

g	50	100	150	200
b	3.65	3.80	3.95	4.10

   b. $b(g) = 0.003g + 3.50$ dollars for g gallons of water
   c. 8.14

10. **a.** $5   **b.** 7.80
    c. $C(m) = 2.60 + 0.40(7m - 1)$ dollars for a cab ride of m miles   **d.** $24.60   **e.** 45 mi

11. **a.** 349 m per second
    b. The speed of sound increases as the temperature increases.   **c.** $48°C$

12. **a.** The Celsius temperature increases as the Fahrenheit temperature increases.   **b.** $16.6°C$

13. The photic zone decreases as the concentration of algae increases.

14. a. $(1.5, 1.8)$ or $x = 1.5, y = 1.8$ **b.** two solutions
   c. no solutions **d.** infinitely many solutions

15. a. $x = -3$ **b.** $x = 4$ **c.** $x = -2.1$

16. a. no **b.** yes

17. Answers vary; for example, $(-12.5, 0)$.

18. a. because A lies on the graph of the equation
   b. because B does not lie on the graph of the equation

19. a. Yes; choose $x = 0$ and $y = -3$.
   b. Yes; choose $y = 0$ and $x = 5$.

20. Answers vary. x-intercepts $= (0.8, 0)$ and $(3.5, 0)$,
   y-intercept $= (0, -2)$

21. y-intercept $= (0, 7)$

22. $(2, -1)$

23. No solution

24. $(3, -2)$

25. $(4, -2)$

26. a. $A = 6\frac{2}{3}$
   b. There are infinitely many solutions to the system of equations.
   c. There are no solutions to the system of equations.

27. a. ☐☐ **b.** ▯▯▯▯ **c.** ■☐☐ **d.** ☐☐ ▯ ■■■

28. a. $3n + 2 = n + 6$ **b.** $3 - 3n = -6$

29.

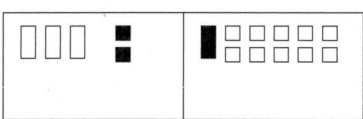

$3n - 2 = 10 - n$

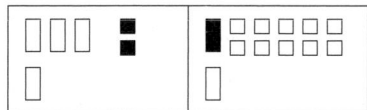

$3n - 2 + n = 10 - n + n$

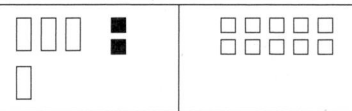

$4n - 2 = 10$

$4n - 2 + 2 = 10 + 2$

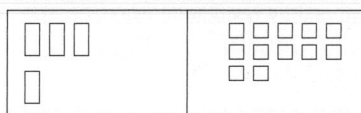

$4n = 12$

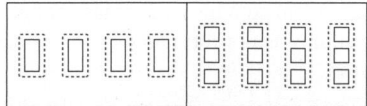

$4n \div 4 = 12 \div 4$

$n = 3$

CHAPTER 8

SECTION 8.1

1. a.

Drink preferred	Tally
soda	||
juice	⼤|

b.

Drink preferred	Frequency
soda	2
juice	6

c.

Drink preferred	Percent
soda	25
juice	75

2.

	Smooth	Chunky
Boy	3	2
Girl	2	1

3. The height of the new cylinder is 3/4 of the original height.

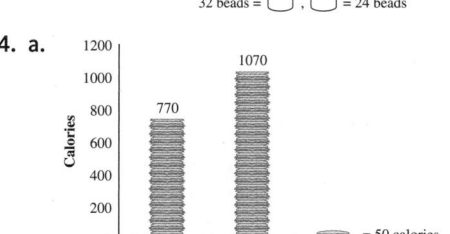

32 beads = ☐ , ☐ = 24 beads

4. a.

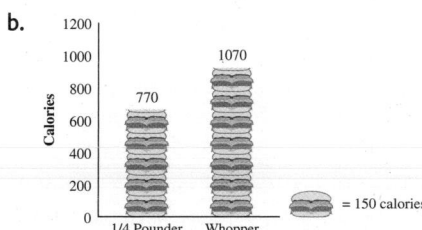

b.

c. Yes; the icon that represents 50 calories seems to exaggerate the differences.

5. a. $160°$ **b.** $80°$ **c.** $120°$

6. a. April, June, and July **b.** June
   c. March and May **d.** March
   e. 50 helmets to make sure it has enough inventory to sell helmets during peak demand

7. a. 28 nonmath majors   **b.** five students
   c. 29% (rounded)   **d.** 52% (rounded)

8. a. 41.2%   **b.** No, they add up to 57%.
   c. One more sector is needed to take into account the category "other."
   d.

Activity	Central angle
social networks	82°
online games	37°
e-mail	30°
portals	16°
instant messaging	14°
videos/movies	14°
search	13°

   e.

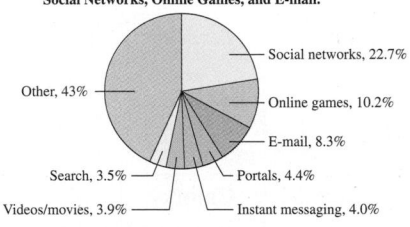
People Spend 41% of Their Internet Time on Social Networks, Online Games, and E-mail.

   f.

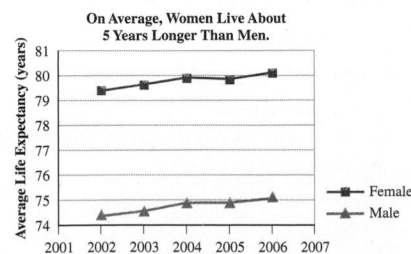
People Spend 41% of Their Internet Time on Social Networks, Online Games, and E-mail.

9. a. More fifth graders participated in each activity.
   b. three more fifth graders   **c.** pull-ups
   d.

	Sit-ups	Pull-ups	Push-ups
fourth graders	8	4	7
fifth graders	9	6	10

10. a. numerical (quantitative)   **b.** categorical (qualitative)
   c. categorical (qualitative)   **d.** categorical (qualitative)
   e. numerical (quantitative)   **f.** categorical (qualitative)
   g. numerical (quantitative)   **h.** numerical (quantitative)

11. monthly homeowner fees (numerical variable), size of the house (numerical variable), type of residence (categorical variable), and zip code (categorical)

12. because the average rating does not make sense

13. a.

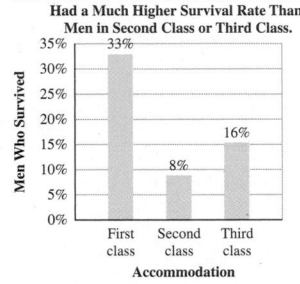
On Average, Women Live About 5 Years Longer Than Men.

b. Females have a longer life expectancy than males, and life expectancies for both genders are increasing.

14.

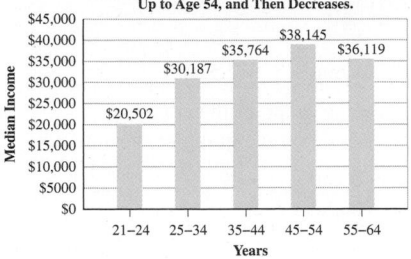
Median Income of Males and Females Increases Up to Age 54, and Then Decreases.

15. a. graph A   **b.** graph B
   c. The median income for males is higher than that for females across all age groups.
   d. Males and females in the 45- to 54-year age group have higher median income levels.

16. a. Yes; men with first-class accommodations had a significantly higher survival rate.
   b.

Men with First Class Accommodations on the *Titanic* Had a Much Higher Survival Rate Than Men in Second Class or Third Class.

17. a. 40%   **b.** 50%
   c. 1980–1981, 1981–1982, 1982–1983, 1990–1991, 1991–1992, and 1992–1993
   d. 1996–1997
   e. From 1993 to 2000, students relied more on loans than on grants.

18. Answers vary.

19. Answers vary.

20.

A Larger Percentage of Women Than Men Support the Smoking Ban, But a Larger Percentage of Men Than Women Oppose the Ban.

21. a. Most water is consumed by residential use.
   b. 51,926 acre-feet ($0.07 \cdot 741,800 = 51,926$)
   c. 59,344 acre-feet   **d.** 2.4   **e.** 1.5

22. a. Students spend more time on homework after school than any other activity.
   b. Students engage in several activities, they may multitask, or perhaps the question was not formulated with mutually exclusive categories.

23. Statistics is the science of collecting, organizing, visualizing, summarizing, and analyzing data.

24. A variable is an attribute that varies from one object of interest to another.

25. Data are observations or measurements from one or more variables.

26. Graphs are visual representations for exploring, identifying, interpreting, and communicating important features of data sets.

27. Labels for the axes, title, and legend as appropriate

28. These critical features help the reader interpret the graph properly.

29. 4, 3, 1, 2

30. They are alike because both show ordered pairs. They are different because a scatterplot is used to see whether an association (shape and the strength of the association) exists between two numerical variables, whereas a line graph is used to show trends (periods of increases or decreases).

31. **a.** pie chart **b.** scatterplot **c.** line graph
    d. frequency table **e.** pictograph **f.** histogram
    g. bar graph

32. **a.** true **b.** false **c.** false **d.** true **e.** true **f.** false

33. **a.** yes = 47.6%, no = 19.0%, and undecided = 33.3%
    b. The percentages do not add to 100% because of rounding.
    c. yes = 171°, no = 69°, and undecided = 120°

34. **a.** The rows record the data for each participant.
    b. The variables are color of car (categorical), gas mileage (numerical), and customer satisfaction (categorical).
    c. The variables are recorded in columns.

35. **a.**
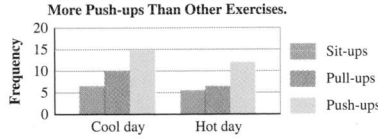

b.
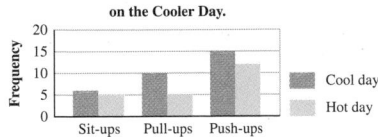

c. the graph in part (a) **d.** the graph in part (b)

36. **a.** yes
    b.
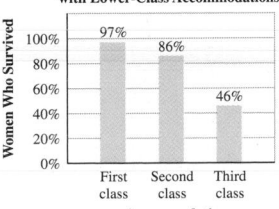

37.
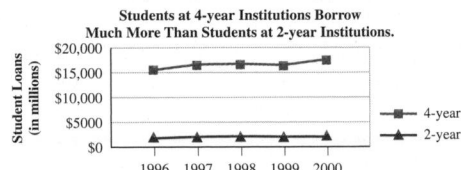

38. **a.**
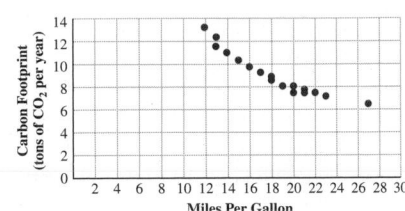

b. There appears to be a negative linear relationship between the variables (one variable increases as the other variable decreases).

39. **a.** Answers vary; for example, "The perception of rising gasoline prices has remained steady" (for the first graph) and "Most Americans think there are major problems with rising gasoline prices" (for the second graph).
    b. Answers vary. The first graph compares the months, and it shows that gasoline prices remain a "major problem."

40. Answers vary.

41.
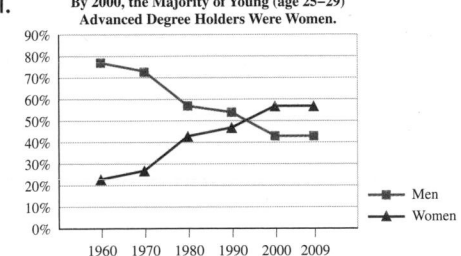

42.
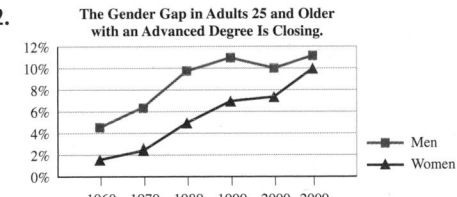

43. **a.**
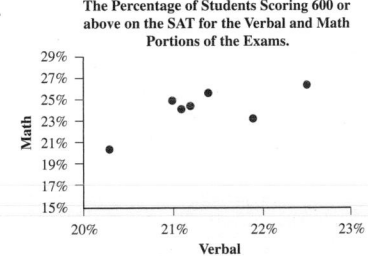

b. There is a weak positive association between math and verbal scores.

44. a.

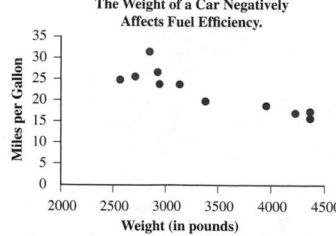

The Weight of a Car Negatively Affects Fuel Efficiency.

b. It makes sense to choose the weight as an independent variable, because we want to see how the weight of a car affects fuel efficiency. Heavier cars tend to have lower fuel efficiency. The graph tends to show a negative association between the two variables.

45. a.

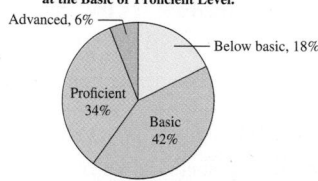

On the Test, 76% of Students Scored at the Basic or Proficient Level.

b. A pie chart seems more appropriate, because it would be natural to compare the parts to the whole.

46. a.

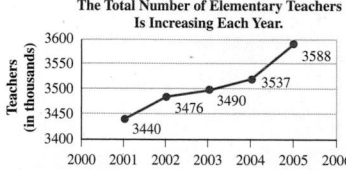

The Total Number of Elementary Teachers Is Increasing Each Year.

b. Answers vary. 3588 + 50 = 3638. At the current rate, the estimated number of elementary teachers in 2006 is about 3,638,000.

47. a. 1509 thousand, or 1,509,000

b. approximately 40%

c.

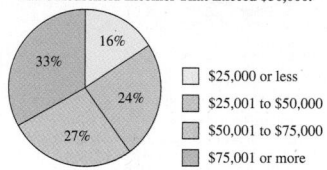

The Majority of Households with Homeschooled Students Have Household Incomes That Exceed $50,000.

- ☐ $25,000 or less
- ▨ $25,001 to $50,000
- ▨ $50,001 to $75,000
- ▨ $75,001 or more

d.

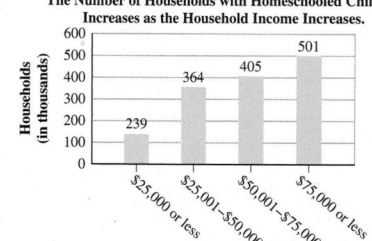

The Number of Households with Homeschooled Children Increases as the Household Income Increases.

48. a.

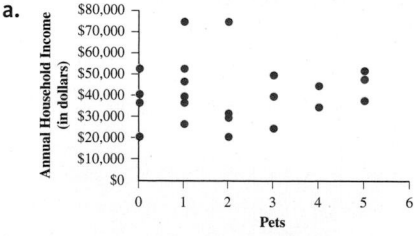

b. no, there is no apparent pattern.

49. a. 2001, 2003, 2004, 2007 **b.** 2007
c. 2002, 2006, 2008 **d.** 2006

50. a. Without regard to age, women have a higher employment rate than men.
b. Older males have a higher employment rate than the younger males, and older females have a higher employment rate than younger females.

51. Sal should choose graph A, because the line graph tends to show more effectively than the bar graph that his sales level is increasing.

52. There seems to be a positive but weak relationship between the two variables.

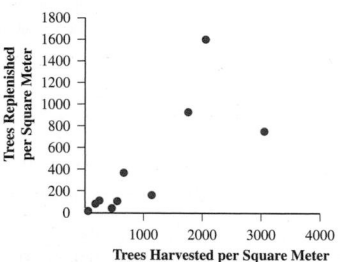

53. a.

Interval	Frequency
$13 \leq x < 16$	2
$16 \leq x < 19$	3
$19 \leq x < 22$	11
$22 \leq x < 25$	5
$25 \leq x < 28$	7
$28 \leq x < 31$	2

b. 30%

54. a.

Interval	Frequency
below 50	0
$50 \leq x < 55$	1
$55 \leq x < 60$	4
$60 \leq x < 65$	5
$65 \leq x < 70$	7
$70 \leq x < 75$	12
$75 \leq x < 80$	14
$80 \leq x < 85$	5
$85 \leq x < 90$	2
above 90	0

b.

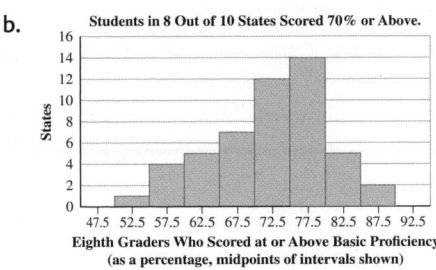

Students in 8 Out of 10 States Scored 70% or Above.

Eighth Graders Who Scored at or Above Basic Proficiency
(as a percentage, midpoints of intervals shown)

55. a. Answers vary, but the values basically range from 0 to 160. A natural starting point would be 0, increasing by 20.

Interval	Frequency
$0 \leq x < 20$	28
$20 \leq x < 40$	15
$40 \leq x < 60$	2
$60 \leq x < 80$	0
$80 \leq x < 100$	2
$100 \leq x < 120$	1
$120 \leq x < 140$	0
$140 \leq x < 160$	1
$160 \leq x < 180$	1
180 or more	0

b.

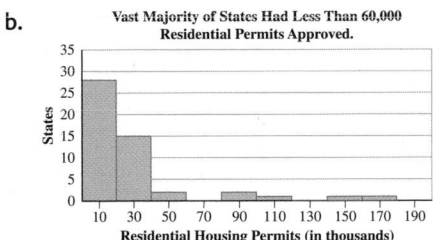

Vast Majority of States Had Less Than 60,000 Residential Permits Approved.

Residential Housing Permits (in thousands)

SECTION 8.2

1. a. median   **b.** mean

2. a.

b. The mean seems fine, because there are no apparent outliers.

3. a. 11 students   **b.** about 1.3 pets

4. 1.0, 1.3, 2.4, 2.5, 2.6, 2.6, 4.0, 4.0, 4.1, 4.2

5. mean = 6, median = 6, mode = 9

6. Use total = $n \cdot$ mean. Then mean = total ÷ 80 = (50 · 76 + 30 · 84) ÷ 80 = 6320 ÷ 80 = 79. The total mean score was 79.

7. $16, because 120 ÷ 15 = 8, 72 ÷ 18 = 4, and mean = $\frac{120 + 72}{8 + 4}$ = 16.

8. $\bar{x}$ = 5.18 hours, MAD = 0.816, and the interval of usual values = mean ± 2.5 · MAD = [3.14, 7.22]. The advertised time may be credible, because it falls within the interval of usual times.

9. a. median = $x_{\frac{n+1}{2}}$ **b.** median = $\frac{x_{\frac{n}{2}} + x_{\frac{n}{2}+1}}{2}$

10. The student did not order the data from least to greatest.

11. a. 31, because $5 \times 7 - 1 - 1 - 1 - 1 = 31$
b. 12, because $35 - 20 - 1 - 1 - 1 = 12$

12. a. Mean = 17.75, median = 6.5, and no mode. The median seems appropriate.
b. Mean ≈ 4.33, median = 3, and mode = 3. The median or mode seems appropriate.
c. Mean ≈ 9.83, median = 9, and mode = 7. The mean seems appropriate.

13. Answers vary.
a. 3, 5, 9, 12, 21; median = 9; mean = 10
b. 3, 5, 9, 12, 16; median = 9; mean = 9
c. 3, 5, 9, 12, 14; median = 9; mean = 8.6

14. Mean ≈ 4.86, and median = 5. The teacher should expect five students to miss the problem.

15. a. usual   **b.** unusual

16. The interval of usual values is [60.85, 83.35]. The score 75 falls in this range, so Jerry's friend probably scored 75.

17. a. $\bar{x}$ = 4.8, MAD ≈ 2.6   **b.** $\bar{x}$ = 6.1, MAD = 2.8

18. Some males and females get married at very early or late ages, and this could affect the mean more than the median. The median is less sensitive to extreme values.

19. a. 5.25   **b.** 0   **c.** −9   **d.** 3
e. Answers vary. For example, using $x = 7$, we get 7.
f. yes

20. $2.15 (the average cost)

21. a. 80   **b.** 80
c. 77, because 77 = (2 · 50 + 3 · 60 + ... + 3 · 100) ÷ 30

22. a. $40   **b.** 40

23. 34.13 or 34.1 ft

24. the math test, because the quotient is higher

25. a package of rollers

26. the gallon of milk, because the quotient is higher

27. Some errors in the measurements will be positive, and some errors will be negative, so when you add the measurements, the absolute value in the error in the mean could be lower because of cancellation. (This is illustrated in the discussion in the chapter.)

28. The student ignored the 0 and computed the mean by averaging 7, 6, and 2. The correct mean is (7 + 6 + 2 + 0) ÷ 4 = 3.75.

29. a. Brand A: mean ≈ 5.5, median = 5.5, mode = 5.5
Brand B: mean ≈ 5.5, median = 5.5, mode = 5.5

b.

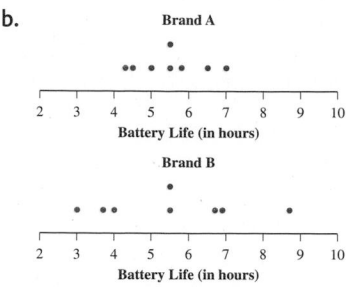

c. The dot plots suggest brand A is preferable, because the life span of the batteries is more predictable (has less variation).

30. You could expect 2 families to have 3 pets between them (say, 1 and 2 pets or 0 and 3 pets). Or you could expect 10 families to have 15 pets among them.

31. Answers vary. First, calculate a quotient of the women's median income and the men's median income for full-time workers. For example, suppose the median income level of women is $74,000 and median income level of men is $80,000. Then the quotient is $q = 74{,}000/80{,}000 = 0.925$. Second, the "wage gap" is $1 - q$. In this example, the wage gap is $1 - 0.925 = 0.075 = 7.5\%$. This means women earn 7.5% less than men. In 2009, the wage gap was 23%, according to the U.S. Census Bureau.

32. **a.** representative **b.** quantifies **c.** sensitive **d.** insensitive **e.** median **f.** extreme values **g.** stem-and-leaf plot **h.** range **i.** small **j.** mean absolute deviation

33. Solve $93 \leq (100 + 100 + n) \div 3$ for n. The lowest score would be 79.

34. Let x be the level value. Then $x + x + x + x + x = 3 + 5 + 2 + 11 + 3$. Then $5x = 24$. Then $x = 4.8$.

35. 9.9 feet, because $(12 \cdot 11.2 + 15 \cdot 8.8) \div 27 = 9.9$ (rounded to the nearest tenth)

36. total dollars/total number of gallons $= (16 + 10)/(5 + 3) = 26/8 = \$3.25$

37. **a.** 6.25 cars **b.** no

c.

x	3	2	11	9
Deviation	-3.25	-4.25	4.75	2.75

d.
$$\text{MAD} = \frac{|-3.25| + |-4.25| + |4.75| + |2.75|}{4} = \frac{15}{4} = 3.75$$

38. **a.** $17/4 = 4.25$ lb **b.** $(17 + 4 \cdot 3)/4 = 7.25$ lb **c.** $(17 + 4 \cdot 7)/4 = 11.25$ lb **d.** $(17 + 4 \cdot k)/4 = 17/4 + (4k)/4 = 4.25 + k$ lb

39. **a.** $12/3 = 4$ ft **b.** $(6 \cdot 2 + 6 \cdot 3 + 6 \cdot 7)/3 = 24$ ft **c.** $(10 \cdot 2 + 10 \cdot 3 + 10 \cdot 7)/3 = 40$ ft **d.** $(k \cdot 2 + k \cdot 3 + k \cdot 7)/4 = k(12/3) = 4k$ ft

40. $5 \cdot 1.4 = 7$. You could tell the students that they could expect that 5 students would have 7 pairs of shoes among them.

41. the second graders (comparing the average amount of money raised)

42. The mean and median times for late arrivals are the same. The MAD for train A is 5.14 minutes, and the MAD for train B is 2.25 minutes. So train B seems more preferable, because it has less variation and therefore may be more predictable.

43. 48.23 cm (rounded to the nearest hundredth), because
$$\frac{(22 \cdot 47 - 36 + 63)}{22} \approx 48.227$$

44. 24.56 cm (rounded to the nearest hundredth), because
$$\frac{(35 \cdot 25 - 40)}{34} \approx 24.558$$

45. Scottsdale is relatively safer. Suppose Scottsdale has population k. Then Boston has population $2.7k$. Then $27{,}876/2.7k = 10{,}324/k > 9474/k$.

46. **a.** mean **b.** mean, median **c.** mode **d.** mean, median **e.** mode **f.** median **g.** median **h.** mean absolute deviation

47. mean $\approx \$1.66$, median $= \$1.65$, mode $= \$1.65$

48. **a.** 113.45 mm (rounded) **b.** 4.47 cm (rounded) **c.** Both measurements equal 11.35 cm.

49. 79.33 (rounded to the nearest hundredth), because
$$\frac{(15 \cdot 78 + 5 \cdot 4)}{15} \approx 79.333$$

50. **a.**

Manufacturing Nondurable Goods		Manufacturing Durable Goods
3.4 = 4|3 Leaf	**Stem**	**Leaf 4|3 = 4.3**
9	1	9
7221	2	4
10	3	34
3	4	
1	5	14578
1	6	0

b. The back-to-back stem-and-leaf plot suggests full-time workers that manufacture durable goods experience higher rates of nonfatal injuries and illness than workers who manufacture nondurable goods. This makes sense, because the categories in the tables suggest that workers who make durable goods have more direct contact with moving machinery, use sharp tools, have jobs that require heavy lifting, and so on.

51. No; a score of 100 on the fifth quiz gives a mean of 91.6.

52. **a.** fair share **b.** reduction of error in measurements **c.** level values **d.** estimation of the total **e.** fair comparisons

53. The fourth-grade class should win the reading contest. Suppose there are k fifth-grade students. Then there are $0.80k$ fourth-grade students, and $15{,}000/k < 12{,}345/(0.80k)$.

54. **a.** mean $= 3.05$, median $= 3$ **b.** mean $= 30.5$, median $= 30$

55. a. The median is less susceptible to the effect of extreme values compared to the mean, because the median depends on position rather than actual values. There are workers that earn millions of dollars (such as actors, bankers, and CEOs), and these high salaries could inflate the mean.
b.

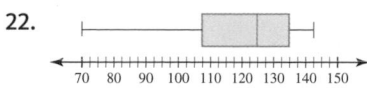

c. The median salary increases as the educational level increases, and men have a higher median salary than women with the same educational level.

56. a. mean = 28.0   **b.** MAD = $4\frac{4}{7}$
   c. interval of usual values = [16.6, 39.4] (rounded)

57. a. mean = 62.5   **b.** MAD = 9

58. brand B, because 6.6 falls within its interval of usual values

SECTION 8.3

1. 14, 20, 28, 30, 32

2.

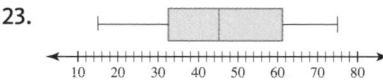

3. a. credit repair because of the highest median cost
   b. credit repair because of the largest IQR

4.

	Percentile		
	25th	50th	75th
Cost for different brands of inkjet printers	$100	$150	$225

5. a. small air conditioners because of the higher median score
   b. large air conditioners because of the larger IQR

6. a. $Q_1 - 1.5 \cdot \text{IQR} = 46 - 1.5 \cdot (66 - 46) = 16$
   b. $Q_3 + 1.5 \cdot \text{IQR} = 66 + 1.5 \cdot (66 - 46) = 96$

7. $Q_3 + 1.5 \cdot \text{IQR} = 167.5$. Any uses of the credit card more than 167.5 miles from his house should be questioned.

8. 16,000 miles (calculate the 15th percentile and round down to a friendly number)

9. The graphs put limitations on the possible values because of the "missing parts."
   a. $a = 15$ (the median must be equal to Q_1)
   b. $b = 15$ (the lowest value must equal Q_1)

10. Answers vary, as long as $x_{\max} - x_{\min} = 25$ and $Q_3 - Q_1 = 8$. For example, 20, 30, 35, 38, 45.

11. IQR

12. a. $40,850   **b.** 90%   **c.** 75%

13. a. at risk of being overweight   **b.** approximately 88 lb

14. a. Answers vary. A possible outlier is $42,000.
   b. $Q_1 = 33{,}400$ and $Q_3 = 35{,}950$. Then $Q_1 - 1.5 \cdot \text{IQR} = 29{,}575$ and $Q_3 + 1.5 \cdot \text{IQR} = 39{,}775$.
   The outliers are child and family studies ($29,500), dietetics ($40,400), and nutrition ($42,200).

15. This means 78% of the people who took the same test scored less than 85.

16. The whisker length gives you a visual sense of the spread of the lower or upper 25% of the data.

17. The length of the box is the interquartile range.

18. Possible sources of outliers are (1) recording error, (2) rare occurrence, (3) equipment malfunction, and (4) value from a different population.

19. Kelly scored higher than 96% of the people who took the same test.

20. a. box plot   **b.** MAD   **c.** outliers
   d. five-number summary   **e.** percentile   **f.** low
   g. high   **h.** 25th percentile   **i.** line   **j.** length
   k. different

21. 18, 31, 40, 61, 82

22.

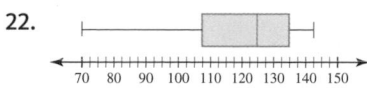

23.

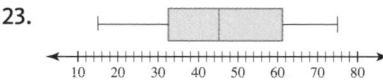

24. a. 60th percentile   **b.** 45th percentile   **c.** 20th percentile
   d. $x_{15} = 5.8$ cents $\left(\dfrac{p}{100}n = \dfrac{72}{100} \cdot 20 = 14.4, \text{round up to } 15\right)$

   e. $x_{12} = 5.2$ cents $\left(\dfrac{p}{100}n = \dfrac{58}{100} \cdot 20 = 11.6, \text{round up to } 12\right)$

   f. $\dfrac{(x_6 + x_7)}{2} = \dfrac{(3.3 + 3.4)}{2} = 3.35$ cents
   $\left(\dfrac{p}{100}n = \dfrac{30}{100} \cdot 20 = 6, \text{so average } x_6 \text{ and } x_7\right)$

25. a.

Type of paint	Price per Gallon			Observations
	Percentile			
	25th	50th	75th	
flat	15	18	21	24
semigloss	17	23	32	15

   b. semigloss   **c.** semigloss because of the larger IQR

26.

	Percentile			Number of observations
	25th	50th	75th	
Miles	19	22	27	19

27. No, it is a ranking or measure of position.

28. **a.** 153   **b.** 137   **c.** 72   **d.** 103

29. **a.** Answers vary. 4186 and possibly 3515
    b. median = 1760.5, Q_1 = 1494, and Q_3 = 2114. Then Q_3 + 1.5 · IQR = 3044 and Q_1 − 1.5 · IQR = 564. The outliers are 4186 (IBM) and 3515 (Samsung).

30. Answers vary; for example, scores on an exam.

31. Answers vary; for example, the amount of water your household wastes compared to others in your neighborhood.

32. **a.** The girl would be between the 50th and the 85th percentiles and therefore in the healthy weight status.
    b. The girl would have a BMI measurement of 23.5 and fall between the 85th and the 95th percentiles; therefore, she would be at risk for being overweight.
    c. The minimum BMI would be 16 (fifth percentile for a girl 14 years old). Solve $16 = \dfrac{703W}{66^2}$ for W to get W = 99 pounds. The minimum healthy weight of a 14-year-old girl with a height of 66 inches is 99 pounds.

33. Yes; the amount $5562 spent on salaries is an outlier.

34. **a.** Answers vary. 214 and 252
    b. There is one outlier: 214. (Q_1 = 232 and Q_3 = 242).

35. **a.** endpoints of whiskers = 21 and 240, Q_1 = 50, median = 98.5, and Q_3 = 129

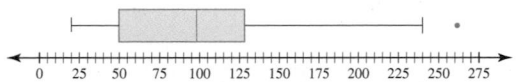

    b. endpoints of whiskers = 67 and 142, Q_1 = 97, median = 120, and Q_3 = 126.5

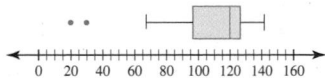

36. **a.** Answers vary. Possible outliers are 14 and 49.
    b. 14 and 49

37. The modified box plot has one outlier ($6015), and there is no whisker on the right side of the box plot. Cars traveling at 10 mph crashed into parked SUVs, resulting in costly damage.

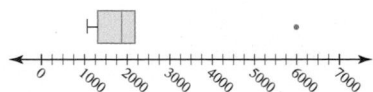

38. **a.** Answers vary. There do not appear to be any outliers.
    b. Q_1 = 69.3, median = 72.5, and Q_3 = 75.5. There are two outliers: 59.1 (HI) and 59.7 (UT).

39. **a.** Answers vary. Possible outliers are 428 and 445.
    b. Q_1 = 12, median = 60, and Q_3 = 138. So 428 and 445 are outliers

40. **a.** Answers vary. There do not appear to be any outliers.
    b. Q_1 = 124.5 and Q_3 = 161.5. So 65 is an outlier.

41. **a.** Answers vary. The values 31 and 69 appear to be outliers.
    b. Q_1 = 44.5 and Q_3 = 48. So 31 and 69 are outliers.

42. **a.** The car suffered costlier damage, based on the higher median.
    b. The car shows more variation in cost because of the larger IQR (wider box).

REVIEW QUESTIONS

1. **a.** numerical   **b.** categorical   **c.** categorical
   d. categorical   **e.** numerical   **f.** categorical
   g. categorical

2. **a.** The data associated with each participant are reported in the rows.
   b. The variables of interest are the student's favorite color and number of pets.
   c. Data for each variable appear in the columns.

3. **a.**

Pet	Tally
dog	I
bird	II
cat	II
other	III

   b.

Pet	Frequency
dog	1
bird	2
cat	2
other	3

   c.

Pet	Percent
dog	12.5
bird	25
cat	25
other	37.5

4. **a.** 7 females   **b.** 19 males   **c.** 43 people   **d.** 55.8%

5. **a.**

Manufacturer	Recommended products
Samsung	7
Motorola	1
LG	4
Casio	2

   b. Answers vary (due to the intervals).

Price range	Recommended products
up to $50	6
$51–$100	4
$101–$200	3
more than $200	1

6. Answers vary. The following are some possible titles:

Less than 10% of tort cases in U.S. district courts are concluded by trial.

The proportion of tort cases concluded by trial in U.S. district courts is declining.

7. Answers vary; for example, "From 1970 to 2007, the number of drug arrests for juveniles has leveled, while the number of arrests for adults has been increasing."

8. yes = 160°; no = 120°, and undecided = 80°

9. a. The graph suggests that class affected the survival rate.

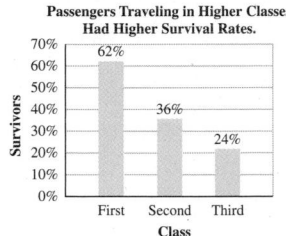

b. The graph suggests that the gender of adults affected the survival rate.

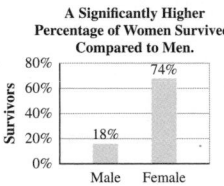

10. a. November and December
b. November
c. August, September, and October
d. September
e. 60 packages to accommodate the peak sales month

11. a. graph A
b. graph B

12. a. graph B
b. graph A
c. Answers vary; for example, "Hospital care dominated the per capita costs associated with hospital, home health, and nursing home care."
d. Answers vary; for example, "Hospital care costs were increasing from 2004–2006, while home health and nursing home care stabilized."

13. a.

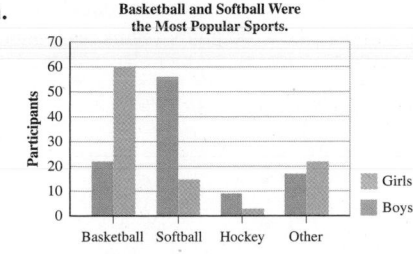

b.

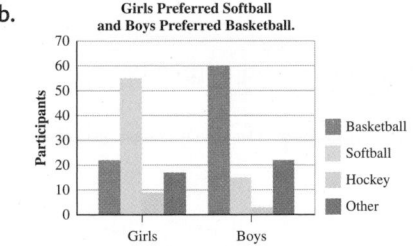

14.

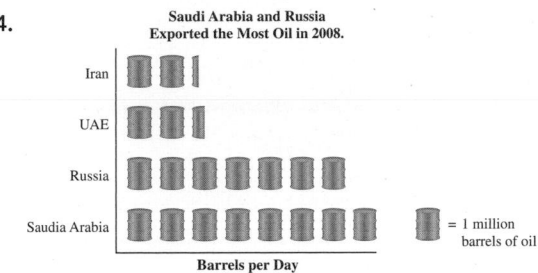

15. a. graph A
b. the scale of the vertical axis

16.

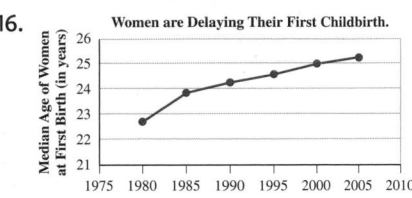

17.

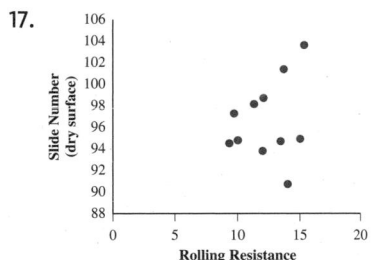

The scatterplot in the exploratory data analysis for all tires in the table does not suggest a weak or strong relationship between the rolling resistance rating and the dry slide number of the tire. But there may be a strong positive relationship for tires with a slide number on dry asphalt greater than 96.

18. a.

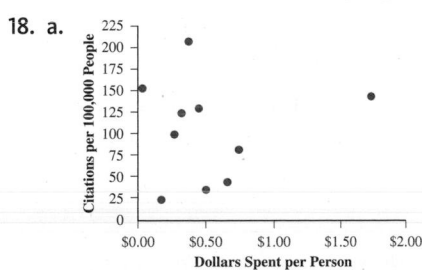

b. The scatterplot does not willingly indicate a relationship between the variables.

19. a.

$0 \leq x < 500$	ⅧⅢ ⅧⅢ ⅧⅢ ‖‖
$500 \leq x < 1000$	ⅧⅢ ‖‖‖
$1000 \leq x < 1500$	‖‖
$1500 \leq x < 2000$	ⅧⅢ
$2000 \leq x < 2500$	‖
$2500 \leq x < 3000$	‖‖
$3000 \leq x < 3500$	‖‖
$3500 \leq x < 4000$	‖
$4000 \leq x < 4500$	⎮
$4500 \leq x < 5000$	⎮
$5000 \leq x < 5500$	
$5500 \leq x < 6000$	
$6000 \leq x < 6500$	‖
6500 or more	⎮

b.

$0 \leq x < 500$	18
$500 \leq x < 1000$	9
$1000 \leq x < 1500$	3
$1500 \leq x < 2000$	5
$2000 \leq x < 2500$	2
$2500 \leq x < 3000$	3
$3000 \leq x < 3500$	3
$3500 \leq x < 4000$	2
$4000 \leq x < 4500$	1
$4500 \leq x < 5000$	1
$5000 \leq x < 5500$	0
$5500 \leq x < 6000$	0
$6000 \leq x < 6500$	2
6500 or more	1

c.

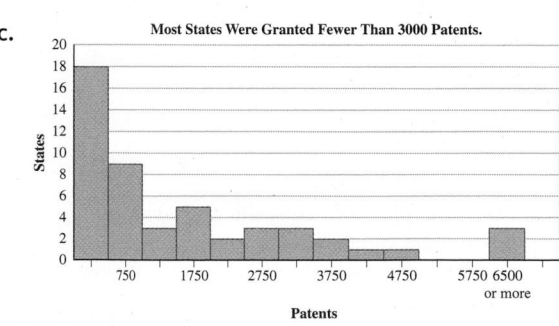

20. a. mean $= 19$, median $= 18$
  b. mean $= 37.75$, median $= 18$
  c. mean $= 37.75$, median $= 18$

21. $2.04/3 = 68$ cents

22. The principal should calculate the average amount of money each student raised for each group of students to take into account the different number of students in each class.

23. $209

24. The mean measurement of 14.7 cm is the most reasonable, because the mean may be closer to the true (but unknown) height of the flower because of cancellation of the errors when adding the measurements to find the mean.

25. a. 25 students   **b.** 2.2 pencils

26. 55.4 cm, because $\dfrac{(20 \cdot 54 - 42 + 70)}{20} = 55.4$

27. 62.7 cm, because $\dfrac{(14 \cdot 65 + 12 \cdot 60)}{26} = 62.7$

28. The student divided the sum 21 by 3 instead of by 4, ignoring the zero.

29. The mean is 79, and the median is 35. The median may be more appropriate.

30. a. 4.7 gal   **b.** 1.46 gal
  c. minimum usual value $= 148.32$, maximum usual value $= 155.64$
  d. 25th percentile $= 150.15$, 75th percentile $= 153.4$

31. a. 21 feet   **b.** 6.8 feet
  c. minimum usual value $= 14.75$, maximum usual value $= 48.92$
  d. 25th percentile $= 24$, 75th percentile $= 38$

32. 66 and 97

33. a. $592.50 and $1967.50
  b. $1187.50 and $1712.50
  c. Ken should choose car B, because his annual budget of $1800 for car repairs fits within the usual operating expenses.

34. a. mean $= 11.11$, median $= 12$, mode $= 3$
  b. mean $= 1.11$, median $= 1.2$, mode $= 0.3$

35. mean $= 13.45$, median $= 14$, mode $= 15$

36. Samantha (2 versus 1.7)

37. a. 43.1 sec   **b.** 62.4 sec   **c.** 40th percentile
  d. 15th percentile   **e.** 28.2, 38.15, 44.55, 51.85, 67.2

38. a. A 23-year-old male with height of 6 feet 1 inch is taller than 85% of males in their 20s.
  b. A 22-year-old female who weighs 150 pounds weighs more than 55% of females in their 20s.

39. Mike should choose a warranty less than or equal to 4231 hours. A number like 4200 hours seems reasonable and memorable.

40. a. 0, 1, 2, 4, 9
  b.

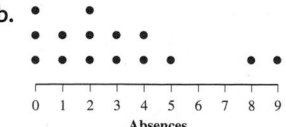

41. a. [85, 138], the numbers from the 25th percentile to the 75th percentile
  b. 138   **c.** 72 ($147 - 75 = 72$)

42. a. Yes; the upper 50% of the data has more variation, because the distance from the median to the highest value is greater than the distance from the median to the lowest value.
  b. 21, 26, 44, 62, 76

43.

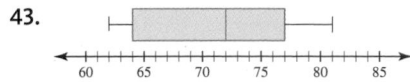

44. a. 850, 884, 939, 1027, 1102   **b.** IQR = 143
  c.

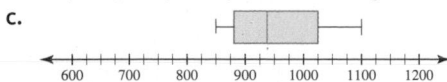

  d. Yes; the distance from the median to the maximum value is greater.

45. a. car B, because the median is lower
  b. car B, because the IQR is larger (the box is wider)

46. a. Truck 1 gets better gas mileage on average, because the median value is higher.
  b. Truck 2 has less variation, because the length of the rectangle in the box plot is shorter.

47. a. 84   **b.** 19

48. a. 2   **b.** 2, 7, and 33

49. a. three outliers   **b.** 15, 70, and 73

50. a.

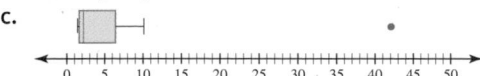

  b. 25th percentile = 1.55, 75th percentile = 6.35, outlier = 42.1% (U.S.)
  c.

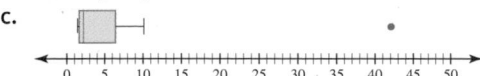

  d. the outlier box plot, because it seems more representative of the data than the standard box plot based on the five-number summary.

CHAPTER 8 TEST

1. a. categorical   **b.** numerical   **c.** categorical
  d. numerical   **e.** categorical   **f.** categorical
  g. numerical   **h.** categorical   **i.** numerical
  j. numerical

2. a.

Subject	Tally
math	ⅢⅢ
history	|||
writing	||

  b.

Subject	Frequency
math	5
history	3
writing	2

  c.

Subject	Percent
math	50
history	30
writing	20

3. a. seven females   **b.** 20%   **b.** ≈43%

4.

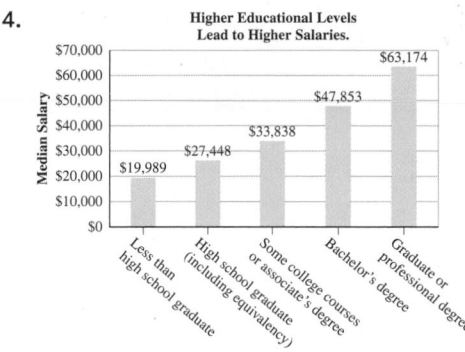

5. Be sure to include the category "other" so that the pie represents 100% of the U.S. searches.

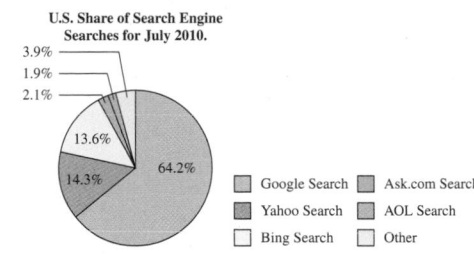

6.

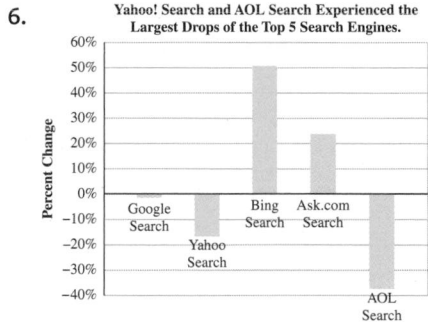

7. a. graph B, because the years are side by side for easy comparison
  b. graph A, because the quarters are side by side for easy comparison
  c. Graph A shows that the rental vacancy rate was generally higher than 10%.

8. a.

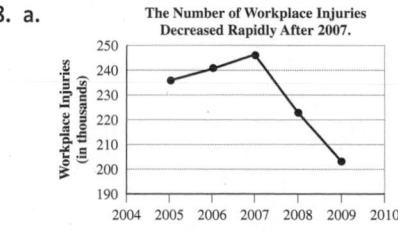

b.

The Number of Workplace Injuries Decreased After 2007.

(line graph: Workplace Injuries (in thousands) vs. year 2004–2010)

9. a. People with less than a high school diploma experience higher unemployment rates.
  b. The unemployment rates rise and fall during the cycles.
  c. Answers vary; for example, "Lower education levels mean higher unemployment rates."

10.

Students Who Took the PSAT Scored Consistently Better on the SAT.

(line graph: Average SAT Score vs. year 1999–2005; legend: ■ Took PSAT, ▲ No PSAT)

11. Since 2001, more workers aged 65 and older are working full time and fewer are working part time.

12. a. no apparent relationship
  b. strong positive linear relationship
  c. weak negative linear relationship

13. a.

Cars With Smaller Carbon Footprints Get Better Gas Mileage.

(scatterplot: Tons of Carbon Dioxide per Year vs. mpg)

  b. The scatterplot suggests a strong negative relationship between gas mileage and CO_2 emissions.

14. a.

(scatterplot: Highway (in miles per gallon) vs. City (in miles per gallon))

  b. The scatterplot suggests a strong positive relationship between city and highway gas mileage.

15. a. 73.025 sec   **b.** 72.8 sec   **c.** no mode

16. a. x_{201} **b.** $(x_{412} + x_{413}) \div 2$

17. a. mean, because there are no outliers
  b. median, because there is an outlier (180)

18. a. 34.8 mpg (34.75 rounded to 34.8)
  b. 1.8 mpg (1.75 rounded to 1.8, use mean = 34.75)

19. The minimum usual height is 56.8 inches, and the maximum usual height is 68.8 inches.

20. Yes; the usual values fall within the interval $5.086 \pm 2.5 \cdot 0.269$, or [4.41, 5.76]. Based on these data, the manufacturer's claim of 5.4 hours seems plausible.

21. a. 43rd percentile   **b.** 83rd percentile
  c. 61.6 pounds, because $70 \cdot 35/100 = 24.5 \rightarrow x_{25}$
  d. 54.75 pounds, because $(52.7 + 56.8) \div 2 = 54.75$

22. Misha scored higher than 85% of the people who took the same exam.

23. 1.2, 1.9, 2.3, 2.5, 3.3

24. 33, 35, 57, 70, 82

25. a. Team B threw the ball farther, on average, because the median is larger for team B.
  b. The distances for team B have more variation, because the box is wider.

26. a. 0.9 and 10.0
  b. 10.0 is an outlier. Workers 65 years old and over suffer an unusually high rate of fatal work injuries: 10.0 per 10,000 workers.

27. a. the least value, $38,400
  b. 25th percentile = $50,700, median = $54,000, and 75th percentile = $56,150. The only outlier is $38,400.
  c.

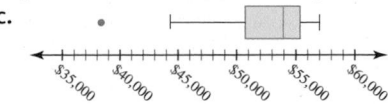

(box plot ranging from $35,000 to $60,000)

CHAPTER 9

SECTION 9.1

1. a. $S = \{1, 2, 3\}$
  b. $P(1) = \dfrac{73}{360} \approx 20.3\%$, $P(2) = \dfrac{107}{360} \approx 29.7\%$, and $P(3) = \dfrac{180}{360} = 50\%$
  c. $P(1) + P(2) + P(3) = \dfrac{73}{360} + \dfrac{107}{360} + \dfrac{180}{360}$
$$= \dfrac{360}{360}$$
$$= 1$$

2. the event that the arrow of the spinner lands on 3, 6, or 7

3. a. 20%   **b.** 16%

4. a. For Raj, $P(E) = \dfrac{68}{120} \approx 57\%$.
    For Gina, $P(E) = \dfrac{147}{250} \approx 59\%$.
    For Taylor, $P(E) = \dfrac{260}{400} \approx 65\%$.
  b. 260/400 seems like the best estimate because of the larger value of n.
  c. Combine the results:
$$P(E) = \dfrac{68 + 147 + 260}{120 + 250 + 400} = \dfrac{475}{770} \approx 62\%.$$

5. The data in table A seem to be the experimental results (generated by a computer), because the quotients 396/855, 840/1724, and 2588/5267 are much closer to what we expect, 0.50, than quotients in table B.

6. a. the probability of drawing a yellow marble
  b. the probability of drawing a green marble
  c. the probability of drawing a blue or green marble

7. a. 15.4% **b.** 30.8% **c.** 23.1%

8. a. $P(A) = \dfrac{18}{36} = 50\%$ **b.** $P(B) = \dfrac{12}{36} \approx 33.3\%$

   c. $P(\text{tie}) = \dfrac{6}{36} \approx 16.7\%$

   d. $250 \times P(B) = 250 \times \dfrac{12}{36} \approx 83$ games

9. 288 blue marbles

10. Solve $\dfrac{4 + n}{12 + n} = 0.80$ to get $n = 28$. Add 28 blue marbles.

11. yellow

12. bag A, because there is a higher probability of picking a blue marble from it

13. 2, because $6 \times \frac{1}{3} = 2$

14. a.

Nickels	1	2	3	4
Pennies	3	6	9	12

   b. 75%, because the ratio of pennies to coins is 3 to 4

15. b = number of blue marbles, and g = number of green marbles. $P(b) = 0.25 = \dfrac{b}{n}$ and $P(g) = 0.60 = \dfrac{g}{n}$, so $b = 0.25n$ and $g = 0.60n$.

   $b{:}g = 0.25n{:}0.60n$
   $\phantom{b{:}g} = 0.25{:}0.60$
   $\phantom{b{:}g} = 25{:}60$
   $\phantom{b{:}g} = 5{:}12$

16. Begin with the equations $P(A) + P(B) \le 1$ and $P(A) = 7 \cdot P(B)$ to get the equation $7 \cdot P(B) \le 1 - P(B)$. Then $8 \cdot P(B) \le 1$. Then $P(B) \le 1/8$. Then $P(B) \le 12.5\%$.

17. a. $P(\text{donuts}) \overset{?}{\approx} 1.7 \cdot P(\text{ice cream})$
   $0.63 \overset{?}{\approx} 1.7 \cdot 0.37$
   $0.63 \approx 0.629$

   b. $P(\text{ice cream}) \overset{?}{\approx} P(\text{donuts}) - 41\% \cdot P(\text{donuts})$
   $0.37 \overset{?}{\approx} 0.63 - 0.41 \cdot 0.63$
   $0.37 \approx 0.3717$

18. a. the relative frequency (percentage) of each outcome
   b. the relative frequency (percentage) of each outcome

19. a.

Green	3	6	9	12
Blue	5	10	15	20

   b. The ratio of the number of green marbles to the total number of marbles in the bag is always 3 to 8 (for example, $6{:}16 = 3{:}8$ and $9{:}24 = 3{:}8$). So $P(\text{green}) = \dfrac{3}{8}$.

20. 75%

21. a. number and operations **b.** algebra
   c. 10% **d.** 45%

22. a. Students are six times more likely to prefer cheese pizza than ham pizza. Students are six times less likely to prefer ham pizza than cheese pizza.

   b. Registered voters are 3.2 times more likely to vote against Proposition A. Registered voters are 3.2 times less likely to vote for Proposition A.

   c. A blue marble is 1.75 times more likely to be randomly picked than a green marble. A green marble is 1.75 times less likely to be randomly picked than a blue marble.

23. a. $\dfrac{15}{105} \approx 14\%$ **b.** $\dfrac{22 + 20 + 8}{105} \approx 48\%$

   c. $48 \times \dfrac{40}{105} \approx 18$ hits

24. a. $360/5 = 72$ and $4 \cdot 72 = 288$. The central angle for A is 288°.

   b. $P(A) = \dfrac{1.3}{2.3}$ and $\dfrac{1.3}{2.3} \cdot 360 \approx 203°$. The central angle for A is about 203°.

25. Suppose you repeat this experiment 100 times. You can "expect" that 32 of the 100 marbles will be green.

26. An outcome is the result of an experiment. An event is a set containing one or more outcomes of an experiment.

27. The experimental probability f/n approaches a fixed number as the number of repetitions n increases. That fixed number is the theoretical probability.

28. You could randomly select 100 students and ask them whether they have two pets. Let f be the number of students who said "yes." Then $f/100$ is an estimate of the probability that a randomly chosen student at the school has two pets.

29. experimental probability, because the situation is too difficult to analyze mathematically

30. a. probability **b.** qualitative **c.** experiment
   d. outcome **e.** sample space **f.** event
   g. experimental probability

31. a. unlikely **b.** likely

32. a. $P(2 \text{ or } 8) = \dfrac{8}{52} \approx 15.4\%$

   b. $P(\text{heart or } 3) = \dfrac{16}{52} \approx 31\%$

33. The probability of any event must be no more than 1.

34. 3/7, or about 43%

35. $1 \cdot 6 = 6$, $2 \cdot 6 = 12$, $3 \cdot 6 = 18$, ..., $16 \cdot 6 = 96$, so there are 16 multiples of 6 from 1 to 100. Then $1 - \dfrac{16}{100} = \dfrac{84}{100} = 84\%$.

36. a. 6/14, or about 43% **b.** 11/14, or about 79%

37. $P(1) + P(2) + P(3) = 1$, so $P(3) = 1 - P(1) - P(2) = 1 - 0.30 - 0.25 = 0.45$

38. Mark, because short-run results are unpredictable and are more likely to differ from expected results.

39. a. experimental **b.** theoretical **c.** experimental

40. Solving the equation $1 - P(B) = 3.5 \cdot P(B)$ for $P(B)$, we get $P(B) = 1/4.5$. Then $(1/4.5) \times 360 \approx 80$. The central angle for B is 80° and for A is 280°. We can check our work: $280 \div 80 = 3.5$.

41. a. 0.45
 b. 0.55

42. Bill has the same chance, because each possibility in the sequence 0000, 0001, 0002, . . . , 9999 is equally likely.

43. a. $3/27 \approx 11\%$ **b.** $7/27 \approx 26\%$
 c. $21/27 \approx 78\%$ **d.** $3/27 \approx 11\%$

44. a. For Mary, $P(E) = \dfrac{3}{15} = 20\%$.

 For Bob, $P(E) = \dfrac{6}{24} = 25\%$.

 For Tina, $P(E) = \dfrac{10}{32} \approx 31\%$.

 b. All three values for n are low, but the experimental probability for Tina seems like the best option because it has a larger number of repetitions.

 c. Combine the results:
 $$P(E) = \frac{3 + 6 + 10}{15 + 24 + 32} = \frac{19}{71} \approx 27\%.$$

45. a. The experimental probability by Bob seems like the best estimate, because it is based on a larger number of repetitions.

 b. Calculate the frequencies: $f_M = 0.58 \cdot 12 \approx 7, f_B = 0.60 \cdot 70 = 42$, and $f_T = 0.80 \cdot 40 = 32$. Then combine the results: $P(E) = \dfrac{7 + 42 + 32}{12 + 70 + 40} = \dfrac{81}{122} \approx 66\%$.

46. a.

W	X	Y	Z
68°	44°	108°	140°

 b. $P(W) = \dfrac{68}{360} \approx 19\%, P(X) = \dfrac{44}{360} \approx 12\%$

 $P(Y) = \dfrac{108}{360} = 30\%, P(Z) = \dfrac{140}{360} \approx 39\%$

47. a. $7/36 \approx 19\%$ **b.** $5/36 \approx 14\%$
 c. $21/36 \approx 58\%$ **d.** $4/36 \approx 11\%$

48. Solve $0.075n = 3$ to get $n = 40$.

49. Answers vary.

 a.

Games ends on two rolls	ꘉꘉ ꘉꘉ ꘉꘉ ꘉꘉ ꘉꘉ ꘉꘉ ꘉꘉ ꘉ
Total two-roll games	100

 b. Based on these results, you won $64 dollars but lost $36. That means that overall you won $28 on 100 games played, or won an average of 28 cents per game.

50. a. Answers vary.

 b. Answers vary. In our experiments, the event occurred 29 out of 50 times. The experimental probability was thus $29/50 = 58\%$.

at least one 6	ꘉꘉ	ꘉꘉ	ꘉꘉ	ꘉꘉ	ꘉꘉ	ꘌꘌꘌꘌ
no sixes	ꘉꘉ	ꘉꘉ	ꘉꘉ	ꘉꘉ	ꘌ	

51. $P(E) \approx 43\%$

52. You expect E to occur half of the times. For example, if you repeat the experiment 500 times, then you expect E to occur 250 times.

53. A is 2.7 times more likely to occur than event B.

54. A is 3.4 times more likely to occur than event B.

55. A is 2.8 times as likely to occur as event B.

56. A is 4.2 times as likely to occur as event B.

57. B is 6.2 times as likely to occur as event A.

58. B is five times as likely to occur as event A.

59. B is eight times less likely to occur than event A.

60. B is 1.7 times less likely to occur than event A.

61. a. $0.48 - 0.21 \cdot 0.48 \approx 0.38$
 b. $0.38 + 0.26 \cdot 0.38 \approx 0.48$ **c.** $1.26 \cdot 0.38 \approx 0.48$

62. a. $0.55 - 0.38 \cdot 0.55 \approx 0.34$
 b. $0.34 + 0.62 \cdot 0.34 \approx 0.55$ **c.** $1.6 \cdot 0.34 \approx 0.55$

63. a. $0.26/0.9 = 2.88 \approx 3$
 b. $0.09 + 189\% \cdot 0.09 = 0.09 + 0.1701 = 0.2601$

64. a. Solve the equation $2.5 \times p = 0.276$ to get $p \approx 0.11$. The likelihood that a randomly selected member of the general population has arthritis is 11%.
 b. $11\% \times 580 \approx 64$. You would expect about 64 out of 580 people to have arthritis.

65. $1.18p$, because $p + 0.18p = 1.18p$

66. $0.76p$, because $p - 0.24p = 0.76p$

67. a. $P(\text{soccer}) \overset{?}{=} 2.5 \cdot P(\text{basketball})$

 $$\frac{20}{30} \overset{?}{=} 2.5 \cdot \frac{8}{30}$$

 $$\frac{20}{30} = \frac{20}{30}$$

 b. $\dfrac{8}{30} \overset{?}{=} \dfrac{20}{30} - 60\% \cdot \dfrac{20}{30}$

 $\dfrac{8}{30} \overset{?}{=} \dfrac{20}{30} - 0.60 \cdot \dfrac{20}{30}$

 $\dfrac{8}{30} \overset{?}{=} \dfrac{20}{30} - \dfrac{12}{30}$

 $\dfrac{8}{30} = \dfrac{8}{30}$

SECTION 9.2

1. a.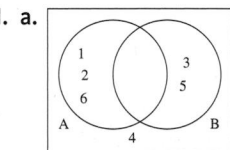

 b. The Venn diagram would show they have no elements in common.

2. a.

 b. The Venn diagram would show the intersection is nonempty.

3. The expression is a number that is the probability that A occurs, given that B has occurred.

4. **a.** There are nine ways A can occur, there are 19 equally likely outcomes in the sample space, so $P(A) = 9/19$.

   b. Given that A has occurred, there are basically only nine equally likely possibilities. Of these, there are four ways B can occur. So $P(B \mid A) = 4/9$.

5. **a.** 6/15, or 40%   **b.** 10/15, or $\approx$66.7%   **c.** $\dfrac{3}{15}$, or 20%

   d. 13/15, or $\approx$86.7%   **e.** 3/10, or 30%   **f.** 3/6, or 50%

   g. 7/9, or $\approx$77.8%

6.
Outcome	BB	BY	GB	GG	GY
Probability	$\dfrac{15}{40}$	$\dfrac{9}{40}$	$\dfrac{4}{35}$	$\dfrac{2}{35}$	$\dfrac{8}{35}$

7. **a.** $P(Y \mid G) = \dfrac{3}{5} = 60\%$

   b. $P(Y \mid Y) = \dfrac{2}{5} = 40\%$

   c. $P(BG) = \dfrac{2}{6} \times \dfrac{1}{5} = \dfrac{1}{15} \approx 6.7\%$

   d. $P(YB) = \dfrac{3}{6} \times \dfrac{2}{5} = \dfrac{1}{5} = 20\%$

   e. $P(YY) + P(GY) + P(BY) = 50\%$

8. **a.** 4/5   **b.** 5/8

9. We draw a tree diagram showing black (B), blue (Bl), red (R), and yellow (Y) marbles to represent the situation.

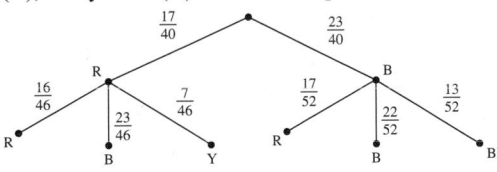

   a. $P(B \mid R) = \dfrac{23}{46}$

   b. $P(R \mid B) = \dfrac{17}{52}$

   c. $P(RY) = \dfrac{17}{40} \cdot \dfrac{7}{46} \approx 6.5\%$

   d. $P(BlB) = \dfrac{23}{40} \cdot \dfrac{13}{52} \approx 14.4\%$

10. **a.** $1/50 = 0.02$ **b.** 0.19
    c. $P(A \text{ and } B) = P(A) \cdot P(B \mid A) = 0.02 \cdot 0.19 = 0.0038$
    d. 0.98   **e.** 0.05
    f. $P(A \text{ and } B) = P(A) \cdot P(B \mid A) = 0.98 \cdot 0.05 = 0.049$
    g. $P(A \text{ and } B) = P(A) \cdot P(B \mid A) = 0.98 \cdot 0.95 = 0.931$

11. **a.** 12/52   **b.** 12/51

12. **a.** $P(A \text{ and } B) = P(A) \cdot P(B) = 0.3 \cdot 0.5 = 0.15$
    b. $P(A \text{ or } B) = P(A) + P(B) - P(A) \cdot P(B) = 0.3 + 0.5 - 0.15 = 0.65$

13. **a.** $P(A \text{ and } B) = P(A) \cdot P(B) = 0.42 \cdot 0.75 = 0.315$
    b. $P(A \text{ or } B) = P(A) + P(B) - P(A) \cdot P(B) = 0.42 + 0.75 - 0.315 = 0.855$

14. No; suppose for a moment that they were mutually exclusive. Then $P(A \text{ or } B)$ would be equal to 1.17, which is greater than 1. But the event "A or B" must have a probability less than or equal to 1. So the events A and B cannot be mutually exclusive.

15. $P(A \text{ and } B) = P(A) \cdot P(B \mid A) = 0.24 \cdot 0.30 = 0.072$

16. $P(A \text{ and } B) = P(A) \cdot P(B \mid A) = 0.35 \cdot 0.15 = 0.0525$, so
    $P(A \text{ or } B) = P(A) + P(B) - P(A \text{ and } B) = 0.35 + 0.22 - 0.0525 = 0.5175$

17. **a.** $\dfrac{300}{600} \times \dfrac{300}{600} = 0.25$ **b.** $\dfrac{300}{600} \times \dfrac{299}{599} \approx 0.2496$
    c. no

18. **a.** $\dfrac{3}{6} \times \dfrac{3}{6} = 0.25$ **b.** $\dfrac{3}{6} \times \dfrac{2}{5} = 0.20$ **c.** yes

19. **a.** $\dfrac{5}{6}$ **b.** $\left(\dfrac{5}{6}\right)^4 \approx 0.4823$

    c. $1 - \left(\dfrac{5}{6}\right)^4 \approx 0.5177$, so de Méré would win slightly more than half of the games.

20. **a.** $\dfrac{35}{36}$ **b.** $\left(\dfrac{35}{36}\right)^{24} \approx 0.5086$

    c. $1 - \left(\dfrac{35}{36}\right)^{24} \approx 0.4914$, so de Méré would win slightly less than half of the games.

21. **a.** 0.77   **b.** 0.054
    c. $P(A \text{ and } B) = P(A) \cdot P(B \mid A) = 0.77 \cdot 0.054 \approx 0.042$

22. **a.** 0.10   **b.** 0.25
    c. $P(A \text{ and } B) = P(A) \cdot P(B \mid A) = 0.10 \cdot 0.25 = 0.025$

23. **a.** $\dfrac{75}{340} \approx 22\%$ **b.** $\dfrac{40}{75} \approx 53\%$

    c. $P(A \text{ and } B) = P(A) \cdot P(B \mid A) = \dfrac{75}{340} \cdot \dfrac{40}{75} \approx 12\%$

24. Suppose for a moment that they were mutually exclusive. Then $P(A \text{ or } B)$ would be equal to 1.3, which is greater than 1. But the event "A or B" must have a probability less than or equal to 1. So the events A and B cannot be mutually exclusive.

25. **a.** $P(B) = \dfrac{7}{15}$

    b. $P(B \mid A) = \dfrac{7}{15}$

    c. $P(B) = P(B \mid A)$, so A and B are independent events.

26. **a.** $P(B) = \dfrac{7}{15}$ **b.** $P(B \mid A) = \dfrac{7}{14}$

    c. $P(B) \neq P(B \mid A)$, so A and B are dependent events.

27. The lottery official is wrong. The lotteries are independent events, so the probability of winning both lotteries is determined by multiplying the probabilities:
    $$\dfrac{1}{2.3 \times 10^6} \times \dfrac{1}{2.3 \times 10^6} \approx 2 \times 10^{-13}.$$

28. **a.** mutually exclusive   **b.** probability tree diagram
    c. independent

29. **a.** yes, provided that $P(A \text{ and } B) = 0.2$
    b. no, because $P(A \text{ or } B) \leq P(A) + P(B)$

30. yes, because a 4 and 1 cannot happen at the same time on one roll

31.

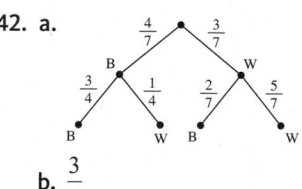

A tree diagram with branches:
- $\frac{40}{52}$ not a face card, $\frac{12}{52}$ face card
- $\frac{1}{2}$ heads, $\frac{1}{2}$ tails, $\frac{3}{5}$ blue, $\frac{2}{5}$ green

32. a.

+	1	2	3	4	5	6
1	2	3	4	5	6	7
2	3	4	5	6	7	8
3	4	5	6	7	8	9
4	5	6	7	8	9	10
5	6	7	8	9	10	11
6	7	8	9	10	11	12

There are $2 + 4 + 6 = 12$ ways the game can end on the first roll. So $P(\text{game ends on first roll}) = 12/36$.

b. The probability that the game does not end on a roll is 24/36. The game does not end on the first three rolls; it ends on the fourth roll. So $P(\text{game ends on fourth}$ roll$) = \frac{24}{36} \times \frac{24}{36} \times \frac{24}{36} \times \frac{12}{36} \approx 0.0988 \approx 10\%$.

33. a.

−	1	2	3	4	5	6
1	0	1	2	3	4	5
2	1	0	1	2	3	4
3	2	1	0	1	2	3
4	3	2	1	0	1	2
5	4	3	2	1	0	1
6	5	4	3	2	1	0

There are $10 + 6 = 16$ ways the game can end on the first roll. So $P(\text{game ends on first roll}) = 16/36$.

b. The probability that the game does not end on a roll is 20/36. The game does not end on the first two rolls; it ends on the third roll. So $P(\text{game ends on third roll}) = \frac{20}{36} \times \frac{20}{36} \times \frac{16}{36} \approx 0.137 \approx 14\%$.

34. a. $\frac{4}{52} \times \frac{12}{52} \approx 1.8\%$ **b.** $\frac{4}{52} \times \frac{4}{52} \approx 0.6\%$

35. a. $P(BG) = P(B) \cdot P(G \mid B) = \frac{6}{14} \cdot \frac{5}{13} \approx 16\%$

b. $P(BB) + P(RR) + P(GG) =$
$$\frac{6}{14} \cdot \frac{5}{13} + \frac{3}{14} \cdot \frac{2}{13} + \frac{5}{14} \cdot \frac{4}{13} = \frac{56}{182} \approx 31\%$$

36. part (c)

37. a. The draws are independent. To need two draws, you will have to draw a marble that is not green followed by a marble that is green. Thus, the probability is

$$P(\text{not green}) \cdot P(\text{green}) = \frac{18}{25} \cdot \frac{7}{25} \approx 20.2\%.$$

b. For three draws, you will have to draw a marble that is not green, followed by a marble that is not

green, followed by a marble that is green. Thus, the probability is $P(\text{not green}) \cdot P(\text{not green}) \cdot P(\text{green}) =$ $\frac{18}{25} \cdot \frac{18}{25} \cdot \frac{7}{25} \approx 14.5\%$.

38. a. To need two draws, you will have to draw a marble that is not green followed by a marble that is green. Thus, the probability is

$$P(\text{not green}) \cdot P(\text{green}) = \frac{18}{25} \cdot \frac{7}{24} = 21\%.$$

b. For three draws, you will have to draw a marble that is not green, followed by a marble that is not green, followed by a marble that is green. Thus, the probability is $P(\text{not green}) \cdot P(\text{not green}) \cdot P(\text{green}) =$ $\frac{18}{25} \cdot \frac{17}{24} \cdot \frac{7}{23} \approx 15.5\%$.

39. $\frac{40}{50} \times \frac{39}{49} \times \frac{10}{48} \approx 13\%$

40. The second candidate wins with a queen of spades, one of the four kings, or one of the four aces. So the probability of the second candidate winning is 9/51, or about 17.6%.

41. a. $0.4 \cdot 0.4 \cdot 0.4 = 0.064$
b. $0.4 \cdot 0.4 \cdot 0.4 + 0.6 \cdot 0.6 \cdot 0.6 = 28\%$

42. a.

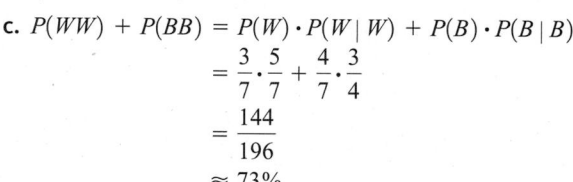

A tree diagram with branches: $\frac{4}{7}$ B, $\frac{3}{7}$ W; $\frac{3}{4}$ B, $\frac{1}{4}$ W; $\frac{2}{7}$ B, $\frac{5}{7}$ W.

b. $\frac{3}{4}$

c. $P(WW) + P(BB) = P(W) \cdot P(W \mid W) + P(B) \cdot P(B \mid B)$
$$= \frac{3}{7} \cdot \frac{5}{7} + \frac{4}{7} \cdot \frac{3}{4}$$
$$= \frac{144}{196}$$
$$\approx 73\%$$

43. part (c)

44. $P(1, 4) + P(1, 2) + P(2, 3) = 0.2 \cdot 0.2 + 0.2 \cdot 0.5 + 0.8 \cdot 0.4 = 46\%$

45. a.

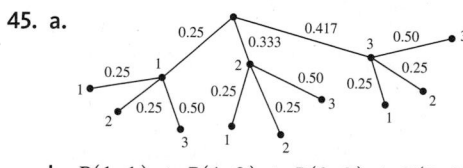

A tree diagram with branches labeled 0.25, 1, 2; 0.25, 0.333, 0.417; 0.50, 0.25; 3, 1, 2; etc.

b. $P(1, 1) + P(1, 3) + P(2, 2) + P(3, 1) + P(3, 3) =$ $0.25 \cdot 0.25 + 0.25 \cdot 0.50 + 0.333 \cdot 0.25 + 0.417 \cdot 0.25 + 0.417 \cdot 0.50 \approx 58\%$

46. part (b)

47. We can predict the proportion of tosses that are tails (or heads).

48. a. $\frac{12,489}{29,903} \approx 42\%$ **b.** $\frac{17,414}{51,014} \approx 34\%$

49. a. $\frac{13,738}{83,339} \approx 16\%$ **b.** $\frac{60,210}{83,339} \approx 72\%$

c. $P(B) = \frac{32,325}{83,339} \approx 39\%$ and $P(B \mid A) = \frac{12,489}{29,903} \approx 42\%$. A and B are not independent because $P(B) \neq P(B \mid A)$.

50. a.

Outcome	HHH	HHT	HTH	HTT	THH	THT	TTH	TTT
Probability	1/8	1/8	1/8	1/8	1/8	1/8	1/8	1/8
Winner		C	B	A	A	B	C	

Each player has the same chance, 2/8, of winning.

b.

Outcome	HHH	HHT	HTH	HTT	THH	THT	TTH	TTT
Probability	0.21	0.09	0.14	0.06	0.21	0.09	0.14	0.06
Winner		C	B	A	A	B	C	

$P(\text{A wins}) = 0.27$, $P(\text{B wins}) = 0.23$, and $P(\text{C wins}) = 0.23$. So A is favored to win.

51. a.

Outcome	HHH	HHT	HTH	HTT	THH	THT	TTH	TTT
Probability	0.144	0.096	0.036	0.024	0.336	0.224	0.084	0.056
Winner		C	B	A	A	B	C	

$P(\text{A wins}) = 0.36$, $P(\text{B wins}) = 0.26$, and $P(\text{C wins}) = 0.18$. So A is favored to win.

b.

Outcome	HHH	HHT	HTH	HTT	THH	THT	TTH	TTT
Probability	0.0525	0.035	0.0975	0.065	0.1575	0.105	0.2925	0.195
Winner		C	B	A	A	B	C	

$P(\text{A wins}) = 0.2225$, $P(\text{B wins}) = 0.2025$, and $P(\text{C wins}) = 0.3275$. So C is favored to win.

52. a. $\dfrac{95}{1150} \approx 8\%$ **b.** $\dfrac{517}{2333} \approx 22\%$

53. a. $\dfrac{2871}{3483} \approx 82\%$ **b.** $\dfrac{1055}{1150} \approx 92\%$

c. $P(B) = \dfrac{2871}{3483} \approx 82\%$ and $P(B \,|\, A) = \dfrac{1055}{1150} \approx 92\%$.
So $P(B) \neq P(B \,|\, A)$, which means A and B are not independent events.

SECTION 9.3

1. There are 8 ways A can occur, and 12 ways $\sim A$ can occur. Therefore, the odds that A will occur are $8:12 = 2:3$.

2. $e = 5 \cdot \dfrac{1}{4} + 12 \cdot \dfrac{3}{4} = 10.25$

3. $e = 8 \cdot \dfrac{115}{360} + 17 \cdot \dfrac{245}{360} = 14.125$

4. The weights are normally distributed.

5. a. 4U, because it looks the least symmetric
b. L8, because it looks more symmetric in the shape of a bell and we would expect a larger sample to contain a wider interval of values.

6. mean ≈ 60

7. The data in graph B have a larger standard deviation.

8. Mario scored relatively higher, because he had a higher z-score.

9. a. more than 3   **b.** less than 6
c. $e = 3 \cdot \dfrac{166}{360} + 6 \cdot \dfrac{124}{360} + 10 \cdot \dfrac{70}{360} \approx 5.4$ (use a protractor to measure the central angles)

10. Dan (z-score $= 2$) scored relatively better than Gary (z-score $= 0.4$).

11. The z-score for Mitchell is $(86 - 74)/5 = 2.4$. Solve $(x - 72)/10 > 2.4$ for x to get $x > 96$. Joey would need to have scored more than 96 to score relatively higher than Mitchell.

12. For the history class, $(82 - 74)/s = 1.4$, which implies $s \approx 5.7$. For the math class, $(88 - 80)/s = 0.8$, which implies $s = 10$. The scores on the math test had more variation.

13. $e = 75 \cdot \dfrac{1}{8} + 45 \cdot \dfrac{1}{8} + 0 \cdot \dfrac{6}{8} = 15$. On average, the player should expect to win \$15 each game.

14. a. $e = 0 \cdot 0.988494 + 250{,}000 \cdot 0.011506 = \$2876.50$
b. $3000 - 2876.50 = \$123.50$
c. $2876.50 + 600 = \$3476.50$

15. C, A, B

16. a. 6   **b.** 4   **c.** $4 \cdot 1 + 6 \cdot 4 = 28$
d. $28 \div 10 = 2.80$ **e.** $\$1 \cdot 0.40 + \$4 \cdot 0.60 = \$2.80$

17. $3 \cdot 0.20 + 4 \cdot 0.15 + 6 \cdot 0.35 + 7 \cdot 0.30 = 5.4$

18. Because 99.7% of all values fall within 3 standard deviations of the mean, minimum $= 80 - 3 \cdot 5 = 65$ and maximum $= 80 + 3 \cdot 5 = 95$. So you would expect values to range from 65 to 95. (In an actual generation of 250 numbers from a normal distribution with a mean of 80 and a standard deviation of 5, the minimum was 66.15 and the maximum value was 94.17.)

19. We expect about 95% of the cancellations and no-shows to be within 2 standard deviations of the mean: $[10.5 - 2 \cdot 3.4, 10.5 + 2 \cdot 3.4]$, or from 3.7 to 17.3. So the manager should accept four more reservations than rooms to offset some cancellations and no-shows yet still be able to honor most reservations.

20. $(60 - 74.5)/8.2 = -1.77$ and $(60 - 68.1)/3.5 = -2.31$. If the score 60 was for test 1, then the z-score would be -1.77, which is within the range of usual z-scores. If the score was from test 2, then the z-score would be -2.31, which is outside the range of usual z-score. So the score was more likely to be from test 1.

21. $P(A):P(\sim A) = 0.42:0.58 = 42:58 = 21:29$

22. $P(A) = \dfrac{4}{4 + 7} = \dfrac{4}{11} \approx 36\%$

23. probability $= \dfrac{\text{area of shaded region}}{\text{area of large circle}} =$
$\dfrac{\pi 24^2 - \pi 14^2}{\pi 24^2} = \dfrac{\pi 380}{\pi 576} \approx 66\%$
odds in favor $= 66:34 = 33:17$

24. Use a protractor the measure the central angle and get 120°.

$$\text{probability} = \frac{\text{area of shaded region}}{\text{area of large circle}} =$$

$$\frac{\frac{120}{360}(\pi 24^2 - \pi 14^2)}{\pi 24^2} = \frac{\frac{120}{360} \cdot \pi 380}{\pi 576} \approx 22\%$$

odds in favor ≈ 22:78 = 11:39

25. **a.** 3:7, because 0.30:0.70 = 3:7
    b. 7:18, because 0.28:0.72 = 28:72 = 7:18

26. $P(8):P(\sim 8) = \frac{5}{36}:\frac{31}{36} = 5:31$

27. There are 10 ways you will roll a 6 or an 8 and 26 ways you will not roll a 7 or 9. Therefore, the odds that you will land on Park Place or Boardwalk are 10:26 or 5:13.

28. **a.** $\frac{9}{19}$ **b.** $\frac{3}{4}$

29. If you take a random sample of many people, ask them how much time they spend on the computer, and then create a histogram for the data, you should expect to see a histogram that is symmetric with the shape of a bell.

30. no, because the outcomes A and B are not numbers

31. Let digits 0 and 1 represent prize A, digits 2 and 3 represent prize B, digits 4 and 5 represent prize C, digits 6 and 7 represent prize D, and digits 8 and 9 represent prize E. An experiment consists of picking digits from a table until you get two digits that represent the same prize. For example, 4170 would represent that Maria bought four boxes and got two A prizes. Then repeat the experiment, say, 25 times. Each time, record the number of boxes purchased. Then average those 25 numbers. The average is an estimate of the expected number of boxes Maria needs to buy to get two identical prizes.

32. **a.** expected value   **b.** $P(E):P(\sim E)$ **c.** $a/(a+b)$
    d. z-scores   **e.** distribution   **f.** normally distributed
    g. 95%   **h.** 3   **i.** simulation

33. **a.**

Payout	$0	$250,000
Probability	0.995587	0.004413

   b. $e = 0 \cdot 0.995587 + 250,000 \cdot 0.004413 = \$1103.25$
   c. $1103.25 + 1200 = \$2303.25$

34. **a.** $e = 15,000 \cdot \frac{1}{10,000} + 1000 \cdot \frac{3}{10,000} +$

$$500 \cdot \frac{5}{10,000} + 0 \cdot \frac{9991}{10,000} = \$2.05$$

   b. 1:9999

35. The expected value of each die is 3.5, so the expected value of two dice is 7. $40 \div 7 = 5$ R5. Therefore, six rolls are expected, on average.

36. $\frac{1}{13,000} \approx 7.7 \times 10^{-5}$

37. **a.** $e \approx 1000 \cdot \frac{1}{6,800,000} + 500 \cdot \frac{1}{6,800,000} +$

$$100 \cdot \frac{1}{6,800,000} + 25 \cdot \frac{97}{70,000} \approx 0.035$$

   The expected value is 3.5 cents per lottery ticket.
   b. less than

38. Let the pairs of digits 00, 01, . . . , 27 represent the batter got a hit. Any pair of digits from 28, 29, . . . , 99 represent the batter did not get a hit. Each pair of digits represents an at-bat. Then the batter has a 28/100 or 0.28 chance of getting a hit. An experiment consists of selecting three pairs of digits. Repeat the experiment, say, 20 times, and count the number of times f the batter gets exactly two hits in three at-bats (see the bold sequences). The empirical probability that the baseball player with a 0.280 batting average got two hits in three at-bats is 4/20, or 20%.

36, 30, 94	15, 52, 67
33, 33, 74	64, 14, 72
17, 15, 04	**00, 15, 28**
28, 58, 68	70, 81, 38
60, 05, 23	21, 66, 37
79, 09, 32	80, 86, 13
47, 99, 57	**19, 58, 14**
67, 20, 62	04, 83, 62
73, 88, 98	39, 05, 42
17, 23, 98	75, 07, 32

39.

−	1	2	3	4	5	6
1	0	1	2	3	4	5
2	1	0	1	2	3	4
3	2	1	0	1	2	3
4	3	2	1	0	1	2
5	4	3	2	1	0	1
6	5	4	3	2	1	0

There are 16 ways the player can win and 36 possible outcomes. Solve the equation $2 = x \cdot \frac{16}{36} + 0 \cdot \frac{20}{36}$ for x to get x = 4.5. The player should be given $4.50 worth of prizes each time he wins.

40. **a.** $e = 1500 \cdot \frac{1}{40} + 800 \cdot \frac{1}{25} + 300 \cdot \frac{4}{15} = 149.50$
    b. $649.50, because 149.50 + 500 = 649.50

41. **a.** The probability that Jack wins is 3/7 because Jack wins about 3 out of 7 games.
    b. Let the digits 0, 1, and 2 represent that Jack won a game, and let the digits 3, 4, 5, and 6 represent that Jill won a game. Each digit from 0 to 6 represents a game played, and we ignore the digits 7, 8, and 9. Each group of three digits represents that they played three games. An experiment consists of picking three digits. Repeat this experiment, say, 20 times, and count the number of times f Jack won exactly two games. Based on the table, an estimate of the probability that Jack won exactly two of three games is 7/20 = 35%.

104	**015**
223	646
241	304
421	613
365	035
210	**060**
562	**205**
630	110
514	342
545	365

	k
10401	5
2236	4
241304	6
42167	5
3757	4
772106	6
5627	4
6301177	7
57143	5
5475	4

42. The probability that a patient fails to show or cancels is 1/5. Let the digits 0 and 1 represent a patient who failed to show or canceled. Let the digits 2, 3, . . . , 9 represent that a patient showed for a scheduled appointment. Each digit represents a scheduled patient. An experiment consists of picking six digits from a table of random digits. Repeat the experiment, say, 20 times, and count the number of times f all six digits are neither 0 nor 1. Based on the table, an estimate of the probability that all six patients will show is 6/20 = 30%.

104801	501101
223684	**657325**
241304	836022
421679	309306
375703	997581
779210	690711
995627	290556
963019	197705
895791	**434263**
854753	**685753**

43. The Westrikeout team has a 3/4 chance of winning one game, or a 6/8 chance. The Werunslow team has a 1/4, or a 2/8, chance of winning a game. Let the digits 0 and 1 represent that Werunslow won a game, and let the digits 2, 3, 4, 5, 6, and 7 represent that Westrikeout team won a game. Ignore the digits 8 and 9. Each digit represents a game played. An experiment consists of picking digits from a table of random digits until a team has won four games. We repeat this experiment a large number of times and keep track of the number of games k required for each World Series. We show the result for 10 experiments: $(5 + 4 + 6 + 5 + 4 + 6 + 4 + 7 + 5 + 4)/10 = 5$. Based on these results, these teams would be expected to play an average of five games in the World Series to determine a winner.

44. Let the digits 0, 1, 2, 3, 4, 5, and 6 each represent a different prize. Ignore the digits 7, 8, and 9. An experiment consists of picking a sequence of digits until two identical digits are picked, which represents two identical prizes. Repeat this experiment a large number of times, recording each time the number of boxes k needed to get two identical prizes. Then find the average number of boxes Maria bought. We show the results for 10 experiments: $(4 + 2 + 6 + 7 + 4 + 5 + 4 + 5 + 5 + 3)/10 = 4.5$. Based on these results, on average, Maria can expect to buy 4.5 boxes to get two identical prizes.

	k
1040	4
2236	2
241304	6
4216303	7
3503	4
21060	5
5622	4
63011	5
51434	5
545	3

45. Let the digits 0, 1, 2, 3, 4, 5, 6, and 7 each represent that Misha wins a prize. The digits 8 and 9 represent that Misha did not win a prize. An experiment consists of picking a sequence of digits until three digits from 0 to 7 are picked, which represents three prizes. Repeat this experiment a large number of times, recording each time the number of games k needed to get three prizes. Then find the average number of games played. We show the results for 10 experiments: $(3 + 3 + 3 + 3 + 3 + 4 + 5 + 4 + 6 + 4)/10 = 3.8$. Based on these results, on average, Misha can expect to play 3.8 games to get three prizes for her friends.

	k
104	3
223	3
241	3
421	3
375	3
7792	4
99562	5
9630	4
895791	6
8547	4

46. Let the digits 0, 1, 2, 3, 4, 5, 6, and 7 each represent that Kelly made a free throw. The digits 8 and 9 represent that Kelly missed a free throw. An experiment consists of picking three digits, which represents three free throws. Repeat this experiment a large number n of times, and record the number of times f Kelly made all three free throws. The quotient f/n is an estimate of the probability that Kelly will make all three of her next three free throws. The table shows the results of the simulation, and the bold sequences indicate all three free throws were made. Based on the results, 8/20 or 40% is an estimate of the probability that Kelly will make all three of her next three free throws.

104	**150**
223	**465**
241	483
421	930
375	399
779	069
995	729
963	919
895	**143**
854	368

47. We assume the interval [130, 163] represents all measurements that are within 3 standard deviations of the mean. The mean is the center of the interval, so we average the endpoints to determine the center: $\bar{x} \approx (130 + 163)/2 = 146.5$ cm. Now we need to estimate the standard deviation. $130 \approx \bar{x} - 3s$, so $130 \approx 146.5 - 3s$. Then $3s \approx 16.5$. Then $s \approx 5.5$.

48. **a.** $\bar{x} = 53$ **b.** $s = 7$
   c. unusual, because $36 < 53 - 2 \cdot 7$
   d. usual, because $45 \not< 53 - 2 \cdot 7$

49. **a.** $\bar{x} = 132.5$ **b.** $s = 17.5$
   c. usual, because $100 \not< 132.5 - 2 \cdot 17.5$
   d. unusual, because $132.5 + 2 \cdot 17.5 < 180$

50. Draw a number line to represent the 68-95-99.7 rule.

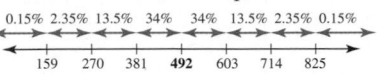

   a. 47.5% **b.** 81.5% **c.** 84% **d.** 2.5%

51. Draw a number line to represent the 68-95-99.7 rule.

| 0.15% | 2.35% | 13.5% | 34% | 34% | 13.5% | 2.35% | 0.15% |

   159 270 381 **492** 603 714 825

   a. 2.5% **b.** 16% **c.** 81.5% **d.** 47.5%

52. We expect the number of people attending the concert to be within 2 standard deviations of the mean: [7400 − 2 · 650, 7400 + 2 · 650], or from 6100 to 8700. Because 8700/500 ≈ 17, the manager should schedule 17 security guards.

REVIEW QUESTIONS

1. **a.** unlikely **b.** likely

2. **a.** $S = \{2, 3, 4, 5, 6, 7, 8, 9, 10, 11, 12\}$
   b. $S = \{0, 1, 2, 3, 4, 5\}$

3. If you repeat the experiment 100 times, then ideally the event E would occur 32 times.

4. **a.**

	1	**2**	**3**	**4**	**5**	**6**
1	1	2	3	4	5	6
2	2	2	3	4	5	6
3	3	3	3	4	5	6
4	4	4	4	4	5	6
5	5	5	5	5	5	6
6	6	6	6	6	6	6

   b. $S = \{1, 2, 3, 4, 5, 6\}$
   c.

Outcome	1	2	3	4	5	6
Probability	$\frac{1}{36}$	$\frac{3}{36}$	$\frac{5}{36}$	$\frac{7}{36}$	$\frac{9}{36}$	$\frac{11}{36}$

5. **a.** $S = \{A, B, C, D\}$
   b.

Outcome	A	B	C	D
Probability	$\frac{75}{360}$	$\frac{64}{360}$	$\frac{146}{360}$	$\frac{75}{360}$

6. **a.** $P(A) = \frac{5}{22} \approx 23\%$ **b.** $P(B) = \frac{15}{22} \approx 68\%$

7. **a.** For Maria, $P(E) = \frac{21}{50} = 42\%$.

   For Ken, $P(E) = \frac{100}{200} = 50\%$.

   For Leila, $P(E) = \frac{301}{500} \approx 60\%$.

   b. the result by Leila, because it has a larger number of repetitions
   c. $P(E) = \frac{21 + 100 + 301}{50 + 200 + 500} = \frac{422}{750} \approx 56\%$.

8. An experiment consists of tossing the bent coin three times and noting the outcomes of all three coin tosses (for example, THT). The students repeat this experiment a large number of times (n) and record the number of times (f) all three tosses landed on tails. The quotient f/n is an estimate of the probability that all three tosses landed on tails. The law of large numbers says that as n increases, the quotient f/n approaches the theoretical but unknown probability that all three tosses land on tails.

9. a. The proportion of times the colors appear is predictable. For example, we expect the green marble to be drawn about 4/9, or 44%, of the times over the long run.
   b. The proportion of times the colors appear is unpredictable when the experiment is repeated just a few times.

10. Valerie probably observed that 35% of the coin tosses were tails, because she tossed the coin only 40 times. Ron tossed the coin 720 times, so he would expect a percentage closer to 50%.

11. bag A, because the probability of drawing a blue marble from it is higher

12. 110 times, because $200 \times 0.55 = 110$

13. There are 17 ways player A can win and 19 ways player B can win ($36 - 17 = 19$).

+	1	2	3	4	5	6
1	2	3	4	5	6	7
2	3	4	5	6	7	8
3	4	5	6	7	8	9
4	5	6	7	8	9	10
5	6	7	8	9	10	11
6	7	8	9	10	11	12

Player B has the advantage, so it would be best to be player B.

14. 95%, because $1 - 0.05 = 0.95$

15. Answers vary, about 42.5%

16. $P(4 \text{ or } 7) = P(4) + P(7) = \frac{4}{52} + \frac{4}{52} = \frac{8}{52} \approx 15\%$

17.

Outcome	0	1	2	3	4	5
Probability	$\frac{6}{36}$	$\frac{10}{36}$	$\frac{8}{36}$	$\frac{6}{36}$	$\frac{4}{36}$	$\frac{2}{36}$

$P(0 \text{ or } 1 \text{ or } 5) = P(0) + P(1) + P(5) = \frac{6}{36} + \frac{10}{36} + \frac{2}{36} = 50\%$

Neither player has the advantage, so you could be either player.

18. a. $2.33 \cdot 0.18 \approx 0.42$ **b.** $1.67 \cdot 0.15 \approx 0.25$
   c. $2.8 \cdot 0.15 = 0.42$ **d.** $0.25 + 0.68 \cdot 0.25 = 0.42$
   e. $0.18 - 0.167 \cdot 0.18 \approx 0.15$

19. a. $P(B) = 12 \cdot P(A) = 12 \cdot 0.042 = 0.504$
   b. $0.06 = 5 \cdot P(B)$, so $P(B) = 0.06/5 = 0.012$
   c. $P(B) = 0.15 + 0.24 \cdot 0.15 = 0.186$
   d. $P(B) = 0.24 - 0.15 \cdot 0.24 = 0.204$

20. A and B are not mutually exclusive because they can occur at the same time; that is, they have the common outcome 3.

21. A and B are mutually exclusive because they cannot occur at the same time; that is, they have no common outcomes.

22. a. $P(B) = 2/11$ **b.** $P(B \mid A) = 2/11$
   c. $P(B) = P(B \mid A)$, so A and B are independent events.

23. a. $P(B) = 4/52$ **b.** $P(B \mid A) = 4/51$
   c. $P(B) \neq P(B \mid A)$, so A and B are dependent events.

24. a. $P(A \text{ and } B) = P(A) \times P(B)$ **b.** $P(A \mid B) = P(A)$
   c. $P(A \text{ or } B) = P(A) + P(B)$
   d. $P(A \text{ or } B) = P(A) + P(B) - P(A \text{ and } B)$
   e. $P(A \text{ and } B) = P(A) \times P(B \mid A)$ or $P(B) \cdot P(A \mid B)$

25. $P(A \text{ and } B) = P(A) \cdot P(B \mid A) = \frac{2}{5} \cdot \frac{1}{2} = \frac{1}{5}$

26. a. $\frac{4}{52} \cdot \frac{13}{52} = \frac{1}{52}$ **b.** $\frac{1}{52} \cdot \frac{12}{51} + \frac{3}{52} \cdot \frac{13}{51} = \frac{1}{52}$

27. a. $\frac{12}{52} \approx 23\%$ **b.** $\frac{12}{52} + \frac{4}{52} = \frac{16}{52} \approx 31\%$
   c. $\frac{4}{52} + \frac{4}{52} = \frac{8}{52} \approx 15\%$
   d. $\frac{26}{52} \cdot \frac{6}{26} = \frac{6}{52} \approx 12\%$
   e. $\frac{26}{52} + \frac{12}{52} - \frac{6}{52} = \frac{32}{52} \approx 62\%$
   f. $\frac{13}{52} + \frac{13}{52} = \frac{26}{52} = 50\%$
   g. $\frac{4}{52} \cdot \frac{1}{4} = \frac{1}{52} \approx 2\%$

28. a. $\frac{64{,}295}{182{,}216} \approx 35\%$
   b. $\frac{32{,}281}{182{,}216} \approx 18\%$ **c.** $\frac{10{,}994}{182{,}216} \approx 6\%$

29. a. $P(B \mid S) = \frac{10{,}994}{64{,}295} \approx 17\%$
   b. $P(S \mid B) = \frac{10{,}994}{32{,}281} \approx 34\%$

30. a. $P(B \text{ or } S) = P(B) + P(S) - P(B \text{ and } S)$
   $= \frac{32{,}281}{182{,}216} + \frac{64{,}295}{182{,}216} - \frac{10{,}994}{182{,}216}$
   $\approx 47\%$
   b. $P(\sim HSG \mid W) = \frac{6452}{39{,}583} \approx 16\%$

31. a. $P(2 \text{ and } FC) = P(2) \cdot P(FC \mid 2) = \frac{4}{52} \cdot \frac{12}{51} = 0.0181$
   b. $P(2 \text{ and } FC) = P(2) \cdot P(FC \mid 2) = \frac{4}{52} \cdot \frac{12}{52} = 0.0178$

32. $\frac{5}{11} \approx 45\%$

33. $\frac{3}{8}$, or 37.5%

34. a. $\frac{10}{20}$, or 50% **b.** $\frac{11}{20}$, or 55% **c.** $\frac{4}{11}$, or about 36%
   d. $\frac{4}{10}$, or 40% **e.** $\frac{7}{10}$, or 70% **f.** $\frac{4}{20}$, or 20%
   g. $\frac{17}{20}$, or 85%

35.

Outcome	BY	BG	GG	GB	GY
Probability	$\frac{2}{28}$	$\frac{5}{28}$	$\frac{9}{40}$	$\frac{6}{40}$	$\frac{15}{40}$

36. a. M = student took math classes
C = student goes to college

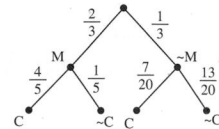

b. $\frac{4}{5}$, or 80% **c.** $\frac{7}{20}$, or 35%

d. $P(M \text{ and } C) = P(M) \cdot P(C \mid M) = \frac{2}{3} \cdot \frac{4}{5} \approx 53\%$

e. $P(\sim M \text{ and } C) = P(\sim M) \cdot P(C \mid \sim M) = \frac{1}{3} \cdot \frac{7}{20} \approx 12\%$

f. $P(C) = P(M \text{ and } C) + P(\sim M \text{ and } C) = \frac{8}{15} + \frac{7}{60} = 65\%$

37. a. There are 12 ways player A can win. There are 11 ways player B can win. Thus, there are 23 ways the game can end in one roll. There are 36 possible ways to roll two dice. So $P(\text{games end on the first roll}) = 23/36$.
b. The probability that the game does not end on a roll is 13/36. So $P(\text{game ends on third roll}) = \frac{13}{36} \cdot \frac{13}{36} \cdot \frac{23}{36} \approx 8\%$.

38. a. $P(\sim G, G) = \frac{13}{15} \cdot \frac{2}{14} \approx 12\%$
b. $P(\sim G, \sim G, G) = \frac{13}{15} \cdot \frac{12}{14} \cdot \frac{2}{13} \approx 11\%$

39. a. $\frac{28}{40} \cdot \frac{28}{40} \cdot \frac{28}{40} \approx 34\%$ **b.** $\frac{28}{40} \cdot \frac{27}{39} \cdot \frac{26}{38} \approx 33\%$

40. a. eight **b.** two **c.** 46, because $8 \cdot 5 + 2 \cdot 3 = 46$
d. 4.60, because $46/10 = 4.6$
e. $e = 3 \cdot 0.20 + 5 \cdot 0.80 = 4.6$. The expected value is $4.60.
f. $4.60

41. $e = 2000 \cdot \frac{1}{8000} + 500 \cdot \frac{2}{8000} + 300 \cdot \frac{3}{8000} + 0 \cdot \frac{5994}{8000} = 0.4875$

The expected value is 48.75 cents. This means that, on average, each ticket is worth 48.75 cents in prizes.

42. a. $3.50 per roll
b. about 21 rolls ($73 \div 3.5 \approx 20.86$)

43. a. one marble **b.** four marbles
c.

Outcome	1	2	3	4
Probability	$\frac{2}{5}$	$\frac{6}{20}$	$\frac{12}{60}$	$\frac{6}{60}$

d. $e = 1 \cdot \frac{2}{5} + 2 \cdot \frac{6}{20} + 3 \cdot \frac{12}{60} + 4 \cdot \frac{6}{60} = 2$, so on average, two draws are required to select a yellow marble.

44. a. There are 11 ways A can occur and 14 ways $\sim A$ can occur, so the odds in favor of A are 11:14.
b. There are 15 ways B can occur and 10 ways $\sim B$ can occur, so the odds against B are 10:15, or 2:3.

45. a. 19:31, because 0.38:0.62 = 38:62 = 19:31
b. 18:7, because 0.72:0.28 = 72:28 = 18:7

46. a. $\bar{x} = 159$ **b.** $s = 21$ **c.** usual value
d. unusual value, since $159 + 2 \cdot 21 < 205$

47. If you take a random sample of many brand X boxes and then create a histogram for the data, you should expect to see a histogram that is symmetric with the shape of a bell.

48. It would reasonable to assume the life span of the trees is a variable that is approximately normally distributed.

49. Most data fall within 3 standard deviations of the mean, so you expect the minimum value to be $\bar{x} - 3s = 55 - 3 \cdot 8 = 31$ and the maximum value to be $\bar{x} + 3s = 55 + 3 \cdot 8 = 79$.

50. Draw the number line.

0.15% 2.35% 13.5% 34% 34% 13.5% 2.35% 0.15%

1226 1484 1742 2000 2258 2516 2774

a. about 81.5% **b.** about 84%
c. about 84% **d.** about 0.15%

51. $\bar{x} = 11.9$ g, $s = 1.1$ g

52. Compare their z-scores: for Laura, $(85 - 73)/8 = 1.5$, and for Charlie, $(70 - 62)/4 = 2$. Charlie scored relatively better.

53. Let the digits 0 and 1 each represent a parent who claimed lack of funding is the biggest problem in school. An experiment consists of picking five random digits, which represent five randomly selected parents. Repeat this experiment a large number n of times, and record the number of times f that you see exactly two of the digits 0 or 1 in the sequence of five digits. The quotient f/n is an estimate of the probability that two out of five randomly selected parents will say lack of funding is the biggest problem at their school. The table shows the results of the simulation. Based on the results, 3/20, or 15%, is an estimate of the probability that two out of five randomly selected parents will say lack of funding is the biggest problem at their school.

10480	15011
22368	46573
24130	48360
42167	93093
37570	39975
77921	**06907**
99562	72905
96301	91977
89579	14342
85475	36857

54. Let the digits 0, 1, 2, and 3 represent that a yellow marble was picked, and let the digits 4, 5, 6, 7, 8, and 9 represent that a blue marble was picked. An experiment consists of picking three random digits. If no 0s, 1s, 2s, or 3s appear, then we consider that to mean four draws were required to pick a yellow marble (because there are only three blue marbles). If a 0, 1, 2, or 3 appears, then we record the position of the first 0, 1, 2, or 3. For example, 503 would mean two draws were needed to get a yellow marble. Repeat this experiment a large number n of times, and average the n numbers. The table shows the results for 20 experiments. The average is $(1 + 1 + 2 + \ldots + 1 + 1)/20 = 46/20 = 2.3$. Based on these results, 2.3 draws are needed on average to get a yellow marble.

	Needed draws		Needed draws
104	1	150	1
223	1	465	4
241	1	483	3
421	2	930	3
375	3	399	1
779	4	069	1
995	4	729	2
963	3	919	2
895	4	143	1
854	4	368	1

CHAPTER 9 TEST

1. a. For Lennie, $P(E) = \dfrac{44}{95} \approx 46\%$.

    For Gina, $P(E) = \dfrac{155}{250} = 62\%$.

    For Taylor, $P(E) = \dfrac{270}{400} \approx 68\%$.

    b. The experimental probability by Taylor seems like the best estimate of the true probability, because of the larger number of repetitions.

    c. Combine the results:
    $$P(E) = \frac{44 + 155 + 270}{95 + 250 + 400} = \frac{469}{745} \approx 63\%.$$

2. a. The proportion of each color is predictable for a large number of repetitions of the experiment. For example, nearly $\frac{8}{15}$ of the marbles drawn should be yellow.

    b. The proportion of each color is not predictable for a few repetitions of the experiment.

3. a. For bag A, $P(\text{blue}) = 8/13 \approx 62\%$. For bag B, $P(\text{blue}) = 45/75 = 60\%$. You have a higher chance of drawing a blue marble from bag A.

    b. 70 times, because $0.28 \times 250 = 70$

4. Player A has 19 chances of winning, and there are 36 possible outcomes. So $P(\text{player A wins}) = 19/36$ and $P(\text{player B wins}) = 17/36$. So player A has the advantage in this game.

5. a. $P(K \text{ or } A) = \dfrac{8}{52} \approx 15\%$

    b. $P(B \text{ or } G) = \dfrac{8}{12} \approx 67\%$

6. a. $P(A) = \dfrac{8}{15} \approx 53\%$

    b. $P(A \mid B) = \dfrac{8}{14} \approx 57\%$

    c. A and B are dependent events, because $P(A) \neq P(A \mid B)$.

7. a. $P(B) = \dfrac{4}{52} = \dfrac{1}{13}$

    b. $P(B \mid A) = \dfrac{4}{52} = \dfrac{1}{13}$

    c. A and B are independent events, because $P(B) = P(B \mid A)$.

8. a. $P(A \text{ and } B) = P(A) \cdot P(B \mid A) = 0.43 \cdot 0.38 = 0.1634$

    b. $P(A \text{ and } B) = P(A) \cdot P(B \mid A) = 0.62 \cdot 0.25 = 0.155$. Then $P(A \text{ or } B) = P(A) + P(B) - P(A \text{ and } B) = 0.62 + 0.37 - 0.155 = 83.5\%$.

9. a. $\dfrac{9}{21}$, or about 43%   b. $\dfrac{13}{21}$, or about 62%

    c. $\dfrac{4}{13}$, or about 31%   d. $\dfrac{4}{9}$, or about 44%

    e. $\dfrac{9}{12}$, or 75%   f. $\dfrac{4}{21}$, or about 19%

    g. $\dfrac{18}{21}$, or about 86%

10. $P(\sim B, B) + P(B, B) = \dfrac{13}{25} \cdot \dfrac{12}{24} + \dfrac{12}{25} \cdot \dfrac{11}{24} = 48\%$

11. There are 13 ways to get a 3, 7, or 8. The probability of the game ending on a roll is 13/36. Neither player wins the first two rolls. So $P(\text{game ends on third roll}) = \dfrac{23}{36} \cdot \dfrac{23}{36} \cdot \dfrac{13}{36} \approx 14.7\%$.

12. a. $\dfrac{2}{9}$ b. $\dfrac{2}{5}$ c. $\dfrac{1}{7} \cdot \dfrac{3}{6} = \dfrac{1}{14}$ d. $\dfrac{3}{7} \cdot \dfrac{1}{5} = \dfrac{3}{35}$

13. a.

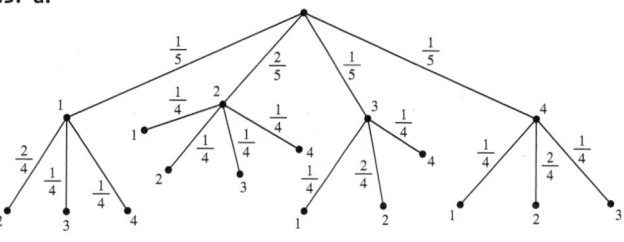

    b.

a	2	3	4	6	8	12
$P(a)$	$\dfrac{4}{20}$	$\dfrac{2}{20}$	$\dfrac{4}{20}$	$\dfrac{4}{20}$	$\dfrac{4}{20}$	$\dfrac{2}{20}$

14. a. $\dfrac{18}{25} \cdot \dfrac{7}{25} \approx 20\%$ b. $\dfrac{18}{25} \cdot \dfrac{18}{25} \cdot \dfrac{7}{25} \approx 15\%$

15. a. 34   b. 66   c. $34 \cdot 4 + 66 \cdot 7 = 598$

    d. 5.98 points, because $598/100 = 5.98$

    e. $e = 4 \cdot 0.34 + 7 \cdot 0.66 = 5.98$ points

16. a. $0.42{:}0.58 = 42{:}58 = 21{:}29$ (almost 2:3)

    b. $68{:}32 = 68{:}32 = 17{:}8$ (almost 2:1)

17. If you take a random sample of many females and measure their height and then create a histogram for the data, you should expect to see a histogram that is symmetric with the shape of a bell.

18. The measurements are normally distributed.

19. a. 81.5% **b.** 83.85% **c.** 16% **d.** 2.5%

20. We can expect 99.7% of the measurements to be within 3 standard deviations of the mean. Let's assume that $28 = \bar{x} - 3s$ and $44 = \bar{x} + 3s$. The mean is the center of the interval: $\bar{x} = (28 + 44)/2 = 36$. Then $28 = 36 - 3s$, so $s = (36 - 28)/3 = 2\frac{2}{3}$.

21. Let the eight digits 0, 1, 2, 3, 4, 5, 6, and 7 represent that the kids asked, "Are we there yet?" The digits 8 and 9 represent that the kids did not ask the question. An experiment consists of picking five random digits. Exactly three of the five digits must be from the list 0, 1, 2, ..., 7. Repeat this experiment a large number n of times, and record the frequency f of times exactly three of the five digits are from the list 0, 1, 2, ..., 7. Then the fraction f/n is an estimate of the probability that three out of five parents will say their kids ask them that question on a trip. Based on the results, our estimate is 4/20, or 20%.

10480	15011
22368	46573
24130	48360
42167	**93093**
37570	**39975**
77921	06907
99562	72905
96301	**91977**
89579	14342
85475	36857

CHAPTER 10

SECTION 10.1

1. Answers may vary (based on the diagram for this problem).
  a. Pick any three points in the plane. For example, pick *G*, *H*, and *K*.
  b. Pick *B* with any three other points in the plane. For example, pick *B*, *G*, *H*, and *K*.
  c. Pick *G*, *C*, and *K*.
  d. Answers vary, such as $\overleftrightarrow{GB}$.
  e. Pick any two points in the plane, because then the line through those two points must be contained in the plane. For example, pick $\overleftrightarrow{GC}$ or $\overleftrightarrow{AG}$ or $\overleftrightarrow{HA}$.

2. statements (b) and (c)

3. a. $\overline{AK}$ **b.** $\overrightarrow{QR}$
  c. $\angle ABC \cong \angle DEF$ or $m\angle ABC = m\angle DEF$
  d. $0° < m\angle ABC < 90°$
  e. *HQW* (the letters can be in any order)

4. a. $\overline{AB}$ is congruent to $\overline{CD}$, or the distance from *A* to *B* equals the distance from *C* to *D*.
  b. $\angle ABC$ is a right angle.
  c. $\angle A$ is congruent to $\angle B$.
  d. *Y* is between *X* and *Z*, or *X*, *Y*, and *Z* are collinear.

5. a. **b.** **c.** **d.**

6. a. **b.** **c.** **d.** **e.**

7. a. **b.** **c.** **d.**

8. a. **b.** **c.**

9. a. Answers vary. About three wedges fit into $\angle A$ and four wedges fit into $\angle B$.
  b. $m\angle A = 3$ wedges, and $m\angle B = 4$ wedges

10. $m\angle A = 120°$, and $m\angle B = 35°$

11. There are 56 ways to choose the first point, say, *A*. There are 55 ways to choose the second point, say, *B*.
  a. There are $56 \times 55 = 3080$ ways to name a line $\overleftrightarrow{AB}$ using the labeled points.
  b. The names $\overleftrightarrow{AB}$ and $\overleftrightarrow{BA}$ may be different names, but they are still the same line. So there are $(56 \times 55)/2 = 1540$ different lines using the labeled points.

12. $m\angle ABD = 40°$, $m\angle DBE = 65°$, and $m\angle EBC = 55°$

13. $GK + KH = 40 + 10 = 50$. You know $GH = 32$. Then $GK + KH \neq GH$, so *K* is not between *G* and *H*.

14. There are two possible answers based on the diagrams shown: $QK = 22$ cm and $QK = 38$ cm.

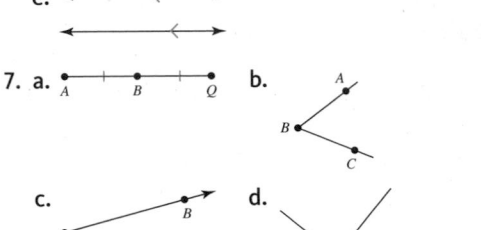

15. $AD = 4$ cm, based on the possible diagrams shown.

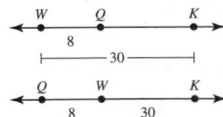

16. a. m∠CPD = 68°   **b.** m∠APC = 78°
c. m∠BPC = 30°

17. Both points lie in the plane. By Postulate 3, given two distinct points in a plane, the line containing the two points lies in the plane.

18. We can choose any point, say, *B*, on line *m* and any point, say, *C*, on line *n*. Then we have the three noncollinear points *A*, *B*, and *C*. By Postulate 2, given three noncollinear points, there is exactly one plane containing the three points. The plane contains *A* and *B*, so by Postulate 3 the plane contains line *m*. The plane contains *A* and *C*, so by Postulate 3, the plane contains line *n*. Therefore, the plane contains lines *m* and *n*.

19. statements (c), (d), and (e)

20. m∠ABC = 132°, m∠DBC = 75°, and m∠ABD = 132° − 75° = 57°.

21. a. two ways ($\overleftrightarrow{AB}$ and $\overleftrightarrow{BA}$)   **b.** 3 · 2 = 6 ways
c. 4 · 3 = 12 ways
d. n(n − 1) ways

22. a. 21.258 degrees   **b.** 30.681 degrees   **c.** 5.343 degrees

23. a.
b.
c.
d.

24. a.
b.
c.

25. A line has infinitely many closely spaced points.

26. collinear, noncollinear, coplanar, noncoplanar, and between

27. coplanar and noncoplanar

28. parallel, perpendicular, and intersecting

29. Answers vary.
a. string on a tennis racquet   **b.** pencil   **c.** taco
d. chair by a pool for relaxing in the Sun
e. door frame   **f.** railroad tracks

30. a. Neither parallel lines nor skew lines intersect.
b. Parallel lines are coplanar, but skew lines are not.

31. They each have a point that must belong in every possible name for the geometric object. For example, *B* belongs to every possible name for ∠ABC, and *D* belongs to every possible name for $\overrightarrow{DE}$.

32. Answers vary.

33. a. $\overleftrightarrow{AB}$ or $\overleftrightarrow{BA}$; order doesn't matter
b. $\overrightarrow{AB}$ or $\overrightarrow{BA}$; order doesn't matter
c. *ABC;* order doesn't matter; 6 orderings are possible

34. a. which point is the endpoint
b. that *A* and *B* are on different sides of the angle

35. a. two points   **b.** three points

36. a. three noncollinear points   **b.** four noncoplanar points

37. a. collinear points   **b.** coplanar points   **c.** parallel lines
d. transversal   **e.** one degree   **f.** between   **g.** postulates
h. protractor   **i.** acute angle   **j.** obtuse angle
k. perpendicular   **l.** openness

38. a. m∠DPE = 53°   **b.** m∠CPD = 29°
c. m∠BPC = 73°

39. a. m∠EBC = 60°   **b.** m∠ABD = 10°
c. m∠FBA = 70°

40. a. $\overrightarrow{OK}$ **b.** $\overline{HI}$ **c.** m ∥ y
d. m∠ABC = 90° or $\overleftrightarrow{AB}$ ⊥ $\overleftrightarrow{BC}$ **e.** m ⊥ y

41. a.

b. not possible, because the vertex of ∠ABC is *B*, not *C*
c.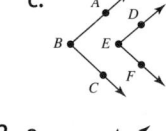

42. a.
b.

43. a. 2 · 3 = 6 regions   **b.** 2 · 4 = 8 regions
c. 2 · 23 = 46 regions

44. a.
b.
c.
d.

45. a. Draw all points on ray $\overrightarrow{AC}$ or $\overrightarrow{AD}$, except for *A*.

b. Draw all points on ray $\overrightarrow{CE}$ or $\overrightarrow{CF}$, except for C.

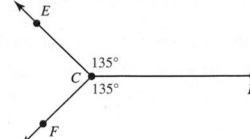

46. a. incorrect **b.** correct **c.** correct **d.** correct

47. P belongs to the interior of m$\angle ABC$, so m$\angle ABP$ + m$\angle PBC$ = m$\angle ABC$ by the angle addition postulate. The measure of each angle is positive, so m$\angle PBC <$ m$\angle ABC$.

48. m$\angle ABC$ is greater than 0° and less than 45°.

49. Answers vary. For example: The order of the letters does not matter. Each geometric object has infinitely many points.

50. 90 ÷ 18 = 5. The walls would form a right angle if the carpenter could squeeze exactly five wedges together.

51. a. 3 · 2 · 1 = 6 names **b.** 4 · 3 · 2 = 24 names
c. 5 · 4 · 3 = 60 names

52. a. 70° **b.** 122°

53. Answers vary. $\overleftrightarrow{EB}$, $\overleftrightarrow{DB}$, and $\overleftrightarrow{AC}$

54. a. 115 **b.** about 3.09 **c.** about 32 **d.** 5 **e.** about 68

55. 32 · 31 · 30 = 29,760 ways

SECTION 10.2

1. a. No, *ABCD* is not a valid name because the vertices must be written in a clockwise or counterclockwise order.
b. eight: *ABCD*, *BCDA*, *CDAB*, *DABC*, *ADCB*, *BADC*, *CBAD*, and *DCBA*.

2. Vertical angles formed by two intersecting lines must be congruent, and 40° ≠ 37°.

3. a. The possible points are indicated by the shaded region but are not on the dotted lines.

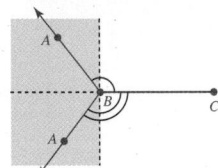

b. The possible points are indicated by the vertical line through *B* but do not include point *B*.

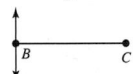

c. The possible points are indicated by the shaded region but are not on the dotted line.

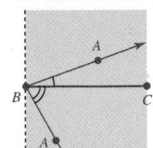

4. $\angle 1$ and $\angle 2$ are complementary angles.

5. Answers vary.

6. a. Draw two lines that intersect.

b. Draw two parallel lines.

7. Answers vary for all parts.

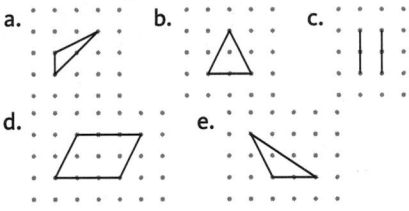

8. Answers vary. For example, use a circle.

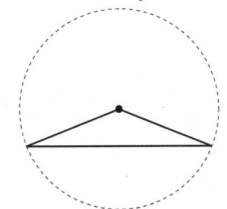

9. a. m$\angle 1$ = 145° **b.** m$\angle 2$ = 70°

10.

A □
B □□□ + 5 | 180
C □□□

m$\angle A$ = 25°, m$\angle B$ = 80°, and m$\angle C$ = 75°.

11. Solve the equation $n + (2n + 3) + (n + 5) = 180$. Then m$\angle B$ = 43°, m$\angle A$ = 89°, and m$\angle C$ = 48°.

12. Use the equations m$\angle T$ + m$\angle Q$ = 90° and $(2 \cdot$ m$\angle Q - 6°)$ + m$\angle Q$ = 90° to get m$\angle Q$ = 32° and m$\angle T$ = 58°.

13. Use the equations m$\angle A$ + m$\angle B$ = 180° and m$\angle A$ = 2m$\angle B - 6°$ to get m$\angle B$ = 62° and m$\angle A$ = 118°.

14. Let $\angle T$ and $\angle Q$ be the two supplementary angles. Then m$\angle T$ + m$\angle Q$ = 180°. Let $\angle Q$ be the smaller angle. Then $(3 \cdot$ m$\angle Q + 5)$ + m$\angle Q$ = 180°. Then m$\angle Q$ = 43.75° and m$\angle T$ = 136.25°.

15. $\triangle ABC$ is a right triangle, where $\angle A$ is the right angle. So m$\angle A$ + m$\angle B$ + $\angle C$ = 180°. Then 90° + m$\angle B$ + $\angle C$ = 180°. Then m$\angle B$ + $\angle C$ = 90°. So $\angle B$ and $\angle C$ are complementary angles.

16. a. false **b.** true **c.** false **d.** true **e.** true
f. true **g.** false **h.** false

17. a. m$\angle A$ + m$\angle B$ + m$\angle C$ + m$\angle D$ = 360°.
b. m$\angle A$ + m$\angle B$ = 180°.
c. m$\angle A$ = m$\angle EBC$. This implies that $\overleftrightarrow{AD} \parallel \overleftrightarrow{BC}$.
d. m$\angle B$ = m$\angle BCF$. This implies that $\overleftrightarrow{AB} \parallel \overleftrightarrow{CD}$.
e. Quadrilateral *ABCD* is a parallelogram.

18. a. We are given $\angle 5 \cong \angle 8$. $\angle 3$ and $\angle 8$ are vertical angles, so $\angle 3 \cong \angle 8$. Then $\angle 5 \cong \angle 3$. $\angle 5$ and $\angle 3$ are congruent corresponding angles, so lines m and n are parallel lines.

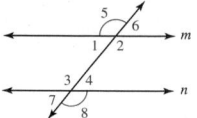

b. We are given $\angle 6 \cong \angle 7$. $\angle 4$ and $\angle 7$ are vertical angles, so $\angle 4 \cong \angle 7$. Then $\angle 6 \cong \angle 4$. $\angle 6$ and $\angle 4$ are congruent corresponding angles, so lines m and n are parallel lines.

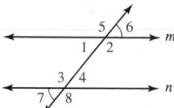

c. the two lines are parallel

19. m and n are parallel lines cut by a transversal, as shown.

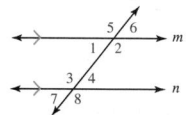

a. m and n are parallel lines cut by a transversal. Corresponding angles are congruent, so $\angle 5 \cong \angle 3$. $\angle 3$ and $\angle 8$ are vertical angles, so $\angle 3 \cong \angle 8$. Then $\angle 5 \cong \angle 8$, so $\angle 5$ and $\angle 8$ are congruent alternate exterior angles.

b. m and n are parallel lines cut by a transversal. Corresponding angles are congruent, so $\angle 6 \cong \angle 4$. $\angle 4$ and $\angle 7$ are vertical angles, so $\angle 4 \cong \angle 7$. Then $\angle 6 \cong \angle 7$, so $\angle 6$ and $\angle 7$ are congruent alternate exterior angles.

c. any two alternate exterior angles are congruent.

20. $145°$, $35°$, and $145°$ (in clockwise order)

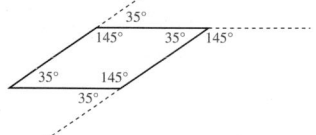

21.

Type of polygon	Angles	Sum of the interior angles for the polygon	Measure of each interior angle for a *regular* polygon
triangle	3	$180°$	$180°/3 = 60°$
quadrilateral	4	$2 \cdot 180° = 360°$	$360°/4 = 90°$
pentagon	5	$3 \cdot 180° = 540°$	$540°/5 = 108°$
hexagon	6	$4 \cdot 180° = 720°$	$720°/6 = 120°$
heptagon	7	$5 \cdot 180° = 900°$	$900°/7 \approx 128.6°$
n-gon	n	$(n-2) \cdot 180°$	$\dfrac{(n-2) \cdot 180°}{n}$

22. a. Drawing a picture could help.

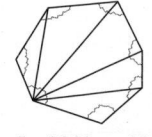

$5 \cdot 180° = 900°$

b. $900°/7 \approx 128.57°$ **c.** $180° - 128.57° \approx 51.43°$

23. a. $7 \cdot 180° = 1260°$ **b.** $1260°/9 = 140°$
c. $180° - 140° = 40°$

24. Draw a diagram of each polygon, draw the diagonals, and count them.

  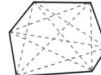

Sides (n)	Diagonals (d)
4	2
5	5
6	9
7	14
8	20

a. 9   **b.** 14   **c.** 20
d. $2 + 3 + 4 + 5 + 6 + 7 + 8 + 9 + 10 = 54$
e. Look at the sequence 2, 5, 9, 14, 20, ... How are n and d related? Look for a pattern.

Sides (n)	Diagonals (d)
4	2
5	$5 = 2 + 3$
6	$9 = 2 + 3 + 4$
7	$14 = 2 + 3 + 4 + 5$
8	$20 = 2 + 3 + 4 + 5 + 6$

The pattern is that each sum begins with 2 and ends with $n - 2$. Then the formula for the number of diagonals of a polygon with n sides is $d = 2 + 3 + 4 + \ldots + (n - 2)$, which equals $(n^2 - 3n)/2$.

25.

Number of lines	2	3	4	5	6	7	8
Maximum possible linear pairs	4	8	12	16	20	24	28

26. When $n = 5$, there are 16 regions.

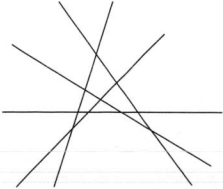

Use patterns ($1 + 1 = 2, 2 + 2 = 4, \ldots, 11 + 5 = 16, \ldots$) to complete the table.

Number of lines	1	2	3	4	5	6	7	8
Maximum regions	2	4	7	11	16	22	29	37

27. a. b.

c. d.

28. A diagonal of a polygon joins two nonadjacent vertices, but in a triangle every pair of vertices are adjacent.

29. There are two corresponding angles, with the measures 61° and 60°, created by the transversal that cuts the lines m and n. Thus, m and n cannot be parallel, because any pair of corresponding angles needs to be congruent.

30. The sum of the angles of any triangle equals 180°. An obtuse angle has a measure greater than 90°. In a triangle with two obtuse angles, the sum of the three angles would be more than 180°; this is impossible, because the sum of the three angles must be exactly 180°. So a triangle cannot have two obtuse angles.

31. a. scalene **b.** complementary **c.** obtuse **d.** 360°
e. nonagon **f.** polygon **g.** corresponding
h. supplementary **i.** alternate **j.** isosceles

32. yes

33. a. b.

c. d.

34. $m\angle A = m\angle D$ and $m\angle B = m\angle E$. The sum of the measure of angles in a triangle equals 180°. So

$$180° = m\angle A + m\angle B + m\angle C$$
$$180° = m\angle D + m\angle E + m\angle F$$
$$m\angle A + m\angle B + m\angle C = m\angle D + m\angle E + m\angle F$$
$$m\angle A + m\angle B + m\angle C = m\angle A + m\angle B + m\angle F$$
$$m\angle C = m\angle F$$

This means $\angle C \cong \angle F$.

35. a. adjacent and complementary angles **b.** vertical angles
c. adjacent and supplementary angles **d.** adjacent angles
e. vertical angles and supplementary angles
f. complementary angles

36. Using a protractor, we get 60° for each angle. The conjecture is that the interior angles of an equilateral triangle are each 60°.

37. Lines m and n are parallel.

38. The markings indicate lines m and n are parallel. $m\angle 1 = 122°$ and $m\angle 2 = 120°$. Then lines m and n have a pair of corresponding angles that are not congruent. This means lines m and n are not parallel, which violates our assumption that they are parallel. So the diagram is impossible.

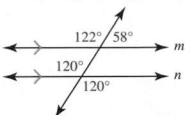

39. a. We are given $m\angle 5 = m\angle 8$. $m\angle 5 = m\angle 2$ and $m\angle 8 = m\angle 3$, because vertical angles are congruent. Then $m\angle 2 = m\angle 3$ because of the substitution property of equality.
b. $m\angle 5 = m\angle 8$ (given) and $m\angle 5 = m\angle 2$ (because vertical angles are congruent). Then $m\angle 2 = m\angle 8$. $\angle 2$ and $\angle 8$ are congruent and corresponding angles, so the lines cut by the transversal are parallel.

40. a. $\angle 1$ and $\angle 3$ **b.** the lines are parallel
c. $\angle 4$ and $\angle 2$ are supplementary angles, as given. $\angle 4$ and $\angle 8$ are also supplementary. So the corresponding angles $\angle 8$ and $\angle 2$ are congruent. Thus, the two lines cut by the transversal are parallel.

41. a. false **b.** true **c.** false **d.** false **e.** true
f. false **g.** false **h.** false **i.** false

42.

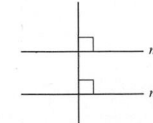

43. First, we extend line segments $\overline{AB}$ and $\overline{CD}$. The two adjacent angles with the common vertex B form a linear pair, so we have two adjacent angles with the measures 110° and 70°. Then we see lines $\overleftrightarrow{AD}$ and $\overleftrightarrow{BC}$ cut by transversal $\overleftrightarrow{AB}$ have a pair of congruent corresponding angles, so $\overleftrightarrow{AD}$ and $\overleftrightarrow{BC}$ are parallel lines. So $\overline{AD}$ and $\overline{BC}$ are parallel sides.

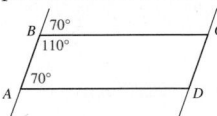

Next, we extend sides $\overline{AD}$ and $\overline{BC}$. The two adjacent angles with the common vertex C also form a linear pair, so we have two adjacent angles with the measures 110° and 70°. Lines $\overleftrightarrow{AB}$ and $\overleftrightarrow{CD}$ cut by the transversal $\overleftrightarrow{BC}$ have a pair of congruent corresponding angles, so $\overleftrightarrow{AB}$ and $\overleftrightarrow{CD}$ are parallel lines. So $\overline{AB}$ and $\overline{CD}$ are parallel sides.

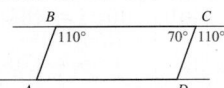

The opposite sides of the quadrilateral $ABCD$ are parallel, so $ABCD$ is a parallelogram.

44. Line k creates a pair of corresponding angles that are congruent, so lines m and n are parallel.

45. Lines *m* and *n* are parallel. Therefore, when they are cut by a transversal *k,* their corresponding angles are congruent. One corresponding angle is 90°, so the other corresponding angle is 90° too. Thus, lines *n* and *k* are also perpendicular.

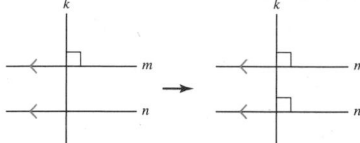

46. *C* must be the right angle. Then solve the equation $3 \cdot m\angle B - 10 + m\angle B = 90$ to get $m\angle A = 65°$ and $m\angle B = 25°$.

47. The bases are $\overline{AD}$ and $\overline{BC}$. The legs are $\overline{AB}$ and $\overline{CD}$.

48. First, we extend line segments $\overline{AB}$ and $\overline{CD}$ as shown. $\angle 2$ and $\angle 5$ are supplementary angles and $\angle 2$ is a right angle, so $\angle 5$ is a right angle. Similarly, $\angle 6$ is a right angle. $\angle 5$ and $\angle 1$ are congruent and corresponding angles formed by the transversal $\overleftrightarrow{AB}$ that cuts $\overleftrightarrow{AD}$ and $\overleftrightarrow{BC}$. Then $\overleftrightarrow{AD}$ and $\overleftrightarrow{BC}$ are parallel. $\angle 6$ and $\angle 2$ are congruent and alternate interior angles formed by the transversal $\overleftrightarrow{BC}$ that cuts $\overleftrightarrow{AB}$ and $\overleftrightarrow{CD}$. Then $\overleftrightarrow{AB}$ and $\overleftrightarrow{CD}$ are parallel. Then opposite sides of rectangle *ABCD* are parallel. So the rectangle *ABCD* is a parallelogram.

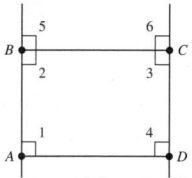

49. $m\angle D = 60°$

50. $m\angle 1 = 144°$

51. **a.** The side opposite the largest interior angle is the longest side.
    b. The side opposite the smallest interior angle is the shortest side.

52. **a.** $\angle 7$ and $\angle 6$, $\angle 4$ and $\angle 6$, $\angle 1$ and $\angle 6$
    b. $\angle 1$ and $\angle 2$, $\angle 4$ and $\angle 2$, $\angle 7$ and $\angle 2$, $\angle 1$ and $\angle 3$, $\angle 4$ and $\angle 3$, $\angle 7$ and $\angle 3$, $\angle 8$ and $\angle 9$, $\angle 5$ and $\angle 8$, $\angle 5$ and $\angle 9$
    c. $\angle 2$ and $\angle 3$, $\angle 8$ and $\angle 5$, $\angle 7$ and $\angle 4$
    d. $\angle 9, \angle 8, \angle 5$ **e.** $\angle 2, \angle 3$ **f.** $\angle 1, \angle 4, \angle 6, \angle 7$
    g. none **h.** $\angle 9$ and $\angle 5$, $\angle 1$ and $\angle 7$
    i. $\angle 1$ and $\angle 4$, $\angle 9$ and $\angle 8$

53. $n = 80°$

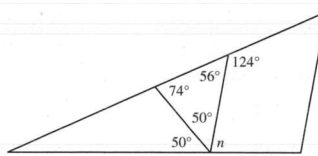

54. **a.** about 154.3° **b.** about 25.7°

55. **a.** 168.75° **b.** 11.25°

56. Solving the equation $\dfrac{(n - 2) \cdot 180}{n} = 165.6$, we get $n = 25$.

So the polygon has 25 sides.

57. $180° - 8° = 172°$. Solving the equation $\dfrac{(n - 2) \cdot 180}{n} = 172$, we get $n = 45$. So the polygon has 45 sides.

58. 80

59. 40

60. (a) obtuse angle

61. (b) They are on the same side of the transversal.

62. (d) $\angle A \cong \angle B$

63. (c) sides

SECTION 10.3

1. **a.** *ABEG* and *FCDH* **b.** *GHIJKL* and *ABCDEF*

2. **a.** *A, B, C, D, E,* and *F* **b.** *D*
   c. *CBEF, ABED,* and *ACFD* **d.** *ABED* and *ACFD*
   e. $\overline{AB}, \overline{AC}, \overline{BC}, \overline{DE}, \overline{DF}, \overline{EF}, \overline{CF}, \overline{AD},$ and $\overline{BE}$
   f. $\overline{AD}, \overline{DE},$ and $\overline{DF}$ **g.** $\triangle ABC$ and $\triangle DEF$
   h. right triangular prism

3. The lateral faces are rectangles.

4. **a.** The bases are regular polygons.
   b. The lateral faces are rectangles.

5. **a.** 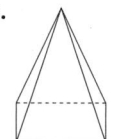 **b.**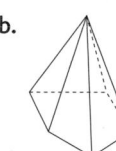

6. **a.** The lateral faces are isosceles triangles.
   b. The bases are regular polygons.

7. **a.** The lateral faces are not isosceles triangles.
   b. The base is not a regular polygon.

8. **a.** **b.**

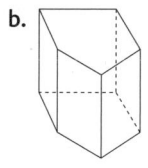

9. **a.** *A, B, C, D, E,* and *F* **b.** *C*
   c. $\triangle ABF, \triangle BCF, \triangle CDF, \triangle DEF,$ and $\triangle AEF$
   d. $\triangle BCF$ and $\triangle FCD$
   e. $\overline{AB}, \overline{BC}, \overline{CD}, \overline{DE}, \overline{AE}, \overline{AF}, \overline{BF}, \overline{CF}, \overline{DF},$ and $\overline{EF}$
   f. $\overline{BC}, \overline{CD},$ and $\overline{FC}$ **g.** regular pentagon *ABCDE*
   h. oblique pentagonal pyramid

10. **a.** regular hexagonal prism **b.** regular hexagonal pyramid

11. Kendra is correct; the name of a regular polyhedron refers to the number of faces. The regular tetrahedron has four vertices and four faces, so it appears Kendra and Daniel could both be correct. However, the regular hexahedron has six faces but not six vertices. So Kendra is correct, and Daniel is incorrect.

12. a.

Type of pyramid	F	V	F + V	E
triangular	4	4	8	6
square	5	5	10	8
pentagonal	6	6	12	10
hexagonal	7	7	14	12

b. $F + V = E + 2$

13. a.

Type of prism	F	V	F + V	E
triangular	5	6	11	9
square	6	8	14	12
pentagonal	7	10	17	15
hexagonal	8	12	20	18

b. $F + V = E + 2$

14. a. The cone is not a polyhedron.
b. The prism has two bases, or the prism does not have an apex.

15. a. The cone has one base, or the cone has an apex.
b. The prism is the only polyhedron.

16. There is at least one lateral face that is not an isosceles or equilateral triangle.

17. Each base is a regular polygon, or the lateral faces for each solid are congruent.

18. Their faces are equilateral triangles.

19. sides, faces

20. a.

n	V	E	F
3	6	9	5
4	8	12	6
5	10	15	7

b. $E = 3n$
c. yes, because the solution to $3n = 456$ is a whole number (the base has 152 sides)
d. no, because the solution to the equation $3n = 314$ is not a whole number
e. $V = 2n$
f. no, because the solution to $2n = 217$ is not a whole number
g. yes, because the solution to $2n = 826$ is a whole number (the base has 413 sides)
h. $F = n + 2$ **i.** yes, because its base has 417 sides
j. yes, because its base has 626 sides
k. 452 vertices **l.** 1113 edges

21. a.

n	V	E	F
3	4	6	4
4	5	8	5
5	6	10	6

b. $E = 2n$
c. yes, because the solution to $2n = 456$ is a whole number (its base has 228 sides)
d. no, because the solution to $2n = 777$ is not a whole number
e. $V = n + 1$ **f.** yes, because its base has 200 sides
g. yes, because its base has 825 sides **h.** $F = n + 1$
i. yes, because its base has 418 sides
j. yes, because its base has 627 sides
k. 340 vertices **l.** 1482 edges

22. a. 27 lateral faces, because $28 - 1 = 27$
b. 804 edges, because $2(403 - 1) = 804$

23. a. pyramid **b.** prism **c.** neither

24. a. a polygon such that all sides are congruent
b. a polyhedron such that all faces are congruent and all vertices are formed by the intersection of the same number of faces

25. a. Each face of a die has the same chance of occurring.
b. Suppose each face on the die has a different symbol or outcome. Then a hexagonal die provides more variety than a tetrahedron.

26. a. edge **b.** vertex

27. a. edge **b.** vertex

28. Prisms and cylinders each have two congruent bases.

29. Pyramids and cones each have one base and one apex.

30. a. They are congruent polygons.
b. Faces of a regular prism are congruent rectangles, and faces of a regular pyramid are congruent isosceles or equilateral triangles.

31. The surface of a sphere does not consist of polygonal regions.

32. The surface of a cylinder does not consist of polygonal regions.

33. a. edges **b.** faces **c.** cone **d.** base **e.** right
f. triangles **g.** apex **h.** oblique pyramid
i. regular pyramid **j.** cylinder **k.** oblique **l.** net

34. a. a simple closed polygonal curve
b. a simple closed surface that consists of polygonal regions

35. a. n lateral faces **b.** $n + 1$ faces

36. a. n lateral faces **b.** $n + 2$ faces

37. a. rectangle or parallelogram, but at least one lateral face is a parallelogram without any right angles
b. rectangle

38. a. triangle, where at least one lateral face is neither an isosceles triangle nor an equilateral triangle
b. congruent isosceles or congruent equilateral triangle

39. The lateral faces of a prism must all be in the shape of a parallelogram, but the polygon GHIJKL is not a parallelogram. So faces ABHG and EDJK cannot be the bases.

40. a. polygon
b. 128.57°, because $(7 - 2) \cdot 180°/7 \approx 128.57°$
c. three **d.** $\approx 385.71°$, because $3 \cdot 128.57 = 385.71$
e. less

41. It is made up of two different regular polygons: regular pentagons and regular hexagons.

42. a. right prism **b.** regular pyramid

43. a. prism **b.** pyramid

44. Yes, both students could be correct. Suppose the polyhedron is a pentagonal pyramid, as Ken exclaimed. This means there are five lateral faces and one base, so there are six faces altogether. So it could also be a hexahedron.

45. A pyramid has at most one nontriangular face. *ABCD* and *CDEF* are nontriangular faces; they are quadrilaterals. So the polyhedron has at least two nontriangular faces.

46. All the lateral faces of a prism are all parallelograms, which each have four vertices.

47. In a pyramid, any two faces share a common vertex. $\triangle ABC$ and $\triangle DEF$ do not have any common points.

48. The base is a polygon, and the lateral faces are triangles.

49. a. three **b.** three **c.** four **d.** three **e.** five

50. (c) three

51. (b) heptahedron

52. (a) pentahedron

53. (c) 8

54. (e) a number not listed here

55. (c) 201

REVIEW QUESTIONS

1. a. $\overline{XY} \cong \overline{DE}$ **b.** $\overleftrightarrow{RT} \parallel \overleftrightarrow{UV}$ **c.** $\angle A \cong \angle X$

2. a. point relationship **b.** line relationship
c. line relationship **d.** line relationship **e.** both
f. point relationship **g.** line relationship

3. a. coplanar **b.** noncollinear
c. noncoplanar **d.** collinear

4. a. coplanar or concurrent **b.** parallel **c.** perpendicular

5. a. obtuse **b.** right **c.** acute **d.** straight **e.** reflex

6. a. acute **b.** straight **c.** reflex **d.** obtuse **e.** right

7. a.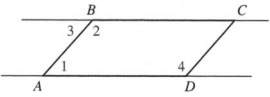
$180° - 12° = 168°$, and $168°/4 = 42°$. Then $m\angle B = 42°$, and $m\angle A = 3 \cdot m\angle B + 12° = 3 \cdot 42° + 12° = 138°$.
b. Solving the equation $m\angle B + (3 \cdot m\angle B + 12°) = 180°$, we get $m\angle B = 42°$ and $m\angle A = 3 \cdot m\angle B + 12° = 3 \cdot 42° + 12° = 138°$.

8. Solving the equation $m\angle B + (4 \cdot m\angle B - 8°) = 202°$, we get $m\angle B = 42°$ and $m\angle A = 4 \cdot 42° - 8° = 160°$.

9. $m\angle ABC = 58°$ and $m\angle DBA = 97°$.

10. a. $m\angle DPE = 28°$ **b.** $m\angle BPC = 35°$

11. $m\angle ABD = 20°$ and $m\angle FBA = 80°$

12. a. corresponding angles **b.** alternate interior angles
c. vertical angles **d.** supplementary angles
e. complementary angles **f.** alternate exterior angles

13. $m\angle CFD = 105°$

14. Vertical angles formed by two intersecting lines are always congruent. But in this diagram, the vertical angles are not congruent ($25° \neq 30°$), so the diagram is impossible.

15. $m\angle Q = 16°$ and $m\angle T = 74°$ by using the equations $m\angle Q + m\angle T = 90°$ and $m\angle T = 5 \cdot m\angle Q - 6°$.

16. Solve the equations $s + 1 = 180$ and $l = 2s + 2l$, where s is the measure of the smaller angle and l is the measure of the larger angle. The angles are $53°$ and $127°$, so the larger angle is $127°$.

17. a. yes, because corresponding angles are congruent
b. yes, because the corresponding angles are congruent
c. no, because the corresponding interior angles are not congruent

18. $m\angle CAB = 40°$, because vertical angles are congruent. Then $m\angle CAB = m\angle EBF$. The transversal that cuts lines $\overleftrightarrow{AC}$ and $\overleftrightarrow{DB}$ creates a pair of congruent corresponding angles, so lines $\overleftrightarrow{AC}$ and $\overleftrightarrow{DB}$ must be parallel.

19. a. Extend lines $\overline{AD}$ and $\overline{BC}$.

$\angle 1$ and $\angle 3$ are congruent alternate interior angles. So $m\angle 1 = m\angle 3$. $\angle 2$ and $\angle 3$ are supplementary, so $m\angle 2 + m\angle 3 = 180°$. Then $m\angle 2 + m\angle 1 = 180°$, because $m\angle 1 = m\angle 3$. So $\angle A$ and $\angle B$ are supplementary angles.
b. The same reasoning in part (a) can be applied to prove that $\angle A$ and $\angle D$ are supplementary angles. Then $\angle B$ and $\angle D$ are both supplementary angles of $\angle A$. Then $\angle B \cong \angle D$.

20. a. obtuse triangle, scalene triangle
b. acute triangle, isosceles triangle
c. acute triangle, equilateral triangle
d. acute triangle, scalene triangle
e. right triangle, isosceles triangle
f. right triangle, scalene triangle
g. obtuse triangle, isosceles triangle

21. Answers vary for all parts.

a. 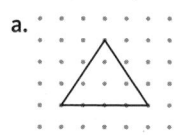 **b.** 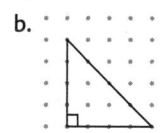 **c.**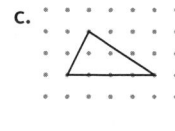

22. $m\angle 1 = 145°$

23. $\angle B$ and $\angle C$ are complementary angles.

24. $m\angle 1 = 69°$

25. a. $38 \cdot 180° = 6840°$ **b.** $6840° / 40 = 171°$

26. a. $1080°$ **b.** $2700°$ **c.** $720°$ **d.** $1800°$

27. Solve the equation $\dfrac{(n - 2) \cdot 180}{n} = 162$ to get $n = 20$. The regular polygon has 20 sides.

28. a. side **b.** vertex **c.** diagonal **d.** interior angle
e. exterior angle **f.** interior

29. a. quadrilateral **b.** parallelogram
c. rectangle, or rhombus **d.** square
e. rhombus, or rectangle **f.** kite, or trapezoid
g. trapezoid, or kite

30. Answers vary for all parts.

a. 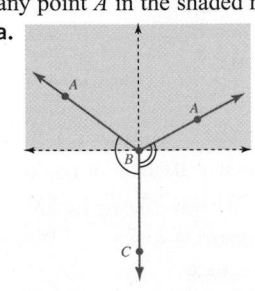   b. 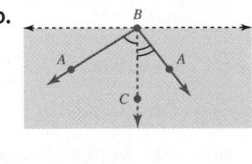   c.

31. a. It is not a closed curve.   **b.** It is not simple.
   c. It is not closed, or it is not a polygonal curve.

32. a. base   **b.** lateral face   **c.** vertex   **d.** edge

33. a. base   **b.** lateral face   **c.** vertex   **d.** edge   **e.** apex

34. a. pentagonal pyramid   **b.** regular octagonal pyramid
   c. oblique heptagonal pyramid

35. a. The base is not a regular polygon.
   b. The lateral faces are not all the same size and shape.

36. a. pentagonal prism   **b.** regular pentagonal prism
   c. regular octagonal prism

37. a. $F = n + 2$ **b.** $E = 3n$ **c.** $V = 2n$

38. a. seven faces   **b.** 15 edges   **c.** 10 vertices

39. a. $F = n + 1$ **b.** $E = 2n$ **c.** $V = n + 1$

40. a. seven faces   **b.** 12 edges   **c.** seven vertices

41. a. a polygon with n congruent sides and n congruent angles
   b. infinitely many
   c. a polyhedron such that its faces are congruent regular
   polygonal regions and each of its vertices is formed by the
   intersection of the same number of faces
   d. five

42. a. oblique cone   **b.** right cone
   c. right cylinder   **d.** oblique cylinder

43. cone

44. cylinder

45. The edges of the rectangle adjacent to each circle are smaller
   than the circumference of the circles.

46. $\overline{AH}$ and $\overline{AE}$ are common sides of two adjacent faces, so
   $AH = AE$.

47. a. (vi) sphere   **b.** (i) rectangular prism
   c. (ii) triangular prism   **d.** (vii) cylinder
   e. (ii) triangular prism   **f.** (iii) cube   **g.** (vii) cylinder
   h. (xii) semi-cylinder   **i.** (iv) pentagonal prism
   j. (ix) square pyramid   **k.** (x) hemisphere   **l.** (viii) cone

CHAPTER 10 TEST

1. a. $5 \cdot 4 = 20$ names   **b.** $5 \cdot 4 \cdot 3 = 60$ names

2. a. The ordering of the letters does not matter.
   b. Each name for the geometric object has a unique letter
   (the endpoint of the ray and the vertex of the angle).

3. any point A in the shaded region (but not on the dashed rays)

4. a. 24 ways
   b. 10 ways
   c. 6 ways

5. The sum of the measures of the two angles in the triangle
   equals the measure of the nonadjacent exterior angle.

6. a. (v) They are complementary angles.
   b. (ii) They are on the same side of the transversal.
   c. (iv) If two lines are cut by a transversal, then corresponding angles must be congruent.

7. $m\angle 1 = 34°$, $m\angle 2 = 56°$, and $m\angle 3 = 70°$

8. a. $m\angle DPE = 24°$ **b.** $m\angle CPD = 54°$
   c. $m\angle BPC = 56°$

9. $m\angle A = 46°$ and $m\angle B = 134°$

10. Yes; lines m and n are not parallel, because they have a pair
   of corresponding angles that are not congruent. Thus, lines
   m and n are not parallel but they are coplanar, so they must
   intersect.

11. Lines m and n are parallel, so any pair of corresponding
   angles must be congruent. $\angle 1$ and $\angle 2$ are corresponding
   angles, but $m\angle 1 \neq m\angle 2$, because $m\angle 1 = 110°$ and
   $m\angle 2 = 115°$.

12. $m\angle 1 = 165°$

13. $\angle A$ and $\angle B$ are complementary angles.

14. a. $n = 16$. Each interior angle has the measure $157.5°$, and
   each exterior angle has the measure $22.5°$.
   b. $n = 13$, so the sum is $1980°$.

15. $11 \cdot 360° - 9 \cdot 180° = 2340°$

16. Solve $\dfrac{(n - 2) \cdot 180}{n} = 165$ to get $n = 24$. The regular
   polygon has 24 sides.

17. a. (i) side, (ii) vertex, and (iii) interior angle
   b. 35 and 51 (look for a pattern: $1 + 4 = 5$, $5 + 7 = 12$,
   $12 + 10 = 22$, $22 + 13 = 35$, and $35 + 16 = 51$)

18. a. n **b.** $2n$

19. Answers vary.

20. a. regular pentagonal prism   **b.** pentagonal pyramid
   c. right cylinder   **d.** regular octagonal pyramid
   e. oblique hexagonal prism   **f.** oblique cone

21. a. 49 faces   **b.** 141 edges   **c.** 94 vertices

22. 18 faces, because $48 \div 3 + 2 = 18$

23. a. eight faces   **b.** 14 edges   **c.** eight vertices

24. 30 vertices

CHAPTER 11

SECTION 11.1

1. a. 1/3 in   **b.** 1/5 m

2. a.

Ruler	Precision
A	1 in
B	1/3 in
C	1/4 in

b.

Ruler	Length of line segment
A	2 in
B	$1\frac{2}{3}$ in
C	$1\frac{2}{4}$ in

   c. Ruler B; the endpoint of the line segment is closer to a tick mark on ruler B, so the rounding error is smaller.

   d. No; ruler C has higher precision than ruler B, but ruler B provides a more accurate measurement than ruler C. So a higher precision ruler does not always lead to a more accurate measurement. However, in general, you should choose a ruler with higher precision.

3. a. The precision is 1/4 inch.

   b. Answers vary. Here are two possible line segments with a length of 1.75 inches.

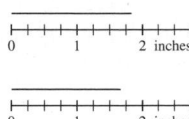

4. The line segment has a length of 4 zippos. Split the line segment into four equal-sized parts to get a line segment with a length of 1 zippo.

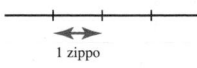

5. a. kilowatt   b. millijoule   c. joules per second

   d. nanometer   e. second   f. megavolt

6. GPE = 1/2 of the precision

	Precision	GPE
a. 14.32 lb	0.01 lb	0.005 lb
b. 37.8 m	0.1 m	0.05 m
c. 57.623 mi	0.001 mi	0.0005 mi
d. 40 cm	1 cm	0.5 cm

7. a. 7.20   b. $\approx$1.76   c. 0.75   d. $\approx$6.38

8. a. how many units of measurement

   b. the measurement unit

9. a. . ⊢——⊣ . . . .

   b. . ⊢——⊣ . . . . .

   c. . ⊢—⊣ . . . . . .

   d. The size of the measurement unit decreases as the number of units in the length increases.

10. Answers vary.

   a. The tenths and hundredths digits of correct answers are 00, 25, 50, or 75, such as 3.50 and 2.00 m.

   b. The tenths and hundredths digits of incorrect answers cannot be 00, 25, 50, or 75, such as 3.54 and 2.06 m.

11. The precision is 0.1 pound, so the GPE is $(1/2)(0.1) = 0.05$. So $3.2 - 0.05 = 3.15$, and $3.2 + 0.05 = 3.25$. The true weight is between 3.15 and 3.25 pounds.

12. a. $6\frac{3}{52}$ blips   b. the blip

13. Partition the line segment into five equal-sized parts to help locate 1 zippo.

⊢+++++++++⊣
    1   2

14. a. mean $= \dfrac{14.3 + 14.2 + 14.7}{3} = 14.4$ cm

   b. The mean measurement could be the most accurate, because the positive errors in the measurements may cancel some of the negative errors in the measurement. The absolute value of the errors are as follows:

$$|14.3 - 14.5| = 0.2$$
$$|14.2 - 14.5| = 0.3$$
$$|14.7 - 14.5| = 0.2$$
$$|14.4 - 14.5| = 0.1$$

In this example, the mean measurement, 14.4 cm, is the most accurate.

15. a. 201 in   b. 68 in   c. 4500 lb

16. The GPE is half the precision.

17. shortest height = 5 ft 8.5 in, tallest height = 5 ft 9.5 in

18. a. $\dfrac{285}{n} = \dfrac{3}{1}$, so $n = 95$ yd

   b. $\dfrac{3.4}{n} = \dfrac{1}{5,280}$, so $n = 17,952$ ft

   c. $\dfrac{7}{n} = \dfrac{1}{12}$, so $n = 84$ in

   d. $\dfrac{45}{n} = \dfrac{1}{10}$, so $n = 450$ mm

19. a. $\approx$113.33   b. 13,200   c. 5   d. $\approx$1.36

20. $\approx$1215.40 mi

21. a. A kilometer is 1000 meters.

   b. A millisecond is one thousandth of a second.

22. Answers vary, such as the area of the deck or the cruising speed.

23. $1\frac{1}{6}$ blips

24. a. 983,571,056.4 ft/s

   b. $5.874601673 \times 10^{12}$ mi/yr

25. a. a quantitative comparison of an attribute of an object to the chosen measurement unit

   b. a collection of units of measurement and rules for relating the various units

26. U.S. customary system and metric system

27. to make trade easier, to accurately compare items for sales, to make sharing scientific information easier, and to reduce fraud and confusion

28. The kilogram is the only unit of measurement in the metric system that has a prefix (*kilo-*) and that is based on a proto-type (a metal alloy in the shape of a cylinder) rather than sci-entific measurements (such as the length of 1 m).

29. millimeter, because centimeters and meters are both much larger than the average ant

30. Answers vary.
    a. weight, height, length   **b.** length, width, height, volume
    c. weight, width, amount

31. Use dimensional analysis, because it tells what and when to multiply and divide.

32. You can use iteration. Be sure to keep track of the endpoint of the yardstick, marking it with a pencil or in some other way.

33. Answers vary. See Problem 7 for an example of a possible answer.

34. **a.** attribute   **b.** iteration   **c.** precision   **d.** accuracy
    e. expect   **f.** 2.54   **g.** GPE   **h.** measurement system
    i. prefix   **j.** dimensional analysis   **k.** gram

35. 14.625 and 14.875 cm

36. **a.** 0 mi   **b.** 0 ft   **c.** 2 in   **d.** 62 mm

37. nearest hundredth: **a.** 2.67   **b.** 0.35   **c.** 2.65   **d.** 0.18

38. **a.** $\frac{n}{35} = \frac{1}{3}$, so $n = 35 \times \frac{1}{3} = 11\frac{2}{3}$ yd

    b. $\frac{n}{60} = \frac{12}{1}$, so $n = 60 \times 12 = 720$ in

    c. $\frac{n}{28} = \frac{2.54}{1}$, so $n = 28 \times \frac{2.54}{1} = 71.12$ in

    d. $\frac{n}{420} = \frac{1}{1000}$, so $n = 420 \times \frac{1}{1000} = 0.42$ km

39. **a.**
    km hm dam m dm cm mm
    1 km = 1000 m

    b.
    km hm dam m dm cm mm
    1 m = 0.001 km

    c.
    km hm dam m dm cm mm
    7.8 hm = 7800 dm

    d.
    km hm dam m dm cm mm
    81.3 cm = 0.00813 hm

40. **a.** 185 yups and 5 peps   **b.** 311 yups and 6 peps

41. **a.** about 1 m   **b.** about 2 m   **c.** about 5 m

42. **a.** 0.01 lb   **b.** 1.715 and 1.725 lb

43. **a.** precision = 100 m, GPE = 50 m
    b. precision = 1 m, GPE = 0.5 m

44. **a.** precision = $\frac{1}{2}$ bar, GPE = $\frac{1}{4}$ bar
    b. precision = 5 km per hour, GPE = 2.5 km per hour

45. **a.** 1908   **b.** 35,904   **c.** 12.192   **d.** ≈752.73

46. **a.** (ii) 1.97 inches, because 2.54 cm equals 1 inch
    b. (iii) 4048 yd, because 2.3 miles and 1760 yards are the greatest distances
    c. (i) 3 m, because 1 m is about 3 feet

47. **a.** d   **b.** h   **c.** min   **d.** sec or s

48. ≈23.9

49. Answers vary. See Example 11.9.

50. The length is not determined by the right endpoint of the line segment, because that would suggest the length depends on where you place the line segment. The length is *l* cm, and it solves the equation $0.5 + l = 2$. Then $l = 2 - 0.5 = 1.5$. The length is 1.5 cm.

51. **a.** Measure the fish from the tip of the nose to the longest part of the tail.
    b. Measure the fish from the tip of the nose to the shortest part of the tail.

52. 11 by 16 mm

53. **a.** The precision is $\frac{1}{7}$ unit.
    b.
    0   1   2

54. **a.** 12 paper clips   **b.** 6 large paper clips
    c. The small paper clip involves more repetitions because it covers less length.
    d. The smaller the unit, the higher the number of repetitions.

55. **a.** precision = 10°C, GPE = 5°C
    b. precision = 2 units, GPE = 1 unit

56. **a.** $2\frac{7}{8}$ units   **b.** $2\frac{14}{16}$ units   **c.** 7.2 units

57. 3.5 cm and 7.25 cm

58.

	Precision	GPE
a. 62.04 lb	0.01 lb	0.005 lb
b. 41.52 cm	0.01 cm	0.005 cm
c. 17.567 mi	0.001 mi	0.0005 mi

59. **a.** 125.98   **b.** 9.14   **c.** 3.28   **d.** 1798.32   **b. e.** 0.91
    f. 2286.00

SECTION 11.2

1. **a.** ▱   **b.** ▯   **c.** ▯
   d. The size of the measurement unit decreases as the number of measurement units increases.

2. **a.** The perimeter is 10 cm. The area is 4 cm².
   b. Answers vary, but the perimeter remains 10 cm as the area increases to 5 cm².

   c. no

3. a.

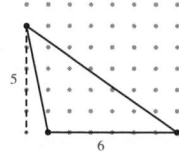

b.

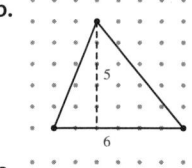

c.

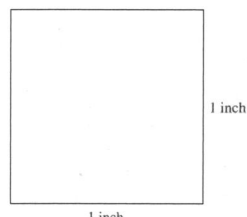

4. a. Draw a square so that the length of each side is exactly 1 inch.

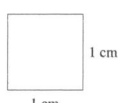

b. Draw a square so that the length of each side is exactly 1 cm.

5. $A = (1/2)bh = (1/2)(6 \cdot 5) = 15$ square units

6. $A = bh = 8 \cdot 3 = 24$ square units

7. a. $A = bh = 6 \cdot 3 = 18$ square units
b. $A = (1/2)bh = (1/2)(5 \cdot 5) = 12.5$ square units
c. $A = (1/2)(b_1 + b_2)h = (1/2)(3 + 8)(2) = 11$ square units

8. a. 7 square units   **b.** 9 square units
c. 6 square units   **d.** 8.5 square units

9. a. $4 \text{ km}^2 = 4 \cdot (10^3 \text{ m})^2 = 4 \cdot 10^6 \text{ m}^2$
b. $1 \text{ m}^2 = (10^{-3} \text{ km})^2 = 10^{-6} \text{ km}^2$
c. $0.5 \text{ hm}^2 = 0.5 \cdot (10^2 \text{ m})^2 = 0.5 \cdot 10^4 \text{ m}^2 = 5000 \text{ m}^2$
d. $567 \text{ cm}^2 = 567 \cdot (10^{-1} \text{ dm})^2 = 567 \cdot 10^{-2} \text{ dm}^2 = 5.67 \text{ dm}^2$

10. a. 7 square units   **b.** 7 para units
c. $4\frac{2}{3}$ trapezoidal units

11. a. the area of rectangle *ABCD*
b. the area of rectangle *EFCD*
c. the area of rectangle *ABFE*
d. $y \times (2y) = (y - 1)(2y) + 1 \times 2y$
e. $(y - 1)(2y) = y \times (2y) - 1 \times 2y$

12.

	$3a$	4
a	$3a \cdot a$	$4 \cdot a$
1	$3a \cdot 1$	$4 \cdot 1$

$$(3a + 4)(a + 1) = 3a \cdot a + 3a \cdot 1 + 4 \cdot a + 4 \cdot 1$$
$$= 3a^2 + 3a + 4a + 4$$
$$= 3a^2 + 7a + 4$$

13.

	$3a + 4$
$a - 3$	$(a - 3)(3a + 4)$
3	$3(3a + 4)$

$a(3a + 4) = (a - 3)(3a + 4) + 3(3a + 4)$, so $(a - 3)(3a + 4) = a(3a + 4) - 3(3a + 4)$.

14. $w = 4l + 3$, $P = 2w + 2l$, and $P = 945$, so $945 = 10l + 6$. Then $l = 939/10 = 93.9$ and $w = 378.6$. The length is 93.9 cm, and the width is 378.6 cm.

15. 12 and 4 cm

16. a.

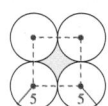

b. $A = \pi(18^2) - \pi(15^2) = 99\pi \approx 311.02 \text{ ft}^2$

17. It will take 120 columns of tiles by 56 rows of tiles: 120×56 tiles $= 6720$ tiles. Then 6720 tiles $\div 24$ tiles per box $= 280$ boxes of tiles.

18. 24 cm^2.

19. $A = 44 \cdot 17 = 748$ square feet. Then $748 \div 145 \approx 5.2$, so you need six buckets of paint.

20. 18 packs

21. $10^2 - 4(\frac{1}{4}(\pi \cdot 5^2)) \approx 21.46 \text{ cm}^2$

22. A piece could have the shape of the shaded parallelogram.

23. a.

b.

24.

The area of the wasted cardboard is $12^2 - \pi \cdot 6^2 \approx 30.9$ square units. Because $(30.9/144) = 0.215 \approx 21.5\%$, 21.5% of the square is wasted.

25. Use P for the first perimeter and P' for the increased-size perimeter. Then $P = 2l + 2w = 2 \cdot 4 + 2 \cdot 6 = 20$ cm and $P' = 2l' + 2w' = 2 \cdot 7 + 2 \cdot 9 = 32$ cm.
a. $32 - 20 = 12$ cm   **b.** $12/20 = 60\%$

26. The directions give you a way to convert square inches to square yards $(1 \text{ in.}^2 = \frac{1}{1296} \text{ yd}^2)$, because fabric is generally sold by the square yard.

27. a. about three times   **b.** exactly π times

28. ≈ 6378 km

29. a. about 26.9 cm^2 **b.** 6 cm^2 **c.** about 129.8 cm^2

30. a. about 2.33 in^2 **b.** $\approx 255{,}483$ mm^2 **c.** 32.3 ft^2
d. ≈ 0.00049 mi^2

31. distance $= 11{,}000 \times 17 = 187{,}000$ miles

32. The front tire travels 54 inches per revolution, and the rear tire travels 36 inches per revolution. LCM$(54, 36) = 108$, $108/36 = 3$, and $108/54 = 2$. So they will touch again after the bike travels 108 inches. (The rear tire makes three revolutions and the front tire makes two revolutions.)

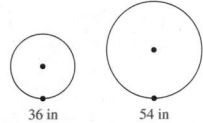

36 in   54 in

33. 25%

34. a.

Base	Height	Area
$BC = 44$ mm	$AE = 58.5$ mm	1287 mm^2
$AB = 59$ mm	$CD = 44$ mm	1296 mm^2
$AC = 68$ mm	$BF = 38$ mm	1292 mm^2

b. The areas are very close in size, but without measurement error the areas would be identical.

35. π is the quotient $C \div d$, where C is the circumference of the circle and d is the diameter of the circle. The size of the circle does not matter.

36. The quotient of two consecutive sides of a square is 1 (because s/s is $= 1$). So rectangle A is $12/9 \approx 1.33$, and rectangle B is $400/340 \approx 1.17$. Rectangle B has a ratio that is closer to 1, so it looks more like a square than rectangle A.

37. a. Samantha confused perimeter and area $(5 \cdot 4 = 20)$.
b. Luis forgot to include the measurement unit (cm).

38. a. The new circumference is four times the original circumference.
b. The new area is 16 times the original area.

39. a. The new perimeter is four times the original perimeter.
b. The new area is 16 times the original area.

40. a. perimeter   **b.** centimeter dot grid   **c.** rectangle
d. square   **e.** incorrect formulas   **f.** square unit
g. unit of measurement   **h.** U.S. customary
i. metric   **j.** altitude   **k.** sector

41. $A = \frac{1}{2}(3 + 5)(4) = 16$ cm^2

42. Answers vary.
a.

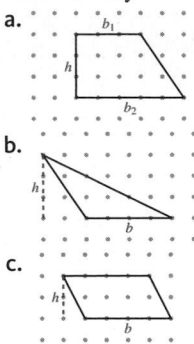

b.

c.

43. 2.4 ft (rounded to the nearest tenth)

44. a. approximately 3963 mi
b. $18 \cdot (2\pi \cdot 4300) \approx 486{,}319$ mi
c. $5 \cdot (2\pi \cdot (250 + 3963.189)) \approx 132{,}361$ mi

45. a.

15 ft   4 ft

b. $A = \pi(19^2) - \pi(15^2) \approx 427$ ft^2

46. $r = 14$ mm, so $C = 2\pi(14) \approx 88$ mm.

47. $l = 18$ mm, $w = 36$ mm, so $P = 2l + 2w = 108$ mm and $A = 18 \cdot 36 = 648$ mm^2.

48. $b = 35$ mm, $h = 35$ mm, so
$$A = \frac{1}{2}b \cdot h = \frac{1}{2}35 \cdot 35 = 612.5 \text{ mm}^2$$

49. $b = 52$ mm, $h = 20$ mm, so $A = b \cdot h = 52 \cdot 20 = 1040$ mm^2.

50. m$\angle APB = 137°$, $C = 2\pi \cdot 8$, and $A = \pi \cdot 8^2$
a. $A = \frac{137}{360}(\pi \cdot 8^2) \approx 76.5$ cm^2
b. arc length $= \frac{137}{360}(2\pi \cdot 8) \approx 19.1$ cm

51. $A_1 = s_1^2$, and $A_2 = s_2^2$. $A_1 = A_2$ implies $s_1^2 = s_2^2$. Then $\sqrt{s_1^2} = \sqrt{s_2^2}$. Then $s_1 = s_2$. Then $4s_1 = 4s_2$. Then $P_1 = P_2$.

52. $C_1 = 2\pi r_1$, and $C_2 = 2\pi r_2$. $C_1 = C_2$ implies $2\pi r_1 = 2\pi r_2$. Then $\frac{2\pi r_1}{2\pi} = \frac{2\pi r_2}{2\pi}$. Then $r_1 = r_2$. Then $\pi r_1^2 = \pi r_2^2$. Then $A_1 = A_2$.

53. 6 yd$^2 = (9 \cdot 6)$ ft$^2 = 54$ ft^2

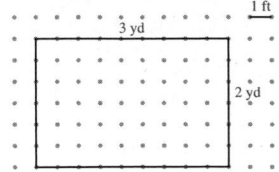

1 ft   3 yd   2 yd

b. $6 \text{ yds}^2 = 6 \text{ yd}^2 \times \left(\frac{3 \text{ ft}}{1 \text{ yd}}\right)^2$
$$= 6 \text{ yd}^2 \times \frac{3^2 \text{ ft}^2}{1^2 \text{ yd}^2}$$
$$= 54 \text{ ft}^2$$

54. No; a 6-by-3 rectangle has a perimeter of 18 units and area of 18 square units, while a 2-by-8 rectangle has a perimeter of 20 units (increased) but an area of 16 square units (decreased).

55. 64

56. The original area is 7.5 cm², and the new area is 31.5 cm².
    a. $31.5 - 7.5 = 24$ cm²   b. $24/7.5 = 3.2 = 320\%$

57. The circumference of a quarter is $2\pi(12.13)$ mm. The perimeter of the rectangle is 22 feet, or 6705.6 mm. So $6705.6 \div 2\pi(12.13) \approx 88$ revolutions (rounded to the nearest whole number).

58. $A(h) = (4h + 3)h$ or $A = (4h + 3)h$

59. No; a 4-by-8-meter rectangle has a perimeter of 24 meters and an area of 32 square meters, while a 10-by-2-meter rectangle has a perimeter of 24 meters but an area of 20 square meters.

60. No; a 3-by-8-meter rectangle has an area of 24 square meters and a perimeter of 22 meters, while a 4-by-6-meter rectangle has an area of 24 square meters but a perimeter of 20 meters.

61. a. $P = 21.9$ cm   b. $A \approx 22.0$ cm²
    c. $22.0 = (8.3)(CD)/2$, so $CD \approx 5.3$ cm.

62. $A = (1/2)(3.2)(6.00) = 9.6$ cm². Solve $9.6 = (1/2)(2.5)AC$ to get $AC = 7.68$ cm.

63. a. $4\sqrt{30}$ m, or about 21.91 m
    b. Answers vary. For example, the length could be 10 m and the width could be 3 m, so the perimeter would be 26 m.
    c. Solve the equation $30 = \pi r^2$ to get $r = \sqrt{30/\pi}$ m. Then $C \approx 2\pi(\sqrt{30/\pi}) \approx 19.42$ m.

64. a.

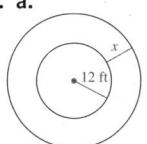

    b. $A = \pi(12 + x)^2 - \pi(12)^2$

65. a. $3s$ b. $4s$ c. $5s$ d. ns

66. A kite has two diagonals. As shown, the diagonal with length d_2 bisects the diagonal with length d_1. We can partition the kite into two equal-sized triangles, each with a height of $\frac{1}{2}d_1$, base of d_2, and area of $\frac{1}{2}(\frac{1}{2}d_1 \cdot d_2)$.

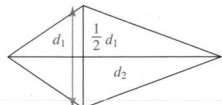

    Then $A = 2[\frac{1}{2}(\frac{1}{2}d_1 \cdot d_2)] = \frac{1}{2}(d_1 \cdot d_2)$.

67. a. the area of rectangle ABCD
    b. the area of rectangle ABFE
    c. the area of rectangle CDEF
    d. $xy = 2x + x(y - 2)$ e. $x(y - 2) = xy - 2x$

68. Solve $12(\pi \cdot 2)^2 = n(\pi \cdot 3)^2$ to get $n \approx 5.33$. Samantha can make five pancakes.

69. Let L and W be the new dimensions. Then $L = 1.15l$ and $lw = LW$. Solve $lw = (1.15l)W$ for W to get $W \approx 0.87w$. You must decrease the width by about 13%.

70. Let L and W be the new dimensions. Then $L = 0.88l$ and $lw = LW$. Solve $lw = (0.88l)W$ for W to get $W \approx 1.14w$. You must increase the width by about 14%.

71. Let B and H be the new dimensions. Then $B = 0.60b$ and $\frac{1}{2}bh = \frac{1}{2}BH$. Solve the equation $\frac{1}{2}bh = \frac{1}{2}0.60bH$ for H to get $H \approx 1.67h$. You must increase the height by about 67%.

72. Let p be the radius of circle P and q be the radius of circle Q. Then $p = 1.20q$. Then the area of circle P is $A = \pi \cdot (1.20q)^2 = 1.44(\pi \cdot q)^2$, so the area of circle P is 1.44 times the area of circle Q. This means that if you increase the radius by 20%, then you increase the area of the circle by 44%.

SECTION 11.3

1. We know $(BC)^2 = (AC)^2 + (AB)^2$. So $(BC)^2 = 4^2 + 5^2 = 16 + 25 = 41$, and $BC = \sqrt{41}$ units (approximately 6.4 units).

2. a.

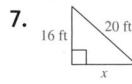

    b. $n^2 + n^2 = 12^2$, $2n^2 = 144$, $n^2 = 72$, $n = \sqrt{72}$. Each side has a length of $\sqrt{72}$ cm (approximately 8.5 cm).

3. a.

    b. $d^2 = 2^2 + 5^2$, $d^2 = 29$, $d = \sqrt{29}$, and $d \approx 5.4$. The bird was approximately 5.4 miles from the nest.

4. a. $180° - 58° - 43° = 79°$. $\angle B$ is the largest angle of the triangle. The opposite side of that angle, $\overline{AC}$, is the longest side.
    b. $2x + 15$ is greater than x and $x + 5$, so $\angle C$ is the largest angle of the triangle. The opposite side of that angle, $\overline{AB}$, is the longest side.

5. a. $A = (1/2)Pa = (1/2)(6 \cdot 12)(10.4) \approx 374.4$ square units
    b. $A = (1/2)Pa = (1/2)(5 \cdot 15)(10.3) \approx 386.25$ square units

6. $20\sqrt{2}$ m (approximately 28.3 m)

7.
    Solve $16^2 + x^2 = 20^2$ to get $x = 12$. The bottom of the ladder is 12 feet from the wall.

8. Solve $15^2 + h^2 = 25^2$ to find the original height of $h = 20$. Then solve $7^2 + h^2 = 25^2$ to find the new height of $h = 24$. Then $24 - 20 = 4$. The ladder is 4 feet higher on the wall when it is 8 feet closer to the wall.

9. a. $\sqrt{1076}$ mi (approximately 32.8 mi)
    b. $\sqrt{527.24}$ mi (approximately 23.0 mi)

10. Comparing $17^2 + 10^2$ and 21^2, we get $17^2 + 10^2 < 21^2$. The triangle is an obtuse triangle.

11. a. $2 < x < 22$ cm   b. $\sqrt{44} < x < 10$ cm

12. a. $8 < x < 38$ cm
    b. $x = \sqrt{304}$ cm ($\overline{AC}$ is not the longest side) or $x = \sqrt{754}$ cm ($\overline{AC}$ is the longest side)

13. a. $17 < x < 47$ cm   **b.** $\sqrt{1249} < x < 47$ cm

14. a. yes, because $4 < 10 + 13$, $10 < 4 + 13$, and $13 < 4 + 10$
   b. no, because $45 < 38 + 92$ and $38 < 45 + 92$, but
      $92 \not< 45 + 38$
   c. yes, because $21 < 17 + 8$, $17 < 21 + 8$, and $8 < 21 + 17$
   d. no, because $1720 \not< 1600 + 5$ even though
      $1600 < 1720 + 5$ and $5 < 1720 + 1600$

15. $n^2 + n^2 = 18^2$
$$2n^2 = 324$$
$$n = \sqrt{162} \text{ ft}$$

Each side has a length of $\sqrt{162}$ feet. Therefore, the area is 162 square feet.

16. a. $\overline{AC}$ **b.** $\overline{AB}$ **c.** $\overline{BC}$ and $\overline{AC}$ **d.** $\overline{AC}$

17. a. obtuse   **b.** right   **c.** right   **d.** acute

18. Answers vary. Let $u = 3$ and $v = 5$. Then $v^2 - u^2 = 5^2 - 3^2 = 16$, $2uv = 2 \cdot 3 \cdot 5 = 30$, and $v^2 + u^2 = 25 + 9 = 34$. So 16, 30, and 34 form a Pythagorean triple. $16^2 + 30^2 = 1156$ and $34^2 = 1156$, so $16^2 + 30^2 = 34^2$.

19. a. The horizontal distance is $16n$ inches, and the vertical distance is $9n$ inches.

Solve $(9n)^2 + (16n)^2 = 32^2$ to get $n \approx 1.743$. Then $16n \approx 16 \cdot 1.743 \approx 28$ in and $9n \approx 9 \cdot 1.743 \approx 16$ in. The horizontal distance is about 28 inches, and the vertical distance is about 16 inches.
   b. The horizontal distance is $3n$ inches, and the vertical distance is $4n$ inches. Solve $(3n)^2 + (4n)^2 = 40^2$ for n to get $n = 8$. Then $3n = 3 \cdot 8 = 24$ in and $4n = 4 \cdot 8 = 32$ in. The horizontal distance is 32 inches, and the vertical distance is 24 inches.

20. The perimeter is 126 cm, and there are 14 line segments on the boundary, so each segment is $126/14 = 9$ cm. Then $AB^2 = 9^2 + 18^2 = 81 + 324 = 405$, so $AB = \sqrt{405} \approx 20.1$ cm.

21. Draw a diagram to represent the situation.

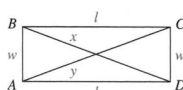

We want to show $AC = BD$ (or $x = y$).

Each diagonal ($\overline{AC}$ and $\overline{BD}$) of the rectangle is a hypotenuse of a right triangle.
$AC^2 = CD^2 + DA^2 = w^2 + l^2$, so $AC = \sqrt{w^2 + l^2}$.
$BD^2 = DA^2 + AB^2 = l^2 + w^2$, so $BD = \sqrt{w^2 + l^2}$.
Then $AC = BD$.

22.

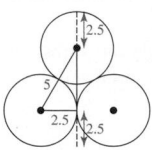

The height is $2.5 + h + 2.5$. Then
$$(2.5)^2 + h^2 = 5^2$$
$$6.25 + x^2 = 25$$
$$x^2 = 18.75$$
$$x \approx 4.33.$$

So $2.5 + 4.33 + 2.5 \approx 9.33$. The height of the stack is about 9.33 cm.

23. a. 17 in
   b. $BD^2 = 12^2 + 12^2 = 144 + 144 = 288$, so $BD = \sqrt{288} = 16.971$ in (rounded to the nearest thousandth).

24. When given the lengths of the sides of a triangle, you can determine the largest angle; it will be opposite the longest side.

25. We know that the sum of the interior angles of a triangle measure $180°$. Subtract the sum of the two given angles from $180°$. Now determine the smallest angle; it will be opposite the shortest side.

26. Fiona can walk due north from point A, and Kim could walk due west from point B, with each counting their steps until they meet. Then they can use the Pythagorean equation to figure out the distance that was between them.

27. You know a 3-4-5 triangle is a right triangle. Place a mark at 3 inches on one leg and a mark at 4 inches on another leg.

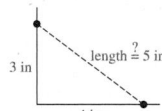

Use the tape measure to measure the distance between the marks. If the distance is 5 inches, then the triangle is a right triangle. Otherwise, the triangle is not a right triangle.

28. the side opposite the right angle of a triangle

29. $a^2 + b^2 = c^2$

30. Yes. Let c represent the length of the longest side. We need to compare c^2 and $a^2 + b^2$. $c^2 < a^2 + b^2$ means the triangle is an acute triangle. $c^2 = a^2 + b^2$ means the triangle is a right triangle. $c^2 > a^2 + b^2$ means the triangle is an obtuse triangle.

31. a. largest angle   **b.** acute   **c.** obtuse   **d.** hypotenuse
   e. Pythagorean equation   **f.** shortest side

32. $l = 40$ cm, and $w = 8$ cm

33. a. $\angle B$ **b.** $\angle A$ **c.** $\angle C$

34. a. $a = 6$ ft   **b.** $b = \sqrt{65}$ cm

35. Draw a diagram to represent the situation.

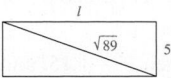

Then $89 = 25 + l^2$ (apply the Pythagorean theorem). Then $64 = l^2$ and $8 = l$. The length is 8 units.

36. Solve $n^2 + (2n - 1)^2 = 17^2$ to get $n = 8$. Then $2n - 1 = 2 \cdot 8 - 1 = 15$. The width is 15 cm and length is 8 cm.

37. a. no, because $15 \nleq 6 + 8$

    b. yes, because $42 < 58 + 96$, $58 < 42 + 96$, and $96 < 42 + 58$

    c. yes, because $4 < 8 + 7$, $8 < 4 + 7$, and $7 < 4 + 8$

    d. no, because $145 \nleq 72 + 60$

38. $A = (1/2)Pa$. Solve the equation $817.6 = (1/2) \cdot 7s \cdot 15.6$ to get $s \approx 14.974$. Then $s \approx 15.0$ cm (rounded to the nearest tenth of a centimeter). Each side of the regular heptagon has a length of approximately 15.0 cm.

39. $(\sqrt{20})^2 = 20 = 16^2 + 4^2 = (4)^2 + (2)^2$. So $\sqrt{20}$ is the length of a hypotenuse of a right triangle with legs of 4 and 2 units.

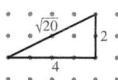

40.

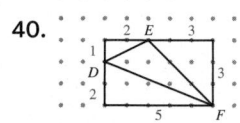

$EF^2 = 3^2 + 3^2 = 9 + 9 = 18$, so $EF = \sqrt{18} \approx 4.2$ units.

$DF^2 = 2^2 + 5^2 = 4 + 25 = 29$, so $DF = \sqrt{29} \approx 5.4$ units.

$ED^2 = 1^2 + 2^2 = 1 + 4 = 5$, so $ED = \sqrt{5} \approx 2.2$ units.

41. Answers vary.

    a. The triangle shown has an area of $A = (1/2)bh = (1/2) \cdot 6 \cdot 4 = (1/2)24 = 12$ square units.

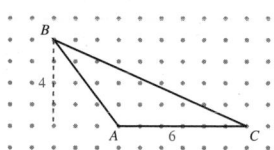

    b. $AB^2 = 4^2 + 3^2$. Then $AB^2 = 16 + 9 = 25$, so $AB = 5$ units. $AC = 6$ units, by design. $BC^2 = 4^2 + 9^2$. Then $BC^2 = 16 + 81 = 97$, so $BC = \sqrt{97}$ units.

42. a. $a \approx 14.51$ cm   **b.** $A \approx 696.40$ cm^2

43. a. $A = 261$ cm^2 **b.** $r \approx 10.03$ cm

44. $A \approx 208.27$ cm^2

45. $A \approx 336.82$ cm^2

46. a. $4 < x < 20$ cm   **b.** $4 < x < 4\sqrt{5}$ cm

47. a. $\angle B$ is the largest angle, so the opposite side $\overline{AC}$ is the longest side.

    b. $\angle B$ is the largest angle, so the opposite side $\overline{AC}$ is the longest side.

48. 14 ft = 168 in, and 20 ft = 240 in. Then $168 \div 3.5 = 48$, so the homeowner needs 48 rows of 3.5-by-7.5-inch wood tiles. Also, $240 \div 7.5 = 32$, so the homeowner needs 32 columns of wood tiles.

    a. $48 \times 32 = 1536$ wood tiles   **b.** none

49. a.

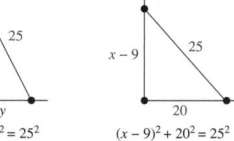

$x^2 + y^2 = 25^2$ $(x - 9)^2 + 20^2 = 25^2$

    b. Solve $(x - 9)^2 + 20^2 = 25^2$ to get $x = 24$, then solve $24^2 + y^2 = 25^2$ to get $y = 7$. The ladder was originally 7 feet from the wall.

50. Bus A travels for 20 minutes at 48 mph. Then $\dfrac{x}{20} = \dfrac{48}{60}$ and $x = \dfrac{20 \times 48}{60} = \dfrac{960}{60} = 16$. In 20 minutes, bus A has traveled 16 miles. Bus B travels for 20 minutes at 36 mph. Then $\dfrac{x}{20} = \dfrac{36}{60}$ and $x = \dfrac{20 \times 36}{60} = \dfrac{720}{60} = 12$. In 20 minutes, bus B has traveled 12 miles. Using the Pythagorean formula, $16^2 + 12^2 = 256 + 144 = 400$, and $\sqrt{400} = 20$. So 20 minutes later, bus A and bus B would be 20 miles apart.

SECTION 11.4

1. a. 8 cm^3 **b.** 7 cm^3 **c.** 11 cm^3

2. a. approximately 10 square units

    b. approximately 10 cubic units

    c. approximately 40 cubic units

3. a. $\overline{BD}$ **b.** $\overline{AD}$ **c.** $\overline{AB}$ **d.** $\overline{CE}$ **e.** $\overline{BE}$ **f.** $90°$

    g. $90°$ **h.** $90°$

4. a. $r^2 = a^2 + \left(\dfrac{1}{2}s\right)^2$ **b.** $l^2 = a^2 + h^2$ **c.** $e^2 = h^2 + r^2$

5. a. $B = \dfrac{1}{2}Pa = \dfrac{1}{2}(5 \cdot 11)(7.6) = 209$ cm^2

    b. To find l, solve $7.6^2 + 15^2 = l^2$ to get $l = \sqrt{282.76}$. Then $\dfrac{1}{2}Pl = \dfrac{1}{2}(5 \cdot 11)\sqrt{282.76} \approx 462.425$ cm^2.

    c. $S.A. = B + \dfrac{1}{2}Pl = 209 + 462.425 \approx 671.425$ cm^2

    d. $V = \dfrac{1}{3}Bh = \dfrac{1}{3} \cdot 209 \cdot 15 = 1045$ cm^3

6. a. $B = \dfrac{1}{2}Pa$. To find a, solve $22^2 + a^2 = 25.2^2$ to get $a = \sqrt{151.04}$. Then $B = \dfrac{1}{2}Pa = \dfrac{1}{2}(5 \cdot 18)\sqrt{151.04} \approx 553.04$ ft^2.

    b. $\dfrac{1}{2}Pl = \dfrac{1}{2}(5 \cdot 18)(25.2) = 1134$ ft^2

    c. $S.A. = B + \dfrac{1}{2}Pl = 553.04 + 1134 \approx 1687$ ft^2

    d. $V = \dfrac{1}{3}Bh = \dfrac{1}{3}(553.04 \cdot 22) \approx 4056$ ft^3

7. a. $B = \dfrac{1}{2}Pa = \dfrac{1}{2}(5 \cdot 15)(10.3) = 386.25$ ft^2

    b. $Ph = (5 \cdot 15)(18) = 1350$ ft^2

    c. $S.A. = 2B + Ph = 2 \cdot 386.25 + 1350 = 2122.5$ ft^2

    d. $V = Bh = 386.25 \cdot 18 = 6952.5$ ft^3

8. **a.** the area of the two bases of the cylinder
   b. the lateral surface area of the cylinder

9. **a.** Draw a cube, and then label the length, width, and height of the cubic as 1 cm.
   b. Draw a cube, and then label the length, width, and height of the cubic as 1 inch.

10. **a.** 9 truckloads   **b.** $2520

11. 7 gal

12. $1.40

13. 1680 cm^3

14. $V = l \cdot w \cdot h$, $1350 = 3n \cdot 5n \cdot 12n$, and $n \approx 1.957$. Then $3n \approx 3 \cdot 1.957 \approx 5.9$. The shortest side is approximately 5.9 cm.

15. **a.** 7.5 cm   **b.** 5 cm

16. yes, because the volume of the prism 1060.5 cm^3 is greater than the capacity of the cylinder 1015.99 cm^3

17. approximately 37 cm

18. **a.** 386.25 cm^2 **b.** $\approx$843.62 cm^2 **c.** $\approx$1229.87 cm^2
    d. 2575 cm^3

19. **a.** $\approx$832.23 cm^2 **b.** 1848 cm^2 **c.** 2680.23 cm^2
    d. 8322.28 cm^3

20. **a.** 25 cm^2 **b.** 122.577 cm^2 **c.** 147.58 cm^2 **d.** 100 cm^3

21. $\approx$10.8%

22. **a.** 0.328125 ft^3 **b.** $\approx$0.0169 yd^3 **c.** $\approx$24.409 in^3
    d. $\approx$20,023.416 ft^3

23. **a.** $\approx$9.6 cm^3 **b.** $\approx$9.6 cm^3

24. 3360 cm^3

25. $V(r) = 3\pi r^3$

26. **a.** $\approx$0.14 cubic zippos   **b.** $\approx$6671.66 cubic leeds

27. **a.** 49 marigold swordtail fish   **b.** 7 marigold swordtail fish

28. **a.** 8 tiger barb fish   **b.** 10 tiger barb fish

29. **a.** 4 cubic units for each
    b. 16 square units for one solid and 18 square units for the other solid
    c. If the volume of two solids is the same, then the surface areas may be different.

30. **a.** 30 square units
    b. 9 cubic units for one solid and 7 cubic units for the other solid
    c. If the surface area of two solids is the same, then the volumes may be different.

31. Capacity and container go together because capacity refers to how much of something a container can hold. Solid and volume go together because you measure a solid by volume. On the other hand, capacity and volume go together because they both refer to the measure of something, and container and solid go together because they are both things that can be measured by volume.

32. **a.**

    b. The square prism has the greater volume, because the cylinder would fit inside the prism with room to spare in the corners.

c. $V_{\text{cylinder}} \approx 196.35$ cubic units
   $V_{\text{prism}} = 250$ cubic units

d. The height of each is the same. The perimeter and surface area of the bases and lateral areas of the prism are greater than the circumference and surface area of the bases and lateral area of the cylinder.

e. $S.A._{\text{cylinder}} = 196.35$ square units
   $S.A._{\text{prism}} = 250$ square units

33. **a.** mL   **b.** g   **c.** in^3 **d.** fl oz

34. **a.** volume   **b.** capacity   **c.** measures of volume
    d. cubic centimeters   **e.** cubic inch   **f.** pyramid
    g. prism   **h.** cylinder

35. **a.** (ii) 15–30 gal   **b.** (iv) 180 gal   **c.** (v) 1/2 gal
    d. (vi) 1 gal   **e.** (i) 4–7 gal   **f.** (iii) 62,600 gal

36. **a.** 9 ft^2 **b.** $\approx$25.6 ft^2 **c.** $\approx$34.6 ft^2 **d.** 12 ft^3

37. **a.** $\approx$12.6 ft^2 **b.** $\approx$37.7 ft^2 **c.** $\approx$62.8 ft^2 **d.** $\approx$37.7 ft^3

38. **a.** $\approx$78.5 in^2 **b.** $\approx$204.2 in^2 **c.** $\approx$282.7 in^2
    d. $\approx$314.2 in^3

39. **a.** $\approx$113.1 ft^2 **b.** $\approx$188.5 ft^2 **c.** $\approx$301.6 ft^2
    d. $\approx$301.6 ft^3

40. **a.** $\approx$158.4 cm^2 **b.** $\approx$505.5 cm^2 **c.** $\approx$663.9 cm^2
    d. $\approx$1056 cm^3

41. **a.** $\approx$166.3 cm^2 **b.** $\approx$374.9 cm^2 **c.** $\approx$541.2 cm^2
    d. $\approx$776.0 cm^3

42. **a.** $\approx$97.5 cm^2 **b.** $\approx$491.3 cm^2 **c.** $\approx$686.3 cm^2
    d. $\approx$1277.3 cm^3

43. **a.** $\approx$406.3 cm^2 **b.** 6.25 cm   **c.** 15 cm   **d.** $\approx$156.3 cm^2
    e. $\approx$562.5 cm^2

44. **a.** $6 \cdot 3^2 = 54$ square units
    b. $6 \cdot 6^2 = 216$ square units
    c. $6 \cdot 9^2 = 486$ square units
    d. $6 \cdot (3n)^2 = 54n^2$ square units
    e. A cube with sides of the length s units has a surface area of $6s^2$ square units. If the sides are multiplied by a positive integer n, then the new surface area of the resulting cube is n^2 times the original surface area.
    f. Suppose the original cube has sides of the length s units. Then the cube has a surface area of $6s^2$ square units. Now multiply each side by n. Then the new surface area is $6(ns)^2 = 6 \cdot n^2 \cdot s^2 = n^2 \cdot 6s^2$. Then the new surface area is n^2 times the original surface area.

45. **a.** $4 \times 4 \times 4 = 64$ m^3
    b. $8 \times 8 \times 8 = 512$ m^3
    c. $12 \times 12 \times 12 = 1728$ m^3
    d. $4n \times 4n \times 4n = 64n^3$ m^3
    e. A cube with sides of the length s m has a volume of s^3 m^3. If the sides are multiplied by a positive integer n, then the volume of the resulting cube is n^3 times the original volume.
    f. Suppose the original cube has sides of the length s units. Then the cube has a volume of s^3 cubic units. Now multiply each side by n. Then the new volume is $(ns)^3 = n^3 \cdot s^3$. Then the new volume is n^3 times the original volume.

46. a. 1 acre-foot = 43,560 ft³
  b. $\approx$325,851.4 gal
  c. 325,851.4 ÷ 20,000 $\approx$ 16.29. So 16 pools can be filled with 1 acre-foot of water.

47. 325,851 ÷ 3 = 108,617 gal, the average amount of water a family uses per year, and 108,617 ÷ 365 $\approx$ 298 gal, the average amount of water each family uses per day

48. $d{:}h = 3{:}5$, so the diameter has the form $d = 3n$ and the height has the form $h = 5n$ for some positive number n. The radius is half the diameter, so $r = (1/2)d$. The radius has the form $r = (1/2)3n$, or $r = 1.5n$. Solve the equation $151.875\pi = \pi(1.5n)^2(5n)$ to get $n \approx 2.38$. Then $r \approx 1.5(2.38) = 3.6$ inches.

49. a. 9 Chinese algae eaters   **b.** 10 Chinese algae eaters

50. a. 43.2 cubic inches   **b.** 0.4 inches

51. $\approx$20.6 cm

52. 15 cm

53. $\approx$1.5 in

54. $S.A. \approx 399$ cm², and $V = 539$ cm³

REVIEW QUESTIONS

1. Answers vary; for example, you can measure weight and diameter.

2. The correct order is (ii), (iv), (i), and (iii).

3. a. · · · · ·   **b.** ⊢——⊣ ·   **c.** · · · · ·
  d. The length of the unit decreases as the number of units in the length increases.

4. a. precision = $\frac{1}{2}$ unit, GPE = $\frac{1}{4}$ unit

  b. precision = $\frac{1}{4}$ unit, GPE = $\frac{1}{8}$ unit

  c. precision = 1 unit, GPE = $\frac{1}{2}$ unit

5. a. 0.05 yd   **b.** 0.5 ft   **c.** 0.05 m   **d.** 0.005 mi
  e. 0.05 lb

6.

	Ruler A	Ruler B	Ruler C
a.	$\frac{1}{2}$ unit	$\frac{1}{4}$ unit	$\frac{1}{6}$ unit
b.	1 unit	$1\frac{1}{4}$ units	$1\frac{1}{6}$ units

  c. ruler B   **d.** no   **e.** ruler C

7. a. 12.315 lb, 12.325 lb   **b.** 26.35 ft, 26.45 ft

8. a. $1\frac{1}{5}$ caps   **b.** $2\frac{6}{7}$ caps   **c.** $8\frac{2}{5}$ pens   **d.** $2\frac{2}{7}$ caps

9. a. $\approx 7.89 \times 10^{-5}$ mi   **b.** $5\frac{1}{3}$ yd   **c.** 1320 ft
  d. $\approx 7.5 \times 10^{-3}$ mi   **e.** $\approx$98.3 ft per sec

10. 5772 mi

11. ink

12. millimeter, centimeter, meter

13. a. approximately 2205 lb   **b.** approximately 441 lb

14. a. $P = 12$ units, $A = 5$ square units
  b. $P = 14$ units, $A = 8$ square units

15. 18 para units

16. a. 6 square units   **b.** 6 square units   **c.** 15 square units
  d. 10π square units

17. a. [dot figure]   **b.** [dot figure]   **c.** It decreases.

18. 12.1 cm

19. a. $r = 13$ mm, so $C = 81.7$ mm.
  b. $r = 15$ mm, so $A = 706.9$ mm².

20. a. The circumference is four times larger.
  b. The area is 16 times larger.

21. a. The perimeter is five times larger.
  b. The area is 25 times larger.

22. approximately 67%

23. a. 675 ft²   **b.** $\approx$36.4 yd²   **c.** $\approx 4.6 \times 10^{-4}$ mi²
  d. $\approx$0.952 yd²

24. a. $\approx$2.79 in²   **b.** $\approx$3716.12 cm²   **c.** $\approx$75.35 ft²
  d. $\approx$0.01 mi²

25. $A = \dfrac{126}{360} \times \pi \cdot 3^2 \approx 9.9$ square units

26. $A = \dfrac{72}{360}\pi \cdot 8^2 \approx 40.2$ cm²

27. Solve $10.47 = \dfrac{n}{360} \cdot \pi \cdot 5^2$ to get $n \approx 48°$.

28. a. [diagram of rectangle with dimensions 2, 12, 2, 5]
  b. $(12 + 4) \cdot (5 + 4) - (12 \cdot 5) = 84$ m²

29. 15.5 cm

30. store A

31. $114 per cubic yard

32. a. 14 cm $\times$ 5 cm = 70 cm². Then 30 mg of lead ÷ 70 cm² $\approx$ 0.43 mg of lead per square centimeter. This does not indicate lead-based paint.
  b. 4 cm $\times$ 3 cm = 12 cm². Then 50 mg of lead ÷ 12 cm² $\approx$ 4.167 mg of lead per square centimeter. This indicates lead-based paint.

33. a. yes, because $6^2 + 8^2 = 10^2$
  b. no, because $7^2 + 9^2 \neq 12^2$

34. $\approx$57 inches

35. $AB = \sqrt{936} \approx 30.6$ cm

36. a. The television has the dimensions $16n$ and $9n$. Solve the equation $(16n)^2 + (9n)^2 = 37^2$ to get $n \approx 2.02$. So the television has dimensions 32-by-18 inches.
  b. The television has the dimensions $4n$ and $3n$. Solve the equation $(4n)^2 + (3n)^2 = 46^2$ to get $n = \sqrt{2116/25}$. So the area of the television screen is $(4\sqrt{2116/25})(3\sqrt{2116/25}) \approx 1016$ in².

37. The length of the unknown base is $x + 5 + y$, where x and y solve the equations $3.54^2 + x^2 = 6.25^2$ and $3.54^2 + y^2 = 4^2$, respectively. Then $x = 5.15$ and $y = 1.86$, to the nearest hundredth. The trapezoid has a height of 3.54 cm, bases of 5.00 cm and 12.01 cm, and an area of 30 cm^2.

38. **a.** obtuse triangle, because $15^2 + 18^2 < 24^2$
    b. acute triangle, because $20^2 < 13^2 + 17^2$
    c. right triangle, because $15^2 + 20^2 = 25^2$

39. **a.** no **b.** yes **c.** no **d.** no

40. The length of the third side must be more than 9 cm and less than 41 cm.

41. **a.** $\overline{BC}$ **b.** $\overline{AB}$ **c.** $\overline{AC}$ and $\overline{BC}$ **d.** $\overline{AC}$

42. **a.** $\approx$3034.5 cm^2 **b.** $\approx$35.7 cm

43. **a.** $\sqrt{702.69} \approx 26.5$ cm **b.** $\approx$2332.7 cm^2

44. **a.** $\approx$2659.2 cm^2 **b.** 32 cm

45. **a.** $\approx$15.6 cm **b.** 18 cm

46. **a.** 15 cm^3 **b.** 14 cm^3

47. **a.** 879.75 cm^2 **b.** $\approx$123.25 cm^2 **c.** $\approx$1126.25 cm^2
    d. $\approx$2551.28 cm^3

48. **a.** 2772 cm^2 **b.** $\approx$509.2 cm^2 **c.** $\approx$3790.4 cm^2
    d. $\approx$16,804.4 cm^3

49. **a.** 23.04 cm^2 **b.** $\sqrt{41.76} \approx 6.46$ cm **c.** $\approx$62.04 cm^2
    d. $\approx$85.08 cm^2 **e.** 46.08 cm^3

50. **a.** $\sqrt{9.72} \approx 3.12$ cm **b.** $\approx$33.67 cm^2
    c. $\sqrt{73.72} \approx 8.59$ cm **d.** $\approx$92.73 cm^2
    e. $\approx$126.40 cm^2 **f.** $\approx$89.79 cm^3

51. **a.** $\approx$50.27 ft^2 **b.** $\approx$251.3 ft^2 **c.** $\approx$351.86 ft^2
    d. $\approx$502.65 ft^3

52. **a.** S.A. $\approx$ 254.16 ft^2 and V $\approx$ 261.80 ft^3
    b. S.A. $\approx$ 678.58 ft^2 and V $\approx$ 1017.88 ft^3

53. **a.** $\approx$80.42 cm^3 **b.** $\approx$80.42 cm^3

54. 9000 cm^3

55. **a.** $\approx$1.41 $\times$ 10^{-6} mi^3 **b.** 6.789 $\times$ 10^{-12} km^3
    c. $\approx$34.60 in^3 **d.** $\approx$0.031 ft^3 **e.** $\approx$0.0031 yd^3 **f.** 20 qt

56. **a.** $\approx$15.9 qt **b.** $\approx$2.2 gal **c.** $\approx$83.3 L **d.** $\approx$1419.5 cm^3

57. $\approx$16.7 cm

58. **a.** $\sqrt[3]{614.125} = 8.5$ cm **b.** 15 cm

CHAPTER 11 TEST

1. Answers vary. For example, possible attributes are volume, weight, or height.

2. **a.** The student could use the endpoint of the nail to determine the measurement.
   b. $\frac{6}{8} + n = 4\frac{1}{8}$, so $n = 4\frac{1}{8} - \frac{6}{8} = 3\frac{3}{8}$. The nail is $3\frac{3}{8}$ inches long.

3. precision = $\dfrac{1}{6}$ unit, GPE = $\dfrac{1}{12}$ unit

4. **a.** 2.38 feet
   b. It is not possible to determine which measurement is more accurate without additional information.
   c. You would expect 2.38 feet to be more accurate than 2.3 feet, because the former may have less rounding error.

5. 46.65 and 46.75 feet

6. **a.** 0.45 mi **b.** 975.36 cm

7. **a.** 10 unit^2 **b.** 19.5 unit^2 **c.** 32 unit^2

8. The radius is 20 mm.
   a. 126 mm **b.** 1257 mm^2

9. $\approx$17.76 cm

10. **a.** 40. 2 cm^2 **b.** $\dfrac{108}{360} \cdot \pi \cdot 5^2 \approx 23.56$ unit^2

11. **a.** The new perimeter is seven times the original perimeter.
    b. The new area is 49 times the original area.

12. **a.** $\approx$27.8 ft **b.** $\approx$8.5 yd **c.** $\approx$1.8 mi

13. 116°

14. **a.** no, because $7 \div 15 \approx 0.47$
    b. yes, because $14 \div 12 \approx 1.17$

15. $\sqrt{10} + 4 + \sqrt{34} + 8 \approx 21.0$ units

16. $4\sqrt{55}$ units

17. $12 < x < 52$ cm

18. **a.** obtuse **b.** acute **c.** right

19. **a.** $\approx$27.22 unit^2 **b.** $a \approx 16.90$ cm, and $r \approx 18.29$ cm

20. **a.** 11 cm^3 **b.** 15 cm^3

21. 24 cm^2

22. **a.** $\sqrt{15.132} \approx 3.89$ cm **b.** $\approx$50.10 cm^2
    c. $\sqrt{241.0329} \approx 15.53$ cm **d.** $\approx$199.97 cm^2
    e. $\approx$250.07 cm^2 **f.** $\approx$251.02 cm^3

23. S.A. $\approx$ 83.395 square units, and V = 50.616 cubic units

24. 12 cm

25. **a.** $\approx$461.8 cm^3 **b.** $\approx$461.8 cm^3

26. **a.** $\approx$21.13 qt **b.** $\approx$0.87 gal **c.** $\approx$56.78 L
    d. $\approx$2839.06 cm^3

27. **a.** $\approx$1.25 $\times$ 10^{-6} mi^3 **b.** $\approx$25.63 in^3 **c.** $\approx$0.17 ft^3

CHAPTER 12

SECTION 12.1

1. **a.** CPCTC **b.** CPCTC **c.** $\triangle BCA$

2. **a.** $AEFG$ **b.** $\angle E$ **c.** FG

3. **a.** $\angle H$
   b. The names of the triangles will vary.

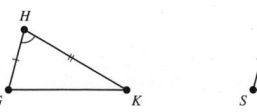 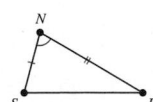

The diagram implies $\triangle GHK \cong \triangle SNU$.

4. **a.** $\overline{QW}$
   b. The names of the triangles will vary.

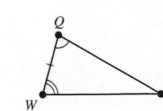 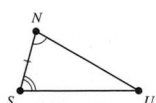

The diagram implies $\triangle QWT \cong \triangle NSU$.

5. a. true **b.** true **c.** true **d.** false **e.** false

6. $\overline{AB}$ bisects $\overline{CD}$ at the point E, so $EC = ED$. The center of the circle is O, and C and D are points on the circle, so $OC = OD$. Also, $OE = OE$ by the reflexive property.

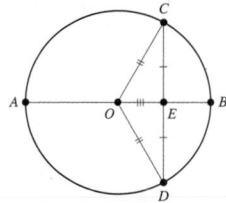

Then $\triangle OEC \cong \triangle OED$ by the SSS congruence axiom. So $\angle OEC \cong \angle OED$ by CPCTC. $\angle OEC \cong \angle OED$ are congruent and supplementary angles, so m$\angle OEC = 90°$. This means $\overline{AB}$ and $\overline{CD}$ are perpendicular.

7. m$\angle 1 = 140°$

m$\angle 2 = 40°$

m$\angle 3 = 20°$

m$\angle 4 = 70°$

m$\angle 5 = 70°$

8.

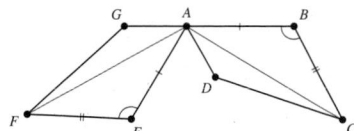

Here, CPCFC represents corresponding parts of congruent figures are congruent.

a.

Statement	Reason
1. $ABCD \cong AEFG$	1. Given
2. $\overline{FE} \cong \overline{CB}$	2. CPCFC
3. $\angle E \cong \angle B$	3. CPCFC
4. $\overline{AE} \cong \overline{AB}$	4. CPCFC
5. $\triangle AEF \cong \triangle ABC$	5. SAS congruence axiom
6. $\overline{AF} \cong \overline{AC}$	6. CPCTC

b.

Statement	Reason
1. $ABCD \cong AEFG$	1. Given
2. $\angle GAE \cong \angle DAB$	2. CPCFC
3. m$\angle DAG =$ m$\angle DAE +$ m$\angle GAE$	3. Angle Addition Postulate
4. m$\angle DAG =$ m$\angle DAE +$ m$\angle DAB$	4. Because m$\angle GAE =$ m$\angle DAB$
5. m$\angle DAG =$ m$\angle BAE$	5. Angle Addition Postulate
6. $\angle DAG \cong \angle BAE$	6. Definition of congruence

9.

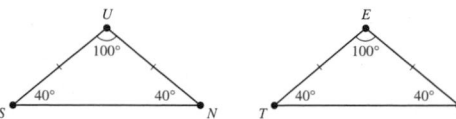

$\triangle SUN \cong \triangle TEA$ by the SAS congruence axiom. Other reasons may be the ASA or AAS congruence axioms.

10. All sides are congruent. We need to prove $ABCD$ is a parallelogram. Draw the diagonal from A to C.

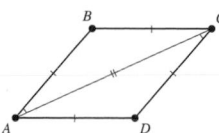

Then $\triangle ABC \cong \triangle CDA$ by the SSS congruence axiom. Then $\angle BAC \cong \angle DCA$ by CPCTC. The transversal $\overleftrightarrow{AC}$ that cuts $\overleftrightarrow{AB}$ and $\overleftrightarrow{CD}$ creates a pair of corresponding angles that are congruent, so $\overleftrightarrow{AB}$ and $\overleftrightarrow{CD}$ are parallel lines. So $\overline{AB}$ and $\overline{CD}$ are parallel. Draw the diagonal from B to D.

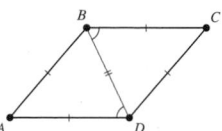

Then $\triangle ADB \cong \triangle CBD$ by the SSS congruence axiom. Then $\angle ADB \cong \angle CBD$ by CPCTC. The transversal $\overleftrightarrow{BD}$ that cuts $\overleftrightarrow{AD}$ and $\overleftrightarrow{CB}$ creates a pair of corresponding angles that are congruent, so $\overleftrightarrow{AD}$ and $\overleftrightarrow{CB}$ are parallel lines. So $\overline{AD}$ and $\overline{CB}$ are parallel. Opposite sides of $ABCD$ are parallel and congruent, so $ABCD$ is a rhombus.

11. Draw a diagram.

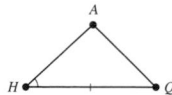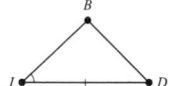

The student would need $\angle Q \cong \angle D$ to use the given information and the ASA congruence axiom.

12. a. no, because AAA is not a congruence axiom for triangles

b. no, because $AC \neq DF$

c. no, because SSA (donkey theorem) is not a triangle congruence axiom

13. a.

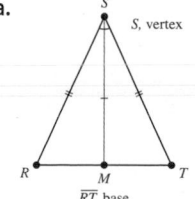

b. $\triangle RSM \cong \triangle TSM$ by the SAS congruence axiom. Then $\angle RMS \cong \angle TMS$ by CPCTC.

$\angle RMS$ and $\angle TMS$ are supplementary and congruent angles, so m$\angle RMS = 90°$. Then $\overline{RT}$ and $\overline{SM}$ are perpendicular.

c. $\triangle RSM \cong \triangle TSM$, so $\overline{RM} \cong \overline{TM}$ by CPCTC. Then $RM = MT$.

So $RM = MT$ and M is between R and T. This means M is the midpoint of $\overline{RT}$.

14. a.

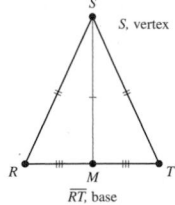

b. $\triangle RSM \cong \triangle TSM$ by the SSS congruence axiom. Then $\angle RSM \cong \angle TSM$ by CPCTC. So $\overline{SM}$ bisects $\angle S$.

c. $\triangle RSM \cong \triangle TSM$ by the SSS congruence axiom, so $\angle RMS \cong \angle TMS$ by CPCTC. $\angle RMS$ and $\angle TMS$ are supplementary and congruent angles, so m$\angle RMS = 90°$. This means $\overline{RT}$ and $\overline{SM}$ are perpendicular.

15.

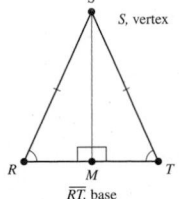

a. $\triangle RSM \cong \triangle TSM$ by the AAS congruence axiom. Then $\angle RSM \cong \angle TSM$ by CPCTC. Then $\overline{SM}$ bisects $\angle S$.

b. $\triangle RSM \cong \triangle TSM$, as shown in part (a). $\overline{RM} \cong \overline{TM}$ by CPCTC. M is between R and T, so

$$RT = RM + MT$$
$$= RM + RM \qquad \textbf{Because } \overline{RM} \cong \overline{TM}$$
$$= 2 \cdot RM$$

So $RM = (1/2)RT$ and M is between R and T. This means M is the midpoint of $\overline{RT}$.

16. a.

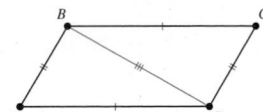

We are given $\overline{AB} \cong \overline{CD}$ and $\overline{AD} \cong \overline{CB}$. Then $\overline{BD} \cong \overline{DB}$ by the reflexive property of congruence. Then $\triangle ABD \cong \triangle CDB$ by the SSS congruence axiom. Then $\angle ABD \cong \angle CDB$ by CPCTC. The transversal $\overleftrightarrow{BD}$ that cuts $\overleftrightarrow{AB}$ and $\overleftrightarrow{CD}$ creates a pair of corresponding angles that are congruent, so $\overleftrightarrow{AB}$ and $\overleftrightarrow{CD}$ are parallel lines. So $\overline{AB}$ and $\overline{CD}$ are parallel.

b.

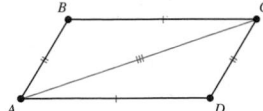

We are given $\overline{AB} \cong \overline{CD}$ and $\overline{BC} \cong \overline{DA}$. Then $\overline{AC} \cong \overline{CA}$ by the reflexive property of congruence. Then $\triangle ABC \cong \triangle CDA$ by the SSS congruence axiom. Then $\angle B \cong \angle D$ by CPCTC.

c. $\triangle ABC \cong \triangle CDA$, as shown in part (b). Then $\angle CAB \cong \angle ACD$ by CPCTC. The transversal $\overleftrightarrow{AC}$ that cuts $\overleftrightarrow{BC}$ and $\overleftrightarrow{AD}$ creates a pair of corresponding angles that are congruent, so $\overleftrightarrow{BC}$ and $\overleftrightarrow{AD}$ are parallel lines. So $\overline{BC}$ and $\overline{AD}$ are parallel.

d. $\triangle ABD \cong \triangle CDB$ by part (a). So $\angle A \cong \angle C$ by CPCTC.

17. a. $\overline{DA} \cong \overline{DC}$, because all sides of a rhombus are congruent. $\overline{BA} \cong \overline{BC}$, because all sides of a rhombus are congruent. $\overline{DB} \cong \overline{BD}$ by the reflexive property of congruence. Then $\triangle DAB \cong \triangle DCB$ by the SSS congruence axiom.

b. $\triangle DAB \cong \triangle DCB$, as shown in part (a). Then $\angle A \cong \angle C$ by CPCTC.

c. $\overline{AB} \cong \overline{AD}$, because all sides of a rhombus are congruent. $\overline{CB} \cong \overline{CD}$, because all sides of a rhombus are congruent. $\overline{AC} \cong \overline{CA}$ by the reflexive property of congruence. Then $\triangle BAC \cong \triangle DCA$ by the SSS congruence axiom. Then $\angle B \cong \angle D$ by CPCTC.

d. Opposite angles of a rhombus are congruent.

18. a. $\overline{AB} \cong \overline{AD}$, because all sides of a rhombus are congruent. $\overline{CB} \cong \overline{CD}$, because all sides of a rhombus are congruent. $\overline{AC} \cong \overline{CA}$ by the reflexive property of congruence. Then $\triangle ABC \cong \triangle ADC$ by the SSS congruence axiom.

b. $\triangle ABC \cong \triangle ADC$, as shown in part (a). Then $\angle BAC \cong \angle DAC$ and $\angle DCA \cong \angle BCA$ by CPCTC. So $\overline{AC}$ bisects $\angle A$ and $\angle C$.

c. $\overline{AB} \cong \overline{CB}$, because all sides of a rhombus are congruent. $\overline{AD} \cong \overline{CD}$, because all sides of a rhombus are congruent. $\overline{BD} \cong \overline{DB}$ by the reflexive property of congruence. Then $\triangle BAD \cong \triangle BCD$ by the SSS congruence axiom. Then $\angle ABD \cong \angle CBD$ and $\angle ADB \cong \angle CDB$ by CPCTC. So $\overline{BD}$ bisects $\angle B$ and $\angle D$.

d. The diagonals of a rhombus bisect the angles.

19. The student can pick the letters in two ways with each of the three picks, and $2 \times 2 \times 2 = 8$. So the student can have eight different arrangements.

20. Suppose $\angle A \cong \angle C$. $\overline{AC} \cong \overline{CA}$ by the reflexive property of congruence. $\angle C \cong \angle A$ by the symmetric property of congruence. Then $\triangle ABC \cong \triangle CBA$ by the ASA congruence axiom. Then $\overline{AB} \cong \overline{BC}$ by CPCTC. Then $\triangle ABC$ is an isosceles triangle.

21. a.

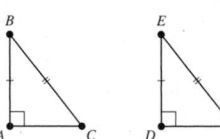

b. $\overline{AB} \cong \overline{DE}$ and $\overline{BC} \cong \overline{EF}$ are given.

$$(AC)^2 = (BC)^2 - (AB)^2 \quad \text{since } (AC)^2 + (AB)^2 = (BC)^2$$
$$= (EF)^2 - (DE)^2 \quad \text{since } BC = EF \text{ and } AB = DE$$
$$= (DF)^2 \quad \text{since } (DF)^2 + (DE)^2 = (EF)^2$$

Then $\overline{AC} \cong \overline{DF}$. Then $\triangle ABC \cong \triangle DEF$ by the SSS Congruence Axiom.

c. the two right triangles are congruent

22. a.

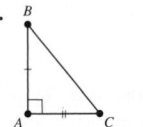 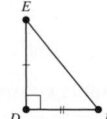

b. $\angle A \cong \angle D$, because right angles are congruent. $\overline{AB} \cong \overline{DE}$ and $\overline{AC} \cong \overline{DF}$ are given. Then $\triangle ABC \cong \triangle DEF$ by the SAS congruence axiom.

c. the two right triangles are congruent

23. a.

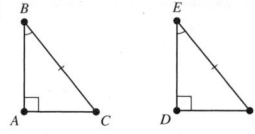

b. $\angle A \cong \angle D$, because right angles are congruent. $\angle B \cong \angle E$ and $\overline{BC} \cong \overline{EF}$ are given. Then $\triangle ABC \cong \triangle DEF$ by the AAS congruence axiom.

c. the two right triangles are congruent

24. a. LL theorem   **b.** HA theorem   **c.** HL theorem

25. the SSS congruence axiom

26. three questions, due to the triangle congruence axioms.

27. $\overline{OH} \cong \overline{EA}$ so that you can use the ASA congruence axiom to conclude $\triangle HOT \cong \triangle AET$. Or, $\overline{OT} \cong \overline{ET}$ so that you can use the AAS congruence axiom to conclude $\triangle HOT \cong \triangle AET$. Or, $\overline{HT} \cong \overline{AT}$ so that you can use the AAS congruence axiom to conclude $\triangle HOT \cong \triangle AET$.

28.

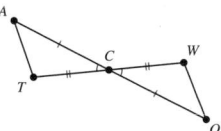

The two vertical angles are congruent, so $\triangle ACT \cong \triangle OCW$ by the SAS congruence axiom. Then $\angle TAC \cong \angle WOC$ by CPCTC. $\overleftrightarrow{AO}$ is a transversal for $\overline{AT}$ and $\overline{WO}$, and it creates a pair of alternate interior angles that are congruent, so $\overleftrightarrow{AT} \parallel \overleftrightarrow{WO}$.

29. No; here's a counterexample.

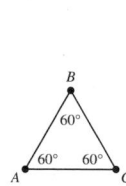 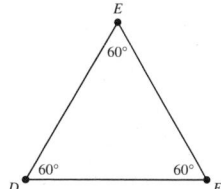

Corresponding angles of $\triangle ABC$ and $\triangle DEF$ are congruent, but $\triangle ABC \not\cong \triangle DEF$ because corresponding sides do not have the same length.

30. Answers vary. Here's a counterexample.

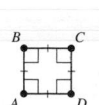 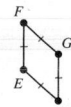

Corresponding sides of $ABCD$ and $EFGH$ are congruent, but $ABCD \not\cong EFGH$ because corresponding angles are not congruent.

31. a. Answers vary.   **b.** Answers vary.

32. a. paragraph form   **b.** two-column format   **c.** proof
   d. axiom   **e.** no   **f.** yes   **g.** corresponding parts

33. a. $\angle RDB$ **b.** $\overline{AT}$
   c. $CATS \cong BIRD$ is given. $\overline{CA} \cong \overline{BI}$ by CPCFC. $\overline{AT} \cong \overline{IR}$ by CPCFC. $\angle A \cong \angle I$ by CPCFC. So $\triangle CAT \cong \triangle BIR$ by the SAS congruence axiom.

34. a. no, because SSA (donkey theorem) is not a triangle congruence axiom
   b. yes, because of the SSS congruence axiom
   c. yes, because of the ASA congruence axiom

35. a.

Statement	Reason
1. $\overline{AD} \cong \overline{BC}$	1. Because opposite sides of a rectangle are congruent
2. $\angle CAD \cong \angle ACB$	2. Because opposite sides of a rectangle are parallel, so pairs of alternate interior angles are congruent
3. $\angle ADB \cong \angle DBC$	3. Because opposite sides of a rectangle are parallel, so pairs of alternate interior angles are congruent
4. $\triangle AED \cong \triangle CEB$	4. ASA congruence axiom

b.

Statement	Reason
1. $\triangle AED \cong \triangle CEB$	1. As shown in part (a)
2. $\overline{AE} \cong \overline{CE}$	2. CPCTC

So $\overline{BD}$ bisects $\overline{AC}$.

c.

Statement	Reason
1. $\triangle AED \cong \triangle CEB$	1. As shown in part (a)
2. $\overline{BE} \cong \overline{DE}$	2. CPCTC

So $\overline{AC}$ bisects $\overline{BD}$.

36.

Statement	Reason
1. $\overline{AB} \cong \overline{CD}$	1. Given
2. $\overline{CD} \cong \overline{DC}$	2. Reflexive property of congruence
3. $\overline{AB} \cong \overline{DC}$	3. Transitive property of congruence
4. $\overline{DC} \cong \overline{AB}$	4. Symmetric property of congruence

37. a.

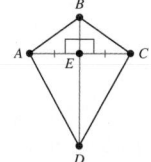

b.

Statement	Reason
1. $\overline{AE} \cong \overline{CE}$	1. $\overline{BD}$ bisects $\overline{AC}$
2. $\angle AEB \cong \angle CEB$	2. $\overline{AC} \perp \overline{BD}$
3. $\overline{BE} \cong \overline{EB}$	3. Reflexive property of congruence
4. $\triangle AEB \cong \triangle CEB$	4. SAS congruence axiom
5. $\angle ABE \cong \angle CBE$	5. CPCTC

Then $\overline{BD}$ bisects $\angle ABC$.

c.

Statement	Reason
1. $\triangle AEB \cong \triangle CEB$	1. As shown in part (b)
2. $\overline{AB} \cong \overline{CB}$	2. CPCTC
3. $\overline{CB} \cong \overline{BC}$	3. Reflexive property of congruence
4. $\overline{AB} \cong \overline{BC}$	4. Transitive property of congruence

d.

Statement	Reason
1. $\overline{AE} \cong \overline{CE}$	1. $\overline{BD}$ bisects $\overline{AC}$
2. $\angle DEA \cong \angle DEC$	2. $\overline{AC} \perp \overline{BD}$
3. $\overline{DE} \cong \overline{DE}$	3. Reflexive property of congruence
4. $\triangle AED \cong \triangle CED$	4. SAS congruence axiom
5. $\overline{AD} \cong \overline{CD}$	5. CPCTC
6. $\overline{AB} \cong \overline{CB}$	6. As shown in part (c)
7. $\overline{BD} \cong \overline{BD}$	7. Reflexive property of congruence
8. $\triangle BAD \cong \triangle BCD$	8. SSS congruence axiom
9. $\angle BAD \cong \angle BCD$	9. CPCTC

38. a.

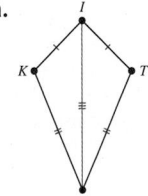

$\overline{KI} \cong \overline{TI}$ and $\overline{KE} \cong \overline{TE}$ are given. $\overline{IE} \cong \overline{IE}$ by the reflexive property of congruence. Then $\triangle KIE \cong \triangle TIE$ by the SSS congruence axiom. Then $\angle KIE \cong \angle TIE$ by CPCTC. So the diagonal $\overline{IE}$ bisects $\angle I$.

b. $\triangle KIE \cong \triangle TIE$, as shown in part (a). Then $\angle KEI \cong \angle TEI$ by CPCTC. So the diagonal $\overline{IE}$ bisects $\angle E$.

c. $\overline{KI} \cong \overline{TI}$ is given. $\angle KIS \cong \angle TIS$, because $\overline{IE}$ bisects $\angle I$ and therefore $\overline{IS}$ bisects $\angle I$. $\overline{IS} \cong \overline{IS}$ by the reflexive property of congruence.

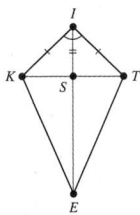

Then $\triangle KIS \cong \triangle TIS$ by the SAS congruence axiom. Then $\angle KSI \cong \angle TSI$ by CPCTC. $\angle KSI$ and $\angle TSI$ are congruent and supplementary angles, so m$\angle KSI = 90°$. Then the diagonals are perpendicular.

39. $\overline{AN} \cong \overline{AP}$ and $\overline{AT} \cong \overline{AE}$ are given. $\angle N \cong \angle P$, because $\triangle ANP$ is an isosceles triangle and the base angles are congruent. $\angle ATE \cong \angle AET$, because $\triangle ATE$ is an isosceles triangle and the base angles are congruent. Then $\angle NTA \cong \angle TEA$, because supplemental angles of congruent angles are congruent. Then by the AAS congruence axiom, $\triangle ANT \cong \triangle APE$.

40.

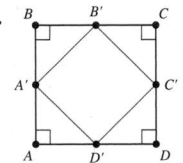

a. the quadrilateral is also a square

b. Let the midpoints of the sides of square $ABCD$ be A', B', C', and D'. Each angle of $ABCD$ is a right angle, each side of $ABCD$ has the same length, and the midpoint splits each line segment into two congruent line segments. The following diagram summarizes the relationships.

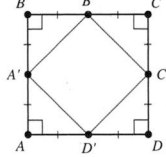

Then $\triangle AA'D' \cong \triangle BB'A'$ by the SAS congruence axiom. Then $\overline{A'D'} \cong \overline{B'A'}$ by CPCTC. We can apply the same reasoning to conclude $\triangle AA'D' \cong \triangle CC'B'$, $\triangle AA'D' \cong \triangle DD'A'$, so $\overline{A'D'} \cong \overline{C'B'}$, and $\overline{A'D'} \cong \overline{D'C'}$ by CPCTC. Then $A'B'C'D'$ is a rhombus. Now we show that $\angle B'$ of $A'B'C'D'$ is a right angle. (The same reasoning can be applied to show the other interior angles of $A'B'C'D'$ are right angles.)

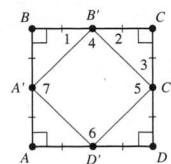

∠2 and ∠3 are complementary. △$A'BB' \cong$ △$C'CB'$ by the SAS congruence axiom. Then ∠1 ≅ ∠2 by CPCTC. △$A'BB' \cong$ △$B'CC'$ by the SAS congruence axiom. Then ∠1 ≅ ∠3 by CPCTC. Then ∠2 ≅ ∠3 by the symmetric property of congruence. ∠2 and ∠3 are congruent and complementary, so they are 45° angles. Then ∠1 is a 45° angle. Then ∠4 is a right angle. Then ∠B' in the rhombus $A'B'C'D'$ is a right angle. The same reasoning can be applied to conclude ∠A', ∠C', and ∠D' are right angles in $A'B'C'D'$. So rhombus $A'B'C'D'$ is a square.

41. corresponding parts of congruent triangles are congruent

42.

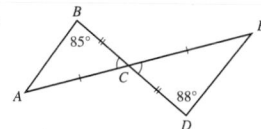

$\overline{CA} \cong \overline{CE}$ is given. ∠ACB ≅ ∠ECD, because vertical angles are congruent. $\overline{BC} \cong \overline{DC}$ is given. Then △$BCA \cong$ △DCE by the SAS congruence axiom. Then ∠B ≅ ∠D by CPCTC. So we cannot have m∠B = 85° and m∠D = 88°.

43. a. $\overline{ON} \cong \overline{ET}$, $\overline{OW} \cong \overline{EA}$, and $\overline{DN} \cong \overline{ST}$ are given. $DN = 2 \cdot WN$ and $ST = 2 \cdot AT$, because W and A are midpoints of $\overline{DN}$ and $\overline{ST}$. $\overline{DN} \cong \overline{ST}$, so $DN = ST$, so $2 \cdot WN = 2 \cdot AT$, then $WN = AT$, then $\overline{WN} \cong \overline{AT}$. Then △$NOW \cong$ △TEA by the SSS congruence axiom.

b.

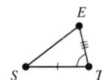

△$NOW \cong$ △TEA by part (a). ∠N ≅ ∠T by CPCTC. $\overline{DN} \cong \overline{ST}$ and $\overline{ON} \cong \overline{ET}$ are given. Then △$DON \cong$ △SET by the SAS congruence axiom.

44. $\overline{AB} \parallel \overline{ET}$ and △$BET \cong$ △ATE are given. Then ∠BET ≅ ∠ATE and $\overline{BE} \cong \overline{AT}$ by CPCTC. By definition, an isosceles trapezoid has congruent base angles, congruent legs, and bases that are parallel. So trapezoid $BETA$ is an isosceles trapezoid.

45. a.

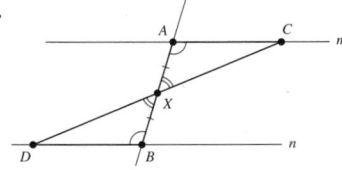

b.

Statement	Reason
1. $m \parallel n$	1. Given
2. $\overline{AX} \cong \overline{BX}$	2. Definition of midpoint
3. ∠A ≅ ∠B	3. The transversal cuts parallel lines, so it creates congruent alternate interior angles
4. ∠AXC ≅ ∠BXD	4. Definition of vertical angles
5. △$AXC \cong$ △BXD	5. By the ASA congruence axiom

46.

Statement	Reason
1. ∠2 ≅ ∠3	1. Given
2. △DBE is isosceles	2. Because its base angles are congruent (See Example 12.5)
3. $\overline{DB} \cong \overline{EB}$	3. Because the legs of an isosceles triangle are congruent
4. ∠ABD ≅ ∠CBE	4. Because vertical angles are congruent
5. ∠5 ≅ ∠6	5. Given
6. △$ABD \cong$ △CBE	6. AAS congruence axiom
7. $\overline{AB} \cong \overline{BC}$	7. CPCTC

47.

a.

Statement	Reason
1. $\overline{AB} \parallel \overline{CD}$	1. Given
2. $\overline{AB} \cong \overline{CD}$	2. $AB = CD$
3. ∠BAC ≅ ∠DCA	3. Because alternate interior angles formed by two parallel lines cut by a transversal are congruent
4. $\overline{AC} \cong \overline{CA}$	4. Reflexive property of congruence
5. △$BAC \cong$ △DCA	5. SAS congruence axiom
6. $\overline{AD} \cong \overline{BC}$	6. CPCTC
7. $\overline{DB} \cong \overline{BD}$	7. Reflexive property of congruence
8. △$ADB \cong$ △CBD	8. SSS congruence axiom
9. ∠ADB ≅ ∠CBD	9. CPCTC
10. $\overline{AB} \parallel \overline{BC}$	10. Because if a transversal cuts two lines and creates a pair of alternate interior angles that are congruent, then the two lines are parallel

Opposite sides of $ABCD$ are parallel, so $ABCD$ is a parallelogram.

b. The quadrilateral is a parallelogram.

48.

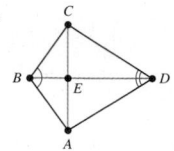

Statement	Reason
1. $\angle CBD \cong \angle ABD$	1. Given that $\overline{BD}$ bisects $\angle B$
2. $\angle CDB \cong \angle ADB$	2. Given that $\overline{BD}$ bisects $\angle D$
3. $\overline{BD} \cong \overline{BD}$	3. Reflexive property of congruence
4. $\triangle CBD \cong \triangle ABD$	4. ASA congruence axiom
5. $\overline{CB} \cong \overline{AB}$	5. CPCTC
6. $\overline{BE} \cong \overline{BE}$	6. Reflexive property of congruence
7. $\triangle CBE \cong \triangle ABE$	7. SAS congruence axiom
8. $\angle BEC \cong \angle BEA$	8. CPCTC
9. $m\angle BEC = 90°$	9. Because $\angle BEC$ and $\angle BEA$ are congruent and supplementary angles, so they are both right angles

This proves the diagonals are perpendicular.

49. a. rectangle **b.** $\angle A \cong \angle C$ **c.** $\angle B \cong \angle D$
d. $\overline{EA} \cong \overline{FC}$, $\angle A \cong \angle C$, and $\overline{AH} \cong \overline{CG}$. Then $\triangle HAE \cong \triangle GCF$ by the SAS congruence axiom.
e. $\overline{HD} \cong \overline{EB}$, $\angle B \cong \angle D$, and $\overline{BF} \cong \overline{DG}$. Then $\triangle HDG \cong \triangle EBF$ by the SAS congruence axiom.
f. $\triangle HAE \cong \triangle GCF$, so $\overline{HE} \cong \overline{GF}$ by CPCTC. $\triangle HDG \cong \triangle EBF$, so $\overline{HG} \cong \overline{EF}$ by CPCTC. The opposite sides of the convex quadrilateral $EFGH$ are congruent, so as shown in Example 12.9, $EFGH$ is a parallelogram.
g. Each interior angle of $EFGH$ has the same measure, and the sum of the measures is 360°. So each angle must be 90° (a right angle).
h. $EFGH$ is a parallelogram with four right angles, so $EFGH$ is a rectangle.

50. The diagram is an aid.

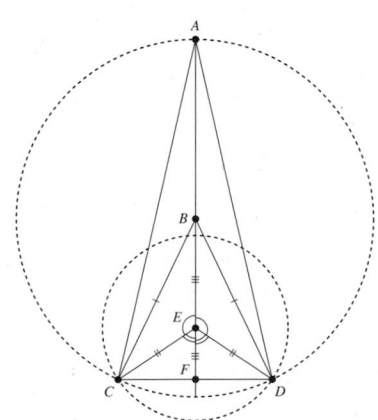

a. $\overline{BC} \cong \overline{BD}$, because C and D lie on the same circle with the center B. $\overline{EC} \cong \overline{ED}$, because C and D lie on the same circle with the center E. $\overline{BE} \cong \overline{BE}$ by the reflexive property of congruence. Then $\triangle BCE \cong \triangle BDE$ by the SSS congruence axiom.
b. $\triangle BCE \cong \triangle BDE$, so $\angle CEB \cong \angle DEB$ by CPCTC. Then $m\angle CEF = 180° - m\angle CEB$ and $m\angle DEF = 180° - m\angle DEB$. So $\angle CEF \cong \angle DEF$. $\overline{EC} \cong \overline{ED}$ by CPCTC and $\overline{EF} \cong \overline{EF}$ by the reflexive property. Then $\triangle CEF \cong \triangle DEF$ by the SAS congruence axiom.

SECTION 12.2

1. a. A and B
b. the line segment through A and B, the arc with the center B, and point C

2. the circle with center P

3. a. point P **b.** vertical line m **c.** points A, B, and C
d. line l
e. a line through P that is perpendicular to the given vertical line m

4. $\sqrt{2}n$ units

5. Answers vary.

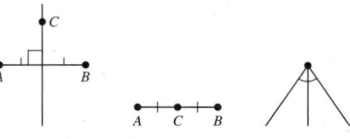

a. **b.** **c.**

 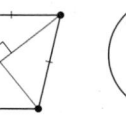 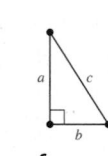

d. **e.** **f.**

6. $\angle A \cong \angle K$

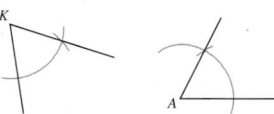

7.

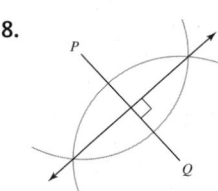

8.

9.

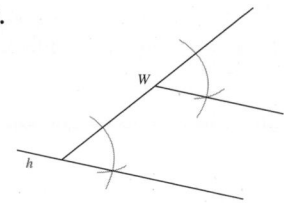

10. Extend the given line segment using a straightedge. Then set the compass opening to radius AB. Place the center point at B, and swing an arc with radius AB so that it intersects the line segment. Label the intersection C. Construct the perpendicular bisector of $\overline{BD}$. Label the point of intersection of the perpendicular bisector and $\overline{BC}$ as D. Then D is the midpoint of $\overline{BC}$. Then $AD = AB + BD = 3 + 1.5 = 4.5$. Then $\overline{AD}$ has a length of 4.5 units.

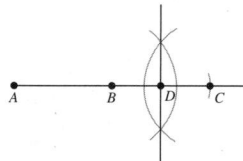

11. Copy the line segment $\overline{AB}$ to get $\overline{CD}$. Set the radius of a compass to AB. Put the center point at C, and swing an arc with radius AB. Maintaining the same compass opening, put the center point at D and swing an arc. Let E be the point of intersection of the two arcs. Then $\triangle CED$ is an equilateral triangle with sides congruent to $\overline{AB}$.

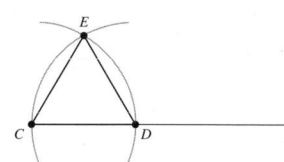

12. Use a straightedge to construct a line segment. Construct the perpendicular bisector of the line segment. The line segment and perpendicular bisector form a right angle.

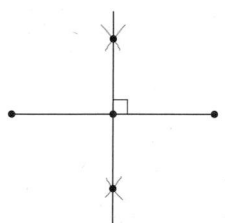

13. Construct a line segment $\overline{AB}$ using the straightedge. Construct the perpendicular bisector of $\overline{AB}$ to create a right angle. Bisect the right angle to create two 45° angles. $\angle NMB$ has the measure 45°.

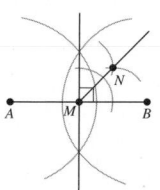

14. Construct any equilateral triangle $\triangle ABC$ as in the answer to Question 11. Then each angle of the triangle has the measure 60°.

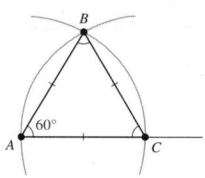

15. Copy the angle, beginning with one of the sides of the given triangle. Put the center point of a compass at A, and swing an arc that intersects both sides of $\angle A$. Label the points of intersection B and C. Set the radius of the compass to BC. Then put the center point of the compass at C, and swing an arc with radius BC. Let D be the point of intersection of the two arcs. Then $m\angle DAB = 2 \cdot m\angle CAB$.

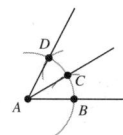

16. Create an equilateral triangle as in the answer to Question 11. Then each interior angle has the measure 60°.

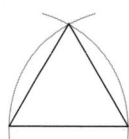

Copy a 60° angle, beginning with one of the sides of the given triangle, as in the answer to Question 15.

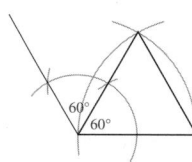

The two adjacent angles form a 120° angle.

17. a. Create a right angle $\angle A$, as described in the answer to Question 8, by constructing the perpendicular bisector of a line segment. Create an angle bisector of $\angle A$.

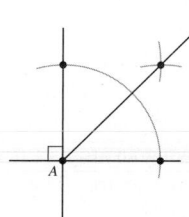

Set the compass opening to r. Put the center point at A, and swing an arc with radius r that intersects the angle bisector. Label the point of intersection C.

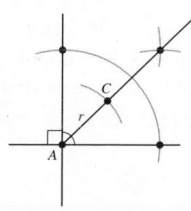

Construct a line through C that is perpendicular to a side of $\angle A$. Label the point of intersection B. Construct a line through C that is perpendicular to the other side of $\angle A$. Label the point of intersection D. Then $ABCD$ is a square.

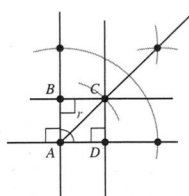

b. Set the compass radius to AB, and place the compass points on consecutive vertices. The sides of $ABCD$ have the same length.

18. Answers vary.

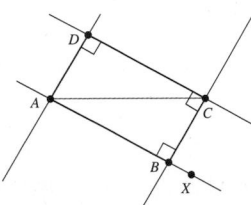

Given line segment $\overline{AC}$, use your straightedge to draw a line segment $\overline{AX}$ as shown. Construct a line through C that is perpendicular to $\overleftrightarrow{AX}$. Let B be the intersection of the new line and $\overleftrightarrow{AX}$. Construct a line through C that is perpendicular to $\overleftrightarrow{BC}$. Construct a line through A that is perpendicular to the perpendicular line you just constructed. Let D be the intersection of the two lines. Then $ABCD$ is a rectangle with the diagonal $\overline{AC}$.

19. Answers vary.

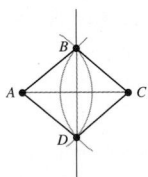

a. a right angle
b. The diagonals of a rhombus are perpendicular, and the diagonals bisect each other. Construct the perpendicular bisector of $\overline{AC}$. Set the radius of the compass to r units so that the radius is greater than $AC/2$. Place the center point of the compass at A, and swing an arc with radius r. Maintaining the same opening of the compass, place the center point of the compass at C and swing an arc. Let B and D be the points of intersection of the two arcs. Then $ABCD$ is a rhombus.

20. Pick two points on the line segment of the length b units; label them X and Y. Then place a straightedge at points X and Y and extend the line segment. Set the radius of a compass to b. Pick a point A on the line segment, and swing an arc so that it intersects the line segment in two locations. Label the points of intersection B and C. Then A is the midpoint of $\overline{BC}$ and $AC = b$. Construct the perpendicular bisector of $\overline{BC}$. Set the radius of the compass to a. Then put the center point of

the compass at A and swing an arc so that it intersects the perpendicular line you just drew. Label the point of intersection D.

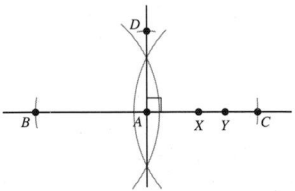

Then $\triangle ADC$ is a right triangle with legs of the lengths a and b units.

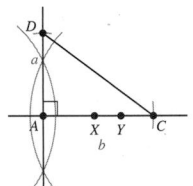

21. a. Suppose C lies on the perpendicular bisector of $\overline{AB}$.

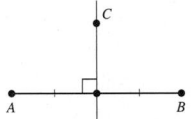

Let M be the midpoint of $\overline{AB}$.

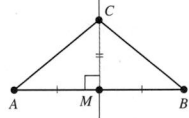

Then $\overline{AM} \cong \overline{BM}$, $\angle AMC \cong \angle BMC$, and $\overline{MC} \cong \overline{MC}$. Then $\triangle AMC \cong \triangle BMC$ by the SAS congruence axiom. Then $\overline{AC} \cong \overline{BC}$ by CPCTC.

b. Suppose C is a point such that $\overline{AC} \cong \overline{BC}$. If C belongs to $\overline{AB}$, then C is the midpoint of $\overline{AB}$. Then C automatically lies on the perpendicular bisector of $\overline{AB}$. Say C does not belong to $\overline{AB}$.

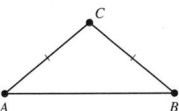

Let M be the midpoint of $\overline{AB}$.

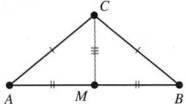

Then $\overline{AM} \cong \overline{BM}$, $\overline{AC} \cong \overline{BC}$, and $\overline{CM} \cong \overline{CM}$. Then $\triangle AMC \cong \triangle BMC$ by the SSS congruence axiom. $\angle AMC$ and $\angle BMC$ are corresponding parts, so they are congruent angles. They are congruent and supplementary angles, so each must be a right angle. So $\overleftrightarrow{CM}$ is perpendicular to $\overline{AB}$. The midpoint M and the point C belong to $\overleftrightarrow{CM}$, so C belongs to the perpendicular bisector of $\overline{AB}$.

22. a.

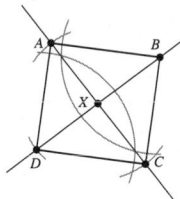

b. Use a straightedge to construct a line segment $\overline{AX}$. Set the compass radius to c. Put the center point of the compass at A, and swing an arc that intersects $\overline{AX}$. Label the point of intersection B. Then $AB = c$. Set the compass radius to b. Put the center point of the compass at A, and swing an arc. Set the compass radius to a. Put the center point of the compass at B, and swing an arc that intersects the previously constructed arc. Label the intersection of the arcs C. Then $AC = b$ and $CB = a$. Then $\triangle ABC$ has sides of the lengths a, b, and c units.

23. a. The diagonals are congruent and perpendicular.

b. Use a straightedge to construct a line segment through B and X. Set the compass radius to BX. Place the center point at X, and swing an arc that intersects the line segment. Label the point of intersection D. Construct the perpendicular bisector of $\overline{DB}$. Set the compass radius to BX. Place the center point at X, and swing an arc that intersects the perpendicular line segment at two points. Label the points of intersection A and C. Then $ABCD$ is a square.

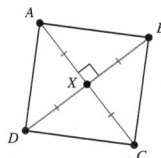

c. The diagonals of a square are congruent, perpendicular, and bisect each other. We first constructed point D so that X is the midpoint of $\overline{BD}$. So $\overline{DX} \cong \overline{XB}$. Then we constructed $\overline{AC}$ so that $\overline{AC} \cong \overline{DB}$, $\overline{AC} \perp \overline{DB}$, and X is the midpoint of $\overline{AC}$. Then $\overline{AX} \cong \overline{XC}$ and $DX = XB = AX = XC$. Then we have

Any two of the four triangles with the vertex X are congruent. For example, $\triangle AXD \cong \triangle AXB$ by the SAS congruence axiom. Then $\overline{AD} \cong \overline{AB}$ by CPCTC. Using this reasoning, all four sides of $ABCD$ are congruent. So $ABCD$ is a rhombus. Now we need to show the interior angles of the rhombus are right angles. $\triangle AXD \cong \triangle AXB$ by the SAS congruence axiom, and $\triangle DXA \cong \triangle AXB$ by the SAS congruence axiom. Then $\angle ADX \cong \angle ABX$ and $\angle DAX \cong \angle ABX$. Then $\angle ADX \cong \angle DAX$. But $\angle ADX$ and $\angle DAX$ are complementary angles, so m$\angle ADX = 45°$ and m$\angle DAX = 45°$. We can use the same reasoning to verify the angles created by the diagonals of the rhombus are $45°$ angles.

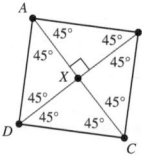

So the interior angles of the rhombus are right angles. Then $ABCD$ is a square.

24. a. Follow the steps in the answer to Question 12 to create a right triangle, making sure the legs have a length of 1 unit.

b. The hypotenuse has a length of $\sqrt{2}$ units because of the Pythagorean theorem:

$$c^2 = a^2 + b^2$$
$$c^2 = 1^2 + 1^2$$
$$c^2 = 2$$
$$c = \sqrt{2}$$

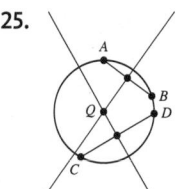

25.

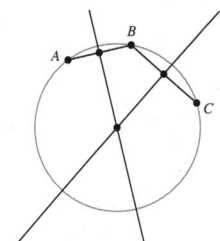

a. See the diagram. **b.** See the diagram.
c. See the diagram. **d.** See the diagram.
e. Q is the center of the circle. (See the diagram.)
f. The center of the circle Q satisfies the equation $AQ = BQ$, so it must lie on the perpendicular bisector of $\overline{AB}$. The center of the circle Q satisfies the equation $CQ = DQ$, so it must lie on the perpendicular bisector of $\overline{CD}$. The point of intersection of the two lines must be the center of the circle.

26. a.

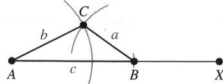

b. Use a straightedge to construct chords $\overline{AB}$ and $\overline{BC}$, and then use the techniques for constructing the perpendicular bisector of a line segment. The center of the circle lies on the perpendicular bisector of a chord. The point that lies on the intersection of two or more perpendicular bisectors of chords is the center of the circle.

27. We know that $1^2 + 2^2 = (\sqrt{5})^2$. If we construct a right triangle with legs of 1 and 2 units, then the hypotenuse of the right triangle has a length of $\sqrt{5}$ units. Use a straightedge to construct a line segment, and then pick a point A on the line segment. Set the compass radius to 1 unit. Put the center point at A, and swing an arc that intersects the line segment.

Label the point of intersection B. Maintaining the same compass opening, put the center point at B and swing another arc that intersects the line segment. Label the point of intersection C. Then $AC = 2$ units. Use a construction technique to construct a line through A that is perpendicular to $\overleftrightarrow{AC}$. Set the compass radius to 1 unit. Put the center point at A, and swing an arc that intersects the line segment. Label the point of intersection E. Then $AE = 1$ and $\overline{AE} \perp \overline{AC}$. Then $\triangle EAC$ is a right triangle with legs of 1 and 2 units, and the hypotenuse $\overline{EC}$ has a length of $\sqrt{5}$ units.

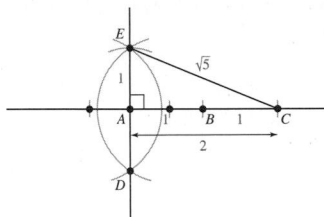

28. Use a straightedge to construct a line segment, and then pick a point A on the line segment. Set the compass radius to 2 units. Put the center point at A, and swing an arc that intersects the line segment. Label the point of intersection B. Then $AB = 2$ units. Maintaining the same compass opening, put the center point at B and swing another arc that intersects the line segment. Label the point of intersection C. Then $BC = 2$ units. Use a construction technique to construct the perpendicular bisector of $\overline{BC}$. Label the midpoint of $\overline{BC}$ as D. Then $AD = 3$ units.

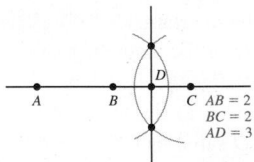

Set the compass radius to 2 units. Place the center point of the compass at D, and swing an arc. Maintaining the same compass opening, place the center point of the compass at A and swing an arc. Label the intersection of the arcs E.

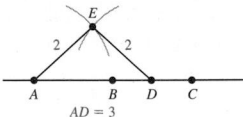

Then $\triangle EAD$ is a triangle with sides that have the ratio 2:2:3.

29. Construct the perpendicular bisector of $\overline{AB}$. Let C be the point of intersection of $\overline{AB}$ and the perpendicular bisector. Set the radius of a compass to CB. Put the center point of the compass at C, and construct a circle with the center C and radius CB. Then $\overline{AB}$ is a diameter of a circle with the center C.

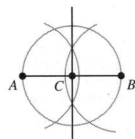

30. The known Fermat prime numbers are 3, 5, 17, 257, and 65,537.
a. yes   **b.** yes   **c.** no   **d.** no   **e.** no

31. Martin demonstrated a conceptual understanding of a tangent line, but he did not use construction techniques to construct the tangent line.

32. Put the center point on X, and swing an arc so that it intersects both sides of $\angle X$. Label the points of intersection A and B. Use a straightedge to draw the rays $\overrightarrow{XA}$ and $\overrightarrow{XB}$. Set the compass radius to a units. Put the center point of the compass at X, and swing an arc so that it intersects $\overrightarrow{XA}$. Label the point of intersection C. Then $XC = a$ units. Set the compass radius to b units. Put the center point of the compass at X, and swing an arc so that it intersects $\overrightarrow{XB}$. Label the point of intersection D. Then $XD = b$ units. Use a construction technique to draw a line through C that is parallel to $\overleftrightarrow{XD}$ and a line through D that is parallel to $\overleftrightarrow{XC}$. Let the intersection of these constructed lines be E. Then $\overline{XC} \parallel \overline{DE}$ and $\overline{XD} \parallel \overline{CE}$. Then quadrilateral $XDEC$ is a parallelogram.

33. The prime number 7 is a factor of 140, and 7 is not a Fermat prime number. So Euclidean tools cannot be used to construct a regular polygon with 140 sides.

34. Use a straightedge to construct a line segment that is longer than $a + b$. Pick a point A on the line segment, placing it near one end of the line segment. Set the compass radius to a. Place the center point at A, and swing an arc so that it intersects the line segment. Label the point of intersection B. Then $AB = a$. Set the compass radius to b. Place the center point at B, and swing an arc so that it intersects the line segment. Label the point of intersection C. Then $BC = b$. Then $AC = AB + BC = a + b$. Thus, $\overline{AC}$ has a length of $a + b$.

35. Use a straightedge to construct a line segment that is longer than b. Pick a point X on the line segment, near one end of the line segment. Set the compass radius to b. Place the center point at X, and swing an arc so that it intersects the line segment. Label the point of intersection Y. Then $XY = b$. Set the compass radius to a. Place the center point at X, and swing an arc so that it intersects $\overline{XY}$. Label the point of intersection Z. Then $XZ = b$. Z is between X and Y, so $XY = XZ + ZY$. Then $b = a + ZY$. Then $ZY = b - a$. Thus, $\overline{ZY}$ has a length of $b - a$.

36. a. The steps are described in the answer to Question 34.

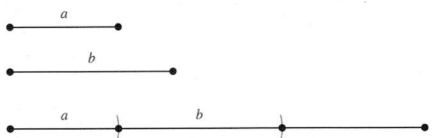

b. The steps are described in the answer to Question 35.

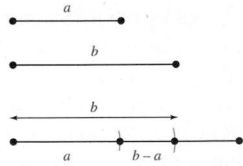

37. a. compass   **b.** straightedge   **c.** radius
   d. constructed   **e.** pencil point   **f.** center point
   g. perpendicular bisector   **h.** Euclidean   **i.** impossible

38.

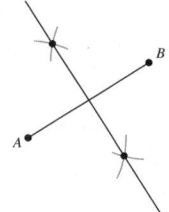

39. Use a straightedge to extend $\overline{AB}$. Construct a line that goes through A and is perpendicular to $\overleftrightarrow{AB}$. Put the center point of a compass at B, and swing an arc so that it intersects the perpendicular line in two locations. Label the points of intersection C and D. Then $\overline{CD} \perp \overline{AB}$ and $BC = BD$. Then $\triangle BCD$ is an isosceles triangle with an apex of B and an altitude of $\overline{AB}$.

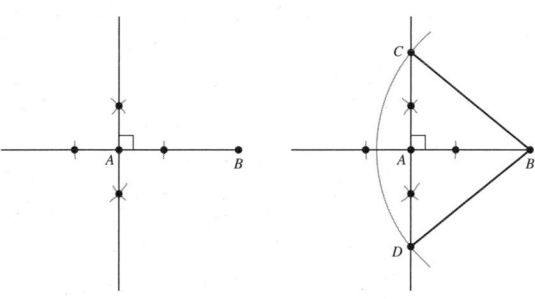

40. $\overrightarrow{BF}$ is the angle bisector for $\angle B$.

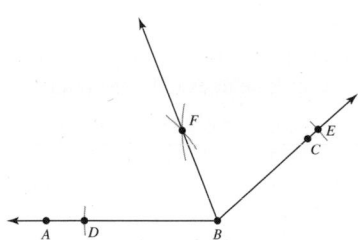

41. Construct a line that goes through A and is perpendicular to a side of $\angle A$. This will create a 40° angle. Bisect the 40° angle to create two 20° angles.

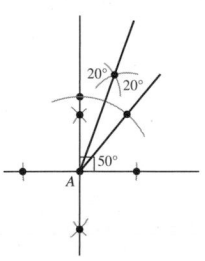

42. Set the compass radius to k units. Put the compass point at A, and swing an arc so that it intersects both sides of $\angle A$. Label the points of intersection B and C. Then $AB = AC$ and $\triangle ABC$ is an isosceles triangle with legs that have the length k units.

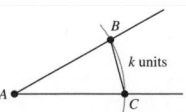

43. Use a straightedge to construct a line segment. Let E be one endpoint of the line segment. Set the radius of a compass to BC units. Put the center point of the compass at E, and swing

an arc that intersects the line segment. Label the point of intersection F. Set the radius of the compass to AC units. Put the center point of the compass at F, and swing an arc. Set the radius of the compass to AB units. Put the center point of the compass at E, and swing an arc so that the two arcs intersect. Label the point of intersection D. Then $\triangle DEF \cong \triangle ABC$ by the SSS congruence axiom.

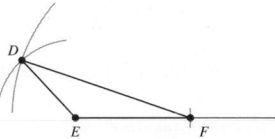

44. Use a straightedge to construct a line segment. Pick a point A on the line segment. Set the compass radius to 1 unit. Put the center point at A, and swing an arc that intersects the line segment. Label the point of intersection B. Repeat this as shown in the diagram so that $AD = 3$ units. Pick a point E on the line segment such that A is between E and D, as shown. Construct a line through E that is perpendicular to $\overleftrightarrow{AD}$. Use the compass to construct a point G on the perpendicular line such that $EG = 2$. Then $\triangle ADG$ is an obtuse triangle with a base of 3 units, a height of 2 units, and an area of 3 square units (because $\frac{1}{2}(3 \cdot 2) = 3$).

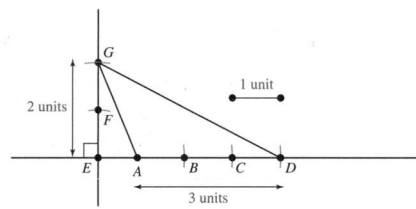

45. a. Use a straightedge to construct a line segment. Pick a point A on the line segment. Set the compass radius to b. Put the center point at A, and swing an arc that intersects the line segment. Let B be the point of intersection. Then $\overline{AB}$ has a length of b units. Construct a line through A and perpendicular to $\overleftrightarrow{AB}$. Set the compass radius to c. Put the center point at B, and swing an arc that intersects the perpendicular line through A. Let C be the point of intersection. Then $\overline{AC} \perp \overline{AB}$ and $\overline{BC}$ has a length of c units. Then $\triangle ABC$ is right triangle, with a hypotenuse of the length c units and a leg of the length b units.

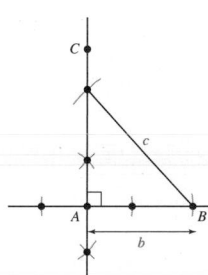

b. The side $\overline{AB}$ has a length of b units, the side $\overline{BC}$ has a length of c units, and $\overline{AC} \perp \overline{AB}$. The right angle is opposite $\overline{BC}$, so $\overline{BC}$ is the hypotenuse.

46. Construct an equilateral triangle, and then bisect one of the interior angles. $\angle OBR$ is a 30° angle.

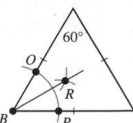

47. Construct an equilateral triangle. Bisect an interior angle to create a 30° angle. Bisect a 30° angle to obtain a 15° angle. Copy a 15° angle so that one of the sides of the angles is a side of the triangle with a common vertex. Then 60° + 15° = 75°, so $\angle ABC$ has the measure 75°.

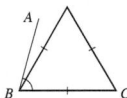

48. Answers vary. The diagonals of a kite are perpendicular, exactly one diagonal bisects the other, and there are two pairs of congruent sides (with no side in common). Use a straightedge to construct a line segment. Pick a point A on the line segment. Set the compass radius to a units. Put the center point at A, and swing an arc that intersects the line segment. Label the point of intersection C. Construct the perpendicular bisector of $\overline{AC}$. Then pick a point B on the perpendicular bisector to create an isosceles triangle $\triangle ABC$. Set the radius of the compass to b units. Put the center point of the compass at B, and swing an arc that intersects the perpendicular line. Label the point of intersection D. Then $ABCD$ is a kite.

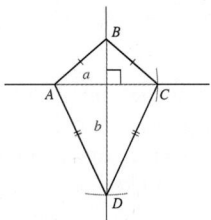

49. 16 + 36 = 52, so $4^2 + 6^2 = (\sqrt{52})^2$. This means a right triangle with legs of the lengths 4 and 6 units will have a hypotenuse of the length $\sqrt{52}$ units.

a. Use a straightedge to construct a line segment with endpoint A, making sure the line segment is longer than 4 units. Set the compass opening to the length of the leg that is 4 units. Put the center point at A, and swing an arc that intersects the line segment. Let B be the point of intersection. Then $AB = 4$ units. Using the techniques in this section, construct a line that passes through A and is perpendicular to $\overline{AB}$. Set the compass opening to the length of the leg that is 6 units. Put the center point at A, and swing an arc that intersects the perpendicular line. Let C be the point of intersection. Then $AC = 6$ units. Use the straightedge to construct the line segment $\overline{BC}$. Then

$\triangle ABC$ is a right triangle with legs of 4 and 6 units and a hypotenuse of $\sqrt{52}$ units.

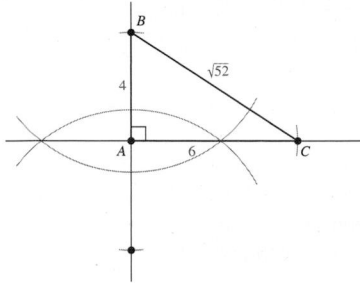

b. The triangle is a right triangle with legs that have the lengths 4 and 6 units. Let h be the hypotenuse. Then

$$h^2 = 4^2 + 6^2$$
$$h^2 = 16 + 36$$
$$h^2 = 52$$
$$h = \sqrt{52} \text{ units.}$$

50. a.

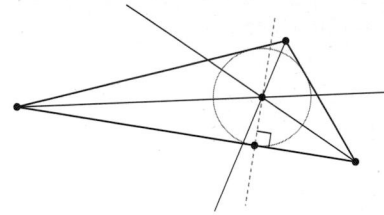

b. The angle bisectors intersect at one point (concurrent).
c. The circle intersects each side at exactly one point.

51. a. Construct the three angle bisectors. The intersection of the angle bisectors is the incenter.
b. Construct a line through the incenter that is perpendicular to one of the sides (shown by the dashed line). The line segment from the incenter to the intersection of the side and the perpendicular bisector is the radius of the incircle.

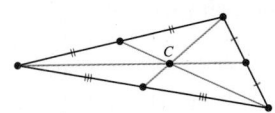

52. Construct the midpoint of each side of the triangle. Use a straightedge to construct the median for each side. The intersection of the medians is the centroid.

53. a.

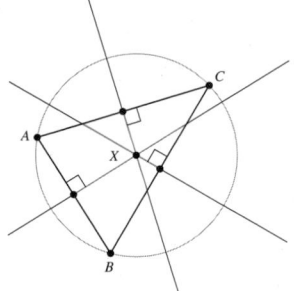

b. The perpendicular bisectors intersect at one point (concurrent).

c. The circle intersects each vertex of the triangle, that is, $XA = XB = XC$.

54.

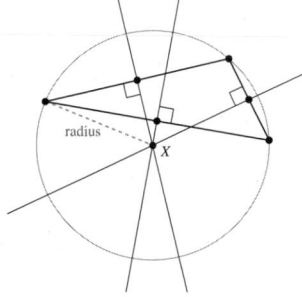

55. a. X lies on the perpendicular bisector of $\overline{AB}$, so $AX = BX$.
b. X lies on the perpendicular bisector of $\overline{BC}$, so $BX = CX$.
c. $AX = BX$ and $BX = CX$, so $AX = CX$. Then $\overline{AX} \cong \overline{BX}$ and $\overline{BX} \cong \overline{CX}$. Then $\overline{AX} \cong \overline{CX}$ by the transitive property of congruence. Then $AX = CX$.
d. $AX = BX = CX$. This means that points A, B, and C lie on a circle with the center X and radius AX. So the circumcenter X of $\triangle ABC$ is equidistant from vertices A, B, and C.

56. X is the orthocenter.

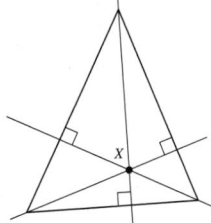

57. X is the orthocenter.

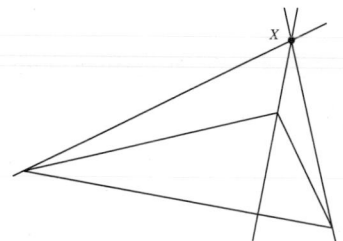

58. a. Use techniques discussed in this section to locate the midpoint of each side.

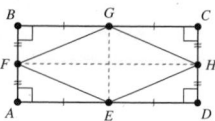

b. $EFGH$ is a rhombus (to see this, think about applying the SAS congruence axiom to show that $FE = EH = HG = GF$).

c. Each diagonal of the rhombus is congruent and parallel to an appropriate side of the rectangle.

59. The points on an arc are equidistant (equal distance) from the center of the arc, and the points on a perpendicular bisector of a line segment are equidistant from the endpoints of the line segment. So the concept of *equidistant* is common to both.

60. Suppose the larger circle has radius R and the smaller circle has radius r. Then

$$\pi R^2 = 2\pi r^2$$
$$R^2 = 2r^2$$
$$R = \sqrt{2r^2}$$
$$R = \sqrt{2}\sqrt{r^2}$$
$$R = \sqrt{2}r$$

Think about a right isosceles triangle with legs of the length r units. The length h of the hypotenuse is $h = \sqrt{r^2 + r^2} = \sqrt{2r^2} = \sqrt{2}r$. Given a circle with the radius r units, we need to construct a right isosceles triangle with legs of the length r units. Then the hypotenuse will have a length of $\sqrt{2}r$ units. Now we can set the compass opening to $\sqrt{2}r$ units and construct a circle with a radius of $\sqrt{2}r$ units. Then the area of the larger circle will be twice the area of the smaller circle.

Construct a circle with the center C and radius r. Use a straightedge to construct a line segment through C and intersecting the circle at two points. Label the points of intersection A and B. Then $\overline{AB}$ is the diameter of the circle. Using the techniques discussed in this section, construct the perpendicular bisector of $\overline{AB}$. Let D be a point of intersection of the circle and the perpendicular bisector. Then $DC = r$ units. Then $\triangle DCB$ is a right isosceles triangle with legs of the length r units and a hypotenuse of $\sqrt{2}r$ units.

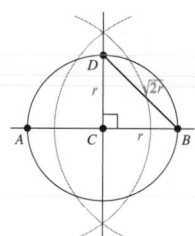

Set the compass opening to the length of $\sqrt{2}r$ units. Put the center point at D (or anywhere), and construct a circle with a radius of $\sqrt{2}r$ units. The area of the newly constructed circle with the radius $\sqrt{2}r$ is twice the area of the circle with the radius r.

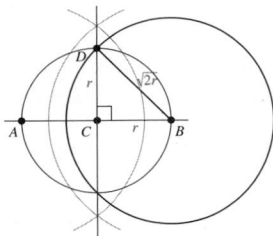

61. The following diagram shows some properties of the diagonals of a square.

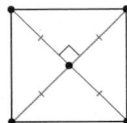

Use a straightedge to construct the diagonals of a square. Label the point of intersection of the diagonals E. Set the radius of a compass to EA. Put the center point of the compass at E, and construct a circle. The circle with the center E and radius EA circumscribes the square.

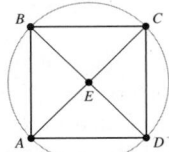

62. The diagonals of the square are also diameters of the circle. Use a straightedge to construct a diameter of the circle. Label the endpoints A and C. Construct a perpendicular bisector of the diameter. Label the points of intersection of the perpendicular line B and D. Then $ABCD$ is a square that is inscribed in the circle.

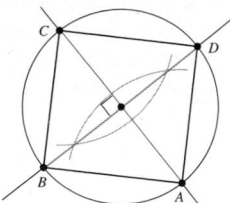

63.

a. See the diagram.   **b.** See the diagram.
c. Lines l and n are parallel by the F Postulate.

64. X and Y are the midpoints of the bases of the trapezoid. We see that the perpendicular bisector of the longer base intersects the midpoint of the shorter base.

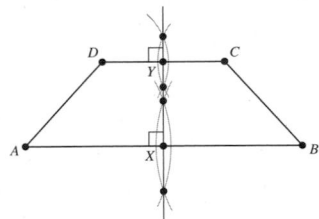

SECTION 12.3

1. no

2. $\dfrac{MN}{ST} = \dfrac{ML}{TU}$, $\dfrac{MN}{ST} = \dfrac{LN}{US}$, and $\dfrac{ML}{TU} = \dfrac{LN}{SU}$

3. a.

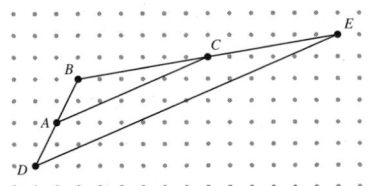

b. $\triangle WIF \sim \triangle OHA$ **c.** SSS similarity axiom

4. a.

b. $\triangle AGM \sim \triangle XBT$ **c.** SAS similarity axiom

5. a.

b. $\triangle QPR \sim \triangle TSU$ **c.** AA similarity axiom

6. If 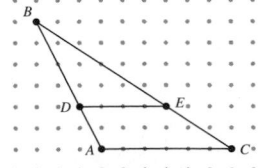, then $\triangle GAM \sim \triangle BXT$.

7. Answers vary. $\triangle ABC \sim \triangle DBE$

8. Answers vary. $\triangle ABC \sim \triangle DBE$

9. part (c)

10. a. $\triangle XYZ \sim \triangle UVW$

b. The ratios of the corresponding sides are identical: $\frac{6k}{6} = \frac{7k}{7} = \frac{4k}{4} = k$. So $\triangle XYZ \sim \triangle UVW$ by the SSS similarity axiom.

11. a.

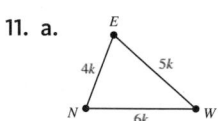

b. $NE = 12.8$ units
$EW = 16$ units
$NW = 19.2$ units

12. a. The triangles are similar because of the AA similarity axiom.

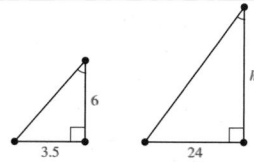

b. approximately 41 ft

13. Solve the equation $\frac{23}{15} = \frac{AB + 7}{AB}$ to get $AB = 13.125$ feet.

14. Every ratio of corresponding sides must be 2.8.

a. not possible, because $\frac{AC}{DC} = \frac{4.0}{11.2} \approx 0.36 \neq 2.8$

b. not possible, because $\frac{AB}{DE} = \frac{7.3}{3.2} \approx 2.3 \neq 2.8$

c. not possible, because $\frac{BC}{EC} = \frac{8.2}{3.8} \approx 2.2 \neq 2.8$

d. possible, because $\frac{AC}{DC} = \frac{9.8}{3.5} = 2.8$

15. a. $\triangle ACE$ and $\triangle BCD$

b. $\overline{BD}$ and $\overline{AE}$ are parallel lines cut by the transversal $\overline{AC}$, and $\angle A$ and $\angle CBD$ are corresponding angles formed by the transversal, so $\angle A \cong \angle CBD$. $\angle C \cong \angle C$ by the reflexive property of congruence. Then $\triangle ACE \sim \triangle BCD$ by the AA similarity axiom.

16. Yes; they are similar triangles because both have a 90° angle and the triangle with the 18° angle also has an angle that measures 72°. By the AA similarity axiom, the two triangles are congruent.

17. a. $m\angle L = 56°$ **b.** $EW = 9$

18. a. 25

b. The given is $\frac{AB}{DE} = 5$. So we know $\frac{b_A}{b_D} = 5$ and $\frac{h_A}{h_D} = 5$. Then $b_A = 5b_D$ and $h_A = 5h_D$. Then

$$\text{area of } \triangle ABC = (1/2)\, b_A h_A$$
$$= (1/2)(5b_D)(5h_D)$$
$$= 25 \cdot [(1/2)\, b_D h_D]$$
$$= 25 \cdot \text{area of } \triangle DEF$$

19. Suppose $\frac{AB}{BC} = \frac{DE}{EF}$. Then $\frac{AB}{AC - AB} = \frac{DE}{DF - DE}$. Then $AB(DF - DE) = DE(AC - AB)$. Then $AB \cdot DF - AB \cdot DE = DE \cdot AC - DE \cdot AB$. Then $AB \cdot DF = DE \cdot AC$. Then $\frac{AB}{AC} = \frac{DE}{DF}$.

20. Answers vary. For example, draw a rectangle and a square. They each have four right angles, but the polygons are not similar.

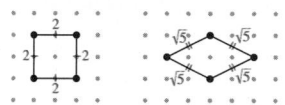

21. Answers vary. For example, the ratios of the sides of a square and the corresponding sides of a rhombus are identical, but the polygons are not similar.

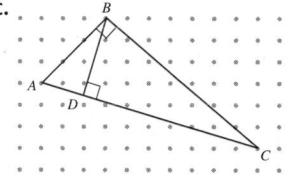

22. The base angles $\angle K$ and $\angle T$ of $\triangle KIT$ are congruent. Then $m\angle I + 2 \cdot m\angle K = 180°$. Similarly, $m\angle O + 2 \cdot m\angle W = 180°$. Then $m\angle I + 2 \cdot m\angle K = m\angle O + 2 \cdot m\angle W$. Then $2 \cdot m\angle K = 2 \cdot m\angle W$, because $\angle I \cong \angle O$. Then $m\angle K = m\angle W$. Then $\triangle KIT \sim \triangle WON$ by the AA similarity axiom.

23. Solve $\frac{20}{5} = \frac{5x + 2}{x + 2}$ to get $x = 6$. Solve $\frac{20}{5} = \frac{4y + 10}{3}$ to get $y = 1/2$.

24. $DE = 14k$, $EC = 10k$, and $DC = 8k$

25. a. $AC = \sqrt{109} \approx 10.4$ units   **b.** $AB = \sqrt{18} \approx 4.2$ units

c.

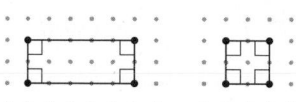

$\angle BAD \cong \angle CAB$, because $\angle A \cong \angle A$. $\angle ADB \cong \angle ABC$, because right angles are congruent. Then $\triangle ADB \sim \triangle ABC$ by the AA similarity axiom.

d. $\triangle ADB \sim \triangle ABC$, as shown. Then $\frac{AB}{AC} = \frac{BD}{CB} = \frac{AD}{AB}$, so $\frac{AB}{AC} = \frac{AD}{AB}$. So

$$AB^2 = AC \cdot AD$$
$$(\sqrt{18})^2 = \sqrt{109} \cdot AD$$
$$18 = \sqrt{109} \cdot AD$$
$$AD = \frac{18}{\sqrt{109}}$$

So $AD \approx 1.7$ units (to the nearest tenth).

26. $\frac{AB}{DE} = 5$, so $AB = 5\, DE$.

a.

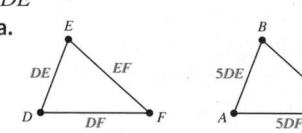

b.
$$\frac{P_A}{P_D} = \frac{AB + BC + AC}{DE + EF + DF}$$
$$= \frac{5DE + 5EF + 5DF}{DE + EF + DF}$$
$$= \frac{5(DE + EF + DF)}{DE + EF + DF}$$
$$= 5$$

So $\frac{P_A}{P_D} = 5$. This means the perimeter of $\triangle ABC$ is five times the perimeter of $\triangle DEF$ (think of the equation $P_A = 5P_D$).

27. a. All the angles are right angles, and the ratios of the longer sides equal the ratios of the shorter sides:
$$\frac{9}{3} = \frac{12}{4} = \frac{9}{3} = \frac{12}{4} = 3.$$ Then $ABCD$ and $EFGH$ are similar because corresponding angles are congruent and corresponding sides have identical ratios.

b.
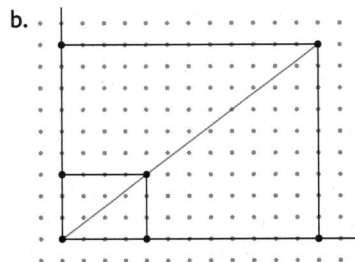

The diagonals have the same slope.

28. a. All the angles are right angles, but the ratios of the longer sides do not equal the ratios of the shorter sides: $\frac{8}{4} \neq \frac{7}{3}$.

Then $ABCD$ and $EFGH$ are not similar rectangles, because their corresponding sides do not have identical ratios.

b.
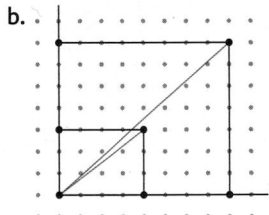

The diagonals have different slopes.

29. The corresponding sides have identical ratios.

30. The corresponding angles are congruent.

31. The two acute angles are congruent, and the two right angles are congruent. So there is a correspondence between the vertices of the triangles such that two corresponding angles are congruent. Then the two triangles are similar because of the AA similarity axiom.

32. Answers vary. There are three possible approaches, as shown in Concept Map 12.1. Each approach relies on parallel lines. For example, given $\triangle ABC$, split two sides of the triangle with a line segment that is parallel to the third side. The two triangles are similar by the AA similarity axiom.

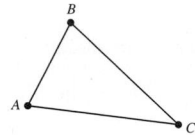
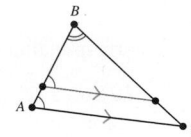

33. If you can show that the ratios of the corresponding sides have identical ratios, then you can use the SSS similarity axiom to prove that the two triangles are similar.

34. If you can show that there are two angles in one triangle with corresponding angles that are congruent in another triangle, then you can use the AA similarity axiom to prove that the two triangles are similar.

35. a. congruent **b.** identical **c.** 7 **d.** 49
e. similarity **f.** ~ **g.** indirect
h. proportional reasoning

36. a. $\triangle YEP \sim \triangle YXZ$
b.
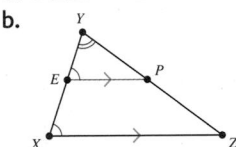

$\overline{YX}$ is a transversal that cuts two parallel line segments $\overline{EP}$ and $\overline{XZ}$, so it creates corresponding angles that are congruent ($\angle E \cong \angle X$, as marked). $\angle Y \cong \angle Y$ by the reflexive property of congruence. So $\triangle YEP \sim \triangle YXZ$ by the AA similarity axiom.

37. $\triangle ATP \sim \triangle HNE$

38.
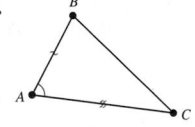
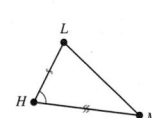

39. a. $\triangle STU \sim \triangle YZX$ by the AA similarity axiom.
b. The two triangles have a pair of congruent angles because they are vertical angles and another pair of congruent angles because of congruent alternate interior angles. Then $\triangle AXB \sim \triangle NXM$, by the AA similarity axiom.
c. $\frac{3.5}{6.5} = \frac{3}{5.4}$, and $\angle D \cong \angle Q$. So two pairs of corresponding sides have identical ratios, and their included angles are congruent. So $\triangle HDT \sim \triangle SQL$, by the SAS similarity axiom.

40. $\triangle ABC \sim \triangle DEC$, so $\angle A \cong \angle D$. The transversal $\overleftrightarrow{AD}$ cuts $\overleftrightarrow{AB}$ and $\overleftrightarrow{ED}$, and there is a pair of alternate interior angles that are congruent, so $\overleftrightarrow{AB}$ and $\overleftrightarrow{ED}$ are parallel. So $\overline{AB}$ and $\overline{ED}$ are parallel.

41. a. $\triangle ACE \sim \triangle BCD$
b.

Statement	Reason
1. $\angle CBD \cong \angle CAE$	1. Because right angles are congruent
2. $\angle C \cong \angle C$	2. Reflexive property of congruence
3. $\triangle ACE \sim \triangle BCD$	3. AA similarity axiom

42. 405 square units

43. $\dfrac{AB}{DE} = \dfrac{15}{3} = 5$, and $\dfrac{AC}{DF} = \dfrac{10}{2} = 5$. $\angle A \cong \angle D$, because right angles are congruent. So two corresponding sides of the triangles have identical ratios (the ratio is 5), and their included angles are congruent. So $\triangle ABC \sim \triangle DEF$ by the SAS similarity axiom.

44. $AB = 2$, $AC = \sqrt{8}$, $BC = \sqrt{20}$. $EF = 3$, $ED = \sqrt{18}$, and $FD = \sqrt{45}$. $\dfrac{BC}{FD} = \dfrac{2}{3}$, $\dfrac{AC}{ED} = \dfrac{2}{3}$, and $\dfrac{AB}{EF} = \dfrac{2}{3}$. The corresponding sides of $\triangle ABC$ and $\triangle EFD$ have a common ratio $\left(\dfrac{2}{3}\right)$, so $\triangle ABC \sim \triangle EFD$ by the SSS similarity axiom.

45. $\angle UTY \cong \angle XVZ$, because $\overleftrightarrow{UT}$ and $\overleftrightarrow{XV}$ are parallel lines cut by a transversal, creating corresponding angles that are congruent. $\angle UYT \cong \angle XZV$, because $\overleftrightarrow{UY}$ and $\overleftrightarrow{XT}$ are parallel lines cut by a transversal, creating corresponding angles that are congruent. Then $\triangle TUY \sim \triangle VXZ$ by the AA similarity axiom.

46. a. $\triangle HOT \sim \triangle AET$ **b.** $n \approx 8.66$

47. $VW = 67.5$ units, $UV = 75$ units, and $UW = 112.5$ units

48. a. $\triangle HAT \sim \triangle PYT$
b. $n = 10$, $t = 6$, and $r = 9$

49. a. The angles in both rectangles are right angles. The ratio of the corresponding sides is 5. By the definition of similar polygons, the two rectangles are similar.
b. Suppose the dimensions of the smaller rectangle are l and w. Then the dimensions of the larger rectangle are $5l$ and $5w$. Then the area of the larger rectangle is $(5l)(5w) = 25(lw)$, which is 25 times the area of the smaller rectangle.

50.

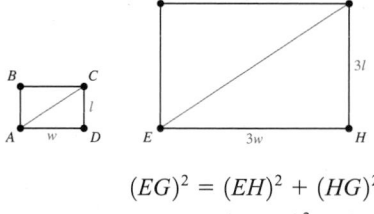

$$(EG)^2 = (EH)^2 + (HG)^2$$
$$= (3 \cdot AD)^2 + (3 \cdot DC)^2$$
$$= 3^2 \cdot AD^2 + 3^2 \cdot DC^2$$
$$= 3^2 (AD^2 + DC^2)$$
$$= 3^2 \cdot AC^2$$

So $EG = 3 \cdot AC$. The diagonal $\overline{EG}$ is three times longer than the diagonal $\overline{AC}$.

51. 7014 square units

52. $ABCD \sim EFGH$ and $\dfrac{AB}{EF} = 8$ are given. Then

$\dfrac{AB}{EF} = \dfrac{BC}{FG} = \dfrac{CD}{GH} = \dfrac{AD}{EH} = 8$. Then $AB = 8 \cdot EF$,

$BC = 8 \cdot FG$, $CD = 8 \cdot GH$, and $AD = 8 \cdot EH$.

$$\dfrac{P_A}{P_E} = \dfrac{AB + BC + CD + AD}{EF + FG + GH + EH}$$
$$= \dfrac{8 \cdot EF + 8 \cdot FG + 8 \cdot GH + 8 \cdot EH}{EF + FG + GH + EH}$$
$$= \dfrac{8(EF + FG + GH + EH)}{EF + FG + GH + EH}$$
$$= 8$$

53. a. no **b.** yes **c.** yes **d.** yes

54. 90 cm

55. 5 cm²

56. $\triangle ABC \sim \triangle DEF$, so $\angle A \cong \angle D$ and $\angle B \cong \angle E$. $\triangle DEF \sim \triangle GHI$, so $\angle D \cong \angle G$ and $\angle E \cong \angle H$. Then $\angle A \cong \angle G$ and $\angle B \cong \angle H$ by the transitive property of congruence. Then $\triangle ABC \sim \triangle GHI$ by the AA similarity axiom.

57. $\triangle SPT \sim \triangle SAK$, so $\dfrac{SP}{SA} = \dfrac{ST}{SK} = \dfrac{PT}{AK}$. Then $\dfrac{SP}{SA} = \dfrac{PT}{AK}$. Then $SP \cdot AK = SA \cdot PT$. Then $\dfrac{SP}{PT} = \dfrac{SA}{AK}$.

58. The perimeter of $\triangle DOG$ is 69 units, and the perimeter of $\triangle RUN$ is 23 units.

59. $x = 2.55$ units

60. a.

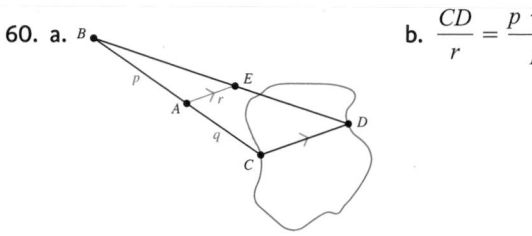

b. $\dfrac{CD}{r} = \dfrac{p + q}{p}$

REVIEW QUESTIONS

1. a. $\triangle YPS$ **b.** $\angle W$ **c.** HO

2. a. $\angle EFG$ **b.** EF **c.** 65°

3. a. $\angle L$ **b.** $\angle KLW$

4. a. CPCTC
b. CPCTC

5. $\overline{XZ}$

6. $\overline{OC}$ and $\overline{OD}$ equal to the radius of the circle. $\overline{DC}$ is longer than the radius. So $\triangle DOC$ is an isosceles triangle with base angles $\angle OCE$ and $\angle ODE$. The base angles of an isosceles triangle are congruent, so $\angle OCE \cong \angle ODE$.

7. $m\angle 1 = 27°$, $m\angle 2 = 126°$, $m\angle 3 = 54°$, $m\angle 4 = 63°$, and $m\angle 5 = 63°$

8. 14 units

9. $\overline{DK} \cong \overline{YL}$

10. $\overline{TU} \cong \overline{WU}$ is given. $\angle TUS \cong \angle WUV$, because vertical angles are congruent. And $\overline{US} \cong \overline{UV}$ is given. So $\triangle TUS \cong \triangle WUV$ by the SAS congruence axiom. Then $\angle S \cong \angle V$ by CPCTC. However, in the diagram, we are given that $\angle S$ is not congruent to $\angle V$. $\angle S$ should be congruent to $\angle V$.

11. a. yes, by the SSS congruence axiom
b. no, because SSA is not a congruence axiom
c. no, because AAA is not a congruence axiom

12.

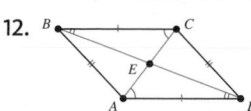

a. $ABCD$ is a parallelogram. $\overline{BC} \cong \overline{DA}$, because opposite sides of a parallelogram are congruent. Then $\angle BCA \cong \angle DAC$, because a transversal that cuts parallel lines creates congruent alternate interior angles. Then $\angle CBE \cong \angle ADE$, because a transversal that cuts parallel lines creates congruent alternate interior angles. So $\triangle BCE \cong \triangle DAE$ by the ASA congruence axiom.

b. From part (a), $\overline{BE} \cong \overline{ED}$ by CPCTC. So the intersection of the diagonals, *E,* is also the midpoint of diagonal $\overline{BD}$.

c. From part (a), $\overline{CE} \cong \overline{AE}$ by CPCTC. So the intersection of the diagonals, *E,* is also the midpoint of diagonal $\overline{AC}$.

13. 240°

14. a.

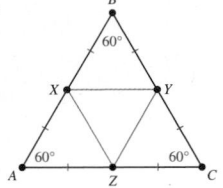

b. $\overline{AX} \cong \overline{BX}$, $\angle A \cong \angle B$, and $\overline{AZ} \cong \overline{BY}$, so $\triangle AXZ \cong \triangle BXY$ by the SAS congruence axiom. Then $\overline{XZ} \cong \overline{XY}$ by CPCTC. $\overline{AX} \cong \overline{CY}$, $\angle A \cong \angle C$, and $\overline{AZ} \cong \overline{CZ}$, so $\triangle AXZ \cong \triangle CYZ$ by the SAS congruence axiom. Then $\overline{XZ} \cong \overline{ZY}$ by CPCTC. Then $XZ = XY = ZY$. Then $\triangle XYZ$ is an equilateral triangle.

15. a.

Statement	Reason
1. $\angle BCE \cong \angle DAE$	1. Because alternate interior angles created by a transversal that cuts parallel lines are congruent
2. $\overline{BC} \cong \overline{DA}$	2. Because the sides of a rhombus are congruent
3. $\angle CBE \cong \angle ADE$	3. Because alternate interior angles created by a transversal that cuts parallel lines are congruent
4. $\triangle BCE \cong \triangle DAE$	4. ASA congruence axiom

b.

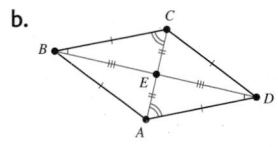

Statement	Reason
1. $\overline{BE} \cong \overline{DE}$	1. Because $\triangle BCE \cong \triangle DAE$ from part (a) implies $\overline{BE} \cong \overline{DE}$ by CPCTC
2. $\overline{BC} \cong \overline{DC}$	2. Because the sides of a rhombus are congruent
3. $\overline{CE} \cong \overline{CE}$	3. Reflexive property of congruence
4. $\triangle BCE \cong \triangle DCE$	4. SSS congruence axiom

c. In part (b), we showed $\triangle BCE \cong \triangle DCE$. Then $\angle BEC \cong \angle DEC$ by CPCTC. $\angle BEC$ and $\angle DEC$ are supplementary angles. Two angles that are congruent and supplementary are right angles. Then $\angle BEC$ and $\angle DEC$ are right angles. Therefore, the diagonals of a rhombus are perpendicular.

16. a. construction   **b.** straightedge   **c.** compass
d. equidistant   **e.** center   **f.** pencil   **g.** radius

17. Use a straightedge to construct a line. Pick a point on the line, and label the point *A.* Set the compass radius to *a.* Place the center point on *A,* and construct a circle. Label one of the points of intersection of the circle and line *D.* Pick a point on the circle, and label it *B.* Maintaining the same compass opening, put the center point at *D* and construct an arc, and then put the center point at *B* and swing an arc that intersects the other arc. Label the point of intersection *C. ABCD* is a parallelogram because opposite sides are congruent (See Example 12.9). All sides have the same length, which make the parallelogram a rhombus.

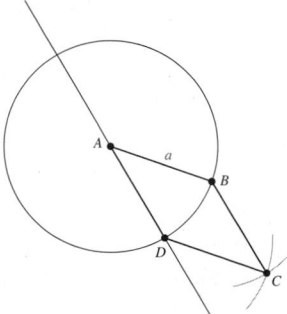

18. Use a straightedge to construct a line. Pick a point on the line, label the point *A.* Set the compass radius to *a.* Place the center point on *A* and construct an arc that intersects the line. Label the point of intersection *B.* Maintaining the same compass opening, put the center point at *A* and construct an arc, and then put the center point at *B* and swing an arc that intersects the other arc. Label the point of intersection *C. $\triangle ABC$* is an equilateral triangle.

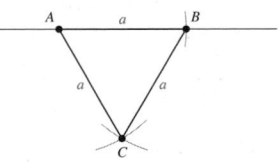

19. Pick a point in the plane, and label it *C.* Set the radius of a compass to *a.* Construct a circle with the center *C* and radius *a.* Pick any point on the circle, and label it *A.* Set the radius of the compass to *b.* Put the center point of the compass at *A,* and swing an arc so that it intersects the circle at one point. Label the point of intersection *B.* Then $\triangle ABC$ is an isosceles triangle with legs that have a length of *a* units and a base that has a length of *b* units.

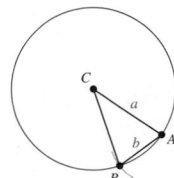

20. Use a straightedge to construct a line. Pick a point on the line, and label it *A.* Set the radius of a compass to *b.* Place the center point at *A,* and swing an arc that intersects the line at two places. Label the points of intersection *B* and *C. A* is the midpoint of $\overline{CB}$. Construct the perpendicular bisector of $\overline{CB}$. Set the radius of the compass to *a.* Place the center point at *A,* and swing an arc that intersects the perpendicular bisector. Label the point of intersection D. Then $\triangle ABD$ is a right triangle with legs that have the lengths a and b units.

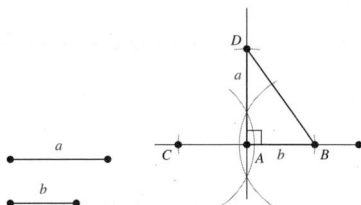

21. a. Use a straightedge to construct a line. Pick a point on the line, and label it A. Set the radius of a compass to b. Place the center point at A, and swing an arc that intersects the line at one place. Label the points of intersection B. Set the radius of the compass to a. Place the center point at A, and swing an arc. Set the radius of the compass to c. Place the center point at B, and swing an arc that intersects the other arc. Label the point of intersection C. Then $\triangle ABC$ is a triangle with sides that have the lengths a, b, and c units.

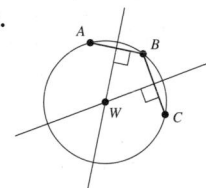

b. B lies on a circle with the center A and radius b, so $AB = b$ units. C lies on a circle with the center A and radius a, so $AC = a$ units. C also lies on a circle with the center B and radius c, so $BC = c$ units. Then $\triangle ABC$ is a triangle with sides that have the lengths a, b, and c units.

22. a.

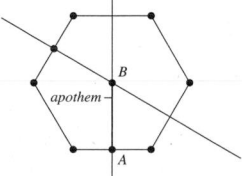

b. The center W is equidistant from A and B, so it lies on the perpendicular bisector of $\overline{AB}$. Similarly, W lies on the perpendicular bisector of $\overline{BC}$. So W is the intersection of the perpendicular bisectors.

23. The center of the circle is the intersection of the perpendicular bisectors of the sides. Construct the perpendicular bisectors for two sides of the polygon. Label the intersection of a side and perpendicular bisector A. Label the point of intersection of the perpendicular bisectors B. Use a straightedge to construct a line segment from A to B. Then $\overline{AB}$ is an apothem of the hexagon.

24. Use a straightedge to construct a line n through P that intersects line l. Label the point of intersection of the two lines A. Put the center point of a compass at A, and swing an arc that intersects lines l and n. Label the points of intersection B and C. Maintaining the same compass opening, put the center point of the compass at P and swing an arc that intersects line n. Label the point of intersection of D. Set the compass radius to BC. Put the center point of the compass at D, and swing an arc that intersects the other arc. Label the point of intersection of the two arcs E. Use the straightedge to construct a line m through P and E. Then lines m and l are parallel.

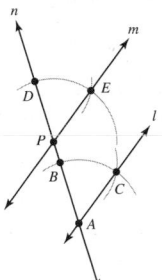

25. a. $\sqrt{5}$ units

b. Construct a right triangle with sides of the lengths 1 and 2 units. The hypotenuse has a length of $\sqrt{5}$ units.

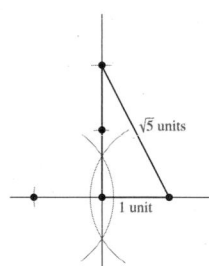

Set the radius of a compass to $\sqrt{5}$. Then use the compass to construct a circle with a radius of $\sqrt{5}$ units.

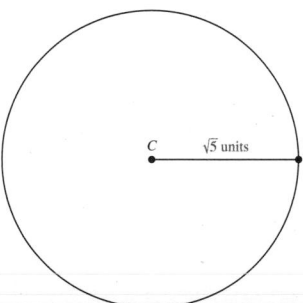

26. Answers may vary. Use a straightedge to construct a line through A and C. Construct a line through B perpendicular to $\overleftrightarrow{AC}$. Label the point of intersection of the perpendicular bisector and $\overleftrightarrow{AC}$ as D. Set the radius of a compass to BD. Then put the center point of the compass at B and swing an arc so that it intersects the perpendicular bisector. Label the point of intersection of the perpendicular bisector and the arc as E. Consider the triangle $\triangle AEC$. The base of $\triangle AEC$ is the same as the base of $\triangle ABC$, but the height of $\triangle AEC$ is twice the height of $\triangle ABC$. So the area of $\triangle AEC = \frac{1}{2}(b \cdot 2h)$ $= 2 \cdot (\frac{1}{2}bh)$; that is, it is twice the area of $\triangle ABC$.

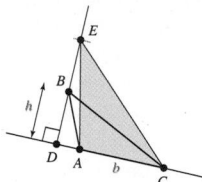

27. a. yes **b.** no **c.** yes **d.** no **e.** yes **f.** no
g. no **h.** no

28. a. Yes; two angles in one triangle are congruent to two angles in another triangle. So $\triangle ASK \sim \triangle OYU$ because of the AA similarity axiom.

b. Yes; $\dfrac{5.5}{4.4} = \dfrac{4.0}{3.2} = \dfrac{3.5}{2.8} = 1.25$, so $\triangle ACT \sim \triangle OGD$ because of the SSS similarity axiom.

c. No; $\dfrac{5.5}{4.4} \neq \dfrac{3.4}{2.6}$. In similar triangles, the longest sides must be corresponding sides, the shortest sides must be corresponding sides, and the ratios of corresponding sides must be identical.

29. a.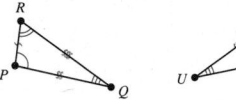

b. $\triangle PQR \sim \triangle SUT$

30. a.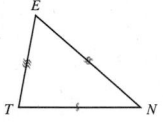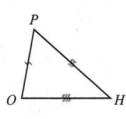

b. $\triangle TEN \sim \triangle OHP$
c. SSS similarity axiom

31. a.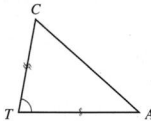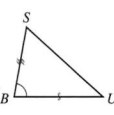

b. $\triangle CAT \sim \triangle SUB$
c. SAS similarity axiom

32. a.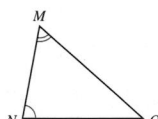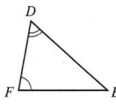

b. $\triangle MNO \sim \triangle DFE$
c. AA similarity axiom

33. No; one triangle has the angle measures 90°, 20°, and 70°, whereas the other triangle has the angle measures 90°, 68°, and 22°. There is no correspondence of the vertices such that corresponding angles are congruent.

34. No; $\triangle ABC$ has angles with the measures 47°, 66.5°, and 66.5° or 47°, 47°, and 86°, whereas $\triangle DEF$ has angles with the measures 130°, 25°, and 25°. There is no correspondence of the vertices such that corresponding angles are congruent.

35. part (a), because $4.2/1.5 = 2.8$

36.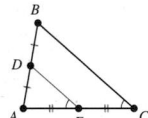
a. **b.**

$$(AC)^2 = (AD)^2 + (CD)^2$$
$$= (5 \cdot WZ)^2 + (5 \cdot YZ)^2$$
$$= 5^2 \cdot (WZ)^2 + 5^2 \cdot (YZ)^2$$
$$= 5^2 \cdot [(WZ)^2 + (YZ)^2]$$
$$= 5^2 \cdot (WY)^2$$

Then $AC = 5 \cdot WY$.

37. a. $\angle OHT \cong \angle TAE$ because they are alternate interior angles created by a transversal that cuts parallel lines, and $\angle HTO \cong \angle ATE$ because they are vertical angles. So the two triangles are similar by the AA similarity axiom.
b. $\triangle HTO \sim \triangle ATE$ **c.** $EA = 7.5$ units

38. a. $m\angle M = 65°$ **b.** $OP \approx 2.8$ cm

39. Solve $\dfrac{7}{5} = \dfrac{4 + BC}{BC}$ to get $BC = 10$ units.

40. a. $\dfrac{AB}{AD} = \dfrac{AC}{AE} = 2$ and $\angle BAC \cong \angle DAE$. So $\triangle BAC \sim \triangle DAE$ by the SAS similarity axiom.

b. $\overleftrightarrow{AC}$ is a transversal for $\overleftrightarrow{DE}$ and $\overleftrightarrow{BC}$, and $\angle DEA \cong \angle BCA$ because corresponding angles of similar triangles are congruent. Then $\overleftrightarrow{DE}$ and $\overleftrightarrow{BC}$ are parallel lines. Then $\overline{DE}$ and $\overline{BC}$ are parallel lines.

41. k, k^2

42. a.

b. $NE = 14.4$ cm, $EW = 24.0$ cm, and $WN = 33.6$ cm

43. ≈ 18.53 cm

44. Solve the proportion $\left(\dfrac{8.4}{14.7}\right)^2 = \dfrac{n}{\frac{1}{2}(14.7 \cdot 3.4)}$ for $n = 8.16$ square feet.

45. Solve the proportion $\dfrac{16}{26} = \dfrac{n}{n+8}$ to get $n = 12.8$. So $AB = 12.8$ feet.

46. 21 ft

47.

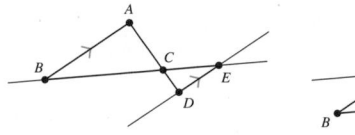

a.   **b.**

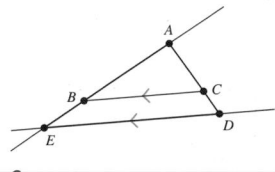

c.

CHAPTER 12 TEST

1. a.

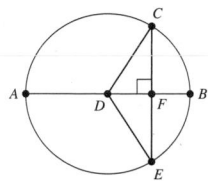

b. Let F be the intersection of the diameter and $\overline{CE}$. C and E lie on the circle with the center D, so $\overline{CD} \cong \overline{DE}$. $\triangle CDE$ is an isosceles triangle, so its base angles are congruent. Then $\angle C \cong \angle E$. We are given that the diameter and $\overline{CE}$ are perpendicular, so $\angle CFD$ and $\angle EFD$ are congruent right angles. So $\triangle CDF \cong \triangle EDF$ by the AAS congruence axiom. Then $\overline{CF} \cong \overline{EF}$ by CPCTC. Thus, the diameter bisects the chord $\overline{CE}$.

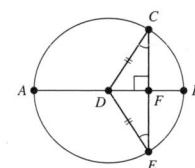

2. $\triangle PQR$ is an isosceles triangle, so its legs are congruent and its base angles are congruent. $\overline{PQ} \cong \overline{RQ}$, $\angle PQS \cong \angle RQT$, and $\angle P \cong \angle R$, so $\triangle PQS \cong \triangle RQT$ by the ASA congruence axiom. Then $\overline{QS} \cong \overline{QT}$ by CPCTC.

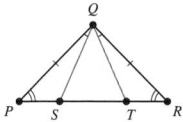

3.

Statement	Reason
1. $\overline{AB} \cong \overline{AD}$	1. Because the sides of a rhombus are congruent
2. $\overline{BC} \cong \overline{DC}$	2. Because the sides of a rhombus are congruent
3. $\overline{AC} \cong \overline{AC}$	3. Reflexive property of congruence
4. $\triangle ABC \cong \triangle ADC$	4. SSS congruence axiom
5. $\angle BAC \cong \angle DAC$	5. CPCTC
6. $\angle BCA \cong \angle DCA$	6. CPCTC

Therefore, the diagonal $\overline{AC}$ bisects $\angle A$ and $\angle C$.

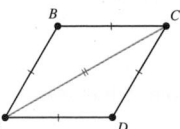

4. $m\angle 1 = 28.5°$, $m\angle 2 = 61.5°$, $m\angle 3 = 61.5°$, $m\angle 4 = 28.5°$, and $m\angle 5 = 57°$

5. a. $\triangle ABC$ is an isosceles triangle, so its base angles are congruent. $(180 - 46)/2 = 67$, so $m\angle BAC = 67°$ and $m\angle BCA = 67°$. Then $m\angle DAC = 67° - 30° = 37°$. $\triangle DAC$ is an isosceles triangle, so its base angles are congruent. Then $m\angle DCA = 37°$. Then $m\angle BCD = 67° - 37° = 30°$.

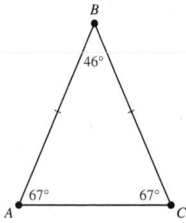 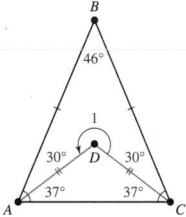

b. The sum of the angles in a quadrilateral is $360°$, so $m\angle 1 = 360° - 46° - 30° - 30° = 254°$.

6.

Statement	Reason
1. $\overline{KI} \cong \overline{IT}$	1. Given
2. $\overline{KE} \cong \overline{TE}$	2. Given
3. $\overline{IE} \cong \overline{IE}$	3. Reflexive property of congruence
4. $\triangle IKE \cong \triangle ITE$	4. SSS congruence axiom
5. $\angle K \cong \angle T$	5. CPCTC

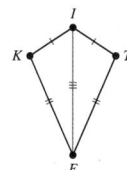

7. a. Construct a line through T that is parallel to $\overleftrightarrow{QR}$.

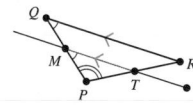

b. $\angle QPR \cong \angle MPT$ and $\angle RQP \cong \angle TMP$. Then $\triangle PQR \sim \triangle PMT$ by the AA similarity axiom.

8. $AH = BH$, so H must lie on the perpendicular bisector of $\overline{AB}$. $AH = CH$, so H must lie on the perpendicular bisector of $\overline{AC}$. $BH = CH$, so H must lie on the perpendicular bisector of $\overline{BC}$. So H must lie on all three perpendicular bisectors.

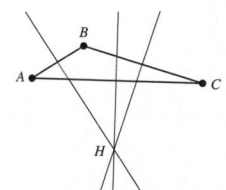

9. a.

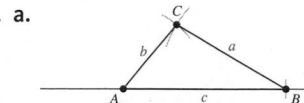

b. B lies on a circle with the center A and radius c, so $AB = c$ units. C lies on a circle with the center A and radius b, so $AC = b$ units. C also lies on a circle with the center B and radius a, so $BC = a$ units. Then $\triangle ABC$ is a triangle with sides that have the lengths a, b, and c units.

10. Construct a line through the vertex of the angle that is perpendicular to one of the sides of the angle. This creates complementary angles with the measures 24° and 66°. Bisect the 66° angle to obtain two angles each with the measure 33°.

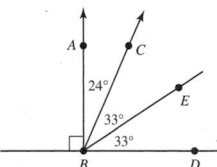

11. Answers vary. For example, if $\triangle AHE$ has a base of 4 units and a height of 3 units, then $\triangle AHE$ has an area of 6 square units, because $\frac{1}{2}(4 \cdot 3) = 6$. So we just need to construct an obtuse triangle with a base of 4 units and a height of 3 units. First, construct a line segment $\overline{AE}$ with a length of 4 units. This line segment will be the base of the triangle. Second, construct a line that is perpendicular to the line that contains $\overline{AE}$ such that you can use your compass to construct a point that leads to an obtuse triangle with a height of 3 units.

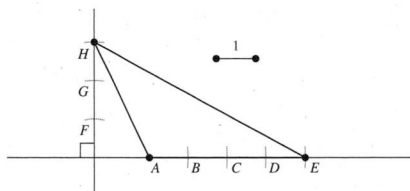

12. a. yes **b.** no **c.** yes **d.** yes $(255 = 3 \cdot 5 \cdot 17)$
e. no **f.** yes $(22{,}282{,}580 = 2^2 \cdot 5 \cdot 17 \cdot 65{,}537)$

13. We know that the longest side of a triangle is opposite the angle with the largest measure. In similar triangles, the corresponding angles are congruent. Then the angles with the largest measure in each triangle must be corresponding parts. The diagram in the definition of similar triangles shows that the sides opposite corresponding angles are corresponding sides. The longest sides are opposite the largest angles, so the longest sides are corresponding parts.

14. a. 45° **b.** 3.1 units

15. a. Answers vary. $\frac{5.40}{4.05} = 1\frac{1}{3}$ and $\frac{3.60}{2.70} = 1\frac{1}{3}$. The scale factor could also be 3/4.

b. $\triangle ABC \sim \triangle ZXY$

c. $\frac{XY}{6.00} = \frac{3.60}{2.70}$, so $XY = 6.00 \cdot \frac{3.60}{2.70} = 8.00$ units.

16. a. $\triangle ABC \sim \triangle DEC$ **b.** 4.5 units

17. a. 12 **b.** 144 (because $12^2 = 144$)

18. 6 cm

19. 36,288 square units

20. $\triangle ABC \sim \triangle DEC$ by the AA similarity axiom. Solve the proportion $\frac{42}{18} = \frac{AB}{14}$ to get $AB = 32\frac{2}{3}$ m.

21. a.

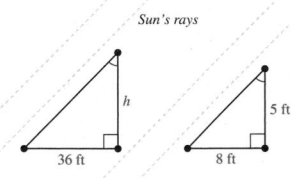

b. the AA similarity axiom **c.** 22.5 ft

CHAPTER 13

SECTION 13.1

1. a. vertical **b.** horizontal **c.** vertical **d.** horizontal
e. oblique **f.** horizontal **g.** vertical

2. The x-intercept is $(3, 0)$, the y-intercept is $(0, -6)$, and the slope is 2.

3. a. l_2 **b.** l_4 **c.** l_3 **d.** l_1

4. a. The slope is -24. This means 24 fewer tickets are sold each day after the release of the movie.
b. The t-intercept is $(16, 0)$. This means that 0 tickets are sold 16 days after the release of the movie.
c. The S-intercept is $(0, 384)$. This means the local movie theater sold 384 tickets to the movie on the first day it was released.

5. a. $p(d) = \frac{5}{11}d + 15$

b. $\frac{5}{11} \cdot 22 + 15 = 10 + 15 = 25$

c. The pressure is 25 pounds per square inch at a depth of 22 feet below the surface of the water.

6. a. $\frac{3}{2}$

b. Tables are produced at the rate of three tables per 2 hours.

7. (x_1, y_1) and (x_2, y_2) belong to the nonvertical line, so $x_1 \neq x_2$ and $y_1 = mx_1 + b$ and $y_2 = mx_2 + b$. Then

$$y_2 - y_1 = (mx_2 + b) - (mx_1 + b)$$
$$= mx_2 + mb - mx_1 - mb$$
$$= mx_2 - mx_1$$
$$= m(x_2 - x_1)$$

Then $m = \dfrac{y_2 - y_1}{x_2 - x_1}$.

8. a. l_1 and l_2 are parallel, so $m_1 = m_2$. l_1 and l_3 are perpendicular, so $m_1 \cdot m_3 = -1$. Then $m_2 \cdot m_3 = -1$ by the substitution property. Then l_2 and l_3 are perpendicular.
b. l_1 and l_2 are perpendicular, so $m_1 \cdot m_2 = -1$. l_1 and l_3 are perpendicular, so $m_1 \cdot m_3 = -1$. Then $m_2 = -1/m_1$ and $m_3 = -1/m_1$. Then $m_2 = m_3$, by the transitive property of equality. Then l_2 and l_3 are parallel.

9. a. Let $x = 1$. Then $y = 4 \cdot 1 + 5 = 9$. Let $x = 5$. Then
$y = 4 \cdot 5 + 5 = 25$. Then $(1, 9)$ and $(5, 25)$ belong to
the line. Then the slope is $\dfrac{25 - 9}{5 - 1} = \dfrac{16}{4} = 4$.

b. Let $x = 1$. Then $y = -8 \cdot 1 + 2 = -6$. Let $x = 5$.
Then $y = -8 \cdot 5 + 2 = -38$. Then $(1, -6)$ and
$(5, -38)$ belong to the line. Then the slope is
$\dfrac{-38 - (-6)}{5 - 1} = \dfrac{-32}{4} = -8$.

c. Let $x = 2$. Then $y = 3 \cdot 2 - 4 = 2$. Let $x = 5$. Then
$y = 3 \cdot 5 - 4 = 11$. Then $(2, 2)$ and $(5, 11)$ belong to
the line. Then the slope is $\dfrac{11 - 2}{5 - 2} = \dfrac{9}{3} = 3$.

d. The slope of the oblique line $y = mx + b$ is m.

10. a. $(0, 5)$ **b.** $(0, 2)$ **c.** $(0, -4)$
d. The y-intercept of the equation $y = mx + b$ is $(0, b)$.

11. a. neither   **b.** parallel   **c.** neither   **d.** perpendicular
e. neither

12. $y = \dfrac{-1}{4}x + \dfrac{23}{4}$

13. $y = 3x - 13$

14. $y = \dfrac{3}{8}x + \dfrac{29}{8}$

15. a. When the femur measures 12.5 inches, the height of the
adult male is 55.75 inches.
b. $H(L) = 1.9L + 32$ **c.** 66.58 in.   **d.** 20 in.

16. a. the position of a term   **b.** the nth term

17. y increases by 14 units.

18. x decreases by $\dfrac{6}{5}$ units.

19.

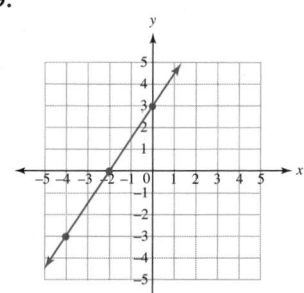

20. a. The nonvertical line with the slope m contains the points
(x, y) and (x_1, y_1). Then the slope m is given by the for-
mula $m = \dfrac{y - y_1}{x - x_1}$. Then $m(x - x_1) = \dfrac{y - y_1}{x - x_1} \cdot (x - x_1)$.
Then $m(x - x_1) = y - y_1$. Then $y - y_1 = m(x - x_1)$.

b. $y - 5 = 3(x - 2)$ **c.** $y - (-5) = -4(x - 3)$
d. $y - 1 = 5[x - (-4)]$

21. $(4, w)$ and $(4, k)$ are distinct points, so $w \neq k$. $(4, w)$ and
$(4, k)$ cannot belong to a horizontal line because $w \neq k$.
Also, $(4, w)$ and $(4, k)$ cannot both belong to an oblique

line because they have the same x-coordinates. So $(4, w)$
and $(4, k)$ belong to a vertical line: $x = 4$.

22. $(2, w)$ and $(5, k)$ cannot belong to a vertical line because
they have different x-coordinates. But if $w = k$, then $(2, w)$
and $(5, k)$ belong to a horizontal line. And if $w \neq k$, then
$(2, w)$ and $(5, k)$ belong to an oblique line.

23. a.

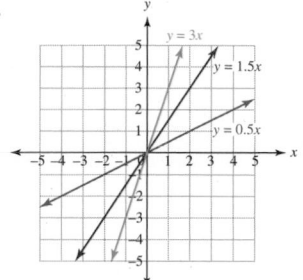

b. The lines become increasingly vertical as the positive
slopes increase.

24. a.

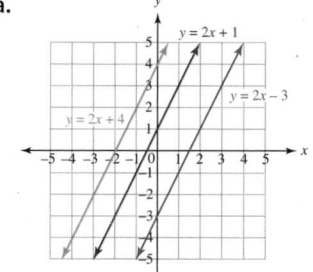

b. The larger constants shift the graphs of the lines upward.

25. a.

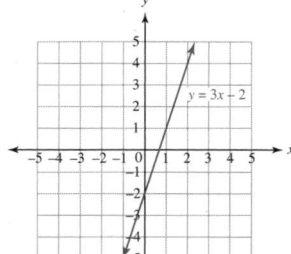
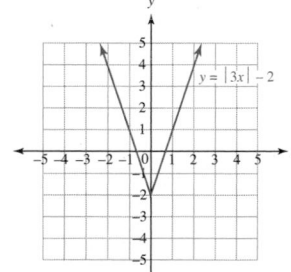

b.

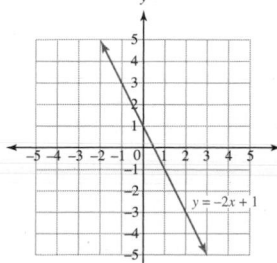
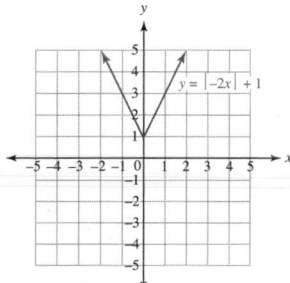

c. The absolute value turns the line into a graph with a
V shape that bends at the y-intercept.

26. a.

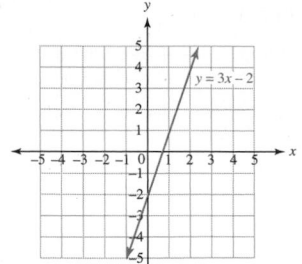

b.

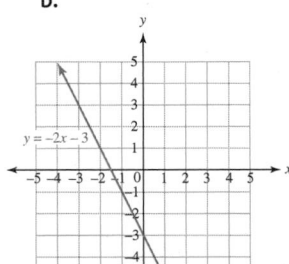 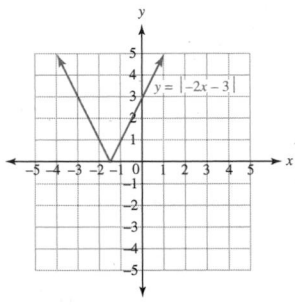

c. The absolute value turns the line into a graph with a V shape that bends at the x-intercept.

27. By definition, two lines are perpendicular if and only if the product of their slopes is -1 or one line is horizontal and the other line is vertical.

a. The line with the equation $y = 3$ is horizontal and the y-axis is a vertical line, so the two lines are perpendicular.

b. The line with the equation $x = 2$ is vertical and the x-axis is a horizontal line, so the two lines are perpendicular.

28. a. horizontal change **b.** vertical change **c.** zero
d. undefined **e.** vertical **f.** horizontal **g.** oblique
h. $-\dfrac{2}{5}$

29. a. no **b.** yes

30. a. slope $= \dfrac{-5 - 7}{-1 - 3} = \dfrac{-12}{-4} = 3$

b. slope $= \dfrac{7 - (-5)}{3 - (-1)} = \dfrac{12}{4} = 3$

c. When applying the formula for the slope, it doesn't matter which ordered pair you choose as (x_1, y_1). Then the other ordered pair is (x_2, y_2).

31. a. no **b.** yes

32. a. y increases by $\dfrac{12}{5}$ units. **b.** x decreases by $\dfrac{5}{2}$ units.

33. a.

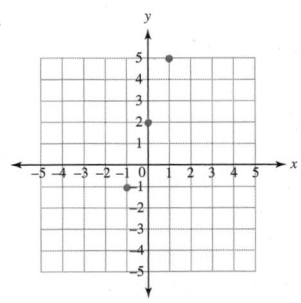

b.

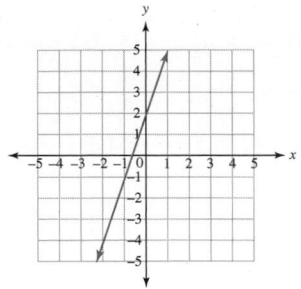

34. a. $\dfrac{-3}{4}$ **b.** 0 **c.** $\dfrac{2}{5}$

35. a. $y = 2x - 7$ **b.** $y = \dfrac{1}{2}x + \dfrac{7}{2}$ **c.** $y = -3x + 23$

36. a.

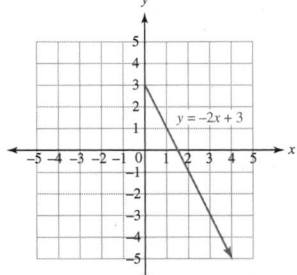

b.

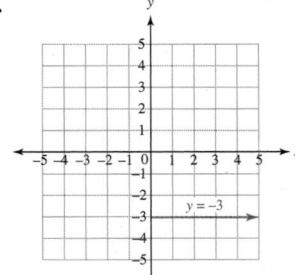

c.

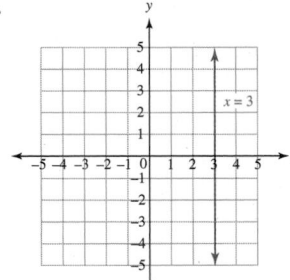

37. a. The y-intercept is $(0, 7)$, and the x-intercept is $\left(\dfrac{7}{4}, 0\right)$.

b. The y-intercept is $(0, -6)$, and the x-intercept is $(8, 0)$.

c. The y-intercept is $(0, 4)$, and there is no x-intercept.

38. a. $y = -4x + 12$ **b.** $y = 2x - 1$ **c.** $y = 3x - 10$

39. a. $y = -4x + 5$ **b.** $y = 3x - 8$

40. a. $y = 5x + 7$ **b.** $y = -2x - 3$

41. a. 13 **b.** 3.4 **c.** -3

42. a. $f(m) = 1.7m + 2$ dollars, because $0.34(5m) + 2 = 1.7m + 2$.

b. $f(3) = 1.7 \cdot 3 + 2 = 7.10$, so cab fare for a 3-mile ride is $7.10.

c. $15.60

d. no, because the function is defined for nonnegative numbers m

e. Solve $29.20 = 1.7m + 2$ to get $m = 16$ miles.

43. a. $\dfrac{-5}{2}$

b. The number of books sold decreases by five books for every \$2 increase in the price of a book.

44. $\dfrac{1}{k}$

45. a. $y(n) = 3n + 1$ **b.** $y(2) = 3 \cdot 2 + 1 = 6 + 1 = 7$
c. $y(15) = 3 \cdot 15 + 1 = 45 + 1 = 46$

46. a. $(k, mk + b)$

b. $\left(\dfrac{k - b}{m}, k \right)$

47. a. $C(m) = 0.30m + 125$ dollars

b. The domain is the set of nonnegative real numbers.

c. The solution to the equation $0 = 0.30m + 125$ does not belong to the domain of the function, so there is no m-intercept.

d. \$202.10

e. The rental car company will charge you \$131.90 for renting the car for 1 week and driving it 23 miles.

f. 886 mi

48. 17 pieces

49.

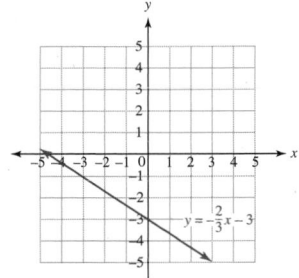

50.

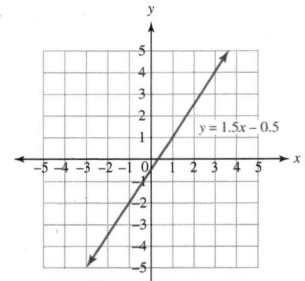

51. The diagram shows a representation of the situation. Solve the equation $-\dfrac{5}{8} = \dfrac{3.5 - 0}{0 - x}$ to get $x = 5.6$ ft.

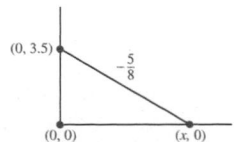

52.

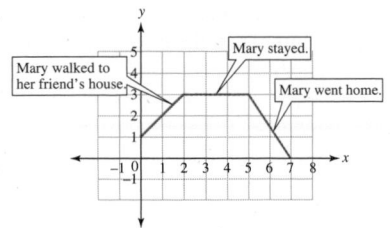

SECTION 13.2

1. $A(-3, -1), B(-5, 4), C(3, 4), D(5, -1)$

2. $A(0, -2), B(-5, 2), C(1, 6), D(6, 2)$

3. $A(2, 5), B(-4, 1), C(0, -5), D(6, -1)$

4. $C(4, 5)$

5. $(x - 4)^2 + (y - 3)^2 = (\sqrt{29})^2$

6. $B(0, k), D(h, 0)$

7. $B(h - BC, k), D(2h - BC, 0)$

8. Answers vary. $k = 2$ or $k = \dfrac{16}{3}$

9. a.

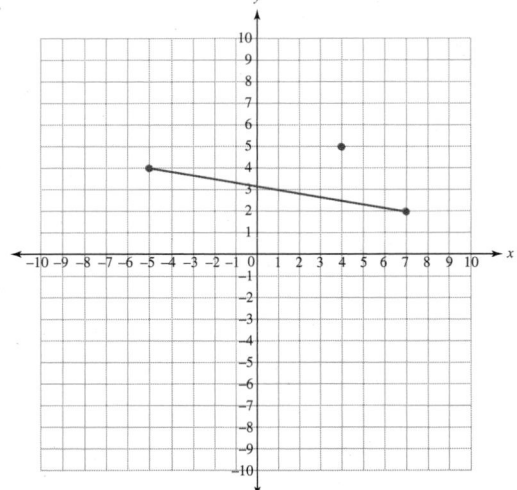

b. $y = 6x - 19$

10. a. 4, because $6 = \dfrac{1}{2}(4 \cdot 3)$

b. Place the base of the triangle along the x-axis, with the vertices $L(0, 0), R(1, 3),$ and $N(4, 0)$.

c.

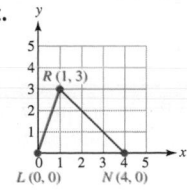

11. From the graph, we see the parallelogram has a base of 7 units and a height of 3 units. Then the area is 21 square units.

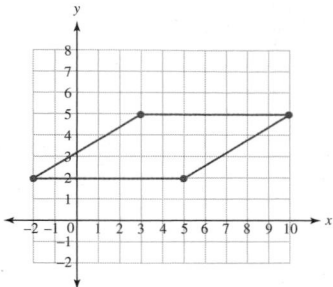

12. Placing the two sides of the rectangle along the axes makes it easier to solve this problem.

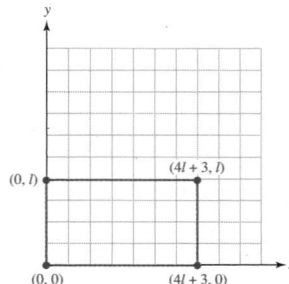

13. The midpoint of $\overline{AC}$ is $\left(\dfrac{1}{2}, 1\right)$, and the midpoint of $\overline{BD}$ is $\left(\dfrac{1}{2}, 1\right)$. The diagonals have the same midpoint, so the diagonals bisect each other.

14. The midpoint of $\overline{AC}$ is $\left(\dfrac{-5}{2}, -2\right)$, and the midpoint of $\overline{BD}$ is $\left(\dfrac{-5}{2}, -2\right)$. The diagonals have the same midpoint, so the diagonals bisect each other.

15. $\overline{AB}$ and $\overline{CD}$ are opposite sides, the slope of $\overline{AB}$ is $\dfrac{4}{6}$, and the slope of $\overline{CD}$ is $\dfrac{4}{6}$. $\overline{BC}$ and $\overline{AD}$ are opposite sides, the slope of $\overline{BC}$ is 2, and the slope of $\overline{AD}$ is 2. The opposite sides of the quadrilateral are parallel, so $ABCD$ is a parallelogram.

16. **a.** The diagonals are $\overline{AC}$ and $\overline{BD}$, and $AC = \sqrt{68}$ and $BD = \sqrt{68}$.
    b. The midpoint of $\overline{AC}$ is $(2, 1)$, and the midpoint of $\overline{BD}$ is $(2, 1)$. The diagonals have the same midpoint, so the diagonals bisect each other.

17. **a.** $AB = \sqrt{45}$ and $CD = \sqrt{45}$, so $\overline{AB} \cong \overline{CD}$.
    b. $AD = \sqrt{50}$ and $BC = \sqrt{50}$, so $\overline{AD} \cong \overline{BC}$.

18. $\dfrac{1}{2} = \dfrac{x_M - x_1}{x_2 - x_1}$. Then $x_2 - x_1 = 2(x_M - x_1)$. Then $x_2 - x_1 = 2x_M - 2x_1$. Then $x_2 + x_1 = 2x_M$. Then $x_M = \dfrac{x_1 + x_2}{2}$.

19. $\dfrac{1}{2} = \dfrac{y_M - y_1}{y_2 - y_1}$. Then $y_2 - y_1 = 2(y_M - y_1)$. Then $y_2 - y_1 = 2y_M - 2y_1$. Then $y_2 + y_1 = 2y_M$. Then $y_M = \dfrac{y_1 + y_2}{2}$.

20. **a.** $\overline{CT}$ is the longest side, so $\angle A$ is the largest angle.
    b. $\overline{AC}$ is the shortest side, so $\angle T$ is the smallest angle.

21. $AB = 5$, $AC = \sqrt{50}$, and $BC = 5$. $(AB)^2 + (BC)^2 = 5^2 + 5^2 = 50$ and $(AC)^2 = 50$. Then $(AB)^2 + (BC)^2 = (AC)^2$, so $\triangle ABC$ is a right triangle.

22. $\overline{PQ}$ is the longest side, so $\overline{PQ}$ is the hypotenuse.

23. The slope of $\overline{AB}$ is $\dfrac{2}{5}$, and the slope of $\overline{CD}$ is $\dfrac{2}{5}$. The slope of $\overline{BC}$ is $\dfrac{5}{2}$, and the slope of $\overline{AD}$ is $\dfrac{5}{2}$. The opposite sides of $ABCD$ are parallel, so the quadrilateral is a parallelogram.

24. The slope of $\overline{AB}$ is $\dfrac{-4}{3}$, and the slope of $\overline{BC}$ is $\dfrac{3}{4}$. The slopes $\overline{AB}$ and $\overline{BC}$ are negative reciprocals of each other, so $\overline{AB}$ is perpendicular to $\overline{BC}$. So $\triangle ABC$ is a right triangle.

25. $y = \dfrac{-3}{4}x + \dfrac{41}{8}$

26. Let B have the coordinates (x, y). W is the midpoint of $\overline{AB}$, so solve the equation $5 = \dfrac{-11 + x}{2}$ for x and solve $7 = \dfrac{18 + y}{2}$ to get $x = 21$ and $y = -4$.

27. $FN = \sqrt{32}$, $UN = \sqrt{122}$, $FU = \sqrt{234}$, and $(\sqrt{32})^2 + (\sqrt{122})^2 < (\sqrt{234})^2$. So $\triangle FUN$ is obtuse.

28. **a.** $x^2 + y^2 = r^2$
    b. The longest side $\overline{PQ}$ has a length of $2r$. We know $b^2 + c^2 = r^2$ since (b, c) lies on a circle with radius r. The legs have the following lengths:
$$RQ = \sqrt{(b - r)^2 + c^2}$$
$$= \sqrt{b^2 - 2br + r^2 + c^2}$$
$$= \sqrt{r^2 - 2br + r^2}$$
$$= \sqrt{2r^2 - 2br}$$
$$PR = \sqrt{(b - (-r))^2 + c^2}$$
$$= \sqrt{b^2 + 2br + r^2 + c^2}$$
$$= \sqrt{r^2 + 2br + r^2}$$
$$= \sqrt{2r^2 + 2br}$$
Then $(RQ)^2 + (PR)^2 = 2r^2 - 2br + 2r^2 + 2rb = 4r^2 = (2r)^2 = (PQ)^2$. Then $(RQ)^2 + (PR)^2 = (PQ)^2$. So $\triangle PQR$ is a right triangle.

29. **a.** $AB = DC = \sqrt{41}$ and $BC = AD = 5$.
    b. The slopes of $\overline{AB}$ and $\overline{CD}$ are $\dfrac{-5}{4}$, and the slopes of $\overline{AD}$ and $\overline{BC}$ are $\dfrac{3}{4}$. So the opposite sides are parallel.
    c. $ABCD$ does not have any right angles because the product of the slopes does not equal -1.

30. **a.** $\left(\dfrac{11}{2}, -4\right)$ **b.** $\left(-1, \dfrac{5}{2}\right)$

31. **a.** $(8, -24)$ **b.** $(6, -36)$

32. The slopes of $\overline{AB}$ and $\overline{CD}$ are 3, and the slopes of $\overline{AD}$ and $\overline{BC}$ are 0. The opposite sides of $ABCD$ are parallel, so the quadrilateral is a parallelogram.

33. a. $(4, 6)$ **b.** $\sqrt{50}$ or $5\sqrt{2}$
   c. $(x - 4)^2 + (y - 6)^2 = (\sqrt{50})^2$

34. a. $(6, 3)$ **b.** $\sqrt{13}$ **b.** $(x - 6)^2 + (y - 3)^2 = (\sqrt{13})^2$

35. $KI = \sqrt{34}$, $KT = \sqrt{13}$, and $IT = \sqrt{89}$.
   $(KI)^2 + (KT)^2 < (IT)^2$, so the triangle is an obtuse triangle.

36. $RP = 8$, $RM = \sqrt{145}$, and $PM = 9$.
   $(RP)^2 + (PM)^2 = (RM)^2$, so the triangle is a right triangle.

37. $UP = \sqrt{82}$, $PS = \sqrt{73}$, and $US = \sqrt{85}$.
   $(US)^2 < (UP)^2 + (PS)^2$, so the triangle is an acute triangle.

38.

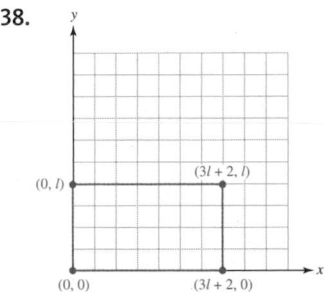

39. a. $AC = 10$ and $BD = 10$, so the diagonals are congruent.
   b. The midpoint of $\overline{AC}$ is $(3, -1)$, and the midpoint of $\overline{BD}$ is $(3, -1)$, so the diagonals bisect.

40. $x = -1$ or 5

41. a. $HA = \sqrt{(\frac{a}{2} - 0)^2 + (b - 0)^2} = \sqrt{\frac{a^2}{4} + b^2}$, and
   $AT = \sqrt{(\frac{a}{2} - a)^2 + (b - 0)^2} = \sqrt{\frac{a^2}{4} + b^2}$. Then
   $HA = AT$.

   b. Let M be the midpoint of $\overline{HT}$. Then M has the coordinates $\left(\dfrac{a}{2}, 0\right)$. The equation of the perpendicular bisector of $\overline{HT}$ is $x = \dfrac{a}{2}$. Any point that is equidistant from H and T must belong to the perpendicular bisector of $\overline{HT}$. So A belongs to the perpendicular bisector of $\overline{HT}$. The A has the x-coordinate $\dfrac{a}{2}$. Then the coordinates of A are $\left(\dfrac{a}{2}, b\right)$.

42. a. $BD = \sqrt{(2 - 0)^2 + (-3 - 2)^2} = \sqrt{29}$, and
   $AC = \sqrt{(-3 - 2)^2 + (2 - 0)^2} = \sqrt{29}$. Then
   $BD = AC$.

   b. The slope of $\overline{BC}$ is $\dfrac{2 - 0}{0 - 2} = -1$, and the slope of $\overline{AD}$ is $\dfrac{-3 - 2}{2 - (-3)} = -1$. The bases have the same slopes, so the bases are parallel.

   c. $AB = 3$ and $CD = 3$, so the legs of the trapezoid are congruent.

43. a. $BD = \sqrt{(-2 - (-1))^2 + (-4 - 4)^2} = \sqrt{65}$, and
   $AC = \sqrt{(4 - (-3))^2 + (5 - 1)^2} = \sqrt{65}$. Then
   $BD = AC$.

   b. The slope of $\overline{AB}$ is $\dfrac{4 - 1}{-1 - (-3)} = \dfrac{3}{2}$, and the slope of $\overline{CD}$ is $\dfrac{-4 - 5}{-2 - 4} = \dfrac{-9}{-6} = \dfrac{3}{2}$. The bases have the same slopes, so the bases are parallel.

c. $AD = \sqrt{(-3 - (-2))^2 + (1 - (-4))^2} = \sqrt{26}$, and
   $BC = \sqrt{(4 - (-1))^2 + (5 - 4)^2} = \sqrt{26}$. Then
   $AD = BC$, so the legs of the trapezoid are congruent.

44. a. $C(n, k)$ and $D(n + h, 0)$
   b. $AB = \sqrt{(h - 0)^2 + (k - 0)^2} = \sqrt{h^2 + k^2}$, and
   $CD = \sqrt{(n + h - n)^2 + (0 - k)^2} = \sqrt{h^2 + k^2}$. Then
   $\overline{AB} \cong \overline{CD}$.
   c. $AC = \sqrt{(n - 0)^2 + (k - 0)^2} = \sqrt{n^2 + k^2}$, and
   $BD = \sqrt{(n + h - h)^2 + (0 - k)^2} = \sqrt{n^2 + k^2}$. Then
   $\overline{AC} \cong \overline{BD}$.

45. $(3, 4)$

46. a. $(p - k, q)$
   b. $AD = DC$, so $(AD)^2 = (DC)^2$. Then $k^2 = (p - k)^2 + q^2$. Then $k^2 = p^2 - 2pk + k^2 + q^2$. Then $p^2 + q^2 = 2pk$.
   c. $A = kq$

47. a. $\overline{BD}$ is a vertical line $(x = 1)$, and $\overline{AC}$ is a horizontal line $(y = 1)$, so $\overline{BD}$ and $\overline{AC}$ are perpendicular.
   b. The midpoint of $\overline{BD}$ is $(1, 1)$, and the midpoint of $\overline{AC}$ is $(1, 1)$. The diagonals intersect at their midpoints, so the diagonals bisect each other.
   c. The slope of $\overline{AB}$ is $\dfrac{3 - 1}{1 - (-2)} = \dfrac{2}{3}$, and the slope of $\overline{DC}$ is $\dfrac{-1 - 1}{1 - 4} = \dfrac{2}{3}$. The slope of $\overline{AD}$ is $\dfrac{-1 - 1}{1 - (-2)} = -\dfrac{2}{3}$, and the slope of $\overline{BC}$ is $\dfrac{3 - 1}{1 - 4} = -\dfrac{2}{3}$. So the opposite sides of the rhombus have the same slope.

48. a. The slope of $\overline{AC}$ is $\dfrac{3 - 1}{2 - (-2)} = \dfrac{1}{2}$, and the slope of $\overline{BD}$ is $\dfrac{-4 - 4}{3 - (-1)} = -2$. The product of the slopes of the diagonals is -1, so the diagonals of the kite are perpendicular.
   b. The midpoint of $\overline{AC}$ is $(0, 2)$, and the midpoint of $\overline{BD}$ is $(1, 0)$. The midpoints of the diagonals are different, so the diagonals do not bisect each other. The points on diagonal $\overline{BD}$ satisfy the equation $y = -2x + 2$ for $-1 \le x \le 3$. The midpoint of $\overline{AC}$ is $(0, 2)$, and it belongs to diagonal $\overline{BD}$ because $2 = 0 \cdot 2 + 2$. So $\overline{BD}$ bisects $\overline{AC}$.

SECTION 13.3

1. A

2. B'

3.

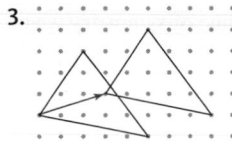

4.

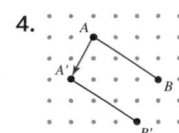

5.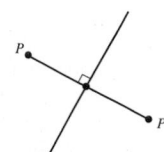

6.

7.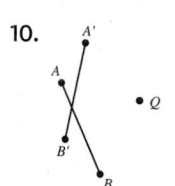

8. Draw the perpendicular bisector of $\overline{PP'}$.

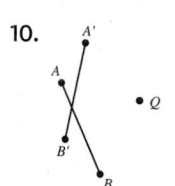

9.

10.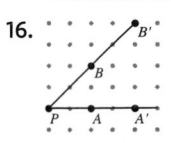

11.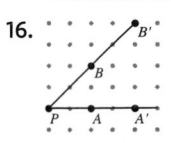

12. It confirms that the opposite sides of a rectangle are congruent.

13. The design has point symmetry with a center of rotation at the center of the circle. It has eight lines of symmetry and an angle of symmetry of 45°.

14. Each has point symmetry, a vertical line of symmetry, and a horizontal line of symmetry.

15. $m\angle BPB' = 25°$, so the angle of rotation is 25°, counterclockwise.

16.

17.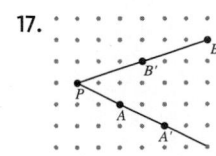

18.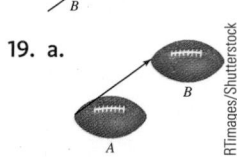

19. a.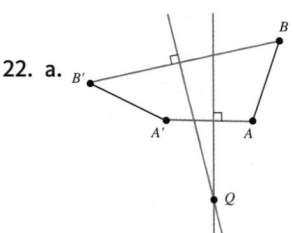

b. about 5.6 cm

20. a. less than 1

b. The scale factor k satisfies the equation $A'B' = k \cdot AB$. Then $k = \dfrac{A'B'}{AB}$. Measuring the line segments, we get $AB \approx 24$ mm, $A'B' \approx 16$ mm, and $k \approx \dfrac{16}{24} = \dfrac{2}{3}$.

21. For any two points A and B in Figure 1, the scale factor k satisfies the equation $A'B' = k \cdot AB$. Then $k = \dfrac{A'B'}{AB}$. Measuring the distance between the axes of the wheels in Figure 2 and dividing by the distance between the axes of the wheels in Figure 1, we get $k \approx \dfrac{9}{12} = 0.75$.

22. a.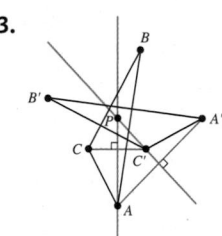

b. 75°   **c.** counterclockwise

23.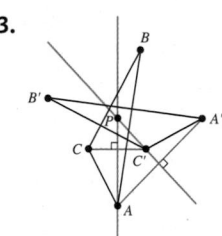

24. a.

b. $QA' = 2 \cdot QA$, $QB' = 2 \cdot QB$, and $A'B' = 2 \cdot AB$. Then $\dfrac{QA'}{QA} = \dfrac{QB'}{QB} = \dfrac{A'B'}{AB} = 2$. Then $\triangle AQB \sim \triangle A'QB'$ by the SSS similarity axiom. Then $\angle QBA \cong \angle QB'A'$, because corresponding angles of similar triangles are congruent.

The transversal $\overleftrightarrow{BB'}$ cuts the lines $\overleftrightarrow{AB}$ and $\overrightarrow{A'B'}$ and creates a pair for corresponding angles that are congruent, so $\overleftrightarrow{AB}$ and $\overleftrightarrow{A'B'}$ are parallel lines. Then $\overline{AB}$ and $\overline{A'B'}$ are parallel.

25. a. 20 ft **b.** 24 ft **c.** 8 ft **d.** 100 ft

26. a. 15 cm **b.** 35 cm **c.** 2 cm **d.** 150 cm²

27. a.

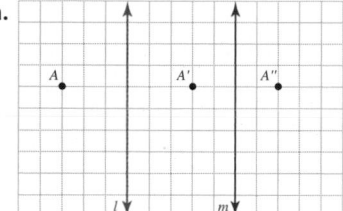

 b. 10 units
 c. If two parallel lines of reflection are n units apart, then the distance between Q and Q'' is $2n$ units.

28. a. The three regular polygons that tessellate the plane are the equilateral triangle, square, and regular hexagon.
 b. The sum of the interior angles that have a common vertex in the tessellation have a sum of 360°.

29. a. m$\angle AQA'' = 80°$ and m$\angle BQB'' = 80°$
 b. m$\angle PQR = 40°$ **c.** $2n$ degrees
 d. Conjecture: the center of rotation is the intersection of the two mirror lines.

30. a. Pick two pairs of points (A and A', and B and B'), draw the lines through each pair. The center of the scale transformation is the intersection of the two lines.

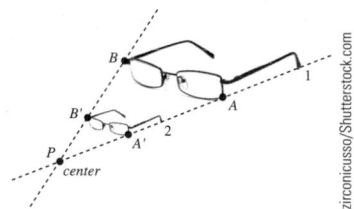

zirconicusso/Shutterstock.com

 b. less than 1
 c. The scale factor k is the ratio $\dfrac{PA'}{PA}$. Use your ruler to measure PA and PA', then divide. Then $k \approx 0.4$.

31. The scale factor is the quotient $\dfrac{A'B'}{AB}$. Draw a line segment $\overline{AB}$ in Figure 1, then draw the corresponding line segment $\overline{A'B'}$ in Figure 2. Measure the length of $\overline{AB}$ and $\overline{A'B'}$, then calculate the quotient $\dfrac{A'B'}{AB}$. We get $k \approx 0.6$.

Memo Angeles/Shutterstock.com

32. An isometry preserves distances, so $AB = A'B'$, $BC = B'C'$, and $AC = A'C'$. Then $\triangle ABC \cong \triangle A'B'C'$ by the SSS congruence axiom.

33. An isometry preserves distances, so $AB = A'B'$, $BC = B'C'$, and $AC = A'C'$. Then $\triangle ABC \cong \triangle A'B'C'$ by the SSS congruence axiom. Then $\angle ABC \cong \angle A'B'C'$ by CPCTC.

34. If a sequence of rigid motions maps one figure to another figure, then the two figures are congruent.

35. $AB = \sqrt{41}$ and $A'B' = \sqrt{29}$. So $AB \neq A'B'$. Then the transformation does not preserve distances; therefore, it cannot be an isometry. So Alicia is correct.

36. The perpendicular bisectors of $\overline{PP'}$ and $\overline{QQ'}$ would be the same under a reflection, but we see that they are different.

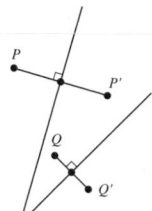

37. A rotation preserves distances, so $PQ = P'Q'$. However, we easily see $P'Q' < PQ$.

38. Draw a point labeled A on helmet 1, and then draw the image A' of that point on helmet 2. The mirror line is the perpendicular bisector of the line segment $\overline{AA'}$.

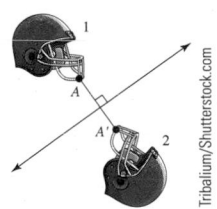

Tribalium/Shutterstock.com

39. a. rotation **b.** rotation **c.** size transformation
 d. translation **e.** glide reflection

40. a. reflection
 b. $AB = \sqrt{(-2 - -3)^2 + (3 - 1)^2} = \sqrt{1^2 + 2^2} = \sqrt{5}$
 and $A'B' = \sqrt{(2 - 3)^2 + (3 - 1)^2} = \sqrt{1^2 + 2^2} = \sqrt{5}$, so $AB = A'B'$.

41. Answers vary. First, translate the triangle with a translation vector that moves from A to X.

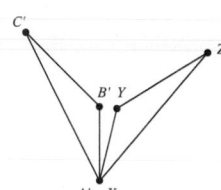

Second, rotate the triangle clockwise by $m\angle B'XY$ about the center A'.

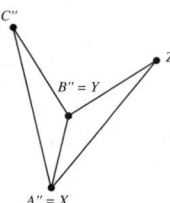

Third, reflect the triangle about the mirror line $\overleftrightarrow{A''B''}$.

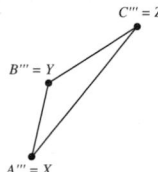

42. Answers vary. The following diagrams show one possibility.

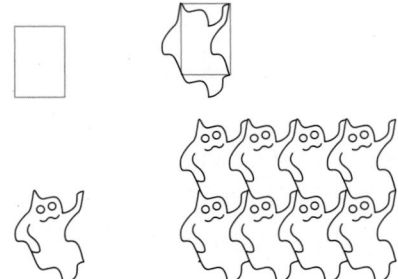

43. Answers vary. The following diagrams show one possibility.

44. a. paper folding   **b.** similar   **c.** $AB = A'B'$
   d. transformation   **e.** preimage   **f.** rigid motion
   g. similarity transformation   **h.** turn   **i.** flip   **j.** slide
   k. direction   **l.** mirror   **m.** image   **n.** mapping
   o. rigid motion

45. a.   **b.**   **c.**

46.

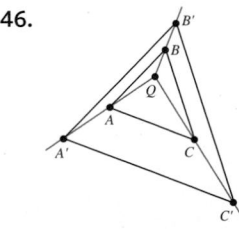

47. a. P is the center

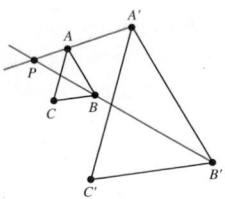

b. larger than 1

c. The scale factor is the quotient $\dfrac{PA'}{PA}$. Using a ruler to measure the line segments $\overline{PA'}$ and $\overline{PA}$ and using a calculator to determine the quotient $\dfrac{PA'}{PA}$, we get $k \approx 3$.

48. a.

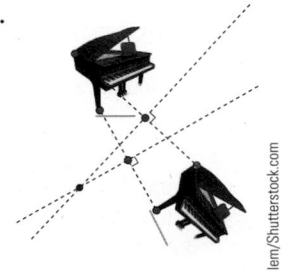

Iem/Shutterstock.com

b. $95°$

49. a. $\angle A$ and $\angle C$ are congruent due to the perfect overlapping.
   b. a right angle   **c.** yes   **d.** yes

50. a. 0   **b.** 2   **c.** 1   **d.** 1

51. $\dfrac{1}{k}$

52. $PA = PA'$ and $PB = PB'$, by definition of a rotation. $P, A,$ and B are collinear, and A is between P and B, so it follows that $PB = PA + AB$. $P, A',$ and B' are collinear, and A' is between P and B', so it follows that $PB' = PA' + A'B'$. Then

$PB = PB'$	Definition of a rotation
$PB = PA' + A'B'$	$P - A' - B'$
$PA + AB = PA' + A'B'$	$P - A - B$
$PA + AB = PA + A'B'$	$PA = PA'$
$AB = A'B'$	Subtraction property of equality

53. No. Suppose k is the mirror line. Then the image of C does not belong to the parallelogram. Suppose h is the mirror line. Then the image of D does not belong to the parallelogram. So the lines through the midpoints of the opposite sides are not lines of symmetry.

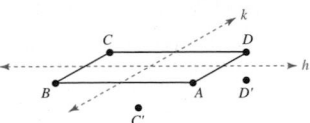

54. A, B, C, D, E, H, I, K, M, O, T, U, V, W, X, and Y

55. Figures on a piece of paper with point symmetry look the same after you turn the page 180°. Thus, the letters with point symmetry are H, I, N, O, S, X, and Z.

56. Answers vary.

a.

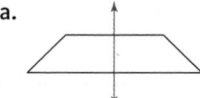

b.

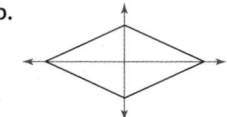

c.

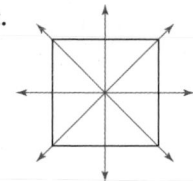

57. a. Answers vary.

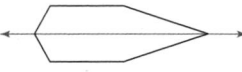

b. Answers vary.

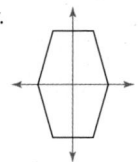

c.

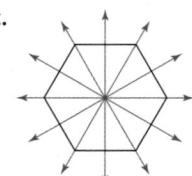

58. $QB' = k \cdot QB$, $\sqrt{360} = k \cdot \sqrt{40}$, and
$k = \sqrt{360}/\sqrt{40} = 3$

59. $PC' = k \cdot PC$, $\sqrt{68} = k \cdot \sqrt{17}$, and $k = \sqrt{68}/\sqrt{17} = 2$

60. $A'B' = k \cdot AB$, and $A'B' = \dfrac{3}{4} \cdot 72 = 54$. So $A'B' = $
54 units.

61. $A'B' = k \cdot AB$, and $72 = 3 \cdot AB$. So $AB = 24$ units.

62. a. $k = \dfrac{6.84}{3.80} = 1.8$ **b.** $1.8 \cdot 3.00 = 5.40$

   c. $1.8^2 \cdot 9.50 = 30.78$ cm^2

63. a. $k = \dfrac{7.50}{6.25} = 1.2$

   b. The perimeter of $\triangle A'B'C'$ is
   $7.5 + 11.5 + (\sqrt{31.25} + \sqrt{107.25})$. Dividing this sum
   by the scale factor 1.2, we find that the perimeter of
   $\triangle ABC$ is 29.12 units, to the nearest hundredth.

64. a.

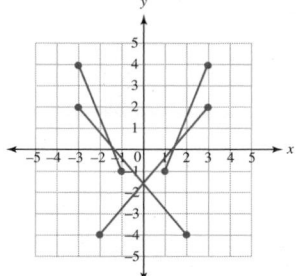

b. The slope of one line segment is $\dfrac{-5}{2}$, and the image of
the line segment has the slope $\dfrac{5}{2}$. The slope of the other
line segment is $\dfrac{6}{5}$, and the image of the line segment has
the slope $\dfrac{-6}{5}$. For each pair, the slopes have opposite
signs but identical absolute values.

c. If an oblique line segment reflected about the y-axis has
the slope $\dfrac{a}{b}$, then the slope of the image of the line segment will be $-\dfrac{a}{b}$.

65. a.

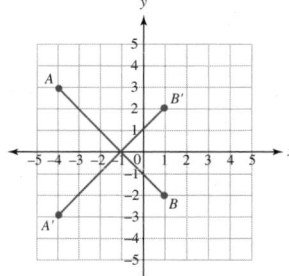 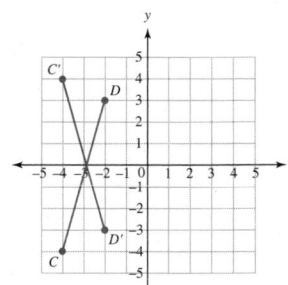

b. The slope of one line segment is -1, and the image of the
line segment has the slope 1. The slope of the other line
segment is $\dfrac{7}{2}$, and the image of the line segment has the
slope $-\dfrac{7}{2}$.

c. For each pair, the slopes have opposite signs but identical
absolute values. If an oblique line segment is reflected
about the x-axis has the slope $\dfrac{a}{b}$, then the slope of the
image of the line segment will be $-\dfrac{a}{b}$.

REVIEW QUESTIONS

1. a. vertical   **b.** horizontal   **c.** vertical   **d.** horizontal
   e. oblique   **f.** vertical

2. a.

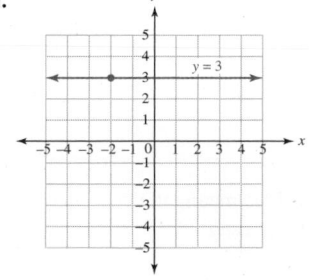

b.

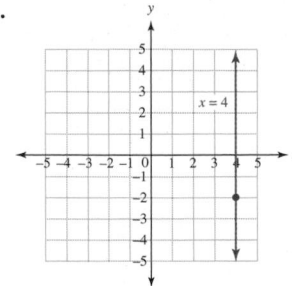

3.

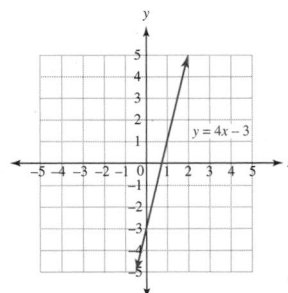

4. l_1: $y = \frac{1}{2}x - \frac{1}{2}$

l_2: $y = -\frac{3}{4}x - 3$

l_3: $y = 6$

l_4: $x = 6$

5. a. $x = 3$ **b.** $y = 5$
   c. Answers vary; for example, $y = 2x - 1$.

6.

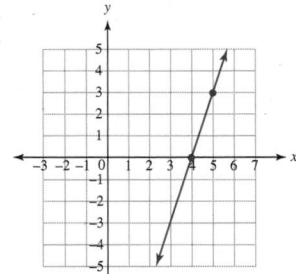

7.

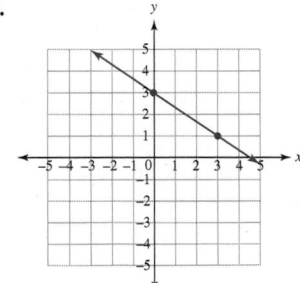

8. a. $y = 3x + 2$ **b.** $y = 2x + 6$

9. a. 3   **b.** $y = 3x - 13$

10. a. \$25
   b. The slope is $m = 0.06$. This means the cost increases by \$0.06 per minute of phone usage.

11. l_1: $-\frac{2}{3}$ l_2: $\frac{4}{5}$

12. The equation of the line is $y = \frac{-4}{7}x + \frac{5}{7}$. Therefore, the x-intercept is $(1.25, 0)$, and the y-intercept is $\left(0, \frac{5}{7}\right)$.

13. a. $m = -\frac{3}{4}$ **b.** $\left(\frac{7}{3}, 0\right)$ **c.** $\left(0, \frac{7}{4}\right)$

14. a. The y value increases by $\frac{10}{3}$ units.
   b. The x value decreases by $\frac{9}{5}$ units.

15. a. The number of tires sold will decrease by 10.
   b. The number of tires sold will increase by 6.

16. a. 0   **b.** undefined   **c.** parallel   **d.** slopes
   e. -1 **f.** perpendicular   **g.** vertical

17. a. neither   **b.** parallel   **c.** neither   **d.** perpendicular
   e. neither

18. a. $m = \frac{5}{3}$ **b.** $m = 0$

19. a. Answers vary; for example, $(3, 1)$.
   b. The slope of $\overline{AB}$ is -2. The slope of the perpendicular line $\overline{BC}$ is $\frac{1}{2}$. Then the rise is 1 and the run is 2, or the rise is 2 and the run is 4. This leads to $(3, 1)$.
   c. The slope of $\overline{AB}$ is $m = -2$, and the slope of $\overline{BC}$ is $m = \frac{1}{2}$. Therefore, $\overline{AB} \perp \overline{BC}$, which means $\angle ABC$ is a right angle. So $\triangle ABC$ must be a right triangle.

20. a. $-\frac{5}{6}$ **b.** $\frac{6}{5}$

21. $y = -\frac{1}{8}x - \frac{39}{8}$

22. $y = 4x + 11$

23. a. $C(m) = 0.25m + 115$ dollars
   b. \$177.50
   c. The total cost to rent the car and drive it 50 miles is \$127.50.
   d. 580 mi

24. a. An adult male with a hand length of 21.3 cm should be 178.25 cm in height.
   b. $H = 3.5L + 103.7$ **c.** 163.20 cm   **d.** ≈ 20.46 cm

25. $\sqrt{73}$ units (about 8.5 units)

26. a. $\angle Q$, because it is opposite the longest side of the triangle
   b. $\angle Q$, because it is opposite the longest side of the triangle

27. a. $\overline{BC}$ is the longest side, so it is the hypotenuse and $\angle A$ is the right angle.
   b. $\overline{AC}$ is the longest side, so it is the hypotenuse and $\angle B$ is the right angle.

28. The lengths of the sides must satisfy the converse of the Pythagorean theorem.
   a. $AB = \sqrt{8}$, $AC = \sqrt{32}$, and $BC = \sqrt{40}$. Then $(AB)^2 + (AC)^2 = 8 + 32 = 40$ and $(BC)^2 = 40$, so $(AB)^2 + (AC)^2 = (BC)^2$. Therefore, $\triangle ABC$ is a right triangle.

b. $AB = \sqrt{29}$, $AC = \sqrt{58}$, and $BC = \sqrt{29}$. Then $(AB)^2 + (BC)^2 = 29 + 29 = 58$ and $(AC)^2 = 58$, so $(AB)^2 + (BC)^2 = (AC)^2$. Therefore, $\triangle ABC$ is a right triangle.

29. $\left(-\dfrac{1}{2}, -\dfrac{3}{2}\right)$

30. $(-5, 5)$

31. $y = -2x + 1$

32. a. $(2, -1)$ **b.** $\sqrt{10}$

33. a. $(x - 4)^2 + [y - (-7)]^2 = (\sqrt{22})^2$
   b. $(4, -7)$ **c** $\sqrt{22}$

34. $[x - (-2)]^2 + (y - 3)^2 = (\sqrt{20})^2$

35. a. $\left(\dfrac{5}{2}, 1\right)$ **b.** $\dfrac{1}{2}\sqrt{145} \approx 6.02$
   c. $\left(x - \dfrac{5}{2}\right)^2 + (y - 1)^2 = \left(\dfrac{1}{2}\sqrt{145}\right)^2$

36. $(-1, 6)$

37. $(0, 5)$

38.

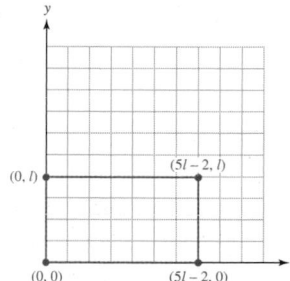

39. Answers vary. One possibility is drawing an obtuse triangle with a base of 5 units and a height of 4 units.

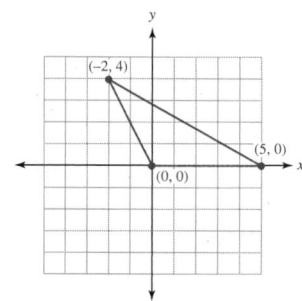

40. Answers vary. One possibility is drawing a parallelogram with a base of 5 units and a height of 2 units.

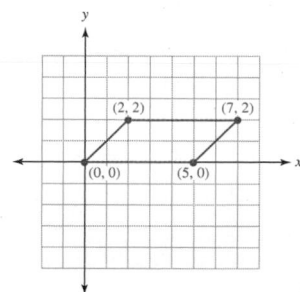

41. The slopes of the nonadjacent sides $\overline{AB}$ and $\overline{CD}$ are 3, so $\overline{AB}$ and $\overline{CD}$ are parallel sides. The slopes of the nonadjacent sides $\overline{BC}$ and $\overline{AD}$ are $\dfrac{1}{5}$, so $\overline{BC}$ and $\overline{AD}$ are parallel sides. The opposite sides of $ABCD$ are parallel, so $ABCD$ is a parallelogram.

42. a. $AC = \sqrt{(2 - (-3))^2 + (2 - (-1)^2} = \sqrt{34}$, and $BD = \sqrt{(2 - (-3))^2 + (-1 - 2)^2} = \sqrt{34}$. Then $AC = BD$. Then $\overline{AC} \cong \overline{BD}$.
   b. The midpoint of $\overline{AC}$ is $\left(-\dfrac{1}{2}, \dfrac{1}{2}\right)$, and the midpoint of $\overline{BD}$ is $\left(-\dfrac{1}{2}, \dfrac{1}{2}\right)$. The midpoint of $\overline{AC}$ equals the mid point of $\overline{BD}$, which is where the two line segments intersect. So $\overline{AC}$ and $\overline{BD}$ bisect each other.

43. a. $AB = \sqrt{(1 - (-1))^2 + (-5 - 0)^2} = \sqrt{29}$
   $CB = \sqrt{(3 - 1)^2 + (0 - (-5))^2} = \sqrt{29}$
   $CD = \sqrt{(1 - 3)^2 + (3 - 0)^2} = \sqrt{13}$
   $AD = \sqrt{(1 - (-1))^2 + (3 - 0)^2} = \sqrt{13}$

   $\overline{AB}$ and $\overline{CB}$ are congruent adjacent sides, $\overline{CD}$ and $\overline{AD}$ are congruent adjacent sides, and the pairs have no sides in common, so quadrilateral $ABCD$ is a kite.
   b. The diagonals are $\overline{AC}$ and $\overline{BD}$. The slope of $\overline{AC}$ is 0, and the slope of $\overline{BD}$ is undefined. The diagonals $\overline{AC}$ and $\overline{BD}$ are perpendicular.

44. a. $\left(\dfrac{a}{2}, \dfrac{b}{2}\right)$ **b.** $\left(\dfrac{a + c}{2}, \dfrac{b}{2}\right)$
   c. $AB = \sqrt{\left(\dfrac{a + c}{2} - \dfrac{a}{2}\right)^2 + \left(\dfrac{b}{2} - \dfrac{b}{2}\right)^2}$
   $= \sqrt{\dfrac{c^2}{4} + \dfrac{0^2}{4}}$
   $= \sqrt{\dfrac{c^2}{4}}$
   $= \dfrac{c}{2}$

   But $WY = c$, so $AB = \dfrac{1}{2}WY$.
   d. The slope of $\overline{WY}$ is $m = \dfrac{0 - 0}{c - 0} = \dfrac{0}{c} = 0$, and the slope of $\overline{AB}$ is $m = \dfrac{\frac{b}{2} - \frac{b}{2}}{\frac{a + c}{2} - \frac{a}{2}} = \dfrac{0}{\frac{c}{2}} = 0$. So $\overline{AB}$ is parallel to $\overline{WY}$.

45. a. translation   **b.** reflection   **c.** rotation
   d. rigid motion or isometry   **e.** symmetry
   f. size transformation, or dilation

46. a. The point A belongs to the mirror line.
   b. The point A is the center of rotation.

47. a. Each point moves 5 units to the left and 3 units upward.
   b. $R'(-3, -1)$

48. $B'(4, -5)$

49. $B(-10, -9)$

50.

51.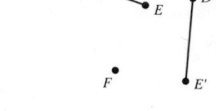

52.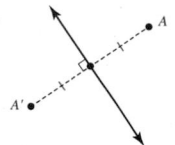

53. reflection

54.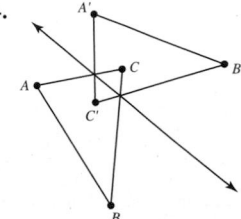

55. a. P is the center of rotation.

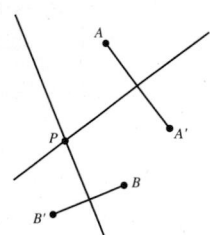

b. 60°

56. 145° or 215°

57. a. 72°   **b.** 60°
   c. There is no angle of symmetry, because the angle of symmetry of the bolts is 90° and the angle of symmetry of the triangular shapes is 72°. So a turn of 90° or 72° will cause one of the patterns to be misaligned.
   d. no angle of symmetry   **e.** 45°   **f.** 40°

58. a. one line of symmetry   **b.** two lines of symmetry
   c. two lines of symmetry   **d.** no lines of symmetry

59. a. S, N **b.** M, K
   c. The final results, N and K, are different. This problem illustrates that the order of the rigid motions may affect the result.

60. a.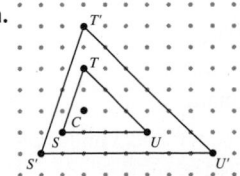

b. $S'T' = \sqrt{40}$ units, $ST = \sqrt{10}$ units, and $S'T'/ST = 2$.

c. $T'U' = \sqrt{72}$ units, $TU = \sqrt{18}$, and $T'U'/TU = 2$.
d. $S'U' = 8$ units, $SU = 4$ units, and $S'U'/SU = 2$.

e. $P'/P = 2$ **f.** $A'/A = \dfrac{24}{6} = 4$

61.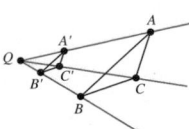

62.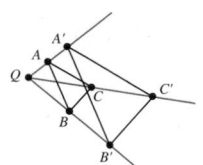

63.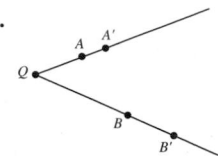

64. a. $QA' = 20$ cm   **b.** $A'B' = 24$ cm

65. $QA = \sqrt{(3-5)^2 + (-5-(-13))^2} = \sqrt{68}$, and
$QA' = \sqrt{(3-14)^2 + (-5-(-49))^2} = \sqrt{2057}$. Then
$k = QA'/QA = \sqrt{2057}/\sqrt{68} = 5.5$.

66. a. $B'C' = k \cdot BC$, so $k = B'C'/BC = \sqrt{80}/\sqrt{20} = 2$.
   b. quadrant II

67. Pick two points A and B in Figure 1, and the corresponding points A' and B' in Figure 2, and then use a ruler to measure AB and $A'B'$. Then $k = A'B'/AB \approx 1.6$.

68. a. 75 cm   **b.** 72 cm²

69. a. 1.25 cm   **b.** 3.2 cm²

70. a. reflection   **b.** rotation   **c.** size transformation
   d. translation

71. Step 1: Begin with a rectangle.

Step 2: Draw any curve from one corner to an adjacent corner of the rectangle.

Step 3: Reflect the curve using a horizontal mirror line. Translate the reflected curve to the opposite side of the rectangle.

Step 4: Draw a curve on the other side of the rectangle.

Step 5: Translate the curve to the other side of the rectangle.

Step 6: Erase the part of the rectangle you do not need to produce the shape of the tile.

Step 7: Reflect the tile.

Step 8: Decorate the tiles, and assemble the interlocking tiles without gaps or overlaps from Steps 6 and 7.

CHAPTER 13 TEST

1. a. $y = 3x - 2$ **b.** $y = -\dfrac{1}{4}x + 1$

2. a. $y = -12x + 38$ **b.** $y = 7x - 3$

3. a. \$2900   **b.** \$40

4. a. $(0, 20)$

   b. The monthly fee to have a phone plan is $20.

5. a. Solve $\dfrac{94.25}{\text{change in } x} = 6.50$ to get change in $x = 14.5$. Then 14.5 more feet of fence will be painted.

   b. Solve $\dfrac{-24.70}{\text{change in } x} = 6.50$ to get change in $x = -3.8$. Then 3.8 fewer feet of fence will be painted.

6. a. parallel **b.** neither **c.** perpendicular

7. a. $-\dfrac{8}{5}$ **b.** undefined

8. $y = -\dfrac{1}{10}x + \dfrac{7}{2}$

9. $PQ = \sqrt{(4 - 7)^2 + (-3 - 4)^2} = \sqrt{58}$, $QR = \sqrt{(7 - (-2))^2 + (4 - 6)^2} = \sqrt{85}$, and $PR = \sqrt{(4 - (-2))^2 + (-3 - 6)^2} = \sqrt{117}$. The longest side is $\overline{PR}$, so $\angle Q$ is the largest angle.

10. $PQ = \sqrt{(-3 - 3)^2 + (3 - (-1))^2} = \sqrt{52}$, $QR = \sqrt{(3 - 8)^2 + (-1 - 1)^2} = \sqrt{29}$, and $PR = \sqrt{(-3 - 8)^2 + (3 - 1)^2} = \sqrt{125}$. The longest side $\overline{PR}$ satisfies the inequality $(PQ)^2 + (QR)^2 < (PR)^2$, so the triangle is obtuse.

11. $\overline{AB}$ has a midpoint of $(3, 12)$ and a slope of -3. The equation of the perpendicular bisector is $y = \dfrac{1}{3}x + 11$.

12. a. $(x - (-8))^2 + (y - 3)^2 = (\sqrt{21})^2$

   b. $(-8, 3)$

   c. $\sqrt{21}$

13. a. $(k + p, q)$

   b. The property $AD = DC$ leads to the equation $p^2 + q^2 = k^2$.

   c. The slope of $\overline{BD}$ is $\dfrac{q}{p - k}$, and the slope of $\overline{AC}$ is $\dfrac{q}{p + k}$. Then

$$\frac{q}{p - k} \cdot \frac{q}{p + k} = \frac{q^2}{p^2 - k^2} = \frac{q^2}{p^2 - (p^2 + q^2)} = \frac{q^2}{-q^2} = -1.$$

   So $\overline{BD}$ and $\overline{AC}$ are perpendicular.

14. $\overline{AC}$ has the midpoint $\left(\dfrac{1}{2}, -1\right)$, and $\overline{BD}$ has the midpoint $\left(\dfrac{1}{2}, -1\right)$. Then $\overline{BD}$ intersects $\overline{AC}$ at the midpoint of $\overline{AC}$ and $\overline{AC}$ intersects $\overline{BD}$ at the midpoint of $\overline{BD}$. So the diagonals of $ABCD$ bisect each other.

15. a. A rigid motion is a transformation of the plane such $AB = A'B'$ for any two points A and B.

   b. Two figures F_1 and F_2 in the plane are congruent, denoted $F_1 \cong F_2$, if and only if there is a sequence of rigid motions that maps F_1 to F_2.

   c. Two figures F_1 and F_2 in the plane are similar, denoted $F_1 \sim F_2$, if and only if there is a sequence of rigid motions and size transformations that maps F_1 to F_2.

16. a. W, H **b.** Y, U

   c. The final images of the two isometries (U and H) are different. This problem illustrates that the order in which the rigid motions are applied may matter.

17.

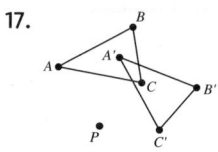

18. $A'(2, 10)$, $B'(-3, 12)$, and $C'(-7, 11)$

19. a.

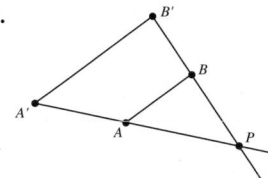

   b. $65°$

20. a. seven lines of symmetry **b.** $\dfrac{360}{7} \approx 51.4$ degrees

21. a. greater than 1

   b. Use the ruler to measure $A'B'$ and AB. Then $k = \dfrac{A'B'}{AB} \approx 1.8$.

   c.

22. $QA' = \sqrt{208}$, and $QA = \sqrt{13}$, so $k = \dfrac{QA'}{QA} = \dfrac{\sqrt{208}}{\sqrt{13}} = 4$.

23. a. 2430 cm **b.** 27 cm²

24. a. $k = \dfrac{10.32}{4.30} = 2.40$.

   b. Use the Pythagorean theorem to determine that $BD = \sqrt{14.49}$ and $DC = \sqrt{2.76}$. Then area of $\triangle A'B'C' = k^2 \cdot$ area of $\triangle ABC = (2.40)^2 \cdot \left(\dfrac{1}{2} \cdot (\sqrt{14.49} + \sqrt{2.76}) \cdot 2.00\right) \approx 31.5$ cm²

25. a. translation **b.** rotation **c.** reflection

   d. size transformation

BIBLIOGRAPHY

Aberg-Bengtsson, L. "Then You Can Take Half . . . Almost—Elementary Students Learning Bar Graphs and Pie Charts in a Computer-Based Context." *Journal of Mathematical Behavior* 25 (2006): 116–135.

Adams, T. L., and Murphy, K. "A Look of Some Numbers of Old: Perfect, Deficient, and Abundant." *Mathematics Teaching in the Middle School* 10 (Feb. 2005): 309–313.

Alexanderson, G. L. *The Random Walks of George Pólya.* Washington, D.C.: Mathematical Association of America, 2000.

Allen, R. M. "Ordered-Pair Relations—A Performance Assessment." *Mathematics Teaching in the Middle School* 5 (Nov. 1999): 190–194.

Ambrose, R. C., and Falkner, K. "Developing Spatial Understanding through Building Polyhedrons." *Teaching Children Mathematics* (Apr. 2002): 442–447.

Anderson, D. "Looking at Probability through a Historical Lens." *Mathematics Teaching in the Middle School* 6 (Sept. 2000): 50–52.

Anthony, G. J., and Walshaw, M. A. "Zero: A 'None' Number?" *Teaching Children Mathematics* 11 (Aug. 2004): 38–42.

Aspinwall, L., and Shaw, K. L. "Enriching Students' Mathematical Intuitions with Probability Games and Tree Diagrams." *Mathematics Teaching in the Middle School* 6 (Dec. 2000): 214–220.

Attia, T. L. "Using School Lunches to Study Proportion." *Mathematics Teaching in the Middle School* 9 (Sept. 2003): 17–21.

Austin, R. A., and Biafore, P. "Perimeter Patterns." *Teaching Children Mathematics* (Dec. 1995): 238–240.

Averbach, B., and Chein, O. *Problem Solving through Recreational Mathematics.* Mineola, NY: Dover, 2000.

Baek, J. Children's Invented Algorithms for Multidigit Multiplication Algorithms. In *The Teaching and Learning of Algorithms in School Mathematics,* L. J. Morrow and M. J. Kenney (eds.). Reston, VA: National Council of Teachers of Mathematics, 1998, pp. 151–160.

Bakker, A. "The Early History of Average Values and Implications for Education." *Journal of Statistics Education* 11 (2003): 1–21.

Ball, D. *The Subject Matter Preparation of Prospective Mathematics Teachers: Challenging the Myths.* East Lansing, MI: National Center for Research on Teacher Education, 1988.

Baltus, C. "A Truth Table on the Island of Truthtellers and Liars." *Mathematics Teacher* 94 (Dec. 2001): 730–732.

Barnes, R., and Hamon, S. "Proof and Prealgebra." *Mathematics Teacher* 103 (Apr. 2010): 597–602.

Barnhardt, R. K. (ed.). *Chambers Dictionary of Etymology.* New York: H. W. Wilson, 1988.

Baroody, A. J. "Why Children Have Difficulties Mastering the Basic Number Combinations and How to Help Them." *Mathematics Teaching in the Middle School* (Aug. 2006): 22–31.

Baroody, A. J., and Bartels, B. H. "Using Concept Maps to Link Mathematical Ideas." *Mathematics Teaching in the Middle School* 5 (May 2000): 604–609.

Battista, M. T. The Development of Geometric and Spatial Thinking. In *Second Handbook of Research on Mathematics Teaching and Learning,* F. K. Lester Jr. (ed.). Reston, VA: National Council of Teachers of Mathematics, 2007, pp. 843–908.

Battista, M. T. "The Importance of Spatial Structuring in Geometric Reasoning." *Teaching Children Mathematics* (Nov. 1999): 170–177.

Battista, M. T., and Clements, D. H. "Geometry and Proof." *Mathematics Teacher* 88 (Jan. 1995): 48–54.

Battista, M. T., Clements, D. H., Arnoff, J., Battista, K., and Borrow, C. "Students' Spatial Structuring of 2D Arrays of Squares." *Journal for Research in Mathematics Education* 29 (1998): 503–532.

Battista, M. T., Clements, D. H., and Wheatley, G. H. "Using Spatial Imagery in Geometric Reasoning." *Arithmetic Teacher* (Nov. 1991): 18–21.

Bay-Williams, J. "What Is Algebra in Elementary School?" *Teaching Children Mathematics* (Dec. 2001): 196–200.

Behr, M., Harel, G., Post, T., and Lesh, R. Rational Number, Ratio, and Proportion. In *Handbook of Research on Mathematics Teaching and Learning,* D. A. Grouws (ed.). Reston, VA: National Council of Teachers of Mathematics, 1992, pp. 296–333.

Behr, M. J., Harel, G., Post, T., and Lesh, R. Units of Quantity: A Conceptual Basis Common to Additive and Multiplicative Structures. In *The Development of Multiplicative Reasoning in the Learning of Mathematics,* G. Harel and J. Confrey (eds.). Albany, NY: State University of New York Press, 1994, pp. 121–176.

Bell, C. J. "Lining Up Arithmetic Sequences." *Mathematics Teaching in the Middle School* 17 (Aug. 2011): 34–39.

Bell, C. J. "Proofs without Words: A Visual Application of Reasoning and Proof." *Mathematics Teacher* 104 (May 2011): 690–695.

Bell, C. V. "Learning Geometric Concepts through Ceramic Tile Design." *Mathematics Teaching in the Middle School* 9 (Nov. 2003): 134–140.

Bennett, A. B., and Nelson, L. T. "A Conceptual Model for Solving Percent Problems." *Mathematics Teaching in the Middle School* 1 (Apr. 1994): 20–25.

Bennett, A. B., and Nelson, L. T. "Divisibility Tests: So Right for Discoveries." *Mathematics Teaching in the Middle School* 7 (Apr. 2002): 460–464.

Bentele, B. "Mathematical Lens." *Mathematics Teacher* 101 (Apr. 2008): 586–590.

Bernstein, J., Boushey, H., McNichol, E., and Zahradnik, R. Pulling Apart: A State-by-State Analysis of Income Trends. The Economic Policy Institute and the Center on Budget and Policy Priorities (Apr. 2002), pp. 1–85. Available at http://www.epinet.org/studies/Pulling_Apart_2002.pdf (see page 31).

Berry, R. Q., III, and Wiggins, J. "Spotlight on the Standards: Measurement in the Middle Grades." *Mathematics Teaching in the Middle School* 3 (Nov. 2001): 154–156.

Bezuszka, S. J., and Kenney, M. J. "Even Perfect Numbers: (Update)." *Mathematics Teacher* 90 (Nov. 1997): 628–633.

Billings, E., and Lakatos, T. "Lisa's Lemonade Stand: Exploring Algebraic Ideas." *Mathematics Teaching in the Middle School* 9 (May 2003): 456–460.

Billings, E., and McClure, M. S. "Mailing a Publication: Exploring Linear and Step Functions in a Real-World Context." *Mathematics Teaching in the Middle School* 10 (Mar. 2005): 349–355.

Binongo, J. N. "Randomness, Statistics, and π." *Mathematics Teacher* 95 (Mar. 2002): 224–230.

Bird, E. "Counting Attribute Blocks: Constructing Meaning for the Multiplication Principle." *Mathematics Teaching in the Middle School* 5 (May 2000): 569–573.

Boats, J. J., Dwyer, N. K., Laing, S., and Fratella, M. P. "Geometric Conjectures: The Importance of Counterexamples." *Mathematics Teaching in the Middle Schools* (Dec. 2003): 210–215.

Bobis, J. "The Empty Number Line: A Useful Tool or Just Another Procedure?" *Teaching Children Mathematics* 11 (Apr. 2007): 410–413.

Bonsanque, M. V., and Gannon, G. E. "From Exploration to Generalization: An Introduction to Necessary and Sufficient Conditions." *Mathematics Teacher* 96 (May 2003): 366–371.

Borko, H., Eisenhart, M., Brown, C. A., Underhill, R. G., Jones, D., and Agard, P. C. "Learning to Teach Hard Mathematics: Do Novice Teachers and Their Instructors Give Up Too Easily?" *Journal for Research in Mathematics Education* 23 (1992): 194–222.

Boston, M., Smith, M. S., and Hillen, A. F. "Building on Students' Intuitive Strategies to Make Sense of Cross Multiplication." *Mathematics Teaching in the Middle School* 9 (Nov. 2003): 150–155.

Botula, M. J., and Ford, M. I. "All about Us: Connecting Statistics with Real Life." *Teaching Children Mathematics* 4 (Sept. 1997): 14–19.

Boyer, C. B. (revised by U. C. Merzbach). *A History of Mathematics* (2nd ed.). New York: John Wiley & Sons, 1991.

Bradley, E. H. "Teacher to Teacher: Finding Common Ground." *Mathematics Teaching in the Middle School* 10 (Dec. 1999): 236.

Brahier, D. J. "Genetics as a Context for the Study of Probability." *Mathematics Teaching in the Middle School* 5 (Dec. 1999): 214–218.

Bray, W.S., and Abreu-Sanchez, L. "Using Number Sense to Compare Fractions." *Teaching Children Mathematics* 17 (Sept. 2010): 90–97.

Bremigan, E. G. "Is It Always True? From Detecting Patterns to Forming Conjectures to Constructing Proofs." *Mathematics Teacher* 97 (Feb. 2004): 96–100.

Bremigan, E. G. "Note: Figures Not Drawn to Scale." *Mathematics Teacher* 98 (Sept. 2004): 74–78.

Breyfogle, M. L., and Herbel-Eisenmann, B. A. "Focusing on Students' Mathematical Thinking." *Mathematics Teacher* 97 (Apr. 2004): 244–247.

Bright, G. W., Joyner, J. M., and Wallis, C. "Assessing Proportional Thinking." *Mathematics Teaching in the Middle School* 9 (Nov. 2003): 166–172.

Britton, B., and Tayeh, C. "Pocketful of Coins." *Teaching Children Mathematics* (Sept. 2004): 70–71.

Brownell, W. A. "Two Kinds of Learning in Arithmetic." *Journal of Educational Research* 31 (1938): 656–664.

Browning, C. A., Garza-Kling, G., and Sundling, E. H. "What's Your Angle on Angles?" *Teaching Children Mathematics* (Dec. 2007/Jan. 2008): 283–287.

Bucher, C. J., and Edwards, M. T. "Deepening Understanding of Transformation through Proof." *Mathematics Teacher* 104 (May 2011): 716–722.

Buczynski, S., Gorsky, J., McGrath, L., and Myers, P. "Sift Like Eratosthenes." *Teaching Children Mathematics* 18 (Sept. 2011): 100–118.

Burger, W., and Shaughnessy, J. "Characterizing the van Hiele Levels of Development in Geometry." *Journal for Research in Mathematics Education* 17 (Jan. 1986): 31–48.

Burke, M. J., and Taggert, D. L. "So That's Why 22/7 Is Used for Pi!" *Mathematics Teaching in the Middle School* 3 (Mar. 2002): 164–169.

Burkhart, J. "Integer Target: Using a Game to Model Integer Addition and Subtraction." *Mathematics Teaching in the Middle School* 7 (Mar. 2007): 388–392.

Burns, B. A., and Brade, G. A. Using the Geoboard to Enhance Measurement Instruction in the Secondary School Mathematics Classroom. In *Learning and Teaching Measurement,* D. H. Clements and G. Bright (eds.). Reston, VA: National Council of Teachers of Mathematics, 2003, pp. 256–270.

Burton, D. M. *History of Mathematics: An Introduction* (3rd ed.). Dubuque, IA: Wm. C. Brown, 1995.

Bush, S. "Unfolding the Solutions of Linear Systems." *Mathematics Teacher* 104 (Sept. 2010): 160

Cai, J., and Sun, W. Developing Students' Proportional Reasoning: A Chinese Perspective. In *Making Sense of Fractions, Ratios, and Proportions,* B. Litwiller and G. Bright (eds.). Reston, VA: National Council of Teachers of Mathematics, 2002, pp. 195–205.

Capps, L. R. "Division of Fractions." *Arithmetic Teacher* 9 (1962): 10–16.

Carnine, D., Jitendra, A. K., and Silbert, J. A. "Descriptive Analysis of Mathematics Curricular Materials from a Pedagogical Perspective: A Case Study of Fractions." *Remedial & Special Education* 18 (1997): 66–81.

Carnine, D., Jones, E. D., and Dixon, R. "Mathematics: Educational Tools for Diverse Learners." *School Psychology Review* 23 (1994): 406–427.

Carpenter, T., Franke, M. L., Jacobs, V. R., Fennema, E., Empson, S. B. "A Longitudinal Study of Invention and Understanding in Children's Multidigit Addition and Subtraction." *Journal for Research in Mathematics Education* 29 (1997): 3–20.

Carpenter, T. P., Franke, M. L., and Levi, L. *Thinking Mathematically: Integrating Arithmetic and Algebra in Elementary School.* Portsmouth, NH: Heinemann, 2003.

Carroll, D. C. "The Relative Effectiveness of Three Geometric Proof Construction Strategies." *Journal for Research in Mathematics Education* 8 (Jan. 1997): 62–67.

Carroll, W. M., and Porter, D. Alternative Algorithms for Whole-Number Operations. In *The Teaching and Learning of Algorithms in School Mathematics,* L. J. Morrow and M. J. Kenney (eds.). Reston, VA: National Council of Teachers of Mathematics, 1998, pp. 106–114.

Caulfield, R., Harkness, S. S., and Riley, R. "Surprise! Turn Routine Problems into Worthwhile Tasks." *Mathematics Teaching in the Middle School* 9 (Dec. 2003): 198–202.

Cengiz, N., and Rathouz, M. "Take a Bite out of Fraction Division." *Mathematics Teaching in the Middle School* 17 (Oct. 2011): 146–153.

Chappell, M. F., and Thompson, D. R. "Modifying our Questions to Assess Students' Thinking." *Mathematics Teaching in the Middle School* 6 (Apr. 1999): 470–474.

Chappell, M. F., and Thompson, D. R. "Perimeter or Area, Which Measure Is It?" *Mathematics Teaching in the Middle School* (Sept. 1999): 20–23.

Chazan, D. "High School Geometry Students' Justification for Their Views of Empirical Evidence and Mathematical Proof." *Educational Studies in Mathematics* 24 (1993): 359–387.

Chen, H., and Rao, A. R. "Two Is Not Equal to Four: Errors in Processing Multiple Percentage Changes." *Journal of Consumer Research* 34 (Oct. 2007): 1–22.

Chissick, N. "Promoting Learning through Inquiry." *Mathematics Teacher* 97 (Jan. 2004): 6–11.

Choppin, J., and Covington, J. "Calender Problems," *Mathematics Teacher* 98 (Sept. 2004): 104–105.

Ciucchi, P. M., and Hutchison, P. S. "Using a Simple Optical Rangefinder to Teach Similar Triangles." *Mathematics Teacher* 96 (Mar. 2003): 166–168.

Claus, A. "Exploring Geometry." *Arithmetic Teacher* (Sept. 1992): 14–17.

Cleaves, W. P. "Promoting Mathematics Accessibility through Multiple Representations Jigsaws." *Mathematics Teaching in the Middle School* 12 (Apr. 2008): 446–452.

Clement, L. "A Model for Understanding, Using, and Connecting Representations." *Teaching Children Mathematics* (Sept. 2004): 97–102.

Clements, D., and Battista, M. "Geometry and Geometric Measurement." *Arithmetic Teacher* (Feb. 1986): 29–32.

Clements, D. H., and Battista, M. T. Geometry and Spatial Reasoning. In *Handbook of Research on Mathematics Teaching and Learning,* D. A. Grouws (ed.). Reston, VA: National Council of Teachers of Mathematics, 1992, pp. 420–464.

Clements, D. H., and Sarama, J. "Young Children's Ideas about Geometric Shapes." *Teaching Children Mathematics* (Apr. 2000): 482–487.

Coffey, D. C., and Richardson, M. G. "Rethinking Fair Games." *Mathematics Teaching in the Middle School* 10 (Feb. 2005): 298–303.

Coffey, M. E. "Irrational Numbers on the Number Line: Perfectly Placed." *Mathematics Teaching in the Middle School* 6 (Sept. 2001): 453–455.

Cognition and Technology Group at Vanderbilt. *The Jasper Project: Lessons in Curriculum, Instruction, Assessment, and Professional Development.* Mahwah, NJ: Erlbaum, 1997.

Cole, S. "Symmetry Gave Me Four Legs!" *Teaching Children Mathematics* 17 (Nov. 2010): 212–217.

Collier, C. P. "By Way of Introduction: Geometry." *Mathematics Teaching in the Middle School* (Mar.–Apr. 1998): 387.

Conference Board of the Mathematical Sciences. *The Mathematical Education of Teachers.* Providence, RI: American Mathematical Society; Washington, D.C.: Mathematical Association of America, 2001.

Consumer Reports. Yonkers, NY: Consumers Union.

Contreras, J. N. "Exploring Nonconvex, Crossed, and Degenerate Polygons." *Mathematics Teacher* 98 (Sept. 2004): 80–86.

Contreras, J. N. "A Problem-Posing Approach to Specializing, Generalizing, and Extending Problems with Interactive Geometry Software." *Mathematics Teacher* 96 (Apr. 2003): 270–276.

Cooper, L. L., and Tomayko, M. C. "Understanding Place Value." *Teaching Children Mathematics* 17 (May 2011): 558–567.

Cox, R. L. "Using Conjectures to Teach Students the Role of Proof." *Mathematics Teacher* 97 (Jan. 2004): 48–52.

Cramer, K., Monson, D., Wyberg, T., Leavitt, S., and Whitney, S. "Models for Initial Decimal Ideas." *Teaching Children Mathematics* 16 (Sept. 2009): 106–117.

Cramer, K., and Post, T. "Proportional Reasoning." *Mathematics Teacher* 5 (May 1993): 404–407.

Cramer, K. A., Post, T. R., and delMas, R. C. "Initial Fraction Learning by Fourth- and Fifth-Grade Students: A Comparison of the Effects of Using Commercial Curricula with the Effects of Using the Rational Number Project Curriculum." *Journal for Research in Mathematics Education* 33 (2002): 111–144.

Daly, F., Hand, D. J., Jones, M. C., Lunn, A. D., and McConway, K. J. Elements of Statistics. Addison Wesley/The Open University, 1995.

Darley, J. W., and Leapard, B. B. "Connecting Arithmetic to Algebra." *Teaching Children Mathematics* 17 (Oct. 2010): 184–191

Davidenko, S. "Building the Concept of Function from Students' Everyday Activities." *Mathematics Teacher* 90 (Feb. 1997): 144–149.

DePeau, E. A., and Kalder, R. S. "Using Dynamic Technology to Present Concepts through Multiple Representations." *Mathematics Teacher 104* (Nov. 2010): 268–273.

DeTemple, D., and Miedema, A. "Patterns and Puzzles for Pyramids and Prisms." *Mathematics Teacher* 90 (May 1997): 370–374.

Devore, J., and Peck, R. Introductory Statistics. Belmont, CA: West Publishing, 1990.

Diezmann, C. M., and English, L. D. Promoting the Use of Diagrams as Tools for Thinking. In *The Roles of Representation in School Mathematics,* A. A. Cuoco and F. R. Curcio (eds.). Reston, VA: National Council of Teachers of Mathematics, 2001, pp. 77–89.

Drum, R. L., and Petty, W. G., Jr. "2 Is Not the Same as 2.0." *Mathematics Teaching in the Middle School* 6 (Sept. 2000): 34–38.

Dugdale, S., Matthews, J. L., and Guerrero, S. "The Art of Posing Problems and Guiding Investigations." *Mathematics Teaching in the Middle School* 10 (Oct. 2004): 140–147.

Dwyer, N. K., Causey-Lee, B. J., and Nekeya, M. I. "Conceptualizing Ratios with Look-Alike Polygons." *Mathematics Teaching in the Middle School* 8 (Apr. 2003): 426–431.

Dyke, F. "Using Graphs to Introduce Functions." *Mathematics Teacher* 96 (Feb. 2003): 126–129.

Eccles, F. M. "The Euler Line and Nine-Point-Circle Theorems." *Mathematics Teacher* 92 (Jan. 1999): 50–54.

Eddins, S. K., Maxwell, E. O., and Stanislaus, F. "Geometrics Transformations: Part 1." *Mathematics Teacher* 87 (Apr. 1994): 177–180.

Edwards, T. G., and Hensien, S. M. "Using Probability Experiments to Foster Discourse." *Teaching Children Mathematics* (Apr. 2000): 524–529.

Embse, C. V., and Engebretsen, A. "Visual Representations of the Mean and Standard Deviation." *Mathematics Teacher* 8 (1996): 688–692.

Empson, S. B. Organizing Diversity in Early Fraction Thinking. In *Making Sense of Fractions, Ratios, and Proportions,* B. Litwiller and G. Bright (eds.). Reston, VA: National Council of Teachers of Mathematics, 2002, pp. 29–40.

Empson, S. B. Using Sharing Situations to Help Children Learn Fractions. In *Putting Research into Practice in the Elementary Grades,* D. Chambers (ed.). Reston, VA: National Council of Teachers of Mathematics, 2002, pp. 122–132.

Enderson, M. Using Measurement to Develop Mathematical Reasoning at the Middle and High School Levels. In *Learning and Teaching Measurement,* D. H. Clements and G. Bright (eds.). Reston, VA: National Council of Teachers of Mathematics, 2003, pp. 271–281.

Englard, L. "Raise the Bar on Problem Solving." *Teaching Children Mathematics* 17 (Oct. 2011): 156–163.

English, L. D., and Warren, E. A. Introducing the Variable through Pattern Recognition. In *Algebraic Thinking, Grades K–12,* B. Moses (ed.). Reston, VA: National Council of Teachers of Mathematics, 1999, pp. 141–145.

Erish, D. J. "Authentic Assessment in the Geometry Classroom: Calculating the Classroom Air-Exchange Rate." *Mathematics Teacher* 95 (Sept. 2002): 422–424.

Even, R. "Factors Involved in Linking Representations of Functions." *Journal of Mathematical Behavior* 17 (1998): 105–121.

Falkner, K., Levi, L., and Carpenter, T. P. Children's Understanding of Equality: A Foundation for Algebra. In *Putting Research into Practice in the Elementary Grades,* D. Chambers (ed.). Reston, VA: National Council of Teachers of Mathematics, 2002, pp. 202–207.

Farmer, J. D., and Powers, R. A. "Exploring Mayan Numerals." *Teaching Children Mathematics* (Sept. 2005): 69–79.

Fawcett, H. P. The Nature of Proof. In *The Thirteenth Yearbook.* Reston, VA: National Council of Teachers of Mathematics, reprinted 2001 (originally published in 1938).

Feicht, L. "Making Charts: Do Your Students Really Understand the Data." *Mathematics Teaching in the Middle School* 5 (Sept. 1999): 16–18.

Feicht, S. N., and O'Conner, W. T. "Sticks to the Roof of Your Mouth?" *Mathematics Teaching in the Middle School* 4 (Mar. 1999): 404–411.

Fennell, F. "Probability." *Arithmetic Teacher* (Dec. 1990): 18–22.

Fennel, F., and Rowan, T. "Representation: An Important Process for Teaching and Learning Mathematics." *Teaching Children Mathematics* (Jan. 2001): 288–292.

Fernández, E. "Understanding Functions without Using the Vertical Line Test." *Mathematics Teacher* 99 (Sept. 2005): 96–100.

Fernández, J. M. L., and Estrella, A. V. "Contexts for Column Addition and Subtraction." *Teaching Children Mathematics* 17 (May 2011): 540–548.

Ferrer, B. B., Hunter, B., Irwin, K. C., Sheldon, M. J., Thompson, C. S., and Vistro-Yu, C. P. "By the Unit or the Square?" *Mathematics Teaching in the Middle School* 3 (Nov. 2001): 132–137.

Ferrini-Mundy, J., Lappan, G., and Phillips, E. Experiences with Patterning. In *Putting Research into Practice in the Elementary Grades,* D. Chambers (ed.). Reston, VA: National Council of Teachers of Mathematics, 2002, pp. 208–215.

Ferrucci, B., Yeap, B., and Carter, J. "A Modeling Approach for Enhancing Problem Solving in the Middle Grades." *Mathematics Teaching in the Middle School* 8 (May 2003): 470–475.

Finzer, W. F., and Bennett, D. S. "From Drawing to Construction with the Geometer's Sketchpad." *Mathematics Teacher* 88 (May 1995): 428–431.

Flores, A., and Regis, T. P. "How Many Times Does a Radius Square Fit into the Circle?" *Mathematics Teaching in the Middle School* 8 (Mar. 2003): 363–368.

Fox, T. B. "Implications of Research on Children's Understanding of Geometry." *Teaching Children Mathematics* (May 2000): 572–576.

Franklin, C. A., and Mewborn, D. S. "Statistics in the Elementary Grades: Exploring Distributions of Data." *Teaching Children Mathematics* (Aug. 2008): 10–16.

Franklin, K., and Kouba, V. L. "Multiplication and Division: Sense Making and Meaning." *Teaching Children Mathematics* (1995): 574–577.

Franzblau, D. S., and Warner, L. From Fibonacci Numbers to Fractals: Recursive Patterns and Subscript Notation. In *The Roles of Representation in School Mathematics,* A. A. Cuoco and F. R. Curcio (eds.). Reston, VA: National Council of Teachers of Mathematics, 2001, pp. 186–200.

Freda, A. "Roll the Dice—An Introduction to Probability." *Mathematics Teaching in the Middle School* 2 (Oct. 1998): 85–89.

Friedlander, A., and Tabach, M. Promoting Multiple Representations in Algebra. In *The Roles of Representation in School Mathematics,* A. A. Cuoco and F. R. Curcio (eds.). Reston, VA: National Council of Teachers of Mathematics, 2001, pp. 173–185.

Friel, S. N., and Bright, G. W. Teach-Stat: A Model for Professional Development in Data Analysis and Statistics for Teachers K–6. In *Reflections on Statistics: Learning, Teaching, and Assessments in Grades K–12,* S. P. Lajoie (ed.). Mahwah, NJ: Erlbaum, 1998, pp. 89–117.

Friel, S. N., Curcio, F. R., and Bright, G. W. "Making Sense of Graphs: Critical Factors Influencing Comprehension and Instructional Implications." *Journal for Research in Mathematics Education* 2 (2001): 124–158.

Frost, J. H., and Dornoo, M. D. "Similar Shapes and Ratios." *Mathematics Teaching in the Middle School* 12 (Nov. 2006): 222–224.

Fung, M. G., and Latulippe, C. L. "Computational Estimation" *Teaching Children Mathematics* 17 (Oct. 2010): 170–176.

Fuson, K. Developing Mathematical Power in Whole Number Operations. In *A Research Companion to Principles and Standards for School Mathematics,* J. Kilpatrick, W. G. Martin, and D. Schifter (eds.). Reston, VA: National Council of Teachers of Mathematics, 2003, pp. 68–94.

Fuson, K. C. Research on Whole Number Addition and Subtraction. In *Handbook of Research on Mathematics Teaching and Learning,* D. A. Grouws (ed.). Reston, VA: National Council of Teachers of Mathematics, 1992, pp. 243–275.

Fuson, K. C., Kalchman, M., and Bransford, J. D. Mathematical Understanding: An Introduction. In *How Students Learn: Mathematics in the Classroom,* M. S. Donovan and J. D. Bransford (eds.). Washington, D.C.: National Academies Press, 2005, pp. 217–256.

Fuys, D. J., and Liebov, A. K. "Concept Learning in Geometry." *Teaching Children Mathematics* (Jan. 1997): 248–251.

Galindo, E. "Assessing Justification and Proof in Geometry Classes Taught Using Dynamic Software." *Mathematics Teacher* 91 (Jan. 1998): 76–82.

Garza-Kling, G. "Fluency with Basic Addition." *Teaching Children Mathematics* 18 (Sept. 2011): 80–88.

Gay, A. S., and Keith, C. J. "Reasoning about Linear Equations." *Mathematics Teaching in the Middle School* 8 (Nov. 2002): 46–148.

Gazella, K. A. "Hydrate for Good Health." *Better Nutrition* (July 2007): 60–61.

Gelman, A., and Nolan, D. "Statistical Sampling and Data Collection Activities." *Mathematics Teacher* 95 (Dec. 2002): 688–693.

Giganti, P., Jr., and Cittadino, M. J. "The Art of Tessellation." *Arithmetic Teacher* (Mar. 1990): 6–16.

Glasgow, R., Ragan, G., Fields, W. M., Reys, R., and Wasman, D. "The Decimal Dilemma." *Teaching Children Mathematics* (Oct. 2000): 89–93.

Glidden, P. L., and Fry, E. K. "Illustrating Mathematical Connections: Two Proofs That Only Five Regular Polyhedra Exist." *Mathematics Teacher* 86 (Nov. 1993): 657–661.

Good, I. J. "The Philosophy of Exploratory Data Analysis." *Philosophy of Science* 50 (June 1983): 283–295.

Goral, M. B. "From Kinesthetic Movement to Algebraic Functions." *Mathematics Teaching in the Middle School* 14 (Mar. 2009): 388–391.

Graeber, A. O., and Tanenhaus, E. Multiplication and Division: From Whole Numbers to Rational Numbers. In *Research Ideas for the Classroom: Middle Grades Mathematics,* D. T. Owens (ed.). New York: Macmillan, 1993, pp. 99–117.

Greenes, C., and Findell, C. Developing Students' Algebraic Reasoning Abilities. In *Developing Mathematical Reasoning in Grades K–12,* L. V. Stiff and F. R. Curcio (eds.). Reston, VA: National Council of Teachers of Mathematics, 1999, pp. 127–137.

Greer, B. Extending the Meaning of Multiplication and Division. In *The Development of Multiplicative Reasoning in the Learning of Mathematics,* G. Harel and J. Confrey (eds.). Albany, NY: State University of New York Press, 1994, pp. 61–85.

Greer, B. Multiplication and Division as Models of Situations. In *Handbook of Research on Mathematics Teaching and Learning,* D. A. Grouws (ed.). Reston, VA: National Council of Teachers of Mathematics, 1992, pp. 276–295.

Gregg, J., and Gregg, D. U. "Interpreting the Standard Division Algorithm in a 'Candy Factory' Context." *Teaching Children Mathematics* (2007): 25–31.

Groth, R. E. "Linking Theory and Practice in Teaching Geometry." *Mathematics Teacher* 99 (Aug. 2005): 27–30.

Gunderson, A., and Gunderson, E. "Fractions Concepts Held by Young Children." *Arithmetic Teacher* 4 (Oct. 1957): 168–173.

Hanna, G. "Proof, Explanation and Exploration: An Overview." *Educational Studies in Mathematics* 44 (2000): 5–23.

Hannibal, M. A. "Young Children's Developing Understanding of Geometric Shapes." *Teaching Children Mathematics* (Feb. 1999): 353–357.

Hansen, D. W. "On Inscribed and Escribed Circles of Right Triangles, Circumscribed Triangles, and the Four-Square, Three-Square Problem." *Mathematics Teacher* 96 (May 2003): 358–364.

Hanson, S. A., and Hogan, T. P. "Computational Estimation Skill of College Students." *Journal for Research in Mathematics Education* 31 (2000): 483–499.

Happs, J., Mansfield, H., and Wheatley, G. H. "Estimation and Mental-Imagery Models in Geometry." *Arithmetic Teacher* (Sept. 1992): 44–46.

Harper, S. R. "Students' Interpretations of Misleading Graphs." *Mathematics Teaching in the Middle School* 9 (Feb. 2004): 340–343.

Hartshorne, R. "Teaching Geometry According to Euclid." *Notices of the AMS* 47 (Apr. 2000): 460–465.

Hartzler, S. J. "Ratios of Linear, Area, and Volume Measures in Similar Solids." *Mathematics Teaching in the Middle School* 8 (Jan. 2003): 228–232.

Haubner, M. A. "Percents: Developing Meaning through Models." *Arithmetic Teacher* 40 (1992): 232–234.

Haznedar, A., Hurwitz, M., and Fromhold, A. T., Jr. "Viewing Standard Problems in Nonstandard Ways." *Mathematics Teacher* 99 (Aug. 2005): 60–64.

Heaton, R. M. *Teaching Mathematics to the New Standards: Relearning the Dance.* New York: Columbia University; London: Teachers College Press, 2000.

Heid, M. K. A Technology-Intensive Functional Approach to the Emergence of Algebraic Thinking. In *Approaches to Algebra: Perspectives for Research and Teaching,* N. Bednarz, C. Kieran, and L. Lee (eds.). Dordrecht, the Netherlands: Kluwer Academic Press, 1996, pp. 239–256.

Heid, M. K., Hollebrands, K. F., and Iseri, L. W. "Reasoning and Justification with Examples from Technological Environments." *Mathematics Teacher* 95 (Mar. 2003): 210–216.

Herrey, E. M. J. "Confidence Intervals Based on the Mean Absolute Deviation of a Normal Sample." *Journal of the American Statistical Association* 60 (Mar. 1965): 257–269.

Hershkowitz, R., and Schwarz, B. "The Emergent Perspective in Rich Learning Environments: Some Roles of Tools and Activities in the Construction of Sociomathematical Norms." *Educational Studies in Mathematics* 39 (1999): 149–166.

Hiebert, J. Decimal Fractions. In *Putting Research into Practice in the Elementary Grades,* D. Chambers (ed.). Reston, VA: National Council of Teachers of Mathematics, 2002, pp. 119–120.

Hiebert, J. Mathematical, Cognitive, and Instructional Analyses of Decimal Fractions. In *Analysis of Arithmetic for Mathematics Teaching,* G. Leinhardt, R. Putnam, and R. Hattrup (eds.). Hillsdale, NJ: Lawrence Erlbaum Associates, 1992, pp. 283–321.

Hiebert, J. What Research Says about the NCTM Standards. In *A Research Companion to Principles and Standards for School Mathematics,* J. Kilpatrick, W. G. Martin, and D. Schifter (eds.). Reston, VA: National Council of Teachers of Mathematics, 2003, pp. 5–23.

Hiebert, J., and Behr, M. Introduction: Capturing the Major Themes. In *Research Agenda for Mathematics Education: Number Concepts and Operations in the Middle Grades,* J. Hiebert and M. Behr (eds.). Hillsdale, NJ: Lawrence Erlbaum

Associates; Reston, VA: National Council of Teachers of Mathematics, 1988, pp. 1–18.

Hiebert, J., and Wearne, D. Developing Understanding through Problem Solving. In *Teaching Mathematics through Problem Solving, Grades 6–12,* H. L. Shoen and R. I. Charles (eds.). Reston, VA: National Council of Teachers of Mathematics, 2003, pp. 3–13.

Hirschhorn, D. B., and Tompson, D. R. "Technology and Reasoning in Algebra and Geometry." *Mathematics Teacher* 89 (Feb. 1996): 138–142.

Hirshfeld, A. W. "The Triangles of Aristarchus." *Mathematics Teacher* 97 (Apr. 2004): 228–231.

Hoehn, L. "The Pythagorean Theorem: An Infinite Number of Proofs?" *Mathematics Teacher* 90 (Sept. 1997): 438–441.

Hoffer, A. R. Geometry and Visual Thinking. In *Teaching Mathematics in Grades K–8: Research-Based Methods,* T. R. Post (ed.). Boston, MA: Allyn and Bacon, 1988, pp. 232–261.

Hoffer, A. R. Ratios and Proportional Thinking. In *Teaching Mathematics in Grades K–8: Research-Based Methods,* T. R. Post (ed.). Boston, MA: Allyn and Bacon, 1988, pp. 285–313.

Hoffer, A. R., and Hoffer, S. A. Geometry and Visual Thinking. In *Teaching Mathematics in Grades K–8* (2nd ed.), T. R. Post (ed.). Needham Heights, MA: Allyn and Bacon, 1992, pp. 249–277.

Hofstetter, E. "Data with Snap, Crackle, and Pop." *Mathematics Teaching in the Middle School* 1 (Mar.–Apr. 1996): 760–764.

Hoiberg, K. B., Sharp, J., Hodgson, T., and Colbert, J. "Geometric Probability and the Area of Leaves." *Mathematics Teaching in the Middle School* 7 (Mar. 2005): 326–332.

Hopkins, T. M., and Cady, J. A. "What Is the Value of @*#? *Teaching Children Mathematics* (Apr. 2007): 434–437.

Horton, B. "Making Connections between Sequences and Mathematical Models." *Mathematics Teacher* 93 (May 2000): 434–436.

Howden, H. Prior Experiences. In *Algebra for Everyone,* E. L. Edwards Jr. (ed.). Reston, VA: National Council of Teachers of Mathematics, 1990, pp. 7–23.

Huinker, D. Letting Fraction Algorithms Emerge through Problem Solving. In *The Teaching and Learning of Algorithms in School Mathematics,* L. J. Morrow and M. J. Kenney (eds.). Reston, VA: National Council of Teachers of Mathematics, 1998, pp. 170–182.

Huinker, D., Freckman, J. L., and Steinmeyer, M. B. "Subtraction Strategies from Children's Thinking: Moving toward Fluency with greater Numbers." *Teaching Children Mathematics* (Feb. 2003): 347–353.

Huntley, M. A., Marcus, R., Kahan, J., and Miller, J. L. "Investigating High-School Students' Reasoning Strategies When They Solve Linear Equations." *Journal of Mathematical Behavior* 26 (2007): 115–139.

Ilayperuma, I., Nanayakkara, G., and Palahepitiya, N. "Prediction of Personal Stature Based on the Hand Length." *Galle Medical Journal* 14 (Sept. 2009): 15–18.

Irwin, K. C. "Using Everyday Knowledge of Decimals to Enhance Understanding." *Journal for Research in Mathematics Education* 32 (2001): 399–420.

Isaacs, A. K., and Kelso, C. R. "Pictures, Graphs, and Questions: Statistical Processes." *Teaching Children Mathematics* 2 (Feb. 1996): 340–345.

Izen, S. P. "Proof in Modern Geometry." *Mathematics Teacher* 91 (Nov. 1998): 718–720.

Jacobs, A., and Rak, S. "Geometry." *Teaching Children Mathematics* (Feb. 1999): 346–347.

Jacobs, V. R. "How Do Students Think about Statistical Sampling Before Instruction?" *Mathematics Teaching in the Middle School* 5 (Dec. 1999): 240–246, 263.

Jaime, A., and Gutiérrez, A. "Guidelines for Teaching Plane Isometries in Secondary School." *Mathematics Teacher* 88 (Oct. 1995): 591–597.

Jardine, D. "Looking at Probability through a Historical Lens." *Mathematics Teaching in the Middle School* 2 (Sept. 2000): 50–52.

Jeon, K. "Mathematics Hiding in the Nets for a Cube." *Teaching Children Mathematics* (Mar. 2009): 394–400.

Johnson, A. "Now & Then. From Shadows to Surveying." *Mathematics Teaching in the Middle School* 6 (Nov. 2000): 170–171.

Johnson, A., and Boswell, L. "Geographic Constructions." *Mathematics Teacher* 85 (Mar. 1992): 184–187.

Johnson, H. C. "Division with Fractions—Levels of Meaning." *Arithmetic Teacher* 12 (1965): 362–368.

Johnson, J. M. "On the Distribution of Primes." *Mathematics Teacher* 96 (Mar. 2003): 198–200.

Johnston, D. E. "Measurement: What's the Big Idea?" *Mathematics Teaching in the Middle School* 9 (Apr. 2004): 430–431.

Jones, G. A., Langrall, C. W., Thornton, C. A., and Mogill, A. T. "Students' Probabilistic Thinking in Instruction." *Journal for Research in Mathematics Education* 30 (1999): 487–519.

Jones, G. A., Langrall, C. W., Thornton, C. A., Mooney, E. S., Wares, A., Jones, M. R., Perry, B., Putt, I. J., and Nisbet, S. "Using Students' Statistical Thinking to Inform Instruction." *Journal of Mathematical Behavior* 20 (2001): 109–144.

Jones, G. A., Langrall, C. W., Thornton, C. A., and Tarr, J. Understanding Students' Probabilistic Thinking. In *Developing Mathematical Reasoning in Grades K–12,* L. V. Stiff and F. R. Curcio (eds.). Reston, VA: National Council of Teachers of Mathematics, 2003, pp. 146–155.

Joram, E. Benchmarks as Tools for Developing Number Sense. In *Learning and Teaching Measurement,* D. H. Clements and G. Bright (eds.). National Council of Teachers of Mathematics 2003 Yearbook. Reston, VA: NCTM, 2003, pp. 57–67.

Joram, E., and Oleson, V. "Learning about Area by Working with Building Plans." *Mathematics Teaching in the Middle School* 9 (Apr. 2004): 450–456.

Kader, G. D. "Means and MADs." *Mathematics Teaching in the Middle School* 6 (Mar. 1999): 398–403.

Kader, G. D., and Perry, M. "Push-Penny: What Is Your Expected Score?" *Mathematics Teaching in the Middle School* 3 (Feb. 1998): pp. 370–377.

Kahan, J. A., and Wyberg, T. R. "Problem Solving Can Generate New Approaches to Mathematics: The Case of Probability." *Mathematics Teacher* 96 (May 2003): 328–332.

Kalchman, M., and Koedinger, K. R. Teaching and Learning Functions. In *How Students Learn: Mathematics in the Classroom,* M. S. Donovan and J. D. Bransford (eds.). Washington, D.C.: National Academies Press, 2005, pp. 351–393.

Kalman, R. "Revisiting the Sum of Odd Natural Numbers." *Mathematics Teaching in the Middle School* 9 (Sept. 2003): 58–61.

Kalman, R. "The Value of Multiple Solutions." *Mathematics Teaching in the Middle School* 10 (Nov. 2004): 174–179.

Kamii, C., and Clark, F. B. "Equivalent Fractions: Their Difficulty and Educational Implications." *Journal of Mathematical Behavior* 14 (1995): 365–378.

Kamii, C., and Dominick, A. The Harmful Effects of Algorithms in Grades 1–4. In *The Teaching and Learning of Algorithms in School Mathematics,* L. J. Morrow and M. J. Kenney (eds.). Reston, VA: National Council of Teachers of Mathematics, 1998, pp. 130–140.

Kamii, C., and Joseph, L. "Teaching Place Value and Double-Column Addition." *Teaching Children Mathematics* (Feb. 1988): 48–52.

Kamii, C., and Lewis, B. A. "Single Digit Subtraction with Fluency." *Teaching Children Mathematics* (2003): 230–236.

Kamii, C., and Warrington, M. A. Teaching Fractions: Fostering Children's Own Reasoning. In *Developing Mathematical Reasoning in Grades K–12,* L. V. Stiff and F. R. Curcio (eds.). Reston, VA: National Council of Teachers of Mathematics, 1999, pp. 82–93.

Kaput, J. J., and West, M. M. Missing-Value Proportional Reasoning Problems: Factors Affecting Informal Reasoning Patterns. In *The Development of Multiplicative Reasoning in the Learning of Mathematics,* G. Harel and J. Confrey (eds.). Albany, NY: State University of New York Press, 1994, pp. 235–287.

Kastberg, S. E. "Euclidean Tools and the Creation of Euclidean Geometry." *Mathematics Teaching in the Middle School* 7 (Jan. 2002): 294–295.

Katz, V. J. *A History of Mathematics* (2nd ed.). Reading, MA: Addison Wesley, 1998.

Keiser, J. M. "The Role of Definition." *Mathematics Teaching in the Middle School* (Apr. 2000): 506–511.

Kenney, P. A., Zawojewski, J. S., and Silver, E. A. Marcy's Dot Pattern. In *Algebraic Thinking, Grades K–12,* B. Moses (ed.). Reston, VA: National Council of Teachers of Mathematics, 1999, pp. 137–140.

Kennis, J. R. "Rare and Exotic Probability Bugs." *Mathematics Teacher* 102 (Mar. 2009): 510–515.

Kent, L. B. "Connecting Integers to Meaningful Contexts." *Mathematics Teaching in the Middle School* 6 (Sept. 2000): 62–66.

Kersaint, G. "A Fruitful Crop." *Mathematics Teaching in the Middle School* 9 (Nov. 2003): 162.

Kersaint, G. "The Rossis' New Kitchen." *Mathematics Teaching in the Middle School* 8 (Mar. 2003): 356–358.

Kieran, C. Helping to Make the Transition to Algebra. In *Putting Research into Practice in the Elementary Grades,* D. Chambers (ed.). Reston, VA: National Council of Teachers of Mathematics, 2002, pp. 221–224.

Kieran, C., and Chalouh, L. Prealgebra: The Transition from Arithmetic to Algebra. In *Algebraic Thinking, Grades K–12,* B. Moses (ed.). Reston, VA: National Council of Teachers of Mathematics, 1999, pp. 59–70.

Killion, K., and Steffe, L. P. Children's Multiplication. In *Putting Research into Practice in the Elementary Grades,* D. Chambers (ed.). Reston, VA: National Council of Teachers of Mathematics, 2002, pp. 90–96.

Kilpatrick, J., Swafford, J., and Findell, B. (eds.). *Adding It Up: Helping Children Learn Mathematics.* National Research Council, Mathematics Learning Study Committee, Center for Education, Division of Behavioral and Social Sciences and Education. Washington, D.C.: National Academies Press, 2001.

Kim, O. K., and Kasmer, L. "Using 'Prediction' to Promote Mathematical Reasoning." *Mathematics in the Middle School* 12 (Feb. 2007): 294–299.

Kincaid, C., Mauldin, G. R., and Mauldin, D. M. "Perimeters, Patterns, and Conjectures." *Mathematics Teacher* 87 (Feb. 1994): 98–100.

Kitchen, R. S., and Wilson, L. D. "Lessons Learned from Students about Assessment and Instruction." *Teaching Children Mathematics* (Apr. 2004): 394–399.

Klein, A. S., and Treffers, A. "The Empty Number Line in Dutch Second Grades: Realistic Versus Gradual Program Design." *Journal for Research in Mathematics Education* 29 (1998): 443–464.

Kloosterman, P., Warfield, J., Wearne, D., Koc, Y., Martin, W. G., and Strutchens, M. Fourth-Grade Students' Knowledge of Mathematics and Perceptions of Learning Mathematics. In *Results and Interpretations of the 1990–2000 Mathematics Assessments of the National Assessment of Educational Progress,* P. Kloosterman and F. K. Lester Jr. (eds.). Reston, VA: National Council of Teachers of Mathematics, 2004, pp. 71–103.

Knuth, E. J. "Secondary School Mathematics Teachers' Conceptions of Proof." *Journal for Research in Mathematics Education* 33 (2002): 397–405.

Knuth, E. J. "Student Understanding of the Cartesian Connection: An Exploratory Study." *Journal for Research in Mathematics Education* 31 (2000): 500–508.

Knuth, E. J. "Understanding Connections between Equations and Graphs." *Mathematics Teacher* 93 (2000): 48–53.

Koehler, M. H. Using Graphing Calculator Simulations in Teaching Statistics. In *Thinking and Reasoning with Data and Chance: Sixty-Eighth Yearbook,* G. F. Burrill and P. C. Elliott (eds.). Reston, VA: National Council of Teachers of Mathematics, 2006, pp. 257–272.

Koester, B. "Prisms and Pyramids: Constructing Three-Dimensional Models to Build Understanding." *Teaching Children Mathematics* (Apr. 2003): 436–442.

Konold, C. "Representing Probability with Pipe Diagrams." *Mathematics Teacher* 89 (May 1996): 378–332.

Konold, C., and Higgins, T. Reasoning about Data. In *A Research Companion to Principles and Standards for School Mathematics,* J. Kilpatrick, W. G. Martin, and D. Schifter (eds.). Reston, VA: National Council of Teachers of Mathematics, 2003, pp. 193–215.

Kouba, V., and Wearne, D. Whole Number Properties and Operations. In *Results from the Seventh Mathematics Assessment of the National Assessment Educational Progress,* E. A. Silver and P. A. Kenney (eds.). Reston, VA: National Council of Teachers of Mathematics, 2000, pp. 141–161.

Kouba, V. L., and Franklin, K. Multiplication and Division: Sense Making and Meaning. In *Putting Research into Practice in the Elementary Grades,* D. Chambers (ed.). Reston, VA: National Council of Teachers of Mathematics, 2002, pp. 93–96.

Kouba, V. L., and Wearne, D. Whole Number Properties and Operations. In *Results from the Seventh Mathematics Assessment of the National Assessment Educational Progress,* E. A. Silver and P. A. Kenney (eds.). Reston, VA: National Council of Teachers of Mathematics, 2000, p. 152.

Kribs-Zaleta, C. M. "Oranges, Posters, Ribbons, and Lemonade." *Mathematics Teaching in the Middle School* 12 (Apr. 2008): 453–457.

Krutchkoff, R. G. "The Correct Use of the Sample Mean Absolute Deviation in Confidence Intervals for a Normal Variate." *Technometrics* 8 (Nov. 1966): 663–674.

Kurz, T., and Garcia, J. "Prime Decomposition Using Tools." *Mathematics Teacher* 104 (Nov. 2010): 256–259.

Lamb, J. F., Jr. "Two Egyptian Construction Tools." *Mathematics Teacher* 86 (Feb. 1993): 166–167.

Lambdin, D. Benefits of Teaching through Problem Solving. In *Teaching Mathematics through Problem Solving, Prekindergarten–Grade 6,* F. K. Lester Jr. and R. I. Charles (eds.). Reston, VA: National Council of Teachers of Mathematics, 2003, pp. 3–13.

Lamm, M. W., and Pugalee, D. K. "Student-Constructed Problems Extend Proportional Reasoning." *Teaching Children Mathematics* 17 (Aug. 2010): 16–19.

Lamon, S. Ratio and Proportion: Cognitive Foundations in Unitizing and Norming. In *The Development of Multiplicative Reasoning in the Learning of Mathematics,* G. Harel and J. Confrey (eds.). Albany, NY: State University of New York Press, 1994, pp. 89–120.

Lamon, S. J. Presenting and Representing from Fractions to Rational Numbers. In *The Roles of Representation in School Mathematics,* A. A. Cuoco and F. R. Curcio (eds.). Reston, VA: National Council of Teachers of Mathematics, 2001, pp. 146–165.

Lamon, S. J. Ratio and Proportion: Cognitive Foundations in Unitizing and Norming. In *The Development of Multiplicative Reasoning in the Learning of Mathematics,* G. Harel and J. Confrey (eds.). Albany, NY: State University of New York Press, 1994, pp. 89–120.

Lamon, S. J. *Teaching Fractions and Ratios for Understanding.* Mahwah, NJ: Erlbaum, 1999.

Lampert, M. Teaching Mathematics and Thinking. In *Putting Research into Practice in the Elementary Grades,* D. Chambers (ed.). Reston, VA: National Council of Teachers of Mathematics, 2002, pp. 68–71.

Lane-Getaz, S. J. "What Is Statistical Thinking, and How Is It Developed?" *Thinking and Reasoning with Data and Chance: Sixty-Eighth Yearbook,* G. F. Burrill and P. C. Elliott (eds.). Reston, VA: National Council of Teachers of Mathematics, 2006, pp. 273–289.

Lanier, S., and Barrs, S. "Let's Play Plinko: A Lesson in Simulations and Experimental Probabilities." *Mathematics Teacher* 96 (Dec. 2003): 626–629.

Lanius, C. S., and Williams, S. E. "Proportionality: A Unifying Theme for the Middle Grades." *Mathematics Teaching in the Middle School* 8 (Apr. 2003): 392–396.

Lannin, J. K. "Developing Mathematical Power by Using Explicit and Recursive Reasoning." *Mathematics Teacher* 98 (Nov. 2004): 216–223.

Lappan, G., Phillips, Fitzgerald, W. M., and Winter, M. J. "Area Models and Expected Value." *Mathematics Teacher* 96 (Nov. 1987): 650–654.

Lappan, G., and Winter, M. J. "Probability Simulation in Middle School." *Mathematics Teacher* 73 (Sept. 1980): 446–449.

Lawrence, S. "Nominals: Numbers as Names." *Teaching Children Mathematics* (Dec. 1995): 242–245.

Lee, J. E. "Making Sense of the Traditional Long Division Algorithm." *Journal of Mathematical Behavior* 26 (2007): 48–59.

Lee, M. A. "Enhancing Discourse on Equations." *Mathematics Teacher* 93 (Dec. 2000): 755–756.

Lehrer, R., and Curtis, C. L. "Why Are Some Solids Perfect?" *Teaching Children Mathematics* (Jan. 2000): 324–329.

Leinhardt, G., Zaslavsky, O., and Stein, M. K. "Functions, Graphs, and Graphing: Tasks, Learning, and Teaching." *Review of Educational Research* 60 (Spring 1990): 1–64.

Leitze, A. R., and Kitt, N. A. "A Modeling Approach for Enhancing Problem Solving in the Middle Grades." *Mathematics Teaching in the Middle School* 8 (May 2003): 470–475.

Leitze, A. R., and Kitt, N. A. "Using Homemade Algebra Tiles to Develop Algebra and Prealgebra Concepts." *Mathematics Teacher* 93 (Sept. 2000): 462–466.

Lembke, L. O., and Reyes, B. J. "The Development of, and Interaction between, Intuitive and School Taught Ideas about Percent." *Journal for Research in Mathematics Education* 25 (1994): 237–259.

Leonard, J., and Campbell, L. "Using the Stock Market for Relevance in Teaching Number Sense." *Mathematics Teaching in the Middle School* 9 (Feb. 2004): 294–299.

Lesh, R., Post, T., and Behr, M. Proportional Reasoning. In *Number Concepts and Operations in the Middle Grades,* J. Hiebert and M. Behr (eds.). Reston, VA: National Council of Teachers of Mathematics, 1988, pp. 93–118.

Levasseur, K., and Cuoco, A. Habits of Mind. In *Teaching Mathematics through Problem Solving, Grades 6–12,* H. L. Shoen and R. I. Charles (eds.). Reston, VA: National Council of Teachers of Mathematics, 2003, pp. 27–37.

Levine, D. R. "Strategy Use and Estimation Ability of College Students." *Journal for Research in Mathematics Education* 13 (1982): 350–359.

Lewis, L. "Irrational Numbers Can 'In-Spiral' You." *Mathematics Teaching in the Middle School* 12 (Apr. 2007): 442–446.

Lloyd, G. M., and Wilson, M. "Supporting Innovation: The Impact of a Teacher's Conceptions of Functions on His Implementation of a Reform Curriculum." *Journal for Research in Mathematics Education* 29 (1998): 248–274.

Lo, J. J., and Watanabe, T. "Developing Ratio and Proportion Schemes: A Story of a Fifth Grader." *Journal for Research in Mathematics Education* 28 (1997): 216–236.

Lo, J. J., Watanabe, T., and Cai, J. "Developing Ratio Concepts: An Asian Perspective." *Mathematics Teaching in the Middle School* 9 (Mar. 2004): 362–367.

Lovin, L.H., Mason, J., and Shifflett, E. "Generating Meaning for Range, Mode, Median, and Mean." *Teaching Children Mathematics* 16 (Nov. 2009): 246–252.

Ma, L. *Knowing and Teaching Elementary Mathematics: Teachers' Understanding of Fundamental Mathematics in China and the United States.* Mahwah, NJ: Lawrence Erlbaum Associates, 1999.

MacGregor, M., and Stacey, K. "Cognitive Models Underlying Students' Formulation of Simple Linear Equations." *Journal for Research in Mathematics Education* 24 (1993): 217–232.

MacGregor, M., and Stacey, K. "A Flying Start to Algebra." *Teaching Children Mathematics* 90 (Oct. 1999): 78–85.

MacGregor, M., and Price, E. An Exploration of Aspects of Language Proficiency and Algebra Learning. In *Lessons Learned* *from Research,* J. Sowder and B. Schappelle (eds.). Reston, VA: National Council of Teachers of Mathematics, 2002, pp. 109–116.

Mack, N. K. Building a Foundation for the Understanding of Multiplication of Fractions. In *Putting Research into Practice in the Elementary Grades,* D. Chambers (ed.). Reston, VA: National Council of Teachers of Mathematics, 2002, pp. 145–149.

Mack, N. K. "Building on Informal Knowledge through Instruction in a Complex Content Domain: Partitioning, Units, and Understanding Multiplication of Fractions." *Journal for Research in Mathematics Education* 32 (2001): 2670–295.

Mack, N. K. "Enriching Number Knowledge." *Teaching Children Mathematics* 18 (Sept. 2011): 100–108.

Mack, N. K. Making Connections to Understand Fractions. In *Putting Research into Practice in the Elementary Grades,* D. Chambers (ed.). Reston, VA: National Council of Teachers of Mathematics, 2002, pp. 137–140.

Madell, R. "Children's Natural Processes." *Arithmetic Teacher* 32 (Mar. 1985): 20–22.

Malloy, C. E. "Perimeter and Area through the Van Hiele Model." *Mathematics Teaching in the Middle School* 5 (Oct. 1999): 87–90.

Mamona-Downs, J., and Downs, M. "The Identity of Problem Solving." *Journal of Mathematical Behavior* 24 (2005): 385–401.

Manaster, A. B., and Schlesinger, B. M. "Geometry Problems Promoting Reasoning and Understanding." *Mathematics Teacher* 92 (Feb. 1999): 114–116.

Mann, R. L. "Balancing Act: The Truth behind the Equals Sign." *Teaching Children Mathematics* (Sept. 2004): 65–69.

Mariorri, M. A. "Introduction to Proof: The Mediation of Dynamic Software Environment." *Educational Studies in Mathematics* 44 (2000): 25–53.

Marrades, R., and Gutiérrez, A. "Proofs Produced by Secondary School Students Learning Geometry in a Dynamic Computer Environment." *Educational Studies in Mathematics* 44 (2000): 87–125.

Martin, G. W., and Harel, G. "Proof Frames of Preservice Elementary Teachers." *Journal for Research in Mathematics Education* 20 (Jan. 1989): 41–51.

Martin, H. M., and Zawojewski, J. S. "Dealing with Data and Chance: An Illustration from the Middle School Addendum to the Standards." *Arithmetic Teacher* (Dec. 1993): 220–223.

Martin, T. S., McCrone, S. M. S., Bower, M. L. W., and Dindyal, J. "The Interplay of Teacher and Student Actions in the Teaching and Learning Geometric Proof." *Educational Studies in Mathematics* 60 (2005): 95–124.

Martin, W. G., and Kasmer, L. "Reasoning and Sense Making." *Teaching Children Mathematics* (Dec. 2009/Jan. 2010): 284–291.

Martin, W. G., and Strutchens, M. E. Geometry and Measurement. In *Results from the Seventh Mathematics Assessment of the National Assessment Educational Progress,* E. A. Solver and P. A. Kenney (eds.). Reston, VA: National Council of Teachers of Mathematics, 2000, pp. 193–234.

Martinie, S. "Data Analysis and Statistics in the Middle School." *Mathematics Teaching in the Middle School* 12 (Aug. 2006): 48.

Martinie, S. L., and Bay-Williams, J. M. "Investigating Students' Conceptual Understanding of Decimal Fractions Using Multiple Representations." *Mathematics Teaching in the Middle School* 8 (Jan. 2003): 244–247.

Martinie, S. L., and Bay-Williams, J. M. "Using Literature to Engage Students in Proportional Reasoning." *Mathematics Teaching in the Middle School* 9 (Nov. 2003): 142–148.

Mason, J. "Enabling Teachers to Be Real Teachers: Necessary Levels of Awareness and Structure of Attention." *Journal for Mathematics Teacher Education* 1 (1998): 243–267.

Matthews, M. E., and Gross, G. "Illumination the Mathematics of Lamp Shades." *Mathematics Teacher* 102 (Dec. 2008/Jan. 2009): 332–335.

McClain, K. "Reflecting on Students' Understanding of Data." *Mathematics Teaching in the Middle School* 4 (Mar. 1999): 374–380.

McClain, K., and Cobb, P. "Supporting Students' Ability to Reason about Data." *Educational Studies in Mathematics* 45 (2001): 103–129.

McClain, K., McGatha, M., and Hodge, L. L. "Improving Data Analysis." *Mathematics Teaching in the Middle School* 5 (Apr. 2000): 548–553.

McClain, K., and Schmitt, P. "Teachers Grow Math: A Case Study from Data Analysis." *Mathematics Teaching in the Middle School* 9 (Jan. 2004): 274–279.

McClure, J. E. "Start Where They Are: Geometry as an Introduction to Proof." *American Mathematical Monthly* 107 (Jan. 2000): 44–52.

McDuffie, A. R., and Morrison, J. A. "Learning about Data Display: Connecting Mathematics and Science Inquiry." *Teaching Children Mathematics* (Feb. 2008): 375–382.

McGatha, M., Cobb, P., and McClain, K. "An Analysis of Students' Initial Statistical Understandings: Developing a Conjectured Learning Trajectory." *Journal of Mathematical Behavior* 21 (2002): 339–355.

McGill, R., Tukey, J. W., and Larsen, W. A. "Variations of Box Plots." *American Statistician* 32 (1978): 12–16.

McGivney, J. M., and DeFranco, T. C. "Geometry Proof Writing: A Problem-Solving Approach à la Pólya." *Mathematics Teacher* 88 (Oct. 1995): 552–555.

Methany, D. "Consumer Investigations: What Is the Best Chip?" *Teaching Children Mathematics* (Mar. 2001): 418–420.

Metz, J. "Reader Reflections." *Mathematics Teacher* 92 (Jan. 1999): 3.

Middleton, J. A., and Van Den Heuvel-Panhuizen, M. "The Ratio Table." *Mathematics Teaching in the Middle School* 4 (Jan.–Mar. 1995): 282–288.

Miller, G. H. "How Effective Is the Meaning Method?" *Arithmetic Teacher* 4 (1957): 45–49.

Miller, J. L., and Fey, J. T. "Proportional Reasoning." *Mathematics Teaching in the Middle School* 5 (Jan. 2000): 310–313.

Mistretta, R. M. "Intersecting and Perpendicular Lines: Activities to Prevent Misconceptions." *Mathematics Teaching in the Middle School* 9 (Oct. 2003): 84–91.

Mitchell, C. E. "Astronomy, Geometry, and the Ancient Greeks." *Arithmetic Teacher* (May 1986): 39–41.

Mokros, J., and Russell, S. J. "Children's Concepts of Average and Representativeness." *Journal for Research in Mathematics Education* 26 (1995): 20–39.

Moldavan, C. C. "Culture in the Curriculum: Enriching Numeration and Number Operations." *Teaching Children Mathematics* (Dec. 2001): 238–243.

Monk, S. Representation in School Mathematics: Learning to Graph and Graphing to Learn. In *A Research Companion to*

Principles and Standards for School Mathematics, J. Kilpatrick, W. G. Martin, and D. Schifter (eds.). Reston, VA: National Council of Teachers of Mathematics, 2003, pp. 250–262.

Moore-Russo, D., and Golzy, J. B. "Helping Students Connect Functions and Their Representations." *Mathematics Teacher* 99 (2005): 156–160.

Morita, J. G. "Capture and Recapture Your Students' Interest in Statistics." *Mathematics Teaching in the Middle School* 4 (Mar. 1999): 412–418.

Moyer, P. S. "Using Representations to Explore Perimeter and Area." *Teaching Children Mathematics* (Sept. 2001): 52–59.

Moyer, P. S., and Mailley, E. "Inchworm and a Half: Developing Fraction and Measurement Concepts Using Mathematical Representations." *Teaching Children Mathematics* 10 (Jan. 2004): 244–252.

Mulligan, J. T., and Mitchelmore, M. C. "Young Children's Intuitive Models of Multiplication and Division." *Journal for Research in Mathematics Education* 28 (1997): 309–330.

Murrey, D. L. "Differentiating Instruction in Mathematics for the English Language Learner." *Mathematics Teaching in the Middle School* 14 (Oct. 2008): 146–153.

Nagel, N., and Swingen, C. C. "Students' Explanations of Place Value in Addition and Subtraction." *Teaching Children Mathematics* (1998): 164–170.

Nathan, M. J., and Koedinger, K. R. "Teachers' and Researchers' Beliefs about the Development of Algebraic Reasoning." *Journal for Research in Mathematics Education* 31 (2000): 168–190.

National Center for Education Statistics, National Assessment of Educational Progress. 2003 Mathematics Assessment. Available at http://nces.ed.gov/nationsreportcard/mathematics/.

National Council of Teachers of Mathematics. *Principles and Standards for School Mathematics.* Reston, VA: NCTM, 2000.

National Mathematics Advisory Panel. "Foundations for Success: The Final Report of the National Mathematics Advisory Panel." Washington, DC: U.S. Department of Education, 2008.

Nickerson, R. S. The Teaching of Thinking and Problem Solving. In *Thinking and Problem Solving,* R. J. Sternberg (ed.). San Diego, CA: Academic Press, 1994, pp. 409–449.

Niezgoda, D. A., and Moyer-Packenham, P. S. "Hickory Dickory Dock: Navigating through Data Analysis." *Teaching Children Mathematics* (Feb. 2005): 292–300.

Nitabach, E., and Lehrer, R. "Developing Spatial Sense through Area Measurement." *Teaching Children Mathematics* 2 (Apr. 1996): 473–476.

Norton, R. M. "Determining Probabilities by Examining Underlying Structure." *Mathematics Teaching in the Middle School* 3 (Oct. 2001): 78–82.

Nowlin, D. "Division with Fractions." *Mathematics Teaching in the Middle School* 3 (Nov.–Dec. 1996): 116–119.

Okolica, S., and Macrina, G. "Integrating Transformation Geometry into Traditional High School Geometry." *Mathematics Teacher* 85 (Dec. 1992): 716–719.

Olsen, A. "Divisibility Tests." *Mathematics Teaching in the Middle School* 100 (Aug. 2006): 46–52.

Olson, M. "Odd Factors and Consecutive Sums: An Interesting Relationship." *Mathematics Teacher* (Jan. 1991): 50–53.

Oppenheimer, L., and Hunting, R. P. "Relating Fractions and Decimals: Listening to Students Talk." *Mathematics Teaching in the Middle School* 4 (Feb. 1999): 318–321.

Osborne, A., and Wilson, P. Moving to Algebraic Thought. In *Teaching Mathematics in Grades K–8: Research-Based Methods,* T. R. Post (ed.). Boston, MA: Allyn and Bacon, 1988, pp. 384–405.

Outhred, L. N., and Mitchelmore, M. C. "Young Children's Intuitive Understanding of Rectangular Area Measurement." *Journal for Research in Mathematics Education* 31 (2000): 144–167.

Owens, D. T. "Spatial Abilities." *Arithmetic Teacher* (Feb. 1990): 48–51.

Parker, D. "Partitioning the Interior of a Circle with Chords." *Mathematics Teacher* 99 (Sept. 2005): 120–124.

Parker, M. "Reasoning and Working Proportionately with Percent." *Mathematics Teaching in the Middle School* 9 (Nov. 2004): 326–330.

Parker, M., and Leinhardt, G. "Percent: A Privileged Proportion." *Review of Educational Research* 65 (1995): 421–481.

Pegg, J., and Redden, E. Procedures for, and Experiences in, Introducing Algebra in New South Wales. In *Algebraic Thinking, Grades K–12,* B. Moses (ed.). Reston, VA: National Council of Teachers of Mathematics, 1999, pp. 71–81.

Pereira-Mendoza, L. "Geometry and Language—A Natural Connection." *Teaching Children Mathematics* (Apr. 1997): 454–457.

Pereira-Mendoza, L. "What Is a Quadrilateral?" *Mathematics Teacher* 86 (Dec. 1993): 774–776.

Pesek, D. D., and Kirshner, D. Interference of Instrumental Instruction in Subsequent Relational Learning. In *Lessons Learned from Research,* J. Sowder and B. Schappelle (eds.). Reston, VA: National Council of Teachers of Mathematics, 2002, pp. 101–107.

Peterson, B. E. "From Tessellations to Polyhedra: Big Polyhedra." *Mathematics Teaching in the Middle School* (Feb. 2000): 348–357.

Petitto, A., and Ginsburg, H. "Mental Arithmetic in Africa and America: Strategies, Principles, and Explanations." *International Journal of Psychology* 17 (1982): 81–102.

Phan-Yamada, T. "How Long Is The Square Root of 2 cm?" *Mathematics Teacher* 105 (Sept. 2011): 160

Philipp, R. A., and Vincent, C. "Reflecting on Learning Fractions without Understanding." *On-Math: Online Journal of School Mathematics* 2 (2003): 1–7.

Pickreign, J., and Rogers, R. "Do You Understand Your Algorithms?" *Mathematics Teaching in the Middle School* 5 (Aug. 2006): 42–47.

Piez, C. M., and Voxman, M. H. "Multiple Representations—Using Different perspectives to Form a Clearer Picture." *Mathematics Teacher* 90 (Feb. 1997): 164–166.

Polly, D. "How Long Can You Stand on One Foot?" *Teaching Children Mathematics* 18 (Aug. 2011): 16–19.

Pólya, G. *How to Solve It* (2nd ed.). Garden City, NY: Doubleday, 1957.

Postlewait, K. B., Adams, M. R., and Shih, J. C. "Promoting Meaningful Mastery of Addition and Subtraction." *Teaching Children Mathematics* (2003): 354–357.

Pratt, D. "Making Sense of the Total of Two Dice." *Journal for Research in Mathematics Education* 31 (2000): 602–625.

Preston, R., and Thompson, T. "Integrating Measurement across the Curriculum." *Mathematics Teaching in the Middle School* (Apr. 2004): 436–441.

Prince, A. A. "Prove It!" *Mathematics Teacher* 91 (Nov. 1998): 726–728.

Proulx, J., Beisiegel, M., Miranda, H., and Simmt, E. "Rethinking the Teaching of Systems of Equations." *Mathematics Teacher* 102 (Mar. 2009): 527–533.

Quesada, A. R. "Recent Improvements to the Sieve of Eratosthenes." *Mathematics Teacher* 90 (Apr. 1997): 304–307.

Quinn, R. J. "Having Fun with Baseball." *Mathematics Teaching in the Middle School* 10 (May 1996): 780–785.

Quinn, R. J., and Tomlinson, S. "Random Variables: Simulations and Surprising Connections." *Mathematics Teacher* 92 (Jan. 1999): 4–9.

Raman, M. "Key Ideas: What Are They and How Can They Help Us Understand How People View Proof?" *Educational Studies in Mathematics* 52 (2003): 319–325.

Randolph, T., and Sherman, H. J. "Alternative Algorithms: Increasing Options, Reducing Errors." *Teaching Children Mathematics* (Apr. 2001): 480–484.

Rathouz, M. M. "Making Sense of Decimal Multiplication." *Mathematics Teaching in the Middle School* 16 (Mar. 2011): 430–437.

Retras, R. "Privacy for the Twenty-First Century: Cryptography." 94 (Nov. 2001): 689–692.

Reynolds, M. J. "Letting the Cat out of the Bag . . . To Make Room for a Triangle!" *Mathematics Teacher* 95 (Jan. 2002): 6–7.

Reys, R. E., and Yang, D. "Relationship between Computational Performance and Number Sense among Sixth- and Eighth-Grade Students in Taiwan." *Journal for Research in Mathematics Education* 29 (1998): 225–237.

Riddle, M., and Rodzelle, B. "Fractions: What Happens between Kindergarten and the Army?" *Teaching Children Mathematics* (Dec. 2000): 202–206.

Rider, R. "Shifting from Traditional to Nontraditional Teaching Practices Using Multiples Representations." *Mathematics Teacher* 100 (Mar. 2007): 494–500.

Rigelman, N. R. "Fostering Mathematical Thinking and Problem Solving: The Teacher's Role." *Teaching Children Mathematics* (Feb. 2007): 308–314.

Roberts, S., and Tayeh, C. "It's the Thought That Counts: Reflecting on Problem Solving." *Mathematics Teaching in the Middle School* 12 (Dec. 2007): 232–237.

Robertson, J. M. "Geometric Constructions Using Hinged Mirrors." *Mathematics Teacher* 79 (May 1986): 380–386.

Robichaux, R. R., and Rodrigue, P. "Polygon Properties: What is Possible?" *Teaching Children Mathematics* 16 (May 2010): 524–531.

Robichaux, R. R., and Rodrique, P. R. "Using Origami to Promote Geometric Communication." *Mathematics Teaching in the Middle School* (Dec. 2003): 222–229.

Rollick, M. B. "Toward a Definition of Reflection." *Mathematics Teaching in the Middle School* 14 (Mar. 2009): 396–398.

Russell, S. J. "What Does It Mean that '5 Has a Lot?'" *Thinking and Reasoning with Data and Chance: Sixty-Eighth Yearbook,* G. F. Burrill and P. C. Elliott (eds.). Reston, VA: National Council of Teachers of Mathematics, 2006, pp. 17–29.

Russell, S. J., and Mokros, J. What Do Children Understand about Average? *Putting Research into Practice in the Elementary Grades,* D. Chambers (ed.). Reston, VA: National Council of Teachers of Mathematics, 2002, pp. 226–231.

Sandefur, J. "Media Clips." *Mathematics Teacher* 98 (Sept. 2004): 129–132.

Sanders, C. V. "Geometric Constructions: Visualizing and Understanding Geometry." *Mathematics Teacher* 91 (Oct. 1998): 554–556.

Saxe, G. B., Taylor, E. V., McIntosh, C., and Gearhart, M. "Representing Fractions with Standard Notation: A Developmental Analysis." *Journal for Research in Mathematics Education* 36 (2005): 137–157.

Schad, B., and Georgeson, J. "Multiplication along the Silk Road." *Teaching Children Mathematics* (Feb. 2010): 321–324.

Scharton, S. "I Did It My Way: Providing Opportunities for Students to Create, Explain, and Analyze Computation Procedures." *Teaching Children Mathematics* (Jan. 2004): 278–283.

Scher, D. P. "Theorems in Motion: Using Dynamic Geometry to Gain Fresh Insights." *Mathematics Teacher* 89 (Apr. 1996): 330–332.

Schifter, D. Reasoning about Operations: Early Algebraic Thinking in Grades K–6. In *Developing Mathematical Reasoning in Grades K–12,* L. V. Stiff and F. R. Curcio (eds.). Reston, VA: National Council of Teachers of Mathematics, 1999, pp. 62–81.

Schliemann, A. D., Araujo, C., Cassunde, M. A., Macedo, S., and Niceas, L. "Use of Multiplicative Commutativity by School Children and Street Sellers." *Journal for Research in Mathematics Education* 29 (1998): 422–435.

Schmandt-Besserat, D. *The History of Counting.* New York: Morrow Junior Books, 1999.

Schneider, S. B., and Thompson, C. S. "Incredible Equations Develop Incredible Number Sense." *Teaching Children Mathematics* (Nov. 2000): 146–168.

Scholemer, C. G. "Tips for Teaching Cartesian Graphing: Linking Concepts and Procedures." *Teaching Children Mathematics* (Sept. 1994): 20–23.

Schwartz, J. E. "A New World of Mathematical Thinking." *Teaching Children Mathematics* 17 (Oct. 2010): 164–169.

Schwartzman, S. "An Unexpected Value." *Mathematics Teacher* 86 (Feb. 1993): 118–120.

Schwarz, B., and Bruckgeimer, M. "Let ABC Be Any Triangle." *Mathematics Teacher* 81 (Nov. 1988): 640–642.

Schwertman, N. C. "Discovering an Optimal Property of the Median." *Mathematics Teacher* 92 (Nov. 1999): 692–696.

Sellers, P. A. "The Trouble with Long Division" *Teaching Children Mathematics* 16 (May 2010): 516–520.

Sellke, D. H. "Geometric Flips via the Arts." *Children Teaching Mathematics* (Feb. 1999): 379–383.

Senk, S. L. "Van Hiele Levels and Achievement in Writing Geometry Proofs." *Journal for Research in Mathematics Education* 20 (May 1989): 309–321.

Seppala-Holtzman, D. N. "Ancient Egyptians Russian Peasants Foretell the Digital Age." *Mathematics Teacher* 100 (May 2007): 632–635.

Sgroi, L. An Exploration of the Russian Peasant Method of Multiplication. In *The Teaching and Learning of Algorithms in School Mathematics,* L. J. Morrow and M. J. Kenney (eds.). Reston, VA: National Council of Teachers of Mathematics, 1998, pp. 81–85.

Sharp, J., and Adams, B. "Children's Constructions of Knowledge for Fraction Division After Solving Realistic Problems." *Journal of Educational Research* 95 (July/Aug. 2002): 333–348.

Sharp, J. G., and Adams, B. Children's Development of Meaningful Fraction Algorithms: A Kid's Cookies and a Puppy's Pills. In *Making Sense of Fractions, Ratios, and Proportions,* B. Litwiller and G. Bright (eds.). Reston, VA: National Council of Teachers of Mathematics, 2002, pp. 18–28.

Shaughnessy, J. M. Research on Statistics Learning and Reasoning. In *Second Handbook of Research on Mathematics Teaching and Learning,* F. K. Lester Jr. (ed.). Charlotte, NC: Information Age Publishing, 2007, pp. 957–1009.

Shaughnessy, J. M. Research on Students' Understandings of Probability. In *A Research Companion to Principles and Standards for School Mathematics,* J. Kilpatrick, W. G. Martin, and D. Schifter (eds.). Reston, VA: National Council of Teachers of Mathematics, 2003, pp. 216–226.

Shaughnessy, J. M., and Dick, T. "Monty's Dilemma: Should You Stick or Switch?" *Mathematics Teacher* 84 (Apr. 1991): 252–256.

Shaughnessy, J. M., and Pfannkuch, M. "How Faithful Is Old Faithful? Statistical Thinking: A Story of Variation and Prediction." *Mathematics Teacher* 4 (Apr. 2002): 252–259.

Shaughnessy, M. H. "Identify Fractions and Decimals on a Number Line." *Teaching Children Mathematics* 17 (Mar. 2011): 428–434.

Shaw, J. M., Thomas, C., Hoffman, A., and Bulgren, J. "Using Concept Diagrams to Promote Understanding in Geometry." *Teaching Children Mathematics* (Nov. 1995): 184–189.

Sherard, W. H. "Is Talk Cheap?" *Mathematics Teaching in the Middle School* 8 (Oct. 2002): 92–94.

Shockey, T., and Snyder, K. "Engaging Preservice Teachers in Tessellating T-Shirts." *Children Teaching Mathematics* (Sept. 2007): 82–87.

Silver, E. A., Shapiro, L. J., and Deutsch, A. "Sense Making and the Solution of Division Problems Involving Remainders: An Examination of Middle School Students' Solution Processes and their Interpretations of Solutions." *Journal for Research in Mathematics Education* 24 (1993): 117–135.

Simon, M. A. "Prospective Elementary Teachers' Knowledge of Division." *Journal for Research in Mathematics Education* 24 (1993): 233–254.

Sincich, T., Levine, D. M., and Stephan, D. *Practical Statistics by Example Using Microsoft Excel.* Upper Saddle River, NJ: Prentice Hall, 2001.

Slovin, H. "Moving to Proportional Reasoning." *Mathematics Teaching in the Middle School* 6 (Sept. 2000): 58–60.

Smith, J., and Thompson, P. W. Quantitative Reasoning and the Development of Algebraic Reasoning. In *Algebra in the Early Grades,* J. Kaput, D. Carraher, and M. Blanton (eds.). Englewood Cliffs, NJ: Erlbaum, in press, pp. 95–132.

Smith, J. P., III. The Development of Students' Knowledge of Fractions and Ratios. In *Making Sense of Fractions, Ratios, and Proportions,* B. Litwiller and G. Bright (eds.). Reston,

VA: National Council of Teachers of Mathematics, 2002, pp. 3–17.

Smith, R. F. "Coordinate Geometry for Third Graders." *Arithmetic Teacher* (Apr. 1986): 6–11.

Smith, S. *Agnesi to Zeno: Over 100 Vignettes from the History of Math.* Berkeley, CA: Key Curriculum Press, 1996.

Snyder, T. D. *Mini-Digest of Education Statistics, 2007* (NCES 2008-023). Washington, D.C.: National Center for Education Statistics, Institute of Educational Sciences, U.S. Department of Education, 2008.

Sorto, M. A. "Exploring the Volume of Mayan and Egyptian Pyramids." *Mathematics Teaching in the Middle School* 15 (Dec. 2009/Jan. 2010): 294–297.

Sowder, J. Estimation and Number Sense. In *Handbook of Research on Mathematics Teaching and Learning,* D. A. Grouws (ed.). Reston, VA: National Council of Teachers of Mathematics, 1992, pp. 371–389.

Sowder, J. Place Value as the Key to Teaching Decimal Operations. In *Putting Research into Practice in the Elementary Grades,* D. Chambers (ed.). Reston, VA: National Council of Teachers of Mathematics, 2002, pp. 113–118.

Sowder, J. T. Making Sense of Numbers in School Mathematics. In *Analysis of Arithmetic for Mathematics Teaching,* G. Leinhardt, R. Putnam, and R. Hattrup (eds.). Hillsdale, NJ: Lawrence Erlbaum Associates, 1992, pp. 1–51.

Star, J. R., Kenyon, M., Joiner, R. M., and Rittle-Johnson, B. "Comparison Helps Students Learn to Be Better Estimators." *Teaching Children Mathematics* 16 (May 2010): 557–563.

Steffe, L. P., and Olive, J. The Problem of Fractions in the Elementary School. In *Putting Research into Practice in the Elementary Grades,* D. Chambers (ed.). Reston, VA: National Council of Teachers of Mathematics, 2002, pp. 128–132.

Stephan, M., and Clements, D. H. Linear and Area Measurement in Prekindergarten to Grade 2. In *Learning and Teaching Measurement,* D. H. Clements and G. Bright (eds.). National Council of Teachers of Mathematics 2003 Yearbook. Reston, VA: NCTM, 2003, pp. 3–16.

Stimpson, V. C. "Sharing Teaching Ideas. A Lesson Designed to Reveal Misconceptions about the Relationship between Area and Perimeter." *Mathematics Teacher* 82 (May 1989): 342–344.

Stocks, C. R., and Lamb, G. "Calculating Pythagorean Triples." *Mathematics Teacher* 104 (Sept. 2010): 152–155.

Strauss, S., and Bichler, E. "The Development of Children's Concepts of the Arithmetic Average." *Journal for Research in Mathematics Education* 19 (Jan. 1988): 64–80.

Strutchens, M. E., Martin, W. G., and Kenney, P. A. "What Students Know about Measurement: Perspectives from the National Assessment of Educational Progress." In *Learning and Teaching Measurement,* D. H. Clements and G. Bright (eds.). Reston, VA: National Council of Teachers of Mathematics. 2003, pp. 197–208.

Stump, C. "Patterns to Develop Algebraic Reasoning." *Teaching Children Mathematics 17* (Mar. 2011): 410–418.

Stump, S. "Designing Fraction-Counting Books." *Teaching Children Mathematics* 9 (May 2003): 546–549.

Stump, S., Bishop, J., and Britton, B. "Building a Vision of Algebra for Preservice Teachers." *Teaching Children Mathematics* (Nov. 2003): 180–186.

Stylianou, D. A., and Blanton, M. L. "Developing Students' Capacity for Constructing Proofs through Discourse." *Mathematics Teacher 104* (Sept. 2011): 140–145.

Sullins, K. "Get More from Pythagorean Ideas." *Mathematics Teacher* 98 (Sept. 2004): 68.

Sundberg, S. "A Plethora of Polyhedra." *Mathematics Teaching in the Middle School* (Mar.–Apr. 1998): 388–391.

Sweeney, E. S., and Quinn, R. J. "Concentration: Connecting Fractions, Decimals, & Percents." *Mathematics Teaching in the Middle School* 5 (Jan. 2000): 324–328.

Symanzik, J., Fischetti, W., Spence, I. "Commemorating William Playfair's 250th Birthday." *Computational Statistics* 24 (2009): 551–566.

Takis, S. L. "*Titanic:* A Statistical Exploration." *Mathematics Teacher* 92 (Nov. 1999): 660–664.

Tall, D. The Transition to Advanced Mathematical Thinking: Functions, Limits, Infinity, and Proof. In *Handbook of Research on Mathematics Teaching and Learning,* D. A. Grouws (ed.). Reston, VA: National Council of Teachers of Mathematics, 1992, pp. 495–511.

Tarr, J. "Providing Opportunities to Learn Probability Concepts." *Teaching Children Mathematics* (Apr. 2002): 482–487.

Tartre, L. A. "Dropping Perpendiculars the Easy Way." *Mathematics Teacher* 80 (Jan. 1987): 30–31.

Tayeh, C. "Solutions to the Risky Allowance Problem." *Teaching Children Mathematics* (Apr. 2006): 423–427.

Telese, J. A., and Abete, J., Jr. "Diet, Ratios, and Proportions." *Mathematics Teaching in the Middle School* 8 (Sept. 2002): pp. 8–13.

Terc, M. "Coordinate Geometry—Art and Mathematics." *Arithmetic Teacher* (Oct. 1985): 22–24.

Thompson, D. R. "Learning and Teaching Indirect Proof." *Mathematics Teacher* 89 (Sept. 1996): 474–481.

Thompson, P. W., and Saldanha, L. A. Fractions and Multiplicative Reasoning. In *A Research Companion to Principles and Standards for School Mathematics,* J. Kilpatrick, W. G. Martin, and D. Schifter (eds.). Reston, VA: National Council of Teachers of Mathematics, 2003, pp. 95–113.

Thompson, T. D., and Preston, R. V. "Measurement in the Middle Grades: Insights from NAEP and TIMMS." *Mathematics Teaching in the Middle School* 9 (May 2004): 514–519.

Tractinsky, N., and Meyer, J. "Chartjunk or Goldgraph? Effects of Presentation Objectives and Content Desirability on Information Presentation." *MIS Quarterly* 23 (Sept. 1999): 397–420.

Tripathi, P. N. "Developing Mathematical Understanding through Multiple Representations." *Mathematics Teaching in the Middle School* 12 (Apr. 2008): 438–445.

Trowell, S. D., and Reynolds, A. M. "How Long Is Its Projection?" *Mathematics Teaching in the Middle School* 9 (Apr. 2004): 444–448.

Tukey, J. W. Box-and-Whisker Plots. In *Explanatory Data Analysis.* Reading, MA: Addison Wesley, 1977, §2C, pp. 39–43.

Uccellini, T. C. "Teaching the Mean Meaningfully." *Mathematics Teaching in the Middle School* 3 (Nov.–Dec. 1996): 112–115.

Urich, J. A., and Sasse, E. A. "An Ap'peel'ing Activity." *Mathematics Teacher* 105 (Oct. 2011): 189–193.

Usnick, V., Mccarthy, J., and Alexander, S. "Mrs. Whatsit 'Socks' It to Probability." *Teaching Children Mathematics* (Dec. 2001): 246–249.

Utley, J., and Wolfe, J. "Geoboard Areas: Students' Remarkable Ideas." *Mathematics Teacher* 97 (Jan. 2004): 18–25.

Van Boening, L. "Growth through Change." *Mathematics Teaching in the Middle School* 7 (Sept. 1999): 27–33.

Van de Walle, J. *Elementary and Middle School Mathematics: Teaching Developmentally* (4th ed.). New York: Addison Wesley Longman, 2001.

Van de Walle, J. Geometric Thinking and Geometric Concepts. In *Elementary and Middle School Mathematics: Teaching Developmentally.* Boston, MA: Allyn and Bacon, 2001, pp. 306–312.

Van Den Heuvel-Panhuizen, M. "The Didactical Use of Models in Realistic Mathematics Education: An Example from a Longitudinal Trajectory on Percentage." *Educational Studies in Mathematics* 54 (2003): 9–35.

Van Dooren, W., De Bock, D., Verschaffel, L., and Janssens, D. "Improper Applications of Proportional Reasoning." *Mathematics Teaching in the Middle School* 9 (Dec. 2003): 204–209.

Van Dooren, W., Verschaffel, L., and Onghena, P. "The Impact of Preservice Teachers' Content Knowledge on Their Evaluation of Students' Strategies for Solving Arithmetic and Algebra Word Problems." *Journal for Research in Mathematics Education* 33 (2002): 319–351.

Van Dyke, F. "A Visual Approach to Deductive Reasoning." *Mathematics Teacher* 88 (Sept. 1995): 481–484.

Van Dyke, F., and Craine, T. V. "Equivalent Representations in the Learning of Algebra." *Mathematics Teacher* 90 (Nov. 1997): 616–619.

Van Dyke, F., and White, A. "Examining Students' Reluctance to Use Graphs." *Mathematics Teacher* 98 (Sept. 2004): 110–117.

van Putten, C. M., van den Brom-Snijders, P. A., and Beishuizen, M. "Progressive Mathematization of Long Division in Dutch Primary Schools." *Journal for Research in Mathematics Education* 36 (2005): 44–73.

Vance, J. H. "Number Operations from an Algebraic Perspective." *Teaching Children Mathematics* (Jan. 1998): 282–285.

Vanderhye, C. M., and Demers, C. M. Z. "Assessing Students' Understanding through Conversations." *Teaching Children Mathematics* (Dec. 2007/Jan. 2008): 260–264.

Vasquez, R., and Villena, M. "Normal Hematological Values for Healthy Persons Living at 4000 Meters in Bolivia." *High Altitude Medicine & Biology* 2 (Sept. 2001): 361–367.

Voza, L. "Winning the "Hundred Years' War." *Teaching Children Mathematics* 18 (Aug. 2011): 32–37.

Wallace, A. H., and Gurganus, S. P. "Teaching for Mastery of Multiplication." *Teaching Children Mathematics* (Aug. 2005): 26–33.

Wallace-Gomez, P. "Slopes of Parallel and Perpendicular Lines: A Visual Justification." *Mathematics Teacher* 104 (May 2011): 728.

Walmsley, A. L. E. "Understanding Aztec and Mayan Number Systems." *Mathematics Teaching in the Middle School* 12 (Aug. 2006): 55–59.

Wanko, J. J. "Trapping into Trapezoids." *Mathematics Teacher* 99 (Oct. 2005): 190–195.

Wanko, J. J., and Venable, C. H. "Investigating Prime Numbers and the Great Internet Mersenne Prime Search." *Mathematics Teaching in the Middle School* 7 (Oct. 2002): 70–76.

Wasdovich, D. H. "Euclid and Descartes: A Partnership." *Mathematics Teacher* 84 (Dec. 1991): 706–709.

Watanabe, T. "Representations in Teaching and Learning Fractions." *Teaching Children Mathematics* (Apr. 2002): 457–463.

Watson, J. "Conditional Probability: Its Place in the Classroom." *Mathematics Teacher* 88 (Jan. 1999): 12–17.

Watson, J. "Statistics in Context." *Mathematics Teacher* 93 (Jan. 2000): 54–58.

Wearne, D., and Kouba, V. Rational Numbers. In *Results from the Seventh Mathematics Assessment of the National Assessment Educational Progress,* E. A. Solver and P. A. Kenney (eds.). Reston, VA: National Council of Teachers of Mathematics, 2000, pp. 163–192.

Wearne, D., and Kouba, V. Whole Number Properties and Operations. In *Results from the Seventh Mathematics Assessment of the National Assessment Educational Progress,* E. A. Solver and P. A. Kenney (eds.). Reston, VA: National Council of Teachers of Mathematics, 2000, pp. 141–161.

Weinberg, S. L. Proportional Reasoning: One Problem, Many Solutions. In *Making Sense of Fractions, Ratios, and Proportions,* B. Litwiller and G. Bright (eds.). Reston, VA: National Council of Teachers of Mathematics, 2002, pp. 138–144.

Weisstein, E. W. Cavalieri's Principle. MathWorld: A Wolfram Web Resource. Available at http://mathworld.wolfram.com/CavalierisPrinciple.html.

Westegaard, S. K. "Stitching Quilts into Coordinate Geometry." *Mathematics Teacher* 91 (91 Oct. 1998): 587–590.

Wheatley, G. H. Reasoning with Images in Mathematical Activity. In *Mathematical Reasoning: Analogies, Metaphors, and Images,* L. D. English (ed.). Mahwah, NJ: Lawrence Erlbaum Associates, 1997, pp. 281–297.

Wheatley, G. H. "Spatial Sense and the Construction of Abstract Units in Tiling." *Arithmetic Teacher* (Apr. 1992): 43–45.

Wheeler, M. Children's Understanding of Zero and Infinity. In *Putting Research into Practice in the Elementary Grades,* D. Chambers (ed.). Reston, VA: National Council of Teachers of Mathematics, 2002, pp. 29–36.

Whitman, N. "Line and Rotational Symmetry." *Mathematics Teacher* 84 (Apr. 1991): 296–298.

Wilburne, J. M. "Preparing Preservice Elementary School Teachers to Teach Problem Solving." *Teaching Children Mathematics* (May 2006): 454–463.

Wilders, R., and VanOyen, L. "Turning Students into Symmetry Detectives." *Mathematics Teaching in the Middle School* 17 (Sept. 2011): 103–107.

Wilson, J. W., Fernandez, M. L., and Hadaway, N. Mathematical Problem Solving. In *Survey of Research in Mathematics Education: Secondary School,* P. S. Wilson (ed.). Reston, VA: National Council of Teachers of Mathematics, 1993, pp. 57–78.

Wilson, P. S. "Understanding Angles: Wedges to Degrees." *Mathematics Teacher* 83 (Apr. 1990): 294–296.

Wilson, P. S. "Zero: A Special Case." *Mathematics Teaching in the Middle School* 6 (Jan. 2001): 300–305.

Winicki-Landman, G. "Equiareal Polygons: A Mathematical Conversation about a 'New' Concept." *Mathematics Teacher* 94 (Mar. 2001): 211–216.

Woleck, K. R. Listen to Their Pictures: An Investigation of Children's Mathematical Drawings. In *The Roles of Representations in School Mathematics* 2001 Yearbook, A. Cuoco and F. Curcio

(eds.). Reston, VA: National Council of Teachers of Mathematics, 2001, pp. 215–227.

Woodward, E., and Brown, R. "Polyhedrons and Three-Dimensional Geometry." *Arithmetic Teacher* (Apr. 1994): 451–458.

Wu, H. "The Role of Euclidean Geometry in High School." *Journal of Mathematical Behavior* (1996): 221–237.

Wu, Z. "Multiplying Fractions." *Teaching Children Mathematics* 8 (Nov. 2001): 174–177.

Yackel, E., and Hanna, G. Reasoning and Proof. In *A Research Companion to Principles and Standards for School Mathematics,* J. Kilpatrick, W. G. Martin, and D. Schifter (eds.). Reston, VA: National Council of Teachers of Mathematics, 2003, pp. 227–236.

Yerushalmy, M., and Shternberg, B. Charting a Visual Course to the Concept of Function. In *The Roles of Representation in School Mathematics,* A. A. Cuoco and F. R. Curcio (eds.). Reston, VA: National Council of Teachers of Mathematics, 2001, pp. 251–268.

Yopp, D. "Identifying Logical Necessity." *Teaching Children Mathematics* 16 (Mar. 2010): 410–418.

Yopp, D. A. "From Inductive Reasoning to Proof." *Mathematics Teaching in the Middle School* 15 (Dec. 2009/Jan. 2010): 287–291.

Young, A. *Travels in France during the Years 1787, 1788 & 1789.* Reprinted by Cambridge: University Press, 1929. Edited by Constance Maxwell.

Young, E. "Probability: A Whale of a Tale." *Teaching Children Mathematics* 17 (Sept. 2010): 106–112.

Young, V. "A Matter of 'Survival.'" *Mathematics Teacher* 95 (Feb. 2002): 100–103.

Zaskis, R., and Liljedahl, P. "Understanding Primes: The Role of Representation." *Journal for Research in Mathematics Education* 35 (2004): 164–186.

Zaslavsky, C. "Developing Number Sense: What Can Other Cultures Tell Us?" *Teaching Children Mathematics* (Feb. 2001): 312–319.

Zaslavsky, C. "The Influence of Ancient Egypt on Greek and Other Numeration Systems." *Mathematics Teaching in the Middle School* 3 (Nov. 2003): 174–178.

Zawojewski, J. Teaching Statistics: Mean, Median, and Mode. In *Putting Research into Practice in the Elementary Grades,* D. Chambers (ed.). Reston, VA: National Council of Teachers of Mathematics, 2002, pp. 238–240.

Zawojewski, J., and Shaughnessy, M. J. "Mean and Median: Are They Really So Easy?" *Mathematics Teaching in the Middle School* 7 (Mar. 2000): 436–44.

Zazkis, R., and Gadowsky, K. Attending to Transparent Features of Opaque Representations of Natural Numbers. In *The Roles of Representation in School Mathematics,* A. A. Cuoco and F. R. Curcio (eds.). Reston, VA: National Council of Teachers of Mathematics, 2001, pp. 44–52.

Zemelman, S., Daniels, H., and Hyde, A. *Today's Standards for Teaching and Learning in America's Schools.* Portsmouth, NH: Heinemann, 2005.

INDEX

deductive reasoning, 35. *See also* logic
  in elementary mathematics curriculum, 35
  vs. inductive reasoning, 46–47
  proof in, 704, 711–712
  three standard rules of, 44–47
deficient number, 216
definitions in geometry, 558, 561
degrees of angle, 563–564
de Moivre, Abraham, 514
denominator(s)
  common denominator
    addition with, 259
    comparing fractions with, 252
    dividing fractions with, 278–279
    subtraction with, 261–262
  definition of, 244
  zero as, 147
density property
  of fractions, 254
  of real numbers, 340
dependent events, 512
dependent variable, 367–368, 371. *See also* output variable
Descartes, René, 25, 140, 768
descriptive statistics, 414. *See also* data; graphs of data; measures of center; measures of variability
detachment, law of, 44–45
deviation from the mean, 452–455
diagonal, of a polygon, 579–580
diagrams. *See also* graph(s)
  in multiplying fractions, 272–274
  as problem-solving strategy, 18, 20, 27–28, 155–156
  of ratio relationships, 290, 297
  of relations, 370
  to represent percents, 344, 345, 346–348
  to represent relationships, 26–27
  to simplify algebraic expressions, 644–645
  for solving word problems, 27–28
    with fractions, 247–248
    multiplicative, 155–156
diameter of a circle, 637
difference. *See also* subtraction
  common, 5
  divisibility of, 190
  estimation of, 113–114
  of integers, 225
  of sets, 61–62
  of whole numbers, 94
digits, 71, 83
dilations (size transformations), 818–822
  with Geometer's Sketchpad, B-13
  homework/review/test problems, 827, 828, 829, 830, 831, 832, 833, 840–841, 843, 844
dimensional analysis, 628–629
  with area, 645–646
  with volume and capacity, 675
Direct Reasoning strategy, 19

disjoint sets, 62
distance. *See also* length
  as absolute value, 226–227
  with Geometer's Sketchpad, B-14
  representations of, 559, 560
  size transformation and, 820–821
distance formula, 784–787
  equation of circle and, 787–788
  in proving properties of polygons, 790–794
distribution of data, 442, 530. *See also* normal distributions
distributive property
  with integers, 228–229
  multiplication algorithm and, 160, 162
  with percent change, 354
  with rational numbers, 275
  with real numbers, 340
  with whole numbers, 136–138
dividend, 147
"divides," 188
divisibility, 188–198
  basic vocabulary of, 188–189
  homework/review/test problems, 198–201, 235–236, 238
  of sums and differences, 190
divisibility rules, 191
  for 2, 191–192, 197
  for 3, 192–193, 197
  for 4, 194, 197
  for 5, 192, 197
  for 6, 195
  for 7, 197
  for 8, 195, 197
  for 9, 193–194, 197
  for 10, 192, 197
  for 11, 197–198
  for 12, 195–196
  connection among, 196–197
  homework/review/test problems, 199–201, 236, 238
  inventing, 195–196
  to test for prime number, 208
  weights for digits in, 196–198
"divisible by," 188
division
  algorithms for, 167–171
    homework/review/test problems, 176, 177, 178, 179–180, 183
  in base five numeration system, 174–176
  checking with quotient–remainder theorem, 151
  connections with other operations, 149–150
    addition, 152
    multiplication, 148–149
  of decimals, 316–318, 326–327
    homework/review/test problems, 322–325, 360, 362

definition of
  for rational numbers, 280, 281
  for whole numbers, 147–148
  Draw a Diagram strategy with, 155–156
  estimation in, 171
    with scientific notation, 339
  of exponential expressions, 154–155, 282
  fact families and, 146–147
  fair share model for, 145, 168
    with algebra tiles, 398
    with decimals, 317–318, 326
  fraction as representation of, 249
  of fractions, 277–281
    homework/review/test problems, 286–289, 303–304, 305–306
  to generate equivalent fractions, 250–251
  with integers, 229–230
  models for, 145–146
  myth of making smaller, 320
  order of operations and, 153
  by powers of 10, 315
  of rational numbers, 277–281
    homework/review/test problems, 286–289, 303–304, 305–306
  repeated subtraction model for, 145
    with decimals, 316–317
    with fractions, 278
  in scientific notation, 339
  sign rules for, 230
  of whole numbers
    algorithms for, 167–171
    with calculator, A-4–A-5
    definition of, 147–148
    homework/review/test problems, 156–159, 176–180, 182, 183, 184, 185
  by zero, 147
division property of equality, 30
divisor, 147, 188
dodecahedron, 596
  regular, 599, 600, 601
domain of a function, 369
donkey theorem, 717
dot plot, 450–451
double-bar graph, 423
Draw a Diagram strategy, 18, 20, 27–28. *See also* diagrams
  multiplicative reasoning with, 155–156

E

edge, of polyhedron, 595, 598
Egyptian mathematics
  fractions in, 241, 242, 261
  numeration system, 70–71, 83
Eiffel Tower, 703
Electronic Numerical Integrator Analyzer and Computer (ENIAC), 154
elementary number theory, 187. *See also* composite numbers; divisibility; divisibility rules; prime factorization; prime numbers
element of a set, 58

WebAssign

ENHANCED

If you elect to use Enhanced WebAssign with this course, you will find problems in Enhanced WebAssign based on exercises from the textbook that are listed below. Visit www.webassign.net/cengage for the most up-to-date list of Enhanced WebAssign problems.

1.1 Patterns and Inductive Reasoning
2, 3, 7, 8, 11, 12, 16, 39, 49

1.2 Problem-Solving Strategies
2, 3, 6, 9, 10, 23, 24, 35, 40

1.3 Algebra and Problem Solving
24, 27, 31, 35, 36, 39, 41, 46, 47

1.4 Logic and Deductive Reasoning
1, 5, 15, 16, 20, 24, 28, 29, 36

2.1 Sets and Operations
1, 3, 5, 11, 26, 29, 30, 39, 46

2.2 Numbers and Numeration
3, 8, 20, 22, 30, 31, 54, 62, 63

2.3 Models and Properties of Addition and Subtraction
13, 31, 32, 38, 39, 42, 51, 54, 62

2.4 Algorithms for Whole Number Addition and Subtraction
9, 10, 11, 17, 28, 34, 48, 50, 51

3.1 Models and Properties of Multiplication
8, 10, 25, 31, 33, 38, 39, 43, 51

3.2 Models of Division
5, 14, 25, 37, 40, 44, 48, 52, 61

3.3 Algorithms for Whole Number Multiplication and Division
4, 5, 14, 37, 43, 50, 55, 65, 68

4.1 Divisibility of Counting Numbers
1, 5, 6, 7, 19, 20, 33, 38, 53

4.2 Prime and Composite Numbers, Least Common Multiple, and Greatest Common Factor
4, 6, 7, 12, 24, 39, 42, 46, 62

4.3 Integers
6, 14, 34, 40, 50, 52, 57, 58, 59

5.1 Concept of Fractions and Representations
6, 11, 37, 38, 39, 44, 53, 57, 60

5.2 Addition and Subtraction with Rational Numbers
8, 9, 21, 27, 33, 34, 42, 46, 52

5.3 Multiplication and Division with Rational Numbers
7, 29, 34, 37, 42, 52, 58, 59, 62

5.4 Ratios and Proportional Reasoning
9, 10, 15, 29, 36, 39, 41, 44, 46

6.1 Decimals and Operations
11, 12, 13, 28, 40, 55, 62, 65, 67

6.2 Repeating Decimals, Irrational Numbers, and Real Numbers
1, 7, 10, 38, 45, 46, 51, 52, 69

6.3 Percent and Percent Change
2, 8, 11, 19, 42, 50, 51, 58, 62

7.1 Representing and Creating Functions
7, 14, 16, 23, 31, 40, 43, 46, 51

7.2 Solving Equations
2, 6, 9, 11, 18, 20, 42, 43, 50

7.3 Algebra Tiles
1, 3, 6, 7, 9, 29, 31, 32, 33

8.1 Graphical Representations of Data
2, 3, 5, 7, 14, 33, 49, 53, 54

8.2 Measures of Center and Measures of Variation
3, 4, 5, 6, 7, 17, 21, 35, 57

8.3 Percentile, Box Plot, and Outliers
1, 3, 8, 9, 10, 12, 21, 24, 41

9.1 Basics of Probability
3, 6, 7, 9, 10, 20, 37, 43, 57

9.2 Probability Rules
5, 9, 11, 12, 15, 22, 34, 44, 52

9.3 Expected Value, Normal Distribution, Simulations, and Odds
2, 11, 12, 13, 21, 24, 34, 39, 51

10.1 Representation of Building Blocks of Geometry
10, 11, 14, 20, 22, 36, 39, 43, 48

10.2 Pairs of Angles and Types of Polygons
4, 11, 13, 20, 43, 46, 50, 53, 57

10.3 Three-Dimensional Shapes
12, 13, 18, 22, 23, 49, 50, 52, 54